ENCYCLOPAEDIA OF OCCUPATIONAL HEALTH AND SAFETY

ENCYCLOPAEDIA OF OCCUPATIONAL HEALTH AND SAFETY

4TH EDITION

3

Editor-in-Chief
Jeanne Mager Stellman, PhD

Senior Associate Editor
Michael McCann, PhD, CIH

Associate Editors
Leon Warshaw, MD   Carole Brabant, PhD

Senior Editors

John Finklea, MD, Dr PH   Jacqueline Messite, MD
Georges H. Coppée, MD   Steven L. Sauter, PhD
Vilma R. Hunt, BDS, AM   Jerry Spiegel, MA, MSc
Richard S. Kraus, PE, CSP   Colin L. Soskolne, PhD
Wolfgang Laurig, Dr-Ing   Benedetto Terracini, MD
Melvin L. Myers, BS, MPA

Managing Editor
Chantal Dufresne, BA

INTERNATIONAL LABOUR OFFICE
GENEVA

Stellman, Jeanne Mager (ed.)
Encyclopaedia of Occupational Health and Safety. 4th ed.
Geneva, International Labour Office, 1998. 4 V.

/Encyclopaedia/, /Occupational health/, /Occupational safety/. 13.04.2
ISBN 92-2-109203-8 (set)
92-2-109814-1 (V. 1)   92-2-109815-X (V. 2)   92-2-109816-8 (V. 3)   92-2-109817-6 (V. 4)

Contents: V. 1. The Body; Health Care; Management and Policy; Tools and Approaches—V. 2. Hazards—V. 3. Chemicals; Industries and Occupations—V. 4.Indexes

ILO Cataloguing in Publication Data

The designations employed in ILO publications, which are in conformity with United Nations practice, and the presentation of material therein do not imply the expression of any opinion whatsoever on the part of the International Labour Office concerning the legal status of any country, area or territory or of its authorities, or concerning the delimitation of its frontiers.
The responsibility for opinions expressed in signed articles, studies and other contributions rests solely with their authors, and publication does not constitute an endorsement by the International Labour Office of the opinions expressed in them.
The reader accepts that the parties make this documentation available without warranty of any kind. The parties do not accept responsibility for the validity or completeness of any data including inaccuracies, errors or omissions or for any consequences arising from the use of such data. Neither the authors, nor the ILO or collaborating institutions shall be liable for damages or other claims and demands arising out of the use of the data.
Reference to names of firms and commercial products and processes does not imply their endorsement by the International Labour Office or any collaborating institution, and any failure to mention a particular firm, commercial product or process is not a sign of disapproval.
ILO publications can be obtained through major booksellers or ILO local offices in many countries, or direct from ILO Publications, International Labour Office, CH-1211 Geneva 22, Switzerland. Catalogues or lists of new publications are available free of charge from the above address.

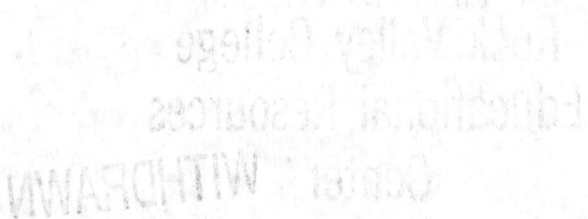

Cover and production design: Robert Silverman Design
Pagesetting by the International Labour Office, Geneva
Printed in the United States of America

Michael Adess, *PhD*
Chief
Human Factors Division Commandant
 (G-WKS-3)
United States Coast Guard Headquarters
Washington, DC
United States

M. Agamennone, *Dr Ing**
Istituto Guidio Donegani
Centro Ricerche Novara
Novara
Italy

Leen Akkers
Managing Director
Stichting Arbouw
Amsterdam
The Netherlands

R.G. Aldi, *MASc, BSc, P Eng*
Director
Quality and Environmental Affairs
Hiram Walker and Sons, Ltd.
Windsor, Ontario
Canada

Priscilla Alexander, *BA*
Coordinator
North American Task Force on
 Prostitution
New York, New York
United States

Sydney Allison, *PhD*
Communications Division
Mintek
Randburg
South Africa

Judith Anderson, *MSc*
Research Associate
Department of Environmental-
 Occupational Health
George Washington University
Washington, DC
United States

W. Stanley Anthony, *MSc*
Supervisory Agricultural Engineer
United States Cotton Ginning Laboratory
Agricultural Research Service
United States Department of Agriculture
Stoneville, Mississippi
United States

Elías Apud, *PhD, MSc*
Professor
Department of Physiopathology
University of Concepción
Concepción
Chile

M.P. Arias, *PhD, MSc*
Head
Environmental Safety and Health
 Department
Hospital Clinic Universitari
Barcelona
Spain

James R. Armstrong, *CIH*
Technical Services Coordinator
Ontario Natural Resources Safety
 Association
North Bay, Ontario
Canada

Ragnar Arnason, *PhD*
Professor
Department of Economics
University of Iceland
Reykjavik
Iceland

Tony Ashdown, *CPS, MS, CSP*
Loss Prevention Manager
Alpharma USPD, Inc.
Baltimore, Maryland
United States

George Astrakianakis, *B Eng, M Eng*
Research Scientist
Cancer Control Research
British Columbia Cancer Agency
Vancouver, British Columbia
Canada

Jörg Augusta, *Dr med*
Arbeitsgruppenleiter
Arbeitsgruppe Ergonomie und Waldarbeit
Landesanstalt für Wald und Forstwirtschaft
Gotha
Germany

William Avery, *AS*
President
Systems Safety Management USA, Inc.
Orlando, Florida
United States

Page Ayres, *MS*
Senior Environmental Engineer
Newport News Shipbuilding
Newport News, Virginia
United States

Angela Babin, *MS*
Associate Director
Center for Safety in the Arts
New York, New York
United States

G. Bachofen*
Chief of Branch
Division Information
Swiss National Accident Insurance
 Organization
Luzern
Switzerland

Dean B. Baker, *MD, MPH*
Professor, Director
Center for Occupational and
 Environmental Health
University of California-Irvine
Irvine, California
United States

David E. Baker, *CSP*
Assistant Program Director
Agriculture, Food and Natural Resources
University of Missouri-Columbia
Columbia, Missouri
United States

David G. Baldwin, *CIH*
Corporate Industrial Hygiene Manager
Hewlett-Packard Company
Palo Alto, California
United States

Gail Coningsby Barazani, *MPH*
Former Environmental Health Consultant
Chicago, Illinois
United States

Hjálmar R. Bárdarson, *MSc*
State Director of Shipping
Gardabaer
Iceland

Donald Barnard, *PhD*
Supervisory Research Entomologist
Agricultural Research Service
United States Department of Agriculture
Gainesville, Florida
United States

Lynn Barroby
Breeder and Trainer of Thoroughbred Racehorses
Langley, British Columbia
Canada

Subhash K. Batra, *PhD*
Director
Nonwovens Cooperative Research Center
 College of Textiles
North Carolina State University
Raleigh, North Carolina
United States

---

* Contributor to the 3rd edition of this ***Encyclopaedia.*** This biographical information has not been updated.

Giuseppe Battista, MD
Professor of Preventive Workers' Medicine
Cattedra di Medicina Preventiva
    dei Lavoratori
University of Siena
Siena
Italy

J.M. Baztarrica*
Facultad de Servicio Social de Higiene
    Industrial y Medicina
Buenos Aires
Argentina

Thomas L. Bean, PhD
Safety Leader, Professor
Department of Food, Agricultural and
    Biological Engineering
Ohio State University
Columbus, Ohio
United States

Luc Beauchamp
ONRSA
North Bay, Ontario
Canada

Bernardo Bedrikow, MD, MPH
Former Chief
Occupational Safety and Health
Serviço Social da Industria
São Paulo
Brazil

Louis S. Beliczky, MS, MPH
Consulting Industrial Hygienist
Technical Advisors and Consultants to
    Trade Unionists
Wickliffe, Ohio
United States

David M. Bell, MD
Assistant to the Director
National Center for Infectious Diseases
Centers for Disease Control and
    Prevention
Atlanta, Georgia
United States

Joel Bender, MD, PhD
Vice President, Chief Medical Officer
Health Sciences
Owens-Corning
Toledo, Ohio
United States

Deborah E. Berkowitz, BA
Director
Office of Safety and Health
United Food and Commercial Workers,
    AFL-CIO
Washington, DC
United States

A.S. Bettenson, MA*
Former Deputy Chief Inspector of Factories
Cambridge
United Kingdom

J.R. Bevan, Dr*
Manager
Coated Products Research
British Steel Corporation, South Wales
    Group
London
United Kingdom

William Blackburn, MS
Senior Research Associate
College of Textiles
North Carolina State University
Raleigh, North Carolina
United States

H.L. Boiteau
Service d'Anesthésiologie
Faculté de Médecine
Nantes
France

Denis Bourcier, PhD
Senior Principle Scientist
Environmental Affairs
Boeing Defence and Space Group
The Boeing Company
Seattle, Washington
United States

Madeleine Bourdouxhe, MSc
Researcher
Work Organization Programme
Institute for Occupational Health and
    Safety Research
Montreal, Quebec
Canada

Carole Brabant, PhD
Associate Editor
Encyclopaedia of Occupational Health and Safety
International Labour Office
Geneva
Switzerland

P.E. Braid, PhD*
Consultant
Laboratory Services
Occupational Health Unit
Medical Services Branch
Health and Welfare Canada
Ottawa, Ontario
Canada

Douglas F. Briggs, MPH, CIH
Group Manager
Safety and Health
Boeing Commercial Airplane Group
The Boeing Company
Seattle, Washington
United States

Jere A. Brittain, PhD
Clemson University
Clemson, South Carolina
United States

T.J. Britton*
Her Majesty's Inspector of Factories
Plastics National Industry Group
Health and Safety Executive
Northampton
United Kingdom

Mary O. Brophy, PhD, CIH, CPE
Former Environmental Toxicologist
Syracuse Research Corporation
North Syracuse, New York
United States

**Jeremy Brown, MD, CM, FRCPC,
    FACP**
Chief
Occupational Health Section
Health Services Directorate
Royal Canadian Mounted Police
Ottawa, Ontario
Canada

Mary E. Brown, DVM, MPH
*Morehouse School of Medicine-Senior Research
    Fellow*
National Institute for Occupational Safety
    and Health
Centers for Disease Control and
    Prevention
Cincinnati, Ohio
United States

Peter J. Bruno, MD, BS
Associate Professor of Medicine
New York University
Senior Consultant
Insall Scott Kelly Institute for Orthopedics
New York, New York
United States

Norman Brusk, JD, CIH, CSP
Health and Safety Manager
Health, Safety and Environment
Resource Partner, Inc.
Columbus, Ohio
United States

---

* Contributor to the 3rd edition of this ***Encyclopaedia.*** This biographical information has not been updated.

LaMont Byrd, *MS*
Director of Safety and Health
International Brotherhood of Teamsters
Washington, DC
United States

Roxanne Cabral, *MPH*
American Federation of State, County and
Municipal Employees
Washington, DC
United States

I.T. Cabrera, *Ing Dipl**
Former Official
International Labour Office
Lima
Peru

Buck Cameron, *CIH*
Director
Health Effects
Carpenters Health and Safety Fund
Seattle, Washington
United States

Giovanni Capelli, *MD*
Assistant Professor
Istituto di Igiene
Università Cattolica Del Sacro Cuore
Rome
Italy

The Carpet and Rug Institute
Melbourne, Victoria
Australia

Melvin E. Cassady, *MS, CIH*
Cassady Safety and Health Services
Southampton, Pennsylvania
United States

Cesare Catananti, *MD*
Medical Director
Policlinico "A. Gemelli" - Istituto di Igiene
Università Cattolica del Sacro Cuore
Rome
Italy

J.A. Catton*
Manager
Safety, Health and Welfare
British Steel Corporation
London
United Kingdom

Larry J. Chapman, *PhD*
Associate Scientist
College of Agricultural and Life Sciences
University of Wisconsin-Madison
Madison, Wisconsin
United States

Tsun-Jen Cheng, *BM, ScD*
Associate Professor
Institute of Occupational Medicine and
Industrial Hygiene
National Taiwan University
College of Public Health
Taipei
Taiwan, China

V.I. Chernyuk, *MD, ScD*
Professor, Scientific Director
Institute for Occupational Health
Kiev
Ukraine

Corky Chew, *MPH, MBA*
Program Manager
Environmental Technologies and
Strategies
Apple Computer, Inc.
Cupertino, California
United States

The Chlorine Institute, Inc.
Washington, DC
United States

John P. Chong, *MD, FRCPC*
Medical Director
Centre for Human Performance and
Health Promotion
Hamilton, Ontario
Canada

Nancy Clark, *MA, CIH, CSP*
Director
Center for Occupational and
Environmental Medicine
Mount Sinai School of Medicine
New York, New York
United States

Esther Cloutier, *PhD*
Researcher
Programme Organisation du Travail
Institute for Occupational Health and
Safety Research
Montreal, Quebec
Canada

Lenora Colbert
Vice-President
National Health and Human Services
Employees Union
New York, New York
United States

James J. Collins, *CSP, CIH*
General Mills
Minneapolis, Minnesota
United States

Zaida Colon, *BS*
Safety and Environmental Specialist
Concentrate Manufacturing Operations
PepsiCo PR, Inc.
Cidra
Puerto Rico

James Cone, *MD*
Assistant Clinical Professor
University of California-Berkeley
Berkeley, California
United States

F.L. Conradi*
Subdirector General
Medicina Laboral
Instituto Nacional de la Salud
Madrid
Spain

George A. Conway, *MD, MPH*
Chief
Alaska Activity Division of Safety Research
National Institute for Occupational Safety
and Health
Anchorage, Alaska
United States

Georges H. Coppée, *MD*
Chief of Medical Section
Occupational Safety and Health Branch
International Labour Office
Geneva
Switzerland

Michael Crane, *MD, MPH*
Assistant Vice-President
Occupational Health
Con Edison
Brooklyn, New York
United States

Charles Crocker
Safety Manager
Burlington Industries, Inc.
Greensboro, North Carolina
United States

Neil Dalhouse
General Manager
Health and Safety Education Program
Tourism and Hospitality Industry
Toronto, Ontario
Canada

Gianfranco Damiani, *MD*
Assistant Professor
Istituto di Igiene
Università Cattolica del Sacro Cuore
Rome
Italy

---

* Contributor to the 3rd edition of this ***Encyclopaedia.*** This biographical information has not been updated.

Hugh Davies, _MSc_
Occupational Hygienist
Occupational Hygiene Programme
University of British Columbia
Vancouver, British Columbia
Canada

L. DeBoer, _Dr*_
Chief Medical Adviser
Shell International Petroleum
The Hague
Netherlands

Paul Demers, _PhD_
Assistant Professor
Occupational Hygiene Program
University of British Columbia
Vancouver, British Columbia
Canada

Louis DiBerardinis, _MS_
Associate Director
Environmental Medical Services
Massachusetts Institute of Technology
Cambridge, Massachusetts
United States

Bertram D. Dinman, _MD, ScD_
Clinical Professor of Occupational Medicine
Graduate School of Public Health
University of Pittsburgh
Pittsburgh, Pennsylvania
United States

Basil Dolphin, _MD, MPH_
Medical Director
Healthworks
Muhlenberg Hospital
Bethlehem, Pennsylvania
United States

Kelley Donham, _DVM_
Department of Preventive Medicine and
    Environmental Health
Institute for Rural and Environmental
    Health
College of Medicine
University of Iowa
Iowa City, Iowa
United States

Kyle B. Dotson, _CIH, CSP, PE_
Group Vice-President, Safety and Health
BHP Copper
San Francisco, California
United States

Aluaro Durao, _MD, OPHS*_
Chief
Occupational Health Department
Siderurgia Nacional
Lisbon
Portugal

Dennis Dykstra, _PhD_
Deputy Director General for Research
Centre for International Forestry Research
Jakarta
Indonesia

Gary S. Earnest, _MS, PE, CSP_
Engineer Officer
Engineering Control Technology Branch
Division of Physical Sciences and
    Engineering
National Institute for Occupational Safety
    and Health
Cincinnati, Ohio
United States

Alan Echt, _MPH_
Industrial Hygienist
Engineering Control Technology Branch
Division of Physical Sciences and
    Engineering
National Institute for Occupational Safety
    and Health
Cincinnati, Ohio
United States

Olli Eeronheimo, _MSc_
Research Scientist
Finnish Forest Research Institute
Vantaa
Finland

M.M. El-Attal, _Dr, MB, ChB, DIH*_
Head
Occupational Health Department
Ministry of Health
Manama
Bahrain

M.A. El Kadeem, _Prof*_
Head
Production Engineering Department
Faculty of Engineering
Alexandria University
Alexandria
Egypt

Carl G. Elinder, _MD, PhD_
Associate Professor
Department of Renal Medicine
Huddinge University Hospital and
    Karolinska Institute
Karolinska
Sweden

Daniel R. English, _PhD_
Unit Director
Environmental Sciences Section
Eastman Kodak Company
Rochester, New York
United States

Claës-W. Englund, _BLL_
Director, Legal Adviser
Association of Swedish Theatres and
    Orchestras
Teatrarnas Riksförbund
Stockholm
Sweden

Madeleine R. Estryn-Béhar, _MD, PhD_
Occupational Health Practitioner
Hôpital Saint-Louis
Paris
France

J.F. Eustace, _MB, DPH*_
Dean of Faculty
Occupational Medicine
Royal College of Physicians of Ireland
Dublin
Ireland

E. Evrard, _Dr*_
Organisation européenne pour la sécurité
    de la navigation aérienne
Brussels
Belgium

Lynda Ewers, _PhD, CHMM_
Industrywide Studies Branch
Division of Surveillance, Hazard
    Evaluations and Field Studies
National Institute for Occupational Safety
    and Health
Cincinnati, Ohio
United States

Michael J. Fagel, _PhD_
Corporate Safety Director
Aurora Packing Co., Inc.
North Aurora, Illinois
United States

John Fajen, _MS_
Director of Industrial Hygiene and Ergonomics
AIG Consultants, Inc.
Cincinnati, Ohio
United States

M. Joseph Fedoruk, _MD_
Medical Director
Center for Occupational and
    Environmental Health
University of California-Irvine
Irvine, California
United States

John B. Feldman, _PE, CIH, CSP, MS_
Corporate Occupational Safety and Health
Raytheon Company
Lexington, Massachusetts
United States

* Contributor to the 3rd edition of this **_Encyclopaedia_**. This biographical information has not been updated.

L.V.R. Fernando, *MBBS, DPH, DHI**
Adviser on Labour and Population
International Labour Office
New Delhi
India

William E. Field, *EdD*
Professor
Agricultural and Biological
Engineering
Purdue University
West Lafayette, Indiana
United States

John Finklea, *MD, Dr PH*
Medical Officer
Center to Protect Workers' Rights
Former Director
National Institute for Occupational Safety
and Health
Washington, DC
United States

Manfred Fischer, *Dr-Ing*
Director of Technical Inspectorate
Verwaltungs-Berufsgenossenschaft
Hamburg
Germany

N. Fish, *MA**
Her Majesty's District Inspector of Factories
Department of Employment and
Productivity
Watford
United Kingdom

Stewart Forbes, *BSc*
Executive Director
Canadian Centre for Pollution Prevention
Sarnia, Ontario
Canada

Janet Fox, *MA*
Director
Safety and Industrial Hygiene
Con Edison
Brooklyn, New York
United States

David Franson, *CSP, ARM*
Occupational Health and Safety Consultant
Safety Management Services Company
Dubuque, Iowa
United States

James S. Frederick
Industrial Hygienist
Health, Safety and Environment
Department
United Steelworkers of America
Pittsburgh, Pennsylvania
United States

Barry R. Friedlander, *MD, MPH*
Senior Environmental Health Adviser
Exxon Biomedical Sciences, Inc.
East Millstone, New Jersey
United States

I.D. Gadaskina*
Doktor biologičeskih nauk
Rukovoditel' toksikologiceskoj laboratorii
Leningradskogo Institut gigieny truda i
profzabolevanij
Leningrad
Former USSR

Nancy Garcia, *MPH*
Airline Division
International Brotherhood of Teamsters
Fremont, California
United States

H. Gartmann, *Dr*
Medical Director
Medical Services
Swissair
Zurich
Switzerland

Joel C. Gaydos, *MD*
Director
Clinical Preventive Medicine
United States Army Center for Health
Promotion and Preventive Medicine
Army Proving Ground, Maryland
United States

E. Gelpi*
Education Permanente
Division des structures, contenus et
méthodes
United Nations Educational, Scientific
and Cultural Organization
Paris
France

Afsaneh Gerami, *BS*
Environmental Health and Safety Consultant
Hewlett-Packard Company
San Jose, California
United States

Gary A. Gibson, *MBA*
Chief Executive Officer
Mines Rescue Board
Sydney
Australia

Gary Gibson, *BSc*
Occupational Health and Safety Officer
Durham Board of Education
Whitby, Ontario
Canada

Denis Giguère, *MSc, DESS*
Ergonomist
Safety-Ergonomics Research Program
Institute for Occupational Health and
Safety Research
Montreal, Quebec
Canada

David Gold, *MOEd*
Occupational Safety and Health Officer
Occupational Safety and Health Branch
International Labour Office
Geneva
Switzerland

J.C. Graham, *MFCM, MFOM, DIH**
Chief Medical Officer
H.J. Heinz Company, Ltd.
London
United Kingdom

Casey C. Grant, *PE*
Assistant Vice-President
Codes and Standards Administration
National Fire Protection Association
International
Quincy, Massachusetts
United States

Alfons Grösbrink, *Dipl-Ing*
Leiter des Technischen Aufsichtsdienstes
Bahnen-Berufsgenossenschaft
Hamburg
Germany

Xavier Guardino Solá, *PhD*
Chief of Department
National Centre for Working Conditions
National Institute for Occupational Safety
and Hygiene
Barcelona
Spain

Tee L. Guidotti, *MD, MPH*
Professor, Director
Occupational Health Program Faculty
of Medicine
University of Alberta
Edmonton, Alberta
Canada

Paul D. Gunderson, *PhD*
Marshfield Clinic
National Farm Medicine Center
Marshfield, Wisconsin
United States

J.C. Gunther, Jr.*
Safety and Training Engineer
Imperial Highway Authority
Addis Ababa
Ethiopia

---

* Contributor to the 3rd edition of this **Encyclopaedia.** This biographical information has not been updated.

H

John G. Hadley, *PhD*
Corporate Toxicologist
Health Sciences
Owens-Corning
Granville, Ohio
United States

Hans Hamrin, *MSc*
Senior Adviser
Mining
Atlas Copco Rock Drills AB
Stockholm
Sweden

Jonathan T. Haney, *MS*
Manlius, New York
United States

David L. Hard, *PhD*
Research Safety Engineer
Division of Safety Research
National Institute for Occupational Safety
   and Health
Morgantown, West Virginia
United States

Francis Hardy, *P Eng*
Project Coordinator
Construction Safety Association of Ontario
South Etobicoke, Ontario
Canada

D.A. Hargrave*
Her Majesty's District Inspector of Factories
Hamilton
United Kingdom

Susan Harman, *MSLS, MEd*
Associate Librarian
Medical and Chirurgical Faculty of
   Maryland
Baltimore, Maryland
United States

Robert Harris, *PhD CIH*
Professor Emeritus
University of North Carolina at
   Chapel Hill
Chapel Hill, North Carolina
United States

**Thomas E. Hawkinson, *MS, CIH,
   ROH, CSP***
Safety and Environmental Engineering Manager
General Mills
Minneapolis, Minnesota
United States

Dick Heederik, *PhD, MSc*
Associate Professor of Occupational Epidemiology
University of Wageningen
Wageningen
The Netherlands

Rudolf Heinrich, *PhD*
Chief
Forest Harvesting, Trade and Marketing
   Branch
Food and Agriculture Organization of the
   United Nations
Rome
Italy

**Jonathan P. Hellerstein, *MS, CIH,
   CSP***
Leader
Occupational Health and Safety
Owens-Corning
Toledo, Ohio
United States

Samuel H. Henao
Principal Technical Assessor
National Manager of Occupational Health
Institute of Social Security
Bogotá
Colombia

Robin Herbert, *MD*
Medical Co-Director
Mount Sinai Center for Environmental
   and Occupational Medicine
New York, New York
United States

Fred W. Hermann, *MSc, BSc, BA*
Chief Inspector of Mines
Ministry of Employment and Investment
Victoria, British Columbia
Canada

Thomas A. Hethmon, *MS, CIH, ROH*
Director
Occupational Health and Safety
Phelps Dodge Corporation
Phoenix, Arizona
United States

Jeffrey Hinksman, *BA Law*
Health and Safety Consultant
Epsom, Surrey
United Kingdom

Matthew Hirsheimer, *BS*
National Safety Manager
Safety and Risk Management
Pepsi-Cola Company
Somers, New York
United States

Robert W. Hites, *BS, AAS*
Corporate Safety Analyst
Delta Airlines
Atlanta, Georgia
United States

Friedrich Hofmann, *PhD, MD*
Professor of Occupational Medicine
University of Wuppertal
Wuppertal
Germany

Charles M. Hohman, *BSME, MBA*
Technical Consultant
East Ohio Machinery Company
Newark, Ohio
United States

Wendy Hord
Occupational Safety and Health Specialist
Civil Service Employees Association
Latham, New York
United States

Ninica Howard, *MS*
Ergonomist
SHARP
Department of Labor and Industries
Olympia, Washington
United States

M. J. Howes, *PhD*
Partner
RHP Consultants
Camborne, Cornwall
United Kingdom

Gordon Huie, *MD*
Insall Scott Kelly Institute
New York, New York
United States

Vilma Hunt, *BDS, AM*
Adjunct Professor
Department of Work Environment
University of Massachusetts-Lowell
Lowell, Massachusetts
United States

David L. Huntzinger, *PhD*, *M Sci*
Vice-President
Corporate Safety
America West Airlines
Phoenix, Arizona
United States

Marit Husmo, *MSc*
Research Fellow
Norwegian College of Fishery Science
University of Tromso
Tromso
Norway

William E. Irwin, *MS, MBA*
*Health Physics Consultant, Radiation Safety
   Officer*
Massachusetts Institute of Technology
Cambridge, Massachusetts
United States

---

* Contributor to the 3rd edition of this ***Encyclopaedia.*** This biographical information has not been updated.

A. Lee Ivester, *MSPH*
Director
Corporate Safety and Workers'
  Compensation
Fieldcrest Cannon, Inc.
Kannapolis, North Carolina
United States

Anthony W. Jackson, *PhD*
Senior Health and Safety Advisor
Fossil Business Unit
Ontario Hydro-Fossil
Toronto, Ontario
Canada

Lars Järup, *MD, PhD*
Environmental Physician
Department of Environmental Health
Sundyberg
Sweden

Norman S. Jennings, *BSc*
Senior Industrial Specialist
Sectoral Activities Department
International Labour Office
Geneva
Switzerland

G. Jensen*
Assistant Director
Danish Labour Inspection Service
Copenhagen
Denmark

Barry L. Johnson, *PhD*
Assistant Surgeon General, Assistant Administrator
Agency for Toxic Substances and Disease
  Registry
Atlanta, Georgia
United States

Steven Johnson, *PhD*
Specialist
Cooperative Extension
University of Maine
Presque Isle, Maine
United States

Alan D. Jones,
Fire Services Advisor
Alberta Fire Training School
Alberta Labour
Vermillion, Alberta
Canada

J.G. Jones, *Dr**
Group Medical Officer
British Steel Corporation, South Wales
  Group
London
United Kingdom

D.D. Joshi, *DVM, MPVM*
Director
National Zoonoses and Food Hygiene
  Research Center
Katmandu
Nepal

Marja-Liisa Juntunen, *MSc*
Research Scientist
Suonenjoki Research Station
Finnish Forest Research Institute
Suonenjoki
Finland

Mike Jurvélius, *BSc*
Senior Consultant
ENSO Forest Development
Imatra
Finland

Yu S. Kagan, *MD, PhD*
Head of Department of General Toxicology
National Institute of Health
Kiev
Ukraine

Juhani Kangas, *PhD, Professor*
Director of the Regional Institute
Finnish Institute of Occupational Health
Kuopio
Finland

Valery P. Kaptsov
Director
Russian Institute of Railway Transport
  Hygiene
Moscow
Russian Federation

Thomas Karsky, *MS*
Extension Safety Specialist
Department of Biological and Agricultural
  Engineering
University of Idaho
Moscow, Idaho
United States

Timo Kauppinen, *PhD*
Head of Register Unit
Finnish Institute of Occupational Health
Helsinki
Finland

Anya Keefe, *MSc*
Research Associate
Occupational Hygiene Program
University of British Columbia
Vancouver, British Columbia
Canada

Anat Keidar, *PhD, CCC-SLP*
Voice Laboratory Director
Vox Humana Voice Laboratory,
  Head and Neck Surgical Group
New York Center for Voice and
  Swallowing Disorders
New York, New York
United States

Barry P. Kelley, *PhD*
Occupational Hygienist
Chloride Industrial Batteries, Ltd.
Manchester
United Kingdom

Susan Kennedy, *PhD*
Associate Professor, Director
Occupational Hygiene Programme
University of British Columbia
Vancouver, British Columbia
Canada

Robert W. Kilpper, *PhD*
Senior Toxicologist
Xerox Corporation
Webster, New York
United States

W. Klost, *Dipl-Ing**
Chief Engineer
Arbeitssicherheit Siemens AG
Berlin
Germany

L.W. Knapp, Jr.*
Department of Preventive Medicine and
  Environmental Health
Institute of Agricultural Medicine
University of Iowa
Iowa City, Iowa
United States

Stephanie Knopp, *MFA*
Associate Professor of Graphic Design
Tyler School of Art
Philadelphia, Pennsylvania
United States

Y.C. Ko, *MD**
Institute of Public Health
College of Medicine
National Taiwan University
Taipei
Taiwan, China

Eero Korhonen, *MSc*
Senior Researcher
Institute of Occupational Health
Vantaa
Finland

---

* Contributor to the 3rd edition of this **Encyclopaedia.** This biographical information has not been updated.

Ludmila P. Korotich
Leading Scientific Researcher
Department of Hygienic Research
RAMS Institute of Occupational Health
Moscow
Russian Federation

Richard S. Kraus, *PE, CSP*
Principal
Petroleum Safety Consultants
Annandale, Virginia
United States

J. Kroeger, *Dipl-Chem**
Mutual Accident Insurance Association of
   the Chemical Industry
Heidelberg
Germany

J. Kubota, *MD**
Director
Occupational Health Service Center
Tokyo
Japan

Yuri Kundiev, *MD, Dr med sci*
Director
Institute for Occupational Health
Kiev
Ukraine

Lucie Laflamme, *PhD*
Senior Researcher
Department of Public Health Sciences
Karolinska Institute
Sundbyberg
Sweden

Paul A. Landsbergis, *EdD, MPH*
Assistant Professor of Epidemiology
Division of Hypertension
Cornell University Medical College
New York, New York
United States

Sverre Langård
Centre of Occupational and
   Environmental Medicine
National Hospital
Oslo
Norway

Donald V. Lassiter, *PhD, MSPH*
Consultant
Environmental and Occupational Health
San Jose, California
United States

Wolfgang Laurig, *Dr-Ing*
Professor, Director
Department of Ergonomics
Institut für Arbeitsphysiologie
University of Dortmund
Dortmund
Germany

P.K. Law*
Group Manager
British Plastics Federation
London
United Kingdom

Pam Tau Lee
Labor Occupational Health Program
University of California-Berkeley
Berkeley, California
United States

Susan B. Lee, *MBA, CIH*
Manager
Environmental Health and Safety
Biogen, Inc.
Cambridge, Massachusetts
United States

David LeGrande, *MA*
Director
Occupational Safety and Health
Communications Workers of America
Washington, DC
United States

Carol J. Lehtola, *PhD*
Assistant Professor
Institute of Food and Agricultural Science
Department of Agricultural and Biological
   Engineering
University of Florida
Gainesville, Florida
United States

Steven W. Lenhart, *CIH*
Industrial Hygienist
Division of Surveillance, Hazard
   Evaluations and Field Studies
National Institute for Occupational Safety
   and Health
Cincinnati, Ohio
United States

Yung Hian Leow, *MD*
Section of Industrial Dermatology
Cleveland Clinic Foundation
Cleveland, Ohio
United States

Charles Levenstein, *PhD, MS*
Professor of Work Environment Policy
Work Environment Department
University of Massachusetts-Lowell
Lowell, Massachusetts
United States

Robert M. Lewy, *MD, MPH*
Director for Medical Affairs
Columbia Presbyterian Medical Center
New York, New York
United States

Norbert Lichtenstein, *PhD*
Berufsgenossenschaftliches Institut für
   Arbeitssicherheit
Sankt Augustin
Germany

Hans Göran Linder, *PhD*
National Board of Occupational Safety
   and Health
Solna
Sweden

Sydney Lipton, *MS*
Consultant
Port Townsend, Washington
United States

J.W.G. Lund, *MD**
Freshwater Biological Association
Windermere Laboratory
Ambleside
United Kingdom

John Lund, *PhD*
Professor
School for Workers
University of Wisconsin-Extension
Madison, Wisconsin
United States

Paul V. Lynch, *PE*
Chief, Safety Staff (Retired)
Bureau of Land Management
United States Department of the Interior
Washington, DC
United States

G.S. Lyndon*
Senior Area Director
West Midlands Area Office
Health and Safety Executive
Birmingham
United Kingdom

Paul Mackenzie-Wood, *BSc*
Manager, Technology
Coal Mines Technical Services
Mines Rescue Services
Corrimal
Australia

Susan Magor, *RN, MSc*
Director
Environment, Health and Safety
Concordia University
Montreal, Quebec
Canada

* Contributor to the 3rd edition of this ***Encyclopaedia.*** This biographical information has not been updated.

Andreas Mahr, *Dipl-Ing*
Technischer Aufsichtsbeamter
Bahnen-Berufsgenossenschaft
Hamburg
Germany

Kathryn A. Makos, *MPH, CIH*
Senior Industrial Hygienist
Office of Environmental Management
    and Safety
Smithsonian Institution
Washington, DC
United States

M. Malagié, *Ing**
Institut national de recherche et de
    sécurité pour la prévention des accidents
    du travail et des maladies
    professionnelles
Paris
France

Bohuslav Málek
Hygienic Institute of Prague
Prague
Czech Republic

David E. Malter, *MS, CIH, CSP,
    ROH*
Malter Associates, Inc.
Downer Grove, Illinois
United States

Adrienne Markowitz, *MSc*
Director of Health and Safety
Retail, Wholesale and Department Store
    Union
United Food and Commercial Workers,
    AFL-CIO
New York, New York
United States

William S. Marras, *PhD*
Professor, Director
Biodynamics Laboratory
Department of Industrial and Systems
    Engineering
Columbus, Ohio
United States

Linda S. Martin, *PhD*
Director, HIV Activity
National Institute for Occupational Safety
    and Health
Altanta, Georgia
United States

John Masaitis, *CIH*
Consultant
New Smyrna Beach, Florida
United States

Steve Mason, *BS*
Senior Manager, Chemical Technology
Operations Technology
Boeing Commercial Airplane Group
The Boeing Company
Seattle, Washington
United States

K.R. Mathisen*
Mechanical Engineering Division
Swedish Standard Commission
Stockholm
Sweden

Toshio Matsushita, *MD, PhD*
Professor
Faculty of Medicine
Kagoshima University
Kagoshima
Japan

Chester Matthews
Bath Iron Works
Brunswick, Maine
United States

R. Mattiussi, *Dr**
Direttore Sanitario
Montedison
Milan
Italy

John May, *MD*
Director
New York Center for Agricultural
    Medicine and Health
Mary Imogene Bassett Hospital
Coopertown, New York
United States

Michael McCann, *PhD, CIH*
Senior Associate Editor
Encyclopaedia of Occupational Health and Safety
International Labour Office
New York, New York
United States

George J. McDonald
Director of Safety and Health
International Transport Workers Union
    of America
New York, New York
United States

Bruce McKay
Senior Researcher
SeaWeb
Montreal, Quebec
Canada

Shane McMahon, *MSc*
Program Manager
Liro Limited
Rotorua
New Zealand

Neil McManus, *MSc, M Eng*
Consulting Industrial Hygienist
NorthWest Occupational Health and
    Safety
North Vancouver, British Columbia
Canada

Nona McQuay, *MS*
Health and Safety Specialist
New York State Public Employees
    Federation, AFL-CIO
Buffalo, New York
United States

Doug J. McVittie, *Dipl Eng*
Manager-Technical Services
Construction Safety Association of Ontario
Etobicoke, Ontario
Canada

Karlheinz Meffert, *Dr-Ing*
Director
Berufsgenossenschaftliches Institut für
    Arbeitssicherheit
Hauptverband der gewerblichen
    Berufsgenossenschaften
Sankt Augustin
Germany

Ronald L. Melnick, *PhD*
Toxicologist
National Institute of Environmental
    Health Sciences
Research Triangle Park, North Carolina
United States

Raji Menon
Research Officer
Mining Association of Canada
Ottawa, Ontario
Canada

Karen Messing, *PhD*
Professor of Biology
CINBIOSE
University of Quebec
Montreal, Quebec
Canada

Jacqueline Messite, *MD*
Clinical Professor
Department of Environmental Medicine
New York University College of Medicine
New York, New York
United States

* Contributor to the 3rd edition of this *Encyclopaedia.* This biographical information has not been updated.

Mark M. Methner, PhD
Industrial Hygienist
Division of Surveillance, Hazard
    Evaluation and Field Studies
National Institute for Occupational Safety
    and Health
Cincinnati, Ohio
United States

John D. Meyer, MD, MPH
Associate Residency Director
Institute of Occupational and
    Environmental Health
West Virginia University School of
    Medicine
Morgantown, West Virginia
United States

Jack L. Mickle, PhD
Professor Emeritus, Consultant
Jack L. Mickle and Associates
Boone, Iowa
United States

John Miles, PhD
Department of Agricultural Engineering
University of California-Davis
Davis, California
United States

Frank Miller, PhD
Hazardous Materials Officer
Environmental Health and Safety Office
Columbia University Health Sciences
New York, New York
United States

Gordon C. Miller, MSPH
Director
Health, Safety and Environment
Rexam, Inc.
Charlotte, North Carolina
United States

Bruce A. Millies, JD, MS, CIH
Industrial Hygienist
International Brotherhood of Teamsters
Bainbridge Island, Washington
United States

Franklin E. Mirer, PhD
Director
Health and Safety Department
International Union of United Auto
    Workers
Detroit, Michigan
United States

Courtney S. Mitchell, MSc, MA
Consultant
CSM Consulting
Golden, Colorado
United States

William S. Mitchell, MSc
Manager, Exploration Administration
BHP Minerals International Exploration,
    Inc.
Golden, Colorado
United States

Augustine Moffitt, ScD
Vice-President
Safety, Health and Environment
Bethlehem Steel Corporation
Pennsylvania
United States

W.G. Morison, BSc, MSc
President
Morwil Inc.
Ontario
Canada

K.M. Morse*
Industrial Health Engineers, Inc.
Altamonte Springs, Florida
United States

Robert J. Mullan, MD
Medical Officer
Centers for Disease Control and
    Prevention
National Institute for Occupational Safety
    and Health
Atlanta, Georgia
United States

Kieran Mulvaney
Editor
Ocean Update
SeaWeb
Washington, DC
United States

Eva Munk-Madsen, PhD
Teacher, Lecturer
Norwegian College of Fishery Science
University of Tromso
Tromso
Norway

R.A. Munoz, MSW*
Subdirector
Technical Programming Department of
    Education
Hato Rey
Puerto Rico

Dennis Murphy, PhD, CSP
Professor
Department of Agricultural and Biological
    Engineering
Pennsylvania State University
University Park, Pennsylvania
United States

Daniel Murphy, MB, FFOM, DIH
Director
Occupational Medical Services
National Authority for Occupational
    Safety and Health
Dublin
Ireland

Joshua E. Muscat, MPH
American Health Foundation
New York, New York
United States

Melvin L. Myers, BS, MPA
Deputy Director
Office of Extramural Coordination and
    Special Projects
National Institute for Occupational Safety
    and Health
Atlanta, Georgia
United States

Pranab Kumar Nag, PhD, DSc, MSc
Deputy Director
Indian Council of Medical Research
National Institute of Occupational Health
Ahmedabad
India

John D. Neefus, PhD, CIH
Industrial Hygiene Consultant
Durham, North Carolina
United States

Barbara Neis, PhD
Associate Professor, Head
Department of Sociology
Memorial University
St. John's, Newfoundland
Canada

Christian E. Newcomer, VMD
Director, Research Associate Professor
Laboratory Animal Medicine
University of North Carolina
Chapel Hill, North Carolina
United States

A.K. Niyogi, MBDPH, DIH*
University Grants Commission Fellow
Department of Preventive and Social
    Medicine
Institute of Medical Sciences
Varanasi
India

Susan Nobel, MSW, CSW
Mount Sinai-Irving J. Selikoff Center for
    Occupational and Environmental
    Medicine
Mount Sinai Medical Center
New York, New York
United States

* Contributor to the 3rd edition of this **Encyclopaedia.** This biographical information has not been updated.

Gunnar Nordberg
Department of Environmental Medicine
University of Umeå
Umeå
Sweden

Jacqueline Nubé, *Dr*
Department of Psychology
Faculty of Methodology
University of Amsterdam
Amsterdam
The Netherlands

Hulda Ólafsdóttir, *MS*
Physiotherapist
Department of Occupational Medicine
Administration of Occupational Safety
   and Health
Reykjavik
Iceland

Edward A. Olmsted, *CIH, CSP*
President
Olmsted Environmental Services
Garrison, New York
United States

Gary W. Olmstead, *PhD, CIH, CSP*
Director
Safety and Environmental Management
General Mills
Minneapolis, Minnesota
United States

David A. O'Malley, *MSc*
Managing Director
Diamond Environmental Ltd.
Chester
United Kingdom

George R. Osborne, *CIH, CSP*
Industrial Hygiene Manager
Lucent Technologies
Norcross, Georgia
United States

Debra Osinsky, *MPH*
Editorial Consultant
Encyclopaedia of Occupational Health and Safety
International Labour Office
Highland Park, New Jersey
United States

Gary A. Page *BS, MS, MBA*
Fertilizer and Agricultural Chemicals
National Safety Council
Ridgewood, New Jersey
United States

N.M. Pant, *Dr, MBBS, DPH**
Medical Officer
Hindustan Lever, Ltd.
Bombay
India

Jon Parish, *BBA*
Director
Loss Control and Environment
Lane Corporation
Altavista, Virginia
United States

Robert M. Park, *MS*
Project Epidemiologist
Health and Safety Department
International Union of United Auto
   Workers
Detroit, Michigan
United States

Relford Patterson, *MD, MPH*
Medical Director
GM Truck Group-Baltimore Assembly
   Plant
General Motors Corporation
Baltimore, Maryland
United States

Gerald F. Peedin, *PhD*
Philip Morris Professor
Crop Science Department
North Carolina State University
Raleigh, North Carolina
United States

Peter W. Pickerill, *BSc, M Eng, MBA*
Regional Director
Asia and Australia
MSA International
Pittsburgh, Pennsylvania
United States

Alexander C. Pittman, Jr., *Dr*
Con Edison
Brooklyn, New York
United States

Philip A. Platcow, *MS, CIH*
Vice-President, Senior Consultant
Risk Management
Sedgwick
Boston, Massachusetts
United States

James W. Platner, *PhD, CIH*
Industrial and Labor Relations
Cornell University
Albany, New York
United States

Rebecca Plattus, *JD*
Political Education Director
Local 89-22-1
Union of Needletrades, Industrial and
   Textile Employees
New York, New York
United States

Lou Piombino, *BS*
Manager
Safety, Health and Environment
Lipton, Inc.
Englewood Cliffs, New Jersey
United States

Bengt Pontén
Forest and Timber Group
Dalarna University
Borlänge
Sweden

William Popendorf, *PhD, CIH*
Professor
Department of Biology
Utah State University
Logan, Utah
United States

Paulo Portich
Fundacentro
Porte Alegre, Rio Grande do Sul
Brazil

Peter Poschen, *PhD*
Forestry and Wood Industries Specialist
Industrial Activities Branch
International Labour Office
Geneva
Switzerland

Christine Proctor, *MS, CIH*
Proctor Occupational Safety and Health
New York, New York
United States

L. Prodan, *Dr**
CLUJ-NAPOCA
Romania

John Quackenbush
International Representative
International Union of Elevator
   Constructors
Springfield, Virginia
United States

A.E. Quinn, *BSc, LLB**
Former Her Majesty's Inspector of Factories
London
United Kingdom

M.E. Radjabi, *Ing**
Assistant Director General, Labour Inspection
Ministry of Labour and Social Affairs
Tehran
Islamic Republic of Iran

* Contributor to the 3rd edition of this ***Encyclopaedia***. This biographical information has not been updated.

Vilhjálmur Rafnsson, MD, PhD
Chief Medical Director
Department of Occupational Medicine
Administration of Occupational Safety
    and Health
Reykjavík
Iceland

Ray RaLonde, MS
Agriculture Specialist
School of Fisheries and Ocean Sciences
University of Alaska
Anchorage, Alaska
United States

Russell B. Rayman, MD, MPH
Executive Director
Aerospace Medical Association
Alexandria, Virginia
United States

Beth Donovan Reh, MHS
Industrial Hygienist
Hazard Evaluations and Technical
    Assistance Branch
National Institute for Occupational Safety
    and Health
Cincinnati, Ohio
United States

John Reimer, P Eng
Environmental Protection Engineer
Health Science Centre
Winnipeg, Manitoba
Canada

Toni Retsch, Dipl.-Ing, ETH*
Bereichsleiter-ALM2
Swiss National Accident Insurance
    Organization
Luzern
Switzerland

Thomas Rhodarmer, BSc
*Corporate Director Environmental Health and
    Safety*
Mark IV Industries Worldwide
Dayco/Mark IV
Waynesville, North Carolina
United States

David Richardson, MPH, DABT
Unit Director, Applied and Regulatory Toxicology
Health and Environment Laboratories
Eastman Kodak Inc.
Rochester, New York
United States

Sandra Karen Richman
Safety Consultant
National Board of Directors
American Federation of Television and
    Radio Artists
New Hope, Pennsylvania
United States

Ted Rickard, MLS, CRSP
Manager of Health, Safety and Security
Ontario College of Art & Design
Toronto, Ontario
Canada

Knut Ringen, Dr PH
Director
Center to Protect Workers' Rights
Washington, DC
United States

Richard D. Ringenwald, Jr., Dr
Exide Corporation
Reading, Pennsylvania
United States

Jorge da Rocha Gomes
Professor Emeritus
Department of Environmental Health,
    School of Public Health
University of São Paulo
São Paulo
Brazil

John G. Rodwan, Jr., MA
International Labour Office
Geneva
Switzerland

T. A. Roščina, Dr*
First Medical Moscow Institute
Moscow
Former USSR

Jonathan Rosen, MS, CIH
Director
Occupational Health and Safety Program
New York State Public Employees
    Federation, AFL-CIO
Albany, New York
United States

Beth Rosenberg, ScD
Assistant Professor
Department of Family Medicine and
    Community Health
Tufts School of Medicine
Boston, Massachusetts
United States

Monona Rossol, MS, MFA
Industrial Hygienist
Arts, Crafts and Theater Safety
New York, New York
United States

Pekka Roto, MD, MSc, PhD
Medical Officer
Tampere Regional Institute of
    Occupational Health
Tampere
Finland

James R. Rubin, MS
Environmental Health and Safety Specialist
Hewlett-Packard Company
Fort Collins, Colorado
United States

Avima M. Ruder, PhD
Chief
Division of Surveillance, Hazard
    Evaluations and Field Studies
National Institute for Occupational Safety
    and Health
Cincinnati, Ohio
United States

L.A. Ryzik, Dr*
Institute of Industrial Hygiene and
    Occupational Diseases
Leningrad
Former USSR

S

David M. Sack, MD
Navy Environmental Health Center
United States Navy
Norfolk, Virginia
United States

Joyce Salg, PhD
Senior Research Scientist
National Institute for Occupational Safety
    and Health
Cincinnati, Ohio
United States

Igor V. Sanotsky, MD, PhD, Prof
Adviser for Science
Institute of Occupational Health
Russian Academy of Medical Sciences
Moscow
Russian Federation

Steven L. Sauter, PhD
Chief
Applied Psychology and Ergonomics
    Branch
National Institute for Occupational Safety
    and Health
Cincinnati, Ohio
United States

E. Neil Schachter, MD
Maurice Hexter Professor of Medicine
Pulmonary Division
Mount Sinai Medical Center
New York, New York
United States

---

* Contributor to the 3rd edition of this ***Encyclopaedia***. This biographical information has not been updated.

Ted Scharf, *PhD*
Division of Biomedical and Behavioral
 Science
National Institute for Occupational Safety
 and Health
Cincinnati, Ohio
United States

Marc B. Schenker, *MD, MPH*
Director
University of California Agricultural
 Health and Safety Center
University of California-Davis
Davis, California
United States

H. Schneider, *Dr med**
Former Medical Director
KRUPP Hüttenwerke AG
Duisburg
Germany

Scott P. Schneider, *MSIH, CIH*
Ergonomics Program Director
Center to Protect Workers' Rights
Washington, DC
United States

Rudolf Scholbeck, *Dipl-Ing Univ*
Head
Technical Inspection Service
Tiefbau-Berufsgenossenschaft
Munich
Germany

Stanley H. Schuman, *MD, PhD,*
 MPH
Professor
Family Medicine
Agromedicine Program
Clemson University
Medical Director
Occupational and Environmental
 Medicine Office
Medical University of South Carolina
Charleston, South Carolina
United States

Charles Schwab, *PhD*
Associate Professor
Agricultural and Biosystems Engineering
Iowa State University
Ames, Iowa
United States

W. Norman Scott, *MD*
Director
Insall Scott Kelly Institute
New York, New York
United States

Jane L. Seegal
Editor
Center to Protect Workers' Rights
Washington, DC
United States

Rita Seguin, *BA*
Safety and Disability Manager
Hiram Walker and Sons, Ltd.
Walkerville, Ontario
Canada

Logan C. Shelman, *BS, ChE, MEA*
Senior Environmental Engineer
Environmental Health and Safety
 Department
Newport News Shipbuilding
Newport News, Virginia
United States

Konstantin K. Sidorov, *Dr med sci*
Deputy Director
Russian Registry of Hazardous Chemical
 and Biological Substances
Moscow
Russian Federation

Itzhak Siev-Ner, *MD*
Orthopedic Surgeon, Physical Medicine and
 Rehabilitation
Sheba Medical Center, Tel-Hashomer
Israel Performing Arts Medicine Center
Tel Aviv
Israel

Ken Sims
Director
Thrigby Hall Wildlife Gardens
Great Yarmouth
United Kingdom

Donald L. Smith, *CIH, CSP, PE, DEE*
Nabisco, Inc.
East Hanover, New Jersey
United States

N.A. Smith, *PhD*
Lighting Consultant
Doncaster
United Kingdom

Marianne Smukowski, *BS*
Dairy Safety Applications Coodinator
Center for Dairy Research
University of Wisconsin-Madison
Madison, Wisconsin
United States

Jack W. Snyder, *MD, JD, MPH, PhD*
Associate Professor
Emergency Medicine and Laboratory
 Medicine
Thomas Jefferson University
Philadelphia, Pennsylvania
United States

Jerzy A. Sokal, *Prof, PhD, DSc*
Director
Institute of Occupational Medicine and
 Environmental Health
Sosnowiec
Poland

Colin L. Soskolne, *PhD*
Professor, Director of Graduate Training
Department of Public Health Sciences
University of Alberta
Edmonton, Alberta
Canada

Jerry Spiegel, *MA, MSc*
Director
Pollution Prevention
Manitoba Environment
Winnipeg, Manitoba
Canada

J. Staal*
Technical Secretary
Fédération européenne de la manutention,
 Section VII: ascenseurs, lifts, Aufzüge
Amsterdam
The Netherlands

Lorann Stallones, *PhD, MPH*
Department of Environmental Health
Colorado State University
Fort Collins, Colorado
United States

Roger Stamm, *Dr*
Head of Central Department
Berufsgenossenschaftliches Institut für
 Arbeitssicherheit
Hauptverband der gewerblichen
 Berufsgenossenschaften
Sankt Augustin
Germany

William E. Steinke, *PhD*
Extension Agricultural Engineer
Biological and Agricultural Engineering
 Department
University of California-Davis
Davis, California
United States

---

* Contributor to the 3rd edition of this **Encyclopaedia.** This biographical information has not been updated.

Jeanne M. Stellman, PhD
Editor-in-Chief
Encyclopaedia of Occupational Health and Safety
International Labour Office
Geneva
Switzerland

School of Public Health
Columbia University
New York, New York
United States

Steven D. Stellman, PhD, MPH
Chief
Division of Epidemiology
American Health Foundation
New York, New York
United States

Frank B. Stern, BBA, MS
Senior Research Epidemiologist
National Institute for Occupational Safety
    and Health
Cincinnati, Ohio
United States

Laura Stock, MPH
Labor Occupational Health Program
School of Public Health
University of California-Berkeley
Berkeley, California
United States

Ulrich Stössel, Dr phil
Academic Lecturer
Department of Medical Sociology
Medical Faculty
University of Freiburg
Freiburg
Germany

J.M. Strother, BS
Manager
Research Analytical and Finishing
    Laboratory
Fieldcrest Cannon, Inc.
Kannopolis, North Carolina
United States

Dean T. Stueland, MD, MPH
Medical Director
National Farm Medicine Center
Marshfield Clinic
Marshfield, Wisconsin
United States

E.A. Suchman, PhD*
Department of Sociology
University of California
Santa Barbara, California
United States

F. William Sunderman, Jr., MD
Professor
Departments of Laboratory Medicine and
    Pharmacology
University of Connecticut Medical School
Farmington, Connecticut
United States

John J. Svagr, CIH
Manager
Industrial Hygiene and Safety-North
    America
Safety and Risk Management Department
Kraft Foods
Rye Brook, New York
United States

William B. Symons, PhD
Associate Professor
Biological Systems Engineering
    Department
Washington State University
Pullman, Washington
United States

Keith Tait, CIH, CSP
Assistant Director
Corporate Health and Safety
Pfizer, Inc.
New York, New York
United States

James S. Taylor, MD
Head
Industrial Dermatology
Cleveland Clinic Foundation
Cleveland, Ohio
United States

Benedetto Terracini, MD
Former Head
Unit of Cancer Epidemiology
University Hospital and University of
    Turin
Turin
Italy

Kay Teschke, PhD, MPH, CIH, ROH
Associate Professor
Department of Health Care and
    Epidemiology
University of British Columbia
Vancouver, British Columbia
Canada

Jamie Tessler, MPH
Occupational Health and Safety Consultant
Brooklyn, New York
United States

Richard J. Thomas, MD, MPH
Officer in Charge, Occupational Medicine
Physician
Navy Environmental and Preventive
    Medicine Unit
United States Navy
Norfolk, Virginia
United States

G. Thomas*
Research Department
British Steel Corporation
Deeside
United Kingdom

Frank H. Thorn, BS
Manager, Environmental Engineering
Environmental Health and Safety
    Department
Newport News Shipbuilding
Newport News, Virginia
United States

James R. Thornton, MS, CIH, CSP
Director, Environmental Health and Safety
Environmental Health and Safety
    Department
Newport News Shipbuilding
Newport News, Virginia
United States

Kendall Thu, PhD
Institute for Rural and Environmental
    Health
College of Medicine
Iowa City, Iowa
United States

Kjell Torén, MD
Associate Professor
Department of Occupational Medicine
Sahlgrenska University Hospital
Göteborg
Sweden

James R. Townhill, CSP
Piedmont Environmental, Inc.
Kannapolis, North Carolina
United States

John N. Trent, PhD
Wildlife Biologist
Division of Wildlife Conservation
Alaska Department of Fish and Game
Anchorage, Alaska
United States

Don Trotter, M Eng
Professor
School of Engineering
Laurentian University
Sudbury, Ontario
Canada

---

* Contributor to the 3rd edition of this **Encyclopaedia**. This biographical information has not been updated.

A. Türkdogan, _Ing-Chim_*
Former Industrial Safety Inspector
Istanbul
Turkey

Timothy J. Ungs, _MD, MS_
Commandant (G-WKS-3)
United States Coast Guard Headquarters
Washington, DC
United States

L.J.L.D. Van Griensven, _PhD_
Professor
Applied Mycology
Catholic University of Nijmegen
Director
Mushroom Experimental Station
Horst
The Netherlands

Anaide Vilasboas de Andrade
Chief of Technical Services
Centro Regional da Bahia
Fundação Jorge Duprat Figueiredo de
    Segurança e Medicina do Trabalho
Salvador
Brazil

R.F. Villard*
Ingénieur EPUL
Chargé de cours à l'Ecole supérieure
    technique de Genève
Geneva
Switzerland

Phillip J. Wakelyn, _PhD_
Senior Scientist, Environmental Health Safety
National Cotton Council of America
Washington, DC
United States

Simon Walker, _BSc, MSc_
Principal
IETS
Oxford
United Kingdom

Anthony D. Walters, _M Eng_
Manager
Coal Division
Kilborn Engineering Pacific, Ltd.
Vancouver, British Columbia
Canada

Jung-Der Wang, _MD, ScD, MIH_
Professor
Institute of Occupational Medicine and
    Epidemiology
National Taiwan University College of
    Public Health
Taipei
Taiwan, China

Lance A. Ward, _BA_
Corporate Director of Health and Safety
Pepsi-Cola General Bottlers, Inc.
Rolling Meadows, Illinois
United States

Leon J. Warshaw, _MD_
Clinical Professor
Department of Environmental Medicine
New York University
New York, New York
United States

James L. Weeks, _ScD, CIH_
Department of Occupational and
    Environmental Health
School of Public Health and Health
    Services
George Washington University
Washington, DC
United States

Beat Wegmüller
Safety Engineer
Swiss National Accident Insurance
    Organization
Luzern
Switzerland

Merri Weinger, _MPH_
Office of Global and Integrated
    Environmental Health
World Health Organization
Geneva
Switzerland

K. Welinder*
Research Director
Slipmaterial-Naxos
Vastervik
Sweden

Paul Westcott, _B Eng_
Director, Consulting Mining Engineer
MineConsult
Chatswood, New South Wales
Australia

Othmar Wettmann, _Dipl Forest Ing, ETH_
Head
Forestry Section
Swiss National Accident Insurance
    Organization
Luzern
Switzerland

Aidan White
General Secretary
International Federation of Journalists
Brussels
Belgium

Michael E. Williams, _CIH, CSP, ARM_
Principal
Health Safety and Risk Management
    Services
Sunnyvale, California
United States

Linda B. Wolfe, _RBP_
Associate Biosafety Officer
Environmental Medical Service
Massachusetts Institute of Technology
Cambridge, Massachusetts
United States

Malinee Wongphanich, _MD_
Consultant on Occupational Health
Department of Health
Ministry of Health
Nondhaburi Province
Thailand

Ray C. Woodcock, _MS, CIH_
Vice-President
Safety and Hygiene Management, Inc.
Waynesville, North Carolina
United States

B. H. Xu, _PhD, MD_
Assistant Professor
Faculty of Medicine
Kagoshima University
Kagoshima
Japan

Annalee Yassi, _MD, MSc_
Director
Occupational and Environmental
    Medicine
Health Sciences Centre and Unit
University of Manitoba
Winnipeg, Manitoba
Canada

Dennis D. Zaebst, _CIH_
Industrial Hygienist
National Institute for Occupational Safety
    and Health
Cincinnati, Ohio
United States

Albert M. Zielinski, _CIH_
Senior Technical Leader, Industrial Hygiene
Lighting Environment
Safety and Health Department
GE Lighting
Cleveland, Ohio
United States

---

* Contributor to the 3rd edition of this **_Encyclopaedia._** This biographical information has not been updated.

A. Zober, *Dr* *
Institute for Occupational Health and
    Social Medicine and Clinic for
    Occupational Diseases
University of Erlangen/Nuremberg
Erlangen
Germany

Craig Zwerling, *MD, PhD, MPH*
Injury Prevention Research Center
College of Medicine
Iowa City, Iowa
United States

* Contributor to the 3rd edition of this ***Encyclopaedia.*** This biographical information has not been updated.

CONTENTS

VOLUME 3

PART IX. CHEMICALS

PART X. INDUSTRIES BASED ON BIOLOGICAL RESOURCES

64. Agriculture and Natural Resources Based Industries

Melvin L. Myers,
Chapter Editor

65. Beverage Industry   Lance A. Ward, *Chapter Editor*

66. Fishing   Hulda Ólafsdóttir and Vilhjálmur Rafnsson, *Chapter Editors*

67. Food Industry — Deborah E. Berkowitz, *Chapter Editor*

68. Forestry — Peter Poschen, *Chapter Editor*

69. Hunting — George A. Conway, *Chapter Editor*

70. Livestock Rearing — Melvin L. Myers, *Chapter Editor*

71. Lumber   Paul Demers and Kay Teschke, *Chapter Editors*

72. Paper and Pulp Industry   Kay Teschke and Paul Demers, *Chapter Editors*

PART XIII. MANUFACTURING INDUSTRIES

PART XVI. CONSTRUCTION

PART XVII. SERVICES AND TRADE

96. Entertainment and the Arts

Michael McCann, *Chapter Editor*

USING, STORING AND TRANSPORTING CHEMICALS

61

Chapter Editors
*Jeanne Mager Stellman and
Debra Osinsky*

Contents

SAFE HANDLING AND USAGE OF CHEMICALS

The ILO Code of Practice*

The objective (section 1.1.1) of the ILO Code of Practice *Safety in the Use of Chemicals at Work* is to protect workers from the hazards of chemicals, to prevent or reduce the incidence of chemically-induced illnesses and injuries resulting from the use of chemicals at work, and consequently to enhance the protection of the general public and the environment by providing guidelines for:

- ensuring that all chemicals for use at work—including impurities, by-products and intermediates, and wastes that may be formed—are evaluated to determine their hazards
- ensuring that employers are provided with a mechanism for obtaining from their suppliers information about the chemicals used at work to enable them to implement effective programmes to protect workers from chemical hazards
- providing workers with information about the chemicals at their workplaces and about appropriate preventive measures to enable them to participate effectively in safety programmes
- establishing principles for such programmes to ensure that chemicals are used safely
- making special provision to protect confidential information, the disclosure of which to a competitor would be liable to cause harm to an employer's business, so long as the safety and health of workers are not compromised thereby.

Section 2 of the ILO Code of Practice outlines the general obligations, responsibilities and duties of the competent authority, the employer and the worker. The section also details the general responsibilities of suppliers and the rights of workers, and it offers guidelines regarding special provisions for the employer's disclosure of confidential information. The final recommendations address the need for cooperation among employers, workers and their representatives.

General Obligations, Responsibilities and Duties

It is the responsibility of the appropriate governmental agency to follow existing national measures and practices, in consultation with the most representative organizations of employers and workers concerned, in order to assure safety in the use of chemicals at work. National practices and laws should be viewed in the context of international regulations, standards and systems, and with the measures and practices recommended by the ILO Code of Practice and the ILO Convention No. 170 and Recommendation No. 177.

The major focus of such measures which provide for safety of workers are, in particular:

- the production and handling of hazardous chemicals
- the storage of hazardous chemicals

---

* Much of the information and excerpts in this chapter are taken from the Code of Practice *Safety in the Use of Chemicals at Work* of the International Labour Organization (ILO 1993). The ILO Code provides practical guidelines on the implementation of the provisions of the Chemicals Convention, 1990 (No. 170), and Recommendation, 1990 (No. 177). The object of the Code is to provide guidance to those who may be engaged in the framing of provisions relating to the use of chemicals at work, such as competent authorities, the management in companies where chemicals are supplied or used, and emergency services, which should also offer guidelines to suppliers', employers' and workers' organizations. The Code provides minimum standards and is not intended to discourage competent authorities from adopting higher standards.

For more detailed information on individual chemicals and chemical families, see the *Guide to chemicals* in Volume IV of this *Encyclopaedia*.

- the transport of hazardous chemicals, consistent with national or international transport regulations
- the disposal and treatment of hazardous chemicals and hazardous waste products, consistent with national or international regulations.

There are various means by which the competent authority may achieve this aim. It may enact national laws and regulations; adopt, approve or recognize existing standards, codes or guidelines; and, where such standards, codes or guidelines do not exist, an authority may encourage their adoption by another authority, which can then be recognized. The governmental agency may also require that employers justify the criteria by which they are working.

According to the Code of Practice (section 2.3.1), it is the responsibility of employers to set out, in writing, their policy and arrangements on safety in the use of chemicals, as part of their general policy and arrangements in the field of occupational safety and health, and the various responsibilities exercised under these arrangements, in accordance with the objectives and principles of the Occupational Safety and Health Convention, 1981 (No. 155), and Recommendation, 1981 (No. 164). This information should be brought to the attention of their workers in a language the latter readily understand.

Workers, in turn, should take care of their own health and safety, and that of other persons who may be affected by their acts or omissions at work, as far as possible and in accordance with their training and with instructions given by their employer (section 2.3.2).

The suppliers of chemicals, whether manufacturers, importers or distributors, should ensure that, in accordance with the guidelines in the relevant paragraphs of the Code and in pursuance of the requirements of Convention No. 170 and Recommendation No. 177:

- such chemicals have been classified or their properties assessed
- such chemicals are marked
- hazardous chemicals are labelled
- chemical safety data sheets for hazardous chemicals are prepared and provided to employers.

Operational Control Measures

Certain general principles exist for the operation control of chemicals at work. These are dealt with in Section 6 of the ILO Code of Practice, which prescribes that after reviewing the chemicals being used at work and obtaining information about their hazards and making an assessment of the potential risks involved, employers should take steps to limit exposure of workers to hazardous chemicals (on the basis of the measures outlined in sections 6.4 to 6.9 of the Code), in order to protect workers against hazards from the use of chemicals at work. The measures taken should eliminate or minimize the risks, preferably by *substitution* of non-hazardous or less hazardous chemicals, or by the choice of better *technology*. When neither substitution nor engineering control are feasible, other measures, such as safe working systems and practices, personal protective equipment (PPE) and the provision of information and training will further minimize risks and may have to be relied upon for some activities entailing the use of chemicals.

When workers are potentially exposed to chemicals that are hazardous to health, they must be safeguarded against the risk of injury or disease from these chemicals. There should be no exposure which exceeds exposure limits or other exposure criteria for the evaluation and control of the working environment established by the competent authority, or by a body approved or recognized by the competent authority in accordance with national or international standards.

Hazard communication: The chemical safety data sheet or the material safety data sheet (MSDS)

A systematic approach to safety requires an efficient flow of information from the suppliers to the users of chemicals on potential hazards and correct safety precautions. In addressing the need for a written hazard communication programme, the ILO Code of Practice *Safety in the Use of Chemicals at Work* (ILO 1993) states, "The supplier should provide an employer with essential information about hazardous chemicals in the form of a chemical safety data sheet." This chemical safety data sheet or material safety data sheet (MSDS) describes the hazards of a material and provides instructions on how the material can be safely handled, used and stored. MSDSs are produced by the manufacturer or importer of hazardous products. The manufacturer must provide distributors and other customers with MSDSs upon first purchase of a hazardous product and if the MSDS changes. Distributors of hazardous chemicals must automatically provide MSDSs to commercial customers. Under the ILO Code of Practice, workers and their representatives should have a right to an MSDS and to receive the written information in forms or languages they easily understand. Because some of the required information might be intended for specialists, further clarification may be needed from the employer. The MSDS is only one source of information on a material and, therefore, it is best used along with technical bulletins, labels, training and other communications.

The requirements for a written hazard communication programme are outlined in at least three major international directives: the US Occupational Safety and Health Administration (OSHA) Hazard Communication Standard, Canada's Workplace Hazardous Materials Information System (WHMIS) and the European Community's Commission Directive 91/155/EEC. In all three directives, the requirements for preparing a complete MSDS are established. Criteria for the data sheets include information about the identity of the chemical, its supplier, classification, hazards, safety precautions and the relevant emergency procedures. The following discussion details the type of required information included in the 1992 ILO Code of Practice *Safety in the Use of Chemicals at Work*. While the Code is not intended to replace national laws, regulations or accepted standards, its practical recommendations are intended for all those who have a responsibility for ensuring the safe use of workplace chemicals.

The following description of chemical safety data sheet content corresponds with section 5.3 of the Code:

Chemical safety data sheets for hazardous chemicals should give information about the identity of the chemical, its supplier, classification, hazards, safety precautions and the relevant emergency procedures.

The information to be included should be that established by the competent authority for the area in which the employer's premises are located, or by a body approved or recognized by that competent authority. Details of the type of information that should be required are given below.

(a) Chemical product and company identification

The name should be the same as that used on the label of the hazardous chemical, which may be the conventional chemical name or a commonly used trade name. Additional names may be used if these help identification. The full name, address and telephone number of the supplier should be included. An emergency telephone number should also be given, for contact in the event of an emergency. This number may be that of the company itself or of a recognized advisory body, so long as either can be contacted at all times.

(b) Information on ingredients (composition)

The information should allow employers to identify clearly the risks associated with a particular chemical so that they may conduct a risk assessment, as outlined in section 6.2 (Procedures for assessment) of this code. Full details of the composition should normally be given but may not be necessary if the risks can be properly assessed. The following should be provided except where the name or concentration of an ingredient in a mixture is confidential information which can be omitted in accordance with section 2.6:

(i) a description of the main components, including their chemical nature;

(ii) the identity and concentrations of components which are hazardous to safety and health

(iii) the identity and maximum concentration to be found of components which are at the concentration or exceed the concentration at which they are classified as hazardous to safety and health in lists approved or recognized by the competent authority, or which are prohibited at higher concentrations by the competent authority.

(c) Hazard identification

The most important hazards, including the most significant health, physical and environmental hazards, should be stated clearly and briefly, as an emergency overview. The information should be compatible with that shown on the label.

(d) First-aid measures

First-aid and self-help measures should be carefully explained. Situations where immediate medical attention is required should be described and the necessary measures indicated. Where appropriate, the need for special arrangements for specific and immediate treatment should be emphasized.

(e) Firefighting measures

The requirements for fighting a fire involving a chemical should be included; for example:

(i) suitable extinguishing agents;

(ii) extinguishing agents which must not be used for safety reasons;

(iii) special protective equipment for firefighters.

Information should also be given on the properties of the chemical in the event of fire and on special exposure hazards as a result of combustion products, as well as the precautions to be taken.

(f) Accidental release measures

Information should be provided on the action to be taken in the event of an accidental release of the chemical. The information should include:

(i) health and safety precautions: removal of sources of ignition, provision of sufficient ventilation, provision of suitable personal protective equipment;

(ii) environmental precautions: keeping away from drains, need to alert the emergency services, and possible need to alert the immediate neighbourhood in the event of an imminent risk;

(iii) methods for making safe and cleaning up: use of suitable absorbent materials, avoiding production of gases/fumes by water or other diluent, use of suitable neutralizing agents;

(iv) warnings: advise against reasonably foreseeable hazardous actions.

(g) Handling and storage

Information should be given about conditions recommended by the supplier for safe storage and handling, including:

(i) design and location of storage rooms or vessels;
(ii) separation from workplaces and occupied buildings;
(iii) incompatible materials;
(iv) conditions of storage (e.g., temperature and humidity, avoidance of sunlight);
(v) avoidance of sources of ignition, including particular arrangements to avoid static build-up;
(vi) provision of local and general ventilation;
(vii) recommended methods of work and those to be avoided.

(h) Exposure controls and personal protection

Information should be given on the need for personal protective equipment during use of a chemical, and on the type of equipment that provides adequate and suitable protection. Where appropriate, a reminder should be given that the primary controls should be provided by the design and installation of any equipment used and by other engineering measures, and information provided on useful practices to minimize exposure of workers. Specific control parameters such as exposure limits or biological standards should be given, along with recommended monitoring procedures.

(i) Physical and chemical properties

A brief description should be given of the appearance of the chemical, whether it is a solid, liquid or gas, and its colour and odour. Certain characteristics and properties, if known, should be given, specifying the nature of the test to determine these in each case. The tests used should be in accordance with the national laws and criteria applying at the employer's workplace and, in the absence of national laws or criteria, the test criteria of the exporting country should be used as guidance. The extent of the information provided should be appropriate to the use of the chemical. Examples of other useful data include:

- viscosity
- freezing point/freezing range
- boiling point/boiling range
- melting point/melting range
- flashpoint
- auto-ignition temperature
- explosive properties
- oxidizing properties
- vapour pressure
- molecular weight
- specific gravity or density
- pH
- solubility
- partition coefficient (water/n-octane)
- parameters such as vapour density
- miscibility
- evaporation rate and conductivity.

(j) Stability and reactivity

The possibility of hazardous reactions under certain conditions should be stated. Conditions to avoid should be indicated, such as:

(i) physical conditions (e.g., temperature, pressure, light, shock, contact with moisture or air);
(ii) proximity to other chemicals (e.g., acids, bases, oxidizing agents or any other specific substance which may cause a dangerous reaction).

Where hazardous decomposition products are given off, these should be specified along with the necessary precautions.

(k) Toxicological information

This section should give information on the effects on the body and on potential routes of entry into the body. Reference should be made to acute effects, both immediate and delayed, and to chronic effects from both short- and long-term exposure. Reference should also be made to health hazards as a result of possible reaction with other chemicals, including any known interactions, for example, resulting from the use of medication, tobacco and alcohol.

(l) Ecological information

The most important characteristics likely to have an effect on the environment should be described. The detailed information required will depend on the national laws and practice applying at the employer's workplace. Typical information that should be given, where appropriate, includes the potential routes for release of the chemical which are of concern, its persistence and degradability, bioaccumulative potential and aquatic toxicity, and other data relating to ecotoxicity (e.g., effects on water treatment works).

(m) Disposal considerations

Safe methods of disposal of the chemical and of contaminated packaging, which may contain residues of hazardous chemicals, should be given. Employers should be reminded that there may be national laws and practices on the subject.

(n) Transport information

Information should be given on special precautions that employers should be aware of or take while transporting the chemical on or off their premises. Relevant information given in the United Nations Recommendations on the Transport of Dangerous Goods and in other international agreements may also be included.

(o) Regulatory information

Information required for the marking and labelling of the chemical should be given here. Specific national regulations or practices applying to the user should be referred to. Employers should be reminded to refer to the requirements of national laws and practices.

(p) Other information

Other information which may be important to workers' health and safety should be included. Examples are training advice, recommended uses and restrictions, references, and sources of key data for compiling the chemical safety data sheet, the technical contact point and date of issue of the sheet.

Control measures to provide protection for workers could be any combination of the following:

1. good design and installation practice:
   - totally enclosed process and handling systems
   - segregation of the hazardous process from the operators or from other processes

2. plants processes or work systems which minimize generation of, or suppress or contain, hazardous dust, fumes, etc., and which limit the area of contamination in the event of spills and leaks:
   - partial enclosure, with local exhaust ventilation (LEV)
   - LEV
   - sufficient general ventilation

3. work systems and practices:
    - reduction of the numbers of workers exposed and exclusion of non-essential access
    - reduction in the period of exposure to workers
    - regular cleaning of contaminated walls, surfaces, etc.
    - use and proper maintenance of engineering control measures
    - provision of means for safe storage and disposal of chemicals hazardous to health
4. personal protection (where the above measures do not suffice, suitable PPE should be provided until such time as the risk is eliminated or minimized to a level that would not pose a threat to health)
5. prohibition of eating, chewing, drinking and smoking in contaminated areas
6. provision of adequate facilities for washing, changing and storage of clothing, including arrangements for laundering contaminated clothing
7. use of signs and notices
8. adequate arrangements in the event of an emergency.

Chemicals known to have carcinogenic, mutagenic or teratogenic health effects should be kept under strict control.

Record Keeping

Record keeping is an essential element of the work practices which provide a safe use of chemicals. Records should be kept by employers on measurements of airborne hazardous chemicals. Such records should be clearly marked by date, work area and plant location. The following are some elements of section 12.4 of the ILO Code of Practice, which deals with record-keeping requirements.

- Personal sampling measurements, including the exposures calculated, should be recorded.
- The workers and their representatives, and the competent authority, should have access to these records.

Besides the numerical results of measurements, the monitoring data should include, for example:

- the marking of the hazardous chemical
- the location, nature, dimensions and other distinctive features of the workplace where static measurements were made; the exact location at which personal monitoring measurements were made, and the names and job titles of the workers involved
- the source or sources of airborne emissions, their location and the type of work and operations being performed during sampling
- relevant information on the functioning of the process, engineering controls, ventilation and weather conditions with respect to the emissions
- the sampling instrument used, its accessories and the method of analysis
- the date and exact time of sampling
- the duration of the workers' exposure, the use or non-use of respiratory protection and other comments relating to the exposure evaluation
- the names of the persons responsible for the sampling and for the analytical determinations.

Records should be kept for a specified period of time determined by the competent authority. Where this has not been prescribed, it is recommended that the employer keep the records, or a suitable summary, for:

1. at least 30 years where the record is representative of the personal exposures of identifiable employees
2. at least 5 years in all other cases.

Information and Training

Correct instruction and quality training are essential components of a successful hazard communication programme. The ILO Code of Practice *Safety in the Use of Chemicals at Work* provides general principles of training (sections 10.1 and 10.2). These include the following:

- Workers should be informed of the hazards associated with chemicals used at their workplace.
- Workers should be instructed about how to obtain and use the information provided on labels and chemical safety data sheets.
- Workers should be trained in the correct and effective use of the control measures, in particular the engineering control measures and measures for personal protection provided, and should be made aware of their significance.
- Employers should use chemical safety data sheets, along with information specific to the workplace, as a basis for the preparation of instruction to workers, which should be in writing if appropriate.
- Workers should be trained on a continuing basis in the working systems and practices to be followed and their significance for safety in the use of chemicals at work, and in how to deal with emergencies.

Review of training needs

The extent of the training and instruction received and required should be reviewed and updated simultaneously with the review of the working systems and practices referred to in section 8.2 (Review of work systems).

The review should include the examination of:

- whether workers understand when protective equipment is required, and its limitations
- whether workers understand the most effective use of the engineering control measures provided
- whether workers are familiar with procedures in the event of an emergency involving a hazardous chemical
- procedures for the exchange of information between shift workers.

CLASSIFICATION AND LABELLING SYSTEMS FOR CHEMICALS

*Konstantin K. Sidorov and
Igor V. Sanotskiy*

Hazard classification and labelling systems are included in legislation covering the safe production, transport, use and disposal of chemicals. These classifications are designed to provide a systematic and comprehensible transfer of health information. Only a small number of significant classification and labelling systems exist at the national, regional and international levels. Classification criteria and their definitions used in these systems vary in the number and degree of hazard scales, specific terminology and test methods, and the methodology for classifying mixtures of chemicals. The establishment of an international structure for harmonizing classification and labelling systems for chemicals would have a beneficial impact on chemical trade, on the exchange of information related to chemicals, on the cost of risk assessment and management of chemicals, and ultimately on the protection of workers, the general public and the environment.

The major basis for classification of chemicals is the assessment of exposure levels and environmental impact (water, air and soil). About half of the international systems contain criteria related to a chemical's production volume or the effects of pollutant emissions. The most widespread criteria used in chemical classification are values of median lethal dose (LD_{50}) and median lethal concentration (LC_{50}). These values are evaluated in laboratory animals via three main pathways—oral, dermal and inhalation—with a one-time exposure. Values of LD_{50} and LC_{50} are evaluated in the same animal species and with the same exposure routes. The Republic of Korea considers LD_{50} with intravenous and intracutaneous administration as well. In Switzerland and Yugoslavia chemical management legislation requires quantitative criteria for LD_{50} with oral administration and adds a provision which specifies the possibility of different hazard classifications based on the route of exposure.

In addition, differences in the definitions of comparable hazard levels exist. While the European Community (EC) system utilizes a three-level acute toxicity scale ("very toxic", "toxic" and "harmful"), the US Occupational Safety and Health Administration (OSHA) Hazard Communication Standard applies two acute toxicity levels ("highly toxic" and "toxic"). Most classifications apply either three categories (United Nations (UN), World Bank, International Maritime Organization (IMO), EC and others) or four (the former Council for Mutual Economic Assistance (CMEA), the Russian Federation, China, Mexico and Yugoslavia).

International Systems

The following discussion of existing chemical classification and labelling systems focuses primarily on major systems with long application experience. Hazard assessments of pesticides are not covered in general chemical classifications, but are included in the Food and Agricultural Organization/World Health Organization (FAO/WHO) classification as well as in various national legislation (e.g., Bangladesh, Bulgaria, China, the Republic of Korea,

---

Classification systems

3.1. General

3.1.1. The competent authority, or a body approved or recognised by the competent authority, should establish systems and specific criteria for classifying a chemical as hazardous and should progressively extend these systems and their application. Existing criteria for classification established by other competent authorities or by international agreement may be followed, if they are consistent with the criteria and methods outlined in this code, and this is encouraged where it may assist uniformity of approach. The results of the work of the UNEP/ILO/WHO International Programme on Chemical Safety (IPCS) coordinating group for the harmonisation of classification of chemicals should be considered when appropriate. The responsibilities and role of competent authorities concerning classification systems are set out in paragraphs 2.1.8 (criteria and requirements), 2.1.9 (consolidated list) and 2.1.10 (assessment of new chemicals).

3.1.2. Suppliers should ensure that chemicals they supplied have been classified or that they have been identified and their properties assessed (see paragraphs 2.4.3 (assessment) and 2.4.4 (classification)).

3.1.3. Manufacturers or importers, unless exempted, should give to the competent authority information about chemical elements and compounds not yet included in the consolidated classification list compiled by the competent authority, prior to their use at work (see paragraph 2.1.10 (assessment of new chemicals)).

3.1.4. The limited quantities of a new chemical required for research and development purposes may be produced by, handled in, and transported between laboratories and pilot plant before all hazards of this chemical are known in accordance with national laws and regulations. All available information found in literature or known to the employer from his or her experience with similar chemicals and applications should be fully taken into account, and adequate protection measures should be applied, as if the chemical were hazardous. The workers involved must be informed about the actual hazard information as it becomes known.

3.2. Criteria for classification

3.2.1. The criteria for the classification of chemicals should be based upon their intrinsic health and physical hazards, including:

(a) toxic properties, including both acute and chronic health effects in all parts of the body;

(b) chemical or physical characteristics, including flammable, explosive, oxidising and dangerously reactive properties;

(c) corrosive and irritant properties;

(d) allergenic and sensitising effects;

(e) carcinogenic effects;

(f) teratogenic and mutagenic effects;

(g) effects on the reproductive system.

3.3. Method of classification

3.3.1. The classification of chemicals should be based on available sources of information, e.g.:

(a) test data;

(b) information provided by the manufacturer or importer, including information on research work done;

(c) information available as a result of international transport rules, e.g., the United Nations Recommendations on the Transport of Dangerous Goods, which should be taken into account for the classification of chemicals in the case of transport, and the UNEP Basel Convention on the Control of Transboundary Movements of Hazardous Wastes and their Disposal (1989), which should be taken into account in respect of hazardous wastes;

(d) reference books or literature;

(e) practical experience;

(f) in the case of mixtures, either on the test of the mixture or on the known hazards of their components;

(g) information provided as a result of the risk evaluation work performed by the International Agency for Research on Cancer (IARC), the UNEP/ILO/WHO International Programme on Chemical Safety (IPCS), the European Communities and various national and international institutions, as well as information available through systems such as the UNEP International Register of Potentially Toxic Chemicals (IRPTC).

3.3.2. Certain classification systems in use may be limited to particular classes of chemicals only. An example is the WHO *Recommended classification of pesticides by hazard and guidelines to classification*, which classifies pesticides by degree of toxicity only and principally by acute risks to health. Employers and workers should understand the limitations of any such system. Such systems can be useful to complement a more generally applicable system.

3.3.3. Mixtures of chemicals should be classified based on the hazards exhibited by the mixtures themselves. Only if mixtures have not been tested as a whole should they be classified on the basis of intrinsic hazards of their component chemicals.

Source: ILO 1993, Chapter 3.

Poland, the Russian Federation, Sri Lanka, Venezuela and Zimbabwe).

Transport-oriented classifications

Transport classifications, which are broadly applied, serve as a basis for regulations governing labelling, packaging and transport of dangerous cargoes. Among these classifications are the UN Recommendations on the Transport of Dangerous Goods (UNRTDG), the International Maritime Dangerous Goods Code developed within the IMO, the classification established by the Group of Experts on the Scientific Aspects of Marine Pollution (GESAMP) for hazardous chemicals carried by ship, as well as national transport classifications. National classifications as a rule comply with UN, IMO and other classifications within international agreements on transportation of dangerous goods by air, rail, road and inland navigation, harmonized with the UN system.

The United Nations Recommendations on the Transport of Dangerous Goods and related transport modal authorities

The UNRTDG create a widely accepted global system which provides a framework for intermodal, international and regional transport regulations. These Recommendations are increasingly being adopted as the basis of national regulations for domestic transport. The UNRTDG is rather general on issues such as notification, identification and hazard communication. The scope has been restricted to the transport of hazardous substances in packaged form; the Recommendations do not apply to exposed hazardous chemicals or to transport in bulk. Originally the objective was to prevent dangerous goods from causing acute injury to workers or the general public, or damage to other goods or the means of transport employed (aircraft, vessel, railcar or road vehicle). The system has now been extended to include asbestos and substances hazardous to the environment.

The UNRTDG focus primarily on hazard communication based on labels which include a combination of graphic symbols, colours, warning words and classification codes. They also provide key data for emergency response teams. The UNRTDG are relevant for the protection of such transport workers as aircrew, mariners and the crews of trains and road vehicles. In many countries the Recommendations have been incorporated in legislation for the protection of dock workers. Parts of the system, such as the Recommendations on explosives, have been adapted to regional and national regulations for the workplace, generally including manufacturing and storage. Other UN organizations concerned with transport have adopted the UNRTDG. The transport classification systems of dangerous goods of Australia, Canada, India, Jordan, Kuwait, Malaysia and United Kingdom basically comply with the major principles of these Recommendations, for example.

The UN classification subdivides chemicals into nine classes of hazards:

- 1st class—explosive substances
- 2nd class—compressed, liquefied, dissolved under pressure or deeply condensed gases
- 3rd class—easily inflammable liquids
- 4th class—easily inflammable solid substances
- 5th class—oxidizing substances, organic peroxides
- 6th class—poisonous (toxic) and infectious substances
- 7th class—radioactive substances
- 8th class—corrosive agents
- 9th class—other dangerous substances.

The packaging of goods for the purpose of transport, an area specified by the UNRTDG, is not covered as comprehensively by other systems. In support of the Recommendations, organizations such as IMO and International Civil Aviation Organization (ICAO) carry out very significant programmes aimed at training dock workers and airport personnel in the recognition of label information and packaging standards.

The International Maritime Organization

The IMO, with a mandate from the 1960 Conference on Safety of Life at Sea (SOLAS 1960), has developed the International Maritime Dangerous Goods (IMDG) Code. This code supplements the mandatory requirements of chapter VII (Carriage of Dangerous Goods) of SOLAS 74 and those of Annex III of the Maritime Pollution Convention (MARPOL 73/78). The IMDG Code has been developed and kept up to date for more than 30 years in close cooperation with the UN Committee of Experts on Transport of Dangerous Goods (CETG) and has been implemented by 50 IMO members representing 85% of the world's merchant tonnage.

Harmonization of the IMDG Code with the UNRTDG ensures compatibility with the national and international rules applicable to the transport of dangerous goods by other modes, in so far as these other modal rules are also based on the recommendations of the UNCETG—that is, ICAO Technical Instructions for the Safe Transport of Dangerous Goods by Air and the European Regulations concerning the international carriage of dangerous goods by road (ADR) and by rail (RID).

In 1991 the 17th IMO Assembly adopted a Resolution on the Coordination of Work in Matters Relating to Dangerous Goods and Hazardous Substances, urging, *inter alia*, UN bodies and governments to coordinate their work in order to ensure the compatibility of any legislation on chemicals, dangerous goods and hazardous substances with established international transport rules.

Basel Convention on the Control of Transboundary Movements of Hazardous Wastes and their Disposal, 1989

The Convention's Annexes define 47 categories of wastes, including domestic wastes. Although the hazard classification parallels that of the UNRTDG, a significant difference includes the addition of three categories reflecting more specifically the nature of toxic wastes: chronic toxicity, liberation of toxic gases from interaction of wastes with air or water, and capacity of wastes to yield secondary toxic material after disposal.

Pesticides

National classification systems related to the hazard assessment of pesticides tend to be quite comprehensive because of the wide use of these chemicals and the potential long-term damage to the environment. These systems may identify from two to five hazard classifications. The criteria are based on median lethal doses with different routes of exposure. While Venezuela and Poland recognize only one route of exposure, ingestion, the WHO and various other countries identify both ingestion and skin application.

The criteria for hazard assessment of pesticides in East European countries, Cyprus, Zimbabwe, China and others are based on median lethal doses via inhalation. Bulgaria's criteria, however, include skin and eye irritation, sensitization, accumulation ability, persistence in environmental media, blastogenic and teratogenic effects, embryotoxicity, acute toxicity and medical treatment. Many classifications of pesticides also include separate criteria based on median lethal doses with different aggregative states. For example, criteria for liquid pesticides are usually more severe than those for solid ones.

WHO Recommended Classification of Pesticides by Hazard

This Classification was first issued in 1975 by the WHO and updated subsequently on a regular basis by the United Nations Environment Programme, the ILO and the WHO

(UNEP/ILO/WHO) International Programme on Chemical Safety (IPCS) with input from the Food and Agriculture Organization (FAO). It consists of one hazard category or classification criterion, acute toxicity, divided in four classification levels based on LD_{50} (rat, oral and dermal values for liquid and solid forms) and ranging from extremely to slightly hazardous. Apart from general considerations, no specific labelling rules are provided. The 1996–97 update contains a guide to classification which includes a list of classified pesticides and comprehensive safety procedures. (See the chapter *Minerals and agricultural chemicals*.)

FAO International Code of Conduct on the Distribution and Use of Pesticides

The WHO Classification is supported by another document, the *FAO International Code of Conduct on the Distribution and Use of Pesticides*. Although it is only a recommendation, this classification is applied most widely in developing countries, where it is often included into pertinent national legislation. With regard to labelling, the FAO has published *Guidelines on Good Labelling Practice for Pesticides* as an addendum to these guidelines.

Regional Systems (EC, EFTA, CMEA)

The EC Council Directive 67/548/EEC has been in application for over two decades and has harmonized the pertinent legislation of 12 countries. It has evolved into a comprehensive system which includes an inventory of existing chemicals, a notification procedure for new chemicals prior to marketing, a set of hazard categories, classification criteria for each category, testing methods, and a hazard communication system including labelling with codified risk and safety phrases and hazard symbols. Chemical preparations (mixtures of chemicals) are regulated by Council Directive 88/379/EEC. The definition of the chemical safety data sheet data elements is practically identical to that defined in ILO Recommendation No. 177, as discussed earlier in this chapter. A set of classification criteria and a label for chemicals that are dangerous to the environment have been produced. The Directives regulate chemicals placed on the market, with the goal of protecting human health and the environment. Fourteen categories are divided into two groups related respectively to physico-chemical properties (explosive, oxidizing, extremely flammable, highly flammable, flammable) and toxicological properties (very toxic, toxic, harmful, corrosive, irritant, carcinogenic, mutagenic, toxic to reproduction, properties dangerous to health or the environment).

The Commission of European Communities (CEC) has an extension to the system specifically addressed to the workplace. In addition, these measures on chemicals should be considered within the overall framework of the protection of the health and safety of workers provided for under Directive 89/391/EEC and its individual Directives.

With the exception of Switzerland, the countries in EFTA follow the EC system to a large degree.

Former Council for Mutual Economic Assistance (CMEA)

This system was elaborated under the umbrella of the Standing Commission for Cooperation in Public Health of the CMEA, which included Poland, Hungary, Bulgaria, the former USSR, Mongolia, Cuba, Romania, Vietnam and Czechoslovakia. China still uses a system which is similar in concept. It consists of two classification categories, namely toxicity and hazard, using a four-level ranking scale. Another element of the CMEA system is its requirement for the preparation of a "toxicological passport of new chemical compounds subjected to introduction in the economy and domestic life". Criteria for irritancy, allergic effects, sensitization, carcinogenicity, mutagenicity, teratogenicity, anti-

fertility and ecological hazards are defined. However, the scientific basis and the testing methodology related to the classification criteria are significantly different from those used by the other systems.

Provisions for workplace labelling and hazard symbols are also different. The UNRTDG system is used for labelling goods for transport, but there does not seem to be any linkage between the two systems. There are no specific recommendations for chemical safety data sheets. The system is described in detail in the UNEP International Register of Potentially Toxic Chemicals (IRPTC) International Survey of Classification Systems. While the CMEA system contains most of the basic elements of the other classification systems, it differs significantly in the area of hazard assessment methodology, and uses exposure standards as one of the hazard classification criteria.

Examples of National Systems

Australia

Australia has enacted legislation for the notification and assessment of industrial chemicals, the Industrial Chemicals Notification and Assessment Act of 1989, with similar legislation enacted in 1992 for agricultural and veterinary chemicals. The Australian system is similar to that of the EC. The differences are mainly due to its utilization of the UNRTDG classification (i.e., the inclusion of the categories compressed gas, radioactive and miscellaneous).

Canada

The Workplace Hazardous Materials Information System (WHMIS) was implemented in 1988 by a combination of federal and provincial legislation designed to enforce the transfer of information about hazardous materials from producers, suppliers and importers to employers and in turn to workers. It applies to all industries and workplaces in Canada. WHMIS is a communication system aimed primarily at industrial chemicals and composed of three interrelated hazard communication elements: labels, chemical safety data sheets and worker education programmes. A valuable support to this system was the earlier creation and commercial distribution worldwide of a computerized database, now available on compact disc, containing over 70,000 chemical safety data sheets voluntarily submitted to the Canadian Centre for Occupational Health and Safety by manufacturers and suppliers.

Japan

In Japan, the control of chemicals is covered mainly by two laws. First, the Chemical Substances Control Law, as amended in 1987, is aimed at preventing environmental contamination by chemical substances that are low in biodegradability and harmful to human health. The law defines a premarket notification procedure and three "hazard" classes:

- Class 1—specified chemical substances (low biodegradation, high bioaccumulation, risk to human health)
- Class 2—specified chemical substances (low biodegradation and bioaccumulation, risk to human health and of contamination of the environment in vast areas)
- Class 3—designated substances (low biodegradation and bioaccumulation, suspicion of risk to human health)

Control measures are defined, and a list of existing chemicals is provided.

The second regulation, the Industrial Safety and Health Law, is a parallel system with its own list of "Specified chemical substances" which require labelling. Chemicals are classified into four groups (lead, tetraalkyl lead, organic solvents, specified chemical substances). The classification criteria are (1) possible occurrence of serious health impairment, (2) possible frequent occurrence of health impairment and (3) actual health impairment. Other laws dealing with the control of hazardous chemicals include the Explosives Control Law; the High Pressure Gas Control Law; the Fire Prevention Law; the Food Sanitation Law; and the Drugs, Cosmetics and Medical Instruments Law.

United States

The Hazard Communication Standard (HCS), a mandatory standard promulgated by OSHA, is a workplace-oriented binding regulation which refers to other existing laws. Its goal is to ensure that all chemicals produced or imported are evaluated, and that information related to their hazards is transmitted to employers and to workers through a comprehensive hazard communication programme. The programme includes labelling and other forms of warning, chemical safety data sheets and training. Label and data sheet minimum contents are defined, but the use of hazard symbols is not mandatory.

Under the Toxic Substances Control Act (TSCA), administered by the Environmental Protection Agency (EPA), an inventory listing approximately 70,000 existing chemicals is maintained. The EPA is developing regulations to complement the OSHA HCS which would have similar hazard evaluation and worker communication requirements for the environmental hazards of chemicals on the inventory. Under TSCA, prior to manufacture or import of chemicals which are not on the inventory, the manufacturer must submit a premanufacture notice. The EPA may impose testing or other requirements based on the premanufacture notice review. As new chemicals are introduced into commerce, they are added to the inventory.

Labelling

Labels on containers of hazardous chemicals provide the first alert that a chemical is hazardous, and should provide basic information about safe handling procedures, protective measures, emergency first aid and the chemical's hazards. The label should also include the identity of the hazardous chemical(s) and the name and address of the chemical manufacturer.

Labelling consists of phrases as well as graphic and colour symbols applied directly on the product, package, label or tag. The marking should be clear, easily comprehensible and able to withstand adverse climatic conditions. The labelling should be placed against a background that contrasts with the product's accompanying data or package colour. The MSDS provides more detailed information on the nature of the chemical product's hazards and the appropriate safety instructions.

While presently there are no globally harmonized labelling requirements, there are established international, national and regional regulations for labelling hazardous substances. Requirements for labelling are incorporated into the Law on Chemicals (Finland), the Act on Dangerous Products (Canada) and EC Directive N 67/548. Minimum label content requirements of the European Union, United States and Canadian systems are relatively similar.

Several international organizations have established labelling content requirements for handling chemicals at the workplace and in transport. The labels, hazard symbols, risk and safety phrases, and emergency codes of the International Organization for Standardization (ISO), the UNRTDG, the ILO and EU are discussed below.

The section on labelling in the ISO/IEC guide 51, *Guidelines for Inclusion of Safety Aspects in Standards*, includes commonly recognized pictograms (drawing, colour, sign). In addition, short and plain warning phrases alert the user to potential hazards and provide information on preventive safety and health measures.

The guidelines recommend the use of the following "signal" words to alert the user:

- DANGER—high danger
- HANDLE WITH CARE—intermediate danger
- BEWARE—potential danger.

The UNRTDG establish five main pictograms for easy visible recognition of dangerous goods and significant hazard identification:

- bomb—explosive
- flame—flammable
- skull and cross-bones—toxic
- trefoil—radioactive
- liquid pouring out of two test-tubes on a hand and a piece of metal—corrosive.

These symbols are supplemented by other representations such as:

- oxidizing substances—flame above a circle
- non-flammable gases—a gas bottle
- infectious substances—three crescent signs superimposed on a circle
- harmful substances which should be stowed away—St. Andrew's cross posed on a wheat-ear.

The Chemicals Convention, 1990 (No. 170), and Recommendation, 1990 (No. 177), were adopted at the 77th Session of the International Labour Conference (ILC). They establish requirements for the labelling of chemicals to ensure the communication of basic hazard information. The Convention states that label information should be easily understandable and should convey the potential risks and appropriate precautionary measures to the user. Regarding the transport of dangerous goods, the Convention refers to the UNRTDG.

The Recommendation outlines labelling requirements in accordance with existing national and international systems, and establishes criteria for classification of chemicals including chemical and physical properties; toxicity; necrotic and irritating properties; and allergic, teratogenic, mutagenic and reproductive effects.

The EC Council Directive N 67/548 stipulates the form of label information: graphic hazard symbols and pictograms including risk and safety phrases. Hazards are coded by the Latin letter R accompanied with combinations of Arabic numerals from 1 to 59. For example, R10 corresponds with "flammable", R23 with "toxic by inhalation". The hazard code is given with a safety code consisting of the Latin letter S and combinations of numerals from 1 to 60. For example, S39 means "Wear eye/face protection". The EC labelling requirements serve as a reference for chemical and pharmaceutical companies throughout the world.

Despite significant efforts in chemical hazard data acquisition, evaluation and organization by different international and regional organizations, there is still a lack of coordination of these efforts, particularly in the standardization of assessment protocols and methods and interpretation of data. The ILO, the Organization for Economic Cooperation and Development (OECD), the IPCS and other concerned bodies have initiated a number of international activities aimed toward establishing a global harmonization of chemical classification and labelling systems. The establishment of an international structure to monitor chemical hazard assessment activities would greatly benefit workers, the general public and the environment. An ideal harmonization process would reconcile the transport, marketing and workplace classification and labelling of hazardous substances, and address consumer, worker and environmental concerns.

SAFE HANDLING AND STORAGE OF CHEMICALS

*A.E. Quinn**

Before a new hazardous substance is received for storage, information concerning its correct handling should be provided to all users. Planning and maintaining of storage areas are necessary to avoid material losses, accidents and disasters. Good housekeeping is essential, and special attention should be paid to incompatible substances, suitable location of products and climatic conditions.

Written instructions of storage practices should be provided, and the chemicals' material safety data sheets (MSDSs) should be available in storage areas. Locations of the different classes of chemicals should be illustrated in a storage map and in a chemical register. The register should contain the maximum allowed quantity of all chemical products and the maximum allowed quantity of all chemical products per class. All substances should be received at a central location for distribution to the storerooms, stockrooms and laboratories. A central receiving area is also helpful in monitoring substances that may eventually enter the waste-disposal system. An inventory of substances contained in the storerooms and stockrooms will give an indication of the quantity and nature of substances targeted for future disposal.

Stored chemicals should be examined periodically, at least annually. Chemicals with expired shelf lives and deteriorated or leaking containers should be disposed of safely. A "first in, first out" system of keeping stock should be used.

The storage of dangerous substances should be supervised by a competent, trained person. All workers required to enter storage areas should be fully trained in appropriate safe work practices, and a periodic inspection of all storage areas should be carried out by a safety officer. A fire alarm should be situated in or near the outside of the storage premises. It is recommended that persons should not work alone in a storage area containing toxic substances. Chemical storage areas should be located away from process areas, occupied buildings and other storage areas. In addition, they should not be in proximity of fixed sources of ignition.

Labelling and Relabelling Requirements

The label is the key to organizing chemical products for storage. Tanks and containers should be identified with signs indicating the name of the chemical product. No containers or cylinders of compressed gases should be accepted without the following identifying labels:

- identification of contents
- description of principal hazard (e.g., flammable liquid)
- precautions to minimize hazards and prevent accidents
- correct first aid procedures
- correct procedures for cleaning up spills
- special instructions to medical personnel in case of an accident.

The label may also offer precautions for correct storage, such as "Keep in a cool place" or "Keep container dry". When certain dangerous products are delivered in tankers, barrels or bags and repackaged at the workplace, each new container should be relabelled so that the user will be able to identify the chemical and recognize the risks immediately.

* Adapted from 3rd edition, *Encyclopaedia of Occupational Health and Safety.*

Explosive Substances

Explosive substances include all chemicals, pyrotechnics and matches which are explosives *per se* and also those substances such as sensitive metallic salts which, by themselves or in certain mixtures or when subject to certain conditions of temperature, shock, friction or chemical action, may transform and undergo an explosive reaction. In the case of explosives, most countries have stringent regulations regarding safe storage requirements and precautions to be taken in order to prevent theft for use in criminal activities.

The storage places should be situated far away from other buildings and structures so as to minimize damage in case of an explosion. Manufacturers of explosives issue instructions as to the most suitable type of storage. The storerooms should be of solid construction and kept securely locked when not in use. No store should be near a building containing oil, grease, waste combustible material or flammable material, open fire or flame.

In some countries there is a legal requirement that magazines should be situated at least 60 m from any power plant, tunnel, mine shaft, dam, highway or building. Advantage should be taken of any protection offered by natural features such as hills, hollows, dense woods or forests. Artificial barriers of earth or stone walls are sometimes placed around such storage places.

The storage place should be well ventilated and free from dampness. Natural lighting or portable electric lamps should be used, or lighting provided from outside the storehouse. Floors should be constructed of wood or other non-sparking material. The area surrounding the storage place should be kept free of dry grass, rubbish or any other material likely to burn. Black powder and explosives should be stored in separate storehouses, and no detonators, tools or other materials should be kept in an explosive store. Non-ferrous tools should be used for opening cases of explosives.

Oxidizing Substances

Oxidizing substances provide sources of oxygen, and thus are capable of supporting combustion and intensifying the violence of any fire. Some of these oxygen suppliers give off oxygen at storage-room temperature, but others require the application of heat. If containers of oxidizing materials are damaged, the contents may mix with other combustible materials and start a fire. This risk can be avoided by storing oxidizing materials in a separate storage place. However, this practice may not always be available, as, for example, in dock warehouses for goods in transit.

It is dangerous to store powerful oxidizing substances near liquids that even have a low flash point or even slightly flammable materials. It is safer to keep all flammable materials away from a place where oxidizing substances are stored. The storage area should be cool, well ventilated and of fire-resisting construction.

Flammable Substances

A gas is deemed to be flammable if it burns in the presence of air or oxygen. Hydrogen, propane, butane, ethylene, acetylene, hydrogen sulphide and coal gas are among the most common flammable gases. Some gases such as hydrogen cyanide and cyanogen are both flammable and poisonous. Flammable materials should be stored in places which are cool enough to prevent accidental ignition if the vapours mix with the air.

Vapours of flammable solvents may be heavier than air and may move along the floor to a distant ignition source. Flammable vapours from spilled chemicals have been known to descend into stairwells and elevator shafts and ignite at a lower storey. It is therefore essential that smoking and open flames be prohibited where these solvents are handled or stored.

Portable, approved safety cans are the safest vessels for storing flammables. Quantities of flammable liquids greater than 1 litre should be stored in metal containers. Two-hundred-litre drums are commonly used to ship flammables, but are not intended as long-term storage containers. The stopper should be removed carefully and replaced by an approved pressure-relief vent to avoid increased internal pressure from heat, fire or exposure to sunlight. When transferring flammables from metal equipment, the worker should use an enclosed transfer system or have adequate exhaust ventilation.

The storage area should be situated away from any source of heat or fire hazard. Highly flammable substances should be kept apart from powerful oxidizing agents or from materials which are susceptible to spontaneous combustion. When highly volatile liquids are stored, any electric light fittings or apparatus should be of certified flameproof construction, and no open flames should be permitted in or near the storage place. Fire extinguishers and absorbent inert materials, such as dry sand and earth, should be available for emergency situations.

The walls, ceilings and floors of the storage room should consist of materials with at least a 2-hour fire resistance. The room should be fitted with self-closing fire doors. The storage-room installations should be electrically grounded and periodically inspected, or equipped with automatic smoke- or fire-detection devices. Control valves on storage vessels containing flammable liquids should be clearly labelled, and pipelines should be painted with distinctive safety colours to indicate the type of liquid and the direction of flow. Tanks containing flammable substances should be situated on ground sloping away from the main buildings and plant installations. If they are on level ground, protection against fire spread can be obtained by adequate spacing and the provision of dykes. The dyke capacity should preferably be 1.5 times that of the storage tank, as a flammable liquid may be likely to boil over. Provision should be made for venting facilities and flame arrestors on such storage tanks. Adequate fire extinguishers, either automatic or manual, should be available. No smoking should be allowed.

Toxic Substances

Toxic chemicals should be stored in cool, well ventilated areas out of contact with heat, acids, moisture and oxidizing substances. Volatile compounds should be stored in spark-free freezers ($-20\ °C$) to avoid evaporation. Because containers may develop leaks, storerooms should be equipped with exhaust hoods or equivalent local ventilation devices. Open containers should be closed with tape or other sealant before being returned to the storeroom. Substances which can react chemically with each other should be kept in separate stores.

Corrosive Substances

Corrosive substances include strong acids, alkalis and other substances which will cause burns or irritation of the skin, mucous membranes or eyes, or which will damage most materials. Typical examples of these substances include hydrofluoric acid, hydrochloric acid, sulphuric acid, nitric acid, formic acid and perchloric acid. Such materials may cause damage to their containers and leak into the atmosphere of the storage area; some are volatile and others react violently with moisture, organic matter or other chemicals. Acid mists or fumes may corrode structural materials and equipment and have a toxic action on personnel. Such materials should be kept cool but well above their freezing point, since a substance such as acetic acid may freeze at a relatively

high temperature, rupture its container and then escape when the temperature rises again above its freezing point.

Some corrosive substances also have other dangerous properties; for example, perchloric acid, in addition to being highly corrosive, is also a powerful oxidizing agent which can cause fire and explosions. *Aqua regia* has three dangerous properties: (1) it displays the corrosive properties of its two components, hydrochloric acid and nitric acid; (2) it is a very powerful oxidizing agent; and (3) application of only a small amount of heat will result in the formation of nitrosyl chloride, a highly toxic gas.

Storage areas for corrosive substances should be isolated from the rest of the plant or warehouses by impervious walls and floor, with provision for the safe disposal of spillage. The floors should be made of cinder blocks, concrete that has been treated to reduce its solubility, or other resistant material. The storage area should be well ventilated. No store should be used for the simultaneous storage of nitric acid mixtures and sulphuric acid mixtures. Sometimes it is necessary to store corrosive and poisonous liquids in special types of containers; for example, hydrofluoric acid should be kept in leaden, gutta percha or ceresin bottles. Since hydrofluoric acid interacts with glass, it should not be stored near glass or earthenware carboys containing other acids.

Carboys containing corrosive acids should be packed with kieselguhr (infusorial earth) or other effective inorganic insulating material. Any necessary first-aid equipment such as emergency showers and eyewash bottles should be provided in or immediately close to the storage place.

Water-reactive Chemicals

Some chemicals, such as sodium and potassium metals, react with water to produce heat and flammable or explosive gases. Certain polymerization catalysts, such as alkyl aluminium compounds, react and burn violently on contact with water. Storage facilities for water-reactive chemicals should not have water in the storage area. Non-water automatic sprinkler systems should be employed.

Legislation

Detailed legislation has been drawn up in many countries to regulate the manner in which various dangerous substances may be stored; this legislation includes the following specifications:

- type of building, its location, the maximum amounts of various substances that may be stored in one place
- type of ventilation required
- precautions to be taken against fire, explosion and the release of dangerous substances
- type of lighting (e.g., flameproof electrical equipment and light fixtures when explosive or flammable materials are stored)
- number and location of fire exits
- security measures against entry by unauthorized persons and against theft
- labelling and marking of storage vessels and pipelines
- warning notices to workers as to the precautions to be observed.

In many countries there is no central authority concerned with the supervision of the safety precautions for the storage of all dangerous substances, but a number of separate authorities exist. Examples include mine and factory inspectorates, dock authorities, transport authorities, police, fire services, national boards and local authorities, each of which deals with a limited range of dangerous substances under various legislative powers. It is usually necessary to obtain a licence or permit from one of these authorities for the storage of certain types of dangerous substances such as petroleum, explosives, cellulose and cellulose solutions. The licensure procedures require that storage facilities comply with specified safety standards.

COMPRESSED GASES: HANDLING, STORAGE AND TRANSPORT

A. Türkdogan and K.R. Mathisen*

Gases in their compressed state, and particularly compressed air, are almost indispensable to modern industry, and are also used widely for medical purposes, for the manufacture of mineral waters, for underwater diving and in connection with motor vehicles.

For purposes of the present article, compressed gases and air are defined as being those with a gauge pressure exceeding 1.47 bar or as liquids having a vapour pressure exceeding 2.94 bar. Thus, consideration is not given to such cases as natural gas distribution, which is dealt with elsewhere in this *Encyclopaedia*.

Table 61.1 shows the gases commonly encountered in compressed cylinders.

All the above gases present either an irritant, asphyxiant or highly toxic respiratory hazard and may also be flammable and an explosive when compressed. Most countries provide for a standard colour-coding system whereby different coloured bands or labels are applied to the gas cylinders to indicate the type of hazard to be expected. Particularly toxic gases, such as hydrogen cyanide, are also given special markings.

All compressed gas containers are so constructed that they are safe for the purposes for which they are intended when first put into service. However, serious accidents may result from their misuse, abuse or mishandling, and the greatest care should be exercised in the handling, transport, storage and even in the disposal of such cylinders or containers.

Characteristics and Production

Depending on the characteristics of the gas, it may be introduced into the container or cylinder in liquid form or simply as a gas under high pressure. In order to liquefy a gas, it is necessary to cool it to below its critical temperature and to subject it to an appropriate pressure. The lower the temperature is reduced below the critical temperature, the less the pressure required.

Certain of the gases listed in table 61.1 have properties against which precautions must be taken. For example, acetylene can react dangerously with copper and should not be in contact with alloys containing more than 66% of this metal. It is usually delivered in steel containers at about 14.7 to 16.8 bar. Another gas that has a highly corrosive action on copper is ammonia, which must also be kept out of contact with this metal, use being made of steel cylinders and authorized alloys. In the case of chlorine, no reaction takes place with copper or steel except in the presence of water, and for this reason all storage vessels or other containers must be kept free from contact with moisture at all times. Fluorine gas, on the other hand, although reacting readily with most metals, will tend to form a protective coating, as, for example, in the case of copper, where a layer of copper fluoride over the metal protects it from further attack by the gas.

Among the gases listed, carbon dioxide is one of the most readily liquefied, this taking place at a temperature of 15 °C and a pressure of about 14.7 bar. It has many commercial applications and may be kept in steel cylinders.

The hydrocarbon gases, of which liquefied petroleum gas (LPG) is a mixture formed mainly of butane (about 62%) and propane (about 36%), are not corrosive and are generally delivered in steel cylinders or other containers at pressures of up to 14.7 to 19.6 bar. Methane is another highly flammable gas that is also generally delivered in steel cylinders at a pressure of 14.7 to 19.6 bar.

Hazards

Storage and transport

When a filling, storage and dispatch depot is being selected, consideration must be given to the safety of both the site and the environment. Pump rooms, filling machinery and so on must be located in fire-resistant buildings with roofs of light construction. Doors and other closures should open outwards from the building. The premises should be adequately ventilated, and a system of lighting with flameproof electrical switches should be installed. Measures should be taken to ensure free movement in the premises for filling, checking and dispatch purposes, and safety exits should be provided.

Compressed gases may be stored in the open only if they are adequately protected from the weather and direct sunlight. Storage areas should be located at a safe distance from occupied premises and neighbouring dwellings.

During the transport and distribution of containers, care must be taken to ensure that valves and connections are not damaged. Adequate precautions should be taken to prevent cylinders from falling off the vehicle and from being subjected to rough usage, excessive shocks or local stress, and to prevent excessive movement of liquids in large tanks. Every vehicle should be equipped with a fire extinguisher and an electrically conductive strip for earthing static electricity, and should be clearly marked "Flammable liquids". Exhaust pipes should have a flame-control device, and engines should be halted during loading and unloading. The maximum speed of these vehicles should be rigorously limited.

Use

The main dangers in the use of compressed gases arise from their pressure and from their toxic and/or flammable properties. The principal precautions are to ensure that equipment is used only with those gases for which it was designed, and that no compressed gases are used for any purpose other than that for which their use has been authorized.

Table 61.1 • Gases often found in compressed form.

Acetylene*	Hydrogen*
Ammonia*	Hydrogen chloride
Butane*	Hydrogen cyanide*
Carbon dioxide	Methane*
Carbon monoxide*	Methylamine*
Chlorine	Neon
Chlorodifluormethane	Nitrogen
Chloroethane*	Nitrogen dioxide
Chloromethane*	Nitrous oxide
Chlorotetrafluoroethane	Oxygen
Cyclopropane*	Phosgene
Dichlorodifluoromethane	Propane*
Ethane*	Propylene*
Ethylene*	Sulphur dioxide
Helium	

*These gases are flammable.

* Adapted from 3rd edition, *Encyclopaedia of Occupational Health and Safety*.

All hoses and other equipment should be of good quality and should be examined frequently. The use of non-return valves should be enforced wherever necessary. All hose connections should be in good condition and no joints should be made by forcing together threads that do not exactly correspond. In the case of acetylene and combustible gases, a red hose should be used; for oxygen the hose should be black. It is recommended that for all flammable gases, the connection-screw thread shall be left-handed, and for all other gases, it shall be right-handed. Hoses should never be interchanged.

Oxygen and some anaesthetic gases are often transported in large cylinders. The transfer of these compressed gases to small cylinders is a hazardous operation, which should be done under competent supervision, making use of the correct equipment in a correct installation.

Compressed air is widely used in many branches of industry, and care should be taken in the installation of pipelines and their protection from damage. Hoses and fittings should be maintained in good condition and subjected to regular examinations. The application of a compressed air hose or jet to an open cut or wound through which air can enter the tissues or the bloodstream is particularly dangerous; precautions should also be taken against all forms of irresponsible behaviour which could result in a compressed air jet coming in contact with any openings in the body (the result of which can be fatal). A further hazard exists when compressed air jets are used to clean machined components or workplaces: flying particles have been known to cause injury or blindness, and precautions against such dangers should be enforced.

Labelling and marking

Labelling and marking should be in accordance with standard practice in the country or region in question. The use of one gas for another by mistake, or the filling of a container with a gas different from that which it previously contained, without the necessary cleaning and decontamination procedures, may cause serious accidents. Colour marking is the best method of avoiding such errors, painting specific areas of containers or piping systems in accordance with the colour code stipulated in national standards or recommended by the national safety organization.

Gas Cylinders

For convenience in handling, transportation and storage, gases are commonly compressed in metal gas cylinders at pressures that range from a few atmospheres overpressure to 200 bar or even more. Alloy steel is the material most commonly used for the cylinders, but aluminium is also widely used for many purposes—for example, for fire extinguishers.

The hazards met with in handling and using compressed gases are:

- normal hazards entailed in handling heavy objects
- hazards connected with pressure (i.e., the amount of stored energy in the gases)
- hazards from the special properties of the gas content, which may be flammable, poisonous, oxidizing and so on.

Cylinder manufacture. Steel cylinders may be seamless or welded. The seamless cylinders are made from high-quality alloy steels and carefully heat-treated in order to obtain the desired combination of strength and toughness for high-pressure service. They may be forged and hot-drawn from steel billets or hot-formed from seamless tubes. Welded cylinders are made from sheet material. The pressed top and bottom parts are welded to a cylindrical seamless or welded tube section and heat-treated to relieve material stresses. Welded cylinders are extensively used in low-

Labelling and marking

4.1.1. The competent authority, or a body approved or recognized by the competent authority, should establish requirements for the marking and labelling of chemicals to enable persons handling or using chemicals to recognize and distinguish between them, both when receiving and when using them, so that they may be used safely (see paragraph 2.1.8 (criteria and requirements)). Existing criteria for marking and labelling established by other competent authorities may be followed where they are consistent with the provisions of this paragraph and are encouraged where this may assist uniformity of approach.

4.1.2. Suppliers of chemicals should ensure that chemicals are marked and hazardous chemicals are labelled, and that revised labels are prepared and provided to employers whenever new relevant safety and health information becomes available (see paragraphs 2.4.1 (suppliers' responsibilities) and 2.4.2 (classification)).

4.1.3. Employers receiving chemicals that have not been labelled or marked should not use them until the relevant information is obtained from the supplier or from other reasonably available sources. Information should be obtained primarily from the supplier but may be obtained from other sources listed in paragraph 3.3.1 (sources of information), with a view to marking and labelling in accordance with the requirements of the national competent authority, prior to use. ...

4.3.2. The purpose of the label is to give essential information on:

(a) the classification of the chemical;
(b) its hazards;
(c) the precautions to be observed.

The information should refer to both acute and chronic exposure hazards.

4.3.3. Labelling requirements, which should be in conformity with national requirements, should cover:

(a) the information to be given on the label, including as appropriate:
   (i) trade names;
   (ii) identity of the chemical;
   (iii) name, address and telephone number of the supplier;
   (iv) hazard symbols;
   (v) nature of the special risks associated with the use of the chemical;
   (vi) safety precautions;
   (vii) identification of the batch;
   (viii) the statement that a chemical safety data sheet giving additional information is available from the employer;
   (ix) the classification assigned under the system established by the competent authority;
(b) the legibility, durability and size of the label;
(c) the uniformity of labels and symbols, including colours.

Source: ILO 1993, Chapter 4.

pressure service for liquefiable gases and for dissolved gases such as acetylene.

Aluminium cylinders are extruded in large presses from special alloys that are heat-treated to give the desired strength.

Gas cylinders must be designed, produced and tested according to strict norms or standards. Every batch of cylinders should be checked for material quality and heat treatment, and a certain number of cylinders tested for mechanical strength. Inspection is often aided by sophisticated instruments, but in all cases the cylinders should be inspected and hydraulically tested to a given test pressure by an approved inspector. Identification data and the inspector's mark should be permanently stamped on the cylinder neck or another suitable place.

Periodic inspection. Gas cylinders in use may be affected by rough treatment, corrosion from inside and outside, fire and so on. National or international codes therefore require that they shall not be filled unless they are inspected and tested at certain intervals, which mostly range between two and ten years, depending on the service. Internal and external visual inspection together with a hydraulic pressure test is the basis for the approval of the cylinder for a new period in a given service. The test date (month and year) is stamped on the cylinder.

Disposal. A large number of cylinders are scrapped every year for various reasons. It is equally important that these cylinders be disposed of in such a way that they will not find their way back into use through uncontrolled channels. The cylinders should therefore be made completely unserviceable by cutting, crushing or a similar safe procedure.

Valves. The valve and any safety attachment must be regarded as a part of the cylinder, which must be kept in good working condition. Neck and outlet threads should be intact, and the valve should close tight without the use of undue force. Shut-off valves are often equipped with a pressure-relief device. This may be in the form of a resetting safety valve, bursting disc, fuse plug (melt plug) or a combination of bursting disc and fuse plug. The practice varies from country to country, but cylinders for low-pressure liquefied gases are always equipped with safety valves connected to the gas phase.

Hazards

Different transport codes classify gases as compressed, liquefied or dissolved under pressure. For the purpose of this article, it is useful to use the type of hazard as a classification.

High pressure. If cylinders or equipment burst, damage and injuries may be caused by flying debris or by the gas pressure. The more a gas is compressed, the higher is the stored energy. This hazard is always present with compressed gases and will increase with temperature if the cylinders are heated. Hence:

- Mechanical damage to the cylinder (dents, cuts and so on) should be avoided.
- Cylinders should be stored away from heat and not in direct sun.
- Cylinders should be removed from fires.
- Cylinders should only be connected to equipment suitable for the intended use.
- The cylinder valve should be protected with the cap during transport.
- Cylinders should be secured in use against falling, which may knock off the valve.
- Tampering with safety devices should be avoided.
- Cylinders should be handled with care to avoid mechanical shocks in very cold climates, since steel may become brittle at low temperature.
- Corrosion, which reduces the strength of the shell, should be avoided.

Low temperature. Most liquefied gases will evaporate rapidly under atmospheric pressure, and may reach very low temperatures. A person whose skin is exposed to such liquid may sustain injuries in the form of "cold burns". (Liquid CO_2 will form snow particles when expanded.) Correct protective equipment (e.g., gloves, goggles) should therefore be used.

Oxidation. The hazard of oxidation is most evident with oxygen, which is one of the most important compressed gases. Oxygen will not burn on its own, but is necessary for combustion. Normal air contains 21% oxygen by volume.

All combustible materials will ignite more easily and burn more vigorously when the oxygen concentration is increased. This is noticeable with even a slight increase in oxygen concentration, and utmost care must be taken to avoid oxygen enrichment in the working atmosphere. In confined spaces small oxygen leaks may lead to dangerous enrichment.

The danger with oxygen increases with increasing pressure to the point where many metals will burn vigorously. Finely divided materials may burn in oxygen with explosive force. Clothing that is saturated with oxygen will burn very rapidly and be difficult to extinguish.

Oil and grease have always been regarded as dangerous in combination with oxygen. The reason is that they react readily with oxygen, their existence is common, the ignition temperature is low and the developed heat may start a fire in the underlying metal. In high-pressure oxygen equipment the necessary ignition temperature may easily be reached by the compression shock that may result from rapid valve opening (adiabatic compression).

Therefore:

- Valves should be operated slowly.
- All oxygen equipment should be kept clean and free from oil and dirt.
- Only materials that are proven to be safe with oxygen should be used.
- Workers should refrain from lubricating oxygen equipment.
- Entering confined spaces where oxygen may exist in higher concentration should be avoided.
- The atmosphere should be checked and the use of oxygen instead of compressed air or some other gas should be strictly avoided.

Flammability. The flammable gases have flashpoints below room temperature and will form explosive mixtures with air (or oxygen) within certain limits known as the lower and upper explosion limits.

Escaping gas (also from safety valves) may ignite and burn with a shorter or longer flame depending on the pressure and amount of gas. The flames may again heat nearby equipment, which may burn, melt or explode. Hydrogen burns with an almost invisible flame.

Even small leaks may cause explosive mixtures in confined spaces. Some gases, such as liquefied petroleum gases, mostly propane and butane, are heavier than air and are difficult to vent away, as they will concentrate in the lower parts of buildings and "float" through channels from one room to another. Sooner or later, the gas may reach an ignition source and explode.

Ignition may be caused by hot sources, but also by electrical sparks, even very small ones.

Acetylene takes a special place among the combustible gases because of its properties and wide use. If heated, the gas may start to decompose with the development of heat even without the presence of air. If allowed to proceed, this may lead to cylinder explosion.

Acetylene cylinders are, for safety reasons, filled with a highly porous mass which also contains a solvent for the gas. Outside heating from a fire or welding torch, or in certain cases internal ignition by strong backfires from welding equipment, may start a decomposition within the cylinder. In such cases:

- The valve should be closed (using protective gloves if necessary) and the cylinder should be removed from fire.
- If part of the cylinder becomes hotter, it should be put into a river, canal or the like to cool down or cooled with water sprays.

- If the cylinder is too hot to be handled, it should be sprayed with water from a safe distance.
- Cooling should continue until the cylinder stays cool by itself.
- The valve should be kept closed, because gas flow will accelerate decomposition.

Acetylene cylinders in several countries are equipped with fuse (melting) plugs. These will release the gas pressure when they melt (usually at about 100 °C) and prevent cylinder explosion. At the same time there is a risk that the released gas may ignite and explode.

Common precautions to observe in respect of combustible gases are as follows:

- Cylinders should be stored separately from other gases in a well ventilated area above ground level.
- Leaking cylinders or equipment should not be used.
- Liquid gas cylinders should be stored and used in an upright position. Larger quantities of gas will come out if liquid is expelled through the safety valves instead of gas. The pressure will be reduced more slowly. Very long flame will result if the gas ignites.
- In case of leaks, any possible ignition source should be avoided.
- Smoking where flammable gases are stored or used should be prohibited.
- The safest way of extinguishing a fire is usually to stop the supply of gas. Merely extinguishing the flame may cause the formation of an explosive cloud, which may re-ignite in contact with a hot object.

Toxicity. Certain gases, if not the most common, may be toxic. At the same time, they may be irritating or corrosive to the skin or eyes.

Persons who handle these gases should be well trained and aware of the danger involved and the necessary precautions. The cylinders should be stored in a well ventilated area. No leaks should be tolerated. Suitable protective equipment (gas masks or breathing equipment) should be used.

Inert gases. Gases such as argon, carbon dioxide, helium and nitrogen are widely used as protective atmospheres to prevent unwanted reactions in welding, chemical plants, steel works and so on. These gases are not labelled as being hazardous, and serious accidents may happen because only oxygen can support life.

When any gas or gas mixture displaces the air so that the breathing atmosphere becomes deficient in oxygen, there is a danger of asphyxiation. Unconsciousness or death may result very rapidly when there is little or no oxygen, and there is no warning effect.

Confined spaces where the breathing atmosphere is deficient in oxygen must be ventilated before entering. When breathing equipment is used, the person entering must be supervised. Breathing equipment must be used even in rescuing operations. Normal gas masks give no protection against oxygen deficiency. The same precaution must be observed with large, permanent firefighting installations, which are often automatic, and those who may be present in such areas should be warned of the danger.

Cylinder filling. Cylinder filling involves the operation of high-pressure compressors or liquid pumps. The pumps may operate with cryogenic (very low-temperature) liquids. The filling stations may also incorporate large storage tanks of liquid gases in a pressurized and/or deeply refrigerated state.

The gas filler should check that the cylinders are in acceptable condition for filling, and should fill the correct gas in not more than the approved amount or pressure. The filling equipment should be designed and tested for the given pressure and type of gas, and protected by safety valves. Cleanliness and material requirements for oxygen service must be observed strictly. When filling flammable or toxic gases, special attention should be given to the safety of the operators. The primary requirement is good ventilation combined with correct equipment and technique.

Cylinders which are contaminated with other gases or liquids by the customers constitute a special hazard. Cylinders with no residual pressure may be purged or evacuated before filling. Special care should be taken to ensure that medical gas cylinders are free from any harmful matter.

Transport. Local transport tends to become more mechanized through the use of fork-lift trucks and so on. Cylinders should be transported only with the caps on and secured against falling from the vehicles. Cylinders must not be dropped from trucks directly onto the ground. For hoisting with cranes, suitable lifting cradles should be used. Magnetic lifting devices or caps with uncertain threads should not be used for lifting cylinders.

When cylinders are manifolded into larger packages, great care should be taken to avoid strain on the connections. Any hazard will be increased because of the greater amount of gas involved. It is good practice to divide larger units into sections and to place shut-off valves where they can be operated in any emergency.

The most frequently occurring accidents in cylinder handling and transport are injuries caused by the hard, heavy and difficult-to-handle cylinders. Safety shoes should be worn. Trolleys should be provided for longer transport of single cylinders.

In international transport codes, compressed gases are classified as dangerous goods. These codes give details about which gases may be transported, cylinder requirements, allowed pressure, marking and so on.

Identification of content. The most important requirement for safe handling of compressed gases is the correct identification of the gas content. Stamping, labelling, stencilling and colour marking are the means that are used for this purpose. Certain requirements for marking are covered in International Organization for Standardization (ISO) standards. The colour marking of medical gas cylinders follows the ISO standards in most countries. Standardized colours are also used in many countries for other gases, but this is not a sufficient identification. In the end only the written word can be regarded as a proof of the cylinder content.

Standardized valve outlets. The use of a standardized valve outlet for a certain gas or group of gases strongly reduces the chance of connecting cylinders and equipment made for different gases. Adapters should therefore not be used, as this sets aside the safety measures. Only normal tools and no excessive force should be used when making connections.

Safe Practice for Users

The safe use of compressed gases entails applying the safety principles outlined in this chapter and the ILO Code of Practice *Safety in the Use of Chemicals at Work* (ILO 1993). This is not possible unless the user has some basic knowledge of the gas and the equipment that he or she is handling. In addition the user should take the following precautions:

- Gas cylinders should only be used for the purpose for which they are intended and not as rollers or work supports.
- The cylinders should be stored and handled in such a way that their mechanical strength is not reduced (e.g., by severe corrosion, sharp dents, cuts and so on).
- The cylinders should be removed from fires or excessive heat.
- Only the necessary number of gas cylinders should be kept in working areas or occupied buildings. It is preferable for them to

be kept near doors and not in emergency escape routes or difficult-to-reach areas.

- Any cylinders that have been exposed to fires should be clearly marked and returned to the filler (owner), since the cylinders may have become brittle or lost their strength.
- Cylinders should be stored in a well-ventilated place, away from rain or snow and any combustible storage.
- Cylinders in use should be secured against falling.
- Gas content should be positively identified before use.
- Labels and instructions should be carefully read.
- Cylinders should only be connected to equipment meant for the particular service.
- Connections should be kept clean and in good order; their condition should be checked at regular intervals.
- Good tools (e.g., normal length, fixed wrenches) should be used.
- Loose valve keys should be left in place when the cylinder is in use.
- Valves should be kept closed when cylinders are not in use.
- Cylinders or connected equipment should be removed from confined spaces when not in use (even during short breaks).
- The atmosphere should be checked for oxygen content and, if possible, for flammable gases before confined spaces are entered and during prolonged working periods.
- It should be kept in mind that heavy gases may concentrate in lower areas and that they may be difficult to remove by ventilation.
- Cylinders should be protected against contamination from pressurized equipment, since backflow of other gases may lead to serious accidents. Proper non-return valves, block-and-bleed arrangements and the like should be used.
- Empty cylinders should be returned to the filler with the valves closed and the caps in place. A little residual pressure should always be left in the cylinder to prevent contamination with air and moisture.
- The filler should be notified of any faulty cylinders.
- Acetylene should only be used at a correctly reduced pressure.
- Flame arrestors should only be used in acetylene lines where acetylene is used with compressed air or oxygen.
- Fire extinguishers and heat-protecting gloves should be available with gas welding equipment.
- Liquid gas cylinders should be stored and used in an upright position.
- Poisonous and irritating gases, such as chlorine, should be handled only by well-informed operators with personal safety equipment.
- Unidentified cylinders should not be kept in stock. Fixed installations, with the gas cylinders connected in separate gas centrals, are safest where gases are used regularly.

• LABORATORY HYGIENE

Frank Miller

Setting up a Safe and Healthy Laboratory

A laboratory can only be safe and hygienic if the work practices and procedures that are followed there are safe and hygienic. Such practices are fostered by first giving responsibility and authority for laboratory safety and chemical hygiene to a laboratory safety officer who, together with a safety committee of laboratory personnel, decides what tasks must be accomplished and assigns responsibility for carrying out each of them.

The safety committee's specific tasks include conducting periodic laboratory inspections and summarizing the results in a report submitted to the laboratory safety officer. These inspections are properly done with a checklist. Another important aspect of safety management is periodic inspections of safety equipment to ensure that all equipment is in good working order and in designated locations. Before this can be done, an annual inventory of all the safety equipment must be made; this includes a brief description, including size or capacity and manufacturer. Of no less importance is a semiannual inventory of all laboratory chemicals, including proprietary products. These should be classified into groups of chemically similar substances and also classified according to their fire hazard. Another essential safety classification depends on the degree of hazard associated with a substance, since the treatment a substance receives is directly related to the harm it can cause and the ease with which the harm is unleashed. Each chemical is put into one of three hazard classes chosen on the basis of grouping according to the order of magnitude of risk involved; they are:

1. ordinary hazard substances
2. high-hazard substances
3. extremely hazardous materials.

Ordinary hazard substances are those that are relatively easily controlled, are familiar to laboratory personnel and present no unusual risk. This class ranges from innocuous substances such as sodium bicarbonate and sucrose to concentrated sulphuric acid, ethylene glycol and pentane.

High-hazard substances present much greater hazards than ordinary hazards. They require special handling or, sometimes, monitoring, and present high fire or explosion hazards or severe health risks. In this group are chemicals that form unstable explosive compounds on standing (e.g., hydroperoxides formed by ethers) or substances that have high acute toxicities (e.g., sodium fluoride, which has an oral toxicity of 57 mg/kg in mice), or that have chronic toxicities such as carcinogens, mutagens or teratogens. Substances in this group often have the same kind of hazard as those in the group that follows. The difference is one of degree—those in group 3, the extremely hazardous materials, have either a greater intensity of hazard, or their order of magnitude is much greater, or the dire effects can be released far more easily.

Extremely hazardous materials, when not handled correctly, can very readily cause a serious accident resulting in severe injury, loss of life or extensive property damage. Extreme caution must be exercised in dealing with these substances. Examples of this class are nickel tetracarbonyl (a volatile, extremely poisonous liquid, the vapours of which have been lethal in concentrations as low as 1 ppm) and triethylaluminium (a liquid that spontaneously ignites on exposure to air and reacts explosively with water).

One of the most important of the safety committee's tasks is to write a comprehensive document for the laboratory, a laboratory safety and chemical hygiene plan, that fully describes its safety policy and standard procedures for carrying out laboratory operations and fulfilling regulatory obligations; these include guidelines for working with substances that may fall into any of the three hazard categories, inspecting safety equipment, responding to a chemical spill, chemical waste policy, standards for laboratory air quality and any recordkeeping required by regulatory standards. The laboratory safety and chemical hygiene plan must be kept in the laboratory or must be otherwise easily accessible to its workers. Other sources of printed information include: chemical information sheets (also called material safety data sheets, MSDSs), a laboratory safety manual, toxicological information and fire hazard information. The inventory of laboratory chemicals and three associated derivative lists (classification of chemicals according to chemical class, fire safety class and the three degrees of hazard) must also be kept with these data.

A file system for records of safety-related activities is also required. It is not necessary that this file either be in the laboratory or be immediately accessible to laboratory workers. The records are mainly for the use of laboratory personnel who oversee laboratory safety and chemical hygiene and for the perusal of regulatory agency inspectors. It should thus be easily available and kept up to date. It is advisable that the file be kept outside the laboratory in order to reduce the possibility of its destruction in the event of a fire. The documents on file should include: records of laboratory inspections by the safety committee, records of inspections by any local regulatory agencies including fire departments and state and federal agencies, records dealing with hazardous waste disposal, records of taxes levied on various classes of hazardous waste, where applicable, a second copy of the inventory of laboratory chemicals, and copies of other pertinent documents dealing with the facility and its personnel (e.g., records of attendance of personnel at annual laboratory safety sessions).

Causes of Illness and Injury in the Laboratory

Measures for the prevention of personal injury, illness and anxiety are an integral part of the plans for the day-to-day operation of a well-run laboratory. The people who are affected by unsafe and unhygienic conditions in a laboratory include not only those who work in that laboratory but also neighbouring personnel and those who provide mechanical and custodial services. Since personal injuries in laboratories stem largely from inappropriate contact between chemicals and people, inappropriate mixing of chemicals or inappropriate supply of energy to chemicals, protecting health entails preventing such undesirable interactions. This, in turn, means suitably confining chemicals, combining them properly and closely regulating the energy supplied to them. The main kinds of personal injury in the laboratory are poisoning, chemical burns and injury resulting from fires or explosions. Fires and explosions are a source of thermal burns, lacerations, concussions and other severe bodily harm.

Chemical attack on the body. Chemical attack takes place when poisons are absorbed into the body and interfere with its normal function through disturbance of metabolism or other mechanisms. Chemical burns, or the gross destruction of tissue, usually occur by contact with either strong acids or strong alkalis. Toxic materials that have entered the body by absorption through the skin, eyes or mucous membranes, by ingestion or by inhalation, can cause systemic poisoning, usually by being spread via the circulatory system.

Poisoning is of two general types—acute and chronic. Acute poisoning is characterized by ill effects appearing during or directly after a single exposure to a toxic substance. Chronic poisoning becomes evident only after the passage of time, which may take weeks, months, years or even decades. Chronic poisoning is said to occur when each of these conditions is met: the victim must have been subjected to multiple exposures over long periods of time and to metabolically significant amounts of a chronic poison.

Chemical burns, usually encountered when liquid corrosives are spilled or splashed on the skin or in the eyes, also occur when those tissues come in contact with corrosive solids, ranging in size from powdery dusts to fairly large crystals, or with corrosive liquids dispersed in the air as mists, or with such corrosive gases as hydrogen chloride. The bronchial tubes, lungs, tongue, throat and epiglottis can also be attacked by corrosive chemicals in either the gaseous, liquid or solid states. Toxic chemicals also, of course, may be introduced into the body in any of these three physical states, or in the form of dusts or mists.

Occupational exposure to hazardous chemicals in laboratories

1990 OSHA Laboratory Standard 29 CFR 1910.1450

The following description of a laboratory chemical hygiene plan corresponds with Section (e:1-4), Chemical hygiene plan—General, of the 1990 OSHA Laboratory Standard. This plan should be made readily available to employees and employee representatives.

The chemical hygiene plan shall include each of the following elements and shall indicate specific measures that the employer will take to ensure laboratory employee protection:

(i) Standard operating procedures relevant to safety and health considerations to be followed when laboratory work involves the use of hazardous chemicals;

(ii) Criteria that the employer will use to determine and implement control measures to reduce employee exposure to hazardous chemicals, including engineering controls, the use of personal protective equipment and hygiene practices; particular attention shall be given to the selection of control measures for chemicals that are known to be extremely hazardous;

(iii) A requirement that fume hoods and other protective equipment are functioning properly, and specific measures that shall be taken to ensure proper and adequate performance of such equipment;

(iv) Provisions for employee information and training as prescribed [elsewhere in this plan];

(v) The circumstances under which a particular laboratory operation, procedure or activity shall require prior approval from the employer or the employer's designee before implementation;

(vi) Provisions for medical consultation and medical examinations…;

(vii) Designation of personnel responsible for implementation of the chemical hygiene plan, including the assignment of a chemical hygiene officer and, if appropriate, establishment of a chemical hygiene committee; and

(viii) Provisions for additional employee protection for work with particularly hazardous substances. These include "select carcinogens", reproductive toxins and substances which have a high degree of acute toxicity. Specific consideration shall be given to the following provisions, which shall be included where appropriate:

(a) establishment of a designated area;

(b) use of containment devices such as fume hoods or glove boxes;

(c) procedures for safe removal of contaminated waste; and

(d) decontamination procedures.

The employer shall review and evaluate the effectiveness of the chemical hygiene plan at least annually and update it as necessary.

Injury through fires or explosions. Both fires or explosions may produce thermal burns. Some of the injuries caused by explosions, however, are particularly characteristic of them; they are injuries engendered either by the concussive force of the detonation itself or by such of its effects as glass fragments hurled through the air, causing loss of fingers or limbs in the first case, or skin lacerations or loss of vision, in the second.

Laboratory injuries from other sources. A third class of injuries may be caused neither by chemical attack nor by combustion. Rather they are produced by a miscellany of all other sources—mechanical, electrical, high-energy light sources (ultraviolet and lasers), thermal burns from hot surfaces, sudden explosive shattering of screw-capped glass chemical containers from the unexpected build-up of high internal gas pressures and lacerations from the sharp, jagged edges of newly broken glass tubing. Among the most serious sources of injury of a mechanical origin are tall, high-pressure gas cylinders tipping over and falling to the floor. Such episodes can injure legs and feet; in addition, should the cylinder stem break during the fall, the gas cylinder, propelled by the rapid, massive, uncontrolled escape of gas, becomes a deadly, undirected missile, a potential source of greater, more widespread harm.

Injury Prevention

Safety sessions and information dissemination. Injury prevention, dependent on performance of laboratory operations in a safe and prudent manner, is, in turn, dependent on laboratory workers being trained in correct laboratory methodology. Although they have received some of this training in their undergraduate and graduate education, it must be supplemented and reinforced by periodic laboratory safety sessions. Such sessions, which should emphasize understanding the physical and biological bases of safe laboratory practice, will enable laboratory workers to reject questionable procedures easily and to select technically sound methods as a matter of course. The sessions should also acquaint laboratory personnel with the kinds of data needed to design safe procedures and with sources of such information.

Workers must also be provided with ready access, from their work stations, to pertinent safety and technical information. Such materials should include laboratory safety manuals, chemical information sheets and toxicological and fire hazard information.

Prevention of poisoning and chemical burns. Poisoning and chemical burns have a common feature—the same four sites of entry or attack: (1) skin, (2) eyes, (3) mouth to stomach to intestines and (4) nose to bronchial tubes to lungs. Prevention consists in making these sites inaccessible to poisonous or corrosive substances. This is done by placing one or more physical barriers between the person to be protected and the hazardous substance or by ensuring that the ambient laboratory air is not contaminated. Procedures that use these methods include working behind a safety shield or using a fume hood, or utilizing both methods. The use of a glove box, of course, of itself affords a twofold protection. Minimization of injury, should contamination of tissue occur, is accomplished by removing the toxic or corrosive contaminant as quickly and completely as possible.

Prevention of acute poisoning and chemical burns in contrast with the prevention of chronic poisoning. Although the basic approach of isolation of the hazardous substance from the person to be protected is the same in preventing acute poisoning, chemical burns and chronic poisoning, its application must be somewhat different in preventing chronic poisoning. Whereas acute poisoning and chemical burns may be likened to massive assault in warfare, chronic poisoning has the aspect of a siege. Usually produced by much lower concentrations, exerting their influence through multiple exposures over long periods of time, its effects surface gradually and insidiously through sustained and subtle action. Corrective action involves either first detecting a chemical capable of causing chronic poisoning before any physical symptoms appear, or recognizing one or more aspects of a laboratory worker's discomfort as possibly being physical symptoms connected with chronic poisoning. Should chronic poisoning be suspected, medical attention must be sought promptly. When a chronic poison is found at a concentration exceeding the allowable level, or even approaching it, steps must be taken either to eliminate that substance or, at the very least, to reduce its concen-

tration to a safe level. Protection against chronic poisoning often requires that protective equipment be used for all or much of the workday; however, for reasons of comfort, the use of a glove-box or a self-contained breathing apparatus (SCBA) is not always feasible.

Protection against poisoning or chemical burns. Protection against contamination of the skin by a particular splashed corrosive liquid or scattered poisonous airborne solid is best done by the use of safety gloves and a laboratory apron made of a suitable natural or synthetic rubber or polymer. The term suitable here is taken to mean a material which is neither dissolved, swelled nor in any other way attacked by the substance against which it must afford protection, nor should it be permeable to the substance. The use of a safety shield on the laboratory bench interposed between apparatus in which chemicals are being heated, reacted or distilled and the experimenter is a further safeguard against chemical burns and poisoning via skin contamination. Since the speed with which a corrosive or a poison is washed from the skin is a critical factor in preventing or minimizing the damage these substances can inflict, a safety shower, conveniently located in the laboratory, is an indispensable piece of safety equipment.

The eyes are best protected from splashed liquids by safety goggles or face shields. Airborne contaminants, in addition to gases and vapours, include solids and liquids when they are present in a finely subdivided state as dusts or mists. These are most effectively kept out of the eyes by conducting operations in a fume hood or glove box, although goggles afford some protection against them. To afford additional protection while the hood is being used, goggles may be worn. The presence of easily accessible eyewash fountains in the laboratory will often eliminate, and certainly will, at least, reduce eye damage through contamination by splashed corrosives or poisons.

The mouth to stomach to intestines route is usually connected with poisoning rather than with attack by corrosives. When toxic materials are ingested, it usually happens unwittingly through the chemical contamination of foods or cosmetics. Sources of such contamination are food stored in refrigerators with chemicals, food and beverages consumed in the laboratory, or lipstick kept or applied in the laboratory. Prevention of this kind of poisoning is done by avoiding practices known to cause it; this is feasible only when refrigerators to be used exclusively for food, and dining space outside of the laboratory, are made available.

The nose to bronchial tubes to lungs route, or respiratory route, of poisoning and chemical burns deals exclusively with airborne substances, whether gases, vapours, dusts or mists. These airborne materials may be kept from the respiratory systems of people within and outside of the laboratory by the concurrent practices of: (1) confining operations that either use or produce them to the fume hood (2) adjusting the laboratory air supply so that the air is changed 10 to 12 times per hour and (3) keeping the laboratory air pressure negative with respect to that of the corridors and rooms around it. Fume- or dust-producing operations that involve very bulky pieces of apparatus or containers the size of a 218-l drum, which are too large to be enclosed by an ordinary fume hood, should be done in a walk-in hood. In general, respirators or SCBA should not be used for any laboratory operations other than those of an emergency nature.

Chronic mercury poisoning, produced by the inhalation of mercury vapours, is occasionally found in laboratories. It is encountered when a pool of mercury that has accumulated in a hidden location—under floorboards, in drawers or a closet—has been emitting vapours over a long enough period of time to affect the health of laboratory personnel. Good laboratory housekeeping will avert this problem. Should a hidden source of mercury be suspected, the laboratory air must be checked for mercury either by the use of a special detector designed for the purpose or by sending an air sample for analysis.

Preventing fires and explosions and extinguishing fires. The principal cause of laboratory fires is the accidental ignition of flammable liquids. Flammable liquid is defined, in the fire safety sense, as being a liquid having a flashpoint of less than 36.7 °C. Ignition sources known to have caused this kind of laboratory fire include open flames, hot surfaces, electric sparks from switches and motors found in such equipment as stirrers, household-type refrigerators and electric fans, and sparks produced by static electricity. When ignition of a flammable liquid occurs, it takes place, not in the liquid itself, but above it, in the mixture of its vapours with air

(when the concentration of vapour falls between certain upper and lower limits).

Preventing laboratory fires is accomplished by confining the vapours of flammables completely within the containers in which the liquids are kept or the apparatus in which they are used. If it is not possible to contain these vapours completely, their rate of escape should be made as low as possible and a continuous vigorous flow of air should be supplied to sweep them away, so as to keep their concentration at any given time well below the lower critical concentration limit. This is done both when reactions involving a flammable liquid are run in a fume hood and when drums of flammables are stored in safety solvent cabinets vented to an exhaust.

A particularly unsafe practice is the storage of such flammables as ethanol in a household-type refrigerator. These refrigerators will not keep vapours of stored flammable liquids from the sparks of its switches, motors and relays. No containers of flammables must ever be put in this type of refrigerator. This is especially true of open vessels and trays containing flammable liquids. However, even flammables in screw-capped bottles, kept in this type of refrigerator, have caused explosions, presumably by vapours leaking through a faulty seal or by the bottles breaking. Flammable liquids that require refrigeration must be kept only in explosion-proof refrigerators.

A significant source of fires that occur when large quantities of flammables are poured or siphoned from one drum to another is sparks produced through the accumulation of electric charge produced by a moving fluid. Spark generation of this sort can be prevented by electrically grounding both drums.

Most chemical and solvent fires that occur in the laboratory and are of manageable size, may be extinguished with either a carbon dioxide or dry-chemical type fire extinguisher. One or more 4.5 kg extinguishers of either kind should be supplied to a laboratory, according to its size. Certain special types of fires require other kinds of extinguishing agents. Many metal fires are put out with sand or graphite. Burning metal hydrides require graphite or powdered limestone.

When clothing is set afire in the laboratory, the flames must be put out quickly to minimize the injury caused by thermal burns. A wall-mounted wrap-around fire blanket extinguishes such fires effectively. It may be used for unassisted smothering of flames by the person whose clothing is on fire. Safety showers may also be used to extinguish these fires.

There are limits to the total volumes of flammable liquids that may be safely kept in a particular laboratory. Such limits, generally written into local fire codes, vary and depend on the materials of construction of the laboratory and on whether it is equipped with an automatic fire-extinguishing system. They usually range from about 55 to 135 litres.

Natural gas is often available from numbers of valves located throughout a typical laboratory. These are the most common sources of gas leaks, along with the rubber tubes and burners leading from them. Such leaks, when not detected soon after their onset, have led to severe explosions. Gas detectors, designed to indicate the level of gas concentration in the air, may be used to locate the source of such leakage quickly.

Prevention of injury from miscellaneous sources. Harm from tall, high-pressure gas cylinders falling, among the most familiar in this group of accidents, is avoided easily by strapping or chaining these cylinders securely to a wall or laboratory bench and putting cylinder caps on all unused and empty cylinders.

Most of the injuries from jagged edges of broken glass tubing are sustained through breakage while the tubing is being put into corks or rubber stoppers. They are avoided by lubricating the tube with glycerol and protecting the hands with leather work gloves.

Incompatible Materials

Incompatible materials are a pair of substances that, on contact or mixing, produce either a harmful or potentially harmful effect. The two members of an incompatible pair may be either a pair of chemicals or a chemical and a material of construction such as wood or steel. The mixing or contact of two incompatible materials leads either to a chemical reaction or to a physical interaction that generates a large amount of energy. Specific harmful or potentially harmful effects of these combinations, which can ultimately lead to serious injury or damage to the health, include liberation of large amounts of heat, fires, explosions, production of a flammable gas or generation of a toxic gas. Since a fairly extensive variety of substances is usually found in laboratories, the occurrence of incompatibles in them is quite common and presents a threat to life and health if they are not handled correctly.

Incompatible materials are seldom mixed intentionally. Most often, their mixing is the result of a simultaneous accidental breaking of two adjacent containers. Sometimes it is the effect of leakage or dripping, or results from the mixing of gases or vapours from nearby bottles. Although in many cases in which a pair of incompatibles is mixed, the harmful effect is easily observed, in at least one instance, a not readily detectable chronic poison is formed. This occurs as the result of the reaction of formaldehyde gas from 37% formalin with hydrogen chloride that has escaped from concentrated hydrochloric acid to form the potent carcinogen bis(chloromethyl) ether. Other instances of not immediately detectable effects are the generation of odourless, flammable gases.

Keeping incompatibles from mixing through the simultaneous breaking of adjacent containers or through escape of vapours from nearby bottles is simple—the containers are moved far apart. The incompatible pair, however, must first be identified; not all such identifications are simple or obvious. To minimize the possibility of overlooking an incompatible pair, a compendium of incompatibles should be consulted and scanned occasionally to acquire an acquaintance with less familiar examples. Preventing a chemical from coming in contact with incompatible shelving material, through dripping or through a bottle breaking, is done by keeping the bottle in a glass tray of sufficient capacity to hold all of its contents.

● METHODS FOR LOCALIZED CONTROL OF AIR CONTAMINANTS

Louis DiBernardinis

Occupational health professionals have generally relied on the following hierarchy of control techniques to eliminate or minimize worker exposures: substitution, isolation, ventilation, work practices, personal protective clothing and equipment. Usually a combination of two or more of these techniques is applied. Although this article focuses primarily on the application of ventilation techniques, the other approaches are briefly discussed. They should not be ignored when attempting to control exposure to chemicals by ventilation.

The occupational health professional should always think of the concept of source-path-receiver. The primary focus should be on control at the source with control of the path the second focus. Control at the receiver should be considered the last choice. Whether it is during the start-up or design phases of a process or during the evaluation of an existing process, the procedure for control of exposure to air contaminants should start at the source and progress to the receiver. It is likely that all or most of these control strategies will need to be used.

Substitution

The principle of substitution is to eliminate or reduce the hazard by substituting non-toxic or less toxic materials or redesigning the process to eliminate escape of contaminants into the workplace. Ideally, substitute chemicals would be non-toxic or the process redesign would completely eliminate exposure. However, since this is not always possible the subsequent controls in the above hierarchy of controls are attempted.

Note that extreme care should be taken to assure that substitution does not result in a more hazardous condition. While this focus is on the toxicity hazard, the flammable and chemical reactivity of substitutes must also be considered when assessing this risk.

Isolation

The principle of isolation is to eliminate or reduce the hazard by separating the process emitting the contaminant from the worker. This is accomplished by completely enclosing the process or locating it a safe distance away from people. However, to accomplish this, the process may need to be operated and/or controlled remotely. Isolation is particularly useful for jobs requiring few workers and when control by other methods is difficult. Another approach is to perform hazardous operations on off shifts where fewer workers may be exposed. Sometimes the use of this technique does not eliminate exposure but reduces the number of people who are exposed.

Ventilation

Two types of exhaust ventilation are commonly employed to minimize airborne exposure levels of contaminants. The first is called general or dilution ventilation. The second is referred to as source control or local exhaust ventilation (LEV) and is discussed in more detail later in this article.

These two types of exhaust ventilation should not be confused with comfort ventilation, whose main purpose is to provide measured amounts of outdoor air for breathing and to maintain design temperature and humidity. Various types of ventilation are discussed elsewhere in this *Encyclopaedia*.

Work Practices

Work practices control encompasses the methods workers employ to perform operations and the extent to which they follow the correct procedures. Examples of this control procedure are given throughout this *Encyclopaedia* wherever general or specific processes are discussed. General concepts such as education and training, principles of management and social support systems include discussions of the importance of work practices in controlling exposures.

Personal Protective Equipment

Personal protective equipment (PPE) is considered the last line of defence for control of worker exposure. It encompasses the use of respiratory protection and protective clothing. It is frequently used in conjunction with other control practices, particularly to minimize the effects of unexpected releases or accidents. These issues are discussed in more detail in the chapter *Personal protection*.

Local Exhaust Ventilation

The most efficient and cost-effective form of contaminant control is LEV. This involves capture of the chemical contaminant at its source of generation. There are three types of LEV systems:

1. enclosures
2. exterior hoods
3. receiving hoods.

Enclosures are the preferable type of hood. Enclosures primarily are designed to contain the materials generated within the

Figure 61.1 • Complete enclosure: Glovebox.

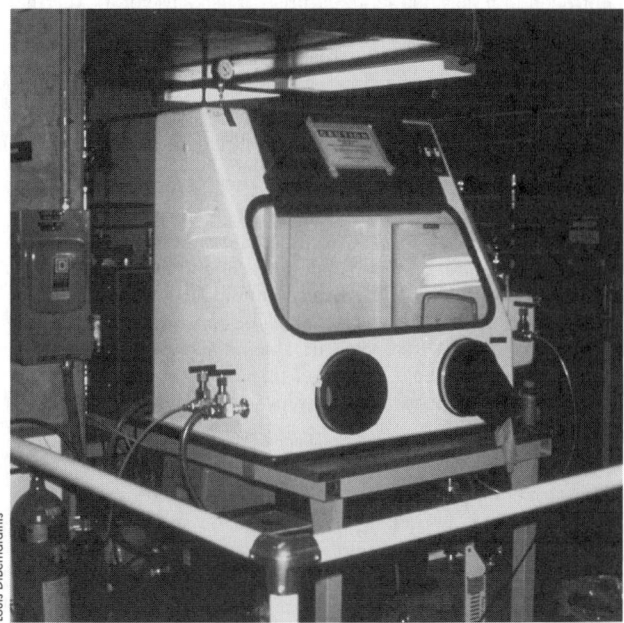

Louis DiBernardinis

enclosure. The more complete the enclosure the more completely the contaminant will be contained. Complete enclosures are those that have no openings. Examples of complete enclosures include

Figure 61.2 • Complete enclosure: Toxic gas storage cabinet.

Louis DiBernardinis

Figure 61.3 • Complete enclosure: Abrasive blasting cabinet.

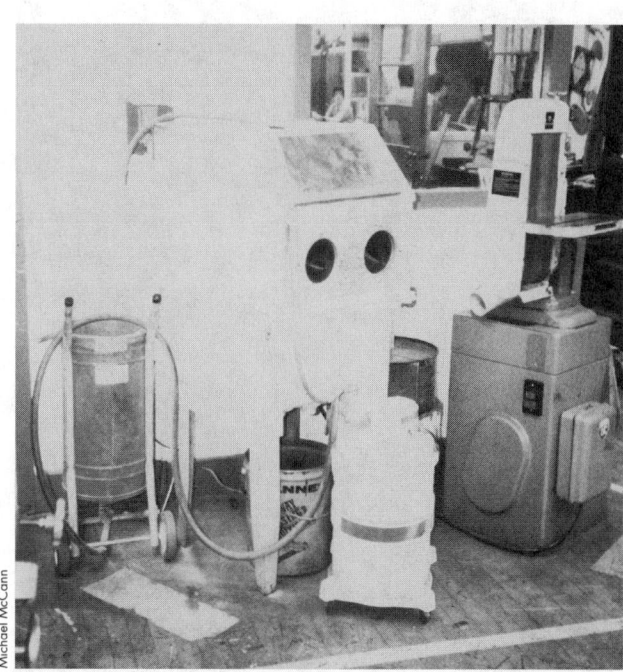

Michael McCann

glove boxes, abrasive blasting cabinets and toxic gas storage cabinets (see figures 61.1, 61.2 and 61.3). Partial enclosures have one or more sides open but the source is still inside the enclosure. Examples of partial enclosures are a spray paint booth (see figure 61.4) and a laboratory hood. Often it might appear that the design of enclosures is more art than science. The basic principle is to design a hood with the smallest opening possible. The volume of air required is usually based on the area of all openings and maintaining an airflow velocity into the opening of 0.25 to 1.0 m/s. The control velocity chosen will depend on the operation's characteristics, including the temperature and the degree to which the contaminant is propelled or generated. For complex enclosures, extreme care must be taken to assure that the exhaust

Figure 61.4 • Partial enclosure: Spray paint booth.

Louis DiBernardinis

Figure 61.5 • Canopy hood: Oven exhaust.

Louis DiBernardinis

flow is evenly distributed throughout the enclosure, particularly if the openings are distributed. Many enclosure designs are evaluated experimentally and if demonstrated to be effective are included as design plates in the American Conference of Governmental Industrial Hygienists' industrial ventilation manual (ACGIH 1992).

Often, total enclosure of the source is not possible, or is not necessary. In these cases, another form of local exhaust, an exterior or capture hood, can be used. An exterior hood prevents the release of toxic materials into the workplace by capturing or entraining them at or close to the source of generation, usually a work station or process operation. Considerably less air volume is usually required than for the partial enclosure. However, since the contaminant is generated outside the hood, it must be designed and used properly in order to be as effective as a partial enclosure. The most effective control is a complete enclosure.

To work effectively, the air inlet of an exterior hood must be of appropriate geometrical design and placed near the point of chemical release. The distance away will depend on the size and shape of the hood and the velocity of air needed at the generation source to capture the contaminant and bring it into the hood. Generally, the closer to the generation source, the better. Design face or slot velocities are typically in the range of 0.25 to 1.0 and 5.0 to 10.0 m/s, respectively. Many design guidelines exist for this class of exhaust hoods in Chapter 3 of the ACGIH manual (ACGIH 1992) or in Burgess, Ellenbecker and Treitman (1989). Two types of exterior hoods that find frequent application are "canopy" hoods and "slot" hoods.

Canopy hoods are used primarily for capture of gases, vapours and aerosols released in one direction with a velocity that can be

used to aid capture. These are sometimes called "receiving" hoods. This type of hood is generally used when the process to be controlled is at elevated temperatures, to make use of the thermal updraft, or the emissions are directed upward by the process. Examples of operations that may be controlled in this manner include drying ovens, melting furnaces and autoclaves. Many equipment manufacturers recommend specific capture hood configurations that are suitable for their units. They should be consulted for advice. Design guidelines are also provided in the ACGIH manual, Chapter 3 (ACGIH 1992). For example, for an autoclave or oven where the distance between the hood and the hot source does not exceed approximately the diameter of the source or 1 m, whichever is smaller, the hood may be considered a low canopy hood. Under such conditions, the diameter or cross-section of the hot air column will be approximately the same as the source. The diameter or side dimensions of the hood therefore need only be 0.3 m larger than the source.

The total flow rate for a circular low canopy hood is

$$Q_t = 4.7 \, (D_f)^{2.33} \, (D_t)^{0.42}$$

where:

Q_t = total hood air flow in cubic feet per minute, ft^3/min
D_f = diameter of hood, ft
D_t = difference between temperature of the hood source, and the ambient, °F.

Similar relationships exist for rectangular hoods and high canopy hoods. An example of a canopy hood can be seen in figure 61.5.

Slot hoods are used for control of operations that cannot be performed inside a containment hood or under a canopy hood. Typical operations include barrel filling, electroplating, welding and degreasing. Examples are shown in figures 61.6 and 61.7. The required flow can be calculated from a series of equations determined empirically by the size and shape of the hood and the distance of the hood from the source. For example, for a flanged slot hood, the flow is determined by

$$Q = 0.0743 LVX$$

where:

Q = total hood air flow, m^3/min
L = the length of the slot, m
V = the velocity needed at the source to capture it, m/min
X = distance from the source to the slot, m.

Figure 61.6 • Exterior hood: Welding.

Michael McCann

The velocity needed at the source is sometimes called "capture velocity" and is usually between 0.25 and 2.5 m/s. Guidelines for selecting an appropriate capture velocity are provided in the ACGIH manual. For areas with excessive cross-drafts or for high-toxicity materials, the upper end of the range should be selected. For particulates, higher capture velocities will be necessary.

Some hoods may be some combination of enclosure, exterior and receiving hoods. For example, the spray paint booth shown in figure 61.4 is a partial enclosure that is also a receiving hood. It is designed to provide efficient capture of particles generated by making use of the particle momentum created by the rotating grinding wheel in the direction of the hood.

Care must be used in selecting and designing local exhaust systems. Considerations should include (1) ability to enclose the operation, (2) source characteristics (i.e., point source vs. widespread source) and how the contaminant is generated, (3) capacity of existing ventilation systems, (4) space requirements and (5) toxicity and flammability of contaminants.

Once the hood is installed, a routine monitoring and maintenance programme for the systems shall be implemented to assure its effectiveness in preventing exposure to workers (OSHA 1993). Monitoring of the standard laboratory chemical hood has become standardized since the 1970s. However, there is no such standardized procedure for other forms of local exhaust; therefore, the user must devise his or her own procedure. The most effective would be a continuous flow monitor. This could be as simple as a magnetic or water pressure gauge measuring static pressure at the hood (ANSI/AIHA 1993). The required hood static pressure (cm of water) will be known from the design calculations, and flow

measurements can be made at the time of installation to verify them. Whether or not a continuous flow monitor is present, there should be some periodic evaluation of the hood performance. This can be done with smoke at the hood to visualize capture and by measuring total flow in the system and comparing that to the design flow. For enclosures it is usually advantageous to measure face velocity through the openings.

Personnel must also be instructed in the correct use of these types of hoods, particularly where the distance from the source and the hood can be easily changed by the user.

If local exhaust systems are designed, installed and used correctly they can be an effective and economical means of controlling toxic exposures.

THE GESTIS CHEMICAL INFORMATION SYSTEM: A CASE STUDY

Karlheinz Meffert and Roger Stamm

GESTIS, the hazardous substance information system of the *Berufsgenossenschaften* (BG, statutory accident insurance carriers) in Germany, is presented here as a case study of an integrated information system for the prevention of risks from workplace chemical substances and products.

With the enactment and application of the regulation on hazardous substances in Germany in the mid-1980s, there was a huge increase in demand for data and information on hazardous substances. This demand had to be met directly by the BG within the framework of their industrial advisory and supervisory activities.

Specialists, including persons working with technical inspection services of the BG, workplace safety engineers, occupational physicians and those cooperating with expert panels, require specific health data. However, information regarding chemical hazards and the necessary safety measures is no less important for the layperson working with hazardous products. In the factory the effectiveness of work protection rules is what finally counts; it is therefore essential that relevant information be easily accessible to the factory owner, safety personnel, workers and, if appropriate, the work committees.

Against this background GESTIS was set up in 1987. Individual BG institutions had maintained databases mostly for more than 20 years. Within the framework of GESTIS, these databases were combined and supplemented with new components, including a "fact" database on substances and products, and information systems specific to particular branches of industry. GESTIS is organized on a central and peripheral basis, with comprehensive data for and about industry in Germany. It is arranged and classified according to branches of industry.

GESTIS consists of four core databases located centrally with the Berufsgenossenschaften Association and their Institute for Occupational Safety (BIA), plus peripheral, branch-specific information systems and documentation on occupational medicine surveillance and interfaces with external databases.

The target groups for hazardous substance information, such as safety engineers and occupational physicians, require different forms and specific data for their work. The form of information directed towards employees should be understandable and related to the specific handling of substances. Technical inspectors may require other information. Finally, the general public has a right to and an interest in workplace health information, including the identification and status of particular risks and the incidence of occupational disease.

Figure 61.7 • Exterior hood: Barrel filling.

Louis DiBernardinis

GESTIS must be able to satisfy the information needs of various target groups by providing accurate information that focuses on practice.

Which data and information are needed?

Core information on substances and products

Hard facts must be the primary foundation. In essence these are facts about pure chemical substances, based on scientific knowledge and legal requirements. The scope of the subjects and information in safety data sheets, as, for example, defined by the European Union in EU Directive 91/155/EEC, correspond to the requirements of work protection in the factory and provide a suitable framework.

These data are found in the GESTIS central substance and product database (ZeSP), an online database compiled since 1987, with an emphasis on substances and in cooperation with the governmental labour inspection services (i.e., the hazardous substance databases of the states). The corresponding facts on products (mixtures) are established only on the basis of valid data on substances. In practice, a large problem exists because producers of safety data sheets often do not identify the relevant substances in preparations. The above-mentioned EU directive provides for improvements in the safety data sheets and requires more precise data on the listing of components (depending on the concentration levels).

The compilation of safety data sheets within GESTIS is indispensable for combining the producer data with substance data that are independent of the producers. This result occurs both through the branch-specific recording activities of the BG and through a project in cooperation with producers, who ensure that the safety data sheets are available, up-to-date and largely in data-processed form (see figure 61.8) in the ISI database (Information System Safety datasheets).

Because safety data sheets often do not adequately consider the special use of a product, specialists in branches of industry compile information on product groups (e.g., cooling lubricants for practical work protection in the factory) from producers' information and substance data. Product groups are defined according to their use and their chemical risk potential. The information made available on product groups is independent of the data provided by producers on the composition of individual products because it is based on general formulae of composition. Thus, the user has access to a supplementary independent information source in addition to the safety data sheet.

Figure 61.8 • Collection and information centre for safety data sheets—basic structure.

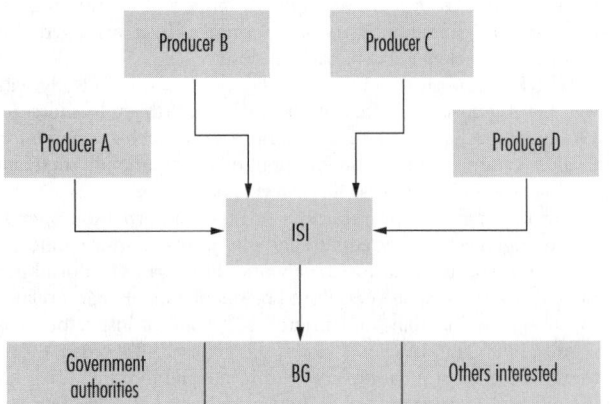

A characteristic feature of ZeSP is the provision of information on the safe handling of hazardous substances in the workplace, including specific emergency and preventive measures. Furthermore, ZeSP contains comprehensive information on occupational medicine in a detailed, understandable and practice-related form (Engelhard et al. 1994).

In addition to the practice-oriented information outlined above, further data are needed in connection with national and international expert panels in order to undertake risk assessments for chemical substances (e.g., the EU Existing Chemicals Regulation).

For the evaluation of risk, data are required for the handling of hazardous substances, including (1) the use category of substances or products; (2) the amounts used in production and handling, and the number of persons working with or exposed to the hazardous substance or product; and (3) exposure data. These data can be obtained from hazardous substance registers at the factory level, which are obligatory under European hazardous substance law, for pooling at a higher level to form branch or general trade registers. These registers are becoming increasingly indispensable for providing the required background for political decision-makers.

Exposure data

Exposure data (i.e., measurement values of hazardous substance concentrations) are obtained through the BG within the framework of the BG measurement system for hazardous substances (BGMG 1993), to carry out compliance measurements in view of threshold values in the workplace. Their documentation is necessary for considering the level of technology when establishing threshold values and for risk analyses (e.g., in connection with the determination of risks in existing substances), for epidemiological studies and for evaluating occupational diseases.

The measurement values determined as part of workplace surveillance are therefore documented in the Documentation for Measurement Data on Hazardous Substances in the Workplace (DOK-MEGA). Since 1972 more than 800,000 measurement values have become available from over 30,000 firms. At present about 60,000 of these values are being added annually. Particular features of the BGMG include a quality assurance system, education and training components, standardized procedures for sampling and analysis, a harmonized measurement strategy on a legal basis and tools supported by data processing for information gathering, quality assurance and evaluation (figure 61.9).

Exposure measurement values must be representative, repeatable and compatible. Exposure data from workplace surveillance in the BGMG are viewed strictly as "representative" of the individual factory situation, since the selection of measurement sites is carried out according to technical criteria in individual cases, not in accordance with statistical criteria. The question of representativeness arises, however, when measurement values for the same or a similar workplace, or even for entire branches of industry, have to be pooled statistically. Measurement data determined as part of surveillance activity generally give higher average values than data that have initially been collected to obtain a representative cross-section of a branch of industry.

For each measurement, differentiated recording and documentation of the relevant factory, process and sampling parameters are required so that the measured values can be combined in a way that is statistically reasonable, and evaluated and interpreted in a technically adequate manner.

In DOK-MEGA this goal is achieved on the following bases of data recording and documentation:

- a standard measurement strategy in accordance with the Technical Rules for Hazardous Substances (TRGS), with documentation of sampling and duration of exposure in particular

Figure 61.9 • BG measurement system for hazardous substances (BGMG)—cooperation between the BIA and the BG.

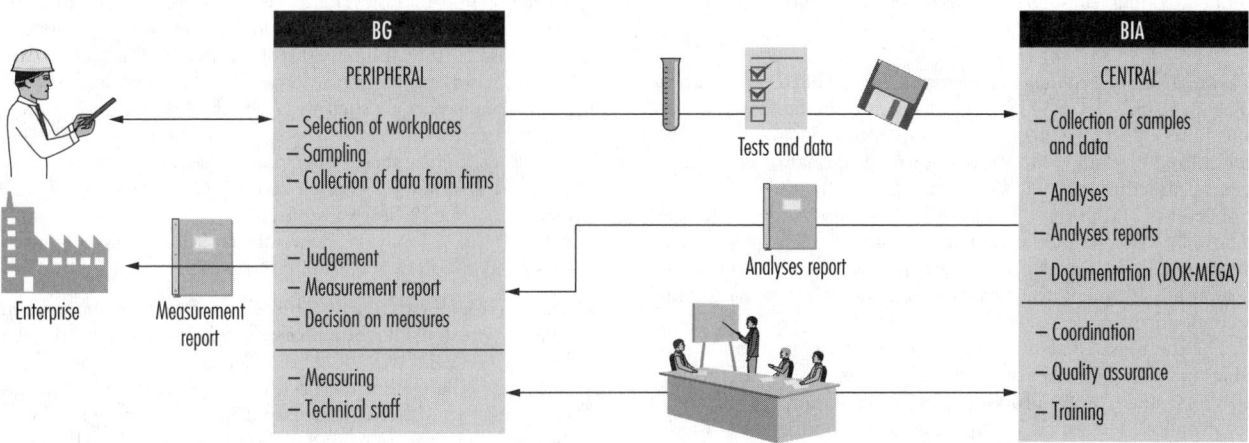

• comparable and reliable procedures for sampling, measuring and analysis
• classification of the measurement values according to industrial area, work process or workplace, and also according to activities in systematized and coded form (GESTIS code directories)
• documentation of process-specific or workplace-specific environmental conditions (e.g., local exhaust ventilation) and chemical substances used (e.g., type of electrodes in welding).

The BIA makes use of its experience with DOK-MEGA in a EU research project with representatives of other national exposure databases with the aim of improving the comparability of exposure and measurement results. In particular, an attempt is being made here to define core information as a basis for comparability and to develop a "protocol" for data documentation.

Health data

In addition to facts about chemical substances and products and about the results of exposure measurements, information is needed on the health effects of actual exposure to hazardous substances in the workplace. Adequate conclusions concerning occupational safety on and beyond the corporate level can be drawn only from an overall view of risk potential, actual risk and effects.

A further component of GESTIS is therefore the occupational disease documentation (BK-DOK), in which all cases of occupational disease reported since 1975 have been registered.

Essential to occupational disease documentation in the area of hazardous substances is the unambiguous, correct determination and recording of the relevant substances and products associated with each case. As a rule the determination is very time-consuming, but acquiring knowledge for prevention is impossible without the accurate identification of substances and products. Thus, for respiratory and skin diseases, which present a particular need for better understanding of possible causative agents, particular effort must be given to record substance and product use information as accurately as possible.

Literature data

The fourth component proposed for GESTIS was background information made available in the form of literature documents, so that the basic facts could be judged appropriately on the basis of current knowledge, and conclusions drawn. For this purpose an interface was developed with the literature database (ZIGUV-

DOK), with a total of 50,000 references at present, of which 8,000 are on the subject of hazardous substances.

Linkage and Problem-oriented Preparation of Data

Information linkage

The components of GESTIS described above cannot stand in isolation if such a system is to be used efficiently. They require appropriate linkage possibilities, for example, between exposure data and cases of occupational disease. This linkage permits the creation of a truly integrated information system. The linkage occurs through core information that is available, coded in the standardized GESTIS coding system (see table 61.2).

With the help of the GESTIS code both individual items of information can be linked to each other (e.g., measurement data from a particular workplace with a case of occupational disease that has occurred in the same or similar workplace) and statistically condensed, "typified" information (e.g., diseases related to particular work processes with average exposure data) can be obtained. With individual linkages of data (e.g., using the pension insurance number) the data protection laws must of course be strictly observed.

It is clear, therefore, that only a systematic coding system is capable of meeting these linkage requirements within the information system. Attention must, however, also be drawn to the possibility of linkage between various information systems

Table 61.2 • Standardized GESTIS code system.

Object	Individual Code	Group Code
Substance, product	ZVG central allocation number (BG)	SGS/PGS, substance/ product group code (BG)
Workplace	IBA sphere of activity of individual factory (BG)	AB sphere of activity (BIA)
Exposed person		Activity (BIA, on the basis of the Federal Statistical Office's systematic listing of occupations)

Origins of codes appear in parentheses.

and across national boundaries. These possibilities of linkage and comparison are crucially dependent on the use of internationally unified coding standards, if necessary in addition to national standards.

Preparation of problem-oriented and use-oriented information

The structure of GESTIS has at its centre the fact databases on substances and products, exposures, occupational diseases and literature, the data compiled both through specialists active at the centre and through the peripheral activities of the BG. For the application and use of the data, it is necessary to reach the users, centrally through publication in relevant journals (e.g., on the subject of the incidence of occupational disease), but also specifically through the advisory activities of the BG in their member firms.

For the most efficient possible use of information made available in GESTIS, the question arises regarding the problem-specific and target-group-specific preparation of facts as information. User-specific requirements are addressed in the fact databases on chemical substances and products—for example, in the depth of information or in the practice-oriented presentation of information. However, not all the specific requirements of possible users can be directly addressed in the fact databases. Target-group-specific and problem-specific preparation, if necessary supported by data processing, is required. Workplace-oriented information must be made available on the handling of hazardous substances. The most important data from the database must be extracted in a generally understandable and workplace-oriented form, for example, in the form of "workplace instructions", which are prescribed in the occupational safety laws of many countries. Frequently too little attention is paid to this user-specific preparation of data as information for workers. Special information systems can prepare this information, but specialized information points which respond to individual queries also provide information and give the necessary support to firms. Within the framework of GESTIS this information-gathering and preparation proceeds, for instance, through branch-specific systems such as GISBAU (Hazardous Substances Information System of the Building Industry BG), GeSi (Hazardous Substances and Safety System), and through specialized information centres in the BG, in the BIA or in the association of the Berufsgenossenschaften.

GESTIS provides the relevant interfaces for data exchange and fosters cooperation by means of task-sharing:

- Direct on-line search is possible for the BG through the central substance and product database (ZeSP) and the literature database (ZIGUV-DOK).
- Off-line exchange between central and peripheral databases is accomplished with the help of appropriate interface formats.
- In the specialized information points within GESTIS, experts carry out targeted evaluations and research on request.

Outlook

The emphasis of further development will be on prevention. In cooperation with the producers, plans encompass a comprehensive and up-to-date preparation of product data; the establishment of statistically determined workplace characteristic values derived from the exposure measurement data and from the substance-specific and product-specific documentation; and an evaluation in the occupational disease documentation.

References

American Conference of Governmental Industrial Hygienists (ACGIH), Committee on Industrial Ventilation. 1992. *Industrial Ventilation: A Manual of Recommended Practices.* 22nd ed. Cincinnati, OH: ACGIH.

American National Standards Institute (ANSI) and American Industrial Hygiene Association (AIHA). 1993. *Laboratory Ventilation.* Standard Z9.5. Fairfax, VA: AIHA.

BG-Measuring System Hazardous Substances (BGMG). 1995. Hauptverband der gewerblichen Berufsgenossenschaften. Sankt Augustin: BGMG.

Burgess, WA, MJ Ellenbecker, and RD Treitman. 1989. *Ventilation for Control of the Work Environment.* New York: John Wiley and Sons.

Engelhard, H, H Heberer, H Kersting, and R Stamm. 1994. Arbeitsmedizinische Informationen aus der Zentralen Stoff- und Productdatenbank ZeSP der gewerblichen Berufsgenossenschaften. *Arbeitsmedizin, Sozialmedizin, Umweltmedizin.* 29(3S):136-142.

International Labour Organization (ILO). 1993. *Safety in the Use of Chemicals at Work.* An ILO Code of Practice. Geneva: ILO.

Occupational Safety and Health Administration (OSHA). 1993. Health and Safety Standard; Occupational exposure to hazardous substances in laboratories. *Federal Register.* 51(42):22660-22684.

Other relevant readings

Commission of European Communities (CEC). 1994. *Working with Dangerous Products.* European Year of Safety, Hygiene and Health. Luxembourg: CEC.

International Labour Organization (ILO). 1993. *Report on the Size of the Task of Harmonization of Existing Systems of Classification and Labelling for Hazardous Chemicals.* Papers of the Governing Body (ILO-GB.255/IO/4/4). Geneva: ILO.

International Programme of Chemical Safety (IPCS) and International Union of Pure and Applied Chemistry (IUPAC). 1992. *Chemical Safety Matters.* IUPAC-IPCS. Cambridge: Cambridge University Press.

Stückrath, M. 1992. Documentation MEGA: Measurement data on hazardous substances at the workplace. In *Clean Air at Work: New Trends in Assessment and Measurement for the 1990s,* edited by RH Brown. London: Royal Society of Chemistry.

Vinzents, P, B Carton, P Fjeldstad, B Rajan, and R Stamm. 1994. *Exposure Registers in Europe. Extraction of Core Information and Possibilities for Comparison between European Databases for Occupational Air Pollutant Measurements.* Luxembourg: Office for Official Publications of the European Communities.

MINERALS AND AGRICULTURAL CHEMICALS

Chapter Editors
Debra Osinsky and
Jeanne Mager Stellman

Contents

MINERALS*

Minerals are used in ceramics, glass, jewellery, insulation, stone carving, abrasives, plastics and numerous other industries in which they present primarily an inhalation hazard. The amount and type of impurities within the minerals may also determine the potential hazard associated with inhalation of the dust. The major concern during mining and production is the presence of silica and asbestos. The silica content in different rock formations, such as sandstone, feldspars, granite and slate, may vary from 20% to nearly 100%. It is therefore imperative that worker exposure to dust concentrations be kept to a minimum by the implementation of strict dust-control measures.

Improved engineering controls, wet drilling, exhaust ventilation and remote handling are recommended to prevent the development of lung disease in mineral workers. Where effective engineering controls are not possible, workers should wear approved respiratory protection, including the proper selection of respirators. Where possible, industrial substitution of less hazardous agents can reduce occupational exposure. Finally, the education of workers and employers regarding the hazards and proper control measures is an essential component of any prevention programme.

Regular medical examinations of mineral-dust-exposed workers should include evaluations for respiratory symptoms, lung function abnormalities and neoplastic disease. Workers showing the first signs of lung changes should be assigned to other jobs entailing no dust hazards. In addition to individual reports of illness, data from groups of workers should be collected for prevention programmes. The chapter *Respiratory system* provides more detail on the health effects of several of the minerals described here.

Apatite (Calcium Phosphate)

Occurrence and uses. Apatite is a natural calcium phosphate, usually containing fluorine. It occurs in the earth's crust as phosphate rock, and it is also the chief component of the bony structure of teeth. Deposits of apatite are located in Canada, Europe, the Russian Federation and the United States.

Apatite is used in laser crystals and as a source of phosphorus and phosphoric acid. It is also employed in the manufacture of fertilizers.

Health hazards. Skin contact, inhalation or ingestion may cause irritation of skin, eyes, nose, throat or gastric system. Fluorine may be present in the dust and may cause toxic effects.

Asbestos

Occurrence and uses. Asbestos is a term used to describe a group of naturally occurring fibrous minerals which are widely distributed throughout the world. The asbestos minerals fall into two groups—the serpentine group, which includes chrysotile, and the amphiboles, which include crocidolite, tremolite, amosite and anthophyllite. Chrysotile and the various amphibole asbestos minerals differ in crystalline structure, in chemical and surface characteristics, and in the physical characteristics of their fibres.

The industrial features which have made asbestos so useful in the past are the high tensile strength and flexibility of the fibres, and their resistance to heat and abrasion and to many chemicals. There are many manufactured products which contain asbestos,

*Adapted from 3rd edition, Encyclopaedia of Occupational Health and Safety. Revision includes information from A. Bruusgaard, L.L. Cash, Jr., G. Donatello, V. D'Onofrio, G. Fararone, M. Kleinfeld, M. Landwehr, A. Meiklejohn, J.A. Pendergrass, S.A. Roach, T.A. Roscina, N.I. Sadkovskaja and R. Stahl.

including construction products, friction materials, felts, packings and gaskets, floor tiles, paper, insulation and textiles.

Health hazards. Asbestosis, asbestos-related pleural disease, malignant mesothelioma and lung cancer are specific diseases associated with exposure to asbestos dust. The fibrotic changes which characterize the pneumoconiosis, asbestosis, are the consequence of an inflammatory process set up by fibres retained in the lung. Asbestos is discussed in the chapter *Respiratory system*.

Bauxite

Occurrence and uses. Bauxite is the principal source of aluminium. It consists of a mixture of minerals formed by the weathering of aluminium-bearing rocks. Bauxites are the richest form of these weathered ores, containing up to 55% alumina. Some lateritic ores (containing higher percentages of iron) contain up to 35% Al_2O_3. The commercial deposits of bauxite are mainly gibbsite ($Al_2O_3 \cdot 3H_2O$) and boehmite ($Al_2O_3 \cdot H_2O$), and are found in Australia, Brazil, France, Ghana, Guinea, Guyana, Hungary, Jamaica and Surinam. Gibbsite is more readily soluble in sodium hydroxide solutions than boehmite, and is therefore preferred for alumina production.

Bauxite is extracted by open-cast mining. The richer ores are used as mined. The lower-grade ores may be upgraded by crushing and washing to remove clay and silica waste.

Health hazards. Severe pulmonary disability has been reported in workers employed on smelting bauxite that is combined with coke, iron and very small amounts of silica. The affliction is known as "Shaver's disease". Because silica contamination of aluminium-containing ores is common, the health hazards associated with the presence of free crystalline silica in bauxite ores must be considered an important causal factor.

Clays (Hydrated Aluminium Silicates)

Occurrence and uses. Clay is a malleable plastic material formed by the weathered disintegration residues of argillaceous silicate rock; it usually contains 15 to 20% water and is hygroscopic. It occurs as a sediment in many geological formations in all parts of the world and contains in varying amounts feldspars, mica and admixtures of quartz, calcspar and iron oxide.

The quality of clay depends on the amount of alumina in it—for example, a good porcelain clay contains about 40% alumina, and the silica content is as low as 3 to 6%. On average the quartz content of clay deposits is between 10 and 20%, but at worst, where there is less alumina than usual, the quartz content may be as high as 50%. Content may vary in a deposit, and separation of grades may take place in the pit. In its plastic state, clay can be moulded or pressed, but when fired it becomes hard and retains the shape into which it has been formed.

Clay is often extracted in open-cast pits but sometimes in underground mines. In open-cast pits the method of extraction depends on the quality of the material and the depth of the deposit; sometimes the conditions require the use of hand-operated pneumatic tools, but, wherever possible, mining is mechanized, using excavators, power shovels, clay cutters, deep digging machines and so on. The clay is taken to the surface by truck or cable transport. The clay brought to the surface may be subjected to preliminary processing before dispatch (drying, crushing, pugging, mixing and so on) or it may be sold whole (see the chapter *Mining and quarrying*). Sometimes, as in many brickyards, the clay pit may be adjacent to the factory where the finished articles are made.

Different types of clay form the basic material in the manufacture of pottery, bricks and tiles, and refractories. Clay may be used without any processing in dam construction; *in situ*, it sometimes serves as a cover for gas stored in lower stratum. Appropriate ventilation and engineering controls are required.

Health hazards. Clays usually contain large amounts of free silica, and chronic inhalation can cause silicosis. Skin contact with wet clay may cause skin drying and irritation. There is a silicosis risk to underground workers where there is mechanized mining of clay with a high quartz content and little natural moisture. Here the decisive factor is not merely the quartz content but also the natural dampness: if the moisture level is less than 12%, much fine dust must be expected in mechanical extraction.

Coal

Occurrence and uses. Coal is a natural, solid, combustible material formed from prehistoric plant life. It occurs in layers or veins in sedimentary rocks. Conditions suitable for the natural formation of coal occurred between 40 and 60 million years ago in the Tertiary Age (brown-coal formation) and over 250 million years ago in the Carboniferous Age (bituminous-coal formation), when swampland forests thrived in a hot climate and then gradually subsided during ensuing geological movements. The main deposits of brown coal are found in Australia, eastern Europe, Germany, the Russian Federation and the United States. Major reserves of bituminous coal are located in Australia, China, India, Japan, the Russian Federation and the United States.

Coal is an important source of chemical raw materials. Pyrolysis or destructive distillation yields coal tar and hydrocarbon gases, which can be upgraded by hydrogenation or methanation to synthetic crude oil and fuel gas. Catalytic hydrogenation yields hydrocarbon oils and gasoline. Gasification produces carbon monoxide and hydrogen (synthetic gas), from which ammonia and other products can be made. While in 1900, 94% of the world's energy requirements were met by coal and only 5% by petroleum and natural gas, coal has been increasingly replaced by liquid and gaseous fuels throughout the world.

Health hazards. Hazards of mining and of coal dust are discussed in the chapters *Mining and quarrying* and *Respiratory system*.

Corundum (Aluminium Oxide)

Occurrence and uses. Corundum is one of the principal natural abrasives. Natural corundum and artificial corundum (alundum or artificial emery) are usually relatively pure. The artificial material is produced from bauxite by smelting in an electric furnace. Because of its hardness, corundum is used to shape metals, wood, glass and ceramics, by a process of grinding or polishing. Health hazards are discussed elsewhere in this *Encyclopaedia*.

Diatomaceous Earth (Diatomite, Kieselguhr, Infusorial Earth)

Occurrence and uses. Diatomaceous earth is a soft, bulky material composed of skeletons of small, prehistoric aquatic plants related to algae (diatoms). Certain deposits comprise up to 90% free amorphous silica. They have intricate geometric forms and are available as light-coloured blocks, bricks, powder and so on. Diatomaceous earth absorbs 1.5 to 4 times its weight of water and has a high oil absorption capacity. Deposits occur in Algeria, Europe, the Russian Federation and the western United States. Diatomaceous earth may be used in foundries, in paper coating, in ceramics and in the maintenance of filters, abrasives, lubricants and explosives. It is used as a filtering medium in the chemical industry. Diatomaceous earth also finds use as a drilling-mud thickener; an extender in paints, rubber and plastic products; and as an anti-caking agent in fertilizers.

Health hazards. Diatomaceous earth is highly respirable. For many industrial purposes diatomaceous earth is calcined at 800 to 1,000 °C to produce a greyish-white powder called *kieselguhr*,

which may contain 60% or more crystobalite. During mining and processing of diatomaceous earth, the risk of death from both respiratory diseases and lung cancer has been related to the inhalation of dust as well as to cumulative crystalline silica exposures, as discussed in the chapter *Respiratory system*.

Erionite

Occurrence and uses. Erionite is a crystalline, fibrous zeolite. Zeolites, a group of alumino-silicates found in the cavities of volcanic rocks, are used in the filtration of hard water and in the refining of oil. Erionite occurs in California, Nevada and Oregon in the United States, and in Ireland, Iceland, New Zealand and Japan.

Health hazards. Erionite is a known human carcinogen. Chronic inhalation may cause mesothelioma.

Feldspar

Occurrence and uses. Feldspar is a general name for a group of sodium, potassium, calcium and barium aluminium silicates. Commercially, feldspar usually refers to the potassium feldspars with the formula $KAlSi_3O_8$, usually with a little sodium. Feldspar occurs in the United States. It is used in pottery, enamel and ceramic ware, glass, soaps, abrasives, cements and concretes. Feldspar serves as a bond for abrasive wheels, and it finds use in insulating compositions, tarred roofing materials and fertilizers.

Health hazards. Chronic inhalation may cause silicosis due to the presence of substantial amounts of free silica. Feldspars may also contain irritating sodium oxide (soda spars), potassium oxide (potash spars), and calcium oxide (lime spars) in insoluble form. See the section "Silica" below.

Flint

Occurrence and uses. Flint is a crystalline form of native silica or quartz. It occurs in Europe and the United States. Flint is used as an abrasive, a paint extender and a filler for fertilizer. In addition, it finds use in insecticides, rubber, plastics, road asphalt, ceramics and chemical tower packing. Historically, flint has been an important mineral because it was used to make some of the first known tools and weapons.

Health hazards are related to the toxic properties of silica.

Fluorspar (Calcium Fluoride)

Occurrence and uses. Fluorspar is a mineral that contains 90 to 95% calcium fluoride and 3.5 to 8% silica. It is extracted by drilling and blasting. Fluorspar is a principal source of fluorine and its compounds. It is used as a flux in open hearth steel furnaces and in metal smelting. In addition, it finds use in the ceramics, paint and optical industries.

Health hazards. The hazards of fluorspar are due primarily to the harmful effects of the fluorine content and its silica content. Acute inhalation may cause gastric, intestinal, circulatory and nervous system problems. Chronic inhalation or ingestion may cause loss of weight and appetite, anaemia, and bone and teeth defects. Pulmonary lesions have been reported among persons inhaling dust containing 92 to 96% calcium fluoride and 3.5% silica. It appears that calcium fluoride intensifies the fibrogenic action of silica in the lungs. Cases of bronchitis and silicosis have been reported among fluorspar miners.

In the mining of fluorspar, dust control should be carefully enforced, including wet drilling, watering of loose rock, and exhaust and general ventilation. When heating fluorspar, there is also the hazard of hydrofluoric acid being formed, and the relevant safety measures should be applied.

Granite

Occurrence and uses. The coarse-grained igneous rock granite consists of quartz, feldspar and mica in shapeless interlocking grains. It finds use as crushed granite and as dimension granite. After it is crushed to the required size, granite may be used for concrete aggregate, road metal, railroad ballast, in filter beds, and for riprap (large chunks) in piers and breakwaters. The colors—pink, grey, salmon, red and white—are desirable for dimension granite. The hardness, uniform texture and other physical properties make dimension granite ideal for monuments, memorials, foundation blocks, steps and columns.

Large production of crushed granite comes mainly from California, with substantial amounts from the other US States of Georgia, North Carolina, South Carolina and Virginia. Major production areas of dimension granite in the United States include Georgia, Maine, Massachusetts, Minnesota, North Carolina, South Dakota, Vermont, and Wisconsin.

Health hazards. Granite is heavily contaminated with silica. Therefore, silicosis is a major health hazard in granite mining.

Graphite

Occurrence and uses. Graphite is found in almost every country of the world, but the majority of production of the natural ore is limited to Austria, Germany, Madagascar, Mexico, Norway, the Russian Federation and Sri Lanka. Most, if not all, natural graphite ores contain crystalline silica and silicates.

Lump graphite is found in veins which cross different types of igneous and metamorphic rock containing mineral impurities of feldspar, quartz, mica, pyroxine, zircon, rutile, apatite and iron sulphides. The impurities are often in isolated pockets in the veins of ore. Mining is commonly underground, with hand drills for selective mining of narrow veins.

Deposits of *amorphous graphite* are also underground, but usually in much thicker beds than the veins of lumps. Amorphous graphite is commonly associated with sandstone, slate, shale, limestone and adjunct minerals of quartz and iron sulphides. The ore is drilled, blasted and hand-loaded into wagons and brought to the surface for grinding and impurity separation.

Flake graphite is usually associated with metamorphosed sedimentary rock such as gneiss, schists and marbles. The deposits are often on or near the surface. Consequently, normal excavating equipment such as shovels, bulldozers and scarifiers are used in open-cast mining, and a minimum of drilling and blasting is necessary.

Artificial graphite is produced by the heating of coal or petroleum coke, and generally contains no free silica. Natural graphite is used in the manufacture of foundry linings, lubricants, paints, electrodes, dry batteries and crucibles for metallurgical purposes. The "lead" in pencils is also graphite.

Health hazards. Inhalation of carbon, as well as associated dusts, may occur during the mining and milling of natural graphite, and during the manufacture of artificial graphite. X-ray examinations of natural and artificial graphite workers have shown varying classifications of pneumoconioses. Microscopic histopathology has revealed pigment aggregates, focal emphysema, collagenous fibrosis, small fibrous nodules, cysts and cavities. The cavities have been found to contain an inky fluid in which graphite crystals were identified. Recent reports note that the materials implicated in exposures leading to severe cases with massive pulmonary fibrosis are likely to be mixed dusts.

Graphite pneumoconiosis is progressive even after the worker has been removed from the contaminated environment. Workers may remain asymptomatic during many years of exposure, and disability often comes suddenly. It is essential that periodic analyses are made of the raw ore and airborne dust for crystalline silica

and silicates, with special attention to feldspar, talc and mica. Acceptable dust levels must be adjusted to accommodate the effect these disease-potentiating dusts may have on workers' health.

In addition to being exposed to the physical hazards of mining, graphite workers may also face chemical hazards, such as hydrofluoric acid and sodium hydroxide used in graphite purification. Protection against the risks associated with these chemicals should be part of any health programme.

Gypsum (Hydrated Calcium Sulphate)

Occurrence and uses. Though it occurs throughout the world, gypsum is rarely found pure. Gypsum deposits may contain quartz, pyrites, carbonates and clayey and bituminous materials. It occurs in nature in five varieties: gypsum rock, gypsite (an impure, earthy form), alabaster (a massive, fine-grained translucent variety), satin spar (a fibrous silky form) and selenite (transparent crystals).

Gypsum rock may be crushed and ground for use in the dihydrate form, calcined at 190 to 200 °C (thus removing part of the water of crystallization) to produce calcium sulphate hemihydrate or plaster of Paris, or completely dehydrated by calcining at over 600 °C to produce anhydrous or dead-burned gypsum.

Ground dihydrate gypsum is used in the manufacture of Portland cement and artificial marble products; as a soil conditioner in agriculture; as a white pigment, filler or glaze in paints, enamels, pharmaceuticals, paper and so on; and as a filtration agent.

Health hazards. Workers employed in the processing of gypsum rock may be exposed to high atmospheric concentrations of gypsum dust, furnace gases and smoke. In gypsum calcining, workers are exposed to high environmental temperatures, and there is also the hazard of burns. Crushing, grinding, conveying and packaging equipment presents a danger of machinery accidents. The pneumoconiosis observed in gypsum miners has been attributed to silica contamination.

Dust formation in gypsum processing should be controlled by mechanization of dusty operations (crushing, loading, conveying and so on), addition of up to 2% by volume of water to gypsum prior to crushing, use of pneumatic conveyors with covers and dust traps, enclosure of dust sources and provision of exhaust systems for kiln openings and for conveyor transfer points. In the workshops containing the calcining kilns, it is advisable to face the walls and floors with smooth materials to facilitate cleaning. Hot piping, kiln walls and drier enclosures should be lagged to reduce the danger of burns and to limit heat radiation to the work environment.

Limestone

Occurrence and uses. Limestone is a sedimentary rock composed mainly of calcium carbonate in the form of mineral calcite. Limestones may be classified either according to the impurities they contain (dolomitic limestone, which contains substantial amounts of magnesium carbonate; argillaceous limestone, with a high clay content; siliceous limestone, which contains sand or quartz; and so on) or according to the formation in which they occur (e.g., marble, which is a crystalline limestone). Limestone deposits are widely distributed throughout the earth's crust and are extracted by quarrying.

Since early times, limestone has been used as a building stone. It is also crushed for use as a flux in smelting, in refining, and for the manufacture of lime. Limestone is used as hardcore and ballast in road and railway construction, and it is mixed with clay for the manufacture of cement.

Health hazards. During extraction, the appropriate quarrying safety measures should be taken, and machinery-guarding principles should be observed on crushers. The main health hazard in limestone quarries is the possible presence, in the airborne limestone dust, of free silica, which normally accounts for 1 to 10% of limestone rock. In studies of limestone quarry and processing workers, x-ray examinations revealed pulmonary changes, and clinical examination showed pharyngitis, bronchitis and emphysema. Workers dressing stone for construction work should observe the safety measures appropriate to the stone industry.

Marble (Calcium Carbonate)

Occurrence and uses. Marble is geologically defined as a metamorphosed (re-crystallized) limestone composed primarily of crystalline grains of calcite, dolomite, or both, having a visible crystalline texture. Long usage of the term *marble* by the quarry and finishing industry has led to the development of the term *commercial marble*, which includes all crystalline rock capable of taking a polish and composed primarily of one or more of the following minerals: calcite, dolomite or serpentine.

Marble has been utilized throughout historic time as an important construction material because of its strength, durability, ease of workability, architectural adaptability and aesthetic satisfaction. The marble industry comprises two major branches—dimension marble and crushed and broken marble. The term *dimension marble* is applied to deposits of marble quarried for the purpose of obtaining blocks or slabs that meet specifications as to size and shape. The uses of dimension marble include building stone, monumental stone, ashlar, veneer panelling, wainscotting, tiling, statuary and so on. Crushed and broken marble ranges in size from large boulders to finely ground products, and products include aggregates, ballast, roofing granules, terrazzo chips, extenders, pigments, agricultural lime and so on.

Health hazards. Occupational diseases specifically connected with the mining, quarrying and processing of marble itself have not been described. In underground mining there may be exposure to toxic gases produced by blasting and some types of motor-driven equipment; adequate ventilation and respiratory protection are necessary. In abrasive blasting there will be exposure to silica if sand is used, but silicon carbide or aluminium oxide are equally effective, carry no silicosis risk, and should be substituted. The large quantities of dust generated in processing marble should be subject to dust control, either by the use of moist methods or by exhaust ventilation.

Mica

Occurrence and uses. Mica (from the Latin *micare*, to gleam or sparkle) is a mineral silicate which occurs as a primary constituent of igneous rocks, particularly granites. It is also a common component of such silicate materials as kaolin, which are produced by the weathering of these rocks. In the rock bodies, particularly in the pegmatite veins, mica occurs as lenticular masses of cleavable sheets (known as books) of up to 1 m in diameter, or as particles. There are many varieties, of which the most useful are *muscovite* (common, clear or white mica), *phlogopite* (amber mica), *vermiculite*, *lepidolite* and *sericite*. Muscovite is generally found in siliceous rocks; there are substantial deposits in India, South Africa and the United States. Sericite is the small plate variety of muscovite. It results from the weathering of schists and gneisses. Phlogopite, which occurs in calcareous rocks, is concentrated in Madagascar. Vermiculite has the outstanding characteristic of expanding considerably when quickly heated to around 300 °C. There are large deposits in the United States. The main value of lepidolite lies in its high content of lithium and rubidium.

Mica is still used for slow-combustion stoves, lanterns or peepholes of furnaces. The supreme quality of mica is that it is dielectric, which makes it a top-priority material in aircraft con-

struction. Mica powder is used in the manufacture of electric cables, pneumatic tyres, welding electrodes, bituminized cardboard, paints and plastics, dry lubricants, dielectric dressings and flameproof insulators. It is often compacted with alkyd resins. Vermiculite is widely used as an insulating material in the building industry. Lepidolite is used in the glass and ceramic industries.

Health hazards. When working with mica, the generation of static electricity is possible. Straightforward engineering techniques can harmlessly discharge it. Mica miners are exposed to the inhalation of a wide variety of dusts, including quartz, feldspar and silicates. Chronic inhalation may cause silicosis. Exposure of workers to mica powder may cause irritation of the respiratory tract, and, after several years, nodular fibrotic pneumoconiosis can occur. It was long considered to be a form of silicosis, but it is now believed not to be, because pure mica dust contains no free silica. The radiological appearance is often close to that of asbestosis. Experimentally, mica has proved to possess a low cytotoxicity on macrophages and to induce only a poor fibrogenic response limited to the formation of thick reticulin fibres.

Chronic inhalation of vermiculite, which often contains asbestos, may cause asbestosis, lung cancer and mesothelioma. Ingestion of vermiculite is also suspected in stomach and intestinal cancer.

Pumice

Occurrence and uses. Pumice is a porous rock, grey or white, fragile and of low specific gravity, coming from recent volcanic magma; it is composed of quartz and silicates (mainly feldspar). It is found either pure or mixed with various substances, chief among them obsidian, which differs by its shiny black colour and its specific gravity, which is four times greater. It occurs principally in Ethiopia, Germany, Hungary, Italy (Sicily, Lipari), Madagascar, Spain and the United States. Some varieties, such as Lipari pumice, have a high content of total silica (71.2 to 73.7%) and a fair amount of free silica (1.2 to 5%).

In commerce and for practical uses, a distinction is made between pumice in blocks and in powder. When it is in block form the designation differs according to the size of block, colour, porosity and so on. The powder form is classified by numbers according to grain size. Industrial processing comprises a number of operations: sorting to separate the obsidian, crushing and pulverizing in machines with stone or metal grinding wheels, drying in open kilns, sifting and screening using hand-operated flat and open sieves and reciprocating or rotating screens, the waste matter generally being recovered.

Pumice is used as an abrasive (block or powder), as a lightweight building material, and in the manufacture of stoneware, explosives and so on.

Health hazards. The most dangerous operations involving exposure to pumice are kiln drying and sifting, because of the large amount of dust produced. Apart from the characteristic signs of silicosis observed in the lungs and sclerosis of the hilar lymphatic glands, the study of some fatal cases has revealed damage to various sections of the pulmonary arterial tree. Clinical examination has revealed respiratory disorders (emphysema and sometimes pleural damage), cardiovascular disorders (cor pulmonale) and renal disorders (albuminuria, haematuria, cylindruria), as well as signs of adrenal deficiency. Radiological evidence of aortitis is more common and serious than in the case of silicosis. A typical radiological appearance of lungs in liparitosis is the presence of linear thickening due to lamellar atelactasis.

Sandstone

Occurrence and uses. Sandstone is a siliciclastic sedimentary rock consisting primarily of sand, usually sand that is predominantly quartz. Sandstones often are poorly cemented and can be easily crumbled into sand. Yet, strong, durable sandstone, with tan and grey colours, is used as dimension sandstone for exterior facing and trim for buildings, in houses, as curbstones, in bridge abutments and in various retaining walls. Firm sandstones are crushed for use as concrete aggregate, railroad ballast and riprap. However, many commercial sandstones are weakly cemented and therefore are crumbled and used for moulding sand and glass sand. Glass sand is the main ingredient in glass. In the metalworking industry, sand with good cohesiveness and refractoriness is used for making special shaped moulds into which molten metal is poured.

Sandstone is found throughout the United States, in Illinois, Iowa, Minnesota, Missouri, New York, Ohio, Virginia and Wisconsin.

Health hazards. The primary risks are from the silica exposure, which is discussed in the chapter *Respiratory system.*

Silica

Occurrence and uses. Silica occurs naturally in crystalline (quartz, cristobalite and tridymite), cryptocrystalline (e.g., chalcedony) and amorphous (e.g., opal) forms, and the specific gravity and melting point depend on the crystalline form.

Crystalline silica is the most widely occurring of all minerals, and it is found in most rocks. The most commonly occurring form of silica is the sand found on beaches throughout the world. The sedimentary rock *sandstone* consists of grains of quartz cemented together with clays.

Silica is a constituent of common glass and most refractory bricks. It is also used extensively in the ceramic industry. Rocks containing silica are used as common building materials.

Free and combined silica. Free silica is silica which is not combined with any other element or compound. The term *free* is used to distinguish it from *combined* silica. *Quartz* is an example of free silica. The term *combined silica* originates from the chemical analysis of naturally occurring rocks, clays and soils. The inorganic constituents are found to consist almost always of oxides bound chemically, commonly including silicon dioxide. Silica so combined with one or more other oxides is known as combined silica. The silica in *mica*, for example, is present in the combined state.

In *crystalline* silica, the silicon and oxygen atoms are arranged in a definite, regular pattern throughout the crystal. The characteristic crystal faces of a crystalline form of silica are the outward expression of this regular arrangement of atoms. The crystalline forms of free silica are *quartz, cristobalite* and *tridymite.* Quartz is crystallized in the hexagonal system, cristobalite in the cubic or tetragonal system and tridymite in the ortho-rhombic system. Quartz is colourless and transparent in the pure form. The colours in naturally occurring quartz are due to contamination.

In amorphous silica the different molecules are in a dissimilar spatial relationship one to another, with the result that there is no definite regular pattern between molecules some distance apart. This absence of long-range order is characteristic of amorphous materials. Cryptocrystalline silica is intermediate between crystalline and amorphous silica in that it consists of minute crystals or crystallites of silica which are themselves arranged in no regular orientation one to another.

Opal is an amorphous variety of silica with a varying amount of combined water. A commercially important form of amorphous silica is *diatomaceous earth*, and *calcinated diatomaceous earth* (kieselguhr). *Chalcedony* is a cryptocrystalline form of silica which occurs filling cavities in lavas or associated with flint. It is also found in the annealing of ceramics when, under certain temperature conditions, the quartz in silicates may crystallize out in minute crystals in the body of the ware.

Health hazards. The inhalation of airborne dust of silica gives rise to silicosis, a serious and potentially fatal fibrotic disease of the lungs. The chronic, accelerated, and acute forms of silicosis reflect differing exposure intensities, latency periods and natural histories. Chronic silicosis may progress to progressive massive fibrosis, even after exposure to silica-containing dust has ceased. Hazards of silica are discussed in more detail in the chapter *Respiratory system.*

Slate

Occurrence and uses. Slate is very fine-grained, sedimentary argillaceous or schisto-argillaceous rock, easily split, of a leaden-grey, reddish or greenish colour. The principal deposits are in France (Ardennes), Belgium, the United Kingdom (Wales, Cornwall), the United States (Pennsylvania, Maryland) and Italy (Liguria). With a high calcium carbonate content, they contain silicates (mica, chlorite, hydrosilicates), iron oxides and free silica, amorphous or crystalline (quartz). The quartz content of hard slates is in the region of 15%, and that of soft slates, less than 10%. In North Wales quarries, respirable slate dust contains between 13 and 32% of respirable quartz.

Slate slabs are used for roofing; stair treads; door, window and porch casements; flooring; fireplaces; billiard tables; electricity switch panels; and school blackboards. Powdered slate has been used as a filler or pigment in rustproofing or insulating paints, in mastics, and in paints and bituminous products for road surfacing.

Health hazards. Disease in slate workers has attracted attention since the early nineteenth century, and cases of "miner's phthisis" uncomplicated by tubercle bacilli were described at an early date. Pneumoconiosis has been found in a third of workers studied in the slate industry in North Wales, and in 54% of slate pencil makers in India. Slateworkers' pneumoconiosis may have features of silicosis due to the high quartz content of some slates. Chronic bronchitis and emphysema are frequently observed, especially in extraction workers.

The replacement of the hand pick by low-velocity mechanical equipment considerably reduces dust generation in slate quarries, and the use of local exhaust ventilation systems makes it possible to maintain airborne dust concentrations within acceptable limits for 8-hour exposure. Ventilation of underground workings, drainage of groundwater into pits, lighting and work organization are improving the general hygiene of working conditions.

Circular sawing should be carried out under water jets, but planing does not usually give rise to dust provided the slivers of slate are not allowed to fall to the ground. Larger sheets are usually wet-polished; however, where dry-polishing is carried out, well-designed exhaust ventilation should be employed since slate dust is not easily collected even when using scrubbers. The dust readily clogs bag filters.

Workshops should be cleaned daily to prevent accumulation of dust deposits; in certain cases, it may be preferable to prevent deposited dust in gangways from becoming airborne again by covering dust with sawdust rather than by wetting it.

Talc

Occurrence and uses. Talc is a hydrous magnesium silicate whose basic formula is $(Mg\,Fe^{+2})_3Si_4O_{10}(OH_2)$, with theoretical weight percentages as follows: 63% SiO_2, 32% MgO and 5% H_2O. Talc is found in a variety of forms and is frequently contaminated with other minerals, including silica and asbestos. Talc production occurs in Australia, Austria, China, France and the United States.

The texture, stability and fibrous or flaky properties of the various talcs have made them useful for many purposes. The purest grades (i.e., those which most nearly approximate the theoretical composition) are fine in texture and colour, and are therefore widely used in cosmetics and toilet preparations. Other varieties, containing admixtures of different silicates, carbonates and oxides, and perhaps free silica, are relatively coarse in texture and are used in the manufacture of paint, ceramics, automobile tyres and paper.

Health hazards. Chronic inhalation may cause silicosis if silica is present, or asbestosis, lung cancer, and mesothelioma if asbestos or asbestos-like minerals are present. Investigations of workers exposed to talc without associated asbestos fibres revealed trends for higher mortality from silicosis, silicotuberculosis, emphysema and pneumonia. The major clinical symptoms and signs of talc pneumoconiosis include chronic productive cough, progressive shortness of breath, diminished breath sounds, limited chest expansion, diffuse rales and clubbing of the finger tips. Lung pathology has revealed various forms of pulmonary fibrosis.

Wollastonite (Calcium Silicate)

Occurrence and uses. Wollastonite ($CaSiO_3$) is a natural calcium silicate found in metamorphic rock. It occurs in many different forms in New York and California in the United States, in Canada, Germany, Romania, Ireland, Italy, Japan, Madagascar, Mexico, Norway and Sweden.

Wollastonite is used in ceramics, welding-rod coatings, silica gels, mineral wool and paper coating. It is also used as a paint extender, a soil conditioner, and as a filler in plastics, rubber, cements and wallboard.

Health hazards. Wollastonite dust may cause skin, eye and respiratory irritation.

● AGRICULTURAL CHEMICALS

Gary A. Page

Agricultural chemicals are usually defined as pesticides, fertilizers and health products. The US Environmental Protection Agency (EPA) defines *pesticides* as any materials manufactured or formulated to kill a pest. This means that herbicides, fungicides, insecticides and miticides are pesticides. *Fertilizers* are nutrient chemicals that enhance the growth of the plant. The important elements in the fertilizers are nitrogen, phosphorus and potassium. Nitrogen is usually in the form of ammonia, ammonium nitrate, ammonium sulphate, ammonium phosphate or solutions of these materials. Other nitrogen-containing chemicals are used for some special nutrient needs. Ammonium phosphate is the normal source of phosphorous. Potash (potassium oxide) is the potassium nutrient. *Animal health products* are any chemicals that are used to promote the health or growth of an animal. This includes products that are used topically by drenching or pouring-on, orally as a tablet or gel, and injectibles.

Pesticides

The most significant development in the pesticide manufacturing industry has been the introduction of the environmentally friendly pesticides. The imidazolinone family of herbicides has been a benefit to soybean and other field crops, as the herbicides are much more effective pound for pound; are less toxic to humans, animals and fish; have less persistence in the soil; and are formulated using water instead of flammable solvents, as compared to the old generation nitroaromatics. Concurrent with these innovations is the development of imidazolinones-resistant seeds that can be protected from weed growth. Corn is in the forefront in this area and has been successfully grown, protected by the imidazolinones. This also makes carry-over from year to year of the herbicide an insignificant problem, as in many areas soybeans and corn are rotated.

A newer development is the production of the synthetic pyrethroids, which are broad-range pesticides. These products are effective pesticides and are less toxic to animals and humans than the old organophosphates and carbamates. They are activated by the insect's biological system and therefore not a danger to vertebrates. They are also less persistent in the environment, as they are biodegradable.

There have also been developments in the use of the old generation pesticides and herbicides. Herbicide formulations have been developed that utilize water dispersion technology that eliminates the use of volatile solvents. This not only reduces the amount of volatile organic chemicals that go to the atmosphere, but also makes handling, storage, formulation and transportation much safer. In the area of pesticides, a superior method of handling the toxic pesticides has been developed that uses closed container transfer of the material from the package to the spreader, called "Lock-N-Load". This reduces the chances of exposure to these toxic materials. Organophosphates are still being used successfully to help eradicate health problems such as malaria and river blindness. Some of the less toxic organophosphates are effective in the treatment of animals for insects, worms and mites by direct application to the skin using pour-on or aerosol formulations.

The pesticide industry is regulated by many countries, and labelling, application to plants and soil, training in pesticide use, and transportation are controlled. Many pesticides can only be spread by licensed applicators. Precautions during pesticide application are discussed elsewhere in this *Encyclopaedia*. Bulk transportation vehicles can only be operated by qualified drivers. The producers of pesticide have a legal obligation to provide safe handling and application methods. This is usually accomplished by providing comprehensive labelling, training and material safety data sheets (MSDSs) (see the chapter *Using, storing and transporting chemicals*).

Another problem is the disposal of empty containers. It is not advisable, and in many places it is illegal, to reuse pesticide containers. Many advances have been made to mitigate this problem. Plastic containers have been collected by the distributors and reprocessed into plastic pipe. Bulk, refillable containers have been used. With the advent of the wettable powders and water-based dispersions, triple rinsing the container into the solutions tank gives the applicator a method to decontaminate the container before landfilling or recycling. Hand lances with spray nozzles that can pierce the container are used to assure proper cleaning and the destruction of the container so that it can not be reused.

Pesticides are made to kill; therefore, care is necessary to handle them safely. Some of the problems have been lessened by the product advances. In most cases, copious quantities of water are the best first-aid treatment for superficial exposures to skin and eyes. For ingestion, it is best to have a specific antidote available. It is important that the nearest health facility know what is being used and have a supply of the appropriate antidote on hand. For instance, organophosphates and carbamates cause cholinesterase inhibition. Atropine, the specific antidote for the treatment of this reaction, should be available wherever these pesticides are used.

For further discussion of pesticides, see the eponymous article in this chapter.

Fertilizers

Ammonia is the base of most important fertilizers. The major fertilizers are ammonia itself, ammonium nitrate, urea, ammonium sulphate and ammonium phosphate. There appears to be an environmental problem associated with nitrogen use, as the ground water in many farming areas is contaminated with nitrates, which causes health problems when the water is consumed as drinking water. There are pressures for farmers to use less fertilizer and to rotate crops of nitrogen-using legumes such as soy beans and rye grass. Ammonium nitrate, an oxidizer, is explosive if heated. The dangers of ammonium nitrate as a blasting agent were demonstrated by the destruction of a US federal building in Oklahoma City, Oklahoma, in 1995. There is some movement to add inert ingredients to make fertilizer-grade ammonium nitrate detonation-resistant. An industrial explosion resulting in multiple fatalities which occurred in an ammonium nitrate solutions plant that was thought to be safe from detonation because the ammonium nitrate was handled as an 85% solution is another example. Investigation results indicated that an intricate condition of temperature and contamination caused the incident. These conditions would not exist in the retail or farming sector. Anhydrous ammonia is a moderately toxic gas at room temperature and must be kept under pressure or refrigeration during storage and use. It is a skin, eye and respiratory irritant, can cause burns, and is flammable. It is directly applied to the soil or used as an aqueous solution. There is significant anhydrous ammonia storage in many farming areas. A hazardous condition is created if the storage is not managed correctly. This should include monitoring for leaks and emergency leak procedures.

Animal Health Products

The development and marketing of bovine somatotropin (BST) has caused controversy. BST, a fermentation product, raises the productivity of milk cows by 10 to 20%. Many people are opposed to the product because it introduces a chemical into the production of milk. However, the BST milk is indistinguishable from ordinary milk since BST is produced naturally by the milk cow. A problem seems to be an increase in infections of the cow's udder. Antibiotics for these infections are available, but the use of these antibiotics is also controversial. The important benefits of BST are the increased production of milk with a reduction in food consumption and a similar reduction in cow manure, a material that is a solid-waste problem in many areas. A similar product, porcine somatotropin (PST), is still in the testing stage. It produces bigger hogs quickly, utilizing less feed, and results in pork containing less fat.

Antibiotic use in the beef-raising industry is also causing controversy. There is fear that consumption of large amounts of beef will result in hormonal problems in humans. There has been little in the way of confirmed problems, but the concern persists. Animal health products have been developed that control worms in animals. The previous generation was a synthetic chemical product, but the new generation products are the result of biological fermentation technology. These products are effective in many types of animals at very low use levels, and include domestic pets in their protection arena. These products are very toxic to aquatic life, though, so much care must be taken to avoid contamination of creeks and streams. These materials do biodegrade, so there appear to be no long-term or residual aquatic problems.

Manufacture of Agricultural Chemicals

The manufacturing of agricultural chemicals entails many processes and raw materials. Some agricultural chemicals are batch chemical syntheses that involve exothermic reactions where temperature control and emergency relief sizing are an issue. Hazard evaluations are necessary to assure that all the hazards are discovered and addressed. Hazard and operability studies (HAZOP) are recommended for conducting reviews. Relief sizing must be conducted using Design Institute for Emergency Relief Systems (DIERS) technology and data from calorimetric equipment. Usually, because of the complexity of the molecules, the production of agricultural chemicals involves many steps. Sometimes there is considerable aqueous and organic liquid waste. Some of the organics may be recyclable, but most of the aqueous waste must be biologically treated or incinerated. Both methods are difficult because of the presence of organic and inorganic salts. The previous generation herbicides, because they involved nitrations, were produced using continuous reactors to minimize the quantities of the nitrated materials at reaction temperatures. Severe runaway reactions, resulting in property damage and injuries, have occurred when batch reactors of nitrated organics have been subjected to a temperature excursion or contamination.

Many modern pesticide products are dry powders. If the concentration, particle size, oxygen concentration and a source of ignition are present at the same time, a dust explosion can occur. The use of inerting, the exclusion of oxygen, and utilization of nitrogen or carbon dioxide minimizes the oxygen source and can make the processes safer. These dusts may also be an industrial hygiene issue. Ventilation, both general and local, is a solutions to these problems.

The major fertilizers are made continuously rather than by the batch process. Ammonia is made by reforming methane at high temperatures utilizing a specific catalyst. Carbon dioxide and hydrogen are also formed and must be separated from the ammonia. Ammonium nitrate is made from ammonia and nitric acid in a continuous reactor. The nitric acid is formed by the continuous oxidation of ammonia on a catalytic surface. Ammonium phosphate is a reaction of ammonia and phosphoric acid. Phosphoric acid is made by reacting sulphuric acid with phosphate -containing ores. Sulphuric acid is formed by burning sulphur to sulphur dioxide, and catalytically converting the sulphur dioxide continuously to sulphur trioxide, and then adding water to form the sulphuric acid. Urea is a continuous high-pressure reaction of carbon dioxide and ammonia, the carbon dioxide usually coming from the ammonia continuous reaction by-product.

Many of these raw materials are toxic and volatile. Release of the raw materials or finished products, through an equipment failure or operator error, can expose employees and others in the community. A detailed emergency response plan is a necessary tool to minimize the effects of a release. This plan should be developed by determining a credible worst-case event through hazard evaluations and then forecasting consequences using dispersion modelling. This plan should include a method to notify employees and the community, an evacuation plan, emergency services and a recovery plan.

Transportation of agricultural chemicals should be thoroughly investigated to choose the safest route—one that minimizes the exposures if an incident occurs. A transportation emergency response plan should be implemented to address transportation incidents. This plan should include a published emergency response telephone number, company personnel to respond to calls and, in some cases, an accident site emergency response team.

Fermentation is the method of producing some of the animal health products. Fermentation is usually not a hazardous process, as it involves growing a culture using a nutritional medium such as lard oil, glucose, or starch. Sometimes anhydrous ammonia is used for pH (acidity) control or as a nutrient, so the process can involve hazards. Solvents may be used to extract the active cells, but the quantities and the methodology are such that is can be done safely. Recycling these solvents is often part of the process.

PESTICIDES*

The word *pesticide* generally denotes a chemical substance (which may be mixed with other substances) that is used for the destruction of an organism deemed to be detrimental to humans. The word clearly has a very wide meaning and includes a number of other terms, such as *insecticides, fungicides, herbicides, rodenticides, bactericides, miticides, nematocides* and *molluscicides,* which individually indicate the organisms or pests that the chemical or class of chemicals is designed to kill. As different types of chemical agents are used for these general classes, it is usually advisable to indicate the particular category of pesticide.

General Principles

Acute toxicity is measured by the LD_{50} value; this is a statistical estimate of the number of mg of the chemical per kg of body weight required to kill 50% of a large population of test animals. The dose may be administered by a number of routes, usually orally or dermally, and the rat is the standard test animal. Oral or dermal LD_{50} values are used according to which route has the lower value for a specific chemical. Other effects, either as a result of short-term exposure (such as neurotoxicity or mutagenicity) or of long-term exposure (such as carcinogenicity), have to be taken into account, but pesticides with such known properties are not registered for use. The *WHO Recommended Classification of Pesticides by Hazard and Guidelines to Classification 1996-1997* issued by the World Health Organization (WHO) classifies technical products according to the acute risk to human health as follows:

- Class IA—extremely hazardous
- Class IB—highly hazardous
- Class II—moderately hazardous
- Class III—slightly hazardous.

The guidelines based on the WHO Classification list pesticides according to toxicity and physical state; these are presented in a separate article in this chapter.

Poisons enter the body through the mouth (ingestion), the lungs (inhalation), the intact skin (percutaneous absorption) or wounds in the skin (inoculation). The inhalation hazard is determined by the physical form and solubility of the chemical. The possibility and degree of percutaneous absorption varies with the chemical. Some chemicals also exert a direct action on the skin, causing dermatitis. Pesticides are applied in many different forms—as solids, by spraying in dilute or concentrated form, as dusts (fine or granulated), and as fogs and gases. The method of use has a bearing on the likelihood of absorption.

The chemical may be mixed with solids (often with food used as bait), water, kerosene, oils or organic solvents. Some of these diluents have some degree of toxicity of their own and may influence the rate of absorption of the pesticide chemical. Many formulations contain other chemicals which are not themselves pesticides but which enhance the effectiveness of the pesticide. Added surface-active agents are a case in point. When two or more pesticides are mixed in the same formulation, the action of one or both may be enhanced by the presence of the other. In many cases, the combined effects of mixtures have not been fully worked out, and it is a good rule that mixtures should always be treated as more toxic than any of the constituents on their own.

By their very nature and purpose, pesticides have adverse biological effects on at least some species, human beings included. The following discussion provides a broad overview of the mechanisms by which pesticides can act, and some of their toxic effects. Carcinogenicity, biological monitoring and safeguards in the use of pesticides are discussed in more detail elsewhere in this *Encyclopaedia.*

Organochlorine Pesticides

The organochlorine pesticides (OCPs) have caused intoxication following skin contact, ingestion or inhalation. Examples are endrin, aldrin and dieldrin. The rate of absorption and toxicity differ depending on the chemical structure and the solvents, surfactants and emulsifiers used in the formulation.

The elimination of OCPs from the body takes place slowly through the kidneys. Metabolism in the cells involves various mechanisms—oxidation, hydrolysis and others. OCPs have a strong tendency to penetrate cell membranes and to be stored in the body fat. Because of their attraction to fatty tissues (lipotropic properties) OCPs tend to be stored in the central nervous system (CNS), liver, kidneys and the myocardium. In these organs they cause damage to the function of important enzyme systems and disrupt the biochemical activity of the cells.

OCPs are highly lipophilic and tend to accumulate in fatty tissue as long as exposure persists. When exposure ceases, they are released slowly into the bloodstream, often over a period of many years, from whence they can be transported to other organs where genotoxic effects, including cancer, may be initiated. The great majority of US residents, for example, have detectable levels of organochlorine pesticides, including breakdown products of DDT, in their adipose (fatty) tissue, and the concentrations increase with age, reflecting lifetime accumulations.

A number of OCPs that have been used throughout the world as insecticides and herbicides are also proven or suspected carcinogens to humans. These are discussed in more detail in the *Toxicology* and *Cancer* chapters of this *Encyclopaedia.*

Acute intoxications

Aldrin, endrin, dieldrin and toxaphene are most frequently implicated in acute poisoning. Delay in the onset of symptoms in severely acute intoxications is about 30 minutes. With lower toxicity OCPs it is several hours but not more than twelve.

Intoxication is demonstrated by gastrointestinal symptoms: nausea, vomiting, diarrhoea and stomach pains. The basic syndrome is cerebral: headache, dizziness, ataxia and paraesthesia. Gradually tremors set in, starting from the eyelids and the face muscles, descending towards the whole body and the limbs; in severe cases this leads to fits of tonic-clonic convulsions, which gradually extend to the different muscle groups. Convulsions may be connected with elevated body temperature and unconsciousness and may result in death. In addition to the cerebral signs, acute intoxications may lead to bulbar paralysis of the respiratory and/or vasomotor centres, which causes acute respiratory deficiency or apnoea, and to severe collapse.

Many patients develop signs of toxic hepatitis and toxic nephropathy. After these symptoms have disappeared some patients develop signs of prolonged toxic polyneuritis, anaemia and haemorrhagic diathesis connected with the impaired thrombocytopoiesis. Typical of toxaphene is an allergic bronchopneumonia.

Acute intoxications with OCPs last up to 72 hours. When organ function has been seriously impaired, the illness may continue up to several weeks. Complications in cases of liver and kidney damage can be long-lasting.

Chronic poisoning

During the application of OCPs in agriculture as well as in their production, poisoning is most commonly chronic—that is, low doses of exposure over time. Acute intoxication (or high-level exposures at a particular instant) are less common and are usually the result of misuse or accidents, both in the home and in indus-

*Adapted from 3rd edition, *Encyclopaedia of Occupational Health and Safety.* Revision includes information from A. Baiinova, J.F. Copplestone, L.A. Dobrobolskij, F. Kaloyanova-Simeonova, Y.I. Kundiev and A.M. Shenker.

62. MINERALS AND AGRICULTURAL CHEMICALS

try. Chronic intoxication is characterized by damage to the nervous, digestive and cardiovascular systems and the blood-formation process. All OCPs are CNS stimulants and are capable of producing convulsions, which frequently appear to be epileptic in character. Abnormal electroencephalographic (EEG) data have been recorded, such as irregular alpha rhythms and other abnormalities. In some cases bitemporal sharp-peaked waves with shifting localization, low voltage and diffuse theta activity have been observed. In other cases paroxysmal emissions have been registered, composed of slow sharp-peaked waves, sharp-peaked complexes and rhythmic peaks with low voltage.

Polyneuritis, encephalopolyneuritis and other nervous system effects have been described following occupational exposure to OCPs. Tremor of the limbs and alterations in the electromyograms (EMGs) have also been observed in workers. In workers handling OCPs such as BHC, polychloropinene, hexachlorobutadiene and dichloroethane, non-specific signs (e.g., diencephalic signs) have been observed and very often develop together with other signs of chronic intoxication. The most common signs of intoxication are headache, dizziness, numbness and tingling in the limbs, rapid changes in blood pressure and other signs of circulatory disturbances. Less frequently, colic pains below the right ribs and in the region of the umbilicus, and dyskinesia of the bile ducts, are observed. Behavioural changes, such as disturbances of sensory and equilibrium functions, are found. These symptoms are often reversible after cessation of the exposure.

OCPs cause liver and kidney damage. Microsomal enzyme induction has been observed, and increased ALF and aldolase activity have also been reported. Protein synthesis, lipoid synthesis, detoxification, excretion and liver functions are all affected. Reduction of creatinine clearance and phosphorus reabsorption are reported in workers exposed to pentachlorophenol, for example. Pentachlorophenol, along with the family of chlorophenols, are also considered possible human carcinogens (group 2B as classified by the International Agency for Research on Cancer (IARC)). Toxaphene is also considered to be a group 2B carcinogen.

Cardiovascular disturbances have been observed in exposed persons, most frequently demonstrated as dyspnoea, high heart rate, heaviness and pain in the heart region, increased heart volume and hollow heart tones.

Blood and capillary disturbances have also been reported following contact with OCPs. Thrombopenia, anaemia, pancytopenia, agranulocytosis, haemolysis and capillary disorders have all been reported. Medullar aplasia can be complete. The capillary damage (purpura) can develop following long- or short-term but intensive exposures. Eosinopenia, neutropenia with lymphocytosis, and hypochromic anaemia have been observed in workers subjected to prolonged exposures.

Skin irritation is reported to follow from skin contact with some OCPs, particularly chlorinated terpenes. Often chronic intoxications are clinically demonstrated by signs of allergic damage.

Organophosphate Pesticides

The organophosphorus pesticides are chemically related esters of phosphoric acid or certain of its derivatives. The organic phosphates are also identified by a common pharmacological property—the ability to inhibit the action of the cholinesterase enzymes.

Parathion is among the most dangerous of the organophosphates and is discussed in some detail here. In addition to parathion's pharmacological effects, no insect is immune to its lethal action. Its physical and chemical properties have rendered it useful as an insecticide and acaricide for agricultural purposes. The description of parathion's toxicity applies to other organophosphates, although their effects may be less rapid and extensive.

The toxic action of all organic phosphates is on the CNS through inhibition of the cholinesterase enzymes. Inhibiting these cholinesterases produces excessive and continuous stimulation of those muscle and gland structures which are activated by acetylcholine, to a point where life can no longer be sustained. Parathion is an indirect inhibitor because it must be converted in the environment or *in vivo* before it can effectively inhibit cholinesterase.

Organophosphates can generally enter the body by any route. Serious and even fatal poisoning may occur by ingesting a small amount of parathion while eating or smoking, for example. Organophosphates may be inhaled when dusts or volatile compounds are even briefly handled. Parathion is easily absorbed through the skin or the eye. The ability to penetrate the skin in fatal quantities without the warning of irritation makes parathion especially difficult to handle.

Signs and symptoms of organophosphate poisoning can be explained on the basis of cholinesterase inhibition. Early or mild poisoning may be hard to distinguish because of a number of other conditions; heat exhaustion, food poisoning, encephalitis, asthma and respiratory infections share some of the manifestations and confuse the diagnosis. Symptoms can be delayed for several hours after the last exposure but rarely longer than 12 hours. Symptoms most often appear in this order: headaches, fatigue, giddiness, nausea, sweating, blurred vision, tightness in the chest, abdominal cramps, vomiting and diarrhoea. In more advanced poisoning, difficult breathing, tremors, convulsions, collapse, coma, pulmonary oedema and respiratory failure follow. The more advanced the poisoning, the more obvious are the typical signs of cholinesterase inhibition, which are: pinpoint pupils; rapid, asthmatic type breathing; marked weakness; excessive sweating; excessive salivation; and pulmonary oedema.

In very severe parathion poisoning, in which the victim has been unconscious for some time, brain damage from anoxia may occur. Fatigue, ocular symptoms, electroencephalogram abnormalities, gastrointestinal complaints, excessive dreams and exposure intolerance to parathion have been reported to persist for days to months following acute poisoning. There is no evidence that permanent impairment occurs.

Chronic exposure to parathion may be cumulative in the sense that repeated exposures closely following each other can reduce cholinesterase faster than it can be regenerated, to the point where a very small exposure can precipitate acute poisoning. If the person is removed from exposure, clinical recovery is usually rapid and complete within a few days. The red blood cells and plasma should be tested for cholinesterase inhibition when phosphate ester poisoning is suspected. Red cell cholinesterase activity is most often reduced and close to zero in severe poisoning. Plasma cholinesterase is also severely reduced and is a more sensitive and more rapid indicator of exposure. There is no advantage in chemical determinations of parathion in the blood because metabolism of the pesticide is too rapid. However, *p*-nitrophenol, an end-product of the metabolism of parathion, can be determined in the urine. Chemical examination to identify the pesticide can be made on contaminated clothing or other material where contact is suspected.

Carbamates and Thiocarbamates

The biological activity of carbamates was discovered in 1923 when the structure of the alkaloid eserine (or physostigmine) contained in the seeds of Calabar beans was first described. In 1929 physostigmine analogues were synthesized, and soon such derivatives of dithiocarbamic acid as thiram and ziram were available. The study of carbamic compounds began in the same year, and now more than 1,000 carbamic acid derivatives are known. More than 50 of them are used as pesticides, herbicides, fungicides and nematocides. In 1947 the first carbamic acid derivatives having insecticide properties were synthesized. Some thiocarbamates have proved effective as vulcanization accelerators, and derivatives of dithiocarbamic acid have been obtained for the treatment of malignant tumours, hypoxia, neuropathies, radiation injuries and other diseases. Aryl esters of alkylcarbamic acid and alkyl esters of arylcarbamic acid are also used as pesticides.

Some carbamates can produce sensitization in exposed individuals, and a variety of foetotoxic, embryotoxic and mutagenic effects have also been observed for members of this family.

Chronic effects

The specific effects produced by acute poisoning have been described for each substance listed. A review of the specific effects gained from an analysis of published data makes it possible to distinguish similar features in the chronic action of the different carbamates. Some authors believe that the main toxic effect of carbamic acid esters is the involvement of the endocrine system. One of the peculiarities of carbamate poisoning is the possible allergic reaction of exposed subjects. The toxic effects of carbamates may not be immediate, which can present a potential hazard because of lack of warning. Results from animal experiments are indicative of embryotoxic, teratogenic, mutagenic and carcinogenic effects of some carbamates.

Baygon (isopropoxyphenyl-N-methylcarbamate) is produced by reaction of alkyl isocyanate with phenols, and is used as an insecticide. Baygon is a systemic poison. It causes inhibition of the serum cholinesterase activity up to 60% after oral administration of 0.75 to 1 mg/kg. This highly toxic substance exerts a weak effect on the skin.

Carbaryl is a systemic poison which produces moderately severe acute effects when ingested, inhaled or absorbed through the skin. It may cause local skin irritation. Being a cholinesterase inhibitor, it is much more active in insects than in mammals. Medical examinations of workers exposed to concentrations of 0.2 to 0.3 mg/m^3 seldom reveal a fall in cholinesterase activity.

Betanal (3-(methoxycarbonyl)aminophenyl-N-(3-methylphenyl) carbamate; N-methylcarbanilate) belongs to the arylcarbamic acid alkyl esters and is used as a herbicide. Betanal is slightly toxic for the gastrointestinal and respiratory tracts. Its dermal toxicity and local irritation are insignificant.

Isoplan is a highly toxic member of the group, its action, like that of Sevin and others, being characterized by the inhibition of acetylcholinesterase activity. Isoplan is used as an insecticide. *Pyrimor* (5,6-dimethyl-2-dimethylamino-4-pyrimidinyl methylcarbamate) is a derivative of arylcarbamic acid alkyl esters. It is highly toxic for the gastrointestinal tract. Its general absorption and local irritative effect are not very pronounced.

Thiocarbamic Acid Esters

Ronite (sym-ethylcyclohexylethyl thiocarbamate; Eurex); *Eptam* (sym-ethyl-N,N-dipropyl thiocarbamate); and *Tillam* (sym-propyl-N-ethyl-N-butylthiocarbamate) are esters which are synthesized by reaction of alkylthiocarbamates with amines and of alkaline mercaptides with carbamoyl chlorides. They are effective herbicides of selective action.

The compounds of this group are slightly to moderately toxic, and the toxicity is reduced when they are absorbed through the skin. They can affect the oxidative processes as well as the nervous and endocrine systems.

Dithiocarbamates and bisdithiocarbamates include the following products, which have much in common as regards their use and their biological effects. *Ziram* is used as a vulcanization accelerator for synthetic rubbers and, in agriculture, as a fungicide and seed fumigant. This compound is very irritant to the conjunctiva and upper airway mucous membranes. It can cause extreme pain in the eyes, skin irritation and liver function disorders. It has embryotoxic and teratogenic effects. *TTD* is used as a seed fumigant, irritates the skin, causes dermatitis and affects the conjunctiva. It increases sensitivity to alcohol. *Nabam* is a plant fungicide and serves as an intermediate in the production of other pesticides. It is irritating to the skin and mucous membranes, and it is a narcotic in high concentrations. In the presence of alcohol it can cause violent vomiting. *Ferbam* is a fungicide of relatively low toxicity, but may cause renal function disorders. It irritates the conjunctiva, the mucous membranes of the nose and upper airways, and the skin. *Zineb* is an insecticide and fungicide that can cause irritation of the eyes, nose and larynx, and is harmful if inhaled or swallowed. *Maneb* is a fungicide that can cause irritation of the eyes, nose and larynx, and is harmful if inhaled or swallowed. *Vapam* (sodium methyldithiocarbamate; carbation) is white crystalline powder of unpleasant smell similar to that of carbon disulphide. It is an effective soil fumigant which destroys weed seeds, fungi and insects. It irritates the skin and mucous membranes.

Rodenticides

Rodenticides are toxic chemicals used for the control of rats, mice and other pest species of rodents. An effective rodenticide must conform to stringent criteria, a fact that is borne out by the small number of compounds that are currently in satisfactory use.

Poisoned baits are the most generally effective and widely used means of formulating rodenticides, but some are used as "contact" poisons (i.e., dusts, foams and gels), where the toxicant adheres to the fur of the animal and is ingested during subsequent grooming, while a few are applied as fumigants to burrows or infested premises. Rodenticides may conveniently be divided into two categories, depending on their mode of action: acute (single dose) poisons and chronic (multiple dose) poisons.

Acute poisons, such as *zinc phosphide, norbormide, fluoracetamide, alpha-chloralose*, are highly toxic compounds, with LD_{50}s that are usually less than 100 mg/kg, and can cause death after a single dose consumed during a period not longer than a few hours.

Most acute rodenticides have the disadvantages of producing symptoms of poisoning rather quickly, of being generally rather non-specific, and lacking satisfactory antidotes. They are used at relatively high concentrations (0.1 to 10%) in bait.

Chronic poisons, which may act, for example, as anticoagulants (e.g., calciferol), are compounds that, having a cumulative mode of action, may need to be eaten by the prey over a succession of days to cause death. Anticoagulants have the advantage of producing symptoms of poisoning very late, usually well after the target species has eaten a lethal dose. An effective antidote to anticoagulants is available for those accidentally exposed. Chronic poisons are used at relatively low concentrations (0.002 to 0.1%).

Application

Rodenticides intended for use in baits are available in one or more of the following forms: technical grade material, concentrate ("master-mix") or ready-to-use bait. Acute poisons are usually acquired as the technical material and mixed with the bait-base shortly before use. Chronic poisons, because they are used at low concentrations, are normally sold as concentrates, where the active ingredient is incorporated into a finely powdered flour (or talc) base.

When the final bait is prepared, the concentrate is added to the bait-base at the relevant rate. If the bait-base is of a coarse consistency, it may be necessary to add a vegetable or mineral oil at a prescribed rate to act as a "sticker", thus ensuring that the poison adheres to the bait-base. It is commonly compulsory for a warning dye to be added to concentrates or ready-to-use baits.

In control treatments against rats and mice, poisoned baits are laid at frequent intervals throughout the infested area. When acute rodenticides are used, better results are obtained when unpoisoned bait ("prebait") is laid for a few days before the poison is given. In "acute" treatments, poisoned bait is presented for a few days only. When anticoagulants are used, prebaiting is unnecessary, but the poison should remain in position for 3 to 6 weeks to achieve complete control.

Contact formulations of rodenticides are especially useful in situations where baiting is difficult for any reason, or where the rodents are not being drawn satisfactorily off their normal diet. The poison is usually incorporated in a finely divided powder (e.g., talc), which is laid on runways or around bait points, or is blown into burrows, wall cavities and so on. The compound may also be formulated in gels or foams, which are inserted into burrows.

The use of contact rodenticides relies on the target animal ingesting the poison while grooming itself. Because the amount of dust (or foam, etc.) adhering to the fur may be small, the concentration of the active ingredient in the formulation is usually relatively high, making it safe to use only where the contamination of food and so on cannot occur. Other specialized formulations of rodenticides include water baits and wax-impregnated blocks. The former, which are aqueous solutions of soluble compounds, are especially useful in dry environments. The latter are made by impregnating the toxicant and bait-base in molten paraffin wax (of low melting point) and casting the mixture into blocks. Wax-impregnated baits are designed to withstand wet climates and insect attack.

Hazards of rodenticides

Although toxicity levels of rodenticides may vary between target and non-target species, all poisons must be presumed to be potentially lethal to humans. Acute poisons are potentially more dangerous than chronic ones because they are rapid in action, non-specific and generally lack effective antidotes. Anticoagulants, on the other hand, are slow and cumulative, allowing adequate time for the administration of a reliable antidote, such as vitamin K.

As stated above, the concentrations of active ingredients in contact formulations of a given poison are higher than those in bait preparations, thus making operator hazard considerably greater. Fumigants present a special danger when used to treat infested premises, holds of ships and so on, and should be used only by trained technicians. The gassing of rodent burrows, although less hazardous, must also be carried out with extreme caution.

Herbicides

Grassy and broad-leaved weeds compete with crop plants for light, space, water and nutrients. They are hosts to bacteria, fungi and viruses, and hamper mechanical harvesting operations. Losses in crop yields as a result of weed infestation can be very heavy, commonly reaching 20 to 40%. Weed-control measures such as hand weeding and hoeing are ineffective in intensive farming. Chemical weedkillers or herbicides have successfully replaced mechanical methods of weed control.

In addition to their use in agriculture in cereals, meadows, open fields, pastures, fruit growing, greenhouses and forestry, herbicides are applied on industrial sites, railway tracks and power lines to remove vegetation. They are used for destroying weeds in canals, drainage channels and natural or artificial pools.

Herbicides are sprayed or dusted on weeds or on the soil they infest. They remain on the leaves (contact herbicides) or penetrate into the plant and so disturb its physiology (systemic herbicides). They are classified as non-selective (total—used to kill all vegetation) and selective (used to suppress the growth of or kill weeds without damaging the crop). Both non-selective and selective can be contact or systemic.

Selectivity is true when the herbicide applied in the correct dose and, at the right time, is active against certain species of weed only. An example of true selective herbicides are the chlorophenoxy compounds, which affect broad-leaved but not grassy plants. Selectivity can also be achieved by placement (i.e., by using the herbicide in such a way that it comes into contact with the weeds only). For example, paraquat is applied to orchard crops, where it is easy to avoid the foliage. Three types of selectivity are distinguished:

1. physiological selectivity, which relies upon the plant's ability to degrade the herbicide into non-phytotoxic components
2. physical selectivity, which exploits the particular habit of the cultivated plant (e.g., the upright in cereals) and/or a specially fashioned surface (e.g., wax-coating, resistant cuticule) protecting the plant against herbicide penetration
3. positional selectivity, in which the herbicide remains fixed in the upper soil layers adsorbed on colloidal soil particles and does not reach the root zone of the cultivated plant, or at least not in harmful quantities. Positional selectivity depends on the soil, precipitation and temperature as well as the water solubility and soil adsorption of the herbicide.

Some commonly used herbicides

Following are brief descriptions of acute and chronic effects associated with some commonly used herbicides.

Atrazine gives rise to decreased body weight, anaemia, disturbed protein and glucose metabolism in rats. It causes occupational contact dermatitis due to skin sensitization. It is considered a possible human carcinogen (IARC group 2B).

Barban, in repeated contact with 5% water emulsion, causes severe skin irritation in rabbits. It provokes skin sensitization in both experimental animals and agricultural workers, and causes anaemia, methaemoglobinaemia and changes in lipid and protein metabolism. Ataxia, tremor, cramps, bradycardia and ECG deviations are found in experimental animals.

Chlorpropharm can produce slight dermal irritation and penetration. In rats, exposure to atrazine causes anaemia, methaemoglobinaemia and reticulocytosis. Chronic application causes skin carcinoma in rats.

Cycloate causes polyneuropathia and liver damage in experimental animals. No clinical symptoms have been described after occupational exposure of workers for three consecutive days.

2,4-D poses moderate dermal toxicity and skin irritancy risks to exposed persons. It is highly irritating to the eyes. Acute exposures in workers provoke headache, dizziness, nausea, vomiting, raised temperature, low blood pressure, leucocytosis, and heart and liver injury. Chronic occupational exposure without protection may cause nausea, liver functional changes, contact toxic dermatitis, irritation of airways and eyes, as well as neurological changes. Some of the derivatives of 2,4-D are embryotoxic and teratogenic for experimental animals in high doses only.

2,4-D and the related phenoxy herbicide 2,4,5-T are rated as group 2B carcinogens (possible human carcinogens) by the IARC. Lymphatic cancers, particularly non-Hodgkin lymphoma (NHL), have been associated in Swedish agricultural workers with exposure to a commercial mixture of 2,4-D and 2,4,5-T (similar to the herbicide Agent Orange used by the US military in Viet Nam during the years 1965 to 1971). Possible carcinogenicity is often ascribed to contamination of 2,4,5-T with 2,3,7,8-tetrachlorodibenzo-*p*-dioxin. However, a US National Cancer Institute research group reported a risk of 2.6 for adult NHL among Kansas residents exposed to 2,4-D alone, which is not thought to be dioxin-contaminated.

Dalapon-Na can cause depression, an unbalanced gait, decreased body weight, kidney and liver changes, thyroid and pituitary dysfunctions, and contact dermatitis in workers who are exposed. *Diallate* has dermal toxicity and causes irritation to the skin, eyes and mucous membranes. *Diquat* is an irritant to the skin, eyes and upper respiratory tract. It can cause a delay in the healing of cuts and wounds, gastrointestinal and respiratory disturbances, bilateral cataract and functional liver and kidney changes.

Dinoseb presents dangers because of its toxicity through dermal contact. It can cause moderate skin and pronounced eye irritation. The fatal dose for humans is about 1 to 3 g. After an acute exposure, Dinoseb causes central nervous system disturbances, vomiting, reddening (erythema) of the skin, sweating and high temperature. Chronic exposure without protection results in decreased weight, contact (toxic or allergic) dermatitis and gastrointestinal, liver and kidney disturbances. Dinoseb is not used in many countries because of its serious adverse effects.

Fluometuron is a moderate skin sensitizer in guinea-pigs and humans. It has been observed to cause decreased body weight, anaemia, and liver, spleen and thyroid gland disturbances. The biological action of *diuron* is similar.

Linuron causes mild irritation to the skin and eyes, and has low cumulative toxicity (threshold value after single inhalation 29 mg/m³). It causes CNS, liver, lung and kidney changes in experimental animals, as well as thyroid dysfunction.

MCPA is highly irritant to skin and mucous membranes, has low cumulative toxicity and is embryotoxic and teratogenic in high doses in rabbits and rats. Acute poisoning in humans (an estimated dose of 300 mg/kg) results in vomiting, diarrhoea, cyanosis, mucus burns, clonic spasms, and myocardium and liver injury. It provokes severe contact toxic dermatitis in workers. Chronic exposure without protection results in dizziness, nausea, vomiting, stomach aches, hypotonia, enlarged liver, myocardium dysfunction and contact dermatitis.

Molinate can reach a toxic concentration after single inhalation of 200 mg/m³ in rats. It causes liver, kidney and thyroid disturbances, and is gonadotoxic and teratogenic in rats. It is a moderate skin sensitizer in humans.

Monuron in high doses can result in liver, myocardium and kidney disturbances. It causes skin irritation and sensitization. Similar effects are shown by *monolinuron, chloroxuron, chlortoluron* and *dodine*.

Nitrofen is a strong skin and eye irritant. Chronic occupational exposure without protection results in CNS disturbances, anaemia, raised temperature, decreased body weight, fatigue and contact dermatitis. It is considered a possible human carcinogen (group 2B) by the IARC.

Paraquat has dermal toxicity and irritant effects on skin or mucous membranes. It causes nail damage and nose bleeding in occupational conditions without protection. Accidental oral poisoning with paraquat has resulted when it was left within reach of children or transferred from the original container into a bottle used for a beverage. Early manifestations of such intoxication are corrosive gastrointestinal effects, renal tubular damage and liver dysfunction. Death is due to circulatory collapse and progressive pulmonary damage (pulmonary oedema and haemorrhage, intra-alveolar and interstitial fibrosis with alveolitis and hyaline membranes), clinically revealed by dyspnoea, hypoxaemia, basal rales and roentgenographic evidence of infiltration and athelectasis. The renal failure is followed by lung damage, and accompanied in some cases by liver or myocardium disturbances. Mortality is higher with poisoning from liquid concentrate formulations (87.8%), and lower from granular forms (18.5%). The fatal dose is 6 g paraquat ion (equivalent to 30 ml *Gramoxone* or 4 packets of

Weedol), and no survivors are reported at greater doses, irrespective of the time or vigour of treatment. Most survivors had ingested less than 1 g paraquat ion.

Potassium cyanate is associated with high inhalation and dermal toxicity in experimental animals and humans due to the metabolic conversion to cyanide, which is discussed elsewhere in this *Encyclopaedia*.

Prometryn exhibits moderate dermal toxicity and skin and eye irritation. It provokes decreased clotting and enzyme abnormalities in animals and has been found to be embryotoxic in rats. Exposed workers may complain of nausea and sore throat. Analogous effects are shown by *propazine* and *desmetryne*.

Propachlor's toxicity is doubled at high environmental temperatures. Skin and mucous membrane irritation and mild skin allergy are associated with exposure. The toxic concentration after single inhalation is 18 mg/m³ in rats, and it is thought to exhibit moderate cumulative toxicity. Propachlor causes polyneuropathies; liver, myocardium and kidney disturbances; anaemia; and damage to testes in rats. During spraying from the air, the concentration in the spray cabin has been found to be about 0.2 to 0.6 mg/m³. Similar toxic properties are shown by *propanil*.

Propham exhibits moderate cumulative toxicity. It causes haemodynamic disturbances, and liver, lung and kidney changes are found in experimental animals.

Simazine causes slight irritation of the skin and mucous membranes. It is a moderate skin sensitizer in guinea-pigs. It also causes CNS, liver and kidney disturbances and has mutagenic effect in experimental animals. Workers may complain of weariness, dizziness, nausea and olfactory deviations after application without protective equipment.

2,4,5-T causes pronounced irritation and embryotoxic, teratogenic and carcinogenic effects in animals; there are also data on its gonadotoxic action in women. Because the extremely toxic chemical *dioxin* can be a contaminant of the trichlorophenoxy acids, use of 2,4,5-T is prohibited in many countries. Agricultural, forestry and industrial workers exposed to mixtures of 2,4-D and 2,4,5-T have been reported at increased risk for both soft-tissue sarcomas and non-Hodgkin lymphomas.

Trifluralin causes slight irritation of skin and mucous membranes. An increased incidence of liver carcinoma has been found in hybrid female mice, probably due to contamination with N-nitroso compounds. Trifluralin causes anaemia and liver, myocardium and kidney changes in experimental animals. Extensively exposed workers have developed contact dermatitis and photodermatitis.

Fungicides

Some fungi, such as rusts, mildews, moulds, smuts, storage rots and seedling blights, are able to infect and cause diseases in plants, animals and humans. Others can attack and destroy non-living materials such as wood and fibre products. Fungicides are used to prevent these diseases and are applied by spraying, dusting, seed dressing, seedling and soil sterilization, and fumigation of warehouses and greenhouses.

Fungi causing plant diseases can be arranged into four subgroups, which differ by the microscopic characters of the mycelium, the spores and the organs on which the spores were developed:

1. phycomycetes—soil-borne organisms causing club rot of brassicae, wart diseases of potatoes and so on
2. ascomycetes—perithecia-forming powdery mildews and fungi causing apple scab, black currant leaf spot and rose black spot
3. basidiomycetes, including loose smut of wheat and barley, and several rusts species
4. fungi imperfecti, which includes the genera *Aspergillus, Fusarium, Penicillium* and so on, that are of great economic impor-

tance because they cause significant losses during plant growth, at harvest, and after harvest. (e.g., *Fusarium* species infect barley, oats and wheat; *Penicillium* species cause brown rot of pomaceous fruit).

Fungicides have been used for centuries. Copper and sulphur compounds were the first to be used, and Bordeaux mixture was applied in 1885 to vineyards. A great number of widely differing chemical compounds with fungicidal action are used in many countries.

Fungicides can be classified into two groups according to their mode of action: protective fungicides (applied at a time prior to the arrival of the fungal spores—e.g., sulphur and copper compounds) or eradicant fungicides (applied after the plant has become infected—e.g., mercury compounds and nitroderivatives of the phenols). The fungicides either act on the surface of the leaves and seeds or penetrate into the plant and exert their toxic action directly on the fungi (systemic fungicides). They can also alter the physiological and biochemical processes in the plant and thus produce artificial chemical immunization. Examples of this group are the antibiotics and the rodananilides.

Fungicides applied to seed act primarily against surface-borne spores. However, in some cases they are required to persist on the seed coat long enough to be effective against the dormant mycelium contained within the seed. When applied to the seed before sowing, the fungicide is called *seed disinfectant* or *seed dressing*, though the latter term may include treatment not intended to counter seed-borne fungi or soil pests. To protect wood, paper, leather and other materials, fungicides are used by impregnation or staining. Special drugs with fungicidal action are also used to control fungal diseases in humans and animals.

Specific field applications include:

- *Seed dressing*. This is a simple and economically efficient method for the control of plant diseases. The pests are destroyed on the seeds and in the soil during the development of the seed. Despite the availability of efficient alternative compounds, the mercury fungicides are still used to a considerable extent for this purpose. Dithiocarbamates, and particularly thiuram, are widely used. Chloranil and dichlone of the quinone group, hexachlorobenzene, formaldehyde and some antibiotics are also used for seed dressing. The seeds can be treated by either the dry or the wet method.
- *Soil disinfection*. This is a more general action, with fungicides incorporated into the soil as solid or liquid formulations that liberate volatile or easily soluble components (e.g., chloropicrin, methyl bromide, dibromomethane, formaldehyde, vapam, dazomet, allyl alcohol, pentachloronitrobenzene and chloroneb). These fungicides are used most intensively on greenhouse soil. Several of them are known or suspected carcinogens.
- *Application on plants*. To control airborne diseases, fungicides are used on annual field crops, fruit trees and berry crops. Almost all fungicide groups are used for this purpose. Copper compounds, dithiocarbamates, aromatic nitro derivatives, quinones, phthalamides, guanidines and chlorinated hydrocarbons are the most frequently used; some heterocyclics, nickel compounds and some antibiotics are also used.

Hazards of fungicides

The fungicides cover a great variety of chemical compounds differing widely in their toxicity. Highly toxic compounds are used as fumigants of foods and warehouses, for seed dressing and for soil disinfection, and cases of poisoning have been described with organomercurials, hexachlorobenzene and pentachlorobenzene, as well as with the slightly toxic dithiocarbamates. These and several other chemicals are discussed in more detail elsewhere in this article, chapter and *Encyclopaedia*. Some are briefly reviewed here.

Chinomethionate has a high cumulative toxicity and inhibits thiol groups and some enzymes containing them; it lowers phagocytic activity and has antispermatogenic effects. It is irritant to the skin and the respiratory system. It can damage the CNS, the liver and the gastrointestinal tract. Glutathione and cysteine provide protection against the acute effects of chinomethionate.

Chloranil is irritating to the skin and the upper respiratory tract; it can also cause depression of the CNS and dystrophic changes in the liver and kidney. The biological monitoring of exposed persons has shown an increased level of the urinary phenols, both free and bound.

Dazomet is used also as a nematocide and a slimicide. This compound and its decomposition products are sensitizers and mild irritants of the eye, nose, mouth and skin. Poisoning is characterized by a variety of symptoms, including anxiety, tachycardia and quick breathing, hypersalivation, clonic cramps, impaired movement coordination, sometimes hyperglycaemia and cholinesterase inhibition. The main pathomorphological findings are enlargement of the liver and degenerative changes of the kidney and other internal organs.

Dichlofluanid inhibits thiol groups. In experimental animals it caused histological changes in liver, proximal tubules of the kidney and adrenal cortex, with the reduction of the lymphatic tissue in the spleen. It is a moderate irritant of the skin and mucous membranes.

Diclone, in addition to sharing the irritant and blood depressant properties common to quinones, is an experimental animal carcinogen.

Dinobuton, like dinitro-*o*-cresol (DNOC), disturbs cell metabolism by inhibiting oxidative phosphorylation, with the loss of energy-rich compounds such as adenosintriphosphoric acid (ATP). It can cause severe liver dystrophy and necrosis of the convoluted tubules of the kidneys. The clinical manifestations of the intoxication are high temperature, methaemoglobinaemia and haemolysis, nervous disturbances and irritation of the skin and mucous membranes.

Dinocap can increase the blood level of alkaline phosphatase and is a moderate irritant of the skin and mucous membranes. It produces distrophic changes in the liver and kidney, and hypertrophy of the myocardium. In acute poisoning, disturbances in thermoregulation, clonic cramps and breathing difficulties have been observed.

Hexachlorobenzene (HCB) is stored in the body fat. It interferes with porphyrin metabolism, increasing the urinary excretion of coproporphyrins and uroporphyrins; it increases also the levels of transaminases and dehydrogenases in the blood. It can produce liver injury (hepatomegaly and cirrhosis), photosensitization of the skin, a porphyria similar to porphyria cutanea tarda, arthritis and hirsutism (monkey disease). It is a skin irritant. Chronic poisoning needs long-term treatment, mainly symptomatic, and it is not always reversible on cessation of exposure. It is classified as a possible human carcinogen (group 2B) by the IARC.

Milneb can cause gastrointestinal disturbances, weakness, decrease of the body temperature and leukopoenia.

Nirit has haemotoxic properties and causes anaemia and leucocytosis with toxic granulation of the leucocytes, in addition to degenerative changes in the liver, spleen and kidneys.

Quinones, in general, cause blood disturbances (methaemoglobinaemia, anaemia), affect the liver, disturb vitamin metabolism, particularly that of ascorbic acid, and are irritant to the respiratory ways and the eye. *Chloranil* and *dichlone* are the quinone derivatives most widely used as fungicides.

Thiabendazole has caused thymus involution, colloid depletion in the thyroid and increase in liver and kidney size. It is also used as an anthelmintic in cattle.

Safety and Health Measures

Labelling and storage

The requirements regarding the labelling of pesticides laid down in national and international legislation should be strictly applied to both imported and locally produced chemicals. The label should give the following essential information: both the approved name and the trade name of the chemical; the name of the manufacturer, packager or supplier; the directions for use; the precautions to be taken during use, including details of protective equipment to be worn; the symptoms of poisoning; and the first-aid treatment for suspected poisoning.

The greater the degree of toxicity or hazard of the chemical, the more precise should be the wording on the label. It is sound practice for the different classes to be clearly distinguished by background colours on the label and, in the case of compounds of high or extreme hazard, for the appropriate danger symbol to be incorporated. It often occurs that an adequately labelled quantity of pesticide in bulk is locally repacked into smaller containers. Each such small package should bear a similar label, and repacking in containers which have held, or are easily identifiable with, containers used for food should be absolutely forbidden. If small packages are to be transported, the same rules apply as for the carriage of larger packages. (See the chapter *Using, storing and transporting chemicals.*)

Pesticides of moderate or higher hazard should be so stored that only authorized persons can have access to them. It is particularly important that children should be excluded from any contact with pesticide concentrates or residues. Spillages often occur in storage and repacking rooms, and they must be cleaned up with care. Rooms used only for storage should be soundly constructed and fitted with secure locks. Floors should be kept clear and the pesticides clearly identified. If repacking is carried out in storage rooms, adequate ventilation and light should be available; floors should be impervious and sound; washing facilities should be available; and eating, drinking and smoking should be prohibited in the area.

A few compounds react with other chemicals or with air, and this has to be taken into account when planning storage facilities. Examples are cyanide salts (which react with acid to produce hydrogen cyanide gas) and dichlorvos (which vaporizes in contact with air). (Dichlorvos is classified as a group 2B possible human carcinogen by the IARC.).

Mixing and application

Mixing and application may comprise the most hazardous phase of the use of pesticides, since the worker is exposed to the concentrate. In any particular situation, only selected persons should be responsible for mixing; they should be thoroughly conversant with the hazards and provided with the proper facilities for dealing with accidental contamination. Even when the mixed formulation is of such a toxicity that it can be used with a minimum of personal protective equipment (PPE), more elaborate equipment may need to be provided for and used by the mixer.

For pesticides of moderate or higher hazard, some type of PPE is almost always necessary. The choice of particular items of equipment will depend on the hazard of the pesticide and the physical form in which it is being handled. Any consideration of PPE must also include not only provision but also adequate cleaning, maintenance and replacement.

Where climatic conditions preclude the use of some types of PPE, three other principles of protection can be applied—protection by distance, protection by time and protection by change of working method. Protection by distance involves modification of the equipment used for application, so that the person is as far away as possible from the pesticide itself, bearing in mind the likely routes of absorption of a specific compound.

Protection by time involves limitation of hours of work. The suitability of this method depends on whether the pesticide is readily excreted or whether it is cumulative. Accumulation of some compounds occurs in the body when the rate of excretion is slower than the rate of absorption. With some other compounds, a cumulative effect may occur when the person is exposed to repeated small doses which, taken individually, may not give rise to symptoms.

Protection by change of working method involves a reconsideration of the whole operation. Pesticides differ from other industrial processes in that they can be applied from the ground or the air. Changes of method on the ground depend largely on the choice of equipment and the physical nature of the pesticide to be applied.

Pesticides that are applied from the air can be in the form of liquids, dusts or granules. Liquids may be sprayed from very low altitudes, frequently as fine droplets of concentrated formulations, known as ultra-low volume (ULV) applications. Drift is a problem particularly with liquids and dusts. Aerial application is an economical way of treating large tracts of land but entails special hazards to pilots and to workers on the ground. Pilots can be affected by leakage from hoppers, by pesticides carried into the cockpit on clothes and boots, and by flying back through the swathe just released or through the drift from the swathe. Even minor degrees of absorption of some pesticides or their local effects (such as may be caused, for instance, by an organophosphorus compound in the eye) can affect a pilot to the extent that he or she cannot maintain the high degree of vigilance necessary for low flying. Pilots should not be allowed to engage in pesticide operations unless they have been specially trained in the items listed above, in addition to any special aviation and agricultural operational requirements.

On the ground, loaders and flaggers may be affected. The same principles apply to loaders as to others dealing with pesticides in bulk. Flaggers mark the swathe to be flown and can be severely contaminated if the pilot misjudges the moment of release. Balloons or flags can be placed in position before or ahead of the operation, and workers should never be used as flaggers within the flight pattern.

Other restrictions

The hazards associated with pesticides do not end with their application; with the more toxic compounds it has been shown that there is a danger to workers entering a sprayed crop too soon after application. It is therefore important that all workers and members of the general public should be informed concerning the areas where a toxic pesticide has been applied and the earliest date on which it is safe to enter and work in these areas. Where a food crop has been sprayed, it is also important that the crop not be harvested until a sufficient period has elapsed for degradation of the pesticide to take place, in order to avoid excessive residues on food.

Disposal of pesticides and containers. Spillage of pesticides at any stage of their storage or handling should be treated with great care. Liquid formulations may be reduced to solid phase by evaporation. Dry sweeping of solids is always hazardous; in the factory environment, these should be removed by vacuum cleaning or by dissolving them in water or other solvent. In the field they may be washed away with water into a suitable soak-hole. Contaminated topsoil should be removed and buried if any domestic animals or fowls are in the area. Soak-holes should be used for disposing of washing waters from cleaning application equipment, clothing or hands. These should be at least 30 cm deep and sited well away from wells or watercourses.

Empty pesticide containers should be collected with care, or disposed of safely. Plastic liners, and paper or card containers should be crushed and buried well below the topsoil or burned, preferably in an incinerator. Metal containers of some pesticides can be decontaminated according to the instructions of the pesticide manufacturers. Such drums should be clearly marked "Not to be used for food or for water for drinking or domestic use". Other metal containers should be punctured, crushed or buried.

Hygiene and first aid

Where a pesticide is of moderate or higher hazard and can be readily absorbed through the skin, special precautions are necessary. In some situations where workers may become accidentally contaminated with large quantities of concentrate, such as in factory situations and mixing, it is necessary to provide a shower bath in addition to the usual washing facilities. Special arrangements for cleaning clothing and overalls may be necessary; in any case, these should not be left for the worker to wash at home.

Since pesticides are often applied outside the factory environment, depending on the chemical used, special care may have to be taken to provide washing facilities at the workplace, even though this may be in remote fields. Workers must never bathe themselves in canals and rivers, the water from which may be subsequently used for other purposes; the washing water provided should be disposed of with care as outlined above. Smoking, eating and drinking before washing should be absolutely prohibited when any pesticide of moderate or higher toxicity is being handled or used.

Where an antidote exists which can be readily used as a first-aid measure for a specific pesticide (e.g., atropine for organophosphorus poisoning), it should be readily available to workers, who should be instructed in the method of its use. When any pesticide is being used on a substantial scale, medical personnel in the area should be informed by the persons responsible for distribution. The nature of the chemical used should be well defined so that medical facilities can be equipped and will know the specific antidotes, where these are applicable and how to recognize cases of poisoning. Facilities should also be available in order to make proper differential diagnosis, even if these are of the simplest type, such as test papers for determining cholinesterase levels. Strict routine medical supervision of workers heavily exposed to concentrates, as in the manufacture and packing of pesticides, is essential and should include laboratory tests and routine surveillance and record keeping.

Training

While all workers using pesticide formulations of moderate or higher hazard should be thoroughly trained in their use, such training is particularly important if the pesticide is extremely toxic. Training programmes must cover: toxicity of compounds used and routes of absorption; handling of concentrates and formulations; methods of use; cleaning of equipment; precautions to be taken and PPE to be worn; maintenance of PPE; avoidance of contamination of other crops, foods and water supplies; early symptoms of poisoning; and first-aid measures to be taken. All training should be strictly relevant to the pesticide actually being used, and, in the case of extremely hazardous compounds, it is wise to license operators following an examination to show that they have, in fact, a good understanding of the hazards and the procedures to be followed.

Public health measures

When pesticides are used, every effort must be made to avoid contamination of water supplies, whether these are officially recognized supplies or not. This not only concerns the actual application (when there may be immediate contamination) but must also include consideration of remote contamination by run-off through rainfall on recently treated areas. While pesticides in natural watercourses may be diluted to such a degree that the contaminated water may not be hazardous in itself, the effect on fish, on water vegetables used as food and grown in the watercourses, and on wild life as a whole must not be overlooked. Such hazards may be economic rather than directly related to health, but are no less important.

THE WHO GUIDELINES TO CLASSIFICATION OF PESTICIDES BY HAZARD*

Individual products are classified in a series of tables according to the products' oral and dermal toxicity and physical states. Technical products classified as Class IA (extremely hazardous, Class IB (highly hazardous), Class II (moderately hazardous) and Class III (slightly hazardous) are listed in tables 62.1, 62.2, 62.3 and 62.4, respectively. Technical products unlikely to present any acute hazard in normal use are listed in table 62.5. The classification given in tables 62.1 to 62.5 is of technical compounds and only forms the starting point for the final classification of an actual formulation: the final classification of any product depends on its formulation. Classification of mixtures of pesticides is not included; many of these mixtures are marketed with varying concentrations of active constituents. (For information on how to find the hazard class of formulations and mixtures, see WHO 1996.) Technical products believed to be absolete or discontinued (see table 62.6) are not inclued in the Classification. Table 62.7 lists gaseous fumigants not included in the *WHO Recommended Classification of Pesticides by Hazard*.

The entries and abbreviations used in the tables' various columns are explained here under the corresponding heading.

Name

The first column in the tables list the approved name of active ingredients. Trade names are not listed since there are many of these.

Status

The following abbreviations are used:

- ISO: Indicates the common name approved by the International Organization for Standardization (ISO). Such names are, when available, preferred by the WHO to all other common names. However, some of these names may not be acceptable for national use in some countries. If the letters ISO appear within parentheses (e.g., with fentin acetate), this indicates that ISO has standardized (or is in the process of standardizing) the name of the base, but not the name of the derivative listed in the "Name" column. (Fentin is an ISO name, but fentin acetate is not.)
- N( ): Indicates approval by a national ministry or other body, which is shown in parentheses as follows: A: United States Environmental Protection Agency (EPA), American National Standards Institute (ANSI), the Weed Science Society of America or the Entomological Society of America; B: British Standards Institution or the British Pharmacopoeia Commission; F: Association française de normalisation; J: Japanese Ministry of Agriculture and Forestry; U: Gosudarstvennyi Komitet Standartov, former USSR.
- C: Chemical, trivial or other common name.

*Adapted from WHO 1996.

Main use

In most cases only a single use is given. This is only for identification purposes and does not exclude other uses. The following abbreviations are used:

- AC: acaricide
- AP: aphicide
- B: bacteriostat (soil)
- FM: fumigant
- F: fungicide, other than for seed treatment
- FST: fungicide, for seed treatment
- H: herbicide
- I: insecticide
- IGR: insect growth regulator
- Ix: ixodicide (for tick control)
- L: larvicide
- M: molluscicide
- N: nematocide
- O: other use for plant pathogens
- PGR: plant growth regulator
- R: rodenticide
- RP( ): repellent (species)
- -S: applied to soil; not used with herbicides or PGRs
- SY: synergist.

Chemical type

A limited number of chemical types are shown in this column. Most have some significance in the sense that they may have a common antidote or may be confused in the nomenclature with other chemical types. For example, thiocarbamates are not cholinesterase inhibitors and do not have the same effects as carbamates. The following abbreviations are used:

- C: carbamate
- CNP: chloronitrophenol derivative
- OC: organochlorine compound
- OM: organomercury compound
- OP: organophosphorus compound
- OT: organotin compound
- P: pyridyl derivative
- PA: phenoxyacetic acid derivative
- PY: pyrethroid
- T: triazine derivative
- TC: thiocarbamate.

These chemical classification are included only for convenience and do not represent a recommendation on the part of the WHO as to the way in which pesticides should be classified. It should, furthermore, be understood that some pesticides may fall into more than one type.

Chemical type is not shown where it is apparent from the name.

Physical state

This refers only to the technical compound. The following are used:

- L: liquid, including solids with a melting point below 50 °C
- oil: oily liquid; refers to physical state only
- S: solid, includes waxes.

It may happen in a few cases that where the technical product is a solid, highly concentrated liquid formulations may need to be classified in a more hazardous class. In most cases, oils have been classified as liquids unless very viscous at ordinary temperatures.

Route

Oral route values are used unless the dermal route values place the compound in a hazardous class or the dermal values are significantly lower than the oral values, although in the same class. The following abbreviations are used:

- D: dermal
- O: oral.

LD$_{50}$ (mg/kg)

The LD$_{50}$ value is a statistical estimate of the number of mg of toxicant per kg of body weight required to kill 50% of a large population of test animals; the rat is used unless otherwise states. A single value is given: "c" preceding the value indicates that it is a value within a wider than usual range, adopted for classification purposes; "+" preceding the value indicates that the kill at the stated dose was less than 50% of the test animals.

The toxicity data for pyrethroids are highly variable according to isomer ratios, the vehicle for oral administration and the husbandry of the test animals. The variability is reflected in the prefix "c". The single LD$_{50}$ value now chosen for classification purposes is based on administration in corn oil and is much lower than that in aqueous solutions. This has resulted in considerable changes in the classification of some products and also underlines the need for classification by formulation if labelling is to reflect true hazard.

The figures in this column are not median values; rather, a safety margin is incorporated by choosing the lower confidence limit in most cases. Where a sex difference occurs in LD$_{50}$ values, the value for the more sensitive sex is used. A number of classification adjustments have been made in respect of some pesticides and these are explained. A borderline case has been classified in the more or less hazardous class after consideration of its toxicology and use experience.

In table 62.5, a number of pesticides are listed as unlikely to present any acute hazard in normal use. The WHO Classification is open-ended but it is clear that there must be a point at which the acute hazard posed by the use of these compounds is so low as to be negligible provided that the necessary precautions are taken. For the purposes of this table, it has been assumed that this point is an oral LD$_{50}$ of 2,000 mg/kg for solids and 3,000 mg/kg for liquids. However, it should not be overlooked that in formulations of these technical products, solvents or vehicles may present a greater hazard than the actual pesticide and therefore classification of a formulation in one of the higher hazard classes may be necessary.

Biological pesticides are not included in the WHO Classification because the methods of the safety testing of live biological agents are not appropriate to classification procedures applied to chemical compounds.

Remarks

Where the classification of a technical product has been adjusted, the basis for this is indicated in this column. Major irritant properties are noted; these do not affect classification. Where the name of a technical product is cross-referenced, the referenced product will be found in the same table. Abbreviations are used to indicate that a WHO/FAO Data Sheet (DS) or an issue of International Programme on Chemical Safety (IPCS) Environmental Health Criteria (EHC) Series or Health and Safety Guide contains further information on the product; the relevant issue numbers follow the abbreviations.

Table 62.1 • List of technical products classified in Class IA: "Extremely hazardous".

Name	Status	Main use	Chemical type	Physical state	Route	LD$_{50}$ (mg/kg)	Remarks
Acrolein	C	H		L	O	29	EHC 127; HSG 67
Alachlor	ISO	H		S	O	930	Adjusted classification; carcinogenic in rats and mice; DS 84
Aldicarb	ISO	I-S	C	S	O	0.93	DS 53; EHC 121; HSG 64
Arsenous oxide	C	R		S	O	180	Adjusted classification; minimum lethal dose for humans of 2 mg/kg; evidence of carcinogenicity for humans is sufficient; EHC 18; HSG 70
Brodifacoum	ISO	R		S	O	0.3	DS 57; EHC 175; HSG 93
Bromadialone	ISO	R		S	O	1.12	DS 88; EHC 175; HSG 94
Bromethalin	ISO	R		S	O	2	
Calcium cyanide	C	FM		S	O	39	Adjusted classification; calcium cyanide is in Class IA as it reacts with moisture to produce hydrogen cyanide gas; the gas is not classified under the WHO system (see table 62.7)
Captafol	ISO	F		S	O	5,000	Adjusted classification; carcinogenic in rats and mice; HSG 49
Chlorfenvinphos	ISO	I	OP	L	O	10	
Chlormephos	ISO	I	OP	L	O	7	
Chlorophacinone	ISO	R		S	O	3.1	DS 62; EHC 175
Chlorthiophos	ISO	I	OP	L	O	9.1	
Coumaphos	ISO	AC, MT	OP	L	O	7.1	
CVP	N(J)						See chlorfenvinphos
Cycloheximide	ISO	F		S	O	2	
DBCP	N(J)						See dibromochloropropane
Demephion-O and -S	ISO	I	OP	L	O	15	
Demeton-O and -S	ISO	I	OP	L	O	2.5	DS 60
Dibromochloropropane	C	F-S		L	O	170	Adjusted classification; has been found to cause sterility in humans and is mutagenic and carcinogenic in animals
Difenacoum	ISO	R		S	O	1.8	EHC 175; HSG 95
Difethialone	ISO	R		S	O	0.56	EHC 175
Difolatan	N(J)						See captafol
Dimefox	ISO	I	OP	L	O	1	Volatile
Diphacinone	ISO	R		S	O	2.3	EHC 175
Disulfoton	ISO	I	OP	L	O	2.6	DS 68
EPN	N(A,J)	I	OP	S	O	14	Has been reported as causing delayed neurotoxicity in hens
Ethoprop	N(A)						See ethoprophos
Ethoprophos	ISO	I-S	OP	L	D	26	DS 70
Ethylthiometon	N(J)						See disulfoton
Fenamiphos	ISO	N	OP	L	O	15	DS 92

Continues on next page.

Table 62.1 • List of technical products classified in Class IA: "Extremely hazardous".
Continued

Name	Status	Main use	Chemical type	Physical state	Route	LD$_{50}$ (mg/kg)	Remarks
Fensulfothion	ISO	I	OP	L	O	3.5	DS 44
Flocoumafen	N(B)	R		S	O	0.25	EHC 175
Fonofos	ISO	I-S	OP	L	O	c8	
Hexachlorobenzene	ISO	FST		S	D	10,000	Adjusted classification; has caused a serious outbreak of porphyria in humans; DS 26
Leptophos	ISO	I	OP	S	O	50	Adjusted classification; has been shown to cause delayed neurotoxicity; DS 38
M74	N(J)						See disulfoton
MBCP	N(J)						See leptophos
Mephosfolan	ISO	I	OP	L	O	9	
Mercuric chloride	ISO	F-S		S	O	1	
Merkaptophos	N(U)						When mixed with merkaptophosteolovy, see demeton -O and -S
Metaphos	N(U)						See parathion-methyl
Mevinphos	ISO	I	OP	L	D	4	DS 14
Nitrofen	ISO	H		S	O	c3,000	Adjusted classification; carcinogenic in rats and mice; teratogenic in several species tested; DS 84
Parathion	ISO	I	OP	L	O	13	DS 6; HSG 74
Parathion-methyl	ISO	I	OP	L	O	14	DS 7; EHC 145; HSG 75
Phenylmercury acetate	ISO	FST		S	O	24	Adjusted classification; highly toxic to mammals and very small doses have produced renal lesions; teratogenic in the rat
Phorate	ISO	I	OP	L	O	2	DS 75
Phosfolan	ISO	I	OP	L	O	9	
Phosphamidon	ISO	I	OP	L	O	7	DS 74
Prothoate	ISO	AC,I	OP	L	O	8	
Red squill							See scilliroside
Schradan	ISO	I	OP	L	O	9	
Scilliroside	C	R		S	O	c0.5	Induces vomiting in mammals
Sodium fluoroacetate	C	R		S	O	0.2	DS 16
Sulfotep	ISO	I	OP	L	O	5	
TEPP	ISO	AC	OP	L	O	1.1	
Terbufos	ISO	I-S	OP	L	O	c2	
Thiofos	N(U)						See parathion
Thionazin	ISO	N	OP	L	O	11	
Timet	N(U)						See phorate

Source: WHO 1996.

62. MINERALS AND AGRICULTURAL CHEMICALS

Table 62.2 • List of technical products classified in Class IB: "Highly hazardous".

Name	Status	Main use	Chemical type	Physical state	Route	LD$_{50}$ (mg/kg)	Remarks
Aldoxycarb	ISO	I,N	C	S	O	27	
Aldrin	ISO	I	OC	S	D	98	DS41; EHC 91; HSG 21
Allyl alcohol	C	H		L	O	64	Highly irritant to skin and eyes
Aminocarb	ISO	I	C	S	O	50	
Antu	ISO	R		S	O	8	Induces vomiting in dogs. Some impurities are carcinogenic
Azinphos-ethyl	ISO	I	OP	S	O	12	DS 72
Azinphos-methyl	ISO	I	OP	S	O	16	DS 59
Benfuracarb	N(B)	I	C	L	O	138	
Bis(tributyltin) oxide	C	F,M		L	O	194	Irritant to skin. DS 65; EHC 15
Blasticidin-S	N(J)	F		S	O	16	
Bromophos-ethyl	ISO	I	OP	L	O	71	
Butocarboxim	ISO	I	C	L	O	158	
Butoxycarboxim	ISO	I	C	L	D	288	
Cadusafos	ISO	N,I	OP	L	O	37	
Calcium arsenate	C	I		S	O	20	
Carbofuran	ISO	I	C	S	O	8	DS 56
Carbophenothion	ISO	I	OP	L	O	32	
3-chloro-1,2-propanediol	C	R		L	O	112	In non-lethal dosage is a sterilant for male rats
Coumachlor	ISO	R		S	D	33	
Coumatetralyl	ISO	R		S	O	16	
Crotoxyphos	ISO	I	OP	L	O	74	
zeta-Cypermethrin	ISO	I	PY	L	O	c86	
DDVF	N(U)						See dichlorvos
DDVP	N(J)						See dichlorvos
Delnav	N(U)						See dioxathion
Demeton-S-methyl	ISO	I	OP	L	O	40	DS 61
Demeton-S-methylsulphon	ISO	I	OP	S	O	37	
Dichlorvos	ISO	I	OP	L	O	56	Volatile, DS 2; EHC 79; HSG 18
Dicrotophos	ISO	I	OP	L	O	22	
Dieldrin	ISO	I	OC	S	O	37	DS 17: EHC 91
Dimetilan	N(A,B)	I	C	S	O	47	
Dinoseb	ISO	H	CNP	L	O	58	
Dinoseb acetate	ISO	H	CNP	L	O	60	
Dinoterb	ISO	H	CNP	S	O	25	
Dioxathion	ISO	I	OP	L	O	23	
DMTP	N(J)						See methidathion
DNBP	N(J)						See dinoseb
DNBPA	N(J)						See dinoseb acetate
DNOC	ISO	I-S,H	CNP	S	O	25	
EDDP	N(J)						See edifenfos
Edifenphos	ISO	F	OP	L	O	150	
Endrin	ISO	I	OC	S	O	7	DS 1; EHC 130; HSG 60
ESP	N(J)	I	OP	L	O	105	
Famphur	N(A)	I	OP	S	O	48	
Flucythrinate	ISO	I	PY	L	O	c67	Irritant to skin and eyes
Fluoroacetamide	C	R		S	O	13	
Formetanate	ISO	AC	C	S	O	21	

Continues on next page.

Table 62.2 • List of technical products classified in Class IB: "Highly hazardous".
Continued

Name	Status	Main use	Chemical type	Physical state	Route	LD$_{50}$ (mg/kg)	Remarks
Fosmethilan	ISO	I	OP	S	O	49	Irritant to skin and eyes.
Furathiocarb	N(B)	I-S	C	L	O	42	
Heptenophos	ISO	I	OP	L	O	96	
Isazofos	ISO	I-S	OP	L	O	60	
Isofenphos	ISO	I	OP	oil	O	28	
Isothioate	ISO	I	OP	L	O	150	
Isoxathion	ISO	I	OP	L	O	112	
Lead arsenate	C	L		S	O	c10	
Mecarbam	ISO	I	C	oil	O	36	
Mercuric oxide	ISO	O		S	O	18	
Methamidophos	ISO	I	OP	L	O	30	HSG 79
Methidathion	ISO	I	OP	L	O	25	
Methomyl	ISO	I	C	S	O	17	DS 55, EHC 178; HSG 97
Methyl-merkapto-phosteolovy	N(U)						See demeton-S-methyl
Metilmerkapto-phosoksid	N(U)						See oxydemeton-methyl
Metriltriazotion	N(U)						See azinphos-methyl
Monocrotophos	ISO	I	OP	S	O	14	HSG 80
MPP	N(J)						See fenthion
Nicotine	ISO			L	D	50	
Omethoate	ISO	I	OP	L	O	50	
Oxamyl	ISO	I	C	S	O	6	DS 54
Oxydemeton-methyl	ISO	I	OP	L	O	65	
Oxydeprofos	N(B)						See ESP
Paris green	C	L		S	O	22	Copper-arsenic complex
Pentachlorophenol	ISO	I,F,H	CNP	S	D	80	Irritant to skin; EHC 71; HSG 19
Phenylmercury nitrate	C	FST	OM	S			Oral LD$_{50}$ not available, rat i.v. LD$_{50}$ is 27 mg/kg
Pirimiphos-ethyl	ISO	I	OP	L	O	140	
Propaphos	N(J)	I	OP	L	O	70	
Propetamphos	ISO	I	OP	L	O	106	
Sodium arsenite	C	R		S	O	10	
Sodium cyanide	C	R		S	O	6	
Strychnine	C	R		S	O	16	
TBTO							See bis-(tributyltin) oxide
Tefluthrin	N(B)	I-S	PY	S	O	c22	
Thallium sulfate	C	R		S	O	11	DS 10
Thiofanox	ISO	I-S	C	S	O	8	
Thiometon	ISO	I	OP	oil	O	120	DS 67
Thioxamyl							See oxyamyl
Triamiphos	ISO	F		S	O	20	
Triazophos	ISO	I	OP	L	O	82	
Triazotion	N(U)						See azinphos-ethyl
Vamidothion	ISO	I	OP	L	O	103	
Warfarin	ISO	R		S	O	10	DS 35, EHC 175; HSG 96
Zinc phosphide	C	R		S	O	45	DS 24, EHC 73

Source = WHO 1996.

Table 62.3 • List of technical products classified in Class II: "Moderately hazardous".

Name	Status	Main use	Chemical type	Physical state	Route	LD$_{50}$ (mg/kg)	Remarks
Alanycarb	ISO	I	C	S	O	330	
Allidochlor	ISO	H		L	O	700	Irritant to skin and eyes
Anilofos	ISO	H		S	O	472	
Azaconazole	N(B)	F		S	O	308	
Azocyclotin	ISO	AC	OT	S	O	80	
Bendiocarb	ISO	I	C	S	O	55	DS 52
Bensulide	ISO	H		L	O	270	
Benzofos	N(U)						See phosalone
BHC	ISO						See HCH
gamma-BHC							See gamma-HCH
Bifenthrin	N(B)	I	PY	S	O	c55	
Bilanafos	ISO	H		S	O	268	
Binapacryl	ISO	AC		S	O	421	
Bioallethrin	C	I	PY	L	O	c700	Bioallethrin, esbiothrin, esbiol and esdepalléthrine are members of the allethrin series; their toxicity varies considerably within this series according to concentrations of isomers.
Bisthiosemi	N(J)	R		S	O	c150	Induces vomiting in non-rodents
BPMC							See fenobucarb
Bromoxynil	ISO	H		S	O	190	
Bronopol	N(B)	B		S	O	254	
Bufencarb	ISO	I	C	S	O	87	
Butamifos	ISO	H		L	O	630	
Butenachlor	ISO	H		L	O	1,630	
Butylamine	ISO	F		L	O	380	Irritant to skin
Camphechlor	ISO	I	OC	S	O	80	DS 20; EHC 45
Carbaryl	ISO	I	C	S	O	c300	DS 3; EHC 153; HSG 78
Carbosulfan	ISO	I		L	O	250	
Cartap	ISO	I		S	O	325	
Chloralose	C	R		S	O	400	
Chlordane	ISO	I	OC	L	O	460	DS 36; EHC 34; HSG 13
Chlordimeform	ISO	AC	OC	S	O	340	
Chlorphenamidine	N(J)						See chlordimeform
Chlorphonium	ISO	PGR		S	O	178	Irritant to skin and eyes
Chlorpyrifos	ISO	I	OP	S	O	135	DS 18
Clomazone	ISO	H		L	O	1,369	
Copper sulfate	C	F		S	O	300	
Cuprous oxide	C	F		S	O	470	
Cyanazine	ISO	H	T	S	O	288	
Cyanofenphos	ISO	I	OP	S	O	89	Has been reported as causing delayed neurotoxicity in hens; no longer manufactured
Cyanophos	ISO	I	OP	L	O	610	

Continues on next page.

Table 62.3 • List of technical products classified in Class II: "Moderately hazardous".
Continued

Name	Status	Main use	Chemical type	Physical state	Route	LD$_{50}$ (mg/kg)	Remarks
CYAP	N(J)						See cyanophos
Cyfluthrin	ISO	I	PY	S	O	c250	
beta-Cyfluthrin	ISO	I	PY	S	O	450	
Cyhalothrin	ISO	Ix	PY	oil	O	c144	EHC 99
lambda-Cyhalothrin	N(B)	I	PY	S	O	c56	EHC 142; HSG 38
CYP	N(J)						See cyanofenphos
Cypermethrin	ISO	I	PY	S	O	c250	DS 58; EHC 82; HSG 22
alpha-Cypermethrin	ISO	I	PY	S	O	c79	EHC 142
beta-Cypermethrin	ISO	I	PY	S	O	166	
Cyphenothrin [(1R)-isomers]	ISO	I	PY	L	O	318	
Cyprofuram	ISO	F		S	O	174	
2,4-D	ISO	H	PA	S	O	375	DS 37; EHC 29; EHC 84
DAPA	N(J)						See fenaminosulf
DDT	ISO	I	OC	S	O	113	DS 21; EHC 9; EHC 83
Deltamethrin	ISO	I	PY	S	O	c135	DS 50; EHC 97; HSG 30
Dialifor	N(A,J)						See dialifos
Dialifos	ISO	I	OP	S	D	145	
Di-allate	ISO	H	TC	L	O	395	
Diazinon	ISO	I	OP	L	O	300	DS 45
Dibrom	N (Denmark)						See naled
Dichlofenthion	ISO	I-S	OP	L	O	270	
Difenzoquat	ISO	H		S	O	470	
Dimethoate	ISO	I	OP	S	O	c150	DS 42; EHC 90; HSG 20
Dinobuton	ISO	AC,F		S	O	140	
Dioxabenzophos	N(B)	I	OP	S	O	125	
Dioxacarb	ISO	I	C	S	O	90	
Diquat	ISO	H	P	S	O	231	Irritant to skin, and eyes, and damages nails; DS 40; EHC 39; HSG 52
Drazoxolon	(ISO)	FST		S	O	126	
ECP	N(J)						See dichlofenthion
Endosulfan	ISO	I	OC	S	O	80	DS 15; EHC 40; HSG 17
Endothal-sodium	(ISO)	H		S	O	51	
EPBP	N(J)	I-S	OP	oil	O	275	
EPTC	ISO	H	TC	L	O	1,652	
Esbiol							See bioallethrin
Esbiothrin							See bioallethrin
Esdepalléthrine							See bioallethrin
Esfenvalerate	ISO	I	PY	S	O	87	
Ethiofencarb	ISO	I	C	L	O	411	

Continues on next page.

Table 62.3 • List of technical products classified in Class II: "Moderately hazardous".
Continued

Name	Status	Main use	Chemical type	Physical state	Route	LD$_{50}$ (mg/kg)	Remarks
Ethion	ISO	I	OP	L	O	208	
Etrimfos	ISO	I	OP	L	O	1,800	
Fenaminosulf	ISO	F-S		S	O	60	
Fenazaquin	ISO	AC		S	O	134	
Fenchlorphos	ISO	I	OP	L	O	1,740	DS 69
Fenitrothion	ISO	I	OP	L	O	503	DS 30; EHC 133; HSG 65
Fenobucarb	N(B)	I	C	S	O	620	
Fenpropathrin	ISO	I	PY	S	O	c66	
Fenthion	ISO	I,L	OP	L	D	586	DS 23
Fentin acetate	(ISO)	F	OT	S	O	125	DS 22
Fentin hydroxide	(ISO)	F	OT	S	O	108	DS 22
Fenvalerate	ISO	I	PY	L	O	c450	EHC 95, DS 90; HSG 34
Fipronil	N(B)	I	Pyrazole	S	O	92	
Fluvalinate	N(B)	I		oil	O	282	Irritant to skin
Fluxofenim	ISO	H		oil	O	670	
Formothion	ISO	I	OP	L	O	365	
Fosfamid	N(U)						See dimethoate
Furconazole-cis	ISO	F		S	O	450	
Guazatine	N(B)	FST		S	O	230	LD$_{50}$ value refers to triacetate
Haloxyfop	N(A,B)	H		S	O	393	
HCH	ISO	I	OC	S	O	100	The LD$_{50}$ varies according to the mixture of isomers. The value shown has been chosen, and the technical product placed in Class II, as a result of the cumulative properties of the beta isomer
Gamma-HCH	ISO	I	OC	S	O	88	DS 12; EHC 124; HSG 54
Heptachlor	ISO	I	OC	S	O	100	DS 19; EHC 38; HSG 14
Imazalil	ISO	F		S	O	320	
Imidacloprid	N(B)	I	Nitro-guanidine	S	O	450	
Iminoctadine	ISO	F		S	O	300	Eye irritant
Ioxynil	ISO	H		S	O	110	
Ioxynil octanoate	(ISO)	H		S	O	390	
Isoprocarb	ISO	I	C	S	O	403	
Karbation	N(U)						See metam-sodium
Lindane	ISO						See gamma-HCH
MEP	N(J)						See fenitrothion
Mercaptodimethur							See methiocarb
Mercurous chloride	C	F		S	O	210	
Metaldehide	ISO	M		S	O	227	
Metam-sodium	(ISO)	F-S		S	O	285	
Methacrifos	ISO	I	OP	L	O	678	

Continues on next page.

Table 62.3 • List of technical products classified in Class II: "Moderately hazardous".
Continued

Name	Status	Main use	Chemical type	Physical state	Route	LD$_{50}$ (mg/kg)	Remarks
Methasulfocarb	ISO	F		S	O	112	
Methiocarb	ISO	I	C	S	O	100	
Methyl isothiocyanate	ISO	F-S		S	O	72	Skin and eye irritant
Metolcarb	ISO	I	C	S	O	268	
MICP	N(J)						See isoprocarb
Molinate	ISO	H	TC	L	O	720	
MPMC							See xylylcarb
Nabam	ISO	F	TC	S	O	395	Goitrogenic in rats
NAC	N(J)						See carbaryl
Naled	ISO	I	OP	L	O	430	DS 39
Norbormide	ISO	R		S	O	52	
2,4-PA	N(J)						See 2,4-D
PAP	N(J)						See phenthoate
Paraquat	ISO	H	P	S	O	150	Has serious delayed effects if absorbed; is relatively low hazard in actual use but is dangerous if accidentally taken orally; DS 4; EHC 39; HSG 51
Pebulate	ISO	H	TC	L	O	1,120	
Permethrin	ISO	I	PY	L	O	c500	DS 51; EHC 94; HSG 33
PHC	N(J)						See propoxur
Phenthoate	ISO	I	OP	L	O	c400	DS 48
Phosalone	ISO	I	OP	L	O	120	
Phosmet	ISO	I,AC	OP	S	O	230	
Phoxim	ISO	I	OP	L	D	1,975	DS 31
Phthalofos	N(U)						See phosmet
Pindone	ISO	R		S	O	50	
Piperophos	ISO	H		oil	O	324	
Pirimicarb	ISO	AP	C	S	O	147	
Polychlorcamphene	N(U)						See camphechlor
Prallethrin	ISO	I	PY	oil	O	460	
Profenofos	ISO	I	OP	L	O	358	
Promacyl	N(Aust)	Ix	C	L	O	1,220	
Promecarb	ISO	I	C	S	O	74	
Propiconazole	ISO	F		L	O	1,520	
Propoxur	ISO	I	C	S	O	95	DS 25
Prosulfocarb	ISO	H		L	O	1,820	
Prothiofos	ISO	I	OP	L	O	925	
Prothiophos							See prothiofos
Pyraclofos	N(B)	I	OP	L	O	237	
Pyrazophos	ISO	F		S	O	435	
Pyrethrins	C	I		L	O	500-1,000	Mixture of compounds present in *Pyrethrum, Cineraefolium* and other flowers; DS 11

Continues on next page.

WHO GUIDELINES TO CLASSIFICATION OF PESTICIDES 62.25

Table 62.3 • List of technical products classified in Class II: "Moderately hazardous".
Continued

Name	Status	Main use	Chemical type	Physical state	Route	LD$_{50}$ (mg/kg)	Remarks
Pyroquilon	ISO	F		S	0	320	
Quinalphos	ISO	I	OP	S	0	62	
Quizalofop-p-tefuryl	ISO	H		L	0	1,012	
Reglon	N(U)						See diquat
Ronnel	N(A)						See fenchlorphos
Rotenone	C	I		S	0	132-1,500	Compounds from roots of *Derris* and *Lonchocarpus* spp.; HSG 73
Salithion							See dioxabenzofos
SAP	N(J)						See bensulide
Sec-butylamine							See butylamine
Sevin	N(U)						See carbaryl
Sodium fluoride	ISO	I		S	0	180	
Sodium hexafluorosilicate	ISO	L-S		S	0	125	
Sulfallate	ISO	H		oil	0	850	Irritant to skin and eyes
Sulprofos	ISO	I	OP	oil	0	130	
2,4,5-T	ISO	H		S	0	500	May contain a contaminant TCDD which affects toxicity: it should not exceed 0.01 mg/kg technical material; DS 13
TCA	ISO						The data shown refer to sodium trichloroacetic acid. In many countries, the term TCA refers to the free acid (now accepted by ISO); this is a solid with an oral LD$_{50}$ of 400 mg/kg and if used as a pesticide is placed in Class II. It is highly corrosive to skin.
Terbumeton	ISO	H	T	S	0	483	
Tetraconazole	ISO	F		oil	0	1,031	
Thiazafluron	ISO	H		S	0	278	
Thiazfluron	N(B)						See thiazafluron
Thicyofen	ISO	F		S	0	368	
Thiobencarb	ISO	H	TC	L	0	1,300	
Thiocyclam	ISO	I		S	0	310	
Thiodan	N(U)						See endosulfan
Thiodicarb	ISO	I		S	0	66	
Tolyl-methyl-carbamate							See metolcarb
Toxaphene	N(A)						See camphechlor
Tralomethrin	N(B)	I	PY	S	0	c85	
Trichloroacetic acid							
Tricyclazole	ISO	F		S	0	305	
Tridemorph	ISO	F		oil	0	650	
Vernolate	ISO	H	TC	L	0	1,780	
Xylylcarb	N(B)	I	C	S	0	380	

Source: WHO 1996.

Table 62.4 • List of technical products classified in Class III: "Slightly hazardous".

Name	Status	Main use	Chemical type	Physical state	Route	LD$_{50}$ (mg/kg)	Remarks
Acephate	ISO	I	OP	S	O	945	
Acetochlor	ISO	H		L	O	2,950	
Acifluorfen	ISO	H		S	O	1,370	Strong irritant to eyes
Allethrin	ISO	I	PY	oil	O	c685	EHC 87; HSG 24
Ametryn	ISO	H	T	S	O	1,110	
Amitraz	ISO	AC		S	O	800	
Azamethiphos	ISO	I	OP	S	O	1,010	
Azidithion	N(F)						See menazon
Barban	ISO	H		S	O	1,300	
Bensultap	ISO	I		S	O	1,100	
Bentazone	ISO	H		S	O	1,100	
Benzoylprop-ethyl	(ISO)	H		S	O	1,555	
Benzthiazuron	ISO	H		S	O	1,280	
Bromofenoxim	ISO	H		S	O	1,217	
Bromophos	ISO	I	OP	S	O	c1,600	DS 76
Buthidazole	ISO	H		S	O	1,480	
Cacodylic acid							See dimethylarsinic acid
Carbofos	N(U)						See malathion
Chlorfenac	ISO	H	OC	S	O	575	
Chlorfenethol	ISO	AC	OC	S	O	930	
Chlorfenson	ISO	AC	OC	S	O	c2,000	Irritant to skin
Chlorinat	N(U)						See barban
Chlormequat (chloride)	ISO	PGR		S	O	670	
Chloroacetic acid	C	H		S	O	650	Irritant to skin and eyes; data refer to sodium salt
Chlorobenzilate	ISO	AC	OC	S	O	700	
Chlorocholine chloride	C						See chlormequat
Chlorthiamid	ISO	H		S	O	757	
Cismethrin	ISO						Resmethrin is a mixture of isomers, the trans isomer (70-80%) being also known as bioresmethrin and the cis isomer (20-30%) as cismethrin. Bioresmethrin (see table 62.5) alone is of much lower toxicity (oral LD$_{50}$ 9,000 mg/kg) (DS 34)
Citrex	N(U)						See dodine
Clofop	ISO	H		L	O	1,208	
Copper hydroxide	C	F		S	O	1,000	
Copper oxychloride	C	F		S	O	1,440	
4-CPA	ISO	PGR		S	O	850	
Crufomate	ISO	I	OP	S	O	770	
Cycloate	ISO	H	TC	L	O	+2,000	
Cyhexatin	ISO	AC	OT	S	O	540	
Cymoxanil	ISO	F		S	O	1,196	
Cyproconazole	N(B)	F		S	O	1,020	

Continues on next page.

Table 62.4 • List of technical products classified in Class III: "Slightly hazardous".
Continued

Name	Status	Main use	Chemical type	Physical state	Route	LD$_{50}$ (mg/kg)	Remarks
Dazomet	ISO	F-S		S	O	640	Irritant to skin and eyes
2,4-DB	N(B)	H		S	O	700	
DCBN	N(J)						See chlorthiamid
Deet							See diethyltoluamide
Dehydroacetic acid	C	F		S	O	1,000	
2,4-DES	N(B,U)						See disul
Desmetryn	ISO	H	T	S	O	1,390	
Diallyl dichloroacetamide							See dichlormid
Dicamba	ISO	H		S	O	1,707	
Dichlone	ISO	FST		S	O	1,300	
Dichlormid	N(A)	H		L	O	2,080	
Dichlorobenzene	C	FM		S	O	500-5,000	Mixture of isomers
Dichlorophen	ISO	F	OC	S	O	1,250	
Dichlorprop	ISO	H		S	O	800	
Diclofop	ISO	H		S	O	565	
Dicofol	ISO	AC		S	O	c690	DS 81
Dienochlor	ISO	AC		S	O	3,160	Acutely toxic by inhalation; skin sensitizer
Diethyltoluamide	ISO	RP (insect)		L	O	c2,000	DS 80
Difenoconazole	ISO	F	T	S	O	1,453	
Dimepiperate	ISO	H	TC	S	O	946	
Dimethachlor	ISO	H		S	O	1,600	
Dimethametryn	ISO	H	T	L	O	3,000	
Dimethipin	ISO	H		S	O	1,180	
Dimethylarsinic acid	C	H		S	O	1,350	
Diniconazole	ISO	F		S	O	639	
Dinocap	ISO	AC,F	CNP	S	O	980	
Diphenamid	ISO	H		S	O	970	
Disul	ISO	H		S	O	730	
Dithianon	ISO	F		S	O	640	
2,4-DP	N(U)						See dichlorprop
Dodine	ISO	F		S	O	1,000	
Doguadine	N(F)						See dodine
DSMA							See methylarsonic acid
Empenthrin [(1R) isomers]	ISO	I	PY	oil	O	+2,280	
Ephirsulphonate	N(U)						See chlorfenson
Esprocarb	ISO	H	TC	L	O	+2,000	Skin and eye irritant
Etacelasil	ISO	PGR		L	O	2,065	
Etaconazole	ISO	F		S	O	1,340	
Ethohexadiol	N(A)	RP (insect)		L	O	2,400	
Etridiazole	ISO	F		L	O	2,000	

Continues on next page.

Table 62.4 • List of technical products classified in Class III: "Slightly hazardous".
Continued

Name	Status	Main use	Chemical type	Physical state	Route	LD$_{50}$ (mg/kg)	Remarks
Fenoprop	ISO	H		S	O	650	
Fenson	ISO	AC		S	O	1,550	
Fenothiocarb	ISO	L	C	S	O	1,150	
Fenpropidin	ISO	F		S	O	1,440	
Fenthiaprop	N(B)	H		S	O	915	
Ferimzone	ISO	F		S	O	725	
Flamprop	ISO	H		S	O	1,210	
Fluchloralin	ISO	H		S	O	1,550	
Fluoroglycofen	N(B)	H		S	O	1,500	
Flurprimidol	ISO	PGR		S	O	709	
Flusilazole	N(B)	F		S	O	1,110	
Flutriafol	ISO	F,FST	T	S	O	1,140	
Fomesafen	ISO	H	OC	S	O	1,250	
Fuberidazole	ISO	F		S	O	1,100	
Furalaxyl	ISO	F		S	O	940	
Glufosinate	ISO	H		S	O	1,625	
Heptopargil	ISO	PGR		L	O	2,100	
Hexazinone	ISO	H		S	O	1,690	
Hydramethylnon	N(A,B)	I		S	O	1,200	
IBP							See iprobenphos
Iprobenphos	N(B)	F		S	O	600	
Isoprothiolane	ISO	F		S	O	1,190	
Isoproturon	ISO	H		S	O	1,800	
Isouron	ISO	H		S	O	630	
Isoxapyrifop	ISO	H		S	O	500	
Kelthane	N(J)						See dicofol
Malathion	ISO	I	OP	L	O	c2,100	LD$_{50}$ value can vary according to impurities. This value has been adopted for classification purposes and is that of a technical product conforming to WHO specifications; DS 29
Maldison	N(Aus,NZ)						See malathion
MCPA	ISO	H		S	O	700	
MCPA-thioethyl	ISO	H		S	O	790	
MCPB	ISO	H		S	O	680	
Mecoprop	ISO	H		S	O	930	
Mecoprop-P	ISO	H		S	O	1,050	
Mefluidide	ISO	H		S	O	1,920	
Menazon	ISO	AP	OP	S	O	1,950	
Mepiquat	ISO	PGR		S	O	1,490	
Metalaxyl	ISO	F		S	O	670	
Metaxon	N(U)						See MCPA

Continues on next page.

Table 62.4 • List of technical products classified in Class III: "Slightly hazardous".
Continued

Name	Status	Main use	Chemical type	Physical state	Route	LD$_{50}$ (mg/kg)	Remarks
Metconazole	ISO	F		S	O	660	
Methazole	N(A,B)	H		S	O	4,543	Slightly irritant to eyes
2-Methoxyethlymercury silicate	C	FST	OM	S	O	1,140	
Methylarsonic acid	ISO	H		S	O	1,800	
Metolachlor	ISO	H		L	O	2,780	
MSMA							See methylarsonic acid
Myclobutanil	N(B)	F		S	O	1,600	
2-Napthyloxy acetic acid	ISO	PGR		S	O	600	
Nitrapyrin	ISO	B-S		S	O	1,072	
Nuarimol	ISO	F		S	O	1,250	
Octhilinone	ISO	F		S	O	1,470	
N-octyl bicycloheptene dicarboxi-mide	C	SY		L	O	2,800	
Oxadixyl	N(B)	F		S	O	1,860	
Paclobutrazol	ISO	PGR		S	O	1,300	
Pallethrine	N(F)						See allethrin
Para-dichlorobenzene							See dichlorobenzene
Pendimethalin	ISO	H		S	O	1,050	
Perfluidone	ISO	H		S	O	920	
Pimaricin	N(B)	F		S	O	2,730	Antibiotic, identical with tennecetin and natamycin
Piproctanyl	ISO	PGR		S	O	820	
Pirimiphos-methyl	ISO	I	OP	L	O	2,018	DS 49
Prochloraz	ISO	F		S	O	1,600	
Propachlor	ISO	H		S	O	1,500	DS 78
Propanil	ISO	H		S	O	c1,400	
Propargite	ISO	AC		L	O	2,200	
Pyrazoxyfen	ISO	H		S	O	1,644	
Pyridaben	ISO	AC		S	O	820	
Pyridaphenthion	N(J)	I	OP	S	O	769	
Pyridate	ISO	H		S	O	c2,000	
Pyrifenox	ISO	F		L	O	2,900	
Quinoclamine	ISO	H		S	O	1,360	
Quizalofop	N(B)	H		S	O	1,670	
Resmethrin	ISO	I	PY	S	O	2,000	See cismethrin; EHC 92, DS 83, HSG 25
Ryania	C	I		S	O	c750	LD$_{50}$ varies: vegetable product
Sesamex	N(A)	SY		L	O	2,000	
Sethoxydim	ISO	H		L	O	3,200	
Silvex	N(A)						See fenoprop
Simetryn	ISO	H	T	S	O	1,830	
Sodium chlorate	ISO	H		S	O	1,200	

Continues on next page.

Table 62.4 • List of technical products classified in Class III: "Slightly hazardous".
Continued

Name	Status	Main use	Chemical type	Physical state	Route	LD$_{50}$ (mg/kg)	Remarks
Sulfluramid	ISO	I		S	0	543	
Sulfoxide	N(A)	SY		L	0	2,000	
2,3,6-TBA	ISO	H		S	0	1,500	
Tebuthiuron	ISO	H		S	0	644	
Thiram	ISO	F		S	0	560	DS 71
TMTD	N(U)						See thiram
2,4,5-TP	N(F,J,U)						See fenoprop
Tralkoxydim	ISO	H		S	0	934	
Triadimefon	ISO	F		S	0	602	
Triadimenol	ISO	FST		S	0	900	
Tri-allate	ISO	H	TC	L	0	2,165	HSG 89
Trichlorfon	ISO	H	OP	S	0	560	DS 27; EHC 132; HSG 66
Triclopyr	ISO	H		S	0	710	
Tridiphane	N(B)	H		S	0	1,740	
Trifenmorph	ISO	M		S	0	1,400	DS 64
Triflumizole	N(B)	F		S	0	695	
Undecan-2-one	C	RP (dogs, cats)		oil	0	2,500	
Uniconazole	ISO	PGR		S	0	1,790	
XMC	N(J)	I	C	S	0	542	
Ziram	ISO	F		S	0	1,400	Irritant to skin; DS 73

Source: WHO 1996.

Table 62.5 • List of technical products unlikely to present acute hazard in normal use.

Name	Status	Main use	Chemical type	Physical state	Route	LD$_{50}$ (mg/kg)	Remarks
Aclonifen	N(B)	H		S	0	+5,000	
Acrinathrin	ISO	MT		S	0	+5,000	
Alloxydim	ISO	H		S	0	2,260	
Aminotriazole	N(F)						See amitrole
Amitrole	ISO	H	T	S	0	5,000	EHC 158, DS 79; HSG 85
Ammonium sulfamate	ISO	H		S	0	3,900	
Ancymidol	ISO	PGR		S	0	4,500	
Anilazine	ISO	F	T	S	0	2,710	Irritant to eyes and skin
Anthraquinone	ISO	RP (birds)		S	0	+5,000	
Asulam	ISO	H	TC	S	0	+4,000	
Atrazine	ISO	H	T	S	0	c2,000	DS 82; HSG 47
Aziprotryne	ISO	H	T	S	0	3,600	
Benalaxyl	ISO	F		S	0	c4,200	
Benazolin	ISO	H		S	0	3,200	Irritant to skin and eyes
Benefin	N(A)						See benfluralin

Continues on next page.

Table 62.5 • List of technical products unlikely to present acute hazard in normal use.
Continued

Name	Status	Main use	Chemical type	Physical state	Route	LD$_{50}$ (mg/kg)	Remarks
Benfluralin	ISO	H		S	O	+10,000	
Benfuresate	ISO	H		S	O	2,031	
Benomyl	ISO	F	TC	S	O	+10,000	EHC 148, DS 87; HSG 81
Benoxacor	ISO	H		S	O	+5,000	
Bensulfuron	N(B)	H		S	O	+5,000	
Benthrodine	N(J)						See benfluralin
Benzamizole							See isoxaben
Benzoximate	ISO	AC		S	O	+10,000	
Bifenox	ISO	H		S	O	+6,400	
Bioresmethrin	ISO	I	PY	L	O	+7,000	DS 34
Biphenyl	ISO	F		S	O	3,280	
Bispyribac	ISO	H		S	O	2,635	
Bitertanol	ISO	F		S	O	+5,000	
Borax	ISO	F		S	O	4,500	
Bromacil	ISO	H		S	O	5,200	
Bromobutide	ISO	H		S	O	+5,000	
Bromocyclen	ISO	I,AC		S	O	+10,000	
Bromopropylate	ISO	AC		S	O	+5,000	
Bupirimate	ISO	F		S	O	c4,000	
Buprofezin	ISO	I		S	O	2,200	
Butachlor	ISO	H		L	O	3,300	
Buthiobate	ISO	F		L	O	3,200	
Butopyronoxyl	N(A)	RP (insects)		L	O	7,840	
Butralin	ISO	H		S	O	+10,000	
Buturon	ISO	H		S	O	3,000	
Butylate	ISO	F	TC	L	O	+4,000	
Captan	ISO	F		S	O	9,000	Irritant to skin; DS 9; HSG 50
Carbendazim	ISO	F		S	O	+10,000	DS 89; EHC 149; HSG 82
Carbetamide	ISO	H		S	O	+10,000	
Carboxin	ISO	FST		S	O	3,820	
Chinomethionat	ISO	AC,F		S	O	2,500	
Chlomethoxyfen	N(B)	H		S	O	+10,000	
Chloramben	ISO	H		S	O	5,620	
Chlorbromuron	ISO	H		S	O	+5,000	
Chlorbufam	ISO	H		S	O	2,500	
Chlorfenidim	N(U)						See monuron
Chlorfluazuron	ISO	IGR		S	O	8,500	
Chlorflurecol	N(B)						See chlorflurenol
Chlorflurenol	ISO	PGR	OC	S	O	+10,000	
Chloridazon	ISO	H		S	O	2,420	

Continues on next page.

Table 62.5 • List of technical products unlikely to present acute hazard in normal use.
Continued

Name	Status	Main use	Chemical type	Physical state	Route	LD$_{50}$ (mg/kg)	Remarks
Chlorimuron	N(B)	H		S	O	4,102	
Chlornitrofen	ISO	H		S	O	+10,000	
Chloromethiuron	ISO	Ix		S	O	2,500	
Chloroneb	ISO	H	OC	S	O	+10,000	
Chloropropylate	ISO	AC	OC	S	O	+5,000	
Chlorothalonil	ISO	F		S	O	+10,000	
Chlorotoluron	ISO	H		S	O	+10,000	
Chloroxifenidim	N(U)						See chloroxuron
Chloroxuron	ISO	H		S	O	+3,000	
Chlorphoxim	ISO	I	OP	S	O	+2,500	DS 32
Chlorpropham	ISO	H		S	O	+5,000	
Chlorpyrifos methyl	ISO	I	OP	L	O	+3,000	DS 33
Chlorsulfuron	ISO	H		S	O	5,545	
Chlorthal-dimethyl	ISO	H		S	O	+3,000	
Chlozolinate	N(B)	F		S	O	+4,000	
Cinmethylin	ISO	H		L	O	3,960	
Cinosulfuron	ISO	H		S	O	+5,000	
Clofentezine	N(B)	AC		S	O	+5,200	
Clomeprop	ISO	H		S	O	+5,000	
Clonitralide	N(A)						See niclosamide
Clopyralid	N(B)	H		S	O	4,300	Severe irritant to eyes
Cloxyfonac	ISO	PGR		S	O	+5,000	
CNA	N(J)						See dicloran
COMU	N(J)						See cycluron
Credazine	N(J)	H		S	O	3,090	
Cryolite	C	I		S	O	+10,000	
Cycloprothrin	ISO	I	PY	L	O	+5,000	
Cycloxydim	N(B)	H		S	O	3,900	
Cycluron	ISO	H		S	O	2,600	
Cyometrinil	N(B)	H		S	O	2,277	
Cyromazine	ISO	L		S	O	3,300	
Caimuron	ISO	H		S	O	+5,000	
Dalapon	N(A,B,F)	H		S	O	9,330	
Daminozide	ISO	H		S	O	8,400	
Desmedipham	ISO	H		S	O	+9,600	
Diafenthiuron	ISO	AC		S	O	2,068	
Dichlobenil	ISO	H		S	O	3,160	
Dichlorfenidim	N(U)						See diuron
Dichlofluanid	ISO	F		S	O	+5,000	
Dichloropicolinic acid							See clopyralid

Continues on next page.

Table 62.5 • List of technical products unlikely to present acute hazard in normal use.
Continued

Name	Status	Main use	Chemical type	Physical state	Route	LD$_{50}$ (mg/kg)	Remarks
Diclobutrazol	ISO	F	T	S	O	+4,000	
Diclomezine	ISO	F		S	O	+10,000	
Dicloran	N(B)	F		S	O	4,000	
Diethatyl	ISO	H		S	O	2,300	
Diethofencarb	ISO	F		S	O	+5,000	
Difenoxuron	ISO	H		S	O	+7,750	
Diflubenzuron	ISO	L		S	O	+4,640	DS 77
Diflufenican	N(B)	H		S	O	+2,000	
Dikegulac	ISO	PGR		S	O	+10,000	
Dimefuron	ISO	H		S	O	+2,000	
Dimethirimol	ISO	F		S	O	2,350	
Dimethomorph	ISO	F		S	O	+5,000	
Dimethyl phthalate	C	RP (insect)		L	O	8,200	
Dinitramine	ISO	H		S	O	3,000	
Diphenyl							See biphenyl
Dipropetryn	ISO	H	T	S	O	4,050	
Dipropyl isocinchomerate	C	RP (fly)		L	O	5,230	
Disodium octaborate							See borax
Ditalimfos	ISO	F	OP	S	O	5,660	Irritant to skin; allergenic
Dithiopyr	ISO	H			O	+5,000	
Diuron	ISO	H		S	O	3,400	
Dodemorph	ISO	H		L	O	4,500	
Eglinazine	ISO	H		S	O	+10,000	
Ethalfluralin	ISO	H		S	O	+10,000	
Ethephon	N(A)	PGR		S	O	+4,000	
Ethidimuron	ISO	H		S	O	+5,000	
Ethirimol	ISO	FST		S	O	6,340	
Ethofumesate	ISO	H		S	O	+6,400	
Etofenprox	N(B)	I		S	O	+10,000	
Fenarimol	ISO	F		S	O	2,500	
Fenbutatin oxide	ISO	MT	OT	S	O	2,630	EHC 15
Fenchlorazole	ISO	H		S	O	+5,000	
Fenclorim	ISO	H		S	O	+5,000	
Fenfuram	ISO	FST		S	O	+10,000	
Fenidim	N(U)						See fenuron
Fenitropan	ISO	F		S	O	3,230	
Fenoxaprop-ethyl	N(B)	H		S	O	2,350	
Fenoxycarb	ISO	I	C	S	O	+10,000	
Fenpiclonil	ISO	FST		S	O	+5,000	
Fenpropimorph	ISO	F		oil	O	3,515	

Continues on next page.

Table 62.5 • List of technical products unlikely to present acute hazard in normal use.
Continued

Name	Status	Main use	Chemical type	Physical state	Route	LD$_{50}$ (mg/kg)	Remarks
Fenuron	ISO	H		S	O	6,400	
Fenuron-TCA	(ISO)	H		S	O	4,000	
Ferbam	ISO	F	TC	S	O	+10,000	
Flamprop-M	ISO	H		S	O	+3,000	
Fluazifop	ISO	H	P	L	O	3,330	
Flubenzimine	ISO	AC		S	O	3,000	
Flucycloxuron	ISO	AC		S	O	+5,000	
Flufenoxuron	ISO	I		S	O	+3,000	
Flumetralin	N(B)	PGR		S	O	+5,000	
Flumetsulam	ISO	H		S	O	+5,000	
Fluometuron	ISO	H		S	O	+8,000	
Fluorodifen	ISO	H		S	O	9,000	
Fluoromide	N(J)	F		S	O	+10,000	
Flupropanate	ISO	H		S	O	+10,000	
Flurecol butyl							See flurenol
Flurenol	ISO	PGR		S	O	+5,000	
Fluridone	ISO	H		S	O	+10,000	
Flurochloridone	ISO	H		S	O	4,000	
Fluthiacet	ISO	H		S	O	+5,000	
Fluroxypyr	N(B)	H		S	O	+5,000	
Fluthiacet	ISO	H		S	O	+5,000	
Flutolanil	ISO	F		S	O	+10,000	
Tau-fluvalinate	ISO	I	PY	oil	O	+3,000	Skin and eye irritant
Folpet	ISO	F		S	O	+10,000	HSG 72
Fosamine	ISO	H		S	O	2,400	
Fosetyl	N(B)	F		S	O	5,800	
Furmecyclox	N(B)	FST		S	O	3,780	
Gibberellic acid	N(B)	PGR		S	O	+10,000	
Glyphosate	ISO	H		S	O	4,230	EHC 159, DS 91
Glyphosine	ISO	H		S	O	3,920	
Hexaconazole	N(B)	F		S	O	2,180	
Hexaflumuron	ISO	I		S	O	+5,000	
Hexythiazox	N(B)	AC		S	O	+5,000	
Hydroprene	N(A)	IGR		L	O	+10,000	
2-Hydroxyethyl octyl sulphide	C	RP (insect)		L	O	8,530	
Hydroxyisoxazole	N(J)						See hymexazol
Hymexazol	N(B)	FST		S	O	3,900	
Imazamethabenz-methyl	(ISO)	H		S	O	+5,000	
Imazapyr	ISO	H		S	O	+5,000	Irritant to eyes
Imazaquin	ISO	H		S	O	+5,000	

Continues on next page.

WHO GUIDELINES TO CLASSIFICATION OF PESTICIDES

Table 62.5 • List of technical products unlikely to present acute hazard in normal use.
Continued

Name	Status	Main use	Chemical type	Physical state	Route	LD$_{50}$ (mg/kg)	Remarks
Imazethapyr	N(B)	H		S	O	+5,000	
Imibenconazole	ISO	F		S	O	+5,000	
Inabenfide	ISO	PGR		S	O	+10,000	
Iodofenphos	N(A,B)						See jodfenphos
Iprodione	ISO	F		S	O	3,500	
Isopropalin	ISO	H		L	O	+5,000	
Isoxaben	N(B)	H		S	O	+10,000	
Jodfenphos	ISO	I	OP	S	O	2,100	DS 43
Karbutilate	ISO	H		S	O	3,000	
Kasugamycin	N(J)	F		S	O	+10,000	
Kinoprene	ISO	IGR		S	O	4,900	
Lenacil	ISO	H		S	O	+10,000	
Linuron	ISO	H		S	O	4,000	
Maleic hydrazide	ISO	PGR		S	O	6,950	
Mancozeb	ISO	F	TC	S	O	+8,000	Irritant to skin on multiple exposure; DS 94
Maneb	ISO	F	TC	S	O	6,750	Irritant to skin on multiple exposure; DS 94
Mefenacet	ISO	H		S	O	+5,000	
Mepanipyrim	ISO	F		S	O	+5,000	
Mepronil	N(J)	F		S	O	+10,000	
Metamitron	ISO	H		S	O	3,343	
Metazachlor	ISO	H		S	O	2,150	
Methabenzthiazuron	ISO	H		S	O	+2,500	
Methoprene	ISO	IGR		L	O	+10,000	DS 47
Methoprotryne	ISO	H		S	O	+5,000	
Methoxychlor	ISO	I	OC	S	O	6,000	DS 28
Methoxyphenone	N(J)	H		S	O	+4,000	
Methyldymron	N(J)	H		S	O	3,948	
Metiram	N(J)	F		S	O	+10,000	
Metobromuron	ISO	H		S	O	2,500	
Metosulam	ISO	H		S	O	+5,000	
Metoxuron	ISO	H		S	O	+3,200	
Metribuzin	ISO	H	T	S	O	2,200	
Metsulfovax	ISO	F		S	O	3,929	
Metsulfuron	N(A,B)	H		S	O	+5,000	
Monalide	ISO	H		S	O	+4,000	
Monolinuron	ISO	H		S	O	2,250	
Monuron	ISO	H		S	O	3,600	
Monuron-TCA	N(A)	H		S	O	3,700	
Naphthalene	C	F		S	O	2,200	
Naphthalic anhydride	C	PGR		S	O	+10,000	

Continues on next page.

Table 62.5 • List of technical products unlikely to present acute hazard in normal use.
Continued

Name	Status	Main use	Chemical type	Physical state	Route	LD$_{50}$ (mg/kg)	Remarks
2-(1-naphthyl) acetamide	ISO	PGR		S	O	6,400	
1-naphthylacetic acid	ISO	PGR		S	O	c3,000	
Napropamide	ISO	H		S	O	5,000	
Naptalam	ISO	PGR		S	O	8,200	
Neburon	ISO	H		S	O	+10,000	
Niclosamide	ISO	M		S	O	5,000	DS 63
Nicosulfuron	ISO	H		S	O	+5,000	Irritant to eyes
Nitralin	ISO	H		S	O	+2,000	
Nitrothal-isopropyl	ISO	F		S	O	6,400	
Norflurazon	ISO	H		S	O	+8,000	
(octylthio)ethanol	C						See 2-hydroxyethyl octyl sulphide
Ofurace	ISO	F		S	O	2,600	
Oryzalin	ISO	H		S	O	+10,000	
Oxabetrinil	ISO	H		S	O	+5,000	
Oxadiazon	ISO	H		S	O	+8,000	
Oxine copper	ISO	F		S	O	10,000	
Oxycarboxin	ISO	F		S	O	2,000	
Oxyfluorfen	ISO	H		S	O	+5,000	
Penconazole	N(B)	F		S	O	2,120	
Pencycuron	ISO	F		S	O	+5,000	
Pentanochlor	ISO	H		S	O	+10,000	
Phenisobromolate	N(J)						See bromopropylate
Phenisopham	ISO	H		S	O	+4,000	
Phenmedipham	ISO	H		S	O	+8,000	
Phenothrin	ISO	I	PY	L	O	+5,000	DS 85; EHC 96; HSG 32
2-Phenylphenol	ISO	F		S	O	2,480	
Phosdiphen	N(J)	F		L	O	6,200	
Phthalide	N(J)	F		S	O	+10,000	
Picloram	ISO	H		S	O	8,200	
Piperonyl butoxide	N(A)	SY		oil	O	+7,500	
Pretilachlor	ISO	H		L	O	6,100	
Primisulfuron	ISO	H		S	O	+5,050	
Probenazole	N(J)	F		S	O	2,030	
Procymidone	ISO	F		S	O	6,800	
Prodiamine	ISO	H		S	O	+5,000	
Profluralin	ISO	H		S	O	c10,000	
Proglinazine	ISO	H		S	O	+8,000	
Prometon	ISO	H	T	S	O	2,980	
Prometryn	ISO	H	T	S	O	3,150	
Pronamide	N(A)						See propyzamide

Continues on next page.

WHO GUIDELINES TO CLASSIFICATION OF PESTICIDES

Table 62.5 • List of technical products unlikely to present acute hazard in normal use.
Continued

Name	Status	Main use	Chemical type	Physical state	Route	LD_{50} (mg/kg)	Remarks
Propamocarb	ISO	F		S	O	8,600	
Propaquizafop	ISO	H		S	O	+5,000	
Propazine	ISO	H	T	S	O	+5,000	
Propham	ISO	H		S	O	5,000	
Propineb	ISO	H	TC	S	O	8,500	
Propyzamide	ISO	H		S	O	5,620	
Pyracarbolid	ISO	F		S	O	+10,000	
Pyrazolynate	ISO	H		S	O	9,550	
Pyrazon	N(A)						See chloridazon
Pyrazosulfuron	ISO	H		S	O	+5,000	
Pyrimethanil	ISO	F		S	O	4,150	
Pyriminobac	ISO	H		S	O	+5,000	
Pyriproxyfen	N(B)	I		S	O	+5,000	
Quinclorac	ISO	H		S	O	2,680	
Quinmerac	ISO	H		S	O	+5,000	
Quinomethinoate	N(B)						See chinomethionat
Quinonamid	ISO	F		S	O	+10,000	
Quintozene	ISO	F		S	O	+10,000	EHC 41
Rimsulfuron	C	H		S	O	+5,000	
Secbumeton	ISO	H	T	S	O	2,680	
Siduron	ISO	H		S	O	+7,500	
Simazine	ISO	H	T	S	O	+5,000	
Sodium metaborate	C						See borax
Sodium trichloracetate							The data shown refer to sodium trichloroacetic acid. In many countries, the term TCA refers to the free acid (now accepted by ISO): this is a solid with an oral LD_{50} of 400 mg/kg and if used as a pesticide is placed in Class II. It is highly corrosive to skin
Solan	N(A)						See pentanochlor
Stirofos	N(A)						See tetrachlorvinphos
Sulfometuron	N(B)	H		S	O	+5,000	
Sulfur	N(A,J)						See sulphur
Sulphur	ISO	F,I		S	O	+3,000	Irritant to skin and mucous membranes. Sulphur dust can spontaneously ignite unless diluted about 50% with inert material
TCA	ISO	H		S	O	3,200	Irritant to skin and eyes; see sodium trichloracetate
Tebuconazole	ISO	F		S	O	4,000	
Tebutam	ISO	H		oil	O	6,210	
Tecnazene	ISO	F		S	O	+10,000	EHC 42; HSG 12
Tedion	N(U)						See tetradifon

Continues on next page.

Table 62.5 • List of technical products unlikely to present acute hazard in normal use.
Continued

Name	Status	Main use	Chemical type	Physical state	Route	LD$_{50}$ (mg/kg)	Remarks
Teflubenzuron	N(B)	I		S	O	+5,000	
Temephos	ISO	I	OP	L	O	8,600	DS 8
Terbacil	ISO	H		S	O	+5,000	
Terbuthylazine	ISO	H	T	S	O	2,160	
Terbutryn	ISO	H	T	S	O	2,400	
Tetrachlorvinphos	ISO	I	OP	S	O	4,000	
Tetradifon	ISO	AC		S	O	+10,000	EHC 67; HSG 11
Tetramethrin	ISO	O	PY	S	O	+5,000	EHC 98; HSG 31
Tetrasul	ISO	AC		S	O	6,810	
Thiabendazole	ISO	F		S	O	3,330	
Thidiazuron	ISO	PGR		S	O	+4,000	
Thifensulfuron	N(B)	H		S	O	+5,000	
Thiophanate	ISO	F		S	O	+10,000	
Thiophanate-methyl	ISO	F		S	O	+6,000	
Tiocarbazil	ISO	H	TC	L	O	10,000	
Tolclofos-methyl	ISO	F-S		S	O	c5,000	
Tolyfluanid	ISO	F		S	O	+5,000	
Transfluthrin	ISO	I	PY	S	O	+5,000	
Triasulfuron	ISO	H		S	O	+5,000	
Tribenuron	N(B)	H		S	O	+5,000	
Trichlamide	ISO	F		S	O	+5,000	
Trietazine	ISO	H	T	S	O	2,830	
Trifluralin	ISO	H		S	O	+10,000	
Triflumuron	ISO	PGR		S	O	+5,000	
Triforine	ISO	F		S	O	+6,000	
Triticonazole	N(B)	F	triazole	S	O	+2,000	
Validamycin	N(J)	F		S	O	+10,000	
Vinclozolin	ISO	F		S	O	10,000	
Zineb	ISO	F		S	O	+5,000	DS 94

Source: WHO 1996.

Table 62.6 • Technical products not included in the WHO Classification and believed to be obsolete or discontinued for use as pesticides.

Allyxycarb	Dinex	Methacarbate
Amidithion	Dinocton	Methiuron
Aramite	Endothion	2-Methoxymethyl mercury chloride (DS 66)
Athidithion	Erbon	Methylmercury dicyandiamide
Atraton	Ethiolate	Mexacarbate
Azothoate	Ethoate-methyl	Mipafox
Barium carbonate	Ethyleneglycol	Mirex (EHC 44; HSG 39)
Benodanil	Bis(trichloracetate)	Morfamquat
Benquinox	EXD	Myclozolin
Butacarb	Fenazaflor	Nitrilacarb
Butam	Fluotrimazole	Noruron
Butonate	Fosthietan	Oxapyrazon
Calcium cyanamide	Fluenetil	Oxydisulfoton
Carbamorph	Glyodin	Parafluron
Carbanolate	Griseofulvin	Phenkapton
Chloethocarb	Halacrinate	Phenobenzuron
Chloraniformethan	Haloxydine	Phenylmercury dimethyldithiocarbamate
Chloranil	Hexachloroacetone	Phosacetim
Chloranocryl	Hexaflurate	Potassium cyanate
Chlorbenside	Hydroxyquinoline sulfate	Propyl isome
Chlorbicyclen	Ipazine	Prothiocarb
Chlordecone (EHC 43; HSG 41)	IPSP	Proxan
Chlorfenprop-methyl	Isobenzan	Pydanon
Chlorfensulphide	Isobornyl thiocyanoacetate	Pyridinitril
Chlorfentezine	Isocarbamid	Quinacetol-sulfate
Chloromebuform	Isocil	Sabadilla
Chlorquinox	Isodrin	Salicylanilide
Crimidine	Isomethiozin	Schradan
Cyanthoate	Isonoruonlisoprothiolane	Swep
Cypendazole	Kelevan (EHC 66; HSG 2)	TDE
Cypromid	Lythidathion	Terbucarb
Delachlor	Malonoben	Thioquinox
Diamidafos	MCC	Triapenthenol
Dibutyl phthalate	Mebenil	Triarimol
Dibutyl succinate	Mecarbinzid	Tricamba
Dichlozoline	Mecarphon	Trichloronat
Dimexano	Medinoterb acetate	Trimethacarb

Source: WHO 1996.

Table 62.7 • List of gaseous or volatile fumigants not classified under the WHO Recommended Classification of Pesticides by Hazard.

Acrylonitrile (EHC 28; HSG 1)	Ethylene dichloride (EHC 176)
Aluminium phosphide (EHC 73; HSG 28)	Ethylene oxide (EHC 55; HSG 16)
Carbon disulfide (EHC 10)	Formaldehyde (EHC 89; HSG 57)
Chloropicrin	Hydrogen cyanide
1,2-Dichloropropane (EHC 146; HSG 76)	Magnesium phosphide (EHC 73; HSG 28)
1,3-Dichloropropene (EHC 146; HSG 76)	Methyl bromide (DS 5; EHC 166; HSG 86)
Epoxyethane (ethylene oxide) (EHC 55; HSG 16)	Phosphine (DS 46; EHC 73; HSG 28)
Ethylene dibromide (EHC 177)	Sulfuryl fluoride

Note: The WHO Classification does not set out any criteria for air concentrations on which classification could be based. Most of these compounds are of high hazard and recommended exposure limits for occupational exposure have been adopted by national authorities in many countries.

Source: WHO 1996.

References

World Health Organization (WHO). 1996. *The WHO Recommended Classification of Pesticides by Hazard and Guidelines to Classification 1996-1997.* International Programme on Chemical Safety (IPCS), WHO/PCS/96.3. Geneva: WHO.

Other relevant readings

Armstrong, LD, and AR Stiles. 1973. Pesticides: Nomenclature, specifications, analysis, uses and residues in food. *Bull Wld Hlth Org* 49:169-204.

International Programme on Chemical Safety (IPCS). 1994. *Summary of Toxicological Evaluations Performed by the Joint FA0/WHO Meeting on Pesticide Residues (JMPR) 1990.* WHO/PCS/95.4. Geneva: IPCS.

Tomlin, C. (ed.). 1994. *The Pesticide Manual: A World Compendium,* 10th ed. Thornton Weath, UK: British Crop Protection Council.

Wiswesser, WJ. 1976. *Pesticide Index.* College Park, MD: College Science Publishers and Entomological Society of America.

METALS: CHEMICAL PROPERTIES AND TOXICITY

Chapter Editor
Gunnar Nordberg

Contents

General profile

This chapter presents a series of short discussions of many metals. It contains a tabulation of major health effects, physical properties and physical and chemical hazards associated with these metals and many of their compounds (see table 63.2 on pp. 63.47–63.55 and table 63.3 on pp. 53.56–63.66). Not every metal is covered in this chapter. Cobalt and beryllium, for example, appear in the chapter *Respiratory sytem*. Other metals are discussed in more detail in articles that present information on the industries in which they predominate. The radioactive elements are discussed in the chapter *Radiation, ionizing*.

The reader is referred to the *Guide to chenicals* in Volume IV of this *Encyclopaedia* for additional information on the toxicity of related chemical substances and compounds. Calcium compounds and boron compounds, in particular, are to be found there. Specific information on biological monitoring is given in the chapter *Biological monitoring*.

Acknowledgements

The material presented here is based on an exhaustive review, revision and expansion of the data on metals found in the 3rd edition of the *Encyclopaedia of Occupational Health and Safety*. Members of the Scientific Committee on the Toxicology of Metals of the International Commission on Occupational Health carried out much of the review. They are listed below, along with other reviewers and authors.

The reviewers are:
L. Alessio
Antero Aitio
P. Aspostoli
M. Berlin
Tom W. Clarkson
C-G. Elinder

Lars Friberg
Byung-Kook Lee
N. Karle Mottet
D.J. Nager
Kogi Nogawa
Tor Norseth
C.N. Ong
Kensaborv Tsuchiva
Nies Tsukuab.

The 4th edition contributors are:
Gunnar Nordberg
Sverre Langård.
F. William Sunderman, Jr.
Jeanne Mager Stellman
Debra Osinsky
Pia Markkanen
Bertram D. Dinman
Agency for Toxic Substances and Disease Registry (ATSDR).

Revisions are based on the contributions of the following 3rd edition authors: A. Berlin, M. Berlin, P.L. Bidstrup, H.L. Boiteau, A.G. Cumpston, B.D. Dinman, A.T. Doig, J.L. Egorov, C-G. Elinder, H.B. Elkins, I.D. Gadaskina, J. Glrmme, J.R. Glover, G.A. Gudzovskij, S. Horiguchi, D. Hunter, Lars Järup, T. Karimuddin, R. Kehoe, R.K. Kye, Robert R. Lauwerys, S. Lee, C. Marti-Feced, Ernest Mastromatteo, O. Ja Mogilevskaja, L. Parmeggiani, N. Perales y Herrero, L. Pilat, T.A. Roščina, M. Saric, Herbert E. Stokinger, H.I. Scheinberg, P. Schuler, H.J. Symanski, R.G. Thomas, D.C. Trainor, Floyd A. van Atta, R. Wagg, Mitchell R. Zavon and R.L. Zielhuis.

● ALUMINIUM

Occurrence and uses

Aluminium is the most abundant metal in the earth's crust, where it is found in combination with oxygen, fluorine, silica, etc., but never in the metallic state. Bauxite is the principal source of aluminium. It consists of a mixture of minerals formed by the weathering of aluminium-bearing rocks. Bauxites are the richest form of these weathered ores, containing up to 55% alumina. Some lateritic ores (containing higher percentages of iron) contain up to 35% Al_2O_3. Commercial deposits of bauxite are mainly gibbsite ($Al_2O_3 \cdot 3H_2O$) and boehmite ($Al_2O_3 \cdot H_2O$) and are found in Australia, Guyana, France, Brazil, Ghana, Guinea, Hungary, Jamaica and Suriname. World production of bauxite in 1995 was 111,064 million tonnes. Gibbsite is more readily soluble in sodium hydroxide solutions than boehmite and is therefore preferred for aluminium oxide production.

Aluminium is used widely throughout industry and in larger quantities than any other non-ferrous metal; worldwide primary metal production in 1995 was estimated at 20,402 million tonnes. It is alloyed with a variety of other material including copper, zinc, silicon, magnesium, manganese and nickel and may contain small amounts of chromium, lead, bismuth, titanium, zirconium and vanadium for special purposes. Aluminium and aluminium alloy ingots can be extruded or processed in rolling mills, wireworks, forges or foundries. The finished products are used in shipbuilding for internal fittings and superstructures; the electrical industry for wires and cables; the building industry for house and window frames, roofs and cladding; aircraft industry for airframes and aircraft skin and other components; automobile industry for bodywork, engine blocks and pistons; light engineering for domestic appliances and office equipment and in the jewellery industry. A major application of sheet is in beverage or food containers, while aluminium foil is used for packaging; a fine particulate form of aluminium is employed as a pigment in paints and in the pyrotechnics industry. Articles manufactured from aluminium are frequently given a protective and decorative surface finish by anodization.

Aluminium chloride is used in petroleum cracking and in the rubber industry. It fumes in air to form hydrochloric acid and combines explosively with water; consequently, containers should be kept tightly closed and protected from moisture.

Alkyl aluminium compounds. These are growing in importance as catalysts for the production of low-pressure polyethylene. They present a toxic, burn and fire hazard. They are extremely reactive with air, moisture and compounds containing active hydrogen and therefore must be kept under a blanket of inert gas.

Hazards

For the production of aluminium alloys, refined aluminium is melted in oil or gas-fired furnaces. A regulated amount of hardener containing aluminium blocks with a percentage of manganese, silicon, zinc, magnesium, etc. is added. The melt is then mixed and is passed into a holding furnace for degassing by passing either argon-chlorine or nitrogen-chlorine through the metal. The resultant gas emission (hydrochloric acid, hydrogen and chlorine) has been associated with occupational illnesses and great care should be taken to see that appropriate engineering controls capture the emissions and also prevent it from reaching the external environment, where it can also cause damage. Dross is skimmed off the surface of the melt and placed in containers to minimize exposure to air during cooling. A flux containing fluoride and/or chloride salts is added to the furnace to assist in separation of pure aluminium from the dross. Aluminium oxide and fluoride fumes may be given off so that this aspect of production must also be carefully controlled. Personal protective equipment (PPE) may be required. The aluminium smelting process is described in the chapter *Metal processing and metal working industry*. In the casting shops, exposure to sulphur dioxide may also occur.

A wide range of different crystalline forms of aluminium oxide is used as smelter feed stock, abrasives, refractories and catalysts. A series of reports published in 1947 to 1949 described a progressive, non-nodular interstitial fibrosis in the aluminium abrasives industry in which aluminium oxide and silicon were processed. This condition, known as Shaver's disease, was rapidly progressive and often fatal. The exposure of the victims (workers producing alundum) was to a dense fume comprising aluminium oxide, crystalline free-silica and iron. The particulates were of a size range that made them highly respirable. It is likely that the preponderence of disease is attributable to the highly damaging lung effects of the finely divided crystalline free-silica, rather than to the inhaled aluminium oxide, although the exact aetiology of the disease is not understood. Shaver's disease is primarily of historical interest now, since no reports have been made in the second half of the 20th century.

Recent studies of the health effects of high level exposures (100 mg/m^3) to the oxides of aluminium amongst workers engaged in the Bayer process (described in the chapter *Metal processing and metal working industry*) have demonstrated that workers with more than twenty years of exposure can develop pulmonary alterations. These changes are clinically characterized by minor, predominantly asymptomatic degrees of restrictive pulmonary function changes. The chest x-ray examinations revealed small, scanty, irregular opacities, particularly at the lung bases. These clinical responses have been attributed to deposition of dust in the lung paraenchyma, which was the result of very high occupational exposures. These signs and symptoms cannot be compared to the extreme response of Shaver's disease. It should be noted that other epidemiological studies in the United Kingdom regarding widespread alumina exposures in the pottery industry have produced no evidence that the inhalation of alumina dust produces chemical or radiographic signs of pulmonary disease or dysfunction.

The toxicological effects of aluminium oxides remain of interest because of its commerical importance. The results of animal experiments are controversial. An especially fine (0.02 μm to 0.04 μm), catalytically active aluminium oxide, uncommonly used commercially, can cause lung changes in animals dosed by injection directly into the lung airways. Lower dose effects have not been observed.

It should also be noted that so-called "potroom asthma" which has frequently been observed among workers in aluminium processing operations, is probably attributable to the exposures to fluoride fluxes, rather than to the aluminium dust itself.

The production of aluminium has been classified as a Group 1, known human carcinogenic exposure situation, by the International Agency for Research on Cancer (IARC). As with the other diseases described above, the carcinogenicity is most likely attributable to the other substances present (e.g., polycyclic aromatic

hydrocarbons (PAHs) and silica dust), although the exact role of the alumina dusts are simply not understood.

Some data on the absorption of high levels of aluminium and nervous tissue damage are found among individuals requiring kidney dialysis. These high levels of aluminium have resulted in severe, even fatal brain damage. This response, however, has also been observed in other patients undergoing dialysis but who did not have similar elevated brain aluminium level. Animal experiments have been unsuccessful in replicating this brain response, or Alzheimer's disease, which has also been postulated in the literature. Epidemiological and clinical follow-up studies on these issues have not been definitive and no evidence of such effects has been observed in the several large-scale epidemiological studies of aluminium workers.

ANTIMONY

Antimony is stable at room temperature but, when heated, burns brilliantly, giving off dense white fumes of antimony oxide (Sb$_2$O$_3$) with a garlic-like odour. It is closely related, chemically, to arsenic. It readily forms alloys with arsenic, lead, tin, zinc, iron and bismuth.

Occurrence and Uses
In nature, antimony is found in combination with numerous elements, and the most common ores are stibnite (SbS$_3$), valentinite (Sb$_2$O$_3$), kermesite (Sb$_2$S$_2$O) and senarmontite (Sb$_2$O$_3$).

High-purity antimony is employed in the manufacture of semiconductors. Normal-purity antimony is used widely in the production of alloys, to which it imparts increased hardness, mechanical strength, corrosion resistance and a low coefficient of friction; alloys combining tin, lead and antimony are used in the electrical industry. Among the more important antimony alloys are babbitt, pewter, white metal, Britannia metal and bearing metal. These are used for bearing shells, storage battery plates, cable sheathing, solder, ornamental castings and ammunition. The resistance of metallic antimony to acids and bases is put to effect in the manufacture of chemical plants.

Hazards
The principal hazard of antimony is that of intoxication by ingestion, inhalation or skin absorption. The respiratory tract is the most important route of entry since antimony is so frequently encountered as a fine airborne dust. Ingestion may occur through swallowing dust or through contamination of beverages, food or tobacco. Skin absorption is less common, but may occur when antimony is in prolonged contact with skin.

The dust encountered in antimony mining may contain free silica, and cases of pneumoconiosis (termed *silico-antimoniosis*) have been reported among antimony miners. During processing, the antimony ore, which is extremely brittle, is converted into fine dust more rapidly than the accompanying rock, leading to high atmospheric concentrations of fine dust during such operations as reduction and screening. Dust produced during crushing is relatively coarse, and the remaining operations—classification, flotation, filtration and so on—are wet processes and, consequently, dust free. Furnace workers who refine metallic antimony and produce antimony alloy, and workers setting type in the printing industry, are all exposed to antimony metal dust and fumes, and may present diffuse miliar opacities in the lung, with no clinical or functional signs of impairment in the absence of silica dust.

Inhalation of antimony aerosols may produce localized reactions of the mucous membrane, respiratory tract and lungs. Examination of miners and concentrator and smelter workers exposed to antimony dust and fumes has revealed dermatitis, rhinitis, inflammation of upper and lower respiratory tracts, including pneumonitis and even gastritis, conjunctivitis and perforations of the nasal septum.

Pneumoconiosis, sometimes in combination with obstructive lung changes, has been reported following long-term exposure in humans. Although antimony pneumoconiosis is regarded as benign, the chronic respiratory effects associated with heavy antimony exposure are not considered harmless. In addition, effects on the heart, even fatal, have been related to long-term occupational exposure to antimony trioxide.

Pustular skin infections are sometimes seen in persons working with antimony and antimony salts. These eruptions are transient and primarily affect the skin areas in which heat exposure or sweating has occurred.

Toxicology

In its chemical properties and metabolic action, antimony has a close resemblance to arsenic, and, since the two elements are sometimes found in association, the action of antimony may be blamed on arsenic, especially in foundry workers. However, experiments with high-purity metallic antimony have shown that this metal has a completely independent toxicology; different authors have found the average lethal dose to be between 10 and 11.2 mg/100 g.

Antimony may enter the body through the skin, but the principal route is through the lungs. From the lungs, antimony, and especially free antimony, is absorbed and taken up by the blood and tissues. Studies on workers and experiments with radioactive antimony have shown that the major part of the absorbed dose enters the metabolism within 48 hours and is eliminated in the faeces and, to a lesser extent, the urine. The remainder stays in the blood for some considerable time, with the erythrocytes containing several times more antimony than the serum. In workers exposed to pentavalent antimony, the urinary excretion of antimony is related to the intensity of exposure. It has been estimated that after 8 hours exposure to 500 μg Sb/m^3, the increase in concentration of antimony excreted in the urine at the end of a shift amounts on average to 35 μg/g creatinine.

Antimony inhibits the activity of certain enzymes, binds sulphydryl groups in the serum, and disturbs protein and carbohydrate metabolism and the production of glycogen by the liver. Prolonged animal experiments with antimony aerosols have led to the development of distinctive endogenous lipoid pneumonia. Cardiac injury and cases of sudden death have also been reported in workers exposed to antimony. Focal fibrosis of the lung and cardiovascular effects have also been observed in animal trials.

The therapeutic use of antimonial drugs has made it possible to detect, in particular, the cumulative myocardial toxicity of the trivalent derivatives of antimony (which are excreted more slowly than pentavalent derivatives). Reduction in amplitude of T wave, increase of QT interval and arrhythmias have been observed in the electrocardiogram.

Symptoms

The symptoms of acute poisoning include violent irritation of the mouth, nose, stomach and intestines; vomiting and bloody stools; slow, shallow respiration; coma sometimes followed by death due to exhaustion and hepatic and renal complications. Those of chronic poisoning are: dryness of throat, nausea, headaches, sleeplessness, loss of appetite, and dizziness. Gender differences in the effects of antimony have been noted by some authors, but the differences are not well established.

Compounds

Stibine (SbH$_3$), or *antimony hydride (hydrogen antimonide)*, is produced by dissolving zinc-antimony or magnesium-antimony alloy in dilute hydrochloric acid. However, it occurs frequently as a by-product in the processing of metals containing antimony with reducing acids or in overcharging storage batteries. Stibine has been used as a fumigating agent. High-purity stibine is used as an n-type gas-phase dopant for silicon in semiconductors. Stibine is an extremely hazardous gas. Like arsine it may destroy blood cells and cause haemoglobinuria, jaundice, anuria and death. Symptoms include headache, nausea, epigastric pain and passage of dark red urine following exposure.

Antimony trioxide (Sb$_2$O$_3$) is the most important of the antimony oxides. When airborne, it tends to remain suspended for an exceptionally long time. It is obtained from antimony ore by a roasting process or by oxidizing metallic antimony and subsequent sublimation, and is used for the manufacture of tartar emetic, as a paint pigment, in enamels and glazes, and as a flameproofing compound.

Antimony trioxide is both a systemic poison and a skin disease hazard, although its toxicity is three times less than that of the metal. In long-term animal experiments, rats exposed to antimony trioxide via inhalation showed a high frequency of lung tumours. An excess of deaths due to cancer of the lung among workers engaged in antimony smelting for more than 4 years, at an average concentration in air of 8 mg/m^3, has been reported from Newcastle. In addition to antimony dust and fumes, the workers were exposed to zircon plant effluents and caustic soda. No other experiences were informative on the carcinogenic potential of antimony trioxide. This has been classified by the American Conference of Governmental Industrial Hygienists (ACGIH) as a chemical substance associated with industrial processes which are suspected of inducing cancer.

Antimony pentoxide (Sb$_2$O$_5$) is produced by the oxidation of the trioxide or the pure metal, in nitric acid under heat. It is used in the manufacture of paints and lacquers, glass, pottery and pharmaceuticals. Antimony pentoxide is noted for its low degree of toxic hazard.

Antimony trisulphide (Sb$_2$S$_3$) is found as a natural mineral, antimonite, but can also be synthesized. It is used in the pyrotechnics, match and explosives industries, in ruby glass manufacture, and as a pigment and plasticizer in the rubber industry. An apparent increase in heart abnormalities has been found in persons exposed to the trisulphide. *Antimony pentasulphide* (Sb$_2$S$_5$) has much the same uses as the trisulphide and has a low level of toxicity.

Antimony trichloride (SbCl$_3$), or *antimonous chloride (butter of antimony)*, is produced by the interaction of chlorine and antimony or by dissolving antimony trisulphide in hydrochloric acid. *Antimony pentachloride* (SbCl$_5$) is produced by the action of chlorine on molten antimony trichloride. The antimony chlorides are used for blueing steel and colouring aluminium, pewter and zinc, and as catalysts in organic synthesis, especially in the rubber and pharmaceutical industries. In addition, antimony trichloride is used in the match and petroleum industries. They are highly toxic substances, act as irritants and are corrosive to the skin. The trichloride has an LD$_{50}$ of 2.5 mg/100 g.

Antimony trifluoride (SbF$_3$) is prepared by dissolving antimony trioxide in hydrofluoric acid, and is used in organic synthesis. It is also employed in dyeing and pottery manufacture. Antimony trifluoride is highly toxic and an irritant to the skin. It has an LD$_{50}$ of 2.3 mg/100 g.

Safety and Health Measures

The essence of any safety programme for the prevention of antimony poisoning should be the control of dust and fume formation at all stages of processing.

In mining, dust prevention measures are similar to those for metal mining in general. During crushing, the ore should be sprayed or the process completely enclosed and fitted with local exhaust ventilation combined with adequate general ventilation. In antimony smelting the hazards of charge preparation, furnace operation, fettling and electrolytic cell operation should be eliminated, where possible, by isolation and process automation. Furnace workers should be provided with water sprays and effective ventilation.

Where complete elimination of exposure is not possible, the hands, arms and faces of workers should be protected by gloves, dustproof clothing and goggles, and, where atmospheric exposure is high, respirators should be provided. Barrier creams should also be applied, especially when handling soluble antimony compounds, in which case they should be combined with the use of waterproof clothing and rubber gloves. Personal hygiene measures should be strictly observed; no food or beverages should be consumed in the workshops, and suitable sanitary facilities should be provided so that workers can wash before meals and before leaving work.

• ARSENIC

Gunnar Nordberg

There are three major groups of arsenic (As) compounds:

1. inorganic arsenic compounds
2. organic arsenic compounds
3. arsine gas and substituted arsines.

Occurrence and Uses

Arsenic is found widely in nature and most abundantly in sulphide ores. Arsenopyrite (FeAsS) is the most abundant one.

Elemental arsenic

Elemental arsenic is utilized in alloys in order to increase their hardness and heat resistance (e.g., alloys with lead in shot-making and battery grids). It is also used in the manufacture of certain types of glass, as a component of electrical devices and as a doping agent in germanium and silicon solid-state products.

Trivalent inorganic compounds

Arsenic trichloride ($AsCl_3$) is used in the ceramics industry and in the manufacturing of chlorine-containing arsenicals. *Arsenic trioxide* (As_2O_3), or *white arsenic*, is useful in the purification of synthesis gas and as a primary material for all arsenic compounds. It is also a preservative for hides and wood, a textile mordant, a reagent in mineral flotation, and a decolourizing and refining agent in glass manufacture. *Calcium arsenite* ($Ca(As_2H_2O_4)$) and *cupric acetoarsenite* (usually considered $Cu(COOCH_3)_2 \cdot 3Cu(AsO_2)_2$) are insecticides. Cupric acetoarsenite is also used for painting ships and submarines. *Sodium arsenite* ($NaAsO_2$) is employed as a herbicide, a corrosion inhibitor, and as a drying agent in the textile industry. *Arsenic trisulphide* is a component of infrared-transmitting glass and a dehairing agent in the tanning industry. It is also used in the manufacturing of pyrotechnics and semiconductors.

Pentavalent inorganic compounds

Arsenic acid ($H_3AsO_4 \cdot \frac{1}{2}H_2O$) is found in the manufacture of arsenates, glass making and wood-treating processes. *Arsenic pentoxide* (As_2O_5), an herbicide and a wood preservative, is also used in the manufacture of coloured glass.

Calcium arsenate ($Ca_3(AsO_4)_2$) is used as an insecticide.

Organic arsenic compounds

Cacodylic acid (($CH_3)_2AsOOH$) is used as a herbicide and a defoliant. *Arsanilic acid* ($NH_2C_6H_4AsO(OH)_2$) finds use as a grasshopper bait and as an additive in animal feeds. Organic arsenic compounds in marine organisms occur in concentrations corresponding to a concentration of arsenic in the range 1 to 100 mg/kg in marine organisms such as shrimp and fish. Such arsenic is mainly made up of *arsenobetaine* and *arsenocholine*, organic arsenic compounds of low toxicity.

Arsine gas and the substituted arsines. Arsine gas is used in organic syntheses and in the processing of solid-state electronic components. Arsine gas may also be generated inadvertently in industrial processes when nascent hydrogen is formed and arsenic is present.

The substituted arsines are trivalent organic arsenical compounds which, depending on the number of alkyl or phenyl groups that they have attached to the arsenic nucleus, are known as mono-, di- or tri-substituted arsines. *Dichloroethylarsine* ($C_2H_5AsCl_2$), or *ethyldichloroarsine*, is a colourless liquid with an irritant odour. This compound, like the following one, was developed as a potential chemical warfare agent.

Dichloro(2-chlorovinyl-)arsine ($ClCH:CHAsCl_2$), or *chlorovinyldichloroarsine* (lewisite), is an olive-green liquid with a germanium-like odour. It was developed as a potential warfare agent but never used. The agent dimercaprol or British anti-lewisite (BAL) was developed as an antidote.

Dimethyl-arsine ($(CH_3)_2AsH$, or *cacodyl hydride* and *trimethylarsine* ($(CH_3)_3As$), or *trimethylarsenic*, are both colourless liquids. These two compounds can be produced after metabolic transformation of arsenic compounds by bacteria and fungi.

Hazards

Inorganic arsenic compounds

General aspects of toxicity. Although it is possible that very small amounts of certain arsenic compounds may have beneficial effects, as indicated by some animal studies, arsenic compounds, particularly the inorganic ones, are otherwise regarded as very potent poisons. Acute toxicity varies widely among compounds, depending on their valency state and solubility in biological media. The soluble trivalent compounds are the most toxic. Uptake of inorganic arsenic compounds from the gastrointestinal tract is almost complete, but uptake may be delayed for less soluble forms such as arsenic trioxide in particle form. Uptake after inhalation is also almost complete, since even less soluble material deposited on the respiratory mucosa, will be transferred to the gastrointestinal tract and subsequently taken up.

Occupational exposure to inorganic arsenic compounds through inhalation, ingestion or skin contact with subsequent absorption may occur in industry. Acute effects at the point of entry may occur if exposure is excessive. Dermatitis may occur as an acute symptom but is more often the result of toxicity from long-term exposure, sometimes subsequent to sensitization (see the section "Long-term exposure (chronic poisoning)").

Acute poisoning

Exposure to high doses of inorganic arsenic compounds by a combination of inhalation and ingestion may occur as a result of accidents in industries where large amounts of arsenic (e.g., arsenic trioxide), are handled. Depending on dose, various symptoms may develop, and when doses are excessive, fatal cases may occur. Symptoms of conjunctivitis, bronchitis and dyspnoea, followed by gastrointestinal discomfort with vomiting, and subsequently cardiac involvement with irreversible shock, may occur in a time course of hours. Arsenic in blood was reported to be above 3 mg/l in a case with fatal outcome.

With exposure to sub-lethal doses of irritant arsenic compounds in air (e.g., arsenic trioxide), there may be symptoms related to acute damage to the mucous membranes of the respiratory system and acute symptoms from exposed skin. Severe irritation of the nasal mucosae, larynx and bronchi, as well as conjunctivitis and dermatitis, occur in such cases. Perforation of the nasal septum can be observed in some individuals only after a few weeks following exposure. A certain tolerance against acute poisoning is believed to develop upon repeated exposure. This phenomenon, however, is not well documented in the scientific literature.

Effects due to accidental ingestion of inorganic arsenicals, mainly arsenic trioxide, have been described in the literature. However, such incidents are rare in industry today. Cases of poisoning are characterized by profound gastrointestinal damage, resulting in severe vomiting and diarrhoea, which may result in shock and subsequent oliguria and albuminuria. Other acute symptoms are facial oedema, muscular cramps and cardiac abnormalities. Symptoms may occur within a few minutes following exposure to the poison in solution, but may be delayed for several hours if the arsenic compound is in solid form or if it is taken with a meal. When ingested as a particulate, toxicity is also dependent on solubility and particle size of the ingested compound. The fatal dose of ingested arsenic trioxide has been reported to range from 70 to 180 mg. Death may occur within 24 hours, but the usual course runs from 3 to 7 days. Acute intoxication with arsenic compounds is usually accompanied by anaemia and leucopenia, especially granulocytopenia. In survivors these effects are usually reversible within 2 to 3 weeks. Reversible enlargement of the liver is also seen in acute poisoning, but liver function tests and liver enzymes are usually normal.

In individuals surviving acute poisoning, peripheral nervous disturbances frequently develop a few weeks after ingestion.

Long-term exposure (chronic poisoning)

General aspects. Chronic arsenic poisoning may occur in workers exposed for a long time to excessive concentrations of airborne arsenic compounds. Local effects in the mucous membranes of the respiratory tract and the skin are prominent features. Involvement of the nervous and circulatory system and the liver may also occur, as well as cancer of the respiratory tract.

With long-term exposure to arsenic via ingestion in food, drinking water or medication, symptoms are partly different from those after inhalation exposure. Vague abdominal symptoms—diarrhoea or constipation, flushing of the skin, pigmentation and hyperkeratosis—dominate the clinical picture. In addition, there may be vascular involvement, reported in one area to have given rise to peripheral gangrene.

Anaemia and leucocytopenia often occur in chronic arsenic poisoning. Liver involvement has been more commonly seen in persons exposed for a long time via oral ingestion than in those exposed via inhalation, particularly in vineyard workers considered to have been exposed mainly through drinking contaminated wine. Skin cancer occurs with excess frequency in this type of poisoning.

Vascular disorders. Long-term oral exposure to inorganic arsenic via drinking water may give rise to peripheral vascular disorders with Raynaud's phenomenon. In one area of Taiwan, China, peripheral gangrene (so-called Blackfoot disease) has occurred. Such severe manifestations of peripheral vascular involvement have not been observed in occupationally exposed persons, but slight changes with Raynaud's phenomenon and an increased prevalence of low peripheral blood presssure on cooling have been found in workers exposed for a long time to airborne inorganic arsenic (doses of absorbed arsenic are given below.

Dermatological disorders. Arsenical skin lesions differ somewhat, depending on the type of exposure. Eczematoid symptoms of varying degrees of severity do occur. In occupational exposure to mainly airborne arsenic, skin lesions may result from local irritation. Two types of dermatological disorders may occur:

1. an eczematous type with erythema (redness), swelling and papules or vesicles
2. a follicular type with erythema and follicular swelling or follicular pustules.

Dermatitis is primarily localized on the most heavily exposed areas, such as the face, back of the neck, forearms, wrists and hands. However, it may also occur on the scrotum, the inner surfaces of the thighs, the upper chest and back, the lower legs and around the ankles. Hyperpigmentation and keratoses are not prominent features of this type of arsenical lesions. Patch tests have demonstrated that the dermatitis is due to arsenic, not to impurities present in the crude arsenic trioxide. Chronic dermal lesions may follow this type of initial reaction, depending on the concentration and duration of exposure. These chronic lesions may occur after many years of occupational or environmental exposure. Hyperkeratosis, warts and melanosis of the skin are the conspicuous signs. Melanosis is most commonly seen on the upper and lower eyelids, around the temples, on the neck, on the areolae of the nipples and in the folds of the axillae. In severe cases arsenomelanosis is observed on the abdomen, chest, back and scrotum, along with hyperkeratosis and warts. In chronic arsenic poisoning, depigmentation (i.e., leukoderma), especially on the pigmented areas, commonly called "raindrop" pigmentation, also occurs. These chronic skin lesions, particularly the hyperkeratoses, may develop into pre-cancerous and cancerous lesions. A transverse striation of the nails (so-called Mees lines) also occurs in chronic arsenical poisoning. It should be noted that the chronic skin lesions may develop long after cessation of exposure, when arsenic concentrations in skin have returned to normal.

Mucous membrane lesions in chronic arsenic exposure is most classically reported as perforation of the nasal septum after inhalation exposure. This lesion is a result of irritation of the mucous membranes of the nose. Such irritation also extends to the larynx, trachea and bronchi. Both in inhalation exposure and in poisoning caused by repeated ingestion, dermatitis of the face and eyelids sometimes extends to keratoconjunctivitis.

Peripheral neuropathy. Peripheral nervous disturbances are frequently encountered in survivors of acute poisoning. They usually start within a few weeks after the acute poisoning, and recovery is slow. The neuropathy is characterized by both motor dysfunction and paresthaesia, but in less severe cases only sensory unilateral neuropathy may occur. Often the lower extremities are more affected than the upper ones. In subjects recovering from arsenical poisoning, Mees lines of the fingernails may develop. Histological examination has revealed Wallerian degeneration, especially in the longer axons. Peripheral neuropathy also may occur in industrial arsenic exposure, in most cases in a subclinical form that can be detected only by neurophysiological methods. In a group of smelter workers with long-term exposure corresponding to a mean cumulative total absorption of approximately 5 g (maximal absorption of 20 g), there was a negative correlation between cumulative absorption of arsenic and nerve conduction velocity. There were also some light clinical manifestations of peripheral vascular involvement in these workers (see above). In children exposed to arsenic, hearing loss has been reported.

Carcinogenic effects. Inorganic arsenic compounds are classified by the International Agency for Research on Cancer (IARC) as lung and skin carcinogens. There is also some evidence to suggest that persons exposed to inorganic arsenic compounds suffer a higher incidence of angiosarcoma of the liver and possibly of stomach cancer. Cancer of the respiratory tract has been reported in excess frequency among workers engaged in the production of insecticides containing lead arsenate and calcium arsenate, in vine-growers spraying insecticides containing inorganic copper and arsenic compounds, and in smelter workers exposed to inorganic compounds of arsenic and a number of other metals. The latency time between onset of exposure and the appearance of cancer is long, usually between 15 and 30 years. A synergistic action of tobacco smoking has been demonstrated for lung cancer.

Long-term exposure to inorganic arsenic via drinking water has been associated with an increased incidence of skin cancer in Taiwan and in Chile. This increase has been shown to be related to concentration in drinking water.

Teratogenic effects. High doses of trivalent inorganic arsenic compounds may cause malformations in hamsters when injected intravenously. With regard to human beings there is no firm evidence that arsenic compounds cause malformations under industrial conditions. Some evidence, however, suggests such an effect in workers in a smelting environment who were exposed simultaneously also to a number of other metals as well as other compounds.

Organic arsenic compounds

Organic arsenicals used as pesticides or as drugs may also give rise to toxicity, although such adverse effects are incompletely documented in humans.

Toxic effects on the nervous system have been reported in experimental animals following feeding with high doses of arsanilic acid, which is commonly used as a feed additive in poultry and swine.

The organic arsenic compounds that occur in foodstuffs of marine origin, such as shrimp, crab and fish, are made up of arsinocholine and arsinobetaine. It is well known that the amounts of organic arsenic that are present in fish and shellfish can be consumed without ill effects. These compounds are quickly excreted, mainly via urine.

Arsine gas and the substituted arsines. Many cases of acute arsine poisoning have been recorded, and there is a high fatality rate. Arsine is one of the most powerful haemolytic agents found in industry. Its haemolytic activity is due to its ability to cause a fall in erythrocyte-reduced glutathion content.

Signs and symptoms of arsine poisoning include haemolysis, which develops after a latent period that is dependent on the intensity of exposure. Inhalation of 250 ppm of arsine gas is instantly lethal. Exposure to 25 to 50 ppm for 30 minutes is lethal, and 10 ppm may be lethal after longer exposures. The signs and symptoms of poisoning are those characteristic of an acute and massive haemolysis. Initially there is a painless haemoglobinuria, gastrointestinal disturbance such as nausea and possibly vomiting. There may also be abdominal cramps and tenderness. Jaundice accompanied by anuria and oliguria subsequently occurs. Evidence of bone marrow depression may be present. After acute and severe exposure, a peripheral neuropathy may develop and can still be present several months after poisoning. Little is known about repeated or chronic exposure to arsine, but since the arsine gas is metabolized to inorganic arsenic in the body, it can be assumed that there is a risk for symptoms similar to those in long-term exposure to inorganic arsenic compounds.

The differential diagnosis should take account of acute haemolytic anaemias that could be caused by other chemical agents such as stibine or drugs, and secondary immunohaemolytic anaemias.

The substituted arsines do not give rise to haemolysis as their main effect, but they act as powerful local and pulmonary irritants and systemic poisons. The local effect on the skin gives rise to sharply circumscribed blisters in the case of dichloro(2-chlorovinyl-)arsine (lewisite). The vapour induces marked spasmodic coughing with frowzy or blood-stained sputum, progressing to acute pulmonary oedema. Dimercaprol (BAL) is an effective antidote if given in the early stages of poisoning.

Safety and Health Measures

The most common type of occupational arsenic exposure is to inorganic arsenic compounds, and these safety and health measures are mainly related to such exposures. When there is a risk of exposure to arsine gas, particular attention needs to be paid to accidental leaks, since peak exposures for short intervals may be of special concern.

The best means of prevention is to keep exposure well below accepted exposure limits. A programme of measurement of air-concentrations of arsenic is thus of importance. In addition to inhalation exposure, oral exposure via contaminated clothes, hands, tobacco and so on should be watched, and biological monitoring of inorganic arsenic in urine may be useful for evaluation of absorbed doses. Workers should be supplied with suitable protective clothing, protective boots and, when there is a risk that the exposure limit for airborne arsenic will be exceeded, respiratory protective equipment. Lockers should be provided with separate compartments for work and personal clothes, and adjacent sanitary facilities of a high standard should be made available. Smoking, eating and drinking at the workplace should not be allowed. Pre-employment medical examinations should be carried out. It is not recommended to employ persons with pre-existing diabetes, cardiovascular diseases, anaemia, allergic or other skin diseases, neurologic, hepatic or renal lesions, in arsenic work. Periodic medical examinations of all arsenic-exposed employees should be performed with special attention to possible arsenic-related symptoms.

Determination of the level of inorganic arsenic and its metabolites in urine allows estimation of the total dose of inorganic arsenic taken up by various exposure routes. Only when inorganic arsenic and its metabolites can be specifically measured is this method useful. Total arsenic in urine may often give erroneous information about industrial exposure, since even a single meal of fish or other marine organisms (containing considerable amounts of non-toxic organic arsenic compound) may cause greatly elevated urinary arsenic concentrations for several days.

Treatment

Arsine gas poisoning. When there is reason to believe that there has been considerable exposure to arsine gas, or upon observation of the first symptoms (e.g., haemoglobinuria and abdominal pain), immediate removal of the individual from the contaminated environment and prompt medical attention are required. The recommended treatment, if there is any evidence of impaired renal function, consists of total-replacement blood transfusion associated with prolonged artificial dialysis. Forced diuresis has proved useful in some cases, whereas, in the opinion of most authors, treatment with BAL or other chelating agents seems to have only limited effect.

Exposure to the substituted arsines should be treated in the same way as inorganic arsenic poisoning (see below).

Poisoning by inorganic arsenic. If there has been exposure to doses that can be estimated to give rise to acute poisoning, or if severe symptoms from the respiratory system, the skin or the gastrointestinal tract occur in the course of long-term exposures, the worker should immediately be removed from exposure and treated with a complexing agent.

The classical agent which has been used most widely in such situations is 2,3-dimercapto-1-propanol or British anti-lewisite (BAL, dimercaprol). Prompt administration in such cases is vital: to obtain maximal benefit such treatment should be given within 4 hours of poisoning. Other pharmaceuticals which may be used are sodium 2,3-dimercaptopropanesulphonate (DMPS or unithiol) or meso-2,3-dimercaptosuccinic acid (DMSA). These drugs are less likely to give side effects and are believed to be more effective than BAL. Intravenous administration of N-acetylcysteine has been reported in one case to be of value; in addition, general treatment, such as prevention of further absorption by removal from exposure and minimizing absorption from the gastrointestinal tract by gastric lavage and administration by gastric tube of chelating agents or charcoal, is mandatory. General supportive therapy, such as maintenance of respiration and circulation, maintenance of water and electrolyte balance, and control of nervous system effects, as well as elimination of absorbed poison through haemodialysis and exchange transfusion, may be used if feasible.

Acute skin lesions such as contact dermatitis and mild manifestations of peripheral vascular involvement, such as Raynaud's syndrome, usually do not require treatment other than removal from exposure.

● BARIUM

Occurrence and Uses

Barium (Ba) is abundant in nature and accounts for approximately 0.04% of the earth's crust. The chief sources are the minerals barite (barium sulphate, $BaSO_4$) and witherite (barium carbonate, $BaCO_3$). Barium metal is produced in only limited quantities, by aluminium reduction of barium oxide in a retort.

Barium is used extensively in the manufacture of alloys for nickel barium parts found in ignition equipment for automobiles and in the manufacture of glass, ceramics and television picture tubes. *Barite* ($BaSO_4$), or *barium sulphate*, is primarily used in the manufacture of lithopone, a white powder containing 20% barium sulphate, 30% zinc sulphide and less than 8% zinc oxide. Lithopone is widely employed as a pigment in white paints. Chemically precipitated barium sulphate—*blanc fixe*—is used in high-quality paints, in x-ray diagnostic work and in the glass and paper industries. It is also used in the manufacture of photographic papers, artificial ivory and cellophane. Crude barite is used as a thixotropic mud in oil-well drilling.

Barium hydroxide ($Ba(OH)_2$) is found in lubricants, pesticides, the sugar industry, corrosion inhibitors, drilling fluids and water softeners. It is also used in glass manufacture, synthetic rubber vulcanization, animal and vegetable oil refining, and fresco painting. *Barium carbonate* ($BaCO_3$) is obtained as a precipitate of barite and is used in the brick, ceramics, paint, rubber, oil-well drilling and paper industries. It also finds use in enamels, marble substitutes, optical glass and electrodes.

Barium oxide (BaO) is a white alkaline powder which is used to dry gases and solvents. At 450 °C it combines with oxygen to produce *barium peroxide* (BaO_2), an oxidizing agent in organic synthesis and a bleaching material for animal substances and vegetable fibres. *Barium peroxide* is used in the textile industry for dyeing and printing, in powder aluminium for welding and in pyrotechnics.

Barium chloride ($BaCl_2$) is obtained by roasting barite with coal and calcium chloride, and is used in the manufacture of pigments, colour lakes and glass, and as a mordant for acid dyes. It is also useful for weighting and dyeing textile fabrics and in aluminium refining. Barium chloride is a pesticide, a compound added to boilers for softening water, and a tanning and finishing agent for leather. *Barium nitrate* ($Ba(NO_3)_2$) is used in pyrotechnics and the electronics industries.

Hazards

Barium metal has only limited use and presents an explosion hazard. The soluble compounds of barium (chloride, nitrate, hydroxide) are highly toxic; the inhalation of the insoluble compounds (sulphate) may give rise to pneumoconiosis. Many of the compounds, including the sulphide, oxide and carbonate, may cause local irritation to the eyes, nose, throat and skin. Certain compounds, particularly the peroxide, nitrate and chlorate, present fire hazards in use and storage.

Toxicity

When the soluble compounds enter by the oral route they are highly toxic, with a fatal dose of the chloride thought to be 0.8 to 0.9 g. However, although poisoning due to the ingestion of these compounds does occasionally occur, very few cases of industrial poisoning have been reported. Poisoning may result when workers are exposed to atmospheric concentrations of the dust of soluble compounds such as may occur during grinding. These compounds exert a strong and prolonged stimulant action on all forms of muscle, markedly increasing contractility. In the heart, irregular contractions may be followed by fibrillation, and there is evidence of a coronary constrictor action. Other effects include intestinal peristalsis, vascular constriction, bladder contraction and an increase in voluntary muscle tension. Barium compounds also have irritant effects on mucous membranes and the eye.

Barium carbonate, an insoluble compound, does not appear to have pathological effects from inhalation; however, it can cause severe poisoning from oral intake, and in rats it impairs the function of the male and female gonads; the foetus is sensitive to barium carbonate during the first half of pregnancy.

Pneumoconiosis

Barium sulphate is characterized by its extreme insolubility, a property which makes it non-toxic to humans. For this reason and due to its high radio-opacity, barium sulphate is used as an opaque medium in x-ray examination of the gastrointestinal, respiratory and urinary systems. It is also inert in the human lung, as has been demonstrated by its lack of adverse effects following deliberate introduction into the bronchial tract as a contrast medium in bronchography and by industrial exposure to high concentrations of fine dust.

Inhalation, however, may lead to deposition in the lungs in sufficient quantities to produce baritosis (a benign pneumoconiosis, which principally occurs in the mining, grinding and bagging of barite, but has been reported in the manufacture of lithopone). The first reported case of baritosis was accompanied by symptoms and disability, but these were associated later with other lung disease. Subsequent studies have contrasted the unimpressive nature of the clinical picture and the total absence of symptoms and abnormal physical signs with the well marked x-ray changes, which show disseminated nodular opacities throughout both lungs. The opacities are discrete but sometimes so numerous as to overlap and appear confluent. No massive shadows have been reported. The outstanding feature of the radiographs is the marked radio-opacity of the nodules, which is understandable in view of the substance's use as a radio-opaque medium. The size of the individual elements may vary between 1 and 5 mm in diameter, although the average is about 3 mm or less, and the shape has been described variously as "rounded" and "dendritic". In some cases, a number of very dense points have been found to lie in a matrix of lower density.

In one series of cases, dust concentrations of up to 11,000 particles/cm^3 were measured at the workplace, and chemical analysis showed that the total silica content lay between 0.07 and 1.96%, quartz not being detectable by x-ray diffraction. Men exposed for up to 20 years and exhibiting x-ray changes were symptomless, had excellent lung function and were capable of carrying out strenuous work. Years after the exposure has ceased, follow-up examinations show a marked clearing of x-ray abnormalities.

Reports of post-mortem findings in pure baritosis are practically non-existent. However, baritosis may be associated with silicosis in mining due to contamination of barite ore by siliceous rock, and, in grinding, if siliceous millstones are used.

Safety and Health Measures

Adequate washing and other sanitary facilities should be provided for workers exposed to toxic soluble barium compounds, and rigorous personal hygiene measures should be encouraged. Smoking and consumption of food and beverages in workshops should be prohibited. Floors in workshops should be made of impermeable materials and frequently washed down. Employees working on such processes as barite leaching with sulphuric acid should be supplied with acid-resistant clothing and suitable hand and face protection. Although baritosis is benign, efforts should still be made to reduce atmospheric concentrations of barite dust to a minimum. In addition, particular attention should be paid to the presence of free silica in the airborne dust.

BISMUTH

Occurrence and Uses

In nature, bismuth (Bi) occurs both as the free metal and in ores such as bismutite (carbonate) and bismuthinite (double bismuth and tellurium sulphide), where it is accompanied by other elements, mainly lead and antimony.

Bismuth is used in metallurgy for the manufacture of numerous alloys, especially alloys with a low melting point. Some of these alloys are used for welding. Bismuth also finds use in safety devices in fire detection and extinguishing systems, and in the production of malleable irons. It acts as a catalyst for making acrylic fibres.

Bismuth telluride is used as a semiconductor. *Bismuth oxide, hydroxide, oxychloride, trichloride* and *nitrate* are employed in the cosmetics industry. Other salts (e.g., *succinate, orthoxyquinoleate, subnitrate, carbonate, phosphate* and so on) are used in medicine.

Hazards

There have been no reports of occupational exposure during the production of metallic bismuth and the manufacture of pharmaceuticals, cosmetics and industrial chemicals. Because bismuth and its compounds do not appear to have been responsible for poisoning associated with work, they are regarded as the least toxic of the heavy metals currently used in industry.

Bismuth compounds are absorbed through the respiratory and gastrointestinal tracts. The main systemic effects in humans and animals are exerted in the kidney and liver. The organic derivatives cause alterations of the convoluted tubules and may result in serious, and sometimes fatal, nephrosis.

Gum discolouration has been reported with exposure to bismuth dusts. The insoluble mineral salts, taken orally over prolonged periods in doses generally exceeding 1 per day, may provoke brain disease characterized by mental disorders (confused state), muscular disorders (myoclonia), motor coordination disorders (loss of balance, unsteadiness) and dysarthria. These disorders stem from an accumulation of bismuth in the nerve centres which manifests itself when bismuthaemia exceeds a certain level, estimated at around 50 mg/l. In most cases, bismuth-linked encephalopathy gradually disappears without medication within a

period of from 10 days to 2 months, during which time the bismuth is eliminated in the urine. Fatal cases of encephalopathy have, however, been recorded.

Such effects have been observed in France and Australia since 1973. They are caused by a factor not yet fully investigated which encourages the absorption of bismuth through the intestinal mucous membrane and leads to an increase in bismuthaemia to a level as high as several hundred mg/l. The danger of encephalopathy caused by inhaling metallic dust or oxide smoke in the workplace is very remote. The poor solubility of bismuth and bismuth oxide in blood plasma and its fairly rapid elimination in the urine (its half-life is about 6 days) argue against the likelihood of a sufficiently acute impregnation of the nerve centres to reach pathological levels.

In animals, inhalation of insoluble compounds such as bismuth telluride provokes the usual lung response of an inert dust. However, long-term exposure to bismuth telluride "doped" with selenium sulphide can produce in various species a mild reversible granulomatous reaction of the lung.

Some bismuth compounds decompose into dangerous chemicals. Bismuth pentafluoride decomposes on heating and emits highly toxic fumes.

CADMIUM

Occurrence and Uses

Cadmium (Cd) has many chemical and physical similarities to zinc and occurs together with zinc in nature. In minerals and ores, cadmium and zinc generally have a ratio of 1:100 to 1:1,000.

Cadmium is highly resistant to corrosion and has been widely used for electroplating of other metals, mainly steel and iron. Screws, screw nuts, locks and various parts for aircraft and motor vehicles are frequently treated with cadmium in order to withstand corrosion. Nowadays, however, only 8% of all refined cadmium is used for platings and coatings. Cadmium compounds (30% of the use in developed countries) are used as pigments and stabilizers in plastics, and cadmium is also used in certain alloys (3%). Rechargeable, small portable cadmium-containing batteries, used, for example, in mobile telephones, comprise a rapidly increasing usage of cadmium (55% of all cadmium in industrialized countries in 1994 was used in batteries).

Cadmium occurs in various inorganic salts. The most important is *cadmium stearate*, which is used as a heat stabilizer in polyvinyl chloride (PVC) plastics. *Cadmium sulphide* and *cadmium sulphoselenide* are used as yellow and red pigments in plastics and colours. Cadmium sulphide is also used in photo- and solar cells. *Cadmium chloride* acts as a fungicide, an ingredient in electroplating baths, a colourant for pyrotechnics, an additive to tinning solution and a mordant in dyeing and printing textiles. It is also used in the production of certain photographic films and in the manufacture of special mirrors and coatings for electronic vacuum tubes. *Cadmium oxide* is an electroplating agent, a starting material for PVC heat stabilizers and a component of silver alloys, phosphors, semiconductors and glass and ceramic glazes.

Cadmium can represent an environmental hazard, and many countries have introduced legislative actions aimed towards decreasing the use and subsequent environmental spread of cadmium.

Metabolism and accumulation

Gastrointestinal absorption of ingested cadmium is about 2 to 6% under normal conditions. Individuals with low body iron stores, reflected by low concentrations of serum ferritin, may have considerably higher absorption of cadmium, up to 20% of a given dose of cadmium. Significant amounts of cadmium may also be absorbed via the lung from the inhalation of tobacco smoke or from occupational exposure to atmospheric cadmium dust. Pulmonary absorption of inhaled respirable cadmium dust is estimated at 20 to 50%. After absorption via the gastrointestinal tract or the lung, cadmium is transported to the liver, where production of a cadmium-binding low-molecular-weight protein, metallothionein, is initiated.

About 80 to 90% of the total amount of cadmium in the body is considered to be bound to metallothionein. This prevents the free cadmium ions from exerting their toxic effects. It is likely that small amounts of metallothionein-bound cadmium are constantly leaving the liver and being transported to the kidney via the blood. The metallothionein with the cadmium bound to it is filtered through the glomeruli into the primary urine. Like other low-molecular-weight proteins and amino acids, the metallothionein-cadmium complex is subsequently reabsorbed from the primary urine into the proximal tubular cells, where digestive enzymes degrade the engulfed proteins into smaller peptides and amino acids. Free cadmium ions in the cells result from degradation of metallothionein and initiate a new synthesis of metallothionein, binding the cadmium, and thus protecting the cell from the highly toxic free cadmium ions. Kidney dysfunction is considered to occur when the metallothionein-producing capacity of the tubular cells is exceeded. The kidney and liver have the highest concentrations of cadmium, together containing about 50% of the body burden of cadmium. The cadmium concentration in the kidney cortex, before cadmium-induced kidney damage occurs, is generally about 15 times the concentration in liver. Elimination of cadmium is very slow. As a result of this, cadmium accumulates in the body, the concentrations increasing with age and length of exposure. Based on organ concentration at different ages the biological half-life of cadmium in humans has been estimated in the range of 7 to 30 years.

Acute toxicity

Inhalation of cadmium compounds at concentrations above 1 mg Cd/m^3 in air for 8 hours, or at higher concentrations for shorter periods, may lead to chemical pneumonitis, and in severe cases pulmonary oedema. Symptoms generally occur within 1 to 8 hours after exposure. They are influenza-like and similar to those in metal fume fever. The more severe symptoms of chemical pneumonitis and pulmonary oedema may have a latency period up to 24 hours. Death may occur after 4 to 7 days. Exposure to cadmium in the air at concentrations exceeding 5 mg Cd/m^3 is most likely to occur where cadmium alloys are smelted, welded or soldered. Ingestion of drinks contaminated with cadmium at concentrations exceeding 15 mg Cd/l gives rise to symptoms of food poisoning. Symptoms are nausea, vomiting, abdominal pains and sometimes diarrhoea. Sources of food contamination may be pots and pans with cadmium-containing glazing and cadmium solderings used in vending machines for hot and cold drinks. In animals parenteral administration of cadmium at doses exceeding 2 mg Cd/kg body weight causes necrosis of the testis. No such effect has been reported in humans.

Chronic toxicity

Chronic cadmium poisoning has been reported after prolonged occupational exposure to cadmium oxide fumes, cadmium oxide dust and cadmium stearates. Changes associated with chronic cadmium poisoning may be local, in which case they involve the respiratory tract, or they may be systemic, resulting from absorption of cadmium. Systemic changes include kidney damage with proteinuria and anaemia. Lung disease in the form of emphysema

is the main symptom at heavy exposure to cadmium in air, whereas kidney dysfunction and damage are the most prominent findings after long-term exposure to lower levels of cadmium in workroom air or via cadmium-contaminated food. Mild hypochromic anaemia is frequently found among workers exposed to high levels of cadmium. This may be due to both increased destruction of red blood cells and to iron deficiency. Yellow discolouration of the necks of teeth and loss of sense of smell (anosmia) may also be seen in cases of exposure to very high cadmium concentrations.

Pulmonary emphysema is considered a possible effect of prolonged exposure to cadmium in air at concentrations exceeding 0.1 mg Cd/m^3. It has been reported that exposure to concentrations of about 0.02 mg Cd/m^3 for more than 20 years can cause certain pulmonary effects. Cadmium-induced pulmonary emphysema can reduce working capacity and may be the cause of invalidity and life shortening. With long-term low-level cadmium exposure the kidney is the critical organ (i.e., the organ first affected). Cadmium accumulates in renal cortex. Concentrations exceeding 200 μg Cd/g wet weight have previously been estimated to cause tubular dysfunction with decreased reabsorption of proteins from the urine. This causes tubular proteinuria with increased excretion of low-molecular-weight proteins such as α, α-1-microglobulin (protein HC), β-2-microglobulin and retinol binding protein (RTB). Recent research suggests, however, that tubular damage may occur at lower levels of cadmium in kidney cortex. As the kidney dysfunction progresses, amino acids, glucose and minerals, such as calcium and phosphorus, are also lost into the urine. Increased excretion of calcium and phosphorous may disturb bone metabolism, and kidney stones are frequently reported by cadmium workers. After long-term medium-to-high levels of exposure to cadmium, the kidney's glomeruli may also be affected, leading to a decreased glomerular filtration rate. In severe cases uraemia may develop. Recent studies have shown the glomerular dysfunction to be irreversible and dose dependent. Osteomalacia has been reported in cases of severe chronic cadmium poisoning.

In order to prevent kidney dysfunction, as manifested by β-2-microglobulinuria, particularly if the occupational exposure to cadmium fumes and dust is likely to last for 25 years (at 8 hours workday and 225 workdays/year), it is recommended that the average workroom concentration of respirable cadmium should be kept below 0.01 mg/m^3.

Excessive cadmium exposure has occurred in the general population through ingestion of contaminated rice and other foodstuffs, and possibly drinking water. The itai-itai disease, a painful type of osteomalacia, with multiple fractures appearing together with kidney dysfunction, has occurred in Japan in areas with high cadmium exposure. Though the pathogenesis of itai-itai disease is still under dispute, it is generally accepted that cadmium is a necessary aetiological factor. It should be stressed that cadmium-induced kidney damage is irreversible and may grow worse even after exposure has ceased.

Cadmium and cancer

There is strong evidence of dose-response relationships and an increased mortality from lung cancer in several epidemiological studies on cadmium-exposed workers. The interpretation is complicated by concurrent exposures to other metals which are known or suspected carcinogens. Continuing observations of cadmium-exposed workers have, however, failed to yield evidence of increased mortality from prostatic cancer, as initially suspected. The IARC in 1993 assessed the risk of cancer from exposure to cadmium and concluded that it should be regarded as a human carcinogen. Since then additional epidemiological evidence has come forth with somewhat contradictory results, and the possible carcinogenicity of cadmium thus remains unclear. It is nevertheless clear that cadmium possesses strong carcinogenic properties in animal experiments.

Safety and Health Measures

The kidney cortex is the critical organ with long-term cadmium exposure via air or food. The critical concentration is estimated at about 200 µg Cd/g wet weight, but may be lower, as stated above. In order to keep the kidney cortex concentration below this level even after lifelong exposure, the average cadmium concentration in workroom air (8 hours per day) should not exceed 0.01 mg Cd/m^3.

Work processes and operations which may release cadmium fumes or dust into the atmosphere should be designed to keep concentration levels to a minimum and, if practicable, be enclosed and fitted with exhaust ventilation. When adequate ventilation is impossible to maintain (e.g., during welding and cutting), respirators should be carried and air should be sampled to determine the cadmium concentration. In areas with hazards of flying particles, chemical splashes, radiant heat and so on (e.g., near electroplating tanks and furnaces), workers should wear appropriate safety equipment, such as eye, face, hand and arm protection and impermeable clothing. Adequate sanitary facilities should be supplied, and workers should be encouraged to wash before meals and to wash thoroughly and change clothes before leaving work. Smoking, eating and drinking in work areas should be prohibited. Tobacco contaminated with cadmium dust from workrooms can be an important exposure route. Cigarettes and pipe tobacco should not be carried in the workroom. Contaminated exhaust air should be filtered, and persons in charge of dust collectors and filters should wear respirators while working on the equipment.

To ensure that excessive accumulation of cadmium in the kidney does not occur, cadmium levels in blood and in urine should be checked regularly. Cadmium levels in blood are mainly an indication of the last few months exposure, but can be used to assess body burden a few years after exposure has ceased. A value of 100 nmol Cd/l whole blood is an approximate critical level if exposure is regular for long periods. Cadmium values in urine can be used to estimate the cadmium body burden, providing kidney damage has not occurred. It has been estimated by the WHO that 10 nmol/mmol creatinine is the concentration below which kidney dysfunction should not occur. Recent research has, however, shown that kidney dysfunction may occur already at around 5 nmol/mmol creatinine. Since the mentioned blood and urinary levels are levels at which action of cadmium on kidney has been observed, it is recommended that control measures be applied whenever the individual concentrations of cadmium in urine and/or in blood exceed 50 nmol/l whole blood or 3 nmol/mmol creatinine respectively. Pre-employment medical examinations should be given to workers who will be exposed to cadmium dust or fumes. Persons with respiratory or kidney disorders should avoid such work. Medical examination of cadmium-exposed workers should be carried out at least once every year. In workers exposed to cadmium for longer periods, quantitative measurements of ß-2-microglobulin or other relevant low-molecular-weight proteins in urine should be made regularly. Concentrations of ß-2-microglobulin in urine should normally not exceed 34 µg/mmol creatinine.

Treatment of cadmium poisoning

Persons who have ingested cadmium salts should be made to vomit or given gastric lavage; persons exposed to acute inhalation should be removed from exposure and given oxygen therapy if necessary. No specific treatment for chronic cadmium poisoning is available, and symptomatic treatment has to be relied upon. As a rule the administration of chelating agents such as BAL and EDTA is contraindicated since they are nephrotoxic in combination with cadmium.

CHROMIUM

Occurrence and Uses

Elemental chromium (Cr) is not found free in nature, and the only ore of any importance is the spinel ore, chromite or chrome iron stone, which is ferrous chromite ($FeOCr_2O_3$), widely distributed over the earth's surface. In addition to chromic acid, this ore contains variable quantities of other substances. Only ores or concentrates containing more than 40% chromic oxide (Cr_2O_3) are used commercially, and countries having the most suitable deposits are the Russian Federation, South Africa, Zimbabwe, Turkey, the Philippines and India. The prime consumers of chromites are the United States, the Russian Federation, Germany, Japan, France and the United Kingdom.

Chromite may be obtained from both underground and open cast mines. The ore is crusted and, if necessary, concentrated.

The most significant usage of pure chromium is for electroplating of a wide range of equipment, such as automobile parts and electric equipment. Chromium is used extensively for alloying with iron and nickel to form stainless steel, and with nickel, titanium, niobium, cobalt, copper and other metals to form special-purpose alloys.

Chromium Compounds

Chromium forms a number of compounds in various oxidation states. Those of II (chromous), III (chromic) and VI (chromate) states are most important; the II state is basic, the III state is amphoteric and the VI state is acidic. Commercial applications mainly concern compounds in the VI state, with some interest in III state chromium compounds.

The chromous state (Cr^{II}) is unstable and is readily oxidized to the chromic state (Cr^{III}). This instability limits the use of chromous compounds. The chromic compounds are very stable and form many compounds which have commercial use, the principal of which are chromic oxide and basic chromium sulphate.

Chromium in the +6 oxidation state (Cr^{VI}) has its greatest industrial application as a consequence of its acidic and oxidant properties, as well as its ability to form strongly coloured and insoluble salts. The most important compounds containing chromium in the Cr^{VI} state are *sodium dichromate, potassium dichromate* and *chromium trioxide*. Most other chromate compounds are produced industrially using dichromate as the source of Cr^{VI}.

Production

Sodium mono- and dichromate are the starting materials from which most of the chromium compounds are manufactured. Sodium chromate and dichromate are prepared directly from chrome ore. Chrome ore is crushed, dried and ground; soda ash is added and lime or leached calcine may also be added. After thorough mixing the mixture is roasted in a rotary furnace at an optimum temperature of about 1,100 °C; an oxidizing atmosphere is essential to convert the chromium to the Cr^{VI} state. The melt from the furnace is cooled and leached and the sodium chromate or dichromate is isolated by conventional processes from the solution.

Chromium^{III} compounds

Technically, *chromium oxide* (Cr_2O_3, or *chromic oxide*), is made by reducing sodium dichromate either with charcoal or with sulphur.

Reduction with sulphur is usually employed when the chromic oxide is to be used as a pigment. For metallurgical purposes carbon reduction is normally employed.

The commercial material is normally basic chromic sulphate $[Cr(OH)(H_2O)_5]SO_4$, which is prepared from sodium dichromate by reduction with carbohydrate in the presence of sulphuric acid; the reaction is vigorously exothermic. Alternatively, sulphur dioxide reduction of a solution of sodium dichromate will yield basic chromic sulphurate. It is used in the tanning of leather, and the material is sold on the basis of Cr_2O_3 content, which ranges from 20.5 to 25%.

Chromium^{VI} compounds

Sodium dichromate can be converted into the anhydrous salt. It is the starting point for preparation of chromium compounds.

Chromium trioxide or *chromium anhydride* (sometimes referred to as "chromic acid", although true chromic acid cannot be isolated from solution) is formed by treating a concentrated solution of a dichromate with strong sulphuric acid excess. It is a violent oxidizing agent, and the solution is the principal constituent of chromium plating.

Insoluble chromates

Chromates of weak bases are of limited solubility and more deeply coloured than the oxides; hence their use as pigments. These are not always distinct compounds and may contain mixtures of other materials to provide the right pigment colour. They are prepared by the addition of sodium or potassium dichromate to a solution of the appropriate salt.

Lead chromate is trimorphic; the stable monoclinic form is orange-yellow, "chrome yellow", and the unstable orthombic form is yellow, isomorphous with lead sulphate and stabilized by it. An orange-red tetragonal form is similar and isomorphous with lead molybdate (VI) $PbMoO_4$ and stabilized by it. On these properties depends the versatility of lead chromate as a pigment in producing a variety of yellow-orange pigments.

Uses

Compounds containing Cr^{VI} are used in many industrial operations. The manufacture of important inorganic pigments such as lead chromes (which are themselves used to prepare chrome greens), molybdate-oranges, zinc chromate and chromium-oxide green; wood preservation; corrosion inhibition; and coloured glasses and glazes. Basic chromic sulphates are widely used for tanning.

The dyeing of textiles, the preparation of many important catalysts containing chromic oxide and the production of light-sensitive dichromated colloids for use in lithography are also well-known industrial uses of chromium-containing chemicals.

Chromic acid is used not only for "decorative" chromium plating but also for "hard" chromium plating, where it is deposited in much thicker layers to give an extremely hard surface with a low coefficient of friction.

Because of the strong oxidizing action of chromates in acid solution, there are many industrial applications particularly involving organic materials, such as the oxidation of trinitrotoluene (TNT) to give phloroglucinol and the oxidation of picoline to give nicotine acid.

Chromium oxide is also used for the production of pure chromium metal that is suitable for incorporation in creep-resistant, high-temperature alloys, and as a refractory oxide. It may be included in a number of refractory compositions with advantage—for example, in magnetite and magnetite-chromate mixtures.

Hazards

Compounds with Cr^{III} oxidation states are considerably less hazardous than are Cr^{VI} compounds. Compounds of Cr^{III} are poorly absorbed from the digestive system. These Cr^{III} compounds may also combine with proteins in the superficial layers of the skin to form stable complexes. Compounds of Cr^{III} do not cause chrome ulcerations and do not generally initiate allergic dermatitis without prior sensitization by Cr^{VI} compounds.

In the Cr^{VI} oxidation state, chromium compounds are readily absorbed after ingestion as well as during inhalation. The uptake through intact skin is less well elucidated. The irritant and corrosive effects caused by Cr^{VI} occur readily after uptake through mucous membranes, where they are readily absorbed. Work-related exposure to Cr^{VI} compounds may induce skin and mucous membrane irritation or corrosion, allergic skin reactions or skin ulcerations.

The untoward effects of chromium compounds generally occur among workers in workplaces where Cr^{VI} is encountered, in particular during manufacture or use. The effects frequently involve the skin or respiratory system. Typical industrial hazards are inhalation of the dust or fumes arising during the manufacture of dichromate from chromite ore and the manufacture of lead and zinc chromates, inhalation of chromic acid mists during electroplating or surface treatment of metals, and skin contact with Cr^{VI} compounds in manufacture or use. Exposure to Cr^{VI}-containing fumes may also occur during welding of stainless steels.

Chrome ulcerations. Such lesions used to be common after work-related exposure to Cr^{VI} compounds. The ulcers result from the corrosive action of Cr^{VI}, which penetrates the skin through cuts or abrasions. The lesion usually begins as a painless papule, commonly on the hands, forearms or feet, resulting in ulcerations. The ulcer may penetrate deeply into soft tissue and may reach underlying bone. Healing is slow unless the ulcer is treated at an early stage, and atrophic scars remain. There are no reports about skin cancer following such ulcers.

Dermatitis. The Cr^{VI} compounds may cause both primary skin irritation and sensitization. In chromate-producing industries, some workers may develop skin irritation, particularly at the neck or wrist, soon after starting work with chromates. In the majority of cases, this clears rapidly and does not recur. However, sometimes it may be necessary to recommend a change of work.

Numerous sources of exposure to Cr^{VI} have been listed (e.g., contact with cement, plaster, leather, graphic work, work in match factories, work in tanneries and various sources of metal work). Workers employed in wet sandpapering of car bodies have also been reported with allergy. Affected subjects react positively to patch testing with 0.5% dichromate. Some affected subjects had only erythema or scattered papules, and in others the lesions resembled dyshidriotic pompholyx; nummular eczema may lead to misdiagnosis of genuine cases of occupational dermatitis.

It has been shown that Cr^{VI} penetrates the skin through the sweat glands and is reduced to Cr^{III} in the corium. It is shown that the Cr^{III} then reacts with protein to form the antigen-antibody complex. This explains the localization of lesions around sweat glands and why very small amounts of dichromate can cause sensitization. The chronic character of the dermatitis may be due to the fact that the antigen-antibody complex is removed more slowly than would be the case if the reaction occurred in the epidermis.

Acute respiratory effects. Inhalation of dust or mist containing Cr^{VI} is irritating to mucous membranes. At high concentrations of such dust, sneezing, rhinorrhoea, lesions of the nasal septum and redness of the throat are documented effects. Sensitization has also been reported, resulting in typical asthmatic attacks, which may recur on subsequent exposure. At exposure for several days to chromic acid mist at concentrations of about 20 to 30 mg/m^3, cough, headache, dyspnoea and substernal pain have also been reported after exposure. The occurrence of bronchospasm in a person working with chromates should suggest chemical irritation of the lungs. Treatment is only symptomatic.

Ulcerations of the nasal septum. In previous years, when the exposure levels to Cr^{VI} compounds could be high, ulcerations of the nasal septum were frequently seen among exposed workers. This untoward effect results from deposition of Cr^{VI}-containing particulates or mist droplets on the nasal septum, resulting in ulceration of the cartilaginous portion followed, in many cases, by perforation at the site of ulceration. Frequent nose-picking may enhance the formation of perforation. The mucosa covering the lower anterior part of the septum, known as the Kiesselbach's and Little's area, is relatively avascular and closely adherent to the underlying cartilage. Crusts containing necrotic debris from the cartilage of the septum continue to form, and within a week or two the septum becomes perforated. The periphery of the ulceration remains active for up to several months, during which time the perforation may increase in size. It heals by the formation of vascular scar tissue. Sense of smell is almost never impaired. During the active phase, rhinorrhoea and nose-bleeding may be troublesome symptoms. When soundly healed, symptoms are rare and many persons are unaware that the septum is perforated.

Effects in other organs. Necrosis of the kidneys has been reported, starting with tubular necrosis, leaving the glomeruli undamaged. Diffuse necrosis of the liver and subsequent loss of architecture has also been reported. Soon after the turn of the century there were a number of reports on human ingestion of Cr^{VI} compounds resulting in major gastro-intestinal bleeding from ulcerations of the intestinal mucosa. Sometimes such bleedings resulted in cardiovascular shock as a possible complication. If the patient survived, tubular necrosis of the kidneys or liver necrosis could occur.

Carcinogenic effects. Increased incidence of lung cancer among workers in manufacture and use of Cr^{VI} compounds has been reported in a great number of studies from France, Germany, Italy, Japan, Norway, the United States and the United Kingdom. Chromates of zinc and calcium appear to be among the most potent carcinogenic chromates, as well as among the most potent human carcinogens. Elevated incidence of lung cancer has also been reported among subjects exposed to lead chromates, and to fumes of chromium trioxides. Heavy exposures to Cr^{VI} compounds have resulted in very high incidence of lung cancer in exposed workers 15 or more years after first exposure, as reported in both cohort studies and case reports.

Thus, it is well established that an increase in the incidence of lung cancer of workers employed in the manufacture of zinc chromate and the manufacture of mono- and dichromates from chromite ore is a long-term effect of work-related heavy exposure to Cr^{VI} compounds. Some of the cohort studies have reported measurements of exposure levels among the exposed cohorts. Also, a small number of studies have indicated that exposure to fumes generated from welding on Cr-alloyed steel may result in elevated incidence of lung cancer among these welders.

There is no firmly established "safe" level of exposure. However, most of the reports on association between Cr^{VI} exposure and cancer of the respiratory organs and exposure levels report on air levels exceeding 50 mg Cr^{VI}/m^3 air.

The symptoms, signs, course, x-ray appearance, method of diagnosis and prognosis of lung cancers resulting from exposure to chromates differ in no way from those of cancer of the lung due to other causes. It has been found that the tumours often originate in the periphery of the bronchial tree. The tumours may be of all histological types, but a majority of the tumours seem to be anaplastic oat-celled tumours. Water-soluble, acid soluble and water insoluble chromium is found in the lung tissues of chromate workers in varying amounts.

Although it has not been firmly established, some studies have indicated that exposure to chromates may result in increased risk of cancer in the nasal sinuses and the alimentary tract. The studies that indicate excess cancer of the alimentary tract are case reports from the 1930s or cohort studies that reflect exposure at high levels than generally encountered today.

Safety and Health Measures

On the technical side, avoidance of exposure to chromium depends on appropriate design of processes, including adequate exhaust ventilation and the suppression of dust or mist containing chromium in the hexavalent state. Built-in control measures are also necessary, requiring the least possible action by either process operators or maintenance staff.

Wet methods of cleaning should be used where possible; at other sites, the only acceptable alternative is vacuum cleaning. Spill of liquids or solids must be removed to prevent dispersion as airborne dust. The concentration in the work environment of chromium-containing dust and fumes should preferably be measured at regular intervals by individual and area sampling. Where unacceptable concentration levels are found by either method, the sources of dust or fumes should be identified and controlled. Dust masks, preferably with an efficiency of more than 99% in retaining particles of 0.5 μm size, should be worn in situations above non-hazardous levels, and it may be necessary to provide air-supplied respiratory protective equipment for jobs considered to be hazardous. Management should ensure that dust deposits and other surface contaminants should be removed by washing down or suction before work of this type begins. Providing laundering overalls daily may help in avoiding skin contamination. Hand and eye protection is generally recommended, as is repair and replacement of all personal protective equipment (PPE).

The medical surveillance of workers on processes in which Cr^{VI} compounds may be encountered should include education in toxic and the carcinogenic properties of both Cr^{VI} and Cr^{III} compounds, as well as on the differences between the two groups of compounds. The nature of the exposure hazards and subsequent risks of various diseases (e.g., lung cancer) should be given at job entry as well as at regular intervals during employment. The need to observe a high standard of personal hygiene should be emphasized.

All untoward effects of exposure to chromium can be avoided. Chrome ulcers of the skin can be prevented by eliminating sources of contact and by preventing injury to the skin. Skin cuts and abrasions, however slight, should be cleaned immediately and treated with 10% sodium EDTA ointment. Together with the use of a frequently renewed impervious dressing, this will enhance rapid healing for any ulcer that may develop. Although EDTA does not chelate Cr^{VI} compounds at room temperature, it reduces the Cr^{VI} to Cr^{III} rapidly, and the excess EDTA chelates Cr^{III}. Both the direct irritant and corrosive action of Cr^{VI} compounds and the formation of protein/Cr^{III} complexes are thus prevented. After accidental ingestion of Cr^{VI} compounds, immediate swallowing of ascorbic acid may also quickly reduce the Cr^{VI}.

Careful washing of the skin after contact and care to avoid friction and sweating are important in the prevention and the control of primary irritation due to chromates. In previous years an ointment containing 10% sodium EDTA was applied regularly to the nasal septum before exposure. This preventive treatment could assist in keeping the septum intact. Soreness of the nose and early ulceration were also treated by regular application of this ointment, and healing could be achieved without perforation.

Results from research indicate that workers exposed to high air concentrations of Cr^{VI} could be monitored successfully by monitoring the excretion of chromium in the urine. Such results, however, bear no relation to the hazard of skin allergy. As of today, with the very long latent period of Cr^{VI}-related lung cancer, hardly anything can be said regarding the cancer hazard on the basis of urinary levels of Cr.

● COPPER

Copper (Cu) is malleable and ductile, conducts heat and electricity exceedingly well and is very little altered in its functional capacity by exposure to dry air. In a moist atmosphere containing carbon dioxide it becomes coated with a green carbonate. Copper is an essential element in human metabolism.

Occurrence and Uses

Copper occurs principally as mineral compounds in which ^{63}Cu constitutes 69.1% and ^{65}Cu, 30.9% of the element. Copper is widely distributed in all continents and is present in most living organisms. Although some natural deposits of metallic copper have been found, it is generally mined either as sulphide ores, including covellite (CuS), chalcocite (Cu$_2$S), chalcopyrite (CuFeS$_2$) and bornite (Cu$_3$FeS$_3$); or as oxides, including malachite (Cu$_2$CO$_3$(OH)$_2$); chrysocolla (CuSiO$_3$·2H$_2$O) and chalcanthite (CuSO$_4$·5H$_2$O).

Because of its electrical properties, more than 75% of copper output is used in the electrical industries. Other applications for copper include water piping, roofing material, kitchenware, chemical and pharmaceutical equipment, and the production of copper alloys. Copper metal is also used as a pigment, and as a precipitant of selenium.

Alloys and Compounds

The most widely used non-ferrous copper alloys are those of copper and zinc (brass), tin (bronze), nickel (monel metal), aluminium, gold, lead, cadmium, chromium, beryllium, silicon or phosphorus.

Copper sulphate is used as an algicide and molluscicide in water; with lime, as a plant fungicide; as a mordant; in electroplating; as a froth flotation agent for the separation of zinc sulphide ore; and as an agent for leather tanning and hide preservation. Copper sulphate neutralized with hydrated lime, known as Bordeaux mixture, is used for the prevention of mildew in vineyards.

Cupric oxide has been used as a component of paint for ship bottoms and as a pigment in glass, ceramics, enamels, porcelain glazes and artificial gems. It is also used in the manufacture of rayon and other copper compounds, and as an optical glass polishing agent and a solvent for chromic iron ores. Cupric oxide is a component of flux in copper metallurgy, pyrotechnic compositions, welding fluxes for bronze and agricultural products such as insecticides and fungicides. Black cupric oxide is used for correcting copper-deficient soils and as a feed supplement.

Copper chromates are pigments, catalysts for liquid-phase hydrogenation and potato fungicides. A solution of cupric hydroxide in excess ammonia is a solvent for cellulose used in the manufacture of rayon (viscose). Cupric hydroxide is used in the manufacture of battery electrodes and for treating and staining paper. It is also a pigment, a feed additive, a mordant in dyeing and an ingredient in fungicides and insecticides.

Hazards

Amine complexes of cupric chlorate, cupric dithionate, cupric azide and cuprous acetylide are explosive but are of no industrial or public health importance. Copper acetylide was found to be the cause of explosions in acetylene plants and has caused the abandonment of the use of copper in the construction of such plants. Fragments of metallic copper or copper alloys that lodge in the eye, a condition known as chalcosis, may lead to uveitis, abscess and loss of the eye. Workers who spray vineyards with Bordeaux mixture may suffer from pulmonary lesions (sometimes called "vineyard sprayer's lung") and copper-laden hepatic granulomas.

Accidental ingestion of soluble copper salts is generally innocuous since the vomiting induced rids the patient of much of the copper. The possibility of copper-induced toxicity may occur in the following situations:

- The oral administration of copper salts is occasionally employed for therapeutic purposes, particularly in India.
- Copper dissolved from the wire used in certain intra-uterine contraceptive devices has been shown to be absorbed systemically.
- An appreciable fraction of the copper dissolved from the tubing commonly used in haemodialysis equipment may be retained by the patient and can produce significant increases in hepatic copper.
- Copper, not uncommonly added to feed for livestock and poultry, concentrates in the liver of these animals and can greatly increase the intake of the element when these livers are eaten. Copper is also added, in large amounts relative to the normal human dietary intake, to a number of pet animal foods that are occasionally consumed by people. Manure from animals with copper-supplemented diets can result in an excessive amount of copper in vegetables and feed grains grown on soil dressed with this manure.

Acute toxicity

Although some chemical reference works contain statements to the effect that soluble salts of copper are poisonous, in practical terms this is true only if such solutions are used with misguided or suicidal intent, or as topical treatment of extensively burned areas. When copper sulphate, known as bluestone or blue vitriol, is ingested in gram quantities, it induces nausea, vomiting, diarrhoea, sweating, intravascular haemolysis and possible kidney failure; rarely, convulsions, coma and death may result. Drinking of carbonated water or citrus fruit juices which have been in contact with copper vessels, pipes, tubing or valves can cause gastrointestinal irritation, which is seldom serious. Such beverages are acidic enough to dissolve irritating levels of copper. There is a report of corneal ulcers and skin irritation, but little other toxicity, in a copper-mine worker who fell into an electrolytic bath, but the acidity, rather than the copper, may have been the cause. In some instances where copper salts have been used in the treatment of burns, high concentrations of serum copper and toxic manifestations have ensued.

The inhalation of dusts, fumes and mists of copper salts can cause congestion of the nasal and mucous membranes and ulceration with perforation of the nasal septum. Fumes from the heating of metallic copper can cause metal fume fever, nausea, gastric pain and diarrhoea.

Chronic toxicity

Chronic toxic effects in human beings attributable to copper appears only to be found in individuals who have inherited a particular pair of abnormal autosomal recessive genes and in whom, as a consequence, hepatolenticular degeneration (Wilson's disease) develops. This is a rare occurrence. Most daily human diets contain 2 to 5 mg of copper, almost none of which is retained. The adult human body copper content is quite constant at about 100 to 150 mg. In normal individuals (without Wilson's disease), almost all of the copper is present as an integral and functional moiety of one of perhaps a dozen proteins and enzyme systems including, for example, cytochrome oxidase, dopa-oxidase and serum ceruloplasmin. Tenfold, or more, increases in the daily intake of copper can occur in individuals who eat large quantities of oysters (and other shellfish), liver, mushrooms, nuts and chocolate—all rich in copper; or in miners who may work and eat meals, for 20 years or more, in an atmosphere laden with 1 to 2% copper ores dusts. Yet evidence of primary chronic copper toxicity (well defined from observations of patients with inherited chronic copper toxicosis—Wilson's disease—as dysfunction of and structural damage to the liver, central nervous system, kidney, bones and eyes) has never been found in any individuals except those with Wilson's disease. However, the excessive copper deposits that are found in the livers of patients with primary biliary cirrhosis, cholestasis and Indian childhood cirrhosis may be one contributing factor to the severity of the hepatic disease that is characteristic of these conditions.

Safety and Health Measures

Workers exposed to copper dusts or mists should be provided with adequate protective clothing to prevent repeated or prolonged skin contact. Where dust conditions cannot be sufficiently controlled, appropriate respirators and eye protection are necessary. Housekeeping and the provision of adequate sanitary facilities is essential since eating, drinking and smoking should be prohibited at the worksite. In mines where there are water-soluble ores such as chalcanthite, workers should be particularly careful to wash their hands with water before eating.

The prevention of metal fume fever is a matter of keeping exposure below the level of concentration currently accepted as satisfactory for working with copper in industry. The employment of local exhaust ventilation (LEV) is a necessary measure to collect copper fumes at the source.

People with Wilson's disease should avoid employment in copper industries. The serum concentration of ceruloplasmin is a screen for this condition, since unaffected individuals have levels which range from 20 to 50 mg/100 cm^3 of this copper protein whereas 97% of patients with Wilson's disease have less than 20 mg/100 cm^3. This is a relatively expensive procedure for broad-based screening programmes.

● IRON

Occurrence and Uses

Iron is second in abundance amongst the metals and is fourth amongst the elements, surpassed only by oxygen, silicon and aluminium. The most common iron ores are: haematite, or red iron ore (Fe_2O_3), which is 70% iron; limonite, or brown iron ore ($FeO(OH) \cdot nH_2O$), containing 42% iron; magnetite, or magnetic iron ore (Fe_3O_4), which has a high iron content; siderite, or spathic iron ore ($FeCO_3$); pyrite (FeS_2), the most common sulphide mineral; and pyrrhotite, or magnetic pyrite (FeS). Iron is used in the manufacture of iron and steel castings, and it is alloyed with other metals to form steels. Iron is also used to increase the density of oil-well drilling fluids.

Alloys and Compounds

Iron itself is not particularly strong, but its strength is greatly increased when it is alloyed with carbon and rapidly cooled to produce steel. Its presence in steel accounts for its importance as an industrial metal. Certain characteristics of steel—that is, whether it is soft, mild, medium or hard—are largely determined by the carbon content, which may vary from 0.10 to 1.15%. About 20 other elements are used in varied combinations and proportions in the production of steel alloys with many different qualities—hardness, ductility, corrosion resistance and so on. The most important of these are manganese (ferromanganese and spiegeleisen), silicon (ferrosilicon) and chromium, which is discussed below.

The most important industrial iron compounds are the oxides and the carbonate, which constitute the principal ores from which the metal is obtained. Of lesser industrial importance are cyanides, nitrides, nitrates, phosphides, phosphates and iron carbonyl.

Hazards

Industrial dangers are present during the mining, transportation and preparation of the ores, during the production and use of the metal and alloys in iron and steel works and in foundries, and during the manufacture and use of certain compounds. Inhalation of iron dust or fumes occurs in iron-ore mining; arc welding; metal grinding, polishing and working; and in boiler scaling. If inhaled, iron is a local irritant to the lung and gastrointestinal tract. Reports indicate that long-term exposure to a mixture of iron and other metallic dusts may impair pulmonary function.

Accidents are liable to occur during the mining, transportation and preparation of the ores because of the heavy cutting, conveying, crushing and sieving machinery that is used for this purpose. Injuries may also arise from the handling of explosives used in the mining operations.

Inhaling dust containing silica or iron oxide can lead to pneumoconiosis, but there are no definite conclusions as to the role of iron oxide particles in the development of lung cancer in humans. Based on animal experiments, it is suspected that iron oxide dust may serve as a "co-carcinogenic" substance, thus enhancing the development of cancer when combined simultaneously with exposure to carcinogenic substances.

Mortality studies of haematite miners have shown an increased risk of lung cancer, generally among smokers, in several mining areas such as Cumberland, Lorraine, Kiruna and Krivoi Rog. Epidemiological studies of iron and steel foundry workers have typically noted risks of lung cancer elevated by 1.5- to 2.5-fold. The International Agency for Research on Cancer (IARC) classifies iron and steel founding as a carcinogenic process for humans. The specific chemical agents involved (e.g., polynuclear aromatic hydrocarbons, silica, metal fumes) have not been identified. An increased incidence of lung cancer has also been reported, but less significantly, among metal grinders. The conclusions for lung cancer among welders are controversial.

In experimental studies, ferric oxide has not been found to be carcinogenic; however, the experiments were not carried out with haematite. The presence of radon in the atmosphere of haematite mines has been suggested to be an important carcinogenic factor.

Serious accidents can occur in iron processing. Burns can occur in the course of work with molten metal, as described elsewhere in this *Encyclopaedia*. Finely divided freshly reduced iron powder is pyrophoric and ignites on exposure to air at normal temperatures. Fires and dust explosions have occurred in ducts and separators of dust-extraction plants, associated with grinding and polishing wheels and finishing belts, when sparks from the grinding operation have ignited the fine steel dust in the extraction plant.

The dangerous properties of the remaining iron compounds are usually due to the radical with which the iron is associated. Thus *ferric arsenate* ($FeAsO_4$) and *ferric arsenite* ($FeAsO_3 \cdot Fe_2O_3$) possess the poisonous properties of arsenical compounds. *Iron carbonyl* ($FeCO_5$) is one of the more dangerous of the metal carbonyls, having both toxic and flammable properties. Carbonyls are discussed in more detail elsewhere in this chapter.

Ferrous sulphide (FeS), in addition to its natural occurrence as pyrite, is occasionally formed unintentionally when materials containing sulphur are treated in iron and steel vessels, such as in petroleum refineries. If the plant is opened and the deposit of ferrous sulphide is exposed to the air, its exothermic oxidation may raise the temperature of the deposit to the ignition temperature of gases and vapours in the vicinity. A fine water spray should be directed on such deposits until flammable vapours have been removed by purging. Similar problems may occur in pyrite mines, where the air temperature is increased by a continuous slow oxidation of the ore.

Safety and health measures

The precautions for the prevention of mechanical accidents include the fencing and remote control of machinery, the design of plant (which, in modern steel-making, includes computerized control) and the safety training of workers.

The danger arising from toxic and flammable gases, vapours and dusts is countered by local exhaust and general ventilation coupled with the various forms of remote control. Protective clothing and eye protection should be provided to safeguard the worker from the effects of hot and corrosive substances, and heat.

It is especially important that the ducting at grinding and polishing machines and at finishing belts be maintained at regular intervals to keep up the efficiency of the exhaust ventilation as well as to reduce the risk of explosion.

Ferroalloys

A ferroalloy is an alloy of iron with an element other than carbon. These metallic mixtures are used as a vehicle for introducing specific elements into the manufacture of steel in order to produce steels with specific properties. The element may alloy with the steel by solution or it may neutralize harmful impurities.

Alloys have unique properties dependent on the concentration of their elements. These properties vary directly in relation to the concentration of the individual components and depend, in part, on the presence of trace quantities of other elements. Although the biological effect of each element in the alloy may be used as a guide, there is sufficient evidence for the modification of action by the mixture of elements to warrant extreme caution in making critical decisions based on extrapolation of effect from the single element.

The ferroalloys constitute a wide and diverse list of alloys with many different mixtures within each class of alloy. The trade generally limits the number of types of ferroalloy available in any one class but metallurgical developments can result in frequent additions or changes. Some of the more common ferroalloys are as follows:

- ferroboron—16.2% boron
- ferrochromium—60 to 70% chromium, that may also contain silicon and manganese
- ferromanganese—78 to 90% manganese; 1.25 to 7% silicon
- ferromolybdenum—55 to 75% molybdenum; 1.5% silicon
- ferrophosphorus—18 to 25% phosphorus
- ferrosilicon—5 to 90% silica

- ferrotitanium—14 to 45% titanium; 4 to 13% silicon
- ferrotungsten—70 to 80% tungsten
- ferrovanadium—30 to 40% vanadium; 13% silicon; 1.5% aluminium.

Hazards

Although certain ferroalloys do have non-metallurgical uses, the main sources of hazardous exposure are encountered in the manufacture of these alloys and in their use during steel production. Some ferroalloys are produced and used in fine particulate form; airborne dust constitutes a potential toxicity hazard as well as a fire and explosion hazard. In addition, occupational exposure to the fumes of certain alloys has been associated with serious health problems.

Ferroboron. Airborne dust produced during the cleaning of this alloy may cause irritation of the nose and throat, which is due, possibly, to the presence of a boron oxide film on the alloy surface. Some animal studies (dogs exposed to atmospheric ferroboron concentrations of 57 mg/m^3 for 23 weeks) found no adverse effects.

Ferrochromium. One study in Norway on the overall mortality and the incidence of cancer in workers producing ferrochromium has shown an increased incidence of lung cancer in causal relationship with the exposure to hexavalent chromium around the furnaces. Perforation of the nasal septum was also found in a few workers. Another study concludes that excess mortality due to lung cancer in steel-manufacturing workers is associated with exposure to polycyclic aromatic hydrocarbons (PAHs) during ferrochromium production. Yet another study investigating the association between occupational exposure to fumes and lung cancer found that ferrochromium workers demonstrated excess cases of both lung and prostate cancer.

Ferromanganese may be produced by reducing manganese ores in an electric furnace with coke and adding dolomite and limestone as flux. Transportation, storage, sorting and crushing of the ores produce manganese dust in concentrations which can be hazardous. The pathological effects resulting from exposure to dust, from both the ore and the alloy, are virtually indistinguishable from those described in the article "Manganese" in this chapter. Both acute and chronic intoxications have been observed. Ferromanganese alloys containing very high proportions of manganese will react with moisture to produce *manganese carbide*, which, when combined with moisture, releases hydrogen, creating a fire and explosion hazard.

Ferrosilicon production can result in both aerosols and dusts of ferrosilicon. Animal studies indicate that ferrosilicon dust can cause thickening of the alveolar walls with the occasional disappearance of the alveolar structure. The raw materials used in alloy production may also contain free silica, although in relatively low concentrations. There is some disagreement as to whether classical silicosis may be a potential hazard in ferrosilicon production. There is no doubt, however, that chronic pulmonary disease, whatever its classification, can result from excessive exposure to the dust or aerosols encountered in ferrosilicon plants.

Ferrovanadium. Atmospheric contamination with dust and fumes is also a hazard in ferrovanadium production. Under normal conditions, the aerosols will not produce acute intoxication but may cause bronchitis and a pulmonary interstitial proliferative process. The vanadium in the ferrovanadium alloy has been reported to be appreciably more toxic than free vanadium as a result of its greater solubility in biological fluids.

Leaded steel is used for automobile sheet steel in order to increase malleability. It contains approximately 0.35% lead. Whenever the leaded steel is subject to high temperature, as in welding, there is always the danger of generating lead fumes.

Safety and health measures

Control of fumes, dust and aerosols during the manufacture and use of ferroalloys is essential. Good dust control is required in the transport and handling of the ores and alloys. Ore piles should be wetted down to reduce dust formation. In addition to these basic dust-control measures, special precautions are needed in the handling of specific ferroalloys.

Ferrosilicon reacts with moisture to produce phosphine and arsine; consequently this material should not be loaded in damp weather, and special precautions should be taken to ensure that it remains dry during storage and transport. Whenever ferrosilicon is being shipped or handled in quantities of any importance, notices should be posted warning workers of the hazard, and detection and analysis procedures should be implemented at frequent intervals to check for the presence of phosphine and arsine in the air. Good dust and aerosol control is required for respiratory protection. Suitable respiratory protective equipment should be available for emergencies.

Workers engaged in the production and use of ferroalloys should receive careful medical supervision. Their working environment should be monitored continuously or periodically, depending on the degree of risk. The toxic effects of the various ferroalloys are sufficiently divergent from those of the pure metals to warrant a more intense level of medical supervision until more data have been obtained. Where ferroalloys give rise to dust, fumes and aerosols, workers should receive periodic chest x-ray examinations for early detection of respiratory changes. Lung function testing and monitoring of metal concentrations in the blood and/or urine of exposed workers may also be required.

GALLIUM

Chemically, gallium (Ga) is similar to aluminium. It is not attacked by air and does not react with water. When cold, gallium reacts with chlorine and bromine, and when heated, with iodine, oxygen and sulphur. There are 12 known artificial radioactive isotopes, with atomic weights between 64 and 74 and half-lives between 2.6 minutes and 77.9 hours. When gallium is dissolved in inorganic acids, salts are formed, which change into insoluble hydroxide $Ga(OH)_3$ with amphoteric properties (i.e., both acidic and basic) when the pH is higher than 3. The three oxides of gallium are GaO, Ga_2O and Ga_2O_3.

Occurrence and Uses

The richest source of gallium is the mineral germanite, a copper sulphide ore which may contain 0.5 to 0.7% gallium and is found in southwest Africa. It is also widely distributed in small amounts together with zinc blendes, in aluminium clays, feldspars, coal and in the ores of iron, manganese and chromium. On a relatively small scale, the metal, alloys, oxides and salts are used in industries such as machine construction (coatings, lubricants), instrument making (solders, washers, fillers), electronics and electrical equipment production (diodes, transistors, lasers, conductor coverings), and in vacuum technology.

In the chemical industries gallium and its compounds are used as catalysts. *Gallium arsenide* has been widely used for semiconductor applications including transistors, solar cells, lasers and microwave generation. Gallium arsenide is used in the production of optoelectronic devices and integrated circuits. Other applications include the use of [72]Ga for the study of gallium interactions in the organism and ^{67}Ga as a tumour-scanning agent. Because of the high affinity of macrophages of the lymphoreticular tissues for

[67]Ga, it can be used in the diagnosis of Hodgkin's disease, Boeck's sarcoid and lymphatic tuberculosis. Gallium scintography is a pulmonary imaging technique which can be used in conjunction with an initial chest radiograph to evaluate workers at risk of developing occupational lung disease.

Hazards

Workers in the electronics industry using gallium arsenide may be exposed to hazardous substances such as arsenic and arsine. Inhalation exposures of dusts are possible during the production of the oxides and powdered salts ($Ga_2(SO_4)_3$, Ga_3Cl) and in the production and processing of monocrystals of semiconductor compounds. The splashing or spilling of the solutions of the metal and its salts may act on the skin or mucous membranes of workers. Grinding of gallium phosphide in water gives rise to considerable quantities of phosphine, requiring preventive measures. Gallium compounds may be ingested via soiled hands and by eating, drinking and smoking in workplaces.

Occupational diseases from gallium have not been described, except for a case report of a petechial rash followed by a radial neuritis after a short exposure to a small amount of fumes containing gallium fluoride. The biological action of the metal and its compounds has been studied experimentally. The toxicity of gallium and compounds depends upon the mode of entry into the body. When administered orally in rabbits over a long period of time (4 to 5 months), its action was insignificant and included disturbances in protein reactions and reduced enzyme activity. The low toxicity in this case is explained by the relatively inactive absorption of gallium in the digestive tract. In the stomach and intestines, compounds are formed which are either insoluble or difficult to absorb, such as metal gallates and hydroxides. The dust of the oxide, nitride and arsenide of gallium was generally toxic when introduced into the respiratory system (intratracheal injections in white rats), causing dystrophy of the liver and kidneys. In the lungs it caused inflammatory and sclerotic changes. One study concludes that exposing rats to gallium oxide particles at concentrations near the threshold limit value induces progressive lung damage that is similar to that induced by quartz. Gallium nitrate has a powerful caustic effect on the conjunctivae, cornea and skin. The high toxicity of the acetate, citrate and chloride of gallium was demonstrated by intraperitoneal injection, leading to death of animals from paralysis of the respiratory centre.

Safety and Health Measures

In order to avoid contamination of the atmosphere of workplaces by the dusts of gallium dioxide, nitride and semiconductor compounds, precautionary measures should include enclosure of dust-producing equipment and effective local exhaust ventilation (LEV). Personal protective measures during the production of gallium should prevent ingestion and contact of gallium compounds with the skin. Consequently, good personal hygiene and the use of personal protective equipment (PPE) are important. The US National Institute for Occupational Safety and Health (NIOSH) recommends control of worker exposure to gallium-arsenide by observing the recommended exposure limit for inorganic arsenic, and advises that concentration of gallium arsenide in air should be estimated by determining arsenic. Workers should be educated in possible hazards, and proper engineering controls should be installed during production of microelectronic devices where exposure to gallium arsenide is likely. In view of the toxicity of gallium and its compounds, as shown by experiments, all persons involved in work with these substances should undergo periodic medical examinations, during which special attention should be paid to the condition of the liver, kidneys, respiratory organs and skin.

GERMANIUM

Occurrence and Uses

Germanium (Ge) is always found in combination with other elements and never in the free state. Among the most common germanium-bearing minerals are argyrodite (Ag_8GeS_6), containing 5.7% germanium, and germanite ($CuS \cdot FeS \cdot GeS_2$), containing up to 10% Ge. Extensive deposits of germanium minerals are rare, but the element is widely distributed within the structure of other minerals, especially in sulphides (most commonly in zinc sulphide and in silicates). Small quantities are also found in different types of coal.

The largest end use of germanium is the production of infrared sensing and identification systems. Its use in fibre-optical systems has increased, while consumption for semiconductors has continued to decline due to advances in silicon semiconductor technology. Germanium is also used in electroplating and in the production of alloys, one of which, germanium-bronze, is characterized by high corrosion resistance. *Germanium tetrachloride* ($GeCl_4$) is an intermediate in the preparation of germanium dioxide and organogermanium compounds. *Germanium dioxide* (GeO_2) is used in the manufacture of optical glass and in cathodes.

Hazards

Occupational health problems may arise from the dispersion of dust during the loading of germanium concentrate, breaking up and loading of the dioxide for reduction to metallic germanium, and loading of powdered germanium for melting into ingots. In the process of producing metal, during chlorination of the concentrate, distillation, rectification and hydrolysis of germanium tetrachloride, the fumes of germanium tetrachloride, chlorine and germanium chloride pyrolysis products may also present a health hazard. Other sources of health hazards are the production of radiant heat from tube furnaces for GeO_2 reduction and during melting of germanium powder into ingots, and the formation of carbon monoxide during GeO_2 reduction with carbon.

The production of single crystals of germanium for the manufacture of semiconductors brings about high air temperatures (up to 45 °C), electromagnetic radiation with field strengths of more than 100 V/m and magnetic radiation of more than 25 A/m, and pollution of the workplace air with metal hydrides. When alloying germanium with arsenic, arsine may form in the air (1 to 3 mg/m^3), and when alloying it with antimony, stibine or antimonous hydride may be present (1.5 to 3.5 mg/m^3). *Germanium hydride*, which is used for the production of high-purity germanium, may also be a pollutant of the workplace air. The frequently required cleaning of the vertical furnaces causes the formation of dust, which contains, apart from germanium, silicon dioxide, antimony and other substances.

Machining and grinding of germanium crystals also give rise to dust. Concentrations of up to 5 mg/m^3 have been measured during dry machining.

Absorbed germanium is rapidly excreted, mainly in urine. There is little information on the toxicity of inorganic germanium compounds to humans. *Germanium tetrachloride* may produce skin irritation. In clinical trials and other long-term oral exposures to cumulative doses exceeding 16 g of *spirogermanium*, an organo-germanium antitumour agent or other germanium compounds have been shown to be neurotoxic and nephrotoxic. Such doses are not usually absorbed in the occupational setting. Animal experiments on the effects of germanium and its compounds have shown that dust of *metallic germanium* and *germanium dioxide* causes general health impairment (inhibition of body weight increase)

when inhaled in high concentrations. The lungs of the animals presented morphological changes of the type of proliferative reactions, such as thickening of the alveolar partitions and hyperplasia of the lymphatic vessels around the bronchi and blood vessels. Germanium dioxide does not irritate the skin, but if it comes into contact with the moist conjunctiva it forms germanic acid, which acts as an eye irritant. Prolonged intra-abdominal administration in doses of 10 mg/kg leads to peripheral blood changes. The effects of germanium concentrate dust are not due to germanium, but to a number of other dust constituents, in particular silica (SiO_2). The concentrate dust exerts a pronounced fibrogenic effect resulting in the development of connective tissue and formation of nodules in the lungs similar to those observed in silicosis.

The most harmful germanium compounds are *germanium hydride* (GeH_4) and *germanium chloride*. The hydride may provoke acute poisoning. Morphological examinations of organs of animals which died during the acute phase revealed circulatory disorders and degenerative cell changes in the parenchymatous organs. Thus the hydride appears to be a multi-system poison that may affect the nervous functions and peripheral blood.

Germanium tetrachloride is a strong irritant of the respiratory system, skin and eyes. Its threshold of irritation is 13 mg/m^3. In this concentration it depresses the pulmonary cell reaction in experimental animals. In stronger concentrations it leads to irritation of the upper airways and conjunctivitis, and to changes in respiratory rate and rhythm. Animals which survive acute poisoning develop catarrhal-desquamative bronchitis and interstitial pneumonia a few days later. Germanium chloride also exerts general toxic effects. Morphological changes have been observed in the liver, kidneys and other organs of the animals.

Safety and Health Measures

Basic measures during the manufacture and use of germanium should be aimed at preventing the contamination of the air by dust or fumes. In the production of metal, continuity of the process and enclosure of the apparatus is advisable. Adequate exhaust ventilation should be provided in areas where the dust of metallic germanium, the dioxide or the concentrate is dispersed. Local exhaust ventilation should be provided near the melting furnaces during the manufacture of semiconductors, for example on zone-refining furnaces, and during the cleaning of the furnaces. The process of manufacturing and alloying monocrystals of germanium should be carried out in a vacuum, followed by the evacuation of the formed compounds under reduced pressure. Local exhaust ventilation is essential in operations such as dry cutting and grinding of germanium crystals. Exhaust ventilation is also important in premises for the chlorination, rectification and hydrolysis of germanium tetrachloride. Appliances, connections and fittings in these premises should be made of corrosion-proof material. The workers should wear acid-proof clothing and footwear. Respirators should be worn during the cleaning of appliances.

Workers exposed to dust, concentrated hydrochloric acid, germanium hydride and germanium chloride and its hydrolysis products should undergo regular medical examinations.

INDIUM

Occurrence and Uses

In nature, Indium (In) is widely distributed and occurs most frequently together with zinc minerals (sphalerite, marmatite, christophite), its chief commercial source. It is also found in the ores of tin, manganese, tungsten, copper, iron, lead, cobalt and bismuth, but generally in amounts of less than 0.1%.

Indium is generally used in industry for surface protection or in alloys. A thin coat of indium increases the resistance of metals to corrosion and wear. It prolongs the life of moving parts in bearings and finds wide use in the aircraft and automobile industries. It is used in dental alloys, and its "wettability" makes it ideal for plating glass. Because of its resistance to corrosion, indium is utilized extensively in making motion picture screens, cathode ray oscilloscopes and mirrors. When joined with antimony and germanium in an extremely pure combination, it is widely used in the manufacture of transistors and other sensitive electronic components. Radioisotopes of indium in compounds such as *indium trichloride* and *colloidal indium hydroxide* are used in organic scanning and in the treatment of tumours.

In addition to the metal, the most common industrial compounds of indium are the trichloride, used in electroplating; the sesquioxide, used in glass manufacture; the sulphate; and the antimonide and the arsenide used as semiconductor material.

Hazards

No cases have been reported of systemic effects in humans exposed to indium. Probably the greatest current potential hazard comes from the use of indium together with arsenic, antimony and germanium in the electronics industry. This is due primarily to the fumes given off during welding and soldering processes in the manufacture of electronic components. Any hazard arising from the purification of indium is probably attributable to the presence of other metals, such as lead, or chemicals, such as cyanide, used in the electroplating process. Exposure of the skin to indium does not seem to present a serious hazard. The tissue distribution of indium in various chemical forms has been studied by administration to laboratory animals.

The sites of highest concentration were kidney, spleen, liver and salivary glands. After inhalation, widespread lung changes were observed, such as interstitial and desquamative pneumonitis with consequent respiratory insufficiency.

The results of animal studies showed that the more soluble salts of indium were very toxic, with lethality occurring after administration of less than 5 mg/kg by way of parenteral routes of injection. However, after gavage, indium was poorly absorbed and essentially non-toxic. Histophathological studies indicated that death was due primarily to degenerative lesions in the liver and kidney. Minor changes in the blood have also been noted. In chronic poisoning by indium chloride the main change is a chronic interstitial nephritis with proteinuria. The toxicity from the more insoluble form, indium sesquioxide, was only moderate to slight, requiring up to several hundred mg/kg for lethal effect. After administration of indium arsenide to hamsters, the uptake in various organs differed from the distribution of ionic indium or arsenic compounds.

Safety and Health Measures

Preventing the inhalation of indium fumes by the use of correct ventilation appears to be the most practical safety measure. When handling indium arsenide, safety precautions such as those applied for arsenic should be observed. In the field of nuclear medicine, correct radiation safety measures must be followed when handling radioactive indium isotopes. Intoxication in rats from indium-induced hepatic necrosis has been reduced considerably by administration of ferric dextran, the action of which is apparently very specific. The use of ferric dextran as a prophylactic treatment in humans has not been possible owing to a lack of serious cases of industrial exposures to indium.

IRIDIUM

Iridium (Ir) belongs to the platinum family. Its name derives from the colours of its salt, which are reminiscent of a rainbow (iris). Although it is very hard and the most corrosion-resistant metal known, it is attacked by some salts.

Occurrence and Uses

Iridium occurs in nature in the metallic state, usually alloyed with osmium (osmiridium), platinum or gold, and it is produced from these minerals. The metal is used to manufacture crucibles for chemical laboratories and to harden platinum. Recent *in vitro* studies indicate the possible effects of iridium on *Leishmania donovani* and the trypanocidal activity of iridium against *Trypanosoma brucei*. Ir is used in industrial radiology and is a gamma emitter (0.31 MeV at 82.7%) and beta emitter (0.67 MeV at 47.2%). ^{192}Ir is a radioisotope which has also been used for clinical treatment, particularly cancer therapy. It is one of the most frequently used isotopes in interstitial brain irradiation.

Hazards

Very little is known about the toxicity of iridium and its compounds. There has been little opportunity to note any adverse human effects since it is used only in small amounts. All radioisotopes are potentially harmful and must be treated with appropriate safeguards required for handling radioactive sources. Soluble iridium compounds such as *iridium tribromide* and *tetrabromide* and *iridium trichloride* could present both toxic effects of the iridium or the halogen, but data as to its chronic toxicity are unavailable. Iridium trichloride has been reported to be a mild irritant to the skin and is positive in eye irritation test. Inhaled aerosol of metallic iridium is deposited in the upper respiratory ways of rats; the metal is then quickly removed via the gastrointestinal tract, and approximately 95% can be found in the faeces. In humans the only reports are those concerning radiation injuries due to accidental exposure to ^{192}Ir.

Safety and Health Measures

A radiation safety and medical surveillance programme should be in place for persons responsible for nursing care during interstitial brachytherapy. Radiation safety principles include exposure reduction by time, distance and shielding. Nurses who care for brachytherapy patients must wear radiation monitoring devices to record the amount of exposure. To avoid industrial radiography accidents, only trained industrial radiographers should be allowed to handle radionuclides.

LEAD*

Occurrence and Uses

Lead ores are found in many parts of the world. The richest ore is galena (lead sulphide) and this is the main commercial source of lead. Other lead ores include cerussite (carbonate), anglesite (sulphate), corcoite (chromate), wulfenite (molybdate), pyromorphite (phosphate), mutlockite (chloride) and vanadinite (vanadate). In many cases the lead ores may also contain other toxic metals.

Lead minerals are separated from gangue and other materials in the ore by dry crushing, wet grinding (to produce a slurry), gravity classification and flotation. The liberated lead minerals are

*Adapted from ATSDR 1995.

smelted by a three-stage process of charge preparation (blending, conditioning, etc.), blast sintering and blast furnace reduction. The blast-furnace bullion is then refined by the removal of copper, tin, arsenic, antimony, zinc, silver and bismuth.

Metallic lead is used in the form of sheeting or pipes where pliability and resistance to corrosion are required, such as in chemical plants and the building industry; it is used also for cable sheathing, as an ingredient in solder and as a filler in the automobile industry. It is a valuable shielding material for ionizing radiations. It is used for metallizing to provide protective coatings, in the manufacture of storage batteries and as a heat treatment bath in wire drawing. Lead is present in a variety of alloys and its compounds are prepared and used in large quantities in many industries.

About 40% of lead is used as a metal, 25% in alloys and 35% in chemical compounds. Lead oxides are used in the plates of electric batteries and accumulators (PbO and Pb_3O_4), as compounding agents in rubber manufacture (PbO), as paint ingredients (Pb_3O_4) and as constituents of glazes, enamels and glass.

Lead salts form the basis of many paints and pigments; lead carbonate and lead sulphate are used as white pigments and the lead chromates provide chrome yellow, chrome orange, chrome red and chrome green. Lead arsenate is an insecticide, lead sulphate is used in rubber compounding, lead acetate has important uses in the chemical industry, lead naphthenate is an extensively used dryer and tetraethyllead is an antiknock additive for gasoline, where still permitted by law.

Lead alloys. Other metals such as antimony, arsenic, tin and bismuth may be added to lead to improve its mechanical or chemical properties, and lead itself may be added to alloys such as brass, bronze and steel to obtain certain desirable characteristics.

Inorganic lead compounds. Space is not available to describe the very large number of organic and inorganic lead compounds encountered in industry. However, the common inorganic compounds include lead monoxide (PbO), lead dioxide (PbO_2), lead tetroxide (Pb_3O_4), lead sesquioxide (Pb_2O_3), lead carbonate, lead sulphate, lead chromates, lead arsenate, lead chloride, lead silicate and lead azide.

The maximum concentration of the *organic (alkyl) lead* compounds in gasolines is subject to legal prescriptions in many countries, and to limitation by the manufacturers with governmental concurrence in others. Many jurisdictions have simply banned its use.

Hazards

The prime hazard of lead is its toxicity. Clinical lead poisoning has always been one of the most important occupational diseases. Medico-technical prevention has resulted in a considerable decrease in reported cases and also in less serious clinical manifestations. However, it is now evident that adverse effects occur at exposure levels hitherto regarded as acceptable.

Industrial consumption of lead is increasing and traditional consumers are being supplemented by new users such as the plastics industry. Hazardous exposure to lead, therefore, occurs in many occupations.

In lead mining, a considerable proportion of lead absorption occurs through the alimentary tract and consequently the extent of the hazard in this industry depends, to some extent, on the solubility of ores being worked. The lead sulphide (PbS) in galena is insoluble and absorption from the lung is limited; however, in the stomach, some lead sulphide may be converted to slightly soluble lead chloride which may then be absorbed in moderate quantities.

In lead smelting, the main hazards are the lead dust produced during crushing and dry grinding operations, and lead fumes and lead oxide encountered in sintering, blast-furnace reduction and refining.

Lead sheet and pipe are used principally for the construction of equipment for storing and handling sulphuric acid. The use of lead for water and town gas pipes is limited nowadays. The hazards of working with lead increase with temperature. If lead is worked at temperatures below 500 °C, as in soldering, the risk of fume exposure is far less than in lead welding, where higher flame temperatures are used and the danger is higher. The spray coating of metals with molten lead is dangerous since it gives rise to dust and fumes at high temperatures.

The demolition of steel structures such as bridges and ships that have been painted with lead-based paints frequently gives rise to cases of lead poisoning. When metallic lead is heated to 550 °C, lead vapour will be evolved and will become oxidized. This is a condition that is liable to be present in metal refining, the melting of bronze and brass, the spraying of metallic lead, lead burning, chemical plant plumbing, ship breaking and the burning, cutting and welding of steel structures coated with paints containing lead tetroxide.

Routes of entry

The main route of entry in industry is the respiratory tract. A certain amount may be absorbed in the air passages, but the main portion is taken up by the pulmonary bloodstream. The degree of absorption depends on the proportion of the dust accounted for by particles less than 5 microns in size and the exposed worker's respiratory minute volume. Increased workload therefore results in higher lead absorption. Although the respiratory tract is the main route of entry, poor work hygiene, smoking during work (pollution of tobacco, polluted fingers while smoking) and poor personal hygiene may considerably increase total exposure mainly by the oral route. This is one of the reasons why the correlation between the concentration of lead in workroom air and lead in blood levels often is very poor, certainly on an individual basis.

Another important factor is the level of energy expenditure: the product of concentration in air and of respiratory minute volume determines lead uptake. The effect of working overtime is to increase exposure time and reduce recovery time. Total exposure time is also much more complicated than official personnel records indicate. Only time analysis in the workplace can yield relevant data. The worker may move around the department or the factory; a job with frequent changes in posture (e.g., turning and bending) results in exposure to a great range of concentrations. A representative measure of lead intake is almost impossible to obtain without the use of a personal sampler applied for many hours and for many days.

Particle size. Since the most important route of lead absorption is by the lungs, the particle size of industrial lead dust is of considerable significance and this depends on the nature of the operation giving rise to the dust. Fine dust of respirable particle size is produced by processes such as the pulverizing and blending of lead colours, the abrasive working of lead-based fillers in automobile bodies and the dry rubbing-down of lead paint. The exhaust gases of gasoline engines yield lead chloride and lead bromide particles of 1 micron diameter. The larger particles, however, may be ingested and be absorbed via the stomach. A more informative picture of the hazard associated with a sample of lead dust might be given by including a size distribution as well as a total lead determination. But this information is probably more important for the research investigator than for the field hygienist.

Biological fate

In the human body, inorganic lead is not metabolized but is directly absorbed, distributed and excreted. The rate at which lead is absorbed depends on its chemical and physical form and on the physiological characteristics of the exposed person (e.g., nutritional status and age). Inhaled lead deposited in the lower respiratory tract is completely absorbed. The amount of lead absorbed from the gastrointestinal tract of adults is typically 10 to 15% of the ingested quantity; for pregnant women and children, the amount absorbed can increase to as much as 50%. The quantity absorbed increases significantly under fasting conditions and with iron or calcium deficiency.

Once in the blood, lead is distributed primarily among three compartments—blood, soft tissue (kidney, bone marrow, liver, and brain), and mineralizing tissue (bones and teeth). Mineralizing tissue contains about 95% of the total body burden of lead in adults.

The lead in mineralizing tissues accumulates in subcompartments that differ in the rate at which lead is resorbed. In bone, there is both a labile component, which readily exchanges lead with the blood, and an inert pool. The lead in the inert pool poses a special risk because it is a potential endogenous source of lead. When the body is under physiological stress such as pregnancy, lactation or chronic disease, this normally inert lead can be mobilized, increasing the lead level in blood. Because of these mobile lead stores, significant drops in a person's blood lead level can take several months or sometimes years, even after complete removal from the source of lead exposure.

Of the lead in the blood, 99% is associated with erythrocytes; the remaining 1% is in the plasma, where it is available for transport to the tissues. The blood lead not retained is either excreted by the kidneys or through biliary clearance into the gastrointestinal tract. In single-exposure studies with adults, lead has a half-life, in blood, of approximately 25 days; in soft tissue, about 40 days; and in the non-labile portion of bone, more than 25 years. Consequently, after a single exposure a person's blood lead level may begin to return to normal; the total body burden, however, may still be elevated.

For lead poisoning to develop, major acute exposures to lead need not occur. The body accumulates this metal over a lifetime and releases it slowly, so even small doses, over time, can cause lead poisoning. It is the total body burden of lead that is related to the risk of adverse effects.

Physiological effects

Whether lead enters the body through inhalation or ingestion, the biologic effects are the same; there is interference with normal cell function and with a number of physiological processes.

Neurological effects. The most sensitive target of lead poisoning is the nervous system. In children, neurological deficits have been documented at exposure levels once thought to cause no harmful effects. In addition to the lack of a precise threshold, childhood lead toxicity may have permanent effects. One study showed that damage to the central nervous system (CNS) that occurred as a result of lead exposure at age 2 resulted in continued deficits in neurological development, such as lower IQ scores and cognitive deficits, at age 5. In another study that measured total body burden, primary school children with high tooth lead levels but with no known history of lead poisoning had larger deficits in psychometric intelligence scores, speech and language processing, attention and classroom performance than children with lower levels of lead. A 1990 follow-up report of children with elevated lead levels in their teeth noted a sevenfold increase in the odds of failure to graduate from high school, lower class standing, greater absenteeism, more reading disabilities and deficits in vocabulary, fine motor skills, reaction time and hand-eye coordination 11 years later. The reported effects are more likely caused by the enduring toxicity of lead than by recent excessive exposures because the blood lead levels found in the young adults were low (less than 10 micrograms per deciliter (μg/dL)).

Hearing acuity, particularly at higher frequencies, has been found to decrease with increasing blood lead levels. Hearing loss may contribute to the apparent learning disabilities or poor classroom behavior exhibited by children with lead intoxication.

Adults also experience CNS effects at relatively low blood lead levels, manifested by subtle behavioural changes, fatigue and impaired concentration. Peripheral nervous system damage, primarily motor, is seen mainly in adults. Peripheral neuropathy with mild slowing of nerve conduction velocity has been reported in asymptomatic lead workers. Lead neuropathy is believed to be a motor neuron, anterior horn cell disease with peripheral dying-back of the axons. Frank wrist drop occurs only as a late sign of lead intoxication.

Haematological effects. Lead inhibits the body's ability to make hemoglobin by interfering with several enzymatic steps in the heme pathway. Ferrochelatase, which catalyzes the insertion of iron into protoporphyrin IX, is quite sensitive to lead. A decrease in the activity of this enzyme results in an increase of the substrate, erythrocyte protoporphyrin (EP), in the red blood cells. Recent data indicate that the EP level, which has been used to screen for lead toxicity in the past, is not sufficiently sensitive at lower levels of blood lead and is therefore not as useful a screening test for lead poisoning as previously thought.

Lead can induce two types of anaemia. Acute high-level lead poisoning has been associated with hemolytic anaemia. In chronic lead poisoning, lead induces anemia by both interfering with erythropoiesis and by diminishing red blood cell survival. It should be emphasized, however, that anemia is not an early manifestation of lead poisoning and is evident only when the blood lead level is significantly elevated for prolonged periods.

Endocrine effects. A strong inverse correlation exists between blood lead levels and levels of vitamin D. Because the vitamin D-endocrine system is responsible in large part for the maintenance of extra- and intra-cellular calcium homeostasis, it is likely that lead impairs cell growth and maturation and tooth and bone development.

Renal effects. A direct effect on the kidney of long-term lead exposure is nephropathy. Impairment of proximal tubular function manifests in aminoaciduria, glycosuria and hyperphosphaturia (a Fanconi-like syndrome). There is also evidence of an association between lead exposure and hypertension, an effect that may be mediated through renal mechanisms. Gout may develop as a result of lead-induced hyperuricemia, with selective decreases in the fractional excretion of uric acid before a decline in creatinine clearance. Renal failure accounts for 10% of deaths in patients with gout.

Reproductive and developmental effects. Maternal lead stores readily cross the placenta, placing the foetus at risk. An increased frequency of miscarriages and stillbirths among women working in the lead trades was reported as early as the end of the 19th century. Although the data concerning exposure levels are incomplete, these effects were probably a result of far greater exposures than are currently found in lead industries. Reliable dose-effect data for reproductive effects in women are still lacking today.

Increasing evidence indicates that lead not only affects the viability of the foetus, but development as well. Developmental consequences of prenatal exposure to low levels of lead include reduced birth weight and premature birth. Lead is an animal teratogen; however, most studies in humans have failed to show a relationship between lead levels and congenital malformations.

The effects of lead on the male reproductive system in humans have not been well characterized. The available data support a tentative conclusion that testicular effects, including reduced sperm counts and motility, may result from chronic exposure to lead.

Carcinogenic effects. Inorganic lead and inorganic lead compounds have been classified as Group 2B, possible human carcinogens, by the International Agency for Research on Cancer (IARC). Case reports have implicated lead as a potential renal carcinogen in humans, but the association remains uncertain. Soluble salts, such as lead acetate and lead phosphate, have been reported to cause kidney tumors in rats.

Continuum of signs and symptoms associated with lead toxicity

Mild toxicity associated with lead exposure includes the following:

- myalgia or paresthesia
- mild fatigue
- irritability
- lethargy
- occasional abdominal discomfort.

The signs and symptoms associated with moderate toxicity include:

- arthralgia
- general fatigue
- difficulty concentrating
- muscular exhaustibility
- tremor
- headache
- diffuse abdominal pain
- vomiting
- weight loss
- constipation.

The signs and symptoms of severe toxicity include:

- paresis or paralysis
- encephalopathy, which may abruptly lead to seizures, changes in consciousness, coma and death
- lead line (blue-black) on gingival tissue
- colic (intermittent, severe abdominal cramps).

Some of the haematological signs of lead poisoning mimic other diseases or conditions. In the differential diagnosis of microcytic anaemia, lead poisoning can usually be ruled out by obtaining a venous blood lead concentration; if the blood lead level is less than 25 µg/dL, the anaemia usually reflects iron deficiency or haemoglobinopathy. Two rare diseases, acute intermittent porphyria and coproporphyria, also result in haeme abnormalities similar to those of lead poisoning.

Other effects of lead poisoning can be misleading. Patients exhibiting neurological signs due to lead poisoning have been treated only for peripheral neuropathy or carpal tunnel syndrome, delaying treatment for lead intoxication. Failure to correctly diagnose lead induced gastrointestinal distress has led to inappropriate abdominal surgery.

Laboratory evaluation

If pica or accidental ingestion of lead-containing objects (such as curtain weights or fishing sinkers) is suspected, an abdominal radiograph should be taken. Hair analysis is not usually an appropriate assay for lead toxicity because no correlation has been found between the amount of lead in the hair and the exposure level. The probability of environmental lead contamination of a laboratory specimen and inconsistent sample preparation make the results of hair analysis difficult to interpret. Suggested laboratory tests to evaluate lead intoxication include the following:

- CBC with peripheral smear
- blood lead level
- erythrocyte protoporphyrin level
- BUN and creatinine level
- urinalysis.

CBC with peripheral smear. In a lead-poisoned patient, the haematocrit and haemoglobin values may be slightly to moderately low. The differential and total white count may appear normal. The peripheral smear may be either normochromic and normocytic or hypochromic and microcytic. Basophilic stippling is usually seen only in patients who have been significantly poisoned for a prolonged period. Eosinophilia may appear in patients with lead toxicity but does not show a clear dose-response effect.

It is important to note that basophilic stippling is not always seen in lead poisoned patients.

Blood lead level. A blood lead level is the most useful screening and diagnostic test for lead exposure. A blood lead level reflects lead's dynamic equilibrium between absorption, excretion and deposition in soft- and hard-tissue compartments. For chronic exposures, blood lead levels often underrepresent the total body burden; nevertheless, it is the most widely accepted and commonly used measure of lead exposure. Blood lead levels srespond relatively rapidly to abrupt or intermittent changes in lead intake (e.g., ingestion of lead paint chips by children) and, within a limited range, bear a linear relationship to those intake levels.

Today, the average blood lead level in the US population, for example, is below 10 µg/dL, down from an average of 16 µg/dL (in the 1970s), the level before the legislated removal of lead from gasoline. A blood lead level of 10 µg/dL is about three times higher than the average level found in some remote populations.

The levels defining lead poisoning have been progressively declining. Taken together, effects occur over a wide range of blood lead concentrations, with no indication of a threshold. No safe level has yet been found for children. Even in adults, effects are being discovered at lower and lower levels as more sensitive analyses and measures are developed.

Erythrocyte protoporhyrin level. Until recently, the test of choice for screening asymptomatic populations at risk was erythrocyte protoporphyrin (EP), commonly assayed as zinc protoporphyrin (ZPP). An elevated level of protoporphyrin in the blood is a result of accumulation secondary to enzyme dysfunction in the erythrocytes. It reaches a steady state in the blood only after the entire population of circulating erythrocyles has turned over, about 120 days. Consequently, it lags behind blood lead levels and is an indirect measure of long-term lead exposure.

The major disadvantage of using EP (ZPP) testing as a method for lead screening is that it is not sensitive at the lower levels of lead poisoning. Data from the second US National Health and Nutrition Examination Survey (NHANES II) indicate that 58% of 118 children with blood lead levels above 30 µg/dL had EP levels within normal limits. This finding shows that a significant number of children with lead toxicity would be missed by reliance on EP (ZPP) testing alone as the screening tool. An EP (ZPP) level is still useful in screening patients for iron deficiency anaemia.

Normal values of ZPP are usually below 35 µg/dL. Hyperbilirubinaemia (jaundice) will cause falsely elevated readings when the haematofluorometer is used. EP is elevated in iron deficiency anaemia and in sickle cell and other haemolytic anaemias. In erythropoietic protoporphyria, an extremely rare disease, EP is markedly elevated (usually above 300 µg/dL).

BUN, creatinine and urinalysis. These parameters may reveal only late, significant effects of lead on renal function. Renal function in adults can also be assessed by measuring the fractional excretion of uric acid (normal range 5 to 10%; less than 5% in saturnine gout; greater than 10% in Fanconi syndrome).

Organic lead intoxication

The absorption of a sufficient quantity of tetraethyllead, whether briefly at a high rate or for prolonged periods at a lower rate, induces acute intoxication of the CNS. The milder manifestations are those of insomnia, lassitude and nervous excitation which reveals itself in lurid dreams and dream-like waking states of anxiety, in association with tremor, hyper-reflexia, spasmodic muscular contractions, bradycardia, vascular hypotension and hypothermia. The more severe responses include recurrent (sometimes nearly continuous) episodes of complete disorientation with hallucinations, facial contortions and intense general somatic muscular activity with resistance to physical restraint. Such episodes may be converted abruptly into maniacal or violent convulsive seizures which may terminate in coma and death.

Illness may persist for days or weeks, with intervals of quietude readily triggered into over-activity by any type of disturbance. In these less acute cases, fall in blood pressure and loss of body weight are common. When the onset of such symptomatology follows promptly (within a few hours) after brief, severe exposure to tetraethyllead, and when the symptomatology develops rapidly, an early fatal outcome is to be feared. When, however, the interval between the termination of brief or prolonged exposure and the onset of symptoms is delayed (by up to 8 days), the prognosis is guardedly hopeful, although partial or recurrent disorientation and depressed circulatory function may persist for weeks.

The initial diagnosis is suggested by a valid history of significant exposure to tetraethyllead, or by the clinical pattern of the presenting illness. It may be supported by the further development of the illness, and confirmed by evidence of a significant degree of absorption of tetraethyllead, provided by analyses of urine and blood which reveal typical findings (i.e., a striking elevation of the rate of excretion of lead in the urine) and a concurrently negligible or slight elevation of the concentration of lead in the blood.

Lead Control in the Working Environment

Clinical lead poisoning has historically been one of the most important occupational diseases, and it remains a major risk today. The considerable body of scientific knowledge concerning the toxic effects of lead has been enriched since the 1980s by significant new knowledge regarding the more subtle subclinical effects. Similarly, in a number of countries it was felt necessary to redraft or modernize work protective measures enacted over the last half-century and more.

Thus, in November 1979, in the US, the Final Standard on Occupational Exposure to Lead was issued by the Occupational Safety and Health Administration (OSHA) and in November 1980 a comprehensive Approved Code of Practice was issued in the United Kingdom regarding the control of lead at work.

The main features of the legislation, regulations and codes of practice emerging in the 1970s concerning the protection of the health of workers at work involved establishing comprehensive systems covering all work circumstances where lead is present and giving equal importance to hygiene measures, ambient monitoring and health surveillance (including biological monitoring).

Most codes of practice include the following aspects:

- assessment of work which exposes persons to lead
- information, instruction and training
- control measures for materials, plant and processes
- use and maintenance of control measures
- respiratory protective equipment and protective clothing
- washing and changing facilities and cleaning
- separate eating, drinking and smoking areas
- duty to avoid spread of contamination by lead
- air monitoring

- medical surveillance and biological tests
- keeping of records.

Some regulation, such as the OSHA lead standard, specifies the permissible exposure limit (PEL) of lead in the workplace, the frequency and extent of medical monitoring, and other responsibilities of the employer. As of this writing, if blood monitoring reveals a blood lead level greater than 40 µg/dL, the worker must be notified in writing and provided with medical examination. If a worker's blood lead level reaches 60 µg/dL (or averages 50 µg/dL or more), the employer is obligated to remove the employee from excessive exposure, with maintenance of seniority and pay, until the employee's blood lead level falls below 40 µg/dL (29 CFR 91 O.1025) (medical removal protection benefits).

Safety and Health Measures

The object of precautions is first to prevent the inhalation of lead and secondly to prevent its ingestion. These objects are most effectively achieved by the substitution of a less toxic substance for the lead compound. The use of lead polysilicates in the potteries is one example. The avoidance of lead carbonate paints for the painting of the interiors of buildings has proved very effective in reducing painters' colic; effective substitutes for lead for this purpose have become so readily available that it has been considered reasonable in some countries to prohibit the use of lead paint for the interiors of buildings.

Even if it is not possible to avoid the use of lead itself, it is still possible to avoid dust. Water sprays may be used in large quantities to prevent the formation of dust and to prevent it from becoming airborne. In lead smelting, the ore and the scrap may be treated in this way and the floors on which it has been lying may be kept wet. Unfortunately, there is always a potential source of dust in these circumstances if the treated material or floors are ever allowed to become dry. In some instances, arrangements are made to ensure that the dust will be coarse rather than fine. Other specific engineering precautions are discussed elsewhere in this *Encyclopaedia*.

Workers who are exposed to lead in any of its forms should be provided with personal protective equipment (PPE), which should be washed or renewed regularly. Protective clothing made of certain man-made fibres retains much less dust than cotton overalls and should be used where the conditions of work render it possible; turn-ups, pleats and pockets in which lead dust may collect should be avoided.

Cloakroom accommodation should be provided for this PPE, with separate accommodation for clothing taken off during working hours. Washing accommodation, including bathing accommodation with warm water, should be provided and used. Time should be allowed for washing before eating. Arrangements should be made to prohibit eating and smoking in the vicinity of lead processes and suitable eating facilities should be provided.

It is essential that the rooms and the plant associated with lead processes should be kept clean by continuous cleaning either by a wet process or by vacuum cleaners. Where, in spite of these precautions, workers may still be exposed to lead, respiratory protective equipment should be provided and properly maintained. Supervision should ensure that this equipment is maintained in a clean and efficient condition and that it is used when necessary.

Organic lead

Both the toxic properties of organic lead compounds, and their ease of absorption, require that contact of the skin of workers with these compounds, alone or in concentrated mixtures in commercial formulations or in gasoline or other organic solvents, must be scrupulously avoided. Both technological and management control are essential, and appropriate training of workers in safe work practices and the use of PPE is required. It is essential that atmospheric concentrations of alkyl lead compounds in the workplace air should be maintained at extremely low levels. Personnel should not be allowed to eat, smoke or keep unsealed food or beverages at the workplace. Good sanitary facilities, including showers, should be provided and workers should be encouraged to practise good personal hygiene, especially by showering or washing after the work shift. Separate lockers should be supplied for working and private clothes.

MAGNESIUM

Magnesium (Mg) is the lightest structural metal known. It is 40% lighter than aluminium. Metallic magnesium can be rolled and drawn when heated between 300 and 475 °C, but is brittle below this temperature and is apt to burn if heated much above it. It is soluble in, and forms compounds with, a number of acids, but is not affected by hydrofluoric or chromic acids. Unlike aluminium, it is resistant to alkali corrosion.

Occurrence and Uses

Magnesium does not exist in a pure state in nature, but is generally found in one of the following forms: dolomite ($CaCO_3 \cdot MgCO_3$), magnesite ($MgCO_3$), brucite ($Mg(OH)_2$), periclase (MgO), carnallite ($KClMgCl_2 \cdot 6H_2O$) or kieserite ($MgSO_4 \cdot H_2O$). In addition, it is found as a silicate in asbestos and talc. Magnesium is so widely distributed over the earth that facilities for processing and transporting the ore are often the determining factors in selecting a site for mining.

Magnesium is used, mainly in alloy form, for components of aircraft, ships, automobiles, machinery and hand tools for which both lightness and strength are required. It is used in the manufacture of precision instruments and optical mirrors, and in the recovery of titanium. Magnesium is also extensively used in military equipment. Because it burns with such intense light, magnesium is widely used in pyrotechnics, signal flares, incendiary and tracer bullets, and in flash bulbs.

Magnesium oxide has a high melting point (2,500 °C) and is often incorporated into the linings of refractories. It is also a component of animal feeds, fertilizers, insulation, wallboard, petroleum additives and electrical heating rods. Magnesium oxide is useful in the pulp and paper industry. In addition, it serves as an accelerator in the rubber industry and as a reflector in optical instruments.

Other important compounds include *magnesium chloride, magnesium hydroxide, magnesium nitrate* and *magnesium sulphate*. Magnesium chloride is a component of fire extinguishers and ceramics. It is also an agent in fireproofing wood and textile and paper manufacture. Magnesium chloride is a chemical intermediate for *magnesium oxychloride*, which is used for cement. A mixture of magnesium oxide and magnesium chloride forms a paste which is useful for floors. *Magnesium hydroxide* is useful for the neutralization of acids in the chemical industry. It is also used in uranium processing and in sugar refining. Magnesium hydroxide serves as a residual fuel-oil additive and an ingredient in toothpaste and antacid stomach powder. *Magnesium nitrate* is used in pyrotechnics and as a catalyst in the manufacture of petrochemicals. *Magnesium sulphate* has numerous functions in the textile industry, including weighting cotton and silk, fireproofing fabrics, and dyeing and printing calicos. It also finds use in fertilizers, explosives, matches, mineral water, ceramics and cosmetic lotions, and in the manufacture of mother-of-pearl and frosted papers. Magnesium sul-

phate increases the bleaching action of chlorinated lime and acts as a water-correcting agent in the brewing industry and a cathartic and analgesic in medicine.

Alloys. When magnesium is alloyed with other metals, such as manganese, aluminium and zinc, it improves their toughness and resistance to strain. In combination with lithium, cerium, thorium and zirconium, alloys are produced which have an enhanced strength-to-weight ratio, along with considerable heat-resisting properties. This renders them invaluable in the aircraft and aerospace industries for the construction of jet engines, rocket launchers and space vehicles. A large number of alloys, all containing over 85% magnesium, are known under the general name of Dow metal.

Hazards

Biological roles. As an essential ingredient of chlorophyll, the magnesium requirements of the human body are largely supplied by the consumption of green vegetables. The average human body contains about 25 g of magnesium. It is the fourth most abundant cation in the body, after calcium, sodium and potassium. The oxidation of foods releases energy, which is stored in the high-energy phosphate bonds. It is believed that this process of oxidative phosphorylation is carried out in the mitochondria of the cells and that magnesium is necessary for this reaction.

Experimentally produced magnesium deficiency in rats leads to a dilation of the peripheral blood vessels and later to hyperexcitability and convulsions. Tetany similar to that associated with hypocalcaemia occurred in calves fed only milk. Older animals with magnesium deficiency developed "grass staggers", a condition which appears to be associated with malabsorption rather than with a lack of magnesium in the fodder.

Cases of magnesium tetany resembling those caused by calcium deficiency have been described in humans. In the reported cases, however, a "conditioning factor", such as an excessive vomiting or fluid loss, has been present, in addition to inadequate dietary intake. Since this tetany clinically resembles that caused by calcium deficiency, a diagnosis can be made only by determining the blood levels of calcium and magnesium. Normal blood levels range from 1.8 to 3 mg per 100 cm^3, and it has been found that persons tend to become comatose when the blood concentration approaches 17 mg per cent. "Aeroform tumours" due to the evolution of hydrogen have been produced in animals by introducing finely divided magnesium into the tissues.

Toxicity. Magnesium and alloys containing 85% of the metal may be considered together in their toxicological properties. In industry, their toxicity is regarded as low. The most frequently used compounds, *magnesite* and *dolomite*, may irritate the respiratory tract. However, the fumes of *magnesium oxide*, as those of certain other metals, can cause metal fume fever. Some investigators have reported a higher incidence of digestive disorders in magnesium plant workers and suggest that a relationship may exist between magnesium absorption and gastroduodenal ulcers. In foundry-casting magnesium or high-magnesium alloys, fluoride fluxes and sulphur-containing inhibitors are used in order to separate the molten metal from the air with a layer of sulphur dioxide. This prevents burning during the casting operations, but the fumes of fluorides or of sulphur dioxide could present a greater hazard.

The greatest danger in handling magnesium is that of fire. Small fragments of the metal, such as would result from grinding, polishing or machining, can readily be ignited by a chance spark or flame, and as they burn at a temperature of 1,250 °C, these fragments can cause deep destructive lesions of the skin. Accidents of this type have occurred when a tool was sharpened on a wheel which was previously used to grind magnesium alloy castings. In addition, magnesium reacts with water and acids, forming combustible hydrogen gas.

Slivers of magnesium penetrating the skin or entering deep wounds could cause "aeroform tumours" of the type already mentioned. This would be rather exceptional; however, wounds contaminated with magnesium are very slow to heal. Fine dust from the buffing of magnesium could be irritating to the eyes and respiratory passages, but it is not specifically toxic.

Safety and Health Measures

As with any potentially hazardous industrial process, constant care is needed in handling and working magnesium. Those engaged in casting the metal should wear aprons and hand protection made of leather or some other suitable material to protect them against the "spatter" of small particles. Transparent face shields should also be worn as face protection, especially for the eyes. Where workers are exposed to magnesium dust, contact lenses should not be worn and eyewash facilities should be immediately available. Workers machining or buffing the metal should wear overalls to which small fragments of the metal will not adhere. Sufficient local exhaust ventilation is also essential in areas where magnesium oxide fumes may develop, in addition to good general ventilation. Cutting tools should be sharp, as blunt ones may heat the metal to the point of ignition.

Buildings in which magnesium is cast or machined should be constructed, if possible, of non-flammable materials and without ledges or protuberances on which magnesium dust might accumulate. The accumulation of shavings and "swarf" should be prevented, preferably by wet sweeping. Until final disposal, the scrapings should be collected in small containers and placed apart at safe intervals. The safest method for disposal of magnesium waste is probably wetting and burying.

Since the accidental ignition of magnesium presents a serious fire hazard, fire training and adequate firefighting facilities are essential. Workers should be trained never to use water in fighting such a blaze, because this merely scatters the burning fragments, and may spread the fire. Among the materials which have been suggested for the control of such fires are carbon and sand. Commercially prepared firefighting dusts are also available, one of which consists of powdered polyethylene and sodium borate.

● MANGANESE

Occurrence and Uses

Manganese (Mn) is one of the most abundant elements in the earth's crust. It is found in soils, sediments, rocks, water and biological materials. At least a hundred minerals contain manganese. Oxides, carbonates and silicates are the most important among manganese-containing minerals. Manganese can exist in eight oxidation states, the most important being +2, +3, and +7. *Manganese dioxide* (MnO_2) is the most stable oxide. Manganese forms various organometallic compounds. Of major practical interest is *methylcyclopentadienyl manganese tricarbonyl* $CH_3C_5H_4Mn(CO)_3$, often referred to as *MMT*.

The most important commercial source of manganese is manganese dioxide (MnO_2), which is found naturally in sedimentary deposits as pyrolusite. Two other types of deposit can be distinguished: carbonate accumulations, which are usually composed mainly of rhodocrosite ($MnCO_3$), and stratiform deposits. However, only the sedimentary deposits are significant, and those are usually worked by opencast techniques. Sometimes underground mining is necessary, and room and pillar extraction is carried out; seldom is there any call for the techniques used in deep metal mining.

Manganese is used in the production of steel as a reagent to reduce oxygen and sulphur and as an alloying agent for special steels, aluminium and copper. It is used in the chemical industry as an oxidizing agent and for the production of potassium permanganate and other manganese chemicals. Manganese is used for electrode coating in welding rods and for rock crushers, railway points and crossings. It also finds use in the ceramics, match, glass and dyestuff industries.

Several manganese salts are used in fertilizers and as driers for linseed oil. They are also utilized for glass and textile bleaching and for leather tanning. MMT has been used as a fuel-oil additive, a smoke inhibitor, and as an antiknock gasoline additive.

Hazards

Absorption, distribution and excretion

In occupational situations manganese is primarily absorbed by inhalation. Manganese dioxide and other manganese compounds which occur as volatile by-products of metal refining are practically insoluble in water. Thus, only particles small enough to reach the alveoli are eventually absorbed into the blood. Large inhaled particles may be cleared from the respiratory tract and swallowed. Manganese may also enter the gastrointestinal tract with contaminated food and water. The rate of absorption can be influenced by a dietary level of manganese and iron, the type of manganese compound, iron deficiency and age. However, the risk of intoxication by this route is not great. Absorption of manganese through the skin is negligible.

After inhalation, or after parenteral and oral exposure, the absorbed manganese is rapidly eliminated from the blood and distributed mainly to the liver. The kinetic patterns for blood clearance and liver uptake of manganese are similar, indicating that these two manganese pools rapidly enter equilibrium. Excess metal may be distributed to other tissues such as kidneys, small intestine, endocrine glands and bones. Manganese preferentially accumulates in tissues rich in mitochondria. It also penetrates the blood-brain barrier and the placenta. Higher concentrations of manganese are also associated with pigmented portions of the body, including the retina, pigmented conjunctiva and dark skin. Dark hair also accumulates manganese. It is estimated that the total body burden for manganese is between 10 and 20 mg for a 70 kg male. The biological half-life for manganese is between 36 and 41 days, but for manganese sequestered in the brain, the half-life is considerably longer. In the blood, manganese is bound to proteins.

The organic compound MMT is rapidly metabolized in the body. The distribution seems to be similar to that seen after exposure to inorganic manganese.

Bile flow is the main route of excretion of manganese. Consequently, it is eliminated almost entirely with faeces, and only 0.1 to 1.3% of daily intake with urine. It seems that biliary excretion is the main regulatory mechanism in the homeostatic control of manganese in the body, accounting for a relative stability of manganese content in tissues. After exposure to the organic compound MMT, excretion of manganese goes to a large extent with urine. This has been explained as a result of biotransformation of the organic compound in the kidney. As a metalloprotein compound of some enzymes, manganese is an essential element for humans.

Exposure

Intoxication by manganese is reported in mining and processing of manganese ores, in the production of manganese alloys, dry-cell batteries, welding electrodes, varnishes and ceramic tiles. Mining of ore can still present important occupational hazards, and the ferromanganese industry is the next most important source of risk. The operations that produce the highest concentrations of manganese dioxide dust are those of drilling and shotfiring. Consequently, the most dangerous job is high-speed drilling.

Considering the dependence of deposition sites and solubility rate of particle size, the dangerous effect of exposure is closely related to the particle size composition of manganese aerosol. There is also evidence that aerosols formed by condensation may be more harmful than those formed by disintegration, which can be connected again with the difference in particle size distribution. The toxicity of different manganese compounds appears to depend on the type of manganese ion present and on the oxidation state of manganese. The less oxidized the compound, the higher the toxicity.

Chronic manganese poisoning (manganism)

Chronic manganese poisoning can take either a nervous or pulmonary form. If the nervous system is attacked, three phases can be distinguished. During the initial period, diagnosis may be difficult. Early diagnosis, however, is critical because cessation of exposure appears to be effective in arresting the course of the disease. Symptoms include indifference and apathy, sleepiness, loss of apetite, headache, dizziness and asthenia. There may be bouts of excitablity, difficulty in walking and coordination, and cramps and pains in the back. These symptoms can be present in varying degrees and appear either together or in isolation. They mark the onset of the disease.

The intermediate stage is marked by the appearance of objective symptoms. First the voice become monotonous and sinks to a whisper, and speech is slow and irregular, perhaps with a stammer. There is fixed and hilarious or dazed and vacant facies, which may be attributable to an increase in the tonus of the facial muscles. The patient may abruptly burst into laughter or (more rarely) into tears. Although the faculties are much decayed, the victim appears to be in a perpetual state of euphoria. Gestures are slow and awkward, gait is normal but there may be a waving movement of the arms. The patient is unable to run and can walk backwards only with difficulty, sometimes with retropulsion. Inability to perform rapid alternating movements (adiadochokinesia) may develop, but neurological examination displays no changes except, in certain cases, exaggeration of the patellar reflexes.

Within a few months, the patient's condition deteriorates noticeably and the various disorders, especially those affecting the gait, grow steadily more pronounced. The earliest and most obvious symptom during this phase is muscular rigidity, constant but varying in degree, which results in a very characteristic gait (slow, spasmodic and unsteady), the patient putting his or her weight on the metatarsus and producing a movement variously described as "cock-walk" or "hen's gait". The victim is totally incapable of walking backwards and, should he or she try to do so, falls; balance can hardly be preserved, even when trying to stand with both feet together. A sufferer can turn round only slowly. There may be tremor, frequently in the lower limbs, even generalized.

The tendinous reflexes, rarely normal, become exaggerated. Sometimes there are vasomotor disorders with sudden sweating, pallor or blushing; on occasion there is cyanosis of the extremities. The sensory functions remain intact. The patient's mind may work only slowly; writing becomes irregular, some words being illegible. There may be changes in the pulse rate. This is the stage at which the disease becomes progressive and irreversible.

Pulmonary form. Reports of "manganese pneumoconiosis" have been contested in view of the high silica content of the rock at the site of exposure; manganese pneumonia has also been described. There is also controversy over the correlation between pneumonia and manganese exposure unless manganese acts as an aggravating factor. In view of its epidemic character and severity, the disease may be a non-typical viral pneumopathy. These manganic pneumonias respond well to antibiotics.

Pathology. Some authors maintain that there are widespread lesions to the *corpus striatum*, then to the cerebral cortex, the hippocampus and *corpora quadrigemina* (in the posterior corpora). However, others are of the opinion that the lesions to the frontal lobes provide a better explanation for all the symptoms observed than do those observed in the basal ganglia; this would be confirmed by electroencephalography. The lesions are always bilateral and more or less symmetrical.

Course. Manganese poisoning ultimately becomes chronic. However, if the disease is diagnosed while still at the early stages and the patient is removed from exposure, the course may be reversed. Once well established, it becomes progressive and irreversible, even when exposure is terminated. The nervous disorders show no tendency to regress and may be followed by deformation of the joints. Although the severity of certain symptoms may be reduced, gait remains permanently affected. The patient's general condition remains good, and he or she may live a long time, eventually dying from an intercurrent ailment.

Diagnosis. This is based primarily on the patient's personal and occupational history (job, length of exposure and so on). However, the subjective nature of the initial symptoms makes early diagnosis difficult; consequently, at this stage, questioning must be supplemented by information supplied by friends, colleagues and relatives. During the intermediate and full-blown stages of the intoxication, occupational history and objective symptoms facilitate diagnosis; laboratory examinations can provide information for supplementing the diagnosis.

Haematological changes are variable; on the one hand, there may be no changes at all, whereas, on the other, there may be leucopenia, lymphocytosis and inversion of leucocyte formula in 50% of cases, or increase in haemoglobin count (considered as the first sign of poisoning) and slight polycythaemia.

There is diminished urinary excretion of 17-ketosteroids, and it may be assumed that the adrenal function is affected. Albumin level in the cerebrospinal fluid is increased, often to a marked degree (40 to 55 and even 75 mg per cent). Digestive and hepatic symptoms are non-indicative; there is no sign of hepatomegalia or splenomegalia; however, accumulation of manganese in the liver may result in metabolic lesions which seem to be related to the patient's endocrinological condition and may be influenced by the existence of neurological lesions.

Differential diagnosis. There may be difficulty in distinguishing between manganese poisoning and the following diseases: nerve syphilis, Parkinson's disease, disseminated sclerosis, Wilson's disease, hepatic cirrhosis and Westphal-Strümpell's disease (pseudosclerosis).

Safety and Health Measures

The prevention of manganese poisoning is primarily a question of suppression of manganese dusts and fumes. In mines, dry drilling should always be replaced by wet drilling. Shotfiring should be carried out after the shift so that the heading can be well ventilated before the next shift starts up. Good general ventilation at source is also essential. Airline respiratory protection equipment as well as independent respirators have to be used in specific situations to avoid excessive short-term exposures.

A high standard of personal hygiene is essential, and personal cleanliness and adequate sanitary facilities, clothing and time must be provided so that compulsory showering after work, a change of clothes and a ban on eating at the workplace can be effected. Smoking at work should be prohibited as well.

Periodic measurements of exposure levels should be performed, and attention should be given to the size distribution of airborne manganese. Contamination of drinking water and food as well as workers' dietary habits ought to be considered as a potential additional source of exposure.

It is inadvisable for workers with psychological or neurological disorders to be employed in work associated with exposure to manganese. Nutritional deficiency states may predispose to anaemia and thus increase susceptibility to manganese. Therefore workers suffering from such deficiencies have to be kept under strict surveillance. During the anaemic state, subjects should avoid exposure to manganese. The same relates to those suffering from lesions of the excretory organs, or from chronic obstructive lung disease. A study has suggested that long-term manganese exposure may contribute to the development of chronic obstructive lung disease, particularly if the exposure is combined with smoking. On the other hand impaired lungs may be more susceptible to the potential acute effect of manganese aerosols.

During the periodic medical examinations the worker should be screened for symptoms which might be connected with the subclinical stage of manganese poisoning. In addition, the worker should be examined clinically, particularly with a view to detecting early psychomotor changes and neurological signs. Subjective symptoms and abnormal behaviour may often constitute the only early indications of health impairment. Manganese can be measured in blood, urine, stools and hair. Estimation of the extent of manganese exposure by means of manganese concentration in urine and blood did not prove to be of great value.

The average manganese blood level in exposed workers seems to be of the same order as that in non-exposed persons. Contamination during sampling and analytical procedures may at least partly explain a rather wide range found in literature particularly for blood. The use of heparin as an anticoagulant is still quite common although the manganese content in heparin may exceed that in blood. The mean concentration of manganese in urine of non-exposed people is usually estimated to be between 1 and 8 mg/l, but values up to 21 mg/l have been reported. Daily manganese intake from human diets varies greatly with the amount of unrefined cereals, nuts, leafy vegetables and tea consumed, owing to their relatively high content of manganese, and thus affects the results of normal manganese content in biological media.

A manganese concentration of 60 mg/kg of faeces and higher has been suggested as indicative of occupational exposure to manganese. Manganese content in hair is normally below 4 mg/kg. As the determination of manganese in urine, which is often used in practice, has not yet been validated enough for assessment of individual exposure, it can be used only as a group indicator of the mean level of exposure. Collection of the stool and the analysis of manganese content is not easy to perform. Our present knowledge does not include any other reliable biological parameter which might be used as an indicator of individual exposure to manganese. Thus the assessment of workers' exposure to manganese still has to rely on manganese air levels. There is also very little reliable information about the correlation between the manganese content in the blood and urine and the findings of neurological symptoms and signs.

Persons with the signs of manganese intoxication should be removed from exposure. If the worker is removed from exposure shortly after the onset of symptoms and signs (before the fully developed stage of manganism) many of the symptoms and signs will disappear. There may be some residual disturbances, however, particularly in speech and gait.

METAL CARBONYLS (especially Nickel Carbonyl)

F. William Sunderman, Jr.

Occurrence and Uses

Metal carbonyls have the general formula $Me_x(CO)_y$, and are formed by combination of the metal (Me) with carbon monoxide (CO). Physical properties of some metal carbonyls are listed in table 63.1. Most are solids at ordinary temperatures, but nickel carbonyl, iron pentacarbonyl and ruthenium pentacarbonyl are liquids, and cobalt hydrocarbonyl is a gas. This article focuses on nickel carbonyl, which, because of its volatility, exceptional toxicity and industrial importance merits special attention in regard to occupational toxicology. Since iron pentacarbonyl and cobalt hydrocarbonyl also have high vapour pressures and potential for inadvertent formation, they warrant serious consideration as possible occupational toxicants. Most metal carbonyls react vigorously with oxygen and oxidizing substances, and some ignite spontaneously. Upon exposure to air and light, nickel carbonyl decomposes to carbon monoxide and particulate nickel metal, cobalt hydrocarbonyl decomposes to cobalt octacarbonyl and hydrogen, and iron pentacarbonyl decomposes to iron nonacarbonyl and carbon monoxide.

Metal carbonyls are used in isolating certain metals (e.g., nickel) from complex ores, for producing carbon steel, and for metallizing by vapour deposition. They are also used as catalysts in organic reactions (e.g., *cobalt hydrocarbonyl* or *nickel carbonyl* in olefin oxidation; *cobalt octacarbonyl* for the synthesis of aldehydes; nickel carbonyl for the synthesis of acrylic esters). *Iron pentacarbonyl* is used as a catalyst for various organic reactions, and is decomposed to make finely powdered, ultra pure iron (so-called carbonyl iron), which is used in the computer and electronics industries. *Methycyclopentadienyl manganese tricarbonyl (MMT)* $(CH_3C_5H_4Mn(CO)_3)$ is an antiknock additive to gasoline and is discussed in the article "Manganese".

Table 63.1 • Physical properties of some metal carbonyls.

Metal carbonyl	Mol. Wt.	Sp. Gr. (20°C)	M.P. (°C)	B.P. (°C)	V.P. (25°C) mm Hg
$Ni(CO)_4$	170.75	1.31	−19	43	390
$CoH(CO)_4$	171.99	–	−26	–	high
$Co_2(CO)_8$	341.95	1.87	51	52*	1.5
$Co_4(CO)_{12}$	571.86	–	60*	–	very low
$Cr(CO)_6$	220.06	1.77	110*	151	0.4
$Fe_2(CO)_9$	363.79	2.08	80*	–	–
$Fe(CO)_5$	195.90	1.46	−25	103	30.5
$Fe(CO)_4$	167.89	2.00	approx. 140*	–	–
$Mo(CO)_6$	264.00	1.96	150*	156	0.2
$Ru(CO)_5$	241.12	–	−22	–	–
$W(CO)_6$	351.91	2.65	approx. 150*	175	0.1

*Decomposition starts at temperature shown.
Source: Adapted from Brief et al. 1971.

Health Hazards

The toxicity of a given metal carbonyl depends on the toxicity of carbon monoxide and of the metal from which it is derived, as well as the volatility and instability of the carbonyl itself. The principal route of exposure is inhalation, but skin absorption can occur with the liquid carbonyls. The relative acute toxicity (LD_{50} for the rat) of nickel carbonyl, cobalt hydrocarbonyl and iron pentacarbonyl may be expressed by the ratio 1:0.52:0.33. Inhalation exposures of experimental animals to these substances induce acute interstitial pneumonitis, with pulmonary oedema and capillary damage, as well as injury to the brain, liver and kidneys.

Judging from the sparse literature on their toxicity, cobalt hydrocarbonyl and iron pentacarbonyl rarely pose health hazards in industry. None the less, iron pentacarbonyl can be formed inadvertently when carbon monoxide, or a gas mixture containing carbon monoxide, is stored under pressure in steel cylinders or fed through steel pipes, when illuminating gas is produced by petroleum reforming, or when gas welding is carried out. Presence of carbon monoxide in emission discharges from blast furnaces, electric arc furnaces and cupola furnaces during steel-making can also lead to the formation of iron pentacarbonyl.

Safety and Health Measures

Special precautions are mandatory in the storage of metal carbonyls; their handling must be mechanized to the maximum degree, and decanting should be avoided wherever possible. Vessels and piping should be purged with an inert gas (e.g., nitrogen, carbon dioxide) before being opened, and carbonyl residues should be burnt or neutralized with bromine water. Where there is an inhalation hazard, workers should be provided with airline respirators or self-contained breathing apparatus. Workshops should be fitted with down-draught ventilation.

Nickel Carbonyl

Nickel carbonyl ($Ni(CO)_4$) is mainly used as an intermediate in the Mond process for nickel refining, but it is also used for vapour-plating in the metallurgical and electronics industries and as a catalyst for synthesis of acrylic monomers in the plastics industry. Inadvertent formation of nickel carbonyl can occur in industrial processes that use nickel catalysts, such as coal gasification, petroleum refining and hydrogenation reactions, or during incineration of nickel-coated papers that are used for pressure-sensitive business forms.

Hazards

Acute, accidental exposure of workers to inhalation of nickel carbonyl usually produces mild, non-specific, immediate symptoms, including nausea, vertigo, headache, dyspnoea and chest pain. These initial symptoms usually disappear within a few hours. After 12 to 36 hours, and occasionally as long as 5 days after exposure, severe pulmonary symptoms develop, with cough, dyspnoea, tachycardia, cyanosis, profound weakness and often gastrointestinal symptoms. Human fatalities have occurred 4 to 13 days after exposure to nickel carbonyl; deaths have resulted from diffuse interstitial pneumonitis, cerebral hemorrhage or cerebral oedema. In addition to pathologic lesions in the lungs and brain, lesions have been found in liver, kidneys, adrenals and spleen. In patients who survive acute nickel carbonyl poisoning, pulmonary insufficiency often causes protracted convalescence. Nickel carbonyl is carcinogenic and teratogenic in rats; the European Union has classified nickel carbonyl as an animal teratogen. Processes that use nickel carbonyl constitute disaster hazards, since fire and explosion can occur when nickel carbonyl is exposed to air, heat, flames or oxidizers. Decomposition of nickel carbonyl is attended by additional toxic hazards from inhalation of its decomposition products, carbon monoxide and finely particulate nickel metal.

Chronic exposure of workers to inhalation of low atmospheric concentrations of nickel carbonyl (0.007 to 0.52 mg/m^3) can cause neurological symptoms (e.g., insomnia, headache, dizziness, memory loss) and other manifestations (e.g., chest tightness, excessive sweating, alopecia). Electroencephalographic abnormalities and elevated serum monoamine oxidase activity have been observed in workers with chronic exposures to nickel carbonyl. A synergistic effect of cigarette smoking and nickel carbonyl exposure on the frequency of sister-chromatid exchanges was noted in a cytogenetic evaluation of workers with chronic exposure to nickel carbonyl.

Safety and Health Measures

Fire and explosion prevention. Because of its flammability and tendency to explode, nickel carbonyl should be stored in tightly closed containers in a cool, well-ventilated area, away from heat and oxidizers such as nitric acid and chlorine. Flames and sources of ignition should be prohibited wherever nickel carbonyl is handled, used or stored. Nickel carbonyl should be transported in steel cylinders. Foam, dry chemical, or CO_2 fire extinguishers should be used to extinguish burning nickel carbonyl, rather than a stream of water, which might scatter and spread the fire.

Health protection. In addition to the medical surveillance measures recommended for all nickel-exposed workers, persons with occupational exposures to nickel carbonyl should have biological monitoring of nickel concentration in urine specimens on a regular basis, typically monthly. Persons who enter confined spaces where they might possibly be exposed to nickel carbonyl should have self-contained breathing apparatus and a suitable harness with lifeline tended by another employee outside the space. Analytical instruments for continuous atmospheric monitoring of nickel carbonyl include (a) Fourier-transform infrared absorption spectroscopes, (b) plasma chromatographs and (c) chemiluminescent detectors. Atmospheric samples can also be analysed for nickel carbonyl by (d) gas chromatography, (e) atomic absorption spectrophotometry and (f) colourimetric procedures.

Treatment. Workers suspected to have been acutely exposed to nickel carbonyl should be immediately removed from the exposure site. Contaminated clothing should be removed. Oxygen should be administered and the patient kept at rest until seen by a physician. Each voiding of urine is saved for nickel analysis. The severity of acute nickel carbonyl poisoning correlates with the urine nickel concentrations during the first 3 days after exposure. Exposures are classified as "mild" if the initial 8-h specimen of urine has a nickel concentration less than 100 μg/l, "moderate" if the nickel concentration is 100 to 500 μg/l, and "severe" if the nickel concentration exceeds 500 μg/l. Sodium diethyldithiocarbamate is the drug of choice for chelation therapy of acute nickel carbonyl poisoning. Ancillary therapeutic measures include bed rest, oxygen therapy, corticosteroids and prophylactic antibiotics. Carbon monoxide poisoning may occur simultaneously and requires treatment.

MERCURY

Inorganic Mercury

Mercury combines readily with sulphur and halogens at ordinary temperatures and forms amalgams with all metals except iron, nickel, cadmium, aluminium, cobalt and platinum. It reacts exothermically (generates heat) with alkaline metals, is attacked by nitric acid but not by hydrochloric acid and, when hot, will combine with sulphuric acid.

Inorganic mercury is found in nature in the form of the sulphide (HgS) as cinnabar ore, which has an average mercury content of 0.1 to 4%. It is also encountered in the earth's crust in the form of geodes of liquid mercury (in Almadén) and as impregnated schist or slate (e.g., in India and Yugoslavia).

Extraction. Mercury ore is extracted by underground mining, and mercury metal is separated from the ore by roasting in a rotary kiln or shaft furnace, or by reduction with iron or calcium oxide. The vapour is carried off in the combustion gases and is condensed in vertical tubes.

The most important uses of metallic mercury and its inorganic compounds have included the treatment of gold and silver ores; the manufacture of amalgams; the manufacture and repair of measurement or laboratory apparatus; the manufacture of incandescent electric bulbs, mercury vapour tubes, radio valves, x-ray tubes, switches, batteries, rectifiers, etc.; as a catalyst for the production of chlorine and alkali and the production of acetic acid and acetaldehyde from acetylene; chemical, physical and biological laboratory research; gold, silver, bronze and tin plating; tanning and currying; feltmaking; taxidermy; textile manufacture; photography and photogravure; mercury-based paints and pigments; and the manufacture of artificial silk. Some of these uses have been discontinued because of the toxic effects that the mercury exposure exerted upon workers.

Organic Mercury Compounds

Organic compounds of mercury may be considered as the organic compounds in which the mercury is chemically linked directly to a carbon atom. Carbon-mercury bonds have a wide range of stability; in general, the carbon-to-mercury bond in aliphatic compounds is more stable than that in aromatic compounds. According to one reliable estimate, more than 400 phenyl mercurials and at least that number of alkyl mercury compounds have been synthesized. The three most important groups in common usage are the alkyls, the aromatic hydrocarbons or aryls and the alkoxyalkyls. Examples of aryl mercury compounds are phenylmercuric acetate (PMA), nitrate, oleate, propionate and benzoate. Most available information is about PMA.

Uses. All the important uses of the organic mercury compounds depend on the biological activity of these substances. In medical practice organic mercury compounds are used as antiseptics, germicides, diuretics and contraceptives. In the field of pesticides they serve as algicides, fungicides, herbicides, slimacides and as preservatives in paints, waxes and pastes; they are used for mildew suppression, in antifouling paints, in latex paints and in the fungus-proofing of fabrics, paper, cork, rubber and wood for use in humid climates. In the chemical industry they act as catalysts in a number of reactions and the mercury alkyls are used as alkylating agents in organic syntheses.

Hazards

Absorption and effects: Inorganic and metallic mercury

Vapour inhalation is the main route for the entry of metallic mercury into the body. Around 80% of inhaled mercury vapour is absorbed in the lung (alveoli). Digestive absorption of metallic mercury is negligible (lower than 0.01% of the administered dose). Subcutaneous penetration of metallic mercury as the result of an accident (e.g. the breakage of a thermometer) is also possible.

The main routes of entry of inorganic mercury compounds (mercury salts) are the lungs (atomization of mercury salts) and the gastrointestinal tract. In the latter case, absorption is often the result of accidental or voluntary ingestion. It is estimated that 2 to 10% of ingested mercury salts are absorbed through the intestinal tract.

Skin absorption of metallic mercury and certain of its compounds is possible, although the rate of absorption is low. After entry into the body, metallic mercury continues to exist for a short time in metallic form, which explains its penetration of the blood-brain barrier. In blood and tissues metallic mercury is rapidly oxidized to Hg^{2+} mercury ion, which fixes to proteins. In the blood, inorganic mercury is also distributed between plasma and red blood cells.

The kidney and brain are the sites of deposition following exposure to metallic mercury vapours, and the kidney following exposure to inorganic mercury salts.

Acute poisoning

The symptoms of acute poisoning include pulmonary irritation (chemical pneumonia), perhaps leading to acute pulmonary oedema. Renal involvement is also possible. Acute poisoning is more often the result of accidental or voluntary ingestion of a mercury salt. This leads to severe inflammation of the gastrointestinal tract followed rapidly by renal insufficiency due to necrosis of the proximal convoluted tubules.

The severe chronic form of mercury poisoning encountered in places like Almadén up until the early 20th century, and which presented spectacular renal, digestive, mental and nervous disorders and terminated in cachexia, was eliminated by means of preventive measures. However, a chronic, "intermittent" poisoning in which periods of active intoxication are interspersed between periods of latent intoxication can still be detected among mercury miners. In the latent periods, symptoms remit to such a degree that they are visible only on close search; only the neurological manifestations persist in the form of profuse sweating, dermographia and, to some extent, emotional instability.

A condition of "micromercurialism" characterized by functional neurosis (frequent hysteria, neurasthenia, and mixed forms), cardiovascular lability and secretory neurosis of the stomach has also been described.

Digestive system. Gingivitis is the most common gastrointestinal disorder encountered in mercury poisoning. It is favoured by poor oral hygiene and is accompanied by an unpleasant, metallic or bitter taste in the mouth. Ulceromembranous stomatitis is much less common and is normally found in persons already suffering from gingivitis who have accidentally inhaled mercury vapours. This stomatitis commences with the subjective symptoms of gingivitis with increased salivation (mercurial ptyalism) and coating of the tongue. Eating and drinking produce a burning sensation and discomfort in the mouth, the gums become increasingly inflamed and swollen, ulcers appear and there is spontaneous bleeding. In acute cases, there is high fever, inflammation of the submaxillary ganglions and extremely fetid breath. Alveolodental periostitis has also been observed.

There may be a bluish line on the tooth edge of the gums, in particular in the vicinity of infected areas; this line is, however, never encountered in persons without teeth. Slate-grey punctiform pigmentation of the oral mucosae—the vestibular side of the gums (usually those of the lower jaw), the palate, and even the inside of the cheeks—has also been observed.

Recurrent gingivitis affects the supporting tissues of the teeth, and in many cases the teeth have to be extracted or merely fall out. Other gastrointestinal disorders encountered in mercury poisoning include gastritis and gastroduodenitis.

Non-specific pharyngitis is relatively common. A rarer manifestation is that of Kussmaul's pharyngitis which presents as a bright-red coloration of the pharynx, tonsils and soft palate with fine arborisation.

Nervous system involvement may occur with or without gastro-intestinal symptoms and may evolve in line with two main clinical pictures: (a) fine-intention tremor reminiscent of that encountered in persons suffering from multiple sclerosis; and (b) Parkinsonism with tremor at rest and reduced motor function. Usually one of these two conditions is dominant in the over-all clinical picture which may be further complicated by morbid irritability and pronounced mental hyperactivity (mercurial erethism).

Mercurial Parkinsonism presents a picture of unsteady and staggering gait, absence of balance-recovery reflexes and hypotonia; vegetative symptoms are slight with mask-like facies, sialorrhea, etc. However, Parkinsonism is usually encountered in milder forms, in particular as micro-Parkinsonism.

The most frequently encountered symptoms resemble those presented by persons with multiple sclerosis, except that there is no nystagmus and the two conditions have a different serology and different clinical courses. The most striking feature is tremor which is usually a late symptom but may develop prior to stomatitis.

Tremor usually disappears during sleep, although sudden generalized cramps or contractions may occur; however, it always increases under emotional stress and this is such a characteristic feature that it provides firm grounds for a diagnosis of mercury poisoning. Tremor is particularly pronounced in situations where the patient feels embarrassed or ashamed; often he or she will have to eat in solitude since otherwise he would be incapable of raising food to his lips. In its most acute form, the tremor may invade all the voluntary muscles and be continuous. Cases still occur in which the patient has to be strapped down to prevent him falling out of bed; such cases also present massive, choreiform movements sufficient to wake the patient from his sleep.

The patient tends to utter his words in staccato fashion, so that his sentences are difficult to follow (psellismus mercurialis); when a spasm ceases, the words come out too fast. In cases more reminiscent of parkinsonism, speech is slow and monotonous and the voice may be low or completely absent; spasmodic utterence is, however, more common.

A highly characteristic symptom is a desire for sleep, and the patient often sleeps for long periods although lightly and is frequently disturbed by cramps and spasms. However, insomnia may occur in some cases.

Loss of memory is an early and dementia a terminal symptom. Dermographia and profuse sweating (for no obvious reason) are frequently encountered. In chronic mercury poisoning, the eyes may show the picture of "mercurialentis" characterized by a light-grey to dark, reddish-grey discoloration of the anterior capsule of the crystalline lens due to the deposition of finely divided particles of mercury. Mercurialentis can be detected by examination with a slit-lamp microscope and is bilateral and symmetrical; it usually appears some considerable time before the onset of general signs of mercury poisoning.

Chronic exposure

Chronic mercury poisoning usually starts insidiously, which makes the early detection of incipient poisoning difficult. The main target organ is the nervous system. Initially, suitable tests can be used to detect psychomotor and neuro-muscular changes and slight tremor. Slight renal involvement (proteinuria, albuminuria, enzymuria) may be detectable earlier than neurological involvement.

If excessive exposure is not corrected, neurological and other manifestations (e.g., tremor, sweating, dermatography) become more pronounced, associated with changes in behaviour and personality disorders and, perhaps, digestive disorders (stomatitis, diarrhoea) and a deterioration in general status (anorexia, weight loss). Once this stage has been reached, termination of exposure may not lead to total recovery.

In chronic mercury poisoning, digestive and nervous symptoms predominate and, although the former are of earlier onset, the latter are more obvious; other significant but less intense symptoms may be present. The duration of the period of mercury absorption preceding the appearance of clinical symptoms depends on the level of absorption and individual factors. The main early signs include slight digestive disorders, in particular, loss of appetite; intermittent tremor, sometimes in specific muscle groups; and neurotic disorders varying in intensity. The course of intoxication may vary considerably from case to case. If exposure is terminated immediately upon the appearance of the first symptoms, full recovery usually occurs; however, if exposure is not terminated and the intoxication becomes firmly established, no more than an alleviation of symptoms can be expected in the majority of cases.

Kidney. There have been studies over the years on the relationships between renal function and urinary mercury levels. The effects of low-level exposures are still not well documented or understood. At higher levels (above 50 µg/g (micrograms per gram) abnormal renal function (as evidenced by N-acetyl-B-D-glucosaminidase (NAG), which is a sensitive indicator of damage to the kidneys) have been observed. The NAG levels were correlated with both the urinary mercury levels and the results of neurological and behavioural testing.

Nervous system. Recent years have seen the development of more data on low levels of mercury, which are discussed in more detail in the chapter *Nervous system* in this *Encyclopaedia*.

Blood. Chronic poisoning is accompanied by mild anaemia sometimes preceded by polycythaemia resulting from bone marrow irritation. Lymphocytosis and eosinophilia have also been observed.

Organic Mercury Compounds

Phenylmercuric acetate (PMA). Absorption may occur through inhalation of aerosols containing PMA, through skin absorption or by ingestion. The solubility of the mercurial and the particle size of the aerosols are determining factors for the extent of absorption. PMA is more efficiently absorbed by ingestion than are inorganic mercuric salts. *Phenylmercury* is transported mainly in blood and distributed in the blood cells (90%), accumulates in the liver and is there decomposed into inorganic mercury. Some phenylmercury is excreted in the bile. The main portion absorbed in the body is distributed in the tissues as inorganic mercury and accumulated in the kidney. On chronic exposure, mercury distribution and excretion follow the pattern seen on exposure to inorganic mercury.

Occupational exposure to phenylmercury compounds occurs in the manufacture and handling of products treated with fungicides containing phenylmercury compounds. Acute inhalation of large amounts may cause lung damage. Exposure of the skin to a concentrated solution of phenylmercury compounds may cause chemical burns with blistering. Sensitization to phenylmercury compounds may occur. Ingestion of large amounts of phenylmercury may cause renal and liver damage. Chronic poisoning gives rise to renal damage due to accumulation of inorganic mercury in the renal tubules.

Available clinical data do not permit extensive conclusions about dose-response relationships. They suggest, however, that phenylmercury compounds are less toxic than inorganic mercury compounds or long-term exposure. There is some evidence of mild adverse effects on the blood.

Alkyl mercury compounds. From a practical point of view, the short-chained alkyl mercury compounds, like *methylmercury* and *ethylmercury*, are the most important, although some exotic mercury compounds, generally used in laboratory research, have led to spectacular rapid deaths from acute poisoning. These compounds have been extensively used in seed treatment where they have been responsible for a number of fatalities. *Methylmercuric chloride* forms white crystals with a characteristic odour, while *ethylmercury chloride*; (chloroethylmercury) forms white flakes. Volatile methylmercury compounds, like methylmercury chloride, are absorbed to about 80% upon inhalation of vapour. More than 95% of short-chained alkyl mercury compounds is absorbed by ingestion, although the absorption of methylmercury compounds by the skin can be efficient, depending on their solubility and concentration and the condition of the skin.

Transport, distribution and excretion. Methylmercury is transported in the red blood cells (95%), and a small fraction is bound to plasma proteins. The distribution to the different tissues of the body is rather slow and it takes about four days before equilibrium is obtained. Methylmercury is concentrated in the central nervous system and especially in grey matter. About 10% of the body burden of mercury is found in the brain. The highest concentration is found in the occipital cortex and the cerebellum. In pregnant women methylmercury is transferred in the placenta to the foetus and especially accumulated in the foetal brain.

Hazards of organic mercury

Poisoning by alkyl mercury may occur on inhalation of vapour and dust containing alkyl mercury and in the manufacture of the mercurial or in handling the final material. Skin contact with concentrated solutions results in chemical burns and blistering. In small agricultural operations there is a risk of exchange between treated seed and products intended for food, followed by involuntary intake of large amounts of alkyl mercury. On acute exposure the signs and symptoms of poisoning have an insidious onset and appear with a latency period which may vary from one to several weeks. The latency period is dependent on the size of the dose—the larger the dose, the shorter the period.

On chronic exposure the onset is more insidious, but the symptoms and signs are essentially the same, due to the accumulation of mercury in the central nervous system, causing neuron damage in the sensory cortex, such as visual cortex, auditory cortex and the pre- and post-central areas. The signs are characterized by sensory disturbances with paresthaesia in the distal extremities, in the tongue and around the lips. With more severe intoxications ataxia, concentric constrictions of the visual fields, impairment of hearing and extrapyramidal symptoms may appear. In severe cases chronic seizures occur.

The period in life most sensitive to methylmercury poisoning is the time *in utero*; the foetus seems to be between 2 and 5 times more sensitive than the adult. Exposure *in utero* results in cerebral palsy, partly due to inhibition of the migration of neurons from central parts to the peripheral cortical areas. In less severe cases retardation in the psychomotor development has been observed.

Alkoxyalkyl mercury compounds. The most common alkoxyalkyl compounds used are *methoxyethyl mercury* salts (e.g., *methoxyethylmercury acetate)*, which have replaced the short-chain alkyl compounds in seed treatment in many industrial countries, in which the alkyl compounds have been banned due to their hazardousness.

The available information is very limited. Alkoxyalkyl compounds are absorbed by inhalation and by ingestion more efficiently than inorganic mercury salts. The distribution and excretion patterns of absorbed mercury follow those of inorganic mercury salts. Excretion occurs through the intestinal tract and the kidney. To what extent unchanged alkoxyalkyl mercury is excreted in humans is unknown. Exposure to alkoxyalkyl mercury compounds can occur in the manufacture of the compound and in handling the final product(s) treated with the mercurial. Methoxyethyl mercury acetate is a vesicant when applied in concentrated solutions to the skin. Inhalation of methoxyethyl mercury salt dust may cause lung damage, and chronic poisoning due to long-term exposure may give rise to renal damage.

Safety and Health Measures

Efforts should be made to replace mercury with less hazardous substances. For example, the felt industry may employ non-mercurial compounds. In mining, wet drilling techniques should be used. Ventilation is the main safety measure and if it is inadequate, the workers should be provided with respiratory protective equipment.

In industry, wherever possible, mercury should be handled in hermetically sealed systems and extremely strict hygiene rules should be applied at the workplace. When mercury is spilt, it very easily infiltrates into crevices, gaps in the floor and workbenches. Due to its vapour pressure, a high atmospheric concentration may occur even following seemingly negligible contamination. It is therefore important to avoid the slightest soiling of work surfaces; these should be smooth, non-absorbent and slightly tilted towards a collector or, failing this, have a metal grill over a gutter filled with water to collect any drops of spilt mercury which fall through the grill. Working surfaces should be cleaned regularly and, in the event of accidental contamination, any drops of mercury collected in a water trap should be drawn off as rapidly as possible.

Where there is a danger of mercury volatilizing, local exhaust ventilation (LEV) systems should be installed. Admittedly, this is a solution which is not always applicable, as is the case in premises producing chlorine by the mercury cell process, in view of the enormous vaporization surface.

Work posts should be planned in such a way as to minimize the number of persons exposed to mercury.

Most exposure to organic mercury compounds involves mixed exposure to mercury vapour and the organic compound, as the organic mercury compounds decompose and release mercury vapour. All technical measures pertaining to exposure to mercury vapour should be applied for exposure to organic mercury compounds. Thus, contamination of clothes and/or parts of the body should be avoided, as it may be a dangerous source of mercury vapour close to the breathing zone. Special protective work clothes should be used and changed after the workshift. Spray painting with paint containing mercurials requires respiratory protective equipment and adequate ventilation. The short-chained alkyl mercury compounds should be eliminated and replaced whenever possible. If handling cannot be avoided, an enclosed system should be used, combined with adequate ventilation, to limit exposure to a minimum.

Great care must be exercised in preventing the contamination of water sources with mercury effluent since the mercury can be incorporated into the food chain, leading to disasters such as that which occurred in Minamata, Japan.

MOLYBDENUM

Occurrence and Uses

Molybdenum (Mo) is widely distributed throughout the earth's crust, but it is mined in only a limited number of countries due to the rarity of bodies of sufficiently high quality molybdenite ore $(MoSO_2)$. A certain amount of molybdenum is obtained as a by-product in the processing of copper ore. Coal-electrical power plants can be significant sources of molybdenum. Molybdenum is an essential trace element.

Molybdenum forms a large variety of commercially useful compounds in which it displays the valence numbers 0, +2, +3, +4, +5 and +6. It readily changes valence states (disproportionates) with only minor changes in external conditions. It has a strong tendency to form complexes; with the exception of the sulphides and halides, very few other simple compounds of molybdenum exist. The +6 molybdenum forms isopoly- and heteropoly- acids.

Over 90% of the molybdenum produced is used as an alloying element for iron, steel and non-ferrous metals, mainly because of its heat-resisting properties; the rest is used in chemicals and lubricants. As a steel alloy, molybdenum is utilized in the electric, electronics, military and automobile industries and in aeronautical engineering. Another important use of molybdenum is in the production of inorganic molybdenum pigments, dyes and lakes. Small but increasing amounts of molybdenum are used as trace elements in fertilizers.

The most important molybdenum chemical is *molybdenum trioxide* (MoO_3), made from roasting the sulphide ore. Pure molybdenum trioxide is used in chemical and catalyst manufacture. The technical product is added to steel as an alloying agent. Molybdenum trioxide also serves as a catalyst in the petroleum industry and as a component of ceramics, enamels and pigments. *Molybdenum disulphide* (MoS_2) is employed as a heat-resistant lubricant or a lubricant additive. *Molybdenum hexacarbonyl* ($Mo(CO)_6$) is the starting product for the manufacture of organomolybdenum dyes. It is increasingly used for molybdenum plating by thermal decomposition.

Molybdenum compounds are widely used as catalysts or catalyst activators or promoters, especially for hydrogenation-cracking, alkylation and reforming in the petroleum industry. They are employed as laboratory reagents (phosphomolybdates). In addition, molybdenum compounds are used in electroplating and in tanning.

Hazards

In the processing and industrial utilization of molybdenum and its compounds there may be exposure to dusts and fumes of molybdenum and its oxides and sulphides. This exposure may occur, especially where high-temperature treatment is being carried out as, for example, in an electric furnace. Exposure to *molybdenum disulphide* lubricant spray, *molybdenum hexacarbonyl* and its breakdown products during molybdenum plating, *molybdenum hydroxide* ($Mo(OH)_3$) mist during electroplating, and molybdenum trioxide fumes which sublime above 800 °C may all prove hazardous to health.

Molybdenum compounds are highly toxic based on animal experiments. Acute poisoning causes severe gastrointestinal irritation with diarrhoea, coma and deaths from heart failure. Pneumoconiosis-like effects in the lungs have been reported in animal studies. Workers exposed to pure molybdenum or to *molybdenum oxide* (MoO_3) (concentration of 1 to 19 mg Mo/m³) over a period of 3 to 7 years have suffered from pneumoconiosis. Inhalation of molybdenum dust from alloys or carbides can cause "hard metal lung disease".

There is a wide degree of variation in the hazard resulting from exposure. Insoluble molybdenum compounds (e.g., molybdenum disulphide and many of the oxides and halides) are characterized by low toxicity; however, the soluble compounds (i.e., those in which molybdenum is an anion, such as *sodium molybdenate*—$Na_2MoO_4 \cdot 2H_2O$) are considerably more toxic and should be handled with care. Likewise, precautions should be taken to prevent over-exposure to freshly generated molybdenum fumes as in the thermal decomposition of molybdenum hexacarbonyl.

Exposure to molybdenum trioxide produces irritation of the eyes and the mucous membranes of the nose and throat. Anaemia is a characteristic feature of molybdenum toxicity, with low haemoglobin concentrations and reduced red-cell counts.

High dietary levels of molybdenum in cattle were found to produce deformities in the joints of the extremities. Among chemists handling molybdenum and tungsten solutions, an abnormally high frequency of cases of gout have been reported, and a correlation has been found between the content of molybdenum in food, the incidence of gout, uricaemia and xanthine oxidase activity.

Safety Measures

While working with molybdenum in industry, proper local exhaust ventilation should be employed to collect fumes at their source. Respirators may be worn when engineering and work practices have failed, when such controls are in the process of being installed, for operations requiring entry into tanks or closed vessels, or in emergencies. In the paint, printing and coatings industries, local and general exhaust ventilation as well as safety glasses, protective clothing, face shields and acceptable respirators should be used to reduce exposure for workers handling molybdenum-based dry ingredients for inorganic and organic colours.

NICKEL

F. William Sunderman, Jr.

Nickel (Ni) compounds of interest include *nickel oxide* (NiO), *nickel hydroxide* ($Ni(OH)_2$), *nickel subsulphide* (Ni_3S_2), *nickel sulphate* ($NiSO_4$) and *nickel chloride* ($NiCl_2$). *Nickel carbonyl* ($Ni(CO)_4$) is considered in a separate article on metal carbonyls.

Occurrence and Uses

Nickel (Ni) comprises 5 to 50% of the weight of meteorites and is found in ores in combination with sulphur, oxygen, antimony, arsenic and/or silica. Ore deposits of commercial importance are principally oxides (e.g., laterite ores containing mixed nickel/iron oxides) and sulphides. Pentlandite (($NiFe)_9S_8$), the major sulphide mineral, is commonly deposited in association with pyrrhotite (Fe_7S_6), chalcopyrite ($CuFeS_2$) and small amounts of cobalt, selenium, tellurium, silver, gold and platinum. Substantial deposits of nickel ores are found in Canada, Russia, Australia, New Caledonia, Indonesia and Cuba.

Since nickel, copper and iron occur as distinct minerals in the sulphide ores, mechanical methods of concentration, such as flotation and magnetic separation, are applied after the ore has been crushed and ground. The nickel concentrate is converted to nickel sulphide matte by roasting or sintering. The matte is refined by electrowinning or by the Mond process. In the Mond process, the matte is ground, calcined and treated with carbon monoxide at 50 °C to form gaseous nickel carbonyl ($Ni(CO)_4$), which is then decomposed at 200 to 250 °C to deposit pure nickel powder. Worldwide production of nickel is approximately 70 million kg/year.

More than 3,000 nickel alloys and compounds are commercially produced. Stainless steel and other Ni-Cr-Fe alloys are widely used for corrosion-resistant equipment, architectural applications and cooking utensils. Monel metal and other Ni-Cu alloys are used in coinage, food-processing machinery and dairy equipment. Ni-Al alloys are used for magnets and catalyst production (e.g., Raney nickel). Ni-Cr alloys are used for heating elements, gas turbines and jet engines. Alloys of nickel with precious metals are used in jewellery. Nickel metal, its compounds and alloys have many other uses, including electroplating, magnetic tapes and computer components, arc-welding rods, surgical and dental prostheses, nickel-cadmium batteries, paint pigments (e.g., yellow nickel titanate), moulds for ceramic and glass containers, and catalysts for hydrogenation reactions, organic syntheses and the final methanation step of coal gasification. Occupational exposures to nickel also occur in recycling operations, since nickel-bearing materials, especially from the steel industry, are commonly melted, refined and used to prepare alloys similar in composition to those that entered the recycling process.

Hazards

Human health hazards from occupational exposures to nickel compounds generally fall into three major categories:

1. allergy
2. rhinitis, sinusitis and respiratory diseases
3. cancers of the nasal cavities, lungs and other organs.

The health hazards from nickel carbonyl are considered separately, in the article on metal carbonyls.

Allergy. Nickel and nickel compounds are among the most common causes of allergic contact dermatitis. This problem is not limited to persons with occupational exposure to nickel compounds; dermal sensitization occurs in the general population from exposures to nickel-containing coins, jewellery, watch cases and clothing fasteners. In nickel-exposed persons, nickel dermatitis usually begins as a papular erythema of the hands. The skin gradually becomes eczematous, and, in the chronic stage, lichenification frequently develops. Nickel sensitization sometimes causes conjunctivitis, eosinophilic pneumonitis, and local or systemic reactions to nickel-containing implants (e.g., intraosseous pins, dental inlays, cardiac valve prostheses and pacemaker wires). Ingestion of nickel-contaminated tap water or nickel-rich foods can exacerbate hand eczema in nickel-sensitive persons.

Rhinitis, sinusitis and respiratory diseases. Workers in nickel refineries and nickel electroplating shops, who are heavily exposed to inhalation of nickel dusts or aerosols of soluble nickel compounds, may develop chronic diseases of the upper respiratory tract, including hypertrophic rhinitis, nasal sinusitis, anosmia, nasal polyposis and perforation of the nasal septum. Chronic diseases of the lower respiratory tract (e.g., bronchitis, pulmonary fibrosis) have also been reported, but such conditions are infrequent. Rendall et al. (1994) reported the fatal acute exposure of a worker to inhalation of particulate nickel from a metal arc process; the authors stressed the importance of wearing protective equipment while using metal arc processes with nickel wire electrodes.

Cancer. Epidemiological studies of nickel-refinery workers in Canada, Wales, Germany, Norway and Russia have documented increased mortality rates from cancers of the lung and nasal cavities. Certain groups of nickel-refinery workers have also been reported to have increased incidences of other malignant tumours, including carcinomas of the larynx, kidney, prostate or stomach, and sarcomas of soft tissues, but the statistical significance of these observations is questionable. The increased risks of cancers of the lungs and nasal cavities have occurred primarily among workers in refinery operations that entail high nickel exposures, including roasting, smelting and electrolysis. Although these cancer risks have generally been associated with exposures to insoluble nickel compounds, such as nickel subsulphide and nickel oxide, exposures to soluble nickel compounds have been implicated in electrolysis workers.

Epidemiological studies of cancer risks among workers in nickel-using industries have generally been negative, but recent evidence suggests slightly increased lung cancer risks among welders, grinders, electroplaters and battery makers. Such workers are often exposed to dusts and fumes that contain mixtures of carcinogenic metals (e.g., nickel and chromium, or nickel and cadmium). Based on an evaluation of epidemiological studies, the International Agency for Research on Cancer (IARC) concluded in 1990: "There is sufficient evidence in humans for the carcinogenicity of nickel sulphate and of the combinations of nickel sulphides and oxides encountered in the nickel refining industry. There is inadequate evidence in humans for the carcinogenicity of nickel and nickel alloys." Nickel compounds have been classified as carcinogenic to humans (Group 1), and metallic nickel as possibly carcinogenic to humans (Group 2B).

Renal effects. Workers with high exposures to soluble nickel compounds may develop renal tubular dysfunction, evidenced by increased renal excretion of β_2-microglobulin (β_2M) and N-acetyl-glucosaminidase (NAG).

Safety and Health Measures

A general protocol for health surveillance of workers exposed to nickel was proposed in 1994 by the Nickel Producers Evironmental Research Association (NiPERA) and the Nickel Development Institute (NiDI). The key elements are as follows:

Pre-placement assessment. The goals of this examination are to identify pre-existing medical conditions that may influence hiring and job placement, and to provide baseline data for subsequent functional, physiological or pathological changes. The assessment includes (i) detailed medical and occupational history, focusing on lung problems, exposures to lung toxins, past or present allergies (particularly to nickel), asthma and personal habits (e.g., smoking, alcohol consumption), (ii) complete physical examination, with attention to respiratory and skin problems and (iii) determination of the respiratory protective equipment that may be worn. Chest x ray, pulmonary function tests, audiometric tests and vision tests may be included. Skin patch testing for nickel sensitivity is not routinely performed, because such tests could possibly sensitize the subject. If the organization conducts a biological monitoring programme for nickel-exposed workers (see below), baseline nickel concentrations in urine or serum are obtained during the pre-placement assessment.

Periodic assessment. The goals of periodic medical examinations, typically performed annually, are to monitor the worker's general health and to address nickel-associated concerns. The examination includes the history of recent illnesses, symptom review, physical examination and re-evaluation of the worker's ability to use the respiratory protective equipment required for particular tasks. Pulmonary symptoms are assessed by a standard questionnaire for chronic bronchitis. Chest x ray may be legally required in some countries; pulmonary function tests (e.g., forced vital capacity (FVC) and forced expiratory volume in 1 second (FEV_1)) are generally left to the physician's discretion. Periodic cancer detection procedures (e.g., rhinoscopy, nasal sinus x rays, nasal mucosal biopsy, exfoliative cytological studies) may be indicated in workers with high-risk exposures in nickel refining.

Biological monitoring. Analyses of nickel concentrations in urine and serum samples may reflect the recent exposures of workers to metallic nickel and soluble nickel compounds, but these assays do not furnish reliable measures of the total body nickel burden. The uses and limitations of biological monitoring of nickel-exposed workers have been summarized by Sunderman et al. (1986). A technical report on analysis of nickel in body fluids was issued in 1994 by the Commission on Toxicology of the International Union of Pure and Applied Chemistry (IUPAC). The National Maximum Workplace Concentration Committee (NMWCC) of the Netherlands proposed that urine nickel concentration 40 µg/g creatinine, or serum nickel concentration 5 µg/l (both measured in samples obtained at the end of a working week or a work shift) be considered warning limits for further investigation of workers exposed to nickel metal or soluble nickel compounds. If a biological monitoring programme is implemented, it should augment an environmental monitoring programme, so that biological data are not used as a surrogate for exposure estimates. A standard method for the analysis of nickel in workplace air was developed in 1995 by the UK Health and Safety Executive.

Treatment. When a group of workers accidently drank water heavily contaminated with nickel chloride and nickel sulphate, conservative treatment with intravenous fluids to induce diuresis was effective (Sunderman et al. 1988). The best therapy for nickel dermatitis is avoidance of exposure, with special attention to work hygienic practices. Therapy of acute nickel carbonyl poisoning is discussed in the article on metal carbonyls.

• NIOBIUM

Occurrence and Uses
Niobium (Nb) is found together with other elements including titanium (Ti), zirconium (Zr), tungsten (W), thorium (Th) and uranium (U) in ores such as tantalite-columbite, fergusonite, samarskite, pyrochlore, koppite and loparite. The largest deposits are located in Australia and Nigeria, and during the last few years extensive deposits have been discovered in Uganda, Kenya, Tanzania and Canada.

Niobium is widely used in the electrovacuum industry and also in the manufacture of anodes, grids, electrolytic condensers and rectifiers. In chemical engineering, niobium is used as a corrosion-proof material for heat exchangers, filters, needle valves and so on. High-quality cutting tools and magnetic materials are made from niobium alloys. Ferroniobium alloy is used in thermonuclear appliances.

Niobium and its refractory alloys are utilized in the field of rocket technology, in the supersonic aircraft industry, interplanetary flight equipment and in satellites. Niobium is also used in surgery.

Hazards
During the mining and concentration of niobium ore and processing of the concentrate, the workers may be exposed to general hazards, such as dust and fumes, which are typical for these operations. In the mines, the action of dust may be aggravated by exposure to radioactive substances such as thorium and uranium.

Toxicity
Much of the information about the behaviour of niobium in the body is based on studies of the radioisotope pair ^{95}Zr-^{95}Nb, a common nuclear fission product. ^{95}Nb is the daughter of ^{95}Zr. One study investigated cancer incidence among niobium mine workers exposed to radon and thoron daughters and found an association between lung cancer and cumulative alpha-radiation.

Intravenous and intraperitoneal injections of niobium (radioactive) and its compounds showed a fairly uniform distribution through the organism, with a tendency to accumulate in the liver, kidneys, spleen and bone marrow. The elimination of radioactive niobium from the organism can be hastened appreciably by the injection of massive doses of zirconium nitrate. After intraperitoneal injections of stable niobium in the form of potassium niobate, the LD_{50} for rats was 86 to 92 mg/kg and for mice 13 mg/kg. Metallic niobium is not absorbed from the stomach or intestines. The LD_{50} of niobium pentachloride in these organs was 940 mg/kg for rats, while the corresponding figure for potassium niobate was 3,000 mg/kg. Niobium compounds administered intravenously, intraperitoneally or per os produce a particularly pronounced effect on the kidneys. This effect can be attenuated by preventive medication with ascorbic acid. Oral intake of niobium pentachloride furthermore causes acute irritation of the mucous membranes of the gullet and stomach, and liver changes; chronic exposure during 4 months causes temporary blood changes (leukocytosis, prothrombin deficiency).

Inhaled niobium is retained in the lung, which is the critical organ for dust. Daily inhalation of niobium nitride dust at a concentration of 40 mg/m^3 of air leads within a few months to signs of pneumoconiosis (while there are no noticeable signs of toxic action): thickening of the interalveolar septa, development of considerable amounts of collagenous fibres in the peribronchial and perivascular tissue, and desquamation of the bronchial epithelium. Analogous changes develop upon intratracheal administration of niobium pentoxide dust; in this case dust is found even in the lymph nodes.

Safety and Health Measures
Atmospheric concentrations of the aerosols of niobium alloys and compounds that contain toxic elements such as fluorine, manganese and beryllium, should be strictly controlled. During the mining and concentration of niobium ore containing uranium and thorium, the worker should be protected against radioactivity. Proper engineering design including adequate ventilation with fresh air is necessary to control dust in mine air. In the extraction of pure niobium from its compounds by powder metallurgy, the workplaces must be kept free from niobium dust and fumes, and workers must be protected against chemicals such as caustic alkalis and benzene. In addition, regular medical examinations which include lung function tests are recommended.

OSMIUM

Occurrence and Uses
Osmium (Os) is found almost exclusively in osmiridium, a natural alloy consisting of osmium and iridium, and in all platinum ores. The major ore deposits are located in the Urals, Canada and Colombia, with less important ores in Australia and in Alaska, California and Oregon in the United States.

Osmium alloys readily with the other platinum metals and with iron, cobalt and nickel. It also forms brittle intermetallic compounds with tin and zinc. One of the distinctive features of osmium is the ease with which it forms osmium tetroxide (OsO_4). Osmium powder always has the characteristic odour of its tetroxide because even at normal temperatures it oxidizes in air to OsO_4, even if only to a slight degree. The tetroxide is extremely volatile and has an unpleasant odour, from which the name of the element was derived (osme = odour). It is a powerful oxidizer and is easily converted to osmium dioxide (OsO_2) or even to metallic osmium. With alkalis it forms unstable compounds such as $OsO_4 \cdot 2KOH$. When heated, osmium readily forms osmium disulphide (OsS_2). The fluorides OsF_4, OsF_6 and OsF_8 are also formed. Various chlorides are formed when osmium is treated with chlorine at high temperatures. With carbon monoxide, it forms carbonyls. It also forms a number of compounds with the complex anion containing osmium, as for example ammonium osmium hexachloride (($NH_4)_2OsCl_6$).

Osmium is used as a catalyst in the synthesis of ammonia and in the hydrogenation of organic compounds. As an alloy with indium it is used for the manufacture of compass needles and fine machine bearings. It is found in the parts of watch and lock mechanisms and in fountain pen points. *Osmium tetroxide*, sometimes incorrectly termed osmic acid, is used as an oxidizing agent, particularly for converting olefins to glycols. The chloro-osmiates are used in place of gold salts in photography.

Hazards
The metal is innocuous, but persons engaged in its production are exposed to the effects of vapours from acids and chlorine. Os-

mium tetroxide vapours are poisonous and extremely irritating to the eyes even at low concentrations, causing weeping and conjunctivitis, and to the upper respiratory system, causing bronchitis, bronchial spasms and difficulty in breathing, which may last for several hours. Longer exposure can result in damage to the cornea, blindness, disturbances of the digestive system and inflammatory disorders of the lungs and kidneys. Upon contact, it discolours the skin green or black and causes dermatitis and ulceration.

Safety and Health Measures

During the production of osmium, local exhaust ventilation should be provided and the apparatus should be sealed if gaseous chlorine is used. An enclosed ventilated area or hood is necessary in order to control the release of osmium tetroxide vapours into the work environment and prevent eye and respiratory irritation. Exposed workers should wear protective clothing, hand protection, gas-tight chemical safety eye protection and appropriate respiratory protective equipment. Containers must be stored in naturally ventilated premises. The vapour has a pronounced and nauseating odour which should serve as a warning of toxic concentration in the air, and personnel should leave the polluted area immediately. Determination in air and blood is possible by colourimetry of the complex with thiourea.

PALLADIUM

Occurrence and Uses

Palladium (Pd) occurs in nature with platinum or gold, as the selenide. It is found in nickel sulphide ores and in the minerals stibiopalladinite, braggite and porpezite. The concentration of palladium in the Earth's crust is 0.01 ppm.

Palladium has been used in gold, silver and copper alloys in dentistry. Alloys are also used for bearings, springs and balance wheels in watches. Palladium is used as a catalyst in the manufacture of sulphuric acid. In powder form it serves as a catalyst in hydrogenation. The sponge form is used for separation of hydrogen from a mixture of gases. Silver alloys are used for electrical contacts. Palladium (II) complexes have been studied as antineoplastic drugs.

Palladium chloride ($PdCl_2 \cdot 2H_2O$), or palladous chloride, is used in photography toning solutions and for the manufacture of indelible ink. It is an agent used for transferring pictures to porcelain, for electroplating watch parts, and for finding leaks in buried gas pipes. Palladium chloride is associated with copper chloride in catalyzing the production of acetaldehyde from ethylene.

Palladium oxide (PdO), or palladous oxide, is used as a reduction catalyst in the synthesis of organic compounds. *Palladium nitrate* ($Pd(NO_3)_2$) is used in the separation of halides. *Palladium trifluoride* (PdF_3) is an active oxidizing agent.

Hazards

Studies indicate cases of allergy and contact dermatitis caused by palladium in dental alloys and fine jewellery. In one study palladium-based alloys were associated with several cases of stomatitis and oral lichenoid reactions. In this same study palladium allergy occurred mainly in patients with a sensitivity to nickel. Palladium chloride produces dermatitis and allergic skin sensitization in workers exposed daily. In addition, it should be regarded as an eye irritant. Palladium hydroxide was used in the past to treat obesity by injection; this form of treatment gave rise to localized necrosis and was discontinued.

Safety and Health Measures

Correct exhaust ventilation is necessary when working with palladium and its compounds. Good personal hygiene, proper protective clothing and medical surveillance are important measures in preventing the risks associated with sensitization. Adequate sanitary facilities must be provided.

PLATINUM

Occurrence and Uses

Platinum (Pt) occurs in native form and in a number of mineral forms, including sperrylite ($PtAs_2$), cooperite (Pt,Pd)S and braggite (Pt,Pd,Ni)S. Platinum is sometimes found with palladium as the arsenide and selenide. The concentration of platinum in the Earth's crust is 0.005 ppm.

Platinum and its alloys are used as catalysts in petroleum reformation, ammonia oxidation, sulphur dioxide oxidation, hydrogenation and dehydrogenation. Platinum is used in the control of automotive emissions, in electrical contacts, electrodes and thermocouples. It is also used in spinnerets for fibrous glass and rayon manufacture, in reflecting or ornamental surfaces and in jewellery. Because of the permanence of platinum, it is utilized for national and international standards for weight, length and temperature measurement. Platinum is manufactured into sheet, wire and foil, and it has wide use in laboratory apparatus.

Nickel, osmium, ruthenium, copper, gold, silver and iridium are alloyed with platinum to increase hardness. Commercially important alloys of platinum are prepared with copper, gold, iridium, rhodium and ruthenium. Alloys with cobalt have become important because of their strong ferromagnetic properties.

Chloroplatinic acid, formed when platinum is dissolved in *aqua regia*, is useful in the manufacture of catalysts. *Potassium hexachloroplatinate* is used in the photographic industry, and *platinum tetrachloride* is used as a catalyst in the chemical industry. *Platinum hexafluoride* is an extremely powerful oxidizing agent, the first substance to oxidize an inert gas (xenon). *Cis-Dichlorodiamineplatinum II*, a complex of platinum and related congeners, was found to be active against a broad spectrum of animal tumours. It has been found useful in producing remissions with a number of human cancers.

Hazards

The toxic and potentially toxic effects of platinum in workers are believed to be related to certain water-soluble platinum salts (e.g., potassium hexachloroplatinate, potassium tetrachloroplatinate, sodium chloroplatinate and ammonium chloroplatinate). Inhalation exposure to these platinum salts is known to give rise to manifestations of respiratory allergy. The first report of such reactions to platinum compounds appeared in 1911 among photographic workers who suffered respiratory and skin disorders. Similar clinical manifestations—rhinitis, conjunctivitis, asthma, urticaria and contact dermatitis—have since been reported mainly in platinum refinery workers and chemists. Allergic respiratory diseases have been reported in a high proportion of refinery workers exposed to soluble hexachloroplatinate salts. Allergic rhinitis and bronchitis in 52 of 91 workers from four platinum refineries in Britain have been described, with most severe symptoms amongst the workers crushing the chloroplatinate salts. The term *platinosis* has been defined as the effects of soluble platinum salts on people exposed to these occupationally and is characterized by pronounced irritation of the nose and upper respiratory passages, with sneezing, running of the eyes, and coughing. Later asthmatic symptoms of cough, tightness of the chest, wheezing and shortness of breath appear. These symptoms become progressively worse with the length of employment. Some workers may show all three allergic manifestations with involvement of the nasal mucosa, bronchi and skin. Reports of allergy among workers exposed to chloroplatinate salts have appeared from the United States, the United Kingdom, Switzerland, Germany and South Africa.

It is of interest to note that anaphylactic reactions have been noted in some patients who have been treated with platinum anti-tumour agents.

In general, the allergic effects of exposure to platinum have been confined to specific platinum complexes. Sensitized workers when tested by pin prick do not respond to the majority of the platinum compounds used in the refinery. Once sensitized the condition persists, and workers generally have to avoid exposure to platinum. Smoking appears to increase the risk of sensitization by platinum salts.

The emissions from catalytic mufflers containing platinum do not appear to present a health hazard from the point of view of the platinum emission.

Safety and Health Measures

Control of platinum hazards can be achieved only by preventing the release of the soluble complex platinum salts to the atmosphere of the workshop. Since platinum dust is more potentially harmful than is the spray, the soluble complex salts should not be dried unless necessary. Good exhaust ventilation is necessary in platinum refineries. Chemical procedures which may generate these salts should be carried out in ventilated fume hoods. Open centrifuges should not be used. Good personal hygiene, proper protective clothing, and medical surveillance are important preventive measures. Workers with a history of allergic or respiratory disease should be advised not to work with soluble platinum compounds.

Pin prick, nasal and bronchial tests have been devised. Skin prick tests with dilute concentrations of the soluble platinum complexes appear to provide reproducible, reliable and highly sensitive biological monitors of allergic response.

RHENIUM

Occurrence and Uses

Rhenium (Re) is found in the combined state in platinum ores, gadolinite, molybdenite (MoS_2) and columbite. It is found in some sulphide ores. It is a rare element making up about 0.001 ppm of the Earth's crust.

Rhenium is used in electron tubes and in semiconductor applications. It is also used as a highly selective catalyst for hydrogenation and dehydrogenation. Rhenium-tagged antibodies have been used experimentally to treat adenocarcinomas of the colon, lung and ovary. Rhenium is used in medical instruments, in high-vacuum equipment, and in alloys for electrical contacts and thermocouples. It is also used for plating of jewellery.

Rhenium is alloyed with tungsten and molybdenum to improve their workability.

Hazards

Chronic toxic manifestations are not known. Some compounds, such as rhenium hexafluoride, are irritating to the skin and eye. In experimental animals, inhalation of rhenium dust causes pulmonary fibrosis. Rhenium VII sulphide ignites spontaneously in air and emits toxic fumes of oxides of sulphur when heated. Hexamethyl rhenium presents a serious explosion hazard and should be handled with extreme caution.

RHODIUM

Occurrence and Uses

Rhodium is one of the rarest elements in the Earth's crust (average concentration 0.001 ppm). It is found in small quantities associated with native platinum and some copper-nickel ores. It occurs in the minerals rhodite, sperrylite and iridosmine (or osmiridium).

Rhodium is used in corrosion-resistant electroplates for protecting silverware from tarnishing and in high-reflectivity mirrors for searchlights and projectors. It is also useful for plating optical instuments and for furnace winding. Rhodium serves as a catalyst for various hydrogenation and oxidation reactions. It is used for spinnerets in rayon production and as an ingredient in gold decorations on glass and porcelain.

Rhodium is alloyed with platinum and palladium to make very hard alloys for use in spinning nozzles.

Hazards

There have been no significant experimental data indicating health problems with rhodium, its alloys or its compounds in humans. Although toxicity is not established, it is necessary to handle these metals carefully. Contact dermatitis in a worker who prepared pieces of metal for plating with rhodium has been reported. The authors argue that the small number of reported cases of sensitization to rhodium may reflect the rarity of use rather than the safety of this metal. The American Conference of Governmental Industrial Hygienists (ACGIH) has recommended a low threshold limit value for rhodium and its soluble salts, based on analogy with platinum. The ability of soluble salts of rhodium to give rise to allergic manifestations in humans has not been completely demonstrated.

RUTHENIUM

Occurrence and Uses

Ruthenium is found in the minerals osmiridium and laurite, and in platinum ores. It is a rare element comprising about 0.001 ppm of the Earth's crust.

Ruthenium is used as a substitute for platinum in jewellery. It is utilized as a hardener for pen nibs, electrical contact relays and electrical filaments. Ruthenium is also used in ceramic colours and in electroplating. It acts as a catalyst in the synthesis of long-chain hydrocarbons. In addition, ruthenium has been used recently in treating eye uveal malignant melanomas.

Ruthenium forms useful alloys with platinum, palladium, cobalt, nickel and tungsten for better wear resistance. *Ruthenium red* ($Ru_3Cl_6H_{42}N_4O_2$) or *ruthenium oxychloride ammoniated* is used as a microscopy reagent for pectin, gum, animal tissues and bacteria. Ruthenium red is an eye inflammatory agent.

Hazards

Ruthenium tetraoxide is volatile and irritating to the respiratory tract.

Some ruthenium electroplating complexes may be skin and eye irritants, but documentation of this is lacking. Ruthenium radioisotopes, chiefly [103]Ru and [106]Ru, occur as fission products in the nuclear fuel cycle. Since ruthenium may transform to volatile compounds (it forms numerous nitrogen complexes as noted above), there has been concern about its uptake in the environment. The significance of radio-ruthenium as a potential radiation hazard is still largely unknown.

SELENIUM

Occurrence and Uses

Selenium (Se) is found in rocks and soils all over the world. There are no true deposits of selenium anywhere, and it cannot economically be recovered directly. Various estimates for selenium in the Earth's crust range from 0.03 to 0.8 ppm; the highest concentrations known are in native sulphur from volcanoes, which contains up to 8,350 ppm. Selenium does, however, occur together with tellurium in the sediments and sludges left from electrolytic copper refining. The chief world supplies are from the copper-refining industries of Canada, the United States and Zimbabwe, where the slimes contain up to 15% selenium.

The manufacture of selenium rectifiers, which convert alternating current to direct current, accounts for over half the world's production of selenium. Selenium is also used for decolourizing green glass and for making ruby glass. It is an additive in the natural and synthetic rubber industries and an insecticide. Selenium is used for alloying with stainless steel and copper.

^{75}Se is used for the radioactive scanning of the pancreas and for photostat and x-ray xerography. *Selenium oxide* or *selenium dioxide* (SeO_2) is produced by burning selenium in oxygen, and it is the most widely used selenium compound in industry. Selenium oxide is employed in the manufacture of other selenium compounds and as a reagent for alkaloids.

Selenium chloride (Se_2Cl_2) is a dark brownish-red stable liquid which hydrolyses in moist air to give selenium, selenious acid and hydrochloric acid. *Selenium hexafluoride* (SeF_6) is used as a gaseous electric insulator.

Hazards

The elemental forms of selenium are probably completely harmless to humans; its compounds, however, are dangerous and their action resembles that of sulphur compounds. Selenium compounds may be absorbed in toxic quantities through the lungs, intestinal tract or damaged skin. Many selenium compounds will cause intense burns of skin and mucous membranes, and chronic skin exposure to light concentrations of dust from certain compounds may produce dermatitis and paronychia.

The sudden inhalation of large quantities of selenium fumes, selenium oxide or hydrogen selenide may produce pulmonary oedema due to local irritant effects on the alveoli; this oedema may not set in for 1 to 4 hours after exposure. Exposure to atmospheric *hydrogen selenide* concentrations of 5 mg/m^3 is intolerable. However, this substance occurs in only small amounts in industry (for example, due to bacterial contamination of selenium-contaminated gloves), although there have been reports of exposure to high concentrations following laboratory accidents.

Skin contact with selenium oxide or *selenium oxychloride* may cause burns or sensitization to selenium and its compounds, especially selenium oxide. Selenium oxychloride readily destroys skin on contact, causing third-degree burns unless immediately removed with water. However, selenium oxide burns are rarely severe and, if properly treated, heal without a scar.

Dermatitis due to exposure to airborne selenium oxide dust usually starts at the points of contact of the dust with the wrist or neck and may extend to contiguous areas of the arms, face and upper portions of the trunk. It usually consists of discrete, red, itchy papules which may become confluent on the wrist, where selenium dioxide is liable to penetrate between the glove and sleeve of the overall. Painful paronychia may also be produced. However, one more frequently sees cases of excruciatingly painful throbbing nail beds, due to the selenium dioxide penetrating

under the free edge of the nails, in workers handling selenium dioxide powder or waste red selenium fume powder without wearing impermeable gloves.

Splashes of *selenium oxide* entering the eye may cause conjunctivitis if not treated immediately. Persons who work in atmospheres containing selenium dioxide dust may develop a condition known among the workers as "rose eye", a pink allergy of the eyelids, which often become puffy. There is usually also a conjunctivitis of the palpebral conjunctiva but rarely of the bulbar conjunctiva.

The first and most characteristic sign of selenium absorption is a garlic odour of the breath. The odour is probably caused by dimethyl selenium, almost certainly produced in the liver by the detoxication of selenium by methylation. This odour will clear quickly if the worker is removed from exposure, but there is no known treatment for it. A more subtle and earlier indication than the garlic odour is a metallic taste in the mouth. It is less dramatic and is often overlooked by the workers. The other systemic effects are impossible to evaluate accurately and are not specific to selenium. They include pallor, lassitude, irritability, vague gastrointestinal symptoms and giddiness.

The possibility of liver and spleen damage in people exposed to high levels of selenium compounds deserves further attention. In addition, more studies of workers are needed to examine the possible protective effects of selenium against lung cancer.

Safety and Health Measures

Selenium oxide is the main selenium problem in industry since it is formed whenever selenium is boiled in the presence of air. All sources of selenium oxide or fumes should be fitted with exhaust ventilation systems with an air speed of at least 30 m/min. Workers should be provided with hand protection, overalls, eye and face protection, and gauze masks. Supplied-air respiratory protective equipment is necessary in cases where good extraction is not possible, such as in the cleaning of ventilation ducts. Smoking, eating and drinking at the workplace should be prohibited, and dining and sanitary facilities, including showers and locker rooms, should be provided at a point distant from exposure areas. Wherever possible, operations should be mechanized, automated or provided with remote control.

SILVER

Occurrence and Uses

Silver (Ag) is found throughout the world, but most of it is produced in Mexico, the western United States, Bolivia, Peru, Canada and Australia. Much of it is obtained as a by-product from argentiferous lead, zinc and copper ores in which it occurs as the silver sulphide, argentite (Ag_2S). It is also recovered during the treatment of gold ores and is an essential constituent of the gold telluride, calaverite (($AuAg$)Te_2).

Because pure silver is too soft for coins, ornaments, cutlery, plate and jewellery, silver is hardened by alloying with copper for all these applications. Silver is extremely resistant to acetic acid and, therefore, silver vats are used in the acetic acid, vinegar, cider and brewing industries. Silver is also used in busbars and windings of electrical plants, in silver solders, dental amalgams, high-capacity batteries, engine bearings, sterling ware and in ceramic paints. It is employed in brazing alloys and in the silvering of glass beads.

Silver finds use in the manufacture of formaldehyde, acetaldehyde and higher aldehydes by the catalytic dehydrogenation of the corresponding primary alcohols. In many installations, the catalyst consists of a shallow bed of crystalline silver of extremely high purity. An important use of silver is in the photography industry. It is the unique and instantaneous reaction of the halides of silver on exposure to light that makes the metal virtually indispensable for films, plates and photographic printing paper.

Silver nitrate ($AgNO_3$) is used in photography, the manufacture of mirrors, silver plating, dyeing, colouring of porcelain, and etching ivory. It is an important reagent in analytical chemistry and a chemical intermediate. Silver nitrate is found in sympathetic and indelible inks. It also serves as a static inhibitor for carpets and woven materials and as a water disinfectant. For medical purposes silver nitrate has been used for the prophylaxis of *ophthalmia neonatorum*. It has been utilized as an antiseptic, an astringent, and in veterinary use for the treatment of wounds and local inflammations.

Silver nitrate is a powerful oxidizing agent and a fire hazard, in addition to being strongly caustic, corrosive and poisonous. In the form of dust or a solid it is dangerous to the eyes, causing burns of the conjunctiva, argyria and blindness.

Silver oxide (Ag_2O) is used in the purification of drinking water, for polishing and colouring glass yellow in the glass industry, and as a catalyst. In veterinary medicine, it is used as an ointment or solution for general germicidal and parasiticidal purposes. Silver oxide is a powerful oxidizing material and a fire hazard.

Silver picrate (($O_2N)_3C_6H_2OAg\cdot H_2O$) is used as a vaginal antimicrobial. In veterinary medicine it is used against granular vaginitis for cattle. It is highly explosive and poisonous.

Hazards

Silver exposure may lead to a benign condition called "argyria". If the dust of the metal or its salts is absorbed, silver is precipitated in the tissues in the metallic state and cannot be eliminated from the body in this state. Reduction to the metallic state takes place either by the action of light on the exposed parts of the skin and visible mucous membranes, or by means of hydrogen sulphide in other tissues. Silver dusts are irritants and can lead to ulceration of the skin and nasal septum.

Occupations involving the risk of argyria can be divided into two groups:

1. workers who handle a compound of silver, either the nitrate, fulminate or cyanide, which, broadly speaking, giving rise to generalized argyria from inhalation and ingestion of the silver salt concerned
2. workers who handle metallic silver, small particles of which accidentally penetrate the exposed skin, giving rise to local argyria by a process equivalent to tattooing.

Generalized argyria is unlikely to occur at respirable silver concentrations in air of 0.01 mg/m^3 or at oral cumulative doses lower than 3.8 g. Persons affected by generalized argyria are often called "blue men" by their fellow workers. The face, forehead, neck, hands and forearms develop a dark slatey-grey colour, uniform in distribution and varying in depth depending on the degree of exposure. Pale scars up to about 6 mm across may be found on the face, hands and forearms due to the caustic effects of silver nitrate. The fingernails are a deep chocolate-brown colour. The buccal mucosa is slatey-grey or bluish in colour. Very slight pigmentation may be detected in the covered parts of the skin. The toenails may show a slight bluish discolouration. In a condition called argyrosis conjunctivae, the colour of the conjunctivae varies from a slight grey to a deep brown, the lower palpebral portion being particularly affected. The posterior border of the lower lid, the caruncle and the plica semilunaris are deeply pigmented and may be almost black. Examination by means of the slit-lamp reveals a delicate network of faint grey pigmentation in the posterior elastic lamina (Descemet's membrane) of the cornea,

known as argyrosis corneae. In cases of long duration, argyrolentis is also found.

Where persons work with metallic silver, small particles may accidentally penetrate the exposed skin surface, giving rise to small pigmented lesions by a process equivalent to tattooing. This may occur in occupations involving the filing, drilling, hammering, turning, engraving, polishing, forging, soldering and smelting of silver. The left hand of the silversmith is more affected than the right, and the pigmentation occurs at the site of injuries from instruments. Many instruments, such as engraving tools, files, chisels and drills, are sharp and pointed and are liable to produce skin wounds. The piercing saw, an instrument resembling a fret saw, may break and run into the worker's hand. If the file slips, the worker's hand may be injured on the silver article; this is especially the case with the prongs of forks. A worker drawing silver wire through a hole in a silver draw-plate may get splinters of silver in his or her fingers. The pigmented points vary from tiny specks to areas 2 mm or more in diameter. They may be linear or rounded and in varying shades of grey or blue. The tattoo marks remain for life and cannot be removed. The use of gloves is usually impractical.

Safety and Health Measures

In addition to the engineering measures necessary to keep the airborne concentrations of silver fumes and dust as low as possible and in any case below the exposure limits, medical precautions for preventing argyria have been recommended. These include, in particular, the periodic medical examination of the eye, because the discolouration of the Descemet's membrane is an early sign of the disease. Biological monitoring seems to be possible via the faecal excretion of silver. There is no recognized effective treatment of argyria. The condition seems to stabilize when exposure to silver is discontinued. Some clinical improvement has been achieved by use of chelating agents and intradermal injection of sodium thiosulphate or potassium ferrocyanide. Sun exposure should be avoided to prevent further discolouration of the skin.

The main incompatibilities of silver with acetylene, ammonia, hydrogen peroxide, ethyleneimine and a number of organic acids should be kept in mind in order to prevent fire and explosion hazards.

The most unstable silver compounds, such as silver acetylide, silver ammonium compounds, silver azide, silver chlorate, silver fulminate and silver picrate, should be kept in cool, well-ventilated places, protected from shock, vibration and contamination by organic or other readily oxidizable materials and away from light.

When working silver nitrate, personal protection should include the wearing of protective clothing to avoid skin contact as well as chemical safety goggles for the protection of the eyes where spillage may occur. Respirators should be available at workplaces in which engineering control cannot maintain an acceptable environment.

TANTALUM

Occurrence and Uses

Tantalum (Ta) is obtained from the ores tantalite and columbite, which are mixed oxides of iron, manganese, niobium and tantalum. Although they are considered rare elements, the earth's crust contains about 0.003% of niobium and tantalum together, which are similar chemically and usually occur in combination.

The chief use of tantalum is in the production of electric capacitators. Tantalum powder is compacted, sintered and subjected to anodic oxidation. The film of oxide on the surface serves as an insulator, and upon introduction of an electrolyte solution, a high-performance capacitator is obtained. Structurally, tantalum is used where its high melting point, high density and resistance to acids are advantageous. The metal is employed widely in the chemical industry. Tantalum has also been used in rectifiers for railway signals, in surgery for suture wire and for bone repair, in vacuum tubes, furnaces, cutting tools, prosthetic appliances, fibre spinnerets and in laboratory ware.

Tantalum carbide is used as an abrasive. *Tantalum oxide* finds use in the manufacture of special glass with a high index of refraction for camera lenses.

Hazards

Metallic tantalum powder presents a fire and explosion hazard, although not as serious as that of other metals (zirconium, titanium and so on). The working of tantalum metal presents the hazards of burns, electric shock, and eye and traumatic injuries. Refining processes involve toxic and hazardous chemicals such as hydrogen fluoride, sodium and organic solvents.

Toxicity. The systemic toxicity of tantalum oxide, as well as that of metallic tantalum, is low, which is probably due to its poor solubility. It does, however, represent a skin, eye and respiratory hazard. In alloys with other metals such as cobalt, tungsten and niobium, tantalum has been attributed an aetiological role in hard-metal pneumoconiosis and in skin affections caused by hard-metal dust. Tantalum hydroxide was found to be not highly toxic to chick embryos, and the oxide was non-toxic to rats by intraperitoneal injection. Tantalum chloride, however, had an LD_{50} of 38 mg/kg (as Ta) while the complex salt K_2TaF_7 was about one-fourth as toxic.

Safety and Health Measures

In most operations, general ventilation can maintain the concentration of the dust of tantalum and its compounds below the threshold limit value. Open flames, arcs and sparks should be avoided in areas where tantalum powder is handled. If workers are regularly exposed to dust concentrations approaching the threshold limit level, periodic medical examinations, with emphasis on pulmonary function, are advisable. For operations involving fluorides of tantalum, as well as hydrogen fluoride, the precautions applicable to these compounds should be observed.

Tantalum bromide ($TaBr_5$), *tantalum chloride* ($TaCl_5$) and *tantalum fluoride* (TaF_5) should be kept in tightly stoppered bottles which are plainly labelled and stored in a cool, ventilated place, away from compounds which are affected by acids or acid fumes. Personnel involved should be cautioned about their hazards.

● TELLURIUM

Tellurium (Te) is a heavy element with the physical properties and silvery lustre of a metal, yet with the chemical properties of a non-metal such as sulphur or arsenic. Tellurium is known to exist in two allotropic forms—the hexagonal crystalline form (isomorphous with grey selenium) and an amorphous powder. Chemically, it resembles selenium and sulphur. It tarnishes slightly in air, but in the molten state it burns to give the white fumes of *tellurium dioxide*, which is only sparingly soluble in water.

Occurrence and Uses

The geochemistry of tellurium is imperfectly known; it is probably 50 to 80 times more rare than selenium in the lithosphere. It is,

like selenium, a by-product of the copper-refining industry. The anodic slimes contain up to 4% tellurium.

Tellurium is used to improve the machinability of "free-cutting" copper and certain steels. The element is a powerful carbide stabilizer in cast irons, and it is used to increase the depth of chill in castings. Additions of tellurium improve the creep strength of tin. The chief use of tellurium is, however, in the vulcanizing of rubber, since it reduces the time of curing and endows the rubber with increased resistance to heat and abrasion. In much smaller quantities, tellurium is used in pottery glazes and as an additive to selenium in metal rectifiers. Tellurium acts as a catalyst in some chemical processes. It is found in explosives, antioxidants and in infrared-transmitting glasses. Tellurium vapour is used in "daylight lamps", and *tellurium-radioiodinated fatty acid* (TPDA) has been used for myocardial scanning.

Hazards

Cases of acute industrial poisoning have occurred as a result of metallic tellurium fumes being absorbed into the lungs.

A study of foundry workers throwing tellurium pellets by hand into molten iron with the emanation of dense white fumes showed that persons exposed to tellurium concentrations of 0.01 to 0.74 mg/m^3 had higher urinary tellurium levels (0.01 to 0.06 mg/l) than workers exposed to concentrations of 0.00 to 0.05 mg/m3 (urinary concentrations of 0.00 to 0.03 mg/l). The most common sign of exposure was a garlic odour of the breath (84% of cases) and a metallic taste in the mouth (30% of cases). Workers complained of somnolence in the afternoons and loss of appetite, but suppression of sweat did not occur; blood and central nervous system test results were normal. One worker still had a garlic odour in his breath and tellurium in the urine after being away from the work for 51 days.

In laboratory workers who were exposed to fumes of melting tellurium-copper (fifty/fifty) alloy for 10 min, there were no immediate symptoms, but the effects of stinking breath were pronounced. Since tellurium forms a sparingly soluble oxide with no acidic reaction, there is no danger to the skin or to the lungs from tellurium dust or fumes. The element is absorbed through the gastrointestinal tract and lungs, and excreted in the breath, faeces and urine.

Tellurium dioxide (TeO_2), *hydrogen telluride* (H_2Te) and *potassium tellurite* (K_2TeO_3) are of industrial health significance. Because tellurium forms its oxide over 450 °C and the dioxide formed is almost insoluble in water and body fluids, tellurium appears to be less of an industrial hazard than is selenium.

Hydrogen telluride is a gas which decomposes slowly to its elements. It has a similar smell and toxicity to hydrogen selenide, and is 4.5 times heavier than air. There have been reports that hydrogen telluride causes irritation to the respiratory tract.

One unique case is reported in a chemist who was admitted to hospital after accidently inhaling tellurium hexafluoride gas whilst engaged on making the tellurium esters. Streaks of blue-black pigmentation below the skin surface were seen on the webs of his fingers and to a lesser degree on his face and neck. The photographs show very clearly this rare example of true skin absorption by a tellurium ester, which was reduced to black elemental tellurium during its passage through the skin.

Animals exposed to tellurium have developed central nervous system and red blood cell effects.

Safety and Health Measures

Where tellurium is being added to molten iron, lead or copper, or being vaporized onto a surface under vacuum, an exhaust system should be installed with a minimum air speed of 30 m/min to control vapour emission. Tellurium should preferably be used in pellet form for alloying purposes. Routine atmospheric determinations should be made to ensure that the concentration is maintained below the recommended levels. Where no specific permissible concentration is given for hydrogen telluride; however, it is considered advisable to adopt the same level as for hydrogen selenide.

Scrupulous hygiene should be observed in tellurium processes. Workers should wear white coats, hand protection and simple gauze mask respiratory protection if handling the powder. Adequate sanitary facilities must be provided. Processes should not require hand grinding, and well-ventilated mechanical grinding stations should be used.

● THALLIUM

Occurrence and Uses

Thallium (Tl) is fairly widely distributed in the earth's crust in very low concentrations; it is also found as an accompanying substance of other heavy metals in pyrites and blendes, and in the manganese nodules on the ocean floor.

Thallium is used in the manufacture of thallium salts, mercury alloys, low-melting glasses, photoelectric cells, lamps and electronics. It is used in an alloy with mercury in low-range glass thermometers and in some switches. It has also been used in semiconductor research and in myocardial imaging. Thallium is a catalyst in organic synthesis.

Thallium compounds are used in infrared spectrometers, crystals and other optical systems. They are useful for colouring glass. While many thallium salts have been prepared, few are of commercial significance.

Thallium hydroxide (TlOH), or thallous hydroxide, is produced by dissolving thallium oxide in water, or by treating thallium sulphate with barium hydroxide solution. It can be used in the preparation of thallium oxide, thallium sulphate or thallium carbonate.

Thallium sulphate (Tl_2SO_4), or thallous sulphate, is produced by dissolving thallium in hot concentrated sulphuric acid or by neutralizing thallium hydroxide with dilute sulphuric acid, followed by crystallization. Because of its outstanding efficacy in the destruction of vermin, particularly rats and mice, thallium sulphate is one of the most important of the thallium salts. However, some western European countries and the United States have prohibited the use of thallium on the grounds that it is inadvisable that such a toxic substance should be easily obtainable. In other countries, following the development of warfarin resistance in rats, the use of thallium sulphate has increased. Thallium sulphate is also used in semiconductor research, optical systems and in photoelectric cells.

Hazards

Thallium is a skin sensitizer and cumulative poison which is toxic by ingestion, inhalation or skin absorption. Occupational exposure may occur during the extraction of the metal from thallium-bearing ores. Inhalation of thallium has resulted from the handling of flue dusts and the dusts from roasting of pyrites. Exposure may also occur during the manufacture and use of thallium-salt vermin exterminators, the manufacture of thallium-containing lenses and separation of industrial diamonds. The toxic action of thallium and its salts is well documented from reports of cases of acute non-occupational poisoning (not infrequently fatal) and from instances of suicidal and homicidal use.

Occupational thallium poisoning is normally the result of moderate, long-term exposure, and the symptoms are usually far less marked than those observed in acute accidental, suicidal or homicidal intoxication. The course is usually unremarkable and characterized by subjective symptoms such as asthenia, irritability, pains in the legs, some nervous system disorders. Objective symptoms of polyneuritis may not be demonstrable for quite some time. The early neurologic findings include changes in the superficially provoked tendon reflexes and a pronounced weakness and fall-off in the speed of pupil reflexes.

The victim's occupational history will usually give the first clue to the diagnosis of thallium poisoning since a considerable time may elapse before the rather vague initial symptoms are replaced by the polyneuritis followed by loss of hair. Where massive hair loss occurs, the likelihood of thallium poisoning is readily suspected. However, in occupational poisoning, where exposure is usually moderate but protracted, the loss of hair may be a late symptom and often noticeable only after the appearance of polyneuritis; in cases of slight poisoning, it may not occur at all.

The two principal criteria for the diagnosis of occupational thallium poisoning are:

1. occupational history which shows that the patient has or may have been exposed to thallium in such work as rodenticide handling, thallium, lead, zinc or cadmium production, or the production or use of various thallium salts
2. neurological symptoms, dominated initially by subjective changes in the form of paraesthesia (both hyperaesthesia and hypoaesthesia) and, subsequently, by reflex changes.

Concentrations of Tl in urine above 500 mg/l have been associated with clinical poisoning. At concentrations of 5 to 500 µg/l the magnitude of risk and severity of adverse effects on humans are uncertain.

Long-term experiments with radioactive thallium have shown marked excretion of thallium in both urine and faeces. On autopsy, the highest thallium concentrations are found in the kidneys, but moderate concentrations may also be present in the liver, other internal organs, muscles and bones. It is striking that, although the principal signs and symptoms of thallium poisoning originate from the central nervous system, only very low concentrations of thallium are retained there. This may be due to extreme sensitivity to even very small amounts of the thallium acting on the enzymes, the transmission substances, or directly on the brain cells.

Safety and Health Measures

The most effective measure against the dangers associated with the manufacture and use of this group of extremely toxic substances is the substitution of a less harmful material. This measure should be adopted wherever possible. When thallium or its compounds must be used, the strictest safety precautions should be taken to ensure that the concentration in the workplace air is kept below permissible limits and that skin contact is prevented. Continuous inhalation of such concentrations of thallium during normal working days of 8 hours may cause the urine level to exceed the above permissible levels.

Persons involved in work with thallium and its compounds should wear personal protective equipment, and respiratory protective equipment is essential where there is the possibility of dangerous inhalation of airborne dust. A complete set of working clothes is essential; these clothes should be washed regularly and kept in accommodation separate from that employed for ordinary clothes. Washing and shower facilities should be provided and scrupulous personal hygiene encouraged. Workrooms must be kept scrupulously clean, and eating, drinking or smoking at the workplace prohibited.

TIN

Tin has been used through the ages up to modern industrial times because it is pliable and easily shaped at normal temperatures, and it mixes readily with other metals to form alloys. One of its outstanding characteristics is its resistance to acids and atmospheric influences.

Occurrence and Uses

Although deposits of tin are widely distributed throughout the world, up to the eighteenth century the world's supply of tin was mainly from England, Saxony and Bohemia. Today, except for some deposits in Nigeria, China, the Congo and Australia, the principal sources are found in Southeast Asia and Bolivia.

Of minerals containing tin, cassiterite (SnO_2) or tinstone is of the greatest commercial importance. It is present in veins closely connected with granite or acid eruptive rocks, but five-sixths of the world's total production is derived from secondary alluvial deposits resulting from the disintegration of the primary deposits. In Bolivia, sulphide ores, such as stannite (Cu_2FeSnS_2) and tealite ($PbZnSnS_2$) are of commercial significance.

Metallic tin is used for Babbitt type metals and for collapsible tubes in the pharmaceutical and cosmetic industries. Because of its resistance to corrosion, tin is used as a protective coating for other metals. *Tinplate* is sheet iron or steel which has been thickly coated with tin by dipping in a molten bath of that metal. It is used mainly for making household utensils and for utensils in food and beverage canning industries. It is often used for decorating purposes. *Terneplate* is sheet iron or steel coated with a lead-tin alloy containing 85% lead and 15% tin. It is used mainly for making roofing tile. *Speculum* is a tin-copper alloy containing 33 to 50% tin, that can be polished to a high degree of reflection. It is used as a coating applied by electrolytic deposition to impart brightness to silverware and similar articles, and for making telescope mirrors. A molten tin bath is also used in the production of window glass.

An important property of tin is its ability to form alloys with other metals, and it has a number of uses in this field. A tin-lead alloy known as *soft solder* is widely used for joining other metals and alloys in the plumbing, automobile, electrical and other industries, and as a filler in the finishing of car bodies. Tin is a constituent of a large number of non-ferrous alloys, including phosphor bronze, light brass, gun-metal, high-tensile brass, manganese bronze, die-casting alloys, bearing metals, type metal and pewter. The tin-niobium alloy is superconductive, and it is used in the manufacture of powerful electromagnets.

Stannic chloride ($SnCl_4$), or tin chloride, is prepared by heating powdered tin with mercuric chloride or by passing a stream of chlorine over molten tin. It is used as a dehydrating agent in organic syntheses, a stabilizer for plastics, and as a chemical intermediate for other tin compounds. Stannic chloride is found in colours and perfumes in the soap industry. It is also employed in ceramics to produce abrasion-resistant or light-reflecting coatings. It is used for the bleaching of sugar and for the surface treatment of glass and other non-conductive materials. The pentahydrate of this salt is used as a mordant. It is also used in treating silk for the purpose of giving weight to the fabric.

Stannous chloride dihydrate ($SnCl_2 \cdot 2H_2O$), or tin salt, is produced by dissolving metallic tin in hydrochloric acid and evaporating until crystallization begins. It is used in dye works as a mordant. It also serves as a reducing agent in the manufacture of glass, ceramics and inks.

The use of *organotin* (alkyl and aryl) compounds has greatly increased in recent years. Disubstituted compounds and, to a lesser degree, monosubstituted compounds, are used as stabilizers and catalysts in the plastics industry. Trisubstituted compounds are used as biocides, and tetrasubstitutes are intermediates in the production of other derivatives. Butyltin trichloride, or trichlorobutyltin; *dibutyltin dichloride*, or dichlorodibutyltin; *trimethyltin*; *triethyltin chloride*; *triphenyltin chloride*, or TPTC; *tetraisobutyltin*, or tetraisobutylstannane are among the most important.

Hazards

In the absence of precautions, mechanical injury can be caused by the heavy, powerful plant and machinery used in the dredging and washing operations. Serious burn hazards are present in the smelting processes when molten metal and hot slags are manipulated.

At the final stage of upgrading of cassiterite concentrate and during the roasting of sulphide ore, sulphur dioxide is evolved. Sulphur dioxide and stannous sulphide constitute a hazard when the rough molten tin is separated from the rest of the charge during refining. This work is done in a very hot environment, and heat exhaustion could arise. The noise on a dredger caused by the discharge from the dredging buckets to the primary washing plant may cause damage to the hearing of the workers.

Several studies report the hazards associated with exposure to radon, radon decay products and silica in tin mines. While most of the operations associated with the extraction and treatment of tin ore are wet processes, tin dust and oxide fumes may escape during bagging of concentrate, in ore rooms and during smelting operations (mixing-plant and furnace tapping), as well as during the periodic cleaning of bag filters used to remove particulate matter from smelter furnace flue gas before release to the atmosphere. The inhalation of tin oxide dust without silica leads to a benign nodular pneumoconiosis without pulmonary disability. The radiological picture is similar to baritosis. This benign pneumoconiosis has been called *stannosis*.

Tin powder is a moderate irritant to the eyes and airways; it is combustible and reacts violently with oxidants, strong acids, powdered sulphur and some extinguishing agents such as bicarbonate powder and carbon dioxide.

Tin ingested in small (mg) quantities is non-toxic (hence, the widespread use of tinplate in the food canning industry). The results of animal experiments indicate that the lethal dose by intravenous injection is about 100 mg/kg body weight, and that the ingestion of considerable quantities of powdered tin may cause vomiting but not permanent injury. It appears that humans can tolerate a daily intake of 800 to 1,000 mg without ill effect. The absorption of metallic tin or its inorganic salts from the alimentary tract seems to be small.

A number of tin alloys are injurious to health (particularly at high temperatures) because of the harmful characteristics of the metals with which may be alloyed (e.g., lead, zinc, manganese).

Organotin compounds are, in general, strong irritants, and acute conjunctivitis has been observed as a result of eye splashes, even when followed by immediate lavage; corneal opacities have also been reported. Prolonged contact of the skin with clothes moistened with vapour, or direct spillage on the skin, have been responsible for acute local burns, subacute diffuse erythematoid dermatitis with pruritus and some pustular eruption in the hair-covered areas. The irritation of the airways and pulmonary tissue can lead to lung oedema; the gastrointestinal tract can also be involved, and inflammatory reactions of the bile duct have been observed, mainly with the dialkyl compounds. Organotin compounds can injure liver and kidneys; they can depress the immune response and have haemolytic activity. In experimental animals they have been in some instances held responsible for reduction in fertility.

Tri- and tetralkyl compounds, in particular *triethyltin chloride*, cause encephalopathy and brain oedema, with clinical effects of depression, convulsions, flaccid paralysis and urinary retention, as seen in therapeutic use following oral administration.

Safety and Health Measures

Wherever possible, safer substitutes should be used in the place of alkyl tin compounds. When it is necessary to make and use them, the widest possible use should be made of enclosed systems and exhaust ventilation. Engineering control should ensure that exposure limits are not exceeded. Personal protective equipment should be worn, and in appropriate circumstances respiratory protection should be used. Emergency showers should be installed at workplaces in order to allow workers to wash immediately after splashes.

Medical surveillance should focus on eyes, skin and chest x rays in the exposure to inorganic tin compounds, and on eyes, skin, central nervous system, liver and kidney function, and blood in the exposure to organic tin compounds. Mercaprol has been reported as useful in the treatment of dialkyltin intoxications. Steroids have been suggested for the treatment of triethyltin poisoning; however only surgical decompression seems to be of value in encephalopathy and brain oedema provoked by tri- and tetraalkyl tin compounds.

Taking into consideration the fact that most tin mines are located in developing countries, attention should also be paid to climatic and other factors influencing the health, well-being and productive capacity of the workers. Where mines are geographically isolated, good housing should be provided for all personnel. Nutritional standards should be upgraded by health education, and workers should be provided with adequate food supplies and good medical care.

● TITANIUM

Occurrence and Uses

Titanium (Ti) is contained in many minerals, but only a few of them are of industrial significance. These include ilmenite ($FeTiO_3$), which contains 52.65% Ti and 47.4% FeO; rutile (TiO_2), with admixtures of ferrous oxide; perovskite ($CaTiO_3$), which contains 58.7% TiO_2 and 41.3% CaO; and sphene, or titanite, ($CaOTiO_2 \cdot SiO_2$), which contains 38.8% TiO_2. Some heterogeneous minerals, such as loparite, pyrochlor, and tailings from bauxite and copper ore processing may also be sources of titanium.

Titanium is used as a pure metal, in alloys, and in the form of various compounds. The bulk of titanium is needed in the iron and steel industry, in shipbuilding, for aircraft and rocket construction, and for the fabrication of chemical plants. Titanium is used as a protective surface on mixers in the pulp and paper industry. It is also found in surgical appliances. Titanium has been employed for the manufacture of electrodes, lamp filaments, paints, dyes and welding rods. Titanium powder is used in pyrotechnics and in vacuum engineering. Titanium is also used in dentistry and in surgery for implants or prostheses.

Titanium carbide and *titanium nitride* are used in powder metallurgy. *Barium titanate* is used for making heavy-duty capacitors. *Titanium dioxide* is utilized as a white pigment in paints, floor coverings, upholstery, electronics, adhesives, roofing, plastics and in cosmetics. It is also useful as a component of porcelain enamels and glazes, as a shrinking agent for glass fibres, and as a delustering agent for synthetic fibre. *Titanium tetrachloride* acts as an intermediate in the production of titanium metal and titanium pigments, and as a catalyst in the chemical industry.

Hazards

The formation of *titanium dioxide* (TiO_2) and concentrate dust, pitch briquette dust arising from crushing, mixing and charging of bulk raw materials, and radiant heat from coking furnaces are hazards in titanium production. There may be chlorine, *titanium tetrachloride* ($TiCl_4$) vapours and their pyrolysis products in the air of the chlorination and rectification plants, arising from leaking or corroded equipment. Magnesium oxide may be present in the air of the reduction area. Titanium dust becomes airborne when titanium sponge is knocked out, crushed, separated and bagged. Exposure to heat and infrared radiation occurs in the arc furnace area (up to 3 to 5 cal/cm^2 per min).

Maintenance and repair of the chlorination and rectification installations, which includes disassembly and cleaning of the equipment and pipework, create particularly adverse conditions of work: high concentrations of $TiCl_4$ vapours and hydrolysis products (HCl, $Ti(OH)_4$), which are highly toxic and irritant. Workers in these plants often suffer from upper-airway disease and acute or chronic bronchitis. Liquid $TiCl_4$ splashed on the skin causes irritation and burns. Even very short contact of the conjunctiva with $TiCl_4$ leads to suppurative conjunctivitis and keratitis, which may result in corneal opacities. Animal experiments have shown that dust of metallic titanium, titanium concentrates, titanium dioxide and titanium carbide is slightly toxic. While titanium dioxide has not been found to be fibrogenic in animals, it seems to increase the fibrogenicity of quartz when given as combined exposure. Long-term exposure to titanium-containing dust may result in mild forms of chronic lung disease (fibrosis). There is radiological evidence that workers who have handled TiO_2 for long periods develop lung changes resembling those observed in mild forms of silicosis. In one worker who had worked in contact with titanium dioxide for several years and died from brain cancer, the lungs displayed accumulations of TiO_2 and changes analogous to anthracosis. Medical examinations of powder metallurgy workers in various countries have disclosed cases of chronic pneumonitis due to mixed dust including titanium carbide. The degree of this disease varied according to conditions of work, length of dust exposure and individual factors.

Workers who have been chronically exposed to titanium and titanium dioxide dust show a high incidence of chronic bronchitis (endobronchitis and peribronchitis). The early stages of the disease are characterized by impaired pulmonary respiration and ventilatory capacity, and by reduced blood alkalinity. Electrocardiographic tracings of these titanium workers revealed cardiac changes characteristic of pulmonary disease with hypertrophy of the right auricle. A considerable number of these cases presented myocardial hypoxia of various degrees, inhibited atrioventricular and intraventricular conductivity, and bradycardia.

Airborne metallic titanium dust is explosive.

Other hazards in titanium production are carbon monoxide exposures at the coking and arc furnaces, and burns.

Safety and Health Measures

Control dust during ore crushing by moistening the material to be processed (up to 6 to 8% moisture content), and by adopting a continuous process, which enables the equipment to be enclosed with exhaust devices at all points where dust may form; the dust-laden air exhausted should be filtered and the dust collected should be recycled. Dust exhaust systems must be provided at the knock-out stations; crushers, separators and baggers in the titanium sponge plant. Knocking out with pneumatic chipping hammers should be replaced by machining out on special milling or turning machines.

TUNGSTEN

Occurrence and Uses

Tungsten (W) never occurs free in nature and is found only in a few minerals as tungstate of calcium, iron or manganese. Of the known tungsten-bearing minerals, scheelite ($CaWO_4$), wolframite ((Fe,Mn)WO_4), hubnerite ($MnWO$) and ferberite ($FeWO_4$) are commercially important. Total world reserves of *tungsten trioxide* (WO_3) are estimated to be about 175,000,000 t. These tungsten minerals are mostly mined from underground workings, but open-cut operations and more primitive methods are also applied. The tungsten content of the ore mined is usually 0.5 to 2.0%. The more common impurities are gangue minerals such as quartz and calcite, and metallic minerals of copper, bismuth, tin and molybdenum.

Tungsten is a component in hard metals. It is used to increase the hardness, toughness, elasticity and tensile strength of steel. It is used in the production of tungsten steels for automobiles and high-speed cutting tools. Tungsten is also used in lamps, vacuum tubes, electric contacts, x-ray tubes and fluorescent light tubes. It serves as a flame retardant in the textile industry.

Tungsten carbide (WC) has replaced diamond in large drawing dies and rock drills because of its extreme hardness. Tungsten compounds are also used in lasers, dyes, inks and ceramic frits. Some tungsten alloys are used in the nuclear and space industries for nozzles of rocket motors and for protecting shields for spacecraft.

Hazards

Little is known of the toxicity of tungsten. The LD_{50} of *sodium tungstate* for 66-day-old rats was between 223 and 255 mg/kg and showed significant postprandial and age effect. Of three tungsten compounds, sodium tungstate is most toxic, *tungstic oxide* is intermediate, and *ammonium paratungstate* is least toxic. The feeding of 2.5 and 10% of diet as tungsten metal over a period of 70 days has been shown to be without marked effect upon the growth of male rats, as measured in terms of gain in weight, though it caused a 15% reduction in weight gain for female rats from that of control.

Industrial exposure is related chiefly to substances associated with the production and uses of tungsten, its alloys and compounds, rather than tungsten itself. In the mining and milling processes, the main hazards seem to be exposure to quartz-containing dust, noise, hydrogen sulphide, sulphur dioxide and chemicals such as sodium cyanide and sodium hydroxide. The exposure may be associated with other metals in the ore, such as nickel.

Hard metal is the mixture of tungsten carbide and cobalt, to which small amounts of other metals may be added. In the tool-cutting industry workers may be exposed to dust of tungsten carbide, cobalt fumes and dust, and carbides of nickel, titanium and tantalum. Following occupational exposure to tungsten carbide dust by inhalation, cases of pneumoconiosis or pulmonary fibrosis have been reported, but it is generally agreed that this "hard-metal disease" is more likely to be caused by the cobalt with which tungsten carbide is fused. Where machining and grinding of tungsten carbide tools is performed, the hard-metal workers may be at risk for the development of interstitial obstructive lung disease, a serious hazard associated with elevated air concentrations of cobalt. The effects of hard metals on the lungs are discussed elsewhere in this *Encyclopaedia*.

Tungsten carbonyl is a moderate fire hazard when exposed to flame. When heated to decomposition, it emits carbon monoxide. The incidence of accidents and diseases in tungsten mines and mills is not well documented. However, from the scarce data available it can be said that it is less than that of coal mines.

VANADIUM

Occurrence and Uses

The most important vanadium (V) ores are patronite (vanadium sulphide), found in Peru, and descloizite (lead-zinc vanadate), found in South Africa. Other ores, such as vanadinite, roscoelite and carnotite, contain vanadium in sufficient quantities for economic extraction. Crude petroleum may contain small amounts of vanadium, and flue-gas deposits from oil-fired furnaces may contain over 50% vanadium pentoxide. Slags from ferrovanadium are another source of the metal. One of the most important sources of human exposure to vanadium is vanadium oxides released when burning fuel oils.

Normally, small amounts of vanadium are found in the human body, particularly in adipose tissue and in the blood.

The larger amount of the vanadium produced is used in *ferrovanadium*, the most important direct use of which is in high-speed steel and tool steelmaking. Addition of 0.05 to 5% of vanadium removes occluded oxygen and nitrogen from the steel, enhances the tensile strength and improves the modulus of elasticity and the rust resistance of the final alloy. In the past vanadium compounds have been used as therapeutic agents in medicine. The vanadium-gallium alloy has shown interesting properties for production of high magnetic fields.

Certain vanadium compounds have a limited use in industry. *Vanadium sulphate* ($VSO_4 \cdot 7H_2O$) and *vanadium tetrachloride* (VCl_4) are used as mordants in the dyeing industry. *Vanadium silicates* are used as catalysts. *Vanadium dioxide* (VO_2) and *vanadium trioxide* (V_2O_3) are employed in metallurgy. However, the most significant compounds in terms of industrial health hazards are *vanadium pentoxide* (V_2O_5) and *ammonium metavanadate* (NH_4VO_3).

Vanadium pentoxide is obtained from patronite. It has for a long time been an important industrial catalyst used in a number of oxidation processes such as those involved in the manufacture of sulphuric acid, phthalic acid, maleic acid and so on. It serves as a photographic developer and as a dyeing agent in the textile industry. Vanadium pentoxide is also used in ceramic colouring materials.

Ammonium metavanadate is employed as a catalyst in the same way as vanadium pentoxide. It is a reagent in analytical chemistry and a developer in the photography industry. Ammonium metavanadate is also used in dyeing and printing in the textile industry.

Hazards

Experience has shown that vanadium oxides and, in particular, the pentoxide and its derivative ammonium metavanadate cause harmful effects in humans. Exposure to vanadium pentoxide is possible at the following points in industry: when vanadium pentoxide is used in particulate form in the production of metallic vanadium; during the repair of installations where vanadium pentoxide is used as a catalyst; and during the cleaning of oil-fired furnace flues in power stations, ships and so on. The presence of vanadium compounds in petroleum products is of particular significance and, because of the possibility of air pollution in the environment of oil-fired power stations, it receives attention from public health authorities as well as from those concerned with industrial health.

The inhalation of vanadium compounds may produce severe toxic effects. The severity of the effects depends on the atmospheric concentration of the vanadium compounds and the duration of exposure. Health impairment may occur after even brief exposure (e.g., 1 hour), and the initial symptoms are profuse lacrimation, burning sensation in the conjunctivae, serous or haemorrhageous rhinitis, sore throat, cough, bronchitis, expectoration and chest pain. Severe exposure may result in pneumonia with fatal outcome; however, following one-time exposure, complete recovery usually occurs within 1 to 2 weeks; prolonged exposure may produce chronic bronchitis with or without emphysema. The tongue may present a greenish discolouration and also the cigarette ends of vanadium workers may show a greenish colour, resulting from chemical interactions.

Local effects in experimental animals are mainly observed in the respiratory tract. Systemic effects have been observed in the liver, kidney, nervous system, cardiovascular system and blood-forming organs. Metabolic effects include interference with biosynthesis of cystine and cholestrol, depression and stimulation of phospholipid synthesis. Higher concentrations have produced inhibition of serotonin oxidation. In addition, vanadate has been shown to inhibit several enzyme systems. In humans, systemic effects of vanadium exposure are less well documented, but reduction of serum cholestrol has been demonstrated. In the work environment, vanadium and its compounds are taken up in the human body by inhalation, mainly during production and boiler cleaning operations. Absorption of vanadium from the gastrointestinal tract is poor, not exceeding 1 to 2%; ingested vanadium compounds are largely eliminated with faeces.

A study was conducted to evaluate the level of bronchial responsiveness among workers recently exposed to vanadium pentoxide during periodic removal of ashes and clinker from boilers of an oil-fired power station. This study suggests that exposure to vanadium increases bronchial responsiveness even without the appearance of bronchial symptoms.

Safety and Health Measures

It is important to prevent the inhalation of airborne particulate vanadium pentoxide. For use as a catalyst, vanadium pentoxide can be produced in an agglomerated or pelleted form which is dust free; however, vibration in the plant may, in time, reduce a certain proportion to dust. In the processes associated with the manufacture of metallic vanadium, and in the sieving of used catalyst during maintenance operations, the escape of dust should be prevented by the enclosure of the process and by the provision of exhaust ventilation. In boiler cleaning in power stations and on ships, maintenance workers may have to enter the boilers to remove soot and to make repairs. These workers should wear adequate respiratory protective equipment with full face mask and eye protection. Wherever possible, on-load cleaning should be improved to reduce the need for workers to enter furnaces; where off-load cleaning proves essential, methods such as water lancing, which do not necessitate physical entry, should be tried.

● ZINC

Occurrence and Uses

Zinc (Zn) is widely distributed in nature in quantities which amount to approximately 0.02% of the earth's crust. It is found in nature as the sulphide (sphalerite), carbonate, oxide or silicate (calamine) in combination with many minerals. Sphalerite, the principal zinc mineral and the source of at least 90% of metallic zinc, contains iron and cadmium as impurities. It is almost always accompanied by galena, the sulphide of lead, and occasionally is found in association with ores containing copper or other base metal sulphides.

On exposure to air, zinc becomes covered with a tenacious film of oxide which protects the metal from further oxidation. This resistance to atmospheric corrosion forms the basis for one of the most common uses of the metal, the protection of steelwork by galvanizing. Zinc's ability to protect ferrous metals against corrosion is reinforced by electrolytic action. It acts as an anode with respect to iron and other structural metals, except aluminium and magnesium, and is thus preferentially attacked by corrosive agents. This property is used in many other important applications of zinc—for example, in the use of zinc plates as anodes for cathodic protection of ships' hulls, underground tanks and so on. Zinc metal is die cast for components in the automobile industry, electrical equipment industry, and in the light machine tool, hardware, toys and fancy goods industries. It is rolled into sheets in rolling mills for the manufacture of roofing, weather stripping, cases for dry batteries, printing plates and so on. Zinc is also alloyed with copper, nickel, aluminium and magnesium. When it is alloyed with copper, it forms the important groups of alloys known as the brasses.

Zinc oxide (ZnO), or zinc white (flowers of zinc) is produced by the oxidation of vaporized pure zinc or by the roasting of zinc oxide ore. It is used as a pigment in paints, lacquers and varnishes, as well as a filler for plastics and rubber. Zinc oxide is found in cosmetics, quick-setting cements, and in pharmaceuticals. It is useful in the manufacture of glass, automobile tyres, matches, white glue and printing inks. Zinc oxide is also used as a semiconductor in the electronics industry.

Zinc chromate ($ZnCrO_4$), or zinc yellow, is produced by the action of chromic acid on slurries of zinc oxide, or on zinc hydroxide. It is used in pigments, paints, varnishes and lacquers, and in the manufacture of linoleum. Zinc chromate acts as a corrosion inhibitor for metals and epoxy laminates.

Zinc cyanide ($Zn(CN)_2$) is produced by precipitation of a solution of zinc sulphate or chloride with potassium cyanide. It is used for metal plating and for gold extraction. Zinc cyanide acts as a chemical reagent and as a pesticide. *Zinc sulphate* ($ZnSO_4 \cdot 7H_2O$), or white vitriol, is produced by roasting zinc blende or by the action of sulphuric acid on zinc or zinc oxide. It is used as an astringent, a preservative for hides and wood, a bleach for paper, a pesticide adjuvant and a fungicide. Zinc sulphate also serves as a fireproofing agent and as a depressant in froth flotation. It is used in water treatment and in textile dyeing and printing. *Zinc sulphide* is used as a pigment for paints, oilcloths, linoleum, leather, inks, lacquers, and cosmetics. *Zinc phosphide* (Zn_3P_2) is produced by passing phosphine through a solution of zinc sulphate. It is used mainly as a rodenticide.

Zinc chloride ($ZnCl_2$), or butter of zinc, has numerous uses in the textile industry, including dyeing, printing, sizing and weighting fabrics. It is a component of cement for metals, dentifrices, and soldering fluxes. It is used alone or with phenol and other antiseptics for preserving railway ties. Zinc chloride is useful for glass etching and for the manufacture of asphalt. It is a vulcanizing agent for rubber, a flame retardant for wood, and a corrosion inhibitor in water treatment.

Hazards

Zinc is an essential nutrient. It is a constituent of metalloenzymes, which play an important role in nucleic acid metabolism and protein synthesis. Zinc is not stored in the body, and a minimum daily intake of zinc is recommended by nutritional experts. Absorption of zinc takes place more readily from animal protein sources than from plant products. The phytate content of plants binds zinc, rendering it unavailable for absorption. Zinc deficiency states have been reported from countries where cereals are the major source of protein consumed by the population. Some of the recognized clinical manifestations of chronic zinc deficiency in humans are growth retardation, hypogonadism in males, skin changes, poor appetite, mental lethargy and delayed wound healing.

In general, zinc salts are astringent, hygroscopic, corrosive and antiseptic. Their precipitating action on proteins forms the basis of their astringent and antiseptic effects, and they are absorbed relatively easily through the skin. The taste threshold for zinc salts is approximately 15 ppm; water containing 30 ppm of soluble zinc salts has a milky appearance, and a metallic taste when the concentration reaches 40 ppm. Zinc salts are irritating to the gastrointestinal tract, and the emetic concentrations for zinc salts in water range from 675 to 2,280 ppm.

The solubility of zinc in weakly acidic solutions, in the presence of iron, has led to accidental ingestion of large quantities of zinc salts when acid foods such as fruit drinks were prepared in worn galvanized iron vessels. Fever, nausea, vomiting, stomach cramps and diarrhoea occurred in 20 minutes to 10 hours following ingestion.

A number of zinc salts may enter the body by inhalation, through the skin or by ingestion and produce intoxication. Zinc chloride has been found to cause skin ulcers. A number of zinc compounds present fire and explosion hazards. The electrolytic manufacturing of zinc can produce mists containing sulphuric acid and zinc sulphate that can irritate the respiratory or digestive systems and lead to dental erosion. Metallurgic processes involving zinc can lead to arsenic, cadmium, manganese, lead and possibly chromium and silver exposures, with their associated hazards. Since arsenic is frequently present in zinc, it can be a source of exposure to highly toxic arsine gas whenever zinc is dissolved in acids or alkalis.

In zinc metallurgy and manufacturing, welding and cutting of galvanized or zinc-coated metal, or melting and casting of brass or bronze, the most frequently encountered hazard from zinc and its compounds is exposure to zinc oxide fumes, which cause metal-fume fever. Symptoms of metal-fume fever include shivering attacks, irregular fever, profuse sweating, nausea, thirst, headache, pains in the limbs and a feeling of exhaustion. Attacks are of short duration (most cases are on the way to complete recovery within 24 hours of the onset of symptoms), and tolerance seems to be acquired. A significant increase in free erythrocyte protoporphyrin has been reported in zinc oxide packing operations.

Zinc chloride fumes are irritating to the eyes and mucous membranes. In an accident involving smoke generators, 70 exposed persons experienced varying degrees of irritation of the eyes, nose, throat and lungs. Of the 10 fatalities, some died within a few hours with pulmonary oedema, and others died later of bronchopneumonia. On another occasion, two firemen were exposed to zinc chloride fumes from a smoke generator during a firefighting demonstration, one briefly, the other for several minutes. The former recovered rapidly while the latter died after 18 days, due to respiratory failure. There was a rapid rise of temperature and marked upper respiratory tract inflammation soon after exposure. Diffuse pulmonary infiltrations were seen on the chest radiograph, and autopsy revealed active fibroblastic proliferation and cor pulmonale.

In an experiment primarily designed to evaluate carcinogenesis, groups of 24 mice received 1,250 to 5,000 ppm of zinc sulphate in drinking water for one year. Apart from severe anaemia in animals receiving 5,000 ppm, there were no adverse effects from zinc. Tumour incidence was not significantly different from that seen in the controls.

Zinc phosphide, which is used as a rodenticide, is toxic to humans whether swallowed, inhaled or injected, and, together with zinc chloride, is the most dangerous of the zinc salts; these two substances have been responsible for the only deaths definitely due to zinc poisoning.

Skin effects. Zinc chromate in primer paints used by car-body builders, tinsmiths and steel cupboard makers has been reported to cause nasal ulceration and dermatitis in exposed workers. Zinc chloride has a caustic action, which may result in ulceration of the fingers, hands and forearms of those who handle timber impregnated with it or use it as a flux in soldering. It has been reported that zinc oxide dust may block the ducts of the sebaceous glands and give rise to a papular, pustular eczema in humans packaging this compound.

Safety and Health Measures

Fire and explosion. Finely divided zinc powder, and other zinc compounds, can be fire and explosion hazards if stored in damp places, sources of spontaneous combustion. Residues from reduction reactions may ignite combustible materials. Zinc ammonium nitrate, zinc bromate, zinc chlorate, zinc ethyl, zinc nitrate, zinc permanganate and zinc picrate are all dangerous fire and explosion hazards. In addition, zinc ethyl will ignite spontaneously in contact with air. It should, therefore, be stored in a cool, dry, well-ventilated place away from acute fire risks, open flames and powerful oxidizing agents.

In all cases where zinc is heated to the point where fumes are produced, it is most important to ensure that adequate ventilation is provided. Individual protection is best ensured by education of the worker concerning metal-fume fever and the provision of local exhaust ventilation, or, in some situations, by wearing of a supplied-air hood or mask.

Workers who are none the less exposed to zinc chloride fumes should wear personal protective equipment including protective clothing, chemical eye and face protection and appropriate respiratory protective equipment. Exposure to zinc chloride fumes should be treated by copious irrigation of the exposed areas.

ZIRCONIUM AND HAFNIUM

Occurrence and Uses

It has been estimated that zirconium (Zr) constitutes about 0.017% of the lithosphere. Because of its very high chemical activity at temperatures only slightly above normal atmospheric temperature, the element occurs only in combined states. The most common ores are zircon (ZrO_2) and baddeleyite ($ZrSiO_4$). Zirconium is found in all animal tissues.

Hafnium (Hf) is found associated with zirconium in all its terrestrial occurrences. The amount of hafnium varies but averages about 2% of the total zirconium plus hafnium. In only one ore, low in both elements, has hafnium been found in greater quantity than zirconium. Spectrographic evidence indicates that the distribution is also about 2% hafnium in the total zirconium-plus-hafnium in the universe. These two elements are more closely identical in their chemical properties than are any other pair in the periodic table. The similarity is so great that no qualitative differences have yet been found which would permit their separation. For this reason, it can be assumed that most of the zirconium which has been used, and on the basis of which physiological effects have been reported, has contained 0.5 to 2% hafnium.

Zircon has been valued since the earliest times as a gem stone, since it occurs quite commonly in large single crystals; however, most of the commercially useful deposits of zirconium ore are in beach sands or other places where the relatively heavy and chemically inert zirconium minerals have been deposited while the lighter portions of the rocks in which they occurred have been disintegrated and washed away by the action of water. Substantial deposits of such beach sands are known in India, Malaya, Australia and the United States. Baddeleyite in commercially useful deposits was first observed in Brazil, and has since been found in a number of other locations including Sweden, India and Italy. Some zirconium ores have also been mined commercially in Madagascar, Nigeria, Senegal and South Africa.

Zircon is used as a foundry sand, an abrasive, and as a component of zircon and zirconia refractory compositions for laboratory crucibles. It is found in ceramic compositions where it acts as an opacifier in glazes and enamels. Zircon and zirconia bricks are used as linings for glass furnaces. Zirconia forms are also used as dies for extrusion of both ferrous and non-ferrous metals and as spout linings for pouring metals, particularly for continuous casting.

More than 90% of zirconium metal is now used in nuclear power generation because zirconium has a low absorption cross-section for neutrons and a high resistance to corrosion inside atomic reactors, provided it is free of hafnium. Zirconium is also used in the manufacture of cast iron, steel and surgical appliances. It is employed in arc lamps, pyrotechnics, in special welding fluxes, and as a pigment in plastics.

Powdered zirconium metal is used as a "getter" in thermionic tubes to absorb the last traces of gas after pumping and out-gassing of the tube elements. In the form of fine ribbon or wool, the metal is also used as the filter in photographic flash-bulbs. The massive metal is used either pure or in alloy form for the lining of reaction vessels. It is also used as a lining for pumps and piping systems for chemical processes. An excellent super-conducting alloy of zirconium and columbium has been used in a magnet with a field of 6.7 T.

Zirconium carbide and *zirconium diboride* are both hard, refractory, metallic compounds which have been used in cutting tools for metals. The diboride has also been used as a thermocouple jacket in open-hearth furnaces, providing very long-lived thermocouples. *Zirconium tetrachloride* is used in organic synthesis and in water repellents for textiles. It is also useful as a tanning agent.

Hafnium metal has been used as a cladding on tantalum for rocket engine parts which must operate in very high-temperature, erosive conditions. Because of its high thermal-neutron cross-section, it is also used as a control rod material for nuclear reactors. In addition, hafnium is used in the manufacture of electrodes and light-bulb filaments.

Hazards

It is inaccurate to state that zirconium compounds are physiologically inert, but the tolerance of most organisms to zirconium appears to be great in comparison to the tolerance for most heavy metals. Zirconium salts have been used in the treatment of plutonium poisoning to displace the plutonium (and yttrium) from its deposition in the skeleton and to prevent the deposition when treatment was started early. In the course of this study, it was determined that the diet of rats could contain as much as 20% of zirconia for comparatively long periods without harmful effects, and that the intravenous LD_{50} of sodium zirconium citrate for rats is about 171 mg/kg body weight. Other investigators have found an intraperitoneal LD_{50} of 0.67 g/kg for zirconium lactate and 0.42 g/kg for barium zirconate in rats and 51 mg/kg of sodium zirconium lactate in mice.

Zirconium compounds have been recommended and used for the topical treatment of Rhus (poison ivy) dermatitis and for body deodorants. Some compounds which have been used are carbonated hydrous zirconia, hydrous zirconia and sodium zirconium lactate. There have been a number of reports of the production of persistent granulomatous conditions of the skin as the result of these applications.

Of more direct interest in connection with occupational exposures is the effect of inhalation of zirconium compounds, and this has been less extensively investigated than the other routes of administration. There have, however, been several experiments and at least one report of human exposure. In this instance, a chemical engineer with seven years' exposure in a zirconium and hafnium processing plant was found to have a granulomatous lung condition. Since examination of all the other employees revealed no comparable lesions, it was concluded that the condition was most probably to be attributed to a relatively heavy beryllium exposure prior to zirconium exposure.

Exposure of experimental animals to zirconium compounds showed that zirconium lactate and barium zirconate both produced severe, persistent, chronic interstitial pneumonitis at atmospheric zirconium concentrations of about 5 mg/m^3. Much higher atmospheric sodium zirconium lactate concentrations of 0.049 mg/cm^3 for shorter exposures have been found to produce peribronchial abscesses, peribronchiolar granulomas and lobular pneumonia. Although documentation of zirconium pneumoconiosis in humans has been lacking, authors of one study conclude that zirconium should be considered a likely cause of pneumoconiosis, and recommend taking appropriate precautions in the workplace.

The small number of investigations on the toxicity of hafnium compounds has indicated an acute toxicity slightly higher than that of zirconium salts. Hafnium and its compounds cause liver damage. Hafnyl chloride at 10 mg/kg produced cardiovascular collapse and respiratory arrest in a cat in the same manner as soluble zirconium salts; the intraperitoneal LD_{50} of 112 mg/kg for hafnium is not much smaller than that for zirconium.

Safety and Health Measures

Fire and explosion. Zirconium metal in the form of a fine powder burns in air, nitrogen or carbon dioxide. The powders are explosive in air in the range of 45 to 300 mg/l, and are self-igniting if disturbed, probably because of static electricity generated by separation of the grains.

The powdered metals should be transported and handled in the wet state; water is usually used for wetting. When the powder is dried prior to use, the quantities employed should be kept as small as possible and operations should be carried out in separate cubicles to prevent propagation in the event of an explosion. All sources of ignition, including static electric charges, should be eliminated from areas in which the powder is to be handled. All surfaces in the area should be impervious and seamless so that they can be washed down with water and kept completely free from dust. Any spilled powder should be cleaned up immediately with water so that it has no chance to dry in place. Used papers and cloths which have become contaminated with the powders should be kept wet in covered containers until they are removed to be burned, which should be done at least daily. The dried powders should be disturbed and handled as little as possible, and then only with non-sparking tools. Rubber or plastic aprons, if worn over work clothes, should be treated with an anti-static compound. Work clothing should be made from non-synthetic fibres unless effectively treated with antistatic materials.

All processes using zirconium and or hafnium should be designed and ventilated to keep airborne contamination below the exposure limits.

Table 63.2 • Physical and chemical hazards.

Chemical name CAS-number	Molecular formula	Physical and chemical hazards	UN class/div/ subsidiary risks
Aluminium chloride 7446-70-0	$AlCl_3$		8
Aluminium hydroxide 21645-51-2	$Al(OH)_3$	• Forms gels ($Al_2 \cdot 3H_2O$) on prolonged contact with water; absorbs acids and carbon dioxide	
Aluminium nitrate 13473-90-0	$Al_2(NO_3)_3$		5.1
Aluminium phosphide 20859-73-8	AlP	• Reacts with moist air, water, acids producing highly toxic fumes of phosphine • Reacts with water, moist air, acids causing fire and toxic (phosphine fumes) hazard	4.3/ 6.1
Diethylaluminium chloride 96-10-6	$AlClC_4H_{10}$		4.2
Ethylaluminium dichloride 563-43-9	$AlCl_2C_2H_5$		4.2
Ethylaluminium sesquichloride 12075-68-2	$Al_2Cl_3C_6H_{15}$		4.2
Sodium aluminate 1302-42-7		• The substance is a strong base, it reacts violently with acid and is corrosive • The solution in water is a strong base, it reacts violently with acid and is corrosive to aluminium and zinc	8
Triethylaluminium 97-93-8	AlC_6H_{15}		4.2
Triisobutylaluminium 100-99-2	$AlC_{12}H_{27}$		4.2
Antimony 7440-36-0	Sb	• On combustion, forms toxic fumes (antimony oxides) • Reacts violently with strong oxidants (e.g., halogens, alkali permanganates and nitrates), causing fire and explosion hazard • Reacts with nascent hydrogen in acid medium producing very toxic gas • On contact with hot concentrated acids, emits toxic gas (stibine)	6.1
Antimony pentachloride 7647-18-9	$SbCl_5$		8
Antimony pentafluoride 7783-70-2	SbF_5		3/ 6.1
Antimony potassium tartrate 28300-74-5	$Sb_2K_2C_8H_4O_{12} \cdot 3H_2O$		6.1
Antimony trichloride 10025-91-9	$SbCl_3$		8
Antimony trioxide 1309-64-4	Sb_2O_3	• The substance decomposes on heating producing toxic fumes of antimony • Reacts under certain circumstances with hydrogen producing a very poisonous gas, stibine	
Stibine 7803-52-3	SbH_3	• The substance decomposes slowly at room temperature producing metallic antimony and hydrogen • Reacts violently with ozone and concentrated nitric acid causing fire and explosion hazard • The substance decomposes on heating producing toxic fumes of antimony • The gas is heavier than air and may travel along the ground; distant ignition possible	2.3/ 2.1
Arsenic 7440-38-2	As	• Reacts with acids, oxidants, halogens • The substance produces toxic fumes	6.1
Arsenic acid, copper salt 10103-61-4	$CuAsOH_4$	• The substance decomposes on heating producing toxic fumes of arsenic by comparation with another compounds • Reacts with acids releasing toxic arsine gas	

Continues on next page.

Table 63.2 • Physical and chemical hazards.
Continued

Chemical name CAS-number	Molecular formula	Physical and chemical hazards	UN class/div/ subsidiary risks
Arsenic acid, diammonium salt 7784-44-3	$(NH_4)_2AsOH_4$	• The substance decomposes on heating producing toxic fumes including arsenic, nitrogen oxides and ammonia • Reacts with acids producing toxic fumes of arsenic • Attacks many metals, such as iron, aluminium and zinc, in presence of water releasing toxic fumes of arsenic and arsine	
Arsenic acid, disodium salt 7778-43-0	Na_2AsOH_4	• The substance decomposes on heating producing toxic fumes of arsenic • Reacts with acids releasing toxic arsine gas • Attacks many metals, such as iron, aluminium and zinc, in presence of water releasing toxic fumes of arsenic and arsine	
Arsenic acid, magnesium salt 10103-50-1	$Mg_xAsO_3H_4$	• The substance decomposes on heating producing toxic fumes of arsenic • Reacts with acids releasing toxic fumes of arsine gas	6.1
Arsenic acid, monopotassium salt 7784-41-0	$KAsO_2H_4$	• The substance decomposes on heating producing toxic fumes of arsenic • Reacts with acids releasing toxic arsine gas • Attacks many metals, such as iron, aluminium and zinc, in presence of water releasing toxic fumes of arsenic and arsine	
Arsenic pentoxide 1303-28-2	As_2O_5	• The substance decomposes on heating above 300 °C producing toxic fumes (arsenic trioxide) and oxygen • The solution in water is a medium strong acid, which may react with reducing substances producing very toxic gas (arsine) • Reacts violently with bromine pentafluoride causing fire and explosion hazard • Corrosive to metals in the presence of moisture	6.1
Arsenic trioxide 1327-53-3	As_2O_3	• The substance is a strong reducing agent and reacts with oxidants • The solution in water is a weak acid which may react with reducing substances producing very toxic gas (arsine) • Gives off toxic fumes in a fire	6.1
Arsenious acid, copper(2+) salt(1:1) 10290-12-7	$CuAsH_3$	• The substance decomposes on heating producing toxic fumes of arsenic • Reacts with acids releasing toxic fumes of arsine gas	6.1
Arsenious acid, lead(II) salt 10031-13-7	$PbAs_2O_4$	• The substance decomposes on heating producing very toxic fumes of arsenic and lead • Reacts with oxidants • Reacts violently with strong acids	
Arsenious acid, potassium salt 10124-50-2	$(KH_3)_x AsO_3$	• The substance decomposes on heating producing toxic fumes of arsenic and potassium oxide • Reacts with acids releasing toxic arsine gas • Decomposes on contact with air (by atmospheric carbon dioxide) and through the skin	6.1
Arsenous trichloride 7784-34-1	$AsCl_3$	• The substance decomposes on heating and under influence of light producing toxic fumes of hydrogen chloride and arsenic oxides • Reacts violently with bases, strong oxidants and water, causing fire and toxic hazard • On contact with air it emits corrosive fumes of hydrogen chloride • Attacks many metals forming combustible gas (hydrogen) in presence of moisture	6.1
Arsine 7784-42-1	AsH_3	• The substance decomposes on heating and under influence of light and moisture producing toxic arsenic fumes • Reacts violently with strong oxidants, fluorine, chlorine, nitric acid, nitrogen trichloride, causing fire and explosion hazard • The gas is heavier than air and may travel along the ground; distant ignition possible • As a result of flow, agitation, etc., electrostatic charges can be generated, conductivity not checked	2.3/ 2.1
Calcium arsenate 7778-44-1	$Ca_3As_2O_8$	• The substance decomposes on heating producing toxic fumes of arsenic • Reacts with acids releasing toxic arsine gas	6.1
Lead arsenate 7784-40-9	$PbAsO_4H$	• The substance decomposes on heating producing toxic fumes of lead, arsenic and its compounds, including arsine	6.1
Methylarsonic acid 124-58-3	$AsCH_5O_3$	• The substance decomposes on heating or on burning producing toxic fumes (arsenic oxides) • The solution in water is a medium strong acid, which may react with reducing substances, active metals (i.e., iron, aluminium, zinc) producing toxic gas (methylarsine)	

Continues on next page.

Table 63.2 • Physical and chemical hazards.
Continued

Chemical name CAS-number	Molecular formula	Physical and chemical hazards	UN class/div/ subsidiary risks
Sodium arsenate 10048-95-0	$Na_2AsO_4H \cdot 7H_2O$	• The substance decomposes on heating producing toxic fumes including arsenic, arsenic oxides • Reacts violently with strong oxidants, strong acids and metals such as iron, aluminium and zinc causing explosion and toxic hazard	6.1
Barium 7440-39-3	Ba	• The substance may spontaneously ignite on contact with air (if in powder form) • The substance is a strong reducing agent and reacts violently with oxidants and acids • Reacts with water, forming combustible gas (hydrogen) and barium hydroxide • Reacts violently with halogenated solvents causing fire and explosion hazard	4.3
Barium carbonate 513-77-9	$BaCO_3$		6.1
Barium chlorate 13477-00-4	$BaCl_2O_6$	• Heating may cause violent combustion or explosion • Shock-sensitive compounds are formed with organic compounds, reducing agents, ammonia-containing agents, metal powders, and sulphuric acid • The substance decomposes violently on warming, on heating and on burning producing oxygen and toxic fumes, causing fire and explosion hazard • The substance is a strong oxidant and reacts with combustible and reducing materials • Dust explosion possible if in powder or granular form, mixed with air	5.1/ 6.1
Barium chloride 10361-37-2	$BaCl_2$	• The substance decomposes on heating producing toxic fumes	6.1
Barium chloride, dihydrate 10326-27-9	$BaCl_2 \cdot 2H_2O$	• The substance decomposes on heating producing toxic fumes	6.1
Barium chromate (VI) 10294-40-3	$BaCrH_2O_4$		6.1
Barium hydroxide 17194-00-2	$Ba(OH)_2$		6.1
Barium nitrate 10022-31-8	$BaNO_3$		5.1/ 6.1
Barium oxide 1304-28-5	BaO	• The solution in water is a medium strong base • Reacts violently with water, hydrogen sulphide, hydroxylamine, and sulphur trioxide, causing fire and explosion hazard	6.1
Barium perchlorate 13465-95-7	$BaCl_2O_8$		5.1/ 6.1
Barium peroxide 1304-29-6	BaO_2	• The substance can presumably form explosive peroxides • The substance is a strong oxidant and reacts with combustible and reducing materials • The substance is a strong reducing agent and reacts with oxidants • Reacts with water and acids forming hydrogen peroxide and barium oxide • Mixtures with organic substances may be ignited or exploded on shock, friction or concussion	5.1/ 6.1
Barium sulphate 7727-43-7	$BaSO_4$	• The substance emits toxic fumes of sulphur oxides when heated to decomposition • Reduction of barium sulphate by aluminium is attended by violent explosions	6.1
Beryllium 7440-41-7	Be		6.1
Beryllium oxide 1304-56-9	BeO		6.1
Cadmium 7440-43-9	Cd	• Reacts with acids giving off flammable hydrogen gas • Dust reacts with oxidants, hydrogen azide, zinc, selenium or tellurium, causing fire and explosion hazard • Dust explosion possible if in powder or granular form, mixed with air	6.1
Cadmium acetate 543-90-8	$Cd(C_2H_4O_2)_2$		6.1

Continues on next page.

Table 63.2 • Physical and chemical hazards.
Continued

Chemical name CAS-number	Molecular formula	Physical and chemical hazards	UN class/div/ subsidiary risks
Cadmium chloride 10108-64-2	$CdCl_2$	• The substance decomposes on heating producing very toxic fumes of cadmium and chlorine • Solution in water is a weak acid • Reacts with strong oxidants • Reacts violently with fluoride, bromide and potassium and acids	6.1
Cadmium oxide 1306-19-0	CdO	• The substance decomposes on heating producing toxic fumes of cadmium • Reacts violently with magnesium when heated causing fire and explosion hazard • Reacts with acids, oxidants	6.1
Cadmium suphate 10124-36-4	$CdSO_4$		6.1
Cadmium sulphide 1306-23-6	CdS	• Upon heating, toxic fumes are formed · Reacts with strong oxidants • Reacts with acids forming toxic gas (hydrogen sulphide) • Gives off toxic fumes in a fire	6.1
Ammonium dichromate(VI) 7789-09-5	$(NH_4)_2Cr_2H_2O_7$		5.1
Chromic acid 7738-94-5	CrH_2O_4		8
Chromium 7440-47-3	Cr		5.1
Chromium trioxide 1333-82-0	CrO_3		5.1
Chromyl chloride 14977-61-8	CrO_2Cl_2	• The substance decomposes violently on contact with water producing toxic and corrosive fumes (hydrochloric acid, chlorine, chromium trioxide and chromium trichloride) • The substance is a strong oxidant and reacts violently with combustible and reducing materials • Reacts violently with water, non-metal halides, non-metal hydrides, ammonia and certain common solvents such as alcohol, ether, acetone, turpentine, causing fire and explosion hazard • Attacks many metals in presence of water • Incompatible with plastics • Can ignite combustible substances	8
Cobalt 7440-48-4	Co	• Reacts with strong oxidants (e.g., fused ammonium nitrate) causing fire and explosion hazard • Certain forms of cobalt metal powder can ignite spontaneously on contact with oxygen or air (pyrophoric) • Can promote decomposition of various organic substances	
Cobalt chloride 7646-79-9	$CoCl_2$	• The substance decomposes on heating producing toxic fumes of chlorine and cobalt • Reacts violently with alkali metals such as potassium or sodium causing fire and explosion hazard	
Cobalt (III) oxide 1308-04-9	Co_2O_3	• Reacts violently with hydrogen peroxide • Reacts with reducing agents	
Cobalt naphthenate 61789-51-3	$CoC_{22}H_{20}O_4$	• Upon heating, toxic fumes are formed • As a result of flow, agitation, etc., electrostatic charges can be generated • Dust explosion possible if in powder or granular form, mixed with air	
Copper 7440-50-8	Cu	• Shock-sensitive compounds are formed with acetylenic compounds, ethylene oxides and azides • Reacts with strong oxidants like chlorates, bromates and iodates, causing explosion hazard	
Copper (I) oxide 1317-39-1	Cu_2O	• Reacts with acids to form cupric salts • Corrodes aluminium	
Cupric acetate 142-71-2	$CuC_4H_6O_4$		6.1
Cupric chloride 7447-39-4	$CuCl_2$		8

Continues on next page.

Table 63.2 • Physical and chemical hazards.
Continued

Chemical name CAS-number	Molecular formula	Physical and chemical hazards	UN class/div/ subsidiary risks
Cupric hydroxide 120427-59-2	$Cu(OH)_2$		6.1
Naphthenic acid, Cu-salt 1338-02-9		• On combustion, forms toxic gases	
Ferric chloride 7705-08-0	$FeCl_3$		8
Iron pentacarbonyl 13463-40-6	C_5FeO_5		6.1/ 3
Lead 7439-92-1	Pb	• The substance decomposes on heating producing toxic fumes including lead oxides • The substance is a strong reducing agent	
Lead acetate 301-04-2	$PbC_4H_6O_4$	• The substance decomposes on heating and on burning producing toxic and corrosive fumes including lead, acetic acid • Reacts violently with bromates, phosphates, carbonates, phenols • Reacts with acids producing corrosive acetic acid	6.1
Lead chromate 7758-97-6	$PbCrO_4$	• The substance decomposes on heating producing toxic fumes including lead oxides • Reacts with strong oxidants, hydrogen peroxide, sodium and potassium • Reacts with aluminium dinitronaphthalene, iron (III) hexacyanoferrate(IV) • Reacts with organics at elevated temperature causing fire hazard	
Lead nitrate 10099-74-8	$Pb(NO_3)_2$		5.1/ 6.1
Lead dioxide 1309-60-0	PbO_2		5.1
Lead(II) oxide 1317-36-8	PbO	• Reacts violently with strong oxidants, aluminium powder and sodium • Upon heating, toxic fumes of lead compounds are formed	
Naphthenic acid, Pb-salt 61790-14-5		• On combustion, forms toxic fumes including lead oxide	
Tetraethyl lead 78-00-2	PbC_8H_{20}	• The substance decomposes on heating above 110 °C and under influence of light producing toxic fumes: carbon monoxide, lead • Reacts violently with strong oxidants, acids, halogens, oils and fats causing fire and explosion hazard • Attacks rubber and some plastics and coatings • The vapour is heavier than air	6.1
Tetramethyl lead 75-74-1	PbC_4H_{12}		6.1
Lithium aluminium hydride 16853-85-3	$LiAlH_4$		4.3
Magnesium 7439-95-4	Mg	• The substance may spontaneously ignite on contact with air or moisture producing irritating or poisonous gases including magnesium oxide • Reacts violently with strong oxidants · Reacts violently with many substances causing fire and explosion hazard • Reacts with acids or water forming flammable hydrogen gas, causing fire and explosion hazard • Dust explosion possible if in powder or granular form, mixed with air	4.1
Magnesium chloride 7786-30-3	$MgCl_2$	• The substance decomposes when slowly heated to 300 °C producing chlorine • Dissolution in water liberates a considerable amount of heat	5.1
Magnesium nitrate 10377-60-3	$Mg(NO_3)_2$		5.1
Magnesium oxide 1309-48-4	MgO	• Readily absorbs moisture and carbon dioxide when exposed to air • Reacts vigorously with halogens and strong acids	

Continues on next page.

Table 63.2 • Physical and chemical hazards.
Continued

Chemical name CAS-number	Molecular formula	Physical and chemical hazards	UN class/div/ subsidiary risks
Magnesium phosphide 12057-74-8	Mg_3P_2	• Reacts with water, air moisture, acids producing highly toxic fumes of phosphine • Reacts with water, air moisture, violently with acids causing fire and toxic (phosphine fumes) hazard	4.3/ 6.1
Mercuric acetate 1600-27-7	$HgC_4H_6O_4$	• The substance decomposes on heating and under influence of light producing toxic fumes of mercury or mercuric oxide	6.1
Mercuric bromide 7789-47-1	$HgBr_2$		6.1
Mercuric chloride 7487-94-7	$HgCl_2$	• The substance decomposes on heating producing toxic vapours of mercury and chloride • Reacts with light metals • Incompatible with formates, sulphites, hypophosphites, phosphates, sulphides, albumin, gelatin, alkalies, alkaloid salts, ammonia, lime water, antimony and arsenic, bromide, borax, carbonate, iron, copper, lead, silver salts	6.1
Mercuric nitrate 10045-94-0	$Hg(NO_3)_2$	• The substance decomposes on heating producing toxic fumes (mercury, nitrogen oxides), or on exposure to light • The substance is a strong oxidant and reacts violently with combustible and reducing materials • Reacts with acetylene, alcohol, phosphine and sulphur to form shock-sensitive compounds • Attacks most metals when in solution • Vigorous reaction with petroleum hydrocarbons	6.1
Mercuric oxide 21908-53-2	HgO	• The substance decomposes on exposure to light, on heating above 500 °C, or on burning under influence of light producing highly toxic fumes including mercury and oxygen, which increases fire hazard • Upon heating, toxic fumes are formed • Reacts violently with chlorine, hydrogen peroxide, hypophosphorous acid, hydrazine hydrate, magnesium (when heated), disulphur dichloride and hydrogen trisulphide • Reacts explosively with acetyl nitrate, butadiene, ethanol, iodine (at 35 °C), chlorine, hydrocarbons, diboron tetrafluoride, hydrogen peroxide, traces of nitric acid, reducing agents • Incompatible with reducing agents	6.1
Mercuric sulphate 7783-35-9	$HgSO_4$	• The substance decomposes on heating or on exposure to light producing toxic fumes of mercury and sulphur oxides • Reacts with water producing insoluble basic mercuric sulphate and sulphuric acid • Reacts violently with hydrogen chloride	6.1
Mercuric thiocyanate 592-85-8	$HgC_2N_2S_2$		6.1
Mercurous chloride 10112-91-1	Hg_2Cl_2	• The substance decomposes on heating producing toxic fumes of chlorine and mercury, or on exposure to sunlight producing metallic mercury and mercuric chloride • Reacts with bromides, iodides, sulphates, sulphites, carbonates, alkali chlorides, hydroxides, cyanides, lead salts, silver salts, soap, sulphides, copper salts, hydrogen peroxide, lime water, iodoform, ammonia, iodine	
Mercury 7439-97-6	Hg	• Reacts violently with acetylene, chlorine, and ammonia • Attacks copper and copper alloy materials • Incompatible with acetylenes and ammonia gases • Toxic vapours are formed on heating	6.1
Phenylmercuric acetate 62-38-4	$C_8H_8HgO_2$	• The substance decomposes on heating producing toxic vapours of mercury	6.1
Phenylmercuric nitrate 55-68-5	$C_6H_5HgNO_3$	• The substance decomposes on heating producing mercury vapours and other toxic fumes • Reacts with reducing agents	6.1
Nickel 7440-02-0	Ni	• Reacts with strong oxidants • Reacts violently, in powder form, with titanium powder and potassium perchlorate, and oxidants such as ammonium nitrate, causing fire and explosion hazard • Reacts slowly with non-oxidizing acids and more rapidly with oxidizing acids • Toxic gases and vapours (such as nickel carbonyl) may be released in a fire involving nickel • Dust explosion possible if in powder or granular form, mixed with air	
Nickel (II) oxide 1313-99-1	NiO	• Reacts violently with iodine and hydrogen sulphide causing fire and explosion hazard	

Continues on next page.

Table 63.2 • Physical and chemical hazards.
Continued

Chemical name CAS-number	Molecular formula	Physical and chemical hazards	UN class/div/ subsidiary risks
Nickel carbonate 3333-67-3	Ni_2CO_3	• The substance decomposes on heating and on contact with acids producing carbon dioxide • Reacts violently with aniline, hydrogen sulphide, flammable solvents, hydrazine and metal powders, especially zinc, aluminium and magnesium, causing fire and explosion hazard	
Nickel carbonyl 13463-39-3	NiC_4O_4	• May explode on heating at 60 °C • The substance may spontaneously ignite on contact with air • The substance decomposes on heating at 180 °C on contact with acids producing highly toxic carbon monoxide • Reacts violently with oxidants, acids and bromine • Reacts violently with oxidants causing fire and explosion hazard • Oxidizes in air forming deposits which become peroxidized causing fire hazard • The vapour is heavier than air and may travel along the ground; distant ignition possible	6.1/ 3
Nickel sulphide 12035-72-2	Ni_3S_2	• The substance decomposes on heating to high temperatures producing sulphur oxides	
Nickel sulphate 7786-81-4	$NiSO_4$	• The substance decomposes on heating at 848 °C, producing toxic fumes of sulphur trioxide and nickel monoxide • The solution in water is a weak acid	
Osmium tetroxide 20816-12-0	OsO_4	• The substance decomposes on heating producing fumes of osmium • The substance is a strong oxidant and reacts with combustible and reducing materials • Reacts with hydrochloric acid to form toxic chlorine gas • Forms unstable compounds with alkalis	6.1
Platinum tetrachloride 13454-96-1	$PtCl_4$	• On combustion, forms corrosive gases such as chlorine • The substance decomposes on heating or on burning producing toxic fumes (chlorine) • Reacts with strong oxidants	
Hydrogen selenide 7783-07-5	SeH_2	• The substance decomposes on heating above 100 °C producing toxic and flammable products including selenium and hydrogen • The substance is a strong reducing agent and reacts violently with oxidants causing fire and explosion hazard • On contact with air it emits toxic and corrosive fumes of selenium dioxide • The gas is heavier than air and may travel along the ground; distant ignition possible	2.3/ 2.1
Selenious acid 7783-00-8	SeH_2O_3	• The substance decomposes on heating producing water and toxic fumes of selenium oxides • Reacts on contact with acids producing toxic gaseous hydrogen selenide	
Selenious acid, disodium salt 10102-18-8	Na_2SeO_3	• On contact with hot surfaces or flames this substance decomposes forming toxic gases • The solution in water is a medium strong base • Reacts with water, strong acids causing toxic hazard	6.1
Selenium 7782-49-2	Se	• Upon heating, toxic fumes are formed • Reacts violently with oxidants and strong acids • Reacts with water at 50 °C forming flammable hydrogen and selenious acids • Reacts with incandescence on gentle heating with phosphorous and metals such as nickel, zinc, sodium, potassium, platinum	6.1
Selenium dioxide 7446-08-4	SeO_2	• The substance decomposes on heating producing toxic fumes of selenium • The solution in water is a medium strong acid (selenious acid) • Reacts with many substances giving off toxic vapours (selenium) • Attacks many metals in presence of water	
Selenium hexafluoride 7783-79-1	SeF_6	• The substance decomposes on heating producing toxic and corrosive fumes including hydrogen fluoride, fluoride and selenium	2.3/ 8
Selenium oxychloride 7791-23-3	$SeOCl_2$	• The substance decomposes on heating producing toxic fumes of chloride and selenium • The solution in water is a strong acid, it reacts violently with bases and is corrosive • Reacts violently with white phosphorus and potassium causing fire and explosion hazard • Reacts violently with metal oxides	3/ 6.1
Selenium trioxide 13768-86-0	SeO_3	• The substance decomposes on heating producing toxic fumes of selenium • The substance is a strong oxidant and reacts with combustible and reducing materials • The solution in water is a strong acid, it reacts violently with bases and is corrosive • Reacts violently with water giving off selenic acid • Attacks many metals when moisture is present	

Continues on next page.

63. METALS: CHEMICAL PROPERTIES AND TOXICITY

Table 63.2 • Physical and chemical hazards.
Continued

Chemical name CAS-number	Molecular formula	Physical and chemical hazards	UN class/div/ subsidiary risks
Silver 7440-22-4	Ag	• Shock-sensitive compounds are formed with acetylene • Finely divided silver and strong hydrogen peroxide solution may explode (violent decomposition to oxygen gas) • Contact with ammonia may cause formation of compounds that are explosive when dry • Readily reacts with diluted nitric acid, hot concentrated sulphuric acid	
Silver nitrate 7761-88-8	$AgNO_3$	Shock-sensitive compounds are formed with acetylene, alcohol, phosphine and sulphur • The substance decomposes on heating producing toxic fumes (nitrogen oxides) • The substance is a strong oxidant and reacts violently with combustible and reducing materials • Reacts with incompatible substances such as acetylene, alkalis, halides and other compounds causing fire and explosion hazard • Attacks some forms of plastics, rubber and coatings • The substance decomposes on contact with organic contaminants when exposed to light	5.1
Strontium chromate 7789-06-2	$SrCrH_2O_4$	• The substance decomposes on burning producing toxic fumes • Reacts violently with hydrazine • Incompatible with combustible, organic or other readily oxidizable materials such as paper, wood, sulphur, aluminium, plastics	
Tellurium 13494-80-9	Te	• Upon heating, toxic fumes are formed • Reacts vigorously with halogens or interhalogens causing flames hazard • Reacts with zinc with incandescence • Lithium silicide attacks tellurium with incandescence	6.1
Tellurium hexafluoride 7783-80-4	TeF_6		2.3/ 8
Thallium 7440-28-0	Tl	• Reacts violently with fluorine • Reacts with halogens at room temperature • Incompatible with strong acids, strong oxidants, and oxygen • The substance forms toxic compounds on contact with moisture	6.1
Thallous sulphate 7446-18-6	$Tl_2 (SO_4)_3$	• The substance decomposes on heating producing highly toxic fumes of thallium and sulphur oxides	6.1
Thorium 7440-29-1	Th		7
Di-N-Butyltin dichloride 683-18-1	$SnCl_2C_8H_{18}$		6.1
Di-N-Dibutyltin oxide 818-08-6	$C_8H_{18}SnO$	• The substance decomposes on heating producing toxic fumes of tin, tin oxides • Reacts with oxidants • Dust explosion possible if in powder or granular form, mixed with air • If dry, it can be charged electrostatically by swirling, pneumatic transport, pouring, etc.	
Dibutyltin dilaurate 77-58-7	$SnC_{32}H_{64}O_4$		6.1
Stannic chloride 7646-78-8	$SnCl_4$	• The vapour is heavier than air • The substance decomposes on heating producing toxic fumes • Reacts violently with water forming corrosive hydrochloric acid and tin oxide fumes • Reacts with turpentine • Attacks many metals, some forms of plastics, rubber and coatings • Contact with alcohol and amines may cause fire and explosion hazard • Reacts with moist air to form hydrochloric acid	8
Stannic oxide 18282-10-5	SnO	• Reacts violently with chlorine trifluoride • Contact with hydrogen trisulphide causes violent decomposition and ignition • Violently reduced by magnesium on heating, with fire and explosion hazard	
Stannous chloride 7772-99-8	$SnCl_2$	• Upon heating, toxic fumes are formed • The substance is a strong reducing agent and reacts violently with oxidants • Reacts violently with bromine trifluoride, sodium and nitrates	
Stannous chloride dihydrate 10025-69-1	$SnCl_2 \cdot 2H_2O$	• The substance is a strong reducing agent and reacts violently with oxidants • Upon heating, toxic and corrosive fumes are formed • The substance absorbs oxygen from air and forms insoluble oxychloride	

Continues on next page.

Table 63.2 • Physical and chemical hazards.
Continued

Chemical name CAS-number	Molecular formula	Physical and chemical hazards	UN class/div/ subsidiary risks
Stannous fluoride 7783-47-3	SnF_2	• Reacts with acids; hydrogen fluoride fumes may be formed • Reacts violently with chlorine • Incompatible with alkaline substances and oxidizing agents	
Tin oxide 21651-19-4	SnO	• On heating at 300 °C in air, oxidation to stannic oxide proceeds incandescently • Ignites in nitrous oxide at 400 °C and incandesces when heated in sulphur dioxide	
Titanium tetrachloride 7550-45-0	$TiCl_4$		8
Titanium trichloride 7705-07-9	$TiCl_3$		8
Vanadium pentoxide 1314-62-1	V_2O_5	• Upon heating, toxic fumes are formed • Acts as a catalyst in oxidation reactions	6.1
Vanadium tetrachloride 7632-51-1	VCl_4		8
Vanadium trioxide 1314-34-7	V_2O_3	• Ignites on heating in air • The substance decomposes on heating or on burning producing irritating and toxic fumes (vanadium oxides)	6.1
Vanadyl trichloride 7727-18-6	$VOCl_3$		8
Zinc 7440-66-6	Zn		4.3/ 4.2
Zinc chloride 7646-85-7	$ZnCl_2$		8
Zinc nitrate 7779-88-6	$Zn(NO_3)_2$		1.5
Zinc phosphide 1314-84-7	Zn_3P_2	• The substance decomposes on heating and on contact with acids or water producing toxic and flammable fumes of phosphorous and zinc oxides, and phosphine • Reacts violently with strong oxidants causing fire hazard	4.3/ 6.1
Zinc stearate 557-05-1	$ZnC_{36}H_{70}O_4$	• The substance decomposes on heating producing acrid smoke and fumes of zinc oxide • Dust explosion possible if in powder or granular form, mixed with air • If dry, it can be charged electrostatically by swirling, pneumatic transport, pouring, etc.	

The data on physical and chemical hazards are adapted from the International Chemical Safety Cards (ICSC) series produced by the International Programme on Chemical Safety (IPCS), a cooperative programme of the World Health Organization (WHO), the International Labour Organization (ILO) and the United Nations Environment Programme (UNEP).
The risk classification data are taken from *Recommendations on the Transport of Dangerous Goods*, 9th edition, developed by the United Nations Committee of Experts on the Transport of Dangerous Goods and published by the United Nations (1995).
In the UN risk classification, the following codes are used: 1.5 = very insensitive substances which have a mass explosion hazard; 2.1 = flammable gas; 2.3 = toxic gas; 3 = flammable liquid; 4.1 = flammable solid; 4.2 = substance liable to spontaneous combustion; 4.3 = substance which in contact with water emits flammable gases; 5.1 = oxidizing substance; 6.1 = toxic; 7 = radioactive; 8 = corrosive substance.

63. METALS: CHEMICAL PROPERTIES AND TOXICITY

Table 63.3 • Health hazards.

Chemical name CAS-Number	Short-term exposure	Long-term exposure	Routes of exposure	Symptoms	Target organs, routes of entry	Symptoms
Aluminium phosphide 20859-73-8	Eyes; skin; resp. tract		Inhalation	Abdominal pain, burning sensation, cough, dizziness, dullness, headache, laboured breathing, nausea, sore throat		
			Skin	Redness, pain		
			Eyes	Redness, pain		
			Ingestion	Abdominal pain, convulsions, nausea, unconsciousness, vomiting		
Antimony 7440-36-0	Eyes; skin; resp. tract; lungs; heart	Skin; lungs; resp. tract	Inhalation	Cough, fever, shortness of breath, vomiting, soreness of upper respiratory tract; See Ingestion	Resp sys; CVS; skin; eyes Inh; ing; con	Irrit eyes, skin, nose, throat, mouth; cough; dizz; head; nau, vomit, diarr; stomach cramps; insom; anor; unable to smell properly
			Skin	Redness		
			Eyes	Redness, pain, conjunctivitis		
			Ingestion	Abdominal pain, burning sensation, diarrhoea, nausea, shortness of breath, vomiting, cardiac arrhythmias		
Antimony trioxide 1309-64-4	Eyes; skin; resp. tract	Skin; lungs	Inhalation	Cough, fever, nausea, sore throat, vomiting		
			Skin	Redness, pain, blisters		
			Eyes	Redness, pain		
			Ingestion	Abdominal pain, diarrhoea, sore throat, vomiting, burning sensation		
Stibine 7803-52-3	Blood; kidneys; liver; CNS		Inhalation	Abdominal pain, headache, nausea, shortness of breath, vomiting, weakness, weak and irregular pulse, haematuria, shock	Blood; liver; kidneys; resp. sys. Inh	Head, weak; nau, abdom pain; lumbar pain, hemog, hema, hemolytic anemia; jaun; pulm irrit
Arsenic 7440-38-2	Eyes; skin; resp. tract; liver; kidneys; GI tract	Skin; liver; CNS; carcinogenic; may cause reproductive toxicity	Inhalation	Chest pain, abdominal pain, cough, headache, weakness, giddiness	Liver; kidneys; skin; lungs; lymphatic sys (lung & lymphatic cancer) Inh; abs; con; ing	Ulceration of nasal septum, derm, GI disturbances, peri neur, resp irrit, hyperpig of skin, [carc]
			Skin	May be absorbed, irritating		
			Eyes	Redness, irritating		
			Ingestion	Diarrhoea, nausea, vomiting		
Arsenic acid, copper salt 10103-61-4	Eyes; resp. tract; CNS;digestive tract	Skin; PNS; mucous membranes; liver	Inhalation	Cough, headache, laboured breathing, weakness; See Ingestion		
			Skin	May be absorbed		
			Eyes	Redness pain		
			Ingestion	Abdominal pain, diarrhoea, vomiting, burning sensation behind breastbone and in the mouth		
Arsenic acid, diammonium salt 7784-44-3	Eyes; skin; resp. tract; CNS; digestive tract; circulatory system	PNS; skin; mucous membranes; liver	Inhalation	Cough, headache, laboured breathing, weakness; See Ingestion		
			Skin	May be absorbed, soluble, redness, pain		
			Eyes	Redness, pain		
			Ingestion	Abdominal pain, diarrhoea, vomiting, burning sensation behind breastbone and in the mouth		
Arsenic acid, disodium salt 7778-43-0	Eyes;skin; resp. tract; CNS; digestive tract; circulatory system	PNS; skin; mucous membranes; liver	Inhalation	Cough, headache, laboured breathing, weakness; See Ingestion		
			Skin	May be absorbed, soluble, redness, pain		
			Eyes	Redness, pain		
			Ingestion	Abdominal pain, diarrhoea, vomiting, burning sensation behind breastbone and in the mouth		

Continues on next page.

Table 63.3 • Health hazards.
Continued

Chemical name CAS-Number	Short-term exposure	Long-term exposure	Routes of exposure	Symptoms	Target organs, routes of entry	Symptoms
Arsenic acid, magnesium salt 10103-50-1	Eyes; resp. tract; CNS; digestive tract; circulatory system	PNS; skin; mucous membranes; liver	Inhalation Skin Eyes Ingestion	Cough, headache, laboured breathing, weakness; *See Ingestion* May be absorbed Redness, pain Abdominal pain, diarrhoea, vomiting, burning sensation behind breastbone and in the mouth		
Arsenic acid, monopotassium salt 7784-41-0	Eyes; skin; resp. tract; mucous membranes	Skin; PNS; mucous membranes; liver	Inhalation Skin Eyes Ingestion	Cough, headache, laboured breathing, weakness; *See Ingestion* May be absorbed, redness, pain Redness, pain Abdominal pain, burning sensation, diarrhoea, vomiting		
Arsenic pentoxide 1303-28-2	Eyes; skin; resp. tract; kidneys; liver; CVS; CNS; blood	Lungs; skin; bone marrow; CVS; CNS; carcinogenic; may cause reproductive toxicity	Inhalation Skin Eyes Ingestion	Cough, headache, dizziness, weakness shortness of breath, pain in chest, symptoms may be delayed; *See Ingestion* Redness, skin burns, pain Redness, pain, conjunctivitis Constriction in throat, vomiting, abdominal pain, diarrhoea, severe thirst, muscular cramps, shock		
Arsenic trioxide 1327-53-3	Eyes; skin; resp. tract; kidneys; liver; CVS; CNS; hemato-poietic	Lungs; skin; bone marrow; PNS; CNS; CVS; heart; kidneys; liver; carcinogenic; may cause birth defects	Inhalation Skin Eyes Ingestion	Cough, dizziness, headache, shortness of breath, weakness, pain in chest, symptoms may be delayed; *See Ingestion* Redness, pain Redness, pain, conjunctivitis Constriction in throat, abdominal pain, diarrhoea, vomiting, severe thirst, muscular cramps, shock		
Arsenious acid, copper (2+) salt (1:1) 10290-12-7	Eyes; skin; resp. tract.; CNS; digestive tract; circulatory system	Skin; PNS; mucous membranes; liver	Inhalation Skin Eyes Ingestion	Cough, headache, laboured breathing, weakness; *See Ingestion* May be absorbed Redness, pain Abdominal pain, diarrhoea, vomiting, burning sensation behind breastbone and in the mouth		
Arsenious acid, lead (II) salt 10031-13-7	Eyes; skin; resp. tract; CNS; GI tract; circulatory system	Skin; PNS; mucous membranes; liver	Inhalation Skin Eyes Ingestion	Cough, headache, laboured breathing, weakness; *See Ingestion* Redness, pain Redness, pain Abdominal pain, diarrhoea, vomiting, burning sensation behind breastbone and in the mouth		
Arsenious acid, potassium salt 10124-50-2	Eyes; skin; resp. tract; CNS; digestive tract; circulatory system		Inhalation Skin Eyes Ingestion	Cough, headache, laboured breathing, weakness; *See Ingestion* May be absorbed, soluble, redness, pain Redness, pain Abdominal pain, diarrhoea, vomiting, burning sensation behind breastbone and in the mouth		

Continues on next page.

Table 63.3 • Health hazards.
Continued

Chemical name CAS-Number	Short-term exposure	Long-term exposure	Routes of exposure	Symptoms	Target organs, routes of entry	Symptoms
Arsenous trichloride 7784-34-1	Eyes; skin; resp. tract; lungs; CVS; CNS; GI tract	Mucous membranes; skin; liver; kidneys; PNS	Inhalation	Corrosive, cough, laboured breathing; *See Ingestion*		
			Skin	Corrosive, may be absorbed, redness, pain		
			Eyes	Corrosive, pain, severe deep burns		
			Ingestion	Corrosive, abdominal pain, burning sensation, diarrhoea, vomiting, collapse		
Arsine 7784-42-1	Lungs; blood; kidneys		Inhalation	Abdominal pain, confusion, dizziness, headache, nausea, shortness of breath, vomiting, weakness	Blood; kidneys; liver (lung & lymphatic cancer)	Head, mal, weak, dizz; dysp; abdom, back pain; nau, vomit, bronze skin; hema; jaun; peri neur, liq: frostbite; [carc]
			Skin	On contact with liquid: frostbite	Inh; con (liq)	
			Eyes	On contact with liquid: frostbite, redness		
Calcium arsenate 7778-44-1	Eyes; skin; resp. tract; CNS; digestive tract; circulatory system	PNS; skin; mucous membranes; liver	Inhalation	Cough, headache, laboured breathing, weakness: *See Ingestion*	Eyes; resp sys; liver; skin; lymphatic sysrtem; CNS; [lymphatic & lung cancer]	Weak; GI dist; peri neur, skin hyperpig, palmar planter hyperkeratoses; derm; [carc]; in animals: liver damage
			Skin	May be absorbed, redness, pain		
			Eyes	Redness, pain	Inh; abs; ing; con	
			Ingestion	Abdominal pain, diarrhoea, vomiting, burning sensation behind breastbone and in the mouth		
Lead arsenate 7784-40-9	Intestines; CVS	Skin; CNS; GI tract; liver; kidneys; blood; carcinogenic; may cause reproductive toxicity	Inhalation	Abdominal cramps, diarrhoea, headache, nausea, vomiting, tightness of chest, constipation, excitation, disorientation		
			Skin	Redness		
			Eyes	Redness		
Methylarsonic acid 124-58-3	Eyes; skin; resp. tract; lungs	Bone marrow; PNS; kidneys; liver	Inhalation	Cough	Organic arsenic compounds: Skin, resp sys, kidneys, CNS, liver, GI tract, repro sys	In animals: irrit skin, possible derm; resp. distress; diarr; kidney damage; musc tremor, sez; possible GI tract, terato, repro effects; possible liver damage
			Skin	Redness		
			Eyes	Redness		
			Ingestion	Abdominal pain, diarrhoea, vomiting, burning sensation in throat		
Sodium arsenate 10048-95-0	Eyes; skin; resp. tract; digestive tract; heart; liver; kidneys; CNS	Skin; CNS; CVS; blood; liver; carcinogenic	Inhalation	Cough, headache, sore throat; *See Ingestion*		
			Skin	Redness, pain		
			Eyes	Redness, pain		
			Ingestion	Abdominal pain, burning sensation, diarrhoea, vomiting		
Barium 7440-39-3	Eyes; skin; resp. tract		Inhalation	Cough, sore throat		
			Skin	Redness		
			Eyes	Redness, pain		
Barium chlorate 13477-00-4	Eyes; skin; resp. tract; various tissues and organs	Tissues and organs	Inhalation	Abdominal pain, abdominal cramps, burning sensation, nausea, vomiting, weakness, paralysis		
			Eyes	Redness, pain		
			Ingestion	Abdominal cramps, abdominal pain, blue lips or fingernails, blue skin, burning sensation, diarrhoea, dizziness, nausea, sore throat, vomiting, weakness, cardiac dysrhythmia		

Continues on next page.

Table 63.3 • Health hazards.
Continued

Chemical name CAS-Number	Short-term exposure	Long-term exposure	Routes of exposure	Symptoms	Target organs, routes of entry	Symptoms
Barium chloride 10361-37-2	Eyes; skin; resp. tract; CNS; muscles		Inhalation	Abdominal cramps, unconsciousness	Heart; CNS; skin; resp sys; eyes	Irrit eyes, skin, upper resp sys; skin burns, gastroenteritis; musc spasm; slow pulse, extrasystoles; hypokalaemia
			Eyes	Redness	Inh; ing; con	
			Ingestion	Abdominal cramps, dullness, unconsciousness		
Barium chloride, dihydrate 10362-27-9	Eyes; skin; resp. tract; CNS; muscles		Inhalation	Abdominal cramps, unconsciousness		
			Eyes	Redness		
			Ingestion	Abdominal cramps, dullness, unconsciousness		
Barium oxide 1304-28-5	Eyes; skin; resp. tract; muscles	Lungs	Inhalation	Cough, shortness of breath, sore throat		
			Skin	Redness		
			Eyes	Redness, pain		
			Ingestion	Abdominal pain, diarrhoea, dizziness, nausea, vomiting, muscle paralysis, cardiac arrhythmia, hypertension, death		
Barium peroxide 1304-29-6		Skin	Inhalation	Cough, nausea, shortness of breath, sore throat		
			Skin	Redness, skin burns, pain, bleaching		
			Eyes	Redness, pain, severe deep burns		
			Ingestion	Abdominal pain, burning sensation, sore throat		
Barium sulphate 7727-43-7		Lungs	Inhalation	Cough	Eyes; resp sys Inh; con	Irrit eyes, nose, upper resp sys; benign pneumoconiosis (baritosis)
Cadmium 7440-43-9	Eyes; resp. tract; lungs	Lungs; kidneys	Inhalation	Cough, headache, symptoms may be delayed	Resp sys; kidneys; prostate; blood (prostatic & lung cancer) Inh; ing	Pulm oedema, dysp, cough, tight chest, subs pain; head; chills, musc aches; nau, vomit, diarr; anos, emphy, prot, mild anaemia; [carc]
			Eyes	Redness, pain		
			Ingestion	Abdominal pain, diarrhoea, headache, nausea, vomiting		
Cadmium chloride 10108-64-2	Resp. tract; digestive tract; lungs	Lungs; kidneys; bone; probably carcinogenic	Inhalation	Cough, laboured breathing, symptoms may be delayed		
			Skin	Redness		
			Eyes	Redness, pain		
			Ingestion	Abdominal pain, burning sensation, diarrhoea, nausea, vomiting		
Cadmium oxide 1306-19-0	Resp. tract; digestive tract; lungs	Lungs; kidneys; carcinogenic	Inhalation	Cough, laboured breathing, shortness of breath, symptoms may be delayed	Resp sys; kidneys; blood; (prostatic & lung cancer) Inh	Pulm oedema, dysp, cough, tight chest, subs pain; head; chills, musc aches; nau, vomit, diarr; anos, emphy, prot, mild anaemia; [carc]
			Skin	Redness		
			Eyes	Redness, pain		
			Ingestion	Abdominal cramps, diarrhoea, nausea, vomiting		
Cadmium sulphide 1306-23-6		Lungs; kidneys; carcinogenic				
Chromium 7440-47-3	Eyes; skin; resp. tract; lungs; kidneys	Skin; asthma; larynx; lungs	Eyes	Irritation	Resp sys; skin; eyes Inh; ing; con	Irrit eyes, skin; lung fib (histologic)
			Ingestion	Diarrhoea, nausea, unconsciousness, vomiting		

Continues on next page.

63. METALS: CHEMICAL PROPERTIES AND TOXICITY

Table 63.3 • Health hazards.
Continued

Chemical name CAS-Number	Short-term exposure	Long-term exposure	Routes of exposure	Symptoms	Target organs, routes of entry	Symptoms
Chromyl chloride 14977-61-8	Eyes; skin; resp. tract; lungs; corrosive on ingestion	Skin; asthma; probably carcinogenic	Inhalation Skin Eyes Ingestion	Cough, laboured breathing, shortness of breath, sore throat Redness, skin burns, pain, blisters Redness, pain, severe deep burns Abdominal pain	Eyes; skin; resp sys (lung cancer) Inh; abs; ing; con	Irrit eyes, skin, upper resp sys; eye, skin burns
Lead chromate 7758-97-6	Resp. tract; may cause perforation of nasal septum	Skin; inhalation may cause asthma; lungs	Inhalation Skin Eyes Ingestion	Cough, headache, laboured breathing, nausea, metallic taste Skin burns, ulcers, blisters Redness Abdominal pain, constipation, convulsions, cough, diarrhoea, vomiting, weakness, anorexia		
Cobalt 7440-48-4		Skin; resp. tract; lungs; heart	Inhalation Skin Eyes Ingestion	Cough, laboured breathing, shortness of breath Redness Redness Abdominal pain, vomiting	Resp sys; skin Inh; ing; con	Cough, dysp, wheez, decr pulm func; low-wgt; derm; diffuse nodular fib; resp hypersensitivity, asthma
Cobalt chloride 7646-79-9	Eyes; skin; resp. tract	Skin; resp. tract ; heart	Inhalation Skin Eyes Ingestion	Cough, laboured breathing, shortness of breath Redness Redness Abdominal pain, diarrhoea, nausea, vomiting		
Cobalt (III) oxide 1308-04-9	Eyes; skin; resp. tract	Skin; may cause asthma; lungs; possibly carcinogenic	Inhalation Eyes	Cough, laboured breathing, shortness of breath Redness		
Cobalt naphthenate 61789-51-3	Eyes; resp. tract	Skin	Inhalation Skin Eyes	Cough, sore throat Redness, pain Redness, pain		
Copper 7440-50-8	Eyes	Skin; lungs	Inhalation Skin Eyes Ingestion	Cough, headache, shortness of breath, sore throat Redness Redness, pain Abdominal pain, nausea, vomiting	Eyes; resp sys; skin; liver; kidneys (incr risk with Wilsons disease) Inh; ing; con	Irrit eyes, nose, pharynx; nasal perf; metallic taste; derm; in animals: lung, liver, kidney damage; anaemia
Copper (I) oxide 1317-39-1	Eyes; resp. tract		Inhalation Eyes Ingestion	Cough, metallic taste, metal fume fever Redness Abdominal cramps, diarrhoea, nausea, vomiting		
Lead 7439-92-1		Nervous system; kidneys; may impair fertility; may cause retarded development of the newborn	Inhalation Ingestion	Headache, nausea, abdominal spasm Headache, nausea, sore throat, abdominal spasm	Eyes; GI tract; CNS; kidneys; blood; gingival tissue Inh; ing; con	Weak, lass, insom; facial pallor; pal eye, anor, low-wgt, malnut; constip, abdom pain, colic; anemia; gingival lead line; tremor; para wrist, ankles; encephalopathy; kidney disease; irrit eyes; hypotension

Continues on next page.

Table 63.3 • Health hazards.
Continued

Chemical name CAS-Number	Short-term exposure	Long-term exposure	Routes of exposure	Symptoms	Target organs, routes of entry	Symptoms
Lead acetate 301-04-2	Eyes; skin; resp. tract; blood; CNS; kidneys	Blood; bone marrow; CVS; kidneys; CNS	Inhalation	Headache, chronic but not described as acute; *See Ingestion*		
			Eyes	Redness, pain		
			Ingestion	Abdominal cramps, constipation, convulsions, headache, nausea, vomiting		
Tetraethyl lead 78-00-2	Eyes; skin; resp. tract; CNS	Skin; CNS; may cause genetic damage; may cause reproductive toxicity	Inhalation	Convulsions, dizziness, headache, unconsciousness, vomiting, weakness	CNS; CVS; kidneys; eyes Inh; abs; ing; con	Insom, lass, anxiety; tremor, hyper-reflexia, spasticity; bradycardia, hypotension, hypothermia, pallor, nau, anor, low-wgt; conf, disorientation, halu, psychosis, mania, convuls, coma; eye irrit
			Skin	May be absorbed, redness		
			Eyes	Pain, blurred vision		
			Ingestion	Convulsions, diarrhoea, dizziness, headache, unconsciousness, vomiting, weakness		
Lead (II) oxide 1317-36-8		CNS; kidneys; blood				
Magnesium 7439-95-4			Inhalation	Cough, laboured breathing		
			Eyes	Redness, pain		
			Ingestion	Abdominal pain, diarrhoea		
Magnesium chloride 7786-30-3	Eyes; resp. tract		Inhalation	Cough		
			Eyes	Redness		
			Ingestion	Diarrhoea		
Magnesium oxide 1309-48-4	Eyes; nose		Inhalation	Cough	Eyes; resp sys Inh; con	Irrit eyes, nose; metal fume fever, cough, chest pain, flu-like fever
			Eyes	Redness		
			Ingestion	Diarrhoea		
Magnesium phosphide 12057-74-8	Eyes; skin; resp. tract		Inhalation	Abdominal pain, burning sensation, cough, dizziness, dullness, headache, laboured breathing, nausea, sore throat		
			Skin	Redness, pain		
			Eyes	Redness, pain		
			Ingestion	Abdominal pain, convulsions, nausea, unconsciousness, vomiting		
Manganese sulphate 10034-96-5	Eyes; skin; resp. tract	Lungs; CNS; liver; kidneys; testes	Inhalation	Burning sensation, cough, laboured breathing		
			Skin	May be absorbed, redness, burning sensation		
			Eyes	Redness, pain, blurred vision		
			Ingestion	Abdominal cramps, nausea, sore throat		
Mercury 7439-97-6	Eyes; skin; lungs; CNS	CNS; nervous system; kidneys	Inhalation	Pulmonary irritation, cough	Skin; resp sys; CNS; kidneys; eyes Inh; abs; ing; con	Irrit eyes, skin; cough, chest pain, dysp, bron pneuitis; tremor, insom, irrity, indecision, head, ftg, weak; stomatitis, salv; GI dist, anor, low-wgt; prot
			Skin	May be absorbed		
			Eyes	Irritating		
Mercuric acetate 1600-27-7	Eyes; skin; resp. tract; lungs; kidneys	Skin; kidneys	Inhalation	Cough, headache, laboured breathing, shortness of breath, sore throat, symptoms may be delayed; *See Ingestion*		
			Skin	May be absorbed, skin burns, pain		
			Eyes	Pain, blurred vision, severe deep burns		
			Ingestion	Abdominal pain, burning sensation, diarrhoea, vomiting, metallic taste		

Continues on next page.

63. METALS: CHEMICAL PROPERTIES AND TOXICITY

Table 63.3 • Health hazards.
Continued

Chemical name CAS-Number	Short-term exposure	Long-term exposure	Routes of exposure	Symptoms	Target organs, routes of entry	Symptoms
Mercuric chloride 7487-94-7	Eyes; skin; resp. tract; lungs; kidneys	Skin; kidneys	Inhalation	Burning sensation, cough, laboured breathing, shortness of breath, sore throat, symptoms may be delayed; *See Ingestion*		
			Skin	May be absorbed, pain, blisters		
			Eyes	Pain, blurred vision, severe deep burns		
			Ingestion	Abdominal cramps, abdominal pain, burning sensation, diarrhoea, nausea, sore throat, vomiting, metallic taste		
Mercuric nitrate 10045-94-0	Skin; resp. tract; eyes; kidneys	Kidneys	Inhalation	Cough, headache, laboured breathing, shortness of breath, sore throat		
			Skin	May be absorbed, redness, pain		
			Eyes	Pain, blurred vision, severe deep burns		
			Ingestion	Abdominal pain, diarrhoea, vomiting, metallic taste		
Mercuric oxide 21908-53-2	Eyes; skin; resp. tract	Skin; kidneys; CNS	Inhalation	Cough		
			Skin	May be absorbed, redness		
			Eyes	Redness		
			Ingestion	Abdominal pain, diarrhoea		
Mercuric sulphate 7783-35-9	Eyes; skin; resp. tract; lungs; GI tract; corrosive on ingestion	Kidneys	Inhalation	Burning sensation, cough, laboured breathing, shortness of breath, weakness, symptoms may be delayed; *See Ingestion*		
			Skin	May be absorbed, redness, burning sensation, pain		
			Eyes	Pain, blurred vision, severe deep burns		
			Ingestion	Abdominal pain, diarrhoea, nausea, vomiting, metallic taste		
Mercurous chloride 10112-91-1	Eyes	Kidneys	Eyes	Redness		
			Ingestion	Weakness		
Mercury organoalkyl compound					Eyes; skin; CNS; PNS; kidneys Inh; abs; ing; con	Pares; ataxia, dysarthria; vision, hearing dist; spasticity; jerking limbs; dizz; salv; lac; nau, vomit, diarr, constip; skin burns; emotional dist; kidney inj; possible terato effects
Phenylmer-curic acetate 62-38-4	Eyes; skin; resp. tract; kidneys	Skin; CNS; possibly causes toxic effects upon human reproduction	Inhalation	Cough, laboured breathing, sore throat, symptoms may be delayed		
			Skin	May be absorbed, redness, pain		
			Eyes	Redness, pain, blurred vision		
			Ingestion	Abdominal pain, diarrhoea, nausea, vomiting, weakness, symptoms of delayed effects		
Phenylmer-curic nitrate 55-68-5	Eyes; skin; resp. tract; kidneys	Skin; CNS; possibly causes toxic effects on human reproduction	Inhalation	Cough, laboured breathing, sore throat, symptoms may be delayed		
			Skin	May be absorbed, redness, pain		
			Eyes	Redness, pain, blurred vision		
			Ingestion	Abdominal pain, diarrhoea, nausea, vomiting, symptoms of delayed effects		

Continues on next page.

Table 63.3 • Health hazards.
Continued

Chemical name CAS-Number	Short-term exposure	Long-term exposure	Routes of exposure	Symptoms	Target organs, routes of entry	Symptoms
Nickel 7440-02-0	Eyes; resp. tract	Skin; inhalation may cause asthma; may effect conjuctiva; possibly carcinogenic			Nasal cavities; lungs; skin (lung & nasal cancer) Inh; ing; con	Sens derm, allergic asthma, pneuitis; [carc]
Nickel (II) oxide 1313-99-1	Eyes; resp. tract	Skin; inhalation may cause asthma; carcinogenic	Inhalation Skin Eyes	Cough Redness Redness		
Nickel carbonate 3333-67-3	Eyes; resp. tract	Skin; carcinogenic; asthma	Inhalation Skin Eyes	Cough Redness Redness		
Nickel carbonyl 13463-39-3	Eyes; skin; resp. tract; lungs; CNS	Possibly carcinogenic; may cause defects on the unborn child	Inhalation Skin Eyes Ingestion	Abdominal pain, blue skin, cough, dizziness, headache, nausea, shortness of breath, vomiting, symptoms may be delayed May be absorbed, redness, pain Redness, pain Abdominal pain, headache, nausea, vomiting	Lungs; paranasal sinus; CNS; repro sys (lung & nasal cancer) Inh; abs; ing; con	Head, verti; nau, vomit, epigastric pain; subs pain; cough, hyperpnea; cyan; weak; leucyt; pneuitis; delirium; convuls; [carc]; in animals: repro, terato effects
Nickel sulphide 12035-72-2	Eyes; skin; resp. tract	Skin; possibly carcinogenic	Inhalation	Cough, sore throat		
Nickel sulphate 7786-81-4	Eyes; skin; resp. tract; GI tract; CNS	Skin; asthma; possibly carcinogenic	Inhalation Skin Eyess Ingestion	Cough, sore throat May be absorbed, redness Redness Abdominal pain, dizziness, headache, nausea, vomiting		
Osmium tetroxide 20816-12-0	Eyes; skin; resp. tract; lungs	Skin; kidneys	Inhalation Skin Eyes Ingestion	Cough, headache, wheezing, shortness of breath, visual disturbances, symptoms may be delayed Redness, skin burns, skin discoloration Blurred vision, loss of vision Burning sensation	Eyes; resp sys; skin Inh; ing; con	Irrit eyes, resp sys; lac, vis dist; conj; head; cough, dysp; derm
Platinium tetrachloride 13454-96-1	Eyes; skin; resp. tract		Inhalation Skin Eyes	Burning sensation, cough Redness Redness	Eyes; skin; resp sys Inh; ing; con	Irrit eyes, nose; cough; dysp, wheez, cyan; derm, sens skin; lymphocytosis
Hydrogen selenide 7783-07-5	Eyes; resp. tract; lungs	Skin; liver; spleen; kidneys	Inhalation Skin Eyes	Burning sensation, cough, laboured breathing, nausea, sore throat, weakness On contact with liquid: frostbite Redness, pain;	Resp sys; eyes; liver Inh; con	Irrit eyes, nose, throat; nau, vomit, diarr; metallic taste, garlic breathy; dizz, lass, ftg; liq: frostbite; in animals: pneuitis; liver damage
Selenious acid 7783-00-8	Eyes; skin; resp. tract	Skin	Inhalation Skin Eyes Ingestion	Burning sensation, cough, laboured breathing, sore throat May be absorbed, redness, pain, blisters Redness, pain, blurred vision, severe deep burns, puffy eyelids Abdominal pain, burning sensation, confusion, nausea, sore throat, weakness, low blood pressure		

Continues on next page.

63. METALS: CHEMICAL PROPERTIES AND TOXICITY

Table 63.3 • Health hazards.
Continued

Chemical name CAS-Number	Short-term exposure	Long-term exposure	Routes of exposure	Symptoms	Target organs, routes of entry	Symptoms
Selenious acid, disodium salt 10102-18-8	Eyes; skin; resp. tract; lungs; liver; kidneys; heart; CNS; GI tract	teeth; bone; blood	Inhalation	Abdominal cramps, diarrhoea, dizziness, headache, hair loss, laboured breathing, nausea, vomiting, symptoms may be delayed		
			Skin	Redness		
			Eyes	Redness		
Selenium 7782-49-2	Lungs	Skin; resp. tract; GI tract; integuments	Inhalation	Irritation of nose, cough, dizziness, headache, laboured breathing, nausea, sore throat, vomiting, weakness, symptoms may be delayed	Resp sys; eyes; skin; liver; kidneys; blood; spleen Inh; ing; con	Irrit eyes, skin, nose, throat; vis dist; head; chills, fever, dysp, bron; metallic taste, garlic breath, GI dist; derm, eye, skin burns; in animals: anemia; liver nec, cirr; kidney, spleen damage
			Skin	Redness, skin burns, pain, discolouration		
			Eyes	Redness, pain, blurred vision		
			Ingestion	Metallic taste, diarrhoea, chills, fever		
Selenium dioxide 7446-08-4	Eyes; skin; resp. tract; lungs	Skin	Inhalation	Burning sensation, cough, laboured breathing, sore throat		
			Skin	May be absorbed, redness, pain, blisters		
			Eyes	Redness, pain, blurred vision, severe deep burns, puffy eyelids		
			Ingestion	Abdominal pain, burning sensation, confusion, nausea, sore throat, weakness, low blood pressure		
Selenium hexafluoride 7783-79-1	Resp. tract; lungs	Skin; CNS; liver; kidneys	Inhalation	Corrosive, cough, headache, nausea, shortness of breath, sore throat	Resp sys Inh	In animals: plum irrit, edema
			Skin	Redness, pain, on contact with liquid: frostbite; corrosive		
			Eyes	Redness, pain, blurred vision;		
Selenium oxychloride 7791-23-3	Eyes; skin; resp. tract; lungs	Skin	Inhalation	Burning sensation, cough, laboured breathing, sore throat		
			Skin	Corrosive, may be absorbed, redness, pain, blisters		
			Eyes	Redness, pain, blurred vision, severe deep burns		
			Ingestion	Abdominal cramps, confusion, nausea, sore throat, hypotension		
Selenium trioxide 13768-86-0	Eyes; skin; resp. tract	Skin; lungs	Inhalation	Burning sensation, cough, laboured breathing, sore throat		
			Skin	May be absorbed, redness, pain		
			Eyes	Redness, pain, blurred vision, puffy eyelids		
			Ingestion	Abdominal cramps, confusion, nausea, sore throat, weakness, low blood pressure		
Silver 7740-22-4		Eyes; nose; throat; skin			Nasal septum; skin; eyes Inh; ing; con	Blue-gray eyes, nasal septum, throat, skin; irrit, ulceration skin; GI dist
Silver nitrate 7761-88-8	Eyes; skin; resp. tract	Blood; skin	Inhalation	Burning sensation, cough, laboured breathing		
			Skin	Redness, skin burns, pain		
			Eyes	Redness, pain, loss of vision, severe deep burns		
			Ingestion	Abdominal pain, burning sensation, weakness		

Continues on next page.

Table 63.3 • Health hazards.
Continued

Chemical name CAS-Number	Short-term exposure	Long-term exposure	Routes of exposure	Symptoms	Target organs, routes of entry	Symptoms
Strontium chromate 7789-06-2	Eyes; skin; resp. tract; kidneys; liver	Skin; lungs; blood; liver; kidneys; brain; red and white blood cells; liver; kidneys; carcinogenic	Inhalation Skin Ingestion	Cough, hoarseness Redness, ulcerations Sore throat		
Tellurium 13494-80-9	Resp. tract; CNS	Possibly causes malformations in human babies	Inhalation Skin Eyes Ingestion	Drowsiness, headache, garlic odour, nausea May be absorbed Redness Abdominal pain, constipation, nausea, vomiting, garlic odour of the breath	Skin; CNS; blood Inh; ing; con	Garlic breath, sweat; dry mouth, metallic taste; som; anor, nau, no sweat; derm; in animals: CNS, red blood cell effects
Thallium metal 7440-28-0	Nervous system	Eyes; liver; lungs; may cause birth defects	Inhalation Skin Eyes Ingestion	Nausea, vomiting, loss of hair, abdominal colic, pain in legs and chest, nervousness, irritability May be absorbed May be absorbed Abdominal pain, constipation, diarrhoea, headache, nausea, vomiting, loss of vision	Eyes; CNS; lungs; liver; kidneys; GI tract, body hair; resp sys Inh; abs; ing; con	Nau, diarr, abdom pain, vomit; ptosis, strabismus; peri neuritis, tremor; retster tight, chest pain, pulm edema; sez, chorea, psychosis; liver, kidney damage; alopecia; pares legs
Thallous sulphate 7446-18-6	Eyes; skin; CNS; CVS; kidneys; GI tract		Inhalation Skin Eyes Ingestion	*See Ingestion* May be absorbed, redness; *See Ingestion* Redness, pain Abdominal pain, convulsions, diarrhoea, headache, vomiting, weakness, delirium, tachycardia		
Di-N-Dibutyltin oxide 818-08-6	Eyes; skin; resp. tract; lungs	Skin; PNS; liver; bile duct; lymphatic system;	Inhalation Skin Eyes	Headache, ringing in the ears, memory loss, disorientation May be absorbed, skin burns, pain Redness, pain		
Stannic chloride 7646-78-8	Eyes; skin; resp. tract; lungs	Skin	Inhalation Skin Eyes Ingestion	Burning sensation, cough, laboured breathing, shortness of breath, sore throat Redness, skin burns, blisters Severe deep burns Abdominal cramps, vomiting		
Stannic oxide 18282-10-5	Resp. tract	Lungs	Inhalation	Cough	Resp sys Inh; con	Stannosis (benign pneumoconiosis): dysp, decr pulm func
Stannous chloride 7772-99-8	Eyes; skin; resp. tract; CNS; blood	Liver	Inhalation Skin Eyes Ingestion	Cough, shortness of breath Redness Redness, pain Abdominal pain, diarrhoea, nausea, vomiting		
Stannous chloride dihydrate 10025-69-1	Eyes; skin; resp. tract; CNS; blood	Liver	Inhalation Skin Eyes Ingestion	Cough, shortness of breath Redness Redness pain Abdominal pain, diarrhoea, nausea, vomiting		

Continues on next page.

63. METALS: CHEMICAL PROPERTIES AND TOXICITY

Table 63.3 • Health hazards.
Continued

Chemical name CAS-Number	Short-term exposure	Long-term exposure	Routes of exposure	Symptoms	Target organs, routes of entry	Symptoms
Stannous fluoride 7783-47-3	Skin; resp. tract; eyes	Teeth; bone	Inhalation Skin Eyes Ingestion	Cough Redness Redness, pain, severe deep burns Abdominal pain, nausea		
Tin oxide 21651-19-4	Resp. tract	Lungs	Inhalation	Cough	Resp sys Inh; con	Stannosis (benign pneumoconiosis): dysp, decr pulm func
Titanium dioxide 13463-67-7	Eyes; lungs	Lungs	Inhalation Eyes	Cough Redness	Resp sys [in animals: lung tumors] Inh	Lung fib; [carc]
Vanadium pentoxide 1314-62-1	Eyes; resp. tract; lungs	Skin; lungs; tongue	Inhalation Skin Eyes Ingestion	Burning sensation, cough, shortness of breath Redness, burning sensation Redness, pain, conjunctivitis Abdominal pain, diarrhoea, drowsiness, unconsciousness, vomiting, symptoms of severe systemic poisoning and death	Resp sys; skin; eyes Inh; con	Irrit eyes, skin, throat; green tongue, metallic taste, eczema; cough; fine râles, wheez, bron, dysp
Vanadium trioxide 1314-34-7	Eyes; skin; resp. tract	Resp. tract; may effect liver and cardiac function	Inhalation Skin Eyes Ingestion	Runny nose, sneezing, cough, diarrhoea, laboured breathing, sore throat, weakness, pain in chest, green to black tongue Dry skin, redness Redness Headache, vomiting, weakness		
Zinc chromate 13530-65-9		Skin; resp. tract	Inhalation Eyes Ingestion	Cough Redness Abdominal pain, diarrhoea, vomiting		
Zinc phosphide 1314-84-7	Resp. tract; lungs; liver; kidneys; heart; CNS		Inhalation Ingestion	Cough, diarrhoea, headache, fatigue, nausea, vomiting Abdominal pain, cough, diarrhoea, dizziness, headache, laboured breathing, nausea, unconsciousness, vomiting, ataxia, fatigue		

The short-term and long-term exposure data area adapted from the International Chemical Safety Cards (ICSC) series produced by the International Programme on Chemical Safety (see notes to table 63.2). The abbreviations used are CNS = central nervous system; CVS = cardiovascular system; PNS = peripheral nervous system; resp. tract = respiratory tract.

The remaining data are adapted from the *NIOSH Pocket Guide to Chemical Hazards* (NIOSH 1994). The following abbreviations are used:
abdom = abdominal; abnor = abnormal/abnormalities; album = albuminuria; anes = anesthesia; anor = anorexia; anos = anosmia (loss of the sense of smell); appre = apprehension; arrhy = arrhythmias; aspir = aspiration; asphy = asphyxia; BP = blood pressure; breath = breathing; bron = bronchitis; broncpneu = bronchopneumonia; bronspas = bronchospasm; BUN = blood urea nitrogen; [carc] = potential occupational carcinogen; card = cardiac; chol = cholinesterase; cirr = cirrhosis; CNS = central nervous system; conc = concentration; conf = confusion; conj = conjunctivitis; constip = constipation; convuls = convulsions; corn = corneal; CVS = cardiovascular system; cyan = cyanosis; decr = decreased; depress = depressant/depression; derm = dermatitis; diarr = diarrhea; dist = disturbance; dizz = dizziness; drow = drowsiness; dysfunc = dysfunction; dysp = dyspnea (breathing difficulty); emphy = emphysema; eosin = eosinophilia; epilep = epileptiform; epis = epistaxis (nosebleed); equi = equilibrium; eryt = erythema (skin redness); euph = euphoria; fail = failure; fasc = fasciculation; FEV = forced expiratory volume; fib = fibrosis; fibri = fibrillation; ftg = fatigue; func = function; GI = gastrointestinal; gidd = giddiness; halu = hallucinations; head = headache; hema = hematuria (blood in the urine); hemato = hematopoietic; hemog = hemoglobinuria; hemorr = hemorrhage; hyperpig = hyperpigmentation; hypox = hypoxemia (reduced oxygen in the blood); inco = incoordination; incr = increase(d); inebri = inebriation; inflamm = inflammation; inj = injury; insom = insomnia; irreg = irregularity/irregularities; irrit = irritation; irrty = irritability; jaun = jaundice; kera = keratitis (inflammation of the cornea); lac = lacrimation (discharge of tears); lar = laryngeal; loss = lassitude (weakness, exhaustion); leth = lethargy (drowsiness or indifference); leucyt = leukocytosis (increased blood leukocytes); leupen = leukopenia (reduced blood leukocytes); li-head = lightheadedness; liq = liquid; local = localized; low-wgt = weight loss; mal = malaise (vague feeling of discomfort); malnut = malnutrition; methemo = methemoglobinemia; monocy = monocytosis (increased blood monocytes); molt = molten; muc memb = mucous membrane; musc = muscle; narco = narcosis; nau = nausea; nec = necrosis; nept = nephritis; ner = nervousness; numb = numbness; opac = opacity; palp = palpitations; para = paralysis; pares = paresthesia; perf = perforation; peri neur = peripheral neuropathy; periorb = periorbital (situated around the eye); phar = pharyngeal; photo = photophobia (abnormal visual intolerance to); pneu = penumonia; pneuitis = pneumonitis; PNS = peripheral nervous system; polyneur = polyneuropathy; prot = proteinuria; pulm = pulmonary; RBC = red blood cell; repro = reproductive; resp = respiratory; restless = restlessness; retster = retrosternal (occurring behind the sternum); rhin = rhinorrhea (discharge of thin nasal mucus); salv = salivation; sens = sensitization; sez = seizure; short = shortness; sneez = sneezing; sol = solid; soln = solution; som = somnolence (sleepiness, unnatural drowsiness); subs = substernal (occurring beneath the sternum); sweat = sweating; swell = swelling; sys = system; tacar = tachycardia; tend = tenderness; terato = teratogenic; throb = throbbing; tight = tightness; trachbronch = tracheobronchitis; twitch = twitching; uncon = unconsciousness; vap = vapor; venfib = ventricular fibrillation; vert = vertigo (an illusion of movement); vesic = vesiculation; vis dist = viszal disturbance; vomit = vomiting; weak = weakness; wheez = wheezing.

References

Agency for Toxic Substances and Disease Registry (ATSDR). 1995. *Case Studies in Environmental Medicine: Lead Toxicity.* Atlanta: ATSDR.

Brief, RS, JW Blanchard, RA Scala, and JH Blacker. 1971. Metal carbonyls in the petroleum industry. *Arch Environ Health* 23:373–384.

International Agency for Research on Cancer (IARC). 1990. *Chromium, Nickel and Welding.* Lyon: IARC.

National Institute for Occupational Safety and Health (NIOSH). 1994. *NIOSH Pocket Guide to Chemical Hazards.* DHHS (NIOSH) Publication No. 94-116. Cincinnati, OH: NIOSH.

Rendall, REG, JI Phillips and KA Renton. 1994. Death following exposure to fine particulate nickel from a metal arc process. *Ann Occup Hyg* 38:921–930.

Sunderman, FW, Jr., and A Oskarsson,. 1991. Nickel. In *Metals and their compounds in the environment,* edited by E Merian, Weinheim, Germany: VCH Verlag.

Sunderman, FW, Jr., A Aitio, LO Morgan, and T Norseth. 1986. Biological monitoring of nickel. *Tox Ind Health* 2:17–78.

United Nations Committee of Experts on the Transport of Dangerous Goods. 1995. *Recommendations on the Transport of Dangerous Goods,* 9th edition. New York: United Nations.

Other relevant readings

Abener, W, H Holub, R Strohal, and R Slavicek. 1993. Palladium in dental alloys—The dermatologists' responsibility to warn? *Contact Dermat* 28 (3):163–165.

Akinfieva, TA, NI Nikolaeva, AA Silaev, IL Gerasimova, and EP Makoilkina. 1992. [Magnesium sulphate as an industrial poison]. *Gig Tr Prof Zabol* 3:33–35.

Alazraki, ND. 1993. Radionuclide imaging in the evaluation of infections and inflammatory disease. *Radiol Clin North Am* (4):783–94.

Bacin, F, E Albuisson, R Rozan, D Donnarieix, P Verrelle, and H Dalens. 1991. [Oncologic and functional results of 57 malignant melanoma of the uvea treated by curietherapy]. *J Fr Opthalmologie* 14 (6–7):383.

Bartter, T, RS Irwin, JL Abraham, A Dascal, G Nash, JS Himmelstein, and PJ Jederlinic. 1991. Zirconium compound–induced pulmonary fibrosis. *Arch Intern Med* 151(6):1197–1201.

Bolm, AU, HG Bienfait, J Burkhard, AH Bury, R Merget, G Pressel, and G Schultze-Werninghaus. 1991. Prevalence of respiratory allergy in a platinum refinery. *Int Arch Occup Environ Health* 64(4):256–60.

Brewer, L, RH Lamoureaux, R Ferro, R Marazza, and K Girgis. 1980. Molybdenum: Physico-chemical properties of its compounds and alloys. *Atomic Energy Review,* Special Issue No.7. Vienna: International Atomic Energy Agency.

Bruevich, TS. 1980. Skin irritation by compounds of the precious metals—Gold, platinum, ruthenium, rhodium, silver. *Gig Tr Prof Zabol* 5:42.

Buchet, JP, R Lauwerys, H Roels, A Bernard, P Bruaux, F Claeys, G Ducoffre, P DePlaen, J Staessen, A Amery, P Lijnen, L Thijs, D Rondia, F Sartor, A Saint Remy, and L Nick. 1990. Renal effects of cadmium body burden of the general population. *Lancet* 336:699–702.

Croft, SL, RA Neal, DG Craciunescu, and G Certad-Fombona. 1992. The activity of platinum, iridium and rhodium drug complexes against Leishmania donovani. *Trop Med Parasitol* 43(1):24–8.

Cromwell, O, J Pepys, WE Parish, and EG Hughes. 1979. Specific IgE antibodies to platinum salts in sensitised workers. *Clinical Allergy* 9(2):109–117.

Decheng, C, J Ming, H Ling, W Shan, X Ziqing, and Z Xinshui. 1987. Cytogenetic analysis in workers occupationally exposed to nickel carbonyl. *Mutat Res* 188:149–152.

Dutkiewicz, B, T Dutkiewicz, and G Milkowska. 1979. The effect of mixed exposure to lead and zinc on ALA level in urine. *International Archives of Occupational and Environmental Health—Internationales Archiv für Arbeits und Umweltmedizin* 42(3–4):341–348.

Elinder, C-G, L Friberg, GF Nordberg, T Kjellström and G Oberdoerster. 1994. *Biological Monitoring of Metals.* Chemical Safety Monographs. WHO/EHG/94.2:1–80. Geneva: International Programme on Chemical Safety.

Fayerweather, WE, ME Karns, PG Gilby and JL Chen. 1992. Epidemiologic study of lung cancer mortality in workers exposed to titanium tetrachloride. *J Occup Med* 34(2):164–9.

Glasgow, GP. 1991. The safety of low melting point bismuth/lead alloys: A review. *Med Dosim* 16(1):13–8.

Greene, RM and WPD Su. 1987. Argyria. *American Family Physician* 36(6):151–4.

Hadjimichael, OC and RE Brubaker. 1981. Evaluation of an occupational respiratory exposure to a zirconium-containing dust. *J Occup Med* 23(8):543–547.

Hensten-Petterson, A. 1992. Casting alloys: Side effects. *Adv Dent Res* 6:38–43.

Hryhorczuk, DO, SE Aks and JW Turk. 1992. Unusual occupational toxins. *Occup Med.* 7(3):567–86.

International Agency for Research on Cancer (IARC). 1984. *Nickel in the Human Environment.* Lyon: IARC.

—. 1987. *Overall Evaluations of Carcinogenicity: An Updating of Vol. 1–42.* Monograph series Suppl. 7, 1987. Lyon: IARC.

—. 1990. *Nickel and Nickel Compounds.* Lyon: IARC.

—. 1993. *Cadmium and Cadmium Compounds.* Lyon: IARC.

Järup, L and C-G Elinder. 1993. Renal stone incidence among cadmium exposed battery workers. *Brit J Ind Med* 50:598–602.

—. 1994. Dose-response relations between urinary cadmium and tubular proteinuria in cadmium exposed workers. *Am J Ind Med* 26:759–769.

Järup, L, B Persson, and C-G Elinder. 1995. Decreased glomerular filtration rate in solderers exposed to cadmium. *Occup Environ Health* 52:818–822.

Joint Expert Committee on Food Additives (JECFA). 1993. *Toxicological Evaluation of Certain Food Additives and Contaminants.* The 41st meeting of the joint FAO/WHO expert committee on food additives. Technical Reports Series No 837. Geneva: WHO.

Kazantsis, G. 1986. Tungsten. *Handbook on the Toxicology of Metals,* edited by G. Friberg, GF Nordberg, and VB Vouk. Amsterdam: Elsevier.

Kron, T, C Hansen, and E Warner. 1991. Renal excretion of tellurium after peroral administration of tellurium in different forms to healthy human volunteers. *J Trace Elem Electrolytes Health Dis* Dec. 5(4):239–44.

Langård, S (ed.). 1982. *Biological and Environmental Aspects of Chromium.* Amsterdam: Elsevier/North-Holland Biomedical Press.

Langård, S. 1990. One hundred years of chromium and cancer; A review of the epidemiological evidence and selected case reports. *Am J Ind Med* 17:189–215.

Langård, S, A Andersen, and B Gylseth. 1980. Incidence of cancer among ferrochromium and ferrosilicon workers. *Brit J Occup Med* 37(2):114–120.

Leonard, JF and PA Templeton. 1992. Pulmonary imaging techniques in the diagnosis of occupational interstitial lung disease. *Occup Med* 7(2):241–60.

Lewis, RJ, Sr. 1992. *Sax's Dangerous Properties of Industrial Materials.* 8th edition, Vol II. New York: Van Nostrand Reinhold.

Loiseau, PM, DG Craciunescu, JC Doadrio-Villarejo, and G Certad-Fombona. 1992. Pharmacomodulations on new organometallic complexes of Ir, Pt, Rh, Pd, Os: In vitro and in vivo trypanocidal study against *Trypanosoma brucei brucei. Trop Med Parasitol* 43(2):110–4.

Maibach, HI and T Menn. 1989. *Nickel and the Skin: Immunology and Toxicology.* Boca Raton, FL: CRC Press.

Mancinella, A. 1993. [Vanadium, an indispensable trace element in living organisms: Current data on biochemical, metabolic levels and therapeutic doses]. *Clinica Terapeutica* 142(3):251–255.

Merck and Co. 1976. *Merck Index,* 9th ed. Rahway, NJ: Merck and Co.

Merget, R, G Schulze-Werninghaus, F Bode, EM Bergmann, W Azchgo, and J Meier-Sydow. 1991. Quantitative skin prick and bronchial provocation tests with platinum salt. *Br J Ind Med* 48(12):830–837.

Morgan, LG and V Usher. 1994. Health problems associated with nickel refining and use. *Ann Occup Hyg* 38:189–198.

Moulin, JJ, P Portefaix, P Wild, JM Mur, G Smaggle, and B Mantout. 1990. Mortality study among workers producing ferroalloys and stainless steel in France. *Brit J Indust Med* 47(8):537–43.

Moulin, JJ, P Wild, B Mantout, M Fournier-Betz, JM Mur, and G Smaggle. 1993. Mortality from lung cancer and cardiovascular diseases among stainless-steel producing workers. *Cancer Causes Control* 4(2):75–81.

National Academy of Sciences (NAS). Committee on Medical and Biological Effects of Environmental Pollutants. 1997. *Platinum-group Metals.* Washington, DC: NAS.

National Institute for Occupational Safety and Health (NIOSH). 1976. *Criteria for a Recommended Standard: Occupational Exposure to Organotin Compounds.* Cincinnati, OH: NIOSH.

—. 1987. *Request for Assistance in Reducing the Potential Risk of Developing Cancer from Exposure to Gallium Arsenide in the Microelectronics Industry. NIOSH Alert.* Cincinnati, OH: NIOSH.

Nemery, B. 1990. Metal toxicity and the respiratory tract. *Eur Resp J* 3(3):202–211.

Nickel Development Institute. 1994. *Health Guide: Safe Use of Nickel in the Workplace.* Toronto: Nickel Development Institute.

Nieboer, E and JO Nriagu. 1992. *Nickel and Human Health: Current Perspectives.* New York: John Wiley.

Nordman, H and M Berlin. 1986. Titanium. In *Handbook on the Toxicology of Metals,* Vol. II, edited by G. Friberg, GF Nordberg, and VB Vouk. Amsterdam: Elsevier.

Organization for Economic and Community Development (OECD). 1994. *Cadmium.* Risk Reduction Monograph No 5:. Paris: OECD.

Pistelli, R, N Pupp, F Forastiere, N Agabiti, GM Corbo, F Tidei, and CA Perucci. 1991. [Increase of nonspecific bronchial reactivity after occupational exposure to vanadium]. *Med Lav* 82(3):270–275.

Rastogi, SK, BN Gupta, T Husain, N Chandra, N Mathur, BS Pangtey, SV Chandra, and N Garg. 1991. A cross-sectional study of pulmonary function among workers exposed to multimetals in the glass bangle industry. *Am J Ind Med* 20(3):391–9.

Reichrtova, E and L Takac. 1992. Issues related to dust aerosols in the magnesite industry. *J Hyg Epi Microbiol Immunol* 36(3):235–44.

Reith, AK, S Reichborn-Kenneruud, M Aubele, UJ Ÿtting, P Gais, and G Burger. 1994. Biological monitoring of chemical exposure in nickel workers by imaging cytometry (ICM) of nasal smears. *Anal Cell Pathol* 6:9–21.

Sax, NI and RJ Lewis, Sr. (eds.). 1989. *Dangerous Properties of Industrial Materials,* 7th ed. New York: Van Nostrand Reinhold.

Scansetti, G. 1992. Exposure to metals that have recently come into use. *Sci Total Environ* 120(1–2):85–91.

Schauss, AG. 1991. Nephrotoxicity-neurotoxicity in humans from organogermanium compounds and germanium dioxide. *Biol Trace Elem Res* 29(3):267–80.

Schrauzer, GN. 1991. Cobalt. In *Metals and Their Compounds in the Environment,* edited by E Merian. Weinheim, Germany: VCH Verlag.

Seidal, K, N Jörgensen, C-G Elinder, B Sjögren, and M Vahter. 1993. A case of fatal cadmium induced pneumonitis. *Scand J Work & Environ Health* 19:429–431.

Sheehy, JW and JH Jones. 1993. Assessment of arsenic exposures and controls in gallium arsenide production. *Am Ind Hyg Assoc J* 54(2):61–69.

Sittig, M. 1985. *Handbook of Toxic and Hazardous Chemicals and Carcinogens,* 2nd ed. Park Ridge, NJ: Noyes Data Corporation.

Spencer, PJ, O Kubascewski-von Goldbeck, R Ferro, R Marazza, K Girgis, and O Kubaschewski. 1981. Hafnium: Physico-chemical properties of its compounds and alloys. *Atomic Energy Review,* Special Issue No. 8. Vienna: International Atomic Energy Agency.

Sprince, NL, RI Chamberlin, CA Hales, AL Weber, and H Kazemi. 1984. Respiratory disease in tungsten carbide production workers. *Chest* 86(4):549–57.

Sunderman, FW, Jr. 1992. Use of sodium diethyldithiocarbamate in the treatment of nickel carbonyl poisoning. In *Nickel and Human Health: Current Perspectives,* edited by E Nieboer and O Nriagu. New York: John Wiley.

—. 1993. Biological monitoring of nickel in humans. *Scand J Work Environ Health* 19: 34–38.

Sunderman, FW, Jr., B Dingle, SM Hopfer, and T Swift. 1988. Acute nickel toxicity in electroplating workers who accidently ingested a solution of nickel sulfate and nickel chloride. *Am J Ind Med* 14:257–266.

Templeton, DM. 1994. Measurement of total nickel in body fluids: Technical report of the IUPAC Commission on Toxicology. *Pure Appl Chem* 66:357–372.

Thun, MJ, C-G Elinder, and L Friberg. 1991. Scientific basis for an occupational standard for cadmium. *Amer J Ind Med* 20:629–42.

Underwood, EJ. 1977. Manganese. In *Trace Elements in Human and Animal Nutrition,* 4th ed. New York: Academic Press.

Venables, KM, MB Dally, AJ Nunn, and JF Stevens. 1989. Smoking and occupational allergy in workers in a platinum refinery. *Brit Med J* 299(6705):939–42.

Vyskocil, A, V Senft, C Viau, M Cizkova, and J Kohout. 1994. Biochemical renal changes in workers exposed to soluble nickel compounds. *Human Exp Toxicol* 13:257–261.

World Health Organization (WHO). 1991. *Nickel.* Environmental Health Criteria 108. Geneva: WHO.

—. 1992. *Cadmium.* Environmental Health Criteria. Geneva: WHO.

Xuan Xz, JH Lubin, JY Li, LF Yang, AS Luo, Y Lan, JZ Wang, and WJ Blot. 1993. A cohort study in Southern China of tin miners exposed to radon and radon decay products. *Health Phys* 64(2);120–31.

Zhicheng, S. 1986. Acute nickel carbonyl poisoning: A report of 179 cases. *Brit J Ind Med* 43:422–424.

Zicheng, S, A Lata, and H Yuhua. 1986. A study of serum monoamine oxidase (MAO) activity and the EEG in nickel carbonyl workers. *Brit J Ind Med* 43:425–426.

Zinsstag, J, R Brun, DG Craciunescu and E Parrondo-Iglesias. 1991. In vitro activity of organometallic complexes of Ir, Pt and Rh on *Trypanosoma b. gambiense, T.b. rhodesiense* and *T.b. brucei. Trop Med Parasitol* 42(1):41–4.

Zwennis, WCM, AC Franssen, and MJ Wijnans. 1991. Biological monitoring of workers exposed to nickel products. *Biol Monit* 1:35–44.

Chapter Editor
Melvin L. Myers

Contents

64. AGRICULTURE AND NATURAL RESOURCE BASED INDUSTRIES

GENERAL PROFILE

Melvin L. Myers

Overview

Twelve millennia ago, humankind moved into the Neolithic era and discovered that food, feed and fibre could be produced from the cultivation of plants. This discovery has led to the food and fibre supply that feeds and clothes more than 5 billion people today.

This general profile of the agricultural industry includes its evolution and structure, economic importance of different crop commodities and characteristics of the industry and workforce. Agricultural workforce systems involve three types of major activities:

1. manual operations
2. mechanization
3. draught power, provided specifically by those engaged in livestock rearing, which is discussed in the chapter *Livestock rearing*.

The agriculture system is shown as four major processes. These processes represent sequential phases in crop production. The agricultural system produces food, feed and fibre as well as consequences for occupational health and, more generally, public health and the environment.

Major commodities, such as wheat or sugar, are outputs from agriculture that are used as food, animal feed or fibre. They are represented in this chapter by a series of articles that address processes, occupational hazards and preventive actions specific to each commodity sector. Animal feed and forage are discussed in the chapter *Livestock rearing*.

Evolution and Structure of the Industry

The Neolithic revolution—the change from hunting and gathering to farming—started in three different places in the world. One was west and southwest of the Caspian Sea, another was in Central America and a third was in Thailand near the Burmese border. Agriculture started in about 9750 BC at the latter location, where seeds of peas, beans, cucumbers and water chestnuts have been found. This was 2,000 years before true agriculture was discovered in the other two regions. The essence of the Neolithic revolution and, thus, agriculture is the harvesting of plant seeds, their reintroduction into the soil and cultivation for another harvest.

In the lower Caspian area, wheat was the early crop of choice. As farmers migrated, taking wheat seed with them, the weeds in other regions were discovered to also be edible. These included rye and oats. In Central America, where maize and beans were the staples, the tomato weed was found to bear nutritious food.

Agriculture brought with it several problems:

- Weeds and other pests (insects in the fields and mice and rats in the granaries) became a problem.
- Early agriculture concerned itself with taking all that it could from the soil, and it would take 50 years to naturally replenish the soil.
- In some places, the stripping of growth from the soil would turn the land to desert. To provide water to crops, farmers discovered irrigation about 7,000 years ago.

Solutions to these problems have led to new industries. Ways to control weeds, insects and rodents evolved into the pesticide industry, and the need to replenish the soil has resulted in the fertilizer industry. The need to provide water for irrigation has spawned systems of reservoirs and networks of pipes, canals and ditches.

Agriculture in the developing nations consists principally of family-owned plots. Many of these plots have been handed down from generation to generation. Peasants make up half of the world's rural poor, but they produce four-fifths of the developing countries' food supply. In contrast, farms are increasing in size in the developed countries, turning agriculture into large-scale commercial operations, where production is integrated with processing, marketing and distribution in an agribusiness system (Loftas 1995).

Agriculture has provided subsistence for farmers and their families for centuries, and it has recently changed into a system of production agriculture. A series of "revolutions" has contributed to an increase in agricultural production. The first of these was the mechanization of agriculture, whereby machines in the fields substituted for manual labour. The second was the chemical revolution that, after the Second World War, contributed to the control of pests in agriculture, but with environmental consequences. A third was the green revolution, which contributed to North American and Asian productivity growth through genetic advances in the new varieties of crops.

Economic Importance

The human population has grown from 2.5 billion in 1950 to 5.6 billion in 1994, and the United Nations estimates that it will continue to grow to 7.9 billion by 2025. The continued rise in the human population will increase the demand for food energy and nutrients, both because of the increase in numbers of people and the global drive to combat malnutrition (Brown, Lenssen and Kane 1995). A list of nutrients derived from food is shown in table 64.1.

Table 64.1 • Sources of nutrients.

Nutrient	Plant sources	Animal sources
Carbohydrates (sugars and starch)	Fruits, cereals, root vegetables, pulses	Honey, milk
Dietary fats	Oilseeds, nuts, and legumes	Meat, poultry, butter, ghee, fish
Proteins	Pulses, nuts, and cereals	Meat, fish, dairy products
Vitamins	Carotenes: carrots, mangoes, papaya Vitamin C: fruits and vegetables Vitamin B complex: cereals, legumes	Vitamin A: liver, eggs, milk Vitamin B complex: meat, poultry, dairy products
Minerals	Calcium: peas, beans Iron: dark green leafy vegetables and nuts	Calcium: milk, meat, cheese Iron: meat, fish, shellfish

Source: Loftas 1995.

Figure 64.1 • Millions of people engaged in agriculture by world region (1994).

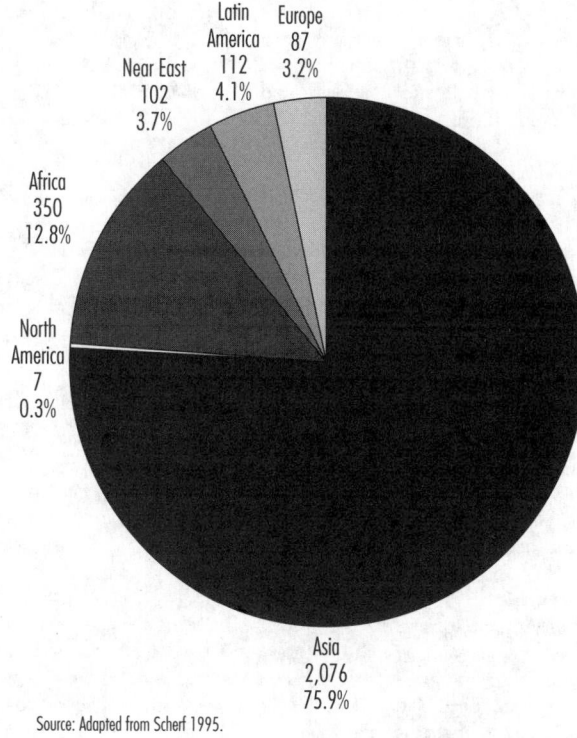

Source: Adapted from Scherf 1995.

Agriculture today can be understood as an enterprise to provide subsistence for those doing the work, staples for the community in which the food is grown and income from the sale of commodities to an external market. A staple food is one that supplies a major part of energy and nutrient needs and constitutes a dominant part of the diet. Excluding animal products, most people live off of one or two of the following staples: rice, wheat, maize (corn), millet, sorghum, and roots and tubers (potatoes, cassava, yams and taro). Although there are 50,000 edible plant species in the world, only 15 provide 90% of the world's food energy intake.

Cereals constitute the principal commodity category that the world depends upon for its staples. Cereals include wheat and rice, the principal food staples, and coarse grains, which are used for animal feed. Three—rice, maize and wheat—are staples to more than 4.0 billion people. Rice feeds about half of the world's population (Loftas 1995).

Another basic food crop is the *starchy* foods: cassava, sweet potatoes, potatoes, yams, taro and plantains. More than 1 billion people in developing nations use roots and tubers as staples. Cassava is grown as a staple in developing countries for 500 million people. For some of these commodities, much of the production and consumption remains at the subsistence level.

An additional basic food crop is the pulses, which comprise a number of dry beans—peas, chickpeas and lentils; all are legumes. They are important for their starch and protein.

Other legumes are used as oil crops; they include soybeans and groundnuts. Additional oil crops, used to make vegetable oil, include coconuts, sesame, cotton seed, oil palm and olive. In addition, some maize and rice bran are used to make vegetable oil. Oil crops also have uses other than for food, such as in manufacturing paints and detergents (Alexandratos 1995).

Small landholders grow many of the same crops as plantation operations do. Plantation crops, typically thought of as tropical export commodities, include natural rubber, palm oil, cane sugar, tropical beverages (coffee, cocoa, tea), cotton, tobacco and bananas. They may include crops that are also grown for both local consumption and export, such as coffee and sugar cane (ILO 1994).

Urban agriculture is labour intensive, occurs on small plots and is present in developed as well as developing countries. In the United States, more than one-third of the dollar value of agricultural crops is produced in urban areas and agriculture may employ as much as 10% of the urban population. In contrast, up to 80% of the population in smaller Siberian and Asian cities may be employed in agricultural production and processing. An urban farmer's produce may also be used for barter, such as paying a landlord (UNDP 1996).

Characteristics of the Industry and Workforce

The 1994 world population totalled 5,623,500,000, and 2,735,021,000 (49%) of this population was engaged in agriculture, as shown in figure 64.1. The largest component of this workforce is in the developing nations and transitional economies. Less than 100 million are in the developed nations, where mechanization has added to their productivity.

Farming employs men and women, young and old. Their roles vary; for example, women in sub-Saharan Africa produce and

Figure 64.2 • Young boy working in agriculture in India.

Family farms

The family farm is an enterprise and a homestead on which both children and the elderly are likely to be present. In some parts of the world, farm families live in villages surrounded by their farm land. The family farm combines family relationships and child raising with the production of food and other raw materials. Family farms range from small, subsistence or part-time operations worked with draught animals and hand tools to very large, family-held corporations with numerous full-time employees. Types of family farms are distinguished by national, regional, cultural, historical, economic, religious and several other factors. The size and type of operations determine the demand for labour from family members and the need for hired full- or part-time workers. A typical farm operation may combine the tasks of livestock handling, manure disposal, grain storage, heavy equipment operation, pesticide application, machinery maintenance, construction and many other jobs.

The Organization for Economic Cooperation and Development (OECD 1994) reports several trends in agriculture, including:

1. the increasing economic dominance of large, highly mechanized producers
2. the increase in off-farm employment as the principal source of income for small farms
3. the controlling role of national and international agricultural policies and trade agreements.

The concentration of farm operations and the reduction in the number of family farms has been recognized for decades. These economic forces affect the work processes, workload and safety and health of the family farm. Several key changes are occurring in family farming as a direct result of these economic forces, including expanding workloads, increasing reliance on hired labor, use of new techniques, unsupervised adolescents and struggling to maintain economic viability.

Children nearing adolescence contribute to family farm productivity. Small and medium-size family farms are likely to rely on this labor, especially when adult family members work off the farm. The result may be unsupervised work by farm children.

Hazards

The family farm is a hazardous work environment. It is one of few hazardous workplaces where multiple generations of family members may live, work and play. A farm can be the source of many and differing life-threatening hazards. The most important indicator for safety and health is workload per worker—both physical labor and decision-making or mental workload. Many serious injuries happen to experienced farmers, working with familiar equipment in familiar fields, while doing tasks that they have been performing for years and even decades.

Hazardous agricultural materials including pesticides, fertilizers, flammable liquids, solvents and other cleaners are responsible for acute and chronic illnesses in farm workers and family members. Tractors, augers and other mechanized equipment have permitted a dramatic increase in the land and livestock that can be worked by a single farmer, but mechanization has contributed to severe injuries in agriculture. Machinery entanglement or tractor rollover, livestock,

operating equipment on public roads, falling or being struck by falling objects, material handling, confined spaces and exposures to toxins, dust, moulds, gases, chemicals, vibration and noise are among the principal risks for illness and injury on farms. Climate and topography (e.g., weather, water, slopes, sinkholes and other obstacles) also contribute to the hazards.

Overall, agricultural occupations produce some of the highest rates of death and injury of all types of jobs. Unfortunately, farm children are at great risk along with their parents. As farm families attempt to remain profitable as they expand, family members may take on too high a workload and place themselves at greatly increased risk of fatigue, stress and injury. It is under these conditions that farm children are most likely to try to help out, often working unsupervised. In addition, unrelenting stressors associated with farming may lead to depression, family breakup and suicide. For example, principal owner-operators on single-family farms appear to be at particularly high risk for suicide when compared to other rural residents (Gunderson 1995). Further, the costs of illnesses and injuries are most often borne by the family member(s), and by the family enterprise—both as direct medical costs and in the reduction of labour necessary to maintain the operation.

Prevention

Classic agricultural safety and health programmes emphasize improved engineering design, education and good practices. Special attention on these farms needs to be placed on age-appropriate tasks for children and older adults. Young children should neither be allowed near operating farm equipment nor ever ride on tractors and other farm equipment. They should also be excluded from farmstead buildings that present hazards including electricity, confined spaces, chemical storage areas and operating equipment (National Committee for Childhood Agricultural Injury Prevention 1996). Warning labels should be maintained on equipment and chemicals so adults are informed of hazards and can thus better protect their families. The availability of experienced part-time or full-time workers reduces the burden on the family during periods of high workloads. The abilities of older adults should be a factor in the tasks that they perform.

Self-reliant farmers, determined to complete tasks regardless of the risks, may ignore safe work practices if they perceive them to interfere with farm productivity. Improving safety and health on family farms requires engaging the active participation of farmers and farm workers; improving attitudes, behavioral intentions and work practices; recognizing farm economics and productivity as powerful determinants in shaping the structure and organization of the enterprise; and including agricultural specialists, equipment dealers, insurance agents, bankers, local media, youth and other community members in generating and sustaining a broad climate of farm and community safety.

Ted Scharf, David E. Baker and Joyce Salg

market 90% of locally grown food. Women are also given the task of growing the subsistence diet for their families (Loftas 1995).

Children become farm labourers around the world at an early age (figure 64.2), working typically 45 hours per week during harvesting operations. Child labour has been a part of plantation agriculture throughout its history, and a prevalent use of contract

labour based upon compensation for tasks completed aggravates the problem of child labour. Whole families work to increase the task completion in order to sustain or increase their income.

Data on plantation employment generally show that the highest incidence of poverty is among agricultural wage labourers working in commercial agriculture. Plantations are located in tropical and subtropical regions of the world, and living and working conditions there may aggravate health problems that accompany the poverty (ILO 1994).

Agriculture in urban areas is another important component of the industry. An estimated 200 million farmers work part-time—equivalent to 150 million full-time workers—in urban agriculture to produce food and other agricultural products for the market. When subsistence agriculture in urban areas is included, the total reaches 800 million (UNDP 1996).

Total agricultural employment by major world region is shown in figure 64.1. In both the United States and Canada, a small proportion of the population is employed in agriculture, and farms are becoming fewer as operations consolidate. In Western Europe, agriculture has been characterized by smallholdings, a relic of equal division of the previous holding among the children. However, with the migration from agriculture, holdings in Europe have been increasing in size. Eastern Europe's agriculture carries a history of socialized farming. The average farm size in the former USSR was more than 10,000 hectares, while in other Eastern European countries it was about one-third that size. This is changing as these countries move toward market economies. Many Asian countries have been modernizing their agricultural operations, with some countries achieving rice surpluses. More than 2 billion people remain engaged in agriculture in this region, and much of the increased production is attributed to high-production species of crops such as rice. Latin America is a diverse region where agriculture plays an important economic role. It has vast resources for agricultural use, which has been increasing, but at the expense of tropical forests. In both the Middle East and Africa, per capita food production has seen a decline. In the Middle East, the principal limiting factor on agriculture is the availability of water. In Africa, traditional farming depends upon small, 3- to 5-hectare plots, which are operated by women while the men are employed elsewhere, some in other countries to earn cash. Some countries are developing larger farming operations.

FARMING SYSTEMS

● PLANTATIONS

Melvin L. Myers and I.T. Cabrera*

The term *plantation* is widely used to describe large-scale units where industrial methods are applied to certain agricultural enterprises. These enterprises are found primarily in the tropical regions of Asia, Africa and Central and South America, but they are also found in certain subtropical areas where the climate and soil are suitable for the growth of tropical fruits and vegetation.

Plantation agriculture includes short-rotation crops, such as pineapple and sugar cane, as well as tree crops, such as bananas and rubber. In addition, the following tropical and subtropical crops are usually considered as plantation crops: tea, coffee, cocoa, coconuts, mango, sisal and palm nuts. However, large-scale cultivation of certain other crops, such as rice, tobacco, cotton, maize, citrus fruits, castor beans, peanuts, jute, hemp and bamboo, is also referred to as plantation cultivation. Plantation crops have several characteristics:

- They are either tropical or subtropical products for which an export market exists.
- Most require prompt initial processing.
- The crop passes through few local marketing or processing centres before reaching the consumer.
- They typically require a significant investment of fixed capital, such as processing facilities.
- They generate some activity for most of the year, and thus offer continuous employment.
- Monocropping is typical, which allows for specialization of technology and management.

While the cultivation of the various plantation crops requires widely different geographic, geological and climatic conditions, practically all of them thrive best in areas where climatic and environmental conditions are arduous. In addition, the extensive nature of plantation undertakings, and in most cases their isolation, has given rise to new settlements that differ considerably from indigenous settlements (NRC 1993).

Plantation Work

The main activity on a plantation is the cultivation of one of two kinds of crops. This involves the following kinds of work: soil preparation, planting, cultivation, weeding, crop treatment, harvesting, transportation and storage of produce. These operations entail the use of a variety of tools, machines and agricultural chemicals. Where virgin land is to be cultivated, it may be necessary to clear forest land by felling trees, uprooting stumps and burning off undergrowth, followed by ditch and irrigation channel digging. In addition to the basic cultivation work, other activities may also be carried out on a plantation: raising livestock, processing crops and maintaining and repairing buildings, plants, machinery, implements, roads and railway tracks. It may be necessary to generate electricity, dig wells, maintain irrigation trenches, operate engineering or woodworking shops and transport products to the market.

Child labour is employed on plantations around the world. Children work with their parents as part of a team for task-based compensation, or they are employed directly for special plantation jobs. They typically experience long and arduous working hours, little safety and health protection and inadequate diet, rest and education. Rather than direct employment, many children are recruited as labour through contractors, which is common for occasional and seasonal tasks. Employing labour through contracted intermediaries is a long-standing practice on plantations. The plantation management thus does not have an employer-employee relationship with the plantation workers. Rather, they contract with the intermediary to supply the labour. Generally, conditions of work for contract labour are inferior to those of directly employed workers.

Many plantation workers are paid based upon the tasks performed rather than the hours worked. For example, these tasks may include lines of sugar cane cut and loaded, number of rubber trees tapped, rows weeded, bushels of sisal cut, kilograms of tea plucked or hectares of fertilizer applied. Conditions such as climate and terrain may affect the time to complete these tasks, and whole families may work from dawn to dusk without taking a break. The majority of countries where plantation commodities are grown report that plantation employees work more than 40 hours per week. Moreover, most plantation workers move to their work location on foot, and since plantations are large, much time and effort are expended on travel to and from the job. This travel can take hours each way (ILO 1994).

* Adapted from 3rd edition, Encyclopaedia of Occupational Health and Safety.

64. AGRICULTURE AND NATURAL RESOURCE BASED INDUSTRIES

Hazards and Their Prevention

Work on plantations involves numerous hazards relating to the work environment, the tools and equipment used and the very nature of the work. One of the first steps toward improving safety and health on plantations is to appoint a safety officer and form a joint safety and health committee. Safety officers should assure that buildings and equipment are kept safe and that work is performed safely. Safety committees bring management and labour together in a common undertaking and enable the workers to participate directly in improving safety. Safety committee functions include developing work rules for safety, participating in injury and disease investigations and identifying locations that place workers and their families in danger.

Medical services and first aid materials with adequate instruction should be provided. Medical doctors should be trained in the recognition of occupational diseases related to plantation work including pesticide poisoning and heat stress. A risk survey should be implemented on the plantation. The purpose of the survey is to comprehend risk circumstances so that preventive action can be taken. The safety and health committee can be engaged in the survey along with experts including the safety officer, the medical supervisor and inspectors. Table 64.2 shows the steps involved in a survey. The survey should result in action including the control of potential hazards as well as hazards that have resulted in an injury or disease (Partanen 1996). A description of some potential hazards and their control follow.

Fatigue and climate-related hazards

The long hours and demanding work make fatigue a major concern. Fatigued workers may be unable to make safe judgements; this may lead to incidents that can result in injuries or other inadvertent exposures. Rest periods and shorter workdays can reduce fatigue.

Physical stress is increased by heat and relative humidity. Frequent water consumption and rest breaks help to avoid problems with heat stress.

Tool and equipment-related injuries

Poorly designed tools will often result in poor work posture, and poorly sharpened tools will require greater physical effort to complete tasks. Working in a bent or stooping position and lifting heavy loads imposes strain on the back. Working with arms above the shoulder can cause upper-extremity musculoskeletal disorders (figure 64.3). Proper tools should be selected to eliminate poor posture, and they should be well maintained. Heavy lifting can be

Table 64.2 • Ten steps for a plantation work risk survey.

1. Define the problem and its priority.
2. Find existing data.
3. Justify the need for more data.
4. Define survey objectives, design, population, time and methods.
5. Define tasks and costs, and their timing.
6. Prepare protocol.
7. Collect data.
8. Analyse data and assess risks.
9. Publish results.
10. Follow up.

Source: Partanen 1996.

Figure 64.3 • Banana cutters at work on "La Julia" plantation in Ecuador.

reduced by lessening the weight of the load or engaging more workers to lift the load.

Injuries can result from improper uses of hand tools such as machetes, scythes, axes and other sharp-edged or pointed tools, or portable power tools such as chain-saws; poor positioning and disrepair of ladders; or unsuitable replacements for broken ropes and chains. Workers should be trained in the proper use and maintenance of equipment and tools. Appropriate replacements should be provided for broken or damaged tools and equipment.

Unguarded machinery can entangle clothing or hair and can crush workers and result in serious injury or death. All machines should have safety built in, and the possibility of dangerous contact with moving parts should be eliminated. A lockout/tagout programme should be in effect for all maintenance and repair.

Machinery and equipment are also sources of excessive noise, resulting in hearing loss among plantation workers. Hearing protection should be used with machinery with high levels of noise. Low noise levels should be a factor in selecting equipment.

Vehicle-related injuries

Plantation roadways and paths may be narrow, thus presenting the hazard of head-on crashes between vehicles or overturns off the side of the road. Safe boarding of transport vehicles including trucks, tractor- or animal-drawn trailers and railways should be ensured. Where two-way roads are used, wider passages should be provided at suitable intervals to allow vehicles to pass. Adequate railing should be provided on bridges and along precipices and ravines.

Tractors and other vehicles pose two principal dangers to workers. One is tractor overturns, which commonly result in the fatal crushing of the operator. Employers should ensure that roll-over protective structures are mounted on tractors. Seat-belts should also be worn during tractor operation. The other major problem is vehicle run-overs; workers should remain clear of vehicle travel paths, and extra riders should not be allowed on tractors unless safe seating is available.

Electricity

Electricity is used on plantations in shops and for processing crops and lighting buildings and grounds. Improper use of electric installations or equipment can expose workers to severe shocks, burns or electrocutions. The danger is more acute in damp places or when working with wet hands or clothing. Wherever water is present, or for electrical outlets outdoors, ground fault interrupter circuits should be installed. Wherever thunderstorms are frequent or severe, lightning protection should be provided for all plantation buildings, and workers should be trained in ways to minimize their danger of being struck and to locate safe refuges.

Fires

Electricity as well as open flames or smouldering cigarettes can provide the ignition source for fuel or organic dust explosions. Fuels—kerosene, gasoline or diesel fuel—can cause fires or explosions if mishandled or improperly stored. Greasy and combustible waste poses a risk of fire in shops. Fuels should be kept clear of any ignition source. Flameproof electrical devices and appliances should be used wherever flammables or explosives are present. Fuses or electrical breaker devices should also be used in electrical circuits.

Pesticides

The use of toxic agrochemicals is a major concern, particularly during the intensive use of pesticides, including herbicides, fungicides and insecticides. Exposures can take place during agricultural production, packaging, storage, transport, retailing, application (often by hand or aerial spraying), recycling or disposal. Risk of exposure to pesticides can be aggravated by illiteracy, poor or faulty labelling, leaking containers, poor or no protective gear, dangerous reformulations, ignorance of the hazard, disregard of rules and a lack of supervision or technical training. Workers applying pesticides should be trained in pesticide use and should wear appropriate clothing and respiratory protection, a particularly difficult behaviour to enforce in tropical areas where protective equipment can add to the heat stress of the wearer (figure 64.4). Alternatives to pesticide use should be a priority, or less toxic pesticides should be used.

Animal-inflicted injuries and illnesses

On some plantations, draught animals are used for dragging or carrying loads. These animals include horses, donkeys, mules and oxen. These types of animals have injured workers by kicking or biting. They also potentially expose workers to zoonotic diseases including anthrax, brucellosis, rabies, Q-fever or tularaemia. Animals should be well trained, and those that exhibit dangerous behaviour should not be used for work. Bridles, harnesses, saddles and so on should be used and maintained in good condition and be properly adjusted. Diseased animals should be identified and treated or disposed of.

Poisonous snakes may be present on the ground or some species may fall from trees onto workers. Snakebite kits should be provided to workers and emergency procedures should be in place for obtaining medical assistance and the appropriate anti-venom drugs should be available. Special hats made of hard materials that are capable of deflecting snakes should be provided and worn in locations where snakes drop on their victims from trees.

Figure 64.4 • Protective clothing worn when applying pesticides.

Gerald Peedin

Infectious diseases

Infectious diseases can be transmitted to plantation workers by rats that infest buildings, or by drinking water or food. Unsanitary water leads to dysentery, a common problem among plantation workers. Sanitary and washing facilities should be installed and maintained in accordance with national legislation, and safe drinking water consistent with national requirements should be provided to workers and their families.

Confined spaces

Confined spaces, such as silos, can pose problems of toxic gases or oxygen deficiency. Good ventilation of confined spaces should be assured prior to entry, or appropriate respiratory protective equipment should be worn.

MIGRANT AND SEASONAL FARMWORKERS

Marc B. Schenker

Migrant and seasonal farmworkers represent a large, global population with the double hazard of occupational health hazards of farming superimposed on a foundation of poverty and migrancy, with its associated health and safety problems. In the United States, for example, there are as many as 5 million migrant and seasonal farmworkers, although precise numbers are not known. As the total farm population has decreased in the United States, the proportion of hired farmworkers has increased. Globally, workers migrate in every region of the world for work, with movement generally from poorer to wealthier countries. In general, migrants are given more hazardous and difficult jobs and have increased rates of illness and injury. Poverty and lack of adequate legal protection exacerbate the risks of occupational and non-occupational disease.

Studies of hazardous exposures and health problems in this population have been limited because of the general paucity of occupational health studies in agriculture and the specific difficulties in studying farmworkers, due to their migratory residence patterns, language and cultural barriers, and limited economic and political resources.

Migrant and seasonal agricultural workers in the United States are predominantly young, Hispanic males, although farmworkers also include whites, blacks, Southeast Asians and other ethnic groups. Almost two-thirds are foreign born; most have low levels of education and do not speak or read English. Poverty is a hallmark of agricultural workers, with over half having family incomes below the poverty level. Substandard working conditions prevail, salaries are low and there are few benefits. For example, less than one-fourth have health insurance. Seasonal and migrant agricultural workers in the United States work about half the year on the farm. Most work is in labour-intensive crops such as harvesting of fruits, nuts or vegetables.

The general health status of agricultural workers directly derives from their working conditions and low income. Deficiencies exist in nutrition, housing, sanitation, education and access to medical care. Crowded living conditions and inadequate nutrition may also contribute to the increased risks of acute, infectious illnesses. Farmworkers see a physician less often than non-farmworking populations, and their visits are overwhelmingly for treatment of acute illnesses and injuries. Preventive care is deficient in farmworker populations, and surveys of farmworker communities find a high prevalence of individuals with medical problems requiring attention. Preventive services such as vision and dental care are seriously deficient, and other preventive services such as immunizations are below the population averages. Anaemia is common, probably reflecting poor nutritional status.

The poverty and other barriers for migrant and seasonal farmworkers generally result in substandard living and working conditions. Many workers still lack access to basic sanitary facilities at the worksite. Living conditions vary from adequate government-maintained housing to substandard shacks and camps used while work exists in a particular area. Poor sanitation and crowding may be particular problems, increasing the risks of infectious diseases in the population. These problems are exacerbated among workers who migrate to follow agricultural work, reducing community resources and interactions at each living site.

Various studies have shown a greater burden of infectious diseases on morbidity and mortality in this population. Parasitic diseases are significantly increased among migrant workers. Increased deaths have been found for tuberculosis, as well as many other chronic diseases such as those of the cardiovascular, respiratory and urinary tracts. The greatest increase in mortality rates is for traumatic injuries, similar to the increase seen for this cause among farmers.

The health status of children of farmworkers is of particular concern. In addition to the stresses of poverty, poor nutrition and poor living conditions, the relative deficiency of preventive health services has a particularly serious impact on children. They also are exposed to the hazards of farming at a young age, both by living in the farming environment and by doing agricultural work. Children under 5 years of age are most at risk of unintentional injury from agricultural hazards such as machinery and farm animals. Above 10 years of age, many children begin working, particularly at times of acute labour need such as during harvesting. Working children may not have the necessary physical strength and coordination for farm labour, nor do they have adequate judgement for many situations. Exposure to agrochemicals is a particular problem, since children may not be aware of recent field application or be able to read warnings on chemical containers.

Farmworkers are at increased risk of pesticide illness during work in the fields. Exposures most commonly occur from direct contact with the spray of application equipment, from prolonged contact with recently sprayed foliage or from drift of pesticide applied by aircraft or other spray equipment. Re-entry intervals exist in some countries to prevent foliar contact while the pesticide on foliage is still toxic, but many places have no re-entry intervals, or they may not be obeyed to hasten the harvest. Mass poisonings from pesticide exposure continue to occur among agricultural workers.

The greatest workplace hazard to farmworkers is from sprains, strains and traumatic injuries. The risk of these outcomes is increased by the repetitive nature of much labour-intensive agricultural work, which often involves workers bending or stooping to reach crops. Some harvesting tasks may require the worker to carry heavy bags full of the harvested commodity, often while balancing on a ladder. There is substantial risk of traumatic injuries and musculoskeletal strains in this situation.

In the United States, one of the most serious causes of fatal injuries to farmworkers is motor vehicle accidents. These often occur when farmworkers are driving or being driven to or from the fields very early or late in the day on unsafe rural roads. Collisions may also occur with slow-moving farm equipment.

Dust and chemical exposures result in an increased risk of respiratory symptoms and disease in farmworkers. The specific hazard will vary with the local conditions and commodities. For example, in dry-climate farming, inorganic dust exposure may result in chronic bronchitis and dust-borne diseases of the lung.

Skin disease is the most common work-related health problem among agricultural workers. There are numerous causes of skin disease in this population, including trauma from using hand equipment such as clippers, irritants and allergens in agrochemicals, allergenic plant and animal materials (including poison ivy and poison oak), nettles and other irritant plants, skin infections caused or exacerbated by heat or prolonged water contact, and sun exposure (which can cause skin cancer).

Many other chronic diseases may be more common among migrant and seasonal farmworkers, but data on actual risks are limited. These include cancer; adverse reproductive outcomes, including miscarriage, infertility and birth defects; and chronic neurologic disorders. All of these outcomes have been observed in other farming populations, or those with high-level exposure to various agricultural toxins, but little is known about actual risk in farmworkers.

URBAN AGRICULTURE

Melvin L. Myers

Agriculture conducted in urban areas is a major contributor to food, fuel and fibre production in the world, and it exists largely for the daily needs of consumers within cities and towns. Urban agriculture uses and reuses natural resources and urban wastes to produce crops and livestock. Table 64.3 summarizes the variety of farming systems in urban areas. Urban agriculture is a source of income for an estimated 100 million people, and a source of food for 500 million. It is oriented to urban markets rather than national or global markets, and it consists of many small-scale farms and some large-scale agribusinesses. Urban farmers range from a household garden in 20 m^2 or less, to a small-scale farmer making a living on 200 m^2, to a large-scale operator who may rent 10 hectares in an industrial zone (UNDP 1996).

Landscaping, an offshoot of architecture, has emerged as another urban agriculture endeavour. Landscape gardening is the tending of plants for their ornamental appearance in public parks and gardens, private yards and gardens, and industrial and commercial building plantings. Landscape gardening includes lawn

Table 64.3 • Farming systems in urban areas.

Farming systems	Product	Location or technique
Aquaculture	Fish and seafood, frogs, vegetables, seaweed and fodder	Ponds, streams, cages, estuaries, sewage, lagoons, wetlands
Horticulture	Vegetables, fruit, herbs, beverages, compost	Homesites, parks, rights-of-way, containers, rooftops, hydroponics, wetlands, greenhouses, shallow bed techniques, layered horticulture
Floriculture	Flowers, insecticides, house plants	Ornamental horticulture, rooftops, containers, greenhouses, rights-of-way
Husbandry	Milk, eggs, meat, manure, hides, and fur	Zero-grazing, rights-of-way, hillsides, cooperatives, pens, open spaces
Agroforestry	Fuel, fruits and nuts, compost, building material	Street trees, homesites, steep slopes, vineyards, green belts, wetlands, orchards, forest parks, hedgerows
Mycoculture	Mushrooms, compost	Sheds, cellers
Vermaculture	Compost, worms for animal and fish feed	Sheds, trays
Sericulture	Silk	Homesites, trays
Apiculture	Honey, pollination, wax	Beehives, rights-of-way
Landscape gardening, arboriculture	Grounds design and upkeep, ornamentation, lawns, gardens	Yards, parks, play fields, commercial frontage, road sides, lawn and garden equipment
Beverage crops cultivation	Grapes (wine), hibiscus, palm tea, coffee, sugar cane, qat (tea substitute), matte (herbed tea), banana (beer)	Steep slopes, beverage processing

Sources: UNDP 1996; Rowntree 1987.

care, planting annuals (bedding plants), and planting and caring for perennials, shrubs and trees. Related to landscape gardening is grounds keeping, in which playing fields, golf courses, municipal parks and so on are tended (Franck and Brownstone 1987).

Table 64.4 • Safety advice for using mechanical lawn and garden equipment.

Tractors (smaller than regular farm equipment)

Prevent rollovers:

• Do not drive where the tractor can tip or slip; avoid steep slopes; watch for rocks, holes and similar hazards.

• Travel up and down slopes or hillsides; avoid travelling across steep slopes.

• Slow down and use care in turning to prevent tipping or losing steering and braking control.

• Stay within the tractor load limits; use ballast for stability; refer to the operator's manual.

Never allow extra riders.

Maintain safety interlocks; they ensure that powered equipment is disengaged when the operator is not seated or when starting the tractor.

Rotary lawn mowers (tractor mounted or walk-behind type)

Maintain safety interlocks.

Use proper blades and guards.

Keep all safety blades and guards in place and in good condition.

Wear substantial closed-toe shoes to prevent slipping and protect against injury.

Do not allow anyone to put their hands or feet near the mower deck or discharge chute while the machine is running; stop the mower if children are nearby.

When leaving the machine, shut it down.

To prevent thrown object injuries:

• Clear the area to be mowed.

• Keep the mower deck guards, discharge chute, or bag in place.

• Stop the mower whenever someone comes near.

When working on mower (on push or walk-behind type mowers), disconnect the spark plug to prevent engine starting.

Avoid fires by not spilling fuel on hot surfaces nor handling fuel near sparks or flames; avoid the accumulation of fuel, oil and trash around hot surfaces.

Front-end loaders (attached to lawn and garden tractors)

Avoid overloading.

Back down ramps and steep inclines with the loader bucket lowered.

Watch the driving route rather than watching the bucket.

Operate the hydraulic loader controls only from the tractor seat.

Use the loader only for materials that it was designed to handle.

Lower the bucket to the ground when leaving the machine.

Utility haulers (similar to all-terrain vehicles but designed for off-the-road work)

Avoid rollovers:

• Practise driving on smooth terrain before driving on rough terrain.

• Do not speed; slow down before turning (especially on slopes).

• Reduce speed on slopes and rough terrain.

• Watch for holes, rocks and other hidden hazards.

Never allow extra riders.

Avoid tipping over by distributing the cargo box load so it is not too high or too far to rear.

Avoid an upset when raising the cargo box by staying clear of the edge of loading docks or embankments.

When towing loads, place weight in the cargo box to assure traction.

Avoid driving on public roads.

Children should not operate these machines.

A helmet is recommended head protection.

Source: Adapted from Deere & Co. 1994.

Process Overview

Urban agriculture is seen as a method for establishing ecological sustainability for towns and cities in the future. Urban agriculture usually engages shorter-cycle, higher-value market crops and uses multi-cropping and integrated farming techniques located where space and water are scarce. It uses both vertical and horizontal space to its best advantage. The principal feature of urban farming is the reuse of waste. The processes are typical of agriculture with similar inputs and steps, but the design is to use both human and animal wastes as fertilizer and water sources for growing vegetation. In this near idealized model, external inputs still exist, however, such as pesticides (UNDP 1996).

In the special case of landscaping, appearance is the product. The care of lawns and ornamental trees, shrubs and flowers are the focus of the landscape operation. In general, the landscaper purchases planting stock from a nursery or a turf farm, plants the stock and cares for it routinely and frequently. It typically is labour and chemical intensive, and the use of hand and power tools and lawn and garden equipment is also common. Grass mowing is a routine chore in landscaping.

Hazards and Their Control

Urban agriculture is typically small scale, close to housing, exposed to urban pollutants, engaged in the reuse of waste and exposed to potential theft of products and related violence. The hazards related to various types of agriculture, pesticides and composting discussed elsewhere in this volume are similar (UNDP 1996).

In the developed countries, suburban farms and landscaping enterprises make use of lawn and garden equipment. This equipment includes small tractors (tractor attachments such as mowers, front-end loaders and blades) and utility haulers (similar to all-terrain vehicles). Other tractor attachments include tillers, carts, snow blowers and trimmers. These tractors all have engines, use fuel, have moving parts, carry an operator and are often used with towed or mounted equipment. They are substantially smaller than the typical agricultural tractor, but they can be overturned and cause serious injury. The fuel used on these tractors poses a fire hazard (Deere & Co. 1994).

Many of the tractor attachments have their own peculiar hazards. Children riding with adults have fallen from the tractor and been crushed under the wheels or chopped by mower blades. Mowers pose two types of hazards: one is potential contact with rotating blades and the other is being struck by objects thrown from the blades. Both front-end loaders and blades are operated hydraulically, and if left unattended and elevated, pose a hazard of falling onto anyone who gets a body part under the attachment. Utility haulers are inexpensive when compared to the cost of a small truck. They can turn over on steep terrain, especially when turning. They are dangerous when used on public roads because of the possibility of collision. (See table 64.4 for several safety tips for operating some types of lawn and garden equipment.)

● GREENHOUSE AND NURSERY OPERATIONS

Mark M. Methner and John A. Miles

The nursery industry raises plants for the replanting market (see figure 64.5). Hardy plants are grown outside, and the less hardy plants are propagated and raised inside, typically in greenhouses, to protect them from cold temperatures or too much solar radi-

ation or wind. Many plants grown inside during harsh growing conditions are grown outside in favourable weather conditions. Typical nursery crops are trees and shrubs, and the typical greenhouse crops include flowers, vegetables and herbs. The nursery industry grows plants for the replanting market, but greenhouses are also used for growing crops for seasonal markets, such as tomatoes during the freezing months of winter.

The plant nursery industry constitutes a large and growing sector of agriculture. In California, where there are more than 3,000 commercial nursery operations, nursery crops are a high value-per-acre commodity, ranking fifth in state farm income. As with much of western US agriculture, the employee population is dominated by workers from Mexico or other Central American countries. The majority of these workers are not migrant, but are settled in local communities with their families (Mines and Martin 1986). Most speak Spanish only or as a primary language and have little or no formal education. Wages are low for most jobs, and there is a labour surplus. Similar situations exist throughout the world.

Nursery work is considered a comparatively good job by most agricultural workers because it is year-round, comparatively well-paid and frequently includes workers' compensation insurance and employee health benefits. Few workers belong to labour organizations in this industry, and most workers are employed directly by the enterprise rather than by farm labour contractors.

Greenhouses provide a controlled environment for plants and are used for a variety of purposes, which include growing rare and exotic plants, protecting producing plants (such as flowers, tomatoes and peppers) from winter weather and starting seedlings. The controlled environment within a greenhouse is advantageous to those who wish to grow crops year-round, regardless of seasonal conditions outdoors. Greenhouse operations have expanded in temperate climates. For example, in the Ukraine, the total area of greenhouses has grown from 3,070 hectares (ha) in 1985 to 3,200 ha in 1990 to an estimated 3,400 ha in 1995 (Viten, Krashyyuh and Ilyna 1994).

The gable (equal sloping roof) greenhouse is typical. It provides good exposure to winter sunlight, drainage and wind protection. The framing materials for greenhouses include wood, aluminium or a combination of steel pipe and wood. Side walls or siding can be made from a variety of materials including plywood, aluminium, wood or vinyl. In the Ukraine, 60% of the greenhouses have masonry block walls. Covers include glass or plastic, and in some parts of the world, the glass-covered house is called a glasshouse. The plastic can be either rigid or a flexible film. Rigid plastics used as covers include fibreglass, acrylic and polycarbonate. Flexible plastic covers include polyethylene, polyvinyl chloride and polyester. Polycarbonate, which withstands breakage from thrown objects, and the flexible plastics require frequent replacement. Covers can vary from clear to opaque, and they serve three purposes. One is to let sunlight in for the plants. Another is for heating within an enclosure. The last is protecting the plants from environmental stress, including snow, rain, hail, high winds, birds, small animals and insects.

The greenhouse operation requires the control of temperature, humidity and ventilation, using artificial heat sources, exhaust and inlet fans, shading (such as with movable slats or netting), cooling equipment (such as wet-pad or evaporative cooling), humidification and climate-control equipment (Jones 1978).

Nursery and greenhouse workers are exposed to a variety of hazards, including skin irritants, dust, noise, heat stress, musculoskeletal disorders (sprains and strains), pesticides and injuries related to vehicles, machines, slips and falls and electricity. The hazards discussed below are limited to ergonomic hazards in nursery work and pesticide hazards in greenhouse work. Many of these hazards are common for the two operations.

Nursery Operations

Typical operations at a large wholesale nursery specializing in container-grown outdoor bedding and ornamental plants consist of four stages:

1. *Propagation stage.* New plants are started in a specialized medium using one of four standard methods: cuttings from mature plants, tissue culture, seeds and grafting.
2. *Replanting stage.* As plants grow they are replanted into individual plastic containers called "cans" (typically 2 or 3 times during the early growth cycle). A powered conveyor carries the new, larger cans past a hopper where they are filled with soil. As the cans continue down the conveyor, plants are manually transplanted into them, and finally they are manually transferred onto a trailer for transport to the field.
3. *Growing stage* or *field operations.* Plants are held in outdoor groups until fully mature. During this period, tasks include watering, pruning, fertilizing and weeding, tying-staking-shaping and spacing as plants grow.
4. *Shipping.* Mature plants are removed to the shipping area, labelled, organized by order load, and loaded into trucks. This operation can also include truck unloading at retail sites.

Ergonomic hazards

Nursery work, as with other agricultural commodities, has a pattern of high rates of sprain and strain injuries. AgSafe data (1992) suggest that 38.9% of all reported injuries in horticultural specialties (including nurseries) were sprains and strains, slightly above the proportion for agriculture as a whole. Overexertion as a cause of injury for this area was cited for 30.2% of reported injuries, also above the proportion for the industry as a whole.

The most common risk factors for the development of work-related musculoskeletal problems have been identified as occurring in the following job tasks:

During propagation, the worker stands or sits at a work table, empties a basket of plant cuttings, and uses hand shears to cut them into smaller pieces. The shears are held in the dominant hand; plant material is grasped with the other hand. After each piece of plant material is cut, the shears must be disinfected by dipping them in a solution in a small container in the work bench.

When cutting, one hand is engaged in very repetitive gripping, with an average of 50 to 60 cuts per minute. Mild to moderate wrist flexion and ulnar deviation occur throughout the cutting cycle. The other hand is used to hold the cuttings, orient them for cutting, and discard the remains in a bin. Moderate wrist extension and ulnar deviation occur throughout this cycle also.

Workers in this specialized job are highly skilled and work virtually full-time year-round without rotation into other jobs. Workers report pain and numbness in the hand, wrist and arm. After a period of years on this job, they demonstrate an elevated incidence of carpal tunnel syndrome.

In transporting plants from a conveyor belt to a trailer, the worker grasps 3 or 4 3.8-litre containers in each hand and places them on a trailer located either to one side of or behind him or her. This job cycle is repeated 13 to 20 times per minute. Risk factors include highly repetitive gripping, high pinch forces and awkward postures, including trunk, lumbar and shoulder flexion.

In transporting plants from a trailer to a planting bed, the worker grasps 3 or 4 3.8-l containers in each hand, carries them up to 17 m, and places them on the ground along a predetermined row. This job cycle is repeated 3 to 5 times per minute. Handling cans is a nearly full-time, year-round job for many workers. It is associated with pain in the fingers and hands, upper extremities and lower back. Because field workers tend to be younger, the predicted high rate of chronic back injury is not documented at this time.

Figure 64.5 • Setting coffee plants in a nursery in Côte d'Ivoire.

The pruner works with various shears to snip unwanted or dead parts off the tops and sides of plants. The worker is usually standing or bent over to reach plants. The dominant hand holds the shears and is engaged in very repetitive gripping, with an average of 40 to 50 cuts per minute. The fingers of the same hand are also used to pinch off small twigs or other plant parts. The nondominant hand grasps the can for a rapid pick and place, and also holds the cuttings in a static grip with a moderate wrist flexion and ulnar deviation present throughout the cutting cycle. Because pruning is a part-time task for most field workers, some relief and recovery are achieved due to task variation. However, it is associated with pain in the fingers and hand, wrist, upper extremities and lower back.

To allow plants adequate room to grow and expand, spacing must be done periodically. This entails grasping and lifting 3 to 4 plants in each hand, carrying them a short distance, and placing them on the ground in rows. This cycle is repeated 3 to 5 times per minute. Like pruning, spacing is a part-time task for most field workers, allowing opportunity for relief and recovery. It is also associated with pain in fingers and hands, wrists, upper extremities and lower back.

Most nursery jobs are human-energy intensive, and this, coupled with the repetitive nature of many tasks, leads to substantial risk of repetitive-motion injuries. Tools to assist the workers by improving body posture and reducing the energy requirements of particular tasks have just begun to be developed.

Greenhouse Operations

Typical operations in a greenhouse vary depending on whether the purpose is to grow rare and exotic plants, production plants or seedlings. The growing of rare or exotic plants is a year-round enterprise. Production plants are typically grown within the greenhouse to protect them from the weather; thus, greenhouses can be used seasonally. The growth of seedlings is similar to nursery operations, but the market is plants for spring replanting after the last freeze. The tasks involved in greenhouse growing include putting the soil into small containers, planting the seed in each of the containers, watering and fertilizing the plants, trim-

Figure 64.6 • Clipping (mowing) tobacco transplants in a greenhouse in North Carolina.

This is done with a conventional lawn mower attached to the sprayer boom, which is also used to apply water and pesticides when needed.

Figure 64.7 • Worker in full protective gear applies pesticides in a greenhouse.

ming or thinning the plants as needed (see figure 64.6), applying fumigants or pesticides and transporting the plants or product from the greenhouse. Soil filling and planting has become a mechanized operation in the production greenhouse. The composition of the potting soil may be a mix of peat, perlite and vermiculite. Trimming may be mechanized, depending upon the crop. Watering may be directly with a hose or through an automated sprinkler or piping system. Nutrients are added to the water to fertilize the plants. Application of pesticides by hand sprayer is typical. Soil sterilization is done either by steam or chemicals, including dibromochloropropane (DBCP). The transport of plants or product is typically a manual exercise.

Pesticides Used in Greenhouses

Diseases and insects that attack plants can result in major problems for greenhouse operators. Often, preventing such damage is easier than trying to eradicate the pests afterward. Some common pests that inflict the most damage on greenhouse crops are insects, fungi, viruses, bacteria and nematodes. To combat these undesirable organisms, special chemicals (pesticides) are applied to the plants to kill the pests.

There are many ways of applying pesticides so that they are effective. The most common application methods are: liquid sprays, mists, dusts, fogs, smokes, aerosol canisters and granules. Pesticide sprays involve the use of a water/pesticide mixture contained in a tank that has a hose with a spray nozzle attached to it. Under pressure, the mixture is directed onto the plants as liquid droplets. Mists are generated by a technique similar to the spray technique, but the resulting droplets are smaller. Pesticide dusts are often released into the air and allowed to settle onto the plant surface. Foggers use heating devices to generate very small droplets directed at the plants. Pesticide smokes are generated by igniting a sparkler and placing it in a canister that contains the chemical.

Aerosol canisters are pressurized metal containers that release the pesticide to the air when a valve is opened. Finally, granular pesticides are placed on top of the soil and then watered. The watering dissolves the granules and transports the chemical to the roots of the plant, where it can either kill organisms in the soil or be absorbed by the plant and kill organisms that feed on it.

With each different method of application of a pesticide comes the hazard of being exposed to the chemical. The two most common routes of exposure are through the skin (dermal) and through the lungs (respiratory). Another, but less common, route of exposure is by ingesting food or drinks contaminated with pesticides. Greenhouse workers who handle the chemicals or the treated plants may be poisoned if proper safety precautions are not followed.

Ways to avoid poisoning include proper use of greenhouse ventilation systems, using and maintaining the appropriate PPE (suits, gloves, respirators, boots—see figure 64.7), observing recommended re-entry times and following the pesticide label instructions. Some additional safety precautions are: storage of all pesticides inside a locked, well-ventilated area; posting signs in areas where plants have been treated; and comprehensive pesticide training that includes proper application and handling techniques. Finally, all pesticide applicators should be trained in appropriate disposal techniques for old pesticides and empty pesticide containers.

FLORICULTURE

Samuel H. Henao

Since the early 1990s, in many countries and across several continents, floriculture as an economic activity has been expanding

Figure 64.8 • Tending flowers in a greenhouse.

Figure 64.9 • Planting cuttings in a greenhouse.

rapidly. Its growing importance in export markets has resulted in an integrated development of several aspects of this field of activity, including production, technology, scientific research, transportation and conservation.

Production

The production of cut flowers has two essential components:

1. the process of production, which involves all activities directly related to the generation and the development of the product up to the moment of packing
2. the various activities that aid in the production and promote the marketing and distribution of cut flowers.

The production process itself can be divided into three basic parts: germination, cultivation and post-harvest procedures.

Germination is carried out by planting parent plants from which cuttings are obtained for cultivation.

The cuttings of different flowers are planted on beds of a rooting medium. The beds are made from steam-treated dross and treated with chemical products to disinfect the growing medium and to facilitate root development.

Cultivation is done in greenhouses which house the beds of rooting medium where the flowers are planted and grown as discussed in the article "Greenhouse and nursery operations" in this chapter and as shown in figure 64.8. Cultivation includes preparing the soil, planting the cuttings (figure 64.9) and harvesting the flowers.

Planting includes the cycle that begins with placing the cuttings in the rooting medium and ends with the flowering plant. It includes the following activities: planting, normal irrigation, drip irrigation with fertilizer, cultivation and weeding of the soil, pinching the tip of the plants to force branching and obtain more

flowers, preparing the props that hold the plants upright, and the growth, branching and flowering of the plant.

Production concludes with the gathering of the flowers and their separation by classification.

At the *post-harvest stage*—in addition to selection and classification—the flowers are covered with plastic hoods, a sanitary treatment is applied, and they are packed for shipment.

Secondary activities include monitoring the health of the plants to detect pests and to diagnose plant illnesses early, obtaining raw materials from the warehouse, and maintaining the furnaces.

Health Risk Factors

The most important risk factors in each of the different areas of work are:

- chemical substances
- extreme temperatures—heat
- non-ionizing radiation
- infectious disease
- ergonomic factors
- mechanical factors
- psychosocial factors.

Chemical substances

Intoxication and chronic illness due to pesticides

The levels of morbidity/mortality found in workers due to exposure to pesticides are not the consequence of a simple relation between the chemical agent and the person who has suffered exposure to it, but also reflect the interplay of many other factors. Among these are the length of exposure, individual susceptibility, the nutritional state of the person exposed, educational and cultural variables and the socioeconomic conditions under which the workers live.

In addition to the active ingredients of pesticides, the substances that convey the active ingredients and the additives should also be taken into consideration, because sometimes those sub-

Figure 64.10 • Bending over for extended periods is a common cause of ergonomic problems.

stances can have adverse effects that are more harmful than those of the active ingredients.

The toxicity of pesticides made with organophosphates is due to their effect on the central nervous system, because they inhibit the activity of the enzyme acetylcholinesterase. The effects are cumulative, and delayed effects have also been noted on the central and the peripheral nervous systems. According to studies carried out in several countries, the prevalence of inhibition of this enzyme among workers who handle these pesticides fluctuates between 3 and 18%.

The long-term effects are pathological processes that develop after a latency period and are due to repeated exposures. Among the long-term effects known to be due to pesticide exposure are skin lesions, nerve damage and mutagenic effects.

Respiratory problems
Decorative plants can irritate the respiratory system and cause coughing and sneezing. In addition, plant scents or odours may exacerbate symptoms of asthma or allergic rhinitis, although they have not been shown to cause allergies. Pollen from the chrysanthemum and the sunflower can cause asthma. Dust from dried plants sometimes causes allergies.

Dermatitis
The cases of occupational dermatitis found in floriculture are about 90% primarily due to contact dermatitis. Of these, about 60% are caused by primary irritants and 40% are due to allergic reactions. The acute form is characterized by reddening (erythema), swelling (oedema), pimples (papules), vesicles or blisters. It is especially localized on the hands, wrists and forearms. The chronic form can have deep fissures, lichenification (thickening and hardening) of the skin, and severe xerosis (dryness). It can be incapacitating and even irreversible.

Floriculture is one of those activities where contact with primary irritants or allergenic substances is high, and for that reason it is important to promote and use preventive measures, such as gloves.

Extreme temperatures—heat
When work must be carried out in a hot environment, as in the case of hothouses, the thermal load on the worker is the sum of the heat of the work environment plus the energy expended on the task itself.

Physical effects of excessive exposure to heat include heat rash, cramps and muscle spasms, exhaustion and fainting spells. Heat rash, in addition to being uncomfortable, lowers the worker's tolerance to heat. If perspiration is abundant and liquids and electrolytes are not replenished adequately, cramps and muscle spasms can set in. Heat exhaustion occurs when vasomotor control and cardiac output are insufficient to compensate for the additional demands placed on these systems by the heat stress. Fainting spells represent a very serious clinical situation that can lead to confusion, delirium and coma.

Precautions include frequent rest breaks in cool areas, availability of beverages to drink, rotating of tasks requiring heavy exertion and wearing of light-coloured clothing.

Non-ionizing radiation
The most important kinds of non-ionizing radiation that floriculture workers are exposed to are ultraviolet (UV) radiation, visible light and infrared radiation. The most serious effects of UV radiation are solar erythema, actinic dermatitis, irritative conjunctivitis and photokeratitis.

Radiation from the visible spectrum of light may cause retinal and macular degeneration. One symptom of exposure to infrared radiation is superficial burn of the cornea, and prolonged exposure can lead to the premature appearance of cataracts.

Precautions include keeping the skin covered, wearing tinted glasses, and medical surveillance.

Ergonomic factors
Workers who maintain a static body posture for long periods of time (see figure 64.10) can suffer from resulting static muscle contractions and from alterations of the peripheral, vascular and nervous systems. Repetitive movements are more common in tasks that require manual dexterity. For example, clipping shears can require a lot of force and involve repetitive motion. The most frequently observed effects are musculoskeletal impairments, including tendinitis of the elbow and wrist, carpal tunnel syndrome and impairment of movement at the shoulder.

Job rotation and the proper ergonomic design of equipment such as clipping shears are needed precautions. Redesigning the workplace to require less bending is another solution.

Infectious diseases
Floriculture may expose workers to a variety of biological agents. Early signs of an infection are rarely specific, although they are generally well-defined enough to lead to a suspicion of illness. The signs, symptomatology and precautions depend on the agent, which includes tetanus, rabies, hepatitis and so on. Preventive measures include a source of potable water, good sanitary facilities, first aid and medical care for cuts and abrasions.

Other factors
The most common health and safety hazards associated with mechanical factors are cuts, abrasions and single and multiple traumas, which most frequently injure the hands and face. Such injuries must be attended to immediately. Workers should have up-to-date tetanus shots and adequate first-aid facilities must be available.

The psychosocial environment can also endanger worker health. The results of exposure to these factors can have the following consequences: physiological changes (indigestion, constipation, palpitations, difficulty breathing, hyperventilation, insomnia and anxiety); psychological disturbances (tension and depression); and behavioural disturbances (absenteeism, instability, dissatisfaction).

FARMWORKER EDUCATION ABOUT PESTICIDES: A CASE STUDY

Merri Weinger

At the San Antonio farm, several workers became poisoned when applying the pesticide Lannate. An investigation of the case revealed that the workers had been using backpack sprayers for application without wearing any protective clothing, gloves or boots. Their employer had never provided the necessary equipment, and soap and showers were also unavailable. Following the poisonings, the employer was directed to take the appropriate corrective actions.

When the Ministry of Health made a follow-up inspection, they discovered that many farmers were still not using any protective clothing or equipment. When they were asked why, some said that the equipment was too hot and uncomfortable. Others explained that they had been working this way for years and never had any problems. Several commented that they didn't need the equipment because they drank a large glass of milk after applying pesticides.

This experience, which took place in Nicaragua, is common to many parts of the world and illustrates the challenge to effective farmworker training. Training must be accompanied by provision of a safe work environment and legislative enforcement, but must also consider the barriers to implementing safe work practices and incorporate them in training programmes. These barriers, such as unsafe work environments, absence of protective equipment and attitudes and beliefs which are not health-promoting, should be directly discussed in training sessions, and strategies to address them should be developed.

This article describes an action-oriented training approach applied in two multidisciplinary pesticide projects that were designed to address the problem of farmworker pesticide poisoning. They were implemented in Nicaragua by CARE, Nicaragua and the American Friends Service Committee (1985 to 1989) and in the Central American region by the International Labour Organization (ILO, 1993 to present). In addition to a strong educational approach, the Nicaraguan project developed improved methods to mix and load pesticides, a medical monitoring plan to screen workers for overexposure to pesticides and a system to collect data for epidemiological investigation (Weinger and Lyons 1992). Within its multifaceted project, the ILO emphasized legislative improvements, training and building a regional network of pesticide educators.

Key elements of both projects were the implementation of a training needs assessment in order to tailor teaching content to the target audience, the use of a variety of participatory teaching approaches (Weinger and Wallerstein 1990) and the production of a teacher's guide and educational materials to facilitate the learning process. Training topics included the health effects of pesticides, symptoms of pesticide poisoning, rights, resources and a problem-solving component which analysed the obstacles to working safely and how to resolve them.

Although there were many similarities between the two projects, the Nicaraguan project emphasized worker education while the regional project focused on teacher training. This article provides selected guidelines for both worker and teacher training.

Worker Education

Needs assessment

The first step in developing the training programme was the needs assessment or "listening phase", which identified problems and obstacles to effective change, recognized factors which were conducive to change, defined values and beliefs held by the farmworkers and identified specific hazardous exposures and experiences which needed to be incorporated into the training. Walkthrough inspections were used by the Nicaraguan project team to observe work practices and sources of worker exposure to pesticides. Photographs were taken of the work environment and work practices for documentation, analysis and discussion during the training. The team also listened for emotional issues which might be barriers to action: worker frustration with inadequate personal protection, lack of soap and water or lack of safe alternatives to currently used pesticides.

Training methods and objectives

The next step in the training process was to identify the content areas to be covered utilizing information gained from listening to workers and then to select appropriate training methods based on the learning objectives. The training had four objectives: providing information; identifying and changing attitudes/emotions; promoting healthy behaviours; and developing action/problem-solving skills. What follows are examples of methods grouped under the objective which they best achieve. The following methods were incorporated into a 2-day training session (Wallerstein and Weinger 1992).

Methods for information objectives

Flipchart. In Nicaragua, the project staff needed visual educational tools which were easily portable and independent of electricity for use during field training or with medical screening on the farms. The flipchart included 18 drawings based on real-life situations, which were designed for use as discussion starters. Each picture had specific objectives and key questions that were outlined in an accompanying guide for instructors.

The flipchart could be used both to provide information and to promote problem analysis leading to action planning. For example, a drawing was used to provide information on the routes of entry by asking "How do pesticides enter the body?" To generate analysis of the problem of pesticide poisoning, the instructor would ask participants: "What's happening here? Is this scene familiar? Why does this occur? What can (he) you do about it?" The introduction of two or more people into a drawing (of two people entering a recently sprayed field) encourages discussion of suspected motivations and feelings. "Why is she reading the sign? Why did he go right in?" With effective visual images, the same picture may trigger a variety of discussions, depending upon the group.

Slides. Slides which portray familiar images or problems were used in the same way as the flipchart. Using photos taken during the needs assessment phase, a slide show was created following the path of pesticide use from selection and purchase to disposal and clean-up at the end of the workday.

Methods for attitude-emotion objectives

Attitudes and emotions may effectively block learning and influence how health and safety practices are implemented back on the job.

Scripted role-play. A scripted role-play was often used to explore attitudes and trigger discussion of the problems of exposure to pesticides. The following script was given to three workers, who read their roles to the entire group.

Jose: What's the matter?

Rafael: I'm about ready to give up. Two workers were poisoned today, just one week after that big training session. Nothing ever changes around here.

Jose: What did you expect? The managers didn't even attend the training.

Sara: But at least they scheduled a training for the workers. That's more than the other farms are doing.

Jose: Setting up a training is one thing, but what about follow-up? Are the managers providing showers and adequate protective equipment?

Sara: Have you ever thought that the workers might have something to do with these poisonings? How do you know they're working safely?

Rafael: I don't know. All I know is that two guys are in the hospital today and I have to go back to work.

The role-play was developed to explore the complex problem of pesticide health and safety and the multiple elements involved in resolving it, including training. In the discussion which followed, the facilitator asked the group if they shared any of the attitudes expressed by the farmworkers in the role-play, explored obstacles to resolving the problems portrayed and solicited strategies for overcoming them.

Worksheet questionnaire. In addition to serving as an excellent discussion starter and providing factual information, a questionnaire can also be a vehicle for eliciting attitudes. Sample questions for a farmworker group in Nicaragua were:

1. Drinking milk before work is effective in preventing pesticide poisoning.

Agree   Disagree

2. All pesticides have the same effect on your health.

Agree   Disagree

A discussion of attitudes was encouraged by inviting participants with conflicting viewpoints to present and justify their opinions. Rather than affirming the "correct" answer, the instructor acknowledged useful elements in the variety of attitudes that were expressed.

Methods for behavioural skill objectives

Behavioural skills are the desired competencies that workers will acquire as a result of training. The most effective way to achieve objectives for behavioural skill development is to provide participants with opportunities to practise in the class, to see an activity and perform it.

Personal protective equipment demonstration. A display of protective equipment and clothing was laid out on a table in front of the class, including an array of appropriate and inappropriate options. The trainer asked a volunteer from the audience to get dressed for work applying pesticides. The farmworker chose clothing from the display and put it on; the audience was asked to comment. A discussion followed concerning appropriate protective clothing and alternatives to uncomfortable clothing.

Hands-on practice. Both trainers and farmworkers in Nicaragua learned to interpret pesticide labels by reading them in small groups during the class. In this activity, the class was divided into groups and given the task of reading different labels as a group. For low-literacy groups, volunteer participants were recruited to read the label aloud and lead their group through a worksheet

questionnaire on the label, which emphasized visual cues to determine level of toxicity. Back in the large group, volunteer spokespeople introduced their pesticide to the group with instructions for potential users.

Methods for action/problem-solving objectives

A primary goal of the training session is to provide farmworkers with the information and skills to make changes back on the job.

Discussion starters. A discussion starter can be used to pose problems or potential obstacles to change, for analysis by the group. A discussion starter can take a variety of forms: a role-play, a picture in a flipchart or slide, a case study. To lead a dialogue on the discussion starter, there is a 5-step questioning process which invites participants to identify the problem, project themselves into the situation being presented, share their personal reactions, analyse the causes of the problem and suggest action strategies (Weinger and Wallerstein 1990).

Case studies. Cases were drawn from real and familiar situations that occurred in Nicaragua that were identified in the planning process. They most commonly illustrated problems such as employer noncompliance, worker noncompliance with safety precautions within their control and the dilemma of a worker with symptoms that may be related to pesticide exposure. A sample case study was used to introduce this article.

Participants read the case in small groups and responded to a series of questions such as: What are some of the causes of pesticide poisoning in this incident? Who's benefiting? Who's being harmed? What steps would you take to prevent a similar problem in the future?

Action planning. Prior to the conclusion of the training session, participants worked independently or in groups to develop a plan of action to increase workplace health and safety when pesticides are used. Using a worksheet, participants identified at least one step they could take to promote safe working conditions and practices.

Evaluation and Teacher Training

Determining the extent to which the sessions met their objectives is a crucial part of training projects. Evaluation tools included a written post-workshop questionnaire and follow-up visits to farms as well as surveys and interviews with participants 6 months following the training session.

Training teachers who would utilize the approach outlined above to provide information and training to farmworkers was an essential component of the ILO-sponsored Central American programmes. The objectives of the teacher training programme were to increase the knowledge on pesticide health and safety and the teaching skill of trainers; to increase the number and quality of training sessions directed toward farmworkers, employers, extension workers and agronomists in project countries; and to initiate a network of educators in pesticide health and safety in the region.

Training topics in the 1-week session included: an overview of the health effects of pesticides, safe work practices and equipment; the principles of adult education; steps in planning an educational programme and how to implement them; demonstration of selected teaching methods; overview of presentation skills; practice teaching by participants using participatory methods, with critique; and development of action plans for future teaching about pesticides and alternatives to their use. A 2-week session allows time to conduct a field visit and training needs assessment during the workshop, to develop educational materials in the classroom and to conduct worker training sessions in the field.

A trainer's guide and sample curricula were provided during the workshop to facilitate practice teaching both in the classroom and following the workshop. The educators' network offers another source of support and a vehicle for sharing innovative teaching approaches and materials.

Conclusion

The success of this teaching approach with workers in the cotton fields of Nicaragua, trade unionists in Panama and trainers from the Ministry of Health in Costa Rica, among others, demonstrates its adaptability to a variety of work settings and target groups. Its goals are not only to increase knowledge and skills, but also to provide the tools for problem-solving in the field after the teaching sessions have ended. One must be clear, however, that education alone cannot resolve the problems of pesticide use and abuse. A multidisciplinary approach which includes farmworker organizing, legislative enforcement strategies, engineering controls, medical monitoring and investigation into alternatives to pesticides is essential to effect comprehensive changes in pesticide practices.

● PLANTING AND GROWING OPERATIONS

Yuri Kundiev and V.I. Chernyuk

Modern agriculture is based on highly efficient equipment, especially high-speed, powerful tractors and agricultural machines. Tractors with mounted and trailed implements allow the mechanization of many agricultural operations.

Use of tractors allows farmers to accomplish the main tillage and care of plants in the optimum time without major manual labour. Permanent enlargement of farms, extension of land under cultivation and intensification of crop rotation promotes more efficient agriculture as well. Widespread use of high-speed assemblies is hampered by two factors: existing agricultural methods based mainly on machines and implements with passive tools; and difficulties in ensuring safe working conditions for the high-speed tractor assembly operator.

Mechanization can accomplish approximately 70% of planting and growing operations. It is used at all stages of crop cultivation and harvesting as well. Nevertheless, each stage of planting and growing has its own requisite set of machines, tools and environmental conditions, and this variability of the production and environmental factors has an influence upon the tractor driver.

Cultivation of the Land

Cultivation of the land (ploughing, harrowing, scuffing, disk harrowing, entire cultivation, rolling-down) is important and the most labour-intensive preliminary stage of crop production. These operations involve 30% of planting and growing operations.

As a rule, loosening of the soil results in the formation of dust. The nature of the dust in the air is variable, and depends on meteorological conditions, season, kind of work, type of soil and so on. Dust concentration in tractor cabs can vary from a few mg/m^3 to hundreds of mg/m^3, depending essentially on the cab enclosure. Approximately 60 to 65% of cases exceed the permissible total dust concentration level; permissible levels of respirable (less than or equal to 5 microns) dust are exceeded 60 to 80% of the time (see figure 64.11). Silica content in the dust varies from 0.5 to 20% (Kundiev 1983).

Cultivation consists of power-consuming operations, especially during ploughing, and it demands a considerable mobilization of the power resources of machines, generating considerable levels of noise where tractor drivers sit. These noise levels amount to 86 to

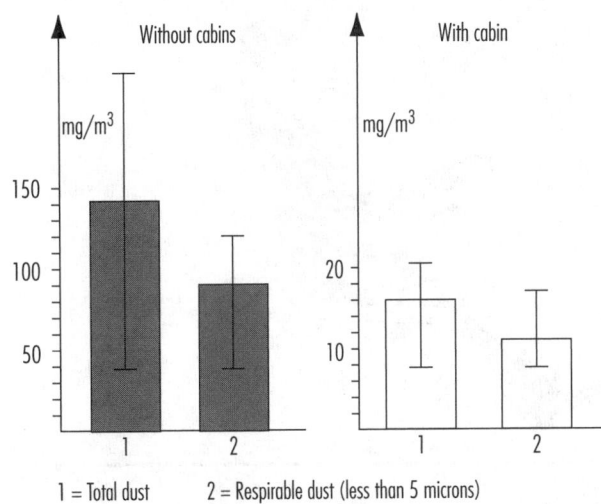

Figure 64.11 • Tractor driver exposures to dust during land cultivation.

Without cabins / With cabin

1 = Total dust   2 = Respirable dust (less than 5 microns)

90 dBA and higher, creating a considerable risk of hearing disorders for these workers.

As a rule, whole-body vibration levels where the tractor driver is seated can be very high, exceeding levels established by the International Organization for Standardization (ISO 1985) for fatigue-decreased proficiency boundary and frequently for exposure limit.

Ground preparation is conducted mainly in early spring and autumn, so the microclimate of cabs in temperate zones for machines without air conditioners is not a health problem except on occasional hot days.

Sowing and Growing

Ensuring that sowing attachments or ploughing implements move in a straight line and that tractors follow marker tracks or the middle of the row are characteristic features of the sowing and care of crops.

In general, these activities require the driver to work in uncomfortable positions and involve considerable nervous and emotional tension due to restricted working-zone visibility, resulting in rapid development of operator fatigue.

The layout of sowing machines and their preparation for use, as well as the necessity of manual auxiliary work, especially materials handling, may involve considerable physical loads.

A wide geographical distribution of grain varieties results in a diversity of meteorological conditions when sowing. Winter crop sowing for different climate zones can be performed, for example, when the outdoor temperature ranges from 3–10 °C to 30–35 °C. Spring crop sowings are performed when the outdoor temperature ranges from 0 °C to 15–20 °C. The temperatures in tractor cabs without air conditioners can be very high in regions where climate is mild and hot.

Microclimate conditions in tractor cabs are favourable as a rule during tilled crops sowing (sugar beet, maize, sunflower) in temperate zones. Cultivation of crops is performed when the outdoor temperature is high and solar radiation is intense. The air temperature in cabs without microclimate control can rise to 40 °C and more. Tractor drivers can work under uncomfortable conditions about 40 to 70% of the total time involved in the care of crops.

Working operations for tilled crops cultivation involve considerable moving of earth, causing formation of dust. Maximum

Figure 64.12 • Angle parameters of optimal work posture of a tractor driver.

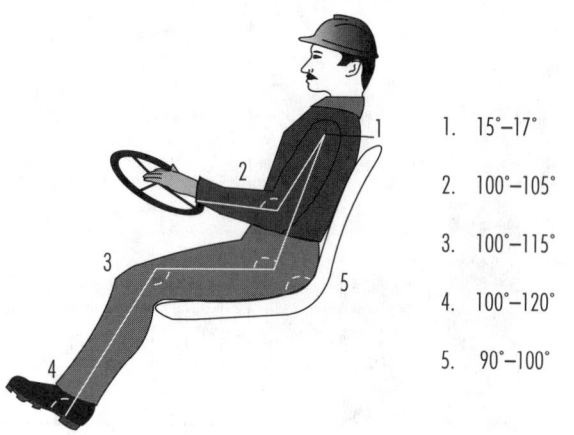

1. 15°–17°
2. 100°–105°
3. 100°–115°
4. 100°–120°
5. 90°–100°

ground dust concentrations in the breathing zone air do not exceed 10 to 20 mg/m³. The dust is 90% inorganic, containing a large amount of free silica. Noise and vibration levels where the driver sits are a little lower than those existing during cultivation.

During sowing and cultivation, workers can be exposed to manures, chemical fertilizers and pesticides. When safety regulations for handling these materials are not followed, and if machines are not working properly, the breathing zone concentration of hazardous materials can exceed permissible values.

Harvesting

As a rule, harvesting lasts from 25 to 40 days. Dust, microclimate conditions and noise can be hazards during harvesting.

Breathing zone dust concentrations depend chiefly on outside concentration and the airtightness of the harvesting machine's cab. Older machines without cabs leave drivers exposed to the dust. Dust formation is most intensive during the harvesting of dry corn, when the dust concentration at non-enclosed combines' cabs can be as much as 60 to 90 mg/m³. Dust consists mainly of plant scraps, pollen and mushroom spores, mostly in large, non-respirable particles (larger than 10 microns). Free silica content is less than 5.5%.

Formation of dust during sugar beet harvesting is lower. Maximum dust concentration at the cab does not exceed 30 mg/m³.

Harvesting of grain is generally performed in the hottest season. Temperature in the cab can rise to 36 to 40 °C. The flux level of direct solar radiation is 500 W/m² and more when ordinary glass is used for cab windows. Tinted glass lowers the temperature of air in the cab by 1 to 1.6 °C. A mechanical forced ventilation system with a flow rate of 350 m³/h can create a temperature difference between inside and outside air of 5 to 7 °C. If the combine is equipped with adjustable louvers, this difference drops to 4 to 6 °C.

Tilled crops are harvested in the autumn months. As a rule conditions of the microclimate in cabs in this time are not a great health problem.

Experience in developed countries points to the fact that agriculture at small farms can be profitable with the use of small-scale mechanization (minitractors—motorized units with a capacity of up to 18 horsepower, with different kinds of auxiliary equipment).

Use of such equipment gives rise to a number of specific health problems. These problems include: intensification of workload in certain seasons, the use of child labour and the labour of elderly persons, absence of the means of protection against intensive

noise, whole-body and local vibration, harmful meteorological conditions, dust, pesticides, and exhaust gases. The effort necessary to move the control levers of motorized units can amount to 60 to 80 N (newtons).

Some kinds of work are performed with the help of draught animals or done manually due to insufficient equipment or because of the impossibility of using machinery for some reason. Manual labour demands as a rule considerable physical effort. Power requirements during ploughing, horse-drawn sowing and manual mowing can amount to 5,000 to 6,000 cal/day and more.

Injuries are common during manual work, especially among inexperienced workers, and cases of plant burns, insect and reptile stings and dermatitis from the sap of some plants are frequent.

Prevention

One of the main trends in tractor construction is the improvement of working conditions of tractor operators. Side by side with perfection of the design of protective cabs is the search for ways of coordinating technical parameters of various tractor units with the functional abilities of operators. The aim of this research consists of ensuring the effectiveness of control and driving functions as well as necessary ergonomic parameters of the workplace environment.

Effectiveness of control and driving of tractor assemblies is ensured by good visibility of the working zone, by optimizing assemblies and control panel design and by proper ergonomic design of tractor seats.

Common ways of increasing visibility are increasing the viewing area of the cab using panoramic glass, improved layout of auxiliary equipment (e.g., fuel tank), rationalization of seat location, use of rear view mirrors and so on.

Optimization of construction control elements is connected with the construction of the control mechanism's drive. Along with hydraulic and electric drives, a new improvement is suspended control pedals. This allows improved access and increased driving comfort. Functional coding (by means of form, colour and/or symbolic signs) plays an important part in recognition of the control elements.

Rational layout of instrumentation (which comprises 15 to 20 units in modern tractors) requires taking into account further increases in indicators due to remote control of technological process conditions, automation of the driving and operating of the technological equipment.

The operator's seat is designed to guarantee a comfortable position and effective driving of the machine and tractor assembly. Design of modern tractor seats takes into account anthropometric data of the human body. Seats have adjustable back and arms and can be adjusted according to the operator's size, in both horizontal and vertical dimensions (figure 64.12).

Precautions against harmful working conditions for tractor drivers include means of protection against noise and vibration, microclimate normalization and airtight sealing of cabs.

Besides special engineering of the engine to reduce noise at its source, considerable effect is achieved by mounting the engine on vibration isolators, isolating the cab from the tractor body with the help of shock absorbers and a number of measures designed for absorption of noise in the cab. Flaky, sound-absorbing lagging with a decorative surface is applied for this purpose to cab wall panels, and rugs made of rubber and porolon are laid on the cab floor. Hard perforated panelling with an air gap of 30 to 50 mm is applied to the ceiling. These measures have reduced noise levels in cabs to 80–83 dBA.

The main means of damping low-frequency vibration in the cab is use of an effective seat suspension. Nevertheless, the effect of whole-body vibration damping achieved this way does not exceed 20 to 30%.

Agricultural ground levelling gives considerable opportunities for decreasing vibration.

Improvement of the microclimate conditions in tractor cabs is reached with the help of both standard equipment (e.g., fans with filter elements, thermo-insulating tinted glass, sun-proof cap peaks, adjustable louvers) and special devices (e.g., air conditioners). Modern tractor heating systems are designed as an autonomous assembly attached to the engine's cooling system and using warmed water to heat the air. Combined air conditioners and air heaters are also available.

Complex solutions of the problem of noise, vibration and heat isolation and sealing of cabs can be reached with the help of sealed cab capsules designed with suspended control pedals and wire rope systems of drives.

Ease of access to tractor engines and assemblies for their maintenance and repairs, as well as obtaining timely information about technical condition of certain units of the assembly, are important indices of the level of tractor operator working conditions. Eliminating the cab bonnet, forward inclination of the cab, detachable panels of the engine's bonnet and so on are available in certain types of tractors.

In the future, tractor cabs are likely to be equipped with automatic control units, with television screens for observation of implements that are out of the operator's field of vision and with units for conditioning of microclimate. Cabs will be mounted on outside rotary rods so they can be moved to a required position.

Rational organization of work and rest is of great importance for the prevention of fatigue and diseases of agricultural workers. In the hot season, daily routine ought to provide for working mainly in the morning and evening hours, reserving the hottest time for rest. During exhausting work (moving, hoeing), short regular breaks are necessary. Special attention has to be devoted to the rational, balanced nourishment of workers with due regard for the energy requirements of the tasks. Drinking regularly during the heat is of great importance. As a rule, workers drink traditional beverages (tea, coffee, fruit juices, infusions, broths and so on) in addition to water. Availability of sufficient amounts of wholesome liquids of high quality is very important.

Availability of comfortable overalls and personal protection equipment (PPE) (respirators, hearing protectors), especially during contact with dust and chemicals, is very important as well.

Medical control of the agricultural workers' health has to be oriented to prevention of common occupational diseases, such as infectious diseases, chemical exposures, injuries, ergonomic problems and so forth. Teaching safe working methods, information about matters of hygiene and sanitation are of great importance.

● HARVESTING OPERATIONS

William E. Field

The gathering in of agricultural crops upon maturity, or the practice of harvesting, signals the end of the production cycle prior to storage and processing. The size and quality of the crop removed from the field, orchard or vineyard represents the most significant measure of a farmer's productivity and success. The value that has been placed on the outcome of the harvest is reflected in the terms used almost universally to measure and compare agricultural productivity, such as kilograms per hectare (kg/ha), bales per hectare, bushels per acre (bu/a) and tons per acre or hectare. From an agronomic perspective, it is actually the inputs that determine the yield; however, it is the harvest that becomes the primary determinant of whether or not there will be

Figure 64.13 • Hand-harvesting millet.

sufficient seed and resources to ensure the sustainability of the farm and those it supports. Because of the significance of harvest and all of its related activities, this part of the agricultural cycle has taken on an almost spiritual role in the lives of farmers throughout the world.

Few agricultural practices illustrate more clearly the scope and diversity of technology- and work-related hazards found in agricultural production than harvesting. Crop harvesting is carried out under a wide variety of conditions, over various types of terrain, utilizing machines from simple to complex that must handle a diversity of crops; it involves considerable physical effort from the farmer (Snyder and Bobick 1995). For these reasons, any attempt to briefly generalize the characteristics or nature of harvest practices and harvest-related hazards is extremely difficult. Small grains (rice, wheat, barley, oats and so on), for example, which dominate much of the planted cropland in the world, represent not only some of the most highly mechanized crops, but in large regions of Africa and Asia are harvested in a manner that would be familiar to farmers 2,500 years ago. The use of hand sickles to harvest a few stalks at a time, hard-packed clay threshing floors and simple threshing devices remain the primary tools of harvest for far too many producers.

The primary hazards associated with the more labour-intensive harvesting practices have changed little with time and are often overshadowed by the perceived increased risks associated with greater mechanization. Long hours of exposure to the elements, the physical demands resulting from lifting heavy loads, repetitive motion and awkward or stooped posture, along with natural hazards such as poisonous insects and snakes, have historically taken, and continue to take, a significant toll (see figure 64.13). Harvesting grain or sugar cane with a sickle or machete, picking fruit or vegetables by hand and manually removing peanuts from the vine are dirty, uncomfortable and exhausting tasks that in many communities frequently are completed by large numbers of children and women. One of the strongest motivating forces that has shaped modern harvesting practices has been the desire to remove the physical drudgery associated with manual harvesting.

Even if the resources were available to mechanize harvesting and reduce its risks (and for many small farmers in many areas of the world, they are not), investments to improve the safety and health aspects of harvesting would likely have smaller returns than would comparable investments to improve housing, water quality or health care. This is especially true if farmers have access to large numbers of unemployed or underemployed workers. High levels of unemployment and limited job opportunities, for example, place large numbers of younger workers at risk of injury during harvest because they are cheaper to use than machines. Even in many countries with highly mechanized agricultural practices, child labour laws frequently exempt children involved in agricultural activities. For example, special provisions of the US Department of Labor child labour laws continue to exempt children under 16 during harvest and allow them to operate agricultural equipment under certain conditions (DOL 1968).

Contrary to a general perception that greater mechanization in agriculture has increased the risks associated with agricultural production, with respect to harvesting, nothing could be further from the truth. Through the introduction of intensive mechanization in major grain- and forage-producing regions, the amount of time required to produce a bushel of grain, for example, has dropped from over an hour to under a minute (Griffin 1973). This accomplishment, though heavily dependent upon fossil fuels, has released tens of millions of people from the drudgery and unsafe working conditions associated with hand harvesting. Mechanization has resulted in not only tremendous increases in productivity and yields, but also the near elimination of the most historically significant harvest-related injuries, such as those involving livestock.

The intensive mechanization of the harvesting process, however, has introduced new hazards, which have required periods of adjustment and in some cases the replacement of machines with improved practices and designs that were either more productive or less hazardous. An example of this technological evolution was experienced with the transition that took place in corn harvesting in North America between the 1930s and 1970s. Up through the 1930s, the corn crop was almost entirely harvested by hand and transported to on-farm storage sites by horse-drawn wagons. The primary cause of harvest-related injuries was related to working with horses (NSC 1942). With the introduction and widespread use of the mechanical, tractor-drawn corn picker in the 1940s, horse- and livestock-related deaths and injuries rapidly declined during the harvest period, and there was a corresponding growth in the number of corn picker-related injuries. This was not because corn pickers were inherently more dangerous, but because the injuries reflected a rapid transition to a new practice that had not been fully refined and that farmers were unfamiliar with. As farmers adjusted to the technology and manufacturers improved the performance of the corn picker, and as more uniform varieties of corn were planted that were better suited to machine harvesting, the number of deaths and injuries quickly declined. In other words, the introduction of the corn picker ultimately resulted in a decline in harvest-related injuries due to exposure to traditional hazards.

With the introduction in the 1960s of the self-propelled combine, which could harvest higher-yielding corn varieties at rates ten or more times faster than the corn picker, corn picker injuries almost disappeared. But, once again, as with the corn picker, the combine introduced a new set of hazards that required a period of adjustment. For example, the ability to gather, cut, separate and clean the grain in the field using one machine changed the handling of grain from a lumpy flow process in the form of ear corn

to shelled corn, which was almost fluid-like. Consequently, in the 1970s, there was a dramatic increase in the number of auger-related injuries, and of engulfments and suffocations in flowing grain that took place in storage structures and grain transport vehicles (Kelley 1996). In addition, there were new categories of injuries being reported that were related to the sheer size and weight of the combine, such as falls from the operator platform and ladders, which can place the operator as much as 4 m off the ground, and operators being crushed beneath the multi-row gathering unit.

The mechanization of the corn harvest directly contributed to one of the most dramatic shifts in rural population ever experienced in North America. The farm population, in less than 75 years after the introduction of hybrid varieties of corn and the mechanical corn picker, went from over 50% to less than 5% of the total population. Through this period of increased productivity and greatly reduced labour demands, the overall exposure to agricultural workplace hazards was substantially reduced, contributing to a drop in reported farm-related deaths from over 14,000 in 1942 to fewer than 900 in 1995 (NSC 1995).

Injuries associated with modern harvesting operations typically relate to tractors, machinery, grain-handling equipment and grain-storage structures. Since the 1950s, tractors have contributed to approximately one-half of all farm-related fatalities, with overturns being the single most important contributing factor. The utilization of rollover protective structures (ROPS) has proven to be the single most important intervention strategy in reducing the number of tractor-related fatalities (Deere & Co. 1994). Other design features that improved the safety and health of tractor operators included wider wheel bases and designs that lowered the centre of gravity to improve stability, all-weather operator enclosures to reduce exposure to the elements and dust, ergonomically designed seating and controls and reduced noise levels.

The problem of tractor-related injuries, however, remains significant and is a growing concern in areas that are being rapidly mechanized, such as China and India. In many areas of the world it is more likely to see the tractor being used as a vehicle of highway transport or a stationary power source than being used in the field to produce crops, as it was designed to do. In these areas, tractors are typically introduced with minimal operator training and are used widely as a means of transporting multiple passengers, another use for which the tractor was not designed. The result has been that runovers of extra riders who have fallen from the tractors during operation has become the second leading cause of tractor-related fatalities. If the trend towards greater utilization of ROPS continues, runovers may eventually become the leading cause of tractor-related fatalities worldwide.

Though used fewer hours during the year than tractors, harvesting equipment such as combines are involved in about twice as many injuries per 1,000 machines (Etherton et al. 1991). These injuries often take place during servicing, repairing or adjusting the machine when the power to machine components is still engaged (NSC 1986). Recent design changes have been made to incorporate more passive and active operator warnings and interlocks, such as safety switches in the operator seat to prevent machine operation when no one is in the seat, and to reduce the number of maintenance points to reduce operator exposure to operating machinery. Many of these design concepts, however, remain voluntary, are frequently by-passed by the operator and are not universally found on all harvesting machines.

Hay and forage harvesting equipment exposes workers to hazards similar to those found on combines. This equipment contains components that cut, crush, grind, chop and blow crop material at high speed, leaving little room for human error. As with grain harvesting, hay and forage harvesting must take place in a timely fashion in order to prevent damage to the crop from the elements. This added stress to complete tasks rapidly, in conjunction with machine hazards, frequently leads to injuries (Murphy and Williams 1983).

Traditionally, the hay baler has been identified as a frequent source of serious injuries. These machines are used under some of the most harsh conditions found in any type of harvesting. High temperature, rough terrain, dusty conditions and the need for frequent adjustments contribute to a high rate of injury. The conversion to large packages or bales of hay and mechanical handling systems has improved safety with a few exceptions, as was the case with the introduction of the early designs of the round baler. The aggressive compression rolls on the front of these machines resulted in a large number of hand and arm amputations. This design was later replaced with a less aggressive gathering unit, which nearly eliminated the problem.

Fire is a potential problem for many types of harvesting operations. Crops that are required to be dried to less than 15% moisture content for proper storage make excellent fuel if ignited. Combines and cotton harvesters are especially vulnerable to fires during field operation. Design features such as the use of diesel engines and protected electrical systems, proper equipment maintenance and operator access to fire extinguishers have been shown to reduce the risk of fire-related damage or injury (Shutske et al. 1991).

Noise and dust are two other hazards that are typically intrinsic to harvesting operations. Both pose serious long-term health risks to the operator of harvesting equipment. The inclusion of environmentally controlled operator enclosures in the design of modern harvesting equipment has done much to reduce operator exposure to excessive noise pressures and dust levels. However, most farmers have yet to benefit from this safety feature. The use of PPE such as ear plugs and disposable dust masks provides an alternative, but less effective, means of protection from these hazards.

As harvesting operations around the world become increasingly mechanized, there will be a continuing shift from environmental-, animal- and hand tool-related injuries to those caused by machines. Drawing upon the experiences of farmers and manufacturers of harvesting equipment who have completed this transition should prove useful in reducing the adjustment period and preventing injuries caused by lack of familiarity and poor design. The experience of farmers with even the most highly mechanized harvesting operations, however, suggests that the injury problem will not be totally eliminated. Contributions of operator error and machine design will continue to play a significant role in injury causation. But there is no question that in addition to greater productivity, the process of mechanization has significantly reduced the risks associated with harvesting.

● STORING AND TRANSPORTATION OPERATIONS

Thomas L. Bean

Storing

The growing and gathering of crops and production of livestock has long been recognized as one of the world's oldest and most important occupations. Farming and ranching today is as diverse as the many crops, fibres and livestock which are produced. At one extreme, the farming unit may consist of a single family that cultivates the soil and plants and harvests the crop, all by hand over a limited area. The opposite extreme includes large corporate farms spanning vast areas that are highly mechanized, using

sophisticated machinery, equipment and facilities. The same is true for the storage of food and fibre. Storage of agricultural products may be as rudimentary as simple huts and hand-dug pits, and as complex as towering silos, bunkers, bins and refrigerated units.

Hazards and their prevention
Agricultural products such as grains, hays, fruit, nuts, vegetables and plant fibre are often stored for later human and livestock consumption or sale to the general populace or to manufacturers. The storage of agricultural products prior to shipment to market may occur in a variety of structures—pits, bunkers, bins, silos, refrigerated units, carts, wagons, barns and railroad cars, to mention a few. Despite the diversity of products being stored and of storage facilities, there are hazards which are common to the storage process:

Falls and falling objects
Falls may occur from heights or at the same level. In the case of bins, silos, barns and other storage structures, falls from heights most often occur from and in storage structures. Most often the cause is unguarded roofs, floor openings, stairways, lofts and shafts, and climbing ladders or standing on raised work areas such as an unprotected platform. Falls from height may also result from climbing on or off the transportation unit (e.g., wagons, carts and tractors). Falls from the same level occur from slippery surfaces, tripping over objects or being pushed by a moving object. Protection against falls includes such measures as:

- provision of safety belts, harnesses, lifelines and safety boots
- installation of guard rails, toeboards, cat-ladders or crawling boards on sloped roofs
- guarded floor openings, lofts and shafts
- use of the standard rise and run of stairways, provision of handrails on both sides, and application non-skid strips where necessary
- maintaining floors in good condition, free from uneven surfaces, holes and accumulations of waste or slippery substances
- provision of handholds on permanent ladders, guard platforms and landings
- maintaining extension or step ladders in good condition and training employees on their use.

Agricultural products may be stored loose in a facility or bundled, bagged, crated or bailed. Loose storage is often associated with grains such as wheat, corn or soybeans. Bundled, bagged, crated or bailed products include hay, straw, vegetables, grains and feeds. Falls of materials occur in all types of storage. Collapse of unsecured stacked foodstuffs, overhead materials and piles of goods are often causes of injury. Employees should be trained in the correct stacking of goods to prevent their collapse. Employers and managers must monitor the workplace for compliance.

Confined spaces
Agricultural products may be stored in two types of facilities—those that contain enough oxygen to sustain life, such as barns, open carts and wagons, and those that do not, such as some silos, tanks and refrigeration units. The latter are confined spaces, and should be treated with appropriate precautions. The oxygen level should be monitored prior to entry and a supplied air or self-contained breathing unit used if necessary; someone else should be on hand. Suffocation may also occur in either type of facility if the goods which it contains have the characteristics of a fluid. This is commonly associated with grains and similar foodstuffs. The worker dies as a result of drowning. In grain bins it is a common practice for an agricultural worker to enter the bin due to difficulties in loading or unloading, often caused by a

condition of the grain resulting in bridging. Workers attempting to alleviate the situation by unbridging the grain may voluntarily walk on the bridged grain. They may fall in and be covered with the grain or be sucked under if the loading or unloading equipment is operational. Bridging also may occur to the sides of such structures, in which case a worker may enter to knock down the material sticking to the sides and become engulfed when the material fails. A lockout/tagout system and fall protection such as a safety belt and rope are essential if workers are to enter this type of structure. Children's safety is of special concern. Often inquisitive, playful and wanting to do adult chores, they are attracted to such structures, and the results are all-too-often fatal.

Fruit and vegetables are often kept in cold storage prior to shipping to market. As indicated in the above paragraph, depending on the type of unit, cold storage may be considered a confined space and should be monitored for oxygen content. Other hazards include frostbite and cold-induced injury or death from body temperature loss following prolonged exposure to cold. Personal protective clothing should be worn appropriate to the temperature within the cold-storage unit.

Gases and poisons

Depending on the moisture content of the product when it is placed in storage and atmospheric and other conditions, feeds, grains and fibres may produce dangerous gases. Such gases include carbon monoxide (CO), carbon dioxide (CO_2) and oxides of nitrogen (NO_x), some of which may cause death in a matter of minutes. This is also especially important if the goods are stored in a facility in which nonlethal gases may be allowed to accumulate to dangerous levels, displacing oxygen. If the potential for gas production exists, then monitoring for gases should be done. In addition, foods and feeds may have been sprayed or treated with a pesticide during the growing period to kill weeds, insects or disease, or during the storage process to reduce spoilage or mould, spore or insect damage. This may add to the hazards of gas production, inhalation of dusts and handling of the product. Special care should be taken by workers to wear PPE depending on the nature and longevity of the treatment, the product used and the label directions.

Machine hazards

Storage facilities may contain a variety of machinery for conveying the product. These range from belt and roller conveyors to blowers, augers, slides and other such product-handling devices, each with its own power source. Hazards and suitable precautions include:

- *Nip points formed by belts, pulleys and gears.* Agricultural workers should be protected from nip and shear points by an appropriate guarding around the point of potential contact.
- *Protruding belt fasteners, setscrews, keys, bolts and grooves.* Protruding setscrews, keys or bolts on revolving shafts should be countersunk, encased or shrouded. Belt fasteners should be inspected and repaired.
- *Shear points caused by flywheel arms, augers and their housing, pulley spokes, crank and lever mechanisms.* These should be guarded or enclosed.
- *Contact with moving transmission or electrical elements.* These should be guarded or enclosed.
- *Inadvertent starting of machinery or equipment.* A system for locking out or tagging out equipment prior to maintenance or repair should be implemented and enforced.
- *Loose clothing or hair getting wound on or caught by shafts.* Clothing that is loose, frayed or that has hanging threads should never be worn. Other personal protective apparel and shoes appropriate to the job task should be worn.

- *Excessive noise.* Noise exposure should be monitored and administrative, engineering and/or personal protective controls should be taken if necessary.

Employees should be trained and aware of the hazards, basic safety rules and safe working methods.

Health outcomes

Agricultural workers who are involved in the handling of agricultural products for storage are at risk for respiratory disorders. Exposures to a variety of dusts, gases, chemicals, silica, fungal spores and endotoxins can result in damage to the lungs. Recent studies link lung disorders caused by these substances to workers who handle grain, cotton, flax, hemp, hay and tobacco. Therefore the populations at risk are worldwide. Agricultural lung disorders have many common names, some of which include: occupational asthma, farmer's lung, green tobacco sickness, brown lung, organic dust toxic syndrome, silo filler's or unloader's disease, bronchitis and airway obstruction. Symptoms may first manifest themselves as being characteristic of influenza (chills, fever, coughing, headaches, myalgias and breathing difficulty). This is especially true for organic dusts. Prevention of lung dysfunction should include an assessment of the worker's environment, health promotion programmes targeted at primary prevention and the use of personal protective respirators and other protective devices based on the environmental assessment.

Transportation Operations

Although it may seem simple, the transportation of goods to market is often as complex and hazardous as growing and storing the crop. The transportation of products to market is as diversified as the types of farming operations. Transportation may range from goods being carried by humans and livestock, to being transported by simple mechanical devices such as bicycles and animal-drawn carts, being hauled by complex mechanical equipment such as large carts and wagons pulled by tractors, to the use of commercial transportation systems, which include large trucks, buses, trains and airplanes. As the world's population increases and urban areas grow, road travel of agricultural equipment and implements of husbandry has increased. In the US, according to the National Safety Council (NSC), 8,000 farm tractors and other agricultural vehicles were involved in highway accidents in 1992 (NSC 1993). Many farming operations are consolidating and expanding by acquiring or renting a number of smaller farms which are typically scattered and not adjoining. A 1991 study in Ohio showed that 79% of the farms surveyed operated in multiple locations (Bean and Lawrence 1992).

Hazards and their prevention

Although each of the modes of transportation mentioned above will have its own unique hazards, it is the intermix of civilian traffic with agricultural transport machinery and equipment that is of major concern. The increase in road travel of agricultural equipment has resulted in a greater number of collisions between motor vehicles and slower moving agricultural equipment. Farm equipment and implements of husbandry may be wider than the width of the road. Due to pressure of planting at the right time to assure a crop or harvesting and getting the crop to a market or storage location as quickly as possible, agricultural machinery must often travel on the·roadways during periods of darkness, early morning or evening. An in-depth study of all 50 states' codes in the United States revealed that the lighting and marking requirements vary greatly from state to state. This diversity in requirements does not communicate a consistent message to motor vehicle drivers (Eicher 1993). Faster speeds of other vehicles combined with inadequate lighting or marking of agricultural equipment is often a deadly combination. A recent study in the United States found that the common accident types are rear end, sideswipe-meeting, sideswipe-passing, angle, head-on, backing and other. In 20% of the 803 two-vehicle crashes studied, the farm vehicle was struck from an angle. In 28% of the crashes, the farm vehicle was sideswiped (15% meeting and 13% passing). Twenty-two per cent of the accidents consisted of rear-end (15%), head-on (4%) and backing (3%) collisions. The remaining 25% were crashes which were caused by something other than a moving vehicle (i.e., a parked vehicle, pedestrian, animal and so on) (Glascock et al. 1993).

Livestock are used in many parts of the world as the "horse-power" to transport agricultural products. Although beasts of burden are generally reliable, most are colourblind, have territorial and maternal instincts, react independently and unexpectedly, and are of great strength. Such animals have caused vehicle crashes. Falls from agricultural machinery and implements of husbandry are common.

The following general safety principles apply to transportation operations:

- Local traffic rules, regulations or laws should be learned and obeyed.
- No riders or passengers other than those that are necessary to accomplish the transport and unloading duties should be permitted.
- Vehicles should stay as close to the shoulder of the road as road conditions will allow.
- Passing other vehicles (moving or parked) and pedestrians must be done with caution.
- Broken-down vehicles should be moved off the road if possible.
- All marking and lighting on machinery and equipment should be maintained and clean.
- Driving should never be done under the influence of alcohol or drugs.

Laws and regulations may dictate the state of acceptable lighting and marking. However, many such regulations only describe the minimal acceptable standards. Unless such regulations specifically prohibit retrofitting and adding additional lighting and marking, farmers should consider adding such devices. It is important that such lighting and marking devices be installed not only on self-propelled implements but also on pieces of equipment that they may be pulling or trailing.

Lights are especially critical for dusk, dawn and night-time movement of agricultural equipment. If the agricultural vehicle has a power source, consideration should be given to having, at a minimum: two headlights, two tail-lights, two turn signals and two brake lights.

Tail-lights, turn signals and brake lights may be incorporated into single units or can be attached as separate entities. Standards for such devices may be found through standard-setting organizations such as the American Society of Agricultural Engineers (ASAE), the American National Standards Institute (ANSI), the European Committee for Standardization (CEN) and the International Organization for Standardization (ISO).

If the agricultural vehicle does not have a power source, battery-powered lights, although not as effective, may be used. Many such lights are commercially available in a variety of types (flood, blinking, rotating and strobe) and sizes. If it is impossible to obtain these devices, then reflectors, flags and other alternative materials discussed below may be used.

Many new retroreflective fluorescent materials are available today to aid in marking agricultural vehicles for enhanced visibility. They are manufactured in patches or strips in a variety of colours. Local regulations should be consulted for acceptable colours or colour combinations.

Fluorescent materials provide excellent daytime visibility by relying on solar radiation for their light-emitting properties. A complex photochemical reaction takes place when the fluorescent pigments absorb non-visible solar radiation and re-emit the energy as a longer wavelength of light. In a sense, fluorescent materials appear to "glow" in the daytime and appear brighter than the conventional colours in the same light conditions. The primary disadvantage of fluorescent materials is their deterioration with prolonged exposure to solar radiation.

Reflection is an element of sight. Wavelengths of light strike an object and are either absorbed or bounced back in all directions (diffused reflection) or at an angle exactly opposite to the angle at which the light struck the object (specular reflection). Retroreflectivity is very similar to specular reflection; however, the light is reflected directly back toward the light source. There are three primary forms of retroreflective materials, each having a different degree of retroreflectivity based on how they were manufactured. They are presented here in increasing order of retroreflectivity: enclosed lens (often called engineering grade or Type ID), encapsulated lens (high intensity) and cube corner (diamond grade, prismatic, DOT C2 or Type IIIB). These retroreflective materials are excellent for night-time visual identification. These materials are also of great assistance in defining the extremities of agricultural implements. In this application, strips of retroreflective and fluorescent material across the width of the machinery, front and back, best communicate to drivers of other, nonagricultural vehicles the actual width of the equipment.

The distinctive red triangle with a yellow-orange centre is used in the United States, Canada and many other parts of the world to designate a class of vehicles as "slow moving". This means the vehicle travels less than 40 km per hour on the roadway. Typically, other vehicles travel much faster, and the difference in speed may result in a misjudgement on the part of the faster vehicle driver, affecting the driver's ability to stop in time to avoid an accident. This emblem or an acceptable substitute should always be used.

Health outcomes

Agricultural workers who are involved in the transportation of agricultural products may be at risk for respiratory disorders. Exposures to a variety of dusts, chemicals, silica, fungal spores and endotoxins may result in damage to the lungs. This is somewhat dependent on whether the transport vehicle has an enclosed cab and whether the operator engages in the loading and unloading process. If the transport vehicle has been used in the process of pesticide application, pesticides could be present and trapped inside the cab unless it has an air filtration system. Nevertheless, symptoms may first manifest themselves as being characteristic of influenza. This is especially true for organic dusts. Prevention of lung dysfunction should include an assessment of the worker's environment, health promotion programmes targeted at primary prevention and the use of personal protective masks, respirators and other protective devices.

MANUAL OPERATIONS IN FARMING

Pranab Kumar Nag

Agricultural methods and practices vary across national boundaries:

- *industrial* agriculture—industrialized countries of the West (temperate climate) and specialized sectors of the tropical countries
- *green revolution* agriculture—well endowed areas in the tropics, primarily irrigated plains and deltas of Asia, Latin America and North Africa

Table 64.5 • Categorization of farm activities.

Work severity	Farm operations			
	Seed bed preparation	Sowing	Weeding and intercultivation	Harvesting
Light work	Laddering (two workers)	Broadcasting seeds/fertilizer, scaring birds, ridging	Fertilizer broadcasting	Grain cleaning, grading, spreading vegetables (squatting), pounding grain (helper), winnowing (sitting)
Moderately heavy work	Walking behind animal-drawn implement, levelling soil surface with wooden rake, laddering (one worker), digging soil with spade, bush cutting	Manual uprooting of seedlings (squatting and bent posture), transplanting seedlings (bent posture), walking on a puddled field	Manual weeding with sickle and hand hoe (squatting and bent posture), channel irrigation, knapsack spraying of pesticides, weeder operation in wet and dry soil	Cutting crops, harvesting paddy, wheat (squatting and bent posture), plucking vegetables, manual winnowing (sitting and standing), cutting sugarcane, pedal-thresher helper, carrying load (20-35 kg)
Heavy work	Ploughing, water lifting (swing busket), hoeing dry soil, bund trimming wet soil, spade work, disc harrowing		Weeder operation in dry soil	Grain threshing by beating, pounding grain
Extremely heavy work	Bund trimming dry soil	Germinating seeder operation in puddled field		Pedal threshing, carrying load on head or yoke (60–80 kg)

Source: Based on data from Nag, Sebastian and Marlankar 1980; Nag and Chatterjee 1981.

- *resource-poor* agriculture—hinterlands, dry lands, forests, mountains and hills, near deserts and swamps. About 1 billion people in Asia, 300 million in sub-Saharan Africa and 100 million in Latin America are dependent on this form of agriculture. Women comprise a large proportion of subsistence farmers—nearly 80% of the food for sub-Saharan Africa, 50 to 60% of Asia's food, 46% of the Caribbean's food, 31% of North Africa and the Middle East's food and 30% of Latin America's food is produced by women (Dankelman and Davidson 1988).

With distinct agro-climatic features, the farm crops are grouped as follows:

- *Field* crops (cereals, oilseeds, fibre, sugar and fodder crops) are rain-fed or cultivated through controlled irrigation.
- *Upland* and *semi-upland* cultivation (wheat, groundnuts, cotton and so on) are practised where irrigation or rain water is not abundantly available.
- *Wetland* cultivation (rice crops) is practised where the land is ploughed and puddled with 5 to 6 cm of standing water and seedlings are transplanted.
- *Horticulture* crops are fruit, vegetable and flower crops.
- *Plantation* or *perennial* crops include coconut, rubber, coffee, tea and so on.
- *Pastures* are anything nature grows without human intervention.

Farming Operations, Hand Tools and Machinery

Farming in the tropical countries is labour intensive. The ratio of rural population to arable land in Asia is twice as great as in Africa and three times that of Latin America. It is estimated that human effort provides more than 70% of the energy required for crop production tasks (FAO 1987). Improvement in the existing tools, equipment and methods of work has significant effects in minimizing human strain and fatigue and increasing farm productivity. For field crops, farm activities may be categorized based on the physiological demand of work with reference to an individual's maximal working capacity (see table 64.5).

Seed-bed preparation

A suitable seed-bed is one that is mellow yet compact and free from vegetation that would interfere with seeding. Seed-bed preparation involves use of different types of hand tools, shallow chisel desi or a mould board plough pulled by draft animals (figure 64.14) or tractor implements for ploughing, harrowing and so on. About 0.4 hectare (ha) of land can be tilled by a bullock-drawn plough in a day, and a pair of bullocks can provide power to the extent of 1 horsepower (hp).

In using animal-drawn equipment, the worker acts as a controller of animals and guides the implement with a handle. In most cases, the operator walks behind the implement or sits on the equipment (e.g., disc harrows and puddlers). The operation of animal-drawn implements involves considerable human energy expenditure. For a 15 cm plough, a person may walk about 67 km to cover a 1-hectare area. At a walking speed of 1.5 km/h, the human energy expenditure amounts to 21 kJ/min (about 5.6 ×

Figure 64.14 • Bullock-drawn shallow chisel desi plough.

Pranab Kumar Nag

10^4 kJ per ha). A handle on implements that is too long or too short results in physical discomfort. Gite (1991) and Gite and Yadav (1990) suggested that the optimum handle height of an implement may be adjusted between 64 and 84 cm (1.0 to 1.2 times the metacarpal III height of the operator).

Hand tools (spade, shovel, hoe and so on) are used for digging and loosening the soil. To minimize drudgery in shovelling work, Freivalds (1984) deduced the optimum rate of work (i.e., shovelling rate) (18 to 21 scoops/minute), shovel load (5 to 7 kg for 15 to 20 scoops/minute, and 8 kg for 6 to 8 scoops/minute), throw distance (1.2 m) and throw height (1 to 1.3 m). Recommendations also include a shovel lift angle of about 32°, a long tool handle, a large, square-pointed blade for shovelling, a round-pointed blade for digging and hollow back construction to reduce shovel weight.

Nag and Pradhan (1992) suggested low-lift and high-lift hoeing tasks (see figure 64.15), based on physiological and biomechanical studies. As a general guide, the method of work and the hoe design are the deciding factors in performance efficiency of hoeing tasks (Pradhan et al. 1986). The mode of striking the blade to the ground determines the angle at which it penetrates the soil. For low-lift work, the work output was optimized at 53 strokes/minute, with a land area dug of 1.34 m²/minute, and a work-rest ratio of 10:7. For high-lift work, the optimal conditions were 21 strokes per minute and 0.33 m²/minute of land dug. The shape of the blade—rectangular, trapezoidal, triangular or circular—depends upon the purpose and preference of the local users. For different modes of hoeing, the recommended design dimensions are: weight 2 kg, angle between blade and handle 65 to 70°, handle length 70 to 75 cm, blade length 25 to 30 cm, blade width 22 to 24 cm and handle diameter 3 to 4 cm.

Sowing/planting and fertilizer application

The sowing of seeds and planting of seedlings involve the use of planters, seeders, drills and the manual broadcasting of seeds. About 8% of total person-hours are required for broadcasting of seeds and uprooting and transplanting of seedlings.

- In the *broadcasting* of seeds/fertilizer by hand, manually operated broadcasters allow uniform distribution with minimum drudgery.
- *Seeding behind a plough* consists of sowing of seeds in a furrow opened by a wooden plough.
- In *drilling*, seeds are placed in the soil by a seed drill or seed-cum-fertilizer drill. The push/pull force required for a worker to operate the drill (manual or animal-drawn units mounted on wheels) is an important design consideration.
- *Dibbling* is the placing of seeds by hand or with a small implement (a *dibbler*), at an average spacing of 15 × 15 cm or 25 × 25 cm. Abrasion of fingers and bodily discomfort due to bent and squat postures are common complaints.
- In *planting*, sugar cane sets are planted at 30 cm length in a furrow; potato seed tubers are planted flat and ridges are made.
- About 1/3 of the world's rice is grown by the *transplanting* system. This is also done for tobacco and some vegetable crops. Usually, germinating seeds are broadcasted densely on a puddled field. The seedlings are uprooted and transplanted to a puddled field by hand or with manual or power-operated transplanters. The operator of a manually operated transplanter walks behind the unit to operate the handle mechanism to pick and transplant the seedlings.

For manual transplanting, the workers are required to be immersed knee deep in mud. The squatting posture used for planting on dry land, with one or two legs flexed at the knee, cannot be adopted in a watered field. About 85 person-hours are required to transplant seedlings for each hectare of land. The awkward posture and static load exert strain on the cardiovascular system and

Figure 64.15 • Hoeing tasks in bund trimming in paddy field.

Pranab Kumar Nag

cause low-back pain (Nag and Dutt 1980). Manually operated seeders produce higher work output (i.e., a seeder is about eight times more efficient than transplanting by hand). However, maintaining the balance of the machine (see figure 64.16) in a puddled field requires about 2.5 times more energy than manual transplanting.

Figure 64.16 • Operating an improved germinated seeder.

Pranab Kumar Nag

Figure 64.17 • Lifting water from irrigation channel using a swing basket.

Pranab Krumar Nag

Plant protection

Fertilizer, pesticide, herbicide and other chemical applicators are operated by pressure through nozzles or by centrifugal force. Large-scale spraying is based on the hydraulic nozzle spray atomizer, either manually operated or using tractor-mounted equipment. Knapsack sprayers are scaled-down models of vehicle-mounted sprayers (Bull 1982).

- A *compression knapsack sprayer* consists of a tank, a pump and a rod with nozzle and hose.
- A *lever-operated knapsack sprayer* (10 to 20 l) has an operating lever.
- A *power knapsack sprayer* consists of a chemical tank of about 10-litre capacity and an air-cooled engine of 1 to 3 hp. The sprayer and engine unit is mounted on a frame and carried on the operator's back.
- A *hand-operated bucket sprayer* and *foot-operated sprayer* require two persons for operating the pump and spraying. A *rocking sprayer* is operated by the rocking (forward and backward) movement of the handle lever.

When carried on the shoulder for prolonged periods, the vibrations of knapsack sprayers/chemical applicators have detrimental effects on the human body. Spraying using a knapsack sprayer results in potential skin exposure (the legs experience 61% of the total contamination, the hands 33%, the torso 3%, the head 2%, and the arms 1%) (Bonsall 1985). Personal protective clothing (including gloves and boots) can reduce the dermal contamination of pesticides (Forget 1991, 1992). The work is quite strenuous, due to carrying of the load on the back as well as continuous operation of the sprayer handle (20 to 30 strokes/minute); in addition, there is the thermoregulatory load due to protective garments. The weight and height of the sprayer, shape of sprayer tank, mounting system and force required to operate the pump are important ergonomic aspects.

Irrigation

Irrigation is a prerequisite for intensive cropping in arid and semi-arid regions. Since time immemorial, various indigenous devices have been used for lifting water. Lifting water by different manual methods is physically strenuous. In spite of the availability of water pump sets (electrical or engine powered), manually operated devices are widely used (e.g., swing baskets, counterpoise water lifts, water wheels, chain and washer pumps, reciprocating pumps).

- A *swing basket* is used for lifting water from an irrigation channel (see figure 64.17). The capacity of the basket is about 4 to 6 l and the frequency of operation is about 15 to 20 swings/minute. Two operators work at right angles to the direction of basket motion. The work demands heavy physical activity, with adoption of awkward body movements and posture.
- A *counterpoise water lift* consists of a container attached to the end of a horizontal lever which is supported on a vertical pole. The worker exerts force on the counterweight to operate the device.
- *Reciprocating pumps* (piston-cylinder type hand pumps) are operated either by hand in reciprocating mode or by pedalling in rotary mode.

Weeding and intercultivation

Undesirable plants and weeds cause losses by impairing crop yields and quality, harbouring plant pests and increasing irrigation cost. Reduction in yield varies from 10 to 60% depending upon the thickness of growth and the kind of weeds. About 15% of human labour is spent in removing weeds during the cultivating season. Women typically comprise a large portion of the workforce engaged in weeding. In a typical situation, a worker spends about 190 to 220 hours weeding one hectare of land by hand or hand hoe. Spades are also used for weeding and intercultivation.

Of several methods (e.g., mechanical, chemical, biological, cultural), mechanical weeding, either by pulling out the weeds by hand or with hand tools like the hand hoe and simple weeders, is useful in both dry and wet land (Nag and Dutt 1979; Gite and Yadav 1990). In dry land, the workers squat on the ground with one or two legs flexed at the knee and remove weeds using a sickle or hand hoe. In watered land, the workers adopt a bent forward

Figure 64.18 • Harvesting wheat crop using a sickle.

Pranab Krumar Nag

Figure 64.19 • Manual harvesting of potatoes with a hand hoe.

stooping posture to remove weeds manually or with the help of weeders.

The physiological demand in using weeders (e.g., blade and rake, projection finger, double sweep type weeders) is relatively higher than in manual weeding. However, the efficiency of work in terms of area covered is significantly better with the weeders than with manual weeding. The energy demand in manual weeding jobs is only about 27% of one's working capacity, whereas for different weeders, the energy demand goes up to 56%. However, the strain is relatively less in the case of wheel hoe-type weeders, with which it takes about 110 to 140 person-hours to cover one hectare. A wheel hoe-type weeder (push/pull) consists of one or two wheels, a blade, a frame and a handle. A force (push or pull) of about 5 to 20 kilograms of force (1 kgf = 9.81 Newtons) is required, with a frequency of about 20 to 40 strokes per minute. The technical specifications of the wheel hoe-type weeders, however, need to be standardized for better operation.

Harvesting

In rice and wheat crops, harvesting requires 8 to 10% of the total person-hours used in crop production. Despite rapid mechanization in harvesting, large-scale dependence on manual methods (see figure 64.18) will continue for years to come. Hand tools (sickle, scythe and so on) are used in manual harvesting. The scythe is commonly used in some parts of the world, because of its large area of coverage. However, it requires more energy than harvesting with a sickle.

The popularity of the sickle is due to its simplicity in construction and operation. A sickle is a curved blade, with a smooth or serrated edge, attached to a wooden handle. Sickle design varies from region to region, and there is a difference in cardiorespiratory load with different types of sickles. The output varies from

110 to 165 m²/hour, values corresponding to 90 and 60 person-hours per hectare of land. Awkward work postures may lead to long-term clinical complications relating to the back and to the joints of the limbs. Harvesting in a bent posture has the advantage of mobility on both dry and wet land, and it is about 16% faster than squatting; however, a bent posture is 18% more energy demanding than squatting (Nag et al. 1988).

Harvesting accidents, lacerations and incised wounds are common in paddy, wheat and cane sugar fields. The hand tools are primarily designed for right-handed persons, but are often used by left-handed users, who are unaware of the possible safety implications. The important factors in a sickle design are the blade geometry, blade serration, handle shape and size. Based on an ergonomics study, suggested design dimensions of a sickle are: weight, 200 g; total length, 33 cm; handle length, 11 cm; handle diameter, 3 cm; radius of blade curvature, 15 cm; blade concavity, 5 cm. For a serrated sickle: tooth pitch, 0.2 cm; tooth angle, 60°; and ratio of the length of cutting surface to chord length, 1.2. Since the workers perform activities under extreme climatic conditions, health and safety issues are critically important in tropical farming. The cardiorespiratory strain accumulates over long hours of work. Extreme climatic conditions and heat disorders place added stress on the worker and diminish working capacity.

Harvesting machines include mowers, choppers, balers and so on. Power-operated or animal-drawn reapers are also used for harvesting field crops. Combine harvesters (self-propelled or tractor operated) are useful where intensive cultivation is practised and the labour shortage is acute.

Harvesting of sorghum is done by cutting the ear-head and then cutting the plant, or vice versa. The cotton crop is collected

Figure 64.20 • Threshing paddy pinnacle by beating.

Figure 64.21 • A pedal thresher in operation.

Pranab Krumar Nag

Self-propelled combines are a combination of a harvester and a thresher unit for grain crops.

Fatal accidents have been reported in grain threshing using power threshers and fodder cutters. The incidence of moderate to severe thresher injuries was 13.1 per thousand threshers (Mohan and Patel 1992). Hands and feet can be injured by the rotor. The position of the feeding chute can result in awkward postures when feeding the crop into the thresher. The belt powering the thresher is also a common cause of injuries. With fodder cutters, the operators can sustain injury while feeding the fodder into the moving blades. Children sustain injury when playing with the machines.

The workers often stand on unstable platforms. In the event of a jerk or loss of balance, the torso weight pushes the hands into the threshing drum/fodder cutter. The thresher must be designed so that the feeding chute is at elbow level and the operators stand on a stable platform. The design of the fodder cutter may be improved for safety as follows (Mohan and Patel 1992):

- a warning roller placed on the chute before the feed rollers
- a locking pin to fix the flywheel when the cutter is not in use
- gear cover and blade guards to push limbs away and prevent clothes from getting entangled.

For threshing groundnuts, the traditional practice is to hold the plants by one hand and strike them against a rod or grill. For threshing maize, tubular maize shellers are used. The worker holds the equipment in his or her palm and inserts and rotates cobs through the equipment to separate the maize grains from the cobs. Output with this equipment is about 25 kg/hour. Hand-operated rotary type maize shellers have higher work output, about 50 to 120 kg/hour. The length of the handle, the force required to operate it and the speed of operation are the important considerations in hand-operated rotary maize shellers.

Winnowing

Winnowing is a process to separate grains from chaff by blowing air, using a hand fan or a pedal- or motor-driven fan. In manual methods (see figure 64.22), the whole content is thrown up in the air, and the grain and chaff get separated out by differential momentum. A mechanical winnower may, with considerable human exertion, be hand or pedal operated.

Other post-harvest operations include cleaning and grading of grains, shelling, decortication, hulling, peeling, slicing, fibre

in 3 to 5 pickings by hand as the ball matures. Harvesting of potatoes and sugar beets is done manually (see figure 64.19) or by using a blade harrow or digger, which may be animal or tractor powered. In the case of groundnuts, the vines are either pulled manually or removed using diggers, and the pods separated.

Threshing

Threshing includes separation of grains from the earheads. Age-old manual methods of threshing of grain from the paddy pinnacle are: rubbing the earheads with one's feet, beating of the harvested crop on a plank, animal treading and so on. Threshing is classified as a moderately heavy task (Nag and Dutt 1980). In manual threshing by beating, (see figure 64.20) one separates about 1.6 to 1.8 kg of grain and 1.8 to 2.1 kg of straw per minute from medium sized paddy/wheat plants.

Mechanical threshers carry out threshing and winnowing operations simultaneously. The pedal thresher (oscillating or rotary mode) increases the output to 2.3 to 2.6 kg of grain (paddy/wheat) and 3.1 to 3.6 kg of straw per min. Pedal threshing (see figure 64.21) is a more strenuous activity than manual threshing by beating. The pedalling and holding of paddy plants on the rolling drum result in high muscular strains. Ergonomic improvements in the pedal thresher may allow a rhythmic pattern of leg work in alternate sitting and standing postures and minimize postural strains. The optimal momentum of the thresher may be reached at about 8 kg weight of the rolling drum.

Power threshers are gradually being introduced in green revolution areas. Essentially they consist of a prime mover, a threshing unit, a winnowing unit, a feeding unit and a outlet for clean grain.

Figure 64.22 • Manual winnowing.

Pranab Krumar Nag

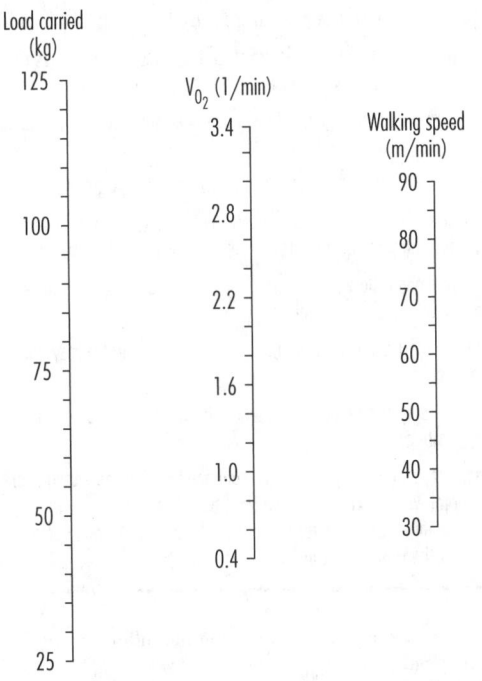

Figure 64.23 • A nomogram to optimize load to be carried on head/yoke, with reference to walking speed and oxygen demand of work.

extraction and so on. Different types of manually operated equipment are used in post-harvest operations (e.g., potato peelers and slicers, coconut dehuskers). *Decortication* involves breaking of shells and removal of seeds (e.g., groundnuts, castor beans). A groundnut decorticator separates kernels from pods. Manual decortication has a very low output (about 2 kg of pod shelling per person-hour). Workers complain of bodily discomfort due to the continuous sitting or squatting posture. Oscillating or rotary-mode decorticators have an output of about 40 to 60 kg of pods per hour. *Shelling* and *hulling* refer to separation of seed coat or husk from the inner portion of the grain (e.g., paddy, soybean). Traditional rice hullers are manually (hand or foot) operated and are widely used in rural Asia. The maximum force which can be exerted by hand or foot determines the size and other characteristics of the device. Nowadays, motorized rice mills are used for hulling. In some grains, such as pigeonpea, the seed coat or husk is tightly attached. Removal of the husk in such cases is called *dehusking*.

For different hand tools and manually operated implements, the grip size and the force exerted on the handles are important considerations. In the case of shears, the force which can be applied by two hands is important. Although most injuries related to hand tools are classified as minor, their consequences are often painful and disabling because of delayed treatment. Design changes in hand tools should be limited to those that can be easily fabricated by village artisans. Safety aspects need to be given due consideration in powered equipment. Safety shoes and gloves available at present are far too expensive and are not suitable for farmers in the tropics.

Manual material-handling tasks

Most agricultural activities involve manual material-handling tasks (e.g., lifting, lowering, pulling, pushing and carrying of heavy loads), resulting in musculoskeletal strains, falls, spinal injuries and

so on. The fall injury rate increases dramatically when the fall height is more than 2 m; impact forces are reduced manyfold if the victim falls on soft earth, hay or sand.

In rural areas, loads weighing 50 to 100 kg might be carried several miles on a daily basis (Sen and Nag 1975). In some countries, women and children have to fetch water in large quantities from a distance. These arduous tasks need to be minimized to the extent possible. Different methods of water carriage involve carrying on the head, on the hip, on the back and on the shoulder. These have been associated with a variety of biomechanical effects and spinal disorders (Dufaut 1988). Attempts have been made to improve shoulder load-carrying techniques, designs of wheelbarrows and so on. Load transportation using transverse yoke and head load are more efficient than the frontal yoke. The load optimization that can be carried by men may be obtained from the nomogram shown (figure 64.23). The nomogram is based on a multiple regression drawn between oxygen demand (the independent variable) and load carried and walking speed (the dependent variables). One may put a scale on the graph across the variables to identify the result. Two variables must be known to find the third. For example, with an oxygen demand of 1.4 l/min (approximate equivalent of 50% of one's maximum working capacity) and walking speed of 30 m/min, the optimum load would be about 65 kg.

In view of the diversity of farm activities, certain organizational measures towards redesigning of tools and machinery, methods of work, installation of safety guards on machinery, optimization of human exposure to adverse work environment and so on may significantly improve conditions of work for farming populations (Christiani 1990). Extensive ergonomic research on farm methods and practices, tools and equipment may generate a great deal of knowledge for the betterment of health, safety and productivity of billions of agricultural workers. This being the world's largest industry, the primitive image of the sector, particularly the resource-poor tropical agriculture, could be transformed as task-oriented. Thus rural workers can undergo systematic training on the hazards of jobs, and safe operational procedures can be developed.

MECHANIZATION

Dennis Murphy

The mechanization of agricultural work and work processes has relieved many workers throughout the world of onerous, back-breaking, monotonous labour. At the same time, the speed and power associated with mechanization contributes greatly toward serious traumatic injury. Throughout the world, countries that practise mechanized agriculture list tractors and field and farmstead machinery as leading agents of fatal and disabling injury in agricultural work. Power tools also contribute to the injury toll, though these injuries are usually less severe. Some machinery also presents environmental hazards such as noise and vibration.

Tractor hazards

Farm tractors have many characteristics that result in their being the most important piece of power equipment on the farm. Most tractors have rubber tyres, hydraulic systems, and power take-off (PTO), and utilize a combination of engine speeds and gear ratios. These characteristics combine to provide tractors with speed, power, flexibility and adaptability. The most serious hazards associated with tractor operation include overturns, runovers and PTO entanglement. Tractor overturns fatally injure far more

Table 64.6 • Common tractor hazards and how they occur.

Hazard	Type of incident	How injury occurs
Overturns	Side rollovers	Operating on slopes, turning corners too fast, rear wheel drops into a hole or off-road surface.
	Rear rollovers	Hitching to a point other than the drawbar, rear wheels are stuck in mudhole or are frozen to the ground.
Runovers	Passenger (extra rider) falls off	Most tractors are designed only for one operator; therefore, there is no safe location for an extra person on a tractor.
	Operator falls off	Knocked off by low-hanging tree limb, bounced out of seat by traversing rough ground.
	Operator is run over while standing on the ground	Jump starting tractor with tractor inadvertently in gear. Tractor rolls while mounting/dismounting. Tractor rolls during hitching/unhitching of equipment.
	Bystander or on-ground helper is run over	Bystander incidents often involve small children the operator does not see. On-ground helper incidents are similar to operator-on-the-ground incidents.
Power take-off (PTO)	Entanglement with PTO stub shaft	Master shield is missing and PTO is left engaged while tractor is running. Operator may be mounting/dismounting from rear of tractor.
Slips and falls	Mounting/dismounting from tractor	Wet and/or muddy feet, first/last step is high off the ground, difficult to reach handholds, hurrying, facing wrong way when dismounting.
Noise-induced hearing loss	Operating tractor	The tractor muffler may be missing, damaged, or is a non-recommended replacement; tractor engine is not maintained properly; metal weather cab redirects sound back to the operator. Damaging noise level may come from a combination of tractor and attached machine. (Older tractors generally produce louder sounds than newer tractors.)

victims than any other type of incident. Table 64.6 provides a listing of tractor hazards and how injuries occur.

Overturns

The central concept in tractor stability/instability is *centre of gravity* (CG). A tractor's CG is the point on the tractor where all parts balance one another. For example, when a two-wheel-drive tractor is sitting with all wheels on level ground, the CG is typically about 25.4 cm above and 0.6 m in front of the rear axle and in the centre of the tractor body. For four-wheel-drive and centre-articulated tractors, the CG is located slightly more forward. For a tractor to stay upright, its CG must stay within the tractor's stability baseline. *Stability baselines* are essentially imaginary lines drawn between points where tractor tires contact the ground (see figure 64.24). A tractor's CG as such does not move, but its relationship with stability baselines may change. This most often occurs as the tractor moves out of a perfectly level position, such as onto a slope. A changing relationship between CG and stability baseline means the tractor is moving toward an unstable position. If the CG-stability baseline relationship changes significantly (e.g., the tractor CG moves beyond the stability baseline), the tractor rolls over. If equipment such as a front-end loader, a round bale lifting fork or a chemical side-saddle tank is mounted on the tractor, the additional weight shifts the CG toward that piece of equipment. As mounted equipment is raised, the CG is raised.

Other factors important to tractor stability/instability include centrifugal force (CF), rear-axle torque (RAT) and drawbar leverage (DBL). Each of these factors works through the CG. Centrifugal force is the outward force nature exerts on objects that move in a circular fashion. Centrifugal force increases both as the turning angle of the tractor becomes sharper (decreases) and as the speed of the tractor increases during a turn. The CF increase is directly proportional to the turning angle of the tractor. For every degree the tractor is turned tighter, there is an equal amount of increased CF. The relationship between CF and tractor speed, however, is not directly proportional. Finding the increase in CF from turning a tractor at a higher speed (assuming the turning

radius stays the same) calls for squaring the difference between the two tractor speeds.

RAT involves energy transfer between the tractor engine and the rear axle of a two-wheel-drive tractor. Engaging the clutch results in a twisting force, called *torque*, to the rear axle. This torque is then transferred to the tractor tyres. Under normal circumstances, the rear axle (and tyres) should rotate, and the tractor will move ahead. In lay terms, the rear axle is said to be rotating about the tractor chassis. If the rear axle should be unable to rotate, the tractor chassis rotates about the axle. This reverse rotation results in the front end of the tractor lifting off the ground until the tractor's CG passes the rear stability baseline. At this point the tractor will continue rearward from its own weight until it crashes into the ground or another obstacle.

Figure 64.24 • The stability baseline of a tricycle tractor and a wide front-end tractor, respectively.

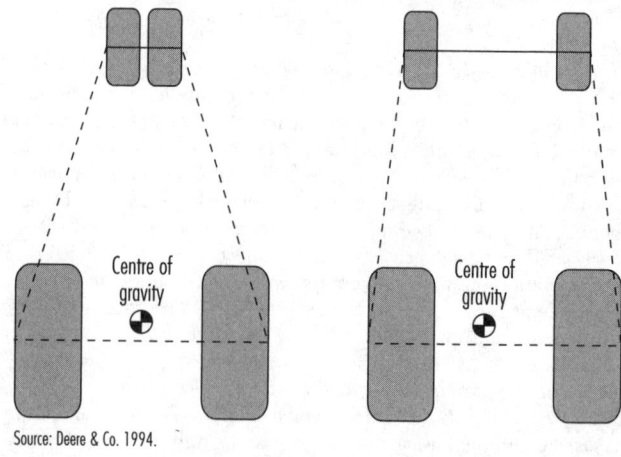

Centre of gravity

Centre of gravity

Source: Deere & Co. 1994.

DBL is another principle of stability/instability related to rear overturns. When a two-wheel-drive tractor is pulling a load, its rear tyres push against the ground. Simultaneously, the load attached to the tractor is pulling back and down against the forward movement of the tractor. The load is pulling down because it is resting on the earth's surface. This backward and downward pull results in the rear tyres becoming a pivot point, with the load acting as a force trying to tip the tractor rearward. An "angle of pull" is created between the ground's surface and the point of attachment on the tractor. The heavier the load, and the higher the angle of pull, the more leverage the load has to tip the tractor rearward.

Runovers

There are three basic types of tractor runover incidents. One is when a passenger (extra rider) on the tractor falls off the tractor. A second is when the tractor operator falls off the tractor. The third type occurs when a person already on the ground is run over by the tractor. The person already on the ground may be a bystander (e.g., a non-working adult or a small child), a co-worker or the tractor operator. The tractor runover event often involves trailing machinery hitched to the tractor; it may be the trailing machinery that inflicts the injury. Extra rider injury incidents occur because there is no safe location for an extra person on a tractor, yet the practice of taking extra riders is common, as a means of saving time, for convenience, work assistance or baby-sitting. Whether an extra rider can be justified for any reason is strictly in the eye of the beholder. Safety experts and tractor manufacturers strongly recommend against an operator carrying an extra rider for any reason. This advice, however, conflicts with several factors that farmers must face daily. For instance, it is human nature to want to complete work tasks as easily and quickly as possible; different

transportation may call for added expenditure of a meagre money supply; other baby-sitting options simply may not exist; and new tractor drivers must be taught how to operate tractors.

Persons already on the ground, usually tractor operators or children, are occasionally run over by tractors and their attached equipment. Tractor operators sometimes try to start their tractor from the ground, instead of from the operator's seat. Most of these incidents occur with older tractors that will start with the tractor in gear, or on newer tractors where the starting interlocks built into the tractor have been by-passed. Small children, usually under the age of five, are sometimes run over by tractors and machinery that is moved around the farmstead. Often, the tractor operator is unaware that the child is even near the equipment. A loud noise, such as the start-up of a tractor, is often attractive to young children and may draw them near. And the practice of allowing extra riders may bring them running to the tractor.

Tractor safety rules include:

- The most important safety device for a tractor is a rollover protective structure (ROPS). This device, along with a properly buckled seat-belt, prevents an operator from being crushed by the tractor during a rollover.
- A ROPS enclosed cab provides even more protection, as cabs also provide protection from adverse weather elements and from falling off the tractor.
- A master shield over the PTO stub shaft protects against PTO entanglement.
- The one seat–one rider rule and other safe operating practices must be followed.
- Operator manuals must be read to learn how to safely operate the machine.
- Workers must be physically, psychologically and physiologically capable of operating a given machine.

Table 64.7 • Common machinery hazards and where they occur.

Hazards	Sources	Locations
Pinch points	Two machine parts moving together with at least one of them moving in a circle	Where drive belts contact pulley wheels, drive chains contact gear sprockets, feed rolls mesh together
Wrap points	An exposed/unguarded rotating machine component	Power take-off (PTO) drive shafts, beater bars on self-unloading ensilage wagons, blades of some manure spreaders
Shear/cutting points	The edges of two moving parts move across one another, or a single edge moves against a stationary edge or soft material	Mowers and forage harvesters, small-grain combine heads, bedding choppers, grain augers
Crush points	Two moving objects moving toward each other, or one moving object moves toward a stationary object	The front and rear tires/sections of articulating tractors, hitching machinery, a hand caught under a piece of hydraulically-controlled equipment
Free-wheeling parts	Machine parts that continue to move after power to the part has stopped, usually from the continuing rotation of knife or fan blades	Forage harvesters, feed grinders, rotary mowers, ensilage blowers
Thrown objects	The chopping, grinding, cutting, and flinging motions of machines. Small objects such as rocks, metal, glass, sticks, and vegetation may be picked up and thrown with great force	Rotary mowers, feed grinders, combines with straw choppers, and manure spreaders
Stored energy	Energy that is confined and released unintentionally or unexpectedly	Machine springs, hydraulic systems, compressed air, electrical systems
Burn points	Skin burns from contacting hot parts of machines	Hot mufflers, engine blocks, pipes, fluids (fuel, oils, chemicals)
Pull-in points	Occurs at the point where the machine takes the crop material in for further processing	Corn pickers and combines, forage choppers, and hay balers
Noise-induced hearing loss	Operating machinery	Tractors, field machinery, grain augers, dryers, silo blowers, bedding choppers, feed grinders. Damaging noise level may come from a combination of one or more machines. Older machines generally produce louder sounds than newer machines.

Agricultural machinery*

Agricultural machinery is designed to till the soil and render it more suitable for crop growth, to sow seeds, to apply agricultural chemicals for improved plant growth and control of pests and diseases, and to harvest and store the mature crops. There is an extremely wide variety of agricultural machines, but all are essentially a combination of gears, shafts, chains, belts, knives, shakers and so on, assembled to perform a certain task. These parts are usually suspended in a frame which may be either stationary or, as is more often the case, mobile and designed to perform the desired operation while moving across a field. The major groups of agricultural machines are: soil tillage machines; planting machines; cultivating machines; forage harvesting machines; grain, fibre, vegetable, and fruit and nut harvesting machines; agricultural chemical applicators; transport and elevating machines; and sorting and packaging machines.

Soil tillage machines. These include ploughs, tillers, subsoilers, harrows, rollers, levellers, graders and so on. They are designed to turn, agitate, level and compact the soil to prepare it for planting. They may be small in size and require only a small power source (as in the case of a one-person roto-tiller for tilling a rice paddy), or they may be large and require a considerable power source (as in the case of a combined subsoiler, drill and harrow).

Planting machines. These include planters, drills, broadcast seeders and so on and are designed to take seeds from a hopper or bin and insert them in the soil at a predetermined depth and spacing or spread them uniformly over the ground. Planters may be of simple design and comprise a single-row seeding mechanism, or they may be highly complex (as is the case with the multi-row planter with attachments that simultaneously add fertilizer, pesticides and herbicides).

Cultivating machines. These include rotary hoes, cultivators, weeders (mechanical and flame) and so on. They are used to eradicate undesirable weeds or grasses which compete with the plant for soil moisture and make the harvest of the crop more difficult. They also improve the soil tillage so as to make it more absorptive of rain.

Forage harvesting machines. These include mowers, choppers, balers and so on and are designed to sever the stems of roughage crops from their roots and prepare them for storage or immediate use. The machines also vary in their complexity: the simple mower merely cuts the crop, whereas the chopper will not only separate the stalk from the root but will also chop the entire plant into small pieces and load it into a vehicle, which may be a towed wagon. Crimpers, which crush or break the stems of plants, are often used to expedite the field-drying process of fodder crops to prevent spoilage, especially of legumes that will be placed in dry storage or baled. Pelleting machines are used to compress fodder crops into compact cubes for mechanical feeding of livestock. Balers are used to compress fodder into square or round bales to facilitate storage and handling. Some bales are small enough (20 to 40 kg) to handle manually, while others may be so large (400 to 500 kg) as to require mechanical handling systems.

Grain and fibre harvesting machines. These include reapers, binders, corn pickers, combines, threshers and so on. They are used to remove the ripe grain or fibre from the plant and place it in a bin or bag for transport to the storage area. Grain harvesting may involve the use of a number of machines, such as a reaper or binder to cut the standing grain, a wagon or truck to transport the crop to the threshing or separating machines and vehicles to transport the grain to a storage area. In other cases many of these functions may be performed by a single machine, the combine harvester (figure 64.25), which cuts the standing grain, separates it from the stalk, cleans it and collects it in a bin, all while moving through the field. Such machines will also load the grain into transport vehicles. Some machines such as cotton pickers and corn pickers may operate selectively and remove only the grain or fibre boll from the stem or stalk.

Vegetable harvesting machines. These include diggers and lifters, and are designed either to dig the crops from the earth and separate them from the soil or to lift or pull the plant free. The potato digger, for example, may form part of a potato combine comprising a sorting, grading device, polisher, bagger and elevator. At the other extreme is the simple two-wheeled, bladed sugar-beet lifter which is followed by hand labourers.

Fruit and nut harvesting machines. These machines are used to harvest berries, fruit and nuts. They may be as simple as a tractor-mounted, vibrating tree shaker which separates the ripe fruit from the tree. Or they may be as complex as the ones which harvest the fruit, catch the falling fruit, place it in a storage container and later transfer it to transport vehicles.

Transport and elevating machines. These also vary considerably in size and complexity ranging, for example, from a simple wagon comprising merely a platform on wheels to a self-loading and stacking transport unit. Inclined chain, flight or belt conveyors or other mechanical handling devices are used to move bulky material (hay, straw, ear corn and so on) from wagon to storage or from one location in a building to another. Screw conveyors are used to move granular material and grain from one level to another, and blowers or pneumatic conveyors are used to move light materials horizontally or vertically.

Agricultural chemical applicators. These are used to apply fertilizers to stimulate plant growth or herbicides and pesticides to control weeds and pests. The chemicals may be liquid, powdered or granular, and the applicator distributes them either by pressure through a nozzle or by centrifugal force. Applicators may be portable or vehicle-mounted; the use of aircraft for chemical application is growing rapidly.

Sorting and packaging machines. These machines are usually stationary. They may be as simple as a fanning mill, which grades and cleans grain merely by passing it over a series of screens, or as complex as a seed mill, which will not only grade and clean but also, for example, separate different types of seeds. Packaging machines usually form part of a sophisticated grading system. They are used primarily for fruit and vegetables and may wrap the produce in paper, bag it or insert it into a plastic container.

Power plants. Electric motors may be used to drive stationary equipment permanently located near a mains supply; however, since many agricultural machines are mobile and must operate in remote areas, they are usually powered by an integral petrol engine or by a separate engine such as that of a tractor. Power from a tractor may be transmitted to the machine via belt, chain, gear or shaft drives; most tractors are fitted with a power take-off coupling specially designed for this purpose.

L.W. Knapp, Jr.

* Adapted from 3rd edition, *Encyclopaedia of Occupational Health and Safety*.

Machinery Hazards

There are a multitude of machines used in mechanized agriculture. These machines are powered in many different ways including PTO shafts, hydraulic oil pressure, electrical power, engine power and ground traction. Many machines have several types of hazards. Table 64.7 gives machine hazards, descriptions of the hazards and examples of where the hazards occur on various machines.

Machinery power and speed

Though workers may understand that machinery is powerful and operates at very high speeds, most workers have not stopped to consider just how powerful machines are in comparison to their own power, nor do they fully comprehend how fast machines are. Machinery power varies considerably, but even small machines generate many times more horsepower than any person. A quick, pull-away action of a human arm normally generates less than 1 horsepower (hp), sometimes much less. A small 16-hp machine, such as a walk-behind mower, may have 20 to 40 times more power pulling a person into the machine than that person can generate pulling away. A medium-sized machine operated at 40 to 60 hp will have hundreds of times more power than a person.

This power and speed combination presents many potentially hazardous situations to workers. For example, the tractor's PTO stub shaft transfers power between the tractor and PTO-powered machinery. Power transfer is accomplished by connecting a drive shaft from the machinery to the tractor's PTO stub. The PTO stub and drive shaft rotate at 540 rpm (9 times/second) or 1,000 rpm (16.7 times/second) when operating at full recommended speed. Most incidents involving PTOs stem from clothing suddenly caught by an engaged but unguarded PTO stub or driveline. Even with a relatively quick reaction of 1 second (i.e., the worker tries to pull away from the shaft) and a shaft with a diameter of 76 mm operating only at half speed (e.g., at 270 rpm (one-half of 540), the victim's clothing has already wrapped 1.1 m around the shaft. A faster-operating PTO and/or a slower reaction provides even less of an opportunity for the worker to avoid entanglement with the shaft.

When a machine is running at full recommended PTO speed, crop material moves into the machine intake or processing area at approximately 3.7 m/s. If a worker is holding onto crop material as it begins entry into the machine, he or she is usually unable to let go quickly enough to release the material before being pulled

Figure 64.25 • Combine for harvesting wheat without an enclosed cabin.

into the machine. In 0.3 second, the worker will be pulled 1.1 m into the machine. This situation most often happens when crop material plugs the intake point of the machine and the worker attempts to unplug it with the PTO engaged.

Machinery safety

Machinery safety is largely a matter of keeping the guards and shields that came with the original in place and properly maintained. Warning decals should be used as a reminder to keep guards and shields in place. If guards or shields must be removed for maintenance, service or adjustment, they must be replaced immediately upon completion of the repair. Safe operating practices must be followed. For example, the tractor must be shut off and the PTO or block hydraulic systems disengaged before unplugging or servicing equipment. Operator manuals must be read and their safety instructions followed. Workers must be properly trained.

FOOD AND FIBRE CROPS

● RICE

Malinee Wongphanich

Rice is the staple food for Asian people; it is prepared by cooking or ground as flour for bread making, thus helping to feed the rest of the world population. Various kinds of rice are produced to suit the taste of the consumers. Rice cultivation is done either in marshy, lowland areas with plenty of water or in plateau or hilly regions where natural rainfall provides adequate amounts of water.

Cultivation Process

Rice can be cultivated either by hand or by partial or full mechanization, according to the technological development of the country and the need for productivity. Whatever kind of operation is done, the following step-by-step processes are necessary.

1. *Ploughing*. The land is ploughed in three stages to eliminate lumps and to make soil as soft and muddy as possible. Buffalo, oxen or cows usually pull the ploughs, though the use of mechanical equipment is increasing.
2. *Weeding* is carried out three times by irrigating the land for 5 days at a time and then letting it dry for 5 days. At the end of each cycle, the land is beaten with a heavy wooden tool to kill off young weeds so they may be used as natural fertilizer.
3. *Preparation of seedlings*. The seeds are soaked in a large water-filled jar with appropriate concentrations of salt added to make the healthy seeds sink. These healthy seeds are then thoroughly washed, soaked overnight, wrapped in a thick

Figure 64.26 • Harvesting of rice plants by hand in China, 1992.

Lenore Manderson

cloth or sack for 2 nights to germinate, sown in the area prepared for them and left to grow for approximately 30 days.

4. *Transplantation*. The young plants, in bunches of 3 to 5, are thrust into the mud in rows and grown for 10 days. After about a total of 45 days, the plant is fully grown and begins to bear seeds.

5. *Harvesting*. When the plant is about 100 days old, it is usually reaped by hand (see figure 64.26); sickles or similar tools are used for cutting the bearing grains off.

6. *Drying* is done in the open air in the sun, to make the moisture content fall below 15%.

7. *Threshing* separates the grain, with its husk or glume, from the stalk. Traditionally, buffaloes or oxen are used to slowly drag the threshing combs over the stalk to force out the grain. Many places use locally made machines for this.

8. *Storage*. Grains and hays are stored in barns or silos.

Hazards

Common and specific hazards are as follows:

- Poor housing, low sanitary standards, inadequate nourishment and the need to drink large quantities of water, which is not always pure, lead to general weakness and fatigue, possible sunstroke, intestinal troubles and diarrhoea.
- Most injuries caused by farm machinery occur when the workers are not familiar with the machines. Muscles, bones and joints are intensively used, both in dynamic and static loads, causing physical fatigue and resulting in the reduction of work capacity and an increase in traumatic injuries and accidents. Children and adolescents, as well as migrant workers, die from farm injuries each year.
- Chemical agents, such as fertilizers, strong weedkillers, pesticides and other extensively used substances, increase the hazards both for the workers and the animal or plant foods they

consume (e.g., fish, field crabs, water plants, mushrooms, medicinal herbs, field rats or even contaminated water).

- Diseases (e.g., malaria, tetanus, hookworm, schistosomiasis, leptospirosis, hay fever, farmer's lung, dermatitis, blepharitis, conjunctivitis, common cold and sunstroke) are very common, as are nutritional disorders (e.g., protein deficiency, toxins), alcoholism, heavy smoking and other addictive habits.
- The most common occupational diseases are skin diseases. These include: redness and blisters from prickly rice leaves; abrasions and skin injuries caused by prickly plants; calluses of the palms, hands, knees and elbows caused by bad posture and the use of hand tools; skin fungal infections (tinea) due to epidermophytes and *Monilia* (candida), which may be complicated by secondary sensitization, redness and blisters, frequently due to *Staphylococcus* bacteria; vesicular dermatitis (small blisters) on the feet sometimes attributed to *Rhizopus parasiticus;* itch commonly caused by the penetration of the skin by *Ancylostoma* (hookworms); schistosome dermatitis caused directly or indirectly by contact with water containing blood flukes from nonhuman hosts; and redness, blisters and oedema resulting from insect stings.
- Respiratory diseases due to organic and inorganic dusts and synthetic chemicals are common. Gram-negative bacterial endotoxin levels in air are high in some countries. Silage gas poisoning of high nitrate soils is also a health problem.
- Climatic agents such as heat, heavy rain, humidity, high wind, storms and lightning strike both workers and cattle.
- Psychological stress factors such as economic problems, sense of insecurity, lack of social standing, lack of educational opportunities, lack of prospects and risk of unexpected calamities are particularly common in the developing countries.

Safety and Health Measures

Working conditions should be improved and the health hazards reduced through increased mechanization. Ergonomic interventions to organize the work and working equipment, and systematic training of the body and its movements to ensure good working methods, are essential.

Necessary medical preventive methods should be strictly applied, including the introduction of first aid instruction, the provision of treatment facilities, health promotion campaigns and medical surveillance of workers.

Improvement of housing, sanitary standards, accessible potable water, nutritional environmental hygiene and economic stability are essential for the quality of life of rice field workers.

Applicable International Labour Organization (ILO) Conventions and Recommendations should be followed. These include:

- The Minimum Age (Agriculture) Convention, 1921 (No.10), provides that children under the age of 14 years may not be employed or work in any public or private agricultural undertakings, or in any branch thereof, when school is in session.
- The Night Work of Children and Young Persons (Agriculture) Recommendation, 1921 (No.14), requires that each Member State regulate the employment of children under the age of 14 years in agricultural tasks at night, leaving not less than 10 consecutive hours for them to rest. For young persons between the age of 14 and 18 years, the period of rest must consist of not less than 9 consecutive hours.
- The Plantations Convention, 1958 (No.110), provides that every recruited worker shall be medically examined. This Convention is obviously of great importance for workers of all ages.
- The Maximum Weight Convention, 1967 (No.127), identified optimum loads that can be handled by 90% of workers for all routine and repetitive manual-handling tasks.

AGRICULTURAL GRAINS AND OILSEEDS

Charles Schwab

Several plants in the grass family, including wheat, rye, barley, oats, corn, rice, sorghum and millet, are valuable agricultural commodities, representing the largest effort in production agriculture. Grains provide a concentrated form of carbohydrates and are an important source of food for animals and humans.

In the human diet, grains make up about 60% of the calories and 55% of the protein, and are used for food as well as beverages. Bread is the most commonly recognized food product made from grains, although grains are also important in the production of beer and liquor. Grain is a basic ingredient in the distillation of neutral spirits that produce liquors with the taste and aroma of grain. Grains also are used to make feed for animals, including pets, working animals and animals raised in the production of meat products for human consumption.

Grain production can be traced to the beginning of civilization. In 1996, world production of cereal grains was 2,003,380,000 tonnes. This volume has increased more than 10% since the mid-1980s (FAO 1997).

Three of the major grains produced for their oil, also called oilseeds, are soybean, rapeseed and sunflower. Although ten different types of oilseed crops exist, these three account for the majority of the market, with soybean as the leader. Virtually all oilseeds are crushed and processed to produce vegetable oils and high-protein meals. Much of the vegetable oil is used as salad or cooking oils, and meal is used predominantly in animal feeds. World oilseed production in 1996 was 91,377,790 tonnes, almost a 41% increase since 1986 (FAO 1997).

The production of grains and oilseeds is affected by regional factors such as weather and geography. Dry soils and environments restrict corn production, while moist soils deter wheat production. Temperature, precipitation, soil fertility and topography also affect the type of grain or oilseed that can be successfully produced in an area.

For production of grain and oilseed crops, work falls into four areas: seed bed preparation and planting, harvest, storage and transportation of the crop to market or processing facilities. In modern agriculture, some of these processes have changed completely, but other processes have changed little since early civilization. However, the mechanization of agriculture has created new situations and safety issues.

Hazards and Their Prevention

All tools used in grain harvest—from complex combines to the simple scythe—have one aspect in common: they are hazardous. Harvest tools are aggressive; they are designed to cut, chew or chop plant materials placed into them. These tools do not discriminate between a crop and a person. Various mechanical hazards associated with grain harvesting include shear-point, pull-in, crush-point, entanglement, wrap-point and pinch-point. A combine pulls in cornstalks at a rate of 3.7 metres per second (m/s), too quickly for humans to avoid entanglement, even with a normal reaction time. Augers and PTO units used to move grain, rotate and have wrapping speeds of 3 m/s and 2 m/s, respectively, and also pose an entanglement hazard.

Agricultural workers also can experience noise-induced hearing loss from large-horsepower machinery and equipment used in crop production. Axial-vane fans that force heated air through a bin or storage structure to dry grain can generate noise levels of 110 dBA or more. Since grain-drying units often are located near living quarters and are operated continuously throughout a season, they often result in substantial hearing loss in farmworkers as well as family members over long periods of time. Other sources of noise that can contribute to hearing loss are machinery such as tractors, combines and conveying equipment, and grain moving through a gravity spout.

Agricultural workers also can be exposed to significant suffocation hazards by engulfment either in flowing grain or collapsing grain surfaces. A person caught in grain is almost impossible to rescue because of the tremendous weight of grain. Workers can prevent engulfment in flowing grain by always turning off all power sources to the unloading and transporting equipment before they enter an area and locking shut all gravity flow gates. Engulfment in a collapsed grain surface is difficult to prevent, but workers can avoid the situation by knowing the history of the storage structure and the grain it contains. All workers should follow confined-space entry procedures for physical engulfment hazards when working with grain.

During the harvest, storage and transportation of grains and oilseeds, agricultural workers are exposed to dusts, spores, mycotoxins and endotoxins that can be harmful to the respiratory system. Biologically active dust is capable of producing irritation and/or allergic, inflammatory or infectious responses in the lungs. Workers can avoid or reduce their exposure to dust, or wear personal protective equipment such as mechanical filter respirators or air-supplied respirators in dusty environments. Some handling and storage systems minimize the creation of dust, and additives such as vegetable oils can keep dust from becoming airborne.

In some conditions during storage, grain can spoil and emit gases that pose a suffocation hazard. Carbon dioxide (CO_2) can collect above a grain surface to displace oxygen, which can cause impairment in workers if oxygen levels drop below 19.5%. Mechanical filter respirators are useless in these situations.

Another hazard is the potential for fires and explosions that can occur when grains or oilseeds are stored or handled. Dust particles that become airborne when grain is moved create an atmosphere ripe for a powerful blast. Only an ignition source is needed, such as an overheated bearing or a belt rubbing against a housing component. The biggest hazards exist at large port elevators or inland community elevators where huge volumes of grain are handled. Regular preventive maintenance and good housekeeping policies minimize the risk of possible ignition and explosive atmospheres.

Chemicals used at the beginning of the crop production cycle for seed-bed preparation and planting also can pose hazards for agricultural workers. Chemicals can increase soil fertility, reduce competition from weeds and insects and boost yields. The biggest concern for agricultural chemicals hazards is long-term exposure; however, anhydrous ammonia, a compressed liquid fertilizer, can cause immediate injury. Anhydrous ammonia (NH_3) is a hygroscopic, or water-seeking, compound, and caustic burns result when it dissolves body tissue. Ammonia gas is a strong lung irritant, but has good warning properties. It also has a low boiling point and freezes on contact, causing another type of severe burn. Wearing protective equipment is the best way to reduce risk of exposure. When exposure occurs, first aid treatment requires immediately flushing of the area with plenty of water.

Grain production workers also are exposed to potential injury from slips and falls. A person can die from injuries in a fall from a height as low as 3.7 m, which is easily exceeded by operator's platforms on most machinery or grain storage structures. Grain storage structures are at least 9 and up to 30 m tall, reachable only by ladders. Inclement weather can cause slippery surfaces from rain, mud, ice or snow build-up, so the use of guards, handrails and footwear with non-slip soles is important. Devices such as a body harness or lanyard also can be used to arrest the fall and minimize injury.

SUGAR CANE CULTIVATION AND PROCESSING

R.A. Munoz, E.A. Suchman, J.M. Baztarrica and Carol J. Lehtola*

Cultivation

Sugar cane is a hardy crop that is cultivated in tropical and sub-tropical regions for its sucrose content and by-products such as molasses and bagasse (the waste fibrous residue). The plant grows in clumps of cylindrical stalks measuring from 1.25 to 7.25 cm in diameter and reaching 6 to 7 m in height. The cane stalks grow straight upward until the stalk becomes too heavy to hold itself up. It then lies on its side and continues to grow upward. This results in a mature cane field lying on top of itself in a mesh pattern. The sugar cane stalks contain a sap from which sugar is processed. Sugar cane is grown throughout the Caribbean, Central and South America, India, the Pacific Islands, Australia, Central and South Africa, Mauritius and the southern United States. Sugar cane's main use is for sugar; however, it can be fermented and distilled to produce rum. Bagasse, the cellulose material that remains after pressing, may be used in the production of paper and other products or as a fuel source.

Under favourable conditions and the appropriate use of pesticides and fertilizers, cane grows rapidly. To ensure the maximum sugar content of 1 to 17% of total weight, the cane must be harvested immediately after it reaches its final growth period. The cane fields are burned prior to harvest, to eliminate weeds (without destroying the crop) and to destroy snakes, dangerous insects and other pests that live in the dense growth of the cane fields. Harvesting is done either by hand (machetes are used to cut the cane) or by a sugar cane harvesting machine. Mechanization of sugar cane harvesting has become more prevalent during the 1990s. However, hand harvesting still occurs in many parts of the world, as well as in field locations that are not conducive for harvesting equipment. Large numbers of seasonal or migrant labourers are employed during cane harvesting, especially in areas of hand harvesting.

To retain the sugar content, the cane has to be processed as soon as possible after harvesting; therefore the processing plants (mills) are located near the major areas of sugar cane production. The crop is transported to the mills by tractors, semi trucks or, in some areas, by internal rail systems.

Hazards and their prevention

In areas where hand harvesting prevails, many of the injuries are machete related. These injuries can range from minor cuts to the severing of body parts. Also, the machete is the tool that is most commonly used by the less skilled workers on the farm or plantation. Keeping the machete sharp aids in reducing injuries, since with a sharp machete the worker does not have to swing as hard and can maintain better control over the machete. There are also instances of workers getting into fights with machetes. Safety gloves armoured with chain mesh have been developed to provide protection for the hand from machete-related injuries. The use of steel-toed boots and arm and leg guards will also reduce these types of injuries. Boots will also provide some protection from snake bites. Working with cane also can very easily produce injuries and cuts to the eyes. Eye protection is recommended during hand harvesting, where workers are exposed to the cane stalks. Since cane is grown in tropical and sub-tropical locations, workers also need to be concerned about heat-related health problems. This can be exacerbated due to use of the necessary

protective clothing. These regions are also areas of high levels of sun exposure, which can result in various types of skin cancer conditions. Precautions need to be taken to limit or protect against sun exposure.

Manual harvesting with machetes can also result in musculoskeletal injuries from the repetitive motions and physical effort. The size of the machete, sharpness and frequency of cutting strokes are factors that affect this. See also the article "Manual operations in farming" in this chapter.

Precautions need to be taken to prevent infection when cuts and abrasions occur. Where the harvesting has become mechanized, hazards exist that are associated with the particular machine being used. These are similar to those of other agricultural harvesting equipment.

Pesticides and other chemicals may involve toxic risks that can lead to poisoning through skin absorption or inhalation. People who apply the pesticides need to be instructed on the hazards of the operation and provided with protective clothing and adequate washing facilities. Their equipment needs to be maintained and repaired as needed in order to prevent spills. Back-pack sprayers are particularly prone to develop leaks that will cause spillage onto the person. Aerial applications of pesticides can affect other people that are in the area of the application. Also, when pesticides are applied, the product label provides both legal and practical requirements for handling and disposal after use, as well as listing time intervals after which it is safe for people to re-enter the field.

Sugar Cane Mills (Processing Plants)

The sugar cane industry is concerned with more than the production of food for human consumption. Certain kinds of sugar and sugar residues provide nutritious supplementary food for animals, and various products of commercial significance are obtained from the raw material and its by-products.

Principal by-products are saccharose, glucose, levulose, raffinose, pectin, waxes and betaines. Subproducts are stalks (used for fodder), bagasse, rum and molasses. Among products manufactured on an industrial scale are saccharose octacetate, ethyl alcohol and acetic, citric, glutamic, oxalic, formic and saccharic acids. Paper and hardboard are produced industrially from bagasse. Bagasse can also, when dried, be used as a biogas source or as fuel in the sugar mill.

In the sugar mill, the cane is crushed and the juice extracted by heavy rollers. The juice contains saccharose, glucose, levulose, organic salts and acids in solution, and is mixed with bagasse fibres, grit, clay, colouring matter, albumin and pectin in suspension. Because of the properties of albumin and the pectin, the juice cannot be filtered cold. Heat and chemicals are required to eliminate the impurities and to obtain saccharose.

The mixture is clarified by heating and the addition of lime-based precipitants. Once clarified, the juice is concentrated by vacuum evaporation until it precipitates in the form of grayish crystals. The concentrated juice, or molasses, is 45% water. Centrifugal treatment produces granulated sugar of a grayish hue (brown sugar), for which there is a market. White sugar is obtained by a refining process. In this process, the brown sugar is dissolved with various chemicals (sulphuric anhydride, phosphoric acid) and filtered with or without bone black, according to the purity desired. The filtered syrup evaporates under a vacuum until it crystallizes. It is then centrifuged until a white crystalline powder is obtained.

Hazards and their prevention

Worker conditions will vary according to geographical locale. Seasonal workers are especially vulnerable to living in substandard conditions. Health risks will vary in relation to the environ-

* Adapted from 3rd edition, *Encyclopaedia of Occupational Health and Safety*.

mental factors, working conditions, living conditions and the socioeconomic class of the worker.

Due to the high temperatures in the areas where cane is produced, workers need to consume large quantities of liquid.

Fumes and gases such as carbon dioxide, sulphur dioxide, carbon monoxide and hydrochloric acid may be given off at various stages of the refining process. The high temperatures of processing can also result in fumes and steam that are not only irritating or hot, but sometimes can be toxic as well.

In some areas of the mill, there are excessive noise levels.

Bagassosis is an occupational lung disease of the extrinsic allergic alveolitis type, caused by breathing dusts containing spores of thermophilic actinomycetes which grow in stored, mouldy bagasse. Hypersensitivity pneumonitis can also result from this exposure.

In developing countries, workers may be unskilled, with no safety training. Also there may be a high turnover rate for employees, which can lead to problems in keeping up with training and increasing skill levels. Although statistical data do not show a high incidence of occupational disease, this can be due in part to reporting and calculating problems, such as the fact that the mills and refining plants are not open year-round, but only for 5 to 6 months of the year. Thus annual accident rates may appear low. During the remainder of the year, seasonal workers will be employed in entirely different jobs, while permanent employees will be maintaining and working with the machinery, equipment and facilities.

Occupational accidents, such as falls, strains, sprains and so on, differ little from those in other industrial and agricultural activities. With increasing mechanization, the occupational accidents are fewer but are often more serious. The more frequent injuries include diseases related to heat stroke or heat stress, dermatitis, conjunctivitis, burns and falls.

In order to plan and put into effect a health and safety programme for a specific sugar mill, it is necessary to conduct a qualitative and quantitative assessment of the risks and hazards involved, including identification of corrective measures, such as the use of local exhaust systems for dust, gas and fumes where appropriate. Dust control can be used effectively for controlling bagasse dust. The facility should be properly aired and ventilated to reduce excessive heat, and adequate lighting should be provided. Machinery should be properly guarded, and proper protective clothing should be provided and easily accessible to workers. Health and safety standards and regulations must be complied with. A proper safety programme, for which trained staff are responsible, to ensure the safety of the workers should be in place.

Noise is a widespread hazard. Noisy machines should be soundproofed, and, in areas where the noise level cannot be reduced adequately, hearing protection must be provided and a hearing conservation programme instituted. That programme should include audiometric testing and worker training.

● POTATO HARVESTING

Steven B. Johnson

Roots and tubers are a major part of the diet, food energy and nutrient source for more than 1 billion people in the developing world. Root crops are used to produce food products including composite flours, noodles, chips and dehydrated products. They provide about 40% of the diet for half of the sub-Saharan African population. Cassava has become one of the developing world's most important staples, providing a basic diet to about 500 mil-

lion people. Cassava has also become an important export crop for animal feed in Europe.

Roots and tubers—potatoes, sweet potatoes, cassava, yams and taro—are known as the starchy foods. They are high in carbohydrates, calcium and vitamin C, but low in protein. These foods are the subsistence crops in some of the poorest countries. Several root food crops are staples in major world regions. These include the yam in Indochina, Indonesia and Africa; the potato in South America, Central America, Mexico and Europe; and the cassava and sweet potato in South America (Alexandratos 1995).

The potato was introduced into Ireland in the 1580s, and a small plot could feed a six-child family, a cow and a pig. Moreover, the crop could remain in the soil protected from the winter freezes and fires. The potato became the food of the poor in Ireland, England, France, Germany, Poland and Russia. In 1845, a blight struck the potato across Europe, which resulted in the great, fatal potato famine in Ireland, where substitute crops were unavailable (Tannahill 1973).

The potato is still a principal crop in the developed world. Its production continues to increase in the United States, and much of this increase is attributed to processed potatoes. Growth in processed potatoes is occurring in chips and shoestrings, frozen French fries, other frozen products and canned potatoes. The principal occupational hazards are related to injury and are experienced during the mechanical harvesting operation. In a Canadian study, potato farmers were found to be at elevated risk of pancreatic cancer, but no association was made with an exposure.

Hazards

Each moving part of the potato harvester carries the potential for injury. The tractor's PTO shaft, which connects the tractor and the harvester by universal joints or yokes, is the source of kinetic energy and of injuries. The PTO shaft should be shielded. The most common injury on a PTO shaft occurs when the yoke catches a loose piece of clothing, entangling the wearer.

All hydraulic systems operate under pressure, even as much as 2,000 pounds per square inch (14,000 Kpa), which is three times the pressure needed to penetrate skin. Thus a worker should never cover a leaking hydraulic hose with a finger since the fluid could be injected through the skin. If any fluid is injected into the skin, it must be surgically removed within a few hours or gangrene may develop. If any point in the hydraulic system fails, a serious injury can occur. A ruptured hydraulic hose can spray fluid a great distance. Hydraulic systems store energy. Careless servicing or adjusting can lead to injury.

A *pinch-type injury* can occur where two machinery parts move together and at least one of them moves in a circle. Gear and belt drives are examples of pinch points. Clothing or body parts can catch and become drawn into the gears. Proper guarding of potato harvester parts reduces the chance of a pinch-type injury.

A *wrap-type injury* can occur when an exposed, unshielded rotating component, such as a PTO shaft, entangles a loose piece of clothing: a sleeve, a shirt-tail, a frayed piece of clothing or even long hair. Smooth PTO shafts with rust or nicks can be rough enough to catch clothing; a slowly rotating PTO shaft must still be regarded with caution. However, the rounder, smoother shafts are less likely to catch clothing than square shafts. The universals at the end of the PTO shafts are the most likely to catch loose clothing and cause a wrap-type injury. These bulky parts extend beyond the PTO shaft and can cause a wrap-type injury even if one is clear of the PTO shaft. PTO shafts from the tractor to the potato harvester must be guarded. No one should work amid unsafe conditions such as unshielded PTO shafts.

Shear points are areas where two pieces move in a cutting motion. A finger placed in a boom joint or between a fan belt and the pulley would be quickly severed. The belt, turned by the engine that drives the fan, is a site for amputation as well as other bodily injuries. Again, proper shielding of potato harvester parts reduces the chance of a shear injury.

Crush points are found where two objects move towards each other, or an object moves toward a stationary object. Big trucks are involved in a potato harvest. Movement in the field and especially in a closed facility such as a potato storage building can lead to runovers and crushed feet or legs.

A *pull-in injury* occurs when a worker is pulled into machinery. Pull-in injuries can occur any time there is an attempt to remove something from a potato harvester while it is operating, even if it is not moving forward.

Thrown-object injuries occur when projectiles are hurled. Air-assisted potato harvesters routinely throw soil and small rocks in the process of separating potato tubers from rocks. The soil and debris are thrown with enough force to cause eye injuries.

Prevention

Fortunately, there is a great deal that can be done to avoid injuries. Clothing can make the difference between being caught in a pinch or wrap point and being safe. Loose, long hair can catch in wrap and pinch points and drag the worker's head into a dangerous spot. Long hair should be securely tied. Skid-resistant shoes help keep the worker from slipping while standing on the sorting platform, which may be treacherous with mud and vines. Gloves, if worn while working on the sorting table, should be tight fitting and not have frayed edges or floppy cuffs.

Attitude, alertness and avoiding dangerous situations complement safe attire. No one should ever mount or dismount a potato harvester while it is in motion. The rider must wait until the harvester stops. Many of the serious and debilitating injuries occur from falling and being crushed while attempting to mount or dismount a moving harvester. One should try to be in a stable position before the tractor starts to pull the potato harvester. This will reduce the possibility of falling down as the tractor jerks forward. No one should ever be between the tractor and the harvester while they are in motion or when they are started. The tractor operator or the workers riding the potato harvester should never be close enough to touch the PTO shaft while it is running or when it is started. Harvesters should not be lubricated, adjusted or repaired while running. No attempt to dislodge anything from the belts should be made while they are in motion.

• VEGETABLES AND MELONS

B.H. Xu and Toshio Matsushita

A wide variety of vegetables (herbaceous plants) is grown for edible leaves, stems, roots, fruits and seeds. Crops include leafy salad crops (e.g., lettuce and spinach), root crops (e.g., beets, carrots, turnips), cole crops (cabbage, broccoli, cauliflower) and many others grown for their fruit or seed (e.g., peas, beans, squashes, melons, tomatoes).

Since the 1940s, the nature of vegetable farming, particularly in North America and Europe, has changed dramatically. Previously, most fresh vegetables were grown close to population centres by garden or truck farmers and were available only during or shortly after harvest. The growth of supermarkets and the development of large food-processing companies created a demand for steady, year-round supplies of vegetables. At the same time, large-scale vegetable production on commercial farms became possible in areas far from major population centres because of rapidly expanding irrigation systems, improved insect sprays and weed control, and the development of sophisticated machin-

ery for planting, spraying, harvesting and grading. Today, the main source of fresh vegetables in the United States is long-season areas, such as the states of California, Florida, Texas and Arizona, and Mexico. Southern Europe and North Africa are major vegetable sources for northern Europe. Many vegetables are also grown in greenhouses. Farmers' markets selling local produce, however, remain the major outlet for vegetable growers throughout much of the world, particularly in Asia, Africa and South America.

Vegetable farming requires substantial skills and care to ensure production of high-quality vegetables that will sell. Vegetable farming operations include soil preparation, planting and growing crops, harvesting, processing and transportation. Weed and pest control and water management are crucial.

Vegetable and melon workers are exposed to many occupational hazards in their working environment, which include plants and their products, agrochemicals for controlling pests and oils and detergents for maintaining and repairing machinery. Manual or automatic work also forces the workers into uncomfortable positions (see figure 64.27). Musculoskeletal disorders such as low-back pain are important health problems in these workers. Agricultural tools and machines used with vegetables and melons give rise to high risks for traumatic injuries and various health impairments similar to those seen in other agricultural work. In addition, outdoor growers are exposed to solar radiation and heat, whereas exposure to pollens, endotoxins and fungi should be taken into account among greenhouse farmers. Therefore, a wide variety of work-related disorders can be found in those populations.

Food allergies to vegetables and melons are well known. They are mostly provoked by vegetable allergens and can cause an immediate reaction. Clinically, mucocutaneous and respiratory

Figure 64.27 • Manual labour on a vegetable farm near Assam, Jordan.

symptoms appear in most patients. Occupational allergy among vegetable workers differs from food allergy in several ways. Occupational allergens are diverse, including those of vegetable origin, chemicals and biological derivatives. Artichoke, brussels sprouts, cabbage, carrot, celery, chicory, chive, endive, garlic, horseradish, leek, lettuce, okra, onion, parsley and parsnip have been reported to contain vegetable allergens and to sensitize vegetable workers. Occupational allergies to melon allergens, however, are seldom reported. Only a few allergens from vegetables and melons have been isolated and identified because of the difficulty and complexity of the laboratory techniques required. Most allergens, especially those of vegetable origin, are fat soluble, but a few are water soluble. The ability to sensitize also varies depending on botanical factors: The allergens may be sequestered in resin canals and released only when the vegetables are bruised. However, in other cases they may be readily released by fragile grandular hairs, or be excreted onto the leaf, coat the pollens or be widely disseminated by the action of wind on trichomes (hair-like growths on the plants).

Clinically, the most common occupational allergic diseases reported in the vegetable workers are allergic dermatitis, asthma and rhinitis. Extrinsic allergic alveolitis, allergic photodermatitis and allergic urticaria (hives) can be seen in some cases. It should be emphasized that vegetables, melons, fruits and pollens have some allergens in common or cross-reacting allergens. This implies that atopic persons and individuals with an allergy to one of those may become more susceptible than others in the development of occupational allergies. To screen and diagnose these occupational allergies, a number of immune tests are currently available. In general, the prick test, intradermal test, measurement of allergen-specific IgE antibody and *in vivo* allergen challenge test are used for immediate allergies, whereas the patch test can be chosen for delayed-type allergy. The allergen-specific lymphocyte proliferation test and cytokine production are helpful in diagnosing both types of allergy. These tests can be performed using native vegetables, their extracts and released chemicals.

Dermatoses such as pachylosis, hyperkeratosis, nail injury chromatosis and dermatitis are observed in vegetable workers. In particular, contact dermatitis, both irritant and allergic, occurs more frequently. Irritant dermatitis is caused by chemical and/or physical factors. Vegetable parts such as thrichomes, spicules, coarse hairs, raphides and spines are responsible for most of this irritation. On the other hand, allergic dermatitis is classified into immediate and delayed types on the basis of their immunopathogenesis. The former is mediated through humoural immune responses, whereas the later is mediated through cellular immune responses.

Clinically, many patients with allergic dermatitis experience a range of symptoms including itching, erythema, rash, swelling and vesicles. The sites of lesions are mainly the hands, arms, face and neck. In a field survey of Japanese okra growers (Nomura 1993), more than 50% of farmers had skin lesions, and these appeared mostly on the hands and arms. About 20 to 30% of farmers showed a positive patch test reaction to okra pad or leaf extracts. Furthermore, proteolytic activity of okra extracts was shown to cause the skin lesions.

Agricultural chemicals are also important allergens responsible for allergic dermatitis. These include insecticides (DDVP, diazinon, EPN, malathion, naled, parathion and so on), fungicides (benomyl, captafol, captan, maneb, manzeb, nitrofen, plondrel®, thiram, zineb, ziram and so on), herbicides (carbyne, randox and so on) and fumigants (D-D® mixture of 1,3-dichloropropene and 1,1,2-dichloropropane and related compounds). Additionally, opportunistic bacteria and *Streptococcus pyogenes* are found to play an important role in allergic dermatitis and urticaria for vegetable workers.

Vegetable workers, especially those working in greenhouses or indoors, are exposed to many vegetable products and to compounds such as pesticides, which are responsible for increased lung diseases. In a national study conducted among Swiss farmers, it was documented that the age-standardized proportional mortality for all lung diseases, bronchitis and asthma, and asthma alone were 127, 140 and 137, respectively. Vegetable products can directly cause occupational allergic asthma, or provide non-specific irritants and/or the vehicle for other allergens including pollens, spores, mites and other substances. Vegetable products which can cause allergic asthma are bromelin, castor beans and wax, freesia, grain pollen, guar gum, papain, paprika, hops, ipecacuanha, plicatic acid, quillaic acid, saponin and sunflower pollen.

Fungi in the work environment produce many spores, some of which cause allergic asthma and/or extrinsic allergic alveolitis. However, it is rare that allergic asthma and extrinsic allergic alveolitis from those allergens occur in the same subjects. As for the causative micro-organisms, *Alternaria*, *Aspergillus niger*, *Cladosporium*, humidifier sludge, *Merulius lacrymans*, *Micropolyspora faei*, *Paecilomyces* and *Verticillium* have been identified. In most cases, antigens of fungal origin are present in spores and breakdown products.

Patients with occupational asthma caused by vegetable products always show elevated serum IgE antibody, eosinophilia and a positive prick test, whereas specific precipitating antibody, positive prick test and distinct radiological findings are seen in patients with extrinsic allergic alveolitis. In addition to pulmonary allergy to vegetable products and fungi spores, nasal symptoms are provoked in atopic patients when handling vegetables such as carrots and lettuce. Gastrointestinal complaints are not generally found.

Agrochemicals are applied for various purposes both in indoor and outdoor vegetable growing. Among the chemicals used, some have been found to have asthmatic potential. They include captafol, chlorothalonil, creosote, formaldehyde, pyrethrin and streptomycin. The improper uses of pesticides potentially can result in soil and vegetable contamination. The application of pesticides without suitable personal protective equipment can lead to both acute or chronic toxic effects.

TREE, BRAMBLE AND VINE CROPS

● BERRIES AND GRAPES

William E. Steinke

This article covers the injury and illness prevention methods against hazards commonly encountered in production of grapes (for fresh consumption, wine, juice or raisins) and berries, including brambles (i.e., raspberries), strawberries and bush berries (i.e., blueberries and cranberries).

Grapevines are stems that climb on supporting structures. Vines planted in commercial vineyards are usually started in spring from year-old rooted or grafted cuttings. They are typically planted 2 to 3.5 m apart. Each year, the vines must be dug over, fertilized, subdivided and pruned. The style of pruning varies in different parts of the world. In the system prevalent in the United States, all the shoots except the strongest ones on the vine are later pruned; the remaining shoots are cut back to 2 or 3 buds. The resulting plant develops a strong main stem which can stand alone, before it is allowed to bear fruit. During the expansion of the main stem, the vine is loosely tied to an upright support 1.8 m tall or higher. After the fruit-producing stage is reached, the vines are carefully pruned to control the number of buds.

Strawberries are planted in early spring, midsummer or later, depending on the latitude. The plants bear fruit in the spring of the following year. A variety called everbearing strawberries produces a second, smaller crop of fruit in the fall. Most strawberries are propagated naturally by means of runners that form about two months after the planting season. The fruit is found at ground level. Brambles such as raspberries are typically shrubs with prickly stems (canes) and edible fruits. The underground parts of brambles are perennial and the canes biennial; only second-year canes bear flowers and fruits. Brambles grow fruit at heights of 2 m or less. Like grapevines, berries require frequent pruning.

Growing practices differ for each fruit species, depending on the type of soil, climate and fertilizer it needs. Close control of insects and diseases is essential, often requiring frequent application of pesticides. Some modern growers have shifted toward biological controls and careful monitoring of pest populations, spraying chemicals only at the most effective times. Most grapes and berries are harvested by hand.

In a study of non-fatal injuries for the 10-year period 1981 through 1990 in California, the most common injury within this category of farms was sprains and strains, accounting for 42% of all injuries reported. Lacerations, fractures and contusions accounted for another 37% of injuries. The most common causes of injuries were being struck by an object (27%), overexertion (23%) and falls (19%) (AgSafe 1992). In a 1991 survey, Steinke (1991) found that 65% of injuries on farms identified as producing this category of crops in California were strains, sprains, lacerations, fractures and contusions. Parts of the body injured were fingers (17%), the back (15%), eyes (14%) and the hand or wrist (11%). Villarejo (1995) reported that there were 6,000 injury claims awarded per 100,000 full-time equivalents to workers in strawberry production in California in 1989. He also noted that most workers do not find employment throughout the year, so that the percentage of workers who suffer injuries could be several times higher than the 6% figure reported.

Musculoskeletal Problems

The major hazard associated with musculoskeletal injuries in these crops is rate of work. If the owner is working in the fields, she or he is typically working quickly to finish one task and move on to the next task. Hired labour is often paid by piece-rate, the practice of paying for work solely based upon what is accomplished (i.e., kilograms of berries harvested or number of grapevines pruned). This type of payment is often at odds with the extra time required to make sure fingers are out of the clipper before squeezing, or carefully walking to and from the edge of the field when exchanging filled baskets for empty ones during harvest. A high rate of work performance can lead to using poor postures, taking undue risks, and not following good safety practices and procedures.

Hand pruning of berries or vines requires the frequent squeezing of the hand to engage a clipper, or the frequent use of a knife. Hazards from the knife are obvious, as there is no solid surface against which to place the vine, shoot or stalk and frequent cuts to the fingers, hands, arms, legs and feet are likely to result. Pruning with a knife should be done only as a last resort.

Although a clipper is the preferred tool for pruning, either in the dormant season or while foliage is on the plants or vines, its use does have hazards. The major safety hazard is the threat of cuts from contact with the open blade while placing a vine or stalk in the jaws, or from inadvertent cutting of a finger while also cutting a vine or stalk. Sturdy leather or cloth gloves are good protection against both hazards and can also provide protection

against contact dermatitis, allergies, insects, bees and cuts from a trellis.

The frequency and effort required for cutting determines the likelihood of development of cumulative-trauma injuries. Although injury reports do not currently show widespread injury, this is believed to be due to the frequent job rotation found on farms. The force required to operate a common clipper is in excess of recommended values, and the frequency of effort indicates the potential for cumulative-trauma disorders, according to accepted guidelines (Miles 1996).

To minimize likelihood of injury, clippers should be kept well lubricated and blades should be sharpened frequently. When large vines are encountered, as they are frequently in grapes, the size of the clipper should be increased accordingly, so as not to overload the wrist or the clipper itself. Lopping shears or pruning saws are often required for safe cutting of large vines or plants.

Lifting and carrying of loads is typically associated with harvesting of these crops. The berries or fruit are usually hand harvested and carried in some type of basket or carrier to the edge of the field, where they are deposited. Loads are often not heavy (10 kg or less), but the distance to be travelled is significant in many cases and over uneven terrain, which may also be wet or slippery. Workers should not run on the uneven terrain and should maintain solid footing at all times.

Harvesting of these crops is often done in awkward postures and at a rapid pace. Persons typically twist and bend, bend to the ground without bending the knees and move quickly between the bush or vine and the container. Containers are sometimes placed upon the ground and pushed or pulled along with the worker. Fruit and berries can be found anywhere from ground level to 2 m in height, depending upon the crop. Brambles are typically found at heights of 1 m or less, leading to almost continuous bending of the back during harvest. Strawberries are at ground level, but workers remain on their feet and bend down to harvest.

Grapes are also commonly cut to free them from the vine during hand harvest. This cutting motion is also very frequent (hundreds of times per hour) and requires sufficient force to cause concern regarding cumulative-trauma injuries if the harvest season were to last more then a few weeks.

Working with trellises or arbours is often involved in production of vines and berries. Installing or repairing arbours frequently involves doing work at heights above one's head and stretching while exerting a force. Sustained effort of this type can lead to cumulative injuries. Each instance is an exposure to strain and sprain injury, particularly to the shoulders and arms, resulting from exerting significant force while working in an awkward posture. Training plants on trellises requires the exertion of substantial force, a force that is increased by the weight of the vines, foliage and fruit. This force is commonly exerted through the arms, shoulders and back, all of which are susceptible to both acute and long-term injury from such overexertion.

Pesticides and Fertilizers

Grapes and berries are subject to frequent pesticide applications for control of insects and disease pathogens. Applicators, mixers, loaders and anyone else in the field or assisting with the application should follow the precautions listed on the pesticide label or as required by local regulations. Applications in these crops can be particularly hazardous because of the nature of the deposit required for pest control. Frequently, all portions of the plant must be covered, including the undersides of the leaves and all surfaces of the fruit or berries. This often implies use of very small droplets and the use of air to promote canopy penetration and deposit of the pesticide. Thus many aerosols are produced, which can be hazardous through inhalation, ocular and dermal exposure routes.

Fungicides are frequently applied as dusts to grapes and many types of berries. The most common of these dusts is sulphur, which may be used in organic farming. Sulphur can be irritating to the applicator and to others in the field. It has also been known to reach air concentrations sufficient to cause explosions and fires. Care should be taken to avoid travelling through a cloud of sulphur dust with any possible ignition source, such as an engine, electric motor or other spark-producing device.

Many fields are fumigated with highly toxic materials before these crops are planted in order to reduce the population of such pests as nematodes, bacteria, fungi and viruses before they can attack the young plants. Fumigation usually involves injection of a gas or liquid into the soil and covering with a plastic sheet to prevent the pesticide from escaping too soon. Fumigation is a specialized practice and should be attempted only by those properly trained. Fumigated fields should be posted with warnings and should not be entered until the cover has been removed and the fumigant has dissipated.

Fertilizers may generate hazards during their application. Inhalation of dust, skin contact dermatitis and irritation of the lungs, throat and breathing passages may occur. A dust mask may be useful in reducing exposure to non-irritating levels.

Workers may be required to enter fields for culturing operations such as irrigation, pruning or harvest soon after pesticides have been applied. If this is sooner than the re-entry interval specified by the pesticide label or local regulations, protective clothing must be worn to protect against exposure. The minimum protection should be a long-sleeved shirt, long-legged pants, gloves, head covering, foot coverings and eye protection. More stringent protection, including a respirator, impermeable clothing and rubber boots may be required based upon the pesticide used, time since the application and regulations. Local pesticide authorities should be consulted to determine the proper level of protection.

Machine Exposures

The use of machinery in these crops is common for soil preparation, planting, weed cultivation and harvest. Many of these crops are grown on hillsides and uneven fields, increasing the chance for tractor and equipment rollovers. General safety rules of tractor and equipment operation to avoid rollovers should be followed, as should the policy of no riders on equipment unless additional personnel must be present for proper equipment operation and a platform is provided for their safety. More information on proper use of equipment can be found in the article "Mechanization" in this chapter and elsewhere in this *Encyclopaedia*.

Many of these crops are also grown in uneven fields, such as on beds or ridges or in furrows. These features increase the danger when they become muddy, slippery or concealed by weeds or the plant canopy. Falling in front of equipment is a hazard, as is falling and straining or spraining a body part. Extra precautions should be taken particularly when fields are wet or at harvest, when discarded fruit may be underfoot.

Mechanical pruning of grapes is increasing around the world. Mechanical pruning typically involves rotating knives or fingers to gather vines and draw them past stationary knives. This equipment can be hazardous to anyone in the vicinity of the entry point for the cutters and should be used only by a properly trained operator.

Harvest operations typically use several machines at once, requiring coordination and cooperation of all equipment operators. Harvesting operations also, by their very nature, include crop gathering and removal, which frequently requires the use of vibrating rods or paddles, stripping fingers, fans, cutting or slicing operations and rakes, any of which are capable of causing great physical harm to persons who become entangled in them. Care should be taken to not place any person near the intake of such machines while they are running. Machine guards should always be kept in place and maintained. If guards must be removed for lubrication, adjustment or cleaning, they should be replaced before the machine is started again. Guards on an operating machine should never be opened or removed.

Other Hazards

Infections

One of the most common injuries suffered by workers in grapes and berries is a cut or puncture, either from thorns on the plant, tools or the trellis or support structure. Such open wounds are always subject to infection from the many bacteria, viruses or infectious agents present in fields. Such infections can cause serious complications, even loss of limb or life. All field workers should be protected with an up-to-date tetanus immunization. Cuts should be washed and cleaned, and antibacterial agent applied; any infections that develop should be treated by a physician immediately.

Insect bites and bee stings

Field workers tending and harvesting are at an increased risk of insect bites and bee stings. Placing hands and fingers into the plant canopy to select and grasp ripe fruit or berries increases the exposure to bees and insects that may be foraging or resting in the canopy. Some insects may be feeding on the ripe berries also, as could rodents and other vermin. The best protection is to wear long sleeves and gloves whenever working in the foliage.

Solar radiation

Heat stress

Exposure to excessive solar radiation and heat can easily lead to heat exhaustion, heat stroke or even death. Heat added to the human body through solar radiation, the effort of work and heat transfer from the environment must be removed from the body through sweat or sensible heat loss. When ambient temperatures are above 37 °C (i.e., normal body temperature), there can be no sensible heat loss, so the body must rely solely on perspiration for cooling.

Perspiration requires water. Anyone working in the sun or in a hot climate should drink plenty of fluids over the entire day. Water or sports drinks should be used, even before one feels thirsty. Alcohol and caffeine should be avoided, as they tend to act as diuretics and actually speed water loss and interfere with the body's heat-regulating process. It is often recommended that persons drink 1 litre per hour of work in the sun or in hot climates. A sign of drinking insufficient fluids is the lack of the need to urinate.

Heat-related diseases can be life-threatening and require immediate attention. Persons suffering from heat exhaustion should be made to lie down in the shade and drink plenty of fluids. Anyone suffering from heat stroke is in grave danger and needs immediate attention. Medical assistance should be summoned immediately. If assistance is not available within a matter of minutes, one should attempt to cool the victim by immersing him or her in cool water. If the victim is unconscious, continued breathing should be assured through first aid. Do not give fluids by mouth.

Signs of heat-related diseases include excessive sweating, weakness in the limbs, disorientation, headaches, dizziness and, in extreme cases, loss of consciousness and also loss of the ability to sweat. The latter symptoms are immediately life-threatening, and action is required.

Working in vineyards and bush berry fields may increase the risk of heat-related illnesses. Air circulation is reduced between

64. AGRICULTURE AND NATURAL RESOURCE BASED INDUSTRIES

the rows, and there is the illusion of working partially in the shade. High relative humidity and cloud covers can also give one a false impression of the effects of the sun. It is necessary to drink plenty of fluids whenever working in fields.

Skin diseases

Long-term exposure to the sun can lead to premature ageing of the skin and increased likelihood of skin cancers. Persons exposed to the direct rays of the sun should wear clothing or sun-screen products to provide protection. At lower latitudes, even a few minutes of exposure to the sun can result in a severe sunburn, especially in those with fair complexions.

Skin cancers can begin on any part of the body, and suspected cancers should immediately be checked by a physician. Some of the frequent signs of skin cancers or pre-cancerous lesions are changes in a mole or birthmark, an irregular border, bleeding or a change in colour, often to a brown or gray tone. Those with a history of sun exposure should undergo annual skin cancer screenings.

Contact dermatitis and other allergies

Frequent and prolonged contact with plant excretions or plant pieces can result in sensitization and cases of contact allergies and dermatitis. Prevention through wearing long-sleeved shirts, long-legged pants and gloves whenever possible is the preferred course of action. Some creams can be used to provide a barrier to the transfer of irritants to the skin. If the skin cannot be protected from exposure to plants, washing immediately after the plant contact ends will minimize the effects. Cases of dermatitis with skin eruptions or which do not heal should be seen by a physician.

● ORCHARD CROPS

Melvin L. Myers

Generally, farms where fruit trees grow in the temperate zones are called orchards; tropical trees are typically grown in plantation or village groves. Naturally occurring fruit trees have been bred and selected over the centuries to produce a diversity of cultivars. Temperate orchard crops include the apple, pear, peach, nectarine, plum, apricot, cherry, persimmon and prune. Nut crops grown in either temperate or semitropical climates include the pecan, almond, walnut, filbert, hazelnut, chestnut and pistachio. Semitropical orchard crops include the orange, grapefruit, tangerine, lime, lemon, figs, kiwis, tangelo, kumquat, calamondin (Panama orange), citron, Javanese pomelo and date.

Orchard Systems

The growing of fruit trees involves several processes. Orchardists may choose to propagate their own stock either by planting seed or asexually through one or more cutting, budding, grafting or tissue culture techniques. Orchardists plow or disk the soil for planting the tree stock, dig holes in the soil, plant the tree and add water and fertilizer.

Growing the tree requires fertilizing, weed control, irrigation and protecting the tree from spring frost. Fertilizer is applied aggressively during the early years of a tree's growth. Components of fertilizers mixtures used include ammonium nitrate and suphate, elemental fertilizer (nitrogen, phosphorus and potassium), cottonseed meal, blood meal, fish meal, sterilized sewage sludge and urea formaldehyde (slow release). Weeds are control-

led by mulching, tilling, mowing, hoeing and applying herbicides. Insecticides and fungicides are applied with sprayers, which are tractor-drawn in the larger operations. Several pests can damage the bark or eat the fruit, including squirrels, rabbits, raccoons, opossums, mice, rats and deer. Controls include netting, live traps, electric fences and guns, as well as visual or odorous deterrents.

Spring freezes can destroy flower blooms in hours. Overhead sprinklers are used to maintain a water-ice mixture so that the temperature does not drop below freezing. Special frost-guard chemicals may be applied with the water to control ice-nucleating bacteria, which can attack damaged tree tissue. Heaters also may be used in the orchard to prevent freezing, and they may be oil-fired in open areas or electric incandescent bulbs under a plastic film supported by plastic pipe frames.

Pruning tools can transmit disease, so they are soaked in a water-chlorine bleach solution or rubbing alcohol after pruning each tree. All limbs and trimmings are removed, shredded and composted. Limbs are trained, which requires the positioning of scaffolds between limbs, building trellises, pounding vertical stakes into the soil and tying limbs to these devises.

The honey-bee is the principal pollinator of fruit trees. Partial girdling—knife cuts into the bark on each side of the trunk—of the peach and pear tree can stimulate production. To avoid excess stunting, limb breakage and irregular bearing, orchardists thin the fruit either by hand or chemically. The insecticide carbaryl (Sevin), a photo inhibitor, is used for chemical thinning.

Manual fruit picking requires climbing ladders, reaching for the fruit or nuts, placing the fruit into containers and carrying the filled container down the ladder and to a collection area. Pecans are knocked from the trees with long poles and gathered manually or by a special machine that envelopes and shakes the tree trunk and catches and automatically funnels the pecans into a container. Trucks and trailers are commonly used in the field during harvest and for transport on public roads.

Tree Crop Hazards

Orchardists use a variety of agricultural chemicals, including fertilizers, herbicides, insecticides and fungicides. Pesticide exposures occur during application, from residues during various tasks, from pesticide drift, during mixing and loading and during harvesting. Employees may also be exposed to noise, diesel exhaust, solvents, fuels and oils. Malignant melanoma is elevated for orchardists as well, especially to the trunk, scalp and arms, presumably from sunlight (ultraviolet exposure). Handling some types of fruit, especially citrus, may cause allergies or other skin problems.

Rotary mowers are popular machines for cutting weeds. These mowers are attached to and powered by tractors. Riders on tractors can fall off and be seriously injured or killed by the mower, and debris can be thrown hundreds of metres and cause injury.

The construction of fences, trellises and vertical stakes in orchards may require the use of tractor-mounted post hole diggers or post drivers. Post hole diggers are tractor-powered augers that drill holes 15 to 30 cm in diameter. Post drivers are tractor-power impact drivers for pounding posts into the soil. Both of these machines are dangerous if not operated properly.

Dry fertilizer can cause skin burns and irritation of the mouth, nose and eyes. The spinning mechanism at the rear of a centrifugal broadcast spreader is also a source of injury. Spreaders are also cleaned with diesel fuel, which presents a fire hazard.

Fatalities among orchard workers may occur from motor vehicle crashes, tractor rollovers, farm machinery incidents and electrocutions from moving irrigation pipe or ladders that come into contact with overhead power lines. For orchard work, rollover protective structures (ROPs) are commonly removed from tractors because of their interference with tree limbs.

Table 64.8 • Safety precautions for rotary mowers, post hole diggers and post drivers.

Rotary mowers (cutters)

- Avoid cutting over tree stumps, metal, and rocks, which can become projectiles thrown from the mower.
- Keep people out of the work area to avoid being struck by flying objects.
- Maintain the chain guards around the mower to prevent projectiles from being thrown from the mower.
- Do not allow riders on the tractor to avoid a fall under the mower.
- Keep PTO shields in place.
- Disengage the PTO before starting the tractor.
- Use care when turning sharp corners and pulling drawn mowers so as not to catch the mower on the tractor wheel, which can result in the mower being thrown towards the operator.
- Use front wheel weights when attached to a mower by the three-point hitch so as to keep the front wheels on the round to maintain steering control.
- Use wide-set tires if possible to add to tractor stability.
- Lower the mower to the ground before leaving it unattended.

Post hole diggers (tractor mounted augers)

- Shift the transmission into park or neutral before operation.
- Set tractor brakes before digging.
- Run the digger slowly to maintain control.
- Dig the hole in small steps.
- Never wear loose hair, clothing, or drawstrings when digging.
- Keep everyone clear of the auger and power shafts when digging.

- Stop the auger and lower it to the ground when not digging.
- Do not engage the power when unlodging an auger. Remove lodged augers manually by turning it counter clockwise and then hydraulically lift the auger with the tractor.

Post drivers (tractor mounted, impact driver)

- Shut off the tractor engine and lower the hammer before lubrication or adjustment.
- Never place hands between the top of the post and the hammer.
- Do not exceed the recommended hammer stroke per minute.
- Use a guide to hold the post during driving in case the post breaks.
- Keep hands clear of posts that are about to be driven.
- Put all shields in place before operation.
- Wear safety glasses and hearing protection during operation.

Fertilizer spreading (mechanical)

- Stay clear of the rear of fertilizer spreaders.
- Do not unplug a spreader while it is operating.
- Work in well-ventilated areas away from fire ignition sources when cleaning the spreaders with diesel fuel.
- Keep the dust off of skin, wear long sleeved shirts, and button collar when handling dry fertilizer. Wash several times a day.
- Work with the wind blowing away from work.
- Tractor operators should drive crosswind to the spreader to avoid dust blowing onto them.

Manual handling of fruit and nuts in the picking and carrying operations places orchardists at risk of sprain and strain injury. In addition, hand tools such as knives and shears are hazards for cuts in orchard work. Orchardists are also exposed to falling objects from the trees during harvesting and injury from falls from ladders.

Hazard Control

In the use of pesticides, the pest must be identified first so that the most effective control method and timing of control can be used. Safety procedures on the label should be followed, including the use of personal protective equipment. Heat stress is a hazard when wearing protective gear, so frequent rest breaks and plenty of drinking water are needed. Attention needs to be given to allowing enough reentry time to prevent hazardous exposures from pesticide residue, and pesticide drift from applications elsewhere in the orchard needs to be avoided. Good sanitary facilities are needed, and gloves may be useful to avoid skin disorders. In addition, table 64.8 shows several safety precautions in operating rotary mowers, post hole diggers, post drivers and fertilizer spreading.

Where ROPs interfere with orchard work, foldable or telescoping ROPs should be installed. The operator should not be belted into the seat when operating without a deployed ROPs. As soon as overhead clearance permits, the ROPs should be deployed and the seat belt fastened.

To prevent falls, use of the top step of the ladder should be prohibited, the ladder rungs should have anti-slip surfaces and workers should be trained and oriented on proper ladder use at the beginning of their employment. Non-conductive ladders or ladders with insulators designed into them should be used to avoid possible electrical shock if they contact a power line.

TROPICAL TREE AND PALM CROPS

Melvin L. Myers*

Although archaeological evidence is inconclusive, tropical forest trees transplanted to the village may have been the first domesticated agricultural crops. More than 200 fruit tree species have been identified in the humid tropics. Several of these trees and palms, such as the banana and coconut, are cultivated in small-holdings, cooperatives or plantations. While the date palm is completely domesticated, other species, such as the Brazil nut, are still harvested in the wild. More than 150 varieties of bananas and 2,500 palm species exist around the world, and they provide a broad range of products for human use. Sago palm wood feeds millions of people around the world. The coconut palm is used in more than 1,000 ways and the palmyra palm in more than 800 ways. About 400,000 people depend on the coconut for their entire livelihood. Several trees, fruits and palms of the tropical and semitropical zones of the world are listed in table 64.9, and table 64.10 shows selected commercial palms or palm types and their products.

Processes

The agriculture of tropical tree and palm growing includes propagation, cultivation, harvesting and post-harvesting processes.

Propagation of tropical trees and palms can be sexual or asexual. Sexual techniques are needed to produce fruit; pollination is criti-

* Some text was revised from the articles "Date palms", by D. Abed; "Raffia" and "Sisal", by E. Arreguin Velez; "Copra", by A.P. Bulengo; "Kapok", by U. Egtasaeng; "Coconut cultivation", by L.V.R. Fernando; "Bananas", by Y. Ko; "Coir", by P.V.C. Pinnagoda; and "Oil palms", by G.O. Sofoluwe from the 3rd edition of this *Encyclopaedia*.

Table 64.9 • Commercial tropical and subtropical trees, fruits and palms.

Categories	Species
Tropical and semitropical fruits (excluding citrus)	Figs, banana, jelly palm, loquat, papaya, guava, mango, kiwis, date, cherimoya, white sapota, durian, breadfruit, Surinam cherry, lychee, olive, carambola, carob, chocolate, loquat, avocado, sapodilla, japoticaba, pomegranate, pineapple
Semitropical citrus fruits	Orange, grapefruit, lime, lemon, tangerine, tangelos, calamondins, kumquats, citrons
Tropical nut trees	Cashew, Brazil, almond, pine, and macadamia nuts
Oil crops	Oil palm, olive, coconut
Insect feed	Mulberry leaf (silkworm feed), decaying sago palm pith (grub feed)
Fibre crops	Kapok, sisal, hemp, coir (coconut husk), raffia palm, piassaba palm, palmyra palm, fishtail palm
Starch	Sago palm
Vanilla bean	Vanilla orchid

cal. The date palm is doecious, and pollen from the male palm must be dispersed upon the female flowers. Pollination is done either by hand or mechanically. The manual process involves the workers climbing the tree by gripping the truck or using tall ladders to hand pollinate the female trees by placing small male clusters in the center of each female cluster. The mechanical process uses a powerful sprayer to carry the pollen over the female clusters. In addition to use for generating products, sexual techniques are used to produce seed, which is planted and cultivated into new plants. An example of an asexual technique is cutting shoots from mature plants for replanting.

Cultivation can be manual or mechanized. Banana cultivation is typically manual, but in flat terrain, mechanization with large tractors is used. Mechanical shovels may be used to dig drainage ditches in banana fields. Fertilizer is added monthly to bananas, and pesticides are applied with boom sprayers or from the air. The plants are supported with bamboo poles against storm damage. A banana plant bears fruit after two years.

Harvesting relies largely on manual labour, though some machinery is also used. Harvesters cut the banana bunches, called hands, from the tree with a knife attached to a long pole. The bunch is dropped onto a worker's shoulder and a second worker attaches a

Table 64.10 • Palm products.

Groups	Products	Uses
Coconut	Nut meat	Food, copra, animal feed
	Copra (desiccated meat)	Food, oil, oilsoap, candle, cooking oil, margarine, cosmetics, detergent, pai, coconut milk, cream, jam
	Nut water	Fuel, charcoal, bowls, scoops, cups
	Nut shells	Mats, string, potting soil mix, brush, rope, cordage
	Coir (husk)	Thatching, weaving
	Leaves	Building
	Wood	Palm honey
	Flower nectar inflorescence	Palm sugar, alcohol, arrack (palm spirits)
Date	Fruit	Dry, sweet and fine dates
	Sap	Date sugar
African oil	Fuit (palm pulp oil; similar to olive oil)	Cosmetics, margarine, dressing, fuel, lubricants
	Seeds (palm kernel oil)	Soap, glycerine
Palmyra	Leaves	Paper, shelter, weaving, fans, buckets, caps
	Petioles and leaf sheaths	Carpets, rope, twine, brooms, brushes
		Timber, sago, cabbage
	Truck	Food, fruit pulp, starch, buttons
	Fruit and seeds	Sugar, wine, alcohol, vinegar, sura (raw sap drink)
	Sap, roots	Food, diuretic
Sago (trunk pith of various species)	Starch	Meals, gruels, puddings, bread, flour
	Insect feed	Food (grubs feeding on decayed sago pith)
Cabbage (various species)	Apical bud (upper trunk)	Salads, canned palm hearts or palmito
Raffia	Leaves	Plaiting, baskets work, tying material
Sugar (various species)	Palm sap	Palm sugar (gur, jaggery)
Wax	Leaves	Candles, lipsticks, shoe polish, car polish, floor wax
Rattan cane	Stems	Furniture
Betel nut	Fruit (nut)	Stimulant (betel chewing)

nylon cord to the bunch, which is then attached to an overhead cable that moves the bunch to a tractor and trailer for transport. Tapping the coconut inflorescence for the juice entails the taper walking from tree to tree on strands of rope high above the ground. Workers climb to the tree tops to pluck the nuts manually or cut the nuts with a knife attached to long bamboo poles. In the Southwest Pacific area the nuts are allowed to fall naturally; then they are gathered. The date ripens in the fall and two or three crops are gathered, requiring climbing the tree or a ladder to the date clusters. An old system of machete harvesting of fruit bunches has been replaced by the use of a hook and pole. However, the machete is still used in harvesting many crops (e.g., sisal leaves).

Post-harvest operations vary between tree and palm and by the expected product. After harvesting, banana workers—typically women and youth—wash the bananas, wrap them in polyethylene and pack them in corrugated cardboard boxes for shipping. Sisal leaves are dried, bound and transported to the factory. Kapok fruit is field dried, and the resulting brittle fruit is broken open with a hammer or pipe. Kapok fibers are then ginned in the field to remove seeds by shaking or stirring, packed in jute sacks, batted in sacks to soften the fibers and baled. After harvest, dates are hydrated and artificially ripened. They are exposed to hot air (100 to 110 °C) to glaze the skin and semi-pasteurize them and then packaged.

The dried meaty endosperm of the coconut is marketed as *copra*, and the prepared husk of the coconut is marketed as *coir*. The fibrous nut husks are stripped off by striking and levering them against spikes firmly fixed into the ground. The nut, stripped of the husk, is split in half with an axe and dried either in the sun, kilns or hot-air dryers. After drying, the meat is separated from the hard woody shell. Copra is used to produce coconut oil, oil extraction residue called copra cake or *poonac* and desiccated food. The coir is retted (partially rotted) by soaking in water for three to four weeks. Workers remove the retted coir from the pits in waist-deep water and send it for decortication, bleaching and processing.

Hazards and Their Prevention

Hazards in tropical fruit and palm crop production include injuries, natural exposures, pesticide exposures and respiratory and dermatitis problems. Working at high elevations is required for much work with many tropical trees and palms. The popular apple banana grows to 5 m, kapok to 15 m, coconut palms to 20 to 30 m, evergreen date palm to 30 m, and the oil palm, 12 m. Falls represent one of the most serious hazards in tropical tree cultivation, and so do falling objects. Safety harnesses and head protection should be used, and workers should be trained in their use. Using dwarf varieties of the palms may help eliminate the tree falls. Falls from the kapok tree because of branches breaking and minor hand injuries during shell cracking are also hazards.

Workers can be injured during the transport on trucks or tractor-drawn trailers. Workers climbing palms receive cuts and abrasions of the hands due to contact with sharp date palm spines and oil palm fruit as well as spiny sisal leaves. Sprains from falling in ditches and holes are a problem. Severe wounds from the machete may be inflicted. Workers, typically women, who lift packed boxes of bananas are exposed to heavy weights. Tractors should have safety cabs. Workers should be trained in the safe handling of agricultural implements, machinery guarding and safe tractor operation. Puncture-resistant gloves should be worn, and arm protection and hooks should be used in harvesting the oil palm fruit. Mechanization of weeding and cultivation reduces sprains from falls in ditches and holes. Safe and proper work practices should be used, such as proper lifting, getting help when lifting to reduce individual loads and taking breaks.

Natural hazards include snakes—a problem during forest clearing and in newly established plantations—and insects as well as diseases. Health problems include malaria, ancylostomiasis, anaemia and enteric diseases. The retting operation exposes workers to parasites and skin infections. Mosquito control, sanitation and safe drinking water are important.

Pesticide poisoning is a hazard in tropical tree production, and pesticides are used in significant quantities in fruit groves. However, palms have few problems with pests, and those that are a problem are unique to specific parts of the life cycle and thus can be identified for specific control. Integrated pest management and, when applying pesticides, following the manufacturer's instructions are important protective measures.

Medical evaluations have identified cases of bronchial asthma among date workers probably from pollen exposure. Also reported among date workers are chronic dry eczema and "nail disease" (onychia). Respiratory protection should be provided during the pollination process, and workers should wear hand protection and frequently wash their hands to protect their skin when working with the trees and dates.

BARK AND SAP PRODUCTION

Melvin L. Myers *

The term *bark* refers to the multilayered protective shell covering a tree, shrub or vine. Some herbaceous plants, such as hemp, are also harvested for their bark. Bark is composed of inner and outer bark. Bark starts at the vascular cambium in the inner bark, where cells are generated for the phloem or conductive tissue that transports sugar from the leaves to the roots and other parts of the plant and the sap wood inside the bark layer with vessels that carry water (sap) up from the roots to the plant. The primary purpose of the outer bark is to protect the tree from injury, heat, wind and infection. A great variety of products are extracted from bark and tree sap, as shown in table 64.11.

Trees are grown for their bark and sap products either by cultivation or in the wild. Reasons for this choice vary. Cork oak groves have advantages over wild trees, which are contaminated by sand and grow irregularly. The control of a rubber tree leaf rust fungus in Brazil is more effective in the sparse tree spacing of the wild. However, in locations free of this fungus, such as in Asia, plantation groves are very effective for cultivating rubber trees.

Processes

Three broad processes are used in harvesting bark and sap: stripping of bark in sheets, debarking for bulk bark and bark ingredients and the extraction of tree fluids by cutting or tapping.

Bark sheets

Stripping sheets of bark from standing trees is easier when the sap is running or after steam injection between the bark and the wood. Two bark stripping technologies are described below, one for cork and the other for cinnamon.

The cork oak is cultivated in the western Mediterranean basin for cork, and Portugal is the largest cork producer. The cork oak, as well as other trees such as the African baobab tree, share the important feature of regrowing outer bark after its removal. Cork

* Some text was revised from the articles "Hemp", by A. Barbero-Carnicero; "Cork", by C. de Abeu; "Rubber cultivation", by the Dunlop Co.; "Turpentine", by W. Grimm and H. Gries; "Tanning and leather finishing", by V.P. Gupta; "Spice industry", by S. Hruby; "Camphor", by Y. Ko; "Resins", by J. Kubota; "Jute", by K.M. Myunt; and "Bark", by F.J. Wenzel from the 3rd edition of this *Encyclopaedia*.

Table 64.11 • Bark and sap products and uses.

Commodity	Product (tree)	Use
Resins (inner bark)	Pine resin, copal, frankincense, myrrh, red resin (climbing palm)	Varnish, shellac, lacquer Incense, perfume, dye
Oleoresins (sapwood)	Turpentine Rosin Benzoin Camphor (camphor laurel tree)	Solvent, thinner, perfume feedstock, disinfectant, pesticide Violin bow treatment, varnish, paint, sealing wax, adhesive, cement, soap Gymnast's powder Perfume, incense, plastic and film feedstock, lacquers, smokeless powder explosives, perfumes, disinfectants, insect repellents
Latex	Rubber Gutta-percha	Tyres, balloons, gaskets, condoms, gloves Insulators, underground and marine cable coatings, golf balls, surgical appliances, some adhesives, chicle/base for chewing gum
Medicines and poisons (bark)	Witch hazel Cascara Quinine (cinchona) Cherry Pacific yew Curarine Caffeine (yoco vine) Lonchocarpus vine	Lotions Emetic Anti-malaria medicinal Cough medicine Ovarian cancer treatment Arrow poison Amazonian soft drink Fish asphyxiate
Flavours (bark)	Cinnamon (cassia tree) Bitters, nutmeg and mace, cloves, sassafras root	Spice, flavouring Root beer (until linked to liver cancer)
Tannins (bark)	Hemlock, oak, acacia, wattle, willow, mangrove, mimosa, quebracho, sumach, birch	Vegetable tanning for heavier leathers, food processing, fruit ripening, beverage (tea, coffee, wine) processing, ink colouring ingredient, dyeing mordants
Cork (outer bark)	Natural cork (cork oak), reconstituted cork	Buoy, bottle cap, gasket, cork paper, cork board, acoustic tile, shoe inner sole
Fibre (bark)	Cloth (birch, tapa, fig, hibiscus, mulberry) Baobab tree (inner) bark Jute (linden family) Bast from flax, hemp (mulberry family), ramie (nettle family)	Canoe, paper, loincloth, skirt, drapery, wall hanging, rope, fishing net, sack, coarse clothing Hat Hessians, sackings, burlap, twine, carpets, clothing Cordage, linen
Sugar	Sugar maple syrup (sapwood) Gur (many palm species)	Condiment syrup Palm sugar
Waste bark	Bark chips, strips	Soil conditioner, mulch (chips), garden pathway covering, fiberboard, particleboard, hardboard, chipboard, fuel

is part of the outer bark that lies beneath the hard outer shell called the rhytidome. The thickness of the cork layer increases year-by-year. After an initial bark removal, harvesters cut regrown cork every 6 to 10 years. Stripping the cork involves cutting two circular and one or more vertical cuts without damaging the inner bark. The cork worker uses a bevelled hatchet handle to remove the cork sheets. The cork is then boiled, scraped and cut into marketable sizes.

Cinnamon tree cultivation has spread from Sri Lanka to Indonesia, East Africa and the West Indies. An ancient tree management technique is still used in cinnamon cultivation (as well as willow and cascara tree cultivation). The technique is called *coppicing*, from the French word *couper*, meaning to cut. In neolithic times, humans discovered that when a tree is cut close to the ground, a mass of similar, straight branches would sprout from the root around the stump, and that these stems could be regenerated by regular cutting just above ground. The cinnamon tree can grow to 18 m but is maintained as 2-metre-high coppices. The main stem is cut at three years, and the resulting coppices are harvested every two to three years. After cutting and bundling the

coppices, the cinnamon gatherers slit the bark sides with a sharp, curved knife. They then strip the bark off and after one to two days separate the outer and inner bark. The outer corky layer is scraped off with a broad, blunt knife and discarded. The inner bark (phloem) is cut into 1-metre lengths called quills; these are the familiar cinnamon sticks.

Bulk bark and ingredients

In the second major process, bark may also be removed from cut trees in large rotating containers called debarking drums. Bark, as a byproduct of lumber, is used as fuel, fibre, mulch or tannin. Tannin is among the most important bark products and is used to produce leather from animal skins and in food processing (see the chapter *Leather, fur and footwear*). Tannins are derived from a variety of tree barks around the world by open diffusion or percolation.

In addition to tannin, many barks are harvested for their ingredients, which include witch hazel and camphor. Witch hazel is a lotion extracted by steam distillation of twigs from the North American witch hazel tree. Similar processes are used in harvesting camphor from branches of the camphor laurel tree.

Tree fluids

The third major process includes the harvesting of resin and latex from the inner bark and oeloresins and syrup from the sapwood. Resin is found especially in the pine. It oozes out of bark wounds to protect the tree from infection. To commercially obtain resin, the worker must wound the tree by peeling off a thin layer of the bark or piercing it.

Most resins thicken and harden when exposed to the air, but some trees produce liquid resins or oleoresins, such as turpentine from conifers. Severe wounds are made into one side of the tree wood to harvest turpentine. The turpentine runs down the wound and is collected and hauled to storage. Turpentine is distilled into turpentine oil with a colophony or rosin residue.

Any milky sap exuded by plants is called latex, which in rubber trees is formed in the inner bark. Latex gatherers tap the rubber trees with spiral cuts around the trunk without damaging the inner bark. They catch the latex in a bowl (see the chapter *Rubber industry*). The latex is kept from hardening either through coagulation or with an ammonium hydroxide fixative. Acid wood smoke in the Amazon or formic acid is used to coagulate raw rubber. Crude rubber is then shipped for processing.

In the early spring in the cold climates of the United States, Canada, and Finland, a syrup is harvested from the sugar maple tree. After the sap starts to run, spouts are placed into drilled holes in the trunk through which sap runs either into buckets or through plastic piping for transport to storage tanks. The sap is boiled to 1/40th of its original volume to produce maple syrup. Reverse osmosis may be used to remove much of the water prior to evaporation. The concentrated syrup is cooled and bottled.

Hazards and Their Prevention

The hazards related to producing bark and sap for processing are natural exposures, injuries, pesticide exposures, allergies and dermatitis. Natural hazards include snake and insect bites and the potential for infection where vector-borne or water-borne diseases are endemic. Mosquito control is important on plantations, and pure water supply and sanitation is important at any tree farm, grove or plantation.

Much of the work with bark stripping, cutting and tapping involves the possibility of cuts, which should be promptly treated to prevent infection. Hazards exist in the manual cutting of trees, but mechanized methods of clearing as well as planting have reduced injury hazards. The use of heat for "smoking" rubber and evaporating oils from bark, resins and sap expose workers to burns. Hot maple syrup exposes workers to scalding injuries during boiling. Special hazards include working with draught animals or vehicles, tool-related injuries and the lifting of bark or containers. Bark stripping machines expose workers to potentially serious injury as well as to noise. Injury control techniques are needed, including safe work practices, personal protection and engineering controls.

Pesticide exposures, especially to the herbicide sodium arsenite on rubber plantations, are potentially hazardous. These exposures can be controlled by following manufacturer recommendations for storage, mixing and spraying.

Allergic proteins have been identified in natural rubber sap, which has been associated with latex allergy (Makinen-Kiljunen et al. 1992). Substances in pine resin and sap can cause allergic reactions in persons sensitive to balsam-of-Peru, colophony or turpentine. Resins, terpenes and oils may cause allergic contact dermatitis in workers handling unfinished wood. Dermal exposures to latex, sap and resin should be avoided through safe work practices and protective clothing.

The disease hypersensitivity pneumonitis is also known as "maple stripper's lung". It is caused by exposure to the spores of *Cryptostroma corticate*, a black mould that grows under the bark, during bark removal from stored maple. Progressive pneumonitis may also be associated with sequoia and cork oak woods. Controls include eliminating the sawing operation, wetting the material during debarking with a detergent and ventilation of the debarking area.

BAMBOO AND CANE

*Melvin L. Myers and Y.C. Ko**

Bamboo, which is a subfamily of the grasses, exists as more than a thousand different species, but only a few species are cultivated in commercial plantations or nurseries. Bamboos are tree-like or shrubby grasses with woody stems, called *culms*. They range from small plants with centimetre-thick culms to giant subtropical species up to 30 m tall and 30 cm in diameter. Some bamboos grow at a prodigious rate, up to 16 cm in height per day. Bamboos rarely flower (and when they do, it may be at intervals of 120 years), but they can be cultivated by planting their stalks. Most bamboos came from Asia, where they grow wild in tropical and subtropical areas. Some species have been exported to temperate climates, where they require irrigation and special care during the winter.

Some bamboo species are used as vegetables and may be pickled or preserved. Bamboo has been used as an oral medicine against poisoning since it contains silicic acid which absorbs poison in the stomach. (Silicic acid is now produced synthetically.)

The wood-like properties of bamboo culms have led to their use for many other purposes. Bamboo is used in building houses, with the culms as uprights and the walls and roofs made from split stems or lattice work. Bamboo is also used for making boats and boat masts, rafts, fences, furniture, containers and handicraft products, including umbrellas and walking sticks. Other uses abound: water pipes, wheelbarrow axles, flutes, fishing rods, scaffolding, roller-blinds, ropes, rakes, brooms and weapons such as bows and arrows. In addition, bamboo pulp has been used to make high-quality paper. It is also grown in nurseries and used in gardens as ornamentals, wind breaks and hedges (Recht and Wetterwald 1992).

Cane is sometimes confused with bamboo, but is botanically different and comes from varieties of the rattan palm. Rattan palms grow freely in tropical and subtropical areas, particularly in Southeast Asia. Cane is used to make furniture (especially chairs), baskets, containers and other handicraft products. It is very popular due to its appearance and elasticity. It is frequently necessary to split the stems when cane is used in manufacturing.

Cultivation Processes

The processes for cultivating bamboo include propagation, planting, watering and feeding, pruning and harvesting. Bamboos are propagated in two ways: by planting seeds or by using sections of the rhizome (the underground stem). Some plantations depend upon natural reseeding. Since some bamboos flower infrequently and seeds remain viable only for a couple of weeks, most propagation is accomplished by dividing a large plant that includes the rhizome with culms. Spades, knives, axes or saws are used to divide the plant.

Growers plant bamboo in groves, and planting and replanting bamboo involves digging a hole, placing the plant into the hole and backfilling soil around its rhizomes and roots. About 10 years is required to establish a healthy grove of bamboo. Although not a

---

* Adapted from Y.C. Ko's article, "Bamboo and cane", *Encyclopaedia of Occupational Health and Safety*, 3rd edition.

concern in its native habitat where it rains often, irrigation is necessary when bamboos are grown in drier areas. Bamboo requires a lot of fertilizer, particularly nitrogen. Both animal dung and commercial fertilizer are used. Silica (SiO_2) is as important for bamboos as is nitrogen. In natural growth, bamboo gains enough silica naturally by recycling it from shed leaves. In commercial nurseries, shed leaves are left around the bamboo and silica-rich clay minerals such as Bentonite may be added. Bamboos are pruned of old and dead culms to provide room for new growth. In Asian groves, dead culms may be split in the fields to hasten their decay and add to the soil's humus.

Bamboo is harvested either as a food or for its wood or pulp. Bamboo shoots are harvested for food. They are dug from the soil and cut with a knife or chopped with an axe. The bamboo culms are harvested when they are 3 to 5 years old. Harvesting is timed for when the culms are neither too soft nor too hard. Bamboo culms are harvested for their wood. They are cut or chopped with a knife or an axe, and the cut bamboo may be heated to bend it or split with a knife and mallet, depending upon its end use.

Rattan palm cane is usually harvested from wild trees often in uncultivated mountainous areas. The stems of the plants are cut near the roots, dragged out from thickets and sun-dried. The leaves and the bark are then removed, and the stems are sent for processing.

Hazards and Their Prevention

Venomous snakes present a hazard in plantation groves. Stumbling over bamboo stumps may cause falls, and cuts can lead to tetanus infection. Bird and chicken droppings in bamboo groves can be contaminated with *Histoplasma capsulatum* (Storch et al. 1980). Working with bamboo culms can lead to knife cuts, particularly when splitting the culms. Sharp edges and the ends of bamboos can cause cuts or punctures. Hyperkeratosis of the palms and fingers has been observed in workers who make bamboo containers. Pesticide exposures are also possible. First aid and medical treatment is required to deal with snake bites. Vaccine and booster vaccine should be used to prevent tetanus.

All cutting knives and saws should be maintained and used with care. Where bird droppings are present, work should be conducted during wet conditions to prevent dust exposure, or respiratory protection should be used.

In harvesting palm cane, workers are exposed to the dangers of remote forests, including snakes and venomous insects. The bark of the tree has thorns that may tear the skin, and workers are exposed to cuts from knives. Gloves should be worn when the stems are handled. Cuts are also a risk during manufacture, and hyperkeratosis of the palms and fingers may often occur among workers, probably because of the friction of the material.

SPECIALITY CROPS

• TOBACCO CULTIVATION

Gerald F. Peedin

Tobacco (*Nicotiana tabacum*) is a unique plant with its characteristic commercial component, nicotine, contained in its leaves. Although cotton is grown on more surface area, tobacco is the most widely grown nonfood crop in the world; it is produced in approximately 100 countries and on every continent. Tobacco is consumed around the world as cigarettes, cigars, chewing or smoking tobaccos and snuff. However, over 80% of world production is consumed as cigarettes, currently estimated at nearly 5.6 trillion annually. China, the United States, Brazil and India produced over 60% of total world production in 1995, which was estimated at 6.8 million tonnes.

The specific uses of tobacco by manufacturers are determined by the chemical and physical properties of the cured leaves, which in turn are determined by interactions among genetic, soil, climatic and cultural management factors. Therefore, many kinds of tobacco are grown in the world, some with rather specific local, commercial uses in one or more tobacco products. In the United States alone, tobacco is categorized into seven major classes which contain a total of 25 different tobacco types. The specific techniques used to produce tobacco vary among and within tobacco classes in various countries, but cultural manipulation of nitrogen fertilization, plant density, time and height of topping, harvesting and curing are used to favourably influence the usability of the cured leaves for specific products; quality of leaves, however, is highly dependent on prevailing environmental conditions.

Flue-cured, Burley and Oriental tobaccos are the major components of the increasingly popular blended cigarette now consumed worldwide, and represented 57, 11 and 12%, respectively, of world production in 1995. Thus, these tobaccos are widely traded internationally; the United States and Brazil are the major exporters of flue-cured and Burley leaf tobaccos, while Turkey and Greece are the major world suppliers of Oriental tobacco. The world's largest tobacco producer and cigarette manufacturer, China, currently consumes most of its production internally. Because of increasing demand for the "American" blended cigarette, the United States became the major cigarette exporter in the early 1990s.

Tobacco is a transplanted crop. In most countries, seedlings are started from tiny seeds (about 12,000 per gram) sown by hand on well-prepared soil beds and manually removed for transplanting to the field after reaching a height of 15 to 20 cm. In tropical climates, seed-beds are usually covered with dried plant materials to preserve soil moisture and reduce disturbance of seeds or seedlings by heavy rains. In cooler climates, seed-beds are covered for frost and freeze protection with one of several synthetic materials or with cotton cheesecloth until several days before transplanting. The bed sites are usually treated before seeding with methyl bromide or dazomet to manage most weeds and soilborne diseases and insects. Herbicides for supplemental grass management are also labelled for use in some countries, but in areas where labour is plentiful and inexpensive, weeds and grasses are often removed by hand. Foliar insects and diseases are usually managed with periodic applications of appropriate pesticides. In the United States and Canada, seedlings are produced primarily in greenhouses covered with plastic and glass, respectively. Seedlings are usually grown in peat- or muck-based media which, in Canada, are steam-sterilized before seeds are sown. In the United States, polystyrene trays are predominantly used to contain the media and are often treated with methyl bromide and/or a chlorine bleach solution between transplant production seasons to protect against fungal diseases. However, only a few pesticides are labelled in the United States for use in tobacco greenhouses, so farmers there depend substantially on proper ventilation, horizontal air movement and sanitation to manage most foliar diseases.

Regardless of the method of transplant production, seedlings are periodically clipped or mowed above the apical meristems for several weeks before transplanting to improve uniformity and survival after transplanting to the field. Clipping is performed mechanically in some developed countries but manually where labour is plentiful (see figure 64.28).

Depending on availability and cost of labour and equipment, seedlings are manually or mechanically transplanted to well-prepared fields previously treated with one or more pesticides for control of soil pathogens and/or grasses (see figure 64.29). In order to protect workers from pesticide exposure, pesticides are seldom applied during the transplanting operation, but additional weed and foliar pest management are often needed during subsequent growth and harvesting of the crop. In many countries, varietal tolerance and 2- to 4-year rotations of tobacco with non-host crops (where sufficient land is available) are widely used to reduce reliance on pesticides. In Zimbabwe, government regulations require seedling beds and stalks/roots in harvested fields to be destroyed by certain dates to reduce the incidence and spread of insect-transmitted viruses.

Depending upon tobacco type, fields receive relatively moderate-to-high rates of fertilizer nutrients, which are usually applied by hand in developing countries. For proper ripening and curing of flue-cured tobacco, it is necessary for nitrogen absorption to decrease rapidly soon after vegetative growth is complete. Therefore, animal manures are not routinely applied to flue-cured soils, and only 35 to 70 kg per hectare of inorganic nitrogen from commercial fertilizers are applied, depending on soil characteristics and rainfall. Burley and most chewing and cigar tobaccos are usually grown on more fertile soils than those used for flue-cured tobacco, but receive 3 to 4 times more nitrogen to enhance certain desirable characteristics of these tobaccos.

Tobacco is a flowering plant with a central meristem which suppresses growth of axillary buds (suckers) by hormonal action until the meristem begins to produce flowers. For most tobacco types, removal of flowers (topping) before seed maturation and control of subsequent sucker growth are common cultural practices used to improve yields by diverting more growth resources into leaf production. Flowers are removed manually or mechanically (primarily in the United States) and sucker growth retarded in most countries with applications of contact and/or systemic growth regulators. In the United States, suckercides are applied mechanically on flue-cured tobacco, which has the longest harvest season of the tobacco types produced in that country. In underdeveloped countries, suckercides are often applied manually. However, regardless of the chemicals and application methods used, complete control is seldom achieved, and some hand labour is usually needed to remove suckers not controlled by the suckercides.

Harvesting practices vary substantially among tobacco types. Flue-cured, Oriental and cigar wrapper are the only types whose leaves are consistently harvested (primed) in sequence as they ripen (senesce) from the bottom to the top of the plant. As leaves ripen, their surfaces become textured and yellow as chlorophyll degrades. Several leaves are removed from each plant in each of several passes over the field during a period of 6 to 12 weeks after topping, depending on rainfall, temperature, soil fertility and variety. Other tobacco types such as Burley, Maryland, cigar binder and filler, and fire-cured chewing tobaccos are "stalk cut", meaning that the entire plant is cut off near ground level when most of the leaves are judged to be ripe. For some air-cured types, the lower leaves are primed while the remainder of the plant is stalk cut. Regardless of tobacco type, harvesting and preparation of the leaves for curing and marketing are the most labour-intensive tasks in tobacco production (see figure 64.30). Harvesting is normally accomplished with manual labour, especially for stalk cutting, which has yet to be totally mechanized (see figure 64.31). Priming of flue-cured tobacco is now highly mechanized in most developed countries, where labour is scarce and expensive. In the United States, about one-half of the flue-cured type is primed with machines, which requires almost complete weed and sucker control to minimize content of these materials in the cured leaves.

Figure 64.28 • Manual clipping of tobacco seedlings with shears in Zimbabwe.

Gerald Peedin

Proper curing of most tobacco types requires management of temperature and moisture content within the curing structure to regulate the drying rate of green leaves. Flue-curing requires the most sophisticated curing structures because temperature and moisture control follow rather specific schedules, and temperatures reach over 70 °C in the latter stages of curing, which totals only 5 to 8 days. In North America and Western Europe, flue-curing is accomplished primarily in gas- or oil-fired metal (bulk) barns equipped with automatic or semiautomatic temperature- and humidity-control devices. In most other countries, the barn environment is controlled manually and the barns are constructed of wood or bricks and often fired by hand with wood (Brazil) or coal (Zimbabwe). The initial and most important stage of flue-

Figure 64.29 • Mechanical transplanting of flue-cured tobacco in North Carolina (US).

Gerald Peedin

About 4 to 5 hectares per day can be transplanted using ten workers and a four-row transplanter. Six workers are needed for a two-row transplanter and four workers for a one-row transplanter.

Figure 64.30 • Preparing Oriental tobacco for air-curing soon after hand harvesting.

The small leaves are collected on a string by pushing a needle through the central vein of each leaf.

curing is called *yellowing*, during which chlorophyll is degraded and most carbohydrates are converted to simple sugars, giving cured leaves a characteristic sweet aroma. The leaf cells are then killed with drier and hotter air to stop respiratory losses of sugars. The products of combustion do not contact the leaves. Most other tobacco types are air-cured in barns or sheds without heat, but usually with some means of partial, manual ventilation control. The air-curing process requires 4 to 8 weeks, depending on prevailing environmental conditions and the ability to control humidity within the barn. This longer, gradual process results in cured

Figure 64.31 • Hand harvesting of flue-cured tobacco by a small farmer in southern Brazil.

Some farmers use small tractors rather than oxen to pull sleds or trailers. Over 90% of harvesting and other labour is provided by family members, relatives and/or neighbours.

leaves with low sugar contents. Fire-cured tobacco, used primarily in chewing and snuff products, is basically air-cured but small, open fires using oak or hickory wood are used to periodically "smoke" the leaves to give them a characteristic wood odour and taste and to improve their keeping properties.

The colours of cured leaves and their uniformity within a lot of tobacco are important characteristics used by buyers to determine the usefulness of tobaccos for specific products. Therefore, leaves with undesirable colours (particularly green, black and brown) are usually manually removed by farmers before offering the tobacco for sale (see figure 64.32). In most countries, the cured tobaccos are further separated into homogeneous lots based on variations in leaf colour, size, texture and other visual characteristics (see figure 64.33). In some southern African countries, where labour is plentiful and inexpensive and most of the production is exported, a crop may be sorted into 60 or more lots (i.e., grades) before being sold (as in figure 64.33). Most tobacco types are packaged in bales weighing 50 to 60 kg (100 kg in Zimbabwe) and delivered to the purchaser in the cured form (see figure 64.34). In the United States, flue-cured tobacco is marketed in burlap sheets averaging about 100 kg each; however, use of bales weighing over 200 kg is currently being evaluated. In most countries, tobacco is produced and sold under contract between the farmer and the purchaser, with predetermined prices for the various grades. In a few large tobacco-producing countries, annual production is controlled by government regulation or by farmer-buyer negotiation, and the tobacco is sold in an auction system with (United States and Canada) or without (Zimbabwe) minimum established prices for the various grades. In the United States, flue-cured or Burley tobacco not sold to commercial buyers is purchased for price support by grower-owned cooperatives and sold later to domestic and foreign buyers. Although some marketing systems have been substantially mechanized, such as that in Zimbabwe (shown in figure 64.35), a great deal of manual labour is still required to unload and present the tobacco for sale, remove it from the sale area and load and transport it to the buyer's processing facilities.

Hazards and Their Prevention

The manual labour required to produce and market tobacco varies greatly around the world, depending primarily on the level of mechanization used for transplanting, harvesting and market preparation. Manual labour involves risks of musculoskeletal problems from activities such as transplanting seedlings, applica-

Figure 64.32 • Manual removal of cured Burley leaves from the stalks.

Figure 64.33 • Manual separation of cured flue-cured tobacco into homogeneous grades in Zimbabwe.

Gerald Peedin

tion of suckercides, harvesting, separation of the cured tobacco into grades and lifting of tobacco bales. Training in proper lifting methods and provision of ergonomically designed tools can help prevent these problems. Knife injuries may occur during cutting, and tetanus may arise in open wounds. Sharp, well-designed knives and training in their use can reduce the number of injuries.

Mechanization can reduce these risks, but carries risks of injury from the machinery used, including transportation accidents.

Figure 64.34 • Loading tobacco bales for transport from the farm to a marketing centre in southern Brazil.

Gerald Peedin

Figure 64.35 • Unloading a farmer's tobacco bales at the auction centre in Zimbabwe, which has the most mechanized and efficient flue-cured marketing system in the world.

Gerald Peedin

Well-designed tractors with safety cabs, properly guarded machinery and adequate training can reduce the number of injuries.

Spraying of pesticides and fungicides can involve the risk of chemical exposures. In the United States, the Environmental Protection Administration (EPA) Worker Protection Standard requires farmers to protect workers from pesticide-related illness or injury by (1) providing training on pesticide safety, specifically those pesticides used on the farm; (2) providing personal protective equipment (PPE) and clothing and assuming responsibility for their proper use and cleaning, plus ensuring that workers do not enter treated fields during specific time intervals after pesticide application; and (3) providing decontamination sites and emergency assistance in case of exposure. Substitution of less hazardous pesticides should also be done where possible.

Field labourers, usually those not accustomed to working in tobacco fields, sometimes become nauseous and/or dizzy soon after direct contact with green tobacco during harvesting, perhaps because nicotine or other substances are absorbed through the skin. In the United States, the condition is called "green tobacco sickness" and affects a small percentage of workers. Symptoms occur most often when sensitive individuals are harvesting wet tobacco and their clothing and/or exposed skin is in almost continuous contact with green tobacco. The condition is temporary and not known to be serious, but causes some discomfort for several hours after exposure. Suggestions for sensitive workers to minimize exposure during harvesting or other tasks requiring prolonged contact with green tobacco include not starting work until the leaves have dried or wearing lightweight rain gear and waterproof gloves when the leaves are wet; wearing long trousers, long-sleeve shirts and possibly gloves as precautions when working in dry tobacco; and leaving the field and washing immediately if symptoms occur.

Skin diseases may occur in workers handling tobacco leaf in warehouses or barns. Sometimes workers in these storage areas, especially new workers, may develop conjunctivitis and laryngitis.

Other preventive measures include good washing and other sanitary facilities, provision of first aid and medical care, and proper training.

GINSENG, MINT AND OTHER HERBS

Larry J. Chapman

There is no standard definition for the term *herb*, and the distinction between the herbs and spice plants is unclear. This article provides an overview of general aspects of some herbs. There are more than 200 herbs, which we are here considering to be those plants originally grown mainly in temperate or Mediterranean climates for their leaves, stems and flowering tops. The primary use for herbs is to flavour foods. Important culinary herbs include basil, bay or laurel leaf, celery seed, chervil, dill, marjoram, mint, oregano, parsley, rosemary, sage, savory, tarragon and thyme. The major demand for culinary herbs comes from the retail sector, followed by the food processing and food service sectors. The United States is by far the major consumer of culinary herbs, followed by the United Kingdom, Italy, Canada, France and Japan. Herbs are also used in cosmetics and pharmaceutical products to impart desirable flavours and odours. Herbs are used medicinally by the pharmaceutical industry and in the practice of herbal medicine.

Ginseng

Ginseng root is used in the practice of herbal medicine. China, the Republic of Korea and the United States are major producers. In China, most operations have historically been plantations owned and run by the government. In the Republic of Korea, the industry is made up of more than 20,000 family operations, most of which are smallholdings, family operations that plant less than an acre each year. In the United States, the largest proportion of producers work on smallholdings and plant less than two acres per year. However, the largest proportion of the US crop is produced by a minority of growers with a hired workforce and mechanization that allows them to plant as much as 60 acres per year. Ginseng is usually grown in open field plots covered by artificial shade structures that simulate the effects of the forest canopy.

Ginseng is also grown in intensively cultivated forest plots. A few per cent of the world's production (and most organic ginseng) is gathered by wild collectors. The roots take 5 to 9 years to reach marketable size. In the United States, bed preparation for either forest plot or open field methods is typically accomplished by a tractor-towed plow. Some hand labour may be required to clear ditches and give the beds their final shape. Mechanized planters pulled behind a tractor are often used for seeding, although the more labour-intensive practice of transplanting nursery seedlings into beds is common in the Republic of Korea and China. Constructing the 7- to 8-foot-high pole and wood lath or cloth shade structures over open field plots is labour intensive and involves considerable lifting and overhead work. In Asia, locally available woods and thatch or woven reeds are used in the shade structures. In mechanized operations in the United States, mulching the plants is accomplished with straw shredders which are adapted from machines used in the strawberry industry and pulled behind a tractor.

Depending on the adequacy and condition of machine guarding, contact with the tractor PTO shaft, the straw shredder's intake or other moving machinery parts can present a risk of entanglement injury. For each year until harvest, three hand weedings are required, which involve crawling, bending and stooping to work at crop level and which place high demands on the musculoskeletal system. Weeding, especially for the first- and second-year plants, is intensive work. One acre of field-grown ginseng may require more than 3,000 total hours of weeding over the 5 to 9 years preceding harvest. New chemical and non-chemical weed control methods, including better mulching, may be able to reduce the musculoskeletal demands posed by weeding. New tools and mechanization also hold promise for reducing the demands of weeding work. In Wisconsin, US, some herb growers are testing an adapted pedal cycle that allows weeding in a seated posture.

Artificial shade creates an especially humid environment susceptible to fungus and mould infestation. Fungicides are routinely applied at least monthly in the United States with tractor-towed application machinery or backpack garden sprayers. Insecticides are also spray applied as needed, and rodenticides put out. The use of lower-toxicity chemicals, improvements in application machinery and alternative pest management practices are strategies for reducing the repeated, low-dose pesticide exposures experienced by employees.

When the roots are ready for harvest, the shade structures are disassembled and stored. Mechanized operations utilize digging machinery adapted from the potato industry which is towed behind a tractor. Here again, inadequate machine guarding of the tractor PTO and moving machinery parts may present a risk of entanglement injuries. Picking, the last step in harvesting, involves hand labour and bending and stooping to gather roots from the soil surface.

On smaller holdings in the United States, China and the Republic of Korea, most or all of the steps in the production process are typically done by hand.

Mint and Other Herbs

There is considerable diversity in herb production methods, geographical locations, work methods and hazards. Herbs can be collected in the wild or grown under cultivation. Cultivated plant production has the advantages of greater efficiency, more consistent quality and timing of the harvest, and the potential for mechanization. Much of the mint and other herb production in the United States is highly mechanized. Soil preparation, planting, cultivation, pest control and harvesting are all done from the seat of a tractor with towed machinery.

Potential hazards resemble those in other mechanized crop production and include motor vehicle collisions on public roads, traumatic injuries involving tractors and machinery and agricultural chemical poisonings and burns.

More labour-intensive cultivation methods are typical in Asia, North Africa, the Mediterranean and other areas (e.g., mint production in China, India, the Philippines and Egypt). Plots are ploughed, often with animals, and then beds are prepared and fertilized by hand. Depending on the climate, a network of irrigation trenches is excavated. Depending on the type of herb produced, seeds, cuttings, seedlings or rhizome portions are planted. Periodic weeding is especially labour intensive and the day-long shifts of stooping, bending and pulling place high demands on the musculoskeletal system. Despite extensive use of manual labour, weed control in herb cultivation is sometimes inadequate. For a few crops, chemical weeding with herbicides, sometimes followed by manual weeding, is used, but herbicide use is not widespread since herb crops are often herbicide sensitive. Mulching crops can reduce weeding labour needs as well as conserve soil and soil moisture. Mulching also generally aids plant growth and yield, since mulch adds organic matter to soils as it decomposes.

Aside from weeding, labour-intensive soil preparation methods, planting, construction of shade or support structures, harvesting and other operations can also result in high musculoskeletal demands for prolonged periods. Modifications in production methods, specialized hand tools and techniques, and mechanization are possible directions to explore for reducing musculoskeletal and labour demands.

The potential for pesticide and other agricultural chemical burns and poisonings can be a concern on labour-intensive operations since backpack sprayers and other manual application methods may not prevent adverse exposures via the skin, mucous membranes or breathing air. Work in greenhouse production poses special hazards due to the confined breathing atmosphere. Substituting lower toxicity chemicals and alternative pest management strategies, improving application equipment and application practices, and making better PPE available may be ways to reduce risks.

The extraction of volatile oils from the harvested crop is common for certain herbs (e.g., mint stills). Cut and chopped plant material is loaded into an enclosed wagon or other structure. Boilers produce live steam which is forced into the sealed structure through low-pressure hoses, and the oil is floated and extracted from the resulting vapour.

Possible hazards associated with the process include burns from live steam and, less frequently, boiler explosions. Preventive measures include regular inspections of boilers and live steam lines to ensure structural integrity.

Herb production with low levels of mechanization may require prolonged close contact with plant surfaces and oils and, less often, associated dusts. Some reports are available in the medical literature of sensitization reactions, occupational dermatitis, occupational asthma and other respiratory and immunological problems associated with a number of herbs and spices. The available literature is small and may reflect underreporting rather than a low likelihood of health problems.

Occupational dermatitis has been associated with mint, laurel, parsley, rosemary and thyme, as well as cinnamon, chicory, cloves, garlic, nutmeg and vanilla. Occupational asthma or respiratory symptoms have been associated with dust from Brazilian ginseng and parsley as well as black pepper, cinnamon, cloves, coriander, garlic, ginger, paprika and red chillies (capsaicin), along with bacteria and endotoxins in dusts from grains and herbs. However, most cases have occurred in the processing industry, and only a few of these reports have described problems arising directly from exposures incurred in herb cultivation work (e.g., dermatitis after parsley picking, asthma after chicory root handling, immunologic reactivity after greenhouse work with paprika plants). In most reports, a proportion of the workforce develops problems while other employees are less affected or asymptomatic.

Processing Industry

The herb and spice crop processing industry represents a higher order of magnitude exposure to certain hazards than herb crop cultivation. For example, the grinding, crushing and mixing of leaves, seeds and other plant materials can involve work in noisy, extremely dusty conditions. Hazards in herb processing operations include hearing loss, traumatic injuries from inadequately guarded moving machinery parts, dust exposures in breathing air, and dust explosions. Closed processing systems or enclosures for machinery can reduce noise. Feed openings of grinding machines should not permit the entry of hands or fingers.

Health conditions including skin diseases, irritation of the eyes, mouth and gastrointestinal tract, and respiratory and immunological problems have been linked to dusts, fungi and other air contaminants. Self selection based on ability to tolerate health effects has been noted in spice grinders, usually within the first 2 weeks of work. Segregation of the process, effective local exhaust ventilation, improved dust collection, regular mopping and vacuuming of

work areas, and personal protective equipment can help reduce risks from dust explosions and contaminants in breathing air.

MUSHROOMS

L.J.L.D. Van Griensven

The world's most widely cultivated edible fungi are: the common white button mushroom, *Agaricus bisporus*, with an annual production in 1991 of approximately 1.6 million tonnes; the oyster mushroom, *Pleurotus* spp. (about 1 million tonnes); and the shiitake, *Lentinus edodes* (about 0.6 million tonnes) (Chang 1993). *Agaricus* is mainly grown in the western hemisphere, whereas oyster mushrooms, shiitake and a number of other fungi of lesser production are mostly produced in East Asia.

The production of *Agaricus* and the preparation of its substrate, compost, are for a large part strongly mechanized. This is generally not the case for the other edible fungi, although exceptions exist.

The Common Mushroom

The common white button mushroom, *Agaricus bisporus,* is grown on compost consisting of a fermented mixture of horse manure, wheat straw, poultry manure and gypsum. The materials are wetted, mixed and set in large heaps when fermented outdoors, or brought into special fermentation rooms, called *tunnels.* Compost is usually made in quantities of up to several hundred tonnes per batch, and large, heavy equipment is used for mixing heaps and for filling and emptying the tunnels. Composting is a biological process that is guided by a temperature regime and that requires thorough mixing of the ingredients. Before being used as a substrate for growth, compost should be pasteurized by heat treatment and conditioned to get rid of the ammonia. During composting, a considerable amount of sulphur-containing organic volatiles evaporates, which can cause odour problems in the surroundings. When tunnels are used, the ammonia in the air can be cleaned by acid washing, and odour escape can be prevented by either biological or chemical oxidation of the air (Gerrits and Van Griensven 1990).

The ammonia-free compost is then *spawned* (i.e., inoculated with a pure culture of *Agaricus* growing on sterilized grain). Mycelial growth is carried out during a 2-week incubation at 25 °C in a special room or in a tunnel, after which the grown compost is placed in growing rooms in trays or in shelves (i.e., a scaffold system with 4 to 6 beds or tiers above each other with a distance of 25 to 40 cm in between), covered with a special casing consisting of peat and calcium carbonate. After a further incubation, mushroom production is induced by a temperature change combined with strong ventilation. Mushrooms appear in flushes with weekly intervals. They are either harvested mechanically or handpicked. After 3 to 6 flushes, the growing room is *cooked out* (i.e., steam pasteurized), emptied, cleaned and disinfected, and the next growing cycle can be started.

Success in mushroom cultivation depends heavily on cleanliness and prevention of pests and diseases. Although management and farm hygiene are key factors in disease prevention, a number of disinfectants and a limited number of pesticides and fungicides are still used in the industry.

Health Risks

Electrical and mechanical equipment

A pre-eminent risk in mushroom farms is the accidental exposure to electricity. Often high voltage and amperage is used in humid environments. Ground fault circuit interrupters and other electrical

64. AGRICULTURE AND NATURAL RESOURCE BASED INDUSTRIES

precautions are necessary. National labour legislation usually sets rules for the protection of labourers; this should be strictly followed.

Also, mechanical equipment may pose dangerous threats by its damaging weight or function, or by the combination of both. Composting machines with their large moving parts require care and attention to prevent accidents. Equipment used in cultivation and harvesting often has rotating parts used as grabbers or harvesting knives; their use and transport require great care. Again, this holds for all machines that are moving, whether they be self-propelled or pulled over beds, shelves or rows of trays. All such equipment should be properly guarded. All personnel whose duties include handling electrical or mechanical equipment in mushroom farms should be carefully trained before work is started and safety rules should be adhered to. Maintenance ordinances of equipment and machines should be taken very seriously. A proper lockout/tagout programme is needed as well. Lack of maintenance causes mechanical equipment to become extremely dangerous. For example, breaking pull chains have caused several deaths in mushroom farms.

Physical factors

Physical factors such as climate, lighting, noise, muscle load and posture strongly influence the health of workers. The difference between ambient outside temperature and that of a growing room can be considerable, especially in the winter. One should allow the body to adapt to a new temperature with every change of location; not doing so may lead to diseases of the airways and eventually to a susceptibility to bacterial and viral infections. Further, exposure to excessive temperature changes may cause muscles and joints to become stiff and inflamed. This may lead to a stiff neck and back, a painful condition causing unfitness for work.

Insufficient lighting in mushroom-growing rooms not only causes dangerous working conditions but also slows down picking, and it prevents pickers from seeing the possible symptoms of disease in the crop. The lighting intensity should be at least 500 lux.

Muscle load and posture largely determine the weight of labour. Unnatural body positions are often required in manual cultivation and picking tasks due to the limited space in many growing rooms. Those positions may damage joints and cause static overload of the muscles; prolonged static loading of muscles, such as that which occurs during picking, can even cause inflammation of joints and muscles, eventually leading to partial or total loss of function. This can be prevented by regular breaks, physical exercises and ergonomic measures (i.e., adaptation of the actions to the dimensions and possibilities of the human body).

Chemical factors

Chemical factors such as exposure to hazardous substances create possible health risks. The large-scale preparation of compost has a number of processes that can pose lethal risks. Gully pits in which recirculation water and drainage from compost is collected are usually devoid of oxygen, and the water contains high concentrations of hydrogen sulphide and ammonia. A change in acidity (pH) of the water may cause a lethal concentration of hydrogen sulphide to occur in the areas surrounding the pit. Piling wet poultry or horse manure in a closed hall may cause the hall to become an essentially lethal environment, due to the high concentrations of carbon dioxide, hydrogen sulphide and ammonia which are generated. Hydrogen sulphide has a powerful odour at low concentrations and is especially threatening, since at lethal concentrations this compound appears to be odourless because it inactivates human olfactory nerves. Indoor compost tunnels do not have sufficient oxygen to support human life. They are confined spaces, and testing of air for oxygen content and toxic gases, wearing of appropriate PPE, having an outside guard and proper training of involved personnel are essential.

Acid washers used for removal of ammonia from the air of compost tunnels require special care because of the large quantities of strong sulphuric or phosphoric acid that are present. Local exhaust ventilation should be provided.

Exposure to disinfectants, fungicides and pesticides can take place through the skin by exposure, through the lungs by breathing, and through the mouth by swallowing. Usually fungicides are applied by a high-volume technique such as by spray lorries, spray guns and drenching. Pesticides are applied with low-volume techniques such as misters, dynafogs, turbofogs and by fumigation. The small particles that are created remain in the air for hours. The right protective clothing and a respirator that has been certified as appropriate for the chemicals involved should be worn. Although the effects of acute poisoning are very dramatic, it should not be forgotten that the effects of chronic poisoning, although less dramatic at first glance, also always require occupational health surveillance.

Biological factors

Biological agents can cause infectious diseases as well as severe allergic reactions (Pepys 1967). No human infectious disease cases caused by the presence of human pathogens in compost have been reported. However, mushroom worker's lung (MWL) is a severe respiratory disease that is associated with handling the compost for *Agaricus* (Bringhurst, Byrne and Gershon-Cohen 1959). MWL, which belongs to the group of diseases designated *extrinsic allergic alveolitis* (EAA), arise from exposure to spores of the thermophilic actinomycetes *Excellospora flexuosa*, *Thermomonospora alba*, *T. curvata* and *T. fusca* that have grown during the conditioning phase in compost. They can be present in high concentrations in the air during spawning of phase 2 compost (i.e., over 10^9 colony-forming units (CFU) per cubic metre of air) (Van den Bogart et al. 1993); for causation of EAA symptoms, 10^8 spores per cubic metre of air are sufficient (Rylander 1986). The symptoms of EAA and thus MWL are fever, difficult respiration, cough, malaise, increase in number of leukocytes and restrictive changes of lung function, starting only 3 to 6 hours after exposure (Sakula 1967; Stolz, Arger and Benson 1976). After a prolonged period of exposure, irreparable damage is done to the lung due to inflammation and reactive fibrosis. In one study in the Netherlands, 19 MWL patients were identified among a group of 1,122 workers (Van den Bogart 1990). Each patient demonstrated a positive response to inhalation provocation and possessed circulating antibodies against spore antigens of one or more of the actinomycetes mentioned above. No allergic reaction had been found with *Agaricus* spores (Stewart 1974), which may indicate low antigenicity of the mushroom itself or low exposure. MWL can easily be prevented by providing workers with powered air-purifying respirators equipped with a fine dust filter as part of their normal work gear during spawning of compost.

Some pickers have been found to suffer from damaged skin of finger tips, caused by exogenous glucanases and proteases of *Agaricus*. Wearing gloves during picking prevents this.

Stress

Mushroom growing has a short and complicated growing cycle. Thus managing a mushroom farm brings worries and tensions which may extend to the workforce. Stress and its management are discussed elsewhere in this *Encyclopaedia*.

The Oyster Mushroom

Oyster mushrooms, *Pleurotus* spp., can be grown on a number of different lignocellulose-containing substrates, even on cellulose itself. The substrate is wetted and usually pasteurized and conditioned. After spawning, mycelial growth takes place in trays, shelves, special containers or in plastic bags. Fructification takes place when the ambient carbon dioxide concentration is decreased by ventilation or by opening the container or bag.

Health risks

Health risks associated with the cultivation of oyster mushrooms are comparable to those linked to *Agaricus* as described above, with one major exception. All *Pleurotus* species have naked lamellae (i.e., not covered by a veil), which results in the early shedding of a large number of spores. Sonnenberg, Van Loon and Van Griensven (1996) have counted spore production in *Pleurotus* spp. and found up to a billion spores produced per gram of tissue per day, depending on species and developmental stage. The so-called sporeless varieties of *Pleurotus ostreatus* produced about 100 million spores. Many reports have described the occurrence of EAA symptoms after exposure to *Pleurotus* spores (Hausen, Schulz and Noster 1974; Horner et al. 1988; Olson 1987). Cox, Folgering and Van Griensven (1988) have established the causal relation between exposure to *Pleurotus* spores and occurrence of EAA symptoms caused by inhalation. Because of the serious nature of the disease and the high sensitivity of humans, all workers should be protected with dust respirators. Spores in the growing room should at least partially be removed before workers enter the room. This can be done by directing the circulation air over a wet filter or by setting ventilation at full power 10 minutes before workers enter the room. Weighing and packing of mushrooms can be done under a hood, and during storage the trays should be covered by foil to prevent release of spores into the working environment.

Shiitake Mushrooms

In Asia this tasty mushroom, *Lentinus edodes,* has been grown on wood logs in the open air for centuries. The development of a low-cost cultivation technique on artificial substrate in growing rooms rendered its culture economically feasible in the western world. The artificial substrates usually consist of a wetted mixture of hardwood sawdust, wheat straw and high-concentration protein meal, which is pasteurized or sterilized before spawning. Mycelial growth takes place in bags, or in trays or shelves, depending on the system used. Fruiting is commonly induced by temperature shock or by immersion in ice-cold water, as is done to induce production on wood logs. Due to its high acidity (low pH), the substrate is susceptible to infection by green moulds such as *Penicillium* spp. and *Trichoderma* spp. Prevention of the growth of those heavy sporulators requires either sterilization of the substrate or use of fungicides.

Health risks

The health risks associated with the cultivation of shiitake are comparable with those of *Agaricus* and *Pleurotus*. Many strains of shiitake sporulate easily, leading to concentrations of up to 40 million spores per cubic metre of air (Sastre et al. 1990).

Indoor cultivation of shiitake has regularly led to EAA symptoms in workers (Cox, Folgering and Van Griensven 1988, 1989; Nakazawa, Kanatani and Umegae 1981; Sastre et al. 1990) and inhalation of spores of shiitake is the cause of the disease (Cox, Folgering and Van Griensven 1989). Van Loon et al. (1992) have shown that in a group of 5 patients tested, all had circulating IgG-type antibodies against shiitake spore antigens. Despite the use of protective mouth masks, a group of 14 workers experienced a rise in antibody titres with increased duration of employment, indicating the need for better prevention, such as powered air-purifying respirators and appropriate engineering controls.

Acknowledgement: The view and results presented here are strongly influenced by the late Jef Van Haaren, M.D., a fine person and gifted occupational health physician, whose humane approach to the effects of human labour was best reflected in Van Haaren (1988), his chapter in my textbook that formed the basis of the present article.

AQUATIC PLANTS

Melvin L. Myers and J.W.G. Lund*

Worldwide aquaculture production totalled 19.3 million tonnes in 1992, of which 5.4 million tonnes came from plants. In addition, much of the feed used on fish farms is water plants and algae, contributing to their growth as a part of aquaculture.

Water plants that are grown commercially include water spinach, watercress, water chestnuts, lotus stems and various seaweeds, which are grown as low-cost foods in Asia and Africa. Floating water plants that have commercial potential are duckweed and water hyacinth (FAO 1995).

Algae are a diverse group of organisms; if the cyanobacteria (blue-green algae) are included, they come in a range of sizes from bacteria (0.2 to 2 microns) to giant kelps (40 m). All algae are capable of photosynthesis and can liberate oxygen.

Algae are nearly all aquatic, but they may also live as a dual organism with fungi as lichens on drier rocks and on trees. Algae are found wherever there is moisture. Plant plankton consists almost exclusively of algae. Algae abound in lakes and rivers, and on the seashore. The slipperiness of stones and rocks, the slimes and discolourations of water usually are formed by aggregations of microscopic algae. They are found in hot springs, snowfields and Antarctic ice. On mountains they can form dark slippery streaks *(Tintenstriche)* that are dangerous to climbers.

There is no general agreement about algae classification, but they are commonly divided into 13 major groups whose members may differ markedly from one group to another in colour. The blue-green algae (Cyanophyta) are also considered by many microbiologists to be bacteria (Cyanobacteria) because they are procaryotes, which lack the membrane-bounded nuclei and other organelles of eukaryotic organisms. They are probably descendants of the earliest photosynthetic organisms, and their fossils have been found in rocks some 2 billion years old. Green algae (Chlorophyta), to which Chlorella belongs, has many of the characteristics of other green plants. Some are seaweeds, as are most of the red (Rhodophyta) and brown (Phaeophyta) algae. Chrysophyta, usually yellow or brownish in colour, include the diatoms, algae with walls made of polymerized silicon dioxide. Their fossil remains form industrially valuable deposits (Kieselguhr, diatomite, diatomaceous earth). Diatoms are the main basis of life in the oceans and contribute about 20 to 25% of the world's plant production. Dinoflagellates (Dinophyta) are free-swimming algae especially common in the sea; some are toxic.

Uses

Water culture can vary greatly from the traditional 2-month to annual growing cycle of planting, then fertilizing and plant maintenance, followed by harvesting, processing, storage and sale. Sometimes the cycle is compressed to 1 day, such as in duckweed farming. Duckweed is the smallest flowering plant.

Some seaweeds are valuable commercially as sources of alginates, carrageenin and agar, which are used in industry and medicine (textiles, food additives, cosmetics, pharmaceuticals, emulsifiers and so on). Agar is the standard solid medium on which bacteria and other micro-organisms are cultivated. In the Far East, especially in Japan, a variety of seaweeds are used as human food. Seaweeds are good fertilizers, but their use is decreasing because of the labour costs and the availability of relatively cheap artificial fertilizers. Algae play an important part in tropical fish farms and in rice fields. The latter are commonly rich

* Adapted from J.W.G. Lund's article, "Algae", *Encyclopaedia of Occupational Health and Safety*, 3rd edition.

64. AGRICULTURE AND NATURAL RESOURCE BASED INDUSTRIES

in Cyanophyta, some species of which can utilize nitrogen gas as their sole source of nitrogenous nutrient. As rice is the staple diet of the majority of the human race, the growth of algae in rice fields is under intensive study in countries such as India and Japan. Certain algae have been employed as a source of iodine and bromine.

The use of industrially cultivated microscopic algae has often been advocated for human food and has a potential for very high yields per unit area. However, the cost of dewatering has been a barrier.

Where there is a good climate and inexpensive land, algae can be used as part of the process of sewage purification and harvested as animal food. While a useful part of the living world of reservoirs, too much algae can seriously impede, or increase the cost of water supply. In swimming pools, algal poisons (algicides) can be used to control algal growth, but, apart from copper in low concentrations, such substances cannot be added to water or domestic supplies. Over-enrichment of water with nutrients, notably phosphorus, with consequent excessive growth of algae, is a major problem in some regions and has led to bans on the use of phosphorus-rich detergents. The best solution is to remove the excess phosphorus chemically in a sewage plant.

Duckweed and a water hyacinth are potential livestock feeds, compost input or fuel. Aquatic plants are also used as feed for noncarnivorous fish. Fish farms produce three primary commodities: finfish, shrimp and mollusc. Of the finfish portion, 85% are made up of noncarnivorous species, primarily the carp. Both the shrimp and mollusc depend upon algae (FAO 1995).

Hazards

Abundant growths of freshwater algae often contain potentially toxic blue-green algae. Such "water blooms" are unlikely to harm humans because the water is so unpleasant to drink that swallowing a large and hence dangerous amount of algae is unlikely. On the other hand, cattle may be killed, especially in hot, dry areas where no other source of water may be available to them. Paralytic shellfish poisoning is caused by algae (dinoflagellates) on which the shellfish feed and whose powerful toxin they concentrate in their bodies with no apparent harm to themselves. Humans, as well as marine animals, can be harmed or killed by the toxin.

Prymnesium (Chrysophyta) is very toxic to fish and flourishes in weakly or moderately saline water. It presented a major threat to fish farming in Israel until research provided a practical method of detecting the presence of the toxin before it reached lethal proportions. A colourless member of the green algae (Prototheca) infects humans and other mammals from time to time.

There have been a few reports of algae causing skin irritations. Oscillatoria nigroviridis are known to cause dermatitis. In freshwater, Anaebaena, Lyngbya majuscula and Schizothrix can cause contact dermatitis. Red algae are known to cause breathing distress. Diatoms contain silica, so they could pose a silicosis hazard as a dust. Drowning is a hazard when working in deeper water while cultivating and harvesting water plants and algae. The use of algicides also poses hazards, and precautions provided on the pesticide label should be followed.

• COFFEE CULTIVATION

*Jorge da Rocha Gomes
and Bernardo Bedrikow*

It is thought that the word *coffee* derives from Kaffa, a village in Ethiopia where the plant is thought to have its origin. Some, however, consider that the word stems from *qahwa*, meaning wine in Arabic. Coffee cultivation spread the world over, starting in Arabia (one species is called *Coffea arabica*, and a variety is *Moka*, named after an Arab village), passing through many countries, such as Ceylon, Java, India, the Philippines, Hawaii and Viet Nam, among others, some of which are important producers to this day. In America, coffee was introduced from plants previously adapted to the climate in Amsterdam and Paris, planted in Martinique, Surinam and French Guyana, from where it was brought to Brazil, the largest producing country in the world.

World production may be estimated from figure 64.36. The 1995–96 crop generated wealth estimated at approximately US$27 million, indicating the economic significance of this product worldwide.

The trend towards a global economy, growing competition and the search for technologies with higher productivity also have effects upon coffee cultivation. Mechanization is being disseminated and updated. Moreover, new methods of cultivation are introduced, among them high-density cultivation, in which the distance between plants is being reduced. This modern method increases the number of coffee trees from 3,000 or 4,000 to 100,000 plants per hectare, with an increase in productivity of around 50% over the traditional method. This procedure is important for workers' health, since lower risks are involved and less herbicide is applied, especially after the third year. On the other

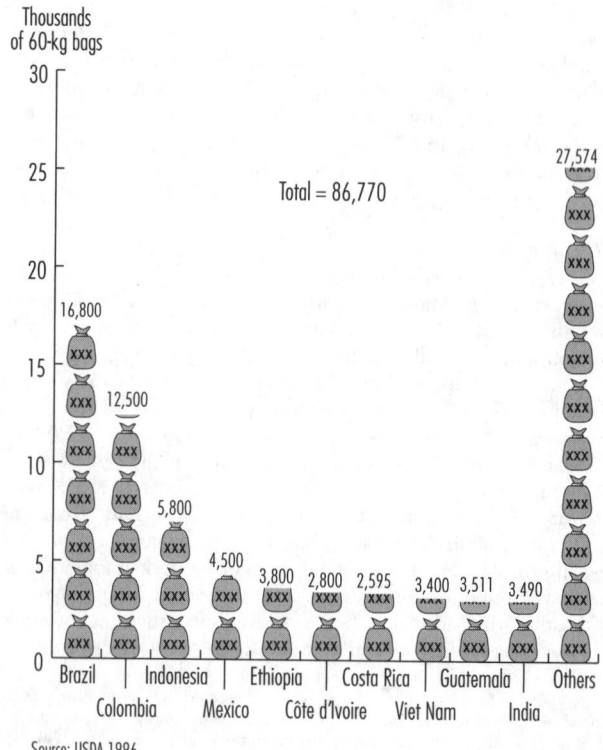

Figure 64.36 • World coffee production for 1995–96.

Thousands of 60-kg bags

Total = 86,770

Brazil 16,800
Colombia 12,500
Indonesia 5,800
Mexico 4,500
Ethiopia 3,800
Côte d'Ivoire 2,800
Costa Rica 2,595
Viet Nam 3,400
Guatemala 3,511
India 3,490
Others 27,574

Source: USDA 1996.

hand, there is an increase in the frequency of tree cutting and higher demand for control of fungus disease in the plants.

Coffee is highly sensitive to fluctuations in international commerce; many countries tend to replace coffee with other crops in which financial return is more predictable. In Brazil, for instance, coffee represented 68% of the total volume of exports in 1920; in the 1990s it is only 4%. Coffee is being replaced by soy bean, citric fruits, corn, latex and especially sugar cane.

It is extremely difficult to obtain a reliable estimate of the total labour force involved in coffee cultivation because the number of employed workers is quite variable. During harvest, a large number of seasonal workers are hired, to be dismissed soon after the crop is over. Moreover, in small properties, very often workers are not legally registered, and therefore are not shown in official reports. In Brazil in 1993, for a production of 28.5 million coffee bags, the number of workers was estimated at 1.1 million in direct and 4 to 5 million in indirect jobs. If the same parameters are applied to world production for the same year, coffee workers around the world could be estimated at approximately 3.6 million.

It is equally difficult to know the average figure of workers per rural property. In general, small or medium-sized properties are predominant. The sex and age distribution of the working population is equally unknown, even though female population among workers is increasing and children are known to be employed in coffee plantations. Figures for unionized workers vary according to the labour policies in each country, but they are known to be generally scarce.

Operations

Coffee cultivation and treatment involve the following steps: tree abatement; soil preparation; planting (small plants are usually grown in nurseries in the same or in external properties); treatment (soil correction, fertilizing, pest control and terrain cleaning manually or with herbicides); fruit picking (ripe fruit is usually red and therefore called a berry—see figure 64.37); sieving to get rid of impurities; transportation; washing to remove pulp and membranes; sun drying, revolving grains with a rake, or mechanical drying through hot air blasting; hand separation of grains; storing in silos; and bagging.

Potential Risks

Risk factors that may affect workers' health in coffee cultivation are the same as for agricultural workers in general.

From tree abatement and terrain preparation to the final storage of coffee bags, each step may involve several risk factors for workers' health and safety. Injury risks are present mainly in mechanized processes, tree abatement, terrain preparation, mechanical picking, transportation of coffee and workers as well, fruit treatment (including the risk of boiler explosion) and use of hand tools (very often improvised or without maintenance).

Potential risks of occupational diseases due to physical conditions are related to heat exposure in drying operations, solar radiation, machine noise, ergonomic problems from hand tools, vibration from machinery and tractors, and cold and humidity from outdoor exposure.

The main chemical agents present as potential risks for workers' health are pesticides and herbicides. Those most often used are gliphosate as an herbicide, copper salts as fungicides and organophosphorus compounds for other pests commonly found on coffee trees. The number of pesticide applications varies according to tree age, soil composition, climatic conditions, vegetation species or variety, cultivation system (e.g., high or low density) and other factors. Spraying is usually done individually with backpack equipment, or from tractors. Large amounts are usually required, and it is said that "without spraying no crop is available".

Figure 64.37 • High-density coffee cultivation showing berries.

Estado de Sao Paulo

Chemical fertilizers may also present a health risk. Often used are compounds derived from boron, zinc, nitrogen, sodium, potassium, calcium, magnesium and sulphur. The release of particles from fertilizer handling should be kept under control.

Biological agents may represent important risks for workers' health. They may include, for instance, bites or stings from snakes, spiders, bees, mosquitoes and acarids, some of them important as disease vectors. In certain areas, endemic diseases may be serious risks for coffee workers.

Ergonomic, psychosocial and organizational factors are discussed below.

Health Effects

Examples of injuries related to work are cuts from hand tools, sprains and fractures from machines and injuries from tractors. Fatal injuries, even if unusual, have occurred as a result of overturning of tractors or inadequate vehicles used in transportation of workers. When artificial drying is employed, heat sources may cause burns and explosions.

Occupational diseases may result from exposure to solar ultraviolet radiation; cutaneous conditions may range from a simple erythema to skin cancer. Hearing loss among machine operators, pulmonary allergic conditions, poisoning from herbicides and pesticides, callosities, lung diseases, bone and circulatory conditions due to vibration, and muscular and skeletal trouble due to poor ergonomic positions or excessive weight (one coffee bag can weigh 60 kg) are other occupational conditions that may occur among coffee cultivation workers. Although primarily a problem among workers processing coffee beans, green bean handlers have complained of respiratory and eye problems. Coffee bean dust has been associated with occupational dust diseases.

Tropical diseases such as malaria, yellow fever, filariasis, trypanossomiasis, leishmaniasis and onchocercosis are prevalent in certain cultivating areas. Tetanus is still prevalent in many rural areas.

More complex health problems related to psychosocial and organizational factors may also affect coffee workers. Since large numbers of workers are required during harvest, and very few during the rest of the year, seasonal contracts are usually practised, often resulting in difficult health problems.

In many cases, workers leave their families and remain during the harvest season in precarious lodgings under inadequate sanitary conditions. If the planting area is close to town, the farmer will contract only one man in the family. However, to increase the profit, the worker himself may bring his whole family to help, including women and children. In some areas, the number of children at work is so high that schools will be closed during the whole harvest season.

In this type of seasonal activity, workers will turn from one type of cultivation to another, according to each harvest period. Since men leave their families, women are called "widows with living husbands". Very often, a man will raise another family, away from his original town.

Proper compliance with labour legislation and social security is usually restricted to large plantations, and labour inspection in rural areas is generally ineffective. Health care is usually very limited. Duration of work is extended to many hours daily; weekends and normal vacations are seldom respected.

These psychosocial and organizational factors result in marked deterioration in workers' health, manifested through early ageing, low life expectancy, increase in prevalence and longer duration of diseases, malnutrition (eating the food taken to the field in cans without heating it has led to workers being given a nickname—*boias frias* in Portuguese), anaemia and hypovitaminoses leading to loss of disposition to work, mental trouble and other manifestations.

Prevention

Preventive measures concerning coffee are the same that apply to rural work in general. Collective protection includes machine guarding, care in application of pesticides and herbicides, mechanizing operations that require undue effort and energy consumption, and adequate transportation of workers. In high-density plantations, regular cutting will not allow the trees to grow, which will eliminate the use of dangerous and uncomfortable ladders for hand picking. When drying requires the use of boilers, careful periodic preventive maintenance is of utmost importance. Biological pest control and proper selection of species resistant to plagues are important preventive measures concerning pesticides, avoiding workers' disease and environmental protection as well.

Implementation of the use of recommended PPE is difficult because such equipment is usually not adapted to climatic conditions or to the biotype of workers. Moreover, there is usually no educational orientation to facilitate the use, and the selection of equipment is not always correct. Equipment in general use is restricted to boots, hats and clothing to protect from the weather, even though hand, lung, eye and ear protection may be required.

Prevention to control psychosocial and organizational factors may bring up many difficulties. Workers' awareness should be raised through educational activities, especially in unions and other workers' organizations, increasing perceptions about workers' rights to better living and working conditions; moreover, employers should develop their perceptions concerning their social responsibilities towards the labour force. The State should exercise an effective and constant orientation and enforcement

wherever legal action is required. Some countries have developed rules and regulations specifically applicable to rural workers. In Brazil, for example, Rural Regulatory Standards establish general directives concerning safety in rural activities, the organization of occupational health services and safety committees in plantations, use of personal protective equipment and handling of chemicals (pesticides, fertilizers and soil-correcting products).

Health control through occupational medicine should cover the evaluation of health effects due to exposure to pesticides, ultraviolet radiation, excessive noise and many other hazards. It may, in many circumstances, be more necessary to control worm diseases, anaemia, hypertension, behavioural problems, eye defects and similar problems, due to their high prevalence in rural areas. Health education should be stressed, as well as tetanus immunization, including for pregnant workers to prevent neonatal tetanus. In some regions, immunization against yellow fever is necessary. Chemoprophylaxis is recommended in areas where malaria is endemic, together with the use of repellents and a preventive orientation against mosquitoes, until sanitation is adequate to control or suppress vectors of the aetiological agent. Serum against snake poison should be available.

Acknowledgement: The authors are obliged to the cooperation received from Professor Nelson Batista Martin, from the Institute of Rural Economy, State Secretary of Agriculture, Sao Paulo; Andre Nasser and Ricardo Luiz Zucas, from the Brazilian Rural Society; and Monica Levy Costa, from the School Health Center, School of Public Health, Sao Paulo University.

TEA CULTIVATION

L.V.R. Fernando*

Tea *(Camellia sinensis)* was originally cultivated in China, and most of the world's tea still comes from Asia, with lesser quantities from Africa and South America. Ceylon and India are now the largest producers, but sizeable quantities also come from China, Japan, the former USSR, Indonesia and Pakistan. The Islamic Republic of Iran, Turkey, Viet Nam and Malaysia are small-scale growers. Since the Second World War, the area under tea cultivation in Africa has been expanding rapidly, particularly in Kenya, Mozambique, Congo, Malawi, Uganda and the United Republic of Tanzania. Mauritius, Rwanda, Cameroon, Zambia and Zimbabwe also have small acreages. The main South American producers are Argentina, Brazil and Peru.

Plantations

Tea is most efficiently and economically produced in large plantations, although it is also grown as a smallholder crop. In Southeast Asia, the tea plantation is a self-contained unit, providing accommodation and all facilities for its workers and their families, each unit forming a virtually closed community. Women form a large proportion of the workers in India and Ceylon, but the pattern is somewhat different in Africa, where mainly male migrant and seasonal labour is employed and families do not have to be housed. See also the article "Plantations" in this chapter.

Cultivation

Land is cleared and prepared for new planting, or areas of old, poor-quality tea are uprooted and replanted with high-yielding vegetatively propagated cuttings. New fields take a couple of years to come into full bearing. Regular programmes of manuring,

* Adapted from 3rd edition, *Encyclopaedia of Occupational Health and Safety*.

Figure 64.38 • Tea pluckers at work on a plantation in Uganda.

Figure 64.39 • Mechanical harvesting on a tea plantation near the Black Sea.

In Asia, where the non-working population resident on the tea estates is almost as great as the workforce itself, the total number of accidents in the home is equal to that of accidents in the field.

Housing is generally substandard. The most common diseases are those of the respiratory system, closely followed by enteric diseases, anaemia and substandard nutrition. The former are mainly the outcome of working and living conditions at high altitudes and exposure to low temperatures and inclement weather. The intestinal diseases are due to poor sanitation and low standards of hygiene among the labour force. These are mainly preventable conditions, which underlines the need for better sanitary facilities and improved health education. Anaemia, particularly among working mothers of child-bearing age, is all too common; it is partly the result of ankylostomiasis, but is due mainly to protein-deficient diets. However, the principal causes of lost work time are generally from the more minor ailments and not serious diseases. Medical supervision of both housing and working conditions is an essential preventive measure, and official inspection, either at local or national level, is also necessary to ensure that proper health facilities are maintained.

weeding and pesticide application are carried on throughout the year.

The plucking of the young tea leaves—the famous "two leaves and a bud"—takes place the year round in most of Southeast Asia, but is restricted in areas with a marked cold season (see figure 64.38). After a cycle of plucking which lasts about 3 to 4 years, bushes are pruned back fairly drastically and the area weeded. Hand weeding is now widely giving way to the use of chemical herbicides. The plucked tea is collected in baskets carried on the backs of the pluckers and taken down to centrally located weighing sheds, and from these to the factories for processing. In some countries, notably Japan and the former USSR, mechanical plucking has been carried out with some success, but this requires a reasonably flat terrain and bushes grown in set rows.

Hazards and Their Prevention

Falls and injuries caused by agricultural implements of the cutting and digging type are the most common types of accidents. This is not unexpected, considering the steep slopes on which tea is generally grown and the type of work involved in the processes of clearing, uprooting and pruning. Apart from exposure to natural hazards like lightning, workers are liable to be bitten by snakes or stung by hornets, spiders, wasps or bees, although highly venomous snakes are seldom found at the high altitudes at which the best tea grows. An allergic condition caused by contact with a certain species of caterpillar has been recorded in Assam, India.

The exposure of workers to ever-increasing quantities of highly toxic pesticides requires careful control. Substitution with less-toxic pesticides and attention to personal hygiene are necessary measures here. Mechanization has been fairly slow, but an increasing number of tractors, powered vehicles and implements are coming into use, with a concomitant increase in accidents from these causes (see figure 64.39). Well-designed tractors with safety cabs, operated by trained, competent drivers will eliminate many accidents.

HOPS

Thomas Karsky and William B. Symons

Hops are used in brewing and are commonly grown in the Pacific Northwest of the United States, Europe (especially Germany and the United Kingdom), Australia and New Zealand.

Hops grow from rhizome cuttings of female hop plants. Hop vines grow up to 4.5 to 7.5 m or more during the growing season. These vines are trained to climb up heavy trellis wire or heavy cords. Hops are traditionally spaced 2 m apart in each direction with two cords per plant going to the overhead trellis wire at about 45° angles. Trellises are about 5.5 m high and are made from 10×10 cm pressure-treated timbers or poles sunk 0.6 to 1 m into the ground.

Manual labour is used to train the vines after the vines reach about a third of a metre in length; additionally, the lowest metre is pruned to allow air circulation to reduce disease development.

Hops vines are harvested in the fall. In the United Kingdom, some hops are grown in trellises 3 m high and harvested with an over-the-row mechanical harvester. In the United States, hop combines are available to harvest 5.5-m-high trellises. The areas that the harvesters (field strippers) are unable to get are harvested by hand with a machete. Newly harvested hops are then kiln dried from 80% moisture to about 10%. Hops are cooled, then baled and taken to cold storage for end use.

Safety Concerns

Workers need to wear long sleeves and gloves when working near the vines, because hooked hairs of the plant may cause a rash on the skin. Some individuals become more sensitized to the vines than others.

A majority of the injuries involve strains and sprains due to lifting materials such as irrigation pipes and bales, and over-reaching when working on trellises. Workers should be trained in lifting or mechanical aids should be used.

Workers need to wear chaps at the knee and below to protect the leg from cuts while cutting the vines by hand. Eye protection is a must while working with the vines.

Many injuries occur while workers tie twine to the wire trellis wire. Most work is performed while standing on high trailers or platforms on tractors. Accidents have been reduced by providing safety belts or guard rails to prevent falls, and by wearing eye protection. Because there is much movement with the hands, carpal tunnel syndrome may be a problem.

Since hops are often treated with fungicides during the season, proper posting of re-entry intervals is needed.

Worker's compensation claims in Washington State (US) tend to indicate that injury incidence ranges between 30 and 40 injuries per 100 person years worked. Growers through their association have safety committees that actively work to lower injury rates. Injury rates in Washington are similar to those found in the tree fruit industry and dairy. Highest injury incidence tends to occur in August and September.

The industry has unique practices in the production of the product, where much of the machinery and equipment is locally manufactured. By the vigilance of the safety committees to provide adequate machine guarding, they are able to reduce "caught in" type injuries within the harvesting and processing operations. Training should focus on proper use of knives, PPE and prevention of falls from vehicles and other machines.

HEALTH AND ENVIRONMENTAL ISSUES

HEALTH PROBLEMS AND DISEASE PATTERNS IN AGRICULTURE

Melvin L. Myers

At the end of the twentieth century, less than 5% of the workforce in industrialized nations is employed in agriculture, while nearly 50% of the worldwide workforce is engaged in agriculture (Sullivan et al. 1992). The work varies from highly mechanized to the manually arduous. Some agribusiness has been historically international, such as plantation farming and the growing of export crops. Today, agribusiness is international and is organized around commodities such as sugar, wheat and beef. Agriculture covers many settings: family farms, including subsistence agriculture; large corporate farms and plantations; urban farms, including specialty enterprises and subsistence agriculture; and migrant and seasonal work. Crops vary from widely used staples, such as wheat and rice, to specialty crops such as coffee, fruits and seaweed. Moreover, the young and the old engage in agricultural work to a greater extent than any other industry. This article addresses health problems and disease patterns among agricultural workers except for livestock rearing, which is covered in another chapter.

Overview

The image of agricultural work is that of a healthy pursuit, far from congested and polluted cities, that provides an opportunity for plenty of fresh air and exercise. In some ways, this is true. US farmers, for example, have a lower mortality rate for ischemic heart disease and cancer as compared with other occupations.

However, agricultural work is associated with a variety of health problems. Agricultural workers are at a high risk for particular cancers, respiratory diseases and injuries (Sullivan et al. 1992). Because of the remote location of much of this work, emergency health services are lacking, and agromedicine has been viewed as a vocation without high social status (see box and table 64.12). The work environment involves exposure to the physical hazards of weather, terrain, fires and machinery; toxicological hazards of pesticides, fertilizers and fuels; and health insults of dust. As shown in tables 64.13 through 64.19, agriculture is associated with a variety of health hazards. In these tables and the corresponding descriptions that follow, six categories of hazards are summarized: (1) respiratory, (2) dermatological, (3) toxic and neoplastic, (4) injury, (5) mechanical and thermal stress and (6) behavioural hazards. Each table also provides a summary of interventions to prevent or control the hazard.

Table 64.12 • Comparison of two types of agromedicine programmes.

Parameter	Model A	Model B
Site (campus)	Medical	Medical and agricultural
Support	Federal, foundation	State, foundation
Research	Primary (basic)	Secondary (applied)
Patient education	Yes	Yes
Producer/worker education	Yes	Yes
Health provider education	Yes	Yes
Extension education	Elective	Yes
Cross-discipline education	Elective	Yes
Statewide community outreach	Intermittent	Ongoing (40 hours/wk)
Constituency: sustainability	Academic peers National peers International peers	Growers, consumers, health professionals, rural physicians
Prestige (academic)	Yes	Little
Growth (capital, grants)	Yes	Little
Administration	Single	Dual (partners)
Primary focus	Research, publication, policy recommendations	Education, public service, client-based research

Agromedicine

Since animal husbandry and crop production began, agriculture and medicine have been interrelated. A healthy farm or livestock operation requires healthy workers. Famine, drought, or pestilence can overwhelm the well-being of all of the interrelated species on the farm; especially in developing countries that depend on agriculture for survival. In colonial times plantation-owners had to be aware of hygienic measures to protect their plants, animals and human workers. At present, examples of agromedical teamwork include: integrated pest management (an ecological approach to pests); tuberculosis (TB) prevention and control (livestock, dairy products and workers); and agricultural engineering (to reduce trauma and farmer's lung). Agriculture and medicine succeed when they work together as one.

Definitions

The following terms are used interchangeably, but there are noteworthy connotations:

- *Agricultural medicine* refers to the subdivision of public health and/or occupational medicine included in the training and practice of health professionals.
- *Agromedicine* is a term coined in the 1950s to emphasize interdisciplinary, programmatic approaches which give a greater role for the agricultural professional based upon the equal partnership of the two disciplines (medicine and agriculture).

In recent years, the definition of *agricultural medicine* as a subspeciality of occupational/environmental medicine located on the health sciences campus has been challenged to develop a broader definition of *agromedicine* as a process of linking agricultural and health resources of a state or a region in a partnership dedicated to public service, along the lines of the original land-grant university model.

The essential unity of biological science is well known to plant chemists (nutrition), animal chemists (nutrition) and human chemists (nutrition); the areas of overlap and integration go beyond the boundaries of narrowly defined specialization.

Content areas

Agromedicine has focused on three core areas:

1. traumatic injury
2. pulmonary exposures
3. agrichemical injury.

Other content areas, including zoonoses, rural health services and other community services, food safety (e.g., the relationship between nutrition and cancer), health education and environmental protection, have received secondary emphasis. Other initiatives relate to biotechnology, the challenge of population growth and sustainable agriculture.

Each core area is emphasized in university training and research programmes depending on faculty expertise, grants and funding initiatives, extension needs, commodity producers' or corporate requests for consultation and networks of inter-university cooperation. For example, traumatic injury skills may be supported by a faculty in agricultural engineering leading to a degree in that branch of agricultural science; farmer's lung will be covered in a pulmonary medicine rotation in a residency in occupational medicine (postgraduate specialization residency) or in preventive medicine (leading to a master's or doctorate in public health); an inter-university food safety programme may link the veterinary discipline, the food science discipline and the infectious disease medical speciality. Table 64.12 compares two types of programmes.

In the United States, a number of states have established agromedicine programmes. Alabama, California, Colorado, Georgia, Iowa, Kansas, Kentucky, Minnesota, Mississippi, Nebraska, New York, Oregon, Pennsylvania, South Carolina, Virginia and Wisconsin have active programmes. Other states have programmes which do not use the terms agromedicine or agricultural medicine or which are at early stages of development. These include Michigan, Florida and Texas. Saskatchewan, Canada, also has an active agromedicine programme.

Conclusion

In addition to collaboration across disciplines in so-called basic science, communities need greater coordination of agricultural expertise and medical expertise. Dedicated localized teamwork is required to implement a preventive, educational approach that delivers the best science and the best outreach that a state-funded university system can provide to its citizens.

Stanley H. Schuman and Jere A. Brittain

Respiratory Hazards

Agricultural workers are subject to several pulmonary diseases related to exposures at work as shown in table 64.13. An excess of these diseases has been found in several countries.

Exacerbation of asthma by specific allergens and nonspecific causes has been associated with airborne dust. Several farm antigen exposures can trigger asthma, and they include pollen, storage mites and grain dust. Mucous membrane inflammation is a common reaction to airborne dust in individuals with allergic rhinitis or a history of atopy. Plant parts in grain dust appear to cause mechanical irritation to the eyes, but endotoxin and mycotoxin exposure may also be associated with the inflammation of the eyes, nasal passages and throat.

Chronic bronchitis is more common among farmers than among the general population. The majority of farmers with this illness have a history of exposure to grain dust or work in swine confinement buildings. It is believed that cigarette smoking is additive and a cause of this illness. In addition, acute bronchitis has been described in grain farmers, especially during grain harvest.

Hypersensitivity pneumonitis is caused by repeated antigen exposures from a variety of substances. Antigens include micro-organisms found in spoiled hay, grain and silage. This problem has also been seen among workers who clean out mushroom bed houses.

Organic dust toxic syndrome was originally associated with exposure to mouldy silage and was, thus, called *silage unloader's syndrome*. A similar illness, called *grain fever*, is associated with exposure to stored grain dust. This syndrome occurs without prior sensitization, as is the case with hypersensitivity pneumonitis. The epidemiology of the syndrome is not well defined.

Farmers may be exposed to several different substances that can cause acute pulmonary responses. Nitrogen dioxide generated in silos can cause death among silo workers. Carbon monoxide generated by combustion sources, including space heaters and internal combustion engines, can cause death of agricultural workers exposed to high concentrations inside of buildings. In addition to toxic exposures, oxygen deficiency in confined spaces on farms is a continuing problem.

Table 64.13 • Respiratory hazards.

Exposures	Health effects
Cereal grain pollen, livestock dander, fungal antigens in grain dust and on crops, dust mites, organophosphorus insecticides	Asthma and rhinitis: Immunoglobin E-mediated asthma
Organic dusts	Nonimmunologic asthma (grain dust asthma)
Specific plant parts, endotoxins, mycotoxins	Mucous membrane inflammation
Insecticides, arsenic, irritant dust, ammonia, fumes, grain dust (wheat, barley)	Bronchospasm, acute and chronic bronchitis
Fungal spores or thermophilic actinomycetes released from mouldy grain or hay, antigens of less than 5 μm in diameter	Hypersensitivity pneumonitis
Thermophilic actinomycetes: mouldy sugar cane	Bagassosis
Mushroom spores (during clean-out of beds)	Mushroom worker's lung
Mouldy hay, compost	Farmer's lung
Fungi: mouldy maple bark	Maple bark stripper's disease
Anthropoids: infested wheat	Wheat weevil disease
Plant debris, starch granules, moulds, endotoxins, mycotoxins, spores, fungi, gram-negative bacteria, enzymes, allergens, insect parts, soil particles, chemical residues	Organic dust toxic syndrome
Dust from stored grain	Grain fever
Mouldy silage on top of silage in silo	Silo unloader's syndrome
Decomposition gases: ammonia, hydrogen sulphide, carbon monoxide, methane, phosgene, chlorine, sulphur dioxide, ozone, paraquat (herbicide), anhydrous ammonia (fertilizer), oxides of nitrogen	Acute pulmonary responses
Nitrogen dioxide from fermenting silage	Silo filler's disease
Welding fumes	Metal fume fever
Oxygen deficiency in confined spaces	Asphyxiation
Soil dust of arid regions	Valley fever (coccidiomycosis)
Mycobacterium tuberculosis	Tuberculosis (migrant workers)

Interventions: ventilation, dust suppression or containment, respirators, mould prevention, smoking cessation.
Sources: Merchant et al. 1986; Meridian Research, Inc. 1994; Sullivan et al. 1992; Zejda, McDuffie et al. 1994.

Many agricultural crops are causative agents for pulmonary diseases when they are processed. These include hypersensitivity pneumonitis caused by mouldy malt (from barley), paprika dust and coffee dust. Byssinosis is caused by cotton, flax and hemp dusts. Several natural products are also associated with occupational asthma when processed: vegetable gums, flax seed, castor bean, soybean, coffee bean, grain products, flour, orris root, papain and tobacco dust (Merchant et al. 1986; Meridian Research, Inc. 1994; Sullivan et al. 1992).

Dermatological Hazards

Farmers are exposed to several skin hazards, as shown in table 64.14. The most common type of agriculture-related skin disease is irritant contact dermatitis. In addition, allergic contact dermatosis is a reaction to exposures to sensitizers including certain plants and pesticides. Other skin diseases include photo-contact, sun-induced, heat-induced, and arthropod-induced dermatoses.

The skin can be burned in several ways. Burns can result from dry fertilizer, which is hygroscopic and attracts moisture (Deere & Co. 1994). When on the skin, it can draw out moisture and cause skin burns. Liquid anhydrous ammonia is used for injecting nitrogen into the soil, where it expands into a gas and readily combines with moisture. If the liquid or gas contacts the body—especially the eyes, skin and respiratory tract—cell destruction and burns can occur, and permanent injury can result without immediate treatment.

Tobacco croppers and harvesters can experience green tobacco sickness when working with damp tobacco. Water from rain or dew on the tobacco leaves probably dissolves nicotine to facilitate its absorption through the skin. Green tobacco sickness is manifested with complaints of headache, pallor, nausea, vomiting and prostration following the worker's contact with wet tobacco leaves. Other insults to the skin include arthropod and reptile stings and bites, and thorn punctures, which can carry diseases.

Toxic and Neoplastic Hazards

The potential for toxic substances exposure in agriculture is great, as can be seen in table 64.15. Chemicals used in agriculture include fertilizers, pesticides (insecticides, fumigants and herbicides) and fuels. Human exposures to pesticides are widespread in developing countries as well as in the developed countries. The United States has registered more than 900 different pesticides with more than 25,000 brand names. About 65% of the registered uses of pesticides are for agriculture. They are primarily used to control insects and to reduce crop loss. Two-thirds (by weight) of the pesticides are herbicides. Pesticides may be applied to seed, soil, crops or the harvest, and they may be applied with spray

Table 64.14 • Dermatological hazards.

Exposures	Health effects
Ammonia and dry fertilizers, vegetable crops, bulb plants, fumigants, oat and barley dust, several pesticides, soaps, petroleum products, solvents, hypochlorite, phenolic compounds, amniotic fluid, animal feeds, furazolidone, hydroquinone, halquinol	Irritant contact dermatitis
Mites	Grain itch
Sensitizing plants (poison ivy or oak), certain pesticides (dithiocarbamates, pyrethrins, thioates, thiurams, parathion, and malathion)	Allergic contact dermatitis
Handling tulips and tulip bulbs	Tulip finger
Creosote, plants containing furocoumarins	Photo-contact dermatitis
Sunlight, ultraviolet radiation	Sun-induced dermatitis, melanoma, lip cancer
Moist and hot environments	Heat-induced dermatitis
Wet tobacco leaf contact	Nicotine poisoning (green tobacco sickness)
Fire, electricity, acid or caustic chemicals, dry (hygroscopic) fertilizer, friction, liquified anhydrous ammonia	Burns
Bites and stings from wasps, chiggers, bees, grain mites, hornets, fire ants, spiders, scorpions, centipedes, other arthropods, snakes	Arthropod-induced dermatitis, envenomation, Lyme disease, malaria
Punctures and thorn pricks	Tetanus

Interventions: Integrated pest management, protective clothing, good sanitation, vaccination, insect control, barrier creams.
Sources: Estlander, Kanerva and Piirilä 1996; Meridian Research, Inc. 1994; Raffle et al. 1994; Sullivan et al. 1992.

equipment or crop dusters. After application, pesticide exposures can result from off-gassing, dispersion by the wind, or contact with the plants through skin or clothing. Dermal contact is the most common type of occupational exposure. A number of health effects have been associated with pesticide exposure. These include acute, chronic, carcinogenic, immunologic, neurotoxic and reproductive effects.

Farmers experience a higher risk for some site-specific cancers. These include brain, stomach, lymphatic and haematopoietic, lip, prostrate and skin cancer. Solar and pesticide (especially herbicide) exposure have been related to higher cancer risks for farm populations (Meridian Research, Inc. 1994; Popendorf and Donham 1991; Sullivan et al. 1992).

Table 64.15 • Toxic and neoplastic hazards.

Exposures	Possible health effects
Solvents, benzene, fumes, fumigants, insecticides (e.g., organophosphates, carbamates, organochlorines), herbicides (e.g., phenoxy-aliphatic acids, bipyridyls, triazines, arsenicals, acentanilides, dinitro-toluidine), fungicides (e.g., thiocarbamates, dicarboximides)	Acute intoxication, Parkinson's disease, peripheral neuritis, Alzheimer's disease, acute and chronic encephalopathy, non-Hodgkin lymphoma, Hodgkin's lymphoma, multiple myeloma, soft-tissue sarcoma, leukaemias, cancers of the brain, prostate, stomach, pancreas and testicle, glioma
Solar radiation	Skin cancer
Dibromochloropropane (DBCP), ethylene dibromide	Sterility (male)

Interventions: integrated pest management, respiratory and dermal protection, good pesticide application practices, safe re-entry time into fields after pesticide application, container labelling with safety procedures, carcinogen identification and elimination.
Sources: Connally et al. 1996; Hanrahan et al. 1996; Meridian Research, Inc. 1994; Pearce and Reif 1990; Popendorf and Donham 1991; Sullivan et al. 1992; Zejda, McDuffie and Dosman 1993.

Injury Hazards

Studies have consistently shown that agricultural workers are at increased risk of death due to injury. In the United States, a study of work-related fatalities for 1980 to 1989 reported rates in agricultural production of 22.9 deaths per 100,000 workers, as compared to 7.0 deaths per 100,000 for all workers. The average fatality rate for males and females, respectively, was 25.5 and 1.5 deaths per 100,000 workers. The leading causes of death in agricultural production were machinery and motor vehicles. Many studies report the tractor as the leading machine involved in fatalities, frequently from tractor rollovers. Other leading causes of death include electrocutions, caught in, flying objects, environmental causes and drowning. Age is an important risk factor related to agricultural fatalities for males. For example, the fatality

Figure 64.40 • Agricultural workers fatality rates, US, 1980-89.

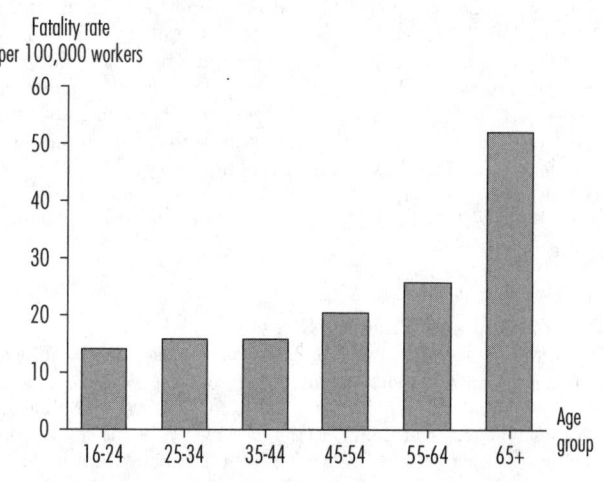

64. AGRICULTURE AND NATURAL RESOURCE BASED INDUSTRIES

Table 64.16 • Injury hazards.

Exposures	Health effects
Road vehicle crashes, machinery and vehicles, struck by objects, falls, oxygen depletion, fires	Fatalities
Tractors	Crushing of the chest, extravasation (escape of fluids—e.g., blood—and surrounding tissue), strangulation/asphyxia, drowning
Augers	Hypovolemia (loss of blood), sepsis and asphyxia
Electricity	Electrocutions
Machinery and vehicles, draught animal kicks and assaults, falls	Nonfatal injuries: injury infection (e.g., tetanus)
Hay balers	Friction burns, crushing, neurovascular disruption, avulsion, fractures, amputation
Power take-offs	Skin or scalp avulsion or degloving, amputation, multiple blunt injury
Corn pickers	Hand injuries (friction burns, crushing, avulsion or degloving, finger amputation)
Fires and explosions	Serious or fatal burns, smoke inhalation,

Interventions: rollover protective structures, guards, good practices, safe electrical wiring, fire prevention, protective equipment, good housekeeping practices.

Sources: Deere & Co. 1994; Meridian Research, Inc. 1994; Meyers and Hard 1995.

Table 64.17 • Percentages of lost time injuries by source of injury, nature of injury, and activity for four types of agricultural operations, United States, 1993.

	Cash grain	Field crops	Vegetables, fruits, nuts	Nursery crops
Source of Injury				
Tractors	11.0	9.7	–	1.0
Machinery	18.2	18.6	25.1	12.5
Livestock	11.0	12.1	1.7	–
Hand tools	13.4	13.0	19.3	3.8
Power tools	4.3	4.6	0.4	17.9
Pesticides/chemicals	1.3	2.8	0.4	0.5
Plants or trees	2.2	3.1	7.4	4.6
Working surfaces	11.5	11.6	6.8	5.1
Trucks or automobiles	4.7	1.4	1.5	–
Other vehicles	3.6	–	3.5	–
Liquids	3.1	1.0	–	–
Other	15.6	22.2	34.0	54.5
Nature of Injury				
Sprain/strain	20.5	23.5	39.3	38.0
Cut	16.4	32.3	18.9	21.7
Fracture	20.3	6.5	4.3	5.6
Bruise	9.3	9.5	12.6	14.8
Crush	10.4	2.6	2.4	1.0
Other	23.1	25.6	22.5	18.9
Activity				
Farm maintenance	23.8	19.1	10.8	33.3
Field work	17.2	34.6	34.0	38.2
Crop handling	14.1	13.8	9.4	7.7
Livestock handling	17.1	14.7	5.5	3.2
Machine maintenance	22.6	10.1	18.0	–
Other	5.1	7.5	22.3	17.6

Source: Meyers 1997.

rate for agricultural workers in the US over the age of 65 was over 50 per 100,000 workers, more than double the overall average (Meyers and Hard 1995) (see figure 64.40). Table 64.16 shows several injury hazard exposures, their consequences and recognized interventions.

A 1993 survey of farm injuries in the United States found the major injury sources to be livestock (18%), machinery (17%) and hand tools (11%). The most frequent injuries reported in this study were sprain and strain (26%), cut (18%) and fracture (15%). Males represented 95% of the injuries, while the highest concentration of injuries occurred among workers 30 to 39 years of age. Table 64.17 shows the source and nature of injury and the activity during injury for four major crop production categories. The National Safety Council estimated a US rate of 13.2 occupational injuries and illnesses per 100 crop production workers in 1992. More than half of these injures and illnesses resulted in an average of 39 days away from work. In contrast, the manufacturing and construction sectors had an injury and illness incidence rate of, respectively, 10.8 and 5.4 per 100 workers. In another study in the United States, investigators determined that 65% of all farm injuries required medical attention and that machinery other than tractors caused nearly half of the injuries that resulted in permanent disability (Meridian Research, Inc. 1994; Boxer, Burnett and Swanson 1995).

Mechanical and Thermal Stress Hazards

As discussed above, sprains and strains are a significant problem among agricultural workers, and as shown in table 64.18, agricultural workers are exposed to several mechanical and thermal stresses that result in injury. Many of these problems result from handling heavy loads, repetitive motion, poor posture and dynamic motion. In addition, agricultural vehicle operators are

exposed to whole-body vibration. One study reported the prevalence of low-back pain to be 10% greater among tractor drivers.

Noise-induced hearing loss is common among agricultural workers. One study reported that farmers more than 50 years of age have as much as 55% hearing loss. A study of rural students found that they have two times greater hearing loss than urban students.

Agricultural workers are exposed to temperature extremes. They may be exposed to hot, humid environments in work in the tropical and subtropical zones, and during the summer in the temperate zones. Heat stress and stroke are hazards under these conditions. Conversely, they may be exposed to extreme cold in the temperate zones in the winters and possible frostbite or death from hypothermia (Meridian Research, Inc. 1994).

Behavioural Hazards

Some aspects of farming can cause stress among farmers. As shown in table 64.19, these include isolation, risk taking, patriarchal attitudes, pesticide exposures, unstable economies and weather, and immobility. Problems associated with these circum-

Table 64.18 • Mechanical and thermal stress hazards.

Exposures	Health effects	Interventions
Tendon overuse, stretching; excessive force	Tendon-related disorders (tendinitis, tenosynovitis)	Ergonomic design, vibration dampening, warm clothing, rest periods
Repetitive motion, awkward wrist posture	Carpal tunnel syndrome	
Vibration of the hands	Raynaud's syndrome	
Repetition, high force, poor posture, whole-body vibration	Degenerative changes, low-back pain, intervertebral disk herniation; peripheral nerve and vascular, gastrointestinal and vestibular system injuries	
Motor and machinery noise	Hearing loss	Noise control, hearing protection
Increased metabolism, high temperatures and humidity, limited water and electrolytes	Heat cramps, heat exhaustion, heat stroke	Drinking water, rest breaks, protection from the sunshine
Low temperatures, lack of dry clothing	Frost nip, chilblains, frostbite, systemic hypothermia	Dry, warm clothing, heat generation from activity

Source: Meridian Research, Inc. 1994.

stances include dysfunctional relationships, conflicts, substance abuse, home violence and suicide. Most suicides associated with depression on farms in North America involve victims who are married and are full-time farmers, and most use firearms to commit suicide. The suicides tend to happen during peak farming periods (Boxer, Burnett and Swanson 1995).

Migrant farm labourers are at high risk of tuberculosis, and where male workers predominate, sexually transmitted diseases are a problem. Female migrant workers experience problems of appropriate perinatal outcome, high infant mortality rates, and low occupational risk perceptions. A broad range of behavioural issues is currently being investigated among migrant workers, including child abuse and neglect, domestic violence, substance abuse, mental disorders and stress-related conditions (ILO 1994).

Table 64.19 • Behavioural hazards.

Exposures	Health effects	Interventions
Isolation, economic threats, intergenerational problems, violence, substance abuse, incest, pesticides, risk taking, patriarchal attitudes, unstable weather, immobility	Depression, anxiety, suicide, poor coping	Early diagnosis, counselling, empowerment, pesticide control, community support
Tuberculosis, sexually transmitted diseases (migrant workers)	Interpersonal illness	Early diagnosis, vaccination, condom use

Sources: Boxer, Burnett and Swanson 1995; Davies 1995; Meridian Research, Inc. 1994; Parrón, Hernández and Villanueva 1996.

ENVIRONMENTAL AND PUBLIC HEALTH ISSUES IN AGRICULTURE

Melvin L. Myers

As the world's population continues to increase, demand grows for more food, but the increasing population is claiming more arable land for non-agricultural uses. Agriculturists need options to feed the world's growing population. These options include augmenting output per hectare, developing unused land into farmland and reducing or stopping the destruction of existing farmland. Over the past 25 years, the world has seen a "green revolution", particularly in North America and Asia. This revolution resulted in a tremendous increase in food production, and it was stimulated by developing new, more productive genetic strains and increasing inputs of fertilizer, pesticides and automation. The equation for producing more food is confounded by the need to address several environmental and public health issues. These issues include the need to prevent pollution and soil depletion, new ways to control pests, making farming sustainable, abating child labour and eliminating illicit drug cultivation.

Water and Conservation

Water pollution may be the most widespread environmental problem caused by agriculture. Agriculture is a large contributor to nonpoint pollution of surface water, including sediments, salts, fertilizers and pesticides. Sediment runoff results in soil erosion, a loss to agricultural production. Replacing 2.5 cm of topsoil naturally from bedrock and surface material takes between 200 and 1,000 years, a long time in human terms.

Sediment loading of rivers, streams, lakes and estuaries increases water turbidity, which results in decreased light for submerged aquatic vegetation. Species that depend upon this vegetation can thus experience a decline. Sediment also causes deposition in waterways and reservoirs, which adds to dredging expense and reduces water storage capacity of water supplies, irrigation systems and hydroelectric plants. Fertilizer waste, both synthetic and natural, contributes phosphorus and nitrates to the water. Nutrient loading stimulates algal growth, which can lead to eutrophication of lakes and related reduction in fish populations. Pesticides, particularly herbicides, contaminate surface water, and conventional water treatment systems are ineffective at removing them from water downstream. Pesticides contaminate food, water and feed. Groundwater is a source of drinking water for many people, and it is also contaminated with pesticides and nitrate from fertilizers. Groundwater is also used for animals and irrigation.

Irrigation has made farming possible in places where intensive farming was previously impossible, but irrigation has its negative consequences. Aquifers are depleted in places where groundwater use exceeds recharging; aquifer depletion can also lead to land subsidence. In arid areas, irrigation has been associated with mineralization and salinization of soils and water, and it has also depleted rivers. More efficient use and conservation of water can help alleviate these problems (NRC 1989).

Pest Control

Following the Second World War, the use of synthetic organic pesticides—fumigants, insecticides, herbicides and fungicides—grew dramatically, but a plethora of problems has resulted from the use of these chemicals. Growers saw the success of broad-spectrum, synthetic pesticides as a solution to pest problems that had plagued agriculture from its beginning. Not only did problems with human health effects emerge, but environmental scientists recognized ecological damage as extensive. For example,

Table 64.20 • Genetically engineered crops.

Crop	Varieties
Cotton	Three varieties, incorporating insect and herbicide resistance
Corn	Two varieties, incorporating insect resistance
Soybeans	One variety, with herbicide resistance
Potatoes	One variety, incorporating insect resistance
Tomatoes	Five varieties, with delayed ripening traits, thicker skin
Squash	One variety, resistant to two viruses
Canola	One variety, engineered to produce oil rich in lauric acid

Source: Toner 1996.

Table 64.21 • Illicit drug cultivation, 1987, 1991 and 1995.

Crop	Product	Hectares cultivated		
		1987	1991	1995
Opium poppy	Opiates	112,585	226,330	234,214
Coca (leaf)	Cocaine	175,210	206,240	214,800
Cannabis	Marijuana	24,423	20,919	12,205

Source: US Department of State 1996.

chlorinated hydrocarbons are persistent in soil and bioaccumulate in fish, shellfish and birds. The body burden of these hydrocarbons has declined in these animals where communities have eliminated or reduced chlorinated hydrocarbon use.

Pesticide applications have adversely affected non-targeted species. In addition, pests can become resistant to the pesticides, and examples of resistant species that became more virulent crop predators are numerous. Thus, growers need other approaches for pest control. Integrated pest management is an approach aimed at putting pest control on a sound ecological basis. It integrates chemical control in a way that is least disruptive to biological control. It aims, not to eliminate a pest, but to control the pest to a level that avoids economic damage (NRC 1989).

Genetically engineered crops are increasing in use (see table 64.20, but in addition to a positive result, they have a negative consequence. An example of a positive result is a genetically engineered strain of insect-resistant cotton. This strain, now in use in the United States, requires only one application of insecticide as contrasted with the five or six applications that would have been typical. The plant generates its own pesticide, and this reduces cost and environmental contamination. The potential negative consequence of this technology is the pest's developing resistance to the pesticide. When a small number of pests survive the engineered pesticide, they can grow resistant to it. The more virulent pest can then survive the engineered pesticide and similar synthetic pesticides. Thus, the pest problem can magnify beyond the one crop to other crops. The cotton boll weevil is now controlled in this way through an engineered cotton strain. With the emergence of a resistant boll weevil, another 200 crops can fall victim to the weevil, which would no longer be susceptible to the pesticide (Toner 1996).

Sustainable Farming

Because of environmental and economic concerns, farmers have started using alternative approaches to farming to reduce input costs, preserve resources and protect human health. The alternative systems emphasize management, biological relationships and natural processes.

In 1987, the World Commission on Environment and Development defined sustainable development to meet "the needs and aspirations of the present without compromising the ability of future generations to meet their own needs" (Myers 1992). A sustainable farm, in the broadest sense, produces adequate amounts of high-quality food, protects its resources, and is both environmentally safe and profitable. It addresses risks to human health using a systems-level approach. The concept of sustainable agriculture incorporates the term *farm safety* across the entire workplace environment. It includes the availability and the appropriate use of all our resources including soil, water, fertilizers, pesticides,

the buildings on our farms, the animals, capital and credit, and the people who are part of the agricultural community.

Child and Migrant Labour

Children labour in agriculture throughout the world. The industrialized world in no exception. Of the 2 million children under age 19 who reside on United States farms and ranches, an estimated 100,000 are injured each year in incidents related to production agriculture. They are typically children of either farmers or farm employees (National Committee for Childhood Agricultural Injury Prevention 1996). Agriculture is one of the few occupational settings in both developed and developing countries where children can engage in work typically done by adults. Children are also exposed to hazards when they accompany their parents during work and during leisure-time visits to the farm. The primary agents of farm injuries are tractors, farm machinery, livestock, building structures and falls. Children are also exposed to pesticides, fuels, noxious gases, airborne irritants, noise, vibration, zoonoses and stress. Child labour is employed on plantations around the world. Children work with their parents as part of a team for task-based compensation on plantations and as migrant farmworkers, or they are employed directly for special plantation jobs (ILO 1994).

Some of the problems and conditions of the migrant labour and child workforce as discussed elsewhere in this chapter and in this *Encyclopaedia*.

Illicit Drug Crops

Some crops do not appear in official records because they are illicit. These crops are cultivated to produce narcotics for human consumption, which alter judgement, are addictive and can cause death. Moreover, they add to the loss of productive land for food production. These crops comprise the poppy (used to make opium and heroine), coca leaf (used to make cocaine and crack) and cannabis (used to produce marijuana). Since 1987, world production of the opium poppy and coca has increased, and cultivation of cannabis has decreased, as shown in table 64.21. Five links are involved in the farm-to-user chain in the illicit drug trade: cultivation, processing, transit, wholesale distribution and retail sale. To interdict the supply of illicit drugs, governments concentrate on eradicating the production of the drugs. For example, eliminating 200 hectares of coca can deprive the drug market of about one metric ton of finished cocaine for a period of 2 years, since that is how long it would take to grow back mature plants. The most efficient means for eliminating the crops is through aerial application of herbicides, although some governments resist this measure. Manual eradication is another option, but it exposes personnel to violent reaction from the growers (US Department of State 1996). Some of these crops have a legal use, such as the manufacture of morphine and codeine from opium, and exposure to their dusts can lead to narcotic hazards in the workplace (Klincewicz et al. 1990).

References

AgSafe—Coalition for Health and Safety in Agriculture. 1992. *Occupational Injuries in California Agriculture 1981–1990.* Berkeley, CA: University of California.

Alexandratos, N. 1995. *World Agriculture: Towards 2010. An FAO Study.* New York: John Wiley & Sons.

Bean, TL and TS Lawrence. 1992. *Vehicles on Public Highways.* National Institute for Farm Safety Paper No. 92-04. Myrtle Beach, SC: National Institute for Farm Safety.

Bonsall, JL. 1985. Measurement of occupational exposure to pesticides. In *Occupational Hazards of Pesticide Use*, edited by GJ Turnbull. London: Taylor and Francis.

Boxer PA, C Burnett, and N Swanson. 1995. Suicide and occupation: A review of the literature. *J Occup Med* 37(4):442–452.

Bringhurst, LS, RN Byrne, and J Gershon-Cohen. 1959. Respiratory disease of mushroom workers. Farmer's lung. *JAMA* 171:15–18.

Brown, LR, N Lenssen, and H Kane. 1995. *Vital Signs 1995: The Trends that Are Shaping Our Future.* New York: WW Norton & Company.

Bull, D. 1982. *A Growing Problem: Pesticides and the Third World Poor.* Washington DC: Oxfam.

Campbell, WP. 1987. *The Condition of Agricultural Driveline System Shielding and Its Impact on Injuries and Fatalities.* MS Thesis. West Lafayette, IN: Purdue University.

Chang, S. 1993. Mushroom biology: The impact on mushroom production and mushroom products. In *Mushroom Biology and Mushroom Products*, edited by S Chang, JA Buswell, and S Chiu. Hong Kong: Chinese University Press.

Christiani, DC. 1990. Occupational health in developing countries: Review of research needs. *Am J Ind Med* 17:393–401.

Connally LB, PA Schulte, RJ Alderfer, LM Goldenhar, GM Calvert, KE Davis-King, and WT Sanderson. 1996. Developing the National Institute for Occupational Safety and Health's cancer control demonstration projects for farm populations. *Journal of Rural Health* suppl 12(4):258–264.

Cox, A, HTM Folgering, and LJLD Van Griensven. 1988. Extrinsic allergic alveolitis caused by the spores of the Oyster mushroom *Pleurotus ostreatus. Eur Respir J* 1:466–468.

—. 1989. Allergische Alveolitis verursacht durch Einatmung von Sporen des Pilzes Shii-take (*Lentinus edodes*). *Atemwegs Lungenkr* 15:233–234.

Dankelman, I and J Davidson. 1988. *Women and Environment in the Third World: Alliance for the Future.* London: Earthscan Publications.

Davies DR. 1995. Organophosphates, affective disorders, and suicide. *Journal of Nutritional and Environmental Medicine* 5:367–374.

Deere & Co. 1994. *Farm and Ranch Safety Management.* Moline, IL: Deere & Company.

Dufaut, A. 1988. Women carrying water: How it affects their health. *Waterlines* 6:23–25.

Eicher, LC. 1993. *State Codes for Road Travel of Agricultural Machinery.* American Society of Agricultural Engineering (ASAE) Paper No. 931513. St. Joseph, MI: ASAE.

Estlander T, L Kanerva and P Piirilä. 1996. Allergic dermatoses and respiratory diseases caused by decorative plants. *Afr Newslttr Occup Health Saf* 6(1):11–13.

Etherton, JR, JR Myers, RC Jensen, JC Russell, and RW Broddee. 1991. Agricultural machine-related deaths. *Am J Public Health* 81(6):776–768.

Food and Agriculture Organization (FAO) of the United Nations. 1987. *African Agriculture: The Next 25 Years.* Rome: FAO.

—. 1995. *The State of World Fisheries and Aquaculture.* Rome: FAO.

—. 1997. FAOSTAT Statistics Database (http://apps.fao.org/Default.htm). Accessed 22 January.

Forget, G. 1991. Pesticides and the third world. *J Toxicol Environ Health* 32:11–31.

—. 1992. Occupational health and development: An overview of the situation. *IDRC Reports: Perils in the Workplace* 20:4–7.

Franck IM and DM Brownstone. 1987. *Harvesters.* New York: Facts on File Publications.

Freivalds, A. 1984. Evaluation of the lift angle in spade work. *Ergonomics* 27 suppl:128–133.

Gerrits, JPG and LJLD Van Griensven. 1990. New developments in indoor composting (tunnel process). *Mushroom J* 205:21–29.

Gite, LP. 1991. Optimum handle height for animal drawn mould board plough. *Appl Ergon* 22:21–28.

Gite, LP and BG Yadav. 1990. Optimum handle height for a push-pull type manually operated dryland weeder. *Ergonomics* 33:1487–1494.

Glascock, LA, TL Bean, RK Wood, TG Carpenter, and RG Holmes. 1993. *Characteristics of SMV Accidents.* American Society of Agricultural Engineering (ASAE) Paper No. 931618. St. Joseph, MI: ASAE.

Griffin, GA. 1973. *Combine Harvesting.* Moline, IL: Deere & Company.

Gunderson, PD. 1995. An analysis of suicides on the farm or ranch within five north central United States, 1980 to 1988. In *Agricultural Health and Safety: Workplace, Environment, Sustainability*, edited by HH McDuffie, JA Dosman, KM Semchuk, SA Olenchock, and A Senthilselvan. Boca Raton, FL: CRC Press.

Hanrahan, LP, HA Anderson, LK Haskins, J Olson, K Lappe, and D Reding. 1996. Wisconsin farmer cancer mortality, 1981 to 1990: Selected malignancies. *Journal of Rural Health* suppl 12(4):273–277.

Hausen, BM, KH Schulz, and U Noster. 1974. Allergic disease caused by the spores of an edible fungus *Pleurotus florida. Mushr Sci* 9:219–225.

Horner, WE, MD Ibanez, V Liengswangwong, JE Salvaggio, and SB Lehrer. 1988. Characterization of allergens from spores of the Oyster mushroom *Pleurotus ostreatus. J Allergy Clin Immunol* 82:978–986.

International Labour Organization (ILO). 1994. *Recent Developments in the Plantation Sector.* Geneva: ILO.

International Organization for Standardization (ISO). 1985. ISO 263. *Evaluation of Human Exposure to Whole-body Vibration: Part I: General Requirements.* Geneva: ISO.

Jones, TH. 1978. *How to Build Greenhouses, Garden Shelters, and Sheds.* New York: Harper & Row.

Kelley, KA. 1996. Characteristics of flowing grain-related entrapments and suffocations with emphasis on grain transport vehicles. *Journal of Agricultural Safety and Health* 96(3):143–151.

Klincewicz, S, AT Fidler, G Siwinski, and A Fleeger. 1990. *Health Hazard Report: Penick Corporation, Newark, New Jersey.* No. HETA -87-311-2087. Cincinnati, OH: NIOSH.

Kundiev, YI. 1983. Conditions of labor in agriculture. In *Occupational Diseases of Agricultural Workers*, edited by YI Kundiev and EP Krasnyu. Kiev: Zdorovye.

Loftas, T (ed.). 1995. *Dimensions of Need: An Atlas of Food and Agriculture.* Santa Barbara, CA: ABC-CLIO, Inc.

Makinen-Kiljunen, S, K Turjanmaa, T Palosuo, and T Reunala. 1992. Characterization of latex antigens and allergens in surgical gloves and natural rubber by immunoelectrophoretic methods. *Journal Allergy Clin Immunol* 90(2):230_235.

McDuffie, HH, JA Dosman, KM Semchuk, SA Olenchock, and A Senthilselvan (eds.). 1994. *Agricultural Health and Safety: Workplace, Environment, Sustainability.* Boca Raton, FL: CRC Press.

Merchant. JP, BA Boehlecke, G Taylor, and M Pickett-Harner (eds.). 1986. *Occupational Respiratory Diseases.* DHHS (NIOSH) Publication No. 86-102. Washington, DC: GPO.

Meridian Research, Inc. 1994. *Occupational Safety and Health Hazards in Agriculture: A Review of the Literature.* Silver Spring, MD: Meridian Research.

Meyers, JR. 1997. Injuries among Farm Workers in the United States, 1993. DHHS (NIOSH) Publication No. 97-115. Cincinnati, OH: NIOSH.

Meyers, JR and DL Hard. 1995. Work-related fatalities in the agricultural production and services sectors, 1980–1989. *Am J Med* 27:51–63.

Miles, J. 1996. Personal communication.

Mines, R and PL Martin. 1986. *A Profile of California Farmworkers.* Giannini Information Series 86-2, Berkeley: University of California, Division of Agriculture and Natural Resources.

Mohan D and R Patel. 1992. Design of safer agricultural equipment: Application of ergonomics and epidemiology. *Int J Ind Erg* 10: 301–310.

Murphy, DJ and RC Williams. 1983. *Safe Forage Harvesting.* Agricultural Engineering Fact Sheet No. 21. State College, PA: Pennsylvania State University Cooperative Extension Service.

Murphy, DJ. 1992. *Safety and Health for Production Agriculture.* St. Joseph, MI: American Society of Agricultural Engineering.

Myers, ML. 1992. *Sustainable Agriculture as a Strategy in Agricultural Safety.* American Society of Agricultural Engineers (ASAE) Paper No. 928510. St. Joseph, MI: ASAE.

Nag, PK and SK Chatterjee. 1981. Physiological reactions of female workers in Indian agricultural work. *Hum Factors* 23:607–614.

Nag, PK and P Dutt. 1979. Effectiveness of some simple agricultural weeders with reference to physiological responses. *J Hum Ergol* 8:13–21.

—. 1980. Circulo-respiratory efficiency in some agricultural work. *Appl Ergon* 11:81–84.

Nag, PK and CK Pradhan. 1992. Ergonomics in the hoeing operation. *Int J Ind Erg* 10:341–350.

Nag, PK, NC Sebastian, and MG Marlankar. 1980. Occupational workload of Indian agricultural workers. *Ergonomics* 23:91–102.

Nag, PK, A Goswami, SP Ashtekar, and CK Pradhan. 1988. Ergonomics in sickle operation. *Appl Ergon* 19:233–239.

Nakazawa, T, K Kanatani and Y Umegae. 1981. Mushroom workers lung due to the inhalation of spores of *Cortinus shii-take. Jpn J Chest Dis* 40:934–938.

National Committee for Childhood Agricultural Injury Prevention. 1996. *Children and Agriculture: Opportunities for Safety and Health.* Marshfield, WI: Marshfield Clinic.

National Research Council (NRC). 1989. *Alternative Agriculture.* Washington, DC: National Academy Press.

—. 1993. *Sustainable Agriculture and the Environment in the Humid Tropics.* Washington, DC: National Academy Press.

National Safety Council (NSC). 1942. *Accident Facts.* Chicago, IL: NSC.

—. 1986. *Grain Harvest Safety.* Chicago, IL: NSC.

—. 1993. *Accident Facts.* Chicago, IL: NSC.

—. 1995. *Accident Facts.* Chicago, IL: NSC.

Nomura, S. 1993. Studies on the work load and health management in agricultural workers. *Journal of Japanese Association of Rural Medicine* 42:1007–1011.

Olson, J.A. 1987. *Pleurotus* spores as allergens. *Mushr J* 172:115–117.

Organization for Economic Cooperation and Development (OECD). 1994. *Farm Employment and Economic Adjustment in OECD Countries*. Paris: OECD.

Parrón, T, AF Hernández, and E Villanueva. 1996. Increased risk of suicide with exposure to pesticides in an intensive agricultural area: A 12-year retrospective study. *Forensic Science International* 79:53–63.

Partanen, T. 1996. Improving the work environment by means of risk surveys. *Afr Newslttr Occup Health Saf* 6(2):28–29.

Pearce, N and JS Reif. 1990. Epidemiologic studies of cancer in agricultural workers. *Am J Ind Med* 18:133–148.

Pepys, J. 1967. Hypersensitivity against inhaled organic antigens. *J Roy Coll Phys London* 2:42–48.

Popendorf, W and KJ Donham. 1991. Agricultural hygiene. In *Patty's Industrial Hygiene and Toxicology*, 4th edition, edited by GD Clayton and FE Clayton. New York: John Wiley & Sons, Inc.

Pradhan, CK, A Goswami, SK Ghosh, and PK Nag. 1986. Evaluation of working with spade in agriculture. *Indian J Med Res* 84:424–429.

Raffle, PAB, PH Adams, PJ Baxter, and WR Lee. 1994. *Hunter's Diseases of Occupations*, 8th edition, London: Edward Arnold.

Recht, C and MF Wetterwald. 1992. *Bamboos*. Portland, OR: Timber Press.

Rowntree, RA. 1987. Contemplating the urban forests. In *Our American Land: 1987 Yearbook of Agriculture*. Washington, DC: USDA.

Rylander, R. 1986. Lung diseases caused by organic dusts in the farm environment. *Am J Ind Med* 10:221–227.

Sakula, A. 1967. Mushroom-worker's lung. *Brit Med J* 3:708–710.

Sastre, J, MD Ibanez, M Lopez, and SB Lehrer. 1990. Respiratory and immunological reactions among Shii-take (*Lentinus edodes*) workers. *Clin Exp Allergy* 20:13–20.

Scherf, BD. 1995. *World Watch List for Domestic Animal Diversity*. Rome: FAO.

Sen, RN and PK Nag. 1975. Work organization of heavy load handling in India. *J Hum Ergol* 4:103–113.

Shutske, JM, WE Field, LD Gaultney, and SD Parsons. 1991. Agricultural machinery fire losses: A preventative approach. *Applied Engineering in Agriculture* 6(5):575–581.

Skillicorn, P, W Spira, and W Journet. 1993. *Duckweed Aquaculture: A New Aquatic Farming System for Developing Countries*. Washington, DC: World Bank.

Snyder, K and T Bobick. 1995. *Safe Grain and Silage Handling*. DHHS (NIOSH) Publication No. 95-109. Cincinnati, OH: NIOSH.

Sonnenberg, ASM, PCC Van Loon, and LJLD Van Griensven. 1996. Het aantal sporen dat *Pleurotus spp.* in de lucht verspreidt (with an English summary). *De Champignoncultuur* 40:269–272.

Steinke, WE. 1991. *Farm Labor, Tractor Use, and Farm Work Injury Survey*. Unpublished data. Davis, CA: University of California.

Stewart, CJ. 1974. Mushroom worker's lung—Two outbreaks. *Thorax* 29:252–257.

Stolz, JL, PH Arger, and JM Benson. 1976. Mushroom worker's lung disease. *Radiology* 119:61–63.

Storch, G, JG Burford, RB George, L Kaufman, and L Ajello. 1980. Acute histoplasmosis: Description of an outbreak in Northern Louisiana. *Chest* 77(1):38–42.

Sullivan JB, M Gonzales, GR Krieger, and CF Runge. 1992. Health-related hazards of agriculture. In *Hazardous Material Toxicology: Clinical Principles of Environmental Health*, edited by JB Sullivan and GR Krieger. London: Williams & Wilkins.

Tannahill, R. 1973. *Food in History*. New York: Stein and Day.

Toner, M. 1996. Debugging king cotton. *Atlanta Journal-Constitution* 47(50):G1.

United Nations Development Programme (UNDP). 1996. *Urban Agriculture: Food, Jobs, and Sustainable Cities*. New York: UNDP.

US Department of Agriculture (USDA). 1996. Foreign Agricultural Service Circular Series FTROP 2-96. Washington, DC: USDA.

US Department of Labor (DOL). 1968. *Fair Labor Standards Act—The Hazardous Occupations Order for Agriculture*. Washington, DC: US DOL.

US Department of State. 1996. *International Narcotics Control Report*. Washington, DC: US Department of State.

Van den Bogart, HGG. 1990. *De champignonkwekerslong: een onderzoek naar voorkomen en etiologie in Nederland*. PhD dissertation. Nijmegen, Netherlands: University of Nijmegen.

Van den Bogart, HGG, G Van den Ende, PGG Van Loon, and LJLD Van Griensven. 1993. Mushroom worker's lung: serologic reactions to thermophilic actinomycetes in the air of compost tunnels. *Mycopathologia* 122:21–28.

Van Haaren, JPM. 1988. Occupational diseases. In *The Cultivation of Mushrooms*, edited by LJLD Van Griensven. Rustington, UK: Darlington Mushroom Laboratories.

Van Loon, PCC, AL Cox, OPJM Wuisman, SLGE Burgers, and LJLD Van Griensven. 1992. Mushroom worker's lung. Detection of antibodies against shii take (*Lentinus edodes*) spore antigens in shii take workers. *J Occup Med* 34:1097–1101.

Villarejo, D. 1995. Issues for farm employees in the United States. In *Agricultural Health and Safety: Workplace, Environment and Sustainability*, edited by HH McDuffie, JA Dosman, KM Semchulk, SA Olenchock, and A Senthilselvan. Boca Raton, FL: CRC Press.

Viten VPh, EP Krashyuh, and OV Ilyna. 1994. Ergonomic and health aspects of pesticide exposure in greenhouses. In *Health, Safety and Ergonomic Aspects in Use of Chemicals in Agriculture and Forestry: Proceedings of the XII Joint GIGR; IAAMRH, IUFRP International Symposium*, edited by Y Kundiev. Kiev: Institute for Occupational Health.

Wallerstein N and M Weinger. 1992. Health and safety education for worker empowerment. *Am J Ind Med* 22:619–635.

Weinger, J and M Lyons. 1992. Problem-solving in the fields: An action-oriented approach to farmworker education about pesticides. *Am J Ind Med* 22:677–690.

Weinger, M and N Wallerstein. 1990. Education for action: An innovative approach to training hospital employees. In *Essentials of Modern Hospital Safety*, edited by W Charney and J Whirmer. Chelsea, MI: Lewis Publishers.

Zejda. JE, HH McDuffie, and JA Dosman. 1993. Epidemiology of health and safety risks in agriculture and related industries: Practical applications for rural physicians. *West J Med* 158:56–63.

Other relevant readings

Adams, WD and TR Leroy. 1992. *Growing Fruits and Nuts in the South: The Definitive Guide*. Dallas, TX: Taylor Publishing Co.

Atta, MV. 1991. *Growing and Using Exotic Foods*. Sarasota, FL: Pineapple Press.

Australian Canegrowers Publication. *Cane Farm Workers Guide*. 1992. Brisbane, Australia: Australian Canegrowers Publication.

Akehurst, BC. 1981. *Tobacco*. New York: Humanities Press.

Ashworth J, FN Curry, IR White, and RJG Rycroft. 1990. Occupationally allergic contact dermatitis in east coast of England fisherman: Newly described hypersensitivities to marine organisms. *Contact Dermat* 22(3):185–186.

Atkin, M. 1992. *The International Grain Trade*. Cambridge: Woodhead Publishing Limited.

Borget, M. 1993. *Spice Plants*. London: Macmillan Press Ltd.

Brittain J, S Caldwell, and S Schuman. 1992. *Agriculture and Medicine: A Partnership*. Videoconference Guide. Clemson, SC: Clemson University.

Cary, AE. 1991. Agriculture, agricultural chemicals, and water quality. In *Agriculture and the Environment: The 1991 Yearbook of Agriculture*. Washington, DC: USDA.

Chan, OY, CS Lee, KT Tan, and T Thirumoorthy. 1990. Health problems among spice grinders. *J Soc Occup Med* 40:111–115.

Christiansson, C, C Folke, and T Karberger (eds.). 1991. *Use and Impacts of Chemical Pesticides in Smallholder Agriculture in the Central Kenya Highlands*. Dordrecht, Netherlands: Kluwer Academic Publishers.

Clerc, J-M (ed.). 1985. *Introduction to Working Conditions and Environment*. Geneva: ILO.

Collins, WK and SN Hawks, Jr. (eds.). 1993. *Principles of Flue-cured Tobacco Production*. Raleigh, NC: North Carolina State University.

Cordes, DH and DF Rea (eds.). 1991. Health hazards of farming. *Occup Med: State Art Rev* 6(3).

Cotes, JE and J Steel. 1987. *Work-related Lung Diseases*. Oxford: Blackwell Scientific Publications.

Coumbis JJ. 1992. Musculoskeletal disorders and hazards. *Papers and Proceedings of the Surgeon General's Conference on Agricultural Safety and Health*. DHHS (NIOSH) Publication No. 92-105. Washington, DC: GPO.

Coye MJ. 1985. The health effects of agricultural production: I. The health of agricultural workers. *J Pub Hlth Policy* 6:349–370.

Cullen M, Johnson L. 1992. *The Urban/suburban Composter*. New York: St. Martin's Press.

Davies JE, RF Smith, and V Freed. 1978. Agromedical approach to pesticide management. *Ann Rev Entomol* 23:353–366.

Dawson, MW, JG Scott, and LM Cox. 1996. The medical and epidemiologic effects on workers of the levels of airborne *Thermoactinomyces spp.* Spores present in Australian raw sugar mills. *Am Ind Hyg Asso J* 57:1002–1012.

Division of Workplace Safety and Health. 1991. *Take Time for Safety: Sugar Industry*. Queensland, Australia: Department of Employment, Vocational Education, Training and Industrial Relations, Division of Workplace Safety and Health.

Dosman, JA and DW Cockcroft. 1989. *Principles of Health and Safety in Agriculture*. Boca Raton, FL: CRC Press.

El Batawi, MA. 1992. Migrant workers. In *Occupational Health in Developing Countries*, edited by J Jeyaratnam. New York: Oxford University Press.

Fenske, R and NJ Simcox. 1995. Agricultural workers. In *Occupational Health: Recognizing and Preventing Work-related Diseases*, edited by BS Levy and DH Wegman. Boston: Little, Brown & Co.

Forsman S and GH Coppee. 1984. *Occupational Health Problems of Young Workers*. Geneva: ILO.

Graber, DR, WJ Jones, and JA Johnson. 1995. Human and ecosystem health: The environment-agricultural connection in developing countries. *J Agromedicine* 2:47–64.

Greenhalgh, P. 1972. *The Market for Culinary Herbs*. London: Tropical Products Institute.

Hay, A. 1991. Recent assessment of cocoa and pesticides in Brazil: An unhealthy blend for plantation workers. *Sci Total Environ* 106(1):97–109.

Hayes, WJJ and ERJ Laws. 1991. *Handbook of Pesticide Toxicology*. San Diego, CA: Academic Press.

Heimlich, RE. 1987. Agriculture and urban areas in perspective. In *Our American Land: 1987 Yearbook of Agriculture*. Washington, DC: GPO.

Helmore, K and A Ratta. 1995. The surprising yields of urban agriculture. *Choices* 4(1):22–27.

International Labour Organization (ILO). 1965. *Safety and Health in Agricultural Work*. Geneva: ILO.

—. 1979. *Guide to Health and Hygiene in Agricultural Work*. Geneva: ILO.

—. 1988. *Maximum Weights in Load Lifting and Carrying*. Geneva: ILO.

James, ER. 1994. Onchocerciasis control by insecticides and chemotherapy stimulates agricultural development in Central West Africa. *J Agromedicine* 1:3–17.

James, PA: Agromedicine: What's in a name? *J Agromedicine* 1:81–87.

Jones, DL. 1995. *Palms throughout the World*. Washington, DC: Smithsonian Institution Press.

Karr, C, J Kalat, D Locke, E Atkinson, and M Rohde. 1995. Farm worker occupational illness and injury in Washington State. In *Agricultural Health and Safety: Workplace, Environment, Sustainability*, edited by HH McDuffie, JA Dosman, KM Semchuk, SA Olenchock, A Senthilselvan. Boca Raton, FL: CRC Press.

Kelley, WD. 1982. *Agricultural Respiratory Hazards*. Cincinnati, OH: American Conference of Governmental Industrial Hygienists.

Kelsey, TW. 1994. The agrarian myth and policy responses to farm safety. *Am J Public Health* 84(7):1171-1177.

Kidd, P, T Scharf, and M Veazie. 1996. Linking stress and injury in the farming environment: A secondary analysis of qualitative data. *Health Education Quarterly* 23(2):224-237.

Levy, BS and DH Wegman. 1995. *Occupational Health: Recognizing and Preventing Work-related Disease*, 3rd edition. Boston: Little, Brown and Co.

Malmros, P and P Jonsson. 1994. Wastes management: Planning for recycling and workers' safety. *Journal of Waste Management and Resource Recovery* 1(3):107–112.

Martin, NB. 1995. Custos e rentabilidade de diferentes sistemas de producao de café. *Informrnacóes Económicas* (Sao Paulo) 5(8):35–47.

Marotz-Baden, R, CB Hennon, and TH Brubaker (eds.) 1988. *Families in Rural America: Stress, Adaptation, and Revitalization*. St. Paul, MN: National Council on Family Relations.

McCurdy, SA, TS Ferguson, DF Goldsmith, JE Parker, and MB Schenker. 1996. Respiratory health of California rice farmers. *Am J Respir Crit Care Med* 153:1553-1559..

Merchant, JP, B Kross, K Donham, and D Pratt. 1989. *Agriculture at Risk: A Report to the Nation*. Kansas City, MO: National Coalition for Agricultural Safety and Health, National Rural Health Association.

Mikheev, M. 1994. Health and safety issues in the use of pesticides: An international perspective. In *Health, Safety and Ergonomic Aspects in Use of Chemicals in Agriculture and Forestry: Proceedings of the XII Joint GIGR, IAAMRH, IUFRP International Symposium*, edited by Y Kundiev. Kiev: Institute for Occupational Health.

Miller, RA. 1992. *The Potential of Herbs as a Cash Crop*. Berkeley, CA: Ten Speed Press.

Mobed, K, E Cold, and MB Schenker. 1992. Occupational health problems among migrant and seasonal farmworkers. *West J Med* 157:367–373.

Morrison, HI, RM Semenciw, D Morrison D, and Y Mao. 1995. Mortality among Canadian fruit and vegetable farmers. *Agricultural Health and Safety: Workplace, Environment, Sustainability*, edited by HH McDuffie, JA Dosman, KM Semchuk, SA Olenchock, and A Senthilselvan. Boca Raton, FL: CRC Press.

Meyers, JR and KA Snyder. 1995. Roll-over protective structure use and the cost of retrofitting tractors in the United States, 1993. *Journal of Agricultural Safety and Health* 1(3):185-197.

Myers, ML, RF Herrick, SA Olenchock, JR Myers, JE Parker, DL Hard, and K Wilson (eds.). 1992. *Papers and Proceedings of the Surgeon General's Conference on Agricultural Safety and Health*. DHHS (NIOSH) Publication No. 92-105. Cincinnati, OH: NIOSH.

National Institute for Occupational Safety and Health (NIOSH). 1977. *Occupational Diseases: A Guide to Their Recognition*. Washington, DC: NIOSH.

—. 1983. *Musculoskeletal Diseases in Agricultural Workers*. Cincinnati, OH: NIOSH.

—. 1993. *Fatal Injuries to Workers in the United States, 1980-1989: A Decade of Surveillance*. Cincinnati, OH: NIOSH.

—. 1996. *Ecologically Based Pest Management: New Solutions for a New Century*. Washington, DC: National Academy Press.

Nelson, PV. 1981. *Greenhouse Operation and Management*, 2nd edition. Reston, VA: Reston Publishing Co.

Nogueira, DP. 1987. Prevention of accidents and injuries in Brazil. *Ergonomics* 30(2):387–393.

Norse, EA (ed.). 1993. *Global Marine Biological Diversity: A Strategy for Building Conservation into Decision Making*. Washington, DC: Island Press.

O'Toole, C. 1995. *Alien Empire: An Exploration of the Lives of Insects*. New York: Harper Collins Publishers.

Persons, WS. 1986. *American Ginseng: Green Gold*. Pompano Beach, FL: Exposition Press of Florida.

Phoolchund, HN. 1991. Aspects of occupational health in the sugar cane industry. *J Soc Occ Med* 41(3):133–136.

Pinstrup-Andersen, P (ed.). 1993. *The Political Economy of Food and Nutrition Policies*. Johns Baltimore, MD: Johns Hopkins University Press.

Prosterman, RL, T Hanstad, and L Ping. 1996. Can China feed itself? *Sci Am* 275(5):90–96.

Rastogi, SK, BN Gupta, T Husain, N Mathur, and N Garg. 1989. Study of respiratory impairment among pesticide sprayers in mango plantations. *Am J Ind Med* 16(5):529–538.

Rodriguez, E. 1993. *Factores de riesgo psicosociales in la organización laboral* (Psychosocial risk factors in labour organization). Medellin, Colombia: Social Security Institute.

Rosenstock, L and M Cullen. 1986. *Clinical Occupational Medicine*. Philadelphia, PA: WB Saunders Company.

Rovell, CR. 1993. *Plants and the Skin*. Oxford: Blackwell Scientific Publications.

Rycroft, RJG, T Menné, and PJ Frosch. 1995. *Textbook of Contact Dermatitis*. Berlin: Springer-Verlag.

Satterwaite, D. 1993. The impact on health of urban environments. *Environment and Urbanization* 5(2):87–111.

Schenker, MB, R Lopez, and G Wintemute. 1995. Farm-related fatalities among children in California, 1980 to 1989. *Am J Public Health* 85(1):89–92.

Schuman, S (ed.). 1995. 1994—A vintage year for agromedicine journals. *J Agromedicine* 2:1–2.

Schuman, SH and WM Simpson Jr. 1997. *AG-MED: The Rural Practitioner's Guide to Agromedicine*. Kansas City, MO: American Academy of Family Physicians.

Sekimpi, DK, EF Agaba, M Okot-Nwang, and DA Orgaram. 1996. Occupational coffee dust allergies in Uganda. *Afr Newslett Occup Health Saf* 6(1):6.

Snyder, K and T Bobick. 1995. *Safe Grain and Silage Handling*. DHHS (NIOSH) Publication No. 95-109. Washington, DC: GPO.

Sobczak, PM, JA Johnson, WJ Jones, and LG Lusby. 1994. Agromedicine: A delphi study of the field—present and future. *J Agromedicine* 1:69–79.

Stransky, L and S Transkov. 1980. Contact dermatitis from parsley. *Contact Dermat* 6:233–234.

Thrupp, LA. 1991. Sterilization of workers from pesticide exposure: The causes and consequences of DBCP-induced damage in Costa Rica and beyond. *Int J Health Serv* 21(4):731–757.

Thune, PO and YJ Solberg. 1980. Photosensitivity and allergy to aromatic lichen acids, compostae, oleoresins and other plant substances. *Contact Dermatitis* 6(2):81–87.

Toorenenbergen, AW and PH Dieges. 1984. Occupational allergy in horticulture: demonstration of immediate-type allergic reactivity to freesia and paprika plants. *International Archives of Allergy and Applied Immunology* 75:44–47.

Tso, TC. 1990. *Production, Physiology, and Biochemistry of the Tobacco Plant*. Beltsville, MD: Ideals, Inc.

US Department of Agriculture (USDA). 1985. *U.S. Agriculture in a Global Economy: 1985 Yearbook of Agriculture*. Washington, DC: GPO.

—. 1988. *Agricultural Statistics 1988*. Washington, DC: GPO.

US Department of Labor. 1991. *Findings from the National Agricultural Workers Survey (NAWS) 1990: A Demographic and Employment Profile of Perishable Crop Farm Workers*. Washington, DC: US Department of Labor.

US General Accounting Office (GAO). 1992. *Report to Congressional Requestors: Hired Farmworkers: Health and Well-being at Risk*. GAO/HRD-92-46. Washington, DC: GAO.

Vasquez-Castelanos, JC. 1991. Coffee cultivation and social history of onchocerciasis in Soconusco, Chiapas, Mexico. *Salud Publica de Mexico* 33:(2):124–135.

Wan, H. 1990. Pesticide exposure of applicators working in tea plantations. *B Environ Contam Tox* 45(3):459–462.

Wheat, JR, MC Nagy, JT McKnight, and RL Anderson. 1994. Alabama agrimedicine program: Rationale, proposal, and supportive study. *J Agromedicine* 1:63–82.

Wilk, VA. 1986. *The Occupational Health of Migrant and Seasonal farmworkers in the United States*, 2nd ed. Washington, DC: Farmworker Justice Fund, Inc.

—. 1993. Health hazards to children in agriculture. *Am J Ind Med* 24(3):283–90.

World Health Organization (WHO). 1987. *Detección precoz de enfermedades profesionales* (Early detection of professional illness). Geneva: WHO.

—. 1990. *Public Health Impact of Pesticides Used in Agriculture*. Geneva: WHO.

64. AGRICULTURE AND NATURAL RESOURCE BASED INDUSTRIES

BEVERAGE INDUSTRY

Chapter Editor
Lance A. Ward

Contents

65. BEVERAGE INDUSTRY

● GENERAL PROFILE

David Franson

Overview of the Sector

The beverage industry consists of two major categories and eight sub-groups. The non-alcoholic category is comprised of soft drink syrup manufacture; soft drink and water bottling and canning; fruit juices bottling, canning and boxing; the coffee industry and the tea industry. Alcoholic beverage categories include distilled spirits, wine and brewing.

Evolution of the industry

Although many of these beverages, including beer, wine and tea, have been around for thousands of years, the industry has developed only over the past few centuries.

The beverage products industry, viewed as an aggregate group, is highly fragmented. This is evident by the number of manufacturers, methods of packaging, production processes and final products. The soft drink industry is the exception to the rule, as it is quite concentrated. Although the beverage industry is fragmented, ongoing consolidation since the 1970s is changing that.

Since the early 1900s beverage companies have evolved from regional firms that mainly produced goods for local markets, to today's corporate giants that make products for international markets. This shift began when companies in this manufacturing sector adopted mass production techniques that let them expand. Also during this time period there were advances in product packaging and processes that greatly increased product shelf life. Air-tight containers for tea prevented absorption of moisture, which is the principle cause of loss of flavour. In addition, the advent of refrigeration equipment enabled lager beers to be brewed during the summer months.

Economic importance

The beverage industry employs several million people worldwide, and each type of beverage grosses billions of dollars in revenue each year. Indeed, in several small, developing countries, the production of coffee is the major support of the entire economy.

Characteristics of the Workforce

Though the ingredients and production of beverages vary, generally the characteristics of those employed in this industry have many commonalties. The process of harvesting raw materials, whether they be coffee beans, barley, hops or grapes, employs low-income, unskilled individuals or families. In addition to being their main source of income, the harvest determines a large part of their culture and lifestyle.

In contrast, the processing of the product involves automated and mechanized operations, usually employing a semi-skilled, blue-collar workforce. In the production facility and warehouse areas, some of the common jobs include packaging and filling machine operator, fork-lift operator, mechanic and manual labourer. The training for these positions is completed onsite with extensive on-the-job instruction. As technology and automation evolve, the workforce diminishes in number and technical training becomes more important. This semi-skilled manufacturing workforce is usually supported by a highly skilled technical group consisting of industrial engineers, manufacturing managers, cost accountants and quality assurance/food safety technicians.

The beverage industry for the most part distributes its products to wholesalers using common carriers. However, soft drink manufacturers usually employ drivers to deliver their products directly to individual retailers. These drivers-salesworkers account for about one-seventh of the workers in the soft drink industry.

The more health-conscious atmosphere in Europe and North America in the 1990s has led to a flat market in the alcoholic beverage industry, with demand shifting to non-alcoholic beverages. Both alcoholic and non-alcoholic beverages, however, are expanding considerably in developing nations in Asia, South America and to some extent Africa. Because of this expansion, numerous local jobs are being created to meet production and distribution needs.

SOFT DRINK CONCENTRATE MANUFACTURING

Zaida Colon

Process Overview

The making of the concentrate is the first step in the production of a carbonated soft drink. At the beginnings of the industry, in the nineteenth century, both concentrate and soft drink were manufactured in the same facility. Sometimes the concentrate was sold to the consumers, who would make their own soft drinks. As the carbonated soft drink business has grown, the concentrate and the soft drink manufacturing have become specialized. Today, a concentrate manufacturing plant sells its product to various bottling companies.

Concentrate plants are constantly optimizing their operation through systems automation. As the demand for concentrate increases, automation has allowed the manufacturer to satisfy the demand without expanding the size of the manufacturing plant. Packaging size has increased too. Early in the industry, 1/2-, 1-

Production of fruit juices

Fruit juices are made from a wide variety of fruits, including oranges and other citrus fruits, apples, grapes, cranberries, pineapples, mangoes and so forth. In many cases, various fruit juices are blended. Usually, the fruit is processed into a concentrate near where it is grown, then shipped to a fruit juice packager. Fruit juices can be sold as concentrates, frozen concentrates (especially orange juice) and as the diluted juice. Often sugar and preservatives are added.

Once received at the processing plant, the oranges are washed, graded to remove damaged fruit, separated according to size and sent to the juice extractors. There the oils are extracted from the peel, and then the juice extracted by crushing. The pulpy juice is screened to remove seeds and pulp, which often end up as cattle feed. If the orange juice is intended for sale as "not from concentrate", it is then pasteurized. Otherwise the juice is sent to evaporators, which remove most of the water by heat and vacuum, then chilled, to produce the frozen, concentrated orange juice. This process also removes many oils and essences which are blended back into the concentrate before shipping to the juice packager.

The frozen concentrate is shipped to the packager in refrigerated trucks or tankers. Many dairies package orange juice using the same equipment used to package milk. (See the article "Dairy products industry" elsewhere in this volume.) The concentrate is diluted with filtered water, pasteurized and packaged under sterile conditions. Depending on the amount of water added, the final product can be cans of frozen orange juice concentrate or ready-to-serve orange juice.

Michael McCann

and 5-gallon containers were the most common. Today 40- and 50-gallon drums and even tank trucks with capacities of 3,000 to 4,000 gallons are used.

Operations in a concentrate manufacturing plant can be divided into five basic processes:

1. treating water
2. receiving raw materials
3. concentrate manufacturing
4. concentrate and additives filling
5. shipping finished products.

Each of these processes has safety hazards that must be evaluated and controlled. Water is a very important ingredient in the concentrate and it must have excellent quality. Each concentrate plant treats water until it reaches the desired quality and is free from micro-organisms. Water treatment is monitored during all stages.

When the plant receives the compounding ingredients, inspection, sampling and analysing of the ingredients in the quality-control department are begun. Only materials that have passed the tests will be used in the concentrate manufacturing process. Some of the raw materials are received in tank trucks and require special handling. Also, packaging material is received, evaluated and analysed in the same way as the raw materials.

During the manufacturing of concentrate, treated water and liquid and solid ingredients are pumped into stainless-steel tanks, where they are mixed, homogenized and/or extracted in accordance with the manufacturing instructions. The tanks have capacities of 50 gallons, 10,000 gallons and even more. These tanks are completely clean and sanitized at the time of mixing.

Once the concentrate is manufactured, the filling stage is started. All the products are piped into the filling room. Filling machines are strictly cleaned and sanitized before the filling process starts. Most of the filling machines are dedicated to specific container sizes. The product is kept inside pipes and tanks at times during the filling process in order to avoid contamination. Each container should be labelled with the product name and handling hazards (if necessary). Full containers are moved by conveyors to the packaging area. Containers are placed on pallets and wrapped in plastic or tied before they are stored. Besides the concentrates, additives to be used in the preparation of carbonated soft drinks are packed. Many of these additives are packed in plastic bags and placed in boxes.

Once at the warehouse, the products are divided and prepared to be sent to the different bottling companies. These products should be labelled following all government regulations. If products are going to another country, the product must be labelled in accordance with the other country's labelling requirements.

Hazard Prevention

Hazards in a concentrate manufacturing plant vary depending on the products manufactured and the size of the plant.

Concentrate plants have a low injury rate due to a high degree of automation and mechanized handling. Materials are handled by fork-lifts, and full containers are placed on pallets by automatic palletizers. Although, employees generally do not have to use excessive force to get the job done, lifting related injuries remain a concern. Major hazards include engines and equipment in motion, objects falling from overhead containers, energy hazards in repair and maintenance, confined space hazards in cleaning mixing tanks, noise, fork-lift accidents and hazardous chemical cleaning agents. See the article "Soft drink bottling and canning" for more information on hazards and precautions.

SOFT DRINK BOTTLING AND CANNING

Matthew Hirsheimer

In most established markets around the world, soft drinks now rank first among manufactured beverages, surpassing even milk and coffee in terms of per capita consumption.

Including ready-to-drink, packaged products and bulk mixes for fountain dispensing, soft drinks are available in almost every conceivable size and flavour and in virtually every channel of retail distribution. Complementing this universal availability, much of the soft drink category's growth can be attributed to convenient packaging. As consumers have become increasingly mobile, they have opted for easier-to-carry packaged goods. With the advent of the aluminium can and, more recently, the resealable plastic bottle, soft drink packaging has become lighter and more portable.

Stringent quality-control standards and state-of-the-art water treatment processes also have afforded the soft drink industry a high degree of confidence regarding product purity. Moreover, the manufacturing or bottling plants that produce soft drinks have evolved into highly mechanized, efficient and spotlessly clean food-processing facilities.

As early as the 1960s, most bottlers were producing beverages through machinery that ran at 150 bottles per minute. As product demand has continued to skyrocket, soft drink manufacturers have shifted to faster machinery. Thanks to advances in production technology, filling lines now are able to run in excess of 1,200 containers per minute, with minimal downtime except for product or flavour changes. This highly automated environment has allowed soft drink manufacturers to reduce the number of employees required to operate the lines (see figure 65.1). Still, as

Figure 65.1 • Control panel in an automated soft drink plant in Novosibirsk, Russia.

65. BEVERAGE INDUSTRY

Figure 65.2 • Flow chart of basic bottling operations.

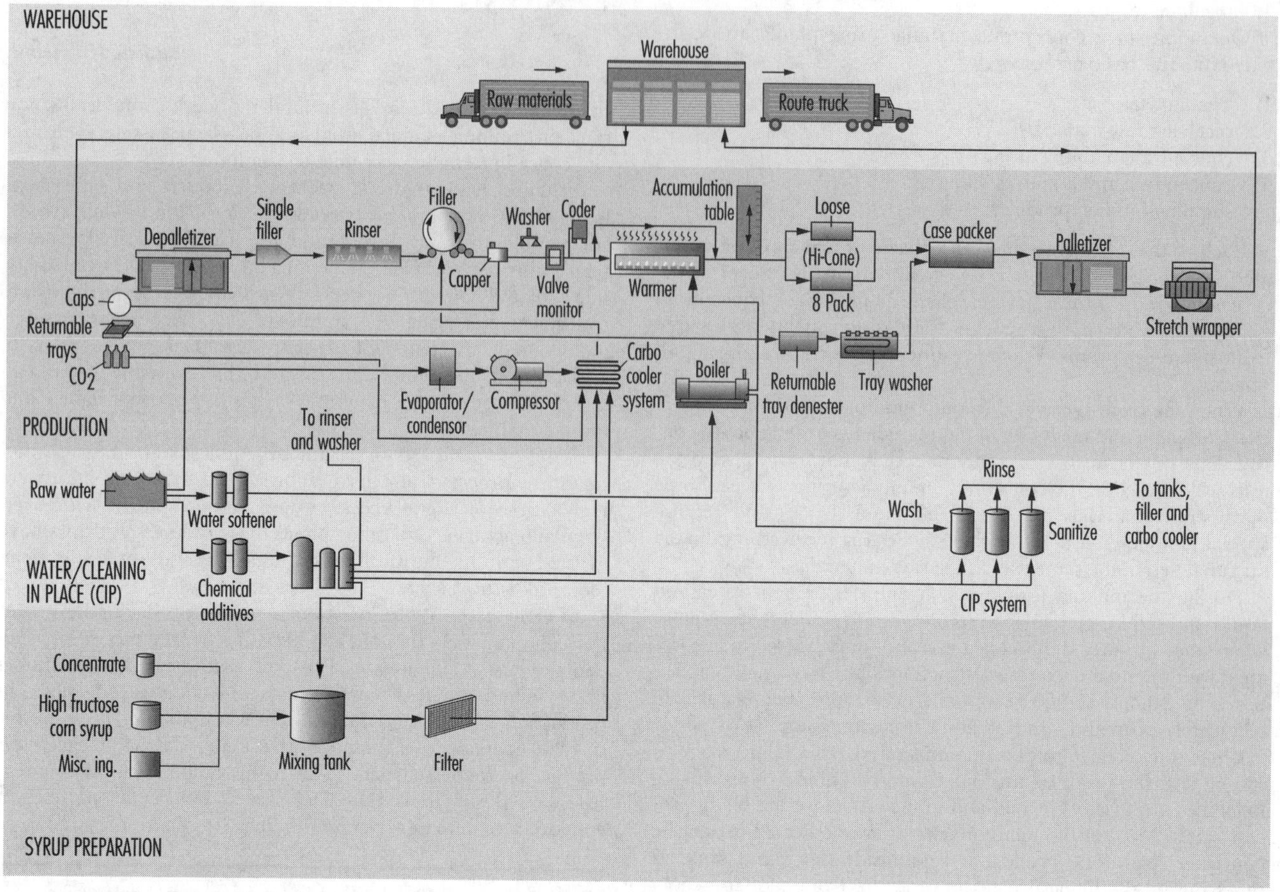

production efficiencies have risen dramatically, plant safety has remained an ever-important consideration.

Soft drink bottling or manufacturing involves five major processes, each with its own safety issues that must be evaluated and controlled:

1. treating water
2. compounding ingredients
3. carbonating product
4. filling product
5. packaging.

See figure 65.2.

Soft drink manufacturing starts with water, which is treated and cleansed to meet exacting quality-control standards, usually exceeding the quality of the local water supply. This process is critical to achieving high product quality and consistent taste profiles.

As ingredients are being compounded, the treated water is piped into large, stainless-steel tanks. This is the stage at which various ingredients are added and mixed. Diet beverages are mixed with artificial, non-nutritive sweeteners such as aspartame or saccharin, whereas regularly sweetened drinks typically use liquid sugars like fructose or sucrose. It is during this stage of the production process that food colouring may be added. Flavoured, sparkling waters receive the desired flavouring at this stage, while plain waters are stored in the mixing tanks until the filling line calls for them. It is common for bottling companies to purchase concentrate from other firms.

In order for carbonation (absorption of carbon dioxide (CO_2)) to occur, soft drinks are cooled using large, ammonia-based refrigeration systems. This is what gives carbonated products their effervescence and texture. CO_2 is stored in a liquid state, and piped into carbonation units as needed. This process can be manipulated to control the required rate of beverage absorption. Depending upon the product, soft drinks may contain from 15 to 75 psi of CO_2. Fruit-flavoured soft drinks tend to have less carbonation than colas or sparkling water. Once carbonated, the product is ready to be dispensed into bottles and cans.

The filling room usually is separated from the rest of the facility, protecting open product from any possible contaminants. Again, the highly automated filling operation requires a minimal number of personnel. See figure 65.3. Filling room operators monitor the equipment for efficiency, adding bulk lids or caps to the capping operation as necessary. Empty bottles and cans are transported automatically to the filling machine via bulk material-handling equipment.

Stringent quality-control procedures are followed throughout the production process. Technicians measure many variables, including CO_2, sugar content and taste, to ensure that finished drinks meet required quality standards.

Packaging is the last stage prior to warehousing and delivery. This process also has become highly automated. Meeting various marketplace requirements, bottles or cans enter the packaging machinery and may be wrapped with cardboard to form cases or placed into reusable plastic trays or shells. The packaged products then enter a palletizing machine, which automatically stacks them

Figure 65.3 • Soft drink canning line showing filling operations.

onto pallets. (See figure 65.4.) Next, the loaded pallets are moved—typically via fork-lift—to a warehouse, where they are stored.

Hazard Prevention

Lifting-related injuries—especially to employees' backs and shoulders—are not uncommon in the beverage business. While many technological advances have been made in material handling over the years, the industry continues to seek safer, more efficient ways to move heavy product.

Certainly, employees must be provided with the proper training on safe work practices. Injuries also can be minimized by limiting exposure to lifting through enhanced work-station design. Adjustable tables can be used to raise or lower material to waist level, for example, so that employees do not have to bend and lift as much. In this manner, most weight-related stress is transferred to a piece of equipment instead of the human body. All beverage manufacturers should implement ergonomics programmes that identify work-related hazards and minimize the risks—either through modification or by developing better equipment. A reasonable means to that end is job rotation, which reduces employee exposure to high-risk tasks.

The use of machine guarding is another critical component of safe beverage manufacturing. Equipment such as fillers and conveyors move at high speeds and, if left unguarded, could snag employee clothing or body parts, causing potentially severe injuries. Conveyors, pulleys, gears and spindles must have appropriate covers to prevent employee contact. Overhead conveyors can create an additional hazard of falling cases. Netting or wire-mesh screens should be installed to protect against this danger. Maintenance programmes should dictate that all guarding which is removed for repair be replaced as soon as repair work is completed.

Since wet conditions are prevalent in the filling room, adequate drainage is necessary to keep liquid from accumulating on nearby walkways. In order to avoid slip-and-fall injuries, proper efforts must be made to keep floors as dry as possible. While steel-toed shoes usually are not required in the filling room, slip-resistant soles are highly recommended. Shoes should be selected based on the slip coefficient of the sole. Additionally, all electrical equipment should be properly grounded and protected from any moisture. Employees must take precautions to dry the areas around equipment before any electrical work begins.

Good housekeeping practices and routine inspections also are beneficial in keeping the workplace hazard-free. By taking these comparatively simple steps, management can be sure that all equipment is in good operating condition and properly stored. Emergency equipment such as fire extinguishers and eyewash stations also should be inspected for proper operation.

Although most of the chemicals present in bottling plants are not extremely hazardous, every operation uses flammable substances, acids, caustics, corrosives and oxidants. Appropriate work practices should be developed so employees know how to work safely with these chemicals. They must be taught how properly to store, handle and dispose of the chemicals and how to wear protective gear. Training should cover the location and operation of emergency response equipment. Eyewash stations and showers can minimize injury to anyone who is accidentally exposed to a hazardous chemical.

It also is necessary to install equipment such as chemical booms and dykes, as well as absorbent material, to be used in the event of a spill. Properly designed hazardous chemical storage facilities will minimize the risk of employee injury, too. Flammables should be separated from corrosives and oxidants.

The large tanks used for mixing ingredients, which need to be entered and cleaned routinely, are considered confined spaces. See the box on confined spaces in this chapter for information on the related hazards and precautions.

Mechanized equipment has become increasingly complex, often controlled by remote computers, pneumatic lines or even gravity. Employees must be sure that this equipment has been de-energized before it is serviced. Proper de-energizing procedures must be developed to guarantee the safety of those who maintain and repair this equipment. Energy must be shut off and locked out at its source so that the unit being serviced cannot be accidentally energized, causing potentially fatal injuries to service employees or nearby line operators.

Safety training and written de-energizing procedures are critical for each piece of equipment. Emergency stop switches should be strategically placed on all equipment. Interlocked safety devices are used to stop the equipment automatically when doors are opened or light beams are interrupted. Employees must be informed, however, that these devices cannot be relied upon to completely de-energize the equipment, but only to stop it in an emergency. Emergency stop switches cannot take the place of a proven de-energizing procedure for equipment maintenance.

Chlorine, which is used in the water treatment area, could be hazardous in the event of an accidental release. Chlorine typically comes in steel cylinders, which should be stored in an isolated,

Figure 65.4 • Eight-packs of 2-litre soft drink plastic bottles on the way to an automatic palletizer.

well-ventilated area and secured from tipping. Employees should be trained to follow safe cylinder-changing procedures. They also should be taught how to take quick, decisive action if an accidental release of chlorine occurs. In the late 1990s new chlorine compounds are gradually replacing the need for chlorine gas. Although still hazardous, these compounds are much safer to handle than gas.

Ammonia is used as a refrigerant in bottling operations. Typically, large ammonia systems can create a health hazard in the event of a leak or a spill. Bottling facilities should develop emergency response procedures to identify the responsibilities of involved employees. Those who are required to respond to such an emergency must be trained in spill response and respirator use. In the event of a leak or spill, respirators should be immediately available, and all non-essential personnel evacuated to safe areas until the situation is controlled.

CO_2, which is used in the filling operation, also can create health concerns. If filling rooms and adjacent work areas are not adequately ventilated, CO_2 accumulation can displace oxygen in employees' breathing zones. Facilities should be monitored regularly for elevated CO_2 levels and, if they are detected, ventilation systems should be inspected to determine the cause for this occurence. Additional ventilation may be required to correct the situation.

Technological advances have made available better sound-absorption material for insulating or muffling motors and gears in most equipment. Still, given the function and size of filling equipment, noise levels generally exceed 90 dBA in this area. Employees who are exposed to this level of noise for an 8-hour weighted average must be protected. Good hearing protection programmes should include research on better ways to control noise; employee education on related health effects; personal noise protection; and training on how to use hearing protection devices, the wearing of which must be enforced in high-noise areas. Employee hearing must be routinely checked.

Fork-lifts are operated throughout the bottling plant and their safe use is imperative. In addition to demonstrating their driving skills, potential operators must understand fork-lift safety principles. Licenses are commonly issued to show that a minimum level of competency has been achieved. Fork-lift safety programmes should include a pre-use inspection process, whereby the vehicles are checked to ensure that all safety equipment is in place and working. Any deficient conditions should be immediately reported and corrected. Gas or liquid petroleum (LP) fork-lifts generate carbon monoxide as a by-product of combustion. Such emissions can be minimized by keeping the fork-lift engines tuned to manufacturers' specifications.

Personal protective equipment (PPE) is common throughout the bottling facility. Filling-room employees wear eye and ear protection. Sanitation crews wear face, hand and foot protection that is appropriate for the chemicals they are exposed to. While slip-resistant shoes are recommended throughout the plant, maintenance employees should also have the added protection of steel-toed shoes. The key to a good PPE programme is to identify and evaluate the potential hazards associated with each job and to determine whether those hazards can be eliminated through engineering changes. If not, PPE must be selected to address the specific hazard at hand.

Management's role is critical in identifying hazards and developing practices and procedures to minimize them in the workplace. Once developed, these practices and procedures must be communicated to employees so that they can perform their jobs safely.

As plant technology continues to advance—providing better equipment, new guards and protective devices—soft drink bottlers will have even more ways to maintain the safety of their workforce.

COFFEE INDUSTRY

Jorge da Rocha Gomes and Bernardo Bedrikow

General Overview

Coffee as a beverage was introduced in Europe during the sixteenth century, first in Germany and then throughout the European continent during the following century, especially to France and Holland. Afterwards, it spread to the rest of the world.

Since coffee will not keep its characteristic smell and flavour for long, after roasting and grinding, industrial establishments to roast and grind coffee have become needed wherever coffee is consumed. The establishments are usually small or medium-sized plants, but large factories do exist, mainly to produce regular as well as instant (soluble) coffee.

It is difficult to estimate the number of workers employed by the coffee industry. Some of the smaller plants do not keep registries, and figures are not entirely reliable. Considering a total consumption of approximately 100 million 60 kg bags of coffee during the year 1995, the worldwide coffee trade represents about US$50 million. Table 65.1 lists selected coffee-importing countries, giving an idea of the present world consumption.

Coffee manufacturing is a relatively simple process, including cleaning, roasting, grinding and packing processes, as shown in figure 65.5. However, modern technology has led to complex processes, with an increase in speed of production and requiring laboratories for quality-control testing of the product.

Coffee beans arrive at factories in 60 kg bags, which are unloaded mechanically or manually. In the latter case, usually two workers hold a bag and place it upon another worker's head. This worker will carry the bag to be stored. Even when transportation is done on coveyor belts, some physical effort with high energy consumption is required.

The use of instant coffee has steadily increased, reaching approximately 20% of the world consumption. Instant coffee is obtained through a complex process in which blasts of hot air blow over coffee extracts, followed by evaporation, cooling and lyophilization (freeze drying), varying in details from one factory to another. In the manufacture of decaffeinated coffee, which represents over 10% of the consumption in the United States and in Europe, some plants still utilize chlorinated solvents (such as methylene chloride), which is removed by a blast of water vapour.

Potential Risks and Health Effects

To start coffee processing, bags are opened with a small knife, and the beans are thrown inside a bin to be cleaned. The work area is noisy and a large amount of residual particulate material remains in suspension, released from the cleaning machine.

Table 65.1 • Selected coffee importers (in tonnes).

Country	1990	1991	1992
United States	1,186,244	1,145,916	1,311,986
France	349,306	364,214	368,370
Japan	293,969	302,955	295,502
Spain	177,681	176,344	185,601
United Kingdom	129,924	119,020	128,702
Austria	108,797	118,935	125,245
Canada	120,955	126,165	117,897

Source: FAO 1992.

Roasting exposes workers to risks of burns and thermal discomfort. Bean mixing, or blending, is done automatically, as is grinding, in areas which may be deficient in lighting due to interference from suspended coffee dust. Dirt may accumulate, noise levels may be high and mechanization requires work at a high speed.

After grinding, bags of different materials and sizes are filled and then packed, usually in cardboard boxes. When performed manually, these operations require high-speed repetitive motion of hands and arms. Cardboard boxes are transported to storage areas and then to their final destination.

The strong odour characteristic of the coffee industry may bother workers inside the plants, and the surrounding community as well. The significance of this problem as a potential health risk has not yet been clarified. The odour of coffee is due to a mixture of different products; research is ongoing to identify individual effects of these chemicals. Some components of the coffee dust and some of the odour-producing substances are known to be allergens.

Potential risks in instant-coffee plants are similar to those in regular coffee production; in addition, there are risks due to hot steam and boiler explosions. In the removal of caffeine, even when performed automatically, the risk of solvent exposure may be present.

Other potential risks which may affect workers' health are similar to those found in food industries in general. Risks for accidents arise from cuts from knives used in bag opening, burns during roasting and crushing during grinding operations, especially in old machinery without automatic machine guarding. There are fire and explosion hazards from the large amounts of dust, unsafe electric wiring and gas used for heating the roasters.

Several hazards may be found in the coffee industry including, among others: hearing loss due to excessive noise, thermal stress during roasting, poisoning from pesticides and musculoskeletal disorders, especially affecting the backs of workers who lift and carry heavy bags.

Allergic disorders affecting the eye, skin or respiratory system may occur in any area in a coffee plant. It is the coffee dust which is associated with bronchitis with lung function impairment; rhinitis and conjunctivitis are also concerns (Sekimpi et al. 1996). Allergic reactions to contaminants of bags previously used for other materials, such as castor bean seeds, have also occurred (Romano et al. 1995).

Repetitive-motion disorders may result from high-speed motion in packing operations, especially where workers are not warned of the risk.

In less developed countries, effects of occupational risks may develop early because conditions of work may be inadequate and, moreover, other social and public health factors may contribute to disease. Such factors include: low salaries, inadequate medical care and social security, improper housing and sanitation, low levels of education, illiteracy, endemic diseases and malnutrition.

Preventive Measures

Machine guarding, general ventilation and local exhaust systems, noise abatement, housekeeping and cleaning, decreased bag weights, substitutes of solvents used in caffeine extraction, periodic inspection and preventive maintenance of boilers are examples of preventive measures that are required for ensuring adequate levels of industrial hygiene and safety. Odour intensity may be reduced through modification of roasting procedures. The organization of work can be modified so that repetitive-motion disorders may be avoided through alteration of working position and rhythm, as well as the introduction of systematic breaks and regular exercises, among other practices.

Periodic health screening should stress evaluation of exposure to herbicides and pesticides, spinal disorders and early signs of repetitive-motion disorders. Scratch tests using extracts from coffee beans, even if not universally accepted as completely reliable, may be useful in the identification of hypersusceptible individuals. Lung function tests may aid in the early diagnosis of obstructive respiratory conditions.

Health education is an important instrument to enable workers to identify health risks and their consequences and to become aware of their right to a healthy working environment.

Governmental action is required, through legislation and enforcement; employers' participation is needed in providing and maintaining adequate working conditions.

TEA INDUSTRY

Lou Piombino

Legend tells us that tea may have been discovered in China by Emperor Shen-Nung, "The Divine Healer". Observant of the fact that people who drank boiled water enjoyed better health, the wise Emperor insisted on this precaution. When adding branches to the fire, some tea leaves accidentally fell into the boiling water. The Emperor approved of the pleasing aroma and delightful flavour and tea was born.

From China, tea spread throughout Asia, soon becoming the national beverage of China and Japan. It was not until the 1600s that Europe became familiar with the beverage. Shortly thereafter, tea was introduced to North America. In the early 1900s, Thomas Sullivan, a New York wholesaler, decided to

Figure 65.5 • Flow chart of coffee manufacturing.

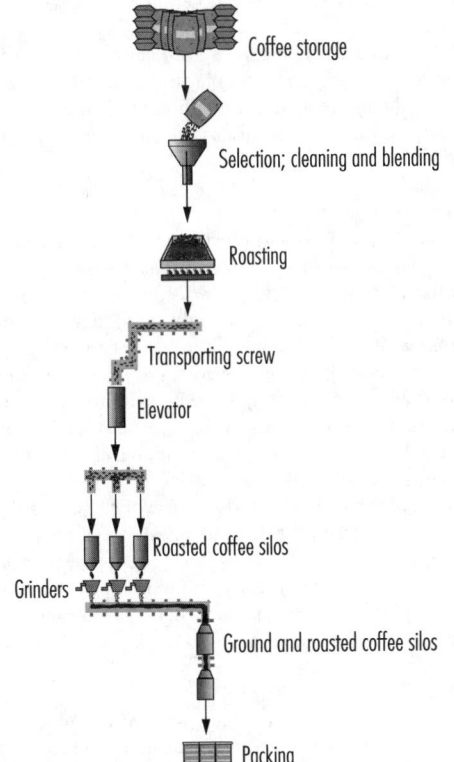

Coffee storage

Selection; cleaning and blending

Roasting

Transporting screw

Elevator

Roasted coffee silos

Grinders

Ground and roasted coffee silos

Packing

package tea in small silk bags rather than in tins. People started brewing the tea in the silk bag rather than removing its contents. Thus the tea bag was first introduced.

Tea is the world's second most popular drink; only water is consumed more often. Consumers can choose from a wide variety of tea products—instant tea, iced tea mixes, specialty and flavoured teas, herbal teas, ready-to-drink teas decaffeinated teas and tea bags. The packaging of tea products has changed significantly; most of the small shops that once dispensed tea from wooden crates into individual tins have given way to sophisticated high-speed production lines which process, package, and/or bottle thousands of pounds of tea and ready-to-drink mixes per hour.

Process Overview

Production of tea bags consists of the blending of various cut and dried leaf teas from a number of regions around the world. Tea is usually received in wooden crates or large bags. The tea is blended and sent to tea packaging machines, where it is packaged either as individual tea bags or in bulk packages. Instant powdered tea requires blended tea in cut leaf form to be brewed using hot water. The liquid tea concentrate is then spray dried into a fine powder and placed in drums. The tea powder may be sent to the packaging lines where it is packaged into canisters or jars, or blended with other ingredients such as sugar or sugar substitutes. Flavouring such as lemon and other fruit flavors may also be added during the blending stage prior to packaging.

Hazards

There are a number of common safety hazards and health issues associated with the blending, processing and packaging of tea. Safety hazards such as machine guarding, noise, slips and falls and lifting-related injuries are quite common within the beverage industry. Other hazards, such as dust in the blending and packaging areas, are not usually found in wet-process bottling and canning operations.

Machine hazards

The blending and packaging of tea involves equipment and machinery where workers are exposed to chains and sprockets, belts and pullies, rotating shafts and equipment and high-speed packaging lines containing a number of dangerous pinch points. Most injuries are the result of lacerations and bruises to the fingers, hands or arms. Guarding of this equipment is critical to protect workers from getting caught in, under or between moving parts. Guards and/or interlocks should be installed to protect workers from moving parts where the potential of injury exists. Whenever a guard is removed (such as for maintenance), all energy sources should be isolated and maintenance and repair of equipment should be with an effective lockout/tagout programme in effect.

Dust hazards

Tea dust can be present in blending and packaging operations. Tea dust may also be present in high concentrations during clean-up or blow-down operations. Tea dust with a diameter greater than 10 micrometers can be classified as "nuisance dust". Nuisance dust has little adverse effect on the lungs and should not produce significant organic disease or toxic effects when exposures are kept under reasonable control. Excessive concentrations of nuisance dust in the workroom air, however, may cause unpleasant deposits in the eyes, ears and nasal passages. Once inhaled, these particles may become entrapped in the nasal and pharyngeal region of the respiratory system, until they are expelled through the body's own cleaning mechanisms (e.g., coughing or sneezing).

Respirable dust particulates are those that are less than 10 micrometers in diameter and therefore small enough to pass through the nasal and pharyngeal regions and enter the lower respiratory tract. Once in the lungs, they may become embedded in the alveolar region, where scar tissue could develop. Respirable particulates can be respiratory irritants, especially in asthmatics. Effective seals and closures will help contain dust particles.

Exhaust ventilation or other types of dust-control equipment should be provided at the site of dust production to maintain dust levels below generally recognized standards (10 mg/m3) or other government regulations that may apply. Dust masks should be worn by workers who may be highly sensitive to dusts and by workers exposed to large concentrations of dust at any one time. Persons with chronic bronchitis or asthma are at higher risk. Workers who suffer from hypersensitivity to tea dust should be removed from the area.

Although there is little information on actual tea dust explosions, test data indicate that the explosion characteristics of tea dust are relatively weak. It appears that the greatest potential for a tea dust explosion exists with storage bins and dust collectors where concentrations and particle size are optimized. Minimizing dust concentration within a room or process will reduce the potential of a dust explosion. Electrical equipment designed for dust hazard areas may also be desirable in some operations.

Although tea and tea dust may not always burst into flames, large quantities of tea will almost always smoulder if ignited. Large quantities of water in a fine mist can be used to cool the smouldering tea below its ignition temperature.

Noise

As in most high-speed packaging operations, high noise levels are almost always present in the tea industry. High noise levels can be generated from vibrating blenders, air-operated and other packaging machines, air conveying systems, dust collectors and box cutters. The noise levels in many of these areas can range from 85 dBA to over 90 dBA. The major potential health hazard associated with exposure to noise lies in the possibility of producing permanent hearing loss. The severity of hearing loss is dependent on the noise levels within the workplace, duration of the exposure and the individual's personal susceptibility. Noise and hearing conservation programmes are discussed further elsewhere in this *Encyclopaedia*.

Chemical hazards

Although most of the production processes and packaging operations do not expose workers to hazardous chemicals, sanitation operations use chemicals to clean and sanitize equipment. Some cleaning chemicals are handled in bulk quantities through fixed pipe systems, while other chemicals are applied by hand using predetermined mixtures. Exposure to these chemicals can cause respiratory problems, dermatitis or skin irritation and chemical burns to the skin. Severe burns to the eyes and/or loss of vision are also hazards associated with the handling of cleaning chemicals. Proper evaluations as to the hazards of the chemicals being used are essential. Proper selection and use of PPE should be part of routine job procedure. PPE such as splash-proof goggles or face shields, chemical-resistant gloves, aprons, boots and a respirator should be considered. Emergency eye and body wash stations should be provided where hazardous chemicals are either stored, mixed or used.

Material handling

Tea arrives on pallets in either bags or crates and is stored in warehouses to await blending and packaging. These bags and crates are moved either by hand or by material-handling devices such as fork-lifts or vacuum lifts. Once blended, the tea is

Figure 65.6 • Packing of tea at the Brooke Bond tea and coffee factory in Dar-es-Salaam, Tanzania.

conveyed to hoppers for packaging. Packaging operations can vary from using highly automated equipment to labour-intensive hand packaging operations (figure 65.6). Injuries to the lower back resulting from lifting tasks are quite common when handling bags weighing 100 pounds (45.5 kg) or more. Repetitive motions on packaging lines can result in cumulative trauma to the wrist, arm and/or shoulder area.

Mechanical devices such as vacuum lifts can aid in reducing heavy lifting tasks. Assigning two workers to a heavy lifting task can help reduce the chances of a serious back injury. Modifying work stations to be more ergonomically correct and/or automating equipment on packaging lines can reduce worker exposure to repetitive tasks. Rotating workers to light duty tasks can also reduce worker exposure to such tasks.

Personal aids such as back belts and wrist bands are also used by some workers to assist them in their lifting tasks or for temporary relief of minor strains. However, these have not been shown to be effective, and they may even be harmful.

Most warehouse operations require the use of fork-lift trucks. Failure to drive at safe speeds, sharp turns, driving with raised forks, failure to observe or yield to pedestrians and loading/ unloading accidents are the leading causes of injuries involving fork-lift operators. Only trained and competent operators should be permitted to drive fork-lifts. Training should consist of formal classroom training and a driving test where operators can demonstrate their skills. Proper maintenance and daily pre-use inspections also help ensure the safe operation of these vehicles.

Slips, trips and falls

Slips, trips and falls are a major concern. In dry blending and packaging operations, fine tea dust will accumulate on walking and working surfaces. Good housekeeping is important. Floors should be swept clean of tea dust on a regular basis. Debris and other items left on the floor should be picked up immediately. Slip-resistant, rubber-soled shoes appear to provide the best traction. Wet-process areas also provide slip and fall hazards. Floors should be kept as dry as possible. Adequate floor drainage should be provided within all wet-process areas. Standing water should

not be permitted to accumulate. Where standing water exists, it should be mopped into floor drains.

Exposure to high temperatures

Contact with hot water, steam lines and process equipment can result in serious injury from burns. Most burns occur on the hands, arms and face. Hot water used for clean-up or wash-down has also been known to cause burns on feet and legs.

Heat sealers and glue operations on packaging lines also can cause burns. Guarding of exposed hot points on equipment is important. The proper evaluation of the hazards, and selection and use of personal protective equipment, will also help reduce or eliminate worker exposure to high temperatures and burns. Use of pipeline breaking and lockout procedures will protect workers from the unexpected release of hot liquids and steam.

Safe Practices

A general safety programme which addresses the use and selection of PPE, entry into confined spaces, isolation of energy sources, identification and communication of hazardous chemicals, self-inspection programmes, hearing conservation programmes, the control of infectious materials, process management and emergency response programmes should also be included as part of the work process. Training of workers in safe work practices is important in reducing worker exposure to hazardous conditions and injuries.

DISTILLED SPIRITS INDUSTRY

R.G. Aldi and Rita Seguin

Distilled spirits can be produced from any number of materials, such as fermented mashes of cereal grains, fermented fruit juices, sugar cane juice, molasses, honey and cactus juice. Fermentation for making wine and beer can be traced back to between 5000 and 6000 BC; however, the history of distillation is much more recent. Although it is uncertain where distillation originated, it was known to alchemists and began to spread in use throughout the thirteenth and fourteenth century. Early uses were primarily pharmaceutical.

Process Overview

Alcoholic beverages are divided into two groups, depending on their mode of preparation: fermented beverages, such as wine and beer, and distilled beverages, such as whisky and brandy. Liqueurs are basically prepared by blending juices or extracts of fruits, nuts or other food products. Wine and beer making are discussed in separate articles in this chapter.

The phases of activity in distilled spirits production include receiving of grain, milling, cooking, fermentation, distillation, storage, blending and bottling (see figure 65.7).

The grain elevator receives and weighs incoming grains and places them in the appropriate bins. Milling consists of grinding the grains necessary for the mash bill. The mash bill is the recipe for the fermentation process.

The cookers receive meal from the mill and slurries with backslop, water and ammonia at a set pH (acidity) and temperature. The starch is solubilized using steam-jet cooking. Enzymes are added to break down starch to smaller starch molecules, reducing mash viscosity. The resulting mash is cooled to fermentation temperature.

Fermentation is the process of converting sugars to alcohol and carbon dioxide by the activities of yeast. Fermenters are cooled to

65. BEVERAGE INDUSTRY

Figure 65.7 • Production flow chart for distilled spirits manufacturing.

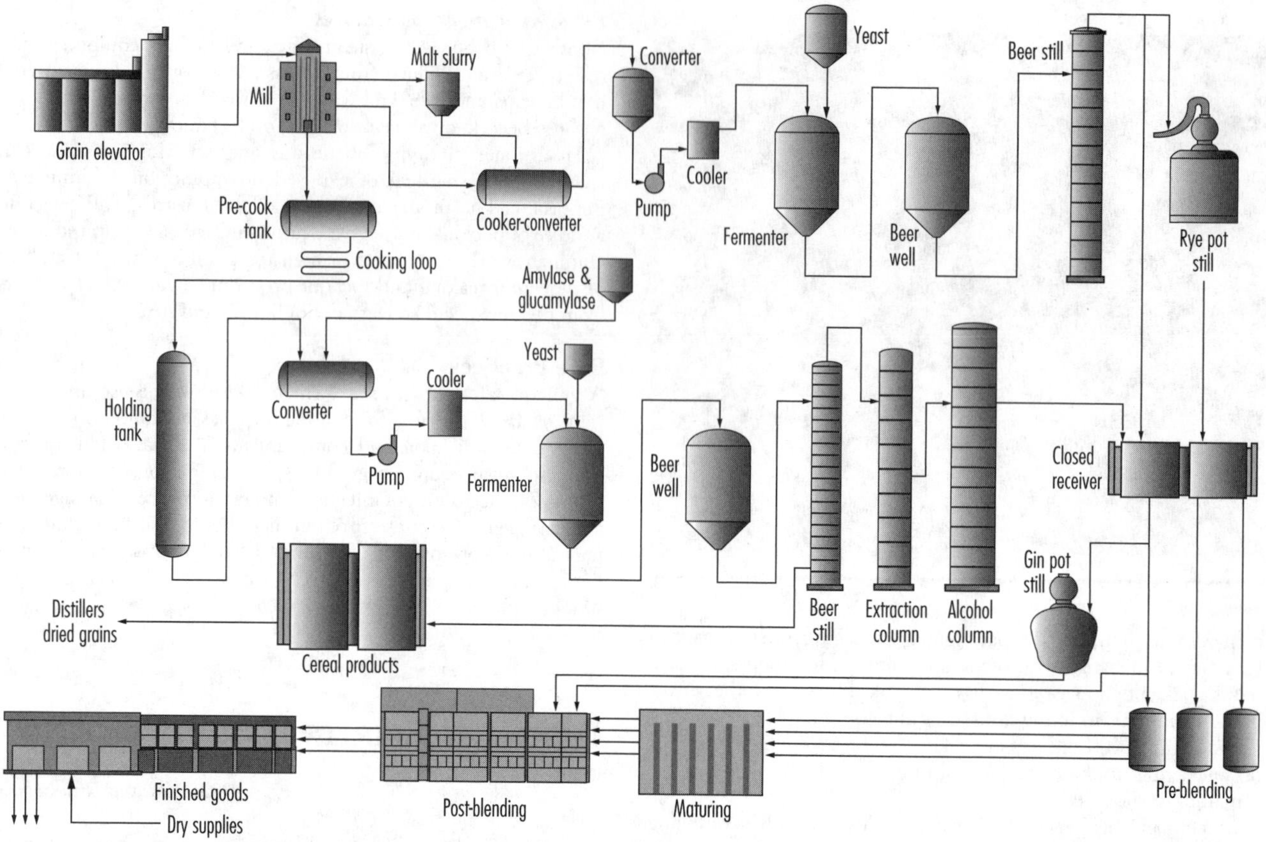

optimum temperature conditions for the yeast, since the reactions that take place are exothermic in nature. Sanitation is important: the biological systems of fermentation are in constant competition with unwanted bacteria that can produce undesirable flavour components.

Distillation type will depend on the spirit being produced. Pot stills are generally used when a particular "character" is required for a product such as cognac and scotches, whereas continuous multicolumn distillation is generally used to produce more neutral spirits which can be used as blenders or neutral grain spirits.

By-product recovery is a very important aspect of the operation of a modern distillery. The residual (fermented and de-alcoholized) grain is rich in protein, vitamins, fibre and fats, and it can be further processed into a valuable animal feed supplement. These processes generally consist of centrifuging, evaporation, drying and mixing.

Whiskies, brandies and rums are aged (matured) in charred oak barrels. Maturation takes place over a number of years to produce the final characteristics that distinguish these products. Once these products have been matured, they are blended and filtered and then packaged as finished products for consumer use.

The bottling room is separated from the rest of the facility, protecting the product from any possible contaminants. The highly automated filling operation requires monitoring for continuous efficiency. Empty bottles are transported by conveyor to the filling machines.

Packaging is the final step prior to warehousing. This process has become automated, although there is a fair amount of manual packing, depending on size of bottle and type of packaging. The packaged product then enters a palletizing machine, which automatically stacks boxes on pallets, which are then removed by fork-lift trucks to warehouses for storage.

Health and Safety Issues

The most obvious safety concern in grain-handling facilities is the threat of dust fires and explosions. High concentrations of grain dust can be explosive; therefore, good housekeeping is the single most important factor in reducing risk of grain dust explosion. Some grains, if damp or kept in storage for a long period, will generate heat, thus becoming a fire hazard. Rotating the grain from bin to bin or adopting a "just-in-time" grain delivery procedure will eliminate this hazard.

Exposure to vapours and gases released throughout the production of distilled spirits is a possible hazard. During the fermentation process, refrigerant gases may cause toxic and explosive risks. Therefore, adequate ventilation and strict maintenance, including the use of intrinsically safe equipment such as air tools, are essential. Particularly significant are the risks of asphyxiation from the vapours of alcohol and carbon dioxide released by the fermentation process, especially when the liquids are transported and decanted into reservoirs, and in confined spaces where ventilation is inadequate. Respirators should be worn by workers in this process. The accompanying box describes some hazards of confined-space entry, which is also discussed elsewhere in this *Encyclopaedia*.

Hazardous materials such as varsol (mineral spirit), caustics, acids and many other solvents and cleaners are used throughout the facility. Employees must be trained to handle these products safely. A yearly review of a workplace hazardous materials information system, such as the Canadian WHMIS, can provide the opportunity for such ongoing training. Workers must be educated on the use of material data safety sheets (MSDSs), which are information sheets available from suppliers, giving information on the contents of the hazardous product and the related health hazards, emergency action, first aid and so on. It is imperative that every worker who is exposed or likely to be exposed to a hazardous material be trained and then provided with an annual review of the handling of hazardous material. In many countries it is required that MSDSs be available at every location where there are controlled substances and should be made convenient for all workers to access. In addition to employee training, eye wash stations, showers and first aid stations should be made available throughout the plant in order to minimize injury to anyone who is accidentally exposed to a hazardous chemical.

Fork-lift trucks are used in many different processes in the plant. The two most common uses are for transfer of barrels for maturing storage and handling of the finished product. There should be a preventive maintenance programme in place for the fork-lifts as well as a safety programme that ensures that all drivers understand fork-lift safety principles. All drivers should be licenced to operate a fork-lift truck.

The occupational hazards associated with the bottling process are similar to those in most bottling facilities. Repetitive-strain injuries such as tendinitis and carpal tunnel syndrome are the most common injuries, resulting from the repetitive work required for packing bottles and operating labellers. However, the frequency of these occupational injuries has declined; this may be due to the technological changes in the plant that have made jobs less labour intensive, including the automation of packing and the use of computerized equipment.

PPE is common throughout the bottling facility. It is mandatory for bottling room employees to wear safety glasses for eye protection, and ear protection where they are exposed to high noise levels. There should be a safety shoe programme in place, with employees expected to wear steel-toed shoes. If a hazard cannot be eliminated at the source (through engineering) or along the path (through barriers), then PPE must be used for the safety of the worker.

There are many key methods in creating a safe work environment. A company must have a health and safety policy and should convey this via a safety manual that outlines safety procedures. Also, monthly plant inspections can prevent hazards and minimize injuries. Communication with employees regarding safety practices is the most essential part of a successful safety programme.

Confined-space entry hazards in the beverage industry

A confined space is defined as a space in which, because of its construction, location, contents or the work activity therein, the accumulation of a hazardous gas, vapour, dust or fumes, or the creation of an oxygen-deficient atmosphere, may occur. Where confined-space entry could occur, it is imperative that a confined-space entry procedure be in place and that all workers be trained and educated on the procedure. Prior to entering a confined space, testing for oxygen deficiency, combustible gases and toxic gases should be conducted. Positive-pressure self-contained breathing apparatus (SCBA) or other approved respirators may have to be worn by workers during entry. Continuous monitoring is mandatory while personnel are inside the confined space. All personnel entering must be properly suited up with a safety harness, complete with shoulder and leg straps. A stand-by observer must be assigned and maintain constant surveillance of employees within a confined space, and a person adequately trained in artificial respiration must be conveniently available.

The beverage industry has many situations in which there are confined-space entry hazards. Examples of such situations include:

- mixing vats in the soft drink industry in which hazardous vapours or gases might be present
- grain bins in brewing and distilled spirits industries
- fermentation vats in brewing and wine making
- fermenters and stills in the distilled spirits industry.

These grain bins, fermenter tanks and so forth may have to be entered from time to time for cleaning, repairing and so on. During the fermentation process, in particular, there are risks of asphyxiation from the vapours of alcohol and carbon dioxide released by the fermentation process when confined spaces are entered where ventilation is inadequate (Giullemin and Horisberger 1994).

R.G. Aldi and Rita Seguin

WINE INDUSTRY

Alvaro Durao*

Wine is produced from grapes. The ripe grape, when crushed, yields the *must* which, by total or partial and normal fermentation, turns into wine. During fermentation, first rapid and turbulent, then gradually slowing down, sugar is transformed into alcohol and carbon dioxide. Many elements contained in the grapes remain in the drink. The various phases of activity in the production of wine from grapes include wine-making, storage and bottling.

Wine-making

Wine-making involves a variety of activities carried out by a variety of methods ranging from traditional "farm production" to modern industrial production. The ancient method of pressing the grapes, in which the harvesters trod during the night the grapes they had gathered during the day, is less and less seen in modern wine-making. Wine is now produced in installations belonging to groups of farmers or to commercial firms, using techniques that produce a more uniform type of wine and reduce the risk of spoilage, especially that which arises from acidification which transforms the wine into vinegar.

On arrival at the cellars, the grapes are crushed in simple mills or large machines, such as centrifugal crushers, by rollers or in other ways. These processes always involve mechanical risks and noise for the entire period during which large quantities of must is being handled. The crushed mass is then transferred to large reservoirs, by pumping or other procedures, where it will be pressed to separate the juice from the skins and stalks. The must is then transferred to fermenting vessels. On completion of fermentation, the wine is drawn off from the dregs and poured into storage bins or tanks. Extraneous matter and impurities are removed by filters. Diatomaceous earth has replaced asbestos as a

* Adapted from 3rd edition, *Encyclopaedia of Occupational Health and Safety*.

filter agent in some countries, such as the United States. Larger foreign matter may be removed by centrifuges.

The quality of the wine can be improved by refrigeration using continuous-flow refrigerators and double-jacketed cooling tanks. In these operations, exposure to vapours and gases released during the various stages of the process—particularly straining, fermentation and the use of disinfectants and other products intended to guarantee the hygienic condition and quality of the wine—must be borne in mind. Refrigerant gases such as ammonia may cause toxic and explosive risks, and adequate ventilation and strict maintenance to prevent leakage are essential. Automatic leak detection and respiratory protective equipment, frequently tested, should be available for emergencies. There are also the common risks due to wet and slippery floors, the disorder characteristic of seasonal activities and the quality of illumination and ventilation (the rooms where the wine is prepared are often also used for storage and are designed to maintain a uniform, relatively low temperature).

Particularly significant are the risks of asphyxiation from the vapours of alcohol and the carbon dioxide released by the fermentation process, especially when the liquids are transported and decanted into reservoirs or confined spaces where ventilation is inadequate.

Certain other harmful substances are used in wine-making. Metabisulphite in concentrated solution is irritating to the skin and the mucous membrane; tartaric acid, which is considered non-toxic, can be slightly irritating in very concentrated solutions; sulphur dioxide provokes an intense irritation of the eyes and the respiratory tract; tannins can dry a worker's skin and make it lose pigmentation; the use of disinfectants and detergents for the washing of storage tanks cause dermatitis; and potassium bitartarate, ascorbic acid, proteolytic enzymes and so on, which may be used in the preparation of alcoholic beverages, can cause diarrhoea or allergic reactions.

When work processes are modernized, workers may need support and assistance in order to adapt. Large production cellars should consider ergonomic principles in the choice of the equipment for such installations. Crushers and presses should have easy access in order to facilitate pouring the grapes and the residues. Whenever possible, suitable pumps should be installed, which should be easy to inspect and should have a solid foundation in order not to cause any obstruction, high noise levels and vibrations.

The general organization of the production cellar should be such that no unnecessary risks are caused and that risks should not spread to other areas; ventilation should conform to standards; temperature control may be necessary; compressors, condensers, electrical equipment and so on must be installed so as to obviate all possible risks. Because of the humidity of several processes, protecting electrical equipment is necessary and, where possible, low voltages should be used, especially for portable equipment and inspection lamps. Ground fault circuit interrupters should be installed where necessary. Electrical equipment in the vicinity of distillation plants should be of flameproof construction.

Wooden vats are decreasingly common, though they can occasionaly be found in small cellars for farm production. In modern wine-making, vats are lined with glass or stainless steel for sanitary and control reasons; lined reinforced concrete and, sometimes, plastics are also used. Vats must have the proper dimensions and be adequately resistant to allow fermentation and decanting (right down to the dregs), to hold the volume of reserves as long as necessary and to allow for easy exchange of their contents, should it prove to be necessary. Cleaning of containers involves especially high risks, and a confined-space programme should be in effect: the gas should be dispelled by mobile ventilators before containers are entered, and safety belts and life-lines and respiratory protective equipment should be worn. A competent worker should be stationed outside to supervise and rescue workers inside, if necessary. See the box on confined spaces for more information.

Wine Storage

Storage involves not only the keeping of large volumes of liquid but also a number of activities such as cleaning and disinfecting the tanks or casks; their maintenance and conservation; application of sulphur dioxide, ascorbic acid, tartaric acid, inert gases, tannins and albumins; and other additional processes, such as mixing, glueing, filtering, centrifugation and so on. Some treatments of wine involve the use of heat and cold to destroy yeast and bacteria; the utilization of carbon and other deodorizers; the application of CO_2, and so on. As an example of this type of installation we may refer to the system of instantaneous refrigeration, for the stabilization of wines at a temperature near the freezing point, which facilitates the elimination of colloids, microbes and other products such as potassium bitartarate, which provokes precipitation in the bottles. It is obvious that these installations imply risks that formerly did not need to be considered in this phase of storage. Prevention is essentially based on ergonomic planning and good maintenance.

Wine Bottling

Wine is usually sold in glass bottles (of 1.0, 0.8, 0.75 or 0.30 l capacity); glass containers of 5 l are occasionally used. Plastic containers are not as common. In the filling plants, bottles are first cleaned and then filled, sealed and labelled. Conveyors are widely used in bottling plants.

The risks of bottling arise from the handling of glass material; these vary according to whether the bottles to be washed are new or returned, and according to the products used (water and detergents) and the techniques applied (washing by hand or mechanically or both). Bottles' shape; how the filling must be done (ranging from manual methods to sophisticated filling machines which can also introduce carbon dioxide); the process of corking; the more or less complicated system of stacking, or placing into boxes or crates after labelling; and other final touches determine the risks.

The risks involved are those which generally correspond to the filling of containers with liquids. The hands are constantly wet; if the bottles break, the projection of glass particles and liquid can cause injuries. The effort required to transport them once they are packed in boxes (usually by dozens) could be eliminated at least partially by mechanization. See also the article "Soft drink bottling and canning".

Acknowledgments: The author would like to thank the Junta Nacional dos Vinhos (Lisbon) for their advice on technical aspects.

BREWING INDUSTRY

J.F. Eustace*

Brewing is one of the oldest industries: beer in different varieties was drunk in the ancient world, and the Romans introduced it to all their colonies. Today it is brewed and consumed in almost every country, particularly in Europe and areas of European settlement.

* Adapted from 3rd edition, *Encyclopaedia of Occupational Health and Safety*.

Process Overview

The grain used as the raw material is usually barley, but rye, maize, rice and oatmeal are also employed. In the first stage the grain is malted, either by causing it to germinate or by artificial means. This converts the carbohydrates to dextrin and maltose, and these sugars are then extracted from the grain by soaking in a mash tun (vat or cask) and then agitating in a lauter tun. The resulting liquor, known as sweet wort, is then boiled in a copper vessel with hops, which give a bitter flavour and helps to preserve the beer. The hops are then separated from the wort and it is passed through chillers into fermenting vessels where the yeast is added—a process known as pitching—and the main process of converting sugar into alcohol is carried out. (For discussion of fermentation see the chapter *Pharmaceutical industry*.) The beer is then chilled to 0 °C, centrifuged and filtered to clarify it; it is then ready for dispatch by keg, bottle, aluminium can or bulk transport. Figure 65.8 is a flow chart of the brewing process.

Hazards and Their Prevention

Manual handling

Manual handling accounts for most of the injuries in breweries: hands are bruised, cut or punctured by jagged hoops, splinters of wood and broken glass. Feet are bruised and crushed by falling or rolling barrels. Much can be done to prevent these injuries by suitable hand and foot protection. Increase in automation and standardization of barrel size (say at 50 l) can reduce the lifting risks. The back pain caused by lifting and carrying of barrels and so on can be dramatically reduced by training in sound lifting techniques. Mechanical handling on pallets can also reduce ergonomic problems. Falls on wet and slippery floors are common. Non-slip surfaces and footwear, and a regular system of cleaning, are the best precaution.

Handling of grain can produce barley itch, caused by a mite infesting the grain. Mill-worker's asthma, sometimes called malt fever, has been recorded in grain handlers and has been shown to be an allergic response to the grain weevil (*Sitophilus granarius*). Manual handling of hops can produce a dermatitis due to the absorption of the resinous essences through broken or chapped skin. Preventive measures include good washing and sanitary facilities, efficient ventilation of the workrooms, and medical supervision of the workers.

When barley is malted by the traditional method of steeping it and then spreading it on floors to produce germination, it may become contaminated by *Aspergillus clavatus*, which can produce growth and spore formation. When the barley is turned to prevent root matting of the shoots, or when it is loaded into kilns, the spores may be inhaled by the workers. This may produce extrinsic allergic alveolitis, which in symptomatology is indistinguishable from farmer's lung; exposure in a sensitized subject is followed by a rise in body temperature and shortness of breath. There is also a fall in normal lung functions and a decrease in the carbon monoxide transfer factor.

A study of organic dusts containing high levels of endotoxin in two breweries in Portugal found the prevalence of symptoms of organic dust toxic syndrome, which is distinct from alveolitis or hypersensitivity pneumonia, to be 18% among brewery workers. Mucous membrane irritation was found among 39% of workers (Carveilheiro et al. 1994).

In an exposed population, the incidence of the disease is about 5%, and continued exposure produces severe respiratory incapacity. With the introduction of automated malting, where workers are not exposed, this disease has largely been eliminated.

Machinery

Where malt is stored in silos, the opening should be protected and strict rules enforced regarding entry of personnel, as described in the box on confined spaces in this chapter. Conveyors are much used in bottling plants; traps in the gearing between belts and drums can be avoided by efficient machinery guarding. There should be an effective lockout/tagout programme for maintenance and repair. Where there are walkways across or above conveyors, frequent stop buttons should also be provided. In the filling process, very serious lesions can be caused by bursting bottles; adequate guards on the machinery and face guards, rubber gloves, rubberized aprons and non-slip boots for the workers can prevent injury.

Electricity

Owing to the prevailing damp conditions, electrical installations and equipment need special protection, and this applies particularly to portable apparatus. Ground fault circuit interrupters should be installed where necessary. Wherever possible, low voltages should be used, especially for portable inspection lamps. Steam is used extensively, and burns and scalds occur; lagging and protection of pipes should be provided, and safety locks on steam valves will prevent accidental release of scalding steam.

Carbon dioxide

Carbon dioxide (CO_2) is formed during fermentation and is present in fermenting tuns, as well as vats and vessels that have contained beer. Concentrations of 10%, even if breathed only for a short time, produce unconsciousness, asphyxia and eventual death. Carbon dioxide is heavier than air, and efficient ventilation with extraction at a low height is essential in all fermentation chambers where open vats are used. As the gas is imperceptible to the senses, there should be an acoustic warning system which will operate immediately if the ventilation system breaks down. Cleaning of confined spaces presents serious hazards: the gas should be dispelled by mobile ventilators before workers are permitted to enter, safety belts and lifelines and respiratory protective equipment of the self-contained or supplied-air type should be available, and another worker should be posted outside for supervision and rescue, if necessary.

Figure 65.8 • Flow chart of the brewing process.

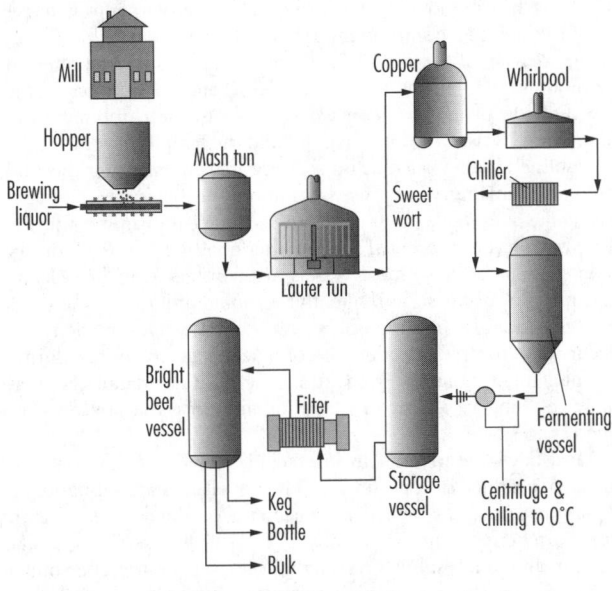

Mill
Hopper
Brewing liquor
Mash tun
Copper
Whirlpool
Sweet wort
Chiller
Lauter tun
Bright beer vessel
Filter
Keg
Bottle
Bulk
Storage vessel
Centrifuge & chilling to 0°C
Fermenting vessel

Gassing

Gassing has occurred during relining of vats with protective coatings containing toxic substances such as trichloroethylene. Precautions should be taken similar to those listed above against carbon dioxide.

Refrigerant gases

Chilling is used to cool the hot wort before fermentation and for storage purposes. Accidental discharge of refrigerants can produce serious toxic and irritant effects. In the past, chloromethane, bromomethane, sulphur dioxide and ammonia were mainly used, but today ammonia is most common. Adequate ventilation and careful maintenance will prevent most risks, but leak detectors and self-contained breathing apparatus should be provided for emergencies frequently tested. Precautions against explosive risks may also be necessary (e.g., flameproof electrical fittings, elimination of naked flames).

Hot work

In some processes, such as cleaning out mash tuns, workers are exposed to hot, humid conditions while performing heavy work; cases of heat stroke and heat cramps can occur, especially in those new to the work. These conditions can be prevented by increased salt intake, adequate rest periods and the provision and use of shower baths. Medical supervision is necessary to prevent mycoses of the feet (e.g., athlete's foot), which spread rapidly in hot, humid conditions.

Throughout the industry, temperature and ventilation control, with special attention to the elimination of steam vapour, and the provision of PPE are important precautions, not only against accident and injury but also against more general hazards of damp, heat and cold (e.g., warm working clothes for workers in cold rooms).

Control should be exercised to prevent excessive consumption of the product by the persons employed, and alternative hot beverages should be available at meal breaks.

Noise

When metal barrels replaced wooden casks, breweries were faced with a severe noise problem. Wooden casks made little or no noise during loading, handling or rolling, but metal casks when empty create high noise levels. Modern automated bottling plants generate a considerable volume of noise. Noise can be reduced by the introduction of mechanical handling on pallets. In the bottling plants, the substitution of nylon or neoprene for metal rollers and guides can substantially reduce the noise level.

● HEALTH AND ENVIRONMENTAL CONCERNS

Lance A. Ward

Beverages, both alcoholic and non-alcoholic, are normally produced under strict sanitary guidelines set by governmental regulations. To meet these guidelines, equipment within beverage plants is constantly cleaned and disinfected with harsh cleaning agents. The copious use of cleaning agents can, in itself, pose health problems to the workers exposed to them in their job duties. Skin and eye contact with the caustic cleansers can cause severe dermatitis. Another concern is that inhalation of the fumes or spray produced when using the cleansers may cause damage to the lungs, nose, mouth or throat. Water or other liquids are commonly found in and around production, making slips and falls a common injury and causing many other injuries simply due to poor traction.

Glass containers, high-speed fillers and overhead conveyors result in a combination of elements that can produce serious harm from flying glass. Cuts and eye injuries are common due to glass breakage. Much of the beverage industry has moved to using larger and larger quantities of aluminium cans and plastic containers; this has reduced the incidence of glass-inflicted injuries. However, in certain countries and specific industries, such as wine and spirits, this has not been the case.

Electrical systems in any industry possess a high degree of potential injury. When mixed with the ever present water in beverage manufacturing, the threat of electrocution becomes extreme. Electrical systems within beverage plants are constantly being reworked as the industry rapidly modernizes with new high-speed equipment that results in increasing exposure.

The manufacturing process in the beverage industry entails the movement of massive quantities of raw materials in bags and barrels, on wooden and plastic pallets; loads of empty bottles and cans; and finished product in a variety of containers. Beverages, being liquid, are naturally heavy. Repetitive-motion injuries due to sorting and inspection of glass bottles and some packaging operations occur frequently. This continuous movement of light and heavy objects presents ergonomic challenges for the beverage industry as well as other industries. The incidence of soft tissue sprain and strain injuries in the United States has risen nearly 400% since 1980, for example. Nations are in different stages of progress in determining preventive measures to reduce these types of injuries.

Modern mechanized equipment has drastically reduced the number of personnel needed to operate the bottling and canning lines, which in itself has reduced the exposure to injury. However, the high-speed conveyers and automatic palletizing and de-palletizing equipment can cause serious, although less frequent, injuries. Personnel tempted to reach into a moving conveyor to put a bottle or can upright can get clothing caught and be dragged into the mechanism. Palletizers and depalletizers can become jammed, and a worker can suffer broken limbs trying to clear the machines.

Modern high-speed equipment has, in most cases, led to increased noise levels, especially at the higher frequencies. Hearing loss caused by workplace noise is classified as a disease, since it occurs insidiously over time and is irreversible. Incidence rates involving hearing loss are increasing. Engineering controls to reduce the noise levels are being tested and used, but enforcement of the wearing of standard hearing protection is still the preferred method used by most employers. New on the horizon is the investigation of the stress on workers due to the combination of high noise levels, 24-hour schedules and the tempo of work.

Confined spaces, such as tanks, casks, vats, wastewater pits and storage or mixing vessels used commonly in beverage manufacturing facilities, have the potential of causing catastrophic injuries. This issue has not received a lot of attention by beverage industry management because most vessels are considered to be "clean" and mishaps occur so infrequently. Although injuries in the types of vessels used by beverage plants are rare, a serious incident can occur due to the introduction of hazardous materials during cleaning operations or from atmospheric abnormalities, potentially resulting in a near or actual fatality. (See the box on confined spaces.)

Most beverage manufacturing facilities have raw material and finished product storage areas. Self-propelled material-handling equipment poses as serious a threat in a production plant as in any warehouse. Injuries involving fork-lift trucks and similar equipment often result in crushing injuries to pedestrian personnel or to the operator if the vehicle overturns. Production plants often entail cramped conditions as expansion of production capability in existing facilities takes place. These cramped conditions are often conducive to a serious accident involving material-handling equipment.

Beverage production usually requires pure water and refrigeration systems. Chemicals used most commonly to satisfy these requirements are chlorine and liquid anhydrous ammonia, respectively, and both are considered extremely hazardous substances. Chlorine is often purchased and stored in pressurized metal cylinders of various sizes. Injuries can occur to personnel during changeover from one cylinder to another or from a leaking or defective valve. An accidental release of anhydrous ammonia can cause burns to the skin and respiratory system on contact. A large, uncontrolled release of anhydrous ammonia can result in air concentrations high enough to explode violently. Emergency systems to detect leaks and automatic ventilation and shut down equipment are used frequently, along with evacuation and response procedures. Chlorine and anhydrous ammonia are chemicals that have strong identifiable odours and are easily detectable in the air. They are considered to have strong warning properties to alert workers of their presence.

Carbon dioxide, most commonly used for pressurization and carbonation, and carbon monoxide, emitted by internal combustion engines, are present in most beverage plants. Beverage filler rooms are usually the most prone to having high levels of carbon dioxide, especially during product changeover procedures. Beverage companies have been increasing the assortment of products offered to the public, so these changeovers occur more frequently, increasing the need for ventilation to exhaust the carbon dioxide. Carbon monoxide can be present if fork-lifts or similar equipment are used. A dangerous concentration can accumulate if engines are not operating within manufacturers' specifications.

Employment in the beverage industry is often seasonal. This is more common in areas of the world with distinct seasons and in northern climates. A combination of worldwide manufacturing trends such as just-in-time inventory control and the use of contract and temporary personnel can have a great impact on safety and health. Often workers employed for short periods of time are not afforded the same amount of safety-related training as permanent employees. In some cases, resultant costs associated with injuries sustained by temporary personnel are not borne by the employer but by an agency supplying the worker to the employer. This has created an apparent "win–win" situation for the employer and the opposite effect on the workers employed in positions such as these. More enlightened governments, employers and trade associations are beginning to look closely at this growing problem and are working on methods to improve the amount and quality of safety training given to workers in this category.

Environmental concerns are not often associated with beverage production, since it is not thought of as a "smokestack industry". Excluding an accidental release of a hazardous chemical such as anhydrous ammonia or chlorine, the main discharge from beverage production is wastewater. Usually this wastewater is treated prior to entry into the waste stream, so it is rare that a problem occurs. Occasionally a bad batch of product has to be discarded, which, depending on the ingredients involved, may have to be transported away for treatment or greatly diluted before release into the waste system. A large quantity of acidic beverage finding its way into a stream or lake can cause large fish kills and must be avoided.

The increasing use of chemical additives for enhancing flavour, extending shelf life or as a substitute sweetener has raised public health concerns. Some chemicals used as artificial sweeteners are prohibited in some countries because they have been found to be carcinogenic. Most, however, present no apparent health risk to the public. The handling of these raw chemicals and their presence in the workplace has not been studied in enough depth to determine if there are worker exposure risks.

References

Carveilheiro, MF, MJM Gomes, O Santo, G Duarte, J Henriques, B Mendes, A Marques, and R Avila. 1994. Symptoms and exposure to endotoxin among brewery employees. *Am J Ind Med* 25:113-115.

Food and Agricultural Organization (FAO) of the United Nations. 1992. *FAO Year Book.* Vol 46. Rome: FAO.

Giullemin, MP and B Horisberger. 1994. Fatal intoxication due to an unexpected presence of carbon dioxide. *Ann Occ Hyg* 38: 951-957.

Sekimpi, DK, DF Agaba, M Okot-Mwang, and DA Ogaram. 1996. Occupational coffee dust allergies in Uganda. *Afr Newslett on Occup and Safety* 6(1):6–9.

Romano, C, F Sulatto, G Piolatto, C Ciacco, E Capellaro, P Falagiani, DW Constabile, A Vaga, and G Scorcetti. 1995. Factors related to the development of sensitization on green coffee and castor bean allergens among coffee workers. *Clin Exp Allergy* 25:643–650.

Other relevant readings

Cartensen, JM, LO Bygren, and T Hatschek. 1990. Cancer incidence among Swedish brewery workers. *Int J Cancer* 45:393-396.

Panzani, RC Palagiani, G Riva, P Mercier, and Y Delord. 1995. Screening for atopy in a coffee processing factory. *Allergol Imunopathol, Madr* 23:29–34.

Reed, G and TW Nagodawithana. 1991. *Yeast Technology,* 2nd edition. New York: Van Nostrand Reinhold.

Sobolov, M, DM Booth, and RG Aldi. 1985. Whisky. In *Comprehensive Biotechnology,* edited by M Moo-Young. Oxford: Pergamon Press.

Tomoda, S. 1993. *Occupational Safety and Health in the Food and Drink Industries.* Sectoral Activities Programme Working Paper. Geneva: ILO.

Zuskin, E, B Kanceljak, TJ Vitek, Jr., and EN Schacter. 1991. Acute ventilatory response to green coffee dust extract. *Annals of Allergy* 66:219–224.

FISHING

66

Chapter Editors
Hulda Ólafsdóttir and Vilhjálmur Rafnsson

Contents

66. FISHING

GENERAL PROFILE

Ragnar Arnason

Overview

Fishing is among the oldest production activities of humankind. Archaeological and historical research shows that fishing—both freshwater and ocean fishing—was widespread in ancient civilizations. In fact, it seems that human settlements were frequently established in areas of good fishing. These findings concerning the role of fishing for human sustenance are confirmed by modern day anthropological research of primitive societies.

During the past few centuries, the world's fisheries have been radically transformed. Traditional fishing methods have to a large extent been superseded by a more modern technology stemming from the industrial revolution. This has been followed by a dramatic increase in effective fishing effort, a much smaller increase in global catch levels and a serious decline in many fish stocks. The industrialization of global fishing has also led to destabilization and decline of many traditional fisheries. Finally, increased worldwide fishing pressure has given rise to international disputes about fishing rights.

In 1993, the world harvest of fish was in the neighbourhood of 100 million metric tonnes per annum (FAO 1995). Of this quantity, fish-farming (aqua- and mariculture) accounted for about 16 million tonnes. So the world's fisheries produced some 84 million tonnes per annum. About 77 million tonnes come from marine fisheries and the rest, some 7 million tonnes, from inland fisheries. To catch this quantity, there was a fishing fleet counting 3.5 million vessels and measuring about 30 million gross registered tonnes (FAO 1993, 1995). There are few hard data about the number of fishermen employed in the operation of this fleet. The Food and Agriculture Organization of the United Nations (FAO 1993) has estimated that they may be as many as 13 million. There is even less information about the number of workers employed in the processing and distribution of the catch. Conservatively estimated they may be 1 to 2 times the number of fishermen. This means that 25 to 40 million people may be directly employed in the fishing industry worldwide.

Asia is by far the largest fishing continent in the world, with close to half of the total annual fish harvest (FAO 1995). North and South America together (30%) come next, followed by Europe (15%). As fishing continents, Africa and Oceania are relatively insignificant, with combined harvest of about 5% of the annual global catch.

In 1993, the largest fishing nation in terms of harvesting volume was China, with about 10 million tonnes of marine catch, corresponding to about 12% of the global marine fish catch. Second and third place were taken by Peru and Japan, with about 10% of the global marine catch each. In 1993, 19 nations had a marine catch in excess of 1 million tonnes.

The world's harvest of fish is distributed over a large number of species and fisheries. Very few fisheries have an annual yield in excess of 1 million tonnes. The largest ones in 1993 were the Peruvian anchovy fishery (8.3 million tonnes), the Alaska pollock fishery (4.6 million tonnes) and the Chilean horse mackerel fishery (3.3 million tonnes). Together these three fisheries account for about 1/5 of the world's total marine harvest.

Evolution and Structure of the Fishing Industry

The combination of population growth and advances in fishing technology has led to a great expansion in fishing activity. Commencing centuries ago in Europe, this expansion has been particularly pronounced worldwide during the current century. According to FAO statistics (FAO 1992, 1995), total world catches have quadrupled since 1948, from under 20 million tonnes to the current level of about 80 million tonnes. This corresponds to almost 3% annual growth. However, during the last few years, the ocean harvest has stagnated at about 80 million tonnes annually. As the global fishing effort has continued to increase, this suggests that the exploitation of the world's most important fish stocks is already at or in excess of the maximum sustainable yield. Hence, unless new fish stocks come under exploitation, the ocean fish catch cannot increase in the future.

The processing and marketing of the fish harvest have also expanded greatly. Assisted by improvements in transportation and conservation technology, and spurred by increased real personal incomes, ever increasing volumes of catch are processed, packaged and marketed as high-value food commodities. This trend is likely to continue at an even faster rate in the future. This means a substantially increased value added per unit of catch. However, it also represents a replacement of the traditional fish-processing and distribution activity by high-technology, industrial production methods. More seriously, this process (sometimes referred to as the globalization of fish markets) threatens to strip underdeveloped communities of their staple fish supply due to overbidding from the industrial world.

The world's fisheries today are composed of two quite distinct sectors: artisanal fisheries and industrial fisheries. Most artisanal fisheries are a continuation of the traditional local fisheries that have changed very little over the centuries. Consequently, they are usually low technology, labour-intensive fisheries confined to near-shore or inshore fishing grounds (see the box on "Indigenous divers"). The industrial fisheries, by contrast, are high technology and extremely capital intensive. The industrial fishing vessels are generally large and well equipped, and can range widely over the oceans.

With regard to vessel numbers and employment, the artisanal sector dominates the world's fisheries. Almost 85% of the world's fishing vessels and 75% of the fishermen are artisanal ones. In spite of this, due to its low technology and limited range, the artisanal fleet accounts for only a small fraction of the world's catch of fish. Moreover, due to the low productivity of the artisanal fleet, the artisanal fishermen's income is generally low and their working conditions poor. The industrial fishing sector is economically much more efficient. Although the industrial fleet only comprises 15% of the world's fishing vessels and approximately 50% of the total tonnage of the world's fishing fleet, it accounts for over 80% of the volume of marine catch in the world.

The increase in fishing during this century is mostly caused by an expansion of the industrial fisheries. The industrial fleet has increased the effectiveness of the harvesting activity in traditional fishing areas and expanded the geographical reach of the fisheries from relatively shallow inshore areas to almost all parts of the oceans where fish are to be found. By contrast, the artisanal fishery has remained relatively stagnant, although there has been technical progress in this part of the fishery as well.

Economic Importance

The current value of the global fish harvest at dockside is estimated to be about US$60 to 70 billion (FAO 1993, 1995). Although fish processing and distribution may be assumed to double or triple this amount, fishing is nevertheless a relatively minor industry from a global perspective, especially when compared to agriculture, the major food production industry of the world. For certain nations and regions, however, fishing is very important. This applies, for instance, to many communities bordering the North Atlantic and North Pacific. Moreover, in many communities of West Africa, South America and Southeast Asia, fishing is the population's main source of animal protein and, consequently, is economically very important.

Indigenous divers

Indigenous peoples living in coastal areas have for centuries depended on the sea for their survival. In the more tropical waters they have not only fished from traditional boats but also engaged in spear fishing and shell gathering activities, diving either from shore or from boats. The waters in the past were plentiful and there was no need to dive deeply for long periods of time. More recently the situation has changed. Overfishing and the destruction of breeding grounds has made it impossible for indigenous peoples to sustain themselves. Many have turned to diving deeper for longer periods of time in order to bring home a sufficient catch. As the capacity of humans to stay underwater without some form of support is quite limited, indigenous divers in several parts of the world have begun using compressors to supply air from the surface or to use self-contained underwater breathing apparatus (SCUBA) to extend the amount of time that they are able to stay underwater (bottom time).

In the developing world, indigenous divers are found in Central and South America, Southeast Asia and the Pacific. It has been estimated by the University of California at Berkeley, Department of Geography's Ocean Conservation and Environmental Action Network (OCEAN) Initiative, that there may be as many as 30,000 working indigenous divers in Central America, South America and the Caribbean. (It is estimated that the Moskito Indians in Central America may have a diving population as high as 450 divers.) Researchers at the Divers Diseases Research Centre of the United Kingdom estimate that in the Philippines there may be between 15,000 to 20,000 indigenous divers; in Indonesia the number has yet to be determined but it may be as many as 10,000.

In Southeast Asia some indigenous divers use compressors on boats with air lines or hoses attached to the divers. The compressors are normally commercial type compressors used in filling stations or are compressors salvaged from large trucks and driven by gasoline or diesel engines. Depths may range to more than 90 m and dives may exceed durations of 2 hours. Indigenous divers work to gather fish and shellfish for human consumption, aquaria fish, seashells for the tourist industry, pearl oysters and, at certain times of the year, sea cucumbers. Their fishing techniques include using underwater fish traps, spear fishing and pounding two stones together to drive fish into a net down current. Lobsters, crabs and shellfish are gathered by hand (see figure 66.1).

The indigenous Sea Gypsy Divers of Thailand

In Thailand there are approximately 400 divers using compressors and living on the west coast. They are known as Sea Gypsies and were once a nomadic people that have settled in 12 rather permanent villages in three provinces. They are literate and almost all have completed compulsory education. Virtually all of the divers speak Thai and most speak their own language, *Pasa Chaaw Lee*, which is an unwritten Malay language.

Only males dive, starting as young as 12 years of age and stopping, if they survive, around the age of 50. They dive from open boats, ranging from 3 to 11 m in length. The compressors used are powered by either a gasoline or a diesel powered motor and are primitive, cycling unfiltered air into a pressure tank and down 100 m of hose to a diver. This practice of using ordinary air compressors without filtration can lead to contamination of breathing air with carbon monoxide, nitrogen dioxide from diesel motors, lead from leaded gasoline and combustion particulates. The hose is attached to a normal diving mask which covers the eyes and nose. Inspiration and expiration is done through the nose, with the expired air escaping from the skirt of the mask. The only protection from marine life and the temperature of the water is a roll collar, a long sleeve shirt, a pair of plastic shoes and a pair of athletic style trousers. A pair of cotton mesh gloves offers the hands a certain degree of protection (see figure 66.2).

A research project was developed in concert with Thailand's Ministry of Public Health to study the diving practices of the Sea Gypsies and to develop educational and informational interventions to raise the divers' awareness of the risks they face and measures that can be taken to reduce those risks. As part of this project 334 divers were interviewed by trained public health care workers in 1996 and 1997. The response rate to the questionnaires was over 90%. Although the survey data are still under analysis, several points have been extracted for this case study.

Regarding diving practices, 54% of the divers were asked how many dives they made on their last day of diving. Of the 310 divers that responded to the question, 54% indicated that they made less than 4 dives; 35% indicated 4 to 6 dives and 11% indicated 7 or more dives.

When asked about the depth of their first dive of their last day of diving, of the 307 divers who responded to this question, 51% indicated 18 m or less; 38% indicated between 18 and 30 m; 8% indicated between 30 and 40 m; 2% indicated more than 40 m, with one diver reporting a dive at a depth of 80 m. A 16 year-old diver in one village reported that he had performed 20 dives on his last day of diving to depths of less than 10 m. Since he has been diving he has been struck 3 times by decompression sickness.

A high frequency of dives, deep depths, long bottom times and short surface intervals are factors which can increase the risk of decompression sickness.

Risks

An early random sampling of the survey revealed that the 3 most significant risks included an interruption of the air supply leading to an emergency ascent, injury from marine life and decompression sickness.

Unlike sport or professional divers, the indigenous diver has no alternative air supply. A cut, crimped or separated air hose leaves only two options. The first is to find a fellow diver and share air from one mask, a skill which is virtually unknown to the Sea Gypsies; the second is an emergency swim to the surface, which can and frequently does lead to barotrauma (injury related to rapidly reducing pressure) and decompression sickness (caused by expanding nitrogen gas bubbles in the blood and tissue as the diver surfaces). When asked about separation from diving partners during working dives, of the 331 divers who responded to the question, 113 (34%) indicated that they worked 10 m or more away from their partners and an additional 24 indicated that they were not concerned about the whereabouts of partners during dives. The research project is currently instructing the divers how to share air from one mask while encouraging them to dive closer together.

Since indigenous divers are frequently working with dead or injured marine life, there is always the potential that a hungry predator may also attack the indigenous diver. The diver may also be handling poisonous marine animals, thus increasing the risk of illness or injury.

Regarding decompression sickness, 83% of divers said they considered pain as part of the job; 34% indicated they had recovered from decompression sickness, and 44% of those had had decompression sickness 3 or more times.

An occupational health intervention

On the implementation side of this project, 16 health care workers at the village level along with 3 Sea Gypsies have been taught to be trainers. Their task is to work with the divers on a boat-by-boat basis

66. FISHING

using short (15 minute) interventions to raise the awareness of the divers about the risks they face; give the divers the knowledge and skills to reduce those risks; and develop emergency procedures to assist sick or injured divers. The train-the-trainer workshop developed 9 rules, a short lesson plan for each rule and an information sheet to use as a handout. The rules are as follows:

1. The deepest dive should be first, with each subsequent dive shallower.
2. The deepest part of any dive should come first, followed by work in shallower water.
3. A safety stop on ascent at 5 m after every deep dive is mandatory.
4. Come up slowly from every dive.
5. Allow a minimum of one hour on the surface between deep dives.
6. Drink large amounts of water before and after each dive.
7. Stay within sight of another diver.
8. Never hold your breath.
9. Always display the international dive flag whenever there are divers underwater.

The Sea Gypsies were born and raised next to or on the sea. They depend on the sea for their existence. Although they are sickened or injured as a result of their diving practices they continue to dive. The interventions listed above will probably not stop the Sea Gypsies from diving, but they will make them aware of the risk they face and provide them the means to reduce this risk.

David Gold

Figure 66.1 • An indigenous diver gathering fish.

Figure 66.2 • A diver off of Phuket, Thailand, preparing to dive from an open boat.

Fisheries Management

The global fishing effort has risen sharply during this century, especially after the end of the Second World War. As a result, many of the world's most valuable fish stocks have been depleted to the point where increased fishing effort actually leads to a drop in the sustainable catch level. The FAO estimates that most of the world's major fish stocks are either fully utilized or overfished in this sense (FAO 1995). As a result, the harvest from many of the world's most important species has actually contracted, and, in spite of continuing advances in fishing technology and increases in the real price of fish, the economic returns from the fishing activity have declined.

Faced with diminishing fish stocks and declining profitability of the fishing industry, most of the world's fishing nations have actively sought means to remedy the situation. These efforts have generally followed two routes: extensions of the national fisheries jurisdictions to 200 nautical miles and more, and an imposition of new fisheries management systems within the national fisheries jurisdictions.

Many different fisheries management methods have been employed for the purpose of improving the economics of fishing. Recognizing that the source of the fisheries problem is the common property nature of the fish stocks, the most advanced fisheries management systems seek to solve the problem by defining quasi-property rights in the fisheries. A common method is to set the total allowable catch for each species and then to allocate this total allowable catch to individual fishing companies in the form of individual catch quotas. These catch quotas constitute a property right in the fishery. Provided the quotas are tradable, the fishing industry finds it to its advantage to restrict fishing effort to the minimum needed to take the total allowable catch and, provided the quotas are also permanent, to adjust the size of the fishing fleet to the long-term sustainable yield of the fishery. This method of fisheries management (usually referred to as the individual transferable quota (ITQ) system) is rapidly expanding in the world today and seems likely to become the management norm for the future.

The expanding range of national fisheries jurisdictions and the property-rights-based management systems being implemented within them imply a substantial restructuring of fishing. The virtual enclosure of the world's oceans by national fisheries jurisdictions, already well under way, will obviously all but eliminate distant water fishing. The property-rights-based fisheries management systems also represent increased incursion of market forces into fishing. Industrial fishing is economically more efficient than artisanal fishing. Moreover, the industrial fishing companies are in a better position to adjust to new fisheries management systems than artisanal fishermen. Hence, it seems that the current evolution of fisheries management poses yet another threat to the artisanal way of fishing. Given this and the need to curtail overall fishing effort, it seems inevitable that the level of employment in the world's fisheries will fall drastically in the future.

● MAJOR SECTORS AND PROCESSES

Hjálmar R. Bárdarson

Characteristics of Work at Sea

Work at sea aboard fishing vessels is in several ways different from work aboard general cargo vessels, although the activity connected to navigation is similar or the same. The principal differ-

ence between a general cargo ship and a fishing vessel is that cargo vessels load their cargo in harbours. After loading, their hatches must be closed watertight and are not normally opened until arrival at the next harbour, where the cargo is to be unloaded.

Fishing vessels, on the other hand, catch fish at fishing grounds and thus take on board their "cargo" at sea. Therefore, a fishing vessel more or less frequently has to operate with some of the hatches open at sea, which can involve a danger of flooding.

Another factor is the catching operation itself. Often there is a heavy drag from fishing gear, even on small vessels. Furthermore, fishing operations often take place at open and unsheltered fishing grounds. In addition, the crew on many smaller fishing vessels still has to work without shelter on open decks.

Fishing vessels are therefore more vulnerable than cargo ships, especially in heavy seas, and require a very different approach at the design stage, as well as guidelines for the education and training of skippers and crew.

Fishing Methods and Types of Fishing Vessels

The types of fishing vessels are generally governed by the fishing methods to be used. Some fishing vessels are designed just for one fishing method, but others are multi-purpose vessels, which are able to use two or more different types of fishing gear. The principal methods in operation from fishing vessels are the following:

1. bottom trawling
2. mid-water trawling
3. purse seining (encircling gear)
4. long-lining
5. drift gill nets
6. linefishing on small boats.

Bottom trawling

Side trawling was the original method of bottom trawling. A side trawler has two gallows, one forward and one aft, usually on the starboard side (the right side of the vessel when looking forward). The trawl net is set over the side by the crew and the warps (wire ropes) passed over blocks hanging from the gallows. Trawl doors

Figure 66.3 • Stern trawler bottom trawling.

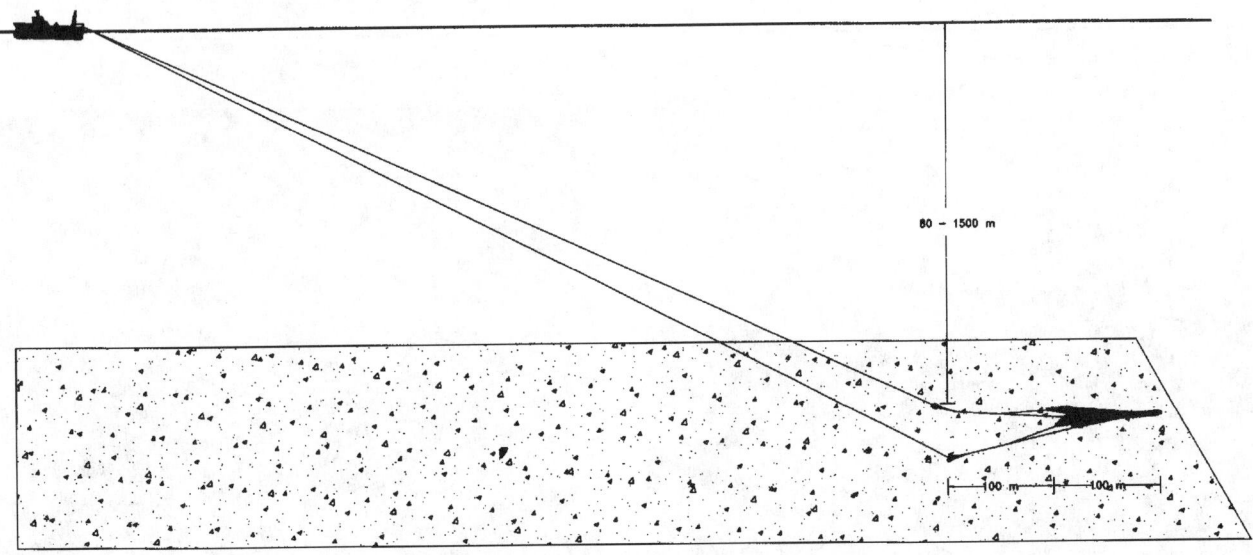

80 – 1500 m

100 m   100 m

Source: Hampidjan Ltd.

66. FISHING

Figure 66.4 • Stern trawler.

Skipataekni Ltd.

Figure 66.6 • Small linefishing high-speed boat (stationary).

Batasmidja Gudmundar

(otter boards), one on each side of the mouth of the net, are set at an angle to keep the net open when pulled by the vessel along the bottom (see figure 66.3). The fish are gathered in the so-called cod end of the net. The superstructure of a side trawler is aft of amidship, with a double-drum trawl winch usually in front of it on the foredeck. The catch is lifted aboard on the foredeck end by a derrick on the forward mast. Very few side trawlers are still in use, as almost all have been replaced by stern trawlers. The stern trawlers have the bridge forward and a large gantry side to side aft instead of the gallows (see figure 66.4). The bigger stern trawlers have a shelterdeck; the main trawl winch is often amidship; and usually there are several smaller winches on the afterdeck for lifting parts of the fishing gear. The trawl net is pulled up a stern ramp on top of the shelterdeck, where the cod end is lifted, and the contents emptied through a hatch into pounds on the main deck below, which is a factory deck on big stern trawlers.

Mid-water trawling

The purpose of mid-water trawls is to catch pelagic and other species of fish in schools at various levels between the bottom of the sea and the surface. Mid-water trawling is operated by same type of ships as bottom trawling, but vessels are usually fitted with

a large net drum for the much bigger nets. There are special mid-water trawl doors, weights and floats on the warps to regulate the depth of the trawl below the surface.

Purse seining (encircling gear)

The purpose of purse seiners is to catch free-swimming species of schooling fish, like herring, capelin and mackerel. Catches can be very large, and high carrying capacity of the vessel can therefore be of importance. The seining net has floats on top and weights on the bottom. As the vessel has to lay out the net in a ring around the school of fish, good manoeuvrability and especially good turning ability are important. There are two types of purse seiners. One of them has been called the American type and the other, the North European (or Nordic) type. Both use hydraulically driven power blocks. The American vessels have the bridge and accommodation forward, with the power block on a derrick from the mast abaft the deckhouse. The Nordic purse seiners were originally of the side-trawler type, with deckhouse, wheelhouse and accommodation aft. The powerblock is usually located on the starboard side of the wheelhouse; a hydraulically driven transport roller carries the net from the power block to the net bin at the stern. After enclosing the school of fish, the purse-seine net is closed at the bottom by the pursing winch on the deck pulling the bottom warp; the fish are then pumped from the purse seine through a fish/water separator into the hold.

Figure 66.5 • Purse seiner.

Skipataekni Ltd.

Figure 66.7 • Small linefishing high-speed boat (running).

Batasmidja Gudmundar

Newly designed and built Nordic purse seiners (see figure 66.5) are now commonly of the same size as the big stern trawlers, with a tweendeck from fore to aft and a separate net bin aft. The arrangement of the powerblock is still similar to the original type of vessels.

Long-lining

Long-lining is a fishing method where a long line is set out, to which several short lengths of line with a baited hook on the end are connected with a separation of 1 to 2 m. After some time, the fishing vessel hauls in the long line and the caught fish are removed from the hooks. This fishing method has for a long time been and still is used on rather small fishing vessels without shelter on the open deck (see figures 66.6 and 66.7). Usually the hooks are baited on land and coiled in tubs. The fishing vessel runs the long line out over the stern and hauls it in from the starboard side with a hydraulic line hauler.

A modern linefishing vessel, equipped for long-lining with autoline, has a shelterdeck, with a side-opening for the hauling and an opening at the stem to set the long line out. Both openings can be closed weathertight, and are bulkheaded off so that only a limited part of the working deck can be flooded, in case of a breaking wave. After the line has been hauled into the vessel through the line hauler, it goes through an automatic baiting machine where old bait is cleaned from the hooks and the new bait is hooked on in one operation, just before the line is run out again. Long-lining vessels can be about 60 m in length with accommodation for around 20 to 40 crew members. The autoline system has up to 40,000 to 50,000 hooks on a longline up to 60 km in length. The line is run out at a speed of 7 to 8 knots, and the line hauler has a pulling power of about 5 t. The fish process space is in the tweendeck, which is fitted with belt conveyors, bins and tables for manual gutting and filleting. In some cases these vessels are equipped for freezing the fish.

Drift gill nets

Gill nets trap fish by entangling their gills. On fishing vessels with superstructure aft and open working deck amidship, several drift gill nets are set end to end over the side. A dan buoy is secured to the free end of the nets, and a number of floats are connected to the top line along the nets. The fishing vessel keeps the nets stretched. This drift net fishing has now in many countries been replaced by purse seiners and mid-water trawlers.

Linefishing on small boats

Coastal fishing on small boats is still an important activity in many countries and has now developed considerably. Small open wooden boats with outboard or inboard motors have largely been replaced by decked or half-decked boats, mostly built of fibreglass and designed as high-speed boats which can reach midshore fishing grounds. The length of these boats is usually from 8 to 15 m. With engines of 250 to 400 horsepower they can reach a cruising speed up to 24 knots. The cabin usually has two berths, a galley and a WC. Several of these boats are fitted with up to four jigging reels, which are computerized automatic linefishing machines. The jigging reel pays out the line and detects when the sinker hits the bottom, positions the hooks at a desired distance from it and performs jigging actions. It detects when a fish bites the hooks and then hauls the catch up to the surface.

Fish Processing on Board and on Shore

With the increasing size of fishing vessels, and also the more extensive deep-sea fishing far away from home ports, fish processing on board fishing vessels has also increased considerably. As space on board is more limited than at processing plants on shore, there has been a need for more compact arrangements and new development of processing lines with automatic fish-processing equipment both for fish and shrimp.

Forward of the upper edge of the stern ramp slipway of a modern stern trawler, the content of the cod end of the trawl is emptied through hydraulically operated hatches from trawl deck down to the stainless steel bins on the receiving deck below, which is abaft of the fish-processing area. Through four hydraulically operated hatches in the front bulkhead of the receiving bins, the fish-processing line receives the fish and carries it between the working stations in the fish-processing area, which is 520 m². The processing is arranged for production of fillets, blocks, mince and headed and gutted fish. See figure 66.8 for an illustration of the process.

The processing line is arranged as much as possible for automatic processing with conveyors, buffer stores, by-pass functions and so on. The layout includes the following items:

- sorting and bleeding conveyor
- one heading and gutting machine
- ten buffer tanks with icewater cooling
- two conveyors for transporting fish from buffer tanks to production

Figure 66.8 • Flow chart of fishing and processing.

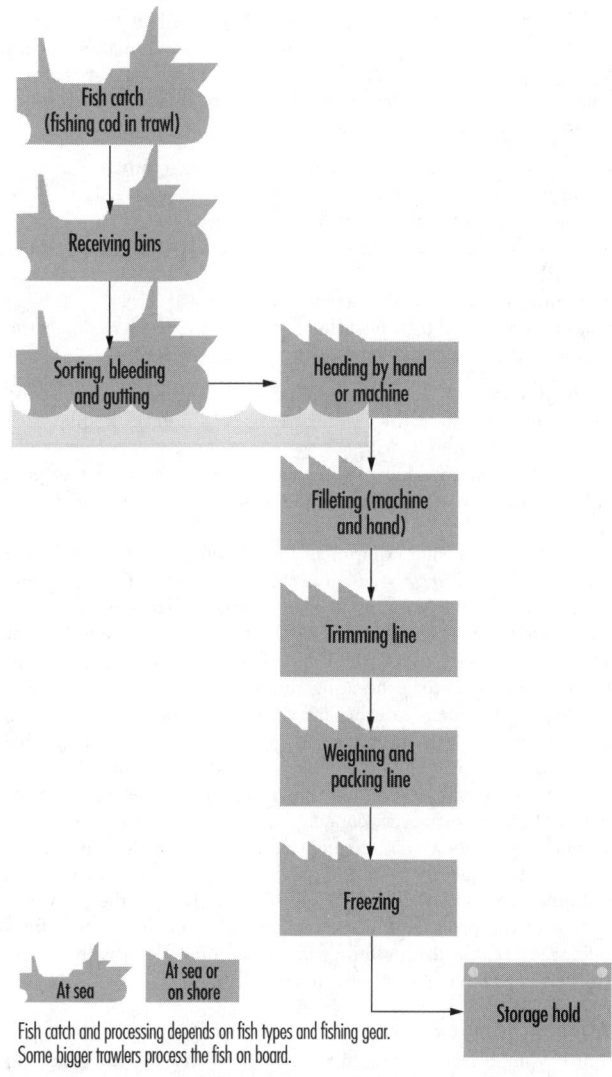

Fish catch and processing depends on fish types and fishing gear. Some bigger trawlers process the fish on board.

- conveyor for bringing fillets from two filleting machines to trimming
- trimming line with eight working stations
- packing line with automatic weighing station (auto-portioning) and five packing stations.

The processing line is also arranged with a hand fillet station with four positions. The freezing system is connected to three horizontal automatic plate freezers and one manually operated freezer. The capacity for freezing is approximately 70 tonnes of fish fillets per 24 hours.

The carton size used is of fixed standard, and the fillets and block are packed into a standard weight of frozen block. A cargo elevator is installed for transporting from the processing line to the hold. The fish hold, with a total volume of 925 m³, can be kept at $-30\,°C$, with an outside temperature of $30\,°C$ and a seawater temperature of $20\,°C$.

In the starboard side of the fish processing area there is a separate shrimp-processing line with sorting conveyor, shrimp grading machine, shrimp cooker, shrimp weighing, freezing tunnel and packing. A part of the fish-processing equipment for whitefish is also utilized for the shrimp processing (e.g., receiving bins, plate freezers, packing, transport conveyors and storage in the fish hold).

A fishmeal factory, with 50 to 60 tonnes capacity of raw material and producing 7 to 9 tonnes of fishmeal in 24 hours, is installed in some bigger freezer trawlers. For good quality, such a factory relies on steam heating of the dryer, with steam from a combined exhaust/oil boiler. Such a fishmeal factory consists of the following machines:

- an indirect cooker with steam-heated jacket and rotor, and nozzles for steam supply direct to the fish
- a strainer conveyor and a twin-screw press
- a tearing conveyor to transport the presscake to a steam-heated rotadisc drier
- a pump to transport the presswater overboard
- a suction pipe to transport the meal from the receiver under the drier outlet to the milling plant.

Ducts then lead from the milling to a bagging station in the fishmeal hold, where the fishmeal is packed into 35 kg paper or jute bags and stored.

For the crew working in the processing area there are adjustable platforms at stations where persons stand for long periods of time.

The fish-processing equipment for whitefish and other seafood on board factory vessels which are not engaged in fishing operations is almost the same as in fishing vessels, like stern trawlers, which are processing their own catch. The main difference is that such factory vessels follow the fishing fleet to the fishing banks and receive their catch for processing and transport to port.

The development of the freezing lines and fish-processing equipment for ships has also had great influence on the equipment in fish-processing factories on land. The automatic but flexible system is built with a number of workstations where product quality, performance, capacity and yield are monitored individually for optional management of the system. Fillets are sent to a portioning machine, and the portions are then sent for individual quick freezing or to packaging stations. Due to the conveyor system of the processing lines for both fish and shrimp, the lines offer remarkable throughput with minimum effort, without the workers ever having to lift or throw the fish.

International Codes

Three United Nations organizations—the FAO, the International Labour Organization (ILO) and the International Maritime Organization (IMO)—entered into an agreement to cooperate in a project to draw up a code of safety for fishers and fishing vessels, each working within its respective field of competence:

- FAO—fisheries in general
- ILO—labour in the fishing industry
- IMO—safety of life, vessels and equipment at sea.

A joint group of consultants from the three organizations drew up the Code of Safety for Fishermen and Fishing Vessels in two parts: Part A, safety and health practice for skippers and crews, containing operational and occupational requirements; and Part B, safety and health requirements for the construction and equipment of fishing vessels. The purpose of this guide is to reduce the risk of injury to fishermen and as far as possible prevent accidents, as well as lessen the risk of danger to the vessel. The IMO coordinated proposed amendments, but any amendments were subject to the final approval of the three organizations. Revised editions of the Code have been published by IMO on behalf of the FAO, the ILO and the IMO.

Part A contains basic information necessary for the safe conduct of fishing operations, such as safety of navigation, seaworthiness of the vessel and proper equipment. Other precautionary measures to be taken include maintaining adequate stability of the vessel; precautions against falling overboard; general safety on deck; safety in machinery spaces and of mechanical equipment; and knowledge of life-saving appliances, fire prevention and precautions and first-aid equipment. The continuous maintenance of all safety devices of the vessel and its equipment is also essential.

For the safety of a fishing vessel, the operation and handling of the ship is a basic factor. Skippers of fishing vessels 24 m in length and over, operating in unlimited waters, must be knowledgeable about all aspects of navigation, fishing vessel manoeuvring and handling, construction and stability. The skipper must be able to use stability data and evaluate the influence of the fish load, of the amount of water and oil in tanks, of water trapped on deck, of closure of openings in the ship and of the pulling of fishing gear.

For the safety of fishing vessels and their crew, it is essential that the education, training and certification for all persons serving on board seagoing fishing vessels is of recognized high standards. To achieve this, an International Convention on Standards of Training, Certification and Watchkeeping for Fishing Vessel Personnel, 1995, was signed at the IMO headquarters in London. Those States for which this Convention has entered into force have undertaken to promulgate all laws, decrees, orders and regulations so as to ensure that, from the point of view of safety of life and property at sea and the protection of the marine environment, seagoing fishing vessel personnel are qualified and fit for their duties. This Convention shall enter into force 12 months after the date on which not less than 15 states have ratified it.

The regulations annexed to the Convention cover mandatory minimum requirements for certification of skippers, officers, engineer officers and radio operators, as well as specified basic safety training for all fishing vessel personnel, and regulations on basic principles to be observed in keeping a navigational watch on board fishing vessels.

Among the items for examination of candidates for certification as skippers and navigational officers on fishing vessels in unlimited waters are the following: navigation, watchkeeping, electronic position-fixing, meteorology, communications, fire prevention, life saving, fishing vessel manoeuvring and handling, fishing vessel construction and stability (including knowledge of effects of free surfaces and ice accretion), catch handling and stowage, English language, medical aid, maritime law, search and rescue, knowledge of the FAO/ILO/IMO Code of Safety for Fishermen and Fishing Vessels, Part A, and prevention of marine pollution.

Crew Accommodation and Equipment for Crew in High-Seas Fishing Vessels

In the bigger types of freezer stern trawlers, intended for fishing in high seas, often staying for months far away from home port, the accommodation and equipment for the crew is usually extensive. For example, a new 68 m long Icelandic stern trawler delivered in 1994 has accommodation for 37 persons. There are 13 one-person cabins and 12 two-person cabins, as well as a hospital cabin with 2 berths and separate toilet and washing basin. The total accommodation area is 625 m². All the cabins have access to separate toilet, washing basin and shower. Besides messroom and galley, there are two TV saloons, one sauna and one trim room. Entertainment equipment includes two 28-inch stereo colour TVs, two video tape recorders, a stereo and receivers. There are radios for each cabin and ten for the process deck. On deck there are a common toilet, wardrobes for the deck crew with lockers, wash basins and wash machines/dryers, and an oil-skin room with high boots dryer and so on.

Fishing Locations

Fishing locations in the world are very different, as are the types and sizes of fishing vessels in use. The most simple dug-out canoe on an inland lake and a sophisticated and well equipped factory trawler in the high seas both have the same purpose—to catch fish. From the safety point of view, fishing sea areas in Part B of the Code are divided into three categories:

1. unlimited sea areas
2. sea areas up to 200 nautical miles from a place of shelter
3. sea areas up to 50 nautical miles from a place of shelter.

Fishing locations or fishing banks are, however, more commonly divided into *coastal* fisheries and *high-sea* fisheries.

Coastal fisheries are located in coastal waters, but the distance from the shore can vary, depending on local conditions. In fjords or other sheltered waters, small (even open or half-decked) motor-boats are used for 1 day fishing trips; for longer trips, small-decked motorboats of very different local types are used.

High-sea fisheries are fishing operations farther from the coast, and the outer limits from the shore are not fixed. Fishing vessels intended for high-sea fisheries are usually designed for unlimited sea areas, since in many coastal countries the high sea (or ocean) is located just outside the sheltered fjords or coastal skerries.

Fishing Vessels

As described above, fishing vessels used for fishing in the high seas are of very variable types and sizes—stern trawlers (fresh-fish vessels with processing lines), purse seiners, long-liners, factory ships and so on. The international definition of a *fishing vessel* is a vessel used commercially for catching fish, whales, seals, walruses or other living resources of the sea. A *processing vessel* is a vessel used exclusively for processing the catch.

The features of fishing vessels are so different from other seagoing ships that they could not be covered individually by the international conventions for safety of life at sea. An International Convention for the Safety of Fishing Vessels was drawn up at the International Conference on Safety of Fishing Vessels held in 1977 in Torremolinos, Spain. This Convention is based on the technical work at IMO over several years, mainly in the Maritime Safety Committee's Subcommittee on Safety of Fishing Vessels. This Committee had previously prepared recommendations on the intact stability of fishing vessels, published by IMO and later included in the 1977 Convention for the Safety of Fishing Vessels. That Convention stated that it shall apply only to new fishing vessels 24 m in length and over. Smaller fishing vessels are not covered by this important safety Convention because the types of smaller vessels of nations' fishing fleets are very different, and very

limited technical information is available. Therefore it was merely due to lack of basic information that safety regulations for these fishing vessels could not be worked out. Even for fishing vessels in the lower ranges above 24 m in length, there is a great difference in hull form and fishing methods. All such features have considerable influence on stability and seaworthiness generally.

The technical information on which the regulations in the Convention are based was supplied mostly by industrialized fishing countries in Europe and North America. Soon after the 1977 conference, it became evident that several countries elsewhere in the world envisaged difficulties in ratifying parts of the Convention for the smallest fishing vessels in their fleet above 24 m in length. A 1993 conference held in Torremolinos resulted in the Torremolinos Protocol of 1993, which relaxed certain items of some of the chapters in the Convention for certain fishing vessels. The chapter on machinery and electrical installations and periodically unattended machinery spaces is, following the Protocol of 1993, applicable only to new vessels 45 m in length and over. The chapter on fire protection, fire detection, fire extinction and fire-fighting was subdivided into two parts: Part A is applicable to new fishing vessels 60 m in length and above, and Part B contains less stringent requirements for vessels between 45 and 60 m. The chapter on radio communications applies to both new and existing vessels 45 m in length and over. The Protocol of 1993 to the 1977 Torremolinos Convention also updates the parent Convention and takes into account technological evolution in the years between 1977 and 1993. The Protocol was extended to include those vessels processing their catch.

The 1977 Torremolinos conference adopted a recommendation concerning the development of safety standards for decked fishing vessels less than 24 m in length, since it was noted that the vast majority of fishing vessels throughout the world are less than 24 m in length. It was recommended that the IMO continue to develop safety standards for design, construction and equipment of such fishing vessels with a view to promoting the safety of those vessels and their crews. Such guidelines have been developed by the IMO in cooperation with the FAO and the ILO.

The Safety of Fishing Vessels

Construction

The safety of ships, including fishing vessels, depends on the construction and strength of the ship itself being sufficient for its intended use. Thus strength and construction of hulls and super-structures must be sufficient to withstand all foreseeable conditions of the intended service. The watertight integrity of the vessel has to be ensured, and all openings through which water can enter have to be provided with suitable closing devices, including deck or side openings which may be open during fishing operations.

Freeing ports are very important for the safety of fishing vessels. They allow water to run off from where bulwarks on weather parts of the working deck form wells that can trap water. On small fishing vessels, the height of such bulwarks has been increased so as to better protect the crew working on open deck. The weight of water on deck can be considerable and can be a great danger to stability if the deck area is not rapidly freed of water. Therefore, a minimum freeing port area to ensure that the deck is rapidly and effectively freed of water is essential.

In more recent designs of even small and medium-sized fishing vessels, the working deck has been covered with a shelterdeck. If the tweendeck of such vessels can be kept completely closed during most fishing operations, or if a watertight opening in the tweendeck is in a small watertight compartment, it is reasonable to accept high-capacity bilge pumps, instead of freeing ports, to empty water from the working deck. This design has increased considerably the form-stability of fishing vessels, by using a much higher freeboard.

Fishing Vessels' Stability and Seaworthiness

Besides strength and watertightness, stability and general seaworthiness are the most important factors in safety of a fishing vessel.

Member countries supplied the IMO Subcommittee on Safety of Fishing Vessels with valuable material on stability calculations for existing vessels with proven records of successful operations, and actual loading conditions of fishing vessels which capsized or suffered large and dangerous heeling. Criteria of minimum stability were developed from this material.

Calculations can be made for static stability, but the movements of a ship in a seaway are governed by dynamic forces which are very difficult, if not impossible, to calculate, since the wind and sea conditions are so irregular. On the other hand, a fishing vessel which has been used without an accident for, say, 15 or 20 years for fishing operations in all normal weather and sea conditions can be considered reasonably safe. The use of so-called weather criteria, where wind and wave action and the effect of water trapped on deck are taken into account in stability considerations, are also recommended. All these calculations and other suitable stability information must be supplied to the skipper, who must assess the stability of the vessel under various operating conditions.

As mentioned before, stability is influenced by the freeboard of the vessel. The stipulation of load lines for fishing vessels was considered by the Fishing Vessel Conference in 1977, as the International Load Line Convention applies only to cargo ships. It was concluded that it was impractical to observe load line marks at fishing grounds when loading. However, the Torremolinos Convention for Safety of Fishing Vessels requires that a maximum permissible operating draught must be approved by the administration in each country and be such that the stability criteria are satisfied.

PSYCHOSOCIAL CHARACTERISTICS OF THE WORKFORCE AT SEA

Eva Munk-Madsen

Two dimensions are of special importance in the psychosocial characteristic of fishwork at sea. One dimension is the issue of scale and technology. Fisheries may be divided into: small-scale, artisanal, coastal or in-shore fisheries; and large-scale, industrial, deep sea, distant water or off-shore fishing. The psychosocial working and living conditions of crew members in small-scale fishing differ tremendously from the conditions faced by crews on large-scale vessels.

The second dimension is gender. Fishing vessels are generally all-male environments. Although exceptions occur in both small-scale and large-scale fishing, one-gender crews are most common worldwide. However, gender plays a role in the character of all crews. The sea/land split which fishers face and have to cope with is to a large extent a gendered division.

Small Fishing Vessels

On board small fishing vessels the crew members are usually related in several ways. A crew may consist of father and son, of brothers or of a mixture of close or more distant kin. Other community members may be in the crew. Depending on availability of male relatives or local customs, women are crewing. Wives may be operating a vessel together with their husbands, or a daughter may be crewing for her father.

A crew is more than a company of workmates. As kinship ties, neighbourhood ties and local community life most often bind them together, the vessel and workforce at sea is socially integrated with family and community life on shore. The ties have a two-way effect. Cooperation in fishing and belonging to a vessel confirms and tightens other social relations as well. When relatives are fishing together, a crew member cannot be replaced by a stranger, even if someone more experienced comes looking for a berth. Fishers have security in their job in such a tight network. On the other hand this also puts restrictions on switching to another vessel out of loyalty to one's family.

The many-sided social relations mitigate conflicts on board. Small-scale fishers share a narrow physical space and are subjected to unpredictable and sometimes dangerous conditions of nature. Under these demanding circumstances it may be necessary to avoid open conflicts. The authority of the skipper is also constrained by the knitted network of relations.

Generally small-scale vessels will come on shore every day, which gives crew members the opportunity to interact with others on a regular basis, although their working hours may be long. Isolation is rare but may be felt by fishers who operate a vessel alone. Nevertheless radio communication at sea and traditions of comrade vessels operating in the vicinity of each other diminish the isolative effects of working alone in modern small-scale fishing.

Learning processes and safety on board are marked by the ties of kinship and locality. The crew are responsible for and dependent on each other. To work skilfully and responsibly may be of utmost importance in unforeseen situations of bad weather or accidents. The spectrum of skills required in small-scale fishing is very wide. The smaller the crew, the lower the level of specialization—workers must have comprehensive knowledge and be able to do a variety of tasks.

Unawareness or unwillingness in work is severely sanctioned by stigmatization. Every crew member has to do necessary tasks willingly, preferably without being told. Orders are supposed to be unnecessary except for the timing of a series of tasks. Cooperation in mutual respect is thus an important skill. The display of serious interest and responsibility is helped by the socialization in a fishing family or village. The diversity of work furthers the respect for experience in any position on board, and egalitarian values are usual.

Successful coping with the demanding cooperation, timing and skills needed in small-scale fishing under changing conditions of weather and seasons creates a high level of job satisfaction and a locally rewarded and strong work identity. Women who go fishing appreciate the status rise connected to their successful participation in men's work. However, they also have to cope with the risk of losing ascriptions of femininity. Men who fish with women, on the other hand, are challenged by the risk of losing ascriptions of masculine superiority when women show their ability in fishing.

Large Fishing Vessels

In large-scale fishing, crew members are isolated from family and community while at sea, and many have only short periods on shore between trips. The duration of a fishing trip generally varies between 10 days and 3 months. Social interaction is limited to the mates on board the vessel. This isolation is demanding. Integration into family and community life when on shore may also be difficult and awaken a sense of homelessness. Fishermen highly depend on wives to keep alive their social network.

In an all-male crew the absence of women and lack of intimacy may contribute to rough sexualized conversations, sexualized bragging and a focus on porno movies. Such a ship culture may develop as an unhealthy way of exposing and confirming masculinity. Partly to prevent the development of a harsh, sexist

Fishing women

The Entangling Net: Alaska's Commercial Fishing Women Tell Their Lives, by Leslie Leyland Fields (Urbana: University of Illinois Press, 1996), is the story, based on the author's own experience and interviews, of some of the women who worked as commercial fishers in the waters of the Pacific Ocean and the Gulf of Alaska surrounding Kodiak Island and the Aleutian Islands. The following excerpts capture some of the flavour of these women's experience, why they chose this line of work and what it entailed.

Theresa Peterson

...The last black cod season started May 15. It was two gals and two guys. The skipper wanted a crew that could bait gear fast; that was what he was looking for. ... To start out, all we were trying to do is turn hooks. Its a numbers game. Ideally you run 18,000-20,000 hooks a day. And so we'd have four people baiting at all times and one person hauling gear. The people baiting would rotate coiling the gear. We went back to the traditional way of fishing. Most Kodiak boats will let the gear fall into a tub, kind of on its own, then you bring that tub back and bait it. On the old halibut schooners they hand coil everything so they're able to offspin every hook. They try to make a really nice coil so when you take it back you can bait it twice as fast. The first couple of days we looked at the time it was taking to bait the messy skates (the long lines on which the hooks are attached). I refuse to bait another skate like that, so then we all started hand coiling our own. When you do that you're able to move from your baiting station. We really worked long hours, often twenty-four hours, then we go into the next day and work through that night until 2:00 A.M. and the next day another twenty hours. Then we'd lie down for about three hours. Then we'd get back up and go another twenty-four hours and a couple of hours down. The first week we averaged ten hours of sleep all together—we figured it out. So we joked, twenty-four on, one off.

I had never fished that hard before. When it opened, we fished Saturday, all through Saturday, all through Sunday and half of Monday. So well over fifty-six hours with no sleep, working as hard, as fast as high paced as you can push yourself. Then we laid down for like three hours. You get up. You are so stiff! Then we brought in a trip, just over 40,000 pounds in four days, so we virtually had been up those entire four days. That was a good load. It was really motivational. I make a thousand dollars a day. ... It's the shorter seasons, the shorter longline seasons, are what are driving the boats back to these schedules. ... with a three-week season, you're almost forced to unless you can rotate a person down [let them sleep] (pp. 31-33).

Leslie Smith

But the reason I feel lucky is because we were out there, a woman running a boat with an all-women crew, and we were doing it. And we were doing it as well as anybody else in the fleet, so I never felt intimidated in thinking, "Oh, a woman can't do this, can't figure it out, or is not capable of it" because the first job I ever had was with women and we did fine. So I had that confidence factor from the beginning of my deckhand career... (p. 35).

When you're on a boat, you don't have a life, you don't have any physical space, you don't have any time to yourself. It's all the boat, the fishing, for four months straight...(p. 36).

...I have a little bit of protection on some of the winds but pretty much I'll get all of it. ... There's also a lot of tide here. You dump these anchors off; you've got fifteen or twenty anchors, some of them three hundred pounders, to try to hold one net in place. And every time you go out there the net's twisted in some different shape and you have to drag these anchors around. And the weather is not very

nice most of the time. You're always fighting the wind. It's a challenge, a physical challenge instead of a mental challenge... (p. 37).

Beating the docks [going from boat to boat seeking a job] was the worst thing. After I did it for a while I realized that probably there's only 15 percent of the boats that you even have a possibility of being hired on because the rest of them will not hire women. Mostly because their wives won't let them or there's another woman on the boat already or they are just flat out sexist—they don't want women. But between those three factors, the number of boats you could get hired on was so slim that it was discouraging. But you had to find out which boats those were. That means walking the docks...(p. 81).

Martha Sutro

I was thinking about the question you asked earlier. Why women are increasingly drawn to this. I don't know. You wonder if there are increasing numbers of women coal mining or trucking. I don't know if it has something to do with Alaska and the whole lure of being able to partake of something that formerly was withheld from you, or maybe its a breed of women who have been raised or somehow have been grown up to understand that certain barriers that supposedly were there are not legitimate. Even withstanding all the dangers, it's an important experience and it's very viable, very—I hate to use the word "fulfilling," but it is very fulfilling. I loved, I loved getting a string of pots over perfectly and not having to ask anyone to help me with one of the doors once and getting all the massive wads of bait that you sort of swoop under the pot in the middle. ...There are elements to it you can't find in any other type of experience. It's almost like farming. It's so elemental. It calls on such an elemental process. Since biblical times we've been talking about these kind of people. There's this ethos surrounding it that's very ancient. And to be able to go to that and draw on it. It gets into this whole mystical realm (p.44).

Lisa Jakubowski

It's very lonely being the only woman on a boat. I make a point of never getting involved with guys on a romantic level or anything. Friends. I'm always open to friends, but you always have to be careful that they don't think it's more. See, there are so many different levels of guys. I don't want to be friends with the drunkards and cocaine addicts. But definitely the more respectable people I became friends with. And I have maintained male friendships and female friendships. There's a lot of loneliness though. I found out that laugh therapy helps. I go out on the back deck and just laugh to myself and feel better (p. 61).

Leslie Leyland Fields

...Each [woman] asked only for equal treatment and equal opportunity. This doesn't come automatically in a job where you need the strength to land a swinging 130-pound crab pot, the endurance to withstand thirty-six straight hours of work without sleep, the moxie to run a 150-horsepowered seine skiff at full speed near reefs, and special hands-on skills like diesel engine repair and maintenance, net mending, operating hydraulics. These are the powers that win the day and the fish; these are the powers fishing women must prove to disbelieving men. And not least of all, there is active resistance from an unexpected quarter—other women, the wives of men who fish (p 53).

This is part of what I know of being a skipper. ... You alone hold the lives of two, three or four people in your hands. Your boat payments and insurance costs run you in the tens of thousands every year—you must catch fish. You manage a potentially volatile mix of personalities and work habits. You must have extensive knowledge of navigation, weather patterns, fishing regulations; you must be able to operate and repair to some degree the array of high-tech electronics that are the brains of the boat. ... The list goes on.

Why does anyone willingly hoist and carry such a load? There is another side, of course. To state it positively, there is independence in skippering, a degree of autonomy seldom found in other professions. You alone control the life within your ark. You can decide where you are going to fish, when the boat goes, how fast it goes, how long and hard the crew will work, how long everyone sleeps, the weather conditions you will work in, the degrees of risk you will take, the kind of food you eat... (p. 75).

In 1992, forty-four vessels in Alaska sunk, eighty-seven people were rescued from sinking vessels, thirty-five died. In Spring 1988 forty-four died after ice fog moved in and consumed boats and crew. To put those numbers in perspective, the National Institute for Occupational Safety and Health reports that the annual death rate for all U.S. Occupations is 7 per 100,000 workers. For commercial fishing in Alaska, the rate jumps to 200 per 100,000, making it the most deadly job in the country. For crab fishermen, whose season runs through the winter, the rate climbs to 660 per 100,000, or almost 100 times the national average (p. 98).

Debra Nielsen

I'm only five feet tall and I weigh one hundred pounds and so men have a protective instinct toward me. I've had to surmount that my whole life to actually get in and do anything. The only way I've been able to get past is by being quicker and knowing what I'm doing. It's about leverage. ... You have to slow down. You have to use your head in a different way and your body in a different way. I think its important that people know how small I am because if I can do it, it means any woman can do it... (p. 86).

Christine Holmes

...I really believe in the North Pacific Vessel Owner's Association, they offer some really good courses, one of which is Medical Emergencies at Sea. I think anytime you take any kind of marine tech class you're doing yourself a favor (p. 106).

Rebecque Raigoza

Developed such a sense of independence and strength. Things I thought I could never do I learned I would do out here. It's just opened a whole new world for myself as a young woman. becoming a woman, I don't know. There are so many possibilities now because I know I can do "a man's job," you know? There's a lot of power that comes with that (p. 129).

and deprived atmosphere, Norwegian companies have since the 1980s employed up to 20% women in the crew on factory ships. A gender-mixed work environment is said to reduce the psychological stress; women are reported to bring a softer tone and more intimacy into the social relations on board (Munk-Madsen 1990).

The mechanization and specialization of work on board industrialized vessels creates a repetitive working routine. Shift work in two watches is usual as fishing goes on round the clock. Life on board consists of a cycle of working, eating and sleeping. In cases of huge catches, sleeping hours may be cut down. The physical space is restricted, the work monotonous and tiring and social interaction with others than the workmates impossible. As long as the vessel is at sea there is no escape from tensions among crew members. This poses a psychological stress on the crew.

The crews of deep-sea vessels with 20 to 80 workers on board cannot be recruited in a tight network of kinship and neighbourhood ties. Yet some Japanese companies have changed recruitment policies and prefer to staff their vessels with personnel who know each other through community or kin relations and who come from communities with traditions of fishing. This is done to solve problems of violent conflicts and excess drinking (Dyer 1988). Also, in the North Atlantic, companies to some extent prefer to hire fishers from the same community to support the social control and create a friendly environment on board.

The major reward in deep sea fishing is the chance of earning good salaries. For women it is furthermore the chance of a rise in status as they cope with work that is traditionally male and culturally ranked as superior to female work (Husmo and Munk-Madsen 1994).

The international deep-sea fishing fleet exploiting global waters may operate their vessels with crews of mixed nationalities. For instance, this is the case with the Taiwanese fleet, the world's largest deep-sea fishing fleet. This may also be the case in joint venture fisheries where industrialized nations' vessels are operating in developing countries' waters. In cross-national crews, communication on board may suffer from language difficulties. Also

the maritime hierarchy on board such vessels may be further stratified by an ethnic dimension. Fish workers of different ethnicity and nationality than the mother country of the vessel, particularly if the vessel is operating in home waters, may be treated far below the level that is otherwise required by officers. This concerns wage conditions and basic provisioning on board as well. Such practices may create racist work environments, increase tensions in crew on board and skew power relations between officers and crew.

Poverty, the hope of good earnings and the globalization of deep-sea fishing has fostered illegal recruitment practices. Crews from the Philippines are reported to be indebted to recruitment agencies and working in foreign waters without contracts and without security in pay or safety measures. Working in a highly mobile deep-sea fleet far from home and without support of any authorities leads to high insecurity, which may exceed the risks faced in stormy weather on the open ocean (Cura 1995; Vacher 1994).

PSYCHOSOCIAL CHARACTERISTICS OF THE WORKFORCE IN ON-SHORE FISH PROCESSING

Marit Husmo

On-shore fish processing includes a variety of activities. The range is from small, low-technology fish processing, like drying or smoking of local catch for the local market, to the large, high-technology modern factory, producing highly specialized products that are consumer packed for an international market. In this article the discussion is limited to industrial fish processing. The level of technology is an important factor for the psychosocial environment in industrialized fish-processing plants. This influences the organization of work tasks, the wage systems, the control and monitoring mechanisms and the opportunities for the employees to have influence on their work and the corporate policy. Another important aspect when discussing psychosocial characteristics of the workforce in the on-shore fish-processing industry is the division of labour by sex, which is widespread in the industry. This means that men and women are assigned to different work tasks according to their sex and not to their skills.

In fish-processing plants, some departments are characterized by high technology and high degree of specialization, while others might use less advanced technology and be more flexible in their organization. The departments characterized by a high degree of specialization are, as a rule, those with a predominantly female workforce, while the departments where the work tasks are less specialized are those with a predominantly male workforce. This is based on an idea that certain work tasks are either fit for males only or females only. Tasks seen as fit only for males will have higher status than the tasks done by female workers only. Consequently, men will be unwilling to do "women's work", while most women are eager to do "men's work" if allowed to. Higher status will also as a rule mean higher salary and better opportunities for advancement (Husmo and Munk-Madsen 1994; Skaptadóttir 1995).

A typical high-technology department is the production department, where the workers are lined up around the conveyor belt, cutting or packing fish fillets. The psychosocial environment is characterized by monotonous and repetitive tasks and a low degree of social interaction among the workers. The wage system is based on individual performance (bonus system), and individual workers are monitored by computer systems in addition to the supervisor. This causes high stress levels, and this type of work also increases the risk of developing strain-related syndromes among the workers. The workers' restriction to the conveyor belt also reduces the possibilities for informal communication with the management in order to influence corporate policy and/or promote one's self for a raise or a promotion (Husmo and Munk-Madsen 1994). Since the workers of highly specialized departments learn only a limited number of tasks, these are the most likely to be sent home when the production is reduced due to temporary lack of raw material or due to market problems. These are also the ones that are most likely to be replaced by machines or industrial robots as new technology is introduced (Husmo and Søvik 1995).

An example of a department of lower technology levels is the raw material department, where workers drive trucks and forklifts at the pier, unload, sort and wash the fish. Here we often find high flexibility in the work tasks, and the workers do different jobs throughout the day. The wage system is based on an hourly rate, and individual performance is not measured by computers, reducing stress and contributing to a more relaxed atmosphere. Variation in work tasks stimulates teamwork and improves the psychosocial environment in many ways. The social interactions increase, and the risk of strain-related syndromes is reduced. Possibilities for promotion increase, since learning a wider range of work tasks makes the workers more qualified for higher positions. Flexibility allows informal communication with the management/supervisor in order to influence corporate policy and individual promotion (Husmo 1993; Husmo and Munk-Madsen 1994).

The general trend is that the level of processing technology increases, leading to more specialization and automation in the fish-processing industry. This has consequences for the psychosocial environment of the workers as outlined above. The division of labour by sex means that the psychosocial environment for most women is worse than it is for men. The fact that women have the work tasks that are the most likely to be replaced by robots adds an additional dimension to this discussion, as it limits the work opportunities for women in general. In some cases these implica-

tions might apply not only to female workers, but also to lower social classes in the workforce or even to different races (Husmo 1995).

SOCIAL EFFECTS OF ONE-INDUSTRY FISHERY VILLAGES

Barbara Neis

With the development of industrialized fish processing in the 19th and 20th centuries, wives and families were displaced from household-based processing and vending, and ended up unemployed or working for fish companies. The introduction of corporate-owned trawlers and, more recently, corporate-owned fish quotas (in the form of enterprise allocations and individual transferable quotas) has displaced male fishers. Changes of this kind have transformed many fishery communities into one-industry villages.

There are different kinds of one-industry fishery villages, but all are characterized by high dependence on a single employer for employment, and significant corporate influence within the community and sometimes the home lives of workers. In the most extreme case, one-industry fishery villages are actually company towns, in which a single corporation owns not only the plant and some of the vessels, but also local housing, stores, medical services and so on, and exercises significant control over local government representatives, the media and other social institutions.

Somewhat more common are villages in which local employment is dominated by a single, often vertically integrated corporate employer that uses its control over employment and markets to indirectly influence local politics and other social institutions associated with the family and community lives of workers. The definition of one-industry fishery villages can also be extended to include fish-processing firms that, despite their location within larger communities that are not fishery dependent, operate with significant autonomy from those communities. This structure is common in the shrimp-processing industry of India, which makes extensive use of young female migrant labourers, often recruited by contractors from nearby states. These workers generally live in compounds on company property. They are cut off from the local community by long working hours, a lack of kinship connections and by linguistic barriers. Such workplaces are like company towns in that companies exert significant influence over the non-working lives of their workers, and workers cannot easily turn to local authorities and other members of the community for support.

Economic uncertainty, unemployment, marginalization within decision-making processes, low income and limited access to and control over services are important determinants of health. These are all, to varying degrees, features of one-industry fishery villages. Fluctuations in fisheries markets and both natural and fishery-related fluctuations in the availability of fishery resources are a fundamental feature of fishery communities. Such fluctuations generate social and economic uncertainty. Fishery communities and households have often developed institutions that help them survive these periods of uncertainty. However, these fluctuations appear to be occurring more frequently in recent years. In the current context of global overfishing of commercial fish stocks, shifting effort to new species and regions, the globalization of markets and the development of aquacultured products which compete with wild fishery products in the marketplace, increased employment uncertainty, plant closures and low incomes are becoming common. In addition, when closures occur, they are more likely to be permanent because the resource is gone and work has moved elsewhere.

Employment uncertainty and unemployment are important sources of psychosocial stress that may affect men and women differently. The displaced worker/fisher must grapple with loss of self-esteem, loss of income, stress and, in extreme cases, loss of family wealth. Other family members must cope with the effects of workers' displacement on their home and working lives. For example, household strategies for coping with prolonged male absence can become a problem when trawler workers find themselves unemployed and their wives find the autonomy and routines that helped them survive male absence threatened by the prolonged presence of displaced husbands. In small-scale fishing households, wives may have to adjust to longer absences and social isolation as their family members go further afield to find fish and employment. Where wives were also dependent on the fishery for wage employment, they may also have to struggle with the effects of their own unemployment on their health.

The stress of unemployment can be greater in one-industry communities where plant closures threaten the future of entire communities and the economic costs of job loss are enhanced by a collapse in the value of such personal assets as homes and cottages. Where, as is often the case, finding alternative employment requires moving away, there will be additional stresses on workers, their spouses and their children associated with displacement. When plant closures are accompanied by the transfer of fish quotas to other communities and the erosion of local educational, medical and other services in response to out migration and the collapse of local economies, the threats to health will be greater.

Dependence on a single employer can make it difficult for workers to participate in decision-making processes. In fisheries, as in other industries, some corporations have used the one-industry structure to control workers, oppose unionization and manipulate public understandings of issues and developments within the workplace and beyond. In the case of the Indian shrimp processing industry, migrant female processing workers suffer from terrible living conditions, extremely long hours, compulsory overtime and routine violation of their work contracts. In western countries, corporations may use their role as gate-keepers controlling seasonal workers' eligibility for such programmes as unemployment insurance in negotiations with workers concerning unionization and working conditions. Workers in some one-industry towns are unionized, but their role in decision-making processes can still be mitigated by limited employment alternatives, by a desire to find local employment for their wives and children and by ecological and economic uncertainty. Workers can experience a sense of helplessness and may feel obliged to keep working despite illness when their ability to access work, housing and social programmes is controlled by a single employer.

Limited access to adequate medical services is also a psychosocial stressor. In company towns, medical professionals may be company employees and, as in mining and other industries, this can limit workers' access to independent medical advice. In all types of one-industry villages, cultural, class and other differences between medical personnel and fishworkers, and high rates of turnover among medical professionals, can limit the quality of local medical services. Medical personnel rarely come from fishery communities and hence are often unfamiliar with the occupational health risks fishworkers encounter and the stresses associated with life in one-industry towns. Turnover rates among such personnel may be high due to relatively low professional incomes and discomfort with rural lifestyles and unfamiliar fishery cultures. In addition, medical personnel may tend to associate more with local elites, such as the plant management, than with workers and their families. These patterns can interfere with doctor-patient relations, continuity of care and medical expertise relevant to fisheries work. Access to appropriate diagnostic services for such fishery-related illnesses as repetitive strain injuries and occupational asthma may be very limited in these communities. Loss of work can also interfere with access to medical services by eliminating access to drug programmes and other insured medical services.

Strong social supports can help mitigate the health effects of unemployment, displacement and economic uncertainty. One-industry villages can encourage the development of dense social and kinship-based ties between workers and, particularly if plants are locally owned, between workers and employers. These social supports can mitigate the effects of economic vulnerability, difficult working conditions and ecological uncertainty. Family members can watch out for each other in the workplace and sometimes help out when workers get into financial trouble. Where fishery workers are able to maintain some economic independence through subsistence activities, they can retain more control over their lives and work than where access to these is lost. Increasing employment uncertainty, plant closures and local competition for jobs and government-adjustment programmes can erode the strength of these local networks, contributing to conflict and isolation within these communities.

When plant closures mean moving away, displaced workers risk loss of access to these social networks of support and subsistence-related sources of independence.

HEALTH PROBLEMS AND DISEASE PATTERNS

Vilhjálmur Rafnsson

Work in the fishing and fish-processing industry shows a clear differentiation according to gender, with the men traditionally doing the actual fishing while the women work at fish processing on shore. Many of the persons working on fishing vessels may be looked upon as unskilled; the deckhands, for instance, receive their training in the work on board. The navigators (captain, skipper and mate), the machine room personnel (engineer, machinist and stoker), the radio operators and the cooks all have different educational backgrounds. The main assignment is to fish; other tasks include loading of the vessel, which is done on the open sea, followed by the fish processing, which takes place to various stages of completion. The only common exposure of these groups occurs during their stay on board the vessel, which is in constant motion both while they are working and resting. Fish processing on shore will be dealt with later.

Accidents

The most dangerous work tasks for the individual fishers are related to the setting out and hauling in of the fishing gear. In trawler fishing, for example, the trawl is laid out in a sequence of tasks involving the complicated coordination of different types of winches (see "Major sectors and processes" in this chapter). All operations take place at great speed, and teamwork is absolutely essential. While setting the trawl, the connecting of the trawl doors to the warp (wire ropes) is one of the most dangerous moments, as these doors weigh several hundred kilograms. Other parts of the fishing gear are also too heavy to be handled without the use of derricks and winches while shooting the trawl (i.e., heavy gear and bobbings move freely around before being hoisted overboard).

The whole procedure of setting and hauling aboard the trawl, purse seine and nets is carried out using wire cables which pass across the working area often. The cables are at high tension, as there is often an extremely heavy pull from the fishing gear in a direction opposite of the forward motion of the fishing vessel itself.

There is a great risk of getting entangled by or falling onto the fishing gear and thus being drawn overboard, or of falling overboard when laying out the fishing gear. There is a risk of crushing and trapping injuries to fingers, hands and arms, and the heavy gear may fall or roll and thus injure legs and feet.

Bleeding and gutting the fish are often done manually and take place on the deck or on a shelterdeck. The pitching and rolling of the vessels make injuries to the hands and fingers common from knife cuts or from pricks of fish bones and spines. Infections in wounds are frequent. Long-line and hand-line fishing involve the risk of wounds to fingers and hands from the hooks. As this type of fishing is becoming more and more automated it is becoming associated with dangers from line haulers and winches.

The method of managing fishing by limiting the amount caught from a restricted natural resource area also influences the injury rate. In some places pursuit quotas allocate to the vessels certain days when they are allowed to fish, and the fishers feel they have to go fishing at these times whatever the weather.

Fatal accidents

Fatal accidents at sea are easily studied through mortality registers, as accidents at sea are coded on the death certificates as water transport accidents according to the International Classification of Diseases, with an indication as to whether the injury was sustained while employed on board. Death rates from work-related fatal accidents among workers in the fishing industry are high, and higher than for many other occupational groups on shore. Table 66.1 shows the mortality rate per 100,000 for fatal accidents in different countries. The fatal injuries are traditionally classified as (1) individual accidents (i.e., individuals falling overboard, being swept overboard by heavy seas or being fatally injured by machinery) or (2) individuals lost as a result of vessel casualties (e.g., because of foundering, capsizing, missing vessels, explosions and fires). Both categories are related to the weather conditions. Accidents to individual crew members outnumber the others. The safety of a vessel depends on its design, size and type, and on factors such as stability, freeboard, weather-tight integrity and structural protection against fire. Negligent navigation or errors of judgement may result in casualties to vessels, and the fatigue which follows long spells of duty may also play a role, as well as being an important cause of personal accidents.

Better safety records of more modern vessels may be due to the combined effects of improved human and technical efficiency. Training of personnel, proper use of flotation support apparatus, suitable clothing and the use of buoyant overalls may all increase the probability of rescue of persons in the event of an accident.

Table 66.1 • Mortality figures on fatal injuries among fishermen as reported in studies from various countries.

Country	Study period	Rates per 100,000
United Kingdom	1958–67	140–230
United Kingdom	1969	180
United Kingdom	1971–80	93
Canada	1975–83	45.8
New Zealand	1975–84	260
Australia	1982–84	143
Alaska	1980–88	414.6
Alaska	1991–92	200
California	1983	84.4
Denmark	1982–85	156
Iceland	1966–86	89.4

More widespread use of other safety measures, including safety lines, helmets and safety shoes, may be needed in the fishing industry in general, as discussed elsewhere in this *Encyclopaedia*.

Non-fatal injuries

Non-fatal injuries are also quite common in the fishing industry (see table 66.2). The body regions of injured workers most frequently mentioned are the hands, lower limbs, head and neck and upper limbs, followed by the chest, spine and abdomen, in decreasing order of frequency. The most common types of traumas are open wounds, fractures, strains, sprains and contusions. Many non-fatal injuries may be serious, involving, for instance, amputation of fingers, hands, arms and legs as well as injuries to the head and neck. Infections, lacerations and minor traumas of the hands and fingers are quite frequent, and treatment with antibiotics is often recommended by the ship's doctors in all cases.

Morbidity

Information on the general health of fishers and overviews of their illnesses are mainly obtained from two types of reports. One source is the case series compiled by ships' doctors, and the other

Table 66.2 • The most important jobs or places related to risk of injuries.

Job or tasks	On board vessels injury	On shore injury
Setting and hauling trawl, purse seine and other fishing gear	Entangled in the fishing gear or wire cables, crushing injuries, fall overboard	
Connecting trawl doors	Crushing injuries, fall overboard	
Bleeding and gutting	Cuts from knives or machines, musculoskeletal disorders	Cuts from knives or machines, musculoskeletal disorders
Long-line and hand-line	Wounds from hooks, entangled in the line	
Heavy lifts	Musculoskeletal disorders	Musculoskeletal disorders
Filleting	Cuts, amputations using knives or machines, musculoskeletal disorders	Cuts, amputations using knives or machines, musculoskeletal disorders
Trimming fillets	Cuts from knives, musculoskeletal disorders	Cuts from knives, musculoskeletal disorders
Work in confined spaces, loading and landing	Intoxication, asphyxia	Intoxication, asphyxia

66. FISHING

is the medical advice reports, which report on evacuations, hospitalizations and repatriations. Unfortunately, most if not all of these reports give only the numbers of patients and percentages.

The most frequently reported non-traumatic conditions leading to consultations and hospitalization arise as a result of dental conditions, gastro-intestinal illness, musculoskeletal conditions, psychiatric/neurological conditions, respiratory conditions, cardiological conditions and dermatological complaints. In one series reported by a ship's doctor, psychiatric conditions were the most common reason for evacuating workers from trawlers on long-term fishing voyages, with injuries only coming in second place as a reason for rescuing fishers. In another series the most common illnesses which necessitated repatriation were cardiological and psychiatric conditions.

Occupational asthma

Occupational asthma is frequently found among workers in the fish industry. It is associated with several types of fish, but most commonly it is related to exposure to crustaceans and molluscs—for example, shrimp, crabs, shellfish and so on. The processing of fishmeal is also often related to asthma, as are similar processes, such as grinding shells (shrimp shells in particular).

Hearing loss

Excessive noise as a cause of decreased hearing acuity is well recognized among workers in the fish-processing industry. The machine room personnel on the vessels are at extreme risk, but so are those working with the older equipment in fish processing. Organized hearing conservation programmes are widely needed.

Suicide

In some studies on fishers and sailors from the merchant fleet, high death rates because of suicide have been reported. There is also an excess of deaths in the category where the doctors were not able to decide whether the injury was accidental or self-inflicted. There is a widespread belief that suicides in general are underreported, and this is rumoured to be even greater in the fishing industry. Psychiatric literature gives descriptions of calenture, a behavioural phenomenon where the predominant symptom is an irresistible impulse for sailors to jump into the sea from their vessels. The underlying causes for the risk for suicide have not been studied among fishermen particularly; however, consideration of the psychosocial situation of the workforce at sea, as discussed in another article in this chapter, seems a not unlikely place to start. There are indications that the suicide risk increases when the workers stop fishing and go ashore both for a short while or definitely.

Fatal poisoning and asphyxia

Fatal poisoning occurs in incidents of fire on board fishing vessels, and is related to inhalation of toxic smoke. There are also reports of fatal and non-fatal intoxication resulting from the leak of refrigerants or the use of chemicals for preserving shrimp or fish, and from toxic gases from the anaerobic decay of organic material in unventilated holds. The refrigerants concerned range from the highly toxic methyl chloride to ammonia. Some deaths have been attributed to exposure to sulphur dioxide in confined spaces, which is reminiscent of the incidents of silo-filler's disease, where there is exposure to nitrogen oxides. Research has similarly shown that there are mixtures of toxic gases (i.e., carbon dioxide, ammonia, hydrogen sulphide and carbon monoxide), along with low partial pressure of oxygen in holds on board ship and on shore, which have resulted in casualties, both fatal and non-fatal, often related to industrial fish such as herring and capelin. In commercial fishing, there are some reports of intoxication when landing fish that have been related to trimethylamine and endotoxins

causing symptoms resembling influenza, which may, however, lead to death. Attempts could be made to reduce these risks through improved education and alterations to equipment.

Skin diseases

Skin diseases affecting hands are common. These may be related to contact with fish proteins or to the use of rubber gloves. If gloves are not used, the hands are constantly wet and some workers may become sensitized. Thus most of the skin diseases are contact eczema, either allergic or non-allergic, and the conditions are often constantly present. Boils and abscesses are recurrent problems also affecting hands and fingers.

Mortality

Some studies, although not all, show low mortality from all causes among fishermen as compared to the general male population. This phenomenon of low mortality in a group of workers is called the "healthy worker effect", referring to the consistent tendency for actively employed people to have more favourable mortality experience than the population at large. However, due to high mortality from accidents at sea, the results from many mortality studies on fishermen show high death rates for all causes.

The mortality from ischemic heart diseases is either elevated or decreased in studies on fishermen. Mortality from cerebrovascular diseases and respiratory diseases is average among fishermen.

Unknown causes

Mortality from unknown causes is higher among fishermen than other men in several studies. Unknown causes are special numbers in the International Classification of Diseases used when the doctor who issues the death certificate is not able to state any specific disease or injury as the cause of death. Sometimes deaths registered under the category of unknown causes are due to accidents in which the body was never found, and are most likely water transport accidents or suicides when the death occurs at sea. In any case an excess of deaths from unknown causes can be an indication, not only of a dangerous job, but also of a dangerous lifestyle.

Accidents occurring other than at sea

An excess of fatal traffic accidents, various poisonings and other accidents, suicide and homicide have been found among fishermen (Rafnsson and Gunnarsdóttir 1993). In this connection the hypothesis has been suggested that seamen are influenced by their dangerous occupation towards hazardous behaviour or a hazardous lifestyle. The fishermen themselves have suggested that they become unaccustomed to traffic, which could provide an explanation for the traffic accidents. Other suggestions have focused on the attempts of fishermen, returning from long voyages during which they have been away from family and friends, to catch up on their social life. Sometimes fishermen spend only a short time ashore (a day or two) between long voyages. The excess of deaths from accidents other than those at sea points to an unusual lifestyle.

Cancer

The International Agency for Research on Cancer (IARC), which among other things has a role in evaluating industries in respect to the potential cancer risks for their workers, has not included fishing or the fish-processing industry among those industrial branches showing clear signs of cancer risk. Several mortality and cancer morbidity studies discuss the cancer risk among fishermen (Hagmar et al. 1992; Rafnsson and Gunnarsdóttir 1994, 1995). Some of them have found an increased risk for different cancers among fishermen, and suggestions are often given as to possible causes for the cancer risks which involve both occupational and lifestyle factors. The cancers which will be discussed here are cancer of the lip, lung and stomach.

Cancer of the lip

Fishing has traditionally been related to lip cancer. Previously this was thought to be related to exposure to tars used to preserve the nets, since the workers had used their mouths as "third hands" when handling the nets. Currently the aetiology of lip cancer among fishermen is considered to be the joint effect of exposure to ultraviolet radiation during outdoor work and smoking.

Cancer of the lung

The studies on lung cancer are not in accord. Some studies have not found increased risk of lung cancer among fishermen. Studies of fishermen from Sweden showed less lung cancer than the reference population (Hagmar et al. 1992). In an Italian study the lung cancer risk was thought to be related to smoking and not to the occupation. Other studies on fishermen have found increased risk of lung cancer, and still others have not confirmed this. Without information on smoking habits it has been difficult to evaluate the role of smoking versus the occupational factors in the possible cases. There are indications of the need to study separately the different occupational groups on the fishing vessels, as engine room personnel have elevated risk for lung cancer, thought to be due to exposure to asbestos or polycyclic aromatic hydrocarbons. Further studies are thus needed to clarify the relation of lung cancer and fishing.

Cancer of the stomach

Many studies have found elevated risk of stomach cancer in fishermen. In the Swedish studies the risk of stomach cancer was thought to be related to high consumption of fatty fish contaminated with organochlorine compounds (Svenson et al. 1995). At present it is uncertain what role dietary, lifestyle and occupational factors play in the association of stomach cancer with fishing.

• MUSCULOSKELETAL DISORDERS AMONG FISHERMEN AND WORKERS IN THE FISH PROCESSING INDUSTRY

Hulda Ólafsdóttir

The term *musculoskeletal disorders* is used collectively for symptoms and diseases of the muscles, tendons and/or joints. Such disorders are often unspecified and can vary in duration. The main risk factors for work-related musculoskeletal disorders are heavy lifting, awkward work postures, repetitive work tasks, psychological stress and improper job organization (see figure 66.9).

In 1985, the World Health Organization (WHO) issued the following statement: "Work-related diseases are defined as multifactorial, where the work environment and the performance of work contribute significantly; but as one of a number of factors to the causation of disease" (WHO 1985). There are, however, no internationally accepted criteria for the causes of work-related musculoskeletal disorders. Work-related musculoskeletal disorders appear in both developing and developed countries. They have not disappeared despite the development of new technologies permitting machines and computers to take over what was previously manual work (Kolare 1993).

Work aboard vessels is physically and mentally demanding. Most of the well-known risk factors for musculoskeletal disorders mentioned above are often present in the fishermen's work situation and organization.

Figure 66.9 • Manual handling of fish in a fish-packing plant in Thailand.

Traditionally most fishery workers have been males. Swedish studies on fishermen have shown that symptoms from the musculoskeletal system are common, and that they follow a logical pattern according to the fishing and type of working tasks on board. Seventy-four per cent of the fishermen had experienced symptoms of the musculoskeletal system during the previous 12 months. The largest number of fishermen considered the motion of the vessel to be a major strain, not only on the musculoskeletal system, but on the individual as a whole (Törner et al. 1988).

There are not many published studies on musculoskeletal disorders among workers in fish processing. There is a long tradition of female domination in the job of cutting and trimming the fillets in the fish-processing industry. Results from Icelandic, Swedish and Taiwanese studies show that female workers in the fish-processing industry had a higher prevalence of symptoms of musculoskeletal disorders of the neck or shoulders than women who had more varied jobs (Ólafsdóttir and Rafnsson 1997; Ohlsson et al. 1994; Chiang et al. 1993). These symptoms were thought to be causally related to the highly repetitive tasks with a short cycle time of less than 30 seconds. Work with highly repetitive tasks without the possibility of rotation between different jobs is a high risk factor. Chiang and co-workers (1993) studied workers in the fish-processing industry (men and women) and found a higher prevalence of symptoms of the upper limbs among those with jobs involving high repetitiveness or forceful movements, as compared to those in the same factories who had jobs with low repetitiveness and low-force movements.

As mentioned above, musculoskeletal disorders have not disappeared despite the development of new technologies. The flow line is an example of one new technique which has been introduced in the fish-processing industry ashore and on board larger processing vessels. The flow line consists of a system of conveyor belts which transport the fish through decapitating and filleting machines to the workers who seize each fillet and cut and trim it with a knife. Other conveyor belts transport the fish to the packing station, after which the fish is quick-frozen. The flow line has changed the prevalence of musculoskeletal symptoms among women working in fish-filleting plants. After the introduction of the flow line, the prevalence of symptoms of the upper limbs increased while the prevalence of symptoms of the lower limbs decreased (Ólafsdóttir and Rafnsson 1997).

In order to develop a strategy for their prevention it is important to understand the causes, mechanisms, prognosis and prevention of musculoskeletal disorders (Kolare et al. 1993). The disorders cannot be prevented by new technologies exclusively. The whole working environment, including the work organization, has to be taken into consideration.

COMMERCIAL FISHERIES: ENVIRONMENTAL AND PUBLIC HEALTH ISSUES

Bruce McKay and Kieran Mulvaney

Fisheries Bycatch and Discards

The capture of non-target species—termed *bycatch* (or in some cases *by-kill*)—ranks as one of the major environmental impacts of the global marine fisheries industry. Bycatch, the vast majority of which is "discarded" overboard, includes:

- marketable species that are too small or that are prohibited from landings
- species that are not marketable
- commercial species that are not the target of a species-specific fishery
- species that are not fishery related, such as sea birds, sea turtles and marine mammals.

In a major study done for the FAO (Alverson et al. 1994) it was provisionally and conservatively estimated that 27.0 million tonnes of fish and invertebrate life (thus not including marine mammals, seabirds or turtles) are caught and then discarded—much of it dead or dying—by commercial fishery operations each year. This is equivalent to more than one-third the weight of all reported marine landings in commercial fisheries worldwide, estimated at some 77 million tonnes.

In addition to the ethical issues associated with wastage, there is great public concern about the environmental impacts of discard mortalities, such as potential biodiversity loss and reduced fish stocks. Perhaps as many as 200,000 marine mammals are killed annually in fishing gear (Alverson et al. 1994). Gill net fishing is likely the most serious threat to many porpoise populations; at least one species (the yaquita in the Gulf of California) and several populations of harbour porpoise are nearing extinction due to this fishery type. The inadvertent capture and mortality of sea turtles, notably those associated with shrimp trawls and some long-line fisheries, is an important factor in the continued endangerment of various populations throughout the world's oceans (Dayton et al. 1995). High numbers of seabirds are also killed in some fisheries; long-line operations kill many tens of thousands of albatross annually and are considered the major threat to the survival of many albatross species and populations (Gales 1993).

The issue of bycatch has been a major factor in the now negative public perception of the commercial marine fisheries. As a consequence, there has been much research in recent years to improve the selectivity of fishing gear and fishing methods. Indeed, the FAO (1995) estimates that a 60% reduction in discards could be achieved by the year 2000 if a major concerted effort is undertaken by governments and industry.

Fish/Seafood Waste and Bycatch Disposal

Fish and seafood wastes can include the internal organs (viscera), heads, tails, blood, scales and wastewater or sludge (e.g., cooker juices, chemical coagulants used in primary treatment systems, oil, grease, suspended solids and so on). In many regions, most seafood-processing material from land-based industry is converted to fishmeal or fertilizer, with any remaining waste either dumped at sea, discharged into coastal waters, applied directly on land or landfilled. Waste from ship-based processing (i.e., fish cleaning) is comprised of fish parts (offal) and is invariably dumped at sea.

The impact of processed fish material on aquatic systems can vary widely according to the type of waste, the rate and amount of discharge, the ecological sensitivity of the receiving environment and physical factors influencing waste mixing and dispersion. The greatest concern involves the discharge of waste by processing companies into coastal environments; here the influx of excessive nutrients can lead to eutrophication and, subsequently, loss of local aquatic plant and animal populations.

The discharge of offal and bycatch from fishing boats can result in oxygen depletion of benthic (i.e., bottom) habitats if sufficient quantities accumulate on the seabed. However, discards and offal are considered factors contributing to the rapid growth of some seabird populations, though this may be to the detriment of less competitive species (Alverson et al. 1994).

Commercial Whaling

Commercial whaling continues to provoke intense public and political focus due (1) to the perceived uniqueness of whales, (2) to concerns about the humaneness of hunting techniques and (3) to the fact that most populations of whales—such as of blues, fins and rights—have been dramatically reduced. The current focus of hunts is the minke whale, which had been spared by the historical whaling fleets because of its small size (7 to 10 m) relative to the much larger "great" whales.

In 1982, the International Whaling Commission (IWC) voted for a global moratorium on commercial whaling. This moratorium came into effect with the 1985/86 whaling season and is scheduled to last for an indefinite period. However, two countries—Norway and Russia—maintain official objections to the moratorium, and Norway uses that objection to continue commercial whaling in the Northeast Atlantic. Although Japan does not maintain an objection to the moratorium, it continues whaling in the North Pacific and the Southern Oceans, taking advantage of an article in the International Convention for the Regulation of Whaling which allows member States to kill whales for purposes of scientific research. Less than 1,000 whales are killed annually by the Japanese and Norwegian fleets; virtually all of the whale meat ends up in the Japanese market for human consumption (Stroud 1996).

Seafood Safety: Pathogens, Chemical Pollutants and Natural Toxins

Human illness can occur from ingestion of contaminated seafood through three main routes:

1. *Raw, undercooked or poorly processed fish and shellfish that are contaminated by pathogens that can cause such diseases as hepatitis A, cholera or typhoid.* Untreated or inadequately treated domestic sewage is the primary source of microbial pathogens, such as viruses and bacteria, in seafood; some disease-causing organisms can persist for months in or on fish or within the digestive tracts or gills of fish and shellfish. The health risks posed by these pathogens can be virtually eliminated with proper sewage treatment and disposal, monitoring programmes, proper food processing and preparation techniques and, most importantly, through thorough cooking of seafood products (Food and Nutrition Board 1991).

2. *Consumption of seafood that has been contaminated by industrial chemicals such as mercury, lead and pesticides.* The global nature and pervasiveness of environmental pollution means that a wide variety of industrial chemicals—such as pesticides and

heavy metals (e.g., lead and mercury)—are typically found in seafood. However, the extent of contamination varies widely from region to region and between species. Of particular concern are those chemicals that can bioaccumulate in humans, such as PCBs, dioxins and mercury. In these cases, contaminant burdens (from a wide variety of sources, including seafood) increase over time to levels where toxic effects may be exerted. Though much remains to be understood concerning the effects on human health of chronic contaminant exposure, an impressive body of information suggests a clear potential for increased cancer risks, immunosuppression, reproductive impacts and subtle impairment of neurological development in foetuses and children. In a major report on seafood safety, the Institute of Medicine of the US Academy of Sciences (Food and Nutrition Board 1991) recommended—as have numerous environmental and human health organizations—that an active environmental stance aimed at pollution prevention would ultimately be the best means to avoid continuing human health problems and pollution disasters as a result of industrial chemicals.

3. *Consumption of seafood contaminated by natural algae-related toxins, such as domoic acid, ciguatoxin and saxitoxin.* A wide range of toxins are produced by various algae species, and these can accumulate in a range of seafood products, notably shellfish (the exception being ciguatoxin, which is found only in reef fish). Resulting illnesses include "shellfish poisoning"—either paralytic (PSP), amnesic (ASP), diarrhetic (DSP) or neurotoxic (NSP)—and ciguatera. Mortalities continue to result from PSP and ciguatera; no fatalities have been reported from ASP since its discovery in 1987, when three people died. There has been what appears to be an increase in toxic algal blooms since the 1970s, as well as changes in the distribution and intensity of fish and shellfish toxicity. Though algal blooms are natural events, it is strongly suspected that coastal nutrient pollution—mainly from fertilizers and sewage—is enhancing bloom formation or duration and thereby increasing the likelihood of seafood toxicity episodes (Anderson 1994). It is important to note that, unlike for pathogens, thorough cooking does *not* reduce the toxicity of seafood contaminated by these natural poisons.

References

Alverson, DL, MH Freeberg, SA Murawski, and JG Pope. 1994. *A Global Assessment of Fisheries Bycatch and Discards.* Rome: FAO.

Anderson, DM. 1994. Red tides. *Sci Am* 271:62–68.

Chiang, H-C, Y-C Ko, S-S Chen, H-S Yu, T-N Wu, and P-Y Chang. 1993. Prevalence of shoulder and upper-limb disorders among workers in the fish-processing industry. *Scand J Work Environment and Health* 19:126–131.

Cura, NM. 1995. Treading on dangerous waters. *Samudra* 13:19–23.

Dayton, PK, SF Thrush, MT Agardy, and RF Hofman. 1995. Environmental effects of marine fishing. *Aquatic Conservation: Marine and Freshwater Ecosystems* 5:205–232.

Dyer, CL. 1988. Social organization as a function of work. Organization aboard a Japanese surimi trawler. *Journal of the Society for Applied Anthropology* 47:76–81.

Food and Agricultural Organization (FAO) of the United Nations. 1992. *Review of the State of World Fishery Resources. Part 1: Marine resources.* Rome: FAO.

—. 1993. *Marine Fisheries and the Law of the Sea: A Decade of Change.* Rome: FAO.

—. 1995. *The State of the World Fisheries and Aquaculture.* Rome: FAO.

Food and Nutrition Board. 1991. *Seafood Safety.* Washington, DC: National Academy Press.

Gales, R. 1993. *Co-operative Mechanisms for the Conservation of Albatross.* Australia: Australian Nature Conservation Agency.

Hagmar, L, K Lindén, A Nilsson, B Norrving, B Åkesson, A Schütz, and T Möller. 1992. Cancer incidence and mortality among Swedish Baltic Sea fishermen. *Scand J Work Environ Health* 18:217–224.

Husmo, M. 1993. *Drømmen om å bli fiskekjøper. Om rekruttering til ledelse og kvinners lederstil i norsk fiskeindustri,* Rap. No. 8. Tromsø, Norway: Fiskeriforskning/Norges fiskerihøgskole, Universitetet i Tromsø.

—. 1995. *Institusjonell endring eller ferniss? Kvalitetsstyringsprosessen i noen norske fiskeindustribedrifter,* Rap. No. 1. Tromsø, Norway: Norges fiskerihøgskole/Seksjon for fiskeriorganisasjon.

Husmo, M and E Munk-Madsen. 1994. Kjønn som kvalifikasjon i fiskeindustrien. In *Leve Kysten?* Strandhogg i fiskeri-Norge, edited by O Otterstad and S Jentoft. Norway: Ad Notam Glydenal.

Husmo, M and G Søvik. 1995. *Ledelsesstrukturen i norsk fiskeforedlingsindustri.* Rap. No. 2. Tromsø, Norway: Norges fiskerihøgskole/Seksjon for fiskeriorganisasjon.

Kolare, S. 1993. Strategies for prevention of work-related musculoskeletal disorders (consensus paper). *Int J of Ind Ergonomics* 11:77–81.

Moore, SRW. 1969. The mortality and morbidity of deep sea fishermen sailing from Grimsby in one year. *Br J Ind Med* 26:25–46.

Munk-Madsen, E. 1990. *Skibet er ladet med køn. En analyse af kønrelationer og kvinders vilkår i fabriksskibsflåden.* Tromsø, Norway: Norwegian College of Fisheries Science, University of Tromsø.

Ohlsson, K, GÅ Hansson, I Balogh, U Strömberg, B Pålsson, C Nordander, L Rylander, and S Skerfving. 1994. Disorders of the neck and upper limbs in women in the fish processing industry. *Occup and Envir Med* 51:826–32.

Ólafsdóttir, H and V Rafnsson. 1997. Increase in musculoskeletal symptoms of upper limbs among women after introduction of the flow-line in fish-fillet plants. *Int J Ind Erg,* in press.

Rafnsson, V and H Gunnarsdóttir. 1992. Fatal accidents among Icelandic seamen: 1966–1986. *Br J Ind Med* 49:694–699.

—. 1993. Risk of fatal accidents occurring other than at sea among Icelandic seamen. *Br Med J* 306:1379-1381.

—. 1994. Mortality among Icelandic seamen. *Int J Epidemiol* 23:730–736.

—. 1995. Cancer incidence among seamen in Iceland. *Am J Ind Med* 27:187–193.

Reilley, MSJ. 1985. Mortality from occupational accidents to United Kingdom fishermen 1961–1980. *Br J Ind Med* 42:806–814.

Skaptadóttir, UD. 1995. *Fishermen's Wives and Fish Processors: Continuity and Change in Women's Position in Icelandic Fishing Villages, 1870–1990.* Ph.D. thesis. New York: University of New York.

Stroud, C. 1996. The ethics and politics of whaling. In *The Conservation of Whales and Dolphins: Science and Practice,* edited by MP Simmons, and JD Hutchinson. Chichester, UK: John Wiley & Sons.

Svenson, B-G, Z Mikoczy, U Strömberg, and L Hagmar. 1995. Mortality and cancer incidence among Swedish fishermen with a high dietary intake of persistent organochlorine compounds. *Scand J Work Environ Health* 21:106–115.

Törner, M, G Blide, H Eriksson, R Kadefors, R Karlsson, and I Petersen. 1988. Musculo-skeletal symptoms as related to working conditions among Swedish professional fishermen. *Applied Ergonomics* 19: 191–201.

Vacher, J. 1994. Be strong by being together. *Samudra* 10 and 11 (special supplement).

World Health Organization (WHO). 1985. *Identification and Control of Work-related Diseases.* Technical Report Series No. 714. Geneva: WHO.

Other relevant readings

Andersen, R and C Wadel (eds.). 1972. *North Atlantic Fishermen: Anthropological Essays on Modern Fishing.* Social and Economic Papers No. 5. St. John's, Newfoundland: Institute of Social and Economic Research, St. John's Memorial University of Newfoundland.

Bárdarson, HR. 1969. Icing of ships. Presented at the Second International Conference on Port and Ocean Engineering under Arctic Conditions, University of Iceland, Department of Engineering and Science, Reykjavik.

Barth, F. 1966. *The Analytical Importance of Transactions. Models of Social Organization.* Royal Anthropological Institute Occasional Paper No. 23. London: RAI.

Bennett, PB and DH Elliott (eds.). 1993. *The Physiology and Medicine of Diving.* London: W.B. Saunders.

Bookspan, J 1995. *Diving Physiology in Plain English.* Kensington: Underseas and Hyperbaric Medical Society, Inc.

Cross, T. 1985. The health of British trawlermen on the arctic fishing grounds. *J Soc Occup Med* 35:55–61.

Dalgaard, JB, F Dencker, B Fallentin, B Hansen, B Kaempe, J Steensberg, and P Wilhardt. 1972. Fatal poisoning and other health hazards connected with industrial fishing. *Br J Ind Med* 29:307–316.

Fields, LL. 1996. *The Entangling Net: Alaska's Commercial Fishing Women Tell Their Lives.* Urbana: University of Illinois Press.

Flemming, NC and MD Max. 1990. *Scientific Diving: A General Code of Practice.* Paris: UNESCO.

Food and Agriculture Organization (FAO) of the United Nations, International Labour Organization (ILO) and International Maritime Organization (IMO). 1980. *Voluntary Guidelines for the Design, Construction and Equipment of Fishing Vessels* (Rome: FAO; Geneva: ILO; London: IMO).

Gerrard, S. 1986. *Kvinners makt og avmakt. Et kjønnsrolleper-spektiv på forvaltning av faglige interesser i fiskeindustrien*, Rap. No.6. Tromsø, Norway: Finmark Distriktshøgskole.

Hagland, K. 1995. *Kvinner i norsk fiskeindustri: deres arbeidsrettslige stilling ved permitteringer*. Tromsø, Norway: Institutt for Rettsvitenskap, Universitetet i Tromsø.

Hale, AR and AI Glendon. 1987. *Individual Behaviour in the Control of Danger*. Amsterdam: Elsevier.

Hornsby, A (ed.). 1993. *Encyclopaedia of Recreational Diving*. Santa Ana, CA: Professional Association of Diving Instructors.

Høst, L and C Wadel (eds.). 1980. *Fiske og Lokalsamfunn*. Oslo, Norway: Universitetsforlaget.

International Maritime Organization (IMO). 1975. *Code of Safety for Fishermen and Fishing Vessels*. Part A. Safety and health practice for skippers and crew. Published on behalf of the FAO, the ILO and the IMO. London: IMO.

—. 1987. *Document for Guidance, 1985: An International Maritime Training Guide*. Published on behalf of the ILO and the IMO. London: IMO.

Kaplan, IM. 1988. Women who go to sea. Working in the commercial fishing industry. *Journal of Contemporary Ethnography* 16: 491–514.

Larsen, M and E Munk-Madsen. 1989. *Kjønnsmyter med konsekvenser. En analyse av skillet mellom kvinner og menn i industriell fiskebearbeiding til lands og til vanns*. Tromsø, Norway: Norges fiskerihøgskole, Universitet i Tromsø.

Melamed, Y, A Shupak, and H Bitterman. 1992. Medical problems associated with underwater diving. *N Engl J Med* 236(1).

Nadel-Klein, J and DL Davis (eds). 1988. *To Work and to Weep: Women in Fishing Economies*. Social and Economic Papers No. 18. St. John's, New Foundland: Institute of Social and Economic Research, St. Johns Memorial University of New Foundland.

Rafnsdottir, GL. 1995. *Kvinnofack eller integrering som strategi mot underordning. Diskussion kring kvinnliga fackföreningar på Island*. Lund, Sweden: Lund University Press.

Schilling, RSF. 1971. Hazards of deep-sea fishing. *Br J Ind Med* 28:27–35.

Wold, TM. 1995. *Kvinner i nord-norsk fiskeindustri - likelønn*. Tromsø, Norway: Institutt for Rettsvitenskap, Universitetet i Tromsø.

Zulaika, J. 1981. *Terranova—The ethos and luck of deep sea fishermen*. St. John's, New Foundland: St. John's Memorial University of New Foundland.

FOOD INDUSTRY

67

Chapter Editor
Deborah E. Berkowitz

Contents

FOOD INDUSTRY PROCESSES

*M. Malagié, G. Jensen, J.C. Graham
and Donald L. Smith**

The term *food industries* covers a series of industrial activities directed at the processing, conversion, preparation, preservation and packaging of foodstuffs (see table 67.1). The raw materials used are generally of vegetable or animal origin and produced by agriculture, farming, breeding and fishing. This article provides an overview of the complex of food industries. Other articles in this chapter and *Encyclopaedia* deal with particular food industry sectors and particular hazards.

The food industry today has become highly diversified, with manufacturing ranging from small, traditional, family-run activities that are highly labour intensive, to large, capital-intensive and highly mechanized industrial processes. Many food industries depend almost entirely on local agriculture or fishing. In the past, this meant seasonal production and hiring of seasonal workers. Improvements in food processing and preservation technologies have taken some of the pressure off workers to process food quickly to prevent spoilage. This has resulted in a decrease in seasonal employment fluctuations. However, certain industries still have seasonal activities, such as fresh fruit and vegetable processing and increases in production of baked goods, chocolate and so forth for holiday seasons. Seasonal workers are often women and foreign workers.

The world's food product output has been increasing. World exports of food products in 1989 totalled US$290 billion, a 30% increase over 1981. Industrialized market economy countries had a 67% share of this export. Much of this increase can be attributed to an increased demand for processed food and drink, especially in developing countries where the market has not yet been saturated.

This increase in output of food and drink products, however, has not resulted in increased employment because of intensified competition, which has resulted in decreased employment in many food industries, especially in industrialized countries. This is due to increased productivity and mechanization in many of these industries.

Demographic pressure, uneven distribution of agricultural resources and the need to insure preservation of food products to facilitate their better distribution explain the rapid technical evolution in the food industries. Constant economic and marketing pressures drive the industry to provide new and different products for market, while other operations may make the same product in the same way for decades. Even highly industrialized facilities often resort to seemingly archaic techniques when starting new products or processes. In practice, to satisfy population requirements, there is a need not only for a sufficient quantity of foodstuffs, which presupposes an increase of production, but also strict control of sanitation to obtain the quality essential to maintain the health of the community. Only modernization of techniques justified by production volumes in a stable production environment will eliminate manual handling hazards. In spite of the extreme diversity of the food industries, the preparation processes can be divided into handling and storage of raw materials, extraction, processing, preservation and packaging.

** This article is adapted from the 3rd edition *Encyclopaedia of Occupational Health* articles "Food industries", by M Malagié; "Frozen food industry", by G. Jenson; and "Canning and food preserving", by J.C. Graham, which were revised by Donald L. Smith.*

Handling and Storage

Manipulation of the raw materials, the ingredients during processing and the finished products is varied and diverse. The current trend is to minimize manual handling by mechanization, through "continuous processing" and automation. Mechanical handling may involve: self-propelled in-plant transport with or without palletization or super or bulk sacks (often containing several thousand pounds of dry powder material); conveyor belts (e.g., with beets, grain and fruit); bucket elevators (e.g., with grain and fish); spiral conveyors (e.g., with confectionery and flour); air fluming (e.g., for unloading grain, sugar or nuts and for transport of flours).

Storage of raw materials is most important in a seasonal industry (e.g., sugar refining, brewing, grain processing and canning). It is usually done in silos, tanks, cellars, bins or cold stores. Storage of the finished products varies according to their nature (liquid or solid), the method of preserving and the method of packaging (loose, in sack or super sack, in bundles, boxes or bottles); and the respective premises must be planned to suit the conditions of handling and preserving (traffic aisles, ease of access, temperature and humidity suited to product, cold-storage installations). Commodities may be held in oxygen-deficient atmospheres or under fumigation while in storage or just before shipment.

Extraction

To extract a specific food product from fruit, cereals or liquids, any of the following methods may be used: crushing, pounding or grinding, extraction by heat (direct or indirect), extraction by solvents, drying and filtration.

Crushing, pounding and grinding are usually preparatory operations—for example, the crushing of cocoa beans and the slicing of sugar beet. In other cases it may be the actual extraction process, as in flour milling.

Heat can be used directly as a means of preparation by extraction, as in roasting (e.g., cocoa, coffee and chicory); in manufacturing it is usually used directly or indirectly in the form of steam (e.g., extraction of edible oils or extraction of sweet juice from thin slices of beet in the sugar industry).

Oils can be extracted equally well by combining and mixing the crushed fruit with solvents that are later eliminated by filtering and reheating. The separation of liquid products is carried out by centrifuging (turbines in a sugar refinery) or by filtering through filter presses in breweries and in oil and fat production.

Production Processes

Operations in processing food products are extremely varied and can be described only after individual study of each industry, but the following general procedures are used: fermentation, cooking, dehydration and distillation.

Fermentation, obtained usually by addition of a micro-organism to the previously prepared product, is practiced in bakeries, breweries, the wine and spirits industry and the cheese products industry. (See also the chapter *Beverage industry*.)

Cooking occurs in many manufacturing operations: canning and preserving of meat, fish, vegetables and fruits; ready-to-serve meat-processing plants (e.g., chicken nuggets); in bakeries, biscuit making, breweries; and so on. In other cases, cooking is done in a vacuum-sealed container and produces a concentration of the product (e.g., sugar refining and tomato-paste production).

Besides the drying of products by the sun, as with many tropical fruits, dehydration can be carried out in hot air (fixed dryers or drying tunnels), by contact (on a drying drum heated by

Table 67.1 • The food industries, their raw materials and processes.

Industry	Materials processed	Storage requirements	Processing techniques	Preserving techniques	Packaging of finished products
Meat processing and preserving	Beef, lamb, pork, poultry	Cold stores	Slaughtering, cutting up, boning, comminuting, cooking	Salting, smoking, refrigeration, deep-freezing, sterilization	Loose or in cans, cardboard
Fish processing	All types of fish	Cold stores or salted loose or in barrels	Heading, gutting, filleting, cooking	Deep-freezing, drying, smoking, sterilization	Loose in refrigerated containers or in cans
Fruit and vegetable preserving	Fresh fruit and vegetables	Processed immediately; fruits may be stabilized with sulphur dioxide	Blanching or cooking, grinding, vacuum-concentration of juices	Sterilization, pasteurization, drying, dehydration, lyophilization (freeze drying)	Bags, cans or glass or plastic bottles
Milling	Grains	Silos may be fumigated in storage	Grinding, sifting, milling, rolling	Drying cooking or baking	Silos (conveyed pneumatically), sacks or bags to other processes, or boxed for retail trade
Baking	Flour and other dry goods, water, oils	Silos, super sacks and bags	Kneading, fermentation, laminating surface treatments of seasoning	Baking, cutting surface treatments and packaging	Packaged for wholesale trades, restaurants and retail markets
Biscuit making	Flour, cream, butter, sugar, fruit and seasoning	Silos, super sacks and bags	Mixing, kneading, laminating moulding	Baking, cutting surface treatments and packaging	Bags, boxes for institutional and retail trades
Pasta manufacture	Flour, eggs	Silos	Kneading, grinding, cutting, extrusion or moulding	Drying	Bags, packets
Sugar processing and refining	Sugar beet, sugar cane	Silos	Crushing, maceration, vacuum concentration, centrifuging, drying	Vacuum cooking	Bags, packets
Chocolate making and confectionery	Cocoa bean sugar, fats	Silos, sacks, conditioned chambers	Roasting, grinding, mixing, conching, moulding	–	Packets
Brewing	Barley, hops	Silos, tanks, conditioned cellars	Grain milling, malting, brewing, filter pressing, fermentation	Pasteurization	Bottles, cans, barrels
Distilling and manufacture of other beverages	Fruit, grain, carbonated water	Silos, tanks, vats	Distillation, blending, aeration	Pasteurization	Barrels, bottles, cans
Milk and milk products processing	Milk, sugar, other constituents	Immediate processing; subsequently in ripening vats, conditioned vats, cold store	Skimming, churning (butter), coagulation (cheese), ripening	Pasteurization, sterilization or concentration, desiccation	Bottles, plastic wrapping, boxes (cheese) or unpacked
Processing of oils and fats	Groundnuts, olives, dates, other fruit and grain, animal or vegetable fats	Silos, tanks, cold stores	Milling, solvent or steam extraction, filter pressing	Pasteurization where necessary	Bottles, packets, cans

steam, such as in the instant-coffee industry and the tea industry), vacuum drying (often combined with filtering) and lyophilization (freeze drying), where the product is first frozen solid and then dried by vacuum in a heated chamber.

Distillation is used in the making of spirits. The fermented liquid, treated to separate grain or fruit, is vaporized in a still; the condensed vapour is then collected as liquid ethyl alcohol.

Preservation Processes

It is important to prevent any deterioration of food products, as much for the quality of the products as for the more serious risk of contamination or threat to the consumers' health.

There are six basic methods of food preservation:

1. radiation sterilization
2. antibiotic sterilization
3. chemical action
4. dehydration
5. refrigeration.

Briefly, the first three methods destroy microbial life; the latter merely inhibit growth. Raw ingredients such as fish and meat, fruit or vegetables are taken fresh and preserved by one of the above methods, or a mixture of different foods are processed to form a product or dish, which is then preserved. Such products include soups, meat dishes and puddings.

Food preservation goes back to the last Ice Age, about 15,000 BC, when Cro-Magnon humans discovered for the first time a way of preserving food by smoking it. The evidence for this lies in the caves at Les Eyzies in the Dordogne in France, where this way of life is well portrayed in carvings, engravings and paintings. From then to the present day, although many methods have been used and still are, heat remains one of the principal cornerstones of food preservation.

High-temperature processes can destroy bacteria, depending on the cooking temperature and duration. Sterilization (mainly used in canneries) involves submitting the already canned product to the action of steam, generally in a closed container such as an autoclave or continuous cooker. Pasteurization—the term is particularly reserved for liquids such as fruit juice, beer, milk or cream—is carried out at a lower temperature and for a short time. Smoking is carried out mainly on fish, ham and bacon, assuring dehydration and giving a distinctive flavor.

Ionizing radiation sterilization is used heavily on spices in some countries to reduce wastage and spoilage. "Radiation pasteurization" using much lower doses enables the refrigerated shelf life of many foods to be considerably extended. However, sterilizing canned foods with radiation requires such high dosage that unacceptable flavours and odours result.

Ionizing radiation has two other well recognized uses in the food industry—the screening of food packs for foreign matter and monitoring to detect underfilling.

Microwave sterilization is another type of electromagnetic emission that is currently finding use in the food industry. It is used for rapidly thawing raw frozen ingredients before further processing, as well as for heating frozen cooked foods in 2 to 3 minutes. Such a method, with its low moisture content loss, preserves the appearance and flavour of the food.

Drying is a common preservation process. Sun drying is the oldest and most widely used method of food preservation. Today foodstuffs may be dried in air, superheated steam, in vacuum, in inert gas and by direct application of heat. Many types of dryers exist, the particular type being dependent on the nature of the material, the desired form of finished product and so on. Dehydration is a process in which heat is transferred into the water in the food, which is vapourized. The water vapour is then removed.

Low-temperature processes involve storage in a cold store (the temperature determined by the nature of the products), freezing and deep-freezing, which allows foodstuffs to be preserved in their naturally fresh state, by various methods of slow or rapid freezing.

With freeze drying, the material to be dried is frozen and placed in a sealed chamber. The chamber pressure is reduced and maintained at a value below 1 mm Hg. Heat is applied to the material, the surface ice heats up and the resultant water vapour is drawn off by the vacuum system. As the ice boundary recedes into the material, the ice sublimes *in situ* and the water percolates to the surface through the pore structure of the material.

Intermediate-moisture foods are foodstuffs that contain relatively large amounts of water (5 to 30%) and yet do not support microbial growth. The technology, which is difficult, is a spin-off from space travel. Open-shelf stability is achieved by suitable control of acidity, redox potential, humectants and preservatives. Most developments to date have been in foods for pet animals.

Whatever the preservation process, the food to be preserved has first to be prepared. Meat preservation involves a butchery department; fish needs cleaning and gutting, filleting, curing and so on. Before fruit and vegetables can be preserved they have to be washed, cleaned, blanched, perhaps graded, peeled, stalked,

shelled and stoned. Many of the ingredients have to be chopped, sliced, minced or pressed.

Packaging

There are many methods of packaging food, including canning, aseptic packaging and frozen packaging.

Canning

The conventional method of canning is based on the original work of Appert in France, for which in 1810 the French government awarded him a prize of 12,000 francs. He preserved food in glass containers. In Dartford, England, in 1812, Donkin and Hall set up the first cannery using tinned iron containers.

Today the world uses several million tonnes of tinplate annually for the canning industry, and a substantial amount of preserved food is packed into glass jars. The process of canning consists of taking cleaned food, raw or partly cooked but not intentionally sterilized, and packing it into a can that is sealed with a lid. The can is then heated, usually by steam under pressure, to a certain temperature for a period of time to allow penetration of the heat to the centre of the can, destroying the microbial life. The can is then cooled in air or chlorinated water, after which it is labelled and packed.

Changes in processing have occurred over the years. Continuous sterilizers cause less damage to cans by impact and allow cooling and drying in a closed atmosphere. Foods can also be heat preserved in retortable pouches. These are bags of small cross-sectional area made from laminates of aluminium and heat-sealable plastics. The process is the same as for conventional canning, but better taste properties are claimed for the products because sterilization times can be reduced. Very careful control of the retorting process is essential to avoid damage to the heat seals with subsequent bacterial spoilage.

Aseptic packaging

There have been recent developments in the aseptic packaging of food. The process is fundamentally different from conventional canning. In the aseptic method the food container and closure are sterilized separately, and the filling and closing are done in a sterile atmosphere. Product quality is optimal because heat treatment of the foodstuff can be controlled precisely and is independent of the size or material of the container. Of concern is employee exposure to the sterilizing agents. It is likely that the method will become more widely used because overall it should result in energy savings. To date most progress has been made with liquids and purées sterilized by the so-called HTST process, in which the product is heated to a high temperature for a few seconds. Developments on particulate foodstuffs will follow. One likely benefit in food factories will be the reduction of noise if rigid metallic containers are replaced. Such containers may also cause problems by contaminating preserved food with lead and tin. These are minimized by new-type two-piece containers drawn from lacquered tinplate and three-piece containers with welded instead of soldered side seams.

Frozen packaging

The frozen food industry utilizes all methods of deep-freezing fresh food at temperatures below their freezing point, thus forming ice crystals in the watery tissues. The food may be frozen raw or partially cooked (e.g., animal carcasses or made-up meat dishes, fish or fish products, vegetables, fruits, poultry, eggs, ready-made meals, bread and cakes). Frozen perishable products can be transported over long distances and stored for processing and/or sale when demand arises, and seasonal products can be available at all times.

Food for freezing must be in prime condition and prepared under strict hygienic control. Packaging materials should be vapour- and aroma-proof and resistant to low temperatures. The quality of the product depends on the rate of freezing: if too slow, the structure of the food may be damaged by large ice crystals and enzymatic and microbiological properties destroyed. Small items, such as shrimps and peas, can be frozen quickly, which makes for an improvement in quality.

The various methods of freezing include: air freezing, blast freezing, fluid-bed freezing, fluid freezing, contact freezing, liqui-freezing and dehydro-freezing.

Air freezing in its simplest form involves placing food in trays on shelves in a cold store at approximately –30 °C for a time varying from a few hours to 3 days, depending on size. Blast freezing, a more complicated technique, uses a rapidly circulating stream of cold air, sometimes combined with cold spirals, which removes heat by means of radiation. Temperatures range between –40 and –50 °C, and the maximum air speed is 5 m/s. Blast freezing may be carried out in tunnel freezers, often equipped with conveyors to carry the food through to cold-storage rooms. When the freezer is adjacent to the cold store, the tunnel is often closed with an air curtain instead of doors.

Fluid-bed freezing is used for chopped or sliced vegetables, peas and so on, which are placed on a perforated belt through which a stream of air is blown. Each item is coated with ice and thus retains its shape and separateness. The frozen vegetables may be stored in large containers and repackaged when needed in small units. In fluid freezing (one of the oldest known methods) the food, usually fish, is immersed in a strong solution of brine. Salt may penetrate unwrapped goods and even wrappings, affecting the flavour and hastening rancidity. This method had declined in use but is now gaining ground again as more effective plastic wrapping materials are developed. Poultry is frozen by a combination of the fluid- and air-freezing methods. Each bird, packed in polyethylene or similar material, is first sprayed or immersed in a fluid to freeze its outer layer; the inside is afterwards frozen in a blast freezer.

Contact freezing is the common method for foodstuffs packed in cartons, which are placed between hollow shelves through which a cooling fluid is circulated; the shelves are pressed flat against the cartons, usually by hydraulic pressure.

In liqui-freezing, the product is placed on a conveyor belt which is passed through a tank of liquid nitrogen (or occasionally liquid carbon dioxide) or through a tunnel where liquid nitrogen is sprayed. Freezing occurs at a temperature as low as –196 °C, and not every type of product or wrapping can withstand this cold. Dehydro-freezing, which removes some of the water before freezing, is used for certain vegetables and fruits. A considerable reduction of weight is achieved, involving lower transport, storage and wrapping costs.

During cold storage, the product must be kept at a temperature of –25 to –30 °C, and good air circulation must be maintained. Transport of frozen goods has to be in refrigerated wagons, lorries, ships and so on, and during loading and unloading, the goods must be exposed to as little heat as possible. Usually, firms producing frozen food also prepare the raw material, but sometimes this treatment is carried out in separate establishments. In beef and poultry operations, carbon dioxide is often used to cool and preserve product during shipping.

Hazards and Their Prevention

Injury hazards

The most common causes of injuries in the food industry are hand tools, especially knives; operation of machinery; collisions with moving or stationary objects; falls or slips; and burns.

Injuries caused by knives in meat and fish preparation can be minimized by design and maintenance, adequate work areas, selection of the right knife for the job, provision of tough protective gloves and aprons and correct training of workers on both the sharpening and the use of the knife. Mechanical cutting devices also pose a hazard, and good maintenance and adequate training of workers is critical to prevent injuries (see figure 67.1).

Although accidents involving transmission machinery are relatively infrequent, they are likely to be serious. Risks related to machines and handling systems must be studied individually in each industry. Handling problems can be addressed by close examination of injury history for each particular process and by use of appropriate personal protection, such as foot and leg protection, hand and arm protection and eye and face protection. Risks from machinery can be prevented by secure machinery guarding. Mechanical handling equipment, especially conveyors, is widely employed, and particular attention should be paid to in-running nips on such equipment. Filling and closing machines should be totally enclosed except for the intake and discharge openings. The intakes of conveyor belts and drums, as well as pulleys and gearing, should be securely protected. To prevent cuts in canning, for example, effective arrangements for clearing up sharp tin or broken glass are required. Serious injury due to the inadvertent start-up of transmission machinery during cleaning or maintenance can be avoided by strict lockout/tagout procedures.

Falling accidents are most often caused by:

- *The state of the floor.* Accidents are possible when floors are uneven, wet or made slippery by the type of surface; by products; by fatty, oily or dusty waste; or, in cold rooms, from humid air condensing on the floors. Anti-slip floors help to prevent slips. Finding the proper surface and cleaning regimen, along with good housekeeping and proper footwear, will help prevent many falls. Curbs around machines containing water will prevent water flowing onto the floor. Good drainage should be provided to remove rapidly any accumulating liquids or spillage that occurs.
- *Uncovered pits or drainage channels.* Maintenance of covers or barricading of the hazard is necessary.

Figure 67.1 • Carving frozen whale meat on a band saw without adequate machine guarding and electrical precautions, Japan, 1989.

L. Manderson.

- *Work at heights.* Provision of safe means of access to equipment and storage areas, sound ladders and fall protection (including body harnesses and lifelines) can prevent many hazards.
- *Steam or dust.* Operations that generate steam or dust may not only make the floor slippery but also prevent good visibility.
- *Insufficient or inconsistent lighting.* Illumination needs to be bright enough for employees to be able to observe the process. The perception of inadequate lighting occurs when warehouses appear dark compared to production areas and people's eyes do not adjust when moving from one light level to the other.

Burns and scalds from hot liquors and cooking equipment are common; similar injuries arise from steam and hot water used in equipment cleaning. Even more serious accidents can occur due to explosion of boilers or autoclaves due to lack of regular examination, poor employee training, poor procedures or poor maintenance. All steam equipment needs regular and careful maintenance to prevent major explosion or minor leaks.

Electrical installations, especially in wet or damp places, require proper grounding and good maintenance to control the common hazard of electrical shock. In addition to proper grounds, outlets protected with ground fault interrupters (GFIs) are effective in protecting from electrical shock. Proper electrical classification for hazardous environments is critical. Often flavours, extracts and dusty flammable powders such as grain dust, corn starch or sugar (thought of as foodstuffs rather than hazardous chemicals) may require classified electrical equipment to eliminate ignition during process upsets or excursions. Fires may also occur if welding is done around explosive/combustible organic dusts in grain elevators and mills. Explosions may also occur in gas or oil-fired ovens or cooking processes if they are not installed, operated or maintained correctly; provided with the essential safety devices; or if proper safety procedures are not followed (especially in open flame operations).

Strict product sanitation control is vital at all stages of food processing, including in slaughterhouses. Personal and industrial hygiene practices are most important in guarding against infection or contamination of the products. The premises and equipment should be designed to encourage personal hygiene through good, conveniently situated and sanitary washing facilities, showerbaths when necessary, provision and laundering of suitable protective clothing and provision of barrier creams and lotions, where appropriate.

Strict equipment sanitation is also vital to all stages of food processing. During the regular operation of most facilities, safety standards are effective to control equipment hazards. During the sanitation cycle, equipment must be opened up, guards removed and interlock systems disabled. A frustration is that the equipment is designed to run, but clean-up is often an afterthought. A disproportional share of the most serious injuries happen during this part of the process. Injuries are commonly caused by exposure to in-running nip points, hot water, chemicals and acid or base splashes, or by cleaning moving equipment. Dangerous high-pressure hoses which carry hot water also pose a hazard. Lack of equipment-specific procedures, lack of training and the low experience level of the typical new employee pressed into a cleaning job can add to the problem. The hazard is increased when equipment to be cleaned is located in areas that are not easily accessible. An effective lockout/tagout programme is essential. Current best practice to help control the problem is designing of clean-in-place facilities. Some equipment is designed to be self-cleaning by use of high-pressure spray balls and self-scrubbing systems, but too often manual labour is required to address trouble spots. In the meat and poultry industries, for example, all cleaning is manual.

Health hazards

Infections and infectious or parasitic diseases spread by animals or the waste products of animals used in manufacture are common occupational problems in the food industry. These zoonoses include anthrax, brucellosis, the leptospiroses, tularemia, bovine tuberculosis, glanders, erysipeloid, Q fever, foot-and-mouth disease, rabies and so on. Some food handlers may be subject to a wide variety of skin infections, including anthrax, actinomycosis and erysipeloid. Certain dried fruits are infested with mites; this can affect workers in sorting operations.

Apart from specific prophylactic vaccination against infectious diseases, proper gloves, good personal hygiene and the sanitary facilities to enable this (which are a prerequisite of any food industry as a protection to the product) are the most valuable preventive measures. Good washing facilities, including showers, and appropriate protective clothing are essential. Efficient medical care, especially for treatment of minor injuries, is an equally important requirement.

Contact dermatitis and allergies of the skin or respiratory system caused by organic products, animal or vegetable, are also common. Primary dermatitis can be caused by irritants such as acids, alkalis, detergents and water used in cleaning; friction from fruit picking and packing; and the handling of sugar, which is much used in food manufacture. Secondary sensitization results from the handling of many fruits and vegetables. Organic dusts from grain or flour can also cause respiratory diseases (e.g., "baker's asthma") and must be controlled. Too often the food industry considers the ingredients they use to be merely ingredients, rather than chemicals that can have health effects when employees are exposed to either industrial strengths or industrial quantities of "normal" household kitchen ingredients.

Cumulative trauma disorders

Many of the meat, poultry, fish and food processing plants involve highly repetitive and forceful work. The very nature of the products is such that manual labour often is needed to manipulate product when inspecting or loading fragile products into packaging or during the scale-up of a product before high-volume equipment is purchased or installed. Further, handling of boxes for shipping can cause back injuries. Three things to watch for are tasks involving extreme postures, high forces or high levels of repetition. Combinations of more than one factor make the problem more critical. Early detection and treatment of affected workers is desirable. Ergonomic redesign of equipment and other changes discussed in specific articles in this chapter will decrease the incidence of these hazards.

Refrigerants such as anhydrous ammonia, methyl chloride and other halogenated aliphatic hydrocarbons used in freezing and cold storage bring risks of poisoning and chemical burns. Emergency planning in addition to the normal fire planning is important. Training of workers in evacuation procedures is also necessary. Escape-type respiratory protection may be needed during evacuation from some areas of the facility. For some chemicals, sensors in the building are used to provide early warning to all employees through a central alarm system to signal the need to evacuate. Worker reactions to increases in ammonia levels must be taken seriously, and affected workers must be evacuated and treated. Ammonia leaks warrant strict attention and contiuous monitoring. Evacuation may be required if levels start to rise, before dangerous levels are reached. A central assembly point should be selected so that those who are evacuated are not in danger of being downwind of the refrigerant leak. Chemical protective clothing will be needed to aggressively approach the system leak to contain the release. Anhydrous ammonia and the less frequently used refrigerants, such as propane, butane, ethane and ethylene, are also flammable and explosive. Leaks from pipes are usually due to inadequate maintenance and can be prevented with adequate attention. Adequate measures should be taken for explosion prevention and firefighting.

Pesticides, fumigants and other hazardous materials must be kept under strict control and used only according to the manufacturer's guidance. Organophosphate pesticides should only be used when accompanied with biological monitoring to assure the control of exposure.

The traditional tin/lead soldering of the side seam of a food can and the awareness of the problem of lead levels in food products have resulted in studies of environmental lead levels in can-making units and blood lead levels in workers. Evidence has shown both to be raised, but neither the environmental threshold limit value (TLV) nor the currently acceptable blood lead levels have ever been found to be exceeded. Thus, the results are consistent with a "low risk" lead process.

Carbon dioxide, used in cooling refrigerated products that are to be shipped, must also be kept under strict controls. Adequate ventilation must be provided over dry ice bins to prevent the gas from causing ill effects.

Exposure to cold can range from handling and storage of raw materials in winter or in processing and store rooms cooled with "still air", to extremes of cold in air-blast refrigeration of raw materials, as in the ice cream and frozen foods industry. Cold-store workers may suffer impairment of health through exposure to cold if adequate protective clothing is not supplied. Exposure to cold is most critical for employees with sedentary jobs in very cold environments. Barriers should be used to deflect cold breezes from workers standing near fans used to circulate air. Job rotation to more active or warmer locations is advisable. In large tunnel freezing plants, it may be fatal for workers to stay in the rapidly moving stream of air, even if dressed in polar clothing. It is particularly important to prohibit entry into a tunnel freezer in operation and to make effective interlocking arrangements or use confined-space entry protocol to ensure that freezers cannot be started up while workers are still inside them. Warm lunchrooms and provision of hot drinks will mitigate the effects of cold work.

Heat, often combined with high humidity in cooking and sterilizing, can produce an equally intolerable physical environment, where heat stroke and heat exhaustion are an issue. These conditions are found especially in processing that entails evaporation of solutions, such as tomato paste production, often in countries where hot conditions already prevail. It is also prevalent on kill floors of slaughterhouses. Effective ventilation systems are essential, with special attention to condensation problems. Air conditioning may be necessary in some areas.

A serious health hazard in most modern plants, especially with canning, is exposure to noise. Putting additional high-speed machines in a limited space continues to drive noise levels up, despite best efforts to keep them below 85 dBA. The manufacture, conveying and filling of cans at speeds of up to 1,000 per minute leads to exposure of operators to a noise level of up to 100 dBA at frequencies ranging from 500 to 4,000 Hz, a dose equivalent of about 96 dBA, which if uncontrolled will lead in many cases to noise-induced deafness over a working lifetime. Certain engineering techniques can lead to some noise reduction; these include sound-absorbent mounting, magnetic elevators, nylon-coated cables and speed-matching in can conveyor systems. However, some radical change in the industry, such as the use of plastic containers, is the only hope for the future of producing a reasonably noise-free environment. At present, a hearing conservation programme based on audiometric examinations, hearing-protection equipment and education should be instituted. Noise refuges and personal ear protection should be provided.

Where ionizing radiation is used, the full precautions applicable to such work (e.g., radiation protection, hazard monitoring, health screening and periodic medical examinations) are necessary.

Medical supervision of workers is desirable; many food factories are small and membership in a group medical service may be the most effective way of securing this.

Health and safety committees that effectively involve the entire organization, including production operators, in the development of plant programmes is the key to a safe operation. Too often the food industry is not considered to be particularly hazardous, and a feeling of complacency develops. Often materials used are ones that people are familiar with and hence individuals may not understand the hazards that can arise when industrial strengths or quantities are employed. Plant employees who understand that safety rules and procedures are in place to protect their health and safety and not simply to meet government requirements are key to the development of a quality safety programme. Management must establish practices and policies that will allow employees to develop those beliefs.

HEALTH EFFECTS AND DISEASE PATTERNS

John J. Svagr

Health effects found in food processing are similar to those found in other manufacturing operations. Respiratory disorders, skin diseases and contact allergies, hearing impairment and musculoskeletal disorders are among the most common occupational health problems in the food and beverage industry (Tomoda 1993; BLS 1991; Caisse nationale d'assurance maladie des travailleurs salariés 1990). Thermal extremes are also a concern. Table 67.2 shows rankings of the three most common occupational diseases in this industry in selected countries.

Respiratory System

Respiratory problems can largely be classified as rhinitis, which affects the nasal passages; broncho-constriction in the major airways; and pneumonitis, which consists of damage to the fine structures of the lung. Exposure to airborne dust from various foodstuffs, as well as chemicals, may lead to emphysema and asthma. A Finnish study found chronic rhinitis common among slaughterhouse and pre-cooked foods workers (30%), mill and bakery workers (26%) and food processing workers (23%). Also, food processing workers (14%) and slaughterhouse/pre-cooked foods workers (11%) suffered from chronic coughs. The causative agent is flour dust in bakery workers, while temperature variations and various kinds of dust (spices) are believed to cause disease in other branches.

Two studies in the former Yugoslavia found a much higher prevalence of chronic respiratory symptoms than in a control group. In a study of spice workers the most common complaint (57.6%) was dyspnea or breathing difficulty, followed by nasal catarrh (37.0%), sinusitis (27.2%), chronic cough (22.8%) and chronic phlegm and bronchitis (19.6%). A study of animal food processing workers found that in addition to the animal food processing ingredients, exposure included powdered coriander, garlic dust, cinnamon dust, red paprika dust and dust from other spices. Non-smokers studied showed a significantly higher prevalence of chronic phlegm and chest tightness. Smokers had a significantly higher prevalence of chronic coughs; chronic phlegm, chronic bronchitis and chest tightness were also observed. The frequency of acute respiratory symptoms associated with the working day was high for the exposed group, and respiratory ventilatory capacity of smokers was significantly lower than predicted. The study therefore concluded an association exists between exposure to animal food dust and the development of respiratory disorders.

Industrial injury compensation in the United Kingdom recognizes occupational asthma from the handling of enzymes, animals, grains and flour. Exposure to cinnamic aldehyde from tree bark and sulphur dioxide, a bleaching agent and fumigant, cause a high prevalence of asthma in cinnamon workers in Sri Lanka. Dust exposure is minimal for the workers who peel the bark, but workers in the local buyers' stores are exposed to high levels of dust and sulphur dioxide. A study found 35 of 40 cinnamon workers complained of chronic coughs (37.5%) or suffered from asthma (22.5%). Other abnormalities included weight loss (65%), skin irritation (50%), hair loss (37.5%), eye irritation (22.5%) and rashes (12.5%). For workers who work under similar high concentrations of airborne dust of vegetable origin, asthma is highest in cinnamon workers (22.5%, compared with 6.4% in tea workers and 2.5% in kapok workers). Smoking is not believed to be directly related to the coughs, since similar symptoms occurred in 8 non-smoking women and 5 men who smoked about 7 cigarettes a day. Irritation of the respiratory mucosa by cinnamon dust causes the coughing.

Other studies examined the relationship between respiratory disorders and the allergens and antigens originating in foodstuffs, such as egg protein and seafood products. While no specific workplace dust could be linked to the various acute and chronic respiratory disorders among the exposed workers, the results of the studies indicate a strong association between the disorders and the work environment.

Use of microbiology has long been a part of food production. In general, most of the micro-organisms used in the food and drink industries are considered to be harmless. Wine, cheese, yogurt and sour dough all use a microbial process to yield a usable product. Production of proteins and enzymes increasingly use biotechnological techniques. Certain species of aspergillus and bacillus produce amylases that convert starches into sugar. Yeasts turn starch into acetone. *Tricoderma* and *Penicillium* produce cellulases that break down cellulose. As a result, spores of fungi and actinomycetes are widely found in food processing. *Aspergillus* and *Penicillium* are frequently present in the air in bakeries. *Penicillium* is also found in dairy and meat processing plants; during the maturation of cheeses and sausages, there can be abundant surface growth. Cleaning steps, prior to sale, disperse them into the air, and workers may develop allergic alveolitis. Occupational asthma cases have association with many of these organisms, while some are suspected of causing infection or carrying mycotoxins. The enzymes trypsin, chymotrypsin and protease are associated with hypersensitivity and respiratory disease, particularly among laboratory workers.

In addition to the airborne particulate originating from foodstuffs and microbial agents, inhalation of hazardous chemical substances used as reagents, refrigerants, fumigants and sanitizers may cause respiratory and other disorders. These substances are found in solid, liquid or gaseous form. Exposure at or above recognized limits often results in skin or eye irritation and respiratory disorders. Headaches, salivation, burning of the throat, perspiration, nausea and vomiting are symptoms of intoxication due to overexposure.

Ammonia is a colourless gas refrigerant, cleaning agent and fumigant for foodstuffs. Exposure to ammonia can result in corrosive burns or blistering of skin. Excessive and prolonged exposure can produce bronchitis and pneumonia.

Trichloroethylene, hexane, benzene, carbon monoxide (CO), carbon dioxide (CO_2) and polyvinyl chloride (PVC) are frequently found in food and beverage plants. Trichloroethylene and hexane are used for olive oil extraction.

CO, a colourless, odourless gas, is difficult to detect. Exposure occurs in smokehouses that are poorly ventilated or while working in grain silos, wine fermentation cellars or where fish are stored. Dry-ice freezing or chilling, CO_2-freeze tunnels and combustion processes expose workers to CO_2. Intoxication symptoms of overexposure to CO and CO_2 include headache, dizziness,

Table 67.2 • Most common occupational diseases in the food and drink industries in selected countries.

Country	Year	Occupational diseases			
		Most common	Second most common	Third most common	Other
Austria	1989	Bronchitis, asthma	Hearing impairment	Skin diseases	Infections transmitted by animals
Belgium (food)	1988	Diseases induced by inhalation of substances	Diseases induced by physical agents	Skin diseases	Infections or parasites from animals
Belgium (drink)	1988	Diseases induced by physical agents	Diseases induced by chemical agents	Diseases induced by inhalation of substances	–
Colombia	1989	Hearing impairment	Respiratory disorders (asthma)	Musculoskeletal disorders	Skin diseases
Czechoslovakia	1988	Respiratory disorders	Musculoskeletal disorders	Digestive disorders	Circulatory disorders, skin diseases
Denmark	1988	Physical coordination disorders	Skin diseases	Hearing impairment	Infections, allergies
France	1988	Asthma and other respiratory disorders	Strains in various parts of body (knees, elbows)	Septicemia (blood poisoning) and other infections	Hearing impairment
Poland	1989	Respiratory disorders	Skin diseases	Infections	Hearing impairment
Sweden	1989	Musculoskeletal disorders	Allergies (contact with chemical agents)	Hearing impairment	Infections
United States	1989	Disorders associated with repeated trauma	Skin diseases	Diseases due to physical agents	Respiratory conditions associated with toxic agents

Source: Tomoda 1993.

drowsiness, nausea, vomiting and, in extreme cases, even death. CO also can aggravate heart and respiratory symptoms. The acceptable exposure limits, set by several governments, permit 100 times greater exposure to CO_2 than CO to trigger the same response.

PVC is used for packaging and food-wrap materials. When PVC film is heated, thermal degradation products cause irritation to the eyes, nose and throat. Workers also report symptoms of wheezing, chest pains, breathing difficulties, nausea, muscle pains, chills and fever.

Hypochlorites, acids (phosphoric, nitric and sulphuric), caustics and quaternary ammonium compounds are frequently used in wet cleaning. Microbiology labs use mercury compounds and formaldehyde (gas and formalin solution). Disinfection in the lab uses phenolics, hypochlorites and glutaraldehyde. Irritation and corrosion to eyes, skin and lungs occur with excessive exposure and contact. Improper handling can release highly toxic substances, like chlorine and sulphur oxides.

The National Institute for Occupational Safety and Health (NIOSH) in the United States reported worker breathing difficulties during washing of poultry with super-chlorinated water. The symptoms included headaches, sore throat, tightness in the chest and difficulty breathing. Chloramine is the suspected agent. Chloromines can form when ammonia-treated water or amine-treated boiler water contacts hypochlorite solutions used in sanitation. Cities have added ammonia to water to prevent the formation of halomethanes. Air sample methods are not available for chloramines. Chlorine and ammonia levels are not predictive as indicators of exposure, as testing found their levels to be well below their limits.

Fumigants prevent infestation during storage and transport of food raw materials. Some fumigants include anhydrous ammonia, phostoxin (phosphine) and methyl bromide. The short duration of this process makes respiratory protection the cost-effective strategy. Proper respiratory protection practices should be observed when handling these items until air measurements of the area are below applicable limits.

Employers should take steps to assess the level of toxic contamination at the workplace and ensure that exposure levels do not exceed limits found in safety and health codes. Contamination levels should be measured frequently, especially following changes in processing methods or the chemicals used.

Engineering controls to minimize the risk of intoxication or infection have two approaches. First, eliminate the use of such materials or substitute a less hazardous material. This may involve replacing a powdered substance with a liquid or slurry. Second, control the exposure through reducing the level of air contamination. Workplace designs include the following: total or partial enclosure of the process, suitable ventilation systems and restricted access (to reduce exposed population). An appropriate ventilation system is instrumental in preventing the dispersal of spores or aerosols throughout the workplace. Substitution of vacuum cleaning or wet cleaning for compressed-air blow-out of equipment is critical for dry materials that could become airborne during cleaning.

Administrative controls include worker rotation (to reduce exposure period) and off-shift/weekend hazardous task work (to reduce exposed population). Personal protective equipment (PPE) is the least favoured exposure control method due to high maintenance, availability issues in developing countries and the fact that the worker must remember to wear it.

PPE consists of splash goggles, face shields and respirators for workers mixing hazardous chemicals. Worker training on use and limitations, plus equipment fitting, must occur for the equipment to adequately serve its purpose. Different types of respirators (masks) are worn depending on the nature of the work and the level of the hazard. These respirators range from the simple half facepiece for dust and mist, through chemical air purifying of various facepiece types, up to self-contained breathing apparatus (SCBA). Proper selection (based on hazard, face-fit and maintenance) and training assure effectiveness of the respirator in reducing exposure and the incidence of respiratory disorders.

Skin

Skin problems found in the food and drink industries are skin disease (dermatitis) and contact allergies (e.g., eczema). Due to sanitation requirements, workers are constantly washing their hands with soap and using hand-dip stations that contain quaternary ammonium solutions. This constant wetting of the hands can reduce the lipid content of the skin and lead to dermatitis. Dermatitis is an inflammation of the skin as a result of contact-exposure to chemicals and food additives. Work with fats and oils can clog the pores of the skin and lead to acne-like symptoms. These primary irritants account for 80% of all occupational dermatitis seen.

There is growing concern that workers may become highly sensitized to microbial proteins and peptides generated by fermentation and extraction, which can lead to eczema and other allergies. An allergy is a hypersensitive response of any type that is greater than that which normally occurs in response to antigens (not-self) in the environment. Allergic contact dermatitis is rarely seen before the fifth or seventh day after exposure is initiated. Hypersensitivity occupational dermatitis is also reported for work with enzymes, such as trypsin, chymotrypsin and protease.

Chlorinated solvents (see "Respiratory system" section above) stimulate the epidermal cells to undertake peculiar growth patterns. This keratin stimulation may lead to tumour formation. Other chlorinated compounds found in soaps for antibacterial purposes can lead to photosensitivity dermatitis.

Reduction of exposure to causative agents is the principle preventive method for dermatitis and contact allergies. Adequately drying foodstuffs prior to storage and clean-condition storage can control airborne spores. PPE such as gloves, masks and uniforms keep workers from direct contact and minimize the risk of dermatitis and other allergies. Latex glove materials can cause allergic skin reactions and should be avoided. Proper application of barrier creams, where permitted, can also minimize contact with the skin irritant.

Infectious and parasitic diseases of animal origin are the occupational diseases most specific to the food and drink industries. The diseases are most common among meat-packing and dairy workers as a result of direct contact with infected animals. Agricultural workers and others are also at risk due to their contact with these animals. Prevention is particularly difficult since the animals may not give any overt signs of disease. Table 67.3 lists the types of infections reported.

The fundamental principle for preventing the contraction and spread of infectious and parasitic skin diseases is personal hygiene. Clean washrooms, toilets and shower facilities should be provided. Uniforms, PPE and hand towels need to be washed and in some cases sterilized frequently. All wounds should be sterilized and dressed, regardless of how slight, and covered with protective gear until healed. Keeping the workplace clean and healthy is just as important. This includes the thorough washing of all equipment and surfaces that contact animal flesh after each workday, the control and extermination of rodents and the exclusion of dogs, cats and other animals from the workplace.

Vaccination of animals and inoculation of workers are measures many countries take to prevent infectious and parasitic diseases. Early detection and treatment of diseases with antibacterial/anti-parasitic drugs is essential to contain and even eradicate them. Workers should be examined as soon as any

Table 67.3 • Types of infections reported in food and drink industries.

Infections	Exposure	Symptoms
Brucellosis (*Brucella melitensis*)	Contact with infected cattle, goats and sheep (Northern and Central Europe and North America)	Constant and recurring fever, headaches, weakness, joint pain, night sweats and loss of appetite; can also give rise to symptoms of arthritis, influenza, asthenia and spondylitis
Erysipeloid	Contact of open wounds with infected pigs and fish (Czechoslovakia)	Localized redness, irritation, a burning sensation, pain in the infected area. It can spread to the bloodstream and lymph nodes.
Leptospirosis	Direct contact with infected animals or their urine	Headaches, aching muscles, eye infections, fever, vomiting and chills; in more serious cases, kidney and liver damage, plus cardiovascular and neurological complications
Epidermycosis	Caused by a parasitic fungus on the skin of animals	Erythema and blistering of skin
Dematophytosis (ringworm)	Fungal disease through contact with skin and hair of infected animals	Localized hair loss and small crusts on the scalp
Toxoplasmosis	Contact with infected sheep, goats, cattle, pigs and poultry	Acute stage: fever, muscle pain, sore throats, headaches, swollen lymph nodes and enlarged spleen. Chronic infection leads to development of cysts in the brain and muscle cells. Foetal transmission causes still- and premature births. Full-term babies can have brain and heart defects and may die.
Papilloma viral lung cancers	Regular contact with live animals or animal flesh coupled with exposure to polycyclic aromatic hydrocarbons and nitrites	Lung cancers in butchers and slaughterhouse workers studied in England, Wales, Denmark and Sweden

symptoms, such as recurring coughs, fever, headaches, sore throats and intestinal disorders, appear. In any case, workers should undergo medical examinations at established frequencies, including pre-placement/post-offer baseline exams. In some countries, authorities must be notified when examination detects work-related infection in the workers.

Noise and Hearing

Hearing impairment occurs as a result of continuous and prolonged exposure to noise above recognized threshold levels. This impairment is an incurable illness causing communication disorders and is stressful if the work demands concentration. As a result, psychological and physiological performance can deteriorate. There is also an association between high noise level exposure and abnormal blood pressure, heartbeat, respiration rate/volume, stomach and intestinal spasms and nervous disorders. Individual susceptibility, exposure duration and noise frequency plus intensity are factors that determine the exposure risk.

Safety and health codes vary from country to country, but worker exposure to noise is usually limited to 85 to 90 dBA for 8 continuous hours, followed by a 16-hour recovery time below 80 dBA. Ear protection should be made available at 85 dBA and is required for workers with a confirmed loss and for 8-hour exposures at or above 90 dBA. Annual audiometric testing is recommended, and in some countries required, for this exposed population. Noise measurements with a meter such as the American National Standards Institute (ANSI) Type II sound meter should be taken at least every 2 years. Readings should be repeated whenever equipment or process changes could increase the ambient noise levels.

Ensuring that noise exposure levels are not hazardous is the primary strategy for noise controls. Good manufacturing practices (GMPs) dictate that control devices and their exposed surfaces be cleanable, do not harbour pests and have necessary approvals to contact food or be ancillary to food production. The methods adopted also depend on the availability of financial resources,

equipment, materials and trained staff. One of the most important factors in noise reduction is the design of the workplace. Equipment should be designed for low noise and low vibration. Replacing metal parts with softer materials, like rubber, can reduce noise. When new or replacement equipment is purchased a low-noise type should be selected. Silencers should be installed at air valves and exhaust pipes. Noise-producing machines and processes should be enclosed to reduce to a minimum the number of workers exposed to high noise levels. Where permitted, noise-proof partitions and noise-absorbing ceilings should be installed. Removal and cleaning of these partitions and ceiling tiles need to be included in the maintenance costs. The optimum solution is usually a combination of these measures, adapted to the needs of each workplace.

When engineering controls are not feasible or when it is impossible to reduce noise below harmful levels, PPE should be used to protect the ears. Protective equipment availability and worker awareness is important to prevent hearing impairment. In general, a selection of plugs and earmuffs will lead to greater acceptance and wearing.

Musculoskeletal System

Musculoskeletal disorders were also reported in the 1988–89 data (see table 67.2). Data in the early 1990s noted more and more workers reporting occupational musculoskeletal disorders. Plant automation and work whose pacing is regulated by a machine or conveyor belt occurs today for more workers in the food industry than ever before. Tasks in automated plants tend to be monotonous, with workers performing the same movement all day long.

A Finnish study found that nearly 40% of survey participants reported performing repetitive work all day. Of those performing repetitive work, 60% used their hands, 37% used more than one part of the body and 3% used their feet. Workers in the following occupational groups perform repetitive work for two-thirds or more of their working hours: 70% of cleaners; 67% of slaughterhouse, pre-cooked food and packaging workers; 56% of warehouse and transport workers; and 54% of dairy workers.

Ergonomic stresses arise because most food products come from natural sources and are not uniform. Meat handling requires workers to handle carcasses of varying sizes. With the introduction of poultry sold in parts in the 1960s, more birds (40%, up from less than 20%) were cut into parts. Workers must make many cuts using sharp tools. Changes in US Department of Agriculture (USDA) inspection procedures now permit average line speeds to increase from 56 to 90 birds per minute. Packaging operations may involve repetitive hand and wrist motions to place finished items undamaged into trays or packs. This is especially true for new products, as the market may not justify high-volume operations. Special promotions, including recipes and coupons, may require that an item be manually inserted into the package. Ingredient packaging and workplace layout may require lifting beyond the action limits recommended by occupational health agencies.

Repetitive strain injuries (RSIs) include inflammation of the tendon (tendinitis) and inflammation of the tendon sheath (tenosynovitis). These are prevalent among workers whose jobs require repetitive hand movements, like meatpacking workers. Tasks that repeatedly combine the bending of the wrist with gripping, squeezing and twisting motion can cause carpal tunnel syndrome (CTS). CTS, characterized by a tingling sensation in the thumb and first three index fingers, is caused by inflammation in the wrist joint creating pressure on the nerve system in the wrist. Misdiagnosis of CTS as arthritis can result in permanent numbness and severe pain in the hands, elbows and shoulders.

Vibration disorders also accompany an increased level of mechanization. Food workers are no exception, although the problem may not be as serious as for certain other industries. Food workers using machines such as band saws, mixers and cutters are exposed to vibration. Cold temperatures also increase the probability of vibration disorders to the fingers of the hand. Five per cent of the participants in the Finnish study noted above were exposed to a fairly high level of vibration, while 9% were exposed to some level of vibration.

Excessive exposure to vibration leads, among other problems, to musculoskeletal disorders in the wrists, elbows and shoulders. The type and degree of disorder depend on the type of machine, how it is used and the level of oscillation involved. High levels of exposure can result in growth of a protuberance on the bone or the gradual destruction of the bone in the joint, resulting in severe pain and/or limited mobility.

Rotation of workers with a view to avoiding repetitive motions may reduce the risk by sharing the critical task across the team. Teamwork by task rotation or two-person handling of awkward/heavy ingredient bags can reduce the stress on a single worker in material handling. Tool maintenance, especially knife sharpening, also plays an important role. An ergonomic team of management and production workers can best address these issues as they arise.

Engineering controls focus on reduction or elimination of the 3 primary causes of musculoskeletal problems—force, position and repetition. The workplace should be analysed to identify needed changes, including workstation design (favouring adjustability), working methods, task automation/mechanical assists and ergonomically sound hand tools.

Adequate training should be provided to workers using knives on keeping the knife sharp to minimize force. Also, plants must provide adequate knife-sharpening facilities and avoid the cutting of frozen meat. Training encourages workers to understand the cause and prevention of musculoskeletal disorders. It reinforces the need to use correctly the tools and machines specified for the task. It should also encourage workers to report medical symptoms as soon as possible. Elimination of more invasive medical intervention by restriction of duties and other conservative care, is effective treatment of these disorders.

Heat and Cold

Thermal extremes exist in the food work area. People must work in freezers with temperatures of −18 °C or below. Freezer clothing helps insulate the worker from the cold, but warm break rooms with access to warm liquids must be provided. Meat-processing plants must be kept at 7 to 10 °C. This is below the comfort zone and workers may need to wear additional clothing layers.

Ovens and steam cookers have radiant and moist heat. Heat stress can occur during season changes and heat waves. Copious amounts of fluids and salting of foods may relieve the symptoms until the worker can acclimatize, usually after 5 to 10 days. Salt tablets are not recommended due to complications of hypertension or gastrointestinal upset.

ENVIRONMENTAL PROTECTION AND PUBLIC HEALTH ISSUES

Jerry Spiegel

Overview

The food industry is directly dependent on the natural environment for a supply of raw materials to produce contaminant-free products for human consumption. Due to the extensive processing of a great volume of materials, potential impact on the environment is considerable. This is also true of the beverage industry.

Environmental concern with respect to the food industry focuses more on organic pollutant loadings than on the impact of toxic substances. If pollutant loadings are inadequately prevented or controlled, they will strain community pollution control infrastructure or produce negative impacts on local ecosystems. Production techniques that control product losses serve the double function of improving yield and efficiency while at the same time reducing potential waste and pollution problems.

While the availability of potable water is essential, the food-processing industry also requires very large volumes of water for a wide variety of non-consumption uses, such as for initial cleaning of raw material, fluming, blanching, pasteurizing, cleaning of processing equipment and cooling of finished product. Water uses are identified by quality criteria for different applications, with the highest quality uses often requiring separate treatment to assure complete freedom from odour and taste and to ensure uniform conditions.

The processing of very large volumes of material introduces a potentially great solid waste problem in the production phase. Packaging waste has been the subject of increasing concern with regard to the post-consumer phase of a product's life cycle. In certain branches of the food industry, processing activities are also associated with potential air emissions and odour control problems.

Despite considerable variation among specific industry subsectors, approaches to the prevention and control of pollution share many general characteristics.

Water Pollution Control

The food-processing industry has a raw waste effluent before treatment that is extremely high in soluble organic matter. Even small, seasonal plants are likely to have waste loads comparable to those of populations of 15,000 to 25,000, with large plants approximating the population-equivalent waste load of a quarter of a million people. If a stream or waterway receiving effluent is too small and organic waste too large in volume, the organic waste will utilize the dissolved oxygen in the process of being stabilized and will pollute or degrade the water body by reducing the dissolved oxygen value below that required by normal aquatic organisms. In most cases the waste from food-processing plants is amenable to biological treatment.

The strength of wastewater varies considerably according to plant, specific process and raw product characteristics. From an economic point of view, it is normally less costly to treat a high-strength, low-volume waste than a large-volume, diluted waste. For this reason, effluent with a high biological oxygen demand (BOD), such as the blood of chickens or meat, should be kept out of poultry and meatpacking plant sewers to reduce pollution load, and retained in containers for separate disposal in a by-products or rendering plant.

Waste streams with extreme pH (acidity) values should be carefully considered because of their effect on biological treatment. The combination of acid and basic waste streams may result in neutralization, and, where possible, cooperation with adjacent industries may be very beneficial.

The liquid portion of food-processing waste is normally screened or separated after settling, as a preliminary step in any treatment process, so that these wastes can be disposed of as garbage or combined with other solids in a by-products recovery programme.

The treatment of wastewater can be accomplished by a variety of physical, chemical and biological methods. As secondary processes are more expensive, maximum use of primary treatment is critical in reducing loads. Primary treatment includes processes such as settling or plain sedimentation, filtration (single, dual and multi-media), flocculation, flotation, centrifugation ion exchange, reverse osmosis, carbon absorption and chemical precipitation. Settling facilities range from simple settling ponds to sophisticated clarifiers designed specifically for the particular waste stream characteristics.

The use of biological secondary treatment to follow primary treatment is frequently a necessity to reach wastewater effluent standards. As most food and beverage industry wastewaters contain mainly biodegradable organic pollutants, biological processes used as secondary treatment seek to reduce the BOD of the waste stream by mixing higher concentrations of organisms and oxygen in the waste stream to provide rapid oxidation and stabilization of the waste stream prior to their discharge back to the environment.

Techniques and combinations of techniques may be adapted to address specific waste situations. For example, for dairy wastes, anaerobic treatment to remove the major portion of the pollutant load, with aerobic post-treatment to further reduce the residual BOD and chemical oxygen demand (COD) down to low values and remove nutrients biologically, has proven to be effective. The biogas mixture of methane (CH_4) and CO_2 that is produced from anaerobic treatment can be captured and used as an alternative to fossil fuels or as a source for electrical power generation (typically $0.30 \, m^3$ biogas per kg of COD removed).

Other secondary methods that are widely used include the activated sludge process, aerobic trickling filters, spray irrigation and the use of a variety of ponds and lagoons. Odour nuisances have been associated with ponds of inadequate depth. Odours from anaerobic processes can be removed by the use of soil filters that can oxidize objectionable polar gases.

Air Pollution Control

Air pollution from the food industry generally revolves around the question of objectionable odours rather than toxic air emissions,

with a few exceptions. For this reason, for example, many cities have regulated the location of slaughterhouses under their health codes. Isolation is one obvious way to reduce community complaints about odours. However, this does not remove the odour. Odour control measures such as absorbers or scrubbers may sometimes be necessary.

One major health concern in the food industries is leaks of ammonia gas from refrigeration units. Ammonia is a severe eye and respiratory irritant, and a major leak into the environment could require evacuation of local residents. A leak control plan and emergency procedures are necessary.

Food processes that use solvents (e.g., edible oil processing) may emit solvent vapours into the atmosphere. Closed systems and recycling of solvents is the best method of control. Industries such as sugar-cane refining, which use sulphuric acid and other acids, may release sulphur oxides and other contaminants into the atmosphere. Controls such as scrubbers should be used.

Solid Waste Management

Solid waste can be quite considerable. Tomato waste for canning, for example, may represent 15 to 30% of total quantity of product processed; with peas and corn, waste is in excess of 75%. By isolating solid wastes, the concentration of soluble organics in

Table 67.4 • Examples of uses for by-products from the food industry.

Method	Examples
Anaerobic digestion	*Digestion by mixed bacteria population to yield methane and CO_2* • Apple press cake, apricot fibre, peach/pear waste, orange peel
Animal feed	*Directly, after pressing or drying, as fodder ensiling or as supplement* • Wide variety of fruit and vegetable processing wastes • Cereal straws with alkali to improve digestibility
Composting	*Natural microbiological process in which organic components decompose under controlled aerobic conditions* • Dewatered sludge from brewery waste • Wide variety of fruit and vegetable wastes • Gelatin wastes
Edible fibre	*Method for utilizing organic solids by filtering and hydration* • Apple/pear pomace fibres used for baked goods, pharmaceuticals • Oat or other seed hulls
Fermentation	*Combination of starch, sugar and alcohol-bearing substances* • Biomass (agricultural wastes, wood, garbage) to produce ethanol • Potato waste to produce methane • Sugar from cornstarch to produce biodegradable plastic
Incineration	*Burning of biomass as fuel* • Pits, leaves, nuts, shells, tree prunings for fuel or cogeneration
Pyrolysis	*Transformation of nut shells and fruit pits into charcoal briquets* • Peach, apricot and olive pits; almond and walnut shells
Soil amendment	*Fertilizing of soils with low nutrient and organic matter content* • Peaches, pears, tomatoes

Source: Adapted from Merlo and Rose 1992.

Dairy industry wastewater treatment

The dairy industry is made up of a large number of relatively small plants supplying products such as milk, cheese, cottage cheese, sour cream, ice cream, whey solids and lactose.

The dairy industry has long been a proponent of aerobic biological wastewater treatment. Many dairy plants have invested heavily in activated sludge, biotower, sequencing batch reactor and package treatment systems. Interest in water and energy conservation has led many dairy facilities to reduce water consumption. This trend, with the presence of normally high-strength wastewater streams in dairy plants, has resulted in the design and construction of numerous anaerobic wastewater treatment systems.

Table 67.5 • Typical water reuse ratios for different industry sub-sectors

Sub-sectors	Reuse ratios
Beet sugar	1.48
Cane sugar	1.26
Corn and wheat milling	1.22
Distilling	1.51
Food processing	1.19
Meat	4.03
Poultry processing	7.56

wastewater may be reduced and the drier solid wastes may be more easily used for by-product or feeding purposes and as fuel.

Utilization of process by-products in a manner that provides income will reduce the total cost of waste treatment and eventually the cost of the final product. Waste solids should be evaluated as sources of food for plants and animals. A growing emphasis has been devoted to the development of markets for by-products or for the compost produced by converting waste organic materials to an innocuous humus. Table 67.4 provides examples of uses for by-products from the food industry.

Water Reuse and Effluent Reduction

Extensive dependence on water by food-processing industries has encouraged the development of conservation and reuse programmes, especially in locations of water scarcity. Reuse of process water can provide substantial reductions in both water consumption and waste load, with reuse in many lower-quality applications not requiring biological treatment. However, any potential for anaerobic fermentation of organic solids must be avoided so that corrosive, odourous decomposition products do not affect equipment, work environment or product quality. Bacterial growth can be controlled by disinfection and by changing environmental factors such as pH and temperature.

Table 67.5 presents typical water reuse ratios. Factors such as the location of sprays, water temperature and pressure are key factors influencing the volume of water required for processing operations. For example, water used as a cooling medium to cool cans and for air conditioning may later be used for primary washing of vegetables and other products. The same water later may be used for fluming waste material, and finally a portion of it may be used to cool ashes in the powerhouse.

Water conservation techniques and waste prevention techniques include the use of high-pressure sprays for clean-up, elimination of excessive overflow from washing and soaking tanks, substitution of mechanical conveyors for water flumes, use of automatic shut-off valves on water hoses, separation of can cooling water from the composite waste flow and recirculation of can cooling water.

Pollution loads at processing plants can be reduced through modified processing methods. For example, most pollution load generated from fruit and vegetable processing originates in the peeling and blanching operations. By moving from conventional water or steam blanching to a hot gas blanching process, pollution loads can be reduced by as much as 99.9%. Similarly, dry caustic peeling can cut BOD by more than 90% in comparison to conventional peeling processes.

Energy Conservation

Energy needs have risen with the increased sophistication of the food industry. Energy is required for a wide a variety of equipment such as gas-fired ovens; dryers; steam boilers; electrical motors; refrigeration units; and heating, ventilation and air-conditioning systems.

As the cost of energy has risen, there has been a trend to install heat recovery equipment to conserve energy and to investigate the feasibility of alternative energy sources in various food-processing situations such as cheese processing, food dehydration and water heating. Energy conservation, waste minimization and water conservation are all mutually supportive strategies.

Consumer Health Issues

The increasing separation of the consumer from the food-production sector that has accompanied urbanization globally has resulted in a loss of the traditional means used by the consumer to ensure the quality and safety of food, making the consumer dependent on a functional and responsible food-processing industry. Increased dependence on food processing has created the possibility of exposure to pathogen-contaminated food from a single production facility. To provide protection from this threat, extensive regulatory structures have been established, especially in the industrialized countries, to protect public health and to regulate the use of additives and other chemicals. Harmonization of regulations and standards across borders is emerging as an issue to ensure the free flow of food among all the world's countries.

MEATPACKING/PROCESSING

Deborah E. Berkowitz and Michael J. Fagel

Sources of meat slaughtered for human consumption include cattle, hogs, sheep, lambs and, in some countries, horses and camels. The size and production of slaughterhouses vary considerably. Except for very small operations located in rural areas, animals are slaughtered and processed in factory-type workplaces. These workplaces are usually subject to food-safety controls by the local government to prevent bacterial contamination that can cause foodborne illnesses in consumers. Examples of known pathogens in meat include salmonella and *Escherichia coli*. In these meat processing plants the work has become very specialized, with almost all the work being done on production disassembly lines where the meat moves on chains and conveyors, and each worker does only one operation. Almost all the cutting and processing is still done by workers. Production jobs can require between 10,000 and 20,000 cuts a day. In some large plants in the United States, for example, a few jobs, such as carcass splitting and bacon slicing, have been automated.

Slaughtering Process

The animals are herded through a holding pen to slaughter (see figure 67.2). The animal must be stunned before being bled, unless slaughtered in accordance with Jewish or Muslim rites. Usually the animal is either knocked to an unconscious state with a bolt stunner gun or with a stunner gun utilizing compressed air that drives a pin into the head (the medulla oblongata) of the animal. After the stunning or "knocking" process, one of the animal's hind legs is secured by a chain hooked onto an overhead conveyor which transfers the animal to the next room, where it is bled by "sticking" the jugular arteries in the neck with a sharp knife. The bleeding-out process follows, and the blood is drained through pipes for processing on floors below.

The skin (hide) is removed by a series of cuts with knives (new air-powered knives are being used in the larger plants for some hide-removal operations) and the animal is then suspended by both hind legs from the overhead conveyor system. In some hog operations, the skin is not removed at this stage. Rather the hair is removed by sending the carcass through tanks of water heated to 58 °C and then through a dehair machine that rubs the hair off the skin. Any remaining hair is removed by singeing and finally shaving.

The front legs and then the viscera (intestines) are removed. The head is then cut and dropped, and the carcass is split in half vertically along the spinal column. Hydraulic band saws are the usual tool for this job. After the carcass is split, it is rinsed with hot water, and may be steam vacuumed or even treated with a newly developed pasteurization process being introduced in some countries.

Government health inspectors usually inspect after the head removal, the viscera removal and the carcass splitting and final wash.

After this, the carcass, still hanging from the overhead conveyor system, moves to a cooler for chilling over the next 24 to 36 hours. The temperature is usually about 2 °C to slow bacterial growth and inhibit spoilage.

Processing

Once chilled, the carcass halves are then cut into front and hind quarters. After this, pieces are further divided into prime cuts, depending on customer specifications. Some quarters are processed for delivery as the front or hind quarters without any further significant trimming. These pieces can weigh from 70 to 125 kg. Many plants (in the United States, the majority of plants) conduct further processing of the meat (some plants do only this processing and receive their meat from slaughterhouses). Products from these plants are shipped in boxes weighing approximately 30 kg.

Cutting is done by hand or powered saws, depending on the cuts, usually following trimming operations to remove skin. Many plants also use large grinders for grinding hamburger and other ground meats. Further processing can involve equipment including bacon presses, ham tumblers and extruders, bacon slicers, electric meat tenderizers and smoke houses. Conveyor belts and screw augers are often used to transport product. Processing areas are also kept cool, with temperatures in the 4 °C range.

Offal meats, such as liver, hearts, sweetbreads, tongues and glands, are processed in a separate area.

Many plants also treat the hides before sending them to a tanner.

Hazards and Their Prevention

Meatpacking has one of the highest rates of injury of all industries. A worker may be injured by the moving animals as they are led through the holding pen into the plant. Adequate training must be given to workers on handling live animals, and minimal worker exposure in this process is advised. Stunner guns may prematurely or inadvertently discharge while workers try to still the animals.

Figure 67.2 • Beef slaughtering flow chart.

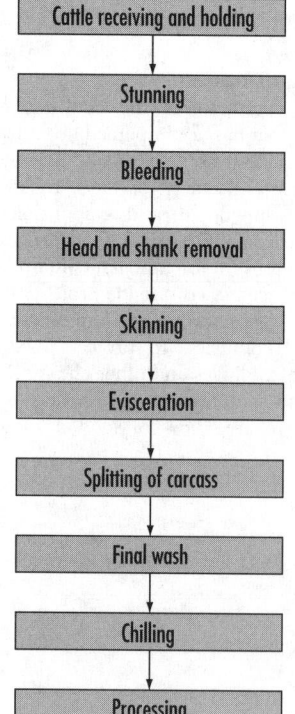

Figure 67.3 • Cutting and sorting meat without protective equipment in a Thai meat packing factory.

Falling animals and nervous system reactions in stunned cattle that cause jerking present hazards to workers in the area. Further, many operations utilize a series of hooks, chains and conveyor tram rails to move the product between processing steps, posing the hazard of falling carcasses and product.

Adequate maintenance of all equipment is necessary, especially equipment used to move meat. Such equipment must be checked frequently and repaired as needed. Adequate safeguards for knocking guns, such as safety switches and making sure there is no blow back, must be taken. Workers involved in knocking and sticking operations must be trained on the hazards of this job, as well as provided with guarded knives and protective equipment to prevent injury. For sticking operations this includes arm guards, mesh gloves and special guarded knives.

Both in the slaughter and further processing of animals, hand knives and mechanical cutting devices are used. Mechanical cutting devices include head splitters, bone splitters, snout pullers, electric band and circular saws, electric- or air-powered circular-blade knives, grinding machines and bacon processors. These types of operations have a high rate of injury, from knife cuts to amputations, because of the speed at which workers operate, the inherent danger of the tools being used and the often slippery nature of the product from fat and wet processes. Workers can be cut by their own knives and by other workers' knives during the butchering process (see figure 67.3).

The above operations require protective equipment, including protective helmets, footwear, mesh gloves and aprons, wrist and forearm guards and waterproof aprons. Protective goggles may be required during boning, trimming and cutting operations to prevent foreign objects from entering workers' eyes. Metal mesh gloves must not be used while operating any type of powered or electrical saw. Powered saws and tools must have proper safety guards, such as blade guards and shut-off switches. Unguarded sprockets and chains, conveyor belts and other equipment can pose a hazard. All such equipment must be properly guarded. Hand knives should also have guards to prevent the hand holding the knife from slipping over the blade. Training and adequate spacing between workers is necessary to conduct operations safely.

Workers maintaining, cleaning or unjamming equipment such as conveyor belts, bacon processors, meat grinders and other processing equipment are subject to the hazard of the inadvertent start-up of equipment. This has caused fatalities and amputations. Some equipment is cleaned while running, subjecting workers to the hazard of getting caught in the machinery.

Workers must be trained in safety lockout/tagout procedures. Implementation of procedures that prevent workers from fixing, cleaning or unjamming equipment until the equipment is off and locked out will prevent injuries. Workers involved in locking out pieces of equipment must be trained on procedures for neutralizing all energy sources.

Wet and treacherously slippery floors and stairs throughout the plant pose a serious hazard to workers. Elevated work platforms also pose a falling hazard. Workers must be provided with safety shoes with non-slip soles. Non-slip floor surfaces and roughened floors, approved by local health agencies, are available and should be used on floors and stairways. Adequate drainage in wet areas must be provided, along with proper and adequate housekeeping of floors during production hours to minimize wet and slippery surfaces. All elevated surfaces must also be properly equipped with guard rails both to prevent workers from accidental falls and to prevent worker contact and materials falling from conveyors. Toe boards should also be used on elevated platforms, where necessary. Guardrails should also be used on stairways on the production floor to prevent slipping.

The combination of wet working conditions and elaborate electrical wiring poses a hazard of electrocution to workers. All equipment must be properly grounded. Electrical outlet boxes should be provided with covers which effectively protect against accidental contact. All electrical wiring should be checked periodically for cracking, fraying or other defects, and all electrical equipment should be grounded. Ground fault circuit interrupters should be used where possible.

Lugging of carcasses (which can weigh up to 140 kg) and repetitive lifting of 30 kg boxes of meat ready for shipping can cause back injuries. Cumulative trauma disorders such as carpal tunnel syndrome, tendinitis and tenosynovitis are widespread in the industry. In the United States, for example, meatpacking operations have higher rates of these disorders than any other industry. The wrist, elbow and shoulder are all affected. These disorders can arise from the highly repetitive and forceful nature of the assembly line work in the plants, the use of vibrating equipment in some jobs, the use of dull knives, the cutting of frozen meat and the use of high-pressure hoses in cleaning

Figure 67.4 • With conveyer belts located beneath worktables, workers can push finished products through a hole in the table instead of having to throw meat over their heads.

United Food & Commercial Workers, AFL-CIO

operations. Prevention of these disorders comes through ergonomic redesign of equipment, use of mechanical assists, vigilant maintenance of vibrating equipment to minimize vibration, and improved worker training and medical programmes. Ergonomic redesign measures include:

- lowering overhead conveyors to reduce repetitive overhead throws on production lines (see figure 67.4)
- moving horizontal platforms that allow workers to split animals with a minimum of reaches
- providing sharp knives with redesigned handles
- building mechanical assists that reduce the force of a job (see figure 67.5)
- increased staffing on high-force jobs, assuring properly sized hand tools and gloves and careful design of packing areas to minimize twisting when lifting, as well as to minimize lifting from below the knees and above the shoulders
- vacuum hoists and other mechanical lifting devices to reduce lifting of boxes (see figure 67.6).

Aisles and walkways should be dry and free of obstacles so that carrying and transporting heavy loads can be done safely.

Workers should be trained or proper use of knives. Cutting frozen meat should be avoided completely.

Early medical intervention and treatment for symptomatic workers is also desirable. Because of the similar nature of the stressors on jobs in this industry, job rotation must be used with caution. Job analyses must be carried out and reviewed to assure that the same muscle tendon groups are not used in different tasks. In addition, workers must be adequately trained in all jobs in any planned rotation.

Machines and equipment found in meatpacking plants produce a high level of noise. Workers must be provided with ear plugs, as well as hearing examinations to ascertain any potential hearing loss. Further, sound-dampening equipment should be used on machinery where possible. Good maintenance on conveyor systems can prevent unnecessary noise.

Workers can be exposed to toxic chemicals during the cleaning and sanitizing of equipment. Compounds used include both alkaline (caustic) and acid cleaners. These can cause dryness, allergic rashes and other skin problems. Liquids can splash up and burn the eyes. Depending on the type of cleaning compound used, PPE—including eye, face and arm coverings, aprons and protective footwear—must be provided. Hand and eye washing facilities should also be available. High-pressure hoses used to transport hot water for disinfecting equipment can also cause burns. Adequate worker training on the use of such hoses is important. Chlorine in the water used to wash the carcasses can also cause eye, throat and skin irritation. New anti-bacterial rinses are being introduced on the slaughter side to decrease bacteria that can cause foodborne illnesses. Adequate ventilation must be provided. Special care to assure that the strength of the chemicals does not exceed manufacturers' instructions must be taken.

Ammonia is used as a refrigerant in the industry, and ammonia leaks from pipes are common. Ammonia gas is irritating to the eyes and skin. Mild to moderate exposure to the gas can produce headaches, burning in the throat, perspiration, nausea and vomiting. If escape is not possible, there may be severe irritation of the respiratory tract, producing cough, pulmonary oedema or respiratory arrest. Adequate maintenance of refrigeration lines is key to preventing such leaks. In addition, once an ammonia leak is detected, monitoring and evacuation procedures must be carried out to prevent dangerous exposures.

Carbon dioxide (CO_2) in the form of dry ice is used in the packaging area. During this process, CO_2 gas may escape from these vats and spread throughout the room. Exposure can cause

Figure 67.5 • Having paddle bones pulled out by the force of an attached chain rather than manually lessens musculoskeletal hazards.

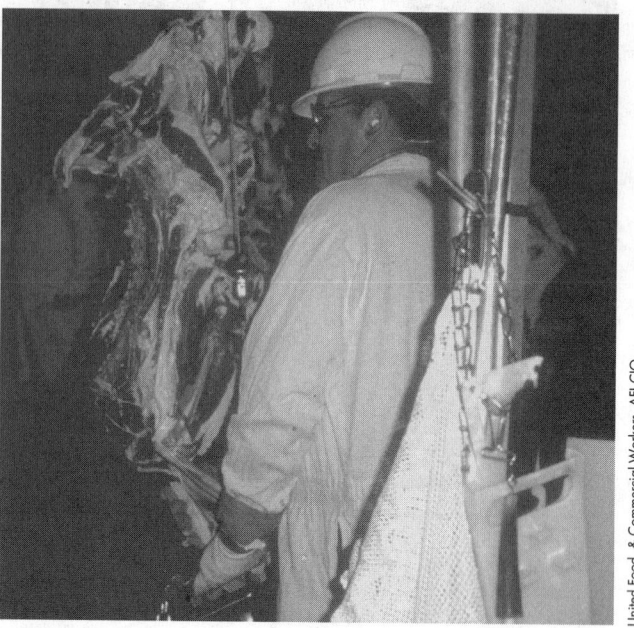

United Food & Commercial Workers, AFL-CIO

headaches, dizziness, nausea, vomiting and, at high levels, death. Adequate ventilation must be provided.

Blood tanks present hazards associated with confined spaces if the plant does not utilize a closed piping and processing system for the blood. Toxic substances emitted from decomposing blood and lack of oxygen pose serious hazards to those having to enter and/or clean tanks or work in the area. Prior to entry, the atmosphere must be tested for toxic chemicals, and the presence of adequate oxygen must be assured.

Figure 67.6 • The use of vacuum hoists for lifting boxes allows workers to guide boxes rather than load them by hand.

United Food & Commercial Workers, AFL-CIO

Workers are exposed to infectious diseases such as brucellosis, erysipeloid, leptospirosis, dermatophytoses and warts.

Brucellosis is caused by a bacterium and is transmitted by the handling of infected cattle or swine. Persons infected by this bacterium experience constant or recurring fever, headaches, weakness, joint pain, night sweats and loss of appetite. Limiting the number of infected cattle slaughtered is one key to preventing this disorder.

Erysipeloid and leptospirosis are also caused by bacteria. Erysipeloid is transmitted by infection of skin puncture wounds, scratches and abrasions; it causes redness and irritation around the site of infection and can spread to the bloodstream and lymph nodes. Leptospirosis is transmitted through direct contact with infected animals or through water, moist soil or vegetation contaminated by the urine of infected animals. Muscular aches, eye infections, fever, vomiting, chills and headaches occur, and kidney and liver damage may develop.

Dermatophytosis, on the other hand, is a fungal disease and is transmitted by contact with the hair and skin of infected persons and animals. Dermatophytosis, also know as ringworm, causes the hair to fall out and small, yellowish cuplike crusts to develop on the scalp.

Verruca vulgaris, a wart caused by a virus, can be spread by infectious workers who have contaminated towels, meat, fish knives, work tables or other objects.

Other diseases that are found in meatpacking plants in some countries include Q fever and tuberculosis. The primary carriers of Q fever are cattle, sheep, goats and ticks. Humans are usually infected by inhaling aerosolized particles from contaminated environments. Typical symptoms include fever, malaise, severe headache and muscular and abdominal pain. The incidence of toxoplasma antibodies amongst abattoir workers is high in certain countries.

Dermatitis is also common in meatpacking plants. Exposure to blood and other animal fluids, exposure to wet conditions, and exposure to cleaning compounds used for cleaning/sanitation in facilities can lead to skin irritation.

Infectious diseases and dermatitis can be prevented with personal hygiene that includes ready and easy access to sanitation and hand-washing facilities that contain soap and disposable hand towels, the provision of proper PPE (which may include protective gloves as well as eye and respiratory protection where exposure to airborne animal body fluids is possible), the use of some barrier creams to provide limited protection against irritants, worker education and early medical care.

The kill floor, where the slaughtering, bleeding and splitting of the animal is done, can be especially hot and humid. A properly working ventilation system that removes the hot, humid air and prevents heat stress should be used. Fans, preferably overhead or roof fans, increase air movement. Beverages should be provided to replace fluids and salts lost through sweating, and frequent rest breaks, in a cool area, should be allowed.

There is also a distinctive smell in slaughterhouses, due to a mixture of odours such as those of wet leather, blood, vomit, urine and faeces of animals. This smell spreads throughout the kill floor, offal, rendering and hide areas. Exhaust ventilation is necessary to remove the odours.

Refrigerated work environments are essential in the meatpacking industry. Processing and transporting meat products generally require temperatures at or below 9 °C. Areas such as freezers may require temperatures to go as low as –40 °C. The most common cold-related injuries are frostnip, frostbite, immersion foot and trenchfoot, which occur in localized areas of the body. A serious consequence of cold stress is hypothermia. The respiratory system, the circulatory system and the osteoarticular system can also be affected by overexposure to the cold.

To prevent the consequences of cold stress and reduce the hazards of cold working conditions, workers should wear appropriate clothing, and the workplace should have proper equipment, administrative controls and engineering controls. Multiple layers of clothing provide better protection than single thick garments. Cooling equipment and air distribution systems should minimize air velocity. Unit coolers should be placed as far away from workers as possible, and wind deflectors and barriers should be used to protect workers from windchill.

POULTRY PROCESSING

Tony Ashdown

Economic Importance
Chicken and turkey production has increased dramatically in the United States since the 1980s. According to a US Department of Labor report this has been due to a change in consumer eating patterns (Hetrick 1994). A shift from red meat and pork to poultry is due in part to early medical studies.

The rise in consumption correspondingly has spurred an increase in the number of processing facilities and growers and a large rise in levels of employment. For example, the United States poultry industry experienced an increase in employment of 64% from 1980 to 1992. Productivity, in terms of pounds yield per worker, increased 3.1% due to mechanization or automation, as well as an increase in line speed, or birds per work hour. However, in comparison to red meat production, poultry production is still very labour intensive.

Globalization is also ocurring. There are production and processing facilities jointly owned by US investors and China and breeding, grow-out and processing facilities in China export product to Japan.

Typical poultry line workers are relatively unskilled, less educated, often members of minority groups and much lower paid than workers in the red meat and manufacturing sectors. Turnover is unusually high in certain aspects of the process. Live hanging, deboning and sanitation jobs are particularly stressful and have high turnover rates. Poultry processing by its nature is a largely rural-based industry found in economically depressed areas where there is a labour surplus. In the United States many processing plants have an increasing number of Spanish-speaking workers. These workers are somewhat transient, working in the processing plants part of the year. As the region's crops near harvest, large segments of the workers move outdoors to pick and harvest.

Processing
Throughout the processing of chicken, rigid sanitation requirements must be met. This means that floors must be washed down periodically and often and that debris, parts and fat must be removed. Conveyors and processing equipment must be accessible, washed down and sanitized also. Condensation must not be allowed to accumulate on ceilings and equipment over exposed chicken; it must be wiped down with long-handled sponge mops. Overhead, unguarded radial-blade fans circulate the air in the processing areas.

Because of these sanitation requirements, guarded rotating equipment often cannot be silenced for noise-abatement purposes. Consequently, in the majority of the processing plant's production areas, there is high noise exposure. A proper and well-run hearing conservation programme is necessary. Not only should initial audiograms and annual audiograms be given, but periodic dosimetry should also be done to document exposure.

Purchased processing equipment should have as low an operating noise level as possible. Particular care needs to be taken in educating and training the workforce.

Receiving and live hang

The first step in processing involves off-loading of the modules and destacking the trays onto a conveyor system to the live hang area. Work here is in almost complete darkness, since this has a quieting effect on the birds. The conveyor belt with a tray is at about waist level. A hanger, with gloved hands, must reach and grab a bird by both thighs and hang its feet in a shackle on an overhead conveyor travelling in the opposite direction.

The hazards of the operation vary. Aside from the normal high level of noise, the darkness and the disorienting effect of opposite running conveyors, there is the dust from flapping birds, suddenly sprayed urine or faeces in the face and the possibility of a gloved finger being caught in a shackle. Conveyor lines need to be equipped with emergency stops. Hangers are constantly striking the backs of their hands against neighboring shackles as they pass overhead.

It is not uncommon for a hanger to be required to hang an average of 23 (or more) birds per minute. (Some positions on the hanger's lines require more physical motions, perhaps 26 birds per minute.) Typically, seven hangers on one line may hang 38,640 birds in 4 hours before they get a break. If each bird weighs approximately 1.9 kg, each hanger conceivably lifts a total of 1,057 kg during the first 4 hours of his or her shift before a scheduled break. The hanger's job is extremely stressful from both a physiological and psychological standpoint. Reducing workload could lessen this stress. The constant grabbing with both hands, pulling in and simultaneously lifting a flapping, scratching bird at shoulder or head height is stressful to the upper shoulder and neck.

The bird's feathers and feet can easily scratch a hanger's unprotected arms. The hangers are required to stand for prolonged periods of time on hard surfaces, which can lead to lower-back discomfort and pain. Proper footwear, possible use of a rump rest stand, protective eyewear, single-use disposable respirators, eyewash facilities and arm guards need to be available for the hanger's protection.

An extremely important element to ensure the worker's health is a proper job conditioning programme. For a period of up to 2 weeks, a new hanger must be acclimated to the conditions and slowly work up to a full shift. Another key ingredient is job rotation; after two hours of hanging birds, a hanger may be rotated to a less strenuous position. The division of labour among the hangers may be such that frequent short rest breaks in an air conditioned area are essential. Some plants have tried double crewing to allow crews to work for 20 minutes and rest for 20 minutes, to reduce the ergonomic stressors.

The health and comfort conditions for the hangers are somewhat dependent on the outside weather conditions and the conditions of the birds. If the weather is hot and dry, the birds carry with them dust and mites, which easily become airborne. If the weather is wet, the birds are harder to handle, the hangers' gloves readily become wet and the hangers must work harder to hold onto the birds. There have been recent developments in reusable gloves with padded backs.

The impact of airborne particulates, feathers, mites and so on may be lessened with an efficient local exhaust ventilation (LEV) system. A balanced system using the push-pull principle, which uses down-draft cooling or heating, would benefit the workers. Additional cooling fans placed about would upset the efficiency of a balanced push-pull system.

Once hung in the shackles, the birds are conveyed to be initially stunned with electricity. The high voltage does not kill them but forces them to hang limply as a rotating wheel (bicycle tyre) guides their neck against a counter-rotating circular cutting blade. The neck is partially severed with the bird's heart still beating to pump out the remainder of blood. There must be no blood in the carcass. A skilled worker must be positioned to slice those birds the kill machine misses. Because of the excessive amount of blood, the worker must be protected by wearing wet gear (a rain suit) and eye protection. Eye washing or flushing facilities must be made available also.

Dressing

The conveyor of birds then passes through a series of troughs or tanks of circulating hot water. These are called scalders. Water is usually heated by steam coils. The water is usually treated or chlorinated to kill bacteria. This phase allows the feathers to be easily removed. Care must be taken when working around the scalders. Often piping and valves are unprotected or poorly insulated and are contact points for burns.

As the birds exit the scalders, the carcass is passed through a U-shaped arrangement which pulls the head off. These parts are usually conveyed in flowing water troughs to a rendering (or by-products) area.

The line of carcasses passes through machines which have a series of rotating drums fixed with rubber fingers which remove the feathers. The feathers drop into a trench below with flowing water leading to the rendering area.

Consistency in bird weight is extremely critical to all aspects of the processing operation. If the weights vary from load to load, the production departments must adjust their processing equipment accordingly. For example, if lighter-weight birds follow heavier birds through the pickers, the rotating drums may not get all the feathers off. This causes rejects and rework. Not only does it add to the processing costs, but it causes additional ergonomic hand stresses, because someone has to hand pick the feathers using a pincer grip.

Once through the pickers, the line of birds passes through a singer. This is a gas-fired arrangement with three burners on each side, used to singe the fine hairs and feathers of each bird. Care must be taken to assure that the gas piping's integrity is maintained due to the corrosive conditions of the picking or dressing area.

The birds then pass a hock cutter to sever the feet (or paws). The paws may be conveyed separately to a separate processing area of the plant for cleaning, sizing, sorting, chilling and packaging for the Asian market.

The birds must be rehung on different shackles before they enter the evisceration section of the plant. The shackles here are configured slightly differently, usually longer. Automation is readily available for this part of the process (see figure 67.7). However, workers need to provide back-up if a machine jams, to rehang dropped birds or to manually cut the feet off with pruning shears if the hock cutter fails to sever properly. From a processing and cost standpoint, it is critical that every shackle be filled. Rehang jobs involve exposure to highly repetitive motions and work involving awkward postures (raised elbows and shoulders). These workers are at increased risk for cumulative trauma disorders (CDTs).

If a machine goes down or gets out of adjustment, a great deal of effort and stress is applied to get the lines running, sometimes at the expense of workers' safety. When climbing to access points on the equipment, a maintenance worker may not take the time to get a ladder, instead stepping on top of wet, slippery equipment. Falls are a hazard. When any such equipment is purchased and installed, provisions must be made for easy access and maintenance. Lockout points and shut-offs need to be placed on each piece of equipment. The manufacturer must consider the environment and hazardous conditions under which their equipment must be maintained.

Evisceration

As the conveyor of birds pass out of dressing into a physically separate part of the process, they usually pass through another singer and then through a rotating circular blade which cuts out the oil sac or gland on each bird's back at the base of the tail. Often such equipment's blades are free rotating and need to guarded properly. Again, if the machine is not adjusted according to the bird's weight, workers must be assigned to remove the sac by slicing it off with a knife.

Next, the conveyor line of birds passes through an automatic venting machine, which pushes up on the abdomen slightly while a blade cuts open the carcass without disturbing the bowel. The next machine or part of the process scoops into the cavity and pulls out the unbroken viscera for inspection. In the United States, the next few processing steps may involve government inspectors who check for growths, air sac disease, faecal contamination and a series of other abnormalities. Usually one inspector checks for only two or three items. If there is a high rate of abnormalities, the inspectors will slow the line down. Often the abnormalities do not cause total rejects, but specific parts of the birds may be washed or salvaged from the carcass to increase yield.

The more rejects, the more manual rework involving repetitive motion due to cutting, slicing and so on the production workers must perform. Government inspectors are usually seated on mandated adjustable elevating stands, whereas production workers called helpers, to their left and right, stand on grating or may use an adjustable sit stand if provided. Foot rests, adjustable height platforms, sit stands and job rotation will help relieve the physical and psychological stresses associated with this part of the process.

Once past the inspections, the viscera are sorted as they pass through a liver/heart or giblet harvester. The separated intestines, stomachs, spleens, kidneys and gall bladders are discarded and flushed into a flowing trench below. The heart and liver are separated and pumped to separate sorting conveyors, where

---

Figure 67.7 • Multi-cut machines reduce repetitive manual repetitive work; workers need to re-work birds that the machines miss.

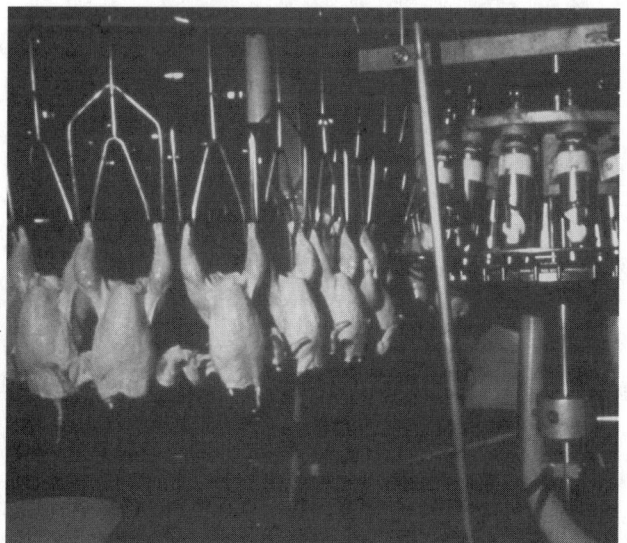

United Food & Commercial Workers, AFL-CIO

---

workers inspect and pick by hand. The remaining intact livers and hearts are pumped or carried to a separate processing area to be bulk-packed by hand or later recombined in a giblet pack for stuffing by hand into the cavity of a whole bird for sale.

Once the carcass clears the harvester, the bird's crop is augered out; each body cavity is probed by hand to pull out the remaining viscera and gizzard if necessary. The worker uses each hand in a separate bird as the conveyor passes in front. A suction device is often used to vacuum out any remaining lungs or kidneys. Frequently, due to the bird's habit of ingesting small pebbles or pieces of litter during grow-out, a worker will reach into the bird's cavity and receive painful puncture wounds in the tips of the fingers or under the finger nails.

The small wounds, if not treated properly, run the risk of serious infection since the bird's cavity still is not cleaned of bacteria. Since tactile sensitivity is necessary for the job, there are no gloves yet available to prevent these frequent incidents. A tight-fitting surgeon's type glove has been tried with some success. The line pace is so fast that it does not allow the worker to carefully insert his or her hands.

Finally, the carcass's neck is removed by machine and harvested. The birds go through a bird washer which uses chlorinated spray to wash out excess viscera inside and outside each bird.

Throughout the dressing and evisceration, workers are exposed to high levels of noise, slippery floors and high ergonomic stress on kill, scissor and packaging jobs. According to a NIOSH study, rates of CTDs documented in poultry plants can range from 20 to 30% of workers (NIOSH 1990).

Chiller operations

Depending on the process, necks are pumped to a open-surfaced chiller tank with rotating arms, paddles or augers. These open tanks pose a serious threat to the safety of the worker during operation and need to be properly guarded by removable covers or grills. The tank's cover must allow for visual inspection of the tank. If a cover is removed or lifted, interlocks must be provided to shut off the rotating arms or auger. The chilled necks are either bulk-packed for later processing or taken to the giblet wrap area for recombining and wrapping.

Once through evisceration, the conveyor lines of birds are either dropped into large, open-surfaced horizontal chilling tanks or, in Europe, pass through refrigerated, circulating air. These chillers are fitted with paddles which slowly rotate through the chiller, bringing down the bird's body temperature. The chilled water is highly chlorinated (20 ppm or greater) and aerated for agitation. Bird carcass residence time in the chiller may be up to an hour.

Due to the high levels of free chlorine released and circulated, workers are exposed and may experience symptoms of eye and throat irritation, coughing and shortness of breath. NIOSH conducted several studies of eye and upper respiratory irritation in poultry processing plants, which recommended that levels of chlorine be monitored and controlled closely, that curtains be used to contain the liberated chlorine (or an enclosure of some sort should surround the open surface of the tank) and that an exhaust ventilation system should be installed (Sanderson, Weber and Echt 1995).

The resident time is critical and a matter of some controversy. Upon exiting evisceration, the carcass is not completely clean, and the skin pores and feather follicles are open and harbour disease-causing bacteria. The main purpose of the trip through the chiller is to chill the bird quickly to reduce spoilage. It does not kill bacteria, and the risk of cross contamination is a serious public health issue. Critics have called the chiller bath method "faecal soup". From a profit perspective, a side benefit is the fact that the meat will absorb the chiller water like a sponge. It adds almost 8% to the market weight of the product (Linder 1996).

Upon exiting the chiller, the carcasses are deposited on a conveyor or shaker table. Specially trained workers called graders inspect the birds for bruises, skin breaks and so on and rehang the birds on separate shackle lines travelling in front of them. Downgraded birds may travel to different processes for parts recovery. Graders stand for prolonged periods handling chilled birds, which can result in numbness and hand pain. Gloves with liners are worn not only to protect the hands of workers from the chlorine residue, but also to provide some degree of warmth.

Cut-up

From grading the birds travel overhead to different processes, machines and lines in an area of the plant called second or further processing. Some machines are hand fed with two-handed trips. Other, more modern European equipment, at separate stations, may remove the thighs and wings and split the breast, without being touched by the worker. Again, consistency in bird size or weight is critical to the successful operation of this automated equipment. Rotating circular blades must be changed every day.

Skilled maintenance technicians and operators must be attentive to the equipment. Access to such equipment for adjustment, maintenance and sanitation needs to be frequent, requiring stairs, not ladders, and substantial work platforms. During blade changing, handling needs to be cautious because of the slipperiness due to fat build-up. Special cut- and slip-resistant gloves with the fingertips removed protect most of the hand, while the tips of the fingers can be used to manipulate the tools, bolts and nuts used for replacement.

Evolving consumer tastes have affected the production process. In some cases, the products (e.g., drumstick, thighs and breasts) are required to be skinless. Processing equipment has been developed to efficiently remove skin so workers do not have to do so by hand. However, as automated processing equipment is added and lines are rearranged, conditions become more crowded and awkward for workers to get around, manoeuvre floor jacks and carry totes, or plastic tubs, of iced product weighing over 27 kg over slippery, wet floors.

Depending on the customer demand and product mix sales, workers stand facing fixed-height conveyors, selecting and arranging product on plastic trays. The product travels in one direction or drops from a chute. The trays arrive on overhead conveyors, descending so the workers can grab a stack and set them in front for easy reach. Product defects may be either placed on a counterflow conveyor below or hung in a shackle travelling in the opposite direction overhead. Workers stand for prolonged periods of time almost shoulder to shoulder, perhaps separated only by a tote into which defects or waste are dropped. Workers need to be provided with gloves, aprons and boots.

Some products may be bulk-packed in cartons covered with ice. This is called ice pack. Workers fill cartons by hand onto scales and manually transfer them to moving conveyors. Later in the ice pack room, ice is added, cartons recovered and the cartons removed and stacked manually on pallets ready for shipment.

Some workers in cut-up are also exposed to high levels of noise.

Deboning

If the carcass is destined for deboning, the product is tanked out in large aluminium bins or cardboard boxes (or gaylords) mounted on pallets. Breast meat must be aged for a certain number of hours before processing either by machine or hand. Fresh chicken is difficult to cut and trim by hand. From an ergonomic standpoint, meat ageing is a key point in helping to reduce repetitive motion injuries to the hand.

There are two methods used in deboning. In the manual method, once ready, carcasses with only the breast meat remaining are dumped into a hopper leading to a conveyor. This section of the line's workers must handle each carcass and hold them against two horizontal, in-running textured skinner rolls. The carcass is rolled over the rolls as the skin is pulled away and down to a conveyor below. There is a risk of workers becoming inattentive or distracted and having their fingers pulled into the rollers. Emergency stop (E-stop) switches need to be provided within easy reach of either the free hand or knee. Gloves and loose clothing cannot be worn around such equipment. Aprons (worn snugly) and protective eyewear must be worn due to the possibility of bone chips or fragments being thrown.

The next step is performed by workers called nickers. They hold a carcass in one hand and make a slice along the keel (or breastbone) with the other. Sharp, short-bladed knives are normally used. Stainless steel mesh gloves are usually worn over a latex- or nitrile-gloved hand holding the carcass. Knives used for this operation do not need to have a sharp point. Protective eye wear needs to be worn.

The third step is performed by the keel pullers. This may be done manually or with a jig or fixture where the carcass is guided over an inexpensive "Y" fixture (made out of stainless steel rod stock) and pulled toward the worker. The working height of each fixture needs to be adjusted to the worker. The manual method simply requires the worker to use a pincer grip with a gloved hand and pull the keel bone out. Protective eyewear must be worn as described above.

The fourth step requires hand filleting. Workers stand shoulder to shoulder reaching for breast meat as it travels on shackle trays in front of them. There are certain techniques that must be observed for this part of the process. Proper job instruction and immediate correction when errors are observed are necessary. Workers are protected with a chain or mesh glove on one hand. In the other, they hold an extremely sharp knife (with a tip that may be too sharply pointed).

The work is fast paced, and workers who get behind are pressured to take short cuts, such as reaching across in front of the associate next to them or reaching for and/or stabbing a piece of meat travelling by out of their reach. Not only does the knife puncture reduce the quality of the product, but it also results in serious injury to fellow workers in the form of lacerations, which are often subject to infection. Protective plastic arm guards are available to prevent this frequent type of injury.

As the fillet meat is replaced on the conveyor shackle, it is picked off by the next section of workers, called trimmers. These workers must trim excess fat, missed skin and bones out of the meat using sharp and adjusted shears. Once trimmed, the finished product is either tray packed by hand or dropped into bulk bags and placed into cartons for restaurant use.

The second method of deboning involves automatic processing equipment developed in Europe. As with the manual method, bulk boxes or tanks of carcasses, sometimes with wings still attached, are loaded into a hopper and chute. Carcasses may then be picked manually and placed into segmented conveyors, or each carcass must be placed manually onto a shoe of the machine. The machine moves rapidly, carrying the carcass through a series of fingers (to remove skin), cutting blades and slitters. All that remains is a meatless carcass that is bulked out and used elsewhere. Most of the manual line's positions are eliminated, except for the trimmers with scissors.

Deboning workers are exposed to serious ergonomic hazards from the forceful, repetitive nature of the work. In each of the deboning positions, especially filleters and trimmers, job rotation may be a key element to reducing ergonomic stresses. It must be understood that the position a worker rotates to must not use the same muscle group. A weak argument has been made that filleters and trimmers may rotate to each other's position. This should not be allowed, because the same gripping, twisting and turning methods are used in the hand not holding the tool (knife or scissors). It may be argued that the muscles holding a knife loosely for twisting and turning while making fillet cuts are used differently when opening and closing scissors. However, twisting and turning of the hand is still required. Line speeds play a critical role in the onset of ergonomic disorders on these jobs.

Overwrap and chilling

After the product is tray packed in either cut-up or deboning, the trays are conveyed to another step in the process called overwrap. Workers retrieve specific product in trays and feed the trays into machines which apply and stretch printed clear wrap over the tray, tuck it under and pass the tray over a heat sealer. The tray may then pass through a washer, where it is retrieved and placed in a basket. The basket containing a particular product is placed on a conveyor where it passes into a chiller area. Trays are then sorted and stacked either manually or automatically.

Workers in the overwrap area stand for prolonged periods of time and are rotated so the hands they use to pick up the product trays are rotated. Normally the overwrap area is relatively dry. Cushioned mats would reduce leg and back fatigue.

Consumer demand, sales and marketing can create special ergonomic hazards. At certain times of the year, large trays are packed with several pounds of product for "convenience and cost savings". This added weight has contributed to additional repetitive motion-related hand injuries simply because the process and conveying system is designed for one-handed pick-up. A worker simply does not have the strength necessary for repeated one-handed lifts of overweight trays.

The clear plastic wrap used in the packing may release slight amounts of monomer or other decomposition products when heated for sealing. If complaints arise concerning the fumes, the manufacturer or supplier of the film should be called in to help assess the problem. LEV may be necessary. The heat-sealing equipment needs to be maintained properly and its E-stops checked for proper operation at the beginning of each shift.

The chilling room or refrigeration area poses a different set of fire, safety and health risks. From a fire standpoint, the product packaging poses a risk since it is usually highly combustible polystyrene. The wall's insulation is usually a polystyrene foam core. Chillers should be properly protected with pre-action dry sprinkler systems designed for extraordinary hazard. (Pre-action systems employ automatic sprinklers attached to piping systems containing dry air or nitrogen as well as a supplemental detection system installed in the same area as the sprinklers.)

Once the baskets of trays enter the chiller, workers must physically pick up a basket and lift it to shoulder height or higher to a stack on a dolly. After so many baskets are stacked, workers are required to assist each other to stack the baskets of product higher.

Temperatures in the chiller may run as low as -2 °C. Workers should be issued and instructed to wear multilayered clothing or "freezer suits" along with insulated safety-toed footwear. Dollies or stacks of baskets must be physically handled and pushed to various areas of the chiller until called for. Often, workers attempt to save time by pushing several stacks of trays at one time, which can result in muscle or lower-back strain.

Basket integrity is an important aspect of both product quality control and worker safety. If broken baskets are stacked with other full baskets stacked on top, the entire load becomes unstable and is easily tipped over. Product packages fall on the floor and become dirty or damaged, resulting in rework and extra manual

handling by workers. Stacks of baskets may also fall on other workers.

When a particular product mix is called for, baskets may be destacked manually. Trays are loaded onto a conveyor with a scale which weighs them and attaches labels marked with the weight and codes for tracking purposes. Trays are packed manually in cartons or boxes sometimes lined with impermeable liners. Workers often have to reach for trays. As in the case of the overwrap process, larger, heavier packages of product can cause stress to the hands, arms and shoulders. Workers stand for prolonged periods in one spot. Antifatigue mats can reduce leg and lower-back stresses.

As the cartons of packages pass down a conveyor, liners may be heat sealed while CO_2 is injected. This, along with continued refrigeration, prolongs product shelf life. Also, as the carton or case continues its progress, a scoop of CO_2 nuggets (dry ice) is added to prolong shelf life on its way to a customer in a refrigerated trailer. However, CO_2 has inherent hazards in enclosed areas. The nuggets may either be dropped by the chute or scooped out of a large, partially covered bin. Though the exposure limit (TLV) for CO_2 is relatively high, and continuous monitors are readily available, workers also need to learn its hazards and symptoms and wear protective gloves and eye protection. Proper warning signs should also be posted in the area.

Cartons or cases of trayed product usually are sealed with hot-melt adhesive injected onto the cardboard. Painful contact burns are possible if adjustments, sensors and pressures are improper. Workers need to wear protective eyewear with side shields. The application and sealing equipment needs to be completely de-energized, with pressure bled off, before adjustments or repairs are made.

Once the cartons are sealed, they may either be manually lifted from the conveyor or run through an automatic palletizer or other remotely operated equipment. Due to the high rate of production, the potential for back injuries exists. This work is usually performed in a cold environment, which has a tendency to lead to strain injuries.

From an ergonomic standpoint, carton retrieval and stacking is easily automated, but investment and maintenance costs will be high.

Thigh deboning and ground chicken

No part of the chicken is wasted in modern poultry processing. Chicken thighs are bulk-packed, stored at or near freezing and then further processed, or deboned, either with scissors or pneumatically actuated hand-operated trimmers. Like the breast deboning operation, thigh deboning workers must remove excess fat and skin with scissors. Work area temperatures may be as low as 4 to 7 °C. Despite the fact that trimmers may wear liners with gloves, their hands are sufficiently chilled to restrict blood circulation, thereby magnifying the ergonomic stresses.

Once chilled, the thigh meat is further processed by adding flavours and grinding under a CO_2 blanket. It is extruded as ground chicken patties or bulk.

Deli processing

Necks, backs and remaining carcasses from breast deboning are not wasted, but dumped into large paddle grinders or mixers, pumped through chilled mixers and extruded into bulk containers. This is usually sold or sent for further processing into what is called "chicken hot dogs" or "frankfurters".

The recent development of convenience foods, which require little processing or preparation in the home, has resulted in high-value-added products for the poultry industry. Select pieces of meat from breast deboning are placed in a rotating vessel;

solutions of flavouring and spices are then mixed under vacuum for a prescribed length of time. The meat gains not only flavour but weight as well, which improves the profit margin. The pieces are then packaged individually in trays. The trays are sealed under vacuum and packed off in small cases for shipment. This process is not time dependent, so workers are not subjected to the same line speeds as others in cut-up. The final product must be handled, inspected and packed carefully so it presents well in the stores.

Summary

Throughout poultry plants, wet processes and fat can create very dangerous floors, with a concurrent high risk of slipping and falling hazards. Proper cleaning of floors, adequate drainage (with protective barriers placed on all floor holes), proper footwear (waterproof and anti-slip) provided to workers and anti-slip floors are key to preventing these hazards.

In addition, high levels of noise are pervasive in poultry plants. Attention must be paid to engineering measures that decrease noise levels. Earplugs and replacements must be provided, as well as a full hearing conservation programme with annual hearing exams.

The poultry industry is an interesting blend of labour-intensive operations and high-tech processing. Human sweat and anguish still characterize the industry. The demands for increased yield and higher line speeds frequently overshadow efforts to properly train and protect the workers. As the technology improves to help eliminate repetitive-motion injuries or disorders, the equipment must be carefully maintained and calibrated by skilled technicians. The industry generally does not attract highly skilled technicians because of the mediocre pay levels, extremely stressful working conditions and often autocratic management, which also often resists positive changes that can be achieved with pro-active safety and health programming.

● DAIRY PRODUCTS INDUSTRY

Marianne Smukowski and Norman Brusk

Dairy products have formed an important element in human food since the earliest days when animals were first domesticated. Originally the work was done within the home or farm, and even now much is produced in small-scale enterprises, although in many countries large-scale industries are common. Cooperatives have been of great importance in the development of the industry and the improvement of its products.

In many countries, there are strict regulations governing the preparation of dairy products—for example, a requirement that all liquids be pasteurized. In most dairies, milk is pasteurized; sometimes it is sterilized or homogenized. Safe, high-quality dairy products are the goal of manufacturing plants today. While recent advances in technology allow for more sophistication and automation, safety is still a concern.

Liquid or fluid milk is the basic raw material for the dairy products industry. The milk is received via tanker trucks (or sometimes in cans) and is unloaded. Each tanker is checked for drug residues and temperature. The milk is filtered and stored in tanks/silos. Temperature of the milk should be less than 7 °C and held for no more than 72 hours. After storage, the milk is separated, the raw cream is stored in house or shipped elsewhere and the remaining milk is pasteurized. The raw cream temperature should also be less than 7 °C and held for no more than 72 hours. Before or after pasteurization (heating to 72 °C for 15 seconds), vitamins may be added. If vitamins are added,

proper concentrations must be administered. After pasteurization, the milk goes into a storage tank. The milk is then packaged, refrigerated and entered into distribution.

In the production of cheddar cheese, the incoming raw milk is filtered, stored, and the cream separated as discussed above. Before pasteurization, the dry and non-dairy ingredients are blended with the milk. This blended product is then pasteurized at a temperature greater than 72 °C for over 15 seconds. After pasteurization, the starter media (which has also been pasteurized) is added. The cheese-milk mixture then enters the cheese vat. At this time colour, salt (NaCl), rennet and calcium chloride ($CaCl_2$) may be added. The cheese then enters the drain table. Salt may also be added at this time. Whey is then expelled and put into a storage tank. A metal detector can be used prior to filling to detect any metal fragments present in the cheese. After filling, the cheese is pressed, packaged, stored and entered into the distribution chain.

For the formation of butter, the raw cream from milk separation is either stored in house or received via trucks or cans. The raw cream is pasteurized at temperatures over 85 °C for over 25 seconds and placed in storage tanks. The cream is pre-heated and pumped into the churn. During churning, water, colour, salt and/or starter distillate may be added. After churning, the buttermilk that is produced is stored in tanks. The butter is pumped into a silo and subsequently packaged. A metal detector may be used prior to or after packaging to detect any metal fragments present in the butter. After packaging, the butter is palletized, stored and entered into the distribution chain.

In the production of dry milk, the raw milk is received, filtered and stored as previously discussed. After storage, the milk is preheated and separated. The raw cream is stored in house or shipped elsewhere. The remaining milk is pasteurized. The temperature of the raw cream and raw skim should be less than 7 °C and held for no more than 72 hours. The raw skim milk is pasteurized at a temperature over 72 °C for 15 seconds, evaporated by drying between heated cylinders or by spray drying and stored in tanks. After storage, the product enters a drying system. After drying, the product is cooled. Both the heated and cool air used must be filtered. After cooling, the product enters a bulk storage tank, is sifted and packaged. A magnet may be used prior to packaging to detect any ferrous metal fragments greater than 0.5 mm in the dry milk. A metal detector may be used prior to or after packaging. After packaging, the dry milk is stored and shipped.

Good Manufacturing Practices

Good manufacturing practices (GMPs) are guidelines to assist in the day-to-day operation of a dairy plant and to ensure the manufacture of a safe dairy product. Areas covered include premises, receiving/storage, equipment performance and maintenance, personnel training programmes, sanitation and recall programmes.

Microbiological, physical and chemical contamination of dairy products is a major industry concern. Microbiological hazards include *Brucella*, *Clostridium botulinum*, *Listeria monocytogenes*, hepatitis A and E, salmonella, *Escherichia coli* 0157:H7, *Bacillus cereus*, *Staphylococcus aureus* and parasites. Physical hazards include metal, glass, insects, dirt, wood, plastic and personal effects. Chemical hazards include natural toxins, metals, drug residues, food additives and inadvertent chemicals. As a result, dairies do extensive drug, microbiological and other testing to ensure product purity. Steam and chemical cleaning of equipment is necessary to maintain sanitary conditions.

Hazards and Their Prevention

Safety hazards include slips and falls caused by wet or soapy floor and ladder surfaces; exposures to unguarded machinery such as pinch points, conveyors, packing machines, fillers, slicers and so forth; and exposure to electrical shock, especially in wet areas.

Aisles should be kept clear. Spilled materials should be cleaned immediately. Floors should be covered with non-slip material. Machinery should be adequately guarded and properly grounded, and ground fault circuit interrupters should be installed in wet areas. Proper lockout/tagout procedures are necessary to ensure that the possibility of unexpected start-up of machines and equipment will not cause injury to plant personnel.

Thermal burns can occur from steam lines and steam cleaning and from leaks or line breaks of high-pressure hydraulic equipment. Cryogenic "burns" can occur from exposure to liquid ammonia refrigerant. Good maintenance, spill and leak procedures and training can minimize the risk of burns.

Fires and explosions. Leaking ammonia systems (the lower explosive limit for ammonia is 16%; the upper explosive limit is 25%), dry milk powder and other flammable and combustible materials, welding and leaking high-pressure hydraulic equipment can all result in fires or explosions. An ammonia leak detector should be installed in areas with ammonia refrigeration systems. Flammable and combustible materials must be stored in closed metal receptacles. Spraying of milk powder should meet appropriate explosion-proof requirements. Only authorized personnel should perform welding. Compressed-gas cylinders should be regularly examined. Precautions should be taken to prevent the mixture of oxygen with flammable gases. Cylinders should be kept away from sources of heat.

Frostbite and *cold stress* can occur from exposure in the freezers and coolers. Adequate protective clothing, job rotation to warmer areas, warm lunchrooms and provision of hot drinks are recommended precautions.

Exposures to *high noise levels* can occur in processing, packaging, grinding and plastic model blow-moulding operations. Precautions include isolation of noisy equipment, proper maintenance, wearing of hearing protectors and a hearing conservation programme.

When entering *confined spaces*—for example, when entering sewer pits or cleaning tanks—ventilation must be provided. The area should be free from equipment, product, gas and personnel. Impellers, agitators and other equipment should be locked out.

Lifting of raw materials, *pulling* cases of product and *packaging* of products are associated with ergonomic problems. Solutions include mechanization and automation of manual operations.

A wide variety of *chemical exposures* can occur in the dairy products industry, including exposure to:

- ammonia vapours due to leaks in ammonia refrigeration systems
- corrosive chemicals (e.g., phosphoric acid used in the manufacture of cottage cheese, cleaning compounds, battery acids and so on)
- chlorine gas generated by inadvertent mixing of chlorinated sanitizer with acids
- hydrogen peroxide generated during ultra-high-temperature packaging operations
- ozone (and ultraviolet) exposure from UV light used in sanitizing operations
- carbon monoxide generated by the action of caustics reacting with milk sugar in clean-in-place (CIP) operations in milk evaporators
- carbon monoxide generated from propane or gasoline lift trucks, gas-fired heaters or gas-fired carton heat sealers
- chromium, nickel and other welding fumes and gases.

Employees should be trained and aware of handling practices for hazardous chemicals. Chemicals must be labelled properly. Standard operating procedures should be established and

followed when cleaning up spills. LEV should be provided where necessary. Protective clothing, safety goggles, face shields, gloves and so on must be available for use and subsequently maintained. An eye wash facility and a quick drench shower should be accessible when working with corrosive materials.

Biological hazards. Employees may be exposed to a variety of bacteria and other microbiological hazards from the unprocessed raw milk and cheeses. Precautions include proper gloves, good personal hygiene and adequate sanitary facilities.

COCOA PRODUCTION AND THE CHOCOLATE INDUSTRY

Anaide Vilasboas de Andrade

Cocoa is indigenous to the Amazon region of South America, and, during the first years of the twentieth century, the southern region of Bahia provided the perfect conditions for its growth. The cocoa-producing region of Bahia is composed of 92 municipalities and Ilheus and Itabuna are its main centres. This region accounts for 87% of the national production of cocoa in Brazil, currently world's the second largest producer of cocoa beans. Cocoa is also produced in about 50 other countries, with Nigeria and Ghana being major producers.

The vast majority of this production is exported to countries like Japan, the Russian Federation, Switzerland and the United States; half of this is sold as processed products (chocolate, vegetable fat, chocolate liquor, cocoa powder and butter) and the rest is exported as cocoa beans.

Process Overview

The industrial method for processing cocoa involves several stages. It begins with the storage of the raw material in adequate sheds, where it undergoes fumigation to prevent the proliferation of rodents and insects. Next, the process of cleaning the grains begins in order to remove any foreign objects or residues. Then all cocoa beans are dried out to extract excess moisture until an ideal level is reached. The next stage is the cracking of the grains in order to separate the skin from the core, followed by the roasting stage, which consists of the heating of the inner part of the grain.

The resulting product, which is in the shape of small particles known as "nibs", is subject to a process of grinding (crushing), thus becoming a liquid paste, which in turn is strained and solidified in refrigeration chambers and sold as paste.

Most grinding companies normally separate the liquor through a process of pressing it until the fat is extracted and converted into two final products: cocoa butter and cocoa cake. The cake is packed in solid pieces while the cocoa butter is filtered, deodorized, cooled in refrigeration chambers and later packaged.

Hazards and Their Prevention

Although, the processing of cocoa is usually automated in such a way that it requires little manual contact and a high level of hygiene is maintained, the great majority of the employees in the industry still are exposed to a variety of occupational risks.

Noise and excessive vibration are problems found throughout the production line since, in order to prevent the easy access of rodents and insects, closed sheds are built with the machinery suspended on metal platforms. These machines must be subjected to proper maintenance and adjustment routines. Anti-vibratory devices should be installed. Noisy machinery should be isolated or noise reduction barriers should be used.

During the fumigation process, tablets of aluminium phosphate are utilized; as these come in contact with humid air, phosphine gas is released. It is recommended that grains remain covered for periods of 48 to 72 hours during and after these fumigation sessions. Air sampling should be done before re-entry.

The operation of grinders, hydraulic presses and drying machinery generate a great deal of heat with the high levels of noise; the high heat is intensified by the type of construction of the buildings. However, many safety measures can be adopted: use of barriers, isolation of the operations, implementation of schedules of working hours and breaks, availability of liquids to drink, use of adequate attire and the appropriate acclimatization of the employees.

In the areas of finished products, where the average temperature is 10 °C, staff members should wear appropriate clothing and have working periods of 20 to 40 minutes. The process of acclimatization is also important. Rest breaks in warm areas are necessary.

In the operations of product reception, where storage of raw materials and all finished products are packaged, ergonomically inadequate procedures and equipment are common. Mechanized equipment should replace manual handling where possible since moving and carrying loads can cause injuries, heavy articles can hit employees and injuries can result from the use of machinery without proper guards.

Procedures and equipment should be evaluated from an ergonomic point of view. Falls due to slippery floors are also a concern. In addition, there are other activities, like the cracking of the grains and the grinding and production of cocoa powder, where there are high levels of organic dust. Adequate dilution ventilation or local exhaust systems should be installed; processes and operations isolated and segregated as appropriate.

A rigorous programme of environmental risks prevention is highly recommended, in addition to the regular system of fire prevention and safety, adequate guarding of machinery and good standards of hygiene. Signs and informational bulletins should be posted in highly visible places and equipment and devices for the personal protection should be distributed to each worker. In maintaining machinery, a lockout/tagout programme should be instituted to prevent injuries.

GRAIN, GRAIN MILLING AND GRAIN-BASED CONSUMER PRODUCTS

Thomas E. Hawkinson, James J. Collins and Gary W. Olmstead

Grain goes through many steps and processes to be prepared for human consumption. The major steps are: collection, consolidation and storage at grain elevators; milling into an intermediate product such as starch or flour; and processing into finished products such as bread, cereal or snacks.

Grain Collection, Consolidation and Storage

Grains are grown on farms and moved to grain elevators. They are transported by truck, rail, barge or ship depending on the location of the farm and the size and type of elevator. Grain elevators are used to collect, classify and store agricultural products. Grains are separated according to their quality, protein content, moisture content and so on. Grain elevators consist of bins, tanks or silos with vertical and horizontal continuous belts. Vertical belts have cups on them to carry the grain up to weighing scales and horizontal belts for distribution of the grain into bins. Bins have discharges on the bottoms which deposit grain on a

horizontal belt which conveys the product to a vertical belt for weighing and transportation or return to storage. Elevators can have capacities ranging from just a few thousand bushels at a country elevator to millions of bushels at a terminal elevator. As these products move towards processing, they may be handled many times through elevators of increasing size and capacity. When they are ready to be transported to another elevator or processing facility, they will be loaded into either truck, railcar, barge or ship.

Grain Milling

Milling is a series of operations involving the grinding of grains to produce starch or flour, most commonly from wheat, oats, corn, rye, barley or rice. The raw product is ground and sifted until the desired size is reached. Typically, milling involves the following steps: raw grain is delivered to a mill elevator; grain is cleaned and prepared for milling; grain is milled and separated by size and grain part; flour, starch and by-products are packaged for consumer distribution or bulk transported to be used in various industrial applications.

Grain-based Consumer Products Manufacturing

Bread, cereal and other baked goods are produced using a series of steps, including: combining raw ingredients, batter production and processing, product forming, baking or toasting, enrobing or frosting, packaging, casing, palletizing and final shipment.

Raw materials are often stored in bins and tanks. Some are handled in large bags or other containers. The materials are transported to processing areas using pneumatic conveyors, pumps or manual material-handling methods.

Dough production is a step where raw ingredients, including flour, sugar and fats or oils, and minor ingredients, such as flavorings, spices and vitamins, are combined in a cooking vessel. Any particulate ingredients are added along with puréed or pulped fruits. Nuts are usually husked and cut to size. Cookers (either continuous process or batch) are used. Processing of the dough into intermediate product stages can involve extruders, formers, pelletizers and shaping systems. Further processing can involve rolling systems, formers, heaters, dryers and fermentation systems.

Packaging systems take the finished product and encase it in a paper or plastic individual wrapping, place individual products in a box and then pack boxes on a pallet to prepare for shipment. Manual pallet stacking or product handling is used along with fork-lift trucks.

Mechanical Safety Issues

Equipment safety hazards include points of operation which can abrade, cut, bruise, crush, fracture and amputate. Workers can be protected by guarding or isolating the hazards, de-energizing all power sources prior to performing any maintenance or adjustment on the equipment and training workers in proper procedures to follow when working on the equipment.

The machines used to mill and convey products can be particularly dangerous. The pneumatic system and its rotary valves can cause severe finger or hand amputations. The equipment must be locked out while maintenance or clean-up is being performed. All equipment must be properly guarded and all workers need to be trained in proper operating procedures.

Processing systems have mechanical parts moving under automatic control which can cause severe injury, especially to fingers and hands. Cookers are hot and noisy, usually involving steam heating under pressure. Extrusion dies can have hazardous moving parts, including knives moving at high speed. Blenders and mixing machines can cause severe injuries and are particularly dangerous during clean-up between batches. Lockout and tagout procedures will minimize risk to workers. Slitter knives and water knives can cause severe lacerations and are especially dangerous during change-outs and adjustment procedures. Further processing can involve rolling systems, formers, heaters, dryers and fermentation systems, which present additional hazards to the extremities in the form of crushing and burn injuries. Manual handling and opening of bags can result in cuts and bruises.

Packaging systems have automated moving parts and can cause crushing or tearing injuries. Maintenance and adjustment procedures are particularly hazardous. Manual pallet stacking or product handling can cause repetitive strain injuries. Fork-lift trucks and hand pallet movers are also dangerous, and poorly stacked or secured loads can fall on nearby personnel.

Fire and Explosion

Fire and explosion can destroy grain-handling facilities and injure or kill workers and others who are in the facility or nearby at the time of explosion. Explosions require oxygen (air), fuel (grain dust), an ignition source of sufficient energy and duration (spark, flame or hot surface) and confinement (to allow pressure build-up). Typically, when an explosion occurs at a grain handling facility, it is not a single explosion but a series of explosions. The primary explosion, which can be quite small and localized, can suspend dust in the air throughout the facility in concentrations sufficient to sustain secondary explosions of great magnitude. The lower explosion limit for grain dust is approximately 20,000 mg/m^3. Prevention of fire and explosion hazards can be accomplished by designing plants with minimal confinement (except for bins, tanks and silos); controlling dust emissions into air and accumulations on floors and equipment surfaces (enclosing product streams, LEV, housekeeping and grain additives such as food-grade mineral oil or water); and controlling the explosion (fire and explosion suppression systems, explosion venting). There should be adequate fire exits or means of escape. Firefighting equipment should be strategically located, and workers should be trained in emergency response; but only very small fires should be fought because of the explosion potential.

Health Hazards

Dust can be created when grain is moved or disturbed. Although most grain dusts are simple respiratory irritants, the dusts from unprocessed grain can contain moulds and other contaminants which can cause fever and allergic asthma reactions in sensitive persons. Employees tend not to work for prolonged times in dusty areas. Typically, a respirator is worn when needed. The highest dust exposures occur during loading/unloading operations or during major cleaning. Some research has indicated pulmonary function changes related to dust exposure. The current American Conference of Governmental Industrial Hygienists (ACGIH) TLVs for occupational exposure to grain dust are 4 mg/m^3 for oat, wheat and barley and 10 mg/m^3 for other grain dust (particulates, not otherwise classified).

Respiratory protection is often worn to minimize dust exposure. Approved dust respirators can be very effective if worn properly. Workers need to be trained in their proper use, maintenance and limitations. Housekeeping is essential.

Pesticides are used in the grain and grain-processing industries to control insects, rodents, birds, mould and so on. Some of the more common pesticides are phosphine, organophosphates and pyrethrins. Potential health effects can include dermatitis, dizziness, nausea and long-term problems with liver, kidney and nervous system functions. These effects occur only if employees are overexposed. Proper use of PPE and following safety procedures will prevent overexposure.

Most grain-processing facilities apply pesticides during shutdown times, when there are few employees in the buildings. Those workers present should be on the pesticide application team and receive special training. Re-entry rules should be followed to prevent overexposure. Many locations heat the entire structure to about 60 °C for 24 to 48 hours in lieu of using chemical pesticides. Workers may also be exposed to pesticides on treated grain being brought to the truck cargo facility in trucks or rail cars.

Noise is a common problem in most grain-processing plants. The predominant noise levels range from 83 to 95 dBA, but can exceed 100 dBA in some areas. Relatively little acoustical absorption can be used due to the need for cleaning of equipment used in these facilities. Most floors and walls are made of cement, tile and stainless steel to allow easy cleaning and to prevent the facility from becoming a refuge for insects. Many employees move from area to area and spend little time working in the noisiest areas. This reduces personal exposure considerably, but hearing protection should be worn to reduce noise exposure to acceptable levels.

Working in a confined space such as a bin, tank or silo can present workers with health and physical hazards. The greatest concern is oxygen deficiency. Tightly sealed bins, tanks and silos can become oxygen deficient due to inert gases (nitrogen and carbon dioxide to prevent pest infestation) and biological action (insect infestation or mouldy grain). Prior to any entry into a bin, tank, silo or other confined space, the atmospheric conditions inside the confined space need to be checked for sufficient oxygen. If oxygen is less than 19.5%, the confined space must be ventilated. Confined spaces should also be checked for recent pesticide application or any other toxic material which may be present. Physical hazards in confined spaces include engulfment in the grain and entrapment in the space due to its configuration (inward sloping walls or entrapment in equipment inside the space). No worker should be in a confined space such as a grain silo, bin or tank while grain is being removed. Injury and death can be prevented by de-energizing and locking out all equipment associated with the confined space, ensuring that workers wear harnesses with lifelines while inside the confined space and maintaining a supply of breathable air. Prior to entry, the atmosphere inside a bin, silo or tank should be tested for the presence of combustible gases, vapours or toxic agents, and for the presence of sufficient oxygen. Employees must not enter bins, silos or tanks underneath a bridging condition, or where build-up of grain products on the sides could fall and bury them.

Medical Screening

Potential employees should be given a medical examination focusing on any pre-existing allergies and checking liver, kidney and lung function. Special examinations may be required for pesticide applicators and workers who use respiratory protection. Evaluations of hearing need to be made to assess any hearing loss. Periodic follow-up should seek to detect any changes.

BAKERIES

R.F. Villard*

The manufacture of foodstuffs from starches and sugars is done in bakeries and biscuit-, pastry- and cake-making establishments. The safety and health hazards presented by the raw materials, the plant and equipment and the manufacturing processes in these plants are similar. This article deals with small-scale bakeries and covers bread and various related products.

* Adapted from 3rd edition, *Encyclopaedia of Occupational Health and Safety*.

Production

There are three main stages in breadmaking—mixing and mould-ing, fermentation and baking. These processes are carried out in different work areas—the raw materials store, the mixing and moulding room, cold and fermentation chambers, the oven, the cooling room and the wrapping and packaging shop. The sales premises are frequently attached to the manufacturing shops.

Flour, water, salt and yeast are mixed together to make dough; hand mixing has been largely replaced by the use of mechanical mixing machines. Beating machines are used in the manufacture of other products. The dough is left to ferment in a warm, humid atmosphere, after which it is divided, weighed, moulded and baked (see figure 67.8).

Small-scale production ovens are of the fixed-hearth type with direct or indirect heat transfer. In the direct type, the refractory lining is heated either intermittently or continuously before each charge. Off-gases pass to the chimney through the adjustable orifices at the rear of the chamber. In the indirect type, the chamber is heated by steam passing through tubes in the chamber wall or by forced hot-air circulation. The oven may be fired by wood, coal, oil, town gas, liquefied petroleum gas or electricity. In rural areas, ovens with hearths heated directly by wood fires are still found. Bread is charged into the oven on paddles or trays. The oven interior can be illuminated so that the baking bread can be observed through the chamber windows. During baking, the air in the chamber becomes charged with water vapour given off by the product and/or introduced in the form of steam. The excess usually escapes up the chimney, but the oven door may also be left open.

Hazards and Their Prevention

Working conditions

The working conditions in artisanal bakehouses can have the following features: night work starting at 2:00 or 3:00 a.m., espe-cially in Mediterranean countries, where the dough is prepared in the evening; premises often infested with parasites such as cock-roaches, mice and rats, which may be carriers of pathogenic micro-organisms (suitable construction materials should be used to ensure that these premises are maintained in an adequate state of hygiene); house-to-house bread delivery, which is not always carried out in adequate conditions of hygiene and which may entail an excess workload; low wages supplemented by board and lodging.

Premises

Premises are often old and dilapidated and lead to considerable safety and health problems. The problem is particularly acute in rented premises for which neither the lessor nor the lessee can afford the cost of renovation. Floor surfaces can be very slippery when wet, although reasonably safe when dry; non-slip surfaces should be provided whenever possible. General hygiene suffers owing to defective sanitary facilities, increased hazards of poisoning, explosions and fire, and the difficulty of modernizing heavy bakehouse plant owing to the terms of the lease. Small premises cannot be suitably divided up; consequently traffic aisles are blocked or littered, equipment is inadequately spaced, handling is difficult, and the danger of slips and falls, collisions with plant, burns and injuries resulting from overexertion is increased. Where premises are located on two or more storeys there is the danger of falls from a height. Basement premises often lack emergency exits, have access stairways which are narrow, winding or steep and are fitted with poor artificial lighting. They are usually inadequately ventilated, and consequently temperatures and humidity levels are excessive; the use of simple

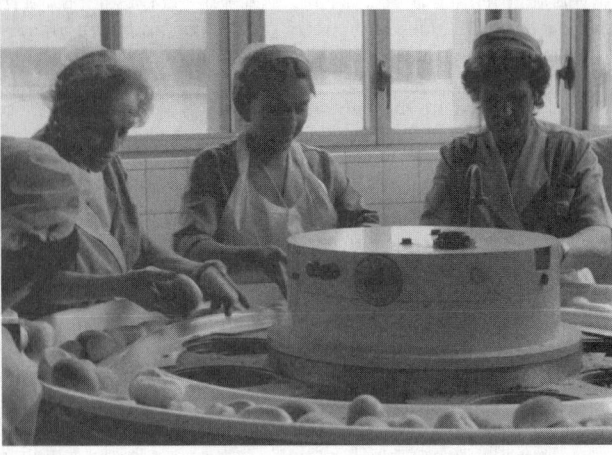

Figure 67.8 • Bread production for a supermarket chain in Switzerland.

cellar ventilators at street level merely leads to the contamination of the bakehouse air by street dust and vehicle exhaust gases.

Accidents

Knives and needles are widely used in artisanal bakeries, with a risk of cuts and puncture wounds and subsequent infection; heavy, blunt objects such as weights and trays may cause crush injuries if dropped on the worker's foot.

Ovens present a number of hazards. Depending on the fuel used, there is the danger of fire and explosion. Flashbacks, steam, cinders, baked goods or uninsulated plant may cause burns or scalds. Firing equipment which is badly adjusted or has insuffi-cient draw, or defective chimneys, may lead to the accumulation of unburnt fuel vapours or gases, or of combustion products, including carbon monoxide, which may cause intoxication or asphyxia. Defective electrical equipment and installations, espe-cially of the portable or mobile type, may cause electric shock. The sawing or chopping of wood for wood-fired ovens may result in cuts and abrasions.

Flour is delivered in sacks weighing up to 100 kg, and these must often be lifted and carried by workers through tortuous gangways (steep inclines and staircases) to the storage rooms. There is the danger of falls while carrying heavy loads, and this arduous manual handling may cause back pain and lesions of intervertebral discs. The hazards may be avoided by: providing suitable access ways to the premises; stipulating a suitable maxi-mum weight for sacks of flour; using mechanical handling equip-ment of a type suitable for use in small undertakings and at a price within the range of most artisanal workers; and by wider use of bulk flour transport, which is, however, suitable only when the baker has a sufficiently large turnover.

Flour dust is also a fire and explosion hazard, and proper precautions should be taken, including fire and explosion suppres-sion systems.

In mechanized bakeries, dough which is in an active state of fermentation may give off dangerous amounts of carbon dioxide; thorough ventilation should therefore be provided in confined spaces wherever the gas is likely to accumulate (dough chutes and so on). Workers should be trained in confined-space procedures.

A wide variety of machines are used in bread manufacture, particularly in industrial bakeries. Mechanization can bring serious accidents in its wake. Modern bakery machines are usually equipped with built-in guards whose correct operation often depends upon the functioning of electrical limit switches and positive interlocks. Feed hoppers and chutes present special hazards which can be eliminated by extending the length of the feed opening beyond arm's length to prevent the operator from reaching the moving parts; hinged double gates or rotary flaps are sometimes used as feeding devices for the same purpose. Nips on dough brakes can be protected by either fixed or automatic guards. A variety of guards (covers, grids and so on) can be used on dough mixers to prevent access to the trapping zone while permitting insertion of additional material and scraping of the bowl. Increasing use is made of bread-slicing and wrapping machines with alternating saw blades or rotary knives; all moving parts should be completely enclosed, interlocking covers being provided where access is necessary. There should be a lockout/tagout programme for maintenance and repair of machinery.

Health Hazards

Bakehouse workers are usually lightly clothed and sweat profusely; they are subject to draughts and pronounced variations in ambient temperature when changing, for example, from oven charging to cooler work. Airborne flour dust may cause rhinitis, throat disorders, bronchial asthma ("baker's asthma") and eye diseases; sugar dust may cause dental caries. Airborne vegetable dust should be controlled by suitable ventilation. Allergic dermatitis may occur in persons with special predisposition. The above health hazards and the high incidence of pulmonary tuberculosis amongst bakers emphasize the need for medical supervision with frequent periodic examinations; in addition, strict personal hygiene is essential in the interests of both workers and the public in general.

● SUGAR-BEET INDUSTRY

Carol J. Lehtola*

Processing

The process of producing sugar from beets consists of many steps, which have been improved continuously throughout the more than century-old history of the sugar-beet industry. Sugar-beet processing facilities have become modernized and use current technology as well as current safety measures. Workers are now trained in using modern and sophisticated equipment.

The sugar content of the beets ranges from 15 to 18%. They are first cleaned in a beet washer. They are then cut in beet slicers and the "cossettes" thus obtained are conveyed via a scalder into the diffuser, where most of the sugar contained in the beets is extracted in hot water. The desugarized cossettes, called "pulps", are pressed mechanically and dried, mostly by heat. The pulps contain many nutrients and are used as animal feed.

The raw juice obtained in the diffuser, in addition to sugar, also contains non-sugar impurities which are precipitated (by adding lime and carbon dioxide) and then filtered. The raw juice thus becomes thin juice, with a sugar content of 12 to 14%. The thin juice is concentrated in evaporators to 65 to 70% dry matter. This thick juice is boiled in a vacuum pan at a temperature of about 70 °C until crystals form. This is then discharged into mixers, and the liquid surrounding the crystals is spun off. The low syrup thus separated from the sugar crystals still contains sugar which can be crystallized. The desugaring process is continued until it is no longer economical. Molasses is the syrup left after the last crystallization.

* This is an update of the article prepared by the European Committee of Sugar Manufacturers (CEFS) for the 3rd edition of the *Encyclopaedia of Occupational Health and Safety*.

After drying and cooling, the sugar is stored in silos, where it can be kept indefinitely if adequately air conditioned and moisture controlled.

The molasses contains approximately 60% sugar and, together with the non-sugar impurities, constitutes valuable animal feed as well as an ideal culture medium for many micro-organisms. For animal feed, part of the molasses is added to the sugar-exhausted pulps before they are dried. Molasses is also used for the production of yeast and alcohol.

With the help of other micro-organisms, other products can be made, such as lactic acid, an important raw material for the food and pharmaceutical industries, or citric acid, which the food industry needs in great quantities. Molasses is also used in the production of antibiotics such as penicillin and streptomycin, and also of sodium glutamate.

Working Conditions

In the highly mechanized sugar-beet industry, the beet is transformed into sugar during what is known as the "campaign". The campaign lasts from 3 to 4 months, during which time the processing plants operate continuously. Personnel work in rotating shifts around the clock. Additional workers may be added temporarily during peak periods. Upon completion of the beet processing, repairs, maintenance and updates are done in the facilities.

Hazards and Their Prevention

Sugar beet processing does not produce or involve working with toxic gases or airborne dusts. Parts of the processing facility may be extremely noisy. In areas where the noise levels cannot be brought down to the threshold limits, hearing protection needs to be provided and a hearing conservation programme instituted. However, for the most part, occupationally related illnesses are rare in the sugar-beet processing plants. This is partially due to the fact that the campaign is only of 3 to 4 months duration per year.

As in most food industries, contact dermatitis and skin allergies from cleaning agents used to clean vats and equipment can be a problem, requiring gloves. When entering vats for cleaning or other reasons, confined space procedures should be in effect.

Care must be taken when entering silos of stored granular sugar, due to the risk of engulfment, a hazard similar to that of grain silos. (See the article "Grain, grain milling and grain-based consumer products" in this chapter for more detailed recommendations.)

Burns from steam lines and hot water are a concern. Proper maintenance, PPE and employee training can help prevent this type of injury.

Mechanization and automation in the sugar-beet industry minimize the risk of ergonomic disorders.

Machinery must be regularly checked and routinely maintained and repaired as required. Safety guards and mechanisms must be kept in place. Employees should have access to protective equipment and devices. Employees should be required to participate in safety training.

OIL AND FAT

N.M. Pant*

The term oils and fats is generally applied to the triglycerides of fatty acids in plant seeds and animal tissues. Oils and fats constitute one of the three main types of organic materials

* Adapted from 3rd edition, *Encyclopaedia of Occupational Health and Safety*.

regarded as the building materials of living organisms, the other two being proteins and carbohydrates.

More than 100 varieties of oil-bearing plants and animals are exploited as sources of oils and fats. The most important vegetable sources are: the olive, coconut, peanut, cotton seed, soya bean, rapeseed (canola oil), mustard seed, flax or linseed, palmfruit, sesame, sunflower, palm kernel, castor bean, hemp seed, tung, cocoa, mowrah, corn and babassu.

The main animal sources are beef cattle, pigs and sheep, the whale, cod and halibut.

Edible oils and fats provide a concentrated source of food energy, serve as carriers of fat-soluble vitamins and also furnish the essential fatty acids which are of vital importance to metabolism. Oils and fats constitute the major raw materials for soaps and detergents, paints, lacquers and varnishes, lubricants and illuminants such as candles. They are also used in the manufacture of linoleum and oiled fabrics, in the manufacture of fixatives and mordants in the tanning of leather, and as feedstock for chemical synthesis.

Processing

Initial processing depends upon the raw material; for example, animal fats are rendered in steam-jacketted vessels, seeds are cleaned, milled and separated and nut-meats are flaked. The fats or oils are extracted by pressing or treatment by solvents, and further processing depends upon the end use. Olives may be pressed several times, but no further treatment is usually required. For other edible oils and fats, processing may comprise a number of different stages, including refining, deodorization, hydrogenation, solidification or emulsification.

Raw oils and fats contain impurities, some of which are objectionable because they darken the oil, cause it to foam and smoke on heating, impart an undesirable flavour or odour or affect processing. Refining, which consists of neutralization and bleaching, removes most of these impurities. Neutralization removes fatty acids and gummy phosphatides by alkali and degumming treatments. The raw materials are bleached by absorption on natural or activated bleaching earths; however, heat bleaching may be employed. Oil temperature does not normally exceed 100 °C during refining.

Deodorization removes the odoriferous compounds by steam distillation at high temperature and low absolute pressure.

Liquid oils and soft fats are converted into firm plastic fats by hydrogenation, which also helps prevent rancidity due to oxidation. In this process, the oil is reacted with hydrogen at a temperature of 180 °C or more in the presence of a catalyst, usually finely divided nickel. The hydrogen is fed in at a pressure of between 2 and 30 atmospheres, depending upon the desired end-product.

If the oil or fat is to be marketed in plastic or emulsion form, further processing is required. Many proprietary brand oils and fats are blended, and shortenings are solidified to yield granules by controlled gradual cooling (fractionation) and separation of crystallized fractions at various temperatures based on their melting points. An alternative method produces a texturized product by rapid chilling in special equipment called a votator.

Hazards and Their Prevention

Hydrogen presents a high risk of explosion and fire in the hydrogenation process. Burning oils and fats may emit highly irritant fumes such as acrolein. The solvents, such as hexane, used for the extraction of oils are highly flammable, although they are commonly used in closed systems. Precautions against fire and explosion include:

- elimination of all sources of ignition
- use of explosion-proof equipment and spark-proof tools

- prohibition of smoking
- ensuring fire exits are not blocked and are well maintained
- provision of appropriate fire extinguishers
- development of procedures for spills and leaks of hydrogen and flammable solvents
- training of staff in firefighting procedures.

Electrical installations present a risk of electrical shock in damp and steamy conditions. All equipment, conductors and so on should be suitably protected with special attention to any portable equipment or lights. Ground fault circuit interrupters should be installed on electrical equipment in wet or steamy areas.

Injuries from moving machinery parts can be prevented by efficient and well maintained machinery guarding. Particular attention should be given to crushing machinery, filling and drum-seaming machines and nips between belts, drums and pulleys of conveyors. Lockout/tagout procedures should be used when maintaining and repairing equipment. Risks of explosion and leakage in steam plant should be prevented by regular inspection and maintenance procedures.

Excessive noise from equipment should be minimized by engineering controls if possible. Employees exposed to excessive noise should wear appropriate hearing protectors, and there should be a hearing conservation programme.

Manual handling of drums may cause musculoskeletal strains and injuries to hands and toes. Mechanical handling equipment should be used when possible. There should be training in correct methods of handling and lifting, foot and hand protection, and checking of containers for sharp edges. Badly stacked drums may fall and cause serious injury; supervision and training in stacking and destacking will reduce the risk involved.

Falls may occur on slippery floors and staircases, and can be prevented by well maintained non-slip floor surfaces, regular cleaning and good housekeeping, and wearing of non-slip footwear.

Burns may be caused by sodium hydroxide during handling of drums for refining and from spurts of liquid caustic when drums are opened; by hot oil or spent catalyst during cleaning of filter presses; from acids; and from steamlines and steam leaks. Protective clothing, boots, aprons and gloves will prevent many injuries; face shields are necessary to protect the eyes from splashes of corrosive or hot material.

Oils are processed at high temperatures, and physical discomfort can result, especially in the tropics, unless effective measures are taken. Muscle cramps, exhaustion and heat strokes may occur. Radiant heat should be reduced by lagging or insulating the vessels and steam pipes. Efficient mechanical ventilation should provide frequent changes of air. Workers should have frequent access to liquids and frequent breaks in cool areas.

Entering bulk tanks for repair or cleaning can be a confined space hazard. Employees should be trained in confined space procedures, such as testing of the confined space air and emergency rescue procedures. A minimum of two workers should be present.

Solvents used for the extraction of fats and oils may present toxic risks. Benzene should not be used, and the least toxic solvent practicable should be substituted (e.g., substitution of heptane for hexane). LEV is required to remove solvent vapours at the point of origin, or closed systems should be used.

Dermatitis may be caused by handling of oils, fats and solvents. Provision and use of adequate washing and sanitary facilities is essential; barrier creams and protective clothing also aid in prevention.

In peanut oil processing plants, under suitable conditions of moisture and temperature, press-cakes can be contaminated by moulds of *Aspergillus flavus*, which contain aflatoxins. Workers exposed to heavy aflatoxin contamination in workroom air have been found to develop acute or subacute liver damage and to present an increased prevalence of tumours.

Rendering of animals to produce animal fats and animal feed can also involve biological hazards. Although most animals and animal materials used as a source for rendering are healthy or from healthy animals, a small percentage comes from animals that have been road-killed or have died of unknown causes and perhaps are diseased. Some animal diseases, such as anthrax and brucellosis, can also affect humans. Workers in slaughterhouses and rendering plants may be at risk. In the United Kingdom, people called knackers make their living going around the countryside picking up dead animals and rendering them in their backyards. They could be at greater risk because of the greater likelihood of their exposure to diseased animals and the crude conditions they work under.

The past rendering of sheep organs, including brains, as a source for cattle feed has resulted in bovine spongiform encephalopathy ("mad cow disease") in some British cows where the sheep had a brain disease called scrapie. It appears that some humans have developed this disease from eating beef from cows with mad cow disease.

Periodic medical examination of workers, selection, training and supervision are aids in prevention of both accidents and occupational diseases.

References

Bureau of Labor Statistics (BLS). 1991. *Occupational Injuries and Illnesses in the United States by Industry, 1989.* Washington, DC: BLS.

Caisse nationale d'assurance maladie des travailleurs salariés. 1990. *Statistiques nationales d'accidents du travail.* Paris: Caisse Nationale d'assurance maladie des Travailleurs Salariés.

Hetrick, RL. 1994. Why did employment expand in poultry processing plants? *Monthly Labor Review* 117(6):31.

Linder, M. 1996. I gave my employer a chicken that had no bone: Joint firm-state responsibility for line-speed-related occupational injuries. *Case Western Reserve Law Review* 46:90.

Merlo, CA and WW Rose. 1992. Alternative methods for disposal/utilization of organic by-products—From the literature". In *Proceedings of the 1992 Food Industry Environmental Conference.* Atlanta, GA: Georgia Tech Research Institute.

National Institute for Occupational Safety and Health (NIOSH). 1990. *Health Hazard Evaluation Report: Perdue Farms, Inc.* HETA 89-307-2009. Cincinnati, OH: NIOSH.

Sanderson, WT, A Weber, and A Echt. 1995. Case reports: Epidemic eye and upper respiratory irritation in poultry processing plants. *Appl Occup Environ Hyg* 10(1): 43-49.

Tomoda, S. 1993. *Occupational Safety and Health in the Food and Drink Industries.* Sectoral Activities Programme Working Paper. Geneva: ILO.

Other relevant readings

Erickson, DE. 1990. *Proceedings of the World Conference on Edible Fats and Oils Processing: Basic Principles and Modern Practices.* Champaign, IL: American Oil Chemists' Society.

—. 1995. *Practical Handbook of Soybean Processing and Utilization.* Champaign, IL: American Oil Chemists' Society; St. Louis, MO: United Soybean Board.

Hui, YH (ed.). 1996. *Bailey's Industrial Oil and Fat Products,* 5th edition. Vol. 4. New York: John Wiley & Sons.

Institute of Shortening and Edible Oils. 1994. *Food Fats and Oils,* 7th edition. Washington, DC: Institute of Shortening and Edible Oils.

National Fire Protection Association (NFPA). 1993. *Solvent Extraction Plants.* NFPA 36. Quincy, MA: NFPA.

Occupational Safety and Health Administration (OSHA). 1992. *OSHA Handbook for Small Businesses.* Washington, DC: OSHA.

US Department of Agriculture (USDA). 1960. *Water Absorption by Eviscerated Broilers during Washing and Chilling.* Marketing Research Report No 438. Washington, DC: USDA.

FORESTRY

68

Chapter Editor
Peter Poschen

Contents

GENERAL PROFILE

Peter Poschen

Forestry—A Definition

For the purposes of the present chapter, forestry is understood to embrace all the fieldwork required to establish, regenerate, manage and protect forests and to harvest their products. The last step in the production chain covered by this chapter is the transport of raw forest products. Further processing, such as into sawnwood, furniture or paper is dealt with in the *Lumber, Woodworking* and *Pulp and paper industries* chapters in this *Encyclopaedia*.

The forests may be natural, human-made or tree plantations. Forest products considered in this chapter are both wood and other products, but emphasis is on the former, because of its relevance for safety and health.

Evolution of the Forest Resource and the Sector

The utilization and management of forests are as old as the human being. Initially forests were almost exclusively used for subsistence: food, fuelwood and building materials. Early management consisted mostly of burning and clearing to make room for other land uses—in particular, agriculture, but later also for settlements and infrastructure. The pressure on forests was aggravated by early industrialization. The combined effect of conversion and over-utilization was a sharp reduction in forest area in Europe, the Middle East, India, China and later in parts of North America. Presently, forests cover about one-quarter of the land surface of the earth.

The deforestation process has come to a halt in industrialized countries, and forest areas are actually increasing in these countries, albeit slowly. In most tropical and subtropical countries, however, forests are shrinking at a rate of 15 to 20 million hectares (ha), or 0.8%, per year. In spite of continuing deforestation, developing countries still account for about 60% of the world forest area, as can be seen in table 68.1. The countries with the largest forest areas by far are the Russian Federation, Brazil, Canada and the United States. Asia has the lowest forest cover in terms of percentage of land area under forest and hectares per capita.

Forest resources vary significantly in different parts of the world. These differences have a direct impact on the working environment, on the technology used in forestry operations and on the level of risk associated with them. Boreal forests in northern parts of Europe, Russia and Canada are mostly made up of conifers and have a relatively small number of trees per hectare. Most of these forests are natural. Moreover, the individual trees are small in size. Because of the long winters, trees grow slowly and wood increment ranges from less than 0.5 to 3 m^3/ha/y.

The temperate forests of southern Canada, the United States, Central Europe, southern Russia, China and Japan are made up of a wide range of coniferous and broad-leaved tree species. Tree densities are high and individual trees can be very large, with diameters of more than 1 m and tree height of more than 50 m. Forests may be natural or human-made (i.e., intensively managed with more uniform tree sizes and fewer tree species). Standing volumes per hectare and increment are high. The latter range typically from 5 to greater than 20 m^3/ha/y.

Tropical and subtropical forests are mostly broad-leaved. Tree sizes and standing volumes vary greatly, but tropical timber harvested for industrial purposes is typically in the form of large trees with big crowns. Average dimensions of harvested trees are highest in the tropics, with logs of more than 2 m^3 being the rule. Standing trees with crowns routinely weigh more than 20 tonnes before felling and debranching. Dense undergrowth and tree climbers make work even more cumbersome and dangerous.

An increasingly important type of forest in terms of wood production and employment is tree plantations. Tropical plantations are thought to cover about 35 million hectares, with about 2 million hectares added per year (FAO 1995). They usually consist of only one very fast growing species. Increment mostly ranges from 15 to 30 m^3/ha/y. Various pines (*Pinus* spp.) and eucalyptus (*Eucalyptus* spp.) are the most common species for industrial uses. Plantations are managed intensively and in short rotations (from 6 to 30 years), while most temperate forests take 80, sometimes up to 200 years, to mature. Trees are fairly uniform, and small to medium in size, with approximately 0.05 to 0.5 m^3/tree. There is typically little undergrowth.

Prompted by wood scarcity and natural disasters like landslides, floods and avalanches, more and more forests have come under some form of management over the last 500 years. Most industrialized countries apply the "sustained yield principle", according to which present uses of the forest may not reduce its potential to produce goods and benefits for later generations. Wood utilization levels in most industrialized countries are below the growth rates. This is not true for many tropical countries.

Economic Importance

Globally, wood is by far the most important forest product. World roundwood production is approaching 3.5 billion m^3 annually. Wood production grew by 1.6% a year in the 1960s and 1970s and by 1.8% a year in the 1980s, and is projected to increase by 2.1% a year well into the 21st century, with much higher rates in developing countries than in industrialized ones.

Industrialized countries' share of world roundwood production is 42% (i.e., roughly proportional to the share of forest area). There is, however, a major difference in the nature of the wood products harvested in industrialized and in developing countries. While in the former more than 85% consists of industrial roundwood to be used for sawnwood, panel or pulp, in the latter 80% is used for fuelwood and charcoal. This is why the list of the ten biggest producers of industrial roundwood in figure 68.1 includes only four developing countries. Non-wood forest products are still very significant for subsistence in many countries. They account for only 1.5% of traded unprocessed forest products, but products like cork, rattan, resins, nuts and gums are major exports in some countries.

Worldwide, the value of production in forestry was US$96,000 million in 1991, compared to US$322,000 million in downstream

Table 68.1 • Forest area by region (1990).

Region	Area (million hectares)	% total
Africa	536	16
North/Central America	531	16
South America	898	26
Asia	463	13
Oceania	88	3
Europe	140	4
Former USSR	755	22
Industrialized (all)	1,432	42
Developing (all)	2,009	58
World	3,442	100

Source: FAO 1995b.

Figure 68.1 • Ten biggest producers of industrial round-wood, 1993 (former USSR 1991).

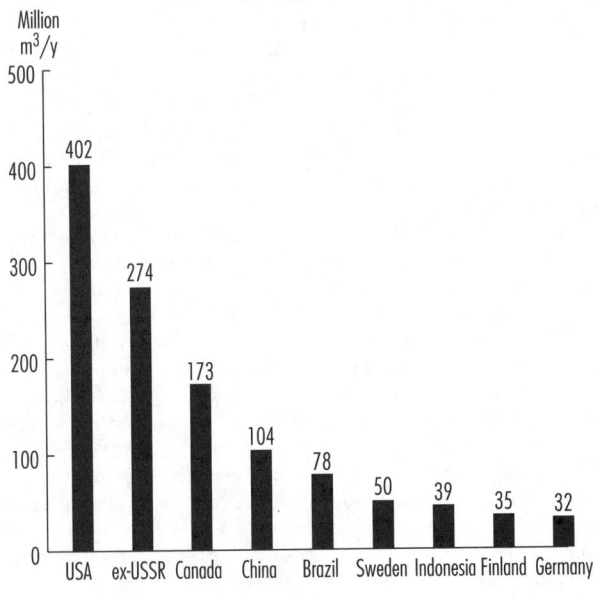

Source: FAO 1995.

forest-based industries. Forestry alone accounted for 0.4% of world GDP. The share of forestry production in GDP tends to be much higher in developing countries, with an average of 2.2%, than in industrialized ones, where it represents only 0.14% of GDP. In a number of countries forestry is far more important than the averages suggest. In 51 countries the forestry and forest-based industries sector combined generated 5% or more of the respective GDP in 1991.

In several industrialized and developing countries, forest products are a significant export. The total value of forestry exports from developing countries increased from about US$7,000 million in 1982 to over US$19,000 million in 1993 (1996 dollars). Large exporters among industrialized countries include Canada, the United States, Russia, Sweden, Finland and New Zealand. Among tropical countries Indonesia (US$5,000 million), Malaysia (US$4,000 million), Chile and Brazil (about US$2,000 million each) are the most important.

While they cannot be readily expressed in monetary terms, the value of non-commercial goods and benefits generated by forests may well exceed their commercial output. According to estimates, some 140 to 300 million people live in or depend on forests for their livelihood. Forests are also home to three-quarters of all species of living beings. They are a significant sink of carbon dioxide and serve to stabilize climates and water regimes. They reduce erosion, landslides and avalanches, and produce clean drinking water. They are also fundamental for recreation and tourism.

Employment

Figures on wage employment in forestry are difficult to obtain and can be unreliable even for industrialized countries. The reasons are the high share of the self-employed and farmers, who do not get recorded in many cases, and the seasonality of many forestry jobs. Statistics in most developing countries simply absorb forestry into the much larger agricultural sector, with no separate figures available. The biggest problem, however, is the fact that most

forestry work is not wage employment, but subsistence. The main item here is the production of fuelwood, particularly in developing countries. Bearing these limitations in mind, figure 68.2 below provides a very conservative estimate of global forestry employment.

World wage employment in forestry is in the order of 2.6 million, of which about 1 million is in industrialized countries. This is a fraction of the downstream employment: wood industries and pulp and paper have at least 12 million employees in the formal sector. The bulk of forestry employment is unpaid subsistence work—some 12.8 million full-time equivalents in developing and some 0.3 million in industrialized countries. Total forestry employment can thus be estimated at some 16 million person years. This is equivalent to about 3% of world agricultural employment and to about 1% of total world employment.

In most industrialized countries the size of the forestry workforce has been shrinking. This is a result of a shift from seasonal to full-time, professional forest workers, compounded by rapid mechanization, particularly of wood harvesting. Figure 68.3 illustrates the enormous differences in productivity in major wood-producing countries. These differences are to some extent due to natural conditions, silvicultural systems and statistical error. Even allowing for these, significant gaps persist. The transformation in the workforce is likely to continue: mechanization is spreading to more countries, and new forms of work organization, namely team work concepts, are boosting productivity, while harvesting levels remain by and large constant. It should be noted that in many countries seasonal and part-time work in forestry are unrecorded, but remain very common among farmers and small woodland owners. In a number of developing countries the industrial forestry workforce is likely to grow as a result of more intensive forest management and tree plantations. Subsistence employment, on the other hand, is likely to decline gradually, as fuelwood is slowly replaced by other forms of energy.

Characteristics of the Workforce

Industrial forestry work has largely remained a male domain. The proportion of women in the formal workforce rarely exceeds 10%. There are, however, jobs that tend to be predominantly carried out by women, such as planting or tending of young stands and raising seedlings in tree nurseries. In subsistence employment women are a majority in many developing countries, because they are usually responsible for fuelwood gathering.

The largest share of all industrial and subsistence forestry work is related to the harvesting of wood products. Even in human-

Figure 68.2 • Employment in forestry (full-time equivalents).

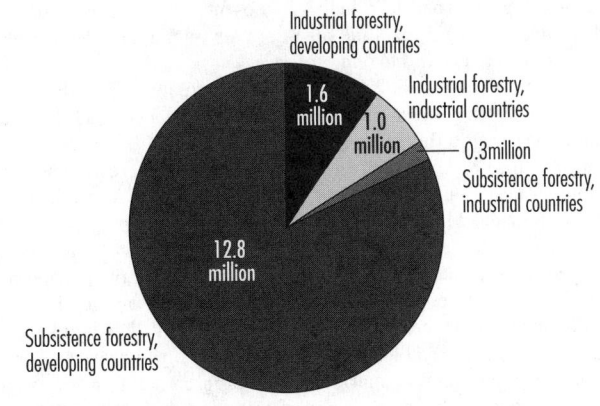

Source: ILO estimate based on partial country data and FAO/ECE/ILO 1989.

Figure 68.3 • Countries with highest wage employment in forestry and industrial roundwood production (late 1980s to early 1990s).

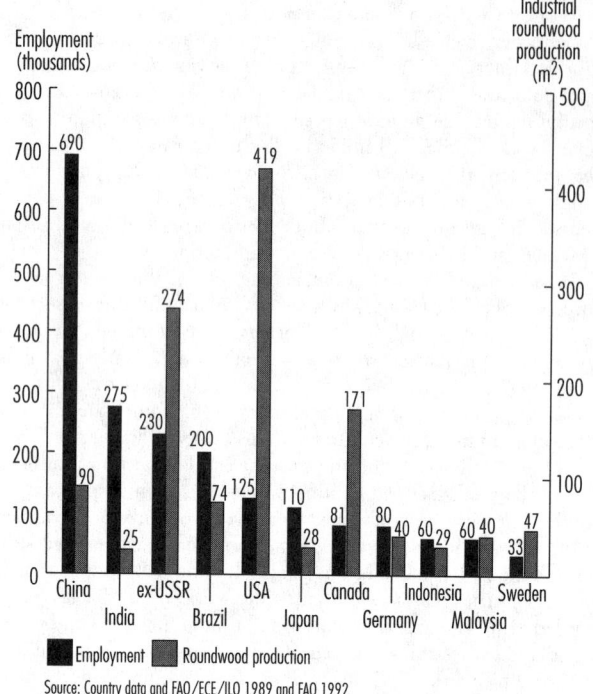

Source: Country data and FAO/ECE/ILO 1989 and FAO 1992.

made forests and plantations, where substantial silvicultural work is required, harvesting accounts for more than 50% of the workdays per hectare. In harvesting in developing countries the ratios of supervisor/technician to foremen and to workers are 1 to 3 and 1 to 40, respectively. The ratio is smaller in most industrialized countries.

Broadly, there are two groups of forestry jobs: those related to silviculture and those related to harvesting. Typical occupations in silviculture include tree planting, fertilization, weed and pest control, and pruning. Tree planting is very seasonal, and in some countries involves a separate group of workers exclusively dedicated to this activity. In harvesting, the most common occupations are chain-saw operation, in tropical forests often with an assistant; choker setters who attach cables to tractors or skylines pulling logs to roadside; helpers who measure, move, load or debranch logs; and machine operators for tractors, loaders, cable cranes, harvesters and logging trucks.

There are major differences between segments of the forestry workforce with respect to the form of employment, which have a direct bearing on their exposure to safety and health hazards. The share of forest workers directly employed by the forest owner or industry has been declining even in those countries where it used to be the rule. More and more work is done through contractors (i.e., relatively small, geographically mobile service firms employed for a particular job). The contractors may be owner-operators (i.e., single-person firms or family businesses) or they have a number of employees. Both the contractors and their employees often have very unstable employment. Under pressure to cut costs in a very competitive market, contractors sometimes resort to illegal practices such as moonlighting and hiring undeclared immigrants. While the move to contracting has in many cases helped to cut costs, to advance mechanization and specialization

as well as to adjust the workforce to changing demands, some traditional ailments of the profession have been aggravated through the increased reliance on contract labour. These include accident rates and health complaints, both of which tend to be more frequent among contract labour.

Contract labour has also contributed to further increasing the high rate of turnover in the forestry workforce. Some countries report rates of almost 50% per year for those changing employers and more than 10% per year leaving the forestry sector altogether. This aggravates the skill problem already looming large among much of the forestry workforce. Most skill acquisition is still by experience, usually meaning trial and error. Lack of structured training, and short periods of experience due to high turnover or seasonal work, are major contributing factors to the significant safety and health problems facing the forestry sector (see the article "Skills and training" in this chapter).

The dominant wage system in forestry by far continues to be piece-rates (i.e., remuneration solely based on output). Piece-rates tend to lead to a rapid pace of work and are widely believed to increase the number of accidents. There is, however, no scientific evidence to back this contention. One undisputed side effect is that earnings fall once workers have reached a certain age because their physical abilities decline. In countries where mechanization plays a major role, time-based wages have been on the increase, because the work rhythm is largely determined by the machine. Various bonus wage systems are also in use.

Forestry wages are generally well below the industrial average in the same country. Workers, the self-employed and contractors often try to compensate by working 50 or even 60 hours per week. Such situations increase strain on the body and the risk of accidents because of fatigue.

Organized labour and trade unions are rather rare in the forestry sector. The traditional problems of organizing geographically dispersed, mobile, sometimes seasonal workers have been compounded by the fragmentation of the workforce into small contractor firms. At the same time, the number of workers in categories that are typically unionized, such as those directly employed in larger forest enterprises, is falling steadily. Labour inspectorates attempting to cover the forestry sector are faced with problems similar in nature to those of trade union organizers. As a result there is very little inspection in most countries. In the absence of institutions whose mission is to protect worker rights, forest workers often have little knowledge of their rights, including those laid down in existing safety and health regulations, and experience great difficulties in exercising such rights.

Health and Safety Problems

The popular notion in many countries is that forestry work is a 3-D job: dirty, difficult and dangerous. A host of natural, technical and organizational factors contribute to that reputation. Forestry work has to be done outdoors. Workers are thus exposed to the extremes of weather: heat, cold, snow, rain and ultraviolet (UV) radiation. Work even often proceeds in bad weather and, in mechanized operations, it increasingly continues at night. Workers are exposed to natural hazards such as broken terrain or mud, dense vegetation and a series of biological agents.

Worksites tend to be remote, with poor communication and difficulties in rescue and evacuation. Life in camps with extended periods of isolation from family and friends is still common in many countries.

The difficulties are compounded by the nature of the work—trees may fall unpredictably, dangerous tools are used and often there is a heavy physical workload. Other factors like work organization, employment patterns and training also play a significant role in increasing or reducing hazards associated with forestry work. In most countries the net result of the above influences are very high accident risks and serious health problems.

Fatalities in Forest Work

In most countries forest work is one of the most dangerous occupations, with great human and financial losses. In the United States accident insurance costs amount to 40% of payroll.

A cautious interpretation of the available evidence suggests that accident trends are more often upward than downward. Encouragingly, there are countries that have a long-standing record in bringing down accident frequencies (e.g., Sweden and Finland). Switzerland represents the more common situation of increasing, or at best stagnating, accident rates. The scarce data available for developing countries indicate little improvement and usually excessively high accident levels. A study of safety in pulpwood logging in plantation forests in Nigeria, for example, found that on average a worker had 2 accidents per year. Between 1 in 4 and 1 in 10 workers suffered a serious accident in a given year (Udo 1987).

A closer inspection of accidents reveals that harvesting is far more hazardous than other forest operations (ILO 1991). Within forest harvesting, tree felling and cross-cutting are the jobs with the most accidents, particularly serious or fatal ones. In some countries, such as in the Mediterranean area, firefighting can also be a major cause of fatalities, claiming up to 13 lives a year in Spain in some years (Rodero 1987). Road transport can also account for a large share of serious accidents, particularly in tropical countries.

The chain-saw is clearly the single most dangerous tool in forestry, and the chain-saw operator the most exposed worker. The situation depicted in figure 68.4 for a territory of Malaysia is found with minor variations in most other countries as well. In spite of increasing mechanization, the chain-saw is likely to remain the key problem in industrialized countries. In developing countries, its use can be expected to expand as plantations account for an increasing share of the wood harvest.

Virtually all parts of the body can be injured in forest work, but there tends to be a concentration of injuries to the legs, feet, back and hands, in roughly that order. Cuts and open wounds are the most common type of injury in chain-saw work while bruises dominate in skidding, but there are also fractures and dislocations.

Two situations under which the already high risk of serious accidents in forest harvesting multiplies severalfold are "hung-up" trees and wind-blown timber. Windblow tends to produce timber under tension, which requires specially adapted cutting techniques (for guidance see FAO/ECE/ILO 1996a; FAO/ILO 1980; and ILO 1998). Hung-up trees are those that have been severed from the stump but did not fall to the ground because the crown became entangled with other trees. Hung-up trees are extremely dangerous and referred to as "widow-makers" in some countries, because of the high number of fatalities they cause. Aid tools, such as turning hooks and winches, are required to bring such trees down safely. In no case should it be permitted that other trees be felled onto a hung-up one in the hope of bringing it down. This practice, known as "driving" in some countries, is extremely hazardous.

Accident risks vary not only with technology and exposure due to the job, but with other factors as well. In almost all cases for which data are available, there is a very significant difference between segments of the workforce. Full-time, professional forest workers directly employed by a forest enterprise are far less affected than farmers, self-employed or contract labour. In Austria, farmers seasonally engaged in logging suffer twice as many accidents per million cubic metres harvested as professional workers (Sozialversicherung der Bauern 1990), in Sweden, even four times

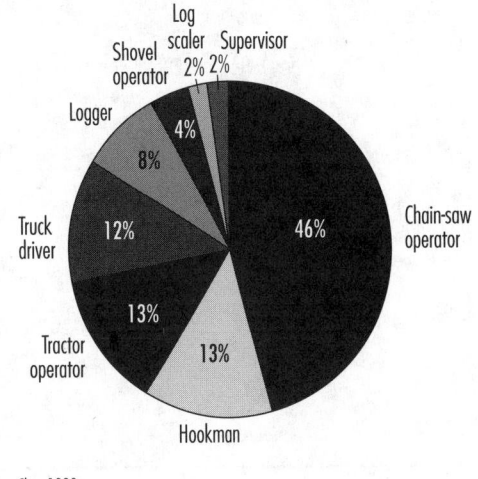

Figure 68.4 • Distribution of logging fatalities among jobs, Malaysia (Sarawak), 1989.

Source: Cheu 1990.

as many. In Switzerland, workers employed in public forests have only half as many accidents as those employed by contractors, particularly where workers are hired only seasonally and in the case of migrant labour (Wettmann 1992).

The increasing mechanization of tree harvesting has had very positive consequences for work safety. Machine operators are well protected in guarded cabins, and accident risks have dropped very significantly. Machine operators experience less than 15% of the accidents of chain-saw operators to harvest the same amount of timber. In Sweden operators have one-quarter of the accidents of professional chain-saw operators.

Growing Occupational Disease Problems

The reverse side of the mechanization coin is an emerging problem of neck and shoulder strain injuries among machine operators. These can be as incapacitating as serious accidents.

The above problems add to the traditional health complaints of chain-saw operators—namely, back injuries and hearing loss. Back pain due to physically heavy work and unfavourable working postures is very common among chain-saw operators and workers doing manual loading of logs. There is a high incidence of premature loss of working capacity and of early retirement among forest workers as a result. A traditional ailment of chain-saw operators that has largely been overcome in recent years through improved saw design is vibration-induced "white finger" disease.

The physical, chemical and biological hazards causing health problems in forestry are discussed in the following articles of this chapter.

Special Risks for Women

Safety risks are by and large the same for men and women in forestry. Women are often involved in planting and tending work, including the application of pesticides. However, women who have smaller body size, lung volume, heart and muscles may have a work capacity on average that is about one-third lower than that of men. Correspondingly, legislation in many countries limits the weight to be lifted and carried by women to about 20 kg (ILO 1988), although such sex-based differences in exposure limits are illegal in many countries. These limits are often exceeded by women working in forestry. Studies in British Columbia, where

Figure 68.5 • Woman fuelwood carrier, Addis Ababa, Ethiopia.

separate standards do not apply, among planting workers showed full loads of plants carried by men and women to average 30.5 kg, often in steep terrain with heavy ground cover (Smith 1987).

Excessive loads are also common in many developing countries where women work as fuelwood carriers. A survey in Addis Ababa, Ethiopia, for example, found that an estimated 10,000 women and children eke out a livelihood from hauling fuelwood into town on their backs (see figure 68.5). The average bundle weighs 30 kg and is carried over a distance of 10 km. The work is highly debilitating and results in numerous serious health complaints, including frequent miscarriages (Haile 1991).

The relationship between the specific working conditions in forestry, workforce characteristics, form of employment, training and other similar factors and safety and health in the sector has been a recurrent theme of this introductory article. In forestry, even more than in other sectors, safety and health cannot be analysed, let alone promoted, in isolation. This theme will also be the *leitmotiv* for the remainder of the chapter.

• WOOD HARVESTING

*Dennis Dykstra and Peter Poschen**

Wood harvesting is the preparation of logs in a forest or tree plantation according to the requirements of a user, and delivery of logs to a consumer. It includes the cutting of trees, their conversion into logs, extraction and long distance transport to a consumer or processing plant. The terms *forest harvesting*, *wood harvesting* or *logging* are often used synonymously. Long-distance transport and the harvesting of non-wood forest products are dealt with in separate articles in this chapter.

Operations

While many different methods are used for wood harvesting, they all involve a similar sequence of operations:

- *tree felling:* severing a tree from the stump and bringing it down

* The present article draws heavily on two publications: FAO 1996 and FAO/ILO 1980. This article is an overview; numerous other references are available. For specific guidance on preventive measures, see ILO 1998.

- *topping and debranching (delimbing):* cutting off the unusable tree crown and the branches
- *debarking:* removing the bark from the stem; this operation is often done at the processing plant rather than in the forest; in fuelwood harvesting it is not done at all
- *extraction:* moving the stems or logs from the stump to a place close to a forest road where they can be sorted, piled and often stored temporarily, awaiting long distance transport
- *log making/cross-cutting (bucking):* cutting the stem to the length specified by the intended use of the log
- *scaling:* determining the quantity of logs produced, usually by measuring volume (for small dimension timber also by weight; the latter is common for pulpwood; weighing is done at the processing plant in that case)
- *sorting, piling and temporary storage:* logs are usually of variable dimensions and quality, and are therefore classified into assortments according to their potential use as pulpwood, sawlogs and so on, and piled until a full load, usually a truckload, has been assembled; the cleared area where these operations, as well as scaling and loading, take place is called a "landing"
- *loading:* moving the logs onto the transport medium, typically a truck, and attaching the load.

These operations are not necessarily carried out in the above sequence. Depending on the forest type, the kind of product desired and the technology available, it may be more advantageous to carry out an operation either earlier (i.e., closer to the stump) or later (i.e., at the landing or even at the processing plant). One common classification of harvesting methods is based on distinguishing between:

- *full-tree systems,* where trees are extracted to the roadside, the landing or the processing plant with the full crown
- *short-wood systems,* where topping, debranching and cross-cutting is done close to the stump (logs are usually not longer than 4 to 6 m)
- *tree-length systems,* where tops and branches are removed before extraction.

The most important group of harvesting methods for industrial wood is based on tree length. Short-wood systems are standard in northern Europe and also common for small-dimension timber and fuelwood in many other parts of the world. Their share is likely to increase. Full-tree systems are the least common in industrial wood harvesting, and are used in only a limited number of countries (e.g., Canada, the Russian Federation and the United States). There they account for less than 10% of volume. The importance of this method is diminishing.

For work organization, safety analysis and inspection, it is useful to conceive of three distinct work areas in a wood harvesting operation:

1. the felling site or stump
2. the forest terrain between the stump and the forest road
3. the landing.

It is also worthwhile to examine whether the operations take place largely independently in space and time or whether they are closely related and interdependent. The latter is often the case in harvesting systems where all steps are synchronized. Any disturbance thus disrupts the entire chain, from felling to transport. These so-called hot-logging systems can create extra pressure and strain if not carefully balanced.

The stage in the life cycle of a forest during which wood harvesting takes place, and the harvesting pattern, will affect both the technical process and its associated hazards. Wood harvesting occurs either as thinning or as final cut. Thinning is the removal of some, usually undesirable, trees from a young stand to improve the growth and quality of the remaining trees. It is usually selective (i.e., individual trees are removed without creating major gaps). The spatial pattern generated is similar to that in selective final cutting. In the latter case, however, the trees are mature and often large. Even so, only some of the trees are removed and a significant tree cover remains. In both cases orientation on the worksite is difficult because remaining trees and vegetation block the view. It can be very difficult to bring trees down because their crowns tend to be intercepted by the crowns of remaining trees. There is a high risk of falling debris from the crowns. Both situations are difficult to mechanize. Thinning and selective cutting therefore require more planning and skill to be done safely.

The alternative to selective felling for final harvest is the removal of all trees from a site, called "clear cutting". Clearcuts can be small, say 1 to 5 hectares, or very large, covering several square kilometres. Large clearcuts are severely criticized on environmental and scenic grounds in many countries. Whatever the pattern of the cut, harvesting old growth and natural forest usually involves greater risk than harvesting younger stands or human-made forests because trees are large and have tremendous inertia when falling. Their branches may be intertwined with the crowns of other trees and climbers, causing them to break off branches of other trees as they fall. Many trees are dead or have internal rot which may not be apparent until late in the felling process. Their behaviour during felling is often unpredictable. Rotten trees may break off and fall in unexpected directions. Unlike green trees, dead and dry trees, called snags in North America, fall quickly.

Technological developments

Technological development in wood harvesting has been very rapid over the second half of the 20th century. Average productivity has been soaring in the process. Today, many different harvesting methods are in use, sometimes side by side in the same country. An overview of systems in use in Germany in the mid-1980s, for example, describes almost 40 different configurations of equipment and methods (Dummel and Branz 1986).

While some harvesting methods are technologically far more complex than others, no single method is inherently superior. The choice will usually depend on the customer specifications for the logs, on forest conditions and terrain, on environmental considerations, and often decisively on cost. Some methods are also technically limited to small and medium-size trees and relatively gentle terrain, with slopes not exceeding 15 to 20°.

Cost and performance of a harvesting system can vary over a wide range, depending on how well the system fits the conditions of the site and, equally important, on the skill of the workers and how well the operation is organized. Hand tools and manual extraction, for example, make perfect economic and social sense in countries with high unemployment, low labour and high capital cost, or in small-scale operations. Fully mechanized methods can achieve very high daily outputs but involve large capital investments. Modern harvesters under favourable conditions can produce upwards of 200 m³ of logs per 8-hour day. A chain-saw operator is unlikely to produce more than 10% of that. A harvester or big cable yarder costs around US$500,000 compared to US$1,000 to US$2,000 for a chain-saw and US$200 for a good quality cross-cut handsaw.

Common Methods, Equipment and Hazards

Felling and preparation for extraction

This stage includes felling and removal of crown and branches; it may include debarking, cross-cutting and scaling. It is one of the most hazardous industrial occupations. Hand tools and chain-saws or machines are used in felling and debranching trees and

crosscutting trees into logs. Hand tools include cutting tools such as axes, splitting hammers, bush hooks and bush knives, and hand saws such as cross-cut saws and bow saws. Chain-saws are widely used in most countries. In spite of major efforts and progress by regulators and manufacturers to improve chain-saws, they remain the single most dangerous type of machine in forestry. Most serious accidents and many health problems are associated with their use.

The first activity to be carried out is felling, or severing the tree from the stump as close to the ground as conditions permit. The lower part of the stem is typically the most valuable part, as it contains a high volume, and has no knots and an even wood texture. It should therefore not split, and no fibre should be torn out from the butt. Controlling the direction of the fall is important, not only to protect the tree and those to be left standing, but also to protect the workers and to make extraction easier. In manual felling, this control is achieved by a special sequence and configuration of cuts.

The standard method for chain-saws is depicted in figure 68.6. After determining the felling direction (1) and clearing the tree's base and escape routes, sawing starts with the undercut (2), which should penetrate approximately one-fifth to one-quarter of the diameter into the tree. The opening of the undercut should be at an angle of about 45°. The oblique cut (3) is made prior to the horizontal cut (4), which must meet the oblique cut in a straight line facing the felling direction at a 90° angle. If stumps are liable to tear splinters from the tree, as is common with softer woods, the undercut should be terminated with small lateral cuts (5) on both sides of the hinge (6). The back cut (7) must also be horizontal . It should be made 2.5 to 5 cm higher than the base of the undercut. If the tree's diameter is smaller than the guide bar, the back cut can be made in a single movement (8). Otherwise, the saw must be moved several times (9). The standard method is used for trees with more than 15 cm butt diameter. The standard technique is modified if trees have one-side crowns, are leaning in one direction or have a diameter more than twice the length of the chain-saw blade. Detailed instructions are included in FAO/ILO (1980) and many other training manuals for chain-saw operators.

Using standard methods, skilled workers can fell a tree with a high degree of precision. Trees that have symmetrical crowns or those leaning a little in a direction other than the intended direction of fall may not fall at all or may fall at an angle from the intended direction. In these cases, tools such as felling levers for small trees or hammers and wedges for big trees need to be used to shift the tree's natural centre of gravity in the desired direction.

Except for very small trees, axes are not suitable for felling and cross-cutting. With handsaws the process is relatively slow and errors can be detected and repaired. With chain-saws cuts are fast and the noise blocks out the signals from the tree, such as the sound of breaking fibre before it falls. If the tree does start to fall but is intercepted by other trees, a "hang-up" results, which is extremely dangerous, and must be dealt with immediately and professionally. Turning hooks and levers for smaller trees and manual or tractor-mounted winches for larger trees are used to bring hung-up trees down effectively and safely.

Hazards involved with felling include falling or rolling trees; falling or snapping branches; cutting tools; and noise, vibration and exhaust gases with chain-saws. Windfall is especially hazardous with wood and partially severed root systems under tension; hung-up trees are a frequent cause of severe and fatal accidents. All workers involved in felling should have received specific training. Tools for felling and for dealing with hung-up trees need to be onsite. Hazards associated with cross-cutting include the cutting tools as well as snapping wood and rolling stems or bolts, particularly on slopes.

Figure 68.6 • Chain-saw felling: Sequence of cuts.

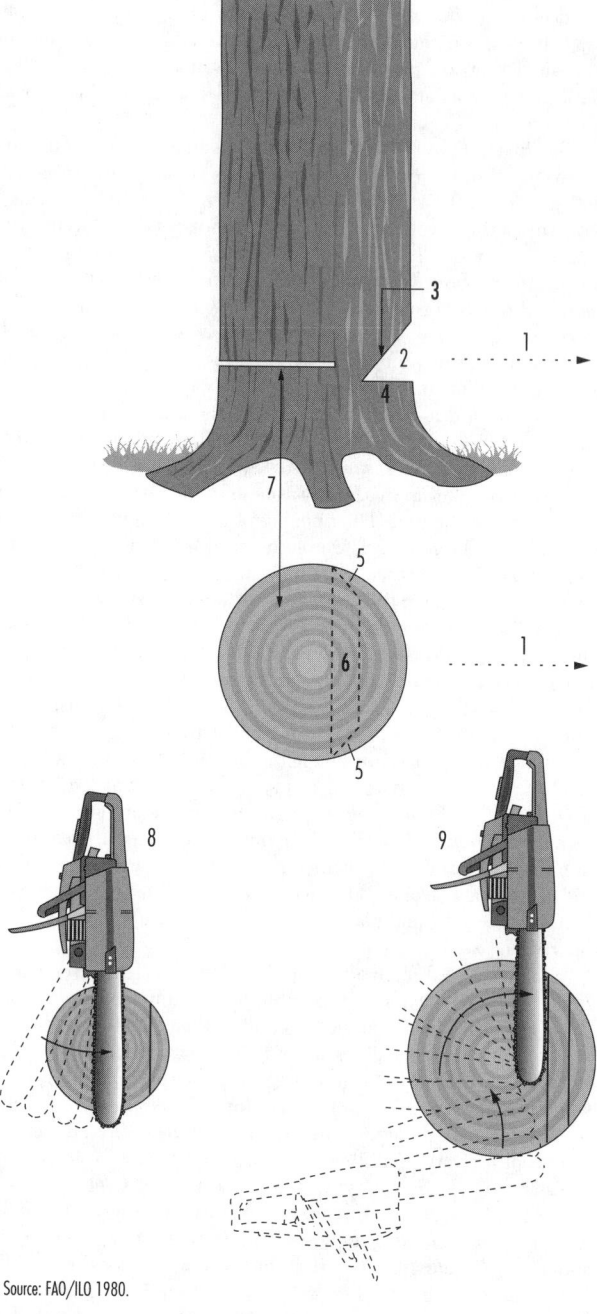

Source: FAO/ILO 1980.

Hazards involved with debranching include cuts with tools or chain-saws; high risk of chain-saw kick-back (see figure 68.7); snapping branches under tension; rolling logs; trips and falls; awkward work postures; and static work load if poor technique is used.

In mechanized operations, the directional fall is achieved by holding the tree with a boom mounted on a sufficiently heavy base machine, and cutting the stem with a shear, circular saw or chain-saw integrated into the boom. To do this, the machine has to be driven rather close to the tree to be felled. The tree is then lowered into the desired direction by movements of the boom or of the base of the machine. The most common types of machines are feller-bunchers and harvesters.

Feller-bunchers are mostly mounted on machines with tracks, but they can also be equipped with tyres. The felling boom usually allows them to fell and collect a number of small trees (a bunch), which is then deposited along a skid trail. Some have a clam bunk to collect a load. When feller-bunchers are used, topping and debranching are usually done by machines at the landing.

With good machine design and careful operation, accident risk with feller-bunchers is relatively low, except when chain-saw operators work along with the machine. Health hazards, such as vibration, noise, dust and fumes, are significant, since base machines often are not built for forestry purposes. Feller-bunchers should not be used on excessive slopes, and the boom should not be overloaded, as felling direction becomes uncontrollable.

Harvesters are machines which integrate all felling operations except debarking. They usually have six to eight wheels, hydraulic traction and suspension, and articulated steering. They have booms with a reach of 6 to 10 m when loaded. A distinction is made between one-grip and two-grip harvesters. One-grip harvesters have one boom with a felling head fitted with devices for felling, debranching, topping and cross-cutting. They are used for small trees up to 40 cm butt diameter, mostly in thinnings but increasingly also in final cutting. A two-grip harvester has separate felling and processing heads. The latter is mounted on the base

Figure 68.7 • Chain-saw kick-back.

Once a tree has been brought down, it is usually topped and debranched. In the majority of cases, this is still done with hand tools or chain-saws at the stump. Axes can be very effective for debranching. Where possible, trees are felled across a stem already on the ground. This stem thus serves as a natural work-bench, raising the tree to be debranched to a more convenient height and allowing for complete debranching without having to turn the tree. The branches and the crown are cut from the stem and left on the site. The crowns of large, broad-leaved trees may have to be cut into smaller pieces or pulled aside because they would otherwise obstruct extraction to the roadside or landing.

machine rather than on the boom. It can handle trees up to a stump diameter of 60 cm. Modern harvesters have an integrated, computer-assisted measuring device that can be programmed to make decisions about optimum cross-cutting depending on the assortments needed.

Harvesters are the dominant technology in large-scale harvesting in northern Europe, but presently account for a rather small share of harvesting worldwide. Their importance is, however, likely to rise fast as second growth, human-made forests and plantations become more important as sources of raw material.

Accident rates in harvester operation are typically low, though accident risk rises when chain-saw operators work along with harvesters. Maintenance of harvesters is hazardous; repairs are always under high work pressure, increasingly at night; there is high risk of slipping and falling, uncomfortable and awkward working postures, heavy lifting, contact with hydraulic oils and hot oils under pressure. The biggest hazards are static muscle tension and repetitive strain from operating controls and psychological stress.

Extraction

Extraction involves moving the stems or logs from the stump to a landing or roadside where they can be processed or piled into assortments. Extraction can be very heavy and hazardous work. It can also inflict substantial environmental damage to the forest and its regeneration, to soils and to watercourses. The major types of extraction systems commonly recognized are:

- *ground-skidding systems:* The stems or logs are dragged on the ground by machines, draught animals or humans.
- *forwarders:* The stems or logs are carried on a machine (in the case of fuelwood, also by humans).
- *cable systems:* The logs are conveyed from the stump to the landing by one or more suspended cables.
- *aerial systems:* Helicopters or balloons are used to airlift the logs.

Ground skidding, by far the most important extraction system both for industrial wood and fuelwood, is usually done with wheeled skidders specially designed for forestry operations. Crawler tractors and, especially, farm tractors can be cost effective in small private forests or for the extraction of small trees from tree plantations, but adaptations are needed to protect both the operators and the machines. Tractors are less robust, less well balanced and less protected than purpose-built machines. As with all machines used in forestry, hazards include over-turning, falling objects, penetrating objects, fire, whole-body vibration and noise. All-wheel drive is preferable, and a minimum of 20% of the machine weight should be maintained as load on the steered axle during operation, which may require attaching additional weight to the front of the machine. The engine and transmission may need extra mechanical protection. Minimum engine power should be 35 kW for small-dimension timber; 50 kW is usually adequate for normal-size logs.

Grapple skidders drive directly to the individual or the pre-bunched stems, lift the front end of the load and drag it to the landing. Skidders with cable winches can operate from skid roads. Their loads are usually assembled through chokers, straps, chains or short cables that are attached to individual logs. A choker setter prepares the logs to be hooked up and, when the skidder returns from the landing, a number of chokers is attached to the main line and winched into the skidder. Most skidders have an arch onto which the front end of the load can be lifted to reduce friction during skidding. When skidders with powered winches are used, good communication between crew members through two-way radios or optical or acoustic signals is essential. Clear signals need to be agreed upon; any signal that is not understood means "Stop!". Figure 68.8 shows proposed hand signals for skidders with powered winches.

As a rule of thumb, ground skidding equipment should not be used on slopes of more than 15°. Crawler tractors may be used to extract large trees from relatively steep terrain, but they can cause substantial damage to soils if used carelessly. For environmental and safety reasons, all skidding operations should be suspended during exceptionally wet weather.

Extraction with draught animals is an economically viable option for small logs, particularly in thinning operations. Skidding distances must be short (typically 200 m or less) and slopes gentle. It is important to use appropriate harnesses providing maximum pulling power, and devices like skidding pans, sulkies or sledges that reduce skidding resistance.

Manual skidding is increasingly rare in industrial logging but continues to be practised in subsistence logging, particularly for fuelwood. It is limited to short distances and usually downhill, making use of gravity to move logs. While logs are typically small, this is very heavy work and can be hazardous on steep slopes. Efficiency and safety can be increased by using hooks, levers and other hand tools for lifting and pulling logs. Chutes, traditionally

Figure 68.8 • International conventions for hand signals to be used for skidders with powered winches.

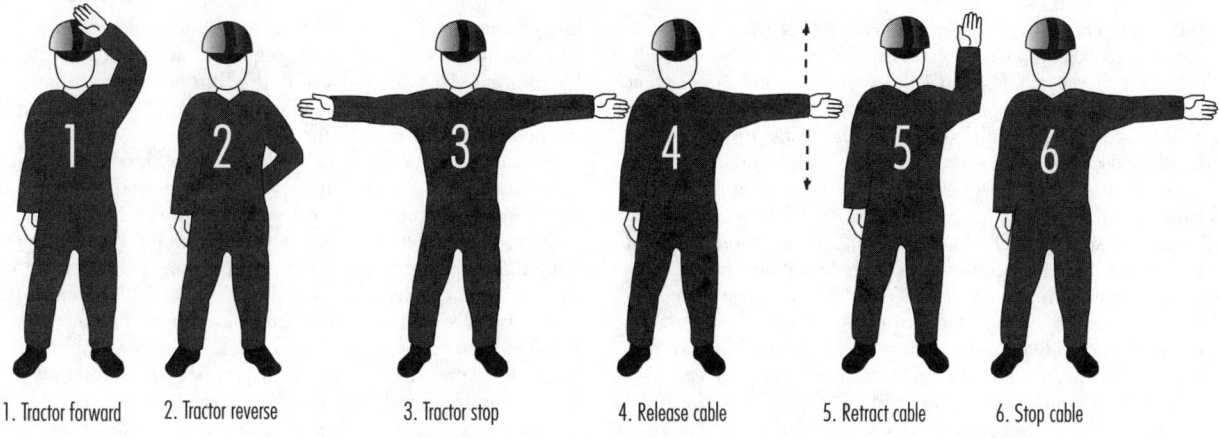

1. Tractor forward   2. Tractor reverse   3. Tractor stop   4. Release cable   5. Retract cable   6. Stop cable

Any signal that is not understood means stop.

made from timber but also available as polyethylene half-tubes, can be an alternative to manual ground skidding of short logs in steep terrain.

Forwarders are extraction machines that carry a load of logs completely off the ground, either within their own frame or on a trailer. They usually have a mechanical or hydraulic crane for self-loading and unloading of logs. They tend to be used in combination with mechanized felling and processing equipment. The economic extraction distance is 2 to 4 times that of ground-skidders. Forwarders work best when logs are approximately uniform in size.

Accidents involving forwarders are typically similar to those of tractors and other forestry machines: overturning, penetrating and falling objects, electric power lines and maintenance problems. Health hazards include vibration, noise and hydraulic oils.

Using human beings to carry loads is still done for short logs like pulpwood or pit props in some industrial harvesting, and is the rule in fuelwood harvesting. Loads carried often exceed all recommended limits, particularly for women, who are often responsible for fuelwood gathering. Training in proper techniques that would avoid extreme strain on the spine and using devices like back packs that give a better weight distribution would ease their burden.

Cable extraction systems are fundamentally different from other extraction systems in that the machine itself does not travel. Logs are conveyed with a carriage moving along suspended cables. The cables are operated by a winching machine, also referred to as a yarder or hauler. The machine is installed either at the landing or at the opposite end of the cableway, often on a ridgetop. The cables are suspended above the ground on one or more "spar" trees, which may either be trees or steel towers. Many different types of cable systems are in use. Skylines or cable cranes have a carriage that can be moved along the mainline, and the cable can be released to allow lateral pulling of logs to the line, before they are lifted and forwarded to the landing. If the system permits full suspension of the load during hauling, soil disturbance is minimal. Because the machine is fixed, cable systems can be used in steep terrain and on wet soils. Cable systems in general are substantially more expensive than ground skidding and require careful planning and skilled operators.

Hazards occur during installation, operation and dismantling of the cable system, and include mechanical impact by deformation of the cabin or stand; breaking of cables, anchors, spars or supports; inadvertent or uncontrollable movements of cables, carriages, chokers and loads; and squeezes, abrasions and so on from moving parts. Health hazards include noise, vibration and awkward working postures.

Aerial extraction systems are those which fully suspend logs in the air throughout the extraction process. The two types currently in use are balloon systems and helicopters, but only helicopters are widely used. Helicopters with a lifting capacity of about 11 tonnes are commercially available. The loads are suspended under the helicopter on a tether line (also called "tagline"). The tether lines are typically between 30 and 100 m long, depending both upon topography and the height of trees above which the helicopter must hover. The loads are attached with long chokers and are flown to the landing, where the chokers are released by remote control from the aircraft. When large logs are being extracted, an electrically operated grapple system may be used instead of chokers. Round-trip times are typically two to five minutes. Helicopters have a very high direct cost, but can also achieve high production rates and reduce or eliminate the need for expensive road construction. They also cause low environmental impact. In practice their use is limited to high-value timber in otherwise inaccessible regions or other special circumstances.

Because of the high production rates required to make the use of such equipment economical, the number of workers employed on helicopter operations is much larger than for other systems. This is true for landings, but also for workers in cutting operations. Helicopter logging can create major safety problems, including fatalities, if precautions are disregarded and crews ill prepared.

Log making and loading

Log making, if it takes place at the landing, is mostly done by chain-saw operators. It can also be carried out by a processor (i.e., a machine that delimbs, tops and cuts to length). Scaling is mostly done manually using measuring tape. For sorting and piling, logs are usually handled by machines like skidders, which use their front blade to push and lift logs, or by grapple loaders. Helpers with hand tools like levers often assist the machine operators. In fuelwood harvesting or where small logs are involved, loading onto trucks is usually done manually or by using a small winch. Loading large logs manually is very arduous and dangerous; these are usually handled by grapple or knuckle boom loaders. In some countries the logging trucks are equipped for self-loading. The logs are secured on the truck by lateral supports and cables that can be pulled tight.

In manual loading of timber, physical strain and workloads are extremely high. In both manual and mechanized loading, there is danger of getting hit by moving logs or equipment. Mechanized loading hazards include noise, dust, vibration, high mental workload, repetitive strain, overturning, penetrating or falling objects and hydraulic oils.

Standards and Regulations

At present most international safety standards applicable to forestry machinery are general—for example, roll-over protection. However, work is under way on specialized standards at the International Organization for Standardization (ISO). (See the article "Rules, legislation, regulations and codes of forest practice" in this chapter.)

Chain-saws are one of the few pieces of forestry equipment for which specific international regulations on safety features exist. Various ISO norms are relevant. They were incorporated and supplemented in 1994 in European Norm 608, *Agricultural and forest machinery: Portable chain-saws—Safety*. This standard contains detailed indications on design features. It also stipulates that manufacturers are required to provide comprehensive instructions and information on all aspects of operator/user maintenance and the safe use of the saw. This is to include safety clothing and personal protective equipment requirements as well as the need for training. All saws sold within the European Union have to be marked "Warning, see instruction handbook". The standard lists the items to be included in the handbook.

Forestry machines are less well covered by international standards, and there is often no specific national regulation about required safety features. Forestry machines may also have significant ergonomic deficiencies. These play a major role in the development of serious health complaints among operators. In other cases, machines have a good design for a particular worker population, but are less suitable when imported into countries where workers have different body sizes, communication routines and so on. In the worst case machines are stripped of essential safety and health features to reduce prices for exports.

In order to guide testing organizations and those responsible for machine acquisition, specialized ergonomic checklists have been developed in various countries. Checklists usually address the following machine characteristics:

- access and exit areas like steps, ladders and doors
- cabin space and position of controls
- seat, arms, back and footrest of operator's chair
- visibility when performing main operations
- "worker-machine interface": type and arrangement of indicators and controls of machine functions
- physical environment, including vibration noise, gases and climatic factors
- safety, including roll-over, penetrating objects, fire and so on
- maintenance.

Specific examples of such checklists can be found in Golsse (1994) and Apud and Valdés (1995). Recommendations for machines and equipment as well as a list of existing ILO standards are included in ILO 1998.

TIMBER TRANSPORT

Olli Eeronheimo

Timber transport provides the link between the forest harvesting and the mill. This operation is of great economic importance: in the northern hemisphere it accounts for 40 to 60% of the total wood procurement cost at the mill (excluding stumpage), and in the tropics the proportion is even higher. The basic factors affecting timber transport include: the size of the operation; the geographic locations of the forest and the mill as well as the distance between them; the assortment of timber for which the mill is designed; and the kinds of transportation that are available and suitable. The main timber assortments are full trees with branches, delimbed tree lengths, long logs (typically 10 to 16 m in length), shortwood (typically 2 to 6 m logs), chips and hog fuel. Many mills can accept varied assortments of timber; some can accept only specific types—for example, shortwood by road. Transport can be by road, rail, ship, floating down a waterway or, depending on the geography and the distance, various combinations of these. Road transport by truck, however, has become the primary form of timber transportation.

In many cases timber transport, especially road transport, is an integrated part of the harvesting operation. Thus, any problem in timber transport may stop the entire harvesting operation. The time pressure can lead to a demand for overtime work and a tendency to cut corners that may compromise the workers' safety.

Both forest harvesting and timber transport are often contracted out. Particularly when there are multiple contractors and subcontractors, there may be a question of who has the responsibility for protecting particular workers' safety and health.

Timber Handling and Loading

When circumstances permit, timber may be loaded directly onto trucks at the stump, eliminating the need for a separate forest transport phase. When distances are short, forest transport equipment (e.g., an agricultural tractor with a trailer or semi-trailer) may convey the timber directly to the mill. Normally, however, the timber is first taken to the forest roadside landing for long-distance transport.

Manual loading is often practised in developing countries and in poorly capitalized operations. Small logs can be lifted and the large ones rolled with the help of ramps (see figure 68.9). Simple hand tools like hooks, levers, sappies, pulleys and so on may be used, and draught animals may be involved.

In most instances, however, loading is mechanized, usually with swing-boom, knuckle-boom or front-end loaders. Swing-boom and knuckle-boom loaders may be mounted on wheeled or tracked carriers or on trucks, and are usually equipped with grapples. Front-end loaders usually have forks or grapples and are mounted on crawler tractors or articulated four-wheel-drive tractors. In semi-mechanized loading, logs may be lifted or rolled up the loading skids by cables and different kinds of tractors and

Figure 68.9 • Manual loading (with and without ramps).

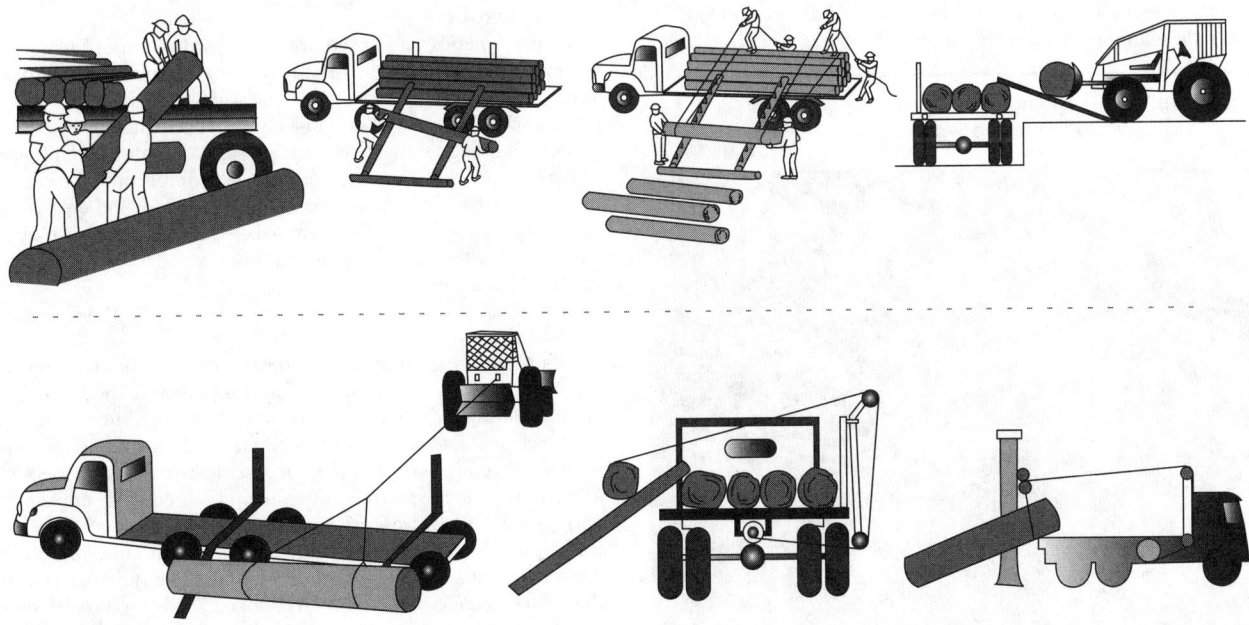

Source: Adapted from Kantola and Harstela 1988.

Figure 68.10 • Mechanized and semi-mechanized loading.

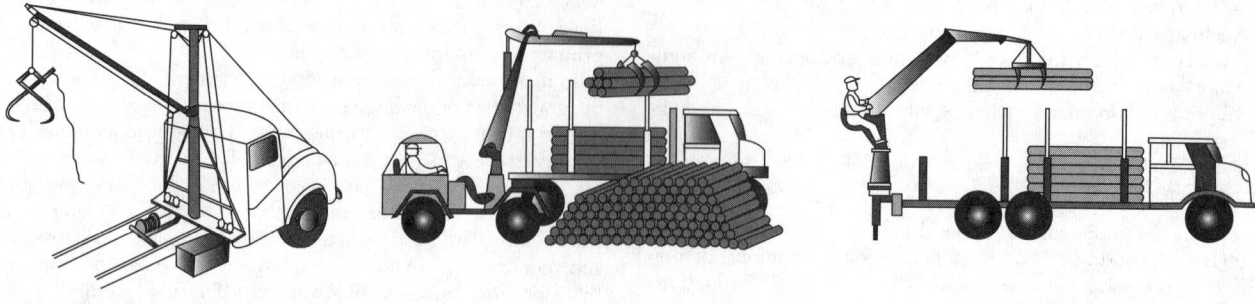

Source: Adapted from Kantola and Harstela 1988.

winches (see figure 68.10). Semi-mechanized loading often re-quires workers to be on the ground attaching and releasing cables, guiding the load and so on, often using hooks, levers and other hand tools. In chipping operations, the chipper usually blows the chips directly into the truck, trailer or semi-trailer.

Landing Operations

Landings are busy, noisy places where many different operations are conducted simultaneously. Depending on the harvesting sys-tem, these include loading and unloading, delimbing, debarking, bucking, sorting, storing and chipping. One or more large ma-chines may be moving and operating at the same time while chain saws are in use close by. During and after rain, snow and frost, the logs may be very slippery and the ground may be very muddy and slick. The area may be littered with debris, and in dry weather it may be very dusty. Logs may be stored in unsecured piles several metres high. All this makes the landing one of the most dangerous working areas in the forestry industry.

Road Transport

Road transport of timber is carried by vehicles the size of which depends on the dimensions of the timber, road conditions and traffic regulations, and the availability of capital to purchase or lease the equipment. Two- or three-axle trucks with a carrying

Figure 68.11 • Logging operations in Nigeria with unprotected workers.

capacity of 5 to 6 tonnes are commonly used in tropical countries. In Scandinavia, for example, the typical logging truck is a 4-axle truck with a 3-axle trailer or vice versa—with a carrying capacity of 20 to 22 tonnes. On private roads in North America, one can encounter rigs with a total weight of 100 to 130 tonnes or more.

Water Transport

The use of waterways for timber transport has been declining as road transport has been increasing, but it still remains important in Canada, the United States, Finland and Russia in the northern hemisphere, in the watersheds of the Amazon, Paraguay and Parana rivers in Latin America, in many rivers and lakes in Western Africa and in most countries in Southeast Asia.

In mangrove and tidal forests, water transport usually starts directly from the stump; otherwise the logs have to be transported to the waterfront, usually by truck. Loose logs or bundles can be drifted downstream in rivers. They can be bound into rafts which can be towed or pushed in rivers, lakes and along coasts, or they may be loaded onto boats and barges of varying size. Ocean-going ships play a large role in the international timber trade.

Rail Transport

In North America and in the tropics, railway transport, like water transport, is giving way to road transport. However, it remains very important in countries like Canada, Finland, Russia and China, where there are good railway networks with suitable inter-mediate landing areas. In some large-scale operations, temporary narrow-gauge railways may be used. The timber may be carried in standard freight cars, or specially constructed timber-carrying cars may be used. In some terminals, large fixed cranes may be used for loading and unloading, but, as a rule, the loading methods described above are used.

Conclusion

Loading and unloading, which sometimes must be done several times as timber travels from the forest to where it will be used, is often a particularly hazardous operation in the timber industry. Even when fully mechanized, workers on foot and using hand tools may be involved and may be at risk. Some larger operators and contractors recognize this, maintain their equipment properly and provide their workers with personal protective equipment (PPE) such as shoes, gloves, helmets, glasses and noise protectors. Even then, trained and diligent supervisors are required, to ensure that safety concerns are not overlooked. Safety often becomes problematic in smaller operations and particularly in developing countries. (For an example see figure 68.11, which shows workers without PPE loading logs in Nigeria.)

HARVESTING OF NON-WOOD FOREST PRODUCTS

Rudolf Heinrich

Operational Environment

There are many hazards associated with the harvest of non-wood forest products because of the wide variety of non-wood products themselves. In order better to define these hazards, non-wood products may be grouped by category, with a few representative examples. Then the hazards associated with their harvest can be more easily identified (see table 68.2).

Non-wood products are harvested for several reasons (subsistence, commercial or hobby/recreational purposes) and for a range of needs. This in turn affects the relative hazard associated with their collection. For example, the hobbyist mushroom picker is much less likely to remain in the open risking exposure to severe climatic conditions than is the commercial picker, dependent on picking for income and competing for a limited supply of seasonally available mushrooms.

The scale of non-wood harvesting operations is variable, with associated positive and negative effects on potential hazards. By its nature non-wood harvesting is often a small, subsistence or entrepreneurial effort. The safety of the lone worker in remote locations can be more problematic than for the non-isolated worker. Individual experience will affect the situation. There may be an emergency or other situation possibly calling for the direct intervention of outside consultative sources of safety and health information. Certain specific non-wood products have, however, been significantly commercialized, even lending themselves to plantation cultivation, such as bamboo, mushrooms, gum naval stores, certain nuts and rubber, to name just a few. Commercialized operations, theoretically, may be more likely to provide and emphasize systematic health and safety information in the course of work.

Collectively, the listed products, the forest environment in which they exist and the methods required to harvest them can be linked with certain inherent health and safety hazards. These hazards are quite elementary because they derive from very common actions, such as climbing, cutting with hand tools, digging, gathering, picking and manual transport. In addition, harvest of a certain food product might include exposure to biological agents (a poisonous plant surface or poisonous snake), biomechanical

Table 68.2 • Non-wood forest product categories and examples.

Categories	Examples
Food products	Animal products, bamboo shoots, berries, beverages, forage, fruits, herbs, mushrooms, nuts, oils, palm hearts, roots, seeds, starches
Chemical and pharmacological products and derivatives	Aromatics, gums and resins, latex and other exudates, medicinal extracts, tans and dyes, toxins
Decorative materials	Bark, foliage, flowers, grasses, potpourri
Non-wood fibre for plaiting, structural purposes, and padding	Bamboo, bark, cork, kapok, palm leaves, rattan, reeds, thatching grasses

Table 68.3 • Non-wood harvesting hazards and examples.

Non-wood harvesting hazards	Examples
Biological agents	Bites and stings (external vector, systemic poisons) Plant contact (external vector, topical poisons) Ingestion (internal vector, systemic poisons)
Biomechanical action	Improper technique or repetitive-use injury related to bending, carrying, cutting, lifting, loading
Climatological conditions	Excessive heat and cold effects, either externally induced (environment) or due to work effort
Tools and techniques	Cuts, mechanical hazards, draught animal handling, small vehicle operation
Other	Altercation, animal attack, difficult terrain, fatigue, loss of orientation, working at heights, working in remote locations, working on or crossing waterways

hazards (e.g., due to a repetitive movement or carrying a heavy load), climatological conditions, safety hazards from tools and techniques (such as a laceration due to careless cutting technique) and other hazards (perhaps due to difficult terrain, river crossings or working off the ground).

Because non-wood products often do not lend themselves to mechanization, and because its cost is frequently prohibitive, there is a disproportionate emphasis on manual harvest or using draught animals for harvest and transport compared to other industries.

Hazard Control and Prevention

A special word about cutting operations is warranted, since cutting is arguably the most recognizable and common source of hazard associated with the harvest of non-wood forest products. Potential cutting hazards are linked to appropriate tool selection and tool quality, size/type of the cut required, the force needed to make the cut, positioning of the worker and worker attitude.

In general, cutting hazards can be reduced or mitigated by:

- *direct training for the work tasks:* proper tool selection, tool maintenance and sharpening, and training of the worker with respect to proper biomechanical technique
- *training in work organization:* job planning, safety/hazard assessment, site preparation and continual worker awareness with respect to work task and surroundings.

The goal of successful training in work technique and philosophy should be: implementation of proper work planning and precautionary measures, hazard recognition, active hazard avoidance and minimization of injury in the event of accident.

Factors Related to Harvesting Hazards

Because non-wood harvesting, by its nature, occurs in the open, subject to changing weather conditions and other natural factors, and because it is predominantly non-mechanized, workers are particularly subject to the environmental effects of geography, topography, climate and season. After considerable physical efforts and fatigue, weather conditions can contribute to work-related health problems and accidents (see table 68.3).

Non-wood harvesting operations tend to be in remote areas. This poses a form of hazard due to a lack of proximity to medical care in the event of accident. This would not be expected to increase accident frequency but certainly may increase the potential severity of any injury.

68. FORESTRY

TREE PLANTING

Denis Giguère

Tree planting consists of putting seedlings or young trees into the soil. It is mainly done to re-grow a new forest after harvesting, to establish a woodlot or to change the use of a piece of land (e.g., from a pasture to a woodlot or to control erosion on a steep slope). Planting projects can amount to several million plants. Projects may be executed by the forest owners' private contractors, pulp and paper companies, the government's forest service, non-governmental organizations or cooperatives. In some countries, tree planting has become a veritable industry. Excluded here is the planting of large individual trees, which is considered more the domain of landscaping than forestry.

The workforce includes the actual tree planters as well as tree nursery staff, workers involved in transporting and maintaining the plants, support and logistics (e.g., managing, cooking, driving and maintaining vehicles and so on) and quality control inspectors. Women comprise 10 to 15% of the tree-planter workforce. As an indication of the importance of the industry and the scale of activities in regions where forestry is of economic importance, the provincial government in Quebec, Canada, set an objective of planting 250 million seedlings in 1988.

Planting Stock

Several technologies are available to produce seedlings or small trees, and the ergonomics of tree planting will vary accordingly. Tree planting on flat land can be done by planting machines. The role of the worker is then limited to feeding the machine manually or merely to controlling quality. In most countries and situations, however, site preparation may be mechanized, but actual planting is still done manually.

In most reforestation, following a forest fire or clear cutting, for example, or in afforestation, seedlings varying from 25 to 50 cm in height are used. The seedlings are either bare-rooted or have been grown in containers. The most common containers in tropical countries are 600 to 1,000 cm^3. Containers may be arranged in plastic or styrofoam trays which usually hold from 40 to 70 identical units. For some purposes, larger plants, 80 to 200 cm, may be needed. They are usually bare-rooted.

Tree planting is seasonal because it depends on rainy and/or cool weather. The season lasts 30 to 90 days in most regions. Although it may seem a lesser seasonal occupation, tree planting must be considered a major long-term strategic activity, both for the environment and for revenue where forestry is an important industry.

Information presented here is based mainly on the Canadian experience, but many of the issues can be extrapolated to other countries with a similar geographical and economic context. Specific practices and health and safety considerations for developing countries are also addressed.

Planting Strategy

Careful evaluation of the site is important for setting adequate planting targets. A superficial approach can hide field difficulties that will slow down the planting and overburden the planters. Several strategies exist for planting large areas. One common approach is to have a team of 10 to 15 planters equally spaced in a row, who progress at the same pace; a designated worker then has the task of bringing in enough seedlings for the whole team, usually by means of small off-road vehicles. One other common method is to work with several pairs of planters, each pair being responsible for fetching and carrying their own small stock of plants. Experienced planters will know how to space out their

Table 68.4 • Typical load carried while planting

Element	Weight in kg
Commercially available harness	2.1
Three 45-seedling container trays, full	12.3
Typical planting tool (dibble)	2.4
Total	16.8

stock to avoid losing time carrying plants back and forth. Planting alone is not recommended.

Seedling Transport

Planting relies on the steady supply of seedlings to the planters. They are brought in several thousands at a time from the nurseries, on trucks or pick-ups as far as the road will go. The seedlings must be unloaded rapidly and watered regularly. Modified logging machinery or small off-road vehicles can be used to carry the seedlings from the main depot to the planting sites. Where seedlings have to be carried by workers, such as in many developing countries, the workload is very heavy. Suitable back-packs should be used to reduce fatigue and risk of injuries. Individual planters will carry from four to six trays to their respective lots. Since most planters are paid at a piece rate, it is important for them to minimize unproductive time spent travelling, or fetching or carrying seedlings.

Equipment and Tools

The typical equipment carried by a tree planter includes a planting shovel or a dibble (a slightly conical metal cylinder at the end of a stick, used to make holes closely fitting the dimensions of containerized seedlings), two or three plant container trays carried by a harness, and safety equipment such as toe-capped boots and protective gloves. When planting bare-rooted seedlings, a pail containing enough water to cover the seedling's roots is used instead of the harness, and is carried by hand. Various types of tree-planting hoes are also widely used for bare-rooted seedlings in Europe and North America. Some planting tools are manufactured by specialized tool companies, but many are made in local shops or are intended for gardening and agriculture, and present some design deficiencies such as excess weight and improper length. The weight typically carried is presented in table 68.4.

Planting Cycle

One tree-planting cycle is defined as the series of steps necessary to put one seedling into the ground. Site conditions, such as slope, soil and ground cover, have a strong influence on productivity. In Canada the production of a planter can vary from 600 plants per day for a novice to 3,000 plants per day for an experienced individual. The cycle may be subdivided as follows:

Selection of a micro-site. This step is fundamental for the survival of the young trees and depends on several criteria taken into account by quality control inspectors, including distance from preceding plant and natural offspring, closeness to organic material, absence of surrounding debris and avoidance of dry or flooded spots. All these criteria must be applied by the planter for each and every tree planted, since their non-observance can lead to a financial penalty.

Ground perforation. A hole is made in the ground with the planting tool. Two operating modes are observed, depending on the type of handle and the length of the shaft. One consists of using the mass of the body applied to a step bar located at the lower extremity of the tool to force it into the ground, while the other one involves

Figure 68.12 • Tree planters in action in Canada.

Denis Giguère, IRSST

raising the tool at arm's length and forcefully plunging it into the ground. To avoid soil particles falling into the hole when the tool is removed, planters have the habit of smoothing its walls either by turning the tool around its long axis with a movement of the hand, or by flaring it with a circular motion of the arm.

Insertion of the plant into the cavity. If the planter is not yet holding a seedling, he or she grabs one from the container, bends down, inserts it into the hole and straightens up. The plant must be straight, firmly inserted into the soil, and the roots must be completely covered. It is interesting to note here that the tool plays an important secondary role by supplying a support for the planter as he or she bends down and straightens up, thus relieving the back muscles. Back movements can be straight or flexed, depending on the length of the shaft and the type of handle.

Soil compaction. Soil is compacted around the newly planted seedling to set it in the hole and to eliminate air that could dry the roots. Even though a trampling action is recommended, a forceful stamping of the feet or heel is more often observed.

Moving to the next micro-site. The planter proceeds to the next micro-site, generally 1.8 m away. This distance is usually evaluated by sight by experienced planters. While proceeding to the site, he or she must identify hazards on the way, plan a path around them, or determine another evasive strategy. In figure 68.12, the planter in the foreground is about to insert the seedling in the hole. The planter in the background is about to make a hole with a straight-handle planting tool. Both carry the seedlings in containers attached to a harness. Seedlings and equipment can weigh up to 16.8 kg (see table 68.4). Also note that the planters are fully covered by clothes to protect themselves against insects and the sun.

Hazards, Outcomes and Preventive Measures

Few studies worldwide have been devoted to the health and safety of tree planters. Although bucolic in appearance, tree planting carried out on an industrial basis can be strenuous and hazardous. In a pioneering study conducted by Smith (1987) in British Columbia, it was found that 90% of the 65 planters interviewed had suffered an illness, injury or accident during life-time tree-planting activities. In a similar study conducted by IRSST, the Quebec Institute of Occupational Health and Safety (Giguère et al. 1991, 1993), 24 out of 48 tree planters reported having suffered from a work-related injury during the course of their planting careers. In Canada, 15 tree planters died between 1987 and 1991 of the

following work-related causes: road accidents (7), wild animals (3), lightning (2), lodging incidents (fire, asphyxia—2) and heat stroke (1).

Although scarce and conducted on a small number of workers, the few investigations of physiological indicators of physical strain (heart rate, blood haematology parameters, elevated serum enzymes activity) all concluded that tree planting is a highly strenuous occupation both in terms of cardiovascular and musculoskeletal strain (Trites, Robinson and Banister 1993; Robinson, Trites and Banister 1993; Giguère et al. 1991; Smith 1987). Banister, Robinson and Trites (1990) defined "tree-planter burnout", a condition originating from haematological deficiency and characterized by the presence of lethargy, weakness and light-headedness similar to the "adrenal exhaustion syndrome" or "sport anaemia" developed by training athletes. (For data on workload in Chile, see Apud and Valdés 1995; for Pakistan, see Saarilahti and Asghar 1994).

Organizational factors. Long workdays, commuting and strict quality control, coupled with the piece-work incentive (which is a widespread practice among tree-planting contractors), may strain the physiological and psychological equilibrium of the worker and lead to chronic fatigue and stress (Trites, Robinson and Banister 1993). A good working technique and regular short pauses improve daily output and help to avoid burnout.

Accidents and injuries. Data presented in table 68.5 provide an indication of the nature and causes of accidents and injuries as they were reported by the tree-planter population participating in the Quebec study. The relative importance of accidents by body part affected shows that injuries to the lower extremities are more frequently reported than those to the upper extremities, if the percentages for knees, feet, legs and ankles are added together. The environmental setting is favourable to tripping and falling accidents. Injuries associated with forceful movements and lesions caused by tools, cutting scraps or soil debris are also of relevance.

A well-prepared planting site, free of bushes and obstacles, will speed up planting and reduce accidents. Scrap should be disposed of in piles instead of furrows to allow easy circulation of the planters on the site. Tools should have straight handles to avoid injuries, and be of a contrasting colour. Shoes or boots should be

Table 68.5 • Frequency grouping of tree-planting accidents by body parts affected (in percentage of 122 reports by 48 subjects in Quebec).

Rank	Body part	% total	Related causes
1	Knees	14	Falls, contact with tool, soil compaction
2	Skin	12	Equipment contact, biting and stinging insects, sunburn, chapping
3	Eyes	11	Insects, insect repellent, twigs
4	Back	10	Frequent bending, load carrying
4	Feet	10	Soil compaction, blisters
5	Hands	8	Chapping, scratches from contact with soil
6	Legs	7	Falls, contact with tool
7	Wrists	6	Hidden rocks
8	Ankles	4	Trips and falls, hidden obstacles, contact with tool
9	Other	18	—

Source: Giguère et al. 1991, 1993.

sturdy enough to protect the feet during the repeated contact with the planting tool and while trampling the soil; sizes should be available for male and female planters, and the sole, sized properly for both men and women, should have a good grip on wet rocks or stumps. Gloves are useful to reduce the occurrence of blistering and of cuts and bruises from inserting the seedling into the soil. They also make the handling of conifer or thorny seedlings more comfortable.

Camp life and outdoor work. In Canada and a number of other countries, planters often have to live in camps. Working in the open requires protection against the sun (sun glasses, hats, sun block) and against biting and stinging insects. Heat stress can also be significant, and prevention calls for the possibility of adjusting the work-rest regimen and the availability of potable liquids to avoid dehydration.

It is important to have first aid equipment and some of the personnel trained as paramedics. Training should include emergency treatment of heat stroke and allergy caused by the venom of wasps or snakes. Planters should be checked for tetanus vaccination and for allergy before being sent to remote sites. Emergency communication systems, evacuation procedures and assembly signal (in case of a forest fire, sudden wind or sudden thunderstorm, or the presence of dangerous wild animals and so on) are essential.

Chemical hazards. The use of pesticides and fungicides to protect the seedlings (during cultivation or storage) is a potential risk when handling freshly sprayed plants (Robinson, Trites and Banister 1993). Eye irritation may occur due to the constant need to apply insect-repelling lotions or sprays.

Musculoskeletal and physiological load. Although there is no specific epidemiological literature linking musculoskeletal problems and tree planting, the forceful movements associated with load carrying, as well as the range of postures and muscular work involved in the planting cycle, undoubtedly constitute risk factors, which are exacerbated by the repetitive nature of the work.

Extreme flexions and extensions of the wrists, in grabbing seedlings in the trays, for example, and shock transmission to the hands and arms occurring when the planting tool hits a hidden rock, are among the possible biomechanical hazards to the upper limbs. The overall weight carried, the frequency of lifting, the repetitive and physical nature of the work, especially the intensive muscular effort required when plunging the dibble into the ground, contribute to the muscular strain exerted on upper limbs.

Low-back problems could be related to the frequency of bending. Handling of seedling trays (3.0 to 4.1 kg each when full) when unloading delivery trucks is also a potential risk. Carrying loads with harnesses, especially if the weight is not properly distributed on the shoulders and around the waist, is also likely to engender back pain.

The muscular load on lower limbs is obviously extensive. Walking several kilometres a day while carrying a load on rough terrain, sometimes going uphill, can rapidly become strenuous. Additionally, the work involves frequent knee flexions, and the feet are used continuously. Most tree planters use their feet to clear local debris with a lateral movement before making a hole. They also use their feet in putting weight on the tool's footrest to aid penetration into the soil and to compact the soil around the seedling after it has been inserted.

Prevention of musculoskeletal strain relies on the minimization of carried loads, in terms of weight, frequency and distance, in conjunction with the optimization of working postures, which implies proper working tools and practices.

If seedlings must be carried in a pail, for instance, water can be replaced by wet peat moss to reduce carried weight. In Chile, replacing heavy wooden boxes for carrying seedlings by lighter cardboard ones increased output by 50% (Apud and Valdés

1995). Tools also have to be well adapted to the job. Replacing a pickaxe and shovel with a specially designed pick-hoe reduced workload by 50% and improved output by up to 100% in reforestation in Pakistan (Saarilahti and Asghar 1994). The weight of the planting tool is also crucial. For example, in a field survey of planting tools conducted in Quebec, variations ranged from 1.7 to 3.1 kg, meaning that choosing the lightest model may save 1,400 kg of lifted weight daily based on 1,000 lifts per day.

Planting tools with long, straight handles are preferred since if the tool hits a hidden rock, the hand will slip on the handle instead of absorbing the shock. A smooth, tapered handle allows an optimum grip for a greater percentage of the population. The Forest Engineering Research Institute of Canada recommends adjustable tools with shock-absorbing properties, but reports that none were available at the time of their 1988 survey (Stjernberg 1988).

Planters should also be educated about optimal working postures. Using the body weight to insert the dibble instead of using muscular effort, avoiding back twisting or exertion of the arms while they are fully extended, avoiding planting downhill and using the planting tool as a support when bending, for example, can all help minimize musculoskeletal strain. Novice planters should not be paid piece rate until they are fully trained.

FOREST FIRE MANAGEMENT AND CONTROL

Mike Jurvélius

The Relevance of Forest Fires

One important task for forest management is the protection of the forest resource base.

Out of many sources of attacks against the forest, fire is often the most dangerous. This danger is also a real threat for the people living inside or adjacent to the forest area. Each year thousands of people lose their homes due to wildfires, and hundreds of people die in these accidents; additionally tens of thousands of domestic animals perish. Fire destroys agricultural crops and leads to soil erosion, which in the long run is even more disastrous than the accidents described before. When the soil is barren after the fire, and heavy rains soak the soil, huge mud- or landslides can occur.

It is estimated that every year:

- 10 to 15 million hectares of boreal or temperate forest burn.
- 20 to 40 million hectares of tropical rain forest burn.
- 500 to 1,000 million hectares of tropical and subtropical savannahs, woodlands and open forests burn.

More than 90% of all this burning is caused by human activity. Therefore, it is quite clear that fire prevention and control should receive top priority among forest management activities.

Risk Factors in Forest Fires

The following factors make fire-control work particularly difficult and dangerous:

- excessive heat radiated by the fire (fires always occur during hot weather)
- poor visibility (due to smoke and dust)
- difficult terrain (fires always follow wind patterns and generally move uphill)

- difficulty getting supplies to the fire-fighters (food, water, tools, fuel)
- often obligatory to work at night (easiest time to "kill" the fire)
- impossibility of outrunning a fire during strong winds (fires move faster than any person can run)
- sudden changes in the wind direction, so that no one can exactly predict the spread of the fire
- stress and fatigue, causing people to make disastrous judgement errors, often with fatal results.

Activities in Forest Fire Management

The activities in forest fire management can be divided into three different categories with different objectives:

- fire prevention (how to prevent fires from happening)
- fire detection (how to report the fires as fast as possible)
- fire suppression (the work to put out the fire, actually fighting the fire).

Occupational dangers

Fire prevention work is generally a very safe activity.

Fire detection safety is mostly a question of safe driving of vehicles, unless aircraft are used. Fixed-wing aircraft are especially vulnerable to strong uplifting air streams caused by the hot air and gases. Each year tens of air crews are lost due to pilot errors, especially in mountainous conditions.

Fire suppression, or actual fighting of the fire, is a very specialized operation. It has to be organized like a military operation, because negligence, non-obedience and other human errors may not only endanger the firefighter, but may also cause the death of many others as well as extensive property damage. The whole organization has to be clearly structured with good coordination between forestry staff, emergency services, fire brigades, police and, in large fires, the armed forces. There has to be a single line of command, centrally and onsite.

Fire suppression mostly involves the establishment or maintenance of a network of fire-breaks. These are typically 10- to 20-metre-wide strips cleared of all vegetation and burnable material. Accidents are mostly caused by cutting tools.

Major wildfires are, of course, the most hazardous, but similar problems arise with prescribed burning or "cold fires", when mild burns are allowed to reduce the amount of inflammable material without damaging the vegetation. The same precautions apply in all cases.

Early intervention

Detecting the fire early, when it is still weak, will make its control easier and safer. Previously, detection was based on observations from the ground. Now, however, infrared and microwave equipment attached to aircraft can detect an early fire. The information is relayed to a computer on the ground, which can process it and give the precise location and temperature of the fire, even when there are clouds. This allows ground crews and/or smoke jumpers to attack the fire before it spreads widely.

Tools and equipment

Many rules are applicable to the firefighter, who may be a forest worker, a volunteer from the community, a government employee or a member of a military unit ordered to the area. The most important is: *never go to fight a fire without your own personal cutting tool.* The only way to escape the fire may be to use the tool to remove one of the components of the "fire triangle", as shown in figure 68.13. The quality of that tool is critical: if it breaks, the fire fighter may lose his or her life.

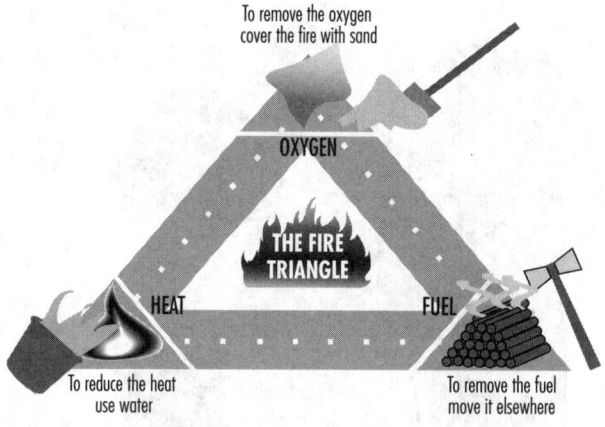

Figure 68.13 • The fire triangle.

This also puts a very special emphasis on the quality of the tool; bluntly put, if the metal part of the tool breaks, the fire-fighter may lose his or her life. Forest firefighter safety equipment is shown in figure 68.14.

Terrestrial firefighting

The preparation of fire breaks during an actual fire is especially dangerous because of the urgency of controlling the advance of the fire. The danger may be multiplied by poor visibility and changing wind direction. In fighting fires with heavy smoke (e.g., peat-land fires), lessons learned from such a fire in Finland in 1995 include:

- Only experienced and physically very fit people should be sent out in heavy smoke conditions.
- Each person should have a radio to receive directions from an hovering aircraft.
- Only people with breathing apparatus or gas masks should be included.

The problems are related to poor visibility and changing wind directions.

When an advancing fire threatens dwellings, the inhabitants may have to be evacuated. This presents an opportunity for thieves and vandals, and calls for diligent policing activities.

The most dangerous work task is the making of backfires: hurriedly cutting through the trees and underbrush to form a path parallel to the advancing line of fire and setting it afire at just the right moment to produce a strong draught of air heading toward the advancing fire, so that the two fires meet. The draught from the advancing fire is caused by the need of the advancing fire to pull oxygen from all sides of the fire. It is very clear that if the timing fails, then the whole crew will be engulfed by strong smoke and exhausting heat and then will suffer a lack of oxygen. Only the most experienced people should set backfires, and they should prepare escape routes in advance to either side of the fire. This backfiring system should always be practised in advance of the fire season; this practice should include the use of equipment like torches for lighting the backfire. Ordinary matches are too slow!

As a last effort for self-preservation, a firefighter can scrape all burning materials in a 5 m diameter, dig a pit in the centre, cover him or herself with soil, soak headgear or jacket and put it over his or her head. Oxygen is often available only at 1 to 2 centimetres from ground level.

Figure 68.14 • Forest firefighter safety equipment.

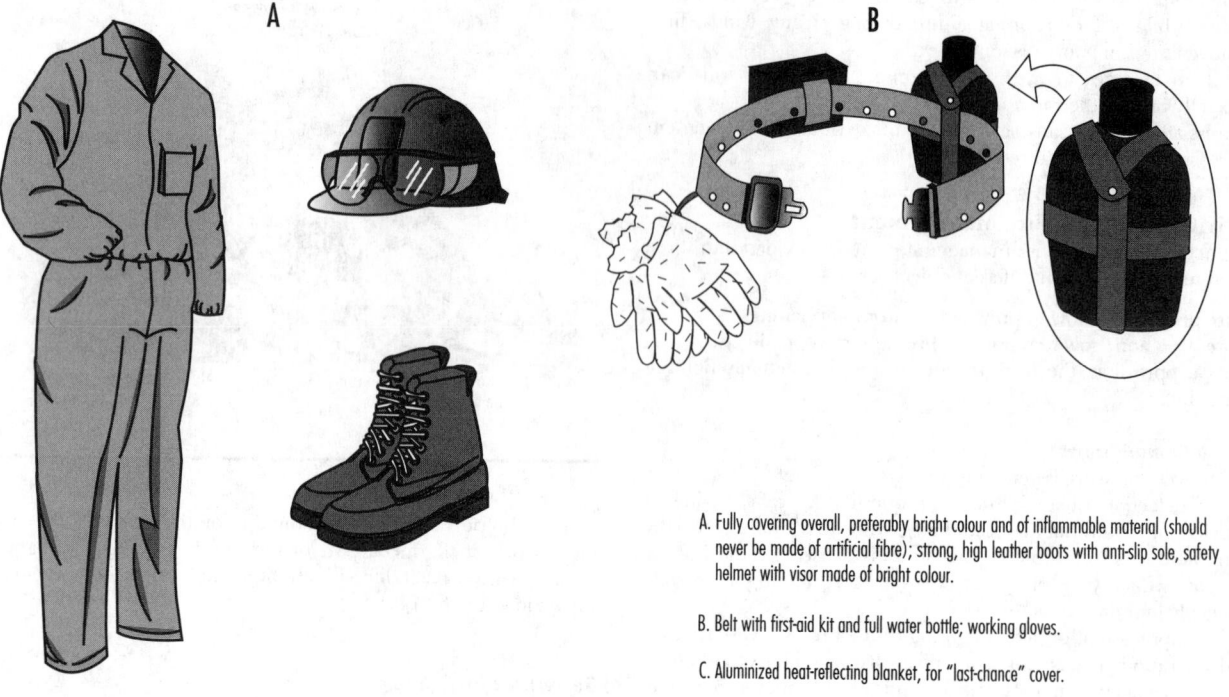

A. Fully covering overall, preferably bright colour and of inflammable material (should never be made of artificial fibre); strong, high leather boots with anti-slip sole, safety helmet with visor made of bright colour.

B. Belt with first-aid kit and full water bottle; working gloves.

C. Aluminized heat-reflecting blanket, for "last-chance" cover.

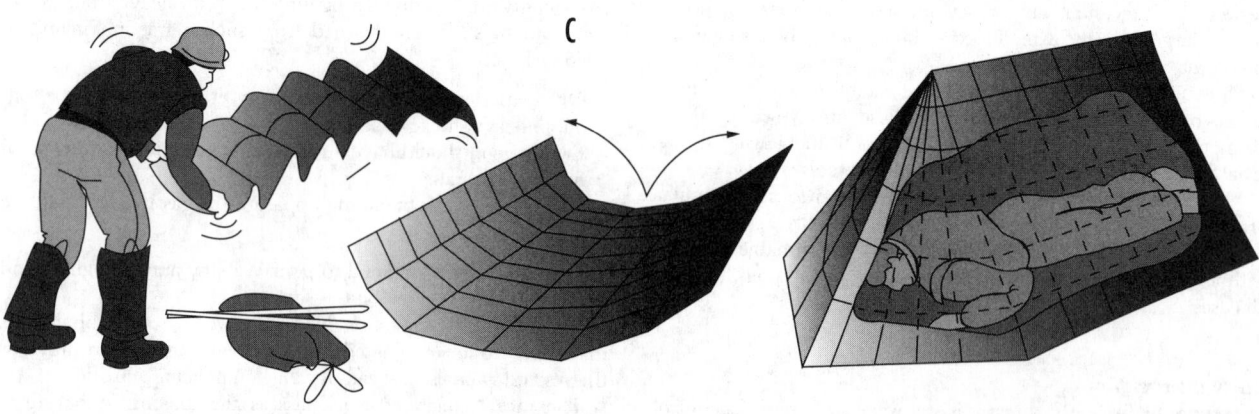

Water bombing by aircraft

The use of aircraft for fighting fires is not new (the dangers in aviation are described elsewhere in this *Encyclopaedia*). There are, however, some activities that are very dangerous for the ground crew in a forest fire. The first is related to the official sign language used in aircraft operations—this has to be practised during training.

The second is how to mark all areas where the aircraft is going to load water for its tanks. To make this operation as safe as possible, these areas should be marked off with floating buoys to obviate the pilot's need to use guesswork.

The third important matter is to keep constant radio contact between the ground crew and the aircraft as it prepares to release its water. The release from small heli-buckets of 500 to 800 litres is not that dangerous. Large helicopters, however, like the MI-6, carry 2,500 litres, while the C-120 aircraft takes 8,000 litres and

the IL-76 can drop 42,000 litres in one sweep. If, by chance, one of these big loads of water lands on crew members on the ground, the impact could kill them.

Training and organization

One essential requirement in firefighting is to line up all firefighters, villagers and forest workers to organize joint firefighting exercises before the beginning of fire season. This is the best way to secure successful and safe firefighting. At the same time, all the work functions of the various levels of command should be practised in the field.

The selected fire chief and leaders should be the ones with the best knowledge of local conditions and of government and private organizations. It is obviously dangerous to assign somebody either too high up the hierarchy (no local knowledge) or too low down the hierarchy (often lacking authority).

PHYSICAL SAFETY HAZARDS

Bengt Pontén

Climate, noise and vibration are common physical hazards in forestry work. Exposure to physical hazards varies greatly depending on the type of work and the equipment used. The following discussion concentrates on forest harvesting and considers manual work and motor-manual (mostly chain-saws) and mechanized operations.

Manual Forest Work

Climate

Working outdoors, subject to climatic conditions, is both positive and negative for the forest worker. Fresh air and nice weather is a good thing, but unfavourable conditions can create problems.

Working in a hot climate puts pressure on the forest worker engaged in heavy work. Among other things, the heart rate increases to keep the body temperature down. Sweating means loss of body fluids. Heavy work in high temperatures means that a worker might need to drink 1 litre of water per hour to keep the body fluid balance.

In a cold climate the muscles function poorly. The risk of musculoskeletal injuries (MSI) and accidents increases. In addition, energy expenditure increases substantially, since it takes a lot of energy just to keep warm.

Rainy conditions, especially in combination with cold, mean higher risk of accidents, since tools are more difficult to grasp. They also mean that the body is even more chilled.

Adequate clothing for different climatic conditions is essential to keep the forest worker warm and dry. In hot climates only light clothing is required. It is then rather a problem to use sufficient protective clothing and footwear to protect him or her against thorns, whipping branches and irritating plants. Lodgings must have sufficient washing and drying facilities for clothes. Improved conditions in camps have in many countries substantially reduced the problems for the workers.

Setting limits for acceptable weather conditions for work based only on temperature is very difficult. For one thing the temperature varies quite a lot between different places in the forest. The effect on the person also depends on many other things such as humidity, wind and clothing.

Tool-related hazards

Noise, vibrations, exhaust gases and so on are seldom a problem in manual forest work. Shocks from hitting hard knots during delimbing with an axe or hitting stones when planting might create problems in elbows or hands.

Motor-Manual Forest Work

The motor-manual forest worker is one who works with hand-held machines such as chain-saws or power brush cutters and is exposed to the same climatic conditions as the manual worker. He or she therefore has the same need for adequate clothing and lodging facilities. A specific problem is the use of personal protective equipment in hot climates. But the worker is also subject to other specific hazards due to the machines he or she is working with.

Noise is a problem when working with a chain-saw, brush saw or the like. The noise level of most chain-saws used in regular forest work exceeds 100 dBA. The operator is exposed to this noise level for 2 to 5 hours daily. It is difficult to reduce the noise levels of these machines without making them too heavy and awkward to work with. The use of ear protectors is therefore

essential. Still, many chain-saw operators suffer loss of hearing. In Sweden around 30% of chain-saw operators had a serious hearing impairment. Other countries report high but varying figures depending on the definition of hearing loss, the duration of exposure, the use of ear protectors and so on.

Hand-induced vibration is another problem with chain-saws. "White finger" disease has been a major problem for some forest workers operating chain-saws. The problem has been brought to a minimum with modern chain-saws. The use of efficient anti-vibration dampers (in cold climates combined with heated handles) has meant, for instance, that in Sweden the number of chain-saw operators suffering from white fingers has dropped to 7 or 8%, which corresponds to the overall figure for natural white fingers for all Swedes. Other countries report large numbers of workers with white finger, but these probably do not use modern, vibration-reduced chain-saws.

The problem is similar when using brush saws and pruning saws. These types of machines have not been under close study, since in most cases the time of exposure is short.

Recent research points to a risk of loss of muscle strength due to vibrations, sometimes even without white finger symptoms.

Machine Work

Exposure to unfavourable climatic conditions is easier to solve when machines have cabins. The cabin can be insulated from cold, provided with air-conditioning, dust filters and so on. Such improvements cost money, so in most older machines and in many new ones the operator is still exposed to cold, heat, rain and dust in a more or less open cabin.

Noise problems are solved in a similar manner. Machines used in cold climates such as the Nordic countries need efficient insulation against cold. They also most often have good noise protection, with noise levels down to 70 to 75 dBA. But machines with open cabins most often have very high noise levels (over 100 dBA).

Dust is a problem especially in hot and dry climates. A cabin well insulated against cold, heat or noise also helps keep out the dust. By using a slight overpressure in the cabin, the situation can be improved even more.

Whole-body vibration in forest machines can be induced by the terrain over which the machine travels, the movement of the crane and other moving parts of the machine, and the vibrations from the power transmission. A specific problem is the shock to the operator when the machine comes down from an obstacle such as a rock. Operators of cross-country vehicles, such as skidders and forwarders, often have problems with low-back pain. The vibrations also increase the risk of repetitive strain injuries (RSI) to the neck, shoulder, arm or hand. The vibrations increase strongly with the speed at which the operator drives the machine.

In order to reduce vibrations, machines in the Nordic countries use vibration-damping seats. Other ways are to reduce the shocks coming from the crane by making it work smoother technically and by using better working techniques. This also makes the machine and the crane last longer. A new interesting concept is the "Pendo cabin". This cabin hangs on its "ears" connected to the rest of the machine by only a stand. The cabin is sealed off from the noise sources and is easier to protect from vibrations. The results are good.

Other approaches try to reduce the shocks that arise from driving over the terrain. This is done by using "intelligent" wheels and power transmission. The aim is to lower environmental impact, but it also has a positive effect on the situation for the operator. Less expensive machines most often have little reduction of noise, dust and vibration. Vibration may also be a problem in handles and controls.

When no engineering approaches to controlling the hazards are used, the only available solution is to reduce the hazards by lowering the time of exposure, for instance, by job rotation.

Ergonomic checklists have been designed and used successfully to evaluate forestry machines, to guide the buyer and to improve machine design (see Apud and Valdés 1995).

Combinations of Manual, Motor-Manual and Machine Work

In many countries, manual workers work together with or close to chain-saw operators or machines. The machine operator sits in a cabin or uses ear protectors and good protective equipment. But, in most cases the manual workers are not protected. The safety distances to the machines are not adhered to, resulting in very high risk of accidents and risk of hearing damage to unprotected workers.

Job Rotation

All the above-described hazards increase with the duration of exposure. To reduce the problems, job rotation is the key, but care has to be taken not to merely change work tasks while in actuality maintaining the same type of hazards.

● PHYSICAL LOAD

Bengt Pontén

Manual Forest Work

Workload. Manual forest work generally carries a high physical workload. This in turn means a high energy expenditure for the worker. The energy output depends on the task and the pace at which it is performed. The forest worker needs a much larger food intake than the "ordinary" office worker to cope with the demands of the job.

Table 68.6 presents a selection of jobs typically performed in forestry, classified into categories of workload by the energy expenditure required. The figures can give only an approximation, as they depend on body size, sex, age, fitness and work pace, as well as on tools and working techniques. It does, however, give a broad indication that nursery work is generally light to moderate; planting work and harvesting with a chain-saw moderate to heavy; and manual harvesting heavy to very heavy. (For case-studies and a detailed discussion of the workload concept applied to forestry see Apud et al. 1989; Apud and Valdés 1995; and FAO 1992.)

Musculoskeletal strain. Manual piling involves repeated heavy lifting. If the working technique is not perfect and the pace too high, the risk of musculoskeletal injuries (MSIs) is very high. Carrying heavy loads over extended periods of time, such as in pulpwood harvesting or fuelwood harvesting and transport, has a similar impact.

A specific problem is the use of maximum body force, which could lead to sudden musculoskeletal injuries in certain situations. An example is bringing down a badly hung-up tree by using a felling lever. Another is "saving" a falling log from a pile.

The work is done using only muscle force, and most often it involves dynamic and not simply repetitive use of the same muscle groups. It is not static. The risk for repetitive strain injuries (RSIs) is usually small. However, working in awkward body positions can create problems such as low-back pain. An example is using an axe to delimb trees which are lying on the ground, which requires working bent over for long periods of time. This puts great strain on the lower back and also means that the muscles in the back do static work. The problem can be reduced by felling trees across a stem that is already on the ground, thus using it as a natural workbench.

Motor-Manual Forest Work

The operation of portable machines such as chain-saws may require even greater energy expenditure than manual work, because of their considerable weight. In fact, the chain-saws used

Table 68.6 • Energy expenditure in forestry work.

	Kj/min/65 kg man		Workload capacity
	Range	Mean	
Work in forestry nursery			
Cultivating tree plants		18.4	L
Hoeing		24.7	M
Weeding		19.7	L
Planting			
Clearing draining ditches with spade		32.7	H
Tractor driving/harrowing while sitting	14.2–22.6	19.3	L
Planting by hand	23.0–46.9	27.2	M
Planting by machine		11.7	L
Work with axe — Horizontal and perpendicular blows			
Weight of axe head / Rate (blows/min)			
1.25 kg 20		23.0	M
0.65-1.25 kg 35	38.0–44.4	41.0	VH
Felling, trimming, etc. with hand tools			
Felling	28.5–53.2	36.0	H
Carrying logs	41.4–60.3	50.7	EH
Dragging logs	34.7–66.6	50.7	EH
Work with saw in forest			
Carrying power saw		27.2	M
Cross-cutting by hand	26.8–44.0	36.0	H
Horizontal-sawing power saw	15.1–26.8	22.6	M
Mechanized logging			
Operating harvester/forwarder	12–20		L
Fuelwood preparation			
Sawing small logs by hand		15.1	L
Cleaving wood	36.0–38.1	36.8	H
Dragging firewood	32.7–41.0	36.8	H
Stacking firewood	21.3–26.0	23.9	M

L = Light; M = Moderate; H = Heavy; VH = Very heavy; EH = Extremely heavy
Source: Adapted from Durnin and Passmore 1967.

are often too big for the task at hand. Instead, the lightest model and the smallest guide bar possible should be used.

Whenever a forest worker who uses machines also does the piling manually, he or she is exposed to the problems described above. Workers have to be instructed to keep the back straight and to rely on the big muscles in the legs to lift loads.

The work is done using machine power and is more static than manual work. The operator's work consists of choosing, moving and holding the machine in the right position.

Many of the problems created originate from working at a low height. Delimbing a tree that is lying flat on the ground means working bent over. This is a similar problem to that described in manual forest work. The problem is compounded when carrying a heavy chain-saw. Work should be planned and organized so the working height is close to the hip of the forest worker (e.g., using other trees as "workbenches" for delimbing, as described above). The saw should be supported by the stem as much as possible.

Highly specialized motor-manual work tasks create very high risk for musculoskeletal injuries since the work cycles are short and the specific movements are repeated many times. An example is the fellers working with chain-saws ahead of a processor (delimbing and cutting). Most of these forest workers that were studied in Sweden had neck and shoulder problems. Doing the whole logging operation (felling, delimbing, crosscutting and certain not-too-heavy piling) means the job is more varied and the exposure to specific unfavourable static, repetitive work is reduced. Even with the appropriate saw and a good working technique, chain-saw operators should not work more than 5 hours a day with the saw running.

Machine Work

The physical workloads in most forest machines are very low compared to manual or motor-manual work. The machine operator or the mechanic is still sometimes exposed to heavy lifting during maintenance and repairs. The operator's work consists of guiding the movements of the machine. He or she controls the force to be exerted by handles, levers, buttons and so on. The work cycles are very short. The work for the most part is repetitive and static, which can lead to a high risk for RSIs in the neck, shoulder, arm, hand or finger regions.

In machinery from the Nordic countries the operator works only with very small tensions in the muscles, using mini–joy sticks, sitting in an ergonomic seat with armrests. But still RSIs are a major problem. Studies show that between 50 and 80% of machine operators have neck or shoulder complaints. These figures are often difficult to compare since the injuries develop gradually over a long period of time. The results depend on the definition of injury or complaints.

Repetitive strain injuries depend on many things in the work situation:

Degree of tension in the muscle. A high static or repeated, monotonous muscle tension can be caused, for example, by using heavy controls, by awkward working positions or whole-body vibrations and shocks, but also by high mental stress. Stress can be generated by high concentration, complicated decisions or by the psychosocial situation, such as lack of control over the work situation and relations with supervisors and workmates.

Time of exposure to static work. Continuous static muscle tensions can be broken only by taking frequent pauses and micropauses, by changing work tasks, by job rotation and so on. A long total exposure to monotonous, repetitive work movements over the years increases the risk of RSIs. The injuries appear gradually and may be irreversible when manifested.

Individual status ("resistance"). The "resistance" of the individual changes over time and depends on his or her inherited predisposition and physical, psychological and social status.

Research in Sweden has shown that the only way to reduce these problems is by working with all these factors, especially through job rotation and job enlargement. These measures decrease the time of exposure and improve the well-being and psychosocial situation of the worker.

The same principles can be applied to all forest work—manual, motor-manual or machine work.

Combinations of Manual, Motor-Manual and Machine Work

Combinations of manual and machine work without job rotation always mean that the work tasks become more specialized. An example is the motor-manual fellers working ahead of a processor which is delimbing and cutting. The work cycles for the fellers are short and monotonous. The risk of MSIs and RSIs is very high.

A comparison between chain-saw and machine operators was made in Sweden. It showed that the chain-saw operators had higher risks of MSIs in the low back, knees and hip as well as high risks of hearing impairment. The machine operators on the other hand had higher risks of RSIs in the neck and shoulders. The two types of work were subject to very different hazards. A comparison with manual work would probably show still another risk pattern. Combinations of different types of work tasks using job rotation and job enlargement give possibilities to reduce the time of exposure for many specific hazards.

PSYCHOSOCIAL FACTORS

Peter Poschen and Marja-Liisa Juntunen

As is apparent from articles in this chapter, physical risks in forestry work are rather well documented. By contrast, comparatively little research has focused on psychological and social factors (Slappendel et al. 1993). In a forestry context such factors include: job satisfaction and security; the mental workload; susceptibility and response to stress; coping with perceived risks; work pressure, overtime and fatigue; need to endure adverse environmental conditions; social isolation in work camps with separation from families; work organization; and teamwork.

The health and safety situation in forest work depends on the wide range of factors described in this chapter: stand and terrain conditions; infrastructure; climate; technology; work methods; work organization; economic situation; contracting arrangements; worker accommodation; and education and training. These factors are known to interact and may actually compound to create higher risk or safer working environments (see "Working conditions and safety in forestry work" in this chapter).

These factors also interact with social and psychological ones, in that they influence the status of forest work, the recruitment base and the pool of skills and abilities that becomes available to the sector. In an unfavourable situation the circle of problems depicted in figure 68.15 can be the result. This situation is unfortunately rather common in developing countries and in segments of the forestry workforce in industrialized countries, in particular among migrant workers.

The social and psychological profile of the forestry workforce and the selection process that leads to it are likely to play a major role in determining the impact of stress and risk situations. They

Figure 68.15 • The circle of problems that may be encountered in forest work.

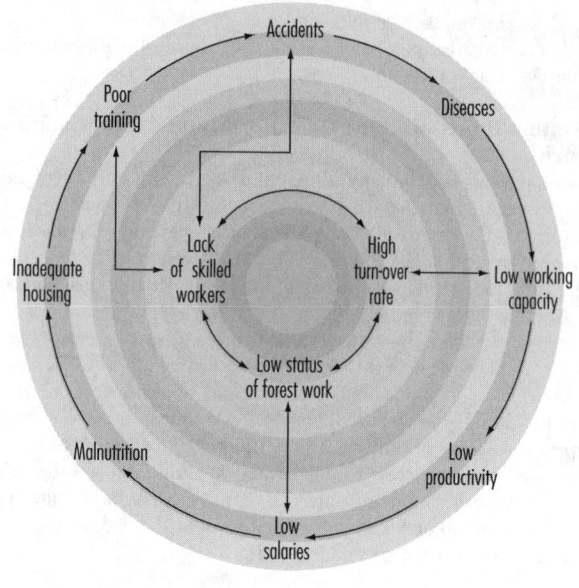

workers develop internal models about their jobs which lead to the development of automatic or semi-automatic routines. The theory of internal models describes the normal activity of a forest worker, like chain-saw or forest machine operation, the changes introduced through experience, the reasons for these and the creation of risk situations (Kanninen 1986). It has helped to provide a coherent explanation for many accidents and to make proposals for their prevention.

According to the theory, internal models evolve at successive levels through experience. Kanninen (1986) has suggested that in chain-saw operations the motion-control model is the lowest in the hierarchy of such models, followed by a tree handling model and a work-environment model. According to the theory, risks develop when the forest worker's internal model deviates from the objective requirements of the situation. The model may not be sufficiently developed, it may contain inherent risk factors, it may not be used at a particular time (e.g., because of fatigue) or there may be no model that fits an unfamiliar situation—say, a windfall. When one of these situations occurs, it is likely to result in an accident.

The development and use of models is influenced by experience and training, which may explain the contradictory findings of studies on risk perception and assessment in the review by Slappendel et al. (1993). Forest workers generally consider risk-taking to be part of their job. Where this is a pronounced tendency, risk compensation can undermine efforts to improve work safety. In such situations workers will adjust their behaviour and return to what they accept as a level of risk. This may, for example, be part of the explanation for the limited effectiveness of personal protective equipment (PPE). Knowing that they are protected by cut-proof trousers and boots, workers go faster, work with the machine closer to their body and take short cuts in violation of safety regulations that they think "take too long to follow". Typically, risk compensation seems to be partial. There are probably differences among individuals and groups in the workforce. Reward factors are probably important to trigger risk compensation. Rewards could be reduced discomfort (such as when not wearing warm protective clothing in a hot climate) or financial benefits (such as in piece-rate systems), but social recognition in a "macho" culture is also a conceivable motive. Worker selection, training and work organization should attempt to minimize incentives for risk compensation.

have probably not received enough attention in forestry. Traditionally, forest workers have come from rural areas and have considered work in the forest as much a way of life as an occupation. It has often been the independent, outdoors nature of the work that attracted them. Modern forest operations often no longer fit such expectations. Even for those whose personal profiles matched the demands of the job rather well when they started, the rapid technological and structural change in forestry work since the early 1980s has created major difficulties. Workers unable to adapt to mechanization and an existence as an independent contractor are often marginalized. To reduce the incidence of such mismatches, the Laboratory of Ergonomics at the University of Concepción in Chile has developed a strategy for forest worker selection, taking into account the needs of the industry, social aspects and psychological criteria.

Moreover, many new entrants still come ill-prepared to the job. On-the-job training, which is often no more than trial and error, is still common. Even where training systems are well developed, the majority of workers may have no formal training. In Finland, for example, forest machine operators have been trained for almost 30 years and a total of over 2,500 graduated. Nonetheless, in the late 1980s, 90% of the contractors and 75% of the operators had received no formal training.

Social and psychological factors are likely to play a major role in determining the impact of risk and stress. Psychological factors featured prominently among the causes given by forest workers in Germany for accidents they suffered. About 11% of the accidents were attributed to stress and another third to fatigue, routine, risk taking and lack of experience. Internal cognitive models may play a significant role in the creation of risk situations leading to logging accidents, and that their study can make an important contribution to prevention.

Risk

Promising work on risk perception, assessment and risk taking in forestry has been done in Finland. The findings suggest that

Mental Workload and Stress

Stress may be defined as the psychological pressure on an individual created by a perceived mismatch between that individual's capacity and perceived demands of the job. Common stressors in forestry include high work speed; repetitive and boring work; heat; work over- or underloads in unbalanced work crews; young or old workers trying to achieve sufficient earnings on low piece-rates; isolation from workmates, family and friends; and a lack of privacy in camps. They can also include a low general social status of forest workers, and conflicts between loggers and the local population or environmental groups. On balance, the transformation of forest work that sharply increased productivity also pushed up stress levels and reduced overall welfare in forest work (see figure 68.16).

Two types of workers are particularly prone to stress: harvester operators and contractors. The operator of a sophisticated harvester is in a multiple-stress situation, because of the short work cycles, the quantity of information that needs to be absorbed and the large number of fast decisions that need to be made. Harvesters are significantly more demanding than more traditional machines like skidders, loaders and forwarders. In addition to machine handling, the operator is usually also

Figure 68.16 • Simplified scheme of cause-and-effect relations in contracting operations.

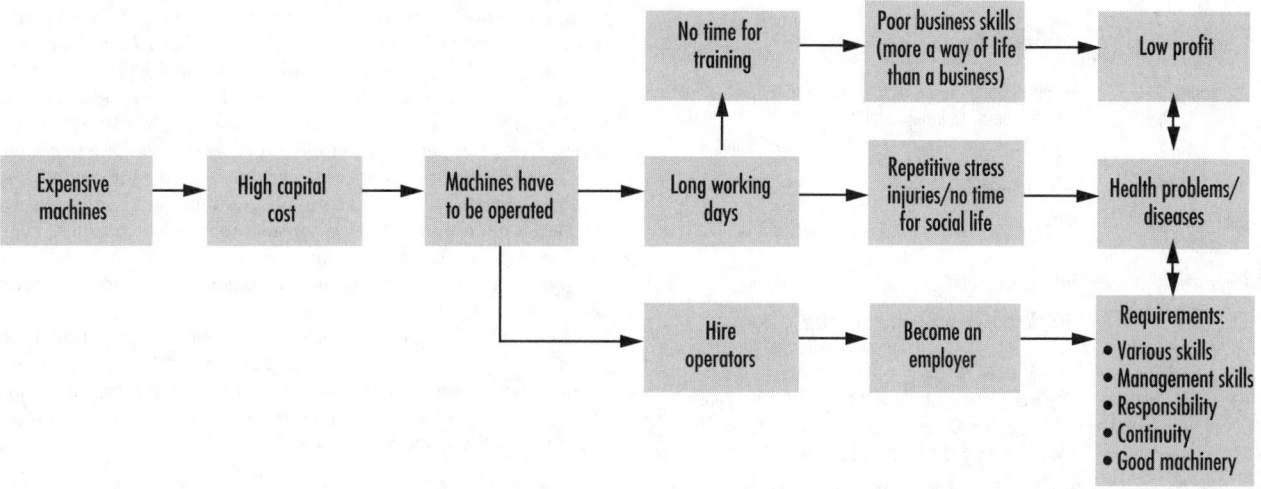

responsible for machine maintenance, planning and skid track design as well as bucking, scaling and other quality aspects that are closely monitored by the company and that have a direct impact on pay. This is particularly true in thinnings, as the operator typically works alone and makes decisions that are irreversible. In a study of thinning with harvesters, Gellerstedt (1993) analysed the mental load and concluded that the operator's mental capacity is the limiting factor for productivity. Operators who were not able to cope with the load were unable to take enough micropauses during the work cycles and developed neck and shoulder problems as a result. Which of these complex decisions and tasks is perceived as most demanding varies considerably among individuals, depending on factors like background, previous work experience and training (Juntunen 1993, 1995).

Added strain may result from the rather common situation in which the operator is also the machine owner, working as a small contractor. This implies a high financial risk, often in the form of a loan involving up to US$1 million, in what often is a very volatile and competitive market. Working weeks often exceed 60 hours for this group. Studies of such contractors show that the ability to withstand stress is a significant factor (Lidén 1995). In one of Lidén's studies in Sweden, as many as 54% of machine contractors were considering leaving the job—first, because it interfered too much with their family life; second, for health reasons; third, because it involved too much work; and, fourth, because it was not profitable. Researchers and contractors themselves consider resilience to stress as a precondition for a contractor to be able to stay in business without developing serious health complaints.

Where the selection process works, the group may show few mental health complaints (Kanninen 1986). In many situations, however, and not only in Scandinavia, the lack of alternatives locks contractors into this sector, where they are exposed to higher health and safety risks than individuals whose personal profile is more in line with that of the job. Good cabins and further improvement in their design, particularly of controls, and measures taken by the individual, such as regular short breaks and physical exercise, can go some way towards reducing such problems. The theory of internal models could be used to improve training to increase the operator-contractors' readiness and ability

to cope with ever more demanding machine operation. That would help lower the level of "background stress". New forms of work organization in teams involving task variety and job rotation are probably the most difficult to put into practice, but are also the potentially most effective strategy.

CHEMICAL HAZARDS

Juhani Kangas

Fuel and Oils for Portable Machines

Portable forestry machines such as chain-saws, brush saws and mobile machines are sources of exhaust emissions of gasoline in logging operations. Gasoline contains mainly aromatic (including up to 5% benzene in some countries) and aliphatic hydrocarbons, additives and some impurities. During the cold season gasoline contains more lightweight and easily evaporating hydrocarbons than during warm season. Additives are organic lead compounds, alcohols and ethers which are used to increase the octane number of gasoline. In many cases, lead has been totally replaced by ethers and alcohols.

The portable machines used in forestry are powered by two-stroke engines, where lubricating oil is mixed with gasoline. Lubrication oils as well as chain oils are mineral oils, synthetic oils or vegetable oils. The exposure to gasoline and lubrication and chain oil may occur during mixing fuel and filling as well as during logging. Fuels are also a fire hazard, of course, and require careful storage and handling.

Oil aerosols may create health hazards such as irritation of the upper respiratory tract and eyes, as well as skin problems. The exposure of lumberjacks to oil aerosols was studied during manual logging. Both mineral and vegetable oils were investigated. The exposure of forestry workers to oil aerosols was on the average 0.3 mg/m^3 for mineral oil and even less for vegetable oil.

The mechanization of forestry work is increasing rapidly. The machines in logging operations use large amounts of fuel oil,

Table 68.7 • Examples of chemicals used in forestry in Europe and North America in the 1980s.

Functions	Chemicals
Fungicides	Benomyl, Borax, Carbendazim, Chlorothalonil, Dicropropene, Endosulphaani, Gamma-HCH, Mancozeb, Maneb, Methyl bromide, Metiram, Thiuram, Zineb
Game control	Polyvinyl acetate
Game damage control	Thiram
Game repellents	Fish oil, tall oil
Herbicides	Allyl alcohol, Cyanazin, Dachtal, Dalapon, Dicamba, Dichlobenil, Diuron, Fosamine, Glyphosate, Hexazinone, MCPA, MCPB, Mecoprop (MCPP), MSMA, Oxyfluorten, Paraquat, Phenoxy herbicides (e.g., 2,4,5-T*, 2,4-D), Picloram, Pronoamide, Simazine, Sulphur, TCA, Terbuthiuron, Terbuthylazine, Trichlopyr, Trifluralin
Insecticides	Azinphos, *Bacillus thuringiens*, Bendiocarbanate, Carbaryl, Cypermethrin, Deltamethrin, Diflubenzuron, Ethylene dibromide, Fenitrothion, Fenvalerate, Lindane, Lindane+promecarb, Malathion, Parathion, Parathionmethyl, Pyrethrin, Permethrin, Propoxur, Propyzamide, Tetrachlorphinos, Trichlorfon
Pesticides	Captan, Chlorpyrifos, Diazinon, Metalyxyl, Napropamide, Sethoxydim, Traiadimefon, Sodium cyanide (rabbits)
Rodenticides	Aluminium phosphide, Strychnine, Warfarin, Zinc phosphide, Ziram
Soil sterilant	Dasomet
Stump protection	Urea
Fuels and oils	Mineral oils, synthetic oils, vegetable oils, gasoline, diesel oil
Other chemicals	Fertilizers (e.g., urea), solvents (e.g., glycol ethers, long-chain alcohols), Desmetryn

* Restricted in some countries.
Source: Adapted from Patosaari 1987.

lubricants and hydraulic oils in their engines and hydraulic systems. During maintenance and repair operations, the hands of machine operators are exposed to lubricants, hydraulic oils and fuel oils, which may cause irritant dermatitis. Mineral oils with short-chain hydrocarbons (C_{14}–C_{21}) are the most irritant. To avoid irritation, the skin must be protected from oil contact by protective gloves and good personal hygiene.

Exhaust Gases

The main component of chain-saw exhaust gases is unburned gasoline. Usually about 30% of the gasoline consumed by a chain-saw engine is emitted unburned. The main components of exhaust emission are hydrocarbons which are typical constituents of gasoline. Aromatic hydrocarbons, particularly toluene, are usually identified among them, but even benzene is found. Some of the exhaust gases are formed during combustion, and the main toxic product among them is carbon monoxide. As a result of combustion there are also aldehydes, mainly formaldehyde, and nitrogen oxides.

The exposure of workers to exhaust gases from chain-saws has been studied in Sweden. Operator exposure to chain-saw exhaust was evaluated under various logging situations. Measurements revealed no difference in average levels of exposure when logging in the presence or in the absence of snow. The felling operation, however, results in short-term high exposure levels, especially when the operation is performed while there is deep snow on the ground. This is judged to be the main cause of the discomfort experienced by loggers. Average exposure levels for loggers engaged only in felling were twice as high as those for cutters who also perform delimbing, bucking and manual skidding of timber. The latter operations involved considerably lower exposure. Typical average levels of exposure are as follows: hydrocarbons, 20 mg/m^3; benzene, 0.6 mg/m^3; formaldehyde, 0.1 mg/m^3; carbon monoxide, 20 mg/m^3.

These values are clearly below the 8-hour occupational exposure limit values in industrialized countries. However, loggers often complain about irritation of the upper respiratory tract and eyes, headache, nausea and fatigue, which can be at least partly explained by these exposure levels.

Pesticides and Herbicides

Pesticides are used in forests and forest nurseries to control fungi, insects and rodents. The overall quantities used are typically small when compared with agricultural use. In forests herbicides are used to control hardwood brush, weeds and grass in young softwood sapling stands. Phenoxy herbicides, glyphosate or triazines are used for this purpose. For occasional needs, insecticides, mainly organophosphorus compounds, organochlorine compounds or synthetic pyredroids may also be used. In forest nurseries dithiocarbamates are used regularly to protect softwood seedlings against fungus of pines. An overview of chemicals used in Europe and North America in the 1980s is provided in table 68.7. Many countries have taken measures to find alternatives to pesticides or to restrict their use. For more detail on the chemistry, chemical symptoms of intoxication and treatment see the chemicals section of this *Encyclopaedia*.

A wide variety of techniques are used for the application of pesticides to their intended target in forests and forestry nurseries. Common methods are aerial spraying, application from tractor-driven equipment, knapsack spraying, ULV spraying and the use of sprayers connected to brush saws.

The risk of exposure is similar to that in other pesticide applications. To avoid exposure to pesticides, forestry workers should use personal protective equipment (PPE) (e.g., cap, coveralls, boots and gloves). If toxic pesticides are applied, a respiratory device should also be worn during applications. Effective PPE often leads to heat build-up and excessive sweating. Applications should be planned for the coolest hours of the day and when it is not too windy. It is also important to wash all spills immediately with water and to avoid smoking and eating during spray operations.

The symptoms caused by excessive exposure to pesticides vary greatly depending on the compound used for application, but most often occupational exposure to pesticides will cause skin disorders. (For a more detailed discussion of pesticides used in forestry in Europe and northern America see FAO/ECE/ILO 1991.)

Others

Other chemicals commonly used in forestry work are fertilizers and colourants used for timber marking. Timber marking is done either with a marking hammer or a spray bottle. The colourants contain glycol ethers, alcohols and other organic solvents, but the exposure level during the work is probably low. The fertilizers used in forestry have low toxicity, and the use of them is seldom a problem in respect of occupational hygiene.

BIOLOGICAL HAZARDS AMONG FORESTRY WORKERS

J. Augusta

People active outdoors, especially in agriculture and forestry, are exposed to health hazards from animals, plants, bacteria, viruses and so on to a greater degree than is the rest of the population.

Plants and Wood

Most common are allergic reactions to plants and wood products (wood, bark components, sawdust), especially pollen. Injuries can result from processing (e.g., from thorns, spines, bark) and from secondary infections, which cannot always be excluded and can lead to further complications. Appropriate protective clothing is therefore especially important.

A comprehensive description of the toxicity of plants and wood products and their components is not possible. Knowledge of a particular area can be acquired only through practical experience—not only from books. Possible safety measures must derive from knowledge of the specific area.

Large Mammals

Using horses, oxen, buffalo, elephants and so on as work animals can result in unforeseen dangerous situations, which may lead to injuries with serious consequences. Diseases transmittable from these animals to humans also pose an important danger.

Infections and Diseases Transmitted by Animals

These constitute the most significant biological hazard. Their nature and incidence varies strongly from region to region. A complete overview is therefore not possible. Table 68.8 (on pages 68.26 and 27) contains a selection of infections common in forestry.

Poisonous Snakes

Poisonous snakebites are always medical emergencies. They require correct diagnosis and immediate treatment. Identifying the snake is of decisive importance. Due to the wide range of varieties and territorial particularities, the knowledge necessary for this can be acquired only locally, and for this reason cannot be described in general. Blocking veins and local incisions (only by experienced people) are not undisputed as a first-aid measure. A prompt dose of a specific antidote is necessary. Attention must also be paid to the possibility of a life-threatening allergic general reaction to the antidote. Injured persons should be transported lying down. Do not administer alcohol or morphine.

Spiders

Few poisons have been researched to date. An attempt should absolutely be made to identify the spider (of which knowledge can be acquired only locally). Actually, there are no valid general first-aid measures (possibly administer available antiserums). In addition, what was said about poisonous snakes applies analogously.

Bees, Wasps, Hornets, Ants

Insect poisons have very different effects, depending on the locale. Removing the stinger from the skin (and being careful not to introduce more poison during handling) and local cooling are recommended first-aid measures. The most-feared complication is a life-threatening general allergic reaction, which can be provoked by an insect sting. People allergic to insect poisons should, therefore, carry adrenalin and an injectable antihistamine with them.

Scorpions

After injury, a dose of antidote should absolutely be given. Local knowledge of first aid is necessary.

RULES, LEGISLATION, REGULATIONS AND CODES OF FOREST PRACTICES

Othmar Wettmann

In a high-risk occupation like forestry, relevant and job-specific safety regulations are a critical element of any strategy to reduce the high frequencies of accidents and health problems. To develop such regulation and to obtain compliance is unfortunately much more difficult in forestry than in many other occupations. Occupational safety legislation and existing general regulations are often not specific for forestry. Moreover, they are often difficult to apply in the highly variable outdoor context of forestry, because they were typically conceived with factory-type workplaces in mind.

This article outlines the route from general legislation to forestry-specific regulations and makes some suggestions for contributions that the various actors in the forestry sector may make to the improvement of compliance with regulations. It concludes with a brief presentation of the concept of codes of forest practices, which holds considerable promise as a form of regulation or self-regulation.

The Law Outlines the Principles

Safety legislation usually merely lays out some basic principles, such as:

- The employer is primarily responsible for the safety of employees and must take the necessary protective measures.
- Employees must be involved in this.
- Employees, in turn, are obliged to support the employer's efforts.
- Laws are enforced through the labour inspectorate, the health service or an analogous body.

What the General Regulations Specify

Regulations on prevention of accidents and occupational diseases often specify a number of points, such as:

- the duties of employers and employees
- the consultation of doctors and other occupational safety specialists
- the safety regulations for buildings and other construction, for technical equipment and devices, and on the working environment and the work organization.

The regulations also contain instructions on:

- organization of workplace safety
- implementing the provisions on workplace safety
- occupational medical care
- financing workplace safety.

As the legislation has evolved over time, there are often laws for other areas and sectors that also contain regulations applicable to

Table 68.8 • Selection of infections common in forestry.

	Cause	Transmission	Locations	Effects	Prevention/therapy
Amoebiasis	*Entamoeba histolytica*	Person-to-person, ingestion with food (water, fruits, vegetables); often asymptomatic carriers	Tropics and temperate zone	Frequent complications of the digestive tract	Personal hygiene; chemoprophylaxis and immunization not possible. Therapy: chemotherapy
Dengue fever	Arboviruses	Aedes mosquito bite	Tropics, subtropics, Caribbean	Sickness results in immunity for one year or longer, not lethal	Control and elimination of carrier mosquitoes, mosquito nets. Therapy: symptomatic
Early summer meningo-encephalitis	Flavivirus	Linked to the presence of the ixodes ricinus tick, vector-free transmission known in individual cases (e.g., milk)	Natural reservoirs confined to certain regions, endemic areas mostly known	Complications with later damages possible	Active and passive immunization possible Therapy: symptomatic
Erysipeloid	*Erysipelotrix rhusiopathiae*	Deep wounds among persons who handle fish or animal tissue	Ubiquitous, especially infects swine	Generally spontaneous cure after 2-3 weeks, bacteremia possible (septic arthritis, affected cardiac valve)	Protective clothing Therapy: antibiotics
Filariasis	*Wuchereria bancrofti, Brugia malayi*	From animal to humans, but also from some types of mosquitoes	Tropics and subtropics	Highly varied	Personal hygiene, mosquito control Therapy: medication possible
Fox tapeworm	*Echinococcus multilocularis*	Wild animals, esp. foxes, less commonly also house pets (cats, dogs)	Knowledge of endemic areas necessary	Mostly affects liver	No consumption of raw wild fruits; dampen fur when handling dead foxes; gloves, mouth protection Therapy: clinical treatment
Gaseous gangrene	Various clostridia	At the onset of infection, anaerobic milieu with low redox potential and necrotic tissue required (e.g., open crushed soft parts)	Ubiquitous, in soil, in intestines of humans and animals	Highly lethal, fatal without treatment (1-3 days)	No known specific antitoxin to date, gaseous gangrene serum controversial Therapy: clinical treatment
Japanese B encephalitis	Arbovirus	From mosquitoes (*Culex* spp.); person-to-person; mammal-to-person	Endemic in China, India, Japan, Korea and neighbouring countries	Mortality to 30%; partial cure to 80%	Mosquito prevention, active immunization possible; Therapy: symptomatic
Leptospirosis	Various leptospira	Urine of infected wild and house animals (mice, rats, field rabbits, foxes, dogs), skin injuries, mucous membrane	Endemic worldwide areas	From asymptomatic to multi-organ infestation	Appropriate protective clothing when around infected animals, immunization not possible Therapy: penicillin, tetracycline
Lyme disease	*Borrelia burgdorferi*	*Ixodes ricinus* tick, other insects also suspected	Europe, North America, Australia, Japan, China	Numerous forms of sickness, complicating organ infection possible	Personal protective measures before tick infestation, immunization not possible Therapy: antibiotics
Meningitis, meningo-encephalitis	Bacteria (meningo-, pneumo-staphylo-cocci and others)	Mostly airborne infection	Meningococci, meningitis epidemic, otherwise ubiquitous	Less than 10% mortality with early diagnosis and specific treatment	Personal hygiene, isolate infected persons Therapy: antibiotics
	Viruses (Poliomyelitis, Coxsackie, Echo, Arbo, Herpes and Varicella viruses)	Mucous and airborne infection (airways, connective tissue, injured skin), mice are source of infection in high percentage of cases	Ubiquitous incidence	High mortality (70%) with herpes infection	Personal hygiene; mouse prevention Therapy: symptomatic, among varicella effective specific treatment possible
	Mushrooms	Mostly systemic infections	Ubiquitous incidence	Uncertain prognosis	Therapy: antibiotics (protracted treatment)
	Mycobacteria (see tuberculosis)				
	Leptospira (see leptospirosis)				

Continues on next page.

Table 68.8 • Selection of infections common in forestry.
Continued

	Cause	Transmission	Locations	Effects	Prevention/therapy
Malaria	Various plasmodia (tropica, vivax, ovale, falciparum, malariae)	mosquitoes (Anopheles species)	Subtropical and tropical regions	30% mortality with M. *tropica*	Chemoprophylaxis possible, not absolutely certain, mosquito nets, repellents, clothing Therapy: medication
Onchocerciasis Loiasis Dracunculiasis Dirofilariasis	Various filaria	Flies, water	West and Central Africa, India, Pakistan, Guinea, Middle East	Highly varied	Fly control, personal hygiene Therapy: surgery, medication, or combined
Ornithosis	Clamydia psittaci	Birds, especially parrot varieties and doves	Worldwide	Fatal cases have been described	Eliminate pathogen reservoir, immunization not possible Therapy: tetracycline
Papatasii fever	Flaviviruses	Mosquitoes (*Phlebotomus papatasii*)	Endemic and epidemic in Mediterranean countries, South and East Asia, East Africa, Central and South America	Mostly favourable, often long convalescence, sickness leaves far-reaching immunity	Insect control Therapy: symptomatic
Rabies	Rhabdovirus	Bite from infected wild or house animals (saliva highly infectious), airborne infection described	Many countries of the world, widely varying frequency	Highly lethal	Active (including after exposure) and passive immunization possible Therapy: clinical treatment
Recurrent fever	Borrelia-spirochetes	Ticks, head and body lice, rodents	America, Africa, Asia, Europe	Extensive fever; up to 5% mortality if untreated	Personal hygiene Therapy: medication (e.g., tetracycline)
Tetanus	Clostridium tetani	Parenteral, deep unclean wounds, introduction of foreign bodies	Ubiquitous, especially common in tropical zones	Highly lethal	Active and passive immunization possible Therapy: clinical treatment
Trichuriasis	*Trichuris trichiura*	Ingested from eggs that were incubated 2–3 weeks in the ground	Tropics, subtropics, seldom in the United States	Only serious infections display symptoms	Personal hygiene Therapy: medication possible
Tsutsugamushi fever	Rickettsia (*R. orientalis*)	Associated with mites (animal reservoir: rats, mice, marsupials); infection from working on plantations and in the bush; sleeping outdoors especially dangerous	Far East, Pacific region, Australia	Serious course; mortality close to zero with timely treatment	Rodent and mite control, chemoprophylaxis controversial Therapy: timely antibiotics
Tuberculosis	Various myco-bacteria (e.g., M. bovis, avium balnei)	Inhaling infected droplets, contaminated milk, contact with infected wild animals (e.g., mountain goats, deer, badgers, rabbits, fish), wounds, mucous membranes	Ubiquitous	Still high mortality, depending on organ infected	Active immunization possible, chemoprophylaxis disputed Therapy: clinical treatment, isolation, medication
Tularemia	*Francisella tularensis*	Digestive tract wounds, contaminated water, rodents, contact with wild rabbits, ticks, arthropods, birds; germs can also enter through uninjured skin	Ubiquitous	Varied forms of sickness; first sickness leads to immunity; mortality with treatment 0%, without treatment appr. 6%	Caution around wild animals in endemic areas, disinfect water Therapy: antibiotics
Yellow fever	Viruses	Bite from forest mosquitoes, which are infected from wild primates	Central Africa, South and Central America	Up to 10% mortality	Active immunization

68. FORESTRY

workplace safety in forestry. In Switzerland, for example, these include the labour code, the law on explosives, the law on poisons and traffic legislation. It would be advantageous to users if all these provisions and related regulations were collected into a single law.

Safety Regulations for Forestry: As Concrete as Possible and Nevertheless Flexible

In most cases, these laws and regulations are too abstract for daily, on-the-job use. They do not correspond to the hazards and risks involved in using machines, vehicles and work materials in the various industries and plants. This is particularly true for a sector with such varied and atypical working conditions as forestry. For this reason, specific safety regulations are worked out by sectoral commissions for the individual industries, their specific jobs, or equipment and devices. In general, this proceeds consciously or unconsciously as follows:

First, the dangers that can arise in an activity or a system are analysed. For example, cuts into the leg are a frequent injury among chain-saw operators.

Second, protection goals that are based on the dangers identified and which describe "what should not happen" are enunciated. For example: "Appropriate measures should be taken to prevent the chain-saw operator from injuring his or her leg".

Only in the third step are solutions or measures sought that, in accordance with the state of technology, reduce or eliminate the dangers. In the above-mentioned example, cut-protected trousers are one of the appropriate measures. The state of technology for this item can be defined by requiring that trousers correspond to European Norms (EN) 381-5, Protective clothing for users of hand-operated chain-saws, Part 5: Regulations for leg protection.

This procedure offers the following advantages:

- Protective goals are based on concrete hazards. The safety requirements are therefore practice-oriented.
- Safety regulations in the form of protective goals allow for greater flexibility in the choice and development of solutions than the prescription of concrete measures. Specific measures can also be adapted continuously to advances in the state of technology.
- When new hazards appear, safety regulations can be supplemented in a targeted manner.

Establishing bi- or tripartite sectoral commissions that involve the interested employer and employee organizations has proven an effective way of improving the acceptance and application of safety regulations in practice.

Content of Safety Rules

When certain jobs or types of equipment have been analysed for their hazards and protective goals derived, measures in the areas of technology, organization and personnel (TOP) can be formulated.

Technical questions

The state of technology for part of the forestry equipment and devices, such as power saws, brush cutters, leg protection for power saw operators and so on, is set in international norms, as discussed elsewhere in this chapter. Over the long term, the EN and the norms of the International Organization for Standardization (ISO) should be unified. Adoption of these norms by the individual countries will contribute to the uniform protection of the employee in the industry. Proof from the seller or manufacturer that a piece of equipment complies with these standards guarantees to the buyer that the equipment corresponds to the state of technology. In the numerous cases where no international standards exist, national minimum requirements need to be defined by groups of experts.

In addition to the state of technology, the following issues, among other things, are important:

- availability of the necessary equipment and materials on the job
- reliable condition of the equipment and materials
- maintenance and repair.

Forestry operations often leave much to be desired in these respects.

Organizational questions

Conditions must be established in the enterprise and at the workplace so that the individual jobs can be carried out safely. In order for this to happen, the following issues must be addressed:

- tasks, authority and responsibilities of all participants clearly defined
- a wage system that promotes safety
- working hours and breaks adapted to the difficulty of the work
- work procedures
- work planning and organization
- first aid and alarms
- where workers have to live in camps, minimum requirements defined for dormitories, sanitation, nutrition, transport and recreation.

Personnel questions

Personnel questions can be divided into:

Training and continuing education. In some countries this includes employees of forestry companies, for example, those who work with power saws are obliged to attend appropriate training and continuing education courses.

Guidance, welfare and support of the employee. Examples include showing new employees how the job is done and supervising the employees. Practice shows that the state of workplace safety in an enterprise depends in large measure on whether and how the management maintains discipline and carries out its supervisory responsibilities.

Doing the job

Most safety regulations contain rules of behaviour that the employee is supposed to abide by in doing the job. In forestry work these rules relate primarily to critical operations such as:

- felling and working with trees
- extraction, storing and transporting wood
- working with wind-felled trees
- climbing trees and working in treetops.

In addition to international standards and national regulations that have proved effective in several countries, the International Labour Organization (ILO) Code of Practice *Safety and Health in Forestry Work* provides examples and guidance for the design and formulation of national or company-level regulations (ILO 1969, 1997, 1998).

Safety regulations have to be reviewed and constantly adapted to changing circumstances or supplemented to cover new technology or work methods. A suitable accident reporting and investigation system can be of great help toward this end. Unfortunately, few countries are making use of this possibility. The ILO (1991) provides some successful examples. Even rather simple systems can provide good pointers. (For further information see Strehlke 1989.) The causes of accidents in forestry are often complex. Without a correct and full understanding, preventive measures and safety regulations often miss the point. A good example is the frequent but often erroneous identification of "unsafe behaviour" as the apparent cause. In accident investigation, the emphasis should as much as possible be on understanding the causes of accidents, rather than on establishing the responsibility of individuals. The "tree of causes" method is too onerous to be used routinely, but has given good results in complicated cases and as a means of raising safety awareness and of improving communication in enterprises. (For a report on the Swiss experience see Pellet 1995.)

Promoting Compliance

Safety regulations remain a dead letter unless all stakeholders in the forestry sector play their part in implementation. Jokulioma and Tapola (1993) give a description of such cooperation in Finland, which has produced excellent results. For information, education and training on safety, including for groups that are difficult to reach like contractors and forest farmers, the contractor and forest owner associations play a critical role.

Safety regulations need to be made available to users in accessible form. A good practice is the publishing in a pocket-size format of illustrated concise extracts relevant to particular jobs such as chain-saw operation or cable cranes. In many countries migrant workers account for a significant percentage of the forestry workforce. Regulations and guides need to be available in their respective languages. Forestry equipment manufacturers should also be required to include in the owner's manual comprehensive information and directions on all aspects of the maintenance and safe use of the equipment.

The cooperation of workers and employers is of course particularly important. This is true at the sectoral level, but even more so at the enterprise level. Examples for successful and very cost effective cooperation are given by the ILO (1991). The generally unsatisfactory safety situation in forestry is often aggravated further where the work is carried out by contractors. In such cases, the contracts offered by the commissioning party, forest owner or industry should always include a clause requiring compliance with safety requirements as well as sanctions in cases of breach of regulations. The regulations themselves should be an annex to the contract.

In some countries, general legislation provides for a joint or subsidiary responsibility and liability of the commissioning party—in this case a forest owner or company—with the contractor. Such a provision can be very helpful in keeping irresponsible contractors out and favouring the development of a qualified service sector.

A more specific measure in the same direction is the accreditation of contractors through government authorities or workers' compensation administrators. In some countries contractors have to demonstrate that they are sufficiently equipped, economically independent and technically competent to carry out forestry work. Contractor associations could conceivably play a similar role, but voluntary schemes have not been very successful.

Labour inspection in forestry is a very difficult task, because of the dispersed, temporary worksites, often in faraway, inaccessible places. A strategy motivating the actors to adopt safe practices is more promising than isolated policing. In countries where large forestry companies or forest owners predominate, self-inspection of contractors by such companies, monitored by the labour inspectorate or workers' compensation administration, is one way of increasing coverage. Direct labour inspection should be focused both in terms of issues and geography, to make optimum use of staff and transport. As labour inspectors are often non-foresters, inspection should best be based on thematic checklists ("chain-saws", "camps" and so on), which inspectors can use after a 1- or 2-day training. A video on labour inspection in forestry is available from the ILO.

One of the biggest challenges is to integrate safety regulations into routine procedures. Where forestry-specific regulations exist as a separate body of rules, they are often perceived by supervisors and operators as an additional constraint on top of technical, logistic and other factors. As a result, safety considerations tend to be ignored. The remainder of this article describes one possibility of overcoming this obstacle.

Codes of Forest Practice

In contrast to general occupational safety and health regulations, codes of practice are sets of rules, prescriptions or recommendations that are forestry-specific and practice-oriented and ideally cover all aspects of an operation. They include safety and health considerations. Codes vary greatly in scope and coverage. Some are very concise while others are elaborate and go into considerable detail. They may cover all types of forest operations or be limited to the ones considered most critical, such as forest harvesting.

Codes of practice can be a very interesting complement to general or forestry-specific safety regulations. Over the last decade, codes have been adopted or are being developed in a growing number of countries. Examples include Australia, Fiji, New Zealand, South Africa and numerous states in the United States. At the time of writing, work was in progress or planned in various other countries, including Chile, Indonesia, Malaysia and Zimbabwe.

There are also two international codes of practice that are designed as guidelines. The *FAO Model Code of Forest Harvesting Practice* (1996) covers all aspects of general forest harvesting practices. The ILO Code of Practice *Safety and Health in Forestry Work*, first published in 1969 and to be published in a completely revised form in 1998 (available in 1997 as a working paper (ILO 1997)), deals exclusively with occupational safety and health.

The driving force behind new codes has been environmental rather than safety concerns. There is, however, a growing recognition that in forestry, operational efficiency, environmental protection and safety are inseparable. They result from the same planning, work methods and practices. Directional felling to reduce impact on the remaining stand or regeneration, and rules for extraction in steep terrain, are good examples. Some codes, like the FAO and the Fiji Codes, make this link explicit and simultaneously address productivity, environmental protection and work safety. Ideally, codes should not have separate chapters on safety, but should have occupational safety and health built into their provisions.

Codes should be based on the safest work methods and technology available, require safety to be considered in planning, establish required safety features for equipment, list required personal protective equipment and contain rules on safe work practices. Where applicable, regulations about camps, nutrition and worker transport should also be included. Safety considerations should also be reflected in rules about supervision and training.

Codes can be voluntary and be adopted as mandatory by groups of companies or the forestry sector of a country as a whole. They can also be legally binding. In all cases they may be enforceable through legal or other complaints procedures.

Many codes are drawn up by the forestry sector itself, which ensures practicability and relevance, and enhances commitment to comply. In the case of Chile, a tripartite committee has been established to develop the code. In Fiji the code was originally designed with strong industry involvement and then made binding by the Ministry of Forests.

The characteristics described above and the experience with existing codes make them a most interesting tool to promote safety in forestry, and offer the possibility of very effective cooperation between safety officers, worker's compensation administrators, labour inspectors and forestry practitioners.

• PERSONAL PROTECTIVE EQUIPMENT

Eero Korhonen

Forestry work is one of those occupations where personal protective equipment (PPE) is always needed. Mechanization has decreased the number of workers using hand-held chain-saws, but the remaining tasks are often in difficult places where the big machines cannot reach.

The efficiency and chain speed of the hand-held chain-saws have increased, while the protection given by protective clothing and footwear has decreased. The higher requirement for the protection has made the equipment heavy. Especially in summertime in Nordic countries, and all around the year in other countries, the protective devices add an extra load to the heavy work of forest workers. This article focuses on chain-saw operators, but protection is needed in most forestry work. Table 68.9 provides an overview of what should normally be required.

Protection Mechanism and Efficiency of Personal Protective Devices

Protective clothing

Protective clothing against cuts protects by three different main mechanisms. In most cases the trousers and gloves contain a safety padding made of multilayer cloth having fibres with high tensile strength. When the moving chain touches the fibres, they are pulled out and will resist the movement of the chain. Second, these padding materials can go around the drive sprocket and the groove of the blade and increase the friction of the chain against the blade so much that the chain will stop. Third, the material can also be made such that the chain glides on the surface and cannot easily penetrate it.

Different work tasks require different protective coverage. For normal forest work the protective padding covers only the front part of the trousers and the back of safety gloves. Special tasks (e.g., gardening or tree surgery) often require a larger area of protective coverage. The protective paddings cover the legs totally, including the back side. If the saw is held above the head, protection of the upper body may be needed.

It must always be remembered that all PPE gives only limited protection, and correct and careful working methods must be used. The new hand-held chain-saws are so effective that the chain can easily go through the best protective material when the chain speed is high or the force of the chain against the protective material is great. Cut-proof protective paddings made of the best materials known at present would be so thick that they could not be used in heavy forest work. The compromise between protection efficiency and comfort is based on field experiments. It has been unavoidable that the protection level has been reduced to be able to increase the comfort of the clothing.

Protective footwear

Protective footwear made of rubber resists against cuts by the chain-saw quite well. The most frequent type of cut comes from contact of the chain with the toe area of the footwear. The safety footwear must have a cut-resistant lining on the front and metallic toe cups; this protects against these cuts very well. In higher

temperatures the use of rubber boots is uncomfortable, and leather boots or ankle-high shoes should be used. These shoes too must be equipped with metallic toe cups. The protection is normally considerably lower than that of the rubber boots, and extra care should be taken when using leather boots or shoes. The working methods must be so planned that the possibility of chain contact with the feet is minimized.

Good fit and construction of the outer sole is essential to avoid slipping and falling accidents, which are very common. In areas where the ground may be covered by ice and snow or where workers walk on slippery logs, boots which can be equipped with spikes are preferred.

Protective helmet

Protective helmets provide protection against falling branches and trees. They also give protection against the chain-saw if a kickback occurs. The helmet should be as light as possible to minimize neck strain. The headband must be correctly adjusted to make the helmet sit firmly on the head. The headbands of most helmets are so designed that vertical adjustment is possible as well. It is important to have the helmet sitting low on the brow so its weight does not cause too much discomfort when working in face-down posture. In cold weather it is necessary to use a textile or fur cap under the helmet. Special caps designed to be used with the helmet should be used. The cap can lower the protection efficiency of the helmet by wrong positioning of the helmet. The protection efficiency of hearing protectors can go to near zero when the cups of the hearing protectors are placed outside the cap. Forestry helmets have built-in devices to attach a visor and earmuffs for hearing protection. The cups of the hearing protectors should be placed directly against the head by insertion of the cups through slits in the cap.

In hot weather, helmets should have ventilation holes. The holes have to be part of the design of the helmet. Under no circumstances should holes be drilled into the helmet, as this may greatly reduce its strength.

Face and eye protection

The face protector or shield is normally attached to the helmet and is most commonly made of a mesh material. The plastic sheets easily get dirty after a relatively short working time. Cleaning is also difficult because the plastics resist solvents poorly. The mesh reduces the light coming to the eyes of the worker, and reflections on the surface of the threads can make seeing difficult. Sealed goggles worn under face protectors mist easily, and distortion of vision is often too high. Metal masks with a black coating and rectangular rather than round openings are preferable.

Hearing protectors

Hearing protectors are efficient only if the cups are placed firmly and tightly against the head. Therefore hearing protectors must be used carefully. Any space between the head and the sealing rings of the cups will decrease the efficiency markedly. For example, the side-arms of spectacles can cause this. The sealing ring shall be inspected often and must be changed when damaged.

Selection of Personal Protective Equipment

Before starting work in a new area, the possible risks should be evaluated. The working tools, methods, environment, the skills of the workers and so on should be evaluated, and all technical and organizational measures should be planned. If the risks cannot be eliminated by those methods, PPE can be used to improve the protection. PPE can never be used as the only preventive method. It must be seen as a complementary means only. The saw must have a chain brake, the worker must be trained and so on.

Table 68.9 • Personal protective equipment appropriate for forestry operations.

Operations	PPE[1]
Planting	
Manual	Safety boots or shoes
Mechanized	Safety boots or shoes, close-fit clothing, ear muffs[2]
Weeding/cleaning	
Smooth-edged tools	Safety boots or shoes, gloves, goggles
Hand-saw	Safety boots or shoes, gloves
Chain-saw	Safety boots or shoes,[3] safety trousers, close-fit clothing, gloves,[4] safety helmet, goggles, visor (mesh), ear muffs
Brush saw:	
with metal blade	Safety boots or shoes,[3] safety trousers, close-fit clothing, gloves,[4] safety helmet, goggles, visor (mesh), ear muffs
with nylon filament	Safety boots or shoes, safety trousers, gloves, goggles, ear muffs
Rotating knife/flail	Safety boots or shoes, close-fit clothing, gloves, ear muffs[2]
Pesticide application	To comply with the specifications for the particular substance and application technique
Pruning[5]	
Hand tools	Safety boots or shoes, gloves, safety helmet,[6] goggles, ear muffs
Felling[7]	
Hand tools	Safety boots or shoes, close-fit clothing, gloves,[8] safety helmet
Chain-saw	Safety boots or shoes, safety trousers, close-fit clothing, gloves,[4] safety helmet, visor (mesh), ear muffs
Mechanized	Safety boots or shoes, close-fit clothing, safety helmet, ear muffs
Debarking	
Manual	Safety boots or shoes, gloves
Mechanized	Safety boots or shoes, close-fit clothing, gloves, goggles, ear muffs[2]
Splitting	
Manual	Safety boots or shoes, gloves, goggles
Mechanized	Safety boots or shoes, close-fit clothing, gloves, goggles, ear muffs
Extraction	
Manual, chute and animal	Safety boots or shoes, gloves, safety helmet[9]
Mechanized	
—skidder	Safety boots or shoes, close-fit clothing, gloves,[10] safety helmet, ear muffs[2]
—forewarder	Safety boots or shoes, close-fit clothing, safety helmet, ear muffs[2]
—cable crane	Safety boots or shoes, close-fit clothing, gloves,[10] safety helmet, ear muffs[2]
—heliocopter	Safety boots or shoes, close-fit clothing,[11] gloves,[10] safety helmet, goggles, ear muffs
Stacking/loading	Safety boots or shoes, close-fit clothing, gloves, safety helmet, ear muffs[2]
Chipping	Safety boots or shoes, close-fit clothing, gloves, safety helmet, visor (mesh), ear muffs[2]
Tree climbing:	
using a chain-saw	Safety boots or shoes,[3] safety trousers, close-fit clothing, gloves,[4] safety helmet,[13] goggles, ear muffs
not using a chain-saw	Safety boots or shoes, safety helmet

[1] Safety boots or shoes should include integrated steel toes for medium or heavy loads. Safety trousers should incorporate clogging material; in hot climates/weather chain-saw leggings or chaps may be used. Safety trousers and chaps contain fibres that are inflammable and can melt; they should not be worn during firefighting. Ear plugs and ear valves are generally not suitable for forestry because of risk of infection.
[2] When noise level at work position exceeds 85 dBA.
[3] Chain-saw boots must have protective guarding at front vamp and instep.
[4] Cut-resistant material must be incorporated.
[5] If pruning involves tree climbing above 3 m, a fall-restricting device should be used. PPE must be used when falling branches are likely to cause injury.
[6] When pruning to a height exceeding 2.5 m.
[7] Felling includes debranching and crosscutting.
[8] When using a hand-saw.
[9] When extracting near unstable trees or branchwood.
[10] Only if manipulating logs; gloves with heavy-duty palm if handling wire choker rope or tether line.
[11] Highly visible colours should be used.
[12] Helmet must have a chin strap.
[13] Climbing helmets are preferable; if they are not available, safety helmets with chin straps may be used.
Source: ILO 1997.

On the basis of this risk analysis, the requirements for personal protective devices must be defined. Environmental factors should be taken into account in order to minimize the load cased by the equipment. The hazard caused by the saw must be evaluated and the protection area and efficiency of clothing defined. If the work- ers are not professionals, the protection area and level should be higher, but this extra loading must be taken into account when the work periods are planned. After the requirements for PPE are defined according to the risks and tasks, the proper equipment is selected from among devices that have been approved. The work-

Figure 68.17 • Bodily location of injuries and personal protective equipment recommended for forest work, the Netherlands, 1989.

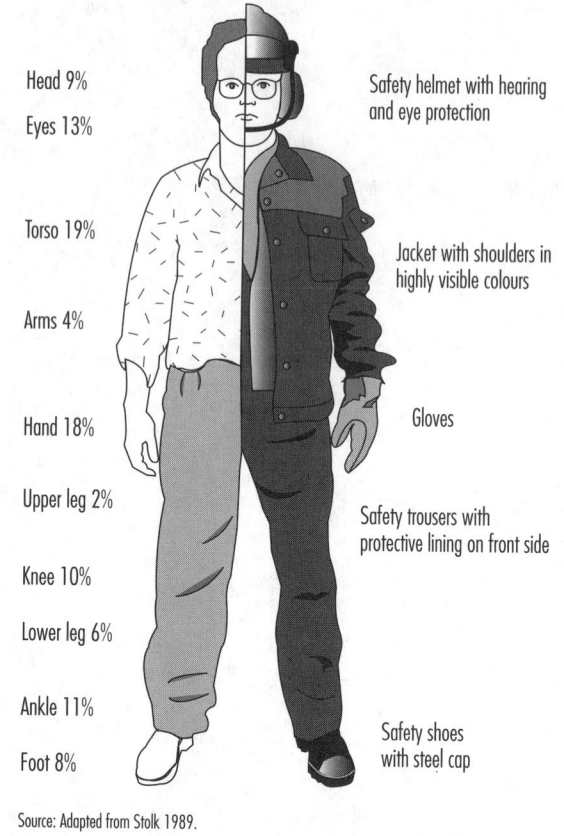

Head 9%

Eyes 13%

Safety helmet with hearing and eye protection

Torso 19%

Jacket with shoulders in highly visible colours

Arms 4%

Hand 18%

Gloves

Upper leg 2%

Safety trousers with protective lining on front side

Knee 10%

Lower leg 6%

Ankle 11%

Foot 8%

Safety shoes with steel cap

Source: Adapted from Stolk 1989.

Some materials are more resistant against the effects of solvents, and those should be selected for forest work use.

Also other environmental factors affect the materials used in a helmet. Plastic materials are sensitive to ultraviolet (UV) radiation of the sun, which makes the shell more rigid, especially at low temperatures; this ageing weakens the helmet, and it will not protect against impacts as planned. The ageing is difficult to see, but small hairline cracks and the loss of gloss can be signs of ageing. Also, when gently twisted, the shell may make cracking noises. The helmets should be carefully visually inspected at least every six months.

If the chain has been in contact with the trousers, the protection efficiency can be much reduced or disappear totally. If the safety padding fibres are drawn out, the trousers should be discarded and new ones should be used. If only the outer material is damaged it can be repaired carefully without making any stitches through the safety padding. The protection efficiency of safety trousers is commonly based on the strong fibres, and if those are fixed tightly during repair they will not provide protection as planned.

Washing must be done according to the instructions given by the manufacturer. It has been shown that wrong washing methods can destroy protection efficiency. The clothing of the forest worker is difficult to clean, and products should be selected which withstand the hard washing methods needed.

How the Approved Protective Equipment is Marked

The design and quality of manufacture of PPE must meet high standards. In the European Economic area, personal protective devices must be tested before they are placed on the market. The basic health and safety requirements for PPE are described in a directive. To clarify those requirements European harmonized standards have been drafted. The standards are voluntary, but devices designed to meet the requirements in the appropriate standards are deemed to meet the requirements of the directive. The International Standards Organization (ISO) and the European Committee for Standardization (CEN) are working on these standards together according to the Vienna Agreement. So there will be technically identical EN and ISO standards.

Accredited test stations are testing the devices and issuing a certificate if they meet the requirements. After that the manufacturer can mark the product with CE-marking, which shows that the conformity assessment has been carried out. In other countries the procedure is similar and the products are marked with the national approval mark.

An essential part of the product is the leaflet giving the user information about its proper use, the degree of protection it can provide and instructions for its cleaning, washing and repair.

ers should have the privilege of trying different models and sizes to select the one that best suits them. Improperly selected clothing can cause abnormal postures and movements, and thus can increase accident and health hazard risks. Figure 68.17 illustrates the selection of equipment.

Determination of the Conditions of Use

All workers should be efficiently instructed and trained in the use of PPE. The protection mechanism must be described so that the workers themselves can inspect and evaluate the condition of the equipment daily. The consequences of non-use must be made clear. Proper cleaning and repair instructions must be given.

The protective equipment used in forestry work may constitute a relatively great extra burden to the worker. This must be taken into account when planning the working times and rest periods.

Often the use of PPE gives a false sense of safety. The supervisors must make sure that risk taking is not increasing and that the workers know well the limits of the protection efficiency.

Care and Maintenance

Improper methods used for maintenance and repair can destroy the protection efficiency of the equipment.

The shell of the helmet must be cleaned by weak detergent solutions. Resins cannot be removed efficiently without the use of solvents, but the use of solvents should be avoided because the shell can be damaged. The instructions of the manufacturer must be followed and the helmet discarded if it cannot be cleaned.

WORKING CONDITIONS AND SAFETY IN FORESTRY WORK

Lucie Laflamme and Esther Cloutier

Safety in the forestry sector depends on matching individuals' work capacities to the conditions under which they perform their tasks. The closer the mental and physical requirements of the work approach the workers' capacities (which, in turn, vary with age, experience and health status), the less likely safety is to be sacrificed in an attempt to satisfy production goals. When individual capacities and working conditions are in a precarious balance, decreased individual and collective safety is inevitable.

Figure 68.18 • Determinants of safety hazards in forestry work.

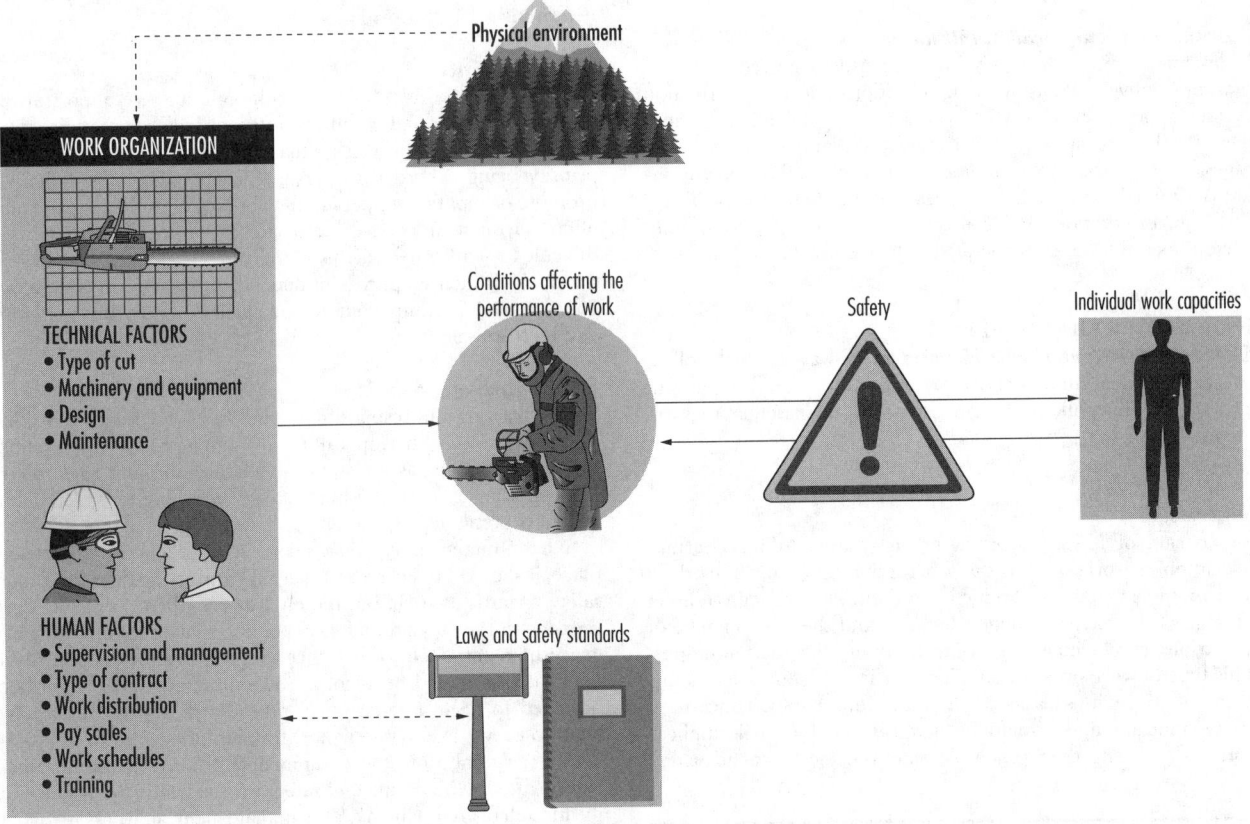

As figure 68.18 illustrates, there are three sources of safety hazards related to working conditions: the physical environment (climate, lighting, terrain, types of trees), deficient safety laws and standards (inadequate content or application) and inappropriate work organization (technical and human).

The technical and human organization of work encompasses potentially hazardous factors that are both distinct and tightly linked: distinct, because they refer to two intrinsically different resources (i.e., humans and machines); linked, because they interact and complement each other during the execution of work activities, and because their interaction allows production goals to be reached safely.

This article details how flaws in the components of work organization listed in figure 68.18 can compromise safety. It should be noted that measures to protect safety and health cannot be retro-fitted onto an existing work method, machine or organization. They need to be part of the design and planning.

Technical Work Organization

The term *technical work organization* refers to operational considerations of forestry work, including the type of cut, the choice of machinery and production equipment, equipment design, maintenance practices, size and composition of the work crew(s) and the time allotted in the production schedule.

Type of cut

There are two main types of cut used in forestry operations, distinguished by the technology used to fell and debranch trees: conventional cutting, which relies on mechanical saws, and mech-

anical cutting, which relies on machines operated from control cabins and equipped with articulated booms. In both cases, skidders, especially chain- or claw-propelled ones, are the usual means of transporting felled trees along the side of the road or waterways. Conventional cutting is the more widespread and the more dangerous of the two.

Mechanization of cutting is known to considerably reduce the frequency of accidents. This is most apparent for accidents occurring during production operations, and is due to the replacement of mechanical saws by machines operated from remote control cabins which isolate operators from hazards. At the same time, however, mechanization appears to increase the risk of accidents during machine maintenance and repair. This effect is due to both technological and human factors. Technological factors include machine deficiencies (see below) and the often improvised, if not frankly ludicrous, conditions under which maintenance and repair operations are performed. Human factors include the existence of production bonuses, which often result in low priority being given to maintenance and repair operations and the tendency to perform them hastily.

Machine design

There are no design codes for forestry machinery, and comprehensive maintenance manuals are rare. Machines such as fellers, debranchers and skidders are often a mixture of disparate components (e.g., booms, cabins, base machines), some of which are designed for use in other sectors. For these reasons, machinery used in forestry operations may be poorly suited to some environmental conditions, especially those related to the state of the forest and the terrain, and to continuous operation. Finally, machine repair is frequently necessary but very difficult to perform.

Machine and equipment maintenance

Maintenance practices in the forest are usually corrective rather than preventive. Various working conditions—such as production pressures, the absence of strict maintenance guidelines and schedules, the lack of appropriate maintenance and repair sites (garages, shelters), the harsh conditions under which these operations are performed, and the lack of adequate tools—may explain this situation. In addition, financial constraints may operate on one-person operations or sites operated by subcontractors.

Human Work Organization

The term *human work organization* refers to the way in which collective or individual human efforts are administered and organized, and to training policies designed to satisfy production requirements.

Supervision

Supervision of forestry work is not easy, due to the constant relocation of worksites and the geographic dispersion of workers over multiple worksites. Production is controlled through indirect strategies, of which production bonuses and the maintenance of precarious employment status are probably the most insidious. This type of work organization does not favour good safety management, since it is easier to transmit information concerning safety guidelines and regulations than it is to ensure their application and evaluate their practical value and the extent to which

they are understood. Managers and supervisors need to be clear that they have primary responsibility for safety. As can be seen in figure 68.19 the worker controls very few of the elements that determine safety performance.

Type of contract

Regardless of the type of cut, work contracts are almost always negotiated individually, and are often of fixed or seasonal duration. This precarious work situation is likely to lead to a low priority being accorded to personal safety, since it is difficult to promote occupational safety in the absence of minimal guarantees of employment. In concrete terms, fellers or operators may find it difficult to work safely if this compromises the production goals upon which their employment depends. Longer-term contracts of guaranteed minimum volumes per year stabilize the workforce and increase safety.

Subcontracting

Subcontracting the responsibility (and costs) for selected production activities to owner-operators is becoming more widespread in the forestry sector, as a result of mechanization and its corollary, work specialization (i.e., using a specific machine for tasks such as felling, pruning, felling-pruning and skidding).

Subcontracting may affect safety in several ways. In the first place, it should be recognized that subcontracting does not reduce safety hazards as such, but merely transfers them from the entrepreneur to the subcontractor. Secondly, subcontracting may also exacerbate certain hazards, since it stimulates production rather than safety-oriented behaviour. Subcontractors have in fact been observed to neglect some safety precautions, especially those related to preventive maintenance, training of new hires, the provision of personal protective equipment (PPE) and the promotion of its use, and the observance of safety rules. Finally, the responsibility for safety maintenance and management at worksites where subcontracting is practised is a judicial grey zone. It may even be difficult to determine the responsibility for declaring accidents to be work related. Work contracts should make compliance with safety regulations binding, include sanctions against offences, and assign responsibility for supervision.

Division of labour

The division of labour on forestry sites is often rigid and encourages specialization rather than flexibility. Task rotation is possible with conventional cutting, but is fundamentally dependent on team dynamics. Mechanized cutting, on the other hand, encourages specialization, although the technology itself (i.e., machine specialization) is not the sole cause of this phenomenon. Specialization is also encouraged by organizational factors (one operator per machine, shift work), geographic dispersion (remoteness of machines and cutting zones) and the fact that operators commonly own their machines.

Isolation and communication problems resulting from this division of labour may have serious consequences for safety, especially when they hamper the efficient circulation of information concerning imminent dangers or the occurrence of an incident or accident.

Work capacities of machines and workers need to be carefully matched and crews composed accordingly, to avoid overloading elements in the production chain. Shift schedules can be designed that maximize the use of expensive machines but give enough rest and variety of tasks to the operators.

Production-based pay scales

Forestry workers are frequently paid on a piece-work basis, which is to say that their salary is determined by their output (number of felled, pruned or transported trees, or some other index of

Figure 68.19 • Human factors have an impact on safety in forest work.

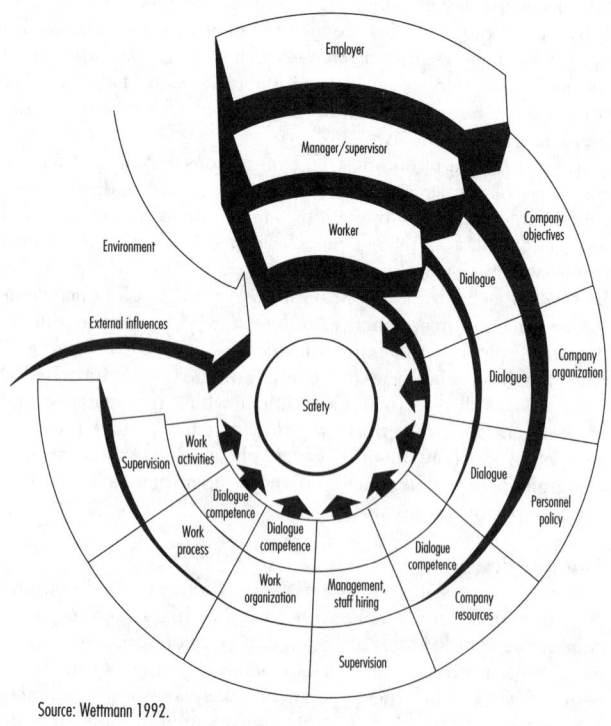

Source: Wettmann 1992.

productivity), not by its duration. For example, the rate which machine owners are paid for the use of their machines is proportional to their productivity. This type of pay scale, while not directly controlling workers, is notorious for stimulating production.

Production-based pay scales may encourage high work rates and the recourse to unsafe work practices during production and short-cuts in maintenance and repair operations. Practices like these persist because they save time, even though they ignore established safety guidelines and the risks involved. The greater the production incentive, the more safety is compromised. Workers paid on the basis of production have been observed to suffer more accidents, as well as different types of accidents, than hourly-paid workers performing the same type of work. Piece rates and prices for contracts need to be adequate for safe execution and acceptable working hours. (For a recent empirical study in Germany, see Kastenholz 1996.)

Work schedules

In the forest, long daily and weekly work schedules are the norm, since worksites and cutting zones are remote, work is seasonal, and the often difficult climatic and environmental factors encourage workers to work as long as possible. Other factors encouraging longer work schedules include production incentives (pay scales, subcontracting) and the possibility of using certain machines on a continuous basis (i.e., without stopping at night).

Long work schedules often result in decreased vigilance and a loss of sensory acuity, both of which may have effects on individual and collective safety. These problems are aggravated by the rarity and brevity of rest periods. Planned breaks and maximum working hours should be observed. Ergonomic research demonstrates that output can actually be increased that way.

Training

There can be no doubt that forestry work is physically and mentally demanding. The skill level required is continually increasing, as a result of technological advances and the growing complexity of machines. Prior and onsite training of forestry workers are therefore very important. Training programmes should be based on clearly defined objectives and reflect the actual work to be performed. The more the training programmes' content corresponds to actual working conditions and the greater the integration of safety and production concerns, the more useful the programmes will be, both individually and collectively. Effective training programmes not only reduce material losses and production delays but also avoid additional safety hazards. For guidance on training, see "Skills and training" in this chapter.

Conclusion

The safety of forestry work is determined by factors related to work organization, and technical and human aspects of work organization may disrupt the equilibrium between production goals and safety. The influence of each individual factor on occupational safety will of course vary from setting to setting, but their combined effect will always be significant. Furthermore, their interaction will be the prime determinant of the degree to which prevention is possible.

It should also be noted that technological developments do not, in and of themselves, eliminate all hazards. Design criteria for machines should take into account their safe operation, maintenance and repair. Finally, it appears that some increasingly widespread management practices, especially subcontracting, may exacerbate rather than reduce safety hazards.

SKILLS AND TRAINING

Peter Poschen

Skills, Training and Exposure

In many industries, attention to safety in the design of equipment, workplaces and work methods can go a long way toward reducing occupational safety and health hazards. In the forestry industry, exposure to risks is largely determined by the technical knowledge, skill and experience of the individual worker and the supervisor, and their commitment to a joint effort in planning and performing the work. Training, therefore, is a crucial determinant of health and safety in forestry.

Studies in different countries and for different jobs in forestry all concur that three groups of workers have a disproportionately high accident frequency: the unskilled, often seasonal, workers; the young; and new entrants. In Switzerland, fully 73% of the accidents affect workers with less than one year in forestry; likewise, three-quarters of the accident victims had no or only rudimentary training (Wettman 1992).

Untrained workers also tend to have a much higher workload and higher risk of back injuries because of poor technique (see "Tree planting" in this chapter for an example). If training is critically important both from a safety and a productivity point of view in normal operations, it is absolutely indispensable in high-risk tasks like salvaging windblown timber or firefighting. No personnel should be allowed to participate in such activities unless they have been especially trained.

Training Forest Workers

On-the-job training is still very common in forestry. It is usually very ineffective, because it is a euphemism for imitation or simply trial and error. Any training needs to be based on clearly established objectives and on well-prepared instructors. For new chainsaw operators, for example, a two-week course followed by systematic coaching at the workplace is the bare minimum.

Fortunately, there has been a trend towards longer and well-structured training in industrialized countries, at least for directly employed workers and most new entrants. Various European countries have 2-to-3-year apprenticeships for forest workers. The structure of training systems is described and contacts to schools are listed in FAO/ECE/ILO 1996b. Even in these countries there is, however, a widening gap between the above and problem groups such as self-employed, contractors and their workers, and farmers working in their own forest. Pilot schemes to provide training for these groups have demonstrated that they can be profitable investments, as their cost is more than offset by savings resulting from reductions in accident frequency and severity. In spite of its demonstrated benefits and of some encouraging examples, like the Fiji Logging School, forest worker training is still virtually non-existent in most tropical and subtropical countries.

Forest worker training has to be based on the practical needs of the industry and the trainee. It has to be hands-on, imparting practical skill rather than merely theoretical knowledge. It can be provided through a variety of mechanisms. Schools or training centres have been used widely in Europe with excellent results. They do, however, carry a high fixed cost, need a fairly high annual enrolment to be cost-effective, and are often far from the workplace. In many countries mobile training has, therefore, been preferred. In its simplest form, specially prepared instructors travel to workplaces and offer courses according to programmes that may be standard or modular and adaptable to local needs. Skilled workers with some further training have been used very effectively as part-time instructors. Where demand for training is higher, specially equipped trucks or trailers are used as mobile classrooms and workshops. Designs and sample equipment lists for such units are available (Moos and Kvitzau 1988). For some target groups, such as contractors or farmers, mobile training may be the only way to reach them.

Minimum Competence Standards and Certification

In all countries, minimum standards of skill should be defined for all major jobs, at least in forest harvesting, the most hazardous operation. A very suitable approach to make sure minimum standards are defined and actually met in the industry is skill certification based on testing workers in short theoretical and practical exams. Most schemes place emphasis on standardized tests of workers' skill and knowledge, rather than on whether these have been acquired through training or long experience. Various certification schemes have been introduced since the mid-1980s. In many cases certification has been promoted by workers' compensation funds or safety and health directorates, but there have also been initiatives by large forest owners and industry. Standard tests are available for chain-saw and skidder operators (NPTC and SSTS 1992, 1993; Ministry of Skills Development 1989). Experience shows that the tests are transferable without or with only minor amendment. In 1995 for example the ILO and the Zimbabwe Forestry Commission successfully introduced the chain-saw test developed in an ILO logging training project in Fiji.

● LIVING CONDITIONS

Elias Apud

Forestry operations, especially in developing countries, tend to be temporary and seasonal. In general, this work takes place far from urban centres, and workers must travel long distances every day or remain for several days or weeks in camps near the worksites. When workers commute from their homes every day, working conditions depend in large measure on their wages, the size of their family, their level of education and the access they have to health services. These variables, which are related to the level of development a nation has achieved and to the organization of the family group, are key to guaranteeing that basic necessities will be covered. These basic necessities include adequate nourishment, which is especially important given the intensity of the effort required of forestry workers. In many regions even commuting workers will still need protection against adverse weather conditions during breaks, particularly against rain and cold. Mobile shelters are available that are specially designed and equipped for forestry. If such forestry shelters are not provided, those used on construction sites can serve the purpose too. The situation in the camps is different, since their quality depends on the facilities provided by the company in terms of infrastructure and maintenance. The discussion which follows therefore refers to living conditions in forestry camps in so far as housing, leisure and nourishment are concerned.

Camp Infrastructure

Camps can be defined as temporary homes for forestry workers when they operate in remote or hard-to-reach locations. To fulfil their purpose, the camps should provide at least minimal levels of sanitation and comfort. It is therefore important to ask: How do different people interpret what these minimal levels should be? The concept is subjective, but it is possible to assert that, in the case of a camp, the minimal conditions required are that the infrastructure provide facilities and basic services that are consistent with human dignity, where each worker can partake with others on the crew without having to significantly alter his or her personal habits or beliefs.

One question that needs to be addressed when planning a forestry camp is the time that the camp will remain in a particular location. Since normally tasks must be shifted from one place to the other, fixed camps, while easier to set up and maintain, are not the solution that is usually required. In general, mobile structures are the most practical, and they should be easy to take down and move from one location to the next. This presents a complex problem, because even well-built modules deteriorate easily as they are moved. Conditions at mobile camps, therefore, tend to be very primitive.

In terms of facilities, a camp should offer an adequate supply of water, enough dormitories, a kitchen, bathrooms and recreation facilities. The size of each site will depend on the number of people who will be using it. In addition there should be separate stores for food, fuel, tools and materials.

Dormitories should allow workers to maintain their privacy. Since this is generally not possible in a camp, the number of people should not exceed six in each dormitory. This number has been arrived at through experience, since it has been found that a collapsible structure can accommodate six workers comfortably, allowing enough room for lockers where they can keep their personal belongings. In sharp contrast to this example, a dormitory that is crowded and dirty is absolutely inadequate for human use. An adequate dormitory is sanitary, with a clean floor, good ventilation and a minimal effort to create a comfortable atmosphere (e.g., with curtains and bedspreads of the same colour).

The kitchen, for its part, constitutes one of the most critical facilities in a camp. The first requirement is that the individuals in charge of the kitchen be skilled in sanitation and food handling. They should be licensed by an authorized authority and be supervised regularly. The kitchen should be easy to clean and should have adequate space for food storage. If food is stocked weekly or biweekly the kitchen should have a refrigerator to keep perishable food. It may be inconvenient and time-consuming for workers to return to camp for lunch: sanitary arrangements should be provided for packing lunches for workers to carry with them or to be delivered to them.

With regards to recreation facilities, mess halls are commonly used for this purpose. If workers are at their tasks all day and the only place to unwind is the eating quarters, these rooms should have enough of an infrastructure to allow workers to feel comfortable and recuperate physically and mentally from their workday. There should be adequate ventilation and, if the season requires, heating. Eating tables should not be for more than six people and should be lined with an easy to clean surface. If the dining-room is also used for recreation it should have, when possible, a television or a radio that can let workers stay in touch with the rest of the world. It is also advisable to provide some table games like checkers, cards and dominoes. Since among forestry workers there is an important contingent of young workers, it is not a bad idea to set up an area where they can play sports.

One aspect that is extremely important is the quality of sanitary facilities, showers and facilities for workers to wash and dry their belongings. It is important to keep in mind that faeces and waste in general are one of the most common avenues for the transmission of disease. It is therefore better to obtain water from a deep well than from a shallow one. If electric pumps can be installed, well-water may be raised into tanks that can then supply the camp. If for any reason it is not possible to erect sanitary services of this kind, chemical latrines should be installed. In any case, the elimination of human and other waste should be done carefully, making especially sure that they are not discharged in areas close to where food is kept or where drinking water is obtained.

68. FORESTRY

Nutrition

Nutrition is a basic necessity for the maintenance of life and for the health of all human beings. Food provides not only nutrients but the energy required to carry out all activities in daily life. In the case of forestry workers, the caloric content of foods consumed is especially important because most of the harvesting, handling and forest protection activities demand great physical exertion (see the article "Physical load" in this chapter for data on energy consumption in forest work). Forestry workers need, therefore, more nourishment than people who do less demanding work. When a worker does not consume enough energy to offset daily energy expenditures, at first he or she will burn the reserves accumulated in body fat, losing weight. However, this can be done for only a limited time. It has been observed that, in the medium term, those workers who do not obtain in their diet the energy equivalent to their daily expenditures will limit their activity and lower their output. As a consequence, if they are paid by piece rate, their income also decreases.

Before analysing just how much energy a worker must consume as part of his or her diet, it bears mentioning that modern forestry work relies on increasingly sophisticated technology, where human energy is replaced by that of machinery. In those situations, operators run the risk of consuming more energy than they require, accumulating the excess as fat and risking obesity. In modern society, obesity is a malady that affects many people, but it is unusual in forestry workers where traditional methods are employed. According to studies carried out in Chile, it is becoming more common among machine operators. Obesity diminishes the quality of life because it is associated with a lower physical aptitude, predisposing those who suffer from it to accidents and to illnesses such as cardiovascular disease and more joint and muscle lesions.

For this reason all forestry workers, whether their daily activity is heavy or sedentary, should have access to a well-balanced diet that provides them with adequate amounts of energy. The key is to educate them so that they can regulate their food needs themselves. Unfortunately, this is a fairly difficult problem to solve; the tendency observed in studies carried out in Chile is for workers to consume all the food provided by the company and, in general, to still find their diet insufficient even though their weight variations indicate the opposite. The solution therefore is to educate the workers so that they learn to eat according to their energy requirements.

If workers are well informed about the problems created by eating too much, camps should offer diets keeping in mind the workers with the highest energy expenditures. The intake and expenditure of human energy is commonly expressed in kilojoules. However, the more widely known unit is the kilocalorie. The amount of energy required by a forestry worker when the job demands intense physical exertion, as in the case of a chain-saw operator or a worker using an axe, can reach 5,000 calories a day or even more. However, to expend those high amounts of energy, a worker must have a very good physical aptitude and reach the end of the workday without undue fatigue. Studies carried out in Chile have resulted in recommendations of an average of 4,000 calories provided daily, in the form of three basic meals at breakfast, lunch and dinnertime. This allows for the possibility of snacking at mid-morning and mid-afternoon so that additional amounts of energy can be provided. Studies over periods of more than a year have shown that, with a system like the one described, workers tend to maintain their body weight and increase their output and their incomes when pay is tied to their output.

A good diet must be balanced and provide, in addition to energy, essential nutrients for the maintenance of life and good health. Among other elements a diet should provide adequate amounts of carbohydrates, proteins, fats, minerals and vitamins.

The tendency in developing countries is for groups that have low incomes to consume fewer proteins and fats and higher amounts of carbohydrates. The lack of the first two elements is due to a low consumption of foods of animal origin. In addition, a lack of certain vitamins and minerals has been observed due to a low consumption of foods of animal origin, fruits and vegetables. To summarize, the diet should be varied to balance the intake of essential nutrients. The most convenient option is to seek the help of specialized dieticians who know about the demands of heavy work. These professionals can develop diets that are reasonably cost efficient and that take into account the tastes, the traditions and the beliefs of the consumers and provide the amounts of energy required by forestry workers for their daily labour.

A very important element is a supply of liquid of good quality—not contaminated and in sufficient quantity. In manual and chain-saw work with high temperatures, a worker needs approximately 1 litre of liquid per hour. Dehydration drastically reduces working capacity and ability to concentrate, thereby increasing the risk of accidents. Therefore water, tea or other suitable drinks need to be available at the worksite as well as in the camp.

Consumption of alcohol and drugs should be strictly forbidden. Cigarette smoking, which is a fire hazard as well as a health hazard, should only be allowed in restricted areas and never in dormitories, recreation areas, dining halls and worksites.

Comments

This article has dealt with some of the general measures that can improve the living conditions and the diet of forestry camps. But while these two aspects are fundamental, they are not the only ones. It is also important to design the work in an ergonomically appropriate way because accidents, occupational injuries and the general fatigue that result from these activities have an impact on output and consequently on incomes. This last aspect of forestry work is of vital importance if workers and their families are to enjoy a better quality of life.

ENVIRONMENTAL HEALTH ISSUES

Shane McMahon

Forestry operations invariably affect the environment in one way or another. Some of these effects can be beneficial to the environment while others can be adverse. Obviously, it is the latter that is regarded with concern by both regulatory authorities and the public.

The Environment

When we speak of the environment, we often think of the physical and biological components of the environment: that is, the soil, the existing vegetation and wildlife and the waterways. Increasingly, the cultural, historic and amenity values associated with these more fundamental components are being considered part of the environment. Considering the impact of forest operations and management at the landscape level, not only on physical and biological objectives but also on the social values, has resulted in the evolution of concepts such as ecosystem management and forest stewardship. Therefore, this discussion of environmental health also draws on some of the social impacts.

Not All Bad News

Understandably, regulation and public concern regarding forestry throughout the world have focused on, and will continue to focus on, the negative impacts on environmental health. Despite this focus, forestry has the potential to benefit the environment.

Table 68.10 • Potential benefits to environmental health.

Forest operations	Potential benefits
Planting (afforestation)	Increased carbon absorption (sequestration) Increased slope stability Increased recreational opportunity (amenity forests) Increased landscape biodiversity Flood control management
Harvesting	Increased public access Reduced wildfire and disease risk Promotion of secessional development of natural forests

Table 68.10 highlights some of the potential benefits of both planting commercial tree species, and harvesting both natural and plantation forests. These benefits can be used to help establish the net effect (sum of positive and negative impacts) of forest management on environmental health. Whether such benefits accrue, and to what extent, often depends on the practices adopted (e.g., biodiversity depends on species mix, extent of tree mono-cultures and treatment of remnants of natural vegetation).

Environmental Health Issues

Despite there being major differences in forest resources, environmental regulations and concerns, as well as in forest practices throughout the world, many of the existing environmental health issues are generic across the forest industry. This overview focuses on the following issues:

- decline in soil quality
- soil erosion
- changes in water quality and quantity (including sedimentation)
- impacts on biodiversity
- adverse public perception of forestry
- discharge of chemicals (oil and pesticides) into the environment.

The degrees to which these general issues are a concern in a particular area will be largely dependent on the sensitivity of the forested area, and the nature of the water resources and water users downstream or offsite from the forest.

Activities within forested areas can affect other areas. These impacts can be direct, such as visual impacts, or they may be indirect, such as the effects of increased suspended sediment on marine farming activities. Therefore, it is important to recognize the pathways linking different parts of the environment. For example: skidder logging → streamside soils → stream water quality → downstream recreational water users.

Decline in soil quality

Forest management can affect soil quality (Powers et al. 1990; FAO/ECE/ILO 1989, 1994). Where forests have been planted to rehabilitate degraded soils, such as eroded soils or mining overburden, this net impact may be an increase in quality by improving soil fertility and structural development. Conversely, forest activities on high-quality soil have the potential to reduce soil quality. Activities causing nutrient depletion, organic matter loss and structural loss through compaction are particularly important.

Soil nutrients are used by vegetation during the growing cycle. Some of these nutrients may be recycled back to the soil through litter fall, death or by residual logging waste. Where all the vegetative material is removed during harvest (i.e., whole tree harvest) these nutrients are removed from the onsite nutrient cycle. With successive growing and harvesting cycles, the store of available

nutrients within the soil may decline to levels where growth rates and tree nutrient status cannot be sustained.

Burning of logging wastes has in the past been a preferred means of promoting regeneration or preparing a site for planting. However, research has shown that intensely hot burns can result in the loss of soil nutrients (carbon, nitrogen, sulphur and some phosphorus, potassium and calcium). The consequences of depleting the store of soil nutrients can be reduced tree growth and changes in species composition. The practice of replacing lost nutrients through inorganic fertilizers may address some of the nutrient depletion. However, this will not mitigate the effects of the loss of organic matter which is an important medium for soil fauna.

The use of heavy machinery for harvesting and preparation for planting can result in soil compaction. Compaction can cause reduced air and water movement in a soil and increase the strength of the soil to the extent that tree roots can no longer penetrate. Consequently, compaction of forest soils can reduce tree survival and growth and increase rainfall runoff and soil erosion. Importantly, without cultivation, compaction of subsoils may persist for 20 to 30 years after logging. Increasingly, logging methods that reduce the areas and degree of compaction are being used to reduce decline in soil quality. The codes of forest practices adopted in a growing number of countries and discussed in the article "Rules, legislation, regulations and codes of forest practices" in this chapter provide guidance on such methods.

Soil erosion

Soil erosion is a major concern to all land users, as it can result in irreversible loss of productive soils, adversely impact visual and amenity values, and may impact water quality (Brown 1985). Forests can protect soils from erosion by:

- intercepting rainfall
- regulating ground water levels
- increasing slope stability because of root growth
- protecting soil from wind and frost action.

However, when an area of forest is harvested, the level of soil protection is significantly reduced, increasing the potential for soil erosion.

It is recognized worldwide that forest operations associated with the following activities are major contributors to increased soil erosion during the forest management cycle:

- road work
- earthworks
- harvesting
- burning
- cultivation.

Road work activities, particularly in steep terrain where cut and fill construction is used, produce significant areas of loose unconsolidated soil material that are exposed to rainfall and runoff. If drainage control on roads and tracks is not maintained, they can channel rainfall runoff, increasing the potential for soil erosion on lower slopes and on the road edges.

Harvesting of forest trees can increase soil erosion in four main ways:

- exposing surface soils to rainfall
- reducing stand water usage, thereby increasing soil water contents and groundwater levels
- causing gradual decline in slope stability as the root system decomposes
- disturbance of soils during wood extraction.

Burning and cultivation are two techniques often used to prepare a site for regeneration or planting. These practices can increase the potential for surface erosion by exposing surface soil to the erosive effects of rainfall.

The degree of increased soil erosion, by either surface erosion or mass wasting, will depend on many factors including the size of the area logged, the slope angles, the strength of slope materials and the time since the harvesting occurred. Large clear cuts (i.e., total removal of almost all trees) can be a cause of severe erosion.

The potential for soil erosion can be very high during the first year after harvest relative to before road construction and harvesting. As the re-established or regenerating crop begins to grow, the risk of increased soil erosion decreases as water interception (protection of surface soils) and transpiration increase. Usually, the potential for increased erosion declines to pre-harvest levels once the forest canopy masks the ground surface (canopy closure).

Forest managers aim to reduce the period of vulnerability or the area of a catchment vulnerable at any one time. Staging the harvesting to spread harvesting over several catchments and reducing the size of individual harvest areas are two alternatives.

Changes in water quality and quantity

The quality of water discharged from undisturbed forest catchments is often very high, relative to agricultural and horticultural catchments. Certain forest activities can reduce the quality of water discharged by increasing nutrient and sediment contents, increasing water temperatures and decreasing dissolved oxygen levels.

Increased nutrient concentrations and exports from forest areas that have been burnt, undergone soil disturbance (scarification) or had fertilizer applied, can adversely effect water weed growth and cause pollution of downstream waters. In particular, nitrogen and phosphorus are important because of their association with toxic algae growth. Similarly, increased sediment input into waterways can adversely affect freshwater and marine life, flooding potential and water utilization for drinking or industrial uses.

The removal of streamside vegetation and the introduction of green and woody material into waterways during thinning or harvesting operations can adversely affect the aquatic ecosystem by increasing water temperatures and levels of dissolved oxygen in the water, respectively.

Forestry can also have an impact on the seasonal volume of water leaving a forest catchment (water yield) and peak discharges during storm events. Planting of trees (afforestation) in catchments previously under a pastoral farming regime can reduce water yields. This issue can be of particular importance where the water resource below an afforested area is utilized for irrigation.

Conversely harvesting within an existing forest can increase water yields because of the loss of water transpiration and interception, increasing the potential for flooding and erosion in the waterways. The size of a catchment and the proportion harvested at any one time will influence the extent of any water yield increase. Where only small proportions of a catchment are harvested, such as patch cuts, the effects on yield may be minimal.

Impacts on biodiversity

Biodiversity of plants and animals within forest areas has become an important issue for the forest industry worldwide. Diversity is a complex concept, not being confined to different plant and animal species alone. Biodiversity also refers to functional diversity (the role of a particular species in the ecosystem), structural diversity (layering within the forest canopy) and genetic diversity (Kimmins 1992). Forest operations have the potential to impact species diversity as well as the structural and functional diversity.

Identifying what is the optimum mix of species, ages, structures and functions is subjective. There is a general belief that a low level of species and structural diversity predisposes a forest to

increased risk of disturbance with a pathogen or pest attack. To some extent this may be true; however, individual species in a mixed natural forest may suffer exclusively from a particular pest. A low level of biodiversity does not imply that a low level of diversity is an unnatural and unwanted outcome of forest management. For instance, many mixed species natural forests which are naturally subject to wildfire and pest attack go through stages of low species and structural diversity.

Adverse public perception of forestry

The public perception and acceptance of forest practice are two increasingly important issues for the forest industry. Many forest areas provide considerable recreational and amenity value to the resident and travelling public. The public often associates pleasurable outdoors experiences with mature managed and natural forested landscapes. Through insensitive harvesting, particularly large clearcuts, the forest industry has the potential to dramatically modify the landscape, the effects of which are often evident for many years. This contrasts with other land uses such as agriculture or horticulture, where the cycles of change are less evident.

Part of the negative public response to such activities stems from a poor understanding of forest management regimes, practices and outcomes. This clearly puts the onus on the forest industry to educate the public while at the same time modifying their own practices to increase public acceptance. Large clearcuts and the retention of logging residues (branch materials and standing dead wood) are two issues often causing public reaction because of the association of these practices with a perceived decline in ecosystem sustainability. However, this association may not be based in fact, as what is valued in terms of visual quality does not imply benefit for the environment. Retention of residues, although looking ugly, does provide habitat and food for animal life, and provides for some cycling of nutrients and organic matter.

Oil in the environment

Oil can be discharged in the forest environment through the dumping of machine oil and filters, the use of oil to control dust on unpaved roads and from chain-saws. Because of concerns about contamination of soil and water by mineral oil, oil dumping and its application on roads are becoming unacceptable practices.

However, the use of mineral oil to lubricate chain-saw bars is still common practice in much of the world. About 2 litres of oil are used by a single chain-saw per day, which adds up to considerable volumes of oil over a year. For example, it has been estimated that chain-saw oil usage was approximately 8 to 11.5 million litres/year in Germany, approximately 4 million litres/year in Sweden and approximately 2 million litres/year in New Zealand.

Mineral oil has been linked with skin disorders (Lejhancova 1968) and respiratory problems (Skyberg et al. 1992) in workers in contact with the oil. Furthermore, the discharge of mineral oil into the environment can result in soil and water contamination. Skoupy and Ulrich (1994) quantified the fate of chain-saw bar lubricant and found that between 50 and 85% was incorporated in the sawdust, 3 to 15% remained on trees, less than 33% was discharged onto the forest floor and 0.5% sprayed onto the operator.

Concerns primarily for the environment have led to biodegradable oils being compulsory in Swedish and German forests. Based on rapeseed or synthetic-based oils, these oils are more friendly to the environmentally and worker, and can also out-perform mineral-based lubricants by offering better chain life and reduced oil and fuel consumption.

Use of herbicides and insecticides

Herbicides (chemicals that kill plants) are employed by the forest industry to reduce weed competition for water, light and nutrients with young planted or regenerating trees. Often herbicides offer a cost-effective alternative to mechanical or manual weed control.

Despite there being a general mistrust of herbicides, possibly as a result of the use of Agent Orange during the Vietnam war, there have been no real documented adverse impacts on soils, wildlife and humans from herbicide use in forestry (Kimmins 1992). Some studies have found decreases in mammal numbers following herbicide treatment. However, by also studying the effects of manual or mechanical weed control, it has been shown that these decreases are coincidental with the loss of vegetation rather than the herbicide itself. Herbicides sprayed near waterways can poten-

tially enter and be transported in the water, although herbicide concentrations are usually low and short term as dilution takes effect (Brown 1985).

Prior to the 1960s, the use of insecticides (chemicals that kill insects) by the agricultural, horticultural and public health sectors was widespread, with lesser amounts being used in forestry. Perhaps one of the more commonly used insecticides used during this time was DDT. Public reaction to health issues has largely curbed the indiscriminate use of insecticides, leading to the development of alternative practices. Since the 1970s, there have been moves towards the use of insect disease organisms, the introduction of insect pests and predators and modification of silvicultural regimes to reduce the risk of insect attack.

References

Apud, E, L Bostrand, I Mobbs, and B Strehlke. 1989. *Guidelines on Ergonomic Study in Forestry*. Geneva: ILO.

Apud, E and S Valdés. 1995. *Ergonomics in Forestry—The Chilean Case*. Geneva: ILO.

Banister, E, D Robinson, and D Trites. 1990. *Ergonomics of Tree Planting*. Canada–British Columbia Forest Resources Development Agreement, FRDA Report 127. Victoria, BC: FRDA.

Brown, GW. 1985. *Forestry and Water Quality*. Corvallis, OR: Oregon State University (OSU) Book Stores Inc.

Chen, KT. 1990. *Logging Accidents—An Emerging Problem*. Sarawak, Malaysia: Occupational Health Unit, Medical Department.

Dummel, K and H Branz. 1986. *"Holzernteverfahren,"* Schriften Reihefdes Bundesministers für Ernätrung, Handwirtschaft und Forsten. Reihe A: Landwirtschafts verlag Münster-Hiltrup.

Durnin, JVGA and R Passmore. 1967. *Energy, Work, Leisure*. London: Heinemann.

Food and Agriculture Organization (FAO) of the United Nations. 1992. *Introduction to Ergonomics in Forestry in Developing Countries*. Forestry Paper 100. Rome:FAO.

—. 1995. *Forestry—Statistics Today for Tomorrow*. Rome: FAO.

—. 1996. *FAO Model Code of Forest Harvesting Practice*. Rome: FAO.

FAO/ECE/ILO. 1989. *Impact of Mechanization of Forest Operations on the Soil*. Proceedings of a seminar, Louvain-la-neuve, Belgium, 11–15 September. Geneva: FAO/ECE/ILO Joint Committee on Forest Technology, Management and Training.

—. 1991. *The Use of Pesticides in Forestry*. Proceedings of a seminar, Sparsholt, UK, 10–14 September 1990.

—. 1994. *Soil, Tree, Machine Interactions, FORSITRISK*. Proceedings of an interactive workshop and seminar, Feldafiraf, Germany, 4–8 July. Geneva: FAO/ECE/ILO Joint Committee on Forest Technology, Management and Training.

—. 1996a. *Manual on Acute Forest Damage*. UN/ECE/FAO discussion papers ECE/TIM/DP/7, New York and Geneva: Joint FAO/ECE/ILO Committee on Forest Technology, Management and Training.

—. 1996b. *Skills and Training in Forestry—Results of a Survey of ECE Member Countries*. Geneva: FAO/ECE/ILO Joint Committee on Forest Technology, Management and Training.

FAO/ILO. 1980. *Chainsaws in Tropical Forests*. Forest Training Series No. 2. Rome: FAO.

Gellerstedt, S. 1993. *Work and Health in Forest Work*. Göteborg: Chalmers University of Technology.

Giguère, D, R Bélanger, J-M Gauthier, and C Larue. 1991. *Étude préliminaire du travail de reboisement*. Rapport IRSST B-026. Montreal: IRSST.

—. 1993. Ergonomics aspects of tree planting using multi-pot technology. *Ergonomics* 36(8):963-972.

Golsse, JM. 1994. *Revised FERIC Ergonomic Checklist for Canadian Forest Machinery*. Pointe Claire: Forest Engineering Research institute of Canada.

Haile, F. 1991. *Women Fuelwood Carriers in Addis Ababa and the Peri-urban Forest*. Research on women in fuelwood transport in Addis Ababa, Ethiopia ETH/88/MO1/IRDC and ETH/89/MO5/NOR. Project report. Geneva: ILO.

Harstela, P. 1990. Work postures and strain of workers in Nordic forest work: A selective review. *Int J Ind Erg* 5:219–226.

International Labour Organization (ILO). 1969. *Safety and Health in Forestry Work*. An ILO Code of Practice. Geneva: ILO.

—. 1988. *Maximum Weights in Load Lifting and Carrying*. Occupational Safety and Health Service, No. 59. Geneva: ILO.

—. 1991. *Occupational Safety and Health in Forestry*. Report II, Forestry and Wood Industries Committee, Second Session. Geneva: ILO.

—. 1997. *Code of Practice on Safety and Health in Forest Work*. MEFW/1997/3. Geneva: ILO.

—. 1998. *Code of Practice on Safety and Health in Forest Work*. Geneva: ILO.

International Standards Organization (ISO). 1986. *Equipment for Working the Soil: ROPS—Laboratory Testing and Performance Specifications*. ISO 3471-1. Geneva: ISO.

Jokulioma, H and H Tapola. 1993. Forest worker safety and health in Finland. *Unasylva* 4(175):57–63.

Juntunen, ML. 1993. Training of harvester operations in Finland. Presented in seminar on the use of multifunctional machinery and equipment in logging operations. Olenino Logging Enterprise, Tvor Region, Russian Federation 22–28 August.

—. 1995. Professional harvester operator: Basic knowledge and skills from training—Operating skills from working life? Presented in IUFRO XX World Congress, Tampre, Finland, 6–12 August.

Kanninen, K. 1986. The occurrence of occupational accidents in logging operations and the aims of preventive measures. In the proceedings of a seminar on occupational health and rehabilitation of forest workers, Kuopio, Finland, 3–7 June 1985. FAO/ECE/ILO Joint Committee on Forest Working Techniques and Training of Forest Workers.

Kastenholz, E. 1996. *Sicheres Handeln bei der Holzernteuntersuchung von Einflüssen auf das Unfallgeschehen bei der Waldarbeit unter besonderer Berücksichtigung der Lohnform*. Doctoral dissertation. Freiburg, Germany: University of Freiburg.

Kantola, M and P Harstela. 1988. *Handbook on Appropriate Technology for Forestry Operations in Developing Counties, Part 2*. Forestry Training Programme Publication 19. Helsinki: National Board of Vocational Education.

Kimmins, H. 1992. *Balancing Act—Environmental Issues in Forestry*. Vancouver, BC: University of British Columbia Press.

Lejhancova, M. 1968. Skin damage caused by mineral oils. *Procovni Lekarstvi* 20(4):164–168.

Lidén, E. 1995. *Forest Machine Contractors in Swedish Industrial Forestry: Significance and Conditions during 1986–1993*. Department of Operational Efficiency Report No. 195. Swedish University of Agricultural Science.

Ministry of Skills Development. 1989. *Cutter-skidder Operator: Competency-based Training Standards*. Ontario: Ministry of Skills Development.

Moos, H and B Kvitzau. 1988. Retraining of adult forest workers entering forestry from other occupation. In *Proceedings of Seminar on the Employment of Contractors in Forestry, Loubières, France 26-30 September 1988*. Loubiéres: FAO/ECE/ILO Joint Committee on Forest Work Techniques and Training of Forest Workers.

National Proficiency Test Council (NPTC) and Scottish Skill Testing Service (SSTS). 1992. *Schedule of Chainsaw Standards*. Warwickshire, UK: NPTC and SSTS.

—. 1993. *Certificates of Competence in Chainsaw Operation*. Warwickshire, United Kingdom: National Proficiency Tests Council and Scottish Skills Testing Service.

Patosaari, P. 1987. *Chemicals in Forestry: Health Hazards and Protection*. Report to the FAO/ECE/ILO Joint Committee on Forest Working Technique and Training of Forest Workers, Helsinki (mimeo).

Pellet. 1995. *Rapport d'étude: L'analyse de l'accident par la méthode de l'arbre des causes*. Luzern: Schweizerische Unfallversicherungsanstalt (SUVA) (mimeo).

Powers, RF, DH Alban, RE Miller, AE Tiarks, CG Wells, PE Avers, RG Cline, RO Fitzgerald, and JNS Loftus. 1990. Sustaining site productivity in North American forests: Problems and prospects. In *Sustained Productivity of Forest Soils*, edited by SP Gessed, DS Lacate, GF Weetman and RF Powers. Vancouver, BC: Faculty of Forestry Publication.

Robinson, DG, DG Trites, and EW Banister. 1993. Physiological effects of work stress and pesticides exposure in tree planting by British Columbian silviculture workers. *Ergonomics* 36(8):951–961.

Rodero, F. 1987. *Nota sobre siniestralidad en incendios forestales*. Madrid, Spain: Instituto Nacional para la Conservación de la Naturaleza.

Saarilahti, M and A Asghar. 1994. Study on winter planting of chir pine. Research paper 12, ILO project, Pakistan.

Skoupy, A and R Ulrich. 1994. Dispersal of chain lubrication oil in one-man chain-saws. *Forsttechnische Information* 11:121–123.

Skyberg, K, A Ronneberg, CC Christensen, CR Naess-Andersen, HE Refsum, and A Borgelsen. 1992. Lung function and radiographic signs of pulmonary fibrosis in oil exposed workers in a cable manufacturing company: A follow up study. *Brit J Ind Med* 49(5):309–315.

Slappendel, C, I Laird, I Kawachi, S Marshal, and C Cryer. 1993. Factors affecting work-related injury among forestry workers: A review. *J Saf Res* 24:19–32.

Smith, TJ. 1987. Occupational characteristics of tree-planting work. *Sylviculture Magazine* II(1):12–17.

Sozialversicherung der Bauern. 1990. Extracts from official Austrian statistics submitted to the ILO (unpublished).

Staudt, F. 1990. *Ergonomics 1990. Proceedings P3.03 Ergonomics XIX World Congress IUFRO, Montreal, Canada, August 1990*. The Netherlands: Department of Forestry, Section Forest Technique and Woodscience, Wageningen Agricultural University.

Stjernberg, EI. 1988. *A Study of Manual Tree Planting Operations in Central and Eastern Canada*. FERIC technical report TR-79. Montreal: Forest Engineering Research Institute of Canada.

Stolk, T. 1989. Gebruiker mee laten kiezen uit persoonlijke beschermingsmiddelen. *Tuin & Landschap* 18.

Strehlke, B. 1989. The study of forest accidents. In *Guidelines on Ergonomic Study in Forestry*, edited by E Apud. Geneva: ILO.

Trites, DG, DG Robinson, and EW Banister. 1993. Cardiovascular and muscular strain during a tree planting season among British Columbian silviculture workers. *Ergonomics* 36(8):935–949.

Udo, ES. 1987. *Working Conditions and Accidents in Nigerian Logging and Sawmilling Industries*. Report for the ILO (unpublished).

Wettman, O. 1992. Securité au travail dans l'exploitation forestière en Suisse. In *FAO/ECE/ILO Proceedings of Seminar on the Future of the Forestry Workforce*, edited by FAO/ECE/ILO. Corvallis, OR: Oregon State University Press.

Other relevant readings

Apud, E and C Ilabaca. 1993. Diagnóstico del estado actual de la mano de obra en algunas empresas de servicio. In *Actas III taller de producción forestal*. Concepción: Fundación Chile.

Arteau, J, D Turcot, R Daigle and P Drouin. 1992. *Findings from Testing Chain-saw Leg Protective Devices and Footwear*. Proceedings of NOKOBETEF IV, Kittilä, Finland, 5–7 February.

Axelsson, S-Å and B Pontén. 1990. New ergonomic problems in mechanized logging. *Int J Ind Erg* 5:267–273.

Axelsson, S-Å. 1995. *Occupational Safety and Health in Forestry—An International Study*. Research Notes No. 280. Garpenberg: Department of Operational Efficiency, College of Forestry, Swedish University of Agricultural Sciences.

Böltz, K. 1988. *Entwicklung der psycho-physischen Belastung und Beanspruchung als Folge der Mechanisierung und Teilautomatisierung der Holsernte*. Doktorwurde der Forstwissenschaftlichen Fakultät Inaugural-Dissertation zur Erlangung, Albert-Ludwigs-Universite Freiburg im Breisgau.

Bünte, H and W Domschke. 1993. *Therapie-Handbuch [Therapy Handbook]*. München-Wien-Baltimore: Urban & Schearzenberg.

BVLB. 1995. *Land-und-fortwirtschaftliche Maschinen, Allegemeine Prüfliste*. München: Bundesverband der Landwirtschaftlichen Berufsgenosschaften.

Cloutier, E and C Pelletier. 1993. *La sécurité en forêt—Machinerie et conditions de travail*. Montreal: IRSST.

European Committee for Standardization (CEN). 1994. *Agricultural and Forest Machinery: Portable Chainsaws—Safety*. Ref. No. EN608:1994. Brussels: CEN.

Fiji Ministry of Forests. 1990. *Fiji National Code of Logging Practice*. Suva: Ministry of Forests.

Florian, HJ and E Stollenz. 1994. *Arbeitsmedizin Aktuell [Current Occupational Medicine]*. Stuttgart-Jena: Gustav Fischer Verlag.

Forest Engineering Working Group of South Africa (FESA). undated. *South African Harvesting Code of Practice*. Matieland: University of Stellenbosch.

Food and Agriculture Organization (FAO) of the United Nations. 1985. *Logging and Transport in Steep Terrain*. Rome: FAO.

—. 1986. *Wood Extraction with Oxen and Agricultural Tractors*. FAO Forestry Paper 49. Rome: FAO.

—. 1986. *Occupational Health and Rehabilitation of Forest Workers*. The proceedings of the seminar on Occupational Health and Rehabilitation of Forest Workers, Kuopio, Finland, 3–7 June 1985.

—. 1987. *Appropriate Wood Harvesting in Plantation Forests*. FAO Forestry Paper 78. Rome: FAO.

—. 1992. *Introduction to Ergonomics in Forestry in Developing Countries*. Rome: FAO.

FAO/ECE/ILO. 1989. *Proceedings of a Seminar, Jämsänkoski, Finland 22–26 May 1989*. Helsinki: FAO/ECE/ILO Joint Committee on Forest Working Techniques and Training of Forest Workers.

FAO/ECE/ILO Joint Committee. 1994. Clothing and safety equipment in forestry. *Proceedings of a Seminar, Kuopio, Finland 27 June–1 July*. Kuopio: FAO/ECE/ILO Joint Committee.

Gäbler, H. 1957. *Wildkrankheiten [Diseases of the wild]*. Berlin: Deutscher Landwirtschaftsverlag.

Gaskin, JE. 1989. Analysis of lost-time accidents 1988 (Accident reporting scheme statistics). *Logging Industry Research Association Report* 14 (6), Rotorua, New Zealand: LIRA.

Golsse, JM and J Rickards. 1990. Woodlands equipment maintenance: An analysis of mechanical labour energy expenditure. *Int J Ind Erg* 5:243–253.

Guo, J. 1989. *Occupational Safety and Health in Chinese Forestry*. Report for the ILO (unpublished).

Hansson, JE. 1990. Design of large forestry machines. *Int J Ind Erg* 5:255–266.

Heikkilä, T, R Grönquist and M Jurvélius. 1993. *Handbook on Forest Fire Control—A Guide for Trainers*. Forestry Training Programme Publication 21. Helsinki: National Board of Education.

Heilmeyer, L. 1955. *Lehrbuch der Inneren Medizin [Textbook of internal medicine]*. Berlin: Springer-Verlag.

International Labour Organization (ILO). 1980. *Forestry Equipment Planning Guide for Vocational and Technical training and education programmes*. Geneva: ILO.

—. 1987. *Wood Harvesting with Hand Tools: An Illustrated Training Manual*. Geneva: ILO.

—. 1991. The future of forestry workforce. In *General Report of the Forestry and Wood Industries Committee*. Geneva: ILO.

—. 1992. *Fitting the Job to the Forest Worker—An Illustrated Training Manual on Ergonomics*. Geneva: ILO.

Juntunen, ML and HL Suomäki. 1992. Continuity in forest contracting companies—A follow up study of 74 Finnish forest contracting entrepreneurs, 1986 and 1991. Presented at the seminar Future of the forestry workforce at Corvallis, OR, 4–8 May.

Kangas, J, A Manninen and J Liesivuori. 1995. Occupational exposure to pesticides in Finland. *International Journal of Environmental Analytical Chemistry* 58:423–429.

Klen, T and S Väyrynen. 1984. The role of personal protection in the prevention of accidental injuries in the logging work. *J Occup Acc* 6:263–275.

Knopp, D and S Glass. 1991. Biological monitoring of the 2,4-dichlorphenoxyacetic acid–exposed workers

in agriculture and forestry. *Int Arch Occup Environ Health* 63:329–333.

Kuratorium für Waldarbeit und Forsttechnik (KWF). 1995. *Prufliste: Fortspezialxchlepper, Rückezüge, Selbstfahrende Vollernter*. Darmstadt: Kuratorium für Waldarbeit und Forsttechnik/Deutsche Prüfstelle für Land-und Forttechnik.

Laflamme, L. 1988. *Modèles et méthodes d'analyse de l'accident du travail, de l'organisation du travail aux stratégies de prévention*. Montréal, PQ: SyGeSa Ltée.

—. 1993. Technological improvement of the production process and accidents: An equivocal relationship. *Saf Sci* 16:249–266.

Laflamme, L and A Arsenault. 1984. Rémunération, postes de travail et accidents: une relation interactive. *Relations Industrielles* 39(3):509–524.

Laflamme, L and E Cloutier. 1988. Mechanization and risk of occupational accidents in the logging industry. *J Occup Acc* 10:191–198.

Lindsay, V, R Visser and M Smith. 1993. *New Zealand Forest Code of Practice*. Rotorua, New Zealand: Logging Industry Research Organization (LIRO).

Marx, HH. 1987. *Medizinische Begutachtung.5., Neubearb. U. Erw. Auflage [Medical expert opinion]*. Stuttgart and New York: Georg Thieme Verlag.

MSD Sharp & Dohme. 1984. *MSD—Manual der Diagnostik und Therapie. 3., Neubearb. Auflage [Manual of diagnosis and therapy]*. München-Wien-Baltimore: Urban & Schwarzenberg.

National Board of Forestry. 1980. *The Chain-saw: Use and Maintenance*. Sweden: Jönköping.

National Board of Labour Protection. 1988. *Industrial Accidents*. Labour Market No. 23. Helsinki, Finland: NBLP.

Nilsson, C-A, R Lindahl and Å Norström. 1987. Occupational exposure to chain-saw exhausts in logging operations. *Am Ind Hyg Assoc J* 48:99–105.

Pontén, B. 1988. *Health Risks in Forest—A Program for Action*. Report No. 77.Thesis. Garpenberg: Department of Operational Efficiency, SUAS.

Poschen, P. 1991. Forest worker training—A step child no longer? Proceedings 10th World Forestry Congress, Paris 1991, *Revue Forestière Française Hors*, série No. 8.

Rummer, R and L Smith. 1990. Ergonomics applied to forest harvesting. *Int J Ind Erg* 5(3):195–302.

Rummer, RB. 1994. Labor for forestry operations—issues for the 1990s. *Transactions of the ASAE* 37(2):639–645.

Staal Wästerlund, D and F Kufakwandi. 1993. Improving working conditions in ZAFFICO, Zambia's parastatal forest industry. *Unasylva* 172:1.

Sturm, A. 1959. *Grundbegriffe der Inneren Medizin. 9. Erg, T. Neubearb. Auflage [Basics of internal medicine]*. Jena: VEB Gustav Fischer Verlag.

Sundstrom-Frisk, C. 1984. Behavioural control through piece-rate wages. *J Occup Acc* 6(1–6):49–59.

Schweizerische Unfallversicherungsanstalt (SUVA). 1986. *Roll-over Protection (ROPS)*. (ISO 8082). Geneva: ISO.

—. 1989. *Protection against Falling Objects (FOPS)*. (ISO 8083). Geneva: ISO.

—. 1992. *Forstliche Seilkrananlagen—Normen, Regeln, Tabellen*. Luzern: SUVA.

Wellburn, V. 1989. *Ergonomics and Training of Workers for Mountain Logging*. Proceedings of a seminar on mechanization of harvesting operations in mountainous terrain, Antalya, Turkey. Geneva and Rome: FAO/ECE/ILO (unpublished).

Wolff, HP and TR Weihrauch. 1988. *Internistische Therapie [Internal therapy]*. München-Wien-Baltimore: Urban & Scharzenberg.

68. FORESTRY

HUNTING

69

Chapter Editor
George A. Conway

Contents

69. HUNTING

A PROFILE OF HUNTING AND TRAPPING IN THE 1990s

John N. Trent

Overview of the Sector

Hunting and trapping of wild animals are two very old human endeavours that persist in a variety of forms throughout the world today. Both involve the capture and death of target species living in wild or relatively undeveloped habitats. A wide variety of species is hunted. Small game mammals like hares, rabbits and squirrels are hunted throughout the world. Examples of big game commonly pursued by hunters are deer, antelope, bears and the large cats. Waterfowl and pheasants are among the commonly hunted game birds. Trapping is limited to animals having fur with either commercial or some practical value for use by the trapper. In the north temperate zones, beaver, muskrat, mink, wolf, bobcat, lynx and raccoons are often trapped.

Hunting is the stalking and killing of individual wild animals, usually for food, clothing or recreational reasons. Recently, hunting in some situations has been viewed as a way of maintaining the cultural continuity of an indigenous culture. Subsistence bowhead whaling in northern Alaska is an example. Hunters usually employ projectile weapons like shotguns, rifles or bow and arrow. Trappers are more specialized and have to obtain numbers of fur-bearing mammals without damaging .the pelts. Snares and deadfalls have been used for millennia. Leghold traps (both padded and unpadded) are still commonly used for some species; killing traps like the Conibear are more widely used for other species.

Evolution and Structure of the Industry

In a few traditional societies throughout the world today, hunting continues as an individual survival activity, essentially unchanged since before the evolution of either animal husbandry or agriculture. However, most people hunt today as some form of leisure time activity; some earn partial incomes as professional hunters or trappers; and relatively few are employed in these occupations on a full-time basis. Commerce in hunting and trapping probably began with the trade of surplus animal food and skins. Trade has gradually evolved into specialized but related occupations. Examples include tanning; hide and fur preparation; clothing manufacture; production of hunting, trapping and outdoor equipment; professional guiding; and regulation of wildlife populations.

Economic Importance

In recent centuries the commercial search for furs influenced the course of history. Wildlife populations, the fate of indigenous people and the character of many nations have been shaped by the quest for wild furs. (For example, see Hinnis 1973.) An important continuing characteristic of the fur trade is that demand for fur, and resulting prices, can fluctuate widely over time. The change in European fashion from beaver felt to silk hats in the early decades of the 19th century brought an end to the era of the mountain men in the Rocky Mountains of North America. The impact on people dependent on fur harvest can be sudden and severe. Organized public protest against the clubbing of harp seal pups in the western North Atlantic in the 1970s wreaked severe economic and social impact on small communities along the Newfoundland coast of Canada.

Trapping and hunting continue to be important in many rural economies. The cumulative expenditures for these activities can be substantial. In 1991 an estimated 10.7 million big game hunters in the United States spent US$5.1 billion on trip and equipment expenditures (US Department of the Interior, Fish and Wildlife Service and US Department of Commerce, Bureau of the Census 1993).

Characteristics of the Workforce

Professional hunting is now rare (except for guiding activities) in developed nations, and confined generally to culling operations (e.g., for predators or overcapacity hooved animals) and nuisance population control (e.g., alligators). Thus, hunting is now largely for subsistence and/or recreation, while trapping remains an income-producing occupation for some rural residents. Most hunters and trappers are men. In 1991, 92% of the 14.1 million people (age 16 or older) hunting in the United States were male. Hunting and trapping attracts independent and vigorous people who enjoy working and living on the land. Both are traditional activities for many rural families, where young people are instructed by their parents or elders in hunting as they are for preparation of food, skins and clothing. It is a seasonal activity used to supplement food supplies and, in the case of trapping, to obtain cash. Consistent success depends upon in-depth knowledge about wildlife habits and competence with a range of outdoor skills. Efficient transportation to good hunting and trapping areas is also an important requirement.

Major Sectors and Processes

Hunting requires locating and closely approaching a wild animal, and then dispatching it, under a combination of formal and informal rules (Ortega y Gasset 1985). Transportation to the hunting area is often a major expense, particularly for recreational hunters who may live in urban centres. Transportation is also a primary source of occupational risk. Automobile, light aircraft and boat accidents as well as mishaps with horses, all-terrain and snow-travel vehicles are all sources of risk. Other sources are weather, exposure and terrain difficulties. Becoming lost in rough country is always a hazard. Injury from wounded dangerous game like bears, elephants and cape buffalo is always possible for hunters seeking those species. In small cabins or tents, fire, carbon monoxide and propane gas all present potential hazards. Both hunters and trappers must contend with self-inflicted injury from knives and, in the case of bowhunters, broad-head arrow points. Firearms accidents are also a well known source of injury and mortality to hunters despite continuing efforts to address the problem.

Trappers are generally exposed to the same hazards as hunters. Trappers in circumpolar areas have more opportunity for frostbite and hypothermia difficulties. The potential for breaking through ice-covered lakes and rivers during the winter months is a serious problem. Some trappers travel long distances alone and must safely operate their traps, often under difficult conditions. Mishandling results in bruised or broken fingers, perhaps a broken arm. Bites from live-trapped animals are always a potential problem. Attacks by rabid foxes or problems with large animals such as bears or moose during the breeding season are unusual but not unknown. Skinning and fur handling expose trappers to knife injuries and, sometimes, wildlife diseases.

Hunting Techniques

Firearms

Firearms are basic equipment for most hunters. Modern rifles and shotguns are the most popular, but hunting with handguns and more primitive muzzle-loading firearms has also increased in some developed countries since the 1970s. All are essentially launching and aiming platforms for a single projectile (a *bullet*) or, in the case of shotguns, a cloud of small, short-range projectiles (called *shot*). Effective range depends on the type of firearm used and the skill of the hunter. It can vary from a few to several hundred metres under most hunting conditions. Rifle bullets can travel thousands of metres and still cause damage or injury.

Most hunting accidents involving firearms are either accidental discharges or vision-related accidents, where the victim is not identified by the shooter. Modern manufacturers of firearms used for hunting and trapping have, with few exceptions, succeeded in producing mechanically safe and reliable equipment at competitive prices. Much effort has been expended at refining mechanical safeties to prevent accidental discharges, but safe operation by the firearm user is still essential. Manufacturers, governments and private groups such as hunting clubs have all worked to promote firearms and hunter safety. Their emphasis has been on safe storage, use and handling of firearms.

The International Hunter Education Association (IHEA) defines a hunting accident as "any event which is attributed directly or indirectly to a firearm or bow, and causes injury or death to any person or persons as a result of a person's actions while hunting" (IHEA 1995). In 1995, 17 million people purchased hunting licenses in the United States (excluding Alaska). For 1995, the IHEA received reports of 107 deaths and 1,094 injuries from hunting accidents in the United States. The most common type of accident occurred when the victim was not identified by the shooter. The use of blaze- or hunter-orange clothing has been shown to reduce visibility-related accidents in states requiring its use. More extensive use of blaze-orange clothing is recommended by the IHEA. Forty states now require use of blaze orange, but in some of them, it is limited to use on public lands or only for big-game hunting. The IHEA reports that self-inflicted injuries are the second most common cause of hunting firearms accidents, accounting for 31% of the total number in 1995.

Governments encourage hunting and firearms safety in various ways. In some European countries, hunters must pass a written examination or demonstrate proficiency in hunting a particular species. The United States emphasizes hunter education, which is administered by each state. All states except Alaska require some form of mandatory hunter education card before allowing hunting in that state. A minimum of 10 hours of instruction is required. Course subjects include hunter responsibility, wildlife conservation, firearms, hunting ethics, specialty hunting, survival skills and first aid.

Other hunting techniques

In recent decades, refinement of the compound bow has made archery hunting available to millions of recreational hunters. Compound bows use a system of pulleys and cables to minimize the strength and training once needed to hunt with traditional bows. Bow hunters use razor-sharp broad-head arrows; cuts from broad heads and falling on unprotected arrowheads are two types of accident common to this hunting specialty. Effective bow hunting requires extensive wildlife knowledge and stalking skills. Bow hunters normally have to be within 30 metres of their prey in order to be able to shoot effectively.

Trapping Techniques

Most of the wild fur production in the world comes from two areas: North America and the former Soviet Union. Trappers normally operate a *line* or series of sets, each with one or more devices intended to restrain or kill the target species without damaging the pelt. Snares and traps (including box, leghold and body-gripping humane traps) are most commonly used. Traplines can vary from a few sets in a creekbed behind a residence to hundreds set out along several hundred miles of trail. The *Alaska Trappers Manual* (ATA 1991) is a recent description of trapping techniques currently in use in that region.

Pelt treatment techniques

Trappers normally skin their catches and sell the dried pelts to a fur buyer or directly to an auction house. The pelts will eventually be sold to a manufacturer who dresses or tans the skins. Afterwards they are prepared into garments. Fur prices vary considerably. The price paid for a pelt depends on size, desired colour, fur condition, the absence of defects and market conditions. Experienced trappers have to catch furbearers and prepare the pelts for sale in a manner that makes the entire process profitable enough to continue operating. For a thorough discussion of the wild fur industry see Novak et al. (1987).

Environmental and Public Health Issues

Technological advances since the Second World War have improved the lot of hunters and trappers in many ways. These improvements have alleviated, at least in the developed countries, the isolation, gruelling physical labour and occasional malnutrition that once had to be endured. Improved navigation and search and rescue methods have improved the safety levels of these occupations generally. Alaska Native walrus and whale hunters, for example, now almost always return home safely from the hunt.

In the 20th century, two major issues have seriously challenged these occupations. They are the continuing need to maintain healthy wildlife ecosystems and the ethical questions resulting from the way hunters and trappers interact with wild animals. Government-sponsored research and regulations are usually the front-line approach to addressing the very old problem of human exploitation of wildlife. The scientific discipline of wildlife management emerged in mid-century and has continued to evolve into the broader concept of conservation biology. The latter seeks to maintain ecosystem health and genetic diversity.

Early in the 20th century, habitat destruction and commercial exploitation in the United States had contributed to depletion of fish and game resources. Hunters, trappers and other outdoor advocates secured passage of legislation that created the US Federal Aid in Wildlife Restoration Act of 1937. This act imposes a 10 to 11% excise tax on the sale of rifles, pistols, shotguns, ammunition and archery equipment. The money is then used to augment revenue obtained from the sale of state hunting/trapping licenses, tags and stamps.

Since the late 1930s, US federal aid has directed millions of dollars into wildlife research, conservation, management and hunter education. One result of these efforts is that North American wildlife populations actively used by hunters and trappers now are generally healthy and capable of sustaining consumptive uses. The federal aid experience suggests that when wildlife has a constituency willing to pay research and management costs, the future for those species is relatively bright. Unfortunately there are many ecosystems and wildlife species throughout the world where this is not the case. As we are about to enter a new century, habitat alteration and species extinction are very real conservation issues.

The other continuing challenge is controversy about animal rights. Is hunting and trapping, especially for recreation or non-subsistence purposes, a socially acceptable activity in a 21st century world of growing human population and shrinking resources? This social debate has intensified in recent decades. One positive side of the dialogue is that those who participate in these activities have had to do a better job of articulating their positions and of maintaining high standards of hunting and trapping performance. Activities offending the sensibilities of the general public, such as the clubbing of baby harp seals off the coast of Newfoundland, have sometimes been eliminated—in this case at enormous social and economic cost to the Newfoundlanders who had for many generations participated in those activities. A recent ban threatened by European communities on importation of fur taken by steel leg-hold traps has intensified the search for practical and more humane methods of killing certain furbearers. This same proposed ban threatens a rural North American subsistence lifestyle that has existed for a long time. (For more details see Herscovici 1985.)

• DISEASES ASSOCIATED WITH HUNTING AND TRAPPING

Mary E. Brown

Hazards

The hazards associated with hunting and trapping are numerous—falls, drownings, frostbite, animal trap injuries, animal bites, reactions to insect bites and stings, wood-cutting wounds, sun glare and many others. However, it is usually the less experienced who suffer such mishaps. The most important factors contributing to the severity of these occupational hazards are isolation and distance. Hunters and trappers frequently work alone in rugged areas remote from any medical treatment centre, and their exact locations may often be unknown to anyone for weeks at a time. A wound, animal bite or other accident that would otherwise be a minor matter can have serious consequences under such circumstances.

Accidents

Since professional trappers work mainly in the winter season in northern climates, sun glare from snow can produce eye injuries, and cold temperatures can produce frostbite and a dangerous lowering of body temperature, known as *hypothermia*; symptoms of hypothermia include euphoria and lethargy, with fatal consequences if not recognized in time. Crossing frozen lakes and rivers requires extreme caution because breaking through a thin layer of ice can result in drowning or hypothermia in a matter of minutes. Prolonged exposure to even moderately cold weather without adequate clothing can lead to hypothermia. Other accidents include gunshot wounds, snowmobile mishaps, wounds from skinning and wood-chopping, the accidental tripping of traps, and bites or injuries from trapped animals, snakes or other animal encounters. In addition to risk of wounds becoming infected, there is also the possibility of contracting certain diseases from animals.

Diseases

Hunters and trappers are potentially exposed to a great variety of infectious agents that can cause illnesses. Among them are *zoonotic* diseases, transmitted from animals to people. Zoonotic diseases are caused by numerous types of bacteria, viruses, parasites and fungi. The risk of acquiring any zoonotic disease varies with location, season and living conditions. A person can become infected directly (e.g., from an animal bite or from contact with blood while skinning an animal) or indirectly (e.g., from an insect bite that transmits the disease from another animal to a human).

Rabies is one of the most serious diseases that can be contracted from wild animals, usually from a bite wound, because it is essentially 100% fatal without medical treatment. Rabies is endemic in many areas and can infect most warm-blooded animals, including foxes, dogs, cats, bats, raccoons, skunks, wolves, bears and beaver as well as larger animals such as caribou, moose, cattle and horses. The rabies virus affects the brain; therefore, any wild animal which appears to lose its fear of man or to show any other unusual behaviour should be considered hazardous. Because the rabies virus, as well as a number of other viruses and bacteria, is transmitted in saliva, all animal bites should be washed thoroughly with soap and water. Any hunter or trapper who is bitten by an animal suspected to be rabid should seek medical assistance immediately and should try to obtain the head of the animal for testing.

Tularaemia, also known as *deer fly fever* and *rabbit fever*, is a bacterial disease that can be transmitted indirectly (by ticks, deer flies and other biting flies) or directly (by bites of infected animals or by handling carcasses, furs and hides of infected animals). It can also infect water supplies and contaminate meat. Its symptoms, similar to those of undulant fever and plague, include fever, chills, fatigue and swollen lymph nodes. In areas in which the disease is suspected, water supplies should be disinfected. Wild game should be thoroughly cooked before eating. Arms and hands should be kept clean and disinfected. Rubber gloves should be worn if there are any cuts or abrasions. The area in which carcasses, hides and pelts are handled should be kept clean and disinfected.

Anthrax is another bacterial disease that may infect trappers and hunters, since it is endemic in both wild and domesticated animals in most parts of the world. A skin infection from contact with contaminated skins and hides is the most frequent form of anthrax; however, people are also infected by eating contaminated meat. Disease caused by inhalation is less common. Treatment should be sought at once.

Tuberculosis is an increasingly significant problem in many areas. Many species of animals can be a source of tuberculosis infection for hunters. Although most cases of human tuberculosis are due to exposure to coughs and sneezes from infected humans, many species of animals, including birds and cold-blooded animals, can be infected with the bacillum. Tuberculosis is also transmitted by consuming unpasteurized dairy products. It is also possible to become infected by inhaling airborne respiratory droplets or by eating the meat of infected animals. People who are immune suppressed (e.g., due to medication or human immunodeficiency virus infection) are at particular risk for the more common agents of tuberculosis, as well as those found in soil and water.

Hunters and trappers may also suffer from several fungal diseases carried by animals as well as soil fungi. *Trichophyton verrucosum* and *T. mentagrophytes* are the main ringworm agents affecting man. Also, dogs serve as a reservoir for *Microsporum canis*, the principal cause of animal ringworm in man. Hunters and trappers may be exposed to fungi that reside in soil and decaying vegetation, especially soils contaminated with bird or bat droppings; these fungi, which are not zoonotic diseases, inhabit specific habitats. *Coccidioides immitis* is common only in arid and semi-arid areas, whereas *Blastomyces dermatitidis* prefers moist soils along waterways and undisturbed areas. *Cryptococcus neoformans* and *Histoplasma capsulatum* are more common and live in soils enriched with bird and bat droppings. When inhaled, these fungi can cause pneumonia-like symptoms as well as serious systemic diseases in both people and animals.

Tetanus is another serious disease that infects both humans and animals. The tetanus bacteria are also very common in soils and other parts of the environment, and are normal inhabitants of many animals' digestive tracts. Wounds, particularly deep puncture wounds, that are contaminated with dirt are the most likely to become infected. Prevention includes proper wound care and routine vaccination.

Wood ticks, mosquitoes, fleas and other biting insects often transmit infections from animals to man. *Bubonic plague* is an example of a bacterial disease transmitted by flea bites. A flea becomes infected when it takes a blood meal from an infected animal—usually a rodent, rabbit or hare, but also various carnivores. The flea then transmits the infection to the next animal it feeds on, including man. People can also become infected by handling tissues of infected animals, or by inhaling

Table 69.1 • Examples of diseases potentially significant to hunters and trappers.

Agent	Disease	Reservoir	Mode of transmission	Occurrence
Bacterial diseases				
Bacillus anthracis	Anthrax	Animals, hides, hair, bone, soil	Direct and indirect contact, insect bites, inhalation, ingestion	Americas, Europe, Asia, Africa
Borellia spp.	Lyme disease, relapsing fever	Rodents, small mammals, deer, ticks	Tick and louse bites	Worldwide except Australia
Brucella spp.	Brucellosis, undulant fever	Animals	Contact, ingestion, inhalation	Worldwide
Campylobacter spp.	Enteritis	Animals	Ingestion	Worldwide
Coxiella burnetii	Q fever	Animals	Inhalation, contact	Worldwide
Clostridium tetani	Tetanus	Soil	Contact	Worldwide
Ehrlichia spp.	Ehrlichiosis	Unknown	Tick bite	North America, Africa, Asia
Francisella tularensis	Tularemia	Animals	Insect bites, contact, ingestion, inhalation	Worldwide except Australia
Leptospira spp.	Leptospirosis	Animals	Contact, ingestion, inhalation	Worldwide
Listeria monocytogenes	Listeriosis	Soil, animals, humans	Ingestion	USA
Mycobacterium spp.	Tuberculosis	Humans, mammals, birds, cold-blooded animals, environment	Inhalation, ingestion, wound contamination	Worldwide
Rickettsia spp.	Tick-borne rickettsioses (spotted fever group)	Ticks, rodents	Tick and mite bites	Worldwide
Salmonella spp.	Salmonellosis	Mammals, birds, cold-blooded animals	Ingestion	Worldwide
Vibrio cholera	Cholera	Humans	Ingestion	Worldwide
Yersinia pestis	Plague, bubonic plague	Rodents, hares, rabbits, humans, carnivores	Flea bites, inhalation, contact	Worldwide
Viral diseases				
Arboviruses (over 100 types)	Fevers, rash, haemorrhagic fevers, encephalitis (includes Dengue, Yellow fever, viral encephalitides, Rift Valley fever, tick fevers)	Humans, animals, insects	Insect bites: mosquitoes, ticks, midges, sandflies, others	Worldwide
Ebola/Marburg viruses	Haemorrhagic fevers	Unknown, monkeys	Unknown, body-fluid contact	Africa, exposure to monkeys
Hantaviruses	Haemorrhagic fever, renal and pulmonary syndromes	Rodents	Inhalation	Asia, former Soviet Union, Americas
Lassa virus	Lassa fever	Rodents	Inhalation, body-fluid contact	West Africa
Rabies virus	Rabies	Mammals	Virus in saliva, usually a bite wound or scratch, occasionally inhalation, organ transplants	Worldwide except some island countries
Fungal diseases				
Blastomyces dermatitidis	Blastomycosis	Soil	Inhalation	Africa, India, Israel, North America, Saudi Arabia, South Africa
Coccidioides immitis	Coccidioidomycosis, valley fever, desert fever	Soil	Inhalation	Argentina, Paraguay, Colombia, Venezuela, Mexico, Central America, USA
Cryptococcus neoformans	Cryptococcosis	Soil, bird and bat droppings	Inhalation	Worldwide
Histoplasma capsulatum	Histoplasmosis	Soil, bird and bat droppings	Inhalation	Americas, Africa, eastern Asia, Australia
Microsporum spp., *Trichophyton* spp.	Ringworm	Humans, animals, soil	Direct or indirect contact	Worldwide

Continues on next page.

69. HUNTING

Table 69.1 • Examples of diseases potentially significant to hunters and trappers.
Continued

Agent	Disease	Reservoir	Mode of transmission	Occurrence
		Parasitic diseases		
Babesia spp.	Babesiosis	Rodents, cattle	Tick bites	Europe, Mexico, Russia, Yugoslavia, USA
Baylisascaris spp.	Baylisascaris larva migrans	Racoons, badgers, skunks, fishers, martens, bears	Ingestion	North America
Cryptosporidium parvum	Cryptosporidiosis	Humans, cattle, domestic animals	Ingestion	Worldwide
Diphyllobothrium latum	Tapeworm infection	Humans, dogs, bears, fish-eating mammals	Ingestion	Lake regions
Echinococcus spp.	Echinococcosis	Animals	Ingestion	Worldwide
Giardia spp.	Giardiasis	Humans, animals	Ingestion	Worldwide
Leishmania spp.	Leishmaniasis	Humans, animals	Sandfly bite	Tropical and sub-tropical areas
Trichinella spiralis	Trichinellosis	Animals	Ingestion	Worldwide
Trypanosoma spp.	Trypanosomiasis	Humans, animals	Insect bites	Africa, Americas

airborne droplets from humans or animals, usually cats, with pneumonic form of plague. The initial symptoms of bubonic plague are non-specific and include fever, chills, nausea and prostration. Later, the lymph nodes may become swollen and inflamed (the *buboes* for which the disease is named).

A more common disease transmitted by the bite of an insect is *Lyme disease*. Lyme disease is one of many transmitted by ticks. The first symptom is often a bull's-eye rash, a red circle with a pale centre at the site of the bite. The rash disappears; however, without treatment, the disease can progress to arthritis and more serious complications.

Hantaviruses infect rodents worldwide, and human infections have been described for decades, most typically affecting the kidneys. In 1993, hantavirus pulmonary syndrome was newly recognized in the United States. This virus caused a rapidly fatal respiratory failure. Transmission of these viruses is likely to be via aerosolized rodent urine and faeces. It is thought that infected people were exposed to mice that contaminated cabins and houses.

In addition, hunters and trappers may be exposed to a wide variety of other viral, bacterial, fungal and parasitic infections that are at times found in wild animals (table 69.1). Standard reference works may be consulted for details.

Most zoonotic diseases and other infectious agents can be avoided by using common sense and some general precautions. Water should be boiled or chemically treated. All foods should be adequately cooked, especially those of animal origin. Meats from all wild animals should be cooked to 71 °C (160 °F). Foods eaten raw should be thoroughly washed. Insect bites and stings should be avoided by tucking trousers into boots; wearing long-sleeved shirts; using repellants and mosquito netting as necessary. Ticks should be removed as soon as possible. Direct contact with animal tissues and bodily fluids should be avoided. Wearing gloves is recommended, particularly if one's hands are cracked or abraded. Hands should be washed with soap and water after animal handling and always prior to eating. Bites and wounds should be washed with soap and water as soon as possible, with follow-up medical treatment especially if exposure to a rabies-infected animal is suspected. Hunters and trappers should be vaccinated against diseases common to their location. Having emergency first aid supplies on hand and a basic knowledge of first aid procedures may make the difference between a major and a minor incident.

References

Alaska Trappers Association (ATA). 1991. *Alaska Trappers Manual*. Fairbanks, AK: ATA.

Herscovici, A. 1985. *Second Nature: The Animal Rights controversy*. Toronto: CBC Enterprises.

Hinnis, HA. 1973. *The Fur Trade in Canada: An Introduction to Economic History*. Toronto: University of Toronto Press.

International Hunter Education Association (IHEA). 1995. *1995 Hunting Accident Report*. Wellington, CO: IHEA.

Novak, M, JA Baker, ME Obbard, and B Malloch (eds.). 1987. *Wild Furbearer Management and Conservation in North America*. Toronto: Ontario Trappers Association.

Ortega y Gasset, J. 1985. *Meditations on Hunting*. New York: Scribner's.

US Department of the Interior, Fish and Wildlife Service, and US Department of Commerce, Bureau of the Census. 1993. *1991 National Survey of Fishing, Hunting and Wildlife-associated Recreation*. Washington DC: US Government Printing Office.

Other relevant readings

Acha, PN and B Szyfres. 1987. *Zoonoses and Communicable Diseases Common to Man and Animals*, 2nd ed. Scientific publication No. 503. Washington, DC: Pan-American Health Organization.

American Public Health Association (APHA). 1995. *Control of Communicable Diseases Manual*, 16th ed., edited by AS Beneson. Washington, DC: APHA.

American Veterinary Medical Association (AVMA). 1996. *Zoonoses Updates from the Journal of the American Veterinary Medical Association*. Schaumberg, IL: AVMA.

Braid, P. 1977. *Guide du trappeur* (Trapper's guide). Brussels: Les Editions de l'Homme. (In French.)

Centers for Disease Control and Prevention (CDC). 1995. *Health Information for International Travel*. Atlanta, GA: CDC.

Docherty, D, J Eckerson, ML Collis, and J Hayward. 1977. Changes in fitness level of humans attributable to hunting activities. *Journal of Sports Medicine and Physical Fitness* 17(3):315-320.

Takeda, J. 1972. An ecological study of bear hunting activities of the Matagi: Japanese traditional hunters. *Journal of Human Ergology* 2:167-187.

Winkler, WG (ed.). 1985. *Rabies Concepts for Medical Professionals*. Miami, FL: Merieux Institute, Inc.

Chapter Editor
Melvin L. Myers

Contents

70. LIVESTOCK REARING

LIVESTOCK REARING: ITS EXTENT AND HEALTH EFFECTS

Melvin L. Myers

Overview

Humans depend upon animals for food and related by-products, work and a variety of other uses (see table 70.1). To meet these demands, they have domesticated or held in captivity species of mammals, birds, reptiles, fish and arthropods. These animals have become known as *livestock*, and rearing them has implications for occupational safety and health. This general profile of the industry includes its evolution and structure, the economic importance of different commodities of livestock, and regional characteristics of the industry and workforce. The articles in this chapter are organized by occupational processes, livestock sectors and consequences of livestock rearing.

Evolution and structure of the industry

Livestock evolved over the past 12,000 years through selection by human communities and adaptation to new environments. Historians believe that goat and sheep were the first species of animals domesticated for human use. Then, about 9,000 years ago, humans domesticated the pig. The cow was the last major food animal that humans domesticated, about 8,000 years ago in Turkey or Macedonia. It was probably only after cattle were domesticated that milk was discovered as a useful foodstuff. Goat, sheep, reindeer and camel milk were also used. People of the Indus valley domesticated the Indian jungle fowl primarily for its egg production, which became the world's chicken, with its source of eggs and meat. People of Mexico had domesticated the turkey (Tannahill 1973).

Humans used several other mammalian and avian species for food, as well as amphibian and fish species and various arthropods. Insects have always provided an important source of protein, and today they are part of the human diet principally in the world's non-western cultures (DeFoliart 1992). Honey from the honey bee was an early food; smoking bees from their nest to collect honey was known in Egypt as early as 5,000 years ago. Fishing is also an ancient occupation used to produce food, but because fishers are depleting wild fisheries, aquaculture has been the fastest growing contributor to fish production since the early 1980s, contributing about 14% to the total current production of fish (Platt 1995).

Humans also domesticated many mammals for use for draught, including the horse, donkey, elephant, dog, buffalo, camel and reindeer. The first animal used for draught, perhaps with the exception of the dog, was likely the goat, which could defoliate scrub for land cultivation through its browsing. Historians believe that Asians domesticated the Asian wolf, which was to become the dog, 13,000 years ago. The dog proved to be useful to the hunter for its speed, hearing and sense of smell, and the sheepdog aided in the early domestication of sheep (Tannahill 1973). The people of the steppe lands of Eurasia domesticated the horse about 4,000 years ago. Its use for work (traction) was stimulated by the invention of the horseshoe, collar harness and feeding of oats. Although draught is still important in much of the world, farmers displace draught animals with machines as farming and transportation becomes more mechanized. Some mammals, such as the cat, are used to control rodents (Caras 1996).

The structure of the current livestock industry can be defined by commodities, the animal products that enter the mar-

Table 70.1 • Livestock uses.

Commodity	Food	By-products and other uses
Dairy	Fluid and dried milk, butter, cheese and curd, casein, evaporated milk, cream, yoghurt and other fermented milk, ice cream, whey	Male calves and old cows sold into the cattle commodity market; milk as an industrial feedstock of carbohydrates (lactose as a diluent for drugs), proteins (used as a surfactant to stabilize food emulsions) and fats (lipids have potential uses as emulsifiers, surfactants and gels), offal
Cattle, buffalo, sheep	Meat (beef, mutton), edible tallow	Hides and skins (leather, collagens for sausage casings, cosmetics, wound dressing, human tissue repair), offal, work (traction), wool, hair, dung (as fuel and fertilizer), bone meal, religious objects, pet food, tallow and grease (fatty acids, varnish, rubber goods, soaps, lamp oil, plastics, lubricants) fat, blood meal
Poultry	Meat, eggs, duck eggs (in India)	Feathers and down, manure (as fertilizer), leather, fat, offal, flightless bird oil (carrier for dermal path pharmaceuticals), weed control (geese in mint fields)
Pig	Meat	Hides and skins, hair, lard, manure, offal
Fish (aquaculture)	Meat	Fishmeal, oil, shell, aquarium pets
Horse, other equines	Meat, blood, milk	Recreation (riding, racing), work (riding, traction), glue, dog feed, hair
Micro-livestock (rabbit, guinea pig), dog, cat	Meat	Pets, furs and skins, guard dogs, seeing-eye dogs, hunting dogs, experimentation, sheep herding (by the dog), rodent control (by the cat)
Bulls		Recreation (bull-fighting, rodeo riding), semen
Insects and other invertebrates (e.g., vermiculture, apiculture)	Honey, 500 species (grubs, grasshoppers, ants, crickets, termites, locusts, beetle larvae, wasps and bees, moth caterpillars) are a regular diet among many non-western societies	Beeswax, silk, predatory insects (>5,000 species are possible and 400 are known as controls for crop pests; the carnivorous "tox" mosquito (*Toxorhynchites spp.*) larvae feeds on the dengue fever vector, vermicompositing, animal fodder, pollination, medicine (honeybee venom to treat arthritis), scale insect products (shellac, red food dye, cochineal)

Sources: DeFoliart 1992; Gillespie 1997; FAO 1995; O'Toole 1995; Tannahil 1973; USDA 1996a, 1996b.

Table 70.2 • International livestock production (1,000 tonnes).

Commodity	1991	1992	1993	1994	1995	1996
Beef and veal carcasses	46,344	45,396	44,361	45,572	46,772	47,404
Pork carcasses	63,114	64,738	66,567	70,115	74,704	76,836
Lamb, mutton, goat carcasses	6,385	6,245	6,238	6,281	6,490	6,956
Bovine hides and skins	4,076	3,983	3,892	3,751	3,778	3,811
Tallow and grease	6,538	6,677	7,511	7,572	7,723	7,995
Poultry meat	35,639	37,527	39,710	43,207	44,450	47,149
Cow's milk	385,197	379,379	379,732	382,051	382,747	385,110
Shrimps	815	884	N/A	N/A	N/A	N/A
Molluscs	3,075	3,500	N/A	N/A	N/A	N/A
Salmonoids	615	628	N/A	N/A	N/A	N/A
Freshwater fish	7,271	7,981	N/A	N/A	N/A	N/A
Egg consumption (million pieces)	529,080	541,369	567,469	617,591	616,998	622,655

Sources: FAO 1995; USDA 1996a, 1996b.

ket. Table 70.2 shows a number of these commodities and the worldwide production or consumption of these products.

Economic importance

The world's growing population and increased per capita consumption both increased the global demand for meat and fish, the results of which are shown in figure 70.1. Global meat production nearly trebled between 1960 and 1994. Over this period, per capita consumption increased from 21 to 33 kilograms per annum. Because of the limitations of available rangeland, beef production levelled off in 1990. As a result, animals that are more efficient in converting feed grain into meat, such as pigs and chickens, have gained a competitive advantage. Both pork and poultry have been increasing in dramatic contrast to beef production. Pork overtook beef in worldwide production in the late 1970s. Poultry may soon exceed beef production. Mutton production remains low and stagnant (USDA 1996a). Milk cows worldwide have been slowly decreasing while milk production has been increasing because of increasing production per cow (USDA 1996b).

Aquaculture production increased at an annual rate of 9.1% from 1984 to 1992. Aquaculture animal production increased from 14 million tonnes worldwide in 1991 to 16 million tonnes in 1992, with Asia providing 84% of world production (Platt 1995). Insects are rich in vitamins, minerals and energy, and provide between 5% and 10% of the animal protein for many people. They also become a vital source of protein during times of famine (DeFoliart 1992).

Regional Characteristics of the Industry and Workforce

Separating the workforce engaged in livestock rearing from other agricultural activities is difficult. Pastoral activities, such as those in much of Africa, and heavy commodity-based operations, such as those in the United States, have differentiated more between livestock and crop raising. However, many agro-pastoral and agronomic enterprises integrate the two. In much of the world, draught animals are still used extensively in crop production. Moreover, livestock and poultry depend upon feed and forage generated from crop operations, and these operations are commonly integrated. The principal aquaculture species in the world is the plant-eating carp. Insect production is also tied directly to crop production. The silkworm feeds exclusively on mulberry leaves; honeybees depend upon flower nectar; plants depend upon them for pollination work; and humans harvest edible grubs from various crops. The 1994 world population totalled 5,623,500,000, and 2,735,021,000 people (49% of the population) were engaged in agriculture (see figure 70.2). The largest contribution to this workforce is in Asia, where 85% of the agricultural population rear draught animals. Regional characteristics related to livestock rearing follow.

Figure 70.1 • World production of meat and fish.

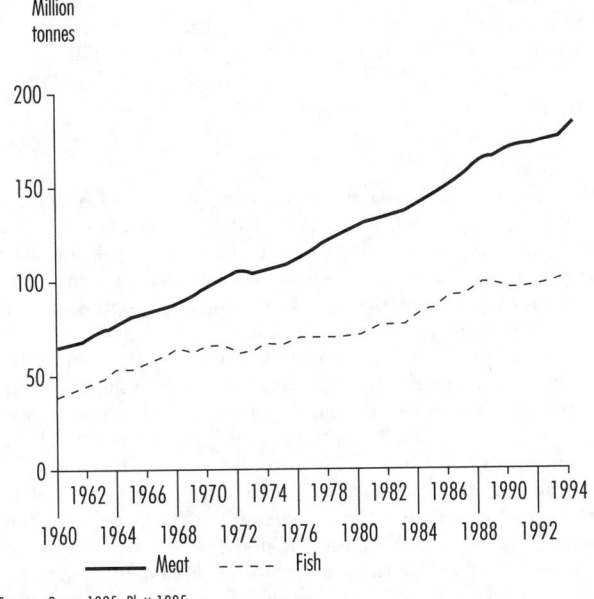

Million tonnes

Sources: Brown 1995; Platt 1995.

Meat ——— Fish - - - -

70. LIVESTOCK REARING

Figure 70.2 • Human population engaged in agriculture by world region, 1994.

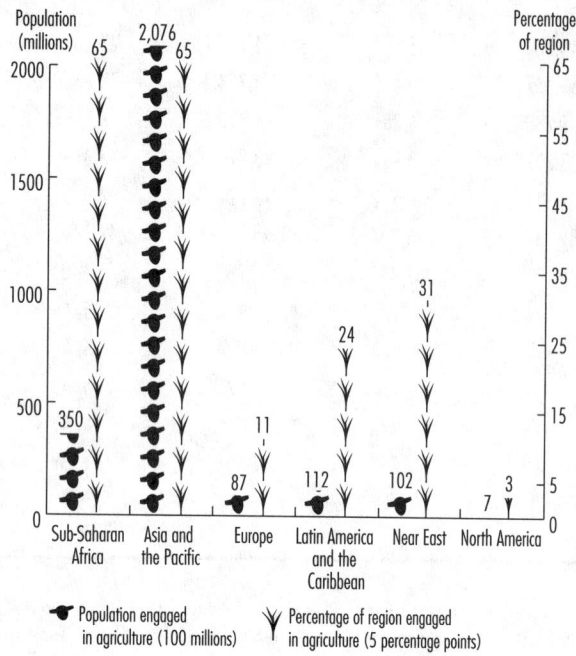

Source: Scherf 1995.

people's diet in this region. Asia contributes 84% of the world's aquaculture production. At 6,856,000 tonnes, China alone produces nearly half of the world production,. Demand for fish is expected to increase rapidly, and aquaculture is expected to meet this demand.

Europe
In this region of 802 million people, 10.8% were engaged in agriculture in 1994, which has decreased significantly from 16.8% in 1975. Increased urbanization and mechanization have led to this decrease. Much of this arable land is in the moist, cool northern climates and is conducive to growing pastures for livestock. As a result, much of the livestock raising is located in the northern part of this region. Europe contributed 8.5% to the world's production of aquaculture in 1992. Aquaculture has concentrated on relatively high-value species of finfish (288,500 tonnes) and shellfish (685,500 tonnes).

Latin America and the Caribbean
The Latin American and Caribbean region differs from other regions in many ways. Large tracts of land remain to be exploited, the region has large populations of domestic animals and much of the agriculture is operated as large operations. Livestock represents about one-third of the agricultural production, which makes up a significant part of the gross domestic product. Meat from beef cattle accounts for the largest share and makes up 20% of the world's production. Most livestock species have been imported. Among those indigenous species that have been domesticated are guinea pigs, dogs, llamas, alpacas, Muscovy ducks, turkeys and black chickens. This region contributed only 2.3% to world aquaculture production in 1992.

Near East
Currently, 31% of the population of the Near East is engaged in agriculture. Because of the shortage of rainfall in this region, the only agricultural use for 62% of this land area is animal grazing. Most of the major livestock species were domesticated in this region (goats, sheep, pigs and cattle) at the confluence of the Tigris and Euphrates rivers. Later, in North Africa, water buffaloes, dromedary camels and asses were domesticated. Some livestock raising systems that existed in ancient times still exist today. These are subsistence systems in Arab tribal society, in which herds and flocks are moved seasonally over great distances in search of feed and water. Intensive farming systems are used in the more developed countries.

North America
Although agriculture is a major economic activity in Canada and the United States, the proportion of the population engaged in agriculture is less than 2.5%. Since the 1950s, agriculture has become more intensive, leading to fewer but larger farms. Livestock and livestock products make up a major proportion of the population's diet, contributing 40% to the total food energy. The livestock industry in this region has been very dynamic. Introduced animals have been bred with indigenous animals to form new breeds. Consumer demand for leaner meats and eggs with less cholesterol is having an impact on breeding policy. Horses were used extensively at the turn of the nineteenth century, but they have declined in numbers because of mechanization. They are currently used in the race horse industry or for recreation. The United States has imported about 700 insect species to control more than 50 pests. Aquaculture in this region is growing, and accounted for 3.7% of the world's aquaculture production in 1992 (FAO 1995; Scherf 1995).

Sub-Saharan Africa
Animal husbandry has been practised in sub-Saharan Africa for more than 5,000 years. Nomadic husbandry of the early livestock has evolved species that tolerate poor nutrition, infectious diseases and long migrations. About 65% of this region, much of it around desert areas, is suitable only for producing livestock. In 1994, 65% of the approximately 539 million people in sub-Saharan Africa depended upon agricultural income, down from 76% in 1975. Although its importance has grown since the mid-1980s, aquaculture has contributed little to the food supply for this region. Aquaculture in this region is based upon pond farming of tilapias, and export enterprises have attempted to culture marine shrimps. An export aquaculture industry in this region is expected to grow because Asian demand for fish is expected to increase, which will be fuelled by Asian investment and technology drawn to the region by a favourable climate and by African labour.

Asia and the Pacific
In Asia and the Pacific region, nearly 76% of the world's agricultural population exists on 30% of the world's arable land. About 85% of the farmers use cattle (bullocks) and buffaloes to cultivate and thresh crops.

Livestock rearing operations are mainly small-scale units in this region, but large commercial farms are establishing operations near urban centres. In rural areas, millions of people depend on livestock for meat, milk, eggs, hides and skins, draught power and wool. China exceeds the rest of the world with 400 million pigs; the remainder of the world has a total of 340 million pigs. India accounts for over one-fourth of the number of cattle and buffaloes worldwide, but because of religious policies that restrict cattle slaughter, India contributes less than 1% to the world's beef supply. Milk production is a part of traditional agriculture in many countries of this region. Fish is a frequent ingredient in most

Environmental and Public Health Issues

Occupational hazards of livestock rearing may lead to injuries, asthma or zoonotic infections. In addition, livestock rearing poses several environmental and public health issues. One issue is the effect of animal waste upon the environment. Other issues include the loss of biological diversity, risks associated with animal and product importation and food safety.

Water and air pollution

Animal wastes pose potential environmental consequences of water and air pollution. Based upon US annual discharge factors shown in table 70.3, major livestock breeds discharged a total of 14.3 billion tonnes of faeces and urine worldwide in 1994. Of this total, cattle (milk and beef) discharged 87%; pigs, 9%; and chickens and turkeys, 3% (Meadows 1995). Because of their high annual discharge factor of 9.76 tonnes of faeces and urine per animal, cattle contributed the most waste among these livestock types for all six United Nations Food and Agricultural Organization (FAO) regions of the world, ranging from 82% in both Europe and Asia to 96% in sub-Saharan Africa.

In the United States, farmers who specialize in livestock rearing do not engage in crop farming, as had been the historical practice. As a result, livestock waste is no longer systematically applied to crop land as a fertilizer. Another problem with modern livestock raising is the high concentration of animals into small areas such as confinement buildings or feedlots. Large operations may confine 50,000 to 100,000 cattle, 10,000 pigs or 400,000 chickens to an area. In addition, these operations tend to cluster near the processing plants to shorten the transportation distance of the animals to the plants.

Several environmental problems result from concentrated operations. These problems include lagoon spills, chronic seepage and runoff and airborne health effects. Nitrate peculation into the groundwater and runoff from fields and feedlots are major contributors to water contamination. A greater use of feedlots leads to concentration of animal manure and a greater risk for contamination of groundwater. Waste from cattle and pig operations is typically collected in lagoons, which are large, shallow pits dug into the ground. Lagoon design depends upon the settling of solids to the bottom, where they anaerobically digest, and the excess liquids are controlled by spraying them onto nearby fields before they overflow (Meadows 1995).

Biodegrading livestock waste also emits odorous gases that contain as many as 60 compounds. These compounds include ammonia and amines, sulphides, volatile fatty acids, alcohols, aldehydes, mercaptans, esters and carbonyls (Sweeten 1995). When humans sense odours from concentrated livestock operations, they can experience nausea, headaches, breathing problems, sleep interruption, appetite loss and irritation of the eyes, ears and throat.

Less understood are the adverse effects of livestock waste upon global warming and atmospheric deposition. Its contribution to global warming is through the generation of the greenhouse gases, carbon dioxide and methane. Livestock manure may contribute to nitrogen depositions because of ammonia release from waste lagoons into the atmosphere. Atmospheric nitrogen re-enters the hydrologic cycle through rain and flows into streams, rivers, lakes and coastal waters. Nitrogen in water contributes to increased algae blooms that reduce the oxygen available to fish.

Two modifications in livestock production offer solutions to some of the problems of pollution. These are less animal confinement and improved waste treatment systems.

Animal diversity

The potential for rapid loss of genes, species and habitats threatens the adaptability and traits of a variety of animals that are or could be useful. International efforts have stressed the need to preserve biological diversity at three levels: genetic, species and habitat. An example of declining genetic diversity is the limited number of sires used to breed artificially females of many livestock species (Scherf 1995).

With the decline of many livestock breeds, and thus the reduction of species diversity, dominant breeds have been increasing, with an emphasis on uniformity in higher production breeds. The problem of a lack of dairy cattle-breed diversity is particularly acute; with the exception of the high-producing Holstein, dairy populations are declining. Aquaculture has not reduced pressure on wild fish populations. For example, the use of fine nets for biomass fishing for shrimp food results in the collection of juveniles of valuable wild species, which adds to their depletion. Some species, such as groupers, milkfish and eels, cannot be bred in captivity, so their juveniles are caught in the wild and raised on fish farms, further reducing the stock of wild populations.

An example of a loss of habitat diversity is the impact of feed for fish farms on wild populations. Fish feed used in coastal areas affects wild populations of shrimp and fish by destroying their natural habitat such as mangroves. In addition, fish faeces and feed can accumulate on the bottom and kill the benthic communities that filter the water (Safina 1995).

Animal species that survive in abundance are those used as a means to human ends, but a social dilemma emerges from an animal rights movement that espouses that animals, especially warm-blooded animals, are not to be used as a means to human ends. Preceding the animal rights movement, an animal welfare movement started before the mid-1970s. Animal welfare proponents advocate the humane treatment of animals that are used for research, food, clothing, sport or companionship. Since the mid-1970s, the animal rights advocates assert that sentient animals have a right not to be used for research. It appears highly unlikely that the human use of animals will be abolished. It is also likely that animal welfare will continue as a popular movement (NIH 1988).

Animal and animal product importation

The history of livestock rearing is closely linked to the history of livestock importation into new areas of the world. Diseases spread with the spread of imported livestock and their products. Animals may carry disease that can infect other animals or humans, and countries have established quarantine services to control the spread of these zoonotic diseases. Among these diseases are scrapie, brucellosis, Q-fever and anthrax. Livestock and food inspection and quarantines have emerged as methods to control disease importation (MacDiarmid 1993).

Public concern about the potential infection of humans with the rare Creutzfeldt-Jakob disease (CJD) emerged among beef-im-

Table 70.3 • Annual US livestock faeces and urine production.

Livestock type	Population	Waste (tonnes)	Tonnes per animal
Cattle (milk and beef)	46,500,000	450,000,000	9.76
Pig	60,000,000	91,000,000	1.51
Chicken and turkey	7,500,000,000	270,000,000	0.04

Source: Meadows 1995.

porting nations in 1996. Eating beef infected with bovine spongiform encephalopathy (BSE), popularly known as mad cow disease, is suspected of leading to CJD infection. Although unproven, public perceptions include the proposition that the disease may have entered cattle from feed containing bone meal and offal from sheep afflicted with the similar disease, scrapie. All three diseases, in humans, cattle and sheep, exhibit common symptoms of sponge-like brain lesions. The diseases are fatal, their causes are unknown, and there are no tests to detect them. Britons launched a pre-emptive slaughter of one-third of their cattle population in 1996 to control BSE and restore consumer confidence in the safety of their beef exports (Aldhous 1996).

The importation of African bees into Brazil has also emerged into a public health issue. In the United States, subspecies of European bees produce honey and beeswax and pollinate crops. They rarely swarm aggressively, which aids safe beekeeping. The African subspecies has migrated from Brazil into Central America, Mexico and the Southeastern United States. This bee is aggressive and will swarm in defence of its colony. It has interbred with the European subspecies, which results in an Africanized bee that is more aggressive. The public health threat is multiple stings when the Africanized bee swarms and severe toxic reactions in humans.

Two controls currently exist for the Africanized bee. One is that they are not hardy in northern climates and may be restricted to warmer temperate climates like the Southern United States. The other control is routinely to replace the queen bee in hives with queen bees of the European subspecies, although this does not control wild colonies (Schumacher and Egen 1995).

Food safety

Many human food-borne illnesses result from pathogenic bacteria of animal origin. Examples include listeria and salmonellae found in dairy products and salmonellae and campylobacter found in meat and poultry. The Centers for Disease Control and Prevention estimates that 53% of all food-borne illness outbreaks in the United States were caused by bacterial contamination of animal products. They estimate that 33 million food-borne illnesses occur each year, from which 9,000 deaths result.

The subtherapeutic feeding of antibiotics and antibiotic treatment of diseased animals are current animal health practices. The potential diminished effectiveness of antibiotics for disease therapy is a rising concern because of the frequent development of antibiotic resistance of zoonotic pathogens. Many antibiotics added to animal feed are also used in human medicine, and antibiotic-resistant bacteria could develop and cause infections in animals and humans.

Drug residues in food that result from medication of livestock also present risks. Residues of antibiotics used in livestock or added to feed have been found in food-producing animals including dairy cows. Among these drugs are chloramphenicol and sulphamethazine. Alternatives to the prophylactic feeding use of antibiotics to maintain animal health include the modification of production systems. These modifications include reduced animal confinement, improved ventilation and improved waste treatment systems.

Diet has been associated with chronic diseases. Evidence of an association between fat consumption and heart disease has stimulated efforts to produce animal products with less fat content. These efforts include animal breeding, feeding intact rather than castrated males and genetic engineering. Hormones are also seen as a method for decreasing fat content in meat. Porcine growth hormones increase growth rate, feed efficiency and the ratio of muscle to fat. The growing popularity of low-fat, low-cholesterol species such as ostriches is another solution (NRC 1989).

HEALTH PROBLEMS AND DISEASE PATTERNS

Kendall Thu, Craig Zwerling and Kelley Donham

The domestication of animals occurred independently in a number of areas of the Old and New World over 10,000 years ago. Until domestication, hunting and gathering was the predominant subsistence pattern. The transformation to human control over animal and plant production and reproduction processes resulted in revolutionary changes in the structure of human societies and their relationships to the environment. The change to agriculture marked an increase in labour intensity and work time spent in food procurement-related activities. Small nuclear families, adapted to nomadic hunting and gathering groups, were transformed into large, extended, sedentary social units suited to labour-intensive domesticated food production.

The domestication of animals increased human susceptibility to animal-related injuries and diseases. Larger non-nomadic populations quartered in close proximity to animals provided greater opportunity for transmission of disease between animals and humans. The development of larger herds of more intensely handled livestock also increased the likelihood of injuries. Throughout the world, differing forms of animal agriculture are associated with varying risks for injury and disease. For example, the 50 million inhabitants who practice swidden (cut and burn) agriculture in equatorial regions face different problems from the 35 million pastoral nomads across Scandinavia and through central Asia or the 48 million food producers who practise an industrialized form of agriculture.

In this article, we provide an overview of selected injury patterns, infectious diseases, respiratory diseases and skin diseases associated with livestock production. The treatment is topically and geographically uneven because most research has been conducted in industrialized countries, where intensive forms of livestock production are common.

Overview

Types of human health problems and disease patterns associated with livestock production can be grouped according to the type of contact between animals and people (see table 70.4). Contact can occur via direct physical interaction, or contact with an organic or inorganic agent. Health problems associated with all types of livestock production can be grouped into each of these areas.

Direct human contact with livestock ranges from the brute force of large animals such as the Chinese buffalo to the undetected skin contact by microscopic hairs of the Japanese oriental tussock moth. A corresponding range of health problems can result, from the temporary irritant to the debilitating physical blow. Notable problems include traumatic injuries from handling large livestock, venom hypersensitivity or toxicosis from venomous arthropod bites and stings, and contact and allergic contact skin dermatitis.

A number of organic agents utilize various pathways from livestock to humans, resulting in a range of health problems. Among the most globally important are zoonotic diseases. Over 150 zoonotic diseases have been identified worldwide, with approximately 40 significant for human health (Donham 1985). The importance of zoonotic diseases depends on regional factors such as agricultural practices, environment and a region's social and economic status. The health consequences of zoonotic diseases range from the relatively benign flu-like symptoms of brucellosis to debilitating tuberculosis or potentially lethal strains of *Escherichia coli* or rabies.

Table 70.4 • Types of human health problems associated with livestock production.

Health problems from direct physical contact

Allergic contact dermatitis
Allergic rhinitis
Bites, kicks, crushing
Envenomation and possible hypersensitivity
Asthma
Scratches
Traumatic injury

Health problems from organic agents

Agrochemical poisoning
Antibiotic resistance
Chronic bronchitis
Contact dermatitis
Allergies from drug residue food exposures
Food-borne illnesses
"Farmer's lung"
Hypersensitivity pneumonitis
Mucous membrane irritation
Occupational asthma
Organic dust toxic syndrome (ODTS)
Allergies from pharmaceutical exposures
Zoonotic diseases

Health problems from physical agents

Hearing loss
Machinery-related trauma
Methane emission and greenhouse effect
Musculoskeletal disorders
Stress

Other organic agents include those associated with respiratory disease. Intensive livestock production systems in confined buildings create enclosed environments where dust, including microbes and their by-products, becomes concentrated and aerosolized along with gases that are in turned breathed by people. Approximately 33% of swine confinement workers in the United States suffer from organic dust toxic syndrome (ODTS) (Thorne et al. 1996). Comparable problems exist in dairy barns, where dust containing endotoxin and/or other biologically active agents in the environment contributes to bronchitis, occupational asthma and inflammation of the mucous membrane. While these problems are most notable in developed countries where industrialized agriculture is widespread, the increasing export of confined livestock production technologies to developing areas such as Southeast Asia and Central America increases the risks for workers there.

Health problems from physical agents typically involve tools or machinery either directly or indirectly involved with livestock production in the agricultural work environment. Tractors are the leading cause of farm fatalities in developed countries. In addition, elevated rates of hearing loss associated with machinery and confined livestock production noises, and musculoskeletal disorders from repetitive motions, are also consequences of industrialized forms of animal agriculture. Agricultural industrialization, characterized by the use of capital-intensive technologies which interface between humans and the physical environment to produce food, is behind the growth of physical agents as significant livestock-related health factors.

Injuries

Direct contact with livestock is a leading cause of injuries in many industrialized regions of the world. In the United States, the national Traumatic Injury Surveillance of Farmers (NIOSH 1993) indicates that livestock is the primary source of injury, with cattle, swine and sheep constituting 18% of all agricultural injuries and accounting for the highest rate of lost workdays. This is consistent with a 1980-81 survey conducted by the US National Safety Council (National Safety Council 1982).

Regional US studies consistently show livestock as a leading cause of injury in agricultural work. Early work on hospital visits by farmers in New York from 1929 to 1948 revealed livestock accounting for 17% of farm-related injuries, second only to machinery (Calandruccio and Powers 1949). Such trends continue, as research indicates livestock account for at least one-third of agricultural injuries among Vermont dairy farmers (Waller 1992), 19% of injuries among a random sample of Alabama farmers (Zhou and Roseman 1995), and 24% of injuries among Iowa farmers (Iowa Department of Public Health 1995). One of the few studies to analyse risk factors for livestock-specific injuries indicates such injuries may be related to the organization of production and specific features of the livestock rearing environment (Layde et al. 1996).

Evidence from other industrialized agricultural areas of the world reveals similar patterns. Research from Australia indicates that livestock workers have the second-highest occupational fatal injury rates in the country (Erlich et al. 1993). A study of accident records and emergency department visits of British farmers in West Wales (Cameron and Bishop 1992) reveals livestock were the leading source of injuries, accounting for 35% of farm-related accidents. In Denmark, a study of 257 hospital-treated agricultural injuries revealed livestock as the second-leading cause of injuries, accounting for 36% of injuries treated (Carstensen, Lauritsen and Rasmussen 1995). Surveillance research is necessary to address the lack of systematic data on livestock-related injury rates in developing areas of the world.

Prevention of livestock-related injuries involves understanding animal behaviour and respecting dangers by acting appropriately and using appropriate control technologies. Understanding animal habits related to feeding behaviours and environmental fluctuations, social relationships such as animals isolated from their herd, nurturing and protective instincts of female animals and the variable territorial nature and feeding patterns of livestock are critical in reducing the risk of injury. Prevention of injury also depends on using and maintaining livestock control equipment such as fences, pens, stalls and cages. Children are at particular risk and should be supervised in designated play areas well away from livestock holding areas.

Infectious Diseases

Zoonotic diseases can be classified according to their modes of transmission, which are in turn linked to forms of agriculture, human social organization and the ecosystem. The four general routes of transmission are:

1. direct single vertebrate host
2. cyclical multiple vertebrate host
3. combination vertebrate-invertebrate host
4. inanimate intermediary host.

Zoonotic diseases can be generally characterized as follows: they are non-fatal, infrequently diagnosed and sporadic rather than epidemic; they mimic other diseases; and humans are typically the dead-end hosts. Primary zoonotic diseases by region are listed in table 70.5.

Rates of zoonotic diseases among human populations are largely unknown owing to the lack of epidemiological data and to misdiag-

Table 70.5 • Primary zoonoses by world region.

Common name	Principal source	Region
Anthrax	Mammals	Eastern Mediterranean, West and Southeast Asia, Latin America
Brucellosis	Goats, sheep, cattle, swine	Europe, Mediterranean area, United States
Encephalitis, arthropod-borne	Birds, sheep, rodents	Africa, Australia, Central Europe, Far East, Latin America, Russia, United States
Hydatidosis	Dogs, ruminants, swine, wild carnivores	Eastern Mediterranean, southern South America, South and East Africa, New Zealand, southern Australia, Siberia
Leptospirosis	Rodents, cattle, swine, wild carnivores, horses	Worldwide, more prevalent in Caribbean
Q fever	Cattle, goats, sheep	Worldwide
Rabies	Dogs, cats, wild carnivores, bats	Worldwide
Salmonellosis	Birds, mammals	Worldwide, most prevalent in regions with industrial agriculture and higher use of antibiotics
Trichinosis	Swine, wild carnivores, Arctic animals	Argentina, Brazil, Central Europe, Chile North America, Spain
Tuberculosis	Cattle, dogs, goats	Worldwide, most prevalent in developing countries

noses. Even in industrialized countries such as the United States, zoonotic diseases such as leptospirosis are frequently mistaken for influenza. Symptoms are non-specific, making diagnosis difficult, a characteristic of many zoonoses.

Prevention of zoonotic diseases consists of a combination of disease eradication, animal vaccinations, human vaccinations, work environment sanitation, cleaning and protecting open wounds, appropriate food handling and preparation techniques (such as pasteurization of milk and thorough cooking of meat), use of personal protection equipment (such as boots in rice fields) and prudent use of antibiotics to reduce the growth of resistant strains. Control technologies and preventive behaviours should be conceptualized in terms of pathways, agents and hosts and specifically targeted to the four routes of transmission.

Respiratory Diseases

Given the variety and extent of exposures related to livestock production, respiratory diseases may be the major health problem. Studies in some sectors of livestock production in developed areas of the world reveal that 25% of livestock workers suffer from some form of respiratory disease (Thorne et al. 1996). The kinds of work most commonly associated with respiratory problems include grain production and handling and working in animal confinement units and dairy farming.

Agricultural respiratory diseases may result from exposures to a variety of dusts, gases, agricultural chemicals and infectious agents. Dust exposures may be divided into those primarily consisting of organic components and those consisting mainly of inorganic components. Field dust is the primary source of inorganic dust exposures. Organic dust is the major respiratory exposure to agricultural production workers. Disease results from periodic short-term exposures to agricultural organic dust containing large numbers of microbes.

ODTS is the acute flu-like illness seen following periodic short-term exposure to high concentrations of dust (Donham 1986). This syndrome has features very similar to those of acute farmer's lung, but does not carry the risk of pulmonary impairment associated with farmer's lung. Bronchitis affecting agricultural workers has both an acute and chronic form (Rylander 1994). Asthma, as defined by reversible airway obstruction associated with airway inflammation, can also be caused by agricultural exposures. In most cases this type of asthma is related to chronic inflammation of the airways rather than a specific allergy.

A second common exposure pattern is daily exposure to a lower level of organic dust. Typically, total dust levels are 2 to 9 mg/m³, microbe counts are at 10^3 to 10^5 organisms/m³ and endotoxin concentration is 50 to 900 EU/m³. Examples of such exposures include work in a swine confinement unit, a dairy barn or a poultry-growing facility. Usual symptoms seen with these exposures include those of acute and chronic bronchitis, an asthma-like syndrome and symptoms of mucous membrane irritation.

Gases play an important role in causing lung disorders in the agricultural setting. In swine confinement buildings and in poultry facilities, ammonia levels often contribute to respiratory problems. Exposure to the fertilizer anhydrous ammonia has both acute and long-term effects on the respiratory tract. Acute poisoning from hydrogen sulphide gas released from manure storage facilities in dairy barns and swine confinement units can cause fatalities. Inhalation of insecticidal fumigants can also lead to death.

Prevention of respiratory illnesses may be aided by controlling the source of dusts and other agents. In livestock buildings, this includes managing a correctly designed ventilation system and frequent cleaning to prevent build-up of dust. However, engineering controls alone are likely insufficient. Correct selection and use of a dust respirator is also needed. Alternatives to confinement operations can also be considered, including pasture-based and partially enclosed production arrangements, which can be as profitable as confined operations, particularly when occupational health costs are considered.

Skin Problems

Skin problems can be categorized as contact dermatitis, sun-related, infectious or insect-induced. Estimates indicate that agricultural workers are at highest occupational risk for certain dermatoses (Mathias 1989). While prevalence rates are lacking, particularly in developing regions, studies in the United States indicate that occupational skin disease may account for up to 70% of all occupational diseases among agricultural workers in certain regions (Hogan and Lane 1986).

There are three types of contact dermatoses: irritant dermatitis, allergic dermatitis and photocontact dermatitis. The most common form is irritant contact dermatitis, while allergic contact dermatitis is less common and photocontact reactions are rare (Zuehlke, Mutel and Donham 1980). Common sources of contact dermatitis on the farm include fertilizers, plants and pesticides. Of

Arthropod-related occupational health problems

Arthropods comprise more than 1 million species of insects and thousands of species of ticks, mites, spiders, scorpions and centipedes. Bees, ants, wasps and scorpions sting and inject venom; mosquitoes and ticks suck blood and transmit diseases; and the scales and hairs from insect bodies can irritate the eyes and skin, as well as tissues in the nose, mouth and respiratory system. Most stings in humans are from social bees (bumble bees, honey bees). Other stings are from paper wasps, yellow jackets, hornets and ants.

Arthropods can be a health hazard in the workplace (see table 70.6), but in most cases, potential arthropod hazards are not unique to specific occupations. Rather, exposure to arthropods in the workplace depends on geographic location, local conditions and the time of year. Table 70.7 lists some of these hazards and their corresponding arthropod agents. For all arthropod hazards, the first line of defence is avoidance or exclusion of the offending agent. Venom immunotherapy may increase a person's tolerance to arthropod venom and is accomplished by injecting increasing doses of venom over time. It is effective in 90 to 100% of venom hypersensitive individuals but involves an indefinite course of expensive injections. Table 70.8 lists normal and allergic reactions to insect stings.

Table 70.6 • Different occupations and their potential for contact with arthropods that may adversely affect health and safety.

Occupation	Arthropods
Construction personnel, environmentalists, farmers, fishers, foresters, fish and wildlife workers, naturalists, transportation workers, park rangers, utility workers	Ants, bees, biting flies, caterpillars, chiggers, centipedes, caddisflies, fly maggots, mayflies, scorpions, spiders, ticks, wasps
Cosmetics manufacturers, dock workers, dye makers, factory workers, food processors, grainery workers, homemakers, millers, restaurant workers	Ants; beetles; bean, grain and pea weevils; mites; scale insects; spiders
Beekeepers	Ants, bumble bees, honey bees, wasps
Insect production workers, laboratory and field biologists, museum curators	Over 500 species of arthropods are reared in the laboratory. Ants, beetles, mites, moths, spiders and ticks are especially important.
Hospital and other health care workers, school administrators, teachers	Ants, beetles, biting flies, caterpillars, cockroaches, mites
Silk producers	Silk worms

Table 70.7 • Potential arthropod hazards in the workplace and their causative agent(s).

Hazard	Arthropod agents
Bites, envenomation[1]	Ants, biting flies, centipedes, mites, spiders
Sting envenomation, venom hypersensitivity[2]	Ants, bees, wasps, scorpions
Tick toxicosis/paralysis	Ticks
Asthma	Beetles, caddisflies, caterpillars, cockroaches, crickets, dust mites, fly maggots, grain mites, grain weevils, grasshoppers, honeybees, mayflies, moths, silk worms
Contact dermatitis[3]	Blister beetles, caterpillars, cockroaches, dried fruit mites, dust mites, grain mites, straw itch mites, moths, silk worms, spiders

[1] Envenomation with poison from glands associated with mouthparts.
[2] Envenomation with poison from glands not associated with mouthparts.
[3] Includes primary irritant and allergic dermatitis.

Table 70.8 • Normal and allergic reactions to insect sting.

Type of response	Reaction
I. Normal, non-allergic reactions at the time of the sting	Pain, burning, itching, redness at the sting site, white area surrounding the sting site, swelling, tenderness
II. Normal, non-allergic reactions hours or days after sting	Itching, residual redness, small brown or red damage spot at sting site, swelling at the sting site
III. Large local reactions	Massive swelling around the sting site extending over an area 10 cm or more and increasing in size for 24 to 72 hours, sometimes lasting up to a week or more
IV. Cutaneous allergic reactions	Hives anywhere on the skin, massive swelling remote from the sting site, generalized itching of the skin, generalized redness of the skin remote from the sting site
V. Non life-threatening systemic allergic reactions	Allergic rhinitis, minor respiratory symptoms, abdominal cramps
VI. Life-threatening systemic allergic reactions	Shock, unconsciousness, hypotension or fainting, difficulty in breathing, massive swelling in the throat.

Source: Schmidt 1992.

Donald Barnard

particular note is dermatitis from contact with livestock feed. Feeds containing additives such as antibiotics may result in allergic dermatitis.

Light-complexioned farmers in developing areas of the world are at particular risk for chronic sun-induced skin problems, including wrinkling, actinic keratoses (scaly non-cancerous lesions) and skin cancer. The two most common types of skin cancer are squamous and basal cell carcinomas. Epidemiological work in Canada indicates that farmers are at higher risk for squamous cell carcinoma than non-farmers (Hogan and Lane 1986). Squamous cell carcinomas often arise from actinic keratoses. Approximately 2 out of 100 squamous cell carcinomas metastasize, and they are most common on the lips. Basal cell carcinomas are more common and occur on the face and ears. While locally destructive, basal cell carcinomas rarely metastasize.

Infectious dermatoses most relevant for livestock workers are ringworm (dermatophytic fungi), orf (contagious ecthyma) and milker's nodule. Ringworm infections are superficial skin infections that appear as red scaling lesions that result from contact with infected livestock, particularly dairy cattle. A study from India, where cattle generally roam free, revealed over 5% of rural inhabitants suffering from ringworm infections (Chaterjee et al. 1980). Orf, by contrast, is a pox virus usually contracted from infected sheep or goats. The result is typically lesions on the backs of hands or fingers which usually disappear with some scarring in about 6 weeks. Milker's nodules result from infection with the pseudocowpox poxvirus, typically from contact with infected udders or teats of milk cows. These lesions appear similar to those of orf, though they are more often multiple.

Insect-induced dermatoses result primarily from bites and stings. Infections from mites that parasitize livestock or contaminate grains is particularly notable among livestock handlers. Chigger bites and scabies are typical skin problems from mites that result in various forms of reddened irritations that usually heal spontaneously. More serious are bites and stings from various insects such as bees, wasps, hornets or ants that result in anaphylactic reactions. Anaphylactic shock is a rare hypersensitivity reaction that occurs with an overproduction of chemicals emitted from white blood cells that result in constriction of the airways and can lead to cardiac arrest.

All of these skin problems are largely preventable. Contact dermatitis can be prevented by reducing exposures through use of protective clothing, gloves and appropriate personal hygiene. Additionally, insect-related problems can be prevented by wearing light-coloured and nonflowery clothing and by avoiding scented skin applications. The risk of skin cancer can be dramatically reduced by using appropriate clothing to minimize exposure, such as a wide-brimmed hat. Use of appropriate sunscreen lotions can also be helpful, but should not be relied upon.

Conclusion

The number of livestock worldwide has grown apace with the increase in human population. There are approximately 4 billion cattle, pigs, sheep, goats, horses, buffalo and camels in the world (Durning and Brough 1992). However, there is a notable lack of data on livestock-related human health problems in developing areas of the world such as China and India, where much of the livestock currently reside and where future growth is likely to occur. However, given the emergence of industrialized agriculture worldwide, it can be anticipated that many of the health problems documented in North American and European livestock production will likely accompany the emergence of industrialized livestock production elsewhere. It is also anticipated that health services in these areas will be inadequate to deal with the health and safety consequences of industrialized livestock production generally described here.

The worldwide emergence of industrialized livestock production with its attendant human health consequences will accompany fundamental changes in the social, economic and political order comparable to those that followed from the domestication of animals over 10,000 years ago. Preventing human health problems will require broad understanding and appropriate engagement of these new forms of human adaptation and the place of livestock production within them.

FORAGE CROPS

Lorann Stallones

As populations tended to concentrate and the need for winter feeding in northern climates grew, the need to harvest, cure and feed hay to domestic animals emerged. Although pasture dates to the earliest domestication of animals, the first cultivated forage plant may have been alfalfa, with its recorded use dating back to 490 BC in Persia and Greece.

Livestock forage is a crucial input for livestock rearing. Forages are grown for their vegetation and not their grains or seeds. Stems, leaves and inflorescences (flower clusters) of some legumes (e.g., alfalfa and clover) and a variety of non-legume grasses are used for grazing or harvested and fed to livestock. When grain crops such as corn, sorghum or straw are harvested for their vegetation, they are considered forage crops.

Production Processes

The major categories of forage crops are pastures and open ranges, hay and silage. Forage crops can be harvested by livestock (in pastures) or by humans, either by hand or machinery. The crop can be used for farm feeding or for sale. In forage production, tractors are a source of traction and processing power, and, in dry areas, irrigation may be required.

Pasture is fed by allowing the livestock to graze or browse. The type of pasture crop, typically grass, varies in its production with the season of the year, and pastures are managed for spring, summer and fall grazing. Range management focuses on not overgrazing an area, which involves rotating livestock from one area to another. Crop residues may be part of the pasture diet for livestock.

Alfalfa, a popular hay crop, is not a good pasture crop because it causes bloating in ruminants, a condition of a gas build-up in the rumen (the first part of the cow's stomach) that can kill a cow. In temperate climates, pastures are ineffective as a feed source in the winter, so stored feed is needed. Moreover, in large operations, harvested forage—hay and silage—is used because pasture is impractical for large concentrations of animals.

Hay is forage that is grown and dry-cured before storage and feeding. After the hay crop has grown, it is cut with a mowing machine or swather (a machine that combines the mowing and raking operations) and raked by a machine into a long row for drying (a windrow). During these two processes it is field cured for baling. Historically harvesting was done by pitchforking loose hay, which may still be used to feed the animals. Once cured, the hay is baled. The baling machine picks up the hay from the windrow, and compresses and wraps it into either a small square bale for manual handling, or large square or round bales for mechanical handling. The small bale may be kicked mechanically from the baler back into a trailer, or it may be picked up by hand and placed—a task called bucking—onto a trailer for transport to the storage area. The bales are stored in stacks, usually under a cover (barn, shed or plastic) to protect them from rain. Wet hay can easily spoil or spontaneously combust from the heat of the decaying process. Hay may be processed for commercial use into compressed pellets or cubes. A crop can be cut several times in a season, three times being typical. When it is fed, a bale is moved to the feeding trough, opened and placed into the trough where the animal can reach it. This part of the operation is typically manual.

Other forage that is harvested for livestock feeding is corn or sorghum for silage. The economic advantage is that corn has as much as 50% more energy when harvested as silage than grain. A machine is used to harvest most of the green plant. The crop is cut, crushed, chopped and ejected into a trailer. The material is then fed as green chop or stored in a silo, where it undergoes fermentation in the first 2 weeks. The fermentation establishes an environment that prevents spoilage. Over a year, the silo is emptied as the silage is fed to livestock. This feeding process is primarily mechanical.

Hazards and Their Prevention

The storage of animal feed presents health hazards for workers. Early in the storage process, nitrogen dioxide is produced and can cause serious respiratory damage and death ("silo filler's disease"). Storage in enclosed environments, such as silos, can create this hazard, which can be avoided by not entering silos or enclosed storage spaces in the first few weeks after feed has been stored. Further problems can occur later if the alfalfa, hay, straw or other forage crop was wet when it was stored and there is a build-up of fungi and other microbial contaminants. This can result in acute respiratory illness ("silo unloader's disease", organic dust toxicity) and/or chronic respiratory diseases ("farmer's lung"). The risk of acute and chronic respiratory diseases can be reduced through the use of appropriate respirators. There should also be appropriate confined space entry procedures.

The straw and hay used for bedding is usually dry and old, but may contain moulds and spores which can cause respiratory symptoms when dust is made airborne. Dust respirators can reduce exposure to this hazard.

Harvesting and baling equipment and bedding choppers are designed to chop, cut and mangle. They have been associated with traumatic injuries to farm workers. Many of these injuries occur when workers try to clear clogged parts while the equipment is still operating. The equipment should be turned off before clearing jams. If more than one person is working, then a lockout/tagout programme should be in effect. Another major source of injuries and fatalities is tractor overturns without proper roll-over protection for the driver (Deere & Co. 1994). More information on farm machinery hazards is also dicussed elsewhere in this *Encyclopaedia*.

Where animals are used to plant, harvest and store feed, there is a possibility of animal-related injuries from kicks, bites, strains, sprains, crush injuries and lacerations. Correct animal handling techniques are the most likely means to reduce these injuries.

Manual handling of bales of hay and straw can result in ergonomic problems. Workers should be trained in correct lifting procedures, and mechanical equipment should be used where possible.

Forage and bedding are fire hazards. Wet hay, as mentioned previously, is a spontaneous combustion hazard. Dry hay, straw and so forth will burn easily, especially when loose. Even bailed forage is a major fuel source in a fire. Basic fire precautions should be instituted, such as no-smoking rules, elimination of spark sources and fire suppression measures.

● LIVESTOCK CONFINEMENT

Kelley Donham

Global economic forces have contributed to the industrialization of agriculture (Donham and Thu 1995). In the developed countries, there are trends toward increased specialization, intensity and mechanization. Increased confinement production of livestock has been a result of these trends. Many developing countries have recognized the need to adopt confinement production in an attempt to transform their agriculture from a subsistence to a globally competitive enterprise. As more corporate organizations obtain ownership and control of the industry, fewer, but larger, farms with many employees replace the family farm.

Conceptually, the confinement system applies principles of industrial mass production to livestock production. The concept of confinement production includes raising animals in high densities in structures that are isolated from the outside environment and equipped with mechanical or automated systems for ventilation, waste handling, feeding and watering (Donham, Rubino et al. 1977).

Several European countries have been using confinement systems since the early 1950s. Livestock confinement started to appear in the United States in the late 1950s. Poultry producers were first to use the system. By the early 1960s, the swine industry had also started to adopt this technique, followed more recently by dairy and beef producers.

Accompanying this industrialization, several worker health and social concerns have developed. In most Western countries, farms are getting fewer in number but larger in size. There are fewer family farms (combined labour and management) and more corporate structures (particularly in North America). The result is that there are more hired workers and relatively fewer family members working. Additionally, in North America, more workers are coming from minority and immigrant groups. Therefore, there is a risk of producing a new underclass of workers in some segments of the industry.

A whole new set of occupational hazardous exposures has arisen for the agricultural worker. These can be categorized under four main headings:

1. toxic and asphyxiating gases
2. bioactive aerosols of particulates
3. infectious diseases
4. noise.

Respiratory hazards are also a concern.

Toxic and Asphyxiating Gases

Several toxic and asphyxiating gases resulting from microbial degradation of animal wastes (urine and faeces) may be associated with livestock confinement. Wastes are most commonly stored in liquid form under the building, over a slatted floor or in a tank or lagoon outside the building. This manure storage system is usually anaerobic, leading to the formation of a number of toxic gases (see table 70.9) (Donham, Yeggy and Dauge 1988). See also the article "Manure and waste handling" in this chapter.

There are four common toxic or asphyxiating gases present in almost every operation where anaerobic digestion of wastes occurs: carbon dioxide (CO_2), ammonia (NH_3), hydrogen sulphide (H_2S) and methane (CH_4). A small amount of carbon monoxide (CO) may also be produced by the decomposing animal wastes, but its main source is heaters used to burn fossil fuels. Typical ambient levels of these gases (as well as particulates) in swine confinement buildings are shown in table 70.10. Also listed are maximum recommended exposures in swine buildings based on recent research (Donham and Reynolds 1995; Reynolds et al. 1996) and threshold limit values (TLVs) set by the American Conference of Governmental Industrial Hygienists (ACGIH 1994). These TLVs have been adopted as legal limits in many countries. It can be seen that in many of the buildings, at least one gas, and often several, exceeds the exposure limits. It should be noted that simultaneous exposure to these toxic substances may

Table 70.9 • Compounds identified in swine confinement building atmospheres.

2-Propanol	Ethanol	Isopropyl acetate
3-Pentanone	Ethyl formate	Isopropyl propionate
Acetaldehyde	Ethylamine	Isovaleric acid
Acetic acid	Formaldehyde	Methane
Acetone	Heptaldehyde	Methyl acetate
Ammonia	Heterocyclic nitrogen	Methylamine
n-Butanol	compound	Methylmercaptan
n-Butyl	Hexanal	Octaldehyde
Butyric acid	Hydrogen sulphide	n-Propanol
Carbon dioxide	Indole	Propionic acid
Carbon monoxide	Isobutanol	Proponaldehyde
Decaldehyde	Isobutyl acetate	Propyl propionate
Diethyl sulphide	Isobutyraldehyde	Skatole
Dimethyl sulphide	Isobutyric acid	Triethylamine
Disulphide	Isopentanol	Trimethylamine

be additive or synergistic—the TLV for the mixture may be exceeded even when individual TLVs are not exceeded. Concentrations are often higher in the winter than in the summer, because ventilation is reduced to conserve heat.

These gases have been implicated in several acute conditions in workers. H_2S has been implicated in many sudden animal deaths and several human deaths (Donham and Knapp 1982). Most acute cases have occurred shortly after the manure pit has been agitated or emptied, which may result in a sudden release of a large volume of the acutely toxic H_2S. In other fatal cases, manure pits had recently been emptied, and workers who entered the pit for inspection, repairs or to retrieve a dropped object collapsed without any forewarning. The available post-mortem results of these cases of acute poisoning revealed massive pulmonary oedema as the only notable finding. This lesion, combined with the history, is compatible with hydrogen sulphide intoxication. Rescue attempts by bystanders have often resulted in multiple fatalities. Confinement workers should therefore be informed of the risks involved and advised never to enter a manure storage facility without testing for the presence of toxic gases, being equipped with a respirator with its own oxygen supply, ensuring adequate ventilation and having at least two other workers stand by, attached by a rope to the worker who enters, so they can effect a

rescue without endangering themselves. There should be a written confined-space programme.

CO may also be present at acute toxic levels. Abortion problems in swine at an atmospheric concentration of 200 to 400 ppm and subacute symptoms in humans, such as chronic headache and nausea, have been documented in swine confinement systems. The possible effects on the human foetus should also be of concern. The primary source of CO is from improperly functioning hydrocarbon-burning heating units. Heavy accumulation of dust in swine confinement buildings makes it difficult to keep heaters in correct working order. Propane-fuelled radiant heaters are also a common source of lower levels of CO (e.g., 100 to 300 ppm). High-pressure washers powered by an internal combustion engine that may be run inside the building are another source; CO alarms should be installed.

Another acutely dangerous situation occurs when the ventilation system fails. Gas levels may then rapidly build up to critical levels. In this case the major problem is replacement of oxygen by other gases, primarily CO_2 produced from the pit as well as from the respiratory activity of the animals in the building. Lethal conditions could be reached in as few as 7 hours. Regarding the health of the pigs, ventilation failure in warm weather may allow temperature and humidity to increase to lethal levels in 3 hours. Ventilation systems should be monitored.

A fourth potentially acute hazard arises from build-up of CH_4, which is lighter than air and, when emitted from the manure pit, tends to accumulate in the upper portions of the building. There have been several instances of explosions occurring when the CH_4 accumulation was ignited by a pilot light or a worker's welding torch.

Bioactive Aerosols of Particulates

The sources of dust in confinement buildings are a combination of feed, dander and hair from the swine and dried faecal material (Donham and Scallon 1985). The particulates are about 24% protein and therefore have the potential not only for initiating an inflammatory response to foreign protein but also for initiating an adverse allergic reaction. The majority of particles are smaller than 5 microns, allowing them to be respired into the deep portions of the lungs, where they may produce a greater danger to health. The particulates are laden with microbes (10^4 to $10^7/m^3$ air). These microbes contribute several toxic/inflammatory substances including, among others, endotoxin (the most documented hazard), glucans, histamine and proteases. The recommended maximum concentrations for dusts are listed in table 70.10. Gases present within the building and bacteria in the atmosphere are adsorbed on the surface of the dust particles. Thus, the inhaled particles have the increased potentially hazardous effect of carrying irritating or toxic gases as well as potentially infectious bacteria into the lungs.

Table 70.10 • Ambient levels of various gases in swine confinement buildings.

Gas	Range (ppm)	Typical ambient concentrations (ppm)	Recommended maximum exposure concentrations (ppm)	Threshold limit values (ppm)
CO	0 to 200	42	50	50
CO_2	1,000 to 10,000	8,000	1,500	5,000
NH_3	5 to 200	81	7	25
H_2S	0 to 1,500	4	5	10
Total dust	2 to 15 mg/m^3	4 mg/m^3	2.5 mg/m^3	10 mg/m^3
Respirable dust	0.10 to 1.0 mg/m^3	0.4 mg/m^3	0.23 mg/m^3	3 mg/m^3
Endotoxin	50 to 500 ng/m^3	200 ng/m^3	100 ng/m^3	(none established)

Infectious Diseases

Some 25 zoonotic diseases have been recognized as having occupational significance for agricultural workers. Many of these may be transmitted directly or indirectly from livestock. The crowded conditions prevailing in confinement systems offer a high potential for transmission of zoonotic diseases from livestock to humans. Swine confinement environment may offer a risk for transmission to workers of swine influenza, leptospirosis, *Streptococcus suis* and salmonella, for example. The poultry confinement environment may offer a risk for ornithosis, histoplasmosis, New Castle disease virus and salmonella. Bovine confinement could offer a risk for Q fever, *Trichophyton verrucosum* (animal ringworm) and leptospirosis.

Biologicals and antibiotics have also been recognized as potential health hazards. Injectable vaccines and various biologicals are commonly used in veterinary preventive medical programmes in animal confinement. Accidental inoculation of Brucella vaccines and *Escherichia coli* bacteria has been observed to cause illness in humans.

Antibiotics are commonly used both parenterally and incorporated in animal feed. Since it is recognized that feed is a common component of the dust present in animal confinement buildings, it is assumed that antibiotics are also present in the air. Thus, antibiotic hypersensitivity and antibiotic-resistant infections are potential hazards for the workers.

Noise

Noise levels of 103 dBA have been measured within animal confinement buildings; this is above the TLV, and offers a potential for noise-induced hearing loss (Donham, Yeggy and Dauge 1988).

Respiratory Symptoms of Livestock Confinement Workers

The general respiratory hazards within livestock confinement buildings are similar regardless of the species of livestock. However, swine confinements are associated with adverse health effects in a larger percentage of workers (25 to 70% of active workers), with more severe symptoms than those in poultry or cattle confinements (Rylander et al. 1989). The waste in poultry facilities is usually handled in solid form, and in this instance ammonia seems to be the primary gaseous problem; hydrogen sulphide is not present.

Subacute or chronic respiratory symptoms reported by confinement workers have been observed to be most frequently associated with swine confinement. Surveys of swine confinement workers have revealed that about 75% suffer from adverse acute upper respiratory symptoms. These symptoms can be broken down into three groups:

1. acute or chronic inflammation of the respiratory airways (manifested as bronchitis)
2. acquired occupational (non-allergic) constriction of the airways (asthma)
3. delayed self-limited febrile illness with generalized symptoms (organic dust toxic syndrome (ODTS)).

Symptoms suggestive of chronic inflammation of the upper respiratory system are common; they are seen in about 70% of swine confinement workers. Most commonly, they include tightness of the chest, coughing, wheezing and excess sputum production.

In approximately 5% of workers, symptoms develop after working in the buildings for only a few weeks. The symptoms include chest tightness, wheezing and difficult breathing. Usually these workers are affected so severely that they are forced to seek employment elsewhere. Not enough is known to indicate whether this reaction is an allergic hypersensitivity or a non-allergic hypersensitivity to dust and gas. More typically, symptoms of bronchitis and asthma develop after 5 years of exposure.

Table 70.11 • Respiratory diseases associated with swine production.

Upper airway disease	Sinusitis
	Irritant rhinitis
	Allergic rhinitis
	Pharyngitis
Lower airway disease	Occupational asthma
	Non-allergic asthma, hyperresponsive airways disease, or reactive airways disease syndrome (RADS)
	Allergic asthma (IgE mediated)
	Acute or subacute bronchitis
	Chronic bronchitis
	Chronic obstructive pulmonary disease (COPD)
Interstitial disease	Alveolitis
	Chronic interstitial infiltrate
	Pulmonary oedema
Generalized illness	Organic dust toxic syndrome (ODTS)

Sources: Donham, Zavala and Merchant 1984; Dosman et al. 1988; Haglind and Rylander 1987; Harries and Cromwell 1982; Heedrick et al. 1991; Holness et al. 1987; Iverson et al. 1988; Jones et al. 1984; Leistikow et al. 1989; Lenhart 1984; Rylander and Essle 1990; Rylander, Peterson and Donham 1990; Turner and Nichols 1995.

Approximately 30% of workers occasionally experience episodes of delayed symptoms. Approximately 4 to 6 hours after working in the building they develop a flu-like illness manifested by fever, headache, malaise, general muscle aches and chest pain. They usually recover from these symptoms in 24 to 72 hours. This syndrome has been recognized as ODTS.

The potential for chronic lung damage certainly seems to be real for these workers. However, this has not been documented so far. It is recommended that certain procedures be followed to prevent chronic exposure as well as acute exposure to the hazardous materials in swine confinement buildings. Table 70.11 summarizes the medical conditions seen in swine confinement workers.

Worker Protection

Acute exposure to hydrogen sulphide. Care should always be taken to avoid exposure to H_2S that may be given off when agitating an anaerobic liquid manure storage tank. If the storage is under the building, it is best to stay out of the building when the emptying procedure is going on and for several hours afterwards, until air sampling indicates it is safe. Ventilation should be at the maximum level during this time. A liquid manure storage facility should never be entered without the safety measures mentioned above being followed.

Particulate exposure. Simple management procedures, such as the use of automated feeding equipment designed to eliminate as much feed dust as possible should be used to control particulate exposure. Adding extra fat to feed, frequent power-washing of the building and installing slatted flooring that cleans well are all proven control measures. An oil-misting dust-control system is presently under study and may be available in the future. In addition to good engineering control, a good-quality dust mask should be worn.

Noise. Ear protectors should be provided and worn, particularly when working in the building in order to vaccinate the animals or for other management procedures. A hearing conservation programme should be instituted.

ANIMAL HUSBANDRY

Dean T. Stueland and Paul D. Gunderson

Animal husbandry—the rearing and use of animals—involves a wide variety of activities, including breeding, feeding, moving animals from one location to another, basic care (e.g., hoof care, cleaning, vaccinations), care for injured animals (either by animal handlers or veterinarians) and activities associated with particular animals (e.g., milking of cows, shearing of sheep, working with draught animals).

Such handling of livestock is associated with a variety of injuries and illnesses among humans. These injuries and illnesses may be due to direct exposure or may be due to environmental contamination from animals. The risk of injury and illness is dependent largely on the type of livestock. The risk of injury also depends on the particulars of animal behaviour (see also the articles in this chapter on specific animals). In addition, persons associated with animal husbandry are often more likely to consume products from the animals. Finally, the specific exposures depend on methods of handling livestock, which have emerged from geographical and social factors that vary across human society.

Hazards and Precautions

Ergonomic Risks

Personnel who work with cattle often have to stand, reach, bend or exert physical effort in sustained or unusual positions. Livestock workers do have an increased risk of joint pain of the back, hips and knees. There are several activities that place the livestock

Figure 70.3 • Panoramic vision of cattle.

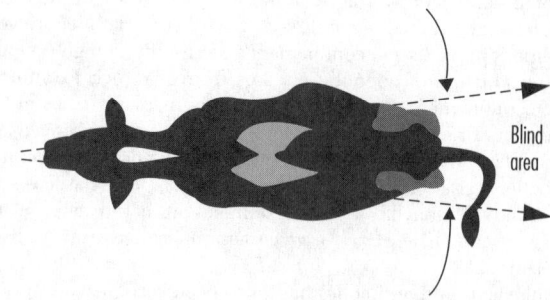

Cattle have panoramic vision which allows them to see everything except what is directly behind them (and right in front of their noses).

worker at ergonomic risk. For example, assisting with birthing of a large animal may put the farmworker in an unusual and strained position, whereas with a small animal, the worker may be required to work or lie in an inclement environment. Further, the worker may be injured by assisting animals who are ill and whose behaviour cannot be anticipated. More commonly, joint and back pain have to do with a repetitive motion, such as milking, during which the worker may crouch or kneel repeatedly.

Other cumulative trauma diseases are recognized in farmworkers, particularly livestock workers. These may be due to repetitive motion or frequent small injuries.

Solutions to reduce ergonomic risk include intensified educational efforts focused upon appropriate handling of animals, as

Animal behaviour

Understanding what influences animal behaviour can help make for a safer work environment. Genetics and learned responses (operant conditioning) influence the way an animal behaves. Certain breeds of bulls are generally more docile than others (genetic influence). An animal that has balked or refused to enter an area, and is successful at not doing so, will likely refuse to do so the next time. On repeated tries it will get more agitated and dangerous. Animals respond to the way in which they are treated, and draw upon past experiences when reacting to a situation. Animals that are chased, slapped, kicked, hit, yelled at, frightened and so on, will naturally have a sense of fear when a human is near. Thus, it is important to do everything possible to make movement of animals successful on the first attempt and as free of stress as possible for the animal.

Domesticated animals living under fairly uniform conditions develop habits which are based on doing the same thing each day at a specific time. Confining bulls in a paddock and feeding them allows them to get used to humans and can be utilized with bull-confinement mating systems. Habits are also caused by regular changes in environmental conditions, such as temperature or humidity fluctuations when daylight turns to darkness. Animals are most active at the time of greatest change, which is at dawn or dusk, and least active either in the middle of the day or the middle of the night. This factor can be used to advantage in the movement or working of animals.

Like animals in the wild, domesticated animals can protect territories. During feeding, this can appear as aggressive behaviour. Studies have shown that feed distributed in large, unpredictable patches eliminates territorial behaviour in livestock. When feed is distributed uniformly or in predictable patterns, it may result in fighting by animals to secure the feed and exclude others. Territorial protection may also occur when a bull is permitted to remain with the herd. The bull may view the herd and the range they cover as his territory, which means he will defend it against perceived and real threats, such as humans, dogs and other animals. Introducing a new or strange bull of breeding age into the herd almost always results in fighting to establish the dominant male.

Bulls, due to having their eyes on the side of their head, have panoramic vision and very little depth perception. This means they can see about 270° around them, leaving a blind spot directly behind them and right in front of their noses (see figure 70.3). Sudden or unexpected movements from behind can "spook" the animal because it cannot determine the proximity or seriousness of the perceived threat. This can cause a "flight or fight" response in the animal. Because cattle have poor depth perception, they can also be easily frightened by shadows and movements outside of working or holding areas. Shadows falling within the working area may appear as a hole to the animal, which can cause it to balk. Cattle are colour blind, but do perceive colours as different shades of black and white.

Many animals are sensitive to noise (compared with humans), especially at high frequencies. Loud, abrupt noises, such as metal gates clanging shut, head chutes latching and/or humans yelling can cause stress in the animals.

David L. Hard

well as engineering efforts to redesign the work environment and its tasks to accommodate animal and human factors.

Injuries

Animals are commonly recognized as agents of injury in surveys of injuries associated with agriculture. There are several postulated explanations for these observations. Close association between the worker and the animal, which often has unpredictable behaviour, puts the livestock worker at risk. Many livestock have superior size and strength. Injuries are often due to direct trauma from kicking, biting or crushing against a structure and often involve the worker's lower extremity. The behaviour of workers may also contribute to risk of injury. Workers who penetrate the "flight zone" of livestock or who position themselves in livestock "blind spots" are at increased risk of injury resulting from flight reaction, butting, kicking and crushing.

Women and children are over-represented among injured livestock workers. This may be due to societal factors resulting in women and children doing more of the animal-related work, or it may be due to exaggerated size differences between the animals and worker or, in the case of children, use of handling techniques to which livestock are unaccustomed.

Specific interventions to prevent animal-associated injuries include intense educational efforts, selecting animals that are more compatible with humans, selecting workers who are less likely to agitate animals and engineering approaches that decrease the risk of exposure of humans to animals.

Zoonotic Diseases

Livestock rearing requires close association of workers and animals. Humans may become infected by organisms normally present on animals, which are rarely human pathogens. In addition, the tissues and behaviour associated with infected animals may expose workers who would experience few, if any, exposures if they were working with healthy livestock.

The relevant zoonotic diseases include numerous viruses, bacteria, mycobacteria, fungi and parasites (see table 70.12). Many zoonotic diseases, such as anthrax, tinea capitis or orf, are associated with skin contamination. In addition, contamination resulting from exposure to a diseased animal is a risk factor for rabies and tularaemia. Because livestock workers often are more likely to ingest under-treated animal products, such workers are at risk of diseases such as *Campylobacter*, cryptosporidiosis, salmonellosis, trichinosis or tuberculosis.

The control of zoonotic diseases must focus on the route and source of exposure. Elimination of the source and/or interruption of the route are essential to disease control. For example, there must be proper disposal of the carcasses of diseased animals. Often, the human disease can be prevented by eliminating the disease in animals. Additionally, there should be adequate processing of animal products or tissues before use in the human food chain.

Some zoonotic diseases are treated in the livestock worker with antibiotics. However, routine prophylactic antibiotic usage on livestock may cause emergence of resistant organisms of general public health concern.

Blacksmithing

Blacksmithing (farrier work) involves primarily musculoskeletal and environmental injury. The manipulation of metal to be used in animal care, such as for horseshoes, does demand heavy work requiring substantial muscle activity to prepare the metal and position animal legs or feet. Furthermore, applying the created product, such as a horseshoe, to the animal in farrier work is an additional source of injury (see figure 70.4).

Often, the heat required to bend metal involves exposure to noxious gases. A recognized syndrome, metal fume fever, has a clinical picture similar to pulmonary infection and results from inhalation of fumes of nickel, magnesium, copper or other metals.

Adverse health effects associated with blacksmithing can be alleviated by working with adequate respiratory protection. Such respiratory devices include respirators or powered air-purifying respirators with cartridges and pre-filters capable of filtering acid gas/organic vapours and metal fumes. If the farrier work occurs in a fixed location, local exhaust ventilation should be installed for the forge. Engineering controls, which place distance or barricades between the animal and the worker, will reduce the risk of injury.

Table 70.12 • Zoonotic diseases of livestock handlers.

Disease	Agent	Animal	Exposure
Anthrax	Bacteria	Goats, other herbivores	Handling hair, bone or other tissues
Brucellosis	Bacteria	Cattle, swine, goats, sheep	Contact with placenta and other contaminated tissues
Campylobacter	Bacteria	Poultry, cattle	Ingestion of contaminated food, water, milk
Cryptosporidiosis	Parasite	Poultry, cattle, sheep, small mammals	Ingestion of animal faeces
Leptospirosis	Bacteria	Wild animals, swine, cattle, dogs	Contaminated water on open skin
Orf	Virus	Sheep, goats	Direct contact with mucous membranes
Psittacosis	Chlamydia	Parakeets, poultry, pigeons	Inhaled desiccated droppings
Q fever	Rickettsia	Cattle, goats, sheep	Inhaled dust from contaminated tissues
Rabies	Virus	Wild carnivores, dogs, cats, livestock	Exposure of virus-laden saliva to breaks in skin
Salmonellosis	Bacteria	Poultry, swine, cattle	Ingestion of food from contaminated organisms
Tinea capitis	Fungus	Dogs, cats, cattle	Direct contact
Trichinosis	Roundworm	Swine, dogs, cats, horses	Eating poorly cooked flesh
Tuberculosis, bovine	Mycobacteria	Cattle, swine	Ingestion of unpasteurized milk; inhalation of airborne droplets
Tularaemia	Bacteria	Wild animals, swine, dogs	Inoculation from contaminated water or flesh

70. LIVESTOCK REARING

Figure 70.4 • Blacksmith shoeing a horse in Switzerland.

Animal Allergies

All animals possess antigens which are non-human and could therefore serve as potential allergens. In addition, livestock are often hosts for mites. Since there are a large number of potential animal allergies, recognition of a specific allergen requires careful and thorough disease and occupational histories. Even with such data, recognition of a specific allergen may be difficult.

The clinical expression of animal allergies may include an anaphylaxis-type picture, with hives, swelling, nasal discharge and asthma. In some patients, itching and nasal discharge may be the only symptoms.

Controlling exposure to animal allergies is a formidable task. Improved practices in animal husbandry and changes in livestock facility ventilation systems may make it less likely that the livestock handler will be exposed. However, there may be little that can be done, other than desensitization, to prevent the formation of specific allergens. In general, desensitizing a worker can be performed only if the specific allergen is adequately characterized.

● MANURE AND WASTE HANDLING

William Popendorf

The importance of the management of waste has increased as the intensity of agricultural production on farms has increased. Waste from livestock production is dominated by manure, but also includes bedding and litter, wasted feed and water and soil. Table 70.13 lists some relevant characteristics of manure; human waste is included both for comparison and because it too must be treated on a farm. The high organic content of manure provides an excellent growth medium for bacteria. The metabolic activity of bacteria will consume oxygen and maintain bulk-stored manure in an anaerobic state. Anaerobic metabolic activity can produce a number of well-known toxic gaseous by-products, including carbon dioxide, methane, hydrogen sulphide and ammonia.

A checklist for livestock rearing safety practices

Feeding

1. Use proper ventilation in buildings and silos.
2. Keep entrances to grain, feed and silage storage areas closed and locked.
3. Post warning signs in feed and silage storage areas about the hazard of entrapment in flowing grain or feed.
4. Maintain silo and bin ladders in good condition.
5. Shield auger inlets to prevent contact with augers.
6. Cover loading troughs on augers, elevators and conveyors with grating.
7. Use caution when moving augers and elevators; check for overhead power lines.
8. Assure that shields are in place for all feeding, grinding and other equipment.
9. Be aware of health effects of breathing organic dust, and inform your doctor about recent dust exposure when seeking treatment for respiratory illness.
10. Use automated or mechanized equipment to move decayed materials.
11. Use source containment, local exhaust ventilation and wet methods to control organic dust.
12. Use appropriate respiratory protection when dust exposure is unavoidable.

Handling

1. Establish good sanitation, vaccination and inoculation programmes.
2. When working with animals, plan an escape exit; have at least two ways out.
3. Livestock handlers should have enough strength and experience for the job.
4. Avoid working with animals when you are tired.
5. Use caution when approaching animals so as not to startle them.
6. Know the animals and be patient with them.
7. Dehorn dangerous animals.
8. Post warning signs where chemicals are stored; lock them in a room or cabinet.
9. Mix all chemicals outside or in a well-ventilated area.
10. Be careful when leading animals.
11. Wear rubber gloves when treating sick animals.
12. Vaccinate animals, and quarantine sick animals.
13. Wash hands after contact with calves with diarrhoea (scours).

Containment and housing

1. Make sure all pens, gates, loading chutes and fences are in good repair and strong enough to contain the animal.
2. Do not allow tobacco smoking around farm buildings and fuel storage and refueling areas; post "no smoking" signs in these areas.
3. Maintain fully charged ABC-type fire extinguishers in major farm buildings.
4. Remove trash and debris around buildings to prevent fires and falls.
5. Keep all buildings in good repair.
6. Keep electrical wiring in good condition.
7. Use adequate lighting in all buildings.
8. Keep floors clean and free of broken concrete and slippery areas.

Waste disposal

1. Correctly dispose of all chemical containers following directions on the label.
2. Install vent pipes and exhaust fans in manure pits.

Melvin L. Myers

Table 70.13 • Physical properties of manure as excreted per day per 1,000 lb of animal weight, excluding moisture.

	Weight (lb)	Volume (ft³)	Volatiles (lb)	Moisture (%)	
				As excreted	As stored
Dairy cow	80–85	1.3	1.4–1.5	85–90	>98
Beef cow	51–63	0.8–1.0	5.4–6.4	87–89	45–55
Pig (grower)	63	1.0	5.4	90	91
Sow (gestation)	27	0.44	2.1	91	97
Sow and piglets	68	1.1	6.0	90	96
Laying hens	60	0.93	10.8	75	50
Broilers	80	1.3	15.	75	24
Turkeys	44	0.69	9.7	75	34
Lamb (sheep)	40	0.63	8.3	75	—
Human	30	0.55	1.9	89	99.5

Source: USDA 1992.

Management Processes

The management of manure involves its collection, one or more transfer operations, storage or/and optional treatment and eventually utilization. The moisture content of manure as listed in table 70.13 determines its consistency. Wastes of different consistencies require different management techniques and therefore can present different health and safety hazards (USDA 1992). The reduced volume of solid or low-moisture manure generally permits lower equipment costs and energy requirements, but handling systems are not easily automated. The collection, transfer and any optional treatments of liquid waste are more easily automated and require less daily attention. Storage of manure becomes increasingly mandatory as the seasonal variability of the local crops increases; the storage method must be sized to meet the production rate and utilization schedule while preventing environmental damage, especially from water runoff. Options for utilization include use as plant nutrients, mulch, animal feed, bedding or a source to produce energy.

Manure Production

Dairy cows are typically raised on pastures, except when in holding areas for pre- and post-milking and during seasonal extremes. Water use for cleaning in milking operations can vary from 5 to 10 gallons per day per cow, where flushing of wastes is not practised, to 150 gallons per day per cow where it is. Therefore, the method used for cleaning has a strong influence on the method chosen for manure transport, storage and utilization. Because the management of beef cattle requires less water, beef manure is more often handled as a solid or semi-solid. Composting is a common storage and treatment method for such dry wastes. The local precipitation pattern also strongly influences the preferred waste management scheme. Excessively dry feedlots are apt to produce a downwind dust and odour problem.

The major problems for swine raised on traditional pastures are the control of runoff and soil erosion due to the gregarious nature of pigs. One alternative is the construction of semi-enclosed pig buildings with paved lots, which also facilitates the separation of solid and liquid wastes; solids require some manual transfer operations but liquids can be handled by gravity flow.

Waste-handling systems for fully enclosed production buildings are designed to collect and store waste automatically in a largely liquid form. Livestock playing with their watering facilities can increase the volumes of swine waste. Manure storage is generally in anaerobic pits or lagoons.

Poultry facilities are generally divided into those for meat (turkeys and broilers) and egg (layers) production. The former are raised directly on prepared litter, which maintains the manure in a relatively dry state (25 to 35% moisture); the only transfer operation is mechanical removal, generally only once per year, and transport directly to the field. Layers are housed in stacked cages without litter; their manure can either be allowed to collect in deep stacks for infrequent mechanical removal or be automatically flushed or scraped in a liquid form much like swine manure.

The consistency of waste from most other animals, like sheep, goats and horses, is largely solid; the major exception is veal calves, because of their liquid diet. Waste from horses contains a high fraction of bedding and may contain internal parasites, which limits its utilization on pasture land. Waste from small animals, rodents and birds may contain disease organisms that can be transmitted to humans. However, studies have shown that faecal bacteria do not survive on forage (Bell, Wilson and Dew 1976).

Storage Hazards

Storage facilities for solid wastes must still control water runoff and leaching into surface and ground water. Thus, they should be paved pads or pits (that may be seasonal ponds) or covered enclosures.

Liquid and slurry storage is basically limited to ponds, lagoons, pits or tanks either below or above ground. Long-term storage is coincident with onsite treatment, usually by anaerobic digestion. Anaerobic digestion will reduce the volatile solids indicated in table 70.13, which also reduces odours emanating from eventual utilization. Unguarded below-surface holding facilities can lead to injuries or fatalities from accidental entry and falls (Knoblauch et al. 1996).

The transfer of liquid manure presents a highly variable hazard from mercaptans produced by anaerobic digestion. Mercaptans (sulphur-containing gases) have been shown to be major contributors to the odour of manure and are all quite toxic (Banwart and Brenner 1975). Perhaps the most dangerous of the effects from H_2S shown in table 70.14 is its insidious capacity to paralyze the sense of smell in the 50- to 100-ppm range, removing the sensory

Table 70.14 • Some important toxicologic benchmarks for hydrogen sulphide (H_2S).

Physiological or regulatory benchmark	Parts per million (ppm)
Odour detection threshold (rotten-egg smell)	.01–.1
Offensive odour	3–5
TLV-TWA = recommended exposure limit	10
TLV-STEL = recommended 15-minute exposure limit	15
Olfactory paralysis (cannot be smelled)	50–100
Bronchitis (dry cough)	100–150
IDLH (pneumonitis and pulmonary oedema)	100
Rapid respiratory arrest (death in 1–3 breaths)	1,000–2,000

TLV-TWA = Threshold limit values–Time weighted average; STEL = Short-term exposure level; IDLH = Immediately dangerous to life and health.

capacity to detect higher, rapidly toxic levels. Liquid storage for as short as 1 week is enough to initiate the anaerobic production of toxic mercaptans. Major differences in long-term manure gas generation rates are thought to be due to uncontrolled variations in the chemical and physical differences within the stored manure, such as temperature, pH, ammonia and organic loading (Donham, Yeggy and Dauge 1985).

The normally slow release of these gases during storage is greatly increased if the slurry is agitated to resuspend the sludge that accumulates at the bottom. H_2S concentrations of 300 ppm have been reported (Panti and Clark 1991), and 1,500 ppm has been measured during the agitation of liquid manure. The rates of gas release during agitation are much too large to be controlled by ventilation. It is most important to realize that natural anaerobic digestion is uncontrolled and therefore highly variable. The frequency of serious and fatal over-exposures can be predicted statistically but not at any individual site or time. A survey of dairy farmers in Switzerland reported a frequency of about one manure gas accident per 1,000 person-years (Knoblauch et al. 1996). Safety precautions are necessary each time agitation is planned to avoid the unusually hazardous event. If the operator does not agitate, sludge will build up until it may have to be removed mechanically. Such sludge should be left to dry before someone physically enters an enclosed pit. There should be a written confined-space programme.

Rarely used alternatives to anaerobic ponds include an aerobic pond, a facultative pond (one using bacteria that can grow under both aerobic and anaerobic conditions), drying (dewatering), composting or an anaerobic digester for biogas (USDA 1992). Aerobic conditions can be created either by keeping the liquid depth no more than 60 to 150 cm or by mechanical aeration. Natural aeration takes more space; mechanical aeration is more costly, as are the circulating pumps of a facultative pond. Composting may be conducted in windrows (rows of manure which must be turned every 2 to 10 days), a static but aerated pile or a specially constructed vessel. The high nitrogen content of manure must be reduced by mixing a high carbon amendment that will support the thermophilic microbial growth necessary for composting to control odours and remove pathogens. Composting is an economical method of treating small carcasses, if local ordinances permit. See also the article "Waste disposal operations" elsewhere in this *Encyclopaedia*. If a rendering or disposal plant is not available, other options include incineration or burial. Their prompt treatment is important to control herd or flock disease. Swine and poultry wastes are particularly amenable to methane production, but this utilization technique is not widely adopted.

Thick crusts can form on top of liquid manure and appear solid. A worker may walk on this crust and break through and drown. Workers can also slip and fall into liquid manure and drown. It is important to keep rescue equipment near the liquid manure storage site and avoid working alone. Some manure gases, such as methane, are explosive, and "no smoking" signs should be posted in or around the manure storage building (Deere & Co. 1994).

Application Hazards

Transfer and utilization of dry manure can be by hand or with mechanical aids like a front-end loader, skid-steer loader and manure spreader, each of which presents a safety hazard. Manure is spread onto land as fertilizer. Manure spreaders are generally pulled behind a tractor and powered by a power-take-off (PTO) from the tractor. They are classified into one of four types: box-type with rear beaters, flail, V-tank with side discharge and closed tank. The first two are used to apply solid manure; the V-tank spreader is used to apply liquid, slurry or solid manure; and the

---

Table 70.15 • Some safety procedures related to manure spreaders.

1. Only one person should operate the machine to avoid inadvertent activation by another person.

2. Keep workers clear of active power-take offs (PTOs), beaters, augers and expellers.

3. Maintain all guards and shields.

4. Keep persons clear of rear and sides of the spreader, which can project heavy objects mixed into the manure as far as 30 m.

5. Avoid dangerous unplugging operations by preventing spreader plugging:
   • Keep stones, boards and other objects out of the spreader.
   • In freezing weather, make sure flails and chains on flail-type spreaders are loose and unfrozen before operation.
   • Keep chains and beaters on beater-type spreaders in good operating order by replacing stretched chains and avoiding dropping loads of frozen manure onto the spreader chains.
   • Never get into an operating spreader to clean it.
   • Maintain the unloading auger and discharge expeller on V-tank spreaders so they operate freely.
   • In cold weather, clean the spreader insides so wet manure will not freeze the moving parts.

6. Use good tractor and PTO safety practices.

7. Make sure the relief valve on closed-tank spreaders is operative to avoid excessive pressures.

8. When unhooking the spreader from the tractor, make sure the jack that holds the weight of the spreader tongue is secure and locked to prevent the spreader from falling.

9. When the spreader is creating airborne dust or aerosols, use respiratory protection.

Source: Deere & Co. 1994.

---

closed tank spreader is used to apply liquid manure. The spreaders throw the manure over large areas either to the rear or sides. Hazards include the machinery, falling objects, dust and aerosols. Several safety procedures are listed in table 70.15.

DAIRY

John May

The dairy farmer is a livestock specialist whose aim is optimizing the health, nutrition and reproductive cycling of a herd of cows with the ultimate goal of maximal milk production. Major determinants of the farmer's exposure to hazards are farm and herd size, labour pool, geography and degree of mechanization. A dairy farm may be a small family business milking 20 or fewer cows per day, or it may be a corporate operation using three shifts of workers to feed and milk thousands of cows around the clock. In regions of the world where the climate is quite mild, the cattle may be housed in open sheds with roofs and minimal walls. Alternatively, in some regions barns must be tightly closed to preserve sufficient heat to protect the animals and the watering and milking systems. All of these factors contribute variability to the risk profile of the dairy farmer. Nevertheless, there are a series of hazards which most people working in dairy farming around the world will encounter to at least some degree.

Hazards and Precautions

Noise

One potential hazard which clearly relates to the degree of mechanization is noise. In dairy farming, harmful noise levels are common and always related to some type of mechanical device. Leading offenders outside of the barn are tractors and chain-saws. Noise levels from these sources are often at or above the 90-100 dBA range. Within the barn, other noise sources include bedding choppers, small skid-steer loaders and milking pipeline vacuum pumps. Here again, sound pressures may exceed those levels generally considered to be damaging to the ear. Although the studies of noise-induced hearing loss in dairy farmers are limited in number, they combine to show a convincing pattern of hearing deficits affecting predominantly the higher frequencies. These losses can be quite substantial and occur considerably more frequently in farmers of all ages than in non-farm controls. In several of the studies, the losses were more notable in the left than the right ear—possibly because farmers spend much of their time with the left ear turned toward the engine and muffler when driving with an implement. Prevention of these losses may be accomplished by efforts directed at noise abatement and muffling, and institution of a hearing-conservation programme. Certainly, the habit of wearing hearing protective devices, either muffs or earplugs, may help substantially to reduce the next generation's risk of noise-induced hearing loss.

Chemicals

The dairy farmer has contact with some chemicals which are commonly found in other types of agriculture, as well as some which are specific to the dairy industry, such as those used for cleaning the automated vacuum-powered milking pipeline system. This pipeline must be effectively cleaned before and after each use. Commonly this is done by first flushing the system with a very strong alkaline soap solution (typically 35% sodium hydroxide), followed by an acidic solution such as 22.5% phosphoric acid. A number of injuries have been observed in association with these chemicals. Spills have resulted in significant skin burns. Splatters may injure the cornea or conjunctivae of unprotected eyes. Tragic accidental ingestion—often by young children—which may occur when these materials are pumped into a cup and then briefly left unattended. These situations can be best prevented by the use of an automated, closed flush system. In the absence of an automated system, precautions must be taken to restrict access to these solutions. Measuring cups should be clearly labelled, reserved for only this purpose, never left unattended and rinsed thoroughly after each use.

Like others working with livestock, dairy farmers may have exposure to a variety of pharmaceutical agents ranging from antibiotics and progestational agents to prostaglandin inhibitors and hormones. Depending upon the country, dairy farmers also may use fertilizers, herbicides and insecticides with varying degrees of intensity. In general, the dairy farmer uses these agrochemicals less intensively than persons working in some other types of farming. However, the same care in mixing, applying and storing these materials is necessary. Appropriate application techniques and protective garb are as important for the dairy farmer as anyone else working with these compounds.

Ergonomic Risks

Although data on the prevalence of all musculoskeletal problems are currently incomplete, it is clear that dairy farmers have increased risk of arthritis of the hip and knee compared to non-farmers. Similarly, their risk of back problems may also be elevated. Although not well studied, there is little question that ergonomics is a major problem. The farmer may routinely carry weights in excess of 40 kg—often in addition to considerable personal body weight. Tractor driving produces abundant vibration exposure. However, it is the portion of the job devoted to milking that seems most ergonomically significant. A farmer may bend or stoop 4 to 6 times in the milking of a single cow. These motions are repeated with each of a number of cows twice daily for decades. Carrying the milking equipment from stall to stall imposes an additional ergonomic load on the upper extremities. In countries where milking is less mechanized, the ergonomic load on the dairy farmer might be different, but still it is likely to reflect considerable repetitive strain. A potential solution in some countries is the shift to milking parlours. In this setting the farmer can milk a number of cows simultaneously while standing several feet below them in the central pit of the parlour. This eliminates the stooping and bending as well as the upper-extremity load of carrying equipment from stall to stall. The latter problem is also addressed by the overhead track systems being introduced in some Scandinavian countries. These support the weight of the milking equipment when moving between stalls, and can even provide a convenient seat for the milker. Even with these potential solutions, much remains to be learned about ergonomic problems and their resolution in dairy farming.

Dust

A closely linked problem is organic dust. This is a complex, often allergenic and generally ubiquitous material on dairy farms. The dust frequently has high concentrations of endotoxin and may contain beta-glucans, histamine and other biologically active materials (Olenchock et al. 1990). Levels of total and respirable dust may exceed 50 mg/m^3 and 5 mg/m^3, respectively, with certain operations. These most commonly involve work with microbially contaminated feed or bedding within a closed space such as a barn, hay loft, silo or grain bin. Exposure to these dust levels may result in acute problems such as ODTS or hypersensitivity pneumonitis ("farmer's lung disease"). Chronic exposure may also play a role in asthma, farmer's lung disease and chronic bronchitis, which seems to occur at twice the rate of a non-farm population (Rylander and Jacobs 1994). The prevalence rates of some of these problems are higher in settings where moisture levels in the feed are likely to be elevated and in areas where barns are more tightly closed because of climatic requirements. Various farming practices such as drying of the hay and shaking out of feed for the animals by hand, and the choice of bedding material, can be major determinants of the levels of both the dust and its associated illnesses. Farmers can often devise a number of techniques to minimize either the amount of microbial overgrowth or its subsequent aerosolization. Examples include the use of sawdust, newspapers and other alternative materials for bedding instead of moulded hay. If hay is used, the addition of a quart of water to the cut surface of the bale minimizes the dust generated by a mechanical bedding chopper. Capping vertical silos with plastic sheets or tarpaulins without additional feed on top of this layer minimizes the dust of subsequent uncapping. The use of small amounts of moisture and/or ventilation in situations where dust is likely to be generated is often possible. Finally, farmers must anticipate potential dust exposures and use appropriate respiratory protection in these situations.

Allergens

Allergens may represent a troublesome health challenge for some dairy farmers. Major allergens appear to be those encountered in the barns, typically animal danders and "storage mites" living in feed stored within the barns. One study has extended the storage mite problem beyond the barn, finding sizeable populations of these species living within farmhouses as well (van Hage-Hamsten, Johansson and Hogland 1985). Mite allergy has been confirmed as a problem in a number of parts of the world, often with differing species of mites. Reactivity to these mites, to cow dander and to multiple other less significant allergens, results in several allergic manifestations (Marx et al. 1993). These include immediate onset of nasal and eye irritation, allergic dermatitis and, of greatest concern, allergy-mediated occupational asthma. This can occur as either an immediate or delayed (up to 12 hours) reaction and may occur in individuals not previously known to be asthmatic. It is of concern because the dairy farmer's involvement in barn activities is daily, intensive and lifelong. With this nearly continual allergic re-challenge, progressively more severe asthma is likely to be seen in some farmers. Prevention includes avoidance of dust, which is the most effective and, unfortunately, the most difficult intervention for most dairy farmers. The results of medical therapies, including allergy shots, topical steroids or other anti-inflammatory agents, and symptomatic relief with bronchodilators, have been mixed.

CATTLE, SHEEP AND GOATS

Melvin L. Myers*

Several animals convert high-fibre feeds, called roughage (over 18% fibre), into edible food that is consumed by humans. This ability comes from their four-stomach digestion system, which includes their largest stomach, the rumen (for which they gain the designation *ruminants*) (Gillespie 1997). Table 70.16 shows the various types of ruminant livestock that have been domesticated and their uses.

Production Processes

Processes for rearing ruminants vary from intensive, high-production operations such as raising beef cattle on large, 2,000-km² ranches in Texas to communal grazing such as the nomadic herders of Kenya and the United Republic of Tanzania. Some farmers use their cattle as oxen for traction power in farm tasks such as ploughing. In humid areas, water buffalo serve the same purpose (Ker 1995). The trend is toward high-production, intensive systems (Gillespie 1997).

High-volume, intensive beef production depends on various interdependent operations. One is the cow-calf system, which involves keeping a herd of cows. The cows are bred by bulls or artificial insemination annually to produce calves, and, after weaning, the calves are sold to cattle feeders to raise for slaughter. Male calves are castrated for the slaughter market; a castrated calf is called a *steer*. Pure-bred breeders maintain the herds of breeding stock, including bulls, which are very dangerous animals.

Sheep are produced in either range or farm flocks. In range production, flocks of 1,000 to 1,500 ewes are common. In farm flocks, production is usually small and typically a secondary enterprise. Sheep are raised for their wool or as feeder lambs for the slaughter market. Lambs are docked, and most male lambs are castrated. Some enterprises specialize in raising rams for pure-bred breeding.

Goats are raised through either range or small-farm production for their mohair, milk and meat. Pure-bred breeders are small operations that raise rams for breeding does. Specific breeds exist for each of these products. The goats are dehorned, and most males are castrated. Goats browse on shoots, twigs and leaves of brush plants, and thus they may also be used to control brush on a ranch or farm.

* Material on hair-cutting and shearing was written with the assistance of J.F. Copplestone's article on the subject in the 3rd edition of this Encyclopaedia.

Table 70.16 • Types of ruminants domesticated as livestock.

Ruminant type	Uses
Cattle	Meat, milk, draught
Sheep	Meat, wool
Goats	Meat, milk, mohair
Camelids (llama, alpaca, dromedary and bactrian camels)	Meat, milk, hair, draught
Buffalo (water buffalo)	Meat, draught
Bison	Meat
Yaks	Meat, milk, wool
Reindeer	Meat, milk, draught

Other major processes involved in rearing cattle, sheep and goats include feeding, disease and parasite control, hair clipping and fleece shearing. The milking process and livestock waste disposal are addressed in other articles in this chapter.

Cattle, sheep and goats are fed in several ways, including grazing or feeding hay and silage. Grazing is the least expensive way to deliver forage to animals. Animals typically graze on pastures, wild lands or crop residues, such as corn stalks, which remain in the field after crop harvests. Hay is harvested from the field and typically stored loose or in stacked bales. The feeding operation includes moving the hay from the stack to the open field or into mangers to feed the animals. Some crops such as corn are harvested and converted into silage. Silage is typically moved mechanically into mangers for feeding.

The control of diseases and parasites in cattle, sheep and goats is an integral part of the livestock-rearing process and requires animal contact. Routine visits to the herd by a veterinarian are an important part of this process, as is observing vital signs. Timely vaccination against diseases and quarantining diseased animals are also important. External parasites include flies, lice, mange, mites and ticks. Chemicals are one control against these parasites. Pesticides are applied by spraying or through insecticide-impregnated ear tags. The heel fly lays eggs on the hair of cattle, and its larva, the cattle grub, burrows into the skin. A control for this grub is systemic pesticides (spread throughout the body through spray, dips or as a feed additive). Internal parasites, including roundworms or flatworms, are controlled with drugs, antibiotics or drenches (oral administration of a liquid medication). Sanitation is also a strategy for the control of infectious diseases and parasite infestations (Gillespie 1997).

The removal of hair from live animals helps to maintain their cleanliness or comfort and to prepare them for exhibitions. Hair may be sheared from live animals as a product, such as the fleece from sheep or mohair from goats. The sheep shearer catches the animal in a pen and drags it to a stand where it is laid on its back for the shearing operation. It is pinned by the shearer's legs. Hair cutters and sheep shearers use a hand-operated scissors or motorized shears to clip the hair. The motorized shears are typically powered by electricity. Prior to shearing and also as part of gestation management, sheep are tagged and crutched (i.e., hair encrusted with faeces is removed). The cut fleece is manually trimmed according to the quality and staple of the hair. It is then compressed into packs for transportation using a hand-operated screw or hydraulic ram.

Facilities used for raising cattle, sheep and goats are generally considered to be either confined or unconfined. Confined facilities include confinement houses, feedlots, barns, corrals (holding, sorting and crowding pens), fences and working and loading chutes. Unconfined facilities refer to pasture or range operations. Feeding facilities include storage facilities (vertical and horizontal silos), feed grinding and mixing equipment, haystacks, conveying equipment (including augers and elevators), feed bunks, water fountains and mineral and salt feeders. In addition, sun protection may be provided by sheds, trees or overhead lattice work. Other facilities include back rubbers for parasite control, creep-feeders (allows feeder calves or lambs to feed without adults feeding), self-feeders, calf shelters, cattle-guard gates and cattle treatment stalls. Fencing may be used around pastures, and these include barbed wire and electric fences. Woven wire may be required to contain goats. Free-ranging animals would require herding to control their movement; goats may be tethered, but require shade. Dipping tanks are used for parasite control in large sheep flocks (Gillespie 1997).

Hazards

Table 70.17 shows several other processes of cattle, sheep and goat handling, with associated hazardous exposures. In a survey of farm workers in the United States (Meyers 1997), handling livestock represented 26% of lost-time injuries. This percentage was higher than any other farm activity, as shown in figure 70.5. These figures would be expected to be representative of the injury rate in other industrialized countries. In countries where draught animals are common, injury rates would be expected to be higher. Injuries from cattle usually occur in farm buildings or in the vicinity of buildings. Cattle inflict injuries when they kick or step on people or crush them against a hard surface such as the side of a pen. People may also be injured by falling when working with cattle, sheep and goats. Bulls inflict the most serious injuries. Most of the people injured are family members rather than hired workers. Fatigue can reduce judgement, and thus increase the chance of injury (Fretz 1989).

Livestock exhibit behaviours that can lead to injuries of workers. The herding instinct is strong among animals such as cattle or

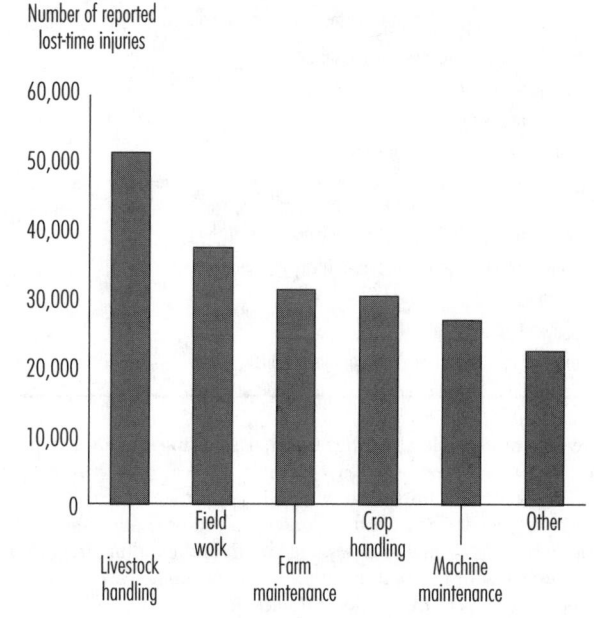

Figure 70.5 • Estimates of lost-time injury frequency by farm activity in the United States, 1993.

Number of reported lost-time injuries

Activity when farm worker was injured

Source: Meyers 1997.

Table 70.17 • Livestock rearing processes and potential hazards.

Process	Potential hazardous exposures
Breeding, artificial inseminating	Violent acts by bulls, rams or bucks; slips and falls; zoonoses; organic dust and dander
Feeding	Organic dust; silo gas; machines; lifting; electricity
Calving, lambing, kidding	Lifting and pulling; animal behaviour
Castrating, docking	Animal behaviour; lifting; cuts from knives
Dehorning	Animal behaviour; cuts from trimmers; caustic salves; burns from electric irons
Branding and marking	Burns; animal behaviour
Vaccinating	Animal behaviour; needle sticks
Spraying and dusting/drenching, worming	Organophosphates
Foot/hoof trimming	Animal behaviour; awkward postures; tool-related cuts and pinches
Shearing, tagging and crutching, washing and clipping	Awkward postures and lifting; animal behaviour; hand-shearer cuts; electricity
Loading and unloading	Animal behaviour
Manure handling	Manure gases; slips and falls; lifting; machines

Sources: Deere & Co. 1994; Fretz 1989; Gillespie 1997; NIOSH 1994.

sheep, and imposed limits such as isolation or overcrowding can lead to unusual behavioural patterns. Reflexive response is a common defensive behaviour among animals, and it can be predicted. Territorialism is another behaviour that is predictable. A reflexive escape struggle is apparent when an animal is removed from its normal quarters and placed in a confined environment. Animals that are restrained by chutes for loading for transportation will exhibit agitated reflex response behaviour.

Dangerous environments are numerous in cattle, sheep and goat production facilities. These include slippery floors, manure pits, corrals, dusty feed areas, silos, mechanized feeding equipment and animal confinement buildings. Confinement buildings may have manure storage pits, which can emit lethal gases (Gillespie 1997).

Heat exhaustion and stroke are potential hazards. Heavy physical labour, stress and strain, heat, high humidity and dehydration from lack of drinking water all contribute to these hazards.

Livestock handlers are at risk for developing respiratory illness from exposure to inhaled dusts. A common illness is organic dust toxic syndrome. This syndrome may follow exposures to heavy concentrations of organic dusts contaminated with micro-organisms. About 30 to 40% of workers who are exposed to organic dusts will develop this syndrome, which includes the conditions shown in table 70.18; this table also shows other respiratory conditions (NIOSH 1994).

Hair cutters and sheep shearers face several hazards. Cuts and abrasions may result during the shearing operation. Animal hoofs and horns also present potential hazards. Slips and falls are an ever-present hazard while handling the animals. Power for the shears is sometimes transferred by belts, and guards must be maintained. Electrical hazards are also present. Shearers also face postural hazards, particularly to the back, as a result of catching and tipping the sheep. Constraining the animal between the shearer's legs tends to strain the back, and torsional movements

Table 70.18 • Respiratory illnesses from exposures on live-stock farms.

Organic dust toxic syndrome conditions
Precipitin-negative farmer's lung disease
Pulmonary mycotoxicosis
Silo unloader's syndrome
Grain fever in grain elevator workers

Other important respiratory illnesses
"Silo fillers' disease" (acute toxic inflammation of the lung)
"Farmer's lung disease" (hypersensitivity pneumonitis)
Bronchitis
Asphyxiation (suffocation)
Toxic gas inhalation (for example, manure pits)

are common while shearing. Manual shearing usually results in tenosynovitis.

The control of insects on cattle, sheep and goats with pesticide spray or powder can expose workers to the pesticide. Sheep dips submerge the animal in a pesticide bath, and handling the animal or contact with the bath solution or contaminated wool can also expose workers to the pesticide (Gillespie 1997).

Common zoonoses include rabies, brucellosis, bovine tuberculosis, trichinosis, salmonella, leptospirosis, ringworm, tapeworm, orf virus disease, Q fever and spotted fever. Diseases that may be contracted while working with hair and fleece include tetanus, salmonellosis from tagging and crutching, leptospirosis, anthrax and parasitic diseases.

Animal faeces and urine also provide a mechanism for infection of workers. Cattle are a reservoir for cryptosporidosis, a disease that can be transmitted from cattle to humans through the faecal-oral route. Calves with diarrhoea (scours) may harbour this disease. Schistosomiasis, an infection by blood flukes, is found in cattle, water buffalo and other animals in several parts of the world; its life cycle goes from eggs excreted in urine and faeces, developing into larvae, which enter snails, then to free-swimming cercariae that attach to and penetrate human skin. Penetration can occur while workers are wading in water.

Some zoonoses are arthropod-borne viral diseases. The primary vectors for these diseases are mosquitoes, ticks and sandflies. These diseases include arboviral encephalitides transmitted by ticks and milk from sheep, babesiosis transmitted by ticks from cattle and Crimean-Congo haemorrhagic fever (Central Asian haemorrhagic fever) transmitted by mosquitoes and ticks from cattle, sheep and goats (as amplifying hosts) during epizootics (Benenson 1990; Mullan and Murthy 1991).

Preventive Action

The principal occupational hazards that occur in rearing ruminants include injuries, respiratory problems and zoonotic diseases. (See the the box "A checklist for livestock rearing safety practices".)

Stair steps should be maintained in good condition, and floors must be even to reduce fall hazards. Guards on belts, mechanical screws, compression rams and shear sharpening equipment should be maintained. Wiring should be maintained in good condition to prevent electrical shock. Ventilation should be assured wherever internal combustion engines are used in barns.

Training and experience in properly handling animals helps to prevent injuries related to the animals' behaviour. Safe livestock handling requires understanding of both innate and acquired

components of animal behaviour. Facilities should be designed so workers do not have to enter small or enclosed areas with animals. Lighting should be diffuse, since animals may become confused and balk around bright lights. Sudden noises or movements may startle cattle, causing them to crowd a person against hard surfaces. Even clothing hanging on fences flapping in the wind can startle cattle. They should be approached from the front so as not to surprise them. Avoid use of contrasting patterns in cattle facilities, because cattle will slow or stop when they see these patterns. Shadows across the floor should be avoided because cattle may refuse to cross over them (Gillespie 1997).

Risks of organic dust exposure can be minimized in several ways. Workers should be aware of the health effects of breathing organic dust and inform their physician about recent dust exposures when seeking help for respiratory illness. Minimizing spoilage of feed can minimize potential fungal spore exposures. To avoid such hazards, workers should use mechanized equipment to move decaying materials. Farm operators should use local exhaust ventilation and wet methods of dust suppression to minimize exposure. Appropriate respirators should be worn when organic dust exposure cannot be avoided (NIOSH 1994).

Preventing zoonoses depends upon maintaining clean livestock facilities, vaccinating the animals, quarantine of sick animals and avoiding exposure to sick animals. Rubber gloves should be worn when treating sick animals to avoid exposures through any cuts in the hands. Workers who become sick after contact with a sick animal should seek medical help (Gillespie 1997).

PIGS

Melvin L. Myers

Pigs were primarily domesticated from two wild stocks—the European wild boar and the East Indian pig. The Chinese domesticated the pig as early as 4900 BC, and today more than 400 million pigs are reared in China out of 840 million worldwide (Caras 1996).

Pigs are reared primarily for food and have many distinguishing attributes. They grow fast and large, and the sows have large litters and short gestation periods of about 100 to 110 days. Pigs are omnivores and eat berries, carrion, insects and garbage, as well as the corn, silage and pasture of high-production enterprises. They convert 35% of their feed into meat and lard, which is more efficient than ruminant species such as cattle (Gillespie 1997).

Production Processes

Some pig holdings are small—for example, one or two animals, which can represent much of a family's wealth (Scherf 1995). Large pig operations include two major processes (Gillespie 1997).

One process is pure-bred production, in which pig breeding stock are improved. Within the pure-bred operation, artificial insemination is prevalent. Pure-bred boars are typically used to breed sows in the other major process, commercial production. The commercial production process rears pigs for the slaughter market and typically follows one of two different types of operations. One operation is a two-stage system. The first stage is feeder pig production, which uses a herd of sows to farrow litters of 14 to 16 piglets per sow. The pigs are weaned, then sold to the next stage of the system, the buying and finishing enterprise, which feeds them for the slaughter market. The most common feeds are corn and soybean oil meal. The feed grains are typically ground.

The other and most common operation is the complete sow and litter system. This production operation rears a herd of breeding sows and farrowing pigs, caring for and feeding the farrowed pigs for the slaughter market.

Some sows give birth to a litter that may outnumber her teats. To feed the excess piglets, a practice is to spread piglets from large litters into other sows' smaller litters. Pigs are born with needle teeth, which are typically clipped at the gum-line before the pig is two days old. Ears are notched for identification. Tail docking occurs when the pig is about 3 days old. Male pigs raised for the slaughter market are castrated before they are 3 weeks old.

Maintaining a healthy herd is the single most important management practice in pig production. Sanitation and the selection of healthy breeding stock are important. Vaccination, sulpha drugs and antibiotics are used to prevent many infectious diseases. Insecticides are used to control lice and mites. The large roundworm and other parasites of pigs are controlled through sanitation and drugs.

Facilities used for pig production include pasture systems, a combination of pasture and low-investment housing and high-investment total-confinement systems. The trend is toward more confinement housing because it produces faster growth than does pasture rearing. However, pasture is valuable in feeding the pig-breeding herd to prevent fattening the breeding herd; it may be used for all or part of the production operation with the use of portable housing and equipment.

Confinement buildings require ventilation to control temperature and moisture. Heat may be added in farrowing houses. Slotted floors are used in confinement houses as a labour-saving approach for handling manure. Fencing and handling feeding and watering equipment are needed for the pig production enterprise. Facilities are cleaned by power washing and disinfecting after all bedding, manure and feed are removed (Gillespie 1997).

Hazards

Injuries from pigs usually occur within or close to farm buildings. Dangerous environments include slippery floors, manure pits, automatic feeding equipment and confinement buildings. Confinement buildings have a manure storage pit that emits gases that, if not ventilated, can kill not only pigs, but workers as well.

Pig behaviour can pose hazards to workers. A sow will attack if her piglets are threatened. Pigs can bite, step on or knock people down. They tend to stay in or return to familiar areas. A pig will try to return to the herd when attempts are made to separate it. Pigs are likely to balk when moved from a dark area into a light area, such as out of a pig house into the daylight. At night, they will resist moving into dark areas (Gillespie 1997).

In a Canadian study of pig farmers, 71% reported chronic back problems. Risk factors include intervertebral disc loading associated with driving and sitting for long periods while operating heavy equipment. This study also identified lifting, bending, twisting, pushing and pulling as risk factors. In addition, more than 35% of these farmers reported chronic knee problems (Holness and Nethercott 1994).

Three types of air exposures pose hazards on pig farms:

1. dust from feed, animal hair and faecal matter
2. pesticides used on pigs and other chemicals, such as disinfectants
3. ammonia, hydrogen sulphide, methane and carbon monoxide from manure storage pits.

Fires in buildings are another potential hazard, as is electricity.

Some zoonotic infections and parasites can be transmitted from the pig to the worker. Common zoonoses associated with pigs include brucellosis and leptospirosis (swineherd's disease).

Preventive Action

Several safety recommendations have evolved for the safe handling of pigs (Gillespie 1997):

- Working with small pigs in the same pen as the sow should be avoided.
- A hurdle or solid panel should be used when handling pigs to avoid bites and being knocked over.
- A pig can be moved backwards by placing a basket over its head.
- Children should be kept out of pig pens and not allowed to reach through fences to pet pigs.
- Because of their herding instincts, it is easier to separate a group of pigs from a herd than a single animal.
- Pigs can be moved from dark to light areas with the use of artificial light. When pigs are moved at night, such as through chutes or alleys, a light should be placed at the destination.
- Loading chutes should be level or at not more than a 25-degree angle.

Musculoskeletal injury risk can be decreased by reducing exposure to repetitive trauma (by taking frequent breaks or by varying the kinds of tasks), improving posture, reducing the weight lifted (use co-worker or mechanical assistance) and avoiding rapid, jerking movements.

Dust control techniques include lowering stock density to reduce dust concentration. In addition, automatic feed delivery systems should be enclosed to contain dust. Water misting can be used, but it is ineffective in freezing weather and can contribute to the survival of bioaerosols and increase endotoxin levels. Filters and scrubbers in the air handling system show promise in cleaning dust particles from recirculated air. Respirators are another way to control dust exposures (Feddes and Barber 1994).

Vent pipes should be installed in manure pits to prevent dangerous gases from recirculating into the farm buildings. Electrical power should be maintained to vent fans at the pits. Workers should be trained in the safe use of pesticides and other chemicals, such as disinfectants, used in pig production.

Cleanliness, vaccination, quarantine of sick animals and avoiding exposures are ways to control zoonoses. When treating sick pigs, wear rubber gloves. A person who becomes sick after working with sick pigs should contact a physician (Gillespie 1997).

POULTRY AND EGG PRODUCTION

Steven W. Lenhart

Farm production of birds weighing 18 kg or less includes not only domestic birds such as chickens, turkeys, ducks, geese and guineas, but also game birds produced for hunting, such as partridges, quail, grouse and pheasants. While some of these birds are raised outdoors, the majority of commercial poultry and egg production occurs in specially designed confinement houses or barns. Larger birds weighing between 40 and 140 kg, such as cassowaries, rheas, emus and ostriches, are also raised on farms for their meat, eggs, leather, feathers and fat. However, because of their larger size, most of these birds, which are known collectively as ratites, are usually raised outdoors in fenced-in areas containing shelters.

Chickens and turkeys comprise the majority of poultry produced in the world. US farmers annually produce one-third of the world's chickens—more than the next six leading chicken-producing countries combined (Brazil, China, Japan, France, the United Kingdom and Spain). Similarly, more than half the world's turkey production occurs in the United States, followed by France, Italy, the United Kingdom and Germany.

While commercial chicken production occurred in the United States as early as 1880, poultry and egg production was not recog-

Figure 70.6 • Part of a commercial flock of 3- to 6-week old ostriches.

Roger Holbrook, Postime Ostrich, Guilford, Indiana

When processed at about 12 months of age, each bird will weigh approximately 100 kg, of which 35 kg is boneless meat. An adult ostrich can weigh as much as 140 kg.

Figure 70.7 • Commercial flock of 12-month old emus.

Volz Emu Farm, Batesville, Indiana

When processed at about 14 months of age, each bird will weigh between 50 and 65 kilograms, of which approximately 15 kilograms is meat and 15 kilograms is fat for oil and lotions.

nized as a large-scale industry until about 1950. In 1900, a chicken weighed slightly less than a kilogram after 16 weeks. Before the emergence of poultry production as an industry, chickens purchased for eating were seasonal, being most abundant in early summer. Improvements in breeding, feed-to-weight conversion, processing and marketing practices, housing and disease control contributed to the poultry industry's growth. The availability of artificial vitamin D also made a major contribution. All these improvements resulted in year-round poultry production, shorter production periods per flock and an increase in the number of birds housed together from only a few hundred to several thousand. The production of broilers (7-week-old chickens weighing approximately 2 kg) increased dramatically in the United States, from 143 million chickens in 1940, to 631 million in 1950, to 1.8 billion in 1960 (Nesheim, Austic and Card 1979). US farmers produced approximately 7.6 billion broilers in 1996 (USDA 1997).

Egg production has also seen dramatic growth similar to broiler production. At the beginning of the twentieth century, a laying hen annually produced about 30 eggs, mostly in the spring. Today, the annual average per layer is more than 250 eggs.

Ratite farming primarily consists of the ostrich from Africa, the emu and cassowary from Australia and the rhea from South America. (Figure 70.6 shows a farm flock of ostriches, and figure 70.7 shows a farm flock of emus.) Ratite farming first started in South Africa in the late 1800s in response to a fashion demand for the wing and tail feathers of ostriches. While ostrich plumes no longer decorate hats and clothing, commercial production still occurs not only in South Africa, but also in other African countries such as Namibia, Zimbabwe and Kenya. Ratite farming also occurs in Australia, Germany, Great Britain, Italy, China and the United States. The meat of these birds is gaining popularity because, while it is a red meat with a beefy taste and texture, it has total and saturated fat levels much lower than beef.

Poultry Confinement Housing

A typical poultry confinement house in the United States is a long (60 to 150 m), narrow (9 to 15 m) single-storey barn with a dirt floor covered with litter (a layer of wood shavings, sphagnum peat

or sawdust). Both ends of a confinement house have large doors, and both sides have half-side curtains running the length of the structure. Watering systems (called *drinkers*) and automatic feeding systems are located close to the floor and run the entire length of a house. Large, 1.2-m diameter propeller fans are also present in a poultry house to keep the birds comfortable. A poultry farmer's daily tasks include maintaining acceptable environmental conditions for the birds, ensuring the continuous flow of feed and water and collecting and disposing of dead birds.

Watering and feeding systems are raised 2.5 to 3 metres above the floor when a flock reaches its processing age to accommodate

Figure 70.8 • Chicken catchers collecting broilers and placing them in crates for delivery to a poultry processing plant.

Steven W. Lenhart

Figure 70.9 • Turkey catchers separating birds from a flock and driving them into a holding pen.

Steven W. Lenhart

catchers, workers who collect the birds for transport to a poultry processing plant. Collecting chickens is usually done by hand. Each member of a crew must bend over or stoop to gather several birds at a time and place them into coops, cages or crates. Each worker will repeat this process several hundred times during a work shift (see figure 70.8). For other types of poultry (e.g., ducks and turkeys), workers herd the birds to a collection area. Turkey catchers wave sticks with red bags tied to them in order to separate several birds at a time from a flock and drive them into a holding pen at the barn's entrance (see figure 70.9).

Poultry confinement houses vary from this general description depending primarily on the type of birds being housed. For example, in commercial egg production, adult hens or layers have traditionally been kept in cages arranged in parallel banks. Caged laying-hen systems-will be banned in Sweden in 1999 and replaced by loose laying-hen systems. (A loose laying system is shown in figure 70.10). Another difference between poultry confinement houses is that some do not have litter-covered floors but

Figure 70.10 • A loose laying system.

Steven W. Lenhart

Poultry catching, live hauling and processing

The potential for back injuries and respiratory disorders is high for poultry catchers. Many poultry companies in the United States contract out catching birds. Due to the transient nature of the catching crews there are no data indicating injuries or losses. Usually, catching crews are picked up and driven to the grower by company-owned truck. The crew members are either given or sold single use disposable respirators and disposable cotton gloves to protect their hands. Companies should make sure that respiratory protection is worn properly and that their crews have been properly medically evaluated and trained.

Each catch crew member must reach down and grab several struggling birds one after another and may be required to handle multiple birds at once. The birds are placed in a tray or drawer of a multi-bay module. The module holds several trays and is loaded by a company-owned fork-lift onto the bed of the company's flat bed trailer. The fork-lift operator may either be the company's truck driver or the contract crew leader. In either case, proper training and operation of the fork-lift must be assured. Speed and coordination are essential among the catching crew.

New methods of catching and loading have been experimented with in the US. One method being tried is a guided gatherer which has arms sweeping inwards guiding the chickens to a vacuum system. Attempts at automation to reduce the physical stresses and potential for respiratory exposure are a long way from success. Only the larger, more efficient poultry companies can afford the capital expenditures necessary to purchase and support such equipment.

A chicken's normal body temperature is 42.2 °C. Consequently, the mortality rate increases in the winter and in locations where the summers are hot and humid. Both in the summer and winter, the flock must be transported as quickly as possible to be processed. In the summer, prior to processing, trailer loads of modules containing birds must be kept out of the sun and cooled with large fans. Dust, dried faecal matter and chicken feathers are often airborne as a result.

Throughout the entire processing of chicken, rigid sanitation requirements must be met. This means floors must be periodically and often washed down and debris, parts and fat removed. Conveyors and processing equipment must be accessible, washed down and sanitized also. Condensation must not be allowed to accumulate on ceilings and equipment over exposed chicken. It must be wiped down with long-handled sponge mops.

In the majority of the processing plant's production areas, there is high noise exposure. Unguarded overhead radial blade fans circulate the air in the processing areas. Because of the sanitation requirements, guarded rotating equipment cannot be silenced for noise abatement purposes. An appropriate and well-run hearing conservation programme is necessary. Initial audiograms and annual audiograms should be given and periodic dosimetry should be performed to document exposure. Purchased processing equipment need to have as low an operating noise level as possible.

Particular care needs to be taken in educating and training the workforce. Workers must understand the full implications of exposure to noise and how to wear their hearing protection correctly.

Tony Ashdown

instead have either slotted or plastic-coated wire floors with manure pits or liquid manure catchment areas under them. In western Europe, poultry confinement houses tend to be smaller than US houses, and they utilize block construction with cement floors for easy litter removal. Western European poultry confinement houses are also decontaminated and floor litter removed after every flock.

Health Risks

The health and safety risks of poultry farmers, their family members (including children) and others who work in poultry confinement houses have increased as the poultry industry has grown. Raising a poultry flock requires a farmer to work 7 days a week. Consequently, unlike most occupations, exposures to contaminants occur over several consecutive days, with the period between flocks (as short as 2 days) being the only time of non-exposure to poultry house contaminants. The air of a poultry house can contain gaseous agents such as ammonia from litter, carbon monoxide from poorly ventilated gas-fired heaters and hydrogen sulphide from liquid manure. Also, particles of organic or agricultural dust are aerosolized from poultry house litter. Poultry house litter contains an assortment of contaminants including bird excreta, feathers and dander; feed dust; insects (beetles and flies), mites and their parts; micro-organisms (viral, bacterial and fungal); bacterial endotoxin; and histamine. The air of a poultry house can be very dusty, and for a first-time or occasional visitor, the smell of manure and the pungent odour of ammonia can at times be overwhelming. However, poultry farmers seemingly develop an adaptive tolerance to the smell and to ammonia's odour.

Because of their inhalation exposures, unprotected poultry workers are at risk of developing respiratory diseases such as allergic rhinitis, bronchitis, asthma, hypersensitivity pneumonitis or allergic alveolitis and organic dust toxic syndrome. Acute and chronic respiratory symptoms experienced by poultry workers include cough, wheezing, excessive mucus secretion, shortness of breath and chest pain and tightness. Pulmonary function testing of poultry workers has provided evidence suggesting not only the risk for chronic obstructive diseases such as chronic bronchitis and asthma, but also restrictive diseases such as chronic hypersensitivity pneumonitis. Common non-respiratory symptoms among poultry workers include eye irritation, nausea, headache and fever. Of approximately 40 zoonotic diseases of agricultural importance, six (*Mycobacterium avium* infection, erysipeloid, listeriosis, conjunctival Newcastle infection, psittacosis and dermatophytosis) are of concern to poultry workers, although they occur only rarely. Non-zoonotic infectious diseases of concern include candidiasis, staphylococcosis, salmonellosis, aspergillosis, histoplasmosis and cryptococcosis.

There are also health issues affecting poultry workers that are as yet unstudied or poorly understood. For example, poultry farmers and especially chicken catchers develop a skin condition they refer to as *galding*. This condition has an appearance of a rash or dermatitis and primarily affects a person's hands, forearms and inner thighs. The ergonomics of poultry catching are also unstudied. Bending to collect several thousand birds every work shift and carrying eight to fifteen chickens, each weighing from 1.8 to 2.3 kg, is physically demanding, but how this work affects a catcher's back and upper extremities is unknown. The extent to which the many psychosocial factors associated with farming have affected the lives of poultry farmers and their families is also unknown, but occupational stress is perceived by many poultry farmers as a problem. Another important but unstudied issue is the extent to which the health of farmers' children is affected as a consequence of work in poultry houses.

Respiratory Health Protection Measures

The best way to protect any worker from exposure to airborne contaminants is with effective engineering controls that capture potential contaminants at their source before they can become airborne. In most industrial environments, airborne contaminants can be reduced to safe levels at their source by the installation of effective engineering control measures. Wearing respirators is the least desirable method for reducing workers' exposures to airborne contaminants, and respirator use is recommended only when engineering controls are not feasible, or while they are being installed or repaired. Nevertheless, at present, wearing a respirator is still probably the most feasible method available for reducing poultry workers' exposures to airborne contaminants. The general ventilation systems in poultry houses are not primarily intended to reduce the exposures of poultry workers. Research is going on to develop appropriate ventilation systems to reduce airborne contamination.

Not all respirators provide the same level of protection, and the type of respirator selected for use in a poultry confinement house can vary depending on the age of the birds being raised, age and condition of the litter, drinker type and position of the side curtains (open or closed). All of these are factors affecting airborne agricultural dust and ammonia concentrations. Airborne dust levels are highest during poultry-catching operations, at times to the point that one cannot see from one end of a poultry house to the other. A full-facepiece respirator with high-efficiency filters is recommended as the minimum protection for poultry workers based on bacterial endotoxin measurements made during chicken catching.

When ammonia levels are high, combination or "piggyback" cartridges are available that filter ammonia and particulates. A more expensive powered air-purifying respirator with a full-facepiece and high-efficiency filters may also be appropriate. These devices have the advantage that filtered air is constantly delivered to the wearer's facepiece, resulting in less breathing resistance. Hooded, powered air-purifying respirators are also available and can be used by bearded workers. Respirators providing less protection than full-facepiece or powered air-purifying types may be adequate for some work situations. However, downgrading the level of protection, such as to a half-mask disposable respirator, is recommended only after environmental measurements and medical monitoring show that the use of a less protective respirator will reduce exposures to safe levels. Repeated exposures of the eyes to poultry dust increase the risk for eye injury and disease. Respirators with full-facepieces and those with hoods have a benefit of also providing eye protection. Poultry workers who choose to wear half-mask respirators should also wear eyecup goggles.

For any respirator to protect its wearer, it must be used in accordance with a complete respiratory-protection programme. However, while poultry farmers experience inhalation exposures for which respirator usage may be beneficial, most of them are not currently prepared to carry out a respiratory protection programme by themselves. This need may be addressed by the development of regional or local respiratory protection programmes in which poultry farmers can participate.

Manure pits should be considered confined spaces. A pit's atmosphere should be tested if entry is unavoidable, and a pit should be ventilated if it is oxygen-deficient or contains toxic levels of gases or vapours. Safe entry may also require wearing a respirator. In addition, a standby person may be needed to stay in constant visual or speech contact with workers inside a manure pit.

Safety Risks

Safety risks associated with poultry and egg production include unguarded chains, sprockets, winches, belts and pulleys on fans, feeding equipment and other machinery. Scratches, pecks and even bites by the larger birds are also safety hazards. A male ostrich is especially protective of his nest during mating season, and when he feels threatened, he will attempt to kick any intruder. Long toes with sharp nails add to the danger of an ostrich's powerful kick.

Electrical hazards created by improperly grounded or non-corrosion-resistant equipment or poorly insulated wires in a poultry house can result in electrocution, non-fatal electrical shock or fire. Poultry dust will burn, and poultry farmers tell anecdotes about accumulated dust exploding within gas-fired heaters when the dust was aerosolized during housekeeping chores. Researchers with the US Bureau of Mines have performed explosiveness testing of agricultural dusts. When aerosolized in a 20-litre test chamber and ignited, dust that was collected from the tops of heater cabinets and from window ledges in chicken houses was determined to have a minimum explosible concentration of 170 g/m^3. Sieved samples of poultry house litter could not be ignited. By comparison, grain dust evaluated under the same laboratory conditions had a minimum explosible concentration of 100 g/m^3.

Safety Measures

Measures can be taken to reduce safety risks associated with poultry and egg production. For protection from moving parts, all machinery should be guarded, and fans should be screened. For tasks involving hand contact with birds, gloves should be worn. High standards of personal hygiene should be maintained, and any injuries, no matter how minor, caused by machinery or birds should be treated immediately to avoid infection. When approaching a ratite, movement toward the bird should be from the side or behind to avoid being kicked. A lockout system should be used when servicing electrical equipment. Poultry farmers should frequently remove settled dust from surfaces, but they should be aware that, on rare occasions, an explosion can result when high concentrations of accumulated dust are aerosolized within an enclosure and ignited.

● HORSES AND OTHER EQUINES

Lynn Barroby

Horses belong to the equine family, which includes the domesticated African wild ass, also known as the donkey or burro. Historians believe that domestication of the horse began circa 6000 BC and the donkey at least as early as 2600 BC. The mule, bred for work, is a cross between a male donkey (jack or jackass) and a female horse (mare). A mule is unable to reproduce. When a male horse (stallion) is bred with a female donkey (jennet), the offspring, also sterile, is called a hinny. Horses and donkeys have also been crossed with another equine, the zebra, and the offspring are collectively called zebroids. Zebroids are also sterile and of little economic importance (Caras 1996).

Processes

Of the 10 million horses in the United States, about 75% are used for personal pleasure riding. Other uses include racing, ranching, breeding and commercial riding. The horse has become a performer in racing, jumping, rodeo and many more events.

The three main horse enterprises are breeding, training and boarding stables. Horse breeding farms breed mares and sell the offspring. Some farms specialize in training horses for show or racing. Boarding stables feed and care for horses for customers who have no facilities to house their horses. All three of these enterprises are labour intensive.

Horse breeding is an increasingly scientific process. Pasture breeding was typical, but now it is generally controlled within a breeding barn or corral. Although artificial insemination is used, it is more common that mares are brought to the stallion for breeding. The mare is checked by a veterinarian and, during breeding, trained workers handle the stallion and the mare.

After giving birth, the mare nurses the foal until it is from 4 to 7 months of age; after weaning, the foal is separated from the mare. Some colts not meant for breeding may be castrated (gelded) as early as 10 months of age.

When a racehorse becomes a two-year-old, professional trainers and riders start breaking it to ride. This involves a gradual process of getting the horse used to human touch, being saddled and bridled, and finally mounted. Horses that race with carts and heavy draught horses are broke to drive at about two years of age, and ranch horses are broke at closer to three years old, sometimes using the rougher method of bucking a horse out.

In horse racing, the groom leads the horse to the saddling paddock, a trainer and a valet saddle it, and a jockey mounts it. The horse is led by a pony horse and rider, warmed up and loaded into the starting gate. Racehorses can become excited, and the noise of a race can further excite and frighten the horse. The groom takes a winning horse to a drug test barn for blood and urine samples. The groom must then cool the horse down with a bath, walking and sipping water.

A groom cares for the performance horse and is responsible for brushing and bathing it, saddling it for the exercise rider, applying any protective bandages or boots to its legs, cleaning the stall and bedding down straw, shavings, peat moss, peanut skins, shredded newspaper or even rice hulls. The groom or a "hot" walker walks the horse; sometimes a mechanical walker is used. The groom feeds the horse hay, grain and water, rakes and sweeps, washes the horse's laundry and carts manure away in a wheelbarrow. The groom holds the horse for others such as the veterinarian or farrier (farrier work is traditionally done by a blacksmith). All horses require parasite control, hoof care and teeth-filing.

Performance horses are typically stabled and given daily exercise. However, young stock and pleasure riding horses are generally stabled at night and released during the day, while others are kept outdoors in paddocks or pastures with sheds for shelter. Race horses in training are fed three or four times a day, while show horses, other performance horses, and breeding stock are fed twice a day. Range or ranch stock are fed once a day, depending on the forage present.

Horses travel for many reasons: shows, races, for breeding or to riding trails. Most are shipped by truck or trailer; however, some travel by rail or plane to major events.

Hazards and Precautions

Several hazards are associated with working around horses. A groom has a physically demanding job with a lot of forking of manure, moving 25 to 50 kg hay and straw bales and handling active horses. Startled or threatened horses may kick; thus, workers should avoid walking behind a horse. A frightened horse may jump and step on a worker's foot; this can also occur accidentally. Various restraints are available to handle fractious horses, such as a chain over the nose or a lip chain. Stress on horses due to shipping may cause balking and injuries to the horses and handlers.

The groom is potentially exposed to hay and grain dust, dust from bedding, moulds, horse dander and ammonia from the urine. Wearing a respirator can provide protection. Grooms do a lot of leg work on the horses, sometimes using liniments containing hazardous chemicals. Gloves are recommended. Some leather-tack care products can contain hazardous solvents, requiring ventilation and skin protection. Cuts can lead to serious infections such as tetanus or

Table 70.19 • Zoonoses associated with horses.

Viral diseases
Rabies (very low occurrence)
Eastern, western and some subtypes of Venezuelan equine encephalomyelitis
Vesicular stomatitis
Equine influenza
Equine morbillvirus disease (first documented in Australia in 1994)

Fungus infections
Ringworm (dermatomycoses)

Parasitic zoonoses
Trichinosis (large outbreaks in France and Italy in the 1970s and 1980s)
Hydatid disease (echinoccosis) (very rare)

Bacterial diseases
Salmonellosis
Glanders (now very rare, restricted to Middle East and Asia)
Brucellosis (rare)
Anthrax
Leptospirosis (relatively rare, direct human contamination not definitively proven)
Melioidosis (outbreaks in France in the 1970s and 1980s; direct transmission not reported)
Tuberculosis (very rare)
Pasteurellosis
Actinobacillus lignieresii, A., A. suis (suspected in Lyme disease transmission, Belgium)

septicaemia. Tetanus shots should be maintained current, especially because of exposure to manure.

A farrier is exposed to injury when shoeing a horse. The groom's job is to hold the horse to keep it from kicking the farrier or pulling its foot in a way that could strain the farrier's back or cut the farrier with the horseshoe and nails.

In the drug test barn, the test person is enclosed in a stall with a loose, excited and unfamiliar horse. He or she holds a stick (with a cup for urine) that may frighten the horse.

When riding horses, it is important to wear a good pair of boots and a helmet. Any mounted person needs a protective vest for racing, jumping, rodeo broncs, and ponying or exercising race-horses. There is always a danger of being bucked off or of a horse stumbling and falling.

Studs can be unpredictable, very strong and can bite or kick viciously. Brood mares are very defensive of their foals and can fight if threatened. Studs are kept individually in high-fenced paddocks, while other breeding stock are kept in groups with their own pecking order. Horses trying to move away from a boss horse or a group of yearlings at play can run over anyone who gets in the way. Foals, weanlings, yearlings and two-year-olds will bite and nip.

Some drugs (e.g., hormones) used in breeding are given orally and can be harmful to humans. Wearing gloves is recommended. Needle-stick injuries are another hazard. Good restraints, including stocks, can be used to control the animal during administration of medication. Topical sprays and automatic stable spray systems to control flies can easily be overused in horse rearing. These insecticides should be used in moderation, and warning labels should be read and recommendations followed.

There are a variety of zoonoses that can be passed from horses to humans, especially skin infections from contact with infected secretions. Horse bites can be a cause of some bacterial infections. See table 70.19 for a list of zoonoses associated with horses.

Elephants

The largest draught animal is the elephant, but its role is slowly becoming one of tradition rather than necessity. Two decades ago, 4,000 Asian elephants were used for logging in Thailand, but the forests there have been clear-cut and mechanization has displaced the elephant. However, they are still used in Myanmar, where elephant logging is prevalent. Logging companies frequently lease working elephants from their owners, who are typically urban businessmen.

The elephant handler (or trainer) is called an *oozie* in Myanmar and a *mahout* in India and Sri Lanka. The trainer mounts a saddle—a thick pad of leaves and bark—on the elephant's back to protect its sensitive spine from the dragging gear, or tack, used in pulling logs. The trainer sits on the elephant's neck as it uses its trunk, tusks, feet, mouth and forehead to accomplish its daily chores. A well-trained elephant in logging work will respond to more than 30 vocal commands and 90 pressure points on its body from a skilled handler. They work until 2:45 every afternoon, then the *oozie* scrubs the elephant in water with coconut halves for up to an hour. The *oozie* then feeds the elephant salted, cooked rice and hobbles and releases it to feed in the forest at night. At about 4:00 a.m., the *oozie* locates the elephant by unique tones of a bell that is attached to the elephant (Schmidt 1997).

Elephant bulls are rarely held in captivity, and cows are traditionally released to be bred in the wild. Artificial insemination is also used to breed elephants. Bull elephants donate semen to an elephant-sized artificial cow. It is impossible to observe visually the cow in oestrus (three times per year), so weekly samples of blood are taken for progesterone analysis. When a cow is in oestrus, she is bred by injecting semen into her vagina with a long, flexible pneumatic insemination tube.

Several hazards are associated with elephant handling; they arise from elephants' size, the massive objects of their work and their behaviour. Mounting the tack on the elephant and manipulating logging gear exposes the handler to injury hazards. In addition, the handler is exposed to falls from the elephant's neck. The potential for injury is aggravated by the logging operations, which include carrying, pushing, pulling and stacking; teak logs can weigh as much as 1,360 kg. The elephant's behaviour may be unpredictable and cause injury to its handler. Captive bulls are very dangerous and are difficult to contain. Breeding bulls are particularly dangerous. A working bull elephant in Sri Lanka has been reported to have killed nine *mahouts*. He was retained after each death, however, because of his value to his owners (Schmidt 1997).

Some elephants will respond only to their trainer. The principal method for controlling unpredictable elephants is to allow only their *oozie* to handle them. Elephants are creatures of habit, so trainers should maintain a daily routine. The afternoon scrubbing by the trainer has been found to be critical in establishing a bond with the elephant. Maintaining the trainer's dominance is another safeguard against unsafe elephant behaviour.

The swimmers who carry blood samples to a laboratory for progesterone analysis are exposed to a particularly dangerous task: they swim across rivers during the monsoon season. This drowning hazard can be corrected by providing laboratory services near the working elephants.

Melvin L. Myers

DRAUGHT ANIMALS IN ASIA

D.D. Joshi

Livestock contributes significantly to the life of small farmers, nomads and foresters all over the world and increases their productivity, income, employment and nutrition. This contribution is expected to rise. The world population will rise from its present 4.8–5.4 billion people to at least 10 billion in the next 100 years. The population of Asia can be expected to double over that same period. The demand for food will rise even more as the standard of living also rises. Along with this will be a rise in the need for draught power to produce the increased food required. According to Ramaswami and Narasimhan (1982), 2 billion people in the developing countries depend on draught animal power for farming and rural transportation. Draught power is critically short at the time of crop planting and is insufficient for other purposes throughout the year. Draught power will remain a major source of energy in agriculture into the foreseeable future, and the lack of draught power in some places may be the primary constraint to increasing crop production.

Animal draught power was the first supplement to human energy inputs in agriculture. Mechanized power has been used in agriculture only in the last century or so. In Asia, a greater proportion of farmers depend on animals for draught power than in any other parts of the world. A large proportion of these animals belong to farmers who have limited resources and cultivate small areas of land. In most parts of Asia, animal power is supplied by bullocks, buffalo and camels. Bullocks will continue to be the common source of farm power, mainly because they are adequate and live on waste residues. Elephants are also used in some places.

Production

In Asian countries, there are three main sources of power used in agriculture: human, mechanical and animal. Human beings provide the main source of power in developing countries for hoeing, weeding, rice transplanting, seed broadcasting and harvesting of crops. Mechanical power with its versatility is used for practically all the field operations, and the intensity of usage varies considerably from one developing country to another (Khan 1983). Animal power is generally used for tillage operations, haulage and operation of some water-lifting devices. A draught cow is a multi-purpose farm animal, providing power, milk, dung, calves and meat. Normal draught power of various animals is presented in table 70.20.

To have better draught animal power the following aspects should be considered:

For landless people to repay a loan for purchase of bullocks, feed them, and earn sufficient income to meet everyday costs, they must be able to work their animals for six hours per day.

- *Draught animal nutrition.* Animal nutrition is a principal factor in increasing the productivity of draught animal power. This is possible only if the necessary feed is available. In some areas, more effort is made to ensure the best use of available resources, such as treating straw with alkali (molasses urea block (MUB)) to improve its nutrient availability. As draught power availability is presently limiting the production of staple crops (there is an estimated 37% deficiency in draught requirements at the time of harvest), a primary objective is to produce draught animals and improve the efficiency of draught power. The opportunity to use improved nutritional technology (e.g., MUB) may assist draught power development through improved animal work capacity and reproduction rates in the

Table 70.20 • Normal draught power of various animals.

Animals	Weight (kg)	Approx. draught (kg)	Average speed of work (m/sec)	Power developed (h.p.)
Light horses	400–700	60–80	1.0	1.00
Bullocks	500–900	60–80	0.6–0.85	0.75
Buffaloes	400–900	50–80	0.8–0.90	0.75
Cows	400–600	50–60	0.7	0.45
Mules	350–500	50–60	0.9–1.0	0.70
Donkeys	200–300	30–40	0.7	0.35

Source: FAO 1966.

female herd as well as better growth of young animals, which will lead to larger body size.

- *Breeding and selection.* Culling of local unproductive breed bulls and selection of the best local bull is necessary. Draught animals are currently selected according to their conformation, temperament and health; however, farmers often must rely on what is available locally.

Some crossbreds show a significant increase not only in milk and meat producing capability, but also in draught power. In India, Pakistan and Australia there have been tremendous efforts made in cross-breeding buffalo, cattle, horses (to produce mules) and, in some places, camels. This has produced very encouraging results. In many other Asian countries, especially developing countries, this research work for improving draught power as well as milk and meat production is very much needed.

- *Equipment.* Most farm equipment is old and unproductive. Much of the equipment that is used in conjunction with draught animals (harnesses, cultivation tools and carts) is of traditional type, the design of which has not changed for hundreds of years. In addition, farm implements are often badly designed and achieve low work output.

- *Health.* The stress of working may upset the balance which often exists between healthy animals and parasites.

Management

The daily feeding of draught animals varies according to work season. Both draught cattle and buffalo are fed in confinement (year-round) through a cut and carry system, with little or no grazing. Rice straw is fed all year long, depending on farmer preference, at either a measured rate of 8 to 10 kg per day or as necessary. Other crop residues such as rice hulls, pulse straw and cane tops are fed when available. In addition to these crop residues, cut or grazed green grass from roadsides and embankments is fed during the rainy season (April into November) at the rate of 5 to 7 kg/day and may be increased during times of heavy work to 10 kg/day.

Draught animal feed is usually supplemented with small amounts of by-product concentrates such as brans, oil cakes, pulses, rice hulls and molasses. The predominant means of feeding concentrates to draught animals is in a liquid form with all of the ingredients mixed together. The types and amounts of ingredients vary according to the daily workload of the animal, the geographical area, farmer preference and capability. Increased amounts of concentrates are fed during the heavy work seasons, and they are reduced during the monsoon season, when the workload is light.

Animal feed ingredients are also chosen by farmers based on availability, price, and their perception and understanding of its

70. LIVESTOCK REARING

feeding value. For example, during the work season from November to June, daily rations may be: 200 g of mustard seed oil cake along with 100 g (dry weight) of boiled rice; 3/4 g of mustard seed oil cake, 100 g boiled rice and 3/4 g of molasses; or 2 kg total of equal parts sesame oil cake, rice polish, wheat bran and boiled rice, along with salt. On actual workdays during this period (163 days), animals are fed an extra 50% of these same rations. If animals are fed any concentrates at all during the non-working season, the rate ranges from 1/4 to 1/2 kg.

Draught Power in Australia

The Australian continent was first colonized by Europeans in 1788. Cattle were introduced with the first ships, but escaped into the surrounding forest. During those days ploughing and other land preparation was done with the heavy bullock plough, and light cultivation either with bullocks or horses. The bullock cart became the standard means of land transport in Australia and remained so until road building and railway construction began and became more widespread following the gold rushes from 1851 onwards.

In Australia other draught animals include the camel and the donkey. Although mules were used, they never became popular in Australia (Auty 1983).

Draught Power in Bangladesh

In Bangladesh livestock play a vital role in the economy, providing both draught power and milk and contributing up to 6.5% of the gross domestic product (GDP) (Khan 1983). Out of the 22 million head of cattle, 90% are used for draught power and transportation. Of this total, 8.2 million are dual purpose, supplying both draught power and dairy products, such as milk and meat (although in minimal amounts) for household consumption and trade. Adding energy value from draught power and dung (fertilizer and fuel), livestock contribute an estimated 11.3% to the GDP.

It has been observed that some cows are used for draught purposes, despite problems with fertility and health complications, which result in lower milk production and fewer calvings per lifetime. While cows are not usually worked during lactation, they contribute significantly to the annual supply of draught power in Bangladesh: 2.14 million (31%) adult female cattle and 60,000 (47%) adult buffalo cows supply animal power (Robertson et al. 1994). When combined with the male workforce, 76% of all adult cattle (11.2 million) and 85 to 90% of all adult buffalo (.41 million) are used for draught purposes (Khan 1983).

There is no aggregate shortage of draught animals. Rather, the shortfall is based on the quality of draught power available, since malnourished animals are largely unproductive (Orlic and Leng 1992).

There are various breeds of cattle used for draught purposes, including pure deshi cattle and deshi cattle crossed with Sahiwal, Haryana and Red Sindhi cattle and Manipuri, Nili-Ravi and Murrah breeds of buffalo. Deshi bullocks weigh an average of 225 kg, crossbreds are slightly heavier at 275 kg and buffalo weigh an average of 400 kg. Bulls, cows, heifers and bullocks all provide animal power, but bullocks constitute the main workforce.

In Bangladesh, land preparation employs the highest percentage of draught animals. Research workers recommend that land be ploughed six to seven times prior to sowing. However, due to the shortage of draught power, many producers plough only four to five times in preparation for each crop. All ploughs in Bangladesh require two animals. Two bullocks can plough 1 acre in 2.75 (at 6 hours each day) (Orlic and Leng 1992; Robertson et al. 1994).

Draught Power in China

China has a long history of buffalo raising. The animals were used for farming as early as 2,500 years ago. Buffalo have a larger body size than the native cattle. Farmers prefer to use buffalo for farm work because of their great draught power, long working life and docile temperament. One buffalo can provide draught power for the production of 7,500 to 12,500 kg of rice (Yang 1995). Most of them are kept by small-scale farmers for draught purpose. The imported dairy buffalo, Murrah and Nili/Ravi, and crossbreds with these two breeds, are mainly raised on state farms and in research institutes. For centuries, buffalo have been reared mainly for draught purposes. The animals were slaughtered for meat only when they become old or disabled. Milking of buffalo was rare. After generations of selection and breeding, the buffalo have become extremely suitable for working, with deep and strong chests, strong legs, large hoofs and a docile temperament.

In China, buffalo are mainly used for paddy land and for field haulage. They are also employed in raising water, pudding clay for bricks, milling and pressing the juice from sugarcane. The extent of such use is declining due to mechanization. Training of buffalo usually starts at the age of two years. They begin to work a year later. Their working life is longer than that of cattle, usually more than 17 years. It is possible to see buffalo more than 25 years old still working in the fields. They work 90 to 120 days per year in the rice-growing area, with intensive work in the spring and autumn, when they work as long as 7 to 8 hours per day. The working capability varies widely with size, age and sex of the animal. The draught power reaches its maximum between the age of five and 12 years, remains high from 13 to 15 and begins to decline from 16 years. Most of the buffalo bulls are castrated (Yang 1995).

The Shanghai buffalo, one of the largest in China, has an excellent working capability. Working for 8 hours a day, one animal can plough 0.27 to 0.4 hectare of paddy land or 0.4 to 0.53 hectare of non-irrigated land (maximum 0.67 hectare). A load of 800 to 1,000 kg on a wooden-wheeled, bearingless vehicle can be drawn by a buffalo over 24 km within a working day. A buffalo can raise enough water to irrigate 0.73 hectares of paddy land in 4 hours.

In some sugar-producing areas, buffalo are used to draw stone rollers for sugar cane pressing. Six buffalo working in shifts can press 7,500 to 9,000 kg of sugar cane, requiring 15 to 20 minutes for every 1,000 kg.

Draught Power in India

According to Ramaswami and Narasimhan (1982) 70 million bullocks and 8 million buffalo generate about 30,000 million watts of power, assuming the Indian Council of Agricultural Research (ICAR) average of 0.5 hp output per animal. To generate, transmit and distribute this power at the same multitudinous points of application would call for an investment of 3,000,000 million rupees. It has also been estimated that an investment of 30,000 million rupees has gone into the Indian bullock cart system as against 45,000 million rupees in railways.

The Ministry of Shipping and Transport estimated that 11,700 to 15,000 million tonnes of freight in the urban areas is carried by cart each year, as against the railway haulage of 200,000 million tonnes. In the rural areas, where railroad service is not available, animal-drawn vehicles carry approximately 3,000 million tonnes of freight (Gorhe 1983).

Draught Power in Nepal

In Nepal, bullocks and male buffalo are the main source of draught power for tilling the fields. They are also used for carting, crushing sugar cane and oil seeds and for tracting loads. Due to the topographic nature of the country as well as the high cost of fuel, there is little opportunity for farm mechanization. Therefore, the demand for draught animal power in the country is high (Joshi 1983).

In wheat production, the contribution of bullocks in terms of labour days is 42% in ploughing, 3% in transplanting and 55% in threshing. In paddy production, it is 63% in ploughing, 9% in transplanting and 28% in threshing (Joshi 1983; Stem, Joshi and Orlic 1995).

Depending on the task, draught animals are generally worked a consistent number of hours each day and for a predetermined number of consecutive days before being allowed to rest. For instance, a full day of ploughing averages 6 hours for a bullock, and the average workday for a cow ranges from 4 to 5 hours per day. Animals used for ploughing follow a pattern of 6 to 8 consecutive days of work, followed by 2 days of rest. In the case of threshing, cows or lighter-weight animals usually work for 6 to 8 hours each day. The length and pattern of use for threshing and transport varies according to need. A bullock in full-time ploughing (maximum heavy labour) typically works for 163 days per year.

Draught Power in Sri Lanka

The total cattle population in Sri Lanka is estimated at 1.3 million. Various breeds are used as draught animals. Cattle breeds are used for draught purposes such as transport and ploughing of both wet and dry fields, as well as in farm operations. Indigenous animals have been used popularly in road transport for several decades. Crosses of Indian breeds with the indigenous cattle have resulted in larger animals that are used extensively for road transport. Out of a total buffalo population of 562,000, the number available in the work age range of three to 12 years is estimated at 200,000 males and 92,000 females.

Potential Hazards and Their Control

Other articles in this chapter address hazards and preventive actions for the draught animals discussed in this article. General information on animal behaviour and a checklist for livestock rearing safety practices are found in boxes on these subjects in the chapter "Animal husbandry". Horses are addressed in the article "Horses and other equines". Cattle (and by close association, bullocks and buffalo) are addressed in the article "Cattle, sheep and goats". "Bull raising" also offers pertinent information on potential hazards and their control.

● BULL RAISING

David L. Hard

While the term *bull* refers to the male of several species of livestock (elephant, water buffalo and cattle) this article will deal specifically with the cattle industry. The National Traumatic Occupational Fatalities (NTOF) surveillance system in the United States, based on death certificates and maintained by the National Institute for Occupational Safety and Health (NIOSH), identified 199 fatalities from 1980 to 1992 associated with the agricultural production industry and inflicted by livestock. Of these, about 46% (92) were directly attributed to beef and dairy bull handling.

Cattle raisers have for centuries used castration of male animals as a means of producing docile males. Castrated males are generally passive, indicating that hormones (largely testosterone) are related to aggressive behaviour. Some cultures place high value on the fighting character of bulls, which is utilized in sports and social events. In this case, certain bloodlines are bred to maintain and enhance these fighting characteristics. In the United States, demand has increased for bulls used in rodeos as these entertainment events have increased in popularity. In Spain, Portugal, parts of France, Mexico and parts of South America, bullfighting has been popular for centuries. (See the article "Bullfighting and rodeos" in the chapter *Entertainment and the arts*.)

The cattle industry can be divided into two major categories—dairy and beef—with some dual-purpose breeds. Most commercial beef operations purchase bulls from pure-bred producers, while dairy operations have moved more toward artificial insemination (AI). Thus, the pure-bred producer generally raises the bulls and then sells them when they are of breeding age (2 to 3 years of age). There are three systems of mating currently used in the cattle industry. Pasture mating allows bull to run with the herd and breed cows as they come into oestrus (heat). This can be for the entire year (historically) or for a specific breeding season. If specific breeding seasons are utilized, this necessitates separating the bull from the herd for periods of time. Hand mating keeps the bull isolated from the cows, except when a cow in oestrus is brought to the bull for mating. Generally, only a single mating is allowed, with the cow being removed after service. Finally, AI is the process of using proven sires, through the use of frozen semen, to be bred to many cows by AI technicians or the producer. This has the advantage of not having a bull at the ranch, which is a reduction of risk for the producer. However, there is still potential for human-animal interaction at the point of semen collection.

When a bull is removed from the herd for hand mating or kept isolated from the herd to establish a breeding season, he may become aggressive when he detects a cow in oestrus. Since he cannot respond naturally through mating, this can lead to the "mean bull" complex, which is an example of abnormal behaviour in bulls. Typical antagonistic or combative behaviour of bulls includes pawing the ground and bellowing. Furthermore, disposition often deteriorates with age. Old breeding stock can be cantankerous, deceptive, unpredictable and large enough to be dangerous.

Facilities

To ensure movement of animals through facilities, chutes should be curved so that the end cannot be seen when first entering, and the corral should be designed with a gap to the left or right so that animals do not sense that they are trapped. Putting rubber bumpers on metal items which create a loud noise when they close can help lessen the noise and reduce stress to the animal. Ideally, facilities should maximize the reduction of hazards due to physical contact between the bull and humans through use of barriers, overhead walkways and gates that can be manipulated from outside the enclosure. Animals are less likely to balk in chutes built with solid walls instead of fencing materials, since they would not be distracted by movement outside the chutes. Alleyways and chutes should be large enough so the animals can move through them, but not so wide they can turn around.

Guidelines for Handling

Male animals should be considered potentially dangerous at all times. When bulls are kept for breeding, injuries can be avoided by having adequate bull-confinement and restraint facilities. Extreme caution should be practised when handling male animals. Bulls may not purposefully hurt people, but their size and bulk make them potentially dangerous. All pens, chutes, gates, fences and loading ramps should be strong and work properly. Proper equipment and facilities are necessary to assure safety. Ideally, when working with bulls, having the handler physically separated from contact with the bull (outside the area and protected by chutes, walls, barriers and so on) greatly reduces the risk of injury. When handlers are with the animal, escape passages should be provided to allow handlers to escape from animals in an emergency. Animals should not be prodded when they have no place to go. Handlers should stay clear of animals that are frightened or "spooked" and be extra careful around strange animals. Solid wall chutes, instead of fencing, will lower the number of animals that balk in the chute. Since bulls see colours as different shades of black and white, facilities should be painted all in the same colour. Properly designed treatment stalls and appropriate animal-restraint equipment and facilities can reduce injuries during animal examination, medication, hoof trimming, dehorning and hand mating.

People who work with animals recognize that animals can communicate despite being unable to speak. Handlers should be sensitive to warnings such as raised or pinned ears, raised tail, pawing the ground and bellowing. General information and guidelines for working with bulls are provided in the checklist and box on animal behaviour in the article "Animal husbandry" in this chapter.

Zoonoses

Handlers should also be concerned with zoonotic diseases. A livestock handler can contract zoonotic illnesses by handling an infected animal or animal products (hides), ingesting animal products (milk, undercooked meat) and disposing of infected tissues. Leptospirosis, rabies, brucellosis (undulant fever in humans), salmonellosis and ringworm are especially important. Tuberculosis, anthrax, Q fever and tularaemia are other illness that should be of concern. To reduce exposure to disease, basic hygiene and sanitation practices should be used, which include prompt treatment or proper disposal of infected animals, adequate disposal of infected tissues, proper cleaning of contaminated sites and proper use of personal protective equipment.

The most sanitary method of carcass disposal is burning it at the site of death, to avoid contamination of the surrounding ground. A hole of appropriate size should be dug, flammable materials of sufficient quantity placed inside and the carcass placed on top in order that it can be consumed in its entirety. However, the most common method of carcass disposal is burial. In this procedure, the carcass should be buried at least 4 feet deep and covered with quicklime in soil that is not susceptible to contamination by drainage and away from flowing streams.

● PET, FURBEARER AND LABORATORY ANIMAL PRODUCTION

Christian E. Newcomer

Processes

Institutional animal programmes involve four major processes:

1. receipt, quarantine and separation of animals
2. separation of species or animals for individual projects when necessary
3. housing, care and sanitation
4. storage.

Husbandry tasks include feeding, watering, providing bedding, maintaining sanitation, disposing of waste including carcasses, controlling pests and veterinarian care. Materials handling is significant in most of these tasks, which include moving cages, feed, pharmaceuticals, biologics and other supplies. Handling and manipulating animals is also fundamental to this work. Sanitation involves changing bedding, cleaning and disinfecting, and cage washing is a significant sanitation task.

Institutional animal facilities include cages, hutches, pens or stalls within a room, barn or outdoor habitat. Adequate space, temperature, humidity, food and water, illumination, noise control and ventilation are provided in a modern facility. The facility is designed for the type of animal that is confined. Animals that are typically confined in institutional settings include group-housed rodents (mice, rats, hamsters and guinea pigs), rabbits, cats, dogs, mink, non-human primates (monkeys, baboons and apes), birds (pigeons, quail and chickens) and farm animals (sheep and goats, swine, cattle, horses and ponies).

Hazards and Precautions

Persons involved with the production, care and handling of pet, furbearer and laboratory animals are potentially exposed to a variety of biological, physical and chemical hazards that can be controlled effectively through available risk reduction practices. The biological hazards intrinsic to the various animal species of concern to personnel include: bites and scratches; highly sensitizing allergens in dander, serum, tissues, urine or salivary secretions; and a wide variety of zoonotic agents. Although the biological hazards are more diverse and potentially more devastating in the work environments supporting these types of animals, the physical and chemical hazards generally are more pervasive, as reflected by their contribution to illness and injury in the workplace.

Personnel involved in the care and production of pet, furbearer or laboratory animals should receive appropriate training in handling techniques and behaviour of the animal species in question, because incorrect handling of an intractable animal frequently is a precipitating cause of a bite or scratch. Such injuries can become contaminated with micro-organisms from the animal's rich oral and skin microflora or the environment, necessitating immediate wound disinfection and prompt and aggressive antimicrobial therapy and tetanus prophylaxis to avert the serious complications of wound infection and disfigurement. Personnel should appreciate that some zoonotic bite infections can produce generalized disease and even death; examples of the former include cat scratch fever, rat bite fever and human orf infection; examples of the latter include rabies, B virus and hantavirus infection.

Due to these extraordinary risks, wire-mesh, bite-proof gloves can be beneficial in some circumstances, and the chemical restraint of animals to facilitate safe handling is sometimes warranted. Personnel also can contract zoonoses through the inhalation of infectious aerosols, contact of the organisms with the skin or mucous membranes, ingestion of infectious materials or transmission by specific fleas, ticks or mites associated with the animals.

All types of zoonotic agents occur within pet, furbearer and laboratory animals, including viruses, bacteria, fungi and internal and external parasites. Some examples of zoonoses include: giardiasis and campylobacterosis from pets; anthrax, tularaemia and ringworm from furbearers; and lymphocytic choriomeningitis, hantavirus and dwarf tapeworm infestation from the laboratory rodent. The distribution of zoonotic agents varies widely according to host animal species, location and isolation from other disease reservoirs, housing and husbandry methods, and history and intensity of veterinary care. For example, some of the commercially produced laboratory animal populations have undergone extensive disease eradication programmes and been maintained subsequently under strict quality control conditions precluding the reintroduction of diseases. However, comparable measures have not been applicable universally in the various settings for pet, furbearer and laboratory animal maintenance and production, enabling the persistence of zoonoses in some circumstances.

Allergic reactions, ranging from ocular and nasal irritation and drainage to asthma or manifesting on the skin as contact urticaria ("hives"), are common in individuals who work with laboratory rodents, rabbits, cats and other animal species. An estimated 10 to 30% of individuals working with these animal species eventually develop allergic reactions, and persons with pre-existing allergic disease from other agents are at higher risk and have an increased incidence of asthma. In rare circumstances, such as a massive exposure to the inciting allergen through an animal bite, susceptible persons can develop anaphylaxis, a potentially life-threatening generalized allergic reaction.

Good personal hygiene practices should be observed by personnel to reduce their likelihood of exposure to zoonoses and allergens during work with animals or animal by-products. These include the use of dedicated work clothing, the availability and use of hand washing and shower facilities and separation of personnel areas from animal housing areas. Work clothing or protective outer garments covering the skin should be worn to prevent exposure to bites, scratches and hazardous microbes and allergens. Personal protective equipment, such as impervious gloves, safety glasses, goggles or other eye protection, and respiratory protection devices (e.g., particle masks, respirators or positive air pressure respirators) appropriate to the potential hazards and the individual's vulnerability, should be provided and worn to promote safe work conditions. Engineering controls and equipment design also can effectively reduce the exposure of personnel to hazardous allergens and zoonoses through directional air flow and the use of isolation caging systems that partition the workers' and animals' environments.

Personnel also encounter significant physical and chemical hazards during animal care. Routine husbandry tasks involve moving or lifting heavy equipment and supplies, and performing repetitive tasks, affording personnel the ubiquitous opportunity to develop cuts and crush injuries, muscular strains and repetitive motion injuries. Work practice redesign, specialized equipment and personnel training in safe work practices can be used to curb these untoward outcomes. Equipment and facility sanitation frequently relies on machinery operating on live steam or extremely hot water, placing personnel at risk of severe thermal injury. The correct design, maintenance and utilization of these devices should be assured to prevent personnel injury and facilitate heat dissipation to provide a comfortable work environment. Personnel who work around large equipment, as well as around rambunctious dog or non-human primate populations, may be exposed to extremely high noise levels, necessitating the use of hearing protection. The various chemicals used for cage and facility sanitation, pest control within the animal facility and external parasite control on animals should be reviewed carefully with personnel to ensure their strict adherence to practices instituted to minimize exposure to these potentially irritating, corrosive or toxic substances.

FISH FARMING AND AQUACULTURE

George A. Conway and Ray RaLonde

Background

Rearing marine organisms for food has been a widespread practice since ancient times. However, large-scale farming of molluscs, crustaceans and bony fishes has rapidly gained momentum since the early 1980s, with 20% of the world's seafood harvest now farmed; this is projected to increase to 25% by 2000 (Douglas 1995; Crowley 1995). Expansion of world markets contemporaneous with depletion of wild stocks has resulted in very rapid growth of this industry.

Land-based aquaculture takes place in tanks and ponds, while water-based culture systems generally employ screened cages or moored net pens of widely varying designs (Kuo and Beveridge 1990) in salt water (mariculture) or fresh rivers.

Aquaculture is performed as either an extensive or intensive practice. Extensive aquaculture entails some form of environmental enhancement for naturally produced species of fish, shellfish or aquatic plants. An example of such a practice would be laying down oyster shells to be used as attachment substrate for juvenile oysters. Intensive aquaculture incorporates more complex technology and capital investment in the culture of aquatic organisms. A salmon hatchery that uses concrete tanks supplied with water via some delivery system is an example. Intensive aquaculture also requires greater allocation of labour in the operation.

The process of intensive aquaculture includes the acquisition of broodstock adults used for production of gametes, gamete collection and fertilization, incubation of eggs and juvenile rearing; it may include rearing of adults to market size or release of the organism into the environment. Herein lies the difference between farming and enhancement aquaculture. Farming means rearing the organism to market size, generally in an enclosed system. Aquaculture for enhancement requires the release of the organism into the natural environment to be harvested at a later date. The essential role of enhancement is to produce a specific organism as a supplement to natural production, not as a replacement. Aquaculture can also be in the form of mitigation for loss of natural production caused by a natural or human-made event—for example, construction of a salmon hatchery to replace lost natural production caused by the damming of a stream for hydroelectric power production.

Aquaculture can occur in land-based facilities, on-bottom marine and freshwater environments and floating structures. Floating net pens are used for fish farming, and cages suspended from raft or buoy flotation are commonly used for shellfish culture.

Land-based operations require the construction of dams and/or excavation of holes for ponds and raceways for water flushing. Mariculture can involve the construction and maintenance of complex structures in harsh environments. Handling of smolt (for bony fishes) or tiny invertebrates, feed, chemical treatments for water and the animals being raised and wastes have all evolved into highly specialized activities as the industry has developed.

Hazards and Controls

Injuries

Fish farming operations afford many injury risks, combining some of those common to all modern agriculture operations (e.g., entanglement in large machinery, hearing loss from prolonged exposure to loud engines) with some hazards unique to these operations. Slips and falls can have particularly bad outcomes if they occur near raceways or pens, as there are the dual added risks of drowning and biological or chemical contamination from polluted water.

Severe lacerations and even amputations may take place during roe-stripping, fish butchering and mollusc shelling and can be prevented by the use of guards, protective gloves and equipment designed specifically for each task. Lacerations contaminated by fish slime and blood can cause serious local and even systemic infections ("fish poisoning"). Prompt disinfection and debridement is essential for these injuries.

Electrofishing (used to stun fish during survey counts, and increasingly in collection of broodstock at hatcheries) carries a high potential for electrical shock to the operators and bystanders (National Safety Council 1985) and should be done only by trained operators, with personnel trained in cardiopulmonary resuscitation (CPR) on site. Only equipment specifically designed for electrofishing operations in water should be employed and scrupulous attention must be paid to establishing and maintaining good insulation and grounding.

All water poses drowning risks, while cold waters pose the additional hazard of hypothermia. Accidental immersions due to falls overboard must be guarded against, as must potential for ensnarement or entrapment in nets. Approved personal flotation devices should be worn by all workers at all times on or near the water, and some thermal protection should also be worn when working around cold waters (Lincoln and Klatt 1994). Mariculture personnel should be trained in marine survival and rescue techniques, as well as CPR.

Repetitive strain injuries may also occur in butchering and hand-feeding operations and can be largely avoided by attention to ergonomics (via task analysis and equipment modifications as necessary) and frequent task rotations of manual workers. Those workers developing repetitive strain injury symptoms should receive prompt evaluation and treatment and possible reassignment.

Sleep deprivation can be a risk factor for injuries in aquaculture facilities requiring intensive labour over a short duration of time (e.g., egg harvest at salmon hatcheries).

Health hazards

Diving is frequently required in construction and maintenance of fishpens. Predictably, decompression illness ("bends") has been observed among divers not carefully observing depth/time limits ("dive tables"). There have also been reports of decompression illness occurring in divers observing these limits but making many repetitive short dives; alternative methods (not using divers) should be developed for clearing dead fish from and maintaining pens (Douglas and Milne 1991). When diving is deemed necessary, observing published dive tables, avoiding repetitive dives, always diving with a second diver ("buddy diving") and rapid evaluation of decompression-like illnesses for possible hyperbaric oxygen therapy should be regular practices.

Severe organophosphate poisoning has occurred in workers incidental to pesticidal treatment of sea lice on salmon (Douglas 1995). Algicides deployed to control blooms may be toxic to workers, and toxic marine and freshwater algae themselves may afford worker hazards (Baxter 1991). Bath treatments for fungal infections in fish may use formaldehyde and other toxic agents (Douglas 1995). Workers must receive adequate instruction and allotment of time for safe handling of all agricultural chemicals and hygienic practices around contaminated waters.

Respiratory illnesses ranging from rhinitis to severe bronchospasm (asthma-like symptoms) have occurred due to sensitization to putative endotoxins of gram-negative bacteria contaminating farmed trout during gutting operations (Sherson, Hansen and Sigsgaard 1989), and respiratory sensitization may occur to antibiotics in medicated fish feeds. Careful attention to personal cleanliness, keeping seafood clean during butchering and handling and respiratory protection will help ensure against these problems. Workers developing sensitivity should avoid subsequent exposures to the implicated antigens. Constant immersion of hands can facilitate dermal sensitization to agricultural chemicals and foreign (fish) proteins. Hygienic practice and use of task-appropriate gloves (such as cuffed, insulated, waterproof neoprene during cold butchering operations) will reduce this risk.

Sunburn and keratotic (chronic) skin injury may result from exposure to sunlight. Wearing hats, adequate clothing and sunscreen should be *de rigueur* for all outdoor agricultural workers.

Large quantities of stored fish feeds are often raided by or infested with rats and other rodents, posing a risk for leptospirosis (Weil's disease). Workers handling fish feeds must be vigilant about feed storage and rodent control and protect abraded skin and mucous membranes from contact with potentially contaminated feeds and soiled pond waters. Feeds with known contamination with rat urine should be handled as potentially infectious, and

discarded promptly (Ferguson and Path 1993; Benenson 1995; Robertson et al. 1981).

Eczema and dermatitis can easily evolve from inflammation of skin macerated by constant water contact. Also, this inflammation and wet conditions can foster reproduction of human papillaviridae, leading to rapid spread of skin warts (*Verruca vulgaris*). Prevention is best accomplished by keeping hands as dry as possible and using appropriate gloves. Emollients are of some value in the management of minor skin irritation from water contact, but topical treatment with corticosteroids or antibiotic creams (after evaluation by a physician) may be necessary if initial treatment is unsuccessful.

Environmental Impacts

Demand for fresh water can be extremely high in all of these systems, with estimates centring on 40,000 litres required for each 0.5 kg of bony fish raised to maturity (Crowley 1995). Recirculation with filtration can greatly reduce demand, but requires intensive application of new technologies (e.g., zeolites to attract ammonia).

Fish farm discharges can include as much faecal waste as that from small cities, and regulations are rapidly proliferating for control of these discharges (Crowley 1995).

Consumption of plankton and krill, and side effects of mariculture such as algal blooms, can lead to major disruptions in species balance in the local ecosystems surrounding fish farms.

BEEKEEPING, INSECT RAISING AND SILK PRODUCTION

Melvin L. Myers and Donald Barnard*

More than a million species of insects exist in the world, and the global mass of insects exceeds the total mass of all other terrestrial animals. Insects such as crickets, grasshoppers, locusts, termites, beetle larvae, wasps, bees and moth caterpillars are among about 500 species that form part of the regular diet of people around the world. Usually humans hunt or gather insects for food rather than intentionally rearing and harvesting them.

In addition to food, humans use insects as sources of pollination, biological controls of pests and fibre. Different uses depend on the four stages of the insect's life cycle, which consist of egg, larva, pupa and adult. Examples of commercial uses of insects include beekeeping (nearly 1 billion tonnes of honey produced annually and pollination of fruit and seed crops), insect rearing (more than 500 species in culture, including those used for insect biological control), shellac production (36,000 tonnes annually) and silk production (180,000 tonnes annually).

Beekeeping

Beekeepers raise the honey-bee in apiaries, a collection of hives that house bee colonies. The honey-bee is a source of flower pollination, honey and wax. Bees are important pollinators, making more than 46,430 foraging trips per bee for each kilogram of honey that they produce. During each foraging trip, the honey-bee will visit 500 flowers within a 25-minute period. The honey-bee's source of honey is flower nectar. The bee uses the enzyme invertase to convert sucrose in the nectar into glucose and fructose and, with water evaporation, honey is produced. In addition, bumble-bees and cutter bees are grown for pollinating, respectively, tomato plants and alfalfa.

---

* Some information on the silk industry was adapted from the article by J. Kubota in the 3rd edition of this *Encyclopaedia*.

The honey-bee colony collects around a single queen bee, and they will colonize in boxes—artificial hives. Beekeepers establish an infant colony of about 10,000 bees in the bottom box of the hive, called a brood chamber. Each chamber contains ten panels with cells that are used for either storing honey or laying eggs. The queen lays about 1,500 eggs per day. The beekeeper then adds a food chamber super (a box placed on top of the brood box), which becomes the storage chamber for honey, on which the bees will survive through the winter. The colony continues to multiply, becoming mature at about 60,000 bees. The beekeeper adds a queen excluder (a flat panel that the larger queen cannot enter) on top of the food super to prevent the queen from laying eggs in additional shallow supers that will be stacked on top of the excluder. These additional supers are designed for harvesting only honey without the eggs.

The beekeeper moves the hives to where flowers are budding. A honey-bee colony can forage over an area of 48 hectares, and 1 hectare can support about two hives. The honey is harvested during the summer from the shallow supers, which can be stacked seven high as the colony grows and the bees fill the panels with honey. The supers with honey-laden panels are transported to the honey "house" for extraction. A sharp, warm knife, called an uncapping knife, is used to remove the wax caps that the bees have placed over the honeycombs within the panels. The honey is then extracted from the panels with a centrifugal force machine. The honey is collected and bottled for sale (Vivian 1986).

At the end of the season, the beekeeper winterizes the hives, wrapping them in tar paper to protect the colonies from the winter wind and to absorb the solar heat. The beekeeper also provides the bees with medicated sugar syrup for their winter consumption. In the spring, the hives are opened to begin production as mature honeybee colonies. If the colony becomes crowded, the colony will create another queen through special feeding, and the old queen will swarm with about half of the colony to find another accommodation. The beekeeper may capture the swarm and treat it as an infant colony.

Beekeepers are exposed to two related hazards from honey-bee stings. One hazard is sting envenomation. The other is venom hypersensitivity reaction and possible anaphylactic shock. Males at 40 years of age and older are at highest risk of fatal reactions. About 2% of the general population is thought to be allergic to venom, but systemic reactions in beekeepers and their immediate family members are estimated at 8.9%. The reaction incidence varies inversely to the numbers of stings received. Anaphylactic reactions to bumble-bee venom are rare except among bumble bee keepers, and their risk is greater if they have been sensitized to honey bee venom.

If a honey-bee stings the beekeeper, the stinger should be removed, and the sting site should be washed. Ice or a paste of baking soda and water should be applied to the site of envenomation. The victim should be watched for signs of systemic reaction, which can be a medical emergency. For anaphylactic reactions, epinephrine is administered subcutaneously at the first sign of symptoms. To assure safe beekeeping, the beekeeper should use smoke at the beehive to neutralize the bees' protective behaviour and should wear a protective hood and veil, thin gloves and log sleeves or coveralls. Bees are attracted to sweat for the moisture, so beekeepers should not wear watch bands or belts where sweat collects. In extracting the honey, the beekeeper should keep his or her thumb and fingers clear of the cutting motion of the uncapping knife.

Mass Insect Raising

More than 500 species of arthropods are reared in the laboratory, including ants, beetles, mites, flies, moths, spiders and ticks. An important use of these arthropods is as biological controls for other animal species. For example, 2,000 years ago, markets in China sold nests of weaver ants to place in citrus orchards to prey on crop pests. Today, more than 5,000 species of insects have been identified worldwide as possible biological controls for crop pests, and 300 are successfully used regularly in 60 countries. Disease vectors have also become targets for biological control. As an example, the carnivorous mosquito from Southeast Asia, *Toxorhynchites spp.*, also called the "tox" mosquito, has a larva that feeds on the larvae of the tiger mosquito, *Aedes spp.*, which transmits diseases such as dengue fever to humans (O'Toole 1995).

Mass rearing facilities have been developed to raise sterile insects as a non-chemical pest-suppression tool. One such facility in Egypt rears a billion fruit flies (about 7 tonnes) each week. This rearing industry has two major cycles. One is the feed conversion or larval incubation cycle, and the other is the propagation or egg-production cycle. The sterile insect technique was first used to eliminate the screw worm, which preyed on cattle. Sterilization is accomplished by irradiating the pupae just prior to adult emergence from the cocoon with either x rays or gamma rays. This technique takes mass quantities of reared, sterile insects and releases them into infested areas where the sterile males mate with the wild, fertile females. Breaking the insect's life cycle has dramatically reduced the fertility rate of these pests. This technique is used on screw worms, gypsy moths, boll weevils and fruit flies (Kok, Lomaliza and Shivhara 1988).

A typical sterile insect facility has an airlock system to restrict unwanted insect entry and fertile insect escape. Rearing tasks include mopping and sweeping, egg stacking, tray washing, diet preparation, inoculation (placing eggs into agar), pupae dyeing, emergence tending, packing, quarantining, irradiating, screening and weighing. In the pupae room, vermiculite is mixed with water and placed in trays. The trays are stacked, and the vermiculite dust is swept with a broom. The pupae are separated from the vermiculite with a sieve. The insect pupae chosen for the sterile insect technique are transported in trays stacked on racks to the irradiation chamber in a different area or facility, where they are irradiated and rendered sterile (Froehlich 1995; Kiefer 1996).

Insect workers, including silkworm workers, may have an allergic reaction to arthropod allergens (scales, hairs, other body parts). Initial symptoms are itchy eyes and irritation of the nose followed by intermittent episodes of wheezing, coughing and breathlessness. Subsequent asthma attacks are triggered by re-exposure to the allergen. Entomologists and workers in sterile fly facilities are exposed to a variety of potentially hazardous, flammable agents. These agents include: in entomology laboratories, isopropyl alcohol, ethyl alcohol and xylene; in the diet preparation room, isopropyl alcohol is used in water solution to sterilize walls and ceilings with a sprayer. Vermiculite dust poses respiratory concerns. Some vermiculites are contaminated with asbestos. Air-handling units in these facilities emit noise that may be damaging to employee hearing. Proper exhaust ventilation and personal respiratory protection can be used in facilities to control exposure to airborne allergens and dusts. Non-dusty working materials should be used. Air conditioning and frequent changes of filters may help reduce airborne levels of spines and hairs. X rays or gamma rays (ionizing radiation) can damage genetic material. Protection is needed against x rays or gamma rays and their sources in the irradiation facilities (Froehlich 1995; Kiefer 1996).

Silkworm Raising

Vermiculture, the raising of worms, has a long history in some cultures. Worms, especially the meal worm (which is a larva rather than a true worm) from the darkling beetle, are raised by the billions as animal fodder for laboratory animals and pets. Worms are also used in composting operations (vermi-composting).

Sericulture is the term used for silkworm cocoon production, which includes silkworm feeding and cocoon formation. Cultivation of the silkworm and the silk moth caterpillar dates back to 3000 BC in China. Silkworm farmers have domesticated the silkworm moth; there are no remaining wild populations. Silkworms eat only white mulberry leaves. Fibre production thus has historically depended upon the leafing season of the mulberry tree. Artificial foods have been developed for the silkworm so that production can extend the year around. Silkworms are raised on trays sometimes mounted on racks. The worms take about 42 days of feeding at a constant temperature of 25 °C. Artificial heating may be required. Silk is a secretion from the silkworm's mouth that solidifies upon contact with air. The silkworm secretes about 2 km of silk fibre to form a cocoon during the pupal stage (Johnson 1982). After the cocoon is formed, the silkworm farmer kills the pupa in a hot oven, and ships the cocoon to a factory. At the factory, silk is harvested from the cocoon and spun into thread and yarn.

Nine per cent of silkworm workers manifest asthma in response to silkworm moth scales, although most asthma in silkworm workers is attributed to inhalation of silkworm faeces. In addition, contact of the skin with silkworm caterpillar hairs may produce a primary irritant contact-dermatitis. Contact with raw silk may also produce allergic skin reactions. For silk moth production, hyposensitization therapy (for moth scales and faeces) provides improvement for 79.4% of recipients. Corticosteroids may reverse the effects of inhaled antigens. Skin lesions may respond to topical corticosteroid lotions and creams. Oral antihistamines relieve itching and burning. Carbon monoxide poisoning has been identified among some silkworm farmers in their homes, where they are maintaining warmth with charcoal fires as they raise the silkworms. Charcoal fires and kerosene heaters should be replaced with electric heaters to avoid carbon monoxide exposures.

References

Aldhous, P. 1996. Scrapie theory fed BSE complacency, now fears grow for unborn babies. *New Scientist* 150:4-5.

Ahlgren, GH. 1956. *Forage Crops*. New York: McGraw-Hill Book Co.

American Conference of Governmental Industrial Hygienists (ACGIH). 1994. *Threshold Limit Values for Chemical Substances and Physical Agents and Biological Exposure Indices*. Cincinnati, OH: ACGIH.

Auty, JH. 1983. Draught animal power in Australia. *Asian Livestock* VIII:83-84.

Banwart, WC and JM Brenner. 1975. Identification of sulfur gases evolved from animal manures. *J Environ Qual* 4:363-366.

Baxter, PJ. 1991. Toxic marine and freshwater algae: An occupational hazard? *Br J Ind Med* 48(8):505-506.

Bell, RG, DB Wilson, and EJ Dew. 1976. Feedlot manure top dressing for irrigated pasture: Good agricultural practice or a health hazard? *B Environ Contam Tox* 16:536-540.

Benenson, AS. 1990. *Control of Communicable Diseases in Man*. Washington, DC: American Public Health Association.

—. 1995. *Control of Communicable Diseases Manual*. Washington, DC: American Public Health Association.

Brown, LR. 1995. Meat production takes a leap. In *Vital Signs 1995: The Trends that are Shaping our Future*, edited by LR Brown, N Lenssen, and H Kane. New York: WW Norton & Company.

Bursey, RG. 1992. New uses of dairy products. In *New Crops, New Uses, New Markets: Industrial and Commercial Products from U.S. Agriculture: 1992 Yearbook of Agriculture*. Washington, DC: USDA.

Calandruccio, RA and JH Powers. 1949. Farm accidents: A clinical and statistical study covering twenty years. *Am Surg* (November):652-660.

Cameron, D and C Bishop. 1992. Farm accidents in adults. *Br Med J* 305:25-26.

Caras, RA. 1996. *A Perfect Harmony: The Intertwining Lives of Animals and Humans throughout History*. New York: Simon & Schuster.

Carstensen, O, J Lauritsen, and K Rasmussen. 1995. The West-Justland study on prevention of farm accidens, Phase 1: A study of work specific factors in 257 hospital-treated agricultural injuries. *Journal of Agricultural Safety and Health* 1:231-239.

Chatterjee, A, D Chattopadhyay, D Bhattacharya, Ak Dutta, and DN Sen Gupta. 1980. Some epidemiologic aspects of zoophilic dermatophytosis. *International Journal of Zoonoses* 7(1):19-33..

Cherry, JP, SH Fearirheller, TA Foglis, GJ Piazza, G Maerker, JH Woychik, and M Komanowski. 1992. Innovative uses of animal byproducts. In *New Crops, New Uses, New Markets: Industrial and Commercial Products from U.S. Agriculture: 1992 Yearbook of Agriculture*. Washington, DC: USDA.

Crowley, M. 1995. Aquaculture trends and technology. *National Fisherman* 76:18-19.

Deere & Co. 1994. *Farm and Ranch Safety Management*. Moline, IL: Deere & Co.

DeFoliart, GR. 1992. Insects as human foods. *Crop Protection* 11:395-399.

Donham, KJ. 1985. Zoonotic diseases of occupational significance in agriculture: A review. *International Journal of Zoonoses* 12:163-191.

—. 1986. Hazardous agents in agricultural dusts and methods of evaluation. *Am J Ind Med* 10:205-220.

Donham, KJ and LW Knapp. 1982. Acute toxic exposure to gases from liquid manure. *J Occup Med* 24:142-145

Donham, KJ and SJ Reynolds. 1995. Respiratory dysfunction in swine production workers: Dose-response relationship of environmental exposures and pulmonary function. *Am J Ind Med* 27:405-418.

Donham, KJ and L Scallon. 1985. Characterization of dusts collected from swine confinement buildings. *Am Ind Hyg Assoc J* 46:658-661.

Donham, KJ and KM Thu. 1995. Agriculture medicine and enivronmental health: The missing component of the sustainable agricultural movement. In *Agricultural health and safety: Workplace, Environment, Sustainability*, edited by HH McDuffie, JA Dosman, KM Semchuk, SA Olenchock, and A Senthilselvan. Boca Raton, FL: CRC Press.

Donham, KJ, MJ Rubino, TD Thedell and J Kammenmeyer. 1977. Potential health hazards of workers in swine confinement buildings. *J Occup Med* 19:383-387.

Donham, KJ, J Yeggy, and RR Dauge. 1985. Chemical and physical parameters of liquid manure from swine confinement facilities: Health implications for workers, swine and the environment. *Agricultural Wastes* 14:97-113.

—. 1988. Production rates of toxic gases from liquid manure: Health implications for workers and animals in swine buildings. *Bio Wastes* 24:161-173.

Donham, KJ, DC Zavala, and JA Merchant. 1984. Acute effects of work environment on pulmonary functions of swine confinement workers. *Am J Ind Med* 5:367-375.

Dosman, JA, BL Graham, D Hall, P Pahwa, H McDuffie, M Lucewicz, and T To. 1988. Respiratory symptoms and alterations in pulmonary function tests in swine producers in Saskatchewan: Results of a survey of farmers. *J Occ Med* 30:715-720.

Douglas, JDM. 1995. Salmon farming: Occupational health in a new rural industry. *Occup Med* 45:89-92.

Douglas, JDM and AH Milne. 1991. Decompression sickness in fish farm workers: A new occupational hazard. *Br Med J* 302:1244-1245.

Durning, AT and HB Brough. 1992. Reforming the livestock economy. In *State of the World*, edited by LR Brown. London: WW Norton & Company.

Erlich, SM, TR Driscoll, JE Harrison, MS Frommer, and J Leight. 1993. Work-related agricultural fatalities in Australia, 1982-1984. *Scand J Work Environ Health* 19:162-167.

Feddes, JJR and EM Barber. 1994. Agricultural engineering solutions to problems of air contaminants in farm silos and animal buildings. In *Agricultural Health and Safety: Workplace, Environment, Sustainability*, edited by HH McDuffie, JA Dosman, KM Semchuk, SA Olenchock and A Senthilselvan. Boca Raton, FL: CRC Press.

Ferguson, IR and LRC Path. 1993. Rats, fish and Weil's disease. *Safety and Health Practitioner* :12-16.

Food and Agriculture Organization (FAO) of the United Nations. 1965. *Farm Implements for Arid and Tropical Regions*. Rome: FAO.

—. 1995. *The State of the World Fisheries and Aquaculture*. Rome: FAO.

Fretz, P. 1989. Injuries from farm animals. In *Principles of Health and Safety in Agriculture*, edited by JA Dosman and DW Crockcroft. Boca Raton, FL: CRC Press.

Froehlich, PA. 1995. *Engineering Control Observations and Recommendations for Insect Rearing Facilities*. Cincinnati, OH: NIOSH.

Gillespie, JR. 1997. *Modern Livestock and Poultry Production*. New York: Delmar Publishers.

Gorhe, DS. 1983. Draught animal power vs mechanization. *Asian Livestock* VIII:90-91.

Haglind, M and R Rylander. 1987. Occupational exposure and lung function measurements among workers in swine confinement buildings. *J Occup Med* 29:904-907

Harries, MG and O Cromwell. 1982. Occupational allergy caused by allergy to pig's urine. *Br Med J* 284:867.

Heederick, D, R Brouwer, K Biersteker, and J. Boleij. Relationship of airborne endotoxin and bacteria levels in pig farms with lung function and respiratory symptoms of farmers. *Intl Arch Occup Health* 62:595-601.

Hogan, DJ and P Lane. 1986. Dermatologic disorders in agriculture. *Occup Med: State Art Rev* 1:285-300.

Holness, DL, EL O'Glenis, A Sass-Kortsak, C Pilger, and J Nethercott. 1987. Respiratory effects and dust exposures in hog confinement farming. *Am J Ind Med* 11:571-580.

Holness, DL and JR Nethercott. 1994. Acute and chronic trauma in hog farmers. In *Agricultural Health and Safety: Workplace, Environment, Sustainability*, edited by HH McDuffie, JA Dosman, KM Semchuk, SA Olenchock, and A Senthilselvan. Boca Raton, FL: CRC Press.

Iowa Department of Public Health. 1995. *Sentinel Project Research Agricultural Injury Notification System*. Des Moines, IA: Iowa Department of Public Health.

Iverson, M, R Dahl, J Korsgaard, T Hallas, and EJ Jensen. 1988. Respiratory symptoms in Danish farmers: An epidemiological study of risk factors. *Thorax* 48:872-877.

Johnson, SA. 1982. *Silkworms*. Minneapolis, MN: Lerner Publications.

Jones, W, K Morring, SA Olenchock, T Williams, and J. Hickey. 1984. Environmental study of poultry confinement buildings. *Am Ind Hyg Assoc J* 45:760-766.

Joshi, DD. 1983. Draught animal power for food production in Nepal. *Asian Livestock* VIII:86-87.

Ker, A. 1995. *Farming Systems in the African Savanna*. Ottawa, Canada: IDRC Books.

Khan, MH. 1983. Animal as power source in Asian agriculture. *Asian Livestock* VIII:78-79.

Kiefer, M. 1996. *Florida Department of Agriculture and Consumer Services Division of Plant Industry, Gainesville, Florida*. Cincinnati, OH: NIOSH.

Knoblauch, A, B Steiner, S Bachmann, G Trachsler, R Burgheer, and J Osterwalder. 1996. Accidents related to manure in eastern Switzerland: An epidemiological study. *Occup Environ Med* 53:577-582.

Kok, R, K Lomaliza, and US Shivhare. 1988. The design and performance of an insect farm/chemical reactor for human food production. *Canadian Agricultural Engineering* 30:307-317.

Kuo, C and MCM Beveridge. 1990. Mariculture: Biological and management problems, and possible engineering solutions. In *Engineering for Offshore Fish Farming*. London: Thomas Telford.

Layde, PM, DL Nordstrom, D Stueland, LB Wittman, MA Follen, and KA Olsen. 1996. Animal-related occupational injuries in farm residents. *Journal of Agricultural Safety and Health* 2:27-37.

Leistikow, B Donham, JA Merchant, and S Leonard. 1989. Assessment of U.S. poultry worker respiratory risk. *Am J Ind Med* 17:73-74.

Lenhart, SW. 1984. Sources of respiratory insult in the poultry processing industry. *Am J Ind Med* 6:89-96.

Lincoln, JM and ML Klatt. 1994. *Preventing Drownings of Commercial Fishermen*. Anchorage, AK: NIOSH.

MacDiarmid, SC. 1993. Risk analysis and the importation of animals and animal products. *Rev Sci Tech* 12:1093-1107.

Marx, J, J Twiggs, B Ault, J Merchant, and E Fernandez-Caldas. 1993. Inhaled aeroallergen and storage mite reactivity in a Wisconsin farmer nested case-control study. *Am Rev Respir Dis* 147:354-358.

Mathias, CGT. 1989. Epidemiology of occupational skin disease in agriculture. In *Principles of Health and Safety in Aagriculture*, edited by JA Dosman and DW Cockroft. Boca Raton, FL: CRC Press.

Meadows, R. 1995. Livestock legacy. *Environ Health Persp* 103:1096-1100.

Meyers, JR. 1997. *Injuries among Farm Workers in the United States, 1993*. DHHS (NIOSH) Publication No. 97-115. Cincinnati, OH: NIOSH.

Mullan, RJ and LI Murthy. 1991. Occupational sentinel health events: An up-dated list for physician recognition and public health surveillance. *Am J Ind Med* 19:775-799.

National Institute for Occupational Safety and Health (NIOSH). 1993. *Injuries among Farm Workers in the United states*. Cincinnati, OH: NIOSH.

—. 1994. *Request for Assistance in Preventing Organic Dust Toxic Syndrome*. Washington, DC: GPO.

National Institutes of Health (NIH). 1988. *Institutional Administrator's Manual for Laboratory Animal Care and Use*. Washington, DC: GPO.

National Research Council (NRC). 1989. *Alternative Agriculture: Committee on the Role of Alternative Farming Methods in Modern Production Agriculture*. Washington, DC: National Academy Press.

National Safety Council. 1982. *Accident Facts*. Chicago, IL: National Safety Council.

—. 1985. *Electrofishing*. NSC data sheet I-696-85. Chicago, IL: National Safety Council.

Nesheim, MC, RE Austic, and LE Card. 1979. *Poultry Production*. Philadelphia, PA: Lea and Febiger.

Olenchock, S, J May, D Pratt, L Piacitelli, and J Parker. 1990. Presence of endotoxins in different agricultural environments. *Am J Ind Med* 18:279-284.

O'Toole, C. 1995. *Alien Empire*. New York: Harper Collins Publishers.

Orlic, M and RA Leng. 1992. *Preliminary Proposal to Assist Bangladesh to Improve Ruminant Livestock Productivity and Reduce Methane Emissions*. Washington, DC: US Environmental Protection Agency, Global Change Division.

Panti, NK and SP Clark. 1991. Transient hazardous conditions in animal building due to manure gas release during slurry mixing. *Applied Engineering in Agriculture* 7:478-484.

Platt, AE. 1995. Aquaculture boosts fish catch. In *Vital Signs 1995: The Trends that Are Shaping our Future*, edited by LR Brown, N Lenssen, and H Kane. New York: WW Norton & Company.

Pursel, VG, CE Rexroad, and RJ Wall. 1992. Barnyard biotchnology may soon produce new medical therapeutics. In *New Crops, New Uses, New Markets: Industrial and Commercial Products from U.S. Agriculture: 1992 Yearbook of Agriculture* Washington, DC: USDA.

Ramaswami, NS and GL Narasimhan. 1982. A case for building up draught animal power. *Kurushetra (India's Journal for Rural Development)* 30:4.

Reynolds, SJ, KJ Donham, P Whitten, JA Merchant, LF Burmeister, and WJ Popendorf. 1996. A longitudinal evaluation of dose-response relationships for environmental exposures and pulmonary function in swine production workers. *Am J Ind Med* 29:33-40.

Robertson, MH, IR Clarke, JD Coghlan, and ON Gill. 1981. Leptospirosis in trout farmers. *Lancet*: 2(8247)626-627.

Robertson, TD, SA Ribeiro, S Zodrow, and JV Breman. 1994. *Assessment of Strategic Livestock Feed Supplementation as an Opportunity for Generating Income for Small Scale Dairy Producers and Reducing Methane Emissions in Bangladesh*. Washington, DC: US Environmental Protection Agency.

Rylander, R. 1994. Symptoms and mechanisms: Inflammation of the lung. *Am J Ind Med* 25:19-24.

Rylander, R, KJ Donham, C Hjort, R Brouwer, and D Heederik. 1989. Effects of exposure to dust in swine confinement buildings: A working group report. *Scand J Work Environ Health* 15:309-312.

Rylander, R and N Essle. 1990. Bronchial hyperactivity among pig and dairy farmers. *Am J Ind Med* 17:66-69.

Rylander, R, Y Peterson, and KJ Donman. 1990. Questionnaire evaluating organic dust exposure. *Am J Ind Med* 17:121-128.

Rylander, R and R Jacobs. 1994. *Organic Dusts: Exposure, Effects and Prevention*. Chicago, IL: Lewis Publishing.

Safina, C. 1995. The world's imperiled fish. *Sci Am* 272:46-53.

Scherf, BD. 1995. *World Watch List for Domestic Animal Diversity*. Rome: FAO.

Schmidt, MJ. 1997. Working elephants. *Sci Am* 279:82-87.

Schmidt, JO. 1992. Allergy to venomous insects. In *The Hive and the Honey Bee*, edited by JM Graham. Hamilton: DaDant & Sons.

Shumacher, MJ and NB Egen. 1995. Significance of Africanized bees on public health. *Arch Int Med* 155:2038-2043.

Sherson, D, I Hansen, and T Sigsgaard. 1989. Occupationally related respiratory symptoms in trout-processing workers. *Allergy* 44:336-341.

Stem, C, DD Joshi, and M Orlic. 1995. *Reducing Methane Emissions from Ruminant Livestock: Nepal prefeasibility Study*. Washington, DC: US Environmental Protection Agency, Global Change Division.

Sweeten, JM. 1995. Odor measurement technology and applications: A state-of-the-art review. In *Seventh International Symposium on Agricultural and Food Processing Wastes: Proceedings of the 7th International Symposium*, edited by CC Ross. American Society of Agricultural Engineering.

Tannahill, R. 1973. *Food in History*. New York: Stein and Day.

Thorne, PS, KJ Donham, J Dosman, P Jagielo, JA Merchant, and S Von Essen. 1996. Occupational health. In *Understanding the Impacts of Large-scale Swine Production*, edited by KM Thu, D Mcmillan, and J Venzke. Iowa City, IA: University of Iowa.

Turner, F and PJ Nichols. 1995. Role of the epithelium in the response of the airways. Abstract for the 19th Cotton and Other Organic Dust Research Conference, 6-7 January, San antonio, TX.

United Nations Development Programme (UNDP). 1996. *Urban Agriculture: Food, Jobs, and Sustainable Cities*. New York: UNDP.

US Department of Agriculture (USDA). 1992. *Agricultural Waste Management Field Handbook*. Washington, DC: USDA Soil Conservation Service.

—. 1996a. *Livestock and Poultry: World Markets and Trade*. Circular Series FL&P 1-96. Washington DC: USDA Foreign Agricultural Service.

—. 1996b. *Dairy: World Markets and Trade*. Circular Series FD 1-96. Washington DC: USDA Foreign Agricultural Service.

—. 1997. *Poultry Production and Value, 1996 Summary*. Washington, DC: National Agricultural Statistics Service.

van Hage-Hamsten, M, S Johansson, and S Hogland. 1985. Storage mite allergy is common in a farming population. *Clin Allergy* 15:555-564.

Vivian, J. 1986. *Keeping Bees*. Charlotte, VT: Williamson Publishing.

Waller, JA. 1992. Injuries to farmers and farm families in a dairy state. *J Occup Med* 34:414-421.

Yang, N. 1995. Research and development of buffalo draught power for farming in China. *Asian Livestock* XX:20-24.

Zhou, C and JM Roseman. 1995. Agriculture-related residual injuries: Prevalence, type, and associated factors among Alabama farm operators, 1990. *Journal of Rural Health* 11:251-258.

Zuehlke, RL, CF Mutel, and KJ Donham. 1980. *Diseases of Agricultural Workers*. Iowa City, IA: Department of Preventive Medicine and Environmental Health, University of Iowa.

Other relevant readings

Alexander, JO. 1984. *Arthropods and Human Skin*. Berlin: Springer-Verlag.

Baker, D and R Lee. 1993. *Animal Handling Safety Considerations*. Columbia, MO: Missouri State University Extension.

Bauer, MA and DP Coppolo. 1993. Agriculture lung disease: Prevention. *Semin Respir Med* 14:83-89.

Bean, T. 1992. *Working Safely with Livestock*. Columbus: Ohio State University Extension.

Beno, J, C Schwab, and L Miller. 1992: *Know Your Livestock and Be Safe.* Fact sheet PM-1265b. Ames, IA: Iowa State University Extension.

Bottcher, RW, RL Langley, and R McLymore. 1994. *Improving the Health and Safety of Poultry Facility Workers.* Raleigh: North Carolina Cooperative Extension Service.

Centers for Disease Control and Prevention (CDC). 1984. Work-related allergies in insect-raising facilities. *Morb Mortal Weekly Rep* 33:448, 453-454.

Cole, WC 1996. Physical hazards in research animal facilities. *Proceedings of the 4th National Symposium on Safety: Working Safely with Research Animals.* 27-31 January Atlanta, GA.

Cotes, JE and J Steel. 1987. *Work-related Lung Disorders.* Oxford: Blackwell Scientific Publications.

Crane, E. 1990. *Bees and Beekeeping: Science, Practice and World Resources.* Oxford: Heinemann Newnes.

—. 1994. Health hazards of pork producers in livestock confinement building: From recognition to control. In *Agricultural Health and Safety: Workplace, Environment, Sustainability,* edited by HH McDuffie, JA Dosman, KM Semchuk, SA Olenchock, and A Senthilselvan. Boca Raton, FL: CRC Press.

Donham, KJ, LW Knapp, R Monoson, and Gustafon. 1982. Acutely toxic exposure to gases from liquid manure. *J Occup Med* 24:142-145.

Ebert, K and M Dennis. 1993a. *Cattle Safety.* Manhattan, KS: Kansas State University Extension.

—. 1993b. *Proper Handling/facilities Critical to Good Working Relationship.* Manhattan, KS: Kansas State University Extension.

Ellis, JL and PR Gordon. 1991. Farm family mental health issues. *Occup Med: State Art Rev* 6:493-502.

Ensminger, ME. 1991. *Animal Science.* Danville, IL: Interstate Publishers.

Fox, JG, CE Newcomer, and H Rozmiarek. 1984. Selected zoonoses and other health hazards. *Laboratory Animal Medicine,* edited by JG Fox, BJ Cohen and FM Loew. New York: Academic Press.

Frazier, CA. 1980. *Occupational Asthma.* New York: Van Nostrand Reinhold Company.

Frazier, CA and FK Brown. 1980. *Insects and Allergy and What to Do about Them.* Norman, OK: University of Oklahoma Press.

Gill, ON, JD Coghlan, and IM Calder. 1985. The risk of leptospirosis in United Kingdom fish farm workers. *J Hyg Camb* 94:81-86.

Goddard, J. 1993. *Physician's Guide to Arthropods of Medical Importance.* Boca Raton, FL: CRC Press.

Gordon, JS. 1996. The chicken story. *American Heritage* 47:52-67.

Graham, JM (ed.). 1992. *The Hive and the Honey Bee.* Hamilton: DaDant & Sons.

King, M. 1993. Environmental hazards and your horse. *Horse Illustrated* :26-35.

Kochuyt, AM, E Van-Hoeyveld and EAM Stevens. 1993. Occupational allergy to bumble-bee venom. *Clin Exp Allergy* 23:190-195.

Langley, RL, RL McLymore, WJ Meggs, and GT Roberson. 1997. Safety and Health in Agriculture, Forestry, and Fisheries. Rockville, MD: Government Institutes.

Layde, PM, DL Nordstrom, D Stueland, LB Wittman, MA Follen and KA Olson. 1996. Animal-related occupational injuries in farm residents. *Journal of Agricultural Safety and Health* 2:27-37.

Lenhart, SW and SA Olenchock. 1984. Sources of respiratory insult in the poultry processing industry. *Am J Ind Med* 6:89-96.

Lenhart, SW and LD Reed. 1989. Respiratory protection for use against organic dust. In *Principles of Health and Safety in Agriculture,* edited by JA Dosman and DW Cockcroft. Boca Raton, FL: CRC Press.

Lenhart, SW, PD Morris, RE Akin, SA Olenchock, WS Service, and WP Boone. 1990. Organic dust, endotoxin, and ammonia exposures in the North Carolina poultry processing industry. *Appl Occup Environ Hyg* 5:611-618.

Levine, ML and RF Lockey. 1986. *Monograph on Insect Allergy.* Milwaukee, WI: American Academy of Allergy Immunology.

Lipman, NS and CE Newcomer. 1989. Hazard control in the animal research facility. In *Biohazards Management Handbook,* edited by DF Liberman and JG Gordon. New York: Marcel Dekker.

Loftas, T. 1995. *Dimensions of Need: An Atlas of Food and Agriculture.* Rome: FAO.

Morgan, WK and A Seaton. 1995. *Occupational Lung Diseases.* Philadelphia: WB Saunders.

Morris, PD, SW Lenhart, and WS Service. 1991. Respiratory symptoms and pulmonary function in chicken catchers in poultry confinement units. *Am J Ind Med* 19:195-204.

Murphy, D. *Animal Handling Tips.* Safety Fact Sheet 14. State College, PA: Pennsylvania State University Extension.

National Research Council (NRC). 1996. *Guide for the Care and Use of Laboratory Animals.* Washington, DC: National Academy Press.

National Technical Information Service (NTIS). 1995. *Health, Safety and Injury Prevention in Agriculture.* National Ag Safety Database CD-ROM #95-503777. Springfield, VA: NTIS.

—. 1997. *Occupational Health and Safety in the Care of Research Animals.* Washington, DC: National Academy Press.

Orkin, M and HI Maibach. 1985. *Cutaneous Infestations and Insect Bites.* New York: Marcel Dekker.

Parkes, WR. 1981. *Occupational Lung Disorders.* London: Butterworths.

Proctor, M, P Yeo, and A Lack. 1996. *The Natural History of Pollination.* Portland, OR: Timber Press.

Reynolds, SJ, D Parker, D Vesley, D Smith, and R Woellner. 1993. Cross-sectional epidemiological study of respiratory disease in turkey farmers. *Am J Ind Med* 24:713-722.

Reynolds, SJ, D Parker, D Vesley, K Janni, and C McJilton. 1994. Occupational exposure to organic dusts and gases in the turkey growing industry. *Appl Occup Environ Hyg* 9:493-502.

Rosenman, K. 1992. *Zoonoses—Animals Can Make You Sick.* East Lansing, MI: Michigan State University Extension.

Rylander, R. 1986. Lung diseases caused by organic dusts in the farm enivronment. *Am J Ind Med* 10:221-227.

Schenker, M, T Ferguson, and T Gamsky. 1991. Respiratory risks associated with agriculture. *Occup Med: State Art Rev* 6:415-428.

Siegel, M. 1996. *Book of Horses.* Davis, CA: University of California-Davis School of Veterinary Medicine.

Tu, AT. 1984. *Handbook of Natural Toxins.* Vol. 2. New York: Marcel Dekker.

Wagstaff, H. 1987. Husbandry methods and farm systems in industrial countries which use lower levels of external inputs: A review. *Agric Ecosyst & Environ* 19:1-27.

Wilkinson, R and A Tilma. 1992. *Livestock Handling and Confinement Safety.* East Lansing, MI: Michigan State University Extension.

71

Chapter Editors
Paul Demers and Kay Teschke

Contents

71. LUMBER

GENERAL PROFILE

Paul Demers

The lumber industry is a major natural resource-based industry around the world. Trees are harvested, for a variety of purposes, in the majority of countries. This chapter focuses on the processing of wood in order to produce solid wood boards and manufactured boards in sawmills and related settings. The term *manufactured boards* is used to refer to lumber composed of wood elements of varying sizes, from veneers down to fibres, which are held together by either additive chemical adhesives or "natural" chemical bonds. The relationship between the various types of manufactured boards is displayed in figure 71.1. Because of differences in process and associated hazards, manufactured boards are divided here into three categories: plywood, particleboard and fibreboard. The term *particleboard* is used to refer to any sheet material manufactured from small pieces of wood such as chips, flakes, splinters, strands or shreds, while the term *fibreboard* is used for all panels produced from wood fibres, including hardboard, medium-density fibreboard (MDF) and insulation board. The other major industrial use for wood is the manufacture of paper and related products, which is covered in the chapter *Pulp and paper industry*.

The sawmill industry has existed in simple forms for hundreds of years, although significant advances in sawmill technology have been made this century by the introduction of electric power, improvements in saw design and, most recently, the automation of sorting and other operations. The basic techniques for making plywood have also existed for many centuries, but the term *plywood* did not enter into common usage until the 1920s, and its manufacture did not become commercially important until this century. The other manufactured board industries, including particleboard, waferboard, oriented strandboard, insulation board, medium-density fibreboard and hardboard, are all relatively new industries which first became commercially important after the Second World War.

Solid wood and manufactured boards may be produced from a wide variety of tree species. Species are selected on the basis of the shape and size of the tree, the physical characteristics of the wood itself, such as strength or resistance to decay, and the aesthetic qualities of the wood. Hardwood is the common name given to broad-leaved trees, which are classified botanically as angiosperms, while softwood is the common name given to conifers, which are classified botanically as gymnosperms. Many hardwoods and some softwoods which grow in tropical regions are commonly referred to as tropical or exotic woods. Although the majority of wood harvested worldwide (58% by volume) is from non-conifers, much of this is consumed as fuel, so that the majority used for industrial purposes (69%) is from conifers (FAO 1993). This may in part reflect the distribution of forests in relation to industrial development. The largest softwood forests are located in the northern regions of North America, Europe and Asia, while the major hardwood forests are located in both tropical and temperate regions.

Almost all wood destined for use in the manufacture of wood products and structures is first processed in sawmills. Thus, sawmills exist in all regions of the world where wood is used for industrial purposes. Table 71.1 presents 1990 statistics regarding the volume of wood harvested for fuel and industrial purposes in the major wood-producing countries on each continent, as well as volumes harvested for saw and veneer logs, a sub-category of industrial wood and the raw material for the industries described in this chapter. In developed countries the majority of wood harvested is used for industrial purposes, which includes wood used for saw and veneer logs, pulpwood, chips, particles and

Table 71.1 • Estimated wood production in 1990 (1,000 m³).

	Wood used for fuel or charcoal	Total wood used for industrial purposes[1]	Saw and veneer logs
NORTH AMERICA	**137,450**	**613,790**	**408,174**
United States	82,900	426,900	249,200
Canada	6,834	174,415	123,400
Mexico	22,619	7,886	5,793
EUROPE	**49,393**	**345,111**	**202,617**
Germany	4,366	80,341	21,655
Sweden	4,400	49,071	22,600
Finland	2,984	40,571	18,679
France	9,800	34,932	23,300
Austria	2,770	14,811	10,751
Norway	549	10,898	5,322
United Kingdom	250	6,310	3,750
FORMER USSR	**81,100**	**304,300**	**137,300**
ASIA	**796,258**	**251,971**	**166,508**
China	188,477	91,538	45,303
Malaysia	6,902	40,388	39,066
Indonesia	136,615	29,315	26,199
Japan	103	29,300	18,377
India	238,268	24,420	18,350
SOUTH AMERICA	**192,996**	**105,533**	**58,592**
Brazil	150,826	74,478	37,968
Chile	6,374	12,060	7,401
Colombia	13,507	2,673	1,960
AFRICA	**392,597**	**58,412**	**23,971**
South Africa	7,000	13,008	5,193
Nigeria	90,882	7,868	5,589
Cameroon	10,085	3,160	2,363
Cote d'Ivoire	8,509	2,903	2,146
OCEANIA	**8,552**	**32,514**	**18,534**
Australia	7,153	17,213	8,516
New Zealand	50	11,948	6,848
Papua New Guinea	5,533	2,655	2,480
WORLD	**1,658,297**	**1,711,629**	**935,668**

[1] Includes wood used for saw and veneer logs, pulpwood, chips, particles and residues.
Source: FAO 1993.

residues. In 1990, three countries—the United States, the former USSR and Canada—produced over half of the world's total industrial wood as well as over half of the logs destined for saw and veneer mills. However, in many of the developing countries in Asia, Africa and South America the majority of wood harvested is used for fuel.

Figure 71.1 • Classification of manufactured boards by particle size, density and process type.

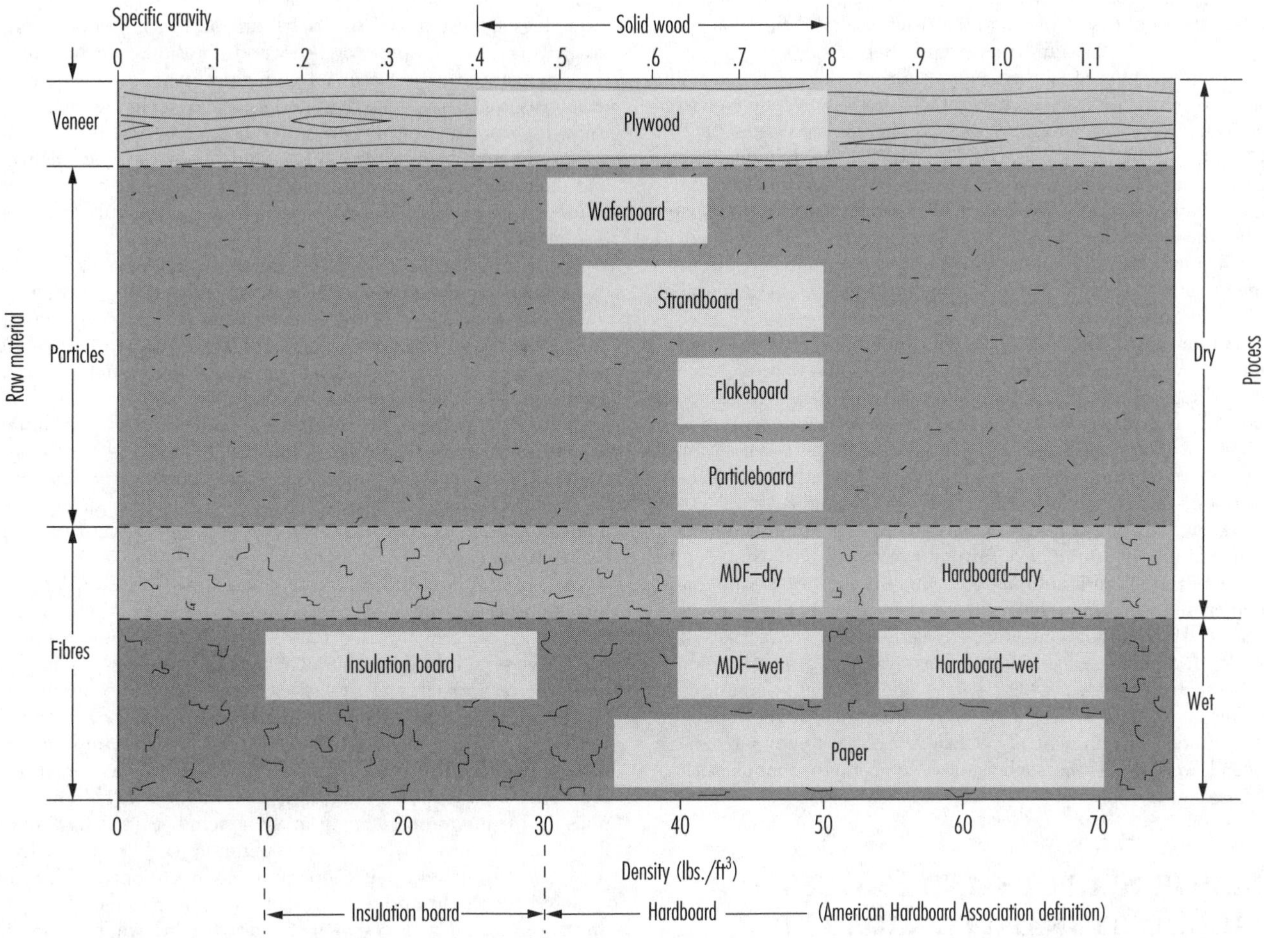

Source: Suchsland and Woodson 1987.

Table 71.2 lists the world's major producers of solid wood lumber, plywood, particleboard and fibreboard. The three largest producers of industrial wood overall also account for over half of world production of solid wood boards, and rank among the top five in each of the manufactured board categories. The volume of manufactured boards produced worldwide is relatively small com-

Table 71.2 • Estimated production of lumber by sector for the 10 largest world producers (1,000 m³).

Solid wood boards		Plywood boards		Particleboard		Fibreboard	
Country	Volume	Country	Volume	Country	Volume	Country	Volume
USA	109,800	USA	18,771	Germany	7,109	USA	6,438
Former USSR	105,000	Indonesia	7,435	USA	6,877	Former USSR	4,160
Canada	54,906	Japan	6,415	Former USSR	6,397	China	1,209
Japan	29,781	Canada	1,971	Canada	3,112	Japan	923
China	23,160	Former USSR	1,744	Italy	3,050	Canada	774
India	17,460	Malaysia	1,363	France	2,464	Brazil	698
Brazil	17,179	Brazil	1,300	Belgium-Luxembourg	2,222	Poland	501
Germany	14,726	China	1,272	Spain	1,790	Germany	499
Sweden	12,018	Korea	1,124	Austria	1,529	New Zealand	443
France	10,960	Finland	643	United Kingdom	1,517	Spain	430
World	505,468	World	47,814	World	50,388	World	20,248

Source: FAO 1993.

pared to the volume of solid wood boards, but the manufactured board industries are growing at a faster rate. While the production of solid wood boards increased by 13% between 1980 and 1990, the volumes of plywood, particleboard and fibreboard increased by 21%, 25% and 19%, respectively.

The proportion of workers in the entire workforce employed in wood products industries is generally 1% or less, even in countries with a large forest industry, such as the United States (0.6%), Canada (0.9%), Sweden (0.8%), Finland (1.2%), Malaysia (0.4%), Indonesia (1.4%) and Brazil (0.4%) (ILO 1993). While some sawmills may be located near urban areas, most tend to be located near the forests that supply their logs, and many are located in small, often isolated communities where they may be the only major source of employment and the most important component of the local economy.

Hundreds of thousands of workers are employed in the lumber industry worldwide, although exact international figures are difficult to estimate. In the United States in 1987 there were 180,000 sawmill and planer mill workers, 59,000 plywood workers and 18,000 workers employed in the production of particleboard and fibreboard (Bureau of the Census 1987). In Canada in 1991 there were 68,400 sawmill and planer mill workers and 8,500 plywood workers (Statistics Canada 1993). Even though wood production is increasing, the number of sawmill workers is decreasing due to mechanization and automation. The number of sawmill and planer mill workers in the United States was 17% higher in 1977 than in 1987, and in Canada there were 13% more in 1986 than in 1991. Similar reductions have been observed in other countries, such as Sweden, where smaller, less efficient operations are being eliminated in favour of mills with much larger capacities and modern equipment. The majority of jobs eliminated have been lower-skilled jobs, such as those involving the manual sorting or feeding of lumber.

● MAJOR SECTORS AND PROCESSES: OCCUPATIONAL HAZARDS AND CONTROLS

Hugh Davies, Paul Demers, Timo Kauppinen and Kay Teschke

Sawmill Process

Sawmills can vary greatly in size. The smallest are either stationary or portable units consisting of a circular saw headrig, a simple log carriage and a two-saw edger (see descriptions below) powered by a diesel or gasoline engine and operated by as few as one or two workers. The largest mills are permanent structures, have much more elaborate and specialized equipment, and can employ over 1,000 workers. Depending on the size of the mill and the climate of the region, operations may be performed outdoors or indoors. While the type and size of logs determine to a large degree what types of equipment are needed, the equipment in sawmills can also vary considerably based on the age and size of the mill as well as the type and quality of boards produced. Below is a description of some of the processes conducted in a typical sawmill.

After transport to a sawmill, logs are stored on land, in water bodies adjacent to the mill or in ponds constructed for storage purposes (see figures 71.2 and 71.3). The logs are sorted according to quality, species or other characteristics. Fungicides and insecticides may be used in land-based log storage areas if the logs will be stored for a long time until further processing. A cut-off saw is used to even up the ends of the logs either before or after

debarking and prior to further processing in the sawmill. The removal of bark from a log may be accomplished by a number of methods. Mechanical methods include peripheral milling by rotating logs against knives; ring debarking, in which tool points are pressed against the log; wood-to-wood abrasion, which pounds the logs against themselves in a rotating drum; and using chains to tear away the bark. Bark may also be removed hydraulically by using high-pressure water jets. After debarking and between all operations within the sawmill, logs and boards are moved from one operation to the next using a system of conveyors, belts and rollers. In large sawmills these systems can become quite complex (see figure 71.4).

The first phase of sawmilling, sometimes referred to as primary breakdown, is performed at a headrig. The headrig is a large, stationary circular saw or band-saw used to cut the log longitudinally. The log is transported back and forth through the headrig using a travelling carriage which can rotate the log for the optimum cut. Multiple band-saw headrigs may also be used, especially for smaller logs. The products of the headrig are a cant (the square centre of the log), a series of slabs (the rounded outer edges of the log) and, in some cases, large boards. Lasers and x rays are becoming common in sawmills for use as viewing and cutting guides in order to optimize wood use and the size and types of boards produced.

In secondary breakdown, the cant and large boards or slabs are further processed into functional lumber sizes. Multiple parallel saw blades are usually used for these operations—for example, quad saws with four linked circular saws, or gang saws which may be of the sash or circular saw type. Boards are cut to the proper width using edgers, consisting of at least two parallel saws, and to the proper length using trim saws. Edging and trimming are usually performed using circular saws, though edgers sometimes are band-saws. Manual chain-saws are usually available in sawmills for freeing lumber caught in the system because it is bent or flared. In modern sawmills, each operation (i.e., headrig, edger) will generally have a single operator, often stationed within an enclosed booth. In addition, workers may be stationed between operations in later stages of secondary breakdown in order to manually ensure that the boards are properly positioned for subsequent operations.

Figure 71.2 ● Chip loading with water storage of logs in background

Source: Canadian Forest Products Ltd.

Figure 71.3 • Logs entering a sawmill; storage and kilns in background.

Canadian Forest Products Ltd.

Figure 71.4 • Mill interior; conveyor belts and rollers transport wood.

British Columbia Ministry of Forests.

After processing in the sawmill, the boards are graded, sorted according to dimensions and quality, then stacked by hand or machine (see figure 71.5). When lumber is manually handled, this area is referred to as a "green chain". Automated sorting bins have been installed in many modern mills to replace labour-intensive manual sorting. In order to increase airflow to assist in drying, small pieces of wood may be placed between the boards as they are being stacked.

Construction grades of lumber may be seasoned in the open air outdoors or dried in kilns, depending on local weather conditions and the wetness of the green lumber; but finishing grades are more commonly kiln dried. There are many kinds of kilns. Compartment kilns and high-temperature kilns are serial kilns. In continuous kilns, stacked bundles can move through the kiln in a perpendicular or parallel position, and the direction of air movement can be perpendicular or parallel to the boards. Asbestos has been used as an insulating material for steam pipes in kilns.

Prior to storage of green lumber, especially in wet or humid locales, fungicides may be applied to prevent growth of fungi which stain wood blue or black (sapstain). Fungicides may be applied in the production line (usually by spraying) or after bundling lumber (usually in dip tanks). The sodium salt of pentachlorophenol was introduced in the 1940s for the control of sapstain, and was replaced in the 1960s by the more water soluble tetrachlorophenate. Chlorophenate use has largely been discontinued because of concern regarding health effects and contamination with polychlorinated dibenzo-p-dioxins. Substitutes include didecyldimethyl ammonium chloride, 3-iodo-2-propynyl butyl carbamate, azaconazole, borax and 2-(thiocyanomethylthio)benzthiazole, most of which have been little studied among user workforces. Often lumber, especially that which has been kiln dried, does not need to be treated. In addition, wood of some tree species, such as Western red cedar, is not susceptible to sapstain fungi.

Either before or after drying, the wood is marketable as green or rough lumber; however, the lumber must be further processed for most industrial uses. Lumber is cut to final size and surfaced in a planing mill. Planers are used to reduce the wood to standard marketable sizes and to smooth the surface. The planer head is a series of cutting blades mounted on a cylinder which revolves at high speed. The operation is generally power fed and performed parallel to the wood grain. Often planing is performed simultaneously on two sides of the board. Planers which operate on four

sides are called matchers. Moulders are sometimes used to round the edges of the wood.

After final processing, the wood must be sorted, stacked and bundled in preparation for shipping. Increasingly, these operations are being automated. In some specialized mills, wood may be further treated with chemical agents used as wood preservatives or fire retardants, or for protection of the surface from mechanical wear or weathering. For example, railroad ties, pilings, fence posts, telephone poles or other wood expected to be in contact with soil or water may be pressure treated with chromated or ammoniacal copper arsenate, pentachlorophenol or creosote in petroleum oil. Stains and colourants may also be used for marketability, and paints may be used to seal the ends of boards or to add company marks.

Large amounts of dust and debris are generated by saws and other wood-processing operations in sawmills. In many sawmills the slabs and other large pieces of wood are chipped. Chippers are generally large rotating discs with straight blades imbedded in the face, and slots for the chips to pass through. The chips are produced when logs or mill wastes are introduced to the blades using inclined gravity feed, horizontal self-feed or controlled power feeding. Generally the cutting action of the chipper is perpendicular to the blades. Different designs are used for whole

Figure 71.5 • Fork-lift with load.

Canadian Forestry Products Ltd.

71. LUMBER

logs than for slabs, edgings and other pieces of waste wood. It is common for a chipper to be integrated into the headrig to chip unusable slabs. Separate chippers to handle waste from the rest of the mill are also used. Wood chips and sawdust may be sold for pulp, reconstituted board manufacturing, landscaping, fuel or other uses. Bark, wood chips, sawdust and other material may also be burned either as fuel or as waste.

Large, modern sawmills will typically have a sizeable maintenance staff which includes clean-up workers, millwrights (industrial mechanics), carpenters, electricians and other skilled workers. Waste material may collect on machinery, conveyors and floors if sawmill operations are not equipped with local exhaust ventilation or the equipment is not operating properly. Clean-up operations are often performed using compressed air to remove wood dust and dirt from machinery, floors and other surfaces. Saws must be regularly inspected for broken teeth, cracks or other defects, and must be properly balanced to prevent vibration. This is done by a trade that is unique to the wood industries—saw filers, who are responsible for the re-toothing, sharpening and other maintenance of circular saws and band-saws.

Sawmill Health and Safety Hazards

Table 71.3 indicates the major types of occupational health and safety hazards found in the major process areas of a typical sawmill. There are many serious safety hazards within sawmills. Machine guarding is necessary at the point of operation for saws and other cutting devices as well as for gears, belts, chains, sprockets and nip points on conveyors, belts and rollers. Anti-kickback devices are necessary on many operations, such as circular saws, to prevent jammed lumber from being ejected from machines. Guard rails are necessary on walkways adjacent to operations or crossing over conveyors and other production lines. Proper housekeeping is necessary to prevent dangerous accumulation of wood dust and debris, which could result in falls as well as presenting a fire and explosion hazard. Many areas which require clean-up and routine maintenance are located in hazardous areas which would normally be inaccessible during times when the sawmill is in operation. Proper adherence to machinery lock-out procedures is extremely important during maintenance, repair and clean-up operations. Mobile equipment should be equipped with audible warning signals and lights. Traffic lanes and pedestrian walkways should be clearly marked. Reflective vests are also necessary to increase the visibility of pedestrians.

Sorting, grading and some other operations may involve the manual handling of boards and other heavy pieces of wood. Ergonomic design of the conveyors and receiving bins, and proper material-handling techniques should be used to help prevent back and upper extremity injuries. Gloves are necessary to prevent splinters, puncture wounds and contact with preservatives. Panels of safety glass or similar material should be placed between operators and points of operation because of the risk of eye and other injuries from wood dust, chips and other debris ejected from saws. Laser beams are also potential ocular hazards, and areas using Class II, III or IV lasers should be identified and warning signs posted. Safety glasses, hardhats and steel-toed boots are standard personal protective gear that should be worn during most sawmill operations.

Noise is a hazard in most areas of sawmills from debarking, sawing, edging, trimming, planing and chipping operations, as well as from logs striking each other on conveyors, rollers and drop-sorters. Feasible engineering controls to reduce noise levels include sound-proof booths for operators, enclosure of cutting machines with sound-absorbent material at the in- and out-feeds, and construction of sound barriers of acoustical materials. Other engineering controls are also possible. For example, idle running noise from circular saws may be reduced by purchasing saws with

a suitable tooth shape or adjusting the speed of rotation. The installation of absorbing material on walls and ceilings may aid in reducing reflected noise throughout the mill, though source control would be necessary where noise exposure is direct.

Workers in almost all areas of the sawmill have the potential for exposure to particulate matter. Debarking operations involve little or no exposure to wood dust, since the goal is to leave the wood intact, but exposure to airborne soil, bark and biological agents, such as bacteria and fungi, is possible. Workers in almost all sawing, chipping and planing areas have the potential for exposure to wood dust. The heat generated by these operations may cause exposure to the volatile elements of the wood, such as monoterpenes, aldehydes, ketones and others, which will vary by tree species and temperature. Some of the highest wood dust exposures may occur among workers using compressed air for clean-up. Workers near kiln drying operations are likely to be exposed to wood volatiles. In addition, there is a potential for exposure to pathogenic fungi and bacteria, which grow at temperatures below 70 °C. Exposure to bacteria and fungi is also possible during the handling of wood chips and waste, and the transport of logs in the yard.

Feasible engineering controls, such as local exhaust ventilation, exist to control the levels of airborne contaminants, and it may be possible to combine noise- and dust-control measures. For example, enclosed booths may reduce both noise and dust exposures (as well as preventing eye and other injuries). However, booths provide protection only to the operator, and controlling exposures at the source through enclosure of operations is preferable. Enclosure of planing operations has become increasingly common and has had the effect of reducing exposure to both noise and dust among persons who do not have to enter the enclosed areas. Vacuum and wet clean-up methods have been used in some mills, usually by clean-up contractors, but are not in general use. Exposure to fungi and bacteria may be controlled by reducing or increasing kiln temperatures and taking other steps to eliminate the conditions which promote the growth of these micro-organisms.

Other potentially hazardous exposures exist within sawmills. Exposure to cold and hot temperature extremes is possible near points where materials enter or leave the building, and heat is also a potential hazard in kiln areas. High humidity may be a problem when sawing wet logs. Exposure to fungicides is primarily via the dermal route and may occur if the boards are handled while still wet during grading, sorting and other operations. Appropriate gloves and aprons are necessary when handling boards that are wet with fungicides. Local exhaust ventilation with spray curtains and mist eliminators should be used in spraying operations. Exposure to carbon monoxide and other combustion products is possible from mobile equipment used to move logs and lumber within storage areas and to load semi-trailers or railroad cars. Saw filers may be exposed to hazardous levels of metal fumes including cobalt, chromium and lead from grinding, welding and soldering operations. Local exhaust ventilation as well as machine guarding are necessary.

Veneer and Plywood Mill Processes

The term *plywood* is used for panels consisting of three or more veneers which have been glued together. The term is also used to refer to panels with a core of solid wood strips or particleboard with top and bottom veneer surfaces. Plywood can be made from a variety of trees, including both conifers and non-conifers.

Veneers are usually created directly from debarked whole logs using rotary peeling. A rotary peeler is a lathe-like machine used to cut veneers, thin sheets of wood, from whole logs using a shearing action. The log is rotated against a pressure bar as it hits a cutting knife to produce a thin sheet between 0.25 and 5 mm in

Table 71.3 • Occupational health and safety hazards by lumber industry process area.

Process area	Safety hazards	Physical hazards	Dust/chemical hazards	Biological hazards
Yard and pond	Mobile equipment;* unsecure logs/lumber;* conveyor belts	Noise; temperate extremes	Road dust, other particulates; pesticides	Mould and bacteria*
Debarking	Elevated walk-ways; machine kick-back; unsecure logs/lumber;* conveyor belts; saws/cutting equipment; flying debris;* failure to lock-out machinery	Noise	Wood dust; road dust; other particulates; volatile wood components	Mould and bacteria*
Sawing, trimming, edging	Elevated walk-ways; machine kick-back;* unsecure logs/lumber; conveyor belts;* saws/cutting equipment;* flying debris; slivers; failure to lock-out machinery*	Noise;* repetitive strain injuries	Wood dust;* volatile wood components*	Mould and bacteria
Kiln drying	Mobile equipment	Temperature extremes	Volatile wood components, asbestos	Mould and bacteria
Planing	Elevated walk-ways; machine kick-back;* unsecure logs/lumber; conveyor belts;* saws/cutting equipment;* flying debris; slivers; failure to lock-out machinery	Noise;* repetitive strain injuries	Wood dust;* volatile wood components; pesticides	
Sorting and grading	Elevated walk-ways; unsecure logs/lumber; conveyor belts;* slivers; failure to lock-out machinery	Noise; repetitive strain injuries*	Wood dust; pesticides	
Chipping and related operations	Elevated walk-ways; machine kick-back; conveyor belts; saws/cutting equipment;* flying debris;* failure to lock-out machinery	Noise*	Wood dust;* volatile wood components	Mould and bacteria*
Veneer cutting	Elevated walk-ways; mobile equipment; conveyor belts; saws/cutting equipment; slivers; failure to lock-out machinery	Noise*	Wood dust; volatile wood components	Mould and bacteria*
Veneer drying	Mobile equipment; slivers	Temperature extremes; repetitive strain injuries	Volatile wood components; asbestos	Mould and bacteria
Glue mixing and patching		Repetitive strain injuries	Formaldehyde;* other resin components*	
Hot press operations	Mobile equipment; slivers; failure to lock-out machinery*	Noise; repetitive strain injuries	Volatile wood components; formaldehyde;* other resin components*	
Panel sanding and finishing	Mobile equipment; saws/cutting equipment; flying debris; slivers; failure to lock-out machinery	Noise;* repetitive strain injuries	Wood dust; formaldehyde; other resin components	
Clean-up operations	Elevated walk-ways; conveyor belts;* flying debris;* slivers; failure to lock-out machinery*	Noise	Wood dust;* formaldehyde; other resin components; asbestos	Mould and bacteria*
Saw filing	Elevated walk-ways; saws/cutting equipment; flying debris; failure to lock-out machinery	Noise	Metal fumes*	
Other maintenance	Elevated walk-ways; mobile equipment;* failure to lock-out machinery*		Wood dust; asbestos; metal fumes	
Packing and shipping	Elevated walk-ways; mobile equipment;* unsecure logs/lumber; conveyor belts; slivers; failure to lock-out machinery	Noise; temperature extremes; repetitive strain injuries	Road dust, other particulates; pesticides	

* Signifies high degree of hazard.

thickness. The logs used in this process may be soaked in hot water or steamed to soften them prior to peeling. The edges of the sheet are usually trimmed by knives attached to the pressure bar. Decorative veneers may be created by slicing a cant (the square centre of the log) using a pressure arm and blade in a manner similar to peeling. After either peeling or slicing, the veneers are collected on long, flat trays or rolled onto reels. The veneer is clipped into functional lengths using a guillotine-like machine, and dried using artificial heating or natural ventilation. The dried panels are inspected and, if necessary, patched using small pieces or strips of wood and formaldehyde-based resins. If the dried veneers are smaller than a standard-size panel, they may be spliced together. This is done by applying a liquid formaldehyde-based adhesive to the edges, pressing the edges together, and applying heat to cure the resin.

To produce the panels, veneers are roller- or spray-coated with formaldehyde-based resins, then placed between two unglued veneers with their grains in the perpendicular direction. The veneers are transferred to a hot press, where they are subjected to both pressure and heat to cure the resin. Phenol-resin adhesives are widely used to produce softwood plywood for severe service conditions, such as for construction and boat building. Urea-resin adhesives are used extensively in producing hardwood plywood for furniture and interior panelling; these can be fortified with

71. LUMBER

melamine resin to increase their strength. The plywood industry has used formaldehyde-based glues in assembling of plywood for over 30 years. Prior to the introduction of formaldehyde-based resins in the 1940s, soybean and blood-albumen adhesives were used, and cold pressing of panels was common. These methods may still be used, but are increasingly rare.

The panels are cut to the proper dimensions using circular saws and are surfaced using large drum or belt sanders. Additional machining may also be performed in order to give the plywood special characteristics. In some cases, pesticides such as chlorophenols, lindane, aldrin, heptachlor, chloronaphthalenes and tributyltin oxide may be added to glues or used to treat the surface of panels. Other surface treatments may include the application of light petroleum oils (for concrete-form panels), paints, stains, lacquers and varnishes. These surface treatments may be performed at separate locations. Veneers and panels are often transported between operations using mobile equipment.

Veneer and Plywood Mill Hazards

Table 71.3 indicates the major types of occupational health and safety hazards found in the major process areas of a typical plywood mill. Many of the safety hazards in plywood mills are similar to those in sawmills, and the control measures are also similar. This section deals with only those issues which differ from sawmill operations.

Both dermal and respiratory exposure to formaldehyde and other components of glues, resins and adhesives is possible among workers in glue preparation, splicing, patching, sanding and hot pressing operations, and among workers nearby. Urea-based resins more readily release formaldehyde during curing than phenol-based ones; however, improvements in resin formulation have reduced exposures. Proper local exhaust ventilation and the use of appropriate gloves and other protective equipment are necessary to reduce respiratory and dermal exposure to formaldehyde and other resin components.

The wood used to produce veneers is wet, and the peeling and clipping operations do not generally produce much dust. The highest wood dust exposures during the production of plywood occur during the sanding, machining and sawing necessary to finish the plywood. Sanding, in particular, can produce large amounts of fine dust because as much as 10 to 15% of the board may be removed during surfacing. These processes should be enclosed and have local exhaust ventilation; hand sanders should have integral exhaust to a vacuum bag. If local exhaust is not present or it is not functioning properly, significant exposure to wood dust may occur. Vacuum and wet clean-up methods are more commonly found in plywood mills because the fine size of the dust makes other methods less effective. Unless noise control measures are in place, noise levels from sanding, sawing and machining operations are likely to exceed 90 dBA.

When veneers are dried, a number of chemical constituents of the wood may be released, including monoterpenes, resin acids, aldehydes and ketones. The types and amounts of chemical released depend on the species of tree and veneer dryer temperature. Proper exhaust ventilation and the prompt repair of veneer dryer leaks are necessary. Exposure to engine exhaust from forklifts may occur throughout plywood mills, and mobile equipment also presents a safety hazard. Pesticides mixed in glues are only slightly volatile and should not be detectable in workroom air, with the exception of chloronaphthalenes, which evaporate substantially. Exposure to pesticides may occur through the skin.

Other Manufactured Board Industries

This group of industries, including the manufacture of particleboard, waferboard, strandboard, insulation board, fibreboard and hardboard, produces boards consisting of wood elements of varying sizes, ranging from large flakes or wafers to fibres, held together by resinous glues or, in the case of wet process fibreboard, "natural" bonding between fibres. In the simplest sense, boards are created using a two-step process. The first step is the generation of the elements either directly from whole logs or as a waste by-product of other wood industries, such as sawmills. The second step is their recombination into sheet or panel form using chemical adhesives.

Particleboard, flakeboard, strandboard and waferboard are made from chips of wood of varying sizes and shapes using similar processes. Particleboard and flakeboard are made from small wood elements and are often used to make wood-veneered or plastic-laminated panels for the manufacture of furniture, cabinets and other wood products. Most elements may be made directly from wood waste. Waferboard and strandboard are made from very large particles—wood shavings and strands, respectively—and are primarily used for structural applications. The elements are generally made directly from logs using a machine containing a series of rotating knives which peel thin wafers. The design can be similar to a chipper, except the wood must be fed to the flaker with the grain oriented parallel to the knives. Peripheral milling designs can also be used. Water-saturated wood works best for these processes and, because the wood must be oriented, short logs are often used.

Before making sheets or panels, the elements must be sorted by size and grade, and then dried using artificial means, to a closely controlled moisture content. The dried elements are mixed with an adhesive and laid out in mats. Both phenol-formaldehyde and urea-formaldehyde resins are used. As is the case with plywood, phenolic resins are likely to be used for panels destined for applications requiring durability under adverse conditions, while the urea-formaldehyde resins are used for less demanding, interior applications. Melamine formaldehyde resins may also be used to increase durability, but rarely are because they are more expensive. In recent decades a new industry has emerged to produce reconstituted lumber for various structural uses as beams, supports and other weight-bearing elements. While the manufacturing processes used may be similar to particleboard, isocyanate-based resins are used because of the added strength needed.

The mats are divided into panel-sized sections, generally using an automated compressed air source or a straight blade. This operation is done in an enclosure so that the excess mat material can be recycled. The panels are formed into sheets by curing the thermosetting resin using a hot press in a manner similar to plywood. Afterwards the panels are cooled and trimmed to size. If necessary, sanders may be used to finish the surface. For example, reconstituted boards which are to be covered with a wood veneer or plastic laminate must be sanded to produce a relatively smooth, even surface. While drum sanders were used early in the industry, wide belt sanders are now generally used. Surface coatings may also be applied.

Fibreboards (including insulation board, medium-density fibreboard (MDF) and hardboard) are panels consisting of bonded wood fibres. Their production varies somewhat from particle- and other manufactured boards (see figure 71.1). To create the fibres, short logs or wood chips are reduced (pulped) in a manner similar to that used for producing pulp for the paper industry (see the chapter *Pulp and paper industry*). In general, a mechanical pulping process is used in which chips are soaked in hot water and then mechanically ground. Fibreboards can vary greatly in density, from low-density insulation boards to hardboards, and can be made from either conifers or non-conifers. Non-conifers generally make better hardboards, while conifers make better insulation boards. The processes involved in pulping have a minor chemical effect on the ground wood, removing a small amount of the lignin and extractive materials.

Two different processes, wet and dry, may be used to bond the fibres and create the panels. Hardboard (high density fibreboard) and MDF can be produced by "wet" or "dry" processes, while insulation board (low density fibreboard) can be produced only by the wet process. The wet process was developed first, and extends from paper production, while the dry process was developed later and stems from particleboard techniques. In the wet process, a slurry of pulp and water is distributed on a screen to form a mat. Afterwards, the mat is pressed, dried, cut and surfaced. The boards created by wet processes are held together by adhesive-like wood components and the formation of hydrogen bonds. The dry process is similar, except that the fibres are distributed on the mat after addition of a binder (either a thermosetting resin, thermoplastic resin or a drying oil) to form a bond between the fibres. Generally, either phenol-formaldehyde or urea-formaldehyde resins are used during the manufacture of dry-process fibreboard. A number of other chemicals may be used as additives, including inorganic salts as fire retardants and fungicides as preservatives.

In general, the health and safety hazards in the particleboard and related manufactured board industries are quite similar to those in the plywood industry, with the exception of pulping operations for fibreboard production (see table 71.3). Exposure to wood dust is possible during the processing to create the elements and may vary greatly depending on the moisture content of the wood and the nature of the processes. The highest wood dust exposures would be expected during the cutting and finishing of panels, especially during sanding operations if engineering controls are not in place or not functioning properly. Most sanders are enclosed systems, and large capacity air systems are needed to remove the dust generated. Exposure to wood dust, as well as fungi and bacteria, is also possible during the chipping and grinding of dried wood and among workers involved in the transport of chips from storage to processing areas. Very high noise exposures are possible near all sanding, chipping, grinding and related wood-processing operations. Exposure to formaldehyde and other resin constituents is possible during the mixing of glues, laying of the mat and the hot pressing operations. The control measures for limiting exposure to safety hazards, wood dust, noise and formaldehyde in the manufactured board industries are similar to those for the plywood and sawmill industries.

● DISEASE AND INJURY PATTERNS

Paul Demers

Injuries

Sawmills and other lumber mills are extremely hazardous work environments due to the nature of the process, which involves the movement and cutting of large, very heavy pieces of wood at relatively high speeds. Even when good engineering controls are in place, strict adherence to safety rules and procedures is necessary. There are a number of general factors which may contribute to the risk of injury. Poor housekeeping can increase the risk of slips, trips and falls, and wood dust may pose a fire or explosion hazard. The high noise levels have been a cause of injuries due to the reduced ability of workers to communicate and hear audible warning signals. Many large mills operate on multiple shifts, and the hours of work, particularly changes in shift, can increase the probability of accidents.

Some common causes of fatal or very serious injuries are being struck by mobile equipment; falls from elevated walkways and platforms; failure to de-energize or lockout equipment during maintenance or attempts to remove jams; kick-backs from saws, edgers and planers; and drowning in log ponds or waterways.

Newly hired workers are at increased risk. For example, in an analysis of the causes of 37 sawmill fatalities between 1985 and 1994 in British Columbia, Canada, 13 (35%) of the fatalities occurred within the first year of employment, and 5 of these occurred within the first week of employment (4 on the first day) (Howard 1995).

There is also a high risk of injuries which are not life threatening. Eye injuries may result from particles and small pieces of wood or debris ejected from machinery. Splinters, cuts and puncture wounds can result from contact between lumber and unprotected skin. Strains, sprains and other musculoskeletal injuries can result from attempts to push, pull or lift heavy materials during sorting, grading and other operations.

Non-Malignant Diseases

Workers in sawmills and related industries are exposed to a variety of respiratory hazards, including wood dust, the volatile components of wood, airborne moulds and bacteria, and formaldehyde. A number of studies have examined respiratory health among sawmill, plywood, particleboard and strandboard workers. The focus of the sawmill studies has generally been on wood dust, while the focus of the plywood and particleboard studies has primarily been on formaldehyde exposure.

Occupational exposure to wood dust has been associated with a broad range of upper- and lower-respiratory effects. Because of the particle sizes generated by operations in the lumber industries, the nose is a natural site for the effects of wood dust exposure. A wide variety of sino-nasal effects have been reported, including rhinitis, sinusitis, nasal obstruction, nasal hypersecretion and impaired mucociliary clearance. Lower-respiratory effects, including asthma, chronic bronchitis and chronic airflow obstruction, have also been associated with exposure to wood dust. Both upper- and lower-respiratory effects have been associated with both softwood and hardwood tree species from both temperate and tropical climates. For example, occupational asthma has been found to be associated with exposure to dust from African maple, African zebra, ash, California redwood, cedar of Lebanon, Central American walnut, Eastern white cedar, ebony, iroko, mahogany, oak, ramin and Western red cedar as well as other tree species.

Wood is primarily composed of cellulose, polyoses and lignin, but also contains a variety of biologically active organic compounds such as monoterpenes, tropolones, resin acids (diterpenes), fatty acids, phenols, tannins, flavinoids, quinones, lignanes and stilbenes. Because health effects have been found to vary by species of tree, it is suspected they may be due to these naturally occurring chemicals, referred to as extractives, which also vary by species. In some cases specific extractives have been identified as the cause of the health effects associated with exposure to wood. For example, plicatic acid, which occurs naturally in Western red cedar and Eastern white cedar, is responsible for asthma and other allergenic effects in humans. While higher-molecular-weight extractives remain with the dust during woodworking operations, other, lighter-weight extractives, such as the monoterpenes, are easily volatilized during kiln drying, sawing and trimming operations. The monoterpenes (such as α-pinene, β-pinene, δ³-carene and limonene) are major components of the resin from many common softwoods and are associated with mouth and throat irritation, shortness of breath, and impaired lung function.

The moulds which grow on timber are another natural, wood-related exposure with potentially harmful effects. Exposure to moulds among sawmill workers appears to be common in regions where the climate is sufficiently damp and warm for moulds to grow. Cases of extrinsic allergic alveolitis, also referred to as hypersensitivity pneumonitis, have been observed among sawmill workers in Scandinavia, Great Britain and North America (Halpin et al. 1994). A much more common, although less serious, effect of exposure to moulds is inhalation fever, also referred to as organic dust toxic syndrome, consisting of acute attacks of fever, malaise, muscular pain and cough. The prevalence of inhalation fever among Swedish wood trimmers has been estimated to be between 5 and 20% in the past, although rates are likely to be much lower now due to the introduction of preventive measures.

Respiratory effects are also possible from exposure to chemicals used as adhesives in the lumber industry. Formaldehyde is an irritant and can cause inflammation of the nose and throat. Acute effects on lung function have been observed and chronic effects are suspected. Exposure has also been reported to cause asthma and chronic bronchitis.

The irritant or allergenic effects of wood dust, formaldehyde and other exposures are not limited to the respiratory system. For example, studies reporting nasal symptoms have often reported an increased prevalence of eye irritation. Dermatitis has been found to be associated with dust from over 100 different species of trees including some common hardwoods, softwoods and tropical species. Formaldehyde is also a skin irritant and can cause allergic contact dermatitis. In addition, a number of the anti-sapstain fungicides used on softwoods have also been found to cause eye and skin irritation.

Workers in sawmills and other lumber industries have a high risk for noise-related hearing loss. For example, in a recent survey in a United States sawmill, 72.5% of workers exhibited some degree of hearing impairment at one or more audiometric test frequencies (Tharr 1991). Workers in the vicinity of saws and other wood processing machinery are typically exposed to levels above 90 or 95 dBA. Despite this well recognized hazard, attempts to reduce noise levels are relatively rare (with the exception of planer mill enclosures), and new cases of noise-induced hearing loss continue to occur.

Cancer

Work in the lumber industries may entail exposure to both known and suspected carcinogens. Wood dust, the most common exposure in the lumber industries, has been classified as a human carcinogen (International Agency for Research on Cancer (IARC)—Group 1). Very high relative risks of sino-nasal cancer, particularly sino-nasal adenocarcinoma, have been observed among workers exposed to high levels of dust from hardwoods, such as beech, oak and mahogany, in the furniture industry. The evidence for softwood dust is less conclusive, and smaller excess risks have been observed. There is evidence of an excess risk among workers in sawmills and related industries based on a pooled re-analysis of the raw data from 12 sino-nasal cancer case-control studies (IARC 1995). Sino-nasal cancer is a relatively rare cancer in almost all regions of the world, with a crude annual incidence rate of approximately 1 per 100,000 population. Ten per cent of all sino-nasal cancers are thought to be adenocarcinomas. Although associations between wood dust and other, more common, cancers have been observed in some studies, the results have been much less consistent than for sino-nasal cancer.

Formaldehyde, a common exposure among workers in the plywood, particleboard and related industries, has been classified as a probable human carcinogen (IARC—Group 2A). Formaldehyde has been found to cause cancer in animals, and excesses of both nasopharyngeal and sino-nasal cancer have been observed in some studies of humans, but the results have been inconsistent. Pentachlorophenol and tetrachlorophenol pesticides, until recently commonly used in the wood industries, are known to be contaminated with furans and dioxins. Pentachlorophenol and 2,3,7,8-tetrachlorodibenzo-para-dioxin have been classified as possible human carcinogens (IARC—Group 2B). Some studies

have found an association between chlorophenols and the risk of non-Hodgkin lymphoma and soft-tissue sarcoma. The results for non-Hodgkin lymphoma have been more consistent than for soft-tissue sarcoma. Other potential carcinogenic exposures which may affect some workers in the lumber industries include asbestos (IARC—Group 1), which is used for insulation of steam pipes and kilns, diesel exhaust (IARC—Group 2A) from mobile equipment, and creosote (IARC—Group 2A), which is used as a wood preservative for railroad ties and telephone poles.

Relatively few studies of cancer among workers specifically employed in sawmills, plywood mills or related board manufacturing industries have been performed. The largest was a cohort study of over 26,000 Canadian sawmill workers conducted by Hertzman and colleagues (1997) in order to examine the risk of cancer associated with exposure to chlorophenol pesticides. A twofold excess of sino-nasal cancer and a smaller excess of non-Hodgkin lymphoma were observed. The excess of non-Hodgkin lymphoma appeared to be associated with exposure to chlorophenates. The remaining studies have been much smaller. Jäppinen, Pukkala and Tola (1989) studied 1,223 Finnish sawmill workers and observed excesses of skin, mouth and pharyngeal cancers, and lymphomas and leukaemias.

Blair, Stewart and Hoover (1990) and Robinson and colleagues (1986) conducted studies of 2,309 and 2,283 US plywood mill workers, respectively. In an analysis of pooled data from the two plywood cohorts, excesses were observed for nasopharyngeal cancer, multiple myeloma, Hodgkin's disease and non-Hodgkin's lymphoma. It is unclear from the results of these studies which, if any, occupational exposures may have been responsible for the excesses observed. The smaller studies have lacked the power to examine the risk of rare cancers, and many of the excesses were based on very small numbers. For example, no sino-nasal cancers were observed, but only 0.3 were expected in the smaller sawmill study, and 0.3 and 0.1 were expected in the plywood mill studies.

ENVIRONMENTAL AND PUBLIC HEALTH ISSUES

Kay Teschke and Anya Keefe

Use and Disposal of Wood Waste

By-products of the lumber industry which can cause environmental problems may include air emissions, liquid effluent and solid wastes. Most of these problems arise from waste wood, which may include wood chips or sawdust from milling operations, bark from debarking operations and log debris in waterways where logs are stored.

Sawdust and other process dust presents a fire and explosion hazard in mills. To minimize this hazard, dust may be removed by manual means or, preferably, gathered by local exhaust ventilation systems and collected in bag houses or cyclones. Larger wood waste is chipped. Most of the sawdust and chips produced in the lumber industry can be used in other wood products (e.g., particleboard, pulp and paper). Efficient use of this type of wood waste is becoming more common as the expense of waste disposal rises, and as forest companies become more vertically integrated. Some types of wood waste, especially fine dust and bark, are not as easily used in other wood products, so other means of disposal must be sought.

Bark can represent a high proportion of tree volume, especially in regions where the logs harvested are of small diameter. Bark and fine sawdust, and, in some operations, all wood waste including chips, may be burned (see figure 71.6). Older style operations have used inefficient burning techniques (e.g., beehive burners, teepee burners) which produce a range of incomplete organic combustion products. Particulate air pollution, which can produce "fog", is a common complaint in the vicinity of these burners. In sawmills where chlorophenols are used, there is also concern about dioxin and furan production in these burners. Some modern sawmills use enclosed temperature-controlled power boilers to produce steam for kilns or power for the mill or other electricity users. Others sell their wood waste to pulp and paper mills, where it is burned to meet their high power requirements (see the chapter *Pulp and paper industry*). Boilers and other burners usually must meet particulate emission control standards using systems such as electrostatic precipitators and wet scrubbers. To minimize burning of wood waste, other uses can be found for bark and fine sawdust, including as compost or mulch in landscaping, agriculture, surface mine revegetation and forest renewal, or as extenders in commercial products. In addition, use of thin-kerf saws in the mill can result in dramatic reductions in sawdust production.

Bark, logs and other wood debris may sink in water-based log storage areas, blanketing the bottom and killing benthic organisms. To minimize this problem, logs in booms can be bundled together and the bundles broken apart on land, where the debris can be easily collected. Even with this modification, sunken debris needs to be dredged from time to time. Recovered logs are available for lumber, but other waste requires disposal. Land-based disposal and deep-water dumping have both been used in the industry. Hydraulic debarking effluent can cause similar problems—thus the trend to mechanical systems.

Chip piles can create storm-water run-off problems since the leachate from wood includes resin and fatty acids and phenolics which are acutely toxic to fish. Landfill disposal of wood waste also produces leachate, requiring mitigation measures to protect ground and surface waters.

Antisapstain and Wood Preservation Fungicides

Wood treatment with fungicides to prevent the growth of sapstain organisms has led to contamination of nearby waterways (sometimes with large fish kills), as well as contamination of the soil on site. Treatment systems which involve driving bundled lumber through large, uncovered dip tanks and drainage in the sawmill yard allow rainfall overflows and widespread travel of runoff. Covered dip tanks with automated dipping elevators, spray booths in the production line, and containment berms around both the treatment system and the lumber drying area greatly reduce the potential for and impact of spills. However, although antisapstain spray booths minimize environmental exposure potential, they may entail more downstream worker exposure than dip tanks that treat finished bundled lumber.

Environmental impacts appear to have been reduced by the new generation of fungicides that have replaced chlorophenols. Although toxicity to aquatic organisms may be the same, certain substitute fungicides bind more strongly to wood, making them less bioavailable, and they are more easily degraded in the environment. In addition, the greater expense of many of the substitutes and the cost of disposal has encouraged recycling of liquid waste and other waste minimization procedures.

Figure 71.6 • Conveyor belts transport waste to a beehive burner.

Léonne Van Zwieten.

Thermal and pressure treatment of wood for long-term resistance to fungi and insects has traditionally been done in more enclosed facilities than antisapstain treatment, and therefore tends not to produce the same liquid waste problems. Disposal of solid wastes including sludge from treatment and storage tanks presents similar problems for both processes. Options may include contained storage in leak-proof containers in a bermed impermeable area, burial in a secure, hydrogeologically isolated hazardous-waste landfill or incineration at high temperatures (e.g., 1,000 °C) with specified residence times (e.g., 2 seconds).

Special Issues in Plywood and Particleboard Operations

Veneer dryers in plywood mills can produce a characteristic blue haze made up of volatile wood extractives such as terpenes and resin acids. This tends to be more of a problem inside plants, but can also be present in the dryer water-vapour plumes. Particleboard and plywood mills often burn wood waste to produce heat for the presses. Vapour and particulate control methods, respectively, can be used for these airborne emissions.

Wash water and other liquid effluents from plywood and particleboard mills can contain the formaldehyde resins used as glues; however, it is now common practice for waste water to be recycled for making up the glue mixtures.

References

Blair, A, PA Stewart and RN Hoover. 1990. Mortality from lung cancer among workers employed in formaldehyde industries. *Am J Ind Med* 17:683-699.

Bureau of the Census. 1987. *1987 Census of Manufacturers*. Washington, DC: US Department of Commerce.

Demers, PA, P Bofetta, M Kogevinas, A Blair, B Miller, C Robinson, R Roscoe, P Winter, D Colin, E Matos and H Vainio. 1995. A pooled re-analysis of cancer mortality among five cohorts of workers in wood-related industries. *Scand J Work Environ Health* 21(3):179-190.

Food and Agricultural Organization of the United Nations (FAO). 1993. *Yearbook of Forest Products 1980-1991*. FAO Statistical Series P6, No.110. Rome: FAO.

Halpin, DMG, BJ Graneek, M Turner-Warwick, and AJ Newman-Taylor. 1994. Extrinsic allergic alveolitis and asthma in a sawmill worker: Case report and review of the literature. *Occup Environ Med* 1(3):160-164.

Hertzman, C., K Teschke, A Ostry, R Herschler, H Dimich-Ward, S Kelly, JJ Spinelli, R Gallagher, M McBride and SA Marion. 1997. Mortality and cancer incidence among a cohort of sawmill workers exposed to chlorophenol pesticides. *Am J Public Health* 87(1):71-79.

Howard, B. 1995. *Fatal Claims in Sawmills. Analysis of Causes and Costs from 1985-1994*. Vancouver: Prevention Division, Workers Compensation Board of British Columbia.

International Agency for Research on Cancer (IARC) Working Group. 1995. *Wood Dust and Formaldehyde*. Vol. 62. Lyon: IARC.

—.1981. *Wood, Leather, and Associated Industries*. Vol. 25. Lyon: IARC.

International Labour Organization (ILO). 1993. *Yearbook of Labour Statistics*. Geneva: ILO.

Jagels, R. 1985. Health hazards of natural and introduced chemical components of boatbuilding woods. *Am J Ind Med* 8:241-251.

Jäppinen, P, E Pukkala and S Tola. 1989. Cancer incidence of workers in a Finnish sawmill. *Scand J Work Environ Health* 15:18-23.

Robinson, C, D Fowler, DP Brown and RA Lemen. 1986. *Plywood Mill Workers Mortality Patterns 1945-1977*.(NTIS Report PB-86 221694). Cincinnati, OH: US NIOSH.

Statistics Canada. 1993. *Industry and the Class of Worker. The Nation*. Ottawa: Statistics Canada.

Suchsland, O and GE Woodson. 1987. *Fiberboard Manufacturing Practices in the United States*. Agricultural handbook No. 640. Washington, DC: US Department of Agriculture, Forest Service.

Tharr, D. 1991. A sawmill environment: Noise levels, controls and audiometric test results. *Appl Occup Environ Hyg* 6(12):1000.

Other relevant readings

Chan-Yeung, M and JL Malo. 1995. Occupational respiratory diseases associated with forest products industries. In *Occupational and Environment Respiratory Diseases*, edited by P Harber, M Schenker, and J Balmes. St. Louis: Mosby.

Hausen, B. 1981. *Woods Injurious to Human Health—A Manual*. Berlin: Walter de Gryter & Co.

Koch, P. 1964. *Wood Machining Processes*. New York: Ronald Press Company.

Maloney, TM. 1977. *Modern Particleboard and Dry-process Fiberboard Manufacturing*. San Francisco: Miller Freeman Publications.

National Institute for Occupational Safety and Health. (NIOSH). 1977. *Health and Safety Guide for Sawmills and Planing Mills*. NIOSH Publication No. 78-102. Cincinnati, OH: US NIOSH.

—.1977. *Health and safety guide for plywood and veneer mills*. NIOSH Publication No. 77-186. Cincinnati, OH: US NIOSH.

Tatken, RL and CA Browning. 1987. *Health Effects of Exposure to Wood Dust: A Summary of the Literature*. Cincinnati, OH: US NIOSH

Timber Industry Ergonomics Group. 1977. *Better Working Environment in Sawmills—Today's Problems, Tomorrow's Environment*. Stockholm: Sagverksindustrins kommitte for arbetsmiliofragor.

Williston, EM. 1988. *Lumber Manufacturing, the Design and Operation of Sawmills and Planer Mills*. San Francisco, CA: Miller Freeman Publications.

Woods, B and CD Calnan. 1976. Toxic Woods. *Brit J Dermatol* 94 Suppl. 13:1-98.

Chapter Editors
Kay Teschke and Paul Demers

Contents

GENERAL PROFILE

Kay Teschke

Evolution and Structure of the Industry

Papermaking is thought to have originated in China in about 100 A.D. using rags, hemp and grasses as the raw material, and beating against stone mortars as the original fibre separation process. Although mechanization increased over the intervening years, batch production methods and agricultural fibre sources remained in use until the 1800s. Continuous papermaking machines were patented at the turn of that century. Methods for pulping wood, a more abundant fibre source than rags and grasses, were developed between 1844 and 1884, and included mechanical abrasion as well as the soda, sulphite, and sulphate (kraft) chemical methods. These changes initiated the modern pulp and paper manufacturing era.

Figure 72.1 illustrates the major pulp and paper making processes in the current era: mechanical pulping; chemical pulping; repulping waste paper; papermaking; and converting. The industry today can be divided into two main sectors according to the types of products manufactured. Pulp is generally manufactured in large mills in the same regions as the fibre harvest (i.e., mainly forest regions). Most of these mills also manufacture paper—for example, newsprint, writing, printing or tissue papers; or they may manufacture paperboards. (Figure 72.2 shows such a mill, which produces bleached kraft pulp, thermomechanical pulp and newsprint. Note the rail yard and dock for shipping, chip storage area, chip conveyors leading to digester, recovery boiler (tall white building) and effluent clarifying ponds). Separate converting operations are usually situated close to consumer markets and use market pulp or paper to manufacture bags, paperboards, containers, tissues, wrapping papers, decorative materials, business products and so on.

There has been a trend in recent years for pulp and paper operations to become part of large, integrated forest product companies. These companies have control of forest harvesting operations (see the *Forestry* chapter), lumber milling (see the *Lumber industry* chapter), pulp and paper manufacturing, as well as converting operations. This structure ensures that the company has an ongoing source of fibre, efficient use of wood waste and assured buyers, which often leads to increased market share. Integration has been operating in tandem with increasing concentration of the industry into fewer companies and increasing globalization as companies pursue international investments. The

Figure 72.1 • Illustration of process flow in pulp and paper manufacturing operations.

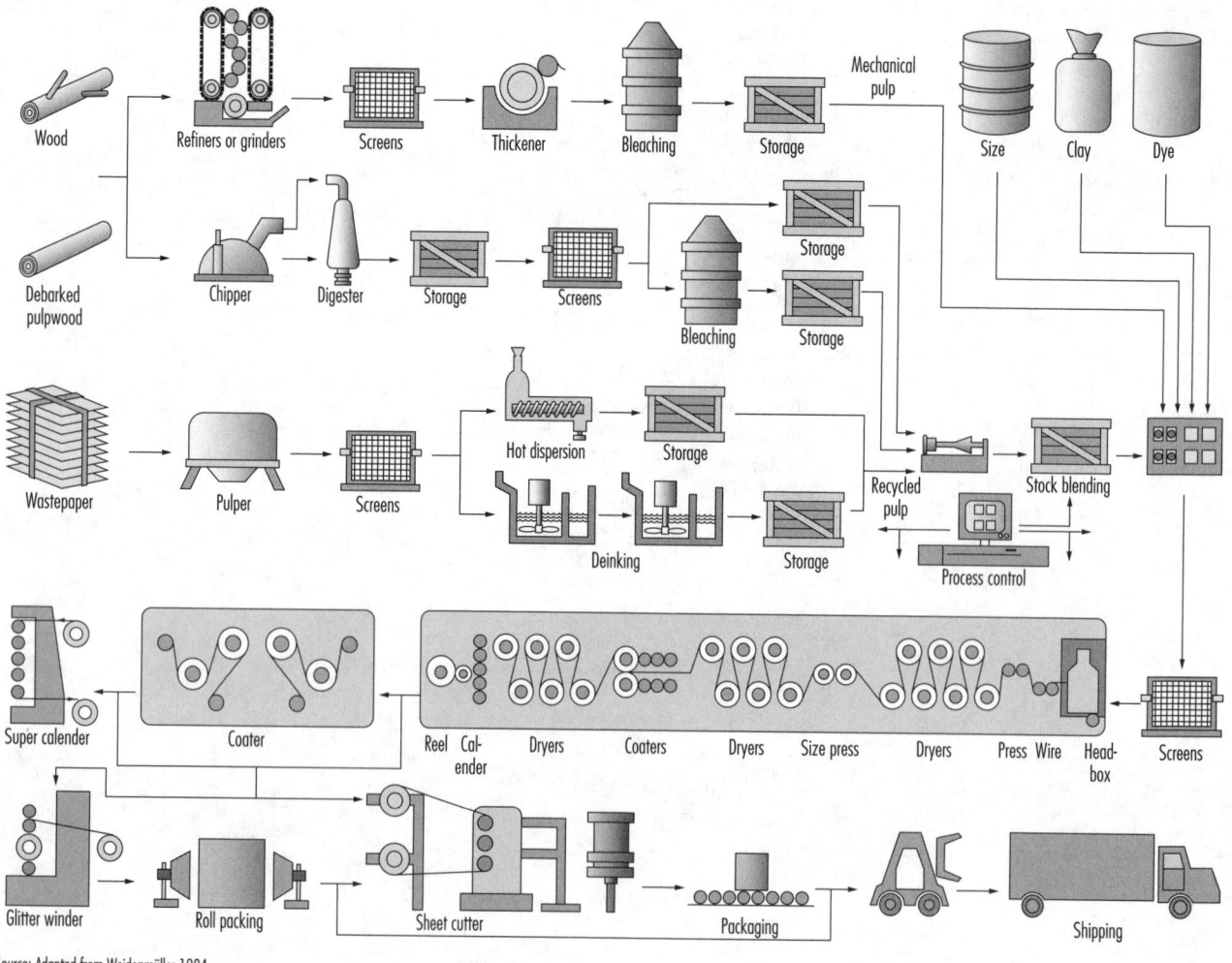

Source: Adapted from Weidenmüller 1984.

Figure 72.2 • Modern pulp and paper mill complex situated on a coastal waterway.

Canfor Library.

Figure 72.3 • Pulp and paper production worldwide, 1980 to 1993.

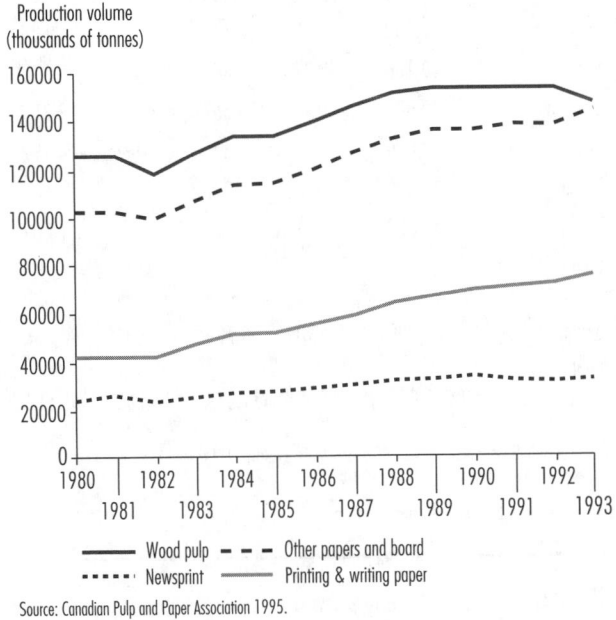

Source: Canadian Pulp and Paper Association 1995.

Figure 72.4 • Paper and paperboard consumption as an indicator of economic development.

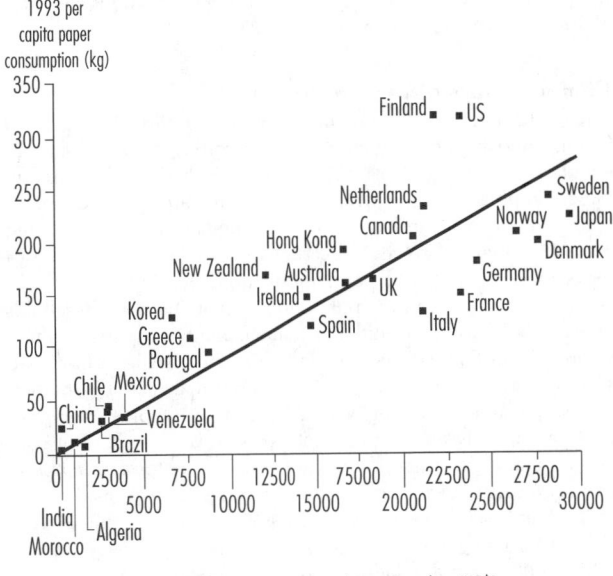

72. PAPER AND PULP INDUSTRY

financial burden of plant development in this industry has encouraged these trends to allow economies of scale. Some companies have now reached production levels of 10 million tonnes, similar to the output of countries with the highest production. Many companies are multinational, some with plants in 20 or more countries worldwide. However, even though many of the smaller mills and companies are disappearing, the industry still has hundreds of participants. As an illustration, the top 150 companies account for two-thirds of pulp and paper output and only one-third of the industry's employees.

Economic Importance

The manufacture of pulp, paper and paper products ranks among the world's largest industries. Mills are found in more than 100 countries in every region of the world, and directly employ more than 3.5 million people. The major pulp and paper producing nations include the United States, Canada, Japan, China, Finland, Sweden, Germany, Brazil and France (each produced more than 10 million tonnes in 1994; see table 72.1).

Every country is a consumer. Worldwide production of pulp, paper and paperboard was about 400 million tonnes in 1993. Despite predictions of decreased paper use in the face of the electronic age, there has been a fairly steady 2.5% annual rate of growth in production since 1980 (figure 72.3). In addition to its economic benefits, the consumption of paper has cultural value resulting from its function in the recording and dissemination of information. Because of this, pulp and paper consumption rates have been used as an indicator of a nation's socioeconomic development (figure 72.4).

The main source of fibre for pulp production over the last century has been wood from temperate coniferous forests, though more recently the use of tropical and boreal woods has been increasing (see the chapter *Lumber* for data on industrial roundwood harvesting worldwide). Because forested regions of the world are generally sparsely populated, there tends to be a dichotomy between the producing and using areas of the world. Pressure from environmental groups to preserve forest resources by using recycled paper stocks, agricultural crops and short-rotation plantation forests as fibre sources may change the distribution of pulp and paper production facilities throughout the world over the coming decades. Other forces, including increased paper consumption in the developing world and globalization, are also expected to play a role in relocating the industry.

Characteristics of the Workforce

Table 72.1 indicates the size of the workforce directly employed in pulp and paper production and converting operations in 27 countries, which together represent about 85% of world pulp and paper employment and over 90% of mills and production. In countries which consume most of what they produce (e.g., United States, Germany, France), converting operations provide two jobs for every one in pulp and paper production.

The labour force in the pulp and paper industry mainly holds full-time jobs within traditional management structures, though some mills in Finland, the United States and elsewhere have had success with flexible working hours and self-managed job-rotation teams. Because of their high capital costs, most pulping operations run continuously and require shift work; this is not true of converting plants. Working hours vary with the patterns of employment prevalent in each country, with a range from about 1,500 to more than 2,000 hours per year. In 1991, incomes in the industry ranged from US$1,300 (unskilled workers in Kenya) to US$70,000 per year (skilled production personnel in the United States) (ILO 1992). Male workers predominate in this industry, with women usually representing only 10 to 20% of the labour

Table 72.1 • Employment and production in pulp, paper, and paperboard operations in 1994, selected countries.*

Country	Number employed in industry	Pulp		Paper and paperboard	
		Number of mills	Production (1,000 tonnes)	Number of mills	Production (1,000 tonnes)
Austria	10,000	11	1,595	28	3,603
Bangladesh	15,000	7	84	17	160
Brazil	70,000	35	6,106	182	5,698
Canada	64,000	39	24,547	117	18,316
China	1,500,000	8,000	17,054	10,000	21,354
Czech Republic	18,000	9	516	32	662
Finland	37,000	43	9,962	44	10,910
Former USSR**	178,000	50	3,313	161	4,826
France	48,000	20	2,787	146	8,678
Germany	48,000	19	1,934	222	14,458
India	300,000	245	1,400	380	2,300
Italy	26,000	19	535	295	6,689
Japan	55,000	49	10,579	442	28,527
Korea, Republic of	60,000	5	531	136	6,345
Mexico	26,000	10	276	59	2,860
Pakistan	65,000	2	138	68	235
Poland**	46,000	5	893	27	1,343
Romania	25,000	17	202	15	288
Slovakia	14,000	3	304	6	422
South Africa	19,000	9	2,165	20	1,684
Spain	20,180	21	626	141	5,528
Sweden	32,000	49	10,867	50	9,354
Taiwan	18,000	2	326	156	4,199
Thailand	12,000	3	240	45	1,664
Turkey	12,000	11	416	34	1,102
United Kingdom	25,000	5	626	99	5,528
United States	230,000	190	58,724	534	80,656
Total worldwide	≈3,500,000	9,100	171,479	14,260	268,551

* Countries included if more than 10,000 people were employed in the industry.

** Data for 1989/90 (ILO 1992).

Source: Data for table adapted from PPI 1995.

force. China and India may form the upper and lower ends of the range with 35% and 5% women respectively.

Management and engineering personnel at pulp and paper mills usually have university-level training. In European countries, most of the skilled blue-collar workforce (e.g., papermakers) and many of the unskilled workforce have had several years of trade-school education. In Japan, formal in-house training and upgrading is the norm; this approach is being adopted by some Latin American and North American companies. However, in many operations in North America and in the developing world, informal on-the-job training is more common for blue-collar jobs. Surveys have shown that, in some operations, many workers have literacy problems and are poorly prepared for the life-long learning required in the dynamic and potentially hazardous environment of this industry.

The capital costs of building modern pulp and paper plants are extremely high (e.g., a bleached kraft mill employing 750 people might cost US$1.5 billion to build; a chemi-thermomechanical pulp (CTMP) mill employing 100 people might cost US$400 million), so there are great economies of scale with high-capacity facilities. New and refitted plants usually use mechanized and continuous processes, as well as electronic monitors and computer controls. They require relatively few employees per unit production (e.g., 1 to 1.2 working hours per tonne of pulp in new Indonesian, Finnish and Chilean mills). Over the last 10 to 20 years, output per employee has increased as a result of incremental advances in technology. The newer equipment allows easier change-overs between product runs, lower inventories and customer-driven just-in-time production. Productivity gains have resulted in job losses in many producing nations in the developed world. However, there have been increases in employment in developing countries, where new mills being constructed, even if sparsely staffed, represent new forays into the industry.

From the 1970s to 1990, there was a decline of about 10% in the proportion of blue-collar jobs in European and North American operations, so that they now represent between 70 and 80% of the workforce (ILO 1992). The use of contract labour for mill construction, maintenance and wood-harvesting operations has been increasing; many operations have reported that 10 to 15% of their on-site workforce are contractors.

MAJOR SECTORS AND PROCESSES

● FIBRE SOURCES FOR PULP AND PAPER

Anya Keefe and Kay Teschke

The basic structure of pulp and paper sheets is a felted mat of cellulose fibres held together by hydrogen bonds. Cellulose is a polysaccharide with 600 to 1,500 repeated sugar units. The fibres have high tensile strength, will absorb the additives used to modify pulp into paper and board products, and are supple, chemically stable and white. The purpose of pulping is to separate cellulose fibres from the other components of the fibre source. In the case of wood, these include hemicelluloses (with 15 to 90 repeated sugar units), lignins (highly polymerized and complex, mainly phenyl propane units; they act as the "glue" that cements the fibres together), extractives (fats, waxes, alcohols, phenols, aromatic acids, essential oils, oleoresins, stearols, alkaloids and pigments), and minerals and other inorganics. As shown in table 72.2, the relative proportions of these components vary according to the fibre source.

Coniferous and deciduous trees are the major fibre sources for pulp and paper. Secondary sources include straws from wheat, rye and rice; canes, such as bagasse; woody stalks from bamboo, flax and hemp; and seed, leaf or bast fibres, such as cotton, abaca

Table 72.2 • Chemical constituents of pulp and paper fibre sources (%).

	Softwoods	Hardwoods	Straw	Bamboo	Cotton
Carbohydrates					
α-cellulose	38–46	38–49	28–42	26–43	80–85
Hemicellulose	23–31	20–40	23–38	15–26	nd
Lignin	22–34	16–30	12–21	20–32	nd
Extractives	1–5	2–8	1–2	0.2–5	nd
Minerals and other inorganics	0.1–7	0.1–11	3–20	1–10	0.8–2

nd = no data available.

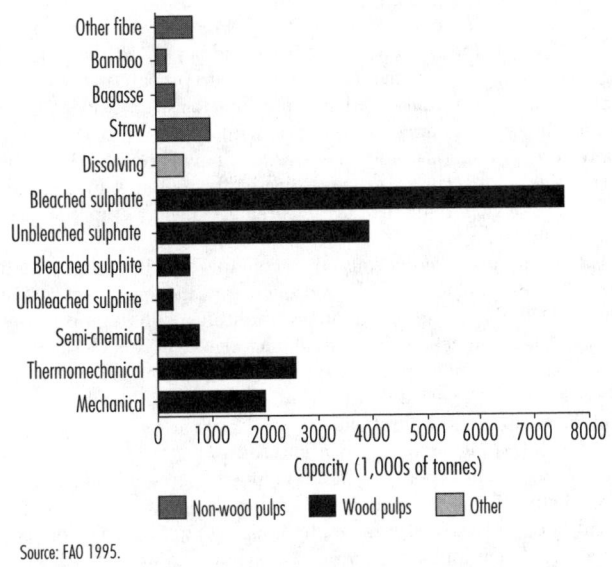

Figure 72.5 • Worldwide pulp capacities, by pulp type.

Source: FAO 1995.

and sisal. The majority of pulp is made from virgin fibre, but recycled paper accounts for an increasing proportion of production, up from 20% in 1970 to 33% in 1991. Wood-based production accounted for 88% of worldwide pulp capacity in 1994 (176 million tonnes, figure 72.5); therefore, the description of pulp and paper processes in the following article focuses on wood-based production. The basic principles apply to other fibres as well.

WOOD HANDLING

Anya Keefe and Kay Teschke

Wood may arrive at a pulp mill woodyard in the form of raw logs or as chips from a lumber mill. Some pulp mill operations have on-site sawmills (often called "woodrooms") which produce both

Figure 72.6 • Chip storage area with front end loaders.

George Astrakianakis.

marketable lumber and stock for the pulp mill. Sawmilling is discussed in detail in the chapter *Lumber*. This article discusses those elements of wood preparation which are specific to pulp mill operations.

The wood preparation area of a pulp mill has several basic functions: to receive and meter the wood supply to the pulping process at the rate demanded by the mill; to prepare the wood so that it meets the mill's feed specifications for species, cleanliness and dimensions; and to collect any material rejected by the previous operations and send it to final disposal. Wood is converted into chips or logs suitable for pulping in a series of steps which may include debarking, sawing, chipping and screening.

Logs are debarked because bark contains little fibre, has a high extractives content, is dark, and often carries large quantities of grit. Debarking can be done hydraulically with high-pressure water jets, or mechanically by rubbing logs against each other or with metal cutting tools. Hydraulic debarkers may be used in coastal areas; however, the effluent generated is difficult to treat and contributes to water pollution.

Debarked logs may be sawn into short lengths (1 to 6 metres) for stone groundwood pulping or chipped for refiner mechanical or chemical pulping methods. Chippers tend to produce chips with a considerable size range, but pulping requires chips of very specific dimensions to ensure constant flow through refiners and uniform cooking in digesters. Chips are therefore passed over a series of screens whose function is to separate chips on the basis of length or thickness. Oversized chips are rechipped, while under-sized chips are either used as waste fuel or are metered back into the chip flow.

The requirements of the particular pulping process and chip conditions will dictate the duration of chip storage (figure 72.6; note the different types of chips available for pulping). Depending on fibre supply and mill demand, a mill will maintain a 2 to 6 week unscreened chip inventory, usually in large outdoor chip piles. Chips may degrade through auto-oxidation and hydrolysis reactions or fungal attack of the wood components. In order to avoid contamination, short-term inventories (hours to days) of screened chips are stored in chip silos or bins. Chips for sulphite pulping may be stored outside for several months to allow volatilization of extractives which may cause problems in subsequent operations. Chips used in kraft mills where turpentine and tall oil are recovered as commercial products typically proceed directly to pulping.

PULPING

Anya Keefe, George Astrakianakis and Judith Anderson

Pulping is the process by which the bonds within the wood structure are ruptured either mechanically or chemically. Chemical pulps can be produced by either alkaline (i.e., sulphate or kraft) or acidic (i.e., sulphite) processes. The highest proportion of pulp is produced by the sulphate method, followed by mechanical (including semi-chemical, thermomechanical and mechanical) and sulphite methods (figure 72.5). Pulping processes differ in the yield and quality of the product, and for chemical methods, in the chemicals used and the proportion that can be recovered for reuse.

Mechanical Pulping

Mechanical pulps are produced by grinding wood against a stone or between metal plates, thereby separating the wood into individual fibres. The shearing action breaks cellulose fibres, so that the resulting pulp is weaker than chemically separated pulps. The lignin connecting cellulose to hemicellulose is not dissolved; it merely softens, allowing the fibres to be ground out of the wood matrix. The yield (proportion of original wood in pulp) is usually greater than 85%. Some mechanical pulping methods also use chemicals (i.e., the chemi-mechanical pulps); their yields are lower since they remove more of the non-cellulosic materials.

In stone groundwood pulping (SGW), the oldest and historically most common mechanical method, fibres are removed from short logs by pressing them against a rotating abrasive cylinder. In refiner mechanical pulping (RMP, figure 72.7), which gained popularity after it became commercially viable in the 1960s, wood chips or sawdust are fed through the centre of a disc refiner, where they are shredded into finer pieces as they are pushed out through progressively narrower bars and grooves. (In figure 72.7, the refiners are enclosed in the middle of the picture and their large motors are on the left. Chips are supplied though the large diameter pipes, and pulp exits the smaller ones.) A modification of RMP is thermomechanical pulping (TMP), in which the chips are steamed before and during refining, usually under pressure.

One of the earliest methods of producing chemi-mechanical pulps involved pre-steaming logs before boiling them in chemical pulping liquors, then grinding them in stone grinders to produce "chemi-groundwood" pulps. Modern chemi-mechanical pulping

Figure 72.7 • Refiner mechanical pulping.

Canfor Library.

uses disc refiners with chemical treatment (e.g., sodium bisulphite, sodium hydroxide) either prior to, during or after refining. Pulps produced in this manner are referred to either as chemi-mechanical pulps (CMP) or chemi-thermomechanical pulps (CTMP), depending on whether refining was carried out at atmospheric or elevated pressure. Specialized variations of CTMP have been developed and patented by a number of organizations.

Chemical Pulping and Recovery

Chemical pulps are produced by chemically dissolving the lignin between the wood fibres, thereby enabling the fibres to separate relatively undamaged. Because most of the non-fibrous wood components are removed in these processes, yields are usually in the order of 40 to 55%.

In chemical pulping, chips and chemicals in aqueous solution are cooked together in a pressure vessel (digester, figure 72.8) which can be operated on a batch or continuous basis. In batch cooking, the digester is filled with chips through a top opening, the digestion chemicals are added, and the contents cooked at elevated temperature and pressure. Once the cook is complete, the pressure is released, "blowing" the delignified pulp out of the digester and into a holding tank. The sequence is then repeated. In continuous digesting, pre-steamed chips are fed into the digester at a continuous rate. Chips and chemicals are mixed together in the impregnation zone at the top of the digester and then proceed through the upper cooking zone, the lower cooking zone, and the washing zone before being blown into the blow tank.

The digesting chemicals are recovered in most chemical pulping operations today. The principal objectives are to recover and reconstitute digestion chemicals from the spent cooking liquor, and to recover heat energy by burning the dissolved organic material from the wood. The resulting steam and electricity supplies some, if not all, of the mill's energy needs.

Sulphate Pulping and Recovery

The sulphate process produces a stronger, darker pulp than other methods and requires chemical recovery to compete economically. The method evolved from soda pulping (which uses only sodium hydroxide for digestion) and began to gain prominence in the industry from the 1930s to 1950s with the development of chlorine dioxide bleaching and chemical recovery processes, which also produced steam and power for the mill. The development of corrosion-proof metals, such as stainless steel, to handle the acidic and alkaline pulp mill environments also played a role.

The cooking mixture (white liquor) is sodium hydroxide (NaOH, "caustic") and sodium sulphide (Na_2S). Modern kraft pulping is usually carried out in continuous digesters often lined with stainless steel (figure 72.8). The temperature of the digester is raised slowly to approximately 170 °C and held at that level for approximately 3 to 4 hours. The pulp (called brown stock because of its colour) is screened to remove uncooked wood, washed to remove the spent cooking mixture (now black liquor), and sent either to the bleach plant or to the pulp machine room. Uncooked wood is either returned to the digester or sent to the power boiler to be burned.

The black liquor collected from the digester and brown stock washers contains dissolved organic material whose exact chemical composition depends on the wood species pulped and the cooking conditions. The liquor is concentrated in evaporators until it contains less than 40% water, then sprayed into the recovery boiler. The organic component is consumed as fuel, generating heat which is recovered in the upper section of the furnace as high-temperature steam. The unburned inorganic component collects at the bottom of the boiler as a molten smelt. The smelt flows out of the furnace and is dissolved in a weak caustic solu-

tion, producing "green liquor" containing primarily dissolved Na_2S and sodium carbonate (Na_2CO_3). This liquor is pumped to a recausticizing plant, where it is clarified, then reacted with slaked lime ($Ca(OH)_2$), forming NaOH and calcium carbonate ($CaCO_3$). The white liquor is filtered and stored for subsequent use. $CaCO_3$ is sent to a lime kiln, where it is heated to regenerate lime (CaO).

Sulphite Pulping and Recovery

Sulphite pulping dominated the industry from the late 1800s to the mid-1900s, but the method used during this era was limited by the types of wood which could be pulped and the pollution created by discharging untreated waste cooking liquor into waterways. Newer methods have overcome many of these problems, but sulphite pulping is now a small segment of the pulp market. Although sulphite pulping usually uses acid digestion, both neutral and basic variations exist.

The cooking liquor of sulphurous acid (H_2SO_3) and bisulphite ion (HSO_3^-) is prepared on-site. Elemental sulphur is burned to produce sulphur dioxide (SO_2), which is passed up through an absorption tower that contains water and one of four alkaline bases ($CaCO_3$, the original sulphite base, Na_2CO_3, magnesium hydroxide ($Mg(OH)_2$) or ammonium hydroxide (NH_4OH)) which produce the acid and ion and control their proportions. Sulphite pulping is usually carried out in brick-lined batch digesters. To avoid unwanted reactions, the digester is heated slowly to a maximum temperature of 130 to 140 °C and the chips are cooked for a long time (6 to 8 hours). As the digester pressure increases,

Figure 72.8 • Continuous kraft digester, with chip conveyor under construction.

Canfor Library.

gaseous sulphur dioxide (SO_2) is bled off and remixed with the raw cooking acid. When approximately 1 to 1.5 hours of cooking time remains, heating is discontinued and the pressure is decreased by bleeding off gas and steam. The pulp is blown into a holding tank, then washed and screened.

The spent digestion mixture, called red liquor, can be used for heat and chemical recovery for all but calcium-bisulphite-base operations. For ammonia-base sulphite pulping, the dilute red liquor is first stripped to remove residual SO_2, then concentrated and burned. The flue gas containing SO_2 is cooled and passed through an absorption tower where fresh ammonia combines with it to regenerate the cooking liquor. Finally, the liquor is filtered, fortified with fresh SO_2 and stored. The ammonia cannot be recovered because it is converted into nitrogen and water in the recovery boiler.

In magnesium-base sulphite pulping, burning the concentrated pulping liquor gives magnesium oxide (MgO) and SO_2, which are easily recovered. No smelt is produced in this process; rather MgO is collected from the flue gas and slaked with water to produce magnesium hydroxide ($Mg(OH)_2$). SO_2 is cooled and combined with the $Mg(OH)_2$ in an absorption tower to reconstitute the cooking liquor. The magnesium bisulphite ($Mg(HSO_3)_2$) is then fortified with fresh SO_2 and stored. Recovery of 80 to 90% of the cooking chemicals is possible.

Recovery of sodium-base sulphite cooking liquor is more complicated. Concentrated spent liquor is incinerated, and approximately 50% of the sulphur is converted into SO_2. The remainder of the sodium and sulphur is collected at the bottom of the recovery boiler as a smelt of Na_2S and Na_2CO_3. The smelt is dissolved to produce green liquor, which is converted to sodium bisulphite ($NaHSO_3$) in several steps. The $NaHSO_3$ is fortified and stored. The regeneration process produces reduced sulphur gases, in particular hydrogen sulphide (H_2S).

BLEACHING

George Astrakianakis and
Judith Anderson

Bleaching is a multi-stage process that refines and brightens raw pulp. The objective is to dissolve (chemical pulps) or modify (mechanical pulps) the brown-coloured lignin that was not removed during pulping, while maintaining the integrity of the pulp fibres. A mill produces customized pulp by varying the order, concentration and reaction time of the bleaching agents.

Each bleaching stage is defined by its bleaching agent, pH (acidity), temperature and duration (table 72.3). After each bleaching stage, the pulp may be washed with caustic to remove spent bleaching chemicals and dissolved lignin before it progresses to the next stage. After the last stage, the pulp is pumped through a series of screens and cleaners to remove any contaminants such as dirt or plastic. It is then concentrated and conveyed to storage.

Historically, the most common bleaching sequence used to produce market-grade bleached kraft pulp is based on the five-stage CEDED process (see table 72.3 for definition of symbols). The first two stages of bleaching complete the delignification process and are considered extensions of pulping. Because of environmental concerns about chlorinated organics in pulp mill effluents, many mills substitute chlorine dioxide (ClO_2) for a portion of the chlorine (Cl_2) used in the first bleaching stage (C_DEDED) and use oxygen (O_2) pretreatment during the first caustic extraction (C_DE_ODED). The current trend in Europe and North America is towards complete substitution with ClO_2 (e.g., DEDED) or elimination of both Cl_2 and ClO_2. Where ClO_2 is used, sulphur dioxide (SO_2) is added during the final washing stage as an "antichlor" to stop the ClO_2 reaction

and to control the pH. Newly developed chlorine-free bleaching sequences (e.g., OAZQP, OQPZP, where Q = chelation) use enzymes, O_2, ozone (O_3), hydrogen peroxide (H_2O_2), peracids and chelating agents such as ethylene diamine tetracetic acid (EDTA). Totally chlorine-free bleaching had been adopted at eight mills worldwide by 1993. Because these newer methods eliminate the acidic bleaching steps, acid washing is a necessary addition to the initial stages of kraft bleaching to allow removal of metals bound to the cellulose.

Sulphite pulps are generally easier to bleach than kraft pulps because of their lower lignin content. Short bleaching sequences (e.g., CEH, DCEHD, P, HP, EPOP) can be used for most paper grades. For dissolving-grade sulphite pulps used in the production of rayon, cellophane and so on, both hemicellulose and lignin are removed, requiring more complex bleaching sequences (e.g., C_1C_2ECHDA). The final acid wash is both for metal control and antichlor purposes. The effluent load for dissolving-grade sulphite pulps is much greater because so much of the raw wood is consumed (typical yield 50%) and more water is used.

The term *brightening* is used to describe bleaching of mechanical and other high-yield pulps, because they are whitened by destroying chromophoric groups without dissolving the lignin. Brightening agents include H_2O_2 and/or sodium hydrosulphite (NaS_2O_4). Historically, zinc hydrosulphite (ZnS_2O_4) was commonly used, but has been largely eliminated because of its toxicity in effluent. Chelating agents are added before bleaching to neutralize any metal ions, thereby preventing the formation of coloured salts or the decomposition of H_2O_2. The effectiveness of mechanical pulp bleaching depends on the species of wood. Hardwoods (e.g., poplar and cottonwood) and softwoods (e.g., spruce and balsam) that are low in lignin and extractives can be bleached to a higher brightness level than the more resinous pine and cedar.

Table 72.3 • Bleaching agents and their conditions of use.

	Symbol	Concentration of agent (%)	pH	Consistency* (%)	Temperature (°C)	Time (h)
Chlorine (Cl_2)	C	2.5–8	2	3	20–60	0.5–1.5
Sodium hydroxide (NaOH)	E	1.5–4.2	11	10–12	<80	1–2
Chlorine dioxide (ClO_2)	D	≈1	0–6	10–12	60–75	2–5
Sodium hypochlorite (NaOCl)	H	1–2	9–11	10–12	30–50	0.5–3
Oxygen (O_2)	O	1.2–1.9	7–8	25–33	90–130	0.3–1
Hydrogen peroxide (H_2O_2)	P	0.25	10	12	35–80	4
Ozone (O_3)	Z	0.5–3.5	2–3	35–55	20–40	<0.1
Acid washing (SO_2)	A	4–6	1.8–5	1.5	30–50	0.25
Sodium dithionite (NaS_2O_4)	Y	1–2	5.5–8	4–8	60–65	1–2

* Concentration of fibre in water solution.

RECYCLED PAPER OPERATIONS

Dick Heederik

The use of waste or recycled paper as the raw material for pulp production has increased during the last several decades, and some paper plants depend almost completely on waste paper. In some countries, waste paper is separated from other household waste at the source before it is collected. In other countries separation by grade (e.g., corrugated board, newsprint, high-grade paper, mixed) takes place in special recycling plants.

Recycled paper can be repulped in a relatively mild process which uses water and sometimes NaOH. Small metal pieces and plastics may be separated during and/or after repulping, using a debris rope, cyclones or centrifugation. Filling agents, glues and resins are removed in a cleaning stage by blowing air through the pulp slurry, sometimes with the addition of flocculating agents. The foam contains the unwanted chemicals and is removed. The pulp can be de-inked using a series of washing steps which may or may not include the use of chemicals (i.e., surfactant fatty acid derivatives) to dissolve remaining impurities, and bleaching agents to whiten the pulp. Bleaching has the disadvantage that it may reduce fibre length and therefore lessen final paper quality. The bleaching chemicals used in recycled pulp production are usually similar to those used in brightening operations for mechanical pulps. After the repulping and de-inking operations, sheet production follows in a manner very similar to that using virgin fibre pulp.

SHEET PRODUCTION AND CONVERTING: MARKET PULP, PAPER, PAPERBOARD

George Astrakianakis and Judith Anderson

End products of pulp and paper mills depend on the pulping process, and may include market pulp and various types of paper or paperboard products. For example, the relatively weak mechanical pulp is converted into single-use products such as newspapers and tissue. Kraft pulp is converted into multi-use paper

Figure 72.9 • Wet end of pulp machine showing fibre mat on the wire.

Canfor Library.

Figure 72.10 • Dry end of a paper machine showing full paper reel and operator using air slitter to cut end.

George Astrakianakis.

products such as high-quality writing paper, books and grocery bags. Sulphite pulp, which is primarily cellulose, can be used in a series of diverse end-products including specialty paper, rayon, photographic film, TNT, plastics, adhesives, and even ice cream and cake mixes. Chemi-mechanical pulps are exceptionally stiff, ideal for the structural support needed for corrugated container board. The fibres in pulp from recycled paper are usually shorter, less flexible and less water permeable, and can therefore not be used for high-quality paper products. Recycled paper is therefore mainly used for the production of soft paper products like tissue paper, toilet paper, paper towelling and napkins.

To produce market pulp, the pulp slurry is usually screened once more and its consistency adjusted (4 to 10%) before it is ready for the pulp machine. The pulp is then spread onto a travelling metal screen or plastic mesh (known as the "wire") at the "wet end" of the pulp machine, where the operator monitors the speed of the moving wire and the water content of the pulp (figure 72.9; the presses and the cover of the drier can be seen in the upper left; in modern mills, operators spend a great deal of time in control rooms). Water and filtrate are drawn through the wire, leaving a web of fibres. The pulp sheet is passed through a series of rotating rolls ("presses") that squeeze out water and air until the fibre consistency is 40 to 45%. The sheet is then floated through a multi-storey sequence of hot-air dryers until the consistency is 90 to 95%. Finally, the continuous pulp sheet is cut into pieces and stacked into bales. The pulp bales are compressed, wrapped and packaged into bundles for storage and transport.

Although similar in principle to making pulp sheets, paper making is considerably more complex. Some mills use a variety of different pulps to optimize paper quality (e.g., a mix of hardwood, softwood, kraft, sulphite, mechanical or recycled pulps). Depending on the type of pulp used, a series of steps is necessary prior to forming the paper sheet. Generally, dried market pulp is rehydrated, while high-consistency pulp from storage is diluted. Pulp fibres may be beaten to increase the fibre-bonding area and thereby improve paper sheet strength. The pulp is then blended with "wet-end" additives (table 72.4) and passed through a final set of screens and cleaners. The pulp is then ready for the paper machine.

The flow spreader and headbox distribute a thin suspension (1 to 3%) of refined pulp onto a moving wire (similar to a pulp machine, only at a much higher speed, sometimes in excess of 55 km/h) which forms the fibres into a thin felted sheet. The sheet moves through a series of press rolls to the dryer section, where a

72. PAPER AND PULP INDUSTRY

Table 72.4 • Papermaking additives.

Additive	Location applied	Purpose and/or examples of specific agents
Most commonly used additives		
Talc	Wet end	Pitch control (prevent deposition and accumulation of pitch) Filler (make brighter, smoother, more opaque)
Titanium dioxide	Wet end	Pigment (brighten sheet, improve printing) Filler (make brighter, smoother, more opaque)
"Alum" ($Al_2(SO_4)_3$)	Wet end	Precipitates rosin sizing onto fibres Retention aid (fix additives to fibres, improve pulp fibre retention)
Rosin	Wet end	Internal sizing (resist liquid penetration)
Clay (kaolin)	Wet/dry	Filler (make brighter, smoother, more opaque) Pigment or surface coating (impart colour)
Starch	Wet/dry	Surface sizing (resist liquid penetration) Dry strength additive (increase strength, reduce surface lint) Retention aid (bind additives to paper, improve pulp fibre retention)
Dyes and pigments	Wet/dry	e.g., acid, basic or direct dyes, colour lakes, $CaCO_3$, may also include solvent vehicles
Latex	Dry end	Adhesive (reinforce sheet, bind additives to paper, fill pores) Waterproofing (resist liquid penetration)
Other additives		
Slimicides	Wet end	e.g., thiones, thiazoles, thiocyanates, thiocarbamates, thiols, isothiazolinones, formaldehyde, glutaraldehyde, glycols, naphthol, chlorinated and brominated organics, organic mercury compounds
Defoamers	Wet end	e.g., pine oil, fuel oil, recycled oils, silicones, alcohols
Wire treatment agents	Wet end	e.g., imidazoles, butyl diglycol, acetone, turpentine, phosphoric acid
Wet and dry strength additives	Wet end	e.g., formaldehyde resins, epichlorohydrin, glyoxal, gums, polyamines, phenolics, polyacrylamides, polyamids, cellulose derivatives
Coatings, adhesives and plasticizers	Dry end	e.g., aluminium hydroxide, polyvinyl acetate, acrylics, linseed oil, gums, protein glues, wax emulsions, azite, glyoxal, stearates, solvents, polyethylene, cellulose derivatives, foil, rubber derivatives, polyamines, polyesters, butadiene-styrene polymers
Others	Wet/dry	Corrosion inhibitors, dispersants, flameproofing, antitarnish agents, drainage aids, deflocculants, pH control agents, preservatives

series of steam-heated rolls evaporate most of the remaining water. Hydrogen bonds between the fibres have fully developed at this stage. Finally, the paper is calendered and reeled. Calendering is the process by which the paper surface is ironed smooth and its thickness reduced. The dried, calendered paper sheet is wound onto a reel, labelled and transported to the warehouse (figure 72.10; note waste paper under reel, and unenclosed operator control panel). "Dry-end" additives can be added before

calendering on the paper machine or in separate "off-machine" coating operations in the converting sector of the industry.

A variety of chemicals are used in the papermaking process to provide the paper with specific surface characteristics and sheet properties. The most commonly used additives (table 72.4) are typically used at the per cent level, though some such as clay and talc may contribute as much as 40% to the dry weight of certain papers. Table 72.4 also indicates the diversity of chemical additives which may be used for specific production purposes and products; some of these are used at very low concentrations (e.g., slimicides are added to process water in parts per million).

The process of making paperboard is similar to that of making paper or pulp. A suspension of pulp and water is dispersed onto a travelling wire, the water is removed, and the sheet dried and stored as a roll. The process differs in the way that the sheet is formed to give thickness, in the combining of multiple layers, and in the drying process. Board can be made from single or multi-layered sheets with or without a core. The sheets are usually high-quality kraft pulp (or kraft and CTMP blend), while the core is made from either a blend of semi-chemical and low-cost recycled pulp or from entirely recycled pulp and other waste material. Coatings, vapour barriers and multiple layers are added according to the end use to protect the contents from water and physical damage.

POWER GENERATION AND WATER TREATMENT

George Astrakianakis and Judith Anderson

In addition to liquor recovery, pulp mills recover a significant portion of energy from burning waste materials and by-products of the process in power boilers. Materials such as bark, wood waste and dried sludge collected from effluent treatment systems may be burned to provide steam to power electrical generators.

Pulp and paper mills consume vast amounts of fresh water. A 1,000 tonne per day bleached kraft pulp mill may use more than 150 million litres of water a day; a paper mill even more. In order to prevent adverse effects on mill equipment and to maintain product quality, the incoming water must be treated to remove contaminants, bacteria and minerals. Several treatments are applied depending on the quality of the incoming water. Sedimentation beds, filters, flocculants, chlorine and ion exchange resins are all used to treat water before it is used in the process. Water that is used in the power and recovery boilers is further treated with oxygen scavengers and corrosion inhibitors such as hydrazine and morpholine to avoid deposits forming in the boiler tubes, to reduce metal corrosion, and to prevent carry-over of water to the steam turbine.

CHEMICAL AND BY-PRODUCT PRODUCTION

George Astrakianakis and Judith Anderson

Because many bleaching chemicals are reactive and hazardous to transport, they are produced on-site or nearby. Chlorine dioxide (ClO_2), sodium hypochlorite (NaOCl) and peracids are always produced on-site, while chlorine (Cl_2) and sodium hydroxide or caustic (NaOH) are usually produced off-site. Tall oil, a product derived from the resin and fatty acids that are extracted during kraft cooking, may be refined on- or off-site. Turpentine, a lighter fraction kraft by-product, is often collected and concentrated on-site, and refined elsewhere.

Chlorine Dioxide

Chlorine dioxide (ClO_2) is a highly reactive greenish-yellow gas. It is toxic and corrosive, explodes at high concentrations (10%) and is quickly reduced to Cl_2 and O_2 in the presence of ultraviolet light. It must be prepared as a dilute gas and stored as a dilute liquid, making bulk transport impossible.

ClO_2 is generated by reducing sodium chlorate (Na_2ClO_3) with either SO_2, methanol, salt or hydrochloric acid. The gas leaving the reactor is condensed and stored as a 10% liquid solution. Modern ClO_2 generators operate at 95% efficiency or greater, and the small amount of Cl_2 that is produced will be collected or scrubbed out of the vent gas. Side reactions may occur depending on the purity of the feed chemicals, the temperature and other process variables. By-products are returned to the process and spent chemicals are neutralized and sewered.

Sodium Hypochlorite

Sodium hypochlorite (NaOCl) is produced by combining Cl_2 with a dilute solution of NaOH. It is a simple, automated process that requires almost no intervention. The process is controlled by maintaining the caustic concentration such that the residual Cl_2 in the process vessel is minimized.

Chlorine and Caustic

Chlorine (Cl_2), used as a bleaching agent since the early 1800s, is a highly reactive, toxic, green-coloured gas which becomes corrosive when moisture is present. Chlorine is usually manufactured by the electrolysis of brine (NaCl) into Cl_2 and NaOH at regional installations, and transported to the customer as a pure liquid. Three methods are used to produce Cl_2 on an industrial scale: the mercury cell, the diaphragm cell, and the most recent development, the membrane cell. Cl_2 is always produced at the anode. It is then cooled, purified, dried, liquefied and transported to the mill. At large or remote pulp mills, local facilities may be constructed, and the Cl_2 can be transported as a gas.

The quality of NaOH depends on which of the three processes is used. In the older mercury cell method, the sodium and mercury combine to form an amalgam that is decomposed with water. The resulting NaOH is nearly pure. One of the shortcomings of this process is that mercury contaminates the workplace and has resulted in serious environmental problems. The NaOH produced from the diaphragm cell is removed with the spent brine and concentrated to allow the salt to crystallize and separate. Asbestos is used as the diaphragm. The purest NaOH is produced in membrane cells. A semi-permeable resin-based membrane allows sodium ions to pass through without the brine or chlorine ions, and combine with water added to the cathode chamber to form pure NaOH. Hydrogen gas is a by-product of each process. It is usually treated and used either in other processes or as fuel.

Tall Oil Production

Kraft pulping of highly-resinous species such as pine produces sodium soaps of resin and fatty acids. The soap is collected from black liquor storage tanks and from soap skimming tanks that are located in the evaporator train of the chemical recovery process. Refined soap or tall oil can be used as a fuel additive, dust control agent, road stabilizer, pavement binder and roofing flux.

At the processing plant, soap is stored in primary tanks to allow the black liquor to settle to the bottom. The soap rises and overflows into a second storage tank. Sulphuric acid and the decanted soap are fed into a reactor, heated to 100 °C, agitated and then allowed to settle. After settling overnight, the crude tall oil is decanted into a storage vessel and allowed to sit for another day. The top fraction is considered dry crude tall oil and is pumped to storage, ready for shipment. The cooked lignin in the bottom fraction will become part of the subsequent batch. The spent sulphuric acid is pumped to a storage tank, and any entrained lignin is allowed to settle to the bottom. The lignin left in the reactor is concentrated for several cooks, dissolved in 20% caustic and returned to the primary soap tank. Periodically, the collected black liquor and the residual lignin from all sources are concentrated and burned as fuel.

Turpentine Recovery

Gases from the digesters and condensate from black liquor evaporators may be collected for recovery of turpentine. The gases are condensed, combined, then stripped of turpentine, which is recondensed, collected and sent to a decanter. The top fraction of the decanter is drawn off and sent to storage, while the bottom fraction is recycled to the stripper. Raw turpentine is stored separately from the rest of the collection system because it is noxious and flammable, and is usually processed off-site. All the non-condensable gases are collected and incinerated either in the power boilers, the lime kiln or a dedicated furnace. The turpentine can be processed for use in camphor, synthetic resins, solvents, flotation agents and insecticides.

OCCUPATIONAL HAZARDS AND CONTROLS

Kay Teschke, George Astrakianakis, Judith Anderson, Anya Keefe and Dick Heederik

Table 72.5 provides an overview of the types of exposures which may be expected in each area of pulp and paper operations. Although exposures may be listed as specific to certain production processes, exposures to employees from other areas may also occur depending on weather conditions, proximity to sources of exposure, and whether they work in more than one process area (e.g., quality control, general labour pool and maintenance personnel).

Exposure to the potential hazards listed in table 72.5 is likely to depend on the extent of automation of the plant. Historically, industrial pulp and paper production was a semi-automatic process which required a great deal of manual intervention. In such facilities, operators would sit at open panels adjacent to the processes to view the effects of their actions. The valves at the top and bottom of a batch digester would be manually opened, and during the filling stages, gases in the digester would be displaced by the incoming chips (figure 72.11). Chemical levels would be adjusted based on experience rather than sampling, and process adjustments would be dependent on the skill and knowledge of the operator, which at times led to upsets. For example, over-chlorination of pulp would expose workers downstream to increased levels of bleaching agents. In most modern mills, progress from manually controlled to electronically controlled pumps and valves allows for remote operation. The demand for process control within narrow tolerances has required computers and sophisticated engineering strategies. Separate control rooms are used to isolate the electronic equipment from the pulp and paper production environment. Consequently, operators usually work in

Table 72.5 • Potential health and safety hazards in pulp and paper production, by process area.

Process area	Safety hazards	Physical hazards	Chemical hazards	Biological hazards
Wood preparation				
Log pond	Drowning; mobile equipment; slipping, falling	Noise; vibration; cold; heat	Engine exhaust	
Wood room	Nip points; slipping, falling	Noise; vibration	Terpenes and other wood extracts; wood dust	Bacteria; fungi
Chip screening	Nip points; slipping, falling	Noise; vibration	Terpenes and other wood extracts; wood dust	Bacteria; fungi
Chip yard	Nip points; mobile equipment	Noise; vibration; cold; heat	Engine exhaust; terpenes and other wood extracts; wood dust	Bacteria; fungi
Pulping				
Stone ground-wood pulping	Slipping, falling	Noise; electric and magnetic fields; high humidity		
RMP, CMP, CTMP	Slipping, falling	Noise; electric and magnetic fields; high humidity	Cooking chemicals and by-products; terpenes and other wood extracts; wood dust	
Sulphate pulping	Slipping, falling	Noise; high humidity; heat	Acids and alkalis; cooking chemicals and by-products; reduced sulphur gases; terpenes and other wood extracts; wood dust	
Sulphate recovery	Explosions; nip points; slipping, falling	Noise; heat; steam	Acids and alkalis; asbestos; ash; cooking chemicals and by-products; fuels; reduced sulphur gases; sulphur dioxide	
Sulphite pulping	Slipping, falling	Noise; high humidity; heat	Acids and alkalis; cooking chemicals and by-products; sulphur dioxide; terpenes and other wood extracts; wood dust	
Sulphite recovery	Explosions; nip points; slipping, falling	Noise; heat; steam	Acids and alkalis; asbestos; ash; cooking chemicals and by-products; fuels; sulphur dioxide	
Repulping/de-inking	Slipping, falling		Acids and alkalis; bleaching chemicals and by-products; dyes and inks; pulp/paper dust; slimicides; solvents	Bacteria
Bleaching	Slipping, falling	Noise; high humidity; heat	Bleaching chemicals and by-products; slimicides; terpenes and other wood extracts	
Sheet forming and converting				
Pulp machine	Nip points; slipping, falling	Noise; vibration; high humidity; heat; steam	Acids and alkalis; bleaching chemicals and by-products; flocculant; pulp/paper dust; slimicides; solvents	Bacteria
Paper machine	Nip points; slipping, falling	Noise; vibration; high humidity; heat; steam	Acids and alkalis; bleaching chemicals and by-products; dyes and inks; flocculant; pulp/paper dust; paper additives; slimicides; solvents	Bacteria
Finishing	Nip points; mobile equipment	Noise	Acids and alkalis; dyes and inks; flocculant; pulp/paper dust; paper additives; slimicides; solvents	
Warehouse	Mobile equipment		Fuels; engine exhaust; pulp/paper dust	
Other operations				
Power generation	Nip points; slipping, falling	Noise; vibration; electric and magnetic fields; heat; steam	Asbestos; ash; fuels; terpenes and other wood extracts; wood dust	Bacteria; fungi
Water treatment	Drowning		Bleaching chemicals and by-products	Bacteria
Effluent treatment	Drowning		Bleaching chemicals and by-products; flocculant; reduced sulphur gases	Bacteria
Chlorine dioxide generation	Explosions; slipping, falling		Bleaching chemicals and by-products	Bacteria
Turpentine recovery	Slipping, falling		Cooking chemicals and by-products; reduced sulphur gases; terpenes and other wood extracts	
Tall oil production			Acids and alkalis; cooking chemicals and by-products; reduced sulphur gases; terpenes and other wood extracts	

RMP = refining mechanical pulping; CMP = chemi-mechanical pulping; CTMP = chemi-thermomechanical pulping.

air-conditioned control rooms which offer refuge from the noise, vibration, temperature, humidity and chemical exposures inherent to mill operations. Other controls which have improved the working environment are described below.

Safety hazards including nip points, wet walking surfaces, moving equipment and heights are common throughout pulp and paper operations. Guards around moving conveyors and machinery parts, quick clean-up of spills, walking surfaces which allow drainage, and guard-rails on walkways adjacent to production lines or at height are all essential. Lock-out procedures must be followed for maintenance of chip conveyors, paper machine rolls and all other machinery with moving parts. Mobile equipment used in chip storage, dock and shipping areas, warehousing and other operations should have roll-over protection, good visibility and horns; traffic lanes for vehicles and pedestrians should be clearly marked and signed.

Noise and heat are also ubiquitous hazards. The major engineering control is operator enclosures, as described above, usually available in wood preparation, pulping, bleaching and sheet-forming areas. Air-conditioned enclosed cabs for mobile equipment used in chip pile and other yard operations are also available. Outside these enclosures, workers usually require hearing protection. Work in hot process or outdoor areas and in vessel maintenance operations requires workers to be trained to recognize symptoms of heat stress; in such areas, work scheduling should allow acclimatization and rest periods. Cold weather may create frostbite hazards in outdoor jobs, as well as foggy conditions near chip piles, which remain warm.

Wood, its extracts and associated micro-organisms are specific to wood preparation operations and the initial stages of pulping. Control of exposures will depend on the particular operation, and may include operator booths, enclosure and ventilation of saws and conveyors, as well as enclosed chip storage and low chip inventory. Use of compressed air to clear wood dust creates high exposures and should be avoided.

Chemical pulping operations present the opportunity for exposures to digestion chemicals as well as gaseous by-products of the cooking process, including reduced (kraft pulping) and oxidized (sulphite pulping) sulphur compounds and volatile organics. Gas formation may be influenced by a number of operating conditions: the wood species used; the quantity of wood pulped; the amount and concentration of white liquor applied; the amount of time required for pulping; and maximum temperature attained. In addition to automatic digester capping valves and operator control rooms, other controls for these areas include local exhaust ventilation at batch digesters and blow tanks, capable of venting at the rate the vessel's gases are released; negative pressure in recovery boilers and sulphite-SO_2 acid towers to prevent gas leaks; ventilated full or partial enclosures over post-digestion washers; continuous gas monitors with alarms where leaks may occur; and emergency response planning and training. Operators taking samples and conducting tests should be aware of the potential for acid and caustic exposure in process and waste streams, and the possibility of side reactions such as hydrogen sulphide gas (H_2S) production if black liquor from kraft pulping comes into contact with acids (e.g., in sewers).

In chemical recovery areas, acidic and alkaline process chemicals and their by-products may be present at temperatures in excess of 800 °C. Job responsibilities may require workers to come into direct contact with these chemicals, making heavy duty clothing a necessity. For example, workers rake the spattering molten smelt that collects at the base of the boilers, thereby risking chemical and thermal burns. Workers may be exposed to dust when sodium sulphate is added to concentrated black liquor, and any leak or opening will release noxious (and potentially fatal) reduced sulphur gases. The potential for a smelt water explosion

Figure 72.11 • Worker opening cap on manually controlled batch digester.

MacMillan Bloedel archives.

always exists around the recovery boiler. Water leaks in the tube walls of the boiler have resulted in several fatal explosions. Recovery boilers should be shut down at any indication of a leak, and special procedures should be implemented for transferring the smelt. Loading of lime and other caustic materials should be done with enclosed and ventilated conveyors, elevators and storage bins.

In bleach plants, field operators may be exposed to the bleaching agents as well as chlorinated organics and other by-products. Process variables such as bleaching chemical strength, lignin content, temperature and pulp consistency are constantly monitored, with operators collecting samples and performing laboratory tests. Because of the hazards of many of the bleaching agents used, continuous alarm monitors should be in place, escape respirators should be issued to all employees, and operators should be trained in emergency response procedures. Canopy enclosures with dedicated exhaust ventilation are standard engineering controls found at the top of each bleaching tower and washing stage.

Chemical exposures in the machine room of a pulp or paper mill include chemical carry-over from the bleach plant, the paper-making additives and the chemical mixture in the waste water. Dusts (cellulose, fillers, coatings) and exhaust fumes from mobile equipment are present in the dry-end and the finishing operations. Cleaning between product runs may be done with solvents, acids and alkalis. Controls in this area may include complete enclosure over the sheet drier; ventilated enclosure of the areas where additives are unloaded, weighed and mixed; use of additives in liquid rather than powder form; use of water-based rather than solvent-based inks and dyes; and eliminating the use of compressed air to clean up trimmed and waste paper.

Paper production in recycled paper plants is generally dustier than conventional paper production using newly produced pulp. Exposure to micro-organisms can occur from the beginning (paper collection and separation) to the end (paper production) of the production chain, but exposure to chemicals is less important than in conventional paper production.

Pulp and paper mills employ an extensive maintenance group to service their process equipment, including carpenters, electricians, instrument mechanics, insulators, machinists, masons, mechanics, millwrights, painters, pipefitters, refrigeration mechanics, tinsmiths and welders. Along with their trade-specific exposures (see the *Metal processing and metal working* and *Occupations* chapters), these tradespeople may be exposed to any of the process-related hazards. As mill operations have become more automated and enclosed, the maintenance, cleaning and quality assurance operations have become the most highly exposed. Plant shutdowns to clean vessels and machines are of special concern. Depending on mill organization, these operations may be carried out by in-house maintenance or production personnel, although subcontracting to non-mill personnel, who may have less occupational health and safety support services, is common.

In addition to process exposures, pulp and paper mill operations entail some noteworthy exposures for maintenance personnel. Because pulping, recovery and boiler operations involve high heat, asbestos was used extensively to insulate pipes and vessels. Stainless steel is often used in vessels and pipes throughout pulping, recovery and bleaching operations, and to some extent in papermaking. Welding this metal is known to generate chromium and nickel fumes. During maintenance shut-downs, chromium-based sprays may be applied to protect the floor and walls of recovery boilers from corrosion during start-up operations. Process quality measurements in the production line are often made using infrared and radio-isotope gauges. Although the gauges are usually well shielded, instrument mechanics who service them may be exposed to radiation.

Some special exposures may also occur among employees in other mill-support operations. Power boiler workers handle bark, waste wood and sludge from the effluent treatment system. In older mills, workers remove ash from the bottom of the boilers and then reseal the boilers by applying a mixture of asbestos and cement around the boiler grate. In modern power boilers, this process is automated. When material is fed into the boiler at too high a moisture level, workers may be exposed to blow-backs of incomplete combustion products. Workers responsible for water treatment may be exposed to chemicals such as chlorine, hydrazine and various resins. Because of the reactivity of ClO_2, the ClO_2 generator is usually located in a restricted area and the operator is stationed in a remote control room with excursions to collect samples and service the saltcake filter. Sodium chlorate (a strong oxidizer) used to generate ClO_2 can become dangerously flammable if it is allowed to spill on any organic or combustible material and then dry. All spills should be wetted down before any maintenance work may proceed, and all equipment should be thoroughly cleaned afterward. Wet clothing should be kept wet and separate from street clothing, until washed.

DISEASE AND INJURY PATTERNS

INJURIES AND NON-MALIGNANT DISEASES

Susan Kennedy and Kjell Torén

Injuries

Only limited statistics are available on accident rates in general in this industry. Compared to other manufacturing industries, the 1990 accident rate in Finland was below the average; in Canada, the rates from 1990 to 1994 were similar to other industries; in the United States, the 1988 rate was slightly above average; in Sweden and Germany, the rates were 25% and 70% above the average (ILO 1992; Workers' Compensation Board of British Columbia 1995).

The most commonly encountered risk factors for serious and fatal accidents in the pulp and paper industry are the papermaking equipment itself and the extreme size and weight of pulp or paper bales and rolls. In a 1993 United States government study of occupational fatalities from 1979 to 1984 in pulp, paper and paperboard mills (US Department of Commerce 1993), 28% were due to workers being caught in or between rotating rolls or equipment ("nip-points") and 18% were due to workers being crushed by falling or tumbling objects, especially rolls and bales. Other causes of multiple deaths included electrocution, hydrogen sulphide and other toxic gas inhalation, massive thermal/chemical burns and one case of heat exhaustion. The number of serious accidents associated with paper machines has been reported to decrease with the installation of newer equipment in some countries. In the converting sector, repetitive and monotonous work, and the use of mechanized equipment with higher speeds and forces, has become more common. Although no sector-specific data are available, it is expected that this sector will experience greater rates of over-exertion injuries associated with repetitive work.

Non-Malignant Diseases

The most well documented health problems encountered by pulp mill workers are acute and chronic respiratory disorders (Torén, Hagberg and Westberg 1996). Exposure to extremely high concentrations of chlorine, chlorine dioxide or sulphur dioxide may occur as a result of a leak or other process upset. Exposed workers may develop acute chemical-induced lung injury with severe inflammation of air passages and release of fluid into the air spaces, requiring hospitalization. The extent of damage depends on the duration and intensity of the exposure, and the specific gas involved. If the worker survives the acute episode, complete recovery may occur. However, in less intense exposure incidents (also usually as a result of process upsets or spills), acute exposure to chlorine or chlorine dioxide may trigger the subsequent development of asthma. This irritant-induced asthma has been recorded in numerous case reports and recent epidemiological studies, and current evidence indicates that it may persist for many years following the exposure incident. Workers similarly exposed who do not develop asthma may experience persistently increased nasal irritation, cough, wheezing and reduction in airflow rates. Workers most at risk for these exposure incidents include maintenance workers, bleach plant workers and construction workers at pulp mill sites. High levels of chlorine dioxide exposure also cause eye irritation and the sensation of seeing halos around lights.

Some mortality studies have indicated increased risk of death from respiratory disease among pulp mill workers exposed to sulphur dioxide and paper dust (Jäppinen and Tola 1990; Torén, Järvholm and Morgan 1989). Increased respiratory symptoms have also been reported in sulphite mill workers who are chronically exposed to low levels of sulphur dioxide (Skalpe 1964), although increased airflow obstruction is not normally reported among pulp mill populations in general. Symptoms of respiratory irritation are also reported by workers exposed to high air concentrations of terpenes in turpentine recovery processes often present at pulp mill sites. Soft paper dust has also been reported to be associated with increased asthma and chronic obstructive pulmonary disease (Torén, Hagberg and Westberg 1996).

Exposure to micro-organisms, especially around wood chip and waste piles, debarkers and sludge presses, creates an increased risk for hypersensitivity responses in the lungs. Evidence for this appears to be limited to isolated case reports of hypersensitivity pneumonitis, which can lead to chronic lung scarring. Bagassosis, or hypersensitivity pneumonitis associated with exposure to thermophylic micro-organisms and bagasse (a sugar cane by-product), is still seen in mills using bagasse for fibre.

Other respiratory hazards commonly encountered in the pulp and paper industry include stainless steel welding fumes and asbestos (see "Asbestos," "Nickel" and "Chromium" elsewhere in the *Encyclopaedia*). Maintenance workers are the group most likely to be at risk from these exposures.

Reduced sulphur compounds (including hydrogen sulphide, dimethyl disulphides and mercaptans) are potent eye irritants and may cause headaches and nausea in some workers. These compounds have very low odour thresholds (ppb range) in individuals not previously exposed; however, among long-time workers in the industry, odour thresholds are considerably higher. Concentrations in the range of 50 to 200 ppm produce olfactory fatigue, and subjects can no longer detect the distinctive "rotten eggs" odour. At higher concentrations, exposure will result in unconsciousness, respiratory paralysis and death. Fatalities associated with exposure to reduced sulphur compounds in confined spaces have occurred at pulp mill sites.

Cardiovascular mortality has been reported to be increased in pulp and paper workers, with some exposure-response evidence suggesting a possible link with exposure to reduced sulphur compounds (Jäppinen 1987; Jäppinen and Tola 1990). However, other causes for this increased mortality may include noise exposure and shift work, both of which have been associated with increased risk for ischaemic heart disease in other industries.

Skin problems encountered by pulp and paper mill workers include acute chemical and thermal burns and contact dermatitis (both irritant and allergic). Pulp mill workers in kraft process mills frequently experience alkali burns to the skin as a result of contact with hot pulping liquors and calcium hydroxide slurries from the recovery process. Contact dermatitis is reported more frequently among paper mill and converting workers, as many of the additives, defoaming agents, biocides, inks and glues used in paper and paper-product making are primary skin irritants and sensitizers. Dermatitis may occur from exposure to the chemicals themselves or from handling freshly treated paper or paper products.

Noise is a significant hazard throughout the pulp and paper industry. The US Department of Labor estimated that noise levels over 85 dBA were found in over 75% of plants in the paper and allied products industries, compared to 49% of plants in manufacturing in general, and that over 40% of workers were exposed regularly to noise levels over 85 dBA (US Department of Commerce 1983). Noise levels around paper machines, chippers and recovery boilers tend to be well over 90 dBA. Conversion operations also tend to generate high noise levels. Reduction in worker exposure around paper machines is usually attempted by the use of enclosed control rooms. In converting, where the operator is usually stationed next to the machine, this type of control measure is seldom used. However where converting machines have been enclosed, this has resulted in decreased exposure to both paper dust and noise.

Excessive heat exposure is encountered by paper mill workers working in paper machine areas, with temperatures of 60 °C being recorded, although no studies of the effects of heat exposure in this population are available in the published scientific literature.

● CANCER

Kjell Torén and Kay Teschke

Exposures to numerous substances designated by the International Agency for Research on Cancer (IARC) as known, probable and possible carcinogens may occur in pulp and paper operations. Asbestos, known to cause lung cancer and mesothelioma, is used to insulate pipes and boilers. Talc is used extensively as a paper additive, and can be contaminated with asbestos. Other paper additives, including benzidine-based dyes, formaldehyde and epichlorohydrin, are considered probable human carcinogens. Hexavalent chromium and nickel compounds, generated in stainless-steel welding, are known lung and nasal carcinogens. Wood dust has recently been classified by IARC as a known carcinogen, based mainly on evidence of nasal cancer among workers exposed to hardwood dust (IARC, 1995). Diesel exhaust, hydrazine, styrene, mineral oils, chlorinated phenols and dioxins, and ionizing radiation are other probable or possible carcinogens which may be present in mill operations.

Few epidemiological studies specific to pulp and paper operations have been conducted, and they indicate few consistent results. Exposure classifications in these studies have often used the broad industrial category "pulp and paper", and even the most specific classifications grouped workers by types of pulping or large mill areas. The three cohort studies in the literature to date involved fewer than 4,000 workers each. Several large cohort studies are currently under way, and IARC is coordinating an international multicentric study likely to include data from more than 150,000 pulp and paper workers, allowing much more specific exposure analyses. This article will review the available knowledge from studies published to date. More detailed information may be obtained from earlier published reviews by IARC (1980, 1987, and 1995) and by Torén, Persson and Wingren (1996). Results for lung, stomach and haematological malignancies are summarized in table 72.6.

Respiratory System Cancers

Maintenance workers in paper and pulp mills experience an increased risk of lung cancer and malignant mesotheliomas, probably because of their exposure to asbestos. A Swedish study showed a threefold increased risk of pleural mesothelioma among pulp and paper workers (Malker et al. 1985). When the exposure was further analysed, 71% of the cases had been exposed to asbestos, the majority having worked in mill maintenance. Elevations in lung cancer risk among maintenance workers have also been shown in Swedish and Finnish pulp and paper mills (Torén, Sällsten and Järvholm 1991; Jäppinen et al. 1987).

In the same Finnish study, a twofold increased risk of lung cancer was also observed among both paper mill and board mill workers. The investigators made a subsequent study restricted to pulp mill workers exposed to chlorine compounds, and found a threefold increased risk of lung cancer.

Few other studies of pulp and paper workers have shown increased risks for lung cancer. A Canadian study showed an increased risk among those exposed to paper dust (Siemiatycki et al. 1986), and US and Swedish studies showed increased risks among paper mill workers (Milham and Demers 1984; Torén, Järvholm and Morgan 1989).

Gastro-intestinal Cancers

Increased risk of stomach cancer has been indicated in many studies, but the risks are not clearly associated with any one area; therefore the relevant exposure is unknown. Socio-economic status and dietary habits are also risk factors for stomach cancer, and might be confounders; these factors were not taken into account in any of the studies reviewed.

The association between gastric cancer and pulp and paper work was first seen in a US study in the 1970s (Milham and Demers 1984). The risk was found to be even higher, nearly doubled, when sulphite workers were examined separately. US sulphite and groundwood workers were also found in a later study to run an increased risk of stomach cancer (Robinson, Waxweiller

Table 72.6 • Summary of studies on lung cancer, stomach cancer, lymphoma and leukaemia in pulp and paper workers.

Process description	Location of study	Type of study	Lung cancer	Stomach cancer	Lymphoma NHL/HD§	Leukaemia
Sulphite	Finland	C	0.9	1.3	X/X	X
Sulphite	USA	C	1.1	0.7	—	0.9
Sulphite	USA	C	0.8	1.5	1.3/X	0.7
Sulphite	USA	PM	0.9	2.2*	2.7*/X	1.3
Sulphate	Finland	C	0.9	0.9	0/0	X
Sulphate	USA	C	0.8	1.0	2.1/0	0.2
Sulphate	USA	PM	1.1	1.9	1.1/4.1*	1.7
Chlorine	Finland	C	3.0*	—	—	—
Sulphite/paper	Sweden	CR	—	2.8*	—	—
Paper dust	Canada	CR	2.0*	—	—	—
Paper mill	Finland	C	2.0*	1.7	X/X	—
Paper mill	Sweden	C	0.7*	—	—	—
Paper mill	USA	C	0.8	2.0	—	2.4
Paper mill	Sweden	CR	1.6	—	—	—
Paper mill	USA	PM	1.3	0.9	X/1.4	1.4
Board mill	Finland	C	2.2*	0.6	X/X	X
Power plant	Finland	C	0.5	2.1	—	—
Maintenance	Finland	C	1.3	0.3*	1.0/X	1.5
Maintenance	Sweden	CR	2.1*	0.8	—	—
Pulp and paper	USA	C	0.9	1.2	0.7/X	1.8
Pulp and paper	USA	C	0.8	1.2	1.7/X	0.5
Pulp and paper	Sweden	CR	0.8	1.3	1.8	1.1
Pulp and paper	Sweden	CR	—	—	2.2/0	—
Pulp and paper	Sweden	CR	1.1	0.6	—	—
Pulp and paper	USA	CR	1.2*	—	—	—
Pulp and paper	USA	CR	1.1	—	—	—
Pulp and paper	USA	CR	—	—	—/4.0	—
Pulp and paper	Canada	PM	—	1.2	3.8*/—	—
Pulp and paper	USA	PM	1.5*	0.5	4.4/4.5	2.3
Pulp and paper	USA	PM	0.9	1.7*	1.6/1.0	1.1
Pulp and paper	USA	PM	0.9	1.2	1.5/1.9*	1.4
Pulp and paper	USA	PM	—	1.7*	1.4	1.6*

C = cohort study, CR = case-referent study, PM = proportionate mortality study. * Statistically significant. § = Where separately reported, NHL = non Hodgkin lymphoma and HD = Hodgkin's disease. X = 0 or 1 case reported, no risk estimate calculated. — = No data reported.

A risk estimate exceeding 1.0 means the risk is increased, and a risk estimate below 1.0 indicates decreased risk.

Source: Adapted from Torén, Persson and Wingren 1996.

and Fowler 1986). A risk of the same magnitude was found in a Swedish study among pulp and paper mill workers from an area where only sulphite pulp was produced (Wingren et al. 1991). American paper, paperboard and pulp mill workers in New Hampshire and Washington state ran an increased mortality from stomach cancer (Schwartz 1988; Milham 1976). The subjects were probably a mixture of sulphite, sulphate and paper mill workers. In a Swedish study, threefold increased mortality due to stomach cancer was found in a group comprising sulphite and paper mill workers (Wingren, Kling and Axelson 1985). The majority of pulp and paper studies reported excesses of stomach cancer, though some did not.

Due to the small number of cases, most studies of other gastrointestinal cancers are inconclusive. An increased risk of colon cancer among workers in the sulphate process and in paper board production has been reported in a Finnish study (Jäppinen et al.

1987), as well as among US pulp and paper workers (Solet et al. 1989). The incidence of biliary tract cancer in Sweden between 1961 and 1979 was linked with occupational data from the 1960 National Census (Malker et al. 1986). An increased incidence of cancer of the gallbladder among male paper mill workers was identified. Increased risks of pancreatic cancer have been observed in some studies of paper mill workers and sulphite workers (Milham and Demers 1984; Henneberger, Ferris and Monson 1989), as well as in the broad group of pulp and paper workers (Pickle and Gottlieb 1980; Wingren et al. 1991). These findings have not been substantiated in other studies.

Haematological Malignancies

The issue of lymphomas among pulp and paper mill workers was originally addressed in a US study from the 1960s, where a fourfold increased risk of Hodgkin's disease was found among pulp and paper workers (Milham and Hesser 1967). In a subsequent study, the mortality among pulp and paper mill workers in the state of Washington between 1950 and 1971 was investigated, and a doubled risk of both Hodgkin's disease and multiple myeloma was observed (Milham 1976). This study was followed by one analysing mortality among pulp and paper union members in the United States and Canada (Milham and Demers 1984). It showed almost a threefold increased risk for lymphosarcoma and reticulum cell sarcoma among sulphite workers, while sulphate workers had a fourfold increased risk of Hodgkin's disease. In a US cohort study, sulphate workers were observed to have a twofold risk of lymphosarcoma and reticulosarcoma (Robinson, Waxweiller and Fowler 1986).

In many of the studies where it was possible to investigate the occurrence of malignant lymphomas, an increased risk has been found (Wingren et al. 1991; Persson et al. 1993). Since the increased risk occurs both in sulphate and sulphite mill workers, this points towards a common source of exposure. In the sorting and chipping departments, the exposures are rather similar. The workforce is exposed to wood dust, terpenes and other extractable compounds from the wood. In addition, both pulping processes bleach with chlorine, which has the potential to create chlorinated organic by-products, including small amounts of dioxins.

Compared with lymphomas, studies on leukaemias show less consistent patterns, and the risk estimates are lower.

Other Malignancies

Among US paper mill workers with presumed exposure to formaldehyde, four cases of urinary tract cancer were found after 30 years' latency, although only one was expected (Robinson, Waxweiller and Fowler 1986). All of these individuals had worked in the paper-drying areas of the paper mills.

In a case-control study from Massachusetts, central nervous system tumours in childhood were associated with an unspecified paternal occupation as a paper and pulp mill worker (Kwa and Fine 1980). The authors regarded their observation as a random event. However, in three subsequent studies, increased risks were also found (Johnson et al. 1987; Nasca et al. 1988; Kuijten, Bunin and Nass 1992). In studies from Sweden and Finland, two- to threefold increased risks of brain tumours were observed among pulp and paper mill workers.

• ENVIRONMENTAL AND PUBLIC HEALTH ISSUES

Anya Keefe and Kay Teschke

Because the pulp and paper industry is a large consumer of natural resources (i.e., wood, water and energy), it can be a major contributor to water, air and soil pollution problems and has come under a great deal of scrutiny in recent years. This concern appears to be warranted, considering the quantity of water pollutants generated per tonne of pulp (e.g., 55 kg of biological oxygen demand, 70 kg of suspended solids, and up to 8 kg of organochlorine compounds) and the amount of pulp produced globally on an annual basis (approximately 180 million tonnes in 1994). In addition, only about 35% of used paper is recycled, and waste paper is a major contributor to total worldwide solid waste (about 150 million of 500 million tonnes annually).

Historically, pollution control was not considered in the design of pulp and paper mills. Many of the processes used in the industry were developed with little regard for minimizing effluent volume and pollutant concentration. Since the 1970s, pollution abatement technologies have become integral components of mill

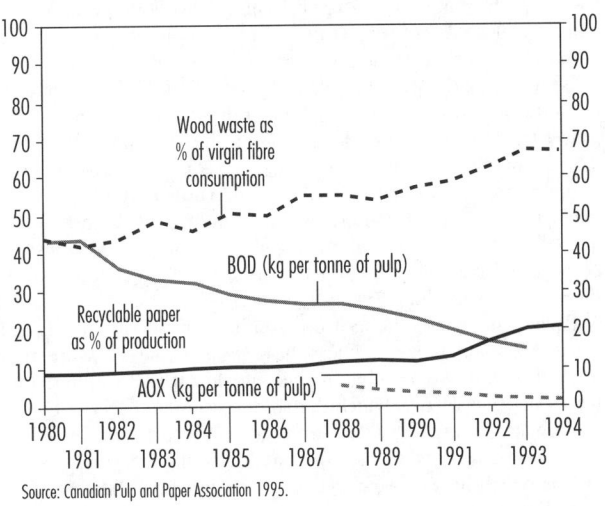

Figure 72.12 • Environmental indicators in Canadian pulp and paper mills, 1980 to 1994, showing use of wood waste and recyclable paper in production, and biological oxygen demand (BOD) and organochlorine compounds (AOX) in wastewater effluent.

Source: Canadian Pulp and Paper Association 1995.

design in Europe, North America and other parts of the world. Figure 72.12 illustrates trends over the period 1980 to 1994 in Canadian pulp and paper mills in response to some of these environmental concerns: increased use of wood waste products and recyclable paper as fibre sources; and decreased oxygen demand and chlorinated organics in wastewater.

This article discusses the major environmental issues associated with the pulp and paper process, identifies the sources of pollution within the process and briefly describes control technologies, including both external treatment and in-plant modifications. Issues arising from wood waste and anti-sapstain fungicides are dealt with in more detail in the chapter *Lumber*.

Air Pollution Issues

Air emissions of oxidized sulphur compounds from pulp and paper mills have caused damage to vegetation, and emissions of reduced sulphur compounds have generated complaints about "rotten egg" odours. Studies among residents of pulp mill communities, in particular children, have shown respiratory effects related to particulate emissions, and mucous membrane irritation and headache thought to be related to reduced sulphur compounds. Of the pulping processes, those with the greatest potential to cause air pollution problems are chemical methods, in particular kraft pulping.

Sulphur oxides are emitted at the highest rates from sulphite operations, especially those using calcium or magnesium bases. The major sources include batch digester blows, evaporators and liquor preparation, with washing, screening and recovery operations contributing lesser amounts. Kraft recovery furnaces are also a source of sulphur dioxide, as are power boilers which use high-sulphur coal or oil as fuel.

Reduced sulphur compounds, including hydrogen sulphide, methyl mercaptan, dimethyl sulphide and dimethyl disulphide, are almost exclusively associated with kraft pulping, and give these mills their characteristic odour. The major sources include the recovery furnace, digester blow, digester relief valves, and washer vents, though evaporators, smelt tanks, slakers, the lime

72. PAPER AND PULP INDUSTRY

kiln and waste water may also contribute. Some sulphite operations use reducing environments in their recovery furnaces and may have associated reduced sulphur odour problems.

Sulphur gases emitted by the recovery boiler are best controlled by reducing emissions at the source. Controls include black liquor oxidation, reduction in liquor sulphidity, low-odour recovery boilers and proper operation of the recovery furnace. Sulphur gases from digester blow, digester relief valves and liquor evaporation can be collected and incinerated—for example, in the lime kiln. Combustion flue gases can be collected using scrubbers.

Nitrogen oxides are produced as products of high-temperature combustion, and may arise in any mill with a recovery boiler, power boiler or lime kiln, depending on the operating conditions. The formation of nitrogen oxides can be controlled by regulating temperatures, air-fuel ratios and residence time in the combustion zone. Other gaseous compounds are minor contributors to mill air pollution (e.g., carbon monoxide from incomplete combustion, chloroform from bleaching operations, and volatile organics from digester relief and liquor evaporation).

Particulates arise mainly from combustion operations, though smelt-dissolving tanks can also be a minor source. More than 50% of pulp mill particulate is very fine (less than 1 μm in diameter). This fine material includes sodium sulphate (Na_2SO_4) and sodium carbonate (Na_2CO_3) from recovery furnaces, lime kilns and smelt-dissolving tanks, and NaCl from burning by-products of logs which have been stored in salt water. Lime kiln emissions include a significant amount of coarse particulates due to entrainment of calcium salts and sublimation of sodium compounds. Coarse particulate may also include fly ash and organic combustion products, especially from power boilers. Reduction of particulate concentrations can be achieved by passing flue gases through electrostatic precipitators or scrubbers. Recent innovations in power boiler technology include fluidized bed incinerators which burn at very high temperatures, result in more efficient energy conversion, and allow burning of less uniform wood waste.

Water Pollution Issues

Contaminated wastewater from pulp and paper mills can cause death of aquatic organisms, allow bioaccumulation of toxic compounds in fish, and impair the taste of downstream drinking water. Pulp and paper wastewater effluents are characterized on the basis of physical, chemical or biological characteristics, with the most important being solids content, oxygen demand and toxicity.

The solids content of wastewater is typically classified on the basis of the fraction that is suspended (versus dissolved), the fraction of suspended solids that is settleable, and the fractions of either that are volatile. The settleable fraction is the most objectionable because it may form a dense sludge blanket close to the discharge point, which rapidly depletes dissolved oxygen in the receiving water and allows the proliferation of anaerobic bacteria which generate methane and reduced sulphur gases. Although non-settleable solids are usually diluted by the receiving water and are therefore of less concern, they may transport toxic organic compounds to aquatic organisms. Suspended solids discharged from pulp and paper mills include bark particles, wood fibre, sand, grit from mechanical pulp grinders, papermaking additives, liquor dregs, by-products of water treatment processes and microbial cells from secondary treatment operations.

Wood derivatives dissolved in the pulping liquors, including oligosaccharides, simple sugars, low-molecular-weight lignin derivatives, acetic acid and solubilized cellulose fibres, are the main contributors to both biological oxygen demand (BOD) and chemical oxygen demand (COD). Compounds which are toxic to aquatic organisms include chlorinated organics (AOX; from bleaching, especially kraft pulp); resin acids; unsaturated fatty acids; diterpene alcohols (especially from debarking and mechanical pulping); juvabiones (especially from sulphite and mechanical pulping); lignin degradation products (especially from sulphite pulping); synthetic organics, such as slimicides, oils and greases; and process chemicals, papermaking additives and oxidized metals. The chlorinated organics have been of particular concern, because they are acutely toxic to marine organisms and may bioaccumulate. This group of compounds, including the polychlorinated dibenzo-p-dioxins, have been the major impetus for minimizing chlorine use in pulp bleaching.

The amount and sources of suspended solids, oxygen demand and toxic discharges are process-dependent (table 72.7). Due to the solubilization of wood extractives with little or no chemical and resin acid recovery, both sulphite and CTMP pulping generate acutely toxic effluents with high BOD. Kraft mills historically used more chlorine for bleaching, and their effluents were more toxic; however, effluents from kraft mills which have eliminated Cl_2 in bleaching and use secondary treatment typically exhibit little acute toxicity if any, and subacute toxicity has been greatly reduced.

Suspended solids have become less of a problem because most mills utilize primary clarification (e.g., gravity sedimentation or dissolved air flotation), which removes 80 to 95% of the settleable solids. Secondary wastewater treatment technologies such as aerated lagoons, activated sludge systems and biological filtration are used for reducing BOD, COD and chlorinated organics in the effluent.

In-plant process modifications to reduce settleable solids, BOD and toxicity include dry debarking and log conveying, improved chip screening to allow uniform cooking, extended delignification during pulping, changes to digestion chemical recovery operations, alternative bleaching technologies, high-efficiency pulp washing, fibre recovery from whitewater and improved spill containment. However, process upsets (particularly if they result in intentional sewering of liquors) and operational changes (particularly the use of unseasoned wood with a higher percentage of extractives) may still cause periodic toxicity breakthroughs.

A relatively recent pollution control strategy to eliminate water pollution entirely is the "closed mill" concept. Such mills are an attractive alternative in locations that lack large water sources to act as process-supply or effluent-receiving streams. Closed systems have been successfully implemented in CTMP and sodium-base sulphite mills. What distinguishes closed mills is that liquid effluent is evaporated and the condensate is treated, filtered, then

Table 72.7 • Total suspended solids and BOD associated with the untreated (raw) effluent of various pulping processes.

Pulping Process	Total Suspended Solids (kg/tonne)	BOD (kg/tonne)
Groundwood	50–70	10–20
TMP	45–50	25–50
CTMP	50–55	40–95
Kraft, unbleached	20–25	15–30
Kraft, bleached	70–85	20–50
Sulphite, low-yield	30–90	40–125
Sulphite, high-yield	90–95	140–250
De-inking, non-tissue	175–180	10–80
Waste paper	110–115	5–15

reused. Other features of closed mills are enclosed screen rooms, counter-current washing in the bleach plant, and salt control systems. Although this approach is effective at minimizing water pollution, it is not yet clear how worker exposures will be affected by concentrating all contaminant streams within the mill. Corrosion is a major issue facing mills using closed systems, and bacteria and endotoxin concentrations are increased in recycled process water.

Solids Handling

The composition of solids (sludges) removed from liquid effluent treatment systems varies, depending on their source. Solids from primary treatment principally consist of cellulose fibres. The major component of solids from secondary treatment is microbial cells. If the mill uses chlorinated bleaching agents, both primary and secondary solids may also contain chlorinated organic compounds, an important consideration in determining the extent of treatment required.

Prior to disposal, sludges are thickened in gravity sedimentation units and mechanically dewatered in centrifuges, vacuum filters or belt or screw presses. Sludges from primary treatment are relatively easy to dewater. Secondary sludges contain a large quantity of intracellular water and exist in a matrix of slime; therefore they require the addition of chemical flocculants. Once sufficiently dewatered, sludge is disposed of in land-based applications (e.g., spread on arable or forested land, used as compost or as a soil conditioner) or incinerated. Although incineration is more costly and can contribute to air pollution problems, it may be advantageous because it can destroy or reduce toxic materials (e.g., chlorinated organics) that could create serious environmental problems if they were to leach into the groundwater from land-based applications.

Solid wastes can be generated in other mill operations. Ash from power boilers can be used in road beds, as construction material and as a dust suppressant. Waste from lime kilns can be used to modify soil acidity and improve soil chemistry.

References

Canadian Pulp and Paper Association. 1995. *Reference Tables 1995*. Montreal, PQ: CPPA.

Food and Agriculture Organization (FAO) of the United Nations. 1995. *Pulp and Paper Capacities, Survey 1994-1999*. Rome: FAO.

Henneberger, PK, JR Ferris, and RR Monson. 1989. Mortality among pulp and paper workers in Berlin. *Br J Ind Med* 46:658-664.

International Agency on the Research of Cancer (IARC). 1980. *Monographs on the Evaluation of Carcinogenic Risks to Humans: Wood, Leather and Some Associated Industries*. Vol. 25. Lyon: IARC.

—.1987. *Monographs on the Evaluation of Carcinogenic Risks to Humans, Overall Evaluations of Carcinogenicity: An Updating of IARC Monographs*. Vol. 1-42 (supplement 7). Lyon: IARC.

—.1995. *Monographs on the Evaluation of Carcinogenic Risks to Humans: Wood Dust and Formaldehyde*. Vol. 62. Lyon: IARC.

International Labour Organization (ILO). 1992. *Social and Labour Issues in the Pulp and Paper Industry*. Geneva: ILO.

Jäppinen, P. 1987. *Exposure to Compounds, Cancer Incidence and Mortality in the Finnish Pulp and Paper Industry*. Thesis, Helsingfors, Finland.

Jäppinen, P and S Tola. 1990. Cardiovascular mortality among pulp mill workers. *Br J Ind Med* 47:259-261.

Jäppinen, P, T Hakulinen, E Pukkala, S Tola, and K Kurppa. 1987. Cancer incidence of workers in the Finnish pulp and paper industry. *Scand J Work Environ Health* 13:197-202.

Johnson, CC, JF Annegers, RF Frankowski, MR Spitz, and PA Buffler. 1987. Childhood nervous system tumors—An evaluation of the association with paternal occupational exposure to hydrocarbons. *Am J Epidemiol* 126:605-613.

Kuijten, R, GR Bunin, and CC Nass. 1992. Parental occupation and childhood astrocytoma: Results of a case-control study. *Cancer Res* 52:782-786.

Kwa, SL and IJ Fine. 1980. The association between parental occupation and childhood malignancy. *J Occup Med* 22:792-794.

Malker, HSR, JK McLaughlin, BK Malker, NJ Stone, JA Weiner, JLE Ericsson, and WJ Blot. 1985. Occupational risks for pleural mesothelioma in Sweden, 1961-1979. *J Natl Cancer Inst* 74:61-66.

—. 1986. Biliary tract cancer and occupation in Sweden. *Br J Ind Med* 43:257-262.

Milham, SJ. 1976. Neoplasias in the wood and pulp industry. *Ann NY Acad Sci* 271:294-300.

Milham, SJ and P Demers. 1984. Mortality among pulp and paper workers. *J Occup Med* 26:844-846.

Milham, SJ and J Hesser. 1967. Hodgkin's disease in woodworkers. *Lancet* 2:136-137.

Nasca, P, MS Baptiste, PA MacCubbin, BB Metzger, K Carton, P Greenwald, and VW Armbrustmacher. 1988. An epidemiologic case-control study of central nervous system tumors in children and parental occupational exposures. *Am J Epidemiol* 128:1256-1265.

Persson, B, M Fredriksson, K Olsen, B Boeryd, and O Axelson. 1993. Some occupational exposures as risk factors for malignant melanomas. *Cancer* 72:1773-1778.

Pickle, L and M Gottlieb. 1980. Pancreatic cancer mortality in Louisiana. *Am J Public Health* 70:256-259.

Pulp and Paper International (PPI). 1995. Vol. 37. Brussels: Miller Freeman.

Robinson, C, J Waxweiller, and D Fowler. 1986. Mortality among production workers in pulp and paper mills. *Scand J Work Environ Health* 12:552-560.

Schwartz, B. 1988. A proportionate mortality ratio analysis of pulp and paper mill workers in New Hampshire. *Br J Ind Med* 45:234-238.

Siemiatycki, J, L Richardson, M Gérin, M Goldberg, R Dewar, M Désy, S Campell, and S Wacholder. 1986. Association between several sites of cancer and nine organic dusts: Results from an hypothesis-generating case control study in Montreal, 1979-1983. *Am J Epidemiol* 123:235-249.

Skalpe, IO. 1964. Long-term effects of sulfur dioxide exposure in pulp mills. *Br J Ind Med* 21:69-73.

Solet, D, R Zoloth, C Sullivan, J Jewett, and DM Michaels. 1989. Patterns of mortality in pulp and paper workers. *J Occup Med* 31:627-630.

Torén, K, S Hagberg, and H Westberg. 1996. Health effects of working in pulp and paper mills: Exposure, obstructive airways diseases, hypersensitivity reactions, and cardiovascular diseases. *Am J Ind Med* 29:111-122.

Torén, K, B Järvholm, and U Morgan. 1989. Mortality from asthma and chronic obstructive pulmonary diseases among workers in a soft paper mill: A case referent study. *Br J Ind Med* 46:192-195.

Torén, K, B Persson, and G Wingren. 1996. Health effects of working in pulp and paper mills: Malignant diseases. *Am J Ind Med* 29:123-130.

Torén, K, G Sällsten, and B Järvholm. 1991. Mortality from asthma, chronic obstructive pulmonary disease, respiratory system cancer among paper mill workers: A case referent study. *Am J Ind Med* 19:729-737.

US Department of Commerce. 1983. *Pulp and Paper Mills*. (PB 83-115766). Washington, DC: US Department of Commerce.

—.1993. *Selected Occupational Fatalities Related to Pulp Paper and Paperboard Mills as Found in Reports of OSHA Fatality/Catastrophe Investigations*. (PB93-213502). Washington, DC: US Department of Commerce.

Weidenmüller, R. 1984. *Papermaking, the Art and Craft of Handmade Paper*. San Diego, CA: Thorfinn International Marketing Consultants Inc.

Wingren, G, H Kling, and O Axelson. 1985. Gastric cancer among paper mill workers. *J Occup Med* 27:715.

Wingren, G, B Persson, K Torén, and O Axelson. 1991. Mortality patterns among pulp and paper mill workers in Sweden: A case-referent study. *Am J Ind Med* 20:769-774.

Workers' Compensation Board of British Columbia. 1995. Personal communication.

Other relevant readings

Bascom, R and P Raford. 1994. Upper airways disorders. In *Textbook of Clinical Occupational and Environmental Medicine*, edited by L Rosenstock and MR Cullen. Philadelphia: WB Saunders Co.

Bernhart, S. 1994. Irritant bronchitis. In *Textbook of Clinical Occupational and Environmental Medicine*, edited by L Rosenstock and MR Cullen. Philadelphia: WB Saunders Co.

Chan-Yeung, M and J Malo. 1995. Forestry products. In *Occupational and Environmental Respiratory Disease*, edited by P Harber, MB Schenker and JR Balmes. St. Louis: Mosby-Yearbook Inc.

Food and Agriculture Organization (FAO) of the United Nations. 1994. *1993 Yearbook of Forest Products*. Rome: FAO.

Rix, BA and E Lynge. 1996. Industrial hygiene measurements in a new industry: The repulping and deinking of paper waste. *Am J Ind Med* 30:142-147.

Schwartz, DA. 1994. Acute inhalational injury. In *Textbook of Clinical Occupational and Environmental Medicine*, edited by L Rosenstock and MR Cullen. Philadelphia: WB Saunders Co.

Smook, GA. 1989. *Handbook for Pulp and Paper Technologists*. Atlanta, GA: Technical Association for the Pulp and Paper Industry.

Springer, AM. 1986. *Industrial Environmental Control Pulp and Paper Industry*. New York: John Wiley and Sons.

United Nations. 1995. *Statistical Yearbook, 1993*. New York: UN.

IRON AND STEEL

73

Chapter Editor
Augustine Moffit

Contents

IRON AND STEEL INDUSTRY

John Masaitis

Iron is most widely found in the crust of the earth, in the form of various minerals (oxides, hydrated ores, carbonates, sulphides, silicates and so on). Since prehistoric times, humans have learned to prepare and process these minerals by various washing, crushing and screening operations, by separating the gangue, calcining, sintering and pelletizing, in order to render the ores smeltable and to obtain iron and steel. In historic times, a prosperous iron industry developed in many countries, based on local supplies of ore and the proximity of forests to supply the charcoal for fuel. Early in the 18th century, the discovery that coke could be used in place of charcoal revolutionized the industry, making possible its rapid development as the base on which all other developments of the Industrial Revolution rested. Great advantages accrued to those countries where natural deposits of coal and iron ore lay close together.

Steel making was largely a development of the 19th century, with the invention of melting processes; the Bessemer (1855), the open hearth, usually fired by producer gas (1864); and the electric furnace (1900). Since the middle of the 20th century, oxygen conversion, pre-eminently the Linz-Donowitz (LD) process by oxygen lance, has made it possible to manufacture high quality steel with relatively low production costs.

Today, steel production is an index of national prosperity and the basis of mass production in many other industries such as shipbuilding, automobiles, construction, machinery, tools, and industrial and domestic equipment. The development of transport, in particular by sea, has made the international exchange of the raw materials required (iron ores, coal, fuel oil, scrap and additives) economically profitable. Therefore, the countries possessing iron ore deposits near coal fields are no longer privileged, and large smelting plants and steelworks have been built in the coastal regions of major industrialised countries and are supplied with raw materials from exporting countries which are able to meet the present-day requirements for high-grade materials.

Figure 73.1 • World pig iron production in 1995, by regions.

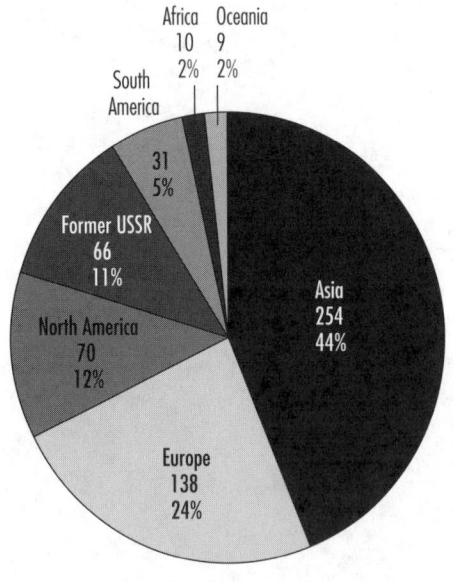

Millions of tonnes

Figure 73.2 • World raw steel production in 1995, by regions.

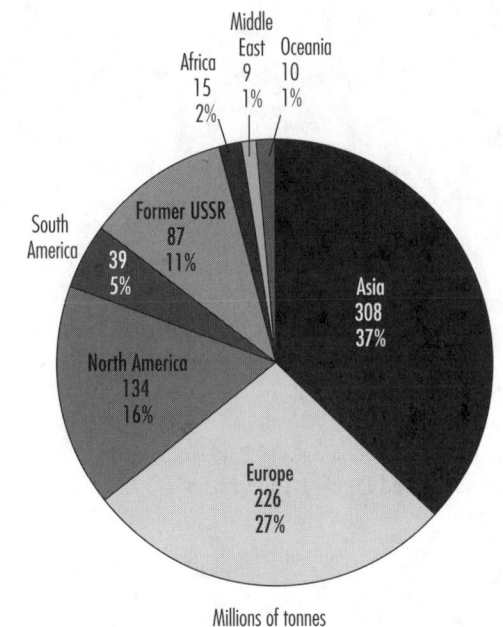

Millions of tonnes

Figure 73.3 • Scrap charges for electric furnaces.

American Iron and Steel Institute

Figure 73.4 • Flow line of steel making.

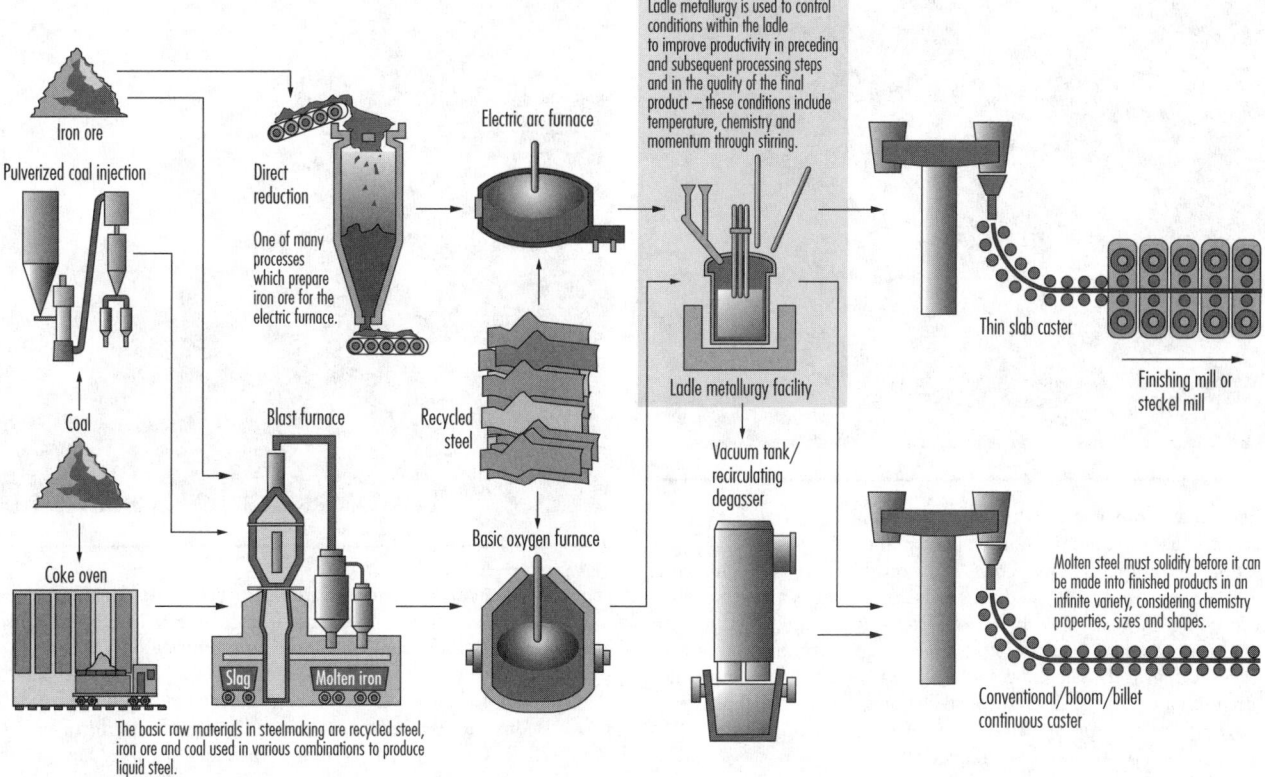

Ladle metallurgy is used to control conditions within the ladle to improve productivity in preceding and subsequent processing steps and in the quality of the final product — these conditions include temperature, chemistry and momentum through stirring.

Iron ore

Pulverized coal injection

Direct reduction

One of many processes which prepare iron ore for the electric furnace.

Electric arc furnace

Thin slab caster

Finishing mill or steckel mill

Coal

Blast furnace

Recycled steel

Coke oven

Basic oxygen furnace

Ladle metallurgy facility

Vacuum tank/ recirculating degasser

Molten steel must solidify before it can be made into finished products in an infinite variety, considering chemistry properties, sizes and shapes.

Slag   Molten iron

Conventional/bloom/billet continuous caster

The basic raw materials in steelmaking are recycled steel, iron ore and coal used in various combinations to produce liquid steel.

Source: American Iron and Steel Institute.

During the past decades, so-called direct-reduction processes have been developed and have met with success. The iron ores, in particular high-grade or upgraded ores, are reduced to sponge iron by extracting the oxygen they contain, thus obtaining a ferrous material that replaces scrap.

Iron and Steel Production

The world's pig iron production was 578 million tonnes in 1995 (see figure 73.1).

The world's raw steel production was 828 million tonnes in 1995 (see figure 73.2).

The steel industry has been undergoing a technological revolution, and the trend in building new production capacity has been towards the recycled steel-scrap-using electric arc furnace (EAF) by smaller mills (see figure 73.3). Although integrated steel works where steel is made from iron ore are operating at record levels of efficiency, EAF steel works with production capacities in the order of less than 1 million tonnes a year are becoming more common in the main steel-producing countries of the world.

Iron making

The overall flow line of iron and steel making is shown in figure 73.4.

For iron making, the essential feature is the blast furnace, where iron ore is melted (reduced) to produce pig iron. The furnace is charged from the top with iron ore, coke and limestone; hot air, frequently enriched with oxygen, is blown in from the bottom; and the carbon monoxide produced from the coke transforms the iron ore into pig iron containing carbon. The limestone acts as a flux. At a temperature of 1,600 °C (see figure 73.5) the pig iron melts and

collects at the bottom of the furnace, and the limestone combines with the earth to form slag. The furnace is tapped (i.e., the pig iron is removed) periodically, and the pig iron may then be poured into

Figure 73.5 • Taking the temperature of molten metal in a blast furnace.

Figure 73.6 • Hot metal charge for basic-oxygen furnace.

American Iron and Steel Institute

Figure 73.8 • Back of hot-metal charge.

American Iron and Steel Institute

pigs for later use (e.g., in foundries), or into ladles where it is transferred, still molten, to the steel-making plant.

Some large plants have coke ovens on the same site. The iron ores are generally subjected to special preparatory processes before being charged into the blast furnace (washing, reduction to ideal lump size by crushing and screening, separation of fine ore for sintering and pelletizing, mechanized sorting to separate the gangue, calcining, sintering and pelletizing). The slag that is removed from the furnace may be converted on the premises for other uses, in particular for making cement.

Steel making

Pig iron contains large amounts of carbon as well as other impurities (mainly sulphur and phosphorus). It must, therefore, be refined. The carbon content must be reduced, the impurities oxidized and removed, and the iron converted into a highly elastic metal which can be forged and fabricated. This is the purpose of the steel-making operations. There are three types of steel-making furnaces: the open-hearth furnace, the basic-oxygen process converter (see figure 73.6) and the electric arc furnace (see figure 73.7). Open-hearth furnaces for the most part have been replaced by basic-oxygen converters (where steel is made by blowing air or oxygen into molten iron) and electric arc furnaces (where steel is made from scrap iron and sponge-iron pellets).

Special steels are alloys in which other metallic elements are incorporated to produce steels with special qualities and for special purposes, (e.g., chromium to prevent rusting, tungsten to give hardness and toughness at high temperatures, nickel to increase

Figure 73.7 • General view of electric furnace casting.

American Iron and Steel Institute

Figure 73.9 • Continuous-casting ladle.

American Iron and Steel Institute

strength, ductility and corrosion resistance). These alloying constituents may be added either to the blast-furnace charge (see figure 73.8) or to the molten steel (in the furnace or ladle) (see figure 73.9). Molten metal from the steel-making process is poured into continuous-casting machines to form billets (see figure 73.10), blooms (see figure 73.11) or slabs. The molten metal can also be poured into moulds to form ingots. The majority of steel is produced by the casting method (see figure 73.12). The benefits of continuous casting are increased yield, higher quality, energy savings and a reduction in both capital and operating costs. Ingot-poured moulds are stored in soaking pits (i.e. underground ovens with doors), where ingots can be reheated before passing to the rolling mills or other subsequent processing (figure 73.4). Recently, companies have begun making steel with continuous casters. Rolling mills are discussed elsewhere in this chapter; foundries, forging and pressing are discussed in the chapter *Metal processing and metal working industry*.

Hazards

Accidents

In the iron and steel industry, large amounts of material are processed, transported and conveyed by massive equipment that

Figure 73.10 • Continuous-casting billet.

American Iron and Steel Institute

Figure 73.11 • Continuous-casting bloom.

American Iron and Steel Institute

Figure 73.12 • Control pulpit for continuous-casting process.

American Iron and Steel Institute

dwarfs that of most industries. Steel works typically have sophisticated safety and health programmes to address hazards in an environment that can be unforgiving. An integrated approach combining good engineering and maintenance practices, safe job procedures, worker training and use of personal protective equipment (PPE) is usually required to control hazards.

Burns may occur at many points in the steel-making process: at the front of the furnace during tapping from molten metal or slag; from spills, spatters or eruptions of hot metal from ladles or vessels during processing, teeming (pouring) or transporting; and from contact with hot metal as it is being formed into a final product.

Water entrapped by molten metal or slag may generate explosive forces that launch hot metal or material over a wide area. Inserting a damp implement into molten metal may also cause violent eruptions.

Mechanical transport is essential in iron and steel manufacturing but exposes workers to potential struck-by and caught-between hazards. Overhead travelling cranes are found in almost all areas of steel works. Most large works also rely heavily on the use of fixed-rail equipment and large industrial tractors for transporting materials.

Safety programmes for crane use require training to ensure proper and safe operation of the crane and rigging of loads to prevent dropped loads; good communication and use of standard hand signals between crane drivers and slingers to prevent injuries from unexpected crane movement; inspection and maintenance programs for crane parts, lifting tackle, slings and hooks to prevent dropped loads; and safe means of access to cranes to avoid falls and accidents on crane transverse ways.

Safety programmes for railways also require good communication, especially during shifting and coupling of rail cars, to avoid catching people between rail car couplings.

Maintaining proper clearance for passage of large industrial tractors and other equipment and preventing unexpected start-up and movement are necessary to eliminate struck-by, struck-against and caught-between hazards to equipment operators, pedestrians and other vehicle operators. Programmes are also necessary for inspection and maintenance of equipment safety appliances and passageways.

Good housekeeping is a cornerstone of safety in iron and steel works. Floors and passageways can quickly become obstructed with material and implements that pose a tripping hazard. Large quantities of greases, oils and lubricants are used and if spilled can easily become a slipping hazard on walking or working surfaces.

Tools are subject to heavy wear and soon become compromised and perhaps dangerous to use. Although mechanization has greatly lessened the amount of manual handling in the industry, ergonomic strains still may occur on many occasions.

Sharp engines or burrs on steel products or metal bands pose laceration and puncture hazards to workers involved in finishing, shipping and scrap-handling operations. Cut-resistant gloves and wrist guards are often used to eliminate injuries.

Protective eye-wear programmes are particularly important in iron and steel works. Foreign-body eye hazards are prevalent in most areas, especially in raw material handling and steel finishing, where grinding, welding and burning are conducted.

Programmed maintenance is particularly important for accident prevention. Its purpose is to ensure the efficiency of the equipment and maintain fully operative guards, because failure may cause accidents. Adhering to safe operating practices and safety rules is also very important because of the complexity, size and speed of process equipment and machinery.

Carbon monoxide poisoning

Blast furnaces, converters and coke ovens produce large quantities of gases in the process of iron and steel manufacturing. After the dust has been removed, these gases are used as fuel sources in the various plants, and some are supplied to chemical plants for use as raw materials. They contain large amounts of carbon monoxide (blast-furnace gas, 22 to 30%; coke oven gas, 5 to 10%; converter gas, 68 to 70%).

Carbon monoxide sometimes emanates or leaks from the tops or bodies of blast furnaces or from the many gas pipelines inside plants, accidentally causing acute carbon monoxide poisoning. Most cases of such poisoning occur during work around blast furnaces, especially during repairs. Other cases occur during work around hot stoves, tours of inspection around the furnace bodies, work near the furnace tops or work near cinder notches or the tapping notches. Carbon monoxide poisoning may also result from gas released from water-seal valves or seal pots in the steel-making plants or rolling mills; from sudden shutdown of blowing equipment, boiler rooms or ventilation fans; from leakage; from failure to properly ventilate or purge process vessels, pipelines or equipment prior to work; and during closing of pipe valves.

Dust and fumes

Dust and fumes are generated at many points in the manufacture of iron and steel. Dust and fumes are found in the preparation processes, especially sintering, in front of the blast furnaces and steel furnaces and in ingot making. Dusts and fumes from iron ore or ferrous metals do not readily cause pulmonary fibrosis and pneumoconiosis is infrequent. Some lung cancers are thought to be connected with carcinogens found in coke-oven emissions. Dense fumes emitted during the use of oxygen lances and from the use of oxygen in open-hearth furnaces may particularly affect crane operators.

Exposure to silica is a risk to workers engaged in lining, relining and repairing blast furnaces and steel furnaces and vessels with refractory materials, which may contain as much as 80% silica. Ladles are lined with fire-brick or bonded crushed silica and this lining requires frequent repair. The silica contained in refractory materials is partly in the form of silicates, which do not cause silicosis but rather pneumoconiosis. Workers are rarely exposed to heavy clouds of dust.

Alloy additions to furnaces making special steels sometimes bring potential exposure risks from chromium, manganese, lead and cadmium.

Miscellaneous hazards

Bench and top-side operations in coking operations in front of blast furnaces in iron making and furnace-front, ingot-making and continuous-casting operations in steel making all involve strenuous activities in a hot environment. Heat-illness prevention programmes must be implemented.

Furnaces may cause glare that can injure eyes unless suitable eye protection is provided and worn. Manual operations, such as furnace bricklaying, and hand-arm vibration in chippers and grinders may cause ergonomic problems.

Blower plants, oxygen plants, gas-discharge blowers and high-power electric furnaces may cause hearing damage. Furnace operators should be protected by enclosing the source of noise with sound-deadening material or by providing sound-proofed shelters. Reducing exposure time may also prove effective. Hearing protectors (earmuffs or earplugs) are often required in high-noise areas due to the unfeasibility of obtaining adequate noise reduction by other means.

Safety and Health Measures

Safety organization

Safety organization is of prime importance in the iron and steel industry, where safety depends so much on workers' reaction to potential hazards. The first responsibility for management is to provide the safest possible physical conditions, but it is usually necessary to obtain everyone's cooperation in safety programmes. Accident-prevention committees, workers' safety delegates, safety incentives, competitions, suggestion schemes, slogans and warning notices can all play an important part in safety programmes. Involving all persons in site hazard assessments, behaviour observation and feedback exercises can promote positive safety attitudes and focus work groups working to prevent injuries and illnesses.

Accident statistics reveal danger areas and the need for additional physical protection as well as greater stress on housekeeping. The value of different types of protective clothing can be evaluated and the advantages can be communicated to the workers concerned.

Training

Training should include information about hazards, safe methods of work, avoidance of risks and the wearing of PPE. When new methods or processes are introduced, it may be necessary to retrain even those workers with long experience on older types of furnaces. Training and refresher courses for all levels of personnel are particularly valuable. They should familiarize personnel with safe working methods, unsafe acts to be proscribed, safety rules and the chief legal provisions associated with accident prevention. Training should be conducted by experts and should make use of effective audio-visual aids. Safety meetings or contacts should be held regularly for all persons to reinforce safety training and awareness.

Engineering and administrative measures

All dangerous parts of machinery and equipment, including lifts, conveyors, long travel shafts and gearing on overhead cranes, should be securely guarded. A regular system of inspection, examination and maintenance is necessary for all machinery and equipment of the plant, particularly for cranes, lifting tackle, chains and hooks. An effective lockout/tagout programme should be in operation for maintenance and repair. Defective tackle should be scrapped. Safe working loads should be clearly marked, and tackle not in use should be stored neatly. Means of access to overhead cranes should, where possible, be by stairway. If a vertical ladder must be used, it should be hooped at intervals. Effective arrangements should be made to limit the travel of overhead cranes when persons are at work in the vicinity. It may be necessary, as required by law in certain countries, to install appropriate switchgear on overhead cranes to prevent collisions if two or more cranes travel on the same runway.

Locomotives, rails, wagons, buggies and couplings should be of good design and maintained in good repair, and an effective system of signalling and warning should be in operation. Riding on couplings or passing between wagons should be prohibited. No operation should be carried on in the track of rail equipment unless measures have been taken to restrict access or movement of equipment.

Great care is needed in storing oxygen. Supplies to different parts of the works should be piped and clearly identified. All lances should be kept clean.

There is a never-ending need for good housekeeping. Falls and stumbles caused by obstructed floors or implements and tools left lying carelessly can cause injury in themselves but can also throw a person against hot or molten material. All materials should be carefully stacked, and storage racks should be conveniently placed for tools. Spills of grease or oil should be immediately cleaned. Lighting of all parts of the shops and machine guards should be of a high standard.

Industrial hygiene

Good general ventilation throughout the plant and local exhaust ventilation (LEV) wherever substantial quantities of dust and fumes are generated or gas may escape are necessary, together with the highest possible standards of cleanliness and housekeeping. Gas equipment must be regularly inspected and well maintained so as to prevent any gas leakage. Whenever any work is to be done in an environment likely to contain gas, carbon monoxide gas detectors should be used to ensure safety. When work in a dangerous area is unavoidable, self-contained or supplied-air respirators should be worn. Breathing-air cylinders should always be kept in readiness, and the operatives should be thoroughly trained in methods of operating them.

With a view to improving the work environment, induced ventilation should be installed to supply cool air. Local blowers may be located to give individual relief, especially in hot working places. Heat protection can be provided by installing heat shields between workers and radiant heat sources, such as furnaces or hot metal, by installing water screens or air curtains in front of furnaces or by installing heat-proof wire screens. A suit and hood of heat-resistant material with air-line breathing apparatus gives the best protection to furnace workers. As work in the furnaces is extremely hot, cool-air lines may also be led into the suit. Fixed arrangements to allow cooling time before entry into the furnaces are also essential.

Acclimatization leads to natural adjustment in the salt content of body sweat. The incidence of heat affections may be much lessened by adjustments of the workload and by well-spaced rest periods, especially if these are spent in a cool room, air-conditioned if necessary. As palliatives, a plentiful supply of water and other suitable beverages should be provided and there should be facilities for taking light meals. The temperature of cool drinks should not be too low and workers should be trained not to swallow too much cool liquid at a time; light meals are to be preferred during working hours. Salt replacement is needed for jobs involving profuse sweating and is best achieved by increasing salt intake with regular meals.

In cold climates, care is required to prevent the ill-effects of prolonged exposure to cold or sudden and violent changes of temperature. Canteen, washing and sanitary facilities should preferably be close at hand. Washing facilities should include showers; changing rooms and lockers should be provided and maintained in a clean and sanitary condition.

Wherever possible, sources of noise should be isolated. Remote central panels remove some operatives from the noisy areas; hearing protection should be required in the worst areas. In addition to enclosing noisy machinery with sound-absorbing material or protecting the workers with sound-proofed shelters, hearing protection programmes have been found to be effective means of controlling noise-induced hearing loss.

Personal protective equipment

All parts of the body are at risk in most operations, but the type of protective wear required will vary according to the location. Those working at furnaces need clothing that protects against burns—overalls of fire-resisting material, spats, boots, gloves, helmets with face shields or goggles against flying sparks and also against glare. Safety boots, safety glasses and hard hats are imperative in almost all occupations and gloves are widely necessary. The protective clothing needs to take account of the risks to health and comfort from excessive heat; for example a fire-resisting hood with wire mesh visor gives good protection against sparks and is resistant to heat; various synthetic fibres have also proved efficient in heat resistance. Strict supervision and continuous propaganda are necessary to ensure that personal protective equipment is worn and correctly maintained.

Ergonomics

The ergonomic approach (i.e. investigation of the worker-machine-environment relationship) is of particular importance at certain operations in the iron and steel industry. An appropriate ergonomic study is necessary not only to investigate conditions while a worker is carrying out various operations, but also to explore the impact of the environment on the worker and the functional design of the machinery used.

Medical supervision

Pre-placement medical examinations are of great importance in selecting persons suitable for the arduous work in iron and steel making. For most work, a good physique is required: hypertension, heart diseases, obesity and chronic gastroenteritis disqualify individuals from work in hot surroundings. Special care is needed in the selection of crane drivers, both for physical and mental capacities.

Medical supervision should pay particular attention to those exposed to heat stress; periodic chest examinations should be provided for those exposed to dust, and audiometric examinations for those exposed to noise; mobile equipment operators should also receive periodic medical examinations to ensure their continued fitness for the job.

Constant supervision of all resuscitative appliances is necessary, as is training of workers in first-aid revival procedure.

A central first-aid station with the requisite medical equipment for emergency assistance should also be provided. If possible, there should be an ambulance for the transport of severely injured persons to the nearest hospital under the care of a qualified ambulance attendant. In larger plants first-aid stations or boxes should be located at several central points.

Coke Operations

Coal preparation

The most important single factor for producing metallurgical coke is the selection of coals. Coals with low ash and low sulphur content are most desirable. Low-volatile coal in amounts up to 40% are usually blended with high-volatile coal to achieve the desired characteristics. The most important physical property of metallurgical coke is its strength and ability to withstand breakage and abrasion during handling and use in the blast furnace. The

---

Table 73.1 • Recoverable by-products of coke ovens.

By-product	Recoverable constituents
Coke oven gas	Hydrogen, methane, ethane, carbon monoxide, carbon dioxide, ethylene, propylene, butylene, acetylene, hydrogen sulphide, ammonia, oxygen and nitrogen
Ammonia liquor	Free and fixed ammonia
Tar	Pyridine, tar acids, naphthalene, creosote oil and coal-tar pitch
Light oil	Varying amounts of coal gas products with boiling points from about 40 °C to 200 °C, and benzene, toluene, xylene and solvent naphtha

coal-handling operations consist of unloading from railroad cars, marine barges or trucks; blending of the coal; proportioning; pulverizing; bulk-density control using diesel grade or similar oil; and conveying to the coke battery bunkers.

Coking

For the most part coke is produced in by-product coking ovens that are designed and operated to collect the volatile material from the coal. The ovens consist of three main parts: the coking chambers, the heating flues and the regenerative chamber. Apart from the steel and concrete structural support, the ovens are constructed of refractory brick. Typically each battery contains approximately 45 separate ovens. The coking chambers are generally 1.82 to 6.7 metres in height, 9.14 to 15.5 metres in length and 1,535 °C at the heating flue base. The time required for coking varies with oven dimensions, but usually ranges between 16 and 20 hours.

In large vertical ovens, the coal is charged through openings in the top from a rail-type "larry car" that transports the coal from the coal bunker. After the coal has become coke, the coke is pushed out of the oven from one side by a power-driven ram or "pusher". The ram is slightly smaller than the oven dimensions so that contact with the oven interior surfaces is avoided. The coke is collected in a rail-type car or in the side of the battery opposite the pusher and transported to the quenching facility. The hot coke is wet quenched with water prior to discharge on the coke wharf. At some batteries, the hot coke is dry quenched to recover sensible heat for the generation of steam.

The reactions during the carbonization of coal for the production of coke are complex. Coal decomposition products initially include water, oxides of carbon, hydrogen sulphide, hydro-aromatic compounds, paraffins, olefins, phenolic and nitrogen-containing compounds. Synthesis and degradation occur among the primary products that produce large amounts of hydrogen, methane, and aromatic hydrocarbons. Further decomposition of the complex nitrogen containing compounds produce ammonia, hydrogen cyanide, pyridine bases and nitrogen. The continual removal of hydrogen from the residue in the oven produces hard coke.

The by-product coke ovens that have equipment for recovering and processing coal chemicals produce the materials listed in table 73.1.

After sufficient cooling so that conveyor-belt damage will not occur, the coke is moved to the screening and crushing station where it is sized for blast-furnace use.

Hazards

Physical hazards

During the coal unloading, preparation and handling operations, thousands of tonnes of coal are manipulated, producing dust, noise and vibrations. The presence of large quantities of accumulated dust can produce an explosion hazard in addition to the inhalation hazard.

During coking, ambient and radiant heat are the major physical concerns, particularly on the topside of the batteries, where the majority of the workers are deployed. Noise may be a problem in mobile equipment, primarily from drive mechanism and vibrating components that are not adequately maintained. Ionizing radiation and/or laser producing devices may be used for mobile equipment alignment purposes.

Chemical hazards

Mineral oil is typically used for operation purposes for bulk density control and dust suppression. Materials may be applied to the coal prior to being taken to the coal bunker to minimize the accumulation and to facilitate the disposal of hazardous waste from the by-products operations.

The major health concern associated with coking operations is emissions from the ovens during charging of the coal, coking and pushing of the coke. The emissions contain numerous polycyclic aromatic hydrocarbons (PAHs), some of which are carcinogenic. Materials utilized for sealing leaks in lids and doors may also be a concern during mixing and when lids and doors are removed. Asbestos and refracting ceramic filters may also be present in the form of insulating materials and gaskets, although suitable replacements have been used for products that previously contained asbestos.

Mechanical hazards

The coal-production hazards associated with railroad car, marine barge and vehicular traffic as well as conveyor belt movement must be recognized. The majority of accidents occur when workers are struck by, caught between, fall from, are entrained and entrapped in, or fail to lockout such equipment (including electrically).

The mechanical hazards of greatest concern are associated with the mobile equipment on the pusher side, coke side and the larry car on top of the battery. This equipment is in operation practically the entire work period and little space is provided between it and the operations. Caught-between and struck-by accidents associated with mobile rail-type equipment account for the highest number of fatal coke-oven production incidents. Skin surface burns from hot materials and surfaces and eye irritation from dust particles are responsible for more numerous, less severe occurrences.

Safety and Health Measures

To maintain dust concentrations during coal production at acceptable levels, containment and enclosure of screening, crushing and conveying systems are required. LEV may also be required in addition to wetting agents applied to the coal. Adequate maintenance programmes, belt programmes and clean-up programmes are required to minimize spillage and keep passageways alongside process and conveying equipment clear of coal. The conveyor system should use components known to be effective in reducing spillage and maintaining containment, such as belt cleaners, skirt boards, proper belt tension and so on.

Due to the health hazards associated with the PAHs released during the coking operations, it is important to contain and collect these emissions. This is best accomplished by a combination of engineering controls, work practices and a maintenance programme. It is also necessary to have an effective respirator programme. The controls should include the following:

- a charging procedure designed and operated to eliminate emissions by controlling the volume of coal being charged, properly

aligning the car over the oven, tightly fitting drop sleeves and charging the coal in a sequence that allows an adequate channel on top of the coal to be maintained for flow of emissions to the collector mains and relidding immediately after charging
- drafting from two or more points in the oven being charged and an aspiration system designed and operated to maintain sufficient negative pressure and flow
- air seals on the pusher machine level bars to control infiltration during charging and carbon cutters to remove carbon build-up
- uniform collector-main pressure adequate to convey the emissions
- chuck door and gaskets as needed to maintain a tight seal and adequately cleaned and maintained pusher side and coke side sealing edges
- luting of lids and doors and maintaining door seals as necessary to control emissions after charging
- green pushes minimized by heating the coal uniformly for an adequate period
- installation of large enclosures over the entire coke side area to control emissions during the pushing of coke or use of travelling hoods to be moved to the individual ovens being pushed
- routine inspection, maintenance and repair for proper containment of emissions
- positive-pressure and temperature controlled operator cabs on mobile equipment to control worker exposure levels. To achieve the positive-pressure cab, structural integration is imperative, with tight fitting doors and windows and the elimination of separations in structural work.

Worker training is also necessary so that proper work practices are used and the importance of proper procedures to minimize emissions is understood.

Routine worker exposure monitoring should also be used to determine that levels are acceptable. Gas monitoring and rescue programmes should be in place, primarily due to the presence of carbon monoxide in coke-gas ovens. A medical surveillance programme should also be implemented.

ROLLING MILLS

H. Schneider*

Hot slabs of steel are converted into long coils of thin sheets in continuous hot strip mills. These coils may be shipped to customers or may be cleaned and cold rolled to make products. See figure 73.13 for a flow line of the processes.

Continuous Hot Rolling

A continuous hot-rolling mill may have a conveyor that is several thousand feet long. The steel slab exits from a slab reheating furnace onto the beginning of the conveyor. Surface scale is removed from the heated slab, which then becomes thinner and longer as it is squeezed by horizontal rolls at each mill, usually called roughing stands. Vertical rolls at the edges help control width. The steel next enters the finishing stands for final reduction, travelling at speeds up to 80 kilometres per hour as it crosses the cooling table and is coiled.

The hot-rolled sheet steel is normally cleaned or pickled in a bath of sulphuric or hydrochloric acid to remove surface oxide (scale) formed during hot rolling. A modern pickler operates continuously. When one coil of steel is almost cleaned, its end is

---

* Adapted from 3rd edition, *Encyclopaedia of Occupational Health and Safety.*

Figure 73.13 • Flow line of hot- and cold-rolled sheet mill products.

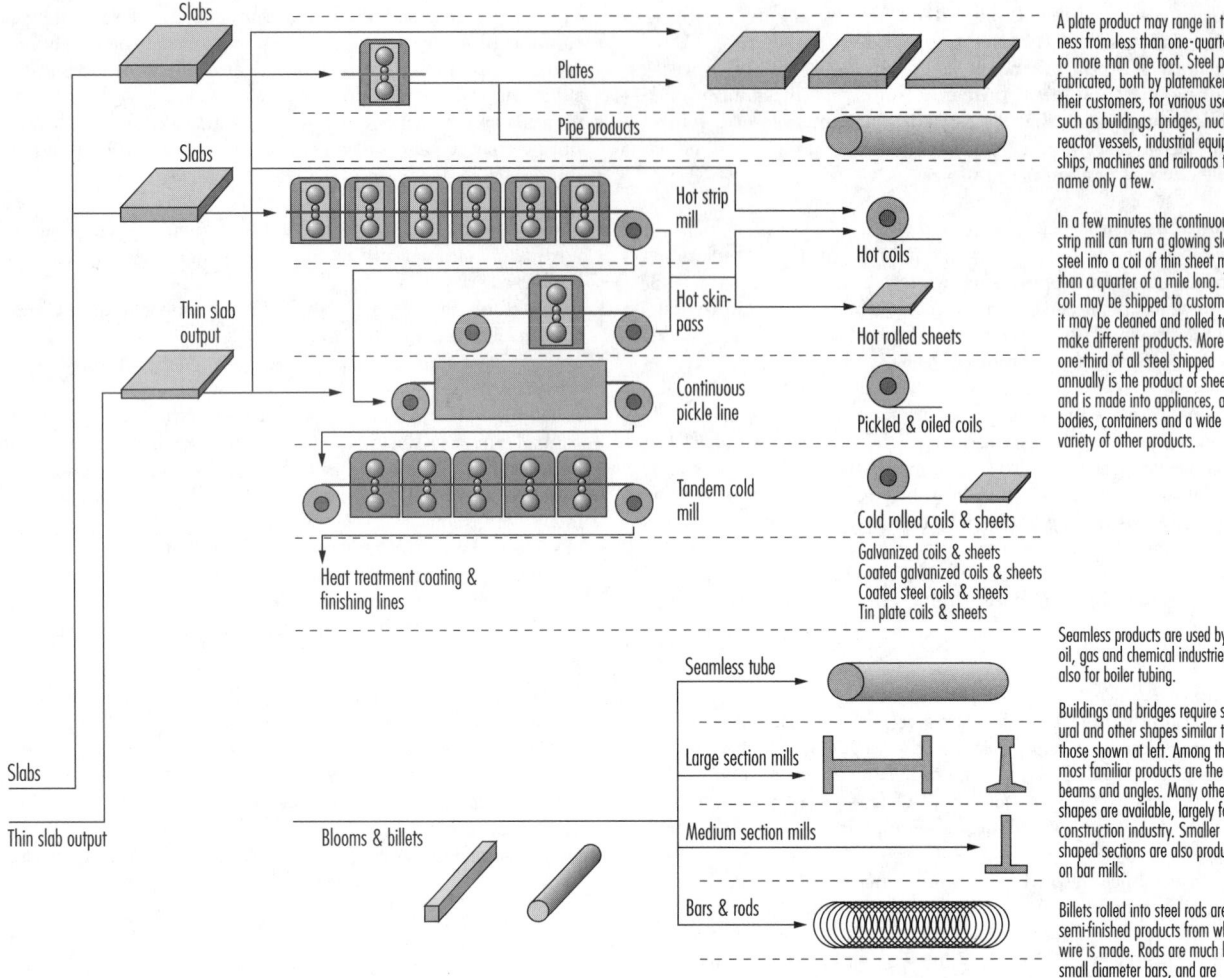

A plate product may range in thickness from less than one-quarter inch to more than one foot. Steel plate is fabricated, both by platemakers and their customers, for various uses such as buildings, bridges, nuclear reactor vessels, industrial equipment, ships, machines and railroads to name only a few.

In a few minutes the continuous hot strip mill can turn a glowing slab of steel into a coil of thin sheet more than a quarter of a mile long. That coil may be shipped to customers, or it may be cleaned and rolled to make different products. More than one-third of all steel shipped annually is the product of sheet mills and is made into appliances, autobodies, containers and a wide variety of other products.

Seamless products are used by the oil, gas and chemical industries and also for boiler tubing.

Buildings and bridges require structural and other shapes similar to those shown at left. Among the most familiar products are the beams and angles. Many other shapes are available, largely for the construction industry. Smaller shaped sections are also produced on bar mills.

Billets rolled into steel rods are the semi-finished products from which wire is made. Rods are much like small diameter bars, and are produced in coils. It has been estimated that there are more than 100,000 uses for wire.

American Iron and Steel Institute

sheared square and welded to the start of a new coil. In the pickler, a temper mill helps break up the scale before the sheet enters the pickling or cleaning section of the line.

An accumulator is located beneath the rubber-lined pickling tanks, the rinsers and the dryers. The sheet accumulated in this system feeds into the pickling tanks when the entry-end of the line is stopped to weld on a new coil. Thus it is possible to clean a sheet continuously at the rate of 360 m (1,200 feet) per minute. A smaller looping system at the delivery end of the line permits continuous line operation during interruptions for coiling.

Cold Rolling

Coils of cleaned, hot-rolled sheet steel may be cold rolled to make a product thinner and smoother. This process gives steel a higher strength-to-weight ratio than can be made on a hot mill. A modern five-stand tandem cold mill may receive a sheet about 1/10 inch (0.25 cm) thick and 3/4 of a mile (1.2 km) long; 2 minutes later that sheet will have been rolled to 0.03 inch (75 mm) thick and be more than 2 miles (3.2 km) long.

The cold-rolling process hardens sheet steel so that it usually must be heated in an annealing furnace to make it more form-

able. Coils of cold-rolled sheets are stacked on a base. Covers are placed over the stacks to control the annealing and then the furnace is lowered over the covered stacks. The heating and re-cooling of sheet steel may take 5 or 6 days.

After the steel has been softened in the annealing process, a temper mill is used to give the steel the desired flatness, metallurgical properties and surface finish. The product may be shipped to consumers as coils or further side-trimmed or sheared into cut lengths.

Hazards and Their Prevention

Accidents. Mechanization has reduced the number of trapping points at machinery but they still exist, especially in cold rolling plants and in finishing departments.

In cold rolling, there is a risk of trapping between the rolls, especially if cleaning in motion is attempted; nips of rolls should be efficiently guarded and strict supervision exercised to prevent cleaning in motion. Severe injuries may be caused by shearing, cropping, trimming and guillotine machines unless the dangerous parts are securely guarded. An effective lockout/tagout programme is essential for maintenance and repair.

Severe injuries may be sustained, especially in hot rolling, if workers attempt to cross roller conveyors at unauthorized points; an adequate number of bridges should be installed and their use enforced. Looping and lashing may cause extensive injuries and burns, even severing of lower limbs; where full mechanization has not eliminated this hazard, protective posts or other devices are necessary.

Special attention should be paid to the hazard of cuts to workers in strip and sheet rolling mills. Such injuries are not only caused by the thin rolled metal, but also by the metal straps used on coils, which may break during handling and constitute a serious hazard.

The use of large quantities of oils, rust inhibitors and so on, which are generally applied by spraying, is another hazard commonly encountered in sheet rolling mills. Despite the protective measures taken to confine the sprayed products, they often collect on the floor and on communication ways, where they may cause slips and falls. Gratings, absorbent materials and boots with non-slip soles should therefore be provided, in addition to regular cleaning of the floor.

Even in automated works, accidents occur in conversion work while changing heavy rollers in the stands. Good planning will often reduce the number of roll changes required; it is important that this work should not be done under pressure of time and that suitable tools be provided.

The automation of modern plants is associated with numerous minor breakdowns, which are often repaired by the crew without stopping the plant or parts of it. In such cases it may happen that it is forgotten to make use of necessary mechanical safeguards, and severe accidents may be the consequence. The fire hazard involved in repairs of hydraulic systems is frequently neglected. Fire protection must be planned and organized with particular care in plants containing hydraulic equipment.

Tongs used to grip hot material may knock together; the square spanners used to move heavy rolled sections by hand may cause serious injuries to the head or upper torso by backlash. All hand tools should be well designed, frequently inspected and well maintained. The tongs used at the mills should have their rivets renewed frequently; ring spanners and impact wrenches should be provided for roll changing crews; bent-out, open-ended spanners should not be used. Workers should receive adequate training in the use of all hand tools. Proper storage arrangements should be made for all hand tools.

Many accidents may be caused by faulty lifting and handling and by defects in cranes and lifting tackle. All cranes and lifting tackle should be under a regular system of examination and inspection; particular care is needed in the storage and use of slings. Crane drivers and slingers should be specially selected and trained. There is always a risk of accidents from mechanical transport: locomotives, wagons and bogies should be well maintained and a well-understood system of warning and signalling should be enforced; clear passage ways should be kept for fork-lifts and other trucks.

Many accidents are caused through falls and stumbles or badly maintained floors, by badly stacked material, by protruding billet ends and cribbing rolls and so on. Hazards can be eliminated by good maintenance of all floor surfaces and means of access, clearly defined walkways, proper stacking of material and regular clearance of debris. Good housekeeping is essential in all parts of the plant including the yards. A good standard of illumination should be kept throughout the plant.

In hot rolling, burns and eye injuries may be caused by flying mill scale; splash guards can effectively reduce the ejection of scale and hot water. Eye injuries may be caused by dust particles or by whipping of cable slings; eyes may also be affected by glare.

Personal protective equipment (PPE) is of great importance in the prevention of rolling mill accidents. Hard hats, safety shoes, gaiters, arm protection, gloves, eye shields and goggles should be worn to meet the appropriate risk. It is essential to secure the cooperation of employees in the use of protective devices and the wearing of protective clothing. Training, as well as an effective accident prevention organization in which workers or their representatives participate, is important.

Heat. Radiant heat levels of up to 1,000 kcal/m^2 have been measured at work points in rolling mills. Heat stress diseases are a concern, but workers in modern mills usually are protected through the use of air-conditioned pulpits. See the article "Iron and steel making" for information on prevention.

Noise. Considerable noise develops in the entire rolling zone from the gearbox of the rolls and straightening machines, from pressure water pumps, from shears and saws, from throwing finished products into a pit and from stopping movements of the material with metal plates. The general level of operating noises can be around 84-90 dBA, and peaks up to 115 dBA or more are not unusual. See the article "Iron and steel making" for information on prevention

Vibration. Cleaning of the finished products with high-speed percussion tools may lead to arthritic changes of the elbows, shoulders, collarbone, distal ulna and radius joint, as well as lesions of the navicular and lunatum bone.

Joint defects in the hand and arm system may be sustained by rolling mill workers, owing to the recoiling and rebounding effect of the material introduced into the gap between the rolls.

Harmful gases and vapours. When lead-alloyed steel is rolled or cutting-off discs containing lead are used, toxic particles may be inhaled. It is therefore necessary constantly to monitor lead concentrations at the workplace, and workers liable to be exposed should regularly undergo medical examination. Lead may also be inhaled by flame scarfers and gas cutters, who may at the same time be exposed to nitrogen oxides (NO_x), chromium, nickel and iron oxide.

Butt welding is associated with the formation of ozone, which may cause, when inhaled, irritation similar to that due to NO_x. Pit-furnace and reheating-furnace attendants may be exposed to harmful gases, the composition of which depends on the fuel used (blast-furnace gas, coke-oven gas, oil) and generally includes carbon monoxide and sulphur dioxide. LEV or respiratory protection may be necessary.

Workers lubricating rolling-mill equipment with oil mist may suffer health impairment due to the oils used and to the additives they contain. When oils or emulsions are used for cooling and lubricating, it should be ensured that the proportions of oil and additives are correct in order to preclude not only irritation of the mucosae but also acute dermatitis in exposed workers. See the article "Industrial lubricants, metal working fluids and automotive oils" in the chapter *Metal processing and metal working industry*.

Large amounts of degreasing agents are used for the finishing operations. These agents evaporate and may be inhaled; their action is not only toxic, but also causes deterioration of the skin, which may be degreased when solvents are not handled properly. LEV should be provided and gloves should be worn.

Acids. Strong acids in pickling shops are corrosive to skin and mucous membranes. Appropriate LEV and PPE should be used.

Ionizing radiation. X rays and other ionizing radiation equipment may be used for gauging and examining; strict precautions in accordance with local regulations are required.

Acknowledgements: The description of hot- and cold-rolling mill operations is used with permission of the American Iron and Steel Institute.

HEALTH AND SAFETY PROBLEMS AND PATTERNS*

The iron and steel industry is a "heavy industry": in addition to the safety hazards inherent in giant plants, massive equipment and movement of large masses of materials, workers are exposed to the heat of molten metal and slag at temperatures up to 1,800 °C, toxic or corrosive substances, respirable air-borne contaminants and noise. Spurred by trade unions, economic pressures for greater efficiency and governmental regulations, the industry has made great strides in the introduction of newer equipment and improved processes which afford greater safety and better control of physical and chemical hazards. Workplace fatalities and lost-time accidents have been significantly reduced, but are still a significant problem (ILO 1992). Steel making remains a dangerous trade in which the potential hazards cannot always be designed out. Accordingly, this presents a formidable challenge to everyday plant management. It calls for ongoing research, continuous monitoring, responsible supervision and updated education and training of workers on all levels.

Physical Hazards

Ergonomic problems

Musculoskeletal injuries are common in steel making. Despite the introduction of mechanization and assistive devices, manual handling of large, bulky and/or heavy objects remains a frequent necessity. Constant attention to housekeeping is necessary to reduce the number of slips and falls. Furnace bricklayers have been shown to be at highest risk of work-related upper arm and low back problems. The introduction of ergonomics into the design of equipment and controls (e.g., crane drivers' cabs) based on study of the physical and mental requirements of the job, coupled with such innovations as job rotation and team working, are recent developments aimed at enhancing the safety, well-being and performance of steel workers.

Noise

Steel making is one of the noisiest industries, although hearing conservation programs are decreasing the risk of hearing loss. The major sources include fume extraction systems, vacuum systems using steam ejectors, electrical transformers and the arc process in electrical arc furnaces, rolling mills and the large fans used for ventilation. At least half of noise-exposed workers will be handicapped by noise-induced hearing loss after as little as 10 or 15 years on the job. Hearing conservation programmes, described in detail elsewhere in this *Encyclopaedia*, include periodic noise and hearing assessments, noise control engineering and maintenance of machines and equipment, personal protection, and worker education and training

Causes of hearing loss other than noise include burns to the eardrum from particles of slag, scale or molten metal, perforation of the drum from intense impulse noise and trauma from falling or moving objects. A survey of compensation claims filed by Canadian steelworkers revealed that half of those with occupational hearing loss also had tinnitus (McShane, Hyde and Alberti 1988).

Vibration

Potentially hazardous vibration is created by oscillating mechanical movements, most often when machine movements have not been balanced, when operating shop floor machines and when using such portable tools as pneumatic drills and hammers, saws and grindstones. Damage to vertebral discs, low back pain and degeneration of the spine have been attributed to whole body vibration in a number of studies of overhead crane operators (Pauline et al. 1988).

Whole body vibration can cause a variety of symptoms (e.g., motion sickness, blurring and loss of visual acuity) which may lead to accidents. Hand-arm vibration has been associated with carpal tunnel syndrome, degenerative joint changes and Reynaud's phenomenon in the finger tips ("white finger disease"), which may cause permanent disability. A study of chippers and grinders showed that they were more than twice as likely to develop Dupuytren's contracture than a comparison group of workers (Thomas and Clarke 1992).

Heat exposure

Heat exposure is a problem throughout the iron and steel industry, especially in plants located in hot climates. Recent research has shown that, contrary to previous belief, the highest exposures occur during forging, when workers are monitoring hot steel continuously, rather than during melting, when, although temperatures are higher, they are intermittent and their effects are limited by the intense heating of the exposed skin and by the use of eye protection (Lydahl and Philipson 1984). The danger of heat stress is reduced by adequate fluid intake, adequate ventilation, the use of heat shields and protective clothing, and periodic breaks for rest or work at a cooler task.

Lasers

Lasers have a wide range of applications in steel making and may cause retinal damage at power levels far below those required to have effects on the skin. Laser operators can be protected by sharp focus of the beam and the use of protective goggles, but other workers may be injured when they unknowingly step into the beam or when it is inadvertently reflected at them.

Radioactive nuclides

Radioactive nuclides are employed in many measuring devices. Exposures can usually be controlled by posting of warning signs and appropriate shielding. Much more dangerous, however, is the accidental or careless inclusion of radioactive materials in the scrap steel being recycled. To prevent this, many plants are using sensitive radiation detectors to monitor all scrap before it is introduced into the processing.

Airborne Pollutants

Steel workers may be exposed to a wide range of pollutants depending on the particular process, the materials involved and the effectiveness of monitoring and control measures. Adverse effects are determined by the physical state and propensities of the pollutant involved, the intensity and duration of the exposure, the extent of accumulation in the body and the sensitivity of the individual to its effects. Some effects are immediate while others may take years and even decades to develop. Changes in processes and equipment, along with improvement of measures to keep exposures below toxic levels, have reduced the risks to the workers. However, these have also introduced new combinations of pollutants and there is always the danger of accidents, fires and explosions.

Dust and fumes

Emissions of fumes and particulates are a major potential problem for employees working with molten metals, making and handling coke, and charging and tapping furnaces. They are also troublesome to workers assigned to equipment maintenance, duct

---

* Adapted in part from an unpublished article by Simon Pickvance.

cleaning and refractory wrecking operations. Health effects are related to the size of the particles (i.e., the proportion that are respirable) and the metals and aerosols that may be adsorbed on their surfaces. There is evidence that exposure to irritant dust and fumes may also make steelworkers more susceptible to reversible narrowing of the airways (asthma) which, over time, may become permanent (Johnson et al. 1985).

Silica

Exposures to silica, with resultant silicosis, once quite common among workers in such jobs as furnace maintenance in melting shops and blast furnaces, have been lowered through the use of other materials for furnace linings as well as automation, which has reduced the number of workers in these processes.

Asbestos

Asbestos, once used extensively for thermal and noise insulation, is now encountered only in maintenance and construction activities when formerly installed asbestos materials are disturbed and generate airborne fibres. The long term effects of asbestos exposure, described in detail in other sections of this *Encyclopaedia*, include asbestosis, mesothelioma and other cancers. A recent cross-sectional study found pleural pathology in 20 out of 900 steelworkers (2%), much of which was diagnosed as restrictive lung disease characteristic of asbestosis (Kronenberg et al. 1991).

Heavy metals

Emissions generated in steel making may contain heavy metals (e.g., lead, chromium, zinc, nickel and manganese) in the form of fumes, particulates, and adsorbates on inert dust particles. They are often present in scrap steel streams and are also introduced in the manufacture of special types of steel products. Research carried out on workers melting manganese alloys has shown impaired physical and mental performance and other symptoms of manganism at exposure levels significantly below the limits currently allowable in most countries (Wennberg et al. 1991). Short-term exposure to high levels of zinc and other vaporized metals may cause "metal fume fever", which is characterized by fever, chills, nausea, respiratory difficulty and fatigue. Details of the other toxic effects produced by heavy metals are found elsewhere in this *Encyclopaedia*.

Acid mists

Acid mists from pickling areas can cause skin, eye and respiratory irritation. Exposure to hydrochloric and sulphuric acid mists from pickling baths have also been associated in one study with a nearly twofold increase in laryngeal cancer (Steenland et al. 1988).

Sulphur compounds

The predominant source of sulphur emissions in steel making is the use of high-sulphur fossil fuels and blast furnace slag. Hydrogen sulphide has a characteristic unpleasant odour and short-term effects of relatively low-level exposures include dryness and irritation of nasal passages and the upper respiratory tract, coughing, shortness of breath and pneumonia. Longer exposures to low levels may cause eye irritation, while permanent eye damage may be produced by higher levels of exposure. At higher levels, there may also be a temporary loss of smell which can delude workers into believing that they are no longer being exposed.

Oil mists

Oil mists generated in the cold rolling of steel can produce irritation of skin, mucous membranes and upper respiratory tract, nausea, vomiting and headache. One study reported cases of

lipoid pneumonia in rolling mill workers who had longer exposures (Cullen et al. 1981).

Polycyclic aromatic hydrocarbons

PAHs are produced in most combustion processes; in steelworks, coke making is the major source. When coal is partially burnt to produce coke, a large number of volatile compounds are distilled off as coal tar pitch volatiles, including PAHs. These may be present as vapours, aerosols or adsorbates on fine particulates. Short-term exposures may cause irritation of the skin and mucous membranes, dizziness, headache and nausea, while long-term exposure has been associated with carcinogenesis. Studies have shown that coke-oven workers have a lung cancer mortality rate twice that of the general population. Those most exposed to coal tar pitch volatiles are at the highest risk. These included workers on the oven topside and workers with the longest period of exposure (IARC 1984; Constantino, Redmond and Bearden 1995). Engineering controls have reduced the numbers of workers at risk in some countries.

Other chemicals

Over 1,000 chemicals are used or encountered in steel making: as raw materials or as contaminants in scrap and/or in fuels; as additives in special processes; as refractories; and as hydraulic fluids and solvents used in plant operation and maintenance. Coke making produces by-products such as tar, benzene and ammonia; others are generated in the different steel-making processes. All may potentially be toxic, depending on the nature of the chemicals, the type, the level and duration of the exposures, their reactivity with other chemicals and the susceptibility of the exposed worker. Accidental heavy exposures to fumes containing sulphur dioxide and nitrogen oxides have caused cases of chemical pneumonitis. Vanadium and other alloy additions may cause chemical pneumonitis. Carbon monoxide, which is released in all combustion processes, can be hazardous when maintenance of equipment and its controls are substandard. Benzene, along with toluene and xylene, is present in coke-oven gas and causes respiratory and central nervous system symptoms on acute exposure; long-term exposures may lead to bone marrow damage, aplastic anaemia and leukaemia.

Stress

High levels of work stress are found in the steel industry. Exposures to radiant heat and noise are compounded by the need for constant vigilance to avoid accidents and potentially hazardous exposures. Since many processes are in continuous operation, shift work is a necessity; its impact on well-being and on workers' essential social support are detailed elsewhere in this *Encyclopaedia*. Finally, there is the potent stressor of potential job loss resulting from automation and changes in processes, plant relocation and downsizing of the workforce.

Preventive Programmes

Protecting steel workers against potential toxicity requires allocation of adequate resources for a continuing, comprehensive and coordinated programme that should include the following elements:

- assessment of all raw materials and fuels and, when possible, substitution of safer products for those known to be hazardous
- effective controls for the storage and safe handling of raw materials, products, by-products and wastes
- continuous monitoring of workers' personal occupational environment and ambient air quality, with biological monitoring when required, and periodic medical surveillance of workers to detect more subtle health effects and verify fitness for their jobs

- engineering systems to control potential exposures (e.g., equipment enclosures and adequate exhaust and ventilation systems) supplemented by personal protective equipment (e.g., shields, gloves, safety glasses and goggles, hearing protectors, respirators, foot and body protection, etc.) when engineering controls do not suffice

- application of ergonomic principles to design of equipment, machine controls and tools and analysis of job structure and content as a guide to interventions that may prevent injury and enhance workers' well-being

- maintenance of readily available, up-to-date information about potential hazards, which must be disseminated among workers and supervisors as part of an ongoing worker education and training programme

- installation and maintenance of systems for the storage and retrieval of the voluminous health and safety data, as well as for the analysis and reporting of records of inspection findings, accidents and worker injury and disease.

● ENVIRONMENTAL AND PUBLIC HEALTH ISSUES*

Because of the sheer volume and complexity of its operations and its extensive use of energy and raw materials, the iron and steel industry, like other "heavy" industries, has the potential of having a significant impact on the environment and the population of nearby communities. Figure 73.14 summarizes the pollutants and wastes generated by its major production processes. They comprise three primary categories: air pollutants, waste water contaminants and solid wastes.

Historically, investigations of the public health impact of the iron and steel industry have concentrated on the localized effects in the densely populated local areas in which steel production has been concentrated and particularly in specific regions where acute air pollution episodes have been experienced, such as the Donora and Meuse valleys, and the triangle between Poland, the former Czechoslovakia and the former German Democratic Republic (WHO 1992).

Air Pollutants

Air pollutants from iron- and steel-making operations have historically been an environmental concern. These pollutants include gaseous substances such as oxides of sulphur, nitrogen dioxide and carbon monoxide. In addition, particulates such as soot and dust, which may contain iron oxides, have been the focus of controls. Emissions from coke ovens and from coke oven by-product plants have been a concern, but the continuous improvements in the technology of steel-making and of emissions control during the past two decades, coupled with more stringent government regulations, have significantly reduced such emissions in North America, Western Europe and Japan. Total pollution control costs, over half of which relate to air emissions, have been estimated to range from 1 to 3% of total production costs; air-pollution control installations have represented approximately 10 to 20% of total plant investments. Such costs create a barrier to the global application of state-of-the-art controls in developing countries and for older, economically marginal enterprises.

* Adapted from UNEP and IISI 1997 and an unpublished article by Jerry Spiegel.

Air pollutants vary with the particular process, the engineering and construction of the plant, the raw materials employed, the sources and amounts of the energy required, the extent to which waste products are recycled into the process and the efficiency of the pollution controls. For example, the introduction of basic-oxygen steel making has permitted the collection and recycling of waste gases in a controlled manner, reducing the amounts to be exhausted, while the use of the continuous-casting process has reduced the consumption of energy, resulting in a reduction of emissions. This has increased product yield and improved quality.

Sulphur dioxide

The amount of sulphur dioxide, formed largely in the combustion processes, depends primarily on the sulphur content of the fossil fuel employed. Both coke and coke-oven gas used as fuels are major sources of sulphur dioxide. In the atmosphere, sulphur dioxide may react with oxygen radicals and water to form a sulphuric acid aerosol and, in combination with ammonia, may form an ammonium sulphate aerosol. The health effects attributed to sulphur oxides are not only due to the sulphur dioxide but also to its tendency to form such respirable aerosols. In addition, sulphur dioxide may be adsorbed onto particulates, many of which are in the respirable range. Such potential exposures may be reduced not only by use of fuels with low sulphur content but also by reduction of the concentration of the particulates. The increased use of electric furnaces has decreased the emission of sulphur oxides by eliminating the need for coke, but this has passed on this pollution control burden to the plants generating electricity. Desulphurization of coke-oven gas is achieved by the removal of reduced sulphur compounds, primarily hydrogen sulphide, prior to combustion.

Nitrogen oxides

Like the sulphur oxides, oxides of nitrogen, primarily nitrogen oxide and nitrogen dioxide, are formed in fuel combustion processes. They react with oxygen and volatile organic compounds (VOCs) in the presence of ultraviolet (UV) radiation to form ozone. They also combine with water to form nitric acid, which, in turn, combines with ammonia to form ammonium nitrate. These may also form respirable aerosols which can be removed from the atmosphere through wet or dry deposition.

Particulate matter

Particulate matter, the most visible form of pollution, is a varying, complex mixture of organic and inorganic materials. Dust may be blown from stockpiles of iron ore, coal, coke and limestone or it may enter the air during their loading and transport. Coarse materials generate dust when they are rubbed together or crushed under vehicles. Fine particles are generated in the sintering, smelting and melting processes, particularly when molten iron comes in contact with air to form iron oxide. Coke ovens produce fine coal coke and tar emissions. Potential health effects depend on the number of particles in the respirable range, the chemical composition of the dust and the duration and concentration of exposure.

Sharp reductions in the levels of particulate pollution have been achieved. For example, by using electrostatic precipitators to clean dry waste gases in oxygen steel making, one German steel works decreased the level of emitted dust from 9.3 kg/t of crude steel in 1960 to 5.3 kg/t in 1975 and to somewhat less than 1 kg/t by 1990. The cost, however, was a marked rise in energy consumption. Other methods of particulate pollution control include the use of wet scrubbers, bag houses and cyclones (which are effective only against large particles).

Figure 73.14 • Flow chart of pollutants and wastes generated by different processes.

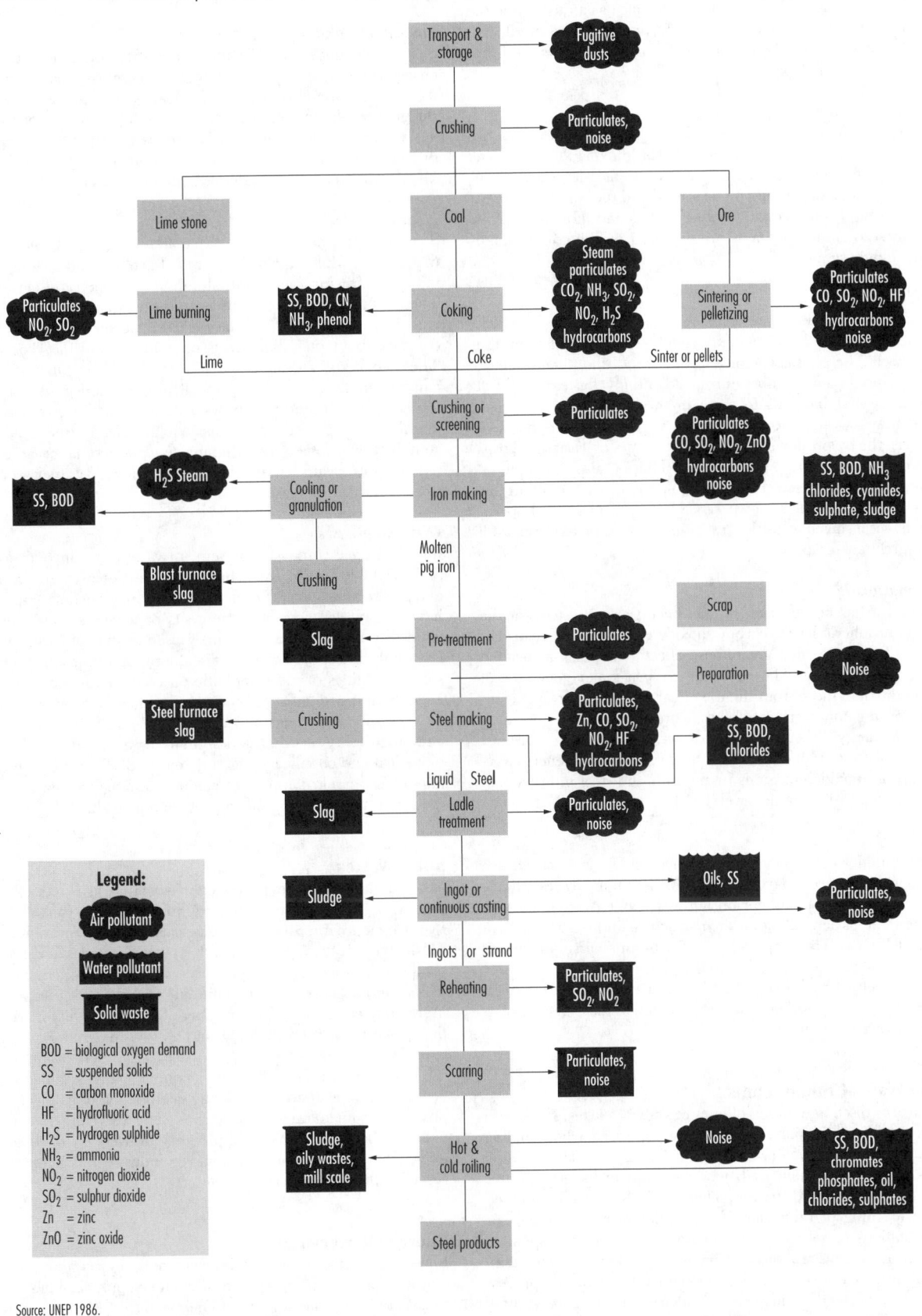

Source: UNEP 1986.

Heavy metals

Metals such as cadmium, lead, zinc, mercury, manganese, nickel and chromium can be emitted from a furnace as a dust, fume or vapour or they may be adsorbed by particulates. Health effects, which are described elsewhere in this *Encyclopaedia*, depend on the level and duration of exposure.

Organic emissions

Organic emissions from primary steel operations may include benzene, toluene, xylene, solvents, PAHs, dioxins and phenols. The scrap steel used as raw material may include a variety of these substances, depending on its source and the way it was used (e.g., paint and other coatings, other metals and lubricants). Not all of these organic pollutants are captured by the conventional gas cleaning systems.

Radioactivity

In recent years, there have been reports of instances in which radioactive materials have inadvertently been included in the scrap steel. The physicochemical properties of the nuclides (e.g., melting and boiling temperatures and affinity for oxygen) will determine what happens to them in the steel making process. There may be an amount sufficient to contaminate the steel products, the by-products and the various types of wastes and thus require a costly clean-up and disposal. There is also the potential contamination of the steel-making equipment, with resultant potential exposure of the steel workers. However, many steel operations have installed sensitive radiation detectors to screen all purchased steel scrap.

Carbon dioxide

Although it has no effect on human health or ecosystems at the usual atmospheric levels, carbon dioxide is important because of its contribution to the "greenhouse effect", which is associated with global warming. The steel industry is a major generator of carbon dioxide, more from the use of carbon as a reducing agent in the production of iron from iron ore than from its use as a source of energy. By 1990, through a variety of measures for blast furnace coke rate reduction, waste-heat recovery and energy saving, carbon dioxide emissions by the iron and steel industry had been reduced to 47% of the levels in 1960.

Ozone

Ozone, a major constituent of atmospheric smog near the surface of the earth, is a secondary pollutant formed in air by the photochemical reaction of sunlight on nitrogen oxides, facilitated to a varying degree, depending on their structure and reactivity, by a range of VOCs. The major source of ozone precursors is motor vehicle exhausts, but some are also generated by iron and steel plants as well as by other industries. As a result of atmospheric and topographic conditions, the ozone reaction may take place at great distances from their source.

Waste Water Contaminants

Steel works discharge large volumes of water to lakes, rivers and streams, with additional volumes being vaporized while cooling coke or steel. Waste water retained in unsealed or leaking holding ponds can seep through and may contaminate the local water table and underground streams. These may also be contaminated by the leaching of rainwater through piles of raw materials or accumulations of solid wastes. Contaminants include suspended solids, heavy metals and oils and greases. Temperature changes in natural waters due to discharge of higher temperature process water (70% of steel-making process water is used for cooling) may affect the ecosystems of these waters. Consequently, cooling treat-

ment prior to discharge is essential and can be achieved through application of available technology.

Suspended solids

Suspended solids (SS) are the main waterborne pollutants discharged during steel production. They comprise mainly iron oxides from scale formation during processing; coal, biological sludge, metallic hydroxides and other solids may also be present. These are largely non-toxic in aqueous environments at normal discharge levels. Their presence at higher levels may lead to discolouration of streams, de-oxygenation and silting.

Heavy metals

Steel-making process water may contain high levels of zinc and manganese, while discharges from cold-rolling and coatings areas may contain zinc, cadmium, aluminium, copper and chromium. These metals are naturally present in the aquatic environment; it is their presence at higher than usual concentrations that creates concern about potential effects on humans and the ecosystems. These concerns are increased by the fact that, unlike many organic pollutants, these heavy metals do not biodegrade to harmless end products and may become concentrated in sediments and in the tissues of fish and other aquatic life. Further, by being combined with other contaminants (e.g., ammonia, organic compounds, oils, cyanides, alkalis, solvents and acids), their potential toxicity may be increased.

Oils and greases

Oils and greases may be present in waste water in both soluble and insoluble forms. Most heavy oils and greases are insoluble and are relatively easily removed. They may become emulsified, however, by contact with detergents or alkalis or by being agitated. Emulsified oils are routinely used as part of the process in cold mills. Except for causing discolouration of the water surface, small quantities of most aliphatic oil compounds are innocuous. Monohydric aromatic oil compounds, however, may be toxic. Further, oil components may contain such toxicants as PCBs, lead and other heavy metals. In addition to the question of toxicity, the biological and chemical oxygen demand (BOD and COD) of oils and other organic compounds can decrease the oxygen content of the water, thus affecting the viability of aquatic life.

Solid Wastes

Much of the solid waste produced in steel making is reusable. The process of producing coke, for example, gives rise to coal derivatives which are important raw materials for the chemical industry. Many by-products (e.g., coke dust) can be fed back into the production processes. Slag produced when the impurities present in coal and iron ore melt and combine with the lime used as a flux in smelting can be used in a number of ways: land fill for reclamation projects, in road building and as raw material for sintering plants that supply blast furnaces. Steel, regardless of grade, size, use or length of time in service, is completely recyclable and can be recycled repeatedly without any degradation of its mechanical, physical or metallurgical properties. The recycling rate is estimated to be 90%. Table 73.2 presents an overview of the degree to which the Japanese steel making industry has achieved the recycling of waste materials.

Energy Conservation

Energy conservation is desirable not only for economic reasons but also for reducing pollution at energy-supply facilities such as electric utilities. The amount of energy consumed in steel production varies widely with the processes used and the mix of scrap

Table 73.2 • Waste generated and recycled in steel production in Japan.

	Generation (A) (1,000 tonnes)	Landfill (B) (1,000 tonnes)	Re-use (A–B/A) %
Slag			
Blast furnaces	24,717	712	97.1
Basic oxygen furnaces	9,236	1,663	82.0
Electric arc furnaces	2,203	753	65.8
Sub-total	36,156	3,128	91.3
Dust	4,763	238	95.0
Sludge	519	204	60.7
Waste oil	81		
Total	41,519	3,570	91.4

Source: IISI 1992.

metal and iron ore in the feed material. The energy intensity of United States scrap-based plants in 1988 averaged 21.1 gigajoules per tonne while the Japanese plants consumed about 25% less. A model International Iron and Steel Institute (IISI) scrap-based plant required only 10.1 gigajoules per tonne (IISI 1992).

Increases in the cost of energy have stimulated development of energy- and materials-saving technologies. Low-energy gases, such as by-product gases produced in the blast-furnace and coke-oven processes, are recovered, cleaned and used as a fuel. Consumption of coke and auxiliary fuel by the German steel industry, which averaged 830 kg/tonne in 1960, was reduced to 510 kg/tonne in 1990. The Japanese steel industry was able to reduce its share of total Japanese energy consumption from 20.5% in 1973 to about 7% in 1988. The United States steel industry has made major investments in energy conservation. The average mill has reduced energy consumption by 45% since 1975 through process modification, new technology and restructuring (carbon dioxide emissions have fallen proportionately).

Facing the Future

Traditionally, governments, trade associations and individual industries have approached environmental concerns on a media-specific basis, dealing separately, for example, with air, water and waste disposal problems. While useful, this has sometimes merely shifted the problem from one environmental area to another, as in the case of costly waste water treatment which leaves the subsequent problem of disposing of the treatment sludge, which can also cause serious ground water pollution.

In recent years, however, the international steel industry has addressed this problem through Integrated Pollution Control, which has further developed into Total Environmental Risk Management, a programme that looks at all impacts simultaneously and addresses the priority areas systematically. A second development of equal importance has been a focus on preventive rather than remedial action. This addresses such issues as plant siting, site preparation, plant layout and equipment, specification of day-to-day management responsibilities, and the assurance of adequate staff and resources to monitor compliance with environmental regulations and report the results to appropriate authorities.

The Industry and Environment Centre, established in 1975 by the United Nations Environment Programme (UNEP), aims to encourage cooperation between the industries and governments in order to promote environmentally sound industrial development. Its goals include:

- encouragement of the incorporation of environmental criteria in industrial development plans
- facilitation of the implementation of procedures and principles for the protection of the environment
- promotion of the use of safe and clean techniques
- stimulation of the exchange of information and experience throughout the world.

The UNEP works closely with the IISI, the first international industry association devoted to a single industry. The IISI's members include publicly- and privately-owned steel-producing companies and national and regional steel industry associations, federations and research institutes in the 51 countries which, together, account for over 70% of the total world steel production. IISI, often in concert with UNEP, produces statements of environmental policy and principles and technical reports such as the one on which much of this article has been based (UNEP and IISI 1997). Together, they are working to address the economic, social, moral, personal, management and technological factors that influence compliance with environmental principles, policies and regulations.

References

Constantino, JP, CK Redmond, and A Bearden. 1995. Occupationally related cancer risk among coke oven workers: 30 years of follow-up. *J Occup Env Med* 37:597–603.

Cullen, MR, JR Balmes, JM Robins, and GJ Walker Smith. 1981. Lipoid pneumonia caused by oil mist exposure from a steel rolling tandem mill. *Am J Ind Med* 2:51–58.

International Agency for Research on Cancer (IARC). 1984. Monographs 1984. 34:101–131.

International Iron and Steel Institute (IISI). 1992. *Environmental Control in the Steel Industry*. Papers prepared for the 1991 ENCOSTEEL World Conference, Brussels.

International Labour Organization (ILO). 1992. *Recent Developments in the Iron and Steel Industry*. Report 1. Geneva: ILO.

Johnson, A, CY Moira, L MacLean, E Atkins, A Dybuncio, F Cheng, and D Enarson. 1985. Respiratory abnormalities amongst workers in iron and steel industry. *Br J Ind Med* 42:94–100.

Kronenberg, RS, JC Levin, RF Dodson, JGN Garcia, and DE Grifith. 1991. Asbestos-related disease in employees of a steel mill and a glass bottle manufacturing plant. *Ann NY Acad Sci* 643:397–403.

Lydahl, E and B Philipson. 1984. Infrared radiation and cataract. 1. Epidemiologic investigation of iron and steel workers. *Acta Ophthalmol* 62:961–975.

McShane, DP, ML Hyde, and PW Alberti. 1988. Tinnitus prevalence in industrial hearing loss compensation claimants. *Clinical Otolaryngology* 13:323–330.

Pauline, MB, CB Hendriek, TJH Carel, and PK Agaath. 1988. Back disorders in crane operators exposed to whole body vibration. *Int Arch Occup Environ Health* 1988:129-137.

Steenland, K, T Schnoor, J Beaumont, W Halperin, and T Bloom. 1988. Incidence of laryngeal cancer and exposure to acid mists. *Br J Ind Med* 45:766–776.

Thomas, PR and D Clarke. 1992. Vibration, White Finger and Dupuytren's Contracture: Are they related? *Occup Med* 42(3):155–158.

United Nations Environment Programme (UNEP). 1986. *Guidelines for Environmental Management of Iron and Steel Works*. Paris: UNEP.

United Nations Environment Programme (UNEP) and Steel Institute (IISI). 1997. *Steel Industry and the Environment: Technical and Management Issues*. Technical Report No. 38. Paris and Brussels: UNEP and IISI.

Wennberg, A, A Iregren, G Strich, G Cizinsky, M Hagman, and L Johansson. Manganese exposure in steel smelters, a health hazard to the nervous system. *Scand J Work Environ Health* 17: 255–62.

World Health Organization (WHO) Commission on Health. 1992. *Report of the Panel on Industry and Health*. Geneva: WHO.

Other relevant readings

American Iron and Steel Institute (AISI). 1995. *Steel Processing Flow Lines*. Washington: AISI.

Dasgupta, AK. 1989. Photodermatitis and photo-aggravated dermatitis in an Indian steel plant. *Contact Dermat* 21:118–119.

Finkelstein, MN and N Wilk. 1990. Investigation of a lung cancer cluster in the melt shop of an Ontario steel producer. *Am J Ind Med* 17:483–491.

Fletcher, AC and A Ades. 1984. Lung cancer mortality in a cohort of English foundary workers. *Scan J Work Environ Health* 10:7-16.

International Iron and Steel Institute (IISI). 1997. *Steel for Sustainable Development*. Brussels: IISI.

Kusiak, R, GM Liss and MM Galitis. 1993. Cor pulmonale and pneumoconiotic lung disease: An investigation using hospital discharge data. *Am J Ind Med* 24:161–173.

Moinov, S. 1995. Falling employment, the trend in steel. *MBM* April 1995:40–45.

Muldoon, SR and DJ Tollerud. 1996. Industries associated with respiratory disease: Foundaries and Steel making. In *Occupational and Environmental Respiratory Disease*, edited by P Harber, MB Schenker, and JR Balmes. St. Louis, MO: Mosby.

Office of Population Censuses and Surveys. 1995. *Occupational Health: Decennial Supplement*. Series DS No. 10. London: Her Majesty's Stationery Office.

Porcq, F. 1977. Storage and handling of coils in the metal trades (Le stockage et la manutention des bo-bines dans les entreprises métallurgiques). *Prevention et securite du travail (Lille)* 114:29–38.

Radford, EP. 1976. Cancer mortality in the steel industry. *Ann NY Acad Sci* 271:228–238.

Rochette, HE and CK Redmond. 1985. Selection, follow-up and analysis in the coke oven study. *National Cancer Institute Monographs* 67:89–94.

Schnauber, H and U Kern. 1980. *Ergonomic Design of Tongs for Rotating Billets* (Ergonomische und sicherheitstechnische Optimierung von Kantwerkzeugen). Dortmund: Bundesanstalt für Arbeitsschutz und Unfallforschung.

Chapter Editors
James R. Armstrong and Raji Menon

74

Contents

● MINING: AN OVERVIEW

Norman S. Jennings

Minerals and mineral products are the backbone of most industries. Some form of mining or quarrying is carried out in virtually every country in the world. Mining has important economic, environmental, labour and social effects—both in the countries or regions where it is carried out and beyond. For many developing countries mining accounts for a significant proportion of GDP and, often, for the bulk of foreign exchange earnings and foreign investment.

The environmental impact of mining can be significant and long-lasting. There are many examples of good and bad practice in the management and rehabilitation of mined areas. The environmental effect of the use of minerals is becoming an important issue for the industry and its workforce. The debate on global warming, for example, could affect the use of coal in some areas; recycling lessens the amount of new material required; and the increasing use of non-mineral materials, such as plastics, affects the intensity of use of metals and minerals per unit of GDP.

Competition, declining mineral grades, higher treatment costs, privatization and restructuring are each putting pressure on mining companies to reduce their costs and increase their productivity. The high capital intensity of much of the mining industry encourages mining companies to seek the maximum use of their equipment, calling in turn for more flexible and often more intensive work patterns. Employment is falling in many mining areas due to increased productivity, radical restructuring and privatization. These changes not only affect mineworkers who must find alternative employment; those remaining in the industry are required to have more skills and more flexibility. Finding the balance between the desire of mining companies to cut costs and those of workers to safeguard their jobs has been a key issue throughout the world of mining. Mining communities must also adapt to new mining operations, as well as to downsizing or closure.

Mining is often considered to be a special industry involving close-knit communities and workers doing a dirty, dangerous job. Mining is also a sector where many at the top—managers and employers—are former miners or mining engineers with wide, first-hand experience of the issues that affect their enterprises and workforces. Moreover, mineworkers have often been the elite of industrial workers and have frequently been at the forefront when political and social changes have taken place faster than was envisaged by the government of the day.

About 23 billion tonnes of minerals, including coal, are produced each year. For high-value minerals, the quantity of waste produced is many times that of the final product. For example, each ounce of gold is the result of dealing with about 12 tonnes of ore; each tonne of copper comes from about 30 tonnes of ore. For lower value materials (e.g., sand, gravel and clay)—which account for the bulk of the material mined—the amount of waste material that can be tolerated is minimal. It is safe to assume, however, that the world's mines must produce at least twice the final amount required (excluding the removal of surface "overburden", which is subsequently replaced and therefore handled twice). Globally, therefore, some 50 billion tonnes of ore are mined each year. This is the equivalent of digging a 1.5 metre deep hole the size of Switzerland every year.

Employment

Mining is not a major employer. It accounts for about 1% of the world's workforce—some 30 million people, 10 million of whom produce coal. However, for every mining job there is at least one job that is directly dependent on mining. In addition, it is estimated that at least 6 million people not included in the above figure work in small-scale mines. When one takes dependants into account, the number of people relying on mining for a living is likely to be about 300 million.

Safety and Health

Mineworkers face a constantly changing combination of workplace circumstances, both daily and throughout the work shift. Some work in an atmosphere without natural light or ventilation, creating voids in the earth by removing material and trying to ensure that there will be no immediate reaction from the surrounding strata. Despite the considerable efforts in many countries, the toll of death, injury and disease among the world's mineworkers means that, in most countries, mining remains the most hazardous occupation when the number of people exposed to risk is taken into account.

Although only accounting for 1% of the global workforce, mining is responsible for about 8% of fatal accidents at work (around 15,000 per year). No reliable data exist as far as injuries are concerned, but they are significant, as is the number of workers affected by occupational diseases (such as pneumoconioses, hearing loss and the effects of vibration) whose premature disability and even death can be directly attributed to their work.

The ILO and Mining

The International Labour Organization (ILO) has been dealing with labour and social problems of the mining industry since its early days, making considerable efforts to improve work and life of those in the mining industry—from the adoption of the Hours of Work (Coal Mines) Convention (No. 31) in 1931 to the Safety and Health in Mines Convention (No. 176), which was adopted by the International Labour Conference in 1995. For 50 years tripartite meetings on mining have addressed a variety of issues ranging from employment, working conditions and training to occupational safety and health and industrial relations. The results are over 140 agreed conclusions and resolutions, some of which have been used at the national level; others have triggered ILO action—including a variety of training and assistance programmes in member States. Some have led to the development of codes of safety practice and, most recently, to the new labour standard.

In 1996 a new system of shorter, more focused tripartite meetings was introduced, in which topical mining issues will be identified and discussed in order to address the issues in a practical way in the countries and regions concerned, at the national level and by the ILO. The first of these, in 1999, will deal with social and labour issues of small-scale mining.

Labour and social issues in mining cannot be separated from other considerations, whether they be economic, political, technical or environmental. While there can be no model approach to ensuring that the mining industry develops in a way that benefits all those involved, there is clearly a need that it should do so. The ILO is doing what it can to assist in the labour and social development of this vital industry. But it cannot work alone; it must have the active involvement of the social partners in order to maximize its impact. The ILO also works closely with other international organizations, bringing the social and labour dimension of mining to their attention and collaborating with them as appropriate.

Because of the hazardous nature of mining, the ILO has been always deeply concerned with the improvement of occupational safety and health. The ILO's International Classification of Radiographs of Pneumoconioses is an internationally recognized tool for recording systematically radiographic abnormalities in the chest provoked by the inhalation of dusts. Two codes of practice on safety and health deal exclusively with underground and surface mines; others are relevant to the mining industry.

The adoption of the Convention on Safety and Health in Mines in 1995, which has set the principle for national action on the improvement of working conditions in the mining industry, is important because:

- Special hazards are faced by mineworkers.
- The mining industry in many countries is assuming increasing importance.
- Earlier ILO standards on occupational safety and health, as well as the existing legislation in many countries, are inadequate to deal with the specific needs of mining.

The first two ratifications of the Convention occurred in mid-1997; it will enter into force in mid-1998.

Training

In recent years the ILO has carried out a variety of training projects aimed at improving the safety and health of miners through greater awareness, improved inspection and rescue training. The ILO's activities to date have contributed to progress in many countries, bringing national legislation into conformity with international labour standards and raising the level of occupational safety and health in the mining industry.

Industrial relations and employment

The pressure to improve productivity in the face of intensified competition can sometimes result in basic principles of freedom of association and collective bargaining being called into question when enterprises perceive that their profitability or even survival is in doubt. But sound industrial relations based on the constructive application of those principles can make an important contribution to productivity improvement. This issue was examined at length at a meeting in 1995. An important point to emerge was the need for close consultation between the social partners for any necessary restructuring to be successful and for the mining industry as a whole to obtain lasting benefits. Also, it was agreed that new flexibility of work organization and work methods should not jeopardize workers' rights, nor adversely affect health and safety.

Small-scale Mining

Small-scale mining falls into two broad categories. The first is the mining and quarrying of industrial and construction materials on a small scale, operations that are mostly for local markets and present in every country (see figure 74.1). Regulations to control and tax them are often in place but, as for small manufacturing plants, lack of inspection and lax enforcement mean that informal or illegal operations persist.

The second category is the mining of relatively high-value minerals, notably gold and precious stones (see figure 74.2). The output is generally exported, through sales to approved agencies or through smuggling. The size and character of this type of small-scale mining have made what laws there are inadequate and impossible to apply.

Small-scale mining provides considerable employment, particularly in rural areas. In some countries, many more people are employed in small-scale, often informal, mining than in the formal mining sector. The limited data that exist suggest that upwards of six million people engage in small-scale mining. Unfortunately, however, many of these jobs are precarious and are far from conforming with international and national labour standards. Accident rates in small-scale mines are routinely six of seven times higher than in larger operations, even in industrialized countries. Illnesses, many due to unsanitary conditions are common at many sites. This is not to say that there are no safe, clean, small-scale mines—there are, but they tend to be a small minority.

Figure 74.1 • Small-scale stone quarry in West Bengal.

A special problem is the employment of children. As part of its International Programme for the Elimination of Child Labour, the ILO is undertaking projects in several countries in Africa, Asia and Latin America to provide educational opportunities and alternative income-generating prospects to remove children from

Figure 74.2 • Small-scale gold mine in Zimbabwe.

74. MINING AND QUARRYING

coal, gold and gemstone mines in three regions in these countries. This work is being coordinated with the international mine-workers union (ICEM) and with local non-governmental organizations (NGOs) and government agencies.

NGOs have also worked hard and effectively at the local level to introduce appropriate technologies to improve efficiency and mitigate the health and environmental impact of small-scale mining. Some international governmental organizations (IGOs) have undertaken studies and developed guidelines and programmes of action. These address child labour, the role of women and indigenous people, taxation and land title reform, and environmental impact but, so far, they appear to have had little discernible effect. It should be noted, however, that without the active support and participation of governments, the success of such efforts is problematic.

Also, for the most part, there seems to be little interest among small-scale miners in using cheap, readily-available and effective technology to mitigate health and environmental effects, such as retorts to recapture mercury. There is often no incentive to do so, since the cost of mercury is not a constraint. Moreover, particularly in the case of itinerant miners, there is frequently no long-term interest in preserving the land for use after the mining has ceased. The challenge is to show small-scale miners that there are better ways to go about their mining that would not unduly constrain their activities and be better for them in terms of health and wealth, better for the land and better for the country. The "Harare Guidelines", developed at the 1993 United Nations Interregional Seminar on Guidelines for the Development of Small/Medium Scale Mining, provide guidance for governments and for development agencies in tackling the different issues in a complete and coordinated way. The absence of involvement by employers' and workers' organizations in most small-scale mining activity puts a special responsibility on the government in bringing small-scale mining into the formal sector, an action that would improve the lot of small-scale miners and markedly increase the economic and social benefits of small-scale mining. Also, at an international roundtable in 1995 organized by the World Bank, a strategy for artisanal mining that aims to minimize negative side effects—including poor safety and health conditions of this activity—and maximize the socio-economic benefits was developed.

The Safety and Health in Mines Convention and its accompanying Recommendation (No. 183) set out in detail an internationally agreed benchmark to guide national law and practice. It covers all mines, providing a floor—the minimum safety requirement against which all changes in mine operations should be measured. The provisions of the Convention are already being included in new mining legislation and in collective agreements in several countries and the minimum standards it sets are exceeded by the safety and health regulations already promulgated in many mining countries. It remains for the Convention to be ratified in all countries (ratification would give it the force of law), to ensure that the appropriate authorities are properly staffed and funded so that they can monitor the implementation of the regulations in all sectors of the mining industry. The ILO will also monitor the application of the Convention in countries that ratify it.

● EXPLORATION

William S. Mitchell and
Courtney S. Mitchell

Mineral exploration is the precursor to mining. Exploration is a high-risk, high-cost business that, if successful, results in the dis-

covery of a mineral deposit that can be mined profitably. In 1992, US$1.2 billion was spent worldwide on exploration; this increased to almost US$2.7 billion in 1995. Many countries encourage exploration investment and competition is high to explore in areas with good potential for discovery. Almost without exception, mineral exploration today is carried out by interdisciplinary teams of prospectors, geologists, geophysicists and geochemists who search for mineral deposits in all terrain throughout the world.

Mineral exploration begins with a *reconnaissance* or *generative* stage and proceeds through a *target evaluation* stage, which, if successful, leads to *advanced exploration*. As a project progresses through the various stages of exploration, the type of work changes as do health and safety issues.

Reconnaissance field work is often conducted by small parties of geoscientists with limited support in unfamiliar terrain. Reconnaissance may comprise prospecting, geologic mapping and sampling, wide-spaced and preliminary geochemical sampling and geophysical surveys. More detailed exploration commences during the target testing phase once land is acquired through permit, concession, lease or mineral claims. Detailed field work comprising geologic mapping, sampling and geophysical and geochemical surveys requires a grid for survey control. This work frequently yields targets that warrant testing by trenching or drilling, entailing the use of heavy equipment such as back-hoes, power shovels, bulldozers, drills and, occasionally, explosives. Diamond, rotary or percussion drill equipment may be truck-mounted or may be hauled to the drill site on skids. Occasionally helicopters are used to sling drills between drill sites.

Some project exploration results will be sufficiently encouraging to justify advanced exploration requiring the collection of large or bulk samples to evaluate the economic potential of a mineral deposit. This may be accomplished through intensive drilling, although for many mineral deposits some form of trenching or underground sampling may be necessary. An exploration shaft, decline or adit may be excavated to gain underground access to the deposit. Although the actual work is carried out by miners, most mining companies will ensure that an exploration geologist is responsible for the underground sampling programme.

Health and Safety

In the past, employers seldom implemented or monitored exploration safety programmes and procedures. Even today, exploration workers frequently have a cavalier attitude towards safety. As a result, health and safety issues may be overlooked and not considered an integral part of the explorer's job. Fortunately, many mining exploration companies now strive to change this aspect of the exploration culture by requiring that employees and contractors follow established safety procedures.

Exploration work is often seasonal. Consequently there are pressures to complete work within a limited time, sometimes at the expense of safety. In addition, as exploration work progresses to later stages, the number and variety of risks and hazards increase. Early reconnaissance field work requires only a small field crew and camp. More detailed exploration generally requires larger field camps to accommodate a greater number of employees and contractors. Safety issues—especially training on personal health issues, camp and worksite hazards, the safe use of equipment and traverse safety—become very important for geoscientists who may not have had previous field work experience.

Because exploration work is often carried out in remote areas, evacuation to a medical treatment centre may be difficult and may depend on weather or daylight conditions. Therefore, emergency procedures and communications should be carefully planned and tested before field work commences.

While outdoor safety may be considered common sense or "bush sense", one should remember that what is considered common sense in one culture may not be so considered in another culture. Mining companies should provide exploration employees with a safety manual that addresses the issues of the regions where they work. A comprehensive safety manual can form the basis for camp orientation meetings, training sessions and routine safety meetings throughout the field season.

Preventing personal health hazards

Exploration work subjects employees to hard physical work that includes traversing terrain, frequent lifting of heavy objects, using potentially dangerous equipment and being exposed to heat, cold, precipitation and perhaps high altitude (see figure 74.3). It is essential that employees be in good physical condition and in good health when they begin field work. Employees should have up-to-date immunizations and be free of communicable diseases (e.g., hepatitis and tuberculosis) that may rapidly spread through a field camp. Ideally, all exploration workers should be trained and certified in basic first aid and wilderness first-aid skills. Larger camps or worksites should have at least one employee trained and certified in advanced or industrial first-aid skills.

Outdoor workers should wear suitable clothing that protects them from extremes of heat, cold and rain or snow. In regions with high levels of ultraviolet light, workers should wear a broad-brimmed hat and use a sunscreen lotion with a high sun protection factor (SPF) to protect exposed skin. When insect repellent is required, repellent that contains DEET (N,N-diethylmeta-toluamide) is most effective in preventing bites from mosquitoes. Clothing treated with permethrin helps protect against ticks.

Training. All field employees should receive training in such topics as lifting, the correct use of approved safety equipment (e.g., safety glasses, safety boots, respirators, appropriate gloves) and health precautions needed to prevent injury due to heat stress, cold stress, dehydration, ultraviolet light exposure, protection from insect bites and exposure to any endemic diseases. Exploration workers who take assignments in developing countries should educate themselves about local health and safety issues, including the possibility of kidnapping, robbery and assault.

Preventive measures for the campsite

Potential health and safety issues will vary with the location, size and type of work performed at a camp. Any field campsite should meet local fire, health, sanitation and safety regulations. A clean, orderly camp will help reduce accidents.

Location. A campsite should be established as close as safely possible to the worksite to minimize travel time and exposure to dangers associated with transportation. A campsite should be located away from any natural hazards and take into consideration the habits and habitat of wild animals that may invade a camp (e.g., insects, bears and reptiles). Whenever possible, camps should be near a source of clean drinking water (see figure 74.4). When working at very high altitude, the camp should be located at a lower elevation to help prevent altitude sickness.

Fire control and fuel handling. Camps should be set up so that tents or structures are well spaced to prevent or reduce the spread of fire. Fire-fighting equipment should be kept in a central cache and appropriate fire extinguishers kept in kitchen and office structures. Smoking regulations help prevent fires both in camp and in the field. All workers should participate in fire drills and know the plans for fire evacuation. Fuels should be accurately labelled to ensure that the correct fuel is used for lanterns, stoves, generators and so on. Fuel caches should be located at least 100 m from camp and above any potential flood or tide level.

Sanitation. Camps require a supply of safe drinking water. The source should be tested for purity, if required. When necessary, drinking water should be stored in clean, labelled containers separate from non-potable water. Food shipments should be examined

Figure 74.3 • Drilling in mountains in British Columbia, Canada, with a light Winkie drill.

William S. Mitchell

for quality upon arrival and immediately refrigerated or stored in containers to prevent invasions from insects, rodents or larger animals. Handwashing facilities should be located near eating areas and latrines. Latrines must conform to public health standards and should be located at least 100 m away from any stream or shoreline.

Camp equipment, field equipment and machinery. All equipment (e.g., chain saws, axes, rock hammers, machetes, radios, stoves, lanterns, geophysical and geochemical equipment) should be kept in good repair. If firearms are required for personal safety from wild animals such as bears, their use must be strictly controlled and monitored.

Communication. It is important to establish regular communication schedules. Good communication increases morale and security and forms a basis for an emergency response plan.

Figure 74.4 • Summer field camp, Northwest Territories, Canada.

William S. Mitchell

Training. Employees should be trained in the safe use all equipment. All geophysicists and helpers should be trained to use ground (earth) geophysical equipment that may operate at high current or voltage. Additional training topics should include fire prevention, fire drills, fuel handling and firearms handing, when relevant.

Preventive measures at the worksite

The target testing and advanced stages of exploration require larger field camps and the use of heavy equipment at the worksite. Only trained workers or authorized visitors should be permitted onto worksites where heavy equipment is operating.

Heavy equipment. Only properly licensed and trained personnel may operate heavy equipment. Workers must be constantly vigilant and never approach heavy equipment unless they are certain the operator knows where they are, what they intend to do and where they intend to go.

Drill rigs. Crews should be fully trained for the job. They must wear appropriate personal protective equipment (e.g., hard hats, steel-toed boots, hearing protection, gloves, goggles and dust masks) and avoid wearing loose clothing that may become caught in machinery. Drill rigs should comply with all safety requirements (e.g., guards that cover all moving parts of machinery, high pressure air hoses secured with clamps and safety chains) (see figure 74.5). Workers should be aware of slippery, wet, greasy, or icy conditions underfoot and the drill area kept as orderly as possible (see figure 74.6).

Excavations. Pits and trenches should be constructed to meet safety guidelines with support systems or the sides cut back to 45° to deter collapse. Workers should never work alone or remain alone in a pit or trench, even for a short period of time, as these excavations collapse easily and may bury workers.

Explosives. Only trained and licensed personnel should handle explosives. Regulations for handling, storage and transportation of explosives and detonators should be carefully followed.

Preventive measures in traversing terrain

Exploration workers must be prepared to cope with the terrain and climate of their field area. The terrain may include deserts, swamps, forests, or mountainous terrain of jungle or glaciers and snowfields. Conditions may be hot or cold and dry or wet. Natural hazards may include lightning, bush fires, avalanches, mudslides or flash floods and so on. Insects, reptiles and/or large animals may present life-threatening hazards. Workers must not take chances or place themselves in danger to secure samples. Employees should receive training in safe traversing procedures for the terrain and climate conditions where they work. They need survival training to recognize and combat hypothermia, hyperthermia and dehydration. Employees should work in pairs and carry enough equipment, food and water (or have access in an emergency cache) to enable them to spend an unexpected night or two out in the field if an emergency situation arises. Field workers should maintain routine communication schedules with the base camp. All field camps should have established and tested emergency response plans in case field workers need rescuing.

Preventive measures in transportation

Many accidents and incidents occur during transportation to or from an exploration worksite. Excessive speed and/or alcohol consumption while driving vehicles or boats are relevant safety issues.

Figure 74.5 • Truck-mounted drill in Australia.

William S. Mitchell

Figure 74.6 • Reverse circulation drilling on a frozen lake in Canada.

William S. Mitchell

Figure 74.7 • Winter field transportation in Canada.

Vehicles. Common causes of vehicle accidents include hazardous road and/or weather conditions, overloaded or incorrectly loaded vehicles, unsafe towing practices, driver fatigue, inexperienced drivers and animals or people on the road—especially at night. Preventive measures include following defensive driving techniques when operating any type of vehicle. Drivers and passengers of cars and trucks must use seatbelts and follow safe loading and towing procedures. Only vehicles that can safely operate in the terrain and weather conditions of the field area, e.g., 4-wheel drive vehicles, 2-wheel motor bikes, all-terrain vehicles (ATVs) or snowmobiles should be used (see figure 74.7). Vehicles must have regular maintenance and contain adequate equipment including survival gear. Protective clothing and a helmet are required when operating ATVs or 2-wheel motor bikes.

Aircraft. Access to remote sites frequently depends on fixed wing aircraft and helicopters (see figure 74.8). Only charter companies with well-maintained equipment and a good safety record should be engaged. Aircraft with turbine engines are recommended. Pilots must never exceed the legal number of allowable flight hours and should never fly when fatigued or be asked to fly in unacceptable weather conditions. Pilots must oversee the proper loading of all aircraft and comply with payload restrictions. To prevent accidents, exploration workers must be trained to work safely around aircraft. They must follow safe embarkation and loading procedures. No one should walk in the direction of the propellers or rotor blades; they are invisible when moving. Helicopter landing sites should be kept free of loose debris that may become airborne projectiles in the downdraft of rotor blades.

Slinging. Helicopters are often used to move supplies, fuel, drill and camp equipment. Some major hazards include overloading, incor-

rect use of or poorly maintained slinging equipment, untidy worksites with debris or equipment that may be blown about, protruding vegetation or anything that loads may snag on. In addition, pilot fatigue, lack of personnel training, miscommunication between parties involved (especially between the pilot and groundman) and marginal weather conditions increase the risks of slinging. For safe slinging and to prevent accidents, all parties must follow safe slinging procedures and be fully alert and well briefed with mutual responsibilities clearly understood. The sling cargo weight must not exceed

Figure 74.8 • Unloading field supplies from Twin Otter, Northwest Territories, Canada.

William S. Mitchell

74. MINING AND QUARRYING

the lifting capacity of the helicopter. Loads should be arranged so they are secure and nothing will slip out of the cargo net. When slinging with a very long line (e.g., jungle, mountainous sites with very tall trees), a pile of logs or large rocks should be used to weigh down the sling for the return trip because one should never fly with empty slings or lanyards dangling from the sling hook. Fatal accidents have occurred when unweighted lanyards have struck the helicopter tail or main rotor during flight.

Boats. Workers who rely on boats for field transportation on coastal waters, mountain lakes, streams or rivers may face hazards from winds, fog, rapids, shallows, and submerged or semi-submerged objects. To prevent boating accidents, operators must know and not exceed the limitations of their boat, their motor and their own boating capabilities. The largest, safest boat available for the job should be used. All workers should wear a good quality personal flotation device (PFD) whenever travelling and/or working in small boats. In addition, all boats must contain all legally required equipment plus spare parts, tools, survival and first aid equipment and always carry and use up-to-date charts and tide tables.

● TYPES OF COAL MINING

Fred W. Hermann

The rationale for selecting a method for mining coal depends on such factors as topography, geometry of the coal seam, geology of the overlying rocks and environmental requirements or restraints. Overriding these, however, are the economic factors. They include: availability, quality and costs of the required work force (including the availability of trained supervisors and managers); adequacy of housing, feeding and recreational facilities for the workers (especially when the mine is located at a distance from a local community); availability of the necessary equipment and machinery and of workers trained to operate it; availability and costs of transportation for workers, necessary supplies, and for getting the coal to the user or purchaser; availability and the cost of the necessary capital to finance the operation (in local currency); and the market for the particular type of coal to be extracted (i.e., the price at which it may be sold). A major factor is the *stripping ratio*, that is, the amount of overburden material to be removed in proportion to the amount of coal that can be extracted; as this increases, the cost of mining becomes less attractive. An important factor, especially in surface mining, that, unfortunately, is often overlooked in the equation, is the cost of restoring the terrain and the environment when the mining operation is closed down.

Health and Safety

Another critical factor is the cost of protecting the health and safety of the miners. Unfortunately, particularly in small-scale operations, instead of being weighed in deciding whether or how the coal should be extracted, the necessary protective measures are often ignored or short-changed.

Actually, although there are always unsuspected hazards—they may come from the elements rather than the mining operations—any mining operation can be safe providing there is a commitment from all parties to a safe operation.

Surface Coal Mines

Surface mining of coal is performed by a variety of methods depending on the topography, the area in which the mining is being undertaken and environmental factors. All methods involve the removal of overburden material to allow for the extraction of the coal. While generally safer than underground mining, surface

operations do have some specific hazards that must be addressed. Prominent among these is the use of heavy equipment which, in addition to accidents, may involve exposure to exhaust fumes, noise and contact with fuel, lubricants and solvents. Climatic conditions, such as heavy rain, snow and ice, poor visibility and excessive heat or cold may compound these hazards. When blasting is required to break up rock formations, special precautions in the storage, handling and use of explosives are required.

Surface operations require the use of huge waste dumps to store overburden products. Appropriate controls must be implemented to prevent dump failure and to protect the employees, the general public and the environment.

Underground Mining

There is also a variety of methods for underground mining. Their common denominator is the creation of tunnels from the surface to the coal seam and the use of machines and/or explosives to extract the coal. In addition to the high frequency of accidents—coal mining ranks high on the list of hazardous workplaces wherever statistics are maintained—the potential for a major incident involving multiple loss of life is always present in underground operations. Two primary causes of such catastrophes are cave-ins due to faulty engineering of the tunnels and explosion and fire due to the accumulation of methane and/or flammable levels of airborne coal dust.

Methane

Methane is highly explosive in concentrations of 5 to 15% and has been the cause of numerous mining disasters. It is best controlled by providing adequate air flow to dilute the gas to a level that is below its explosive range and to exhaust it quickly from the workings. Methane levels must be continuously monitored and rules established to close down operations when its concentration reaches 1 to 1.5% and to evacuate the mine promptly if it reaches levels of 2 to 2.5%.

Coal dust

In addition to causing black lung disease (anthracosis) if inhaled by miners, coal dust is explosive when fine dust is mixed with air and ignited. Airborne coal dust can be controlled by water sprays and exhaust ventilation. It can be collected by filtering recirculating air or it can be neutralized by the addition of stone dust in sufficient quantities to render the coal dust/air mixture inert.

TECHNIQUES IN UNDERGROUND MINING ●

Hans Hamrin

There are underground mines all over the world presenting a kaleidoscope of methods and equipment. There are approximately 650 underground mines, each with an annual output that exceeds 150,000 tonnes, which account for 90% of the ore output of the western world. In addition, it is estimated that there are 6,000 smaller mines each producing less than 150,000 tonnes. Each mine is unique with workplace, installations and underground workings dictated by the kinds of minerals being sought and the location and geological formations, as well as by such economic considerations as the market for the particular mineral and the availability of funds for investment. Some mines have been in continuous operation for more than a century while others are just starting up.

Mines are dangerous places where most of the jobs involve arduous labour. The hazards faced by the workers range from such catastrophes as cave-ins, explosions and fire to accidents, dust exposure, noise, heat and more. Protecting the health and safety of the workers is a major consideration in properly conducted mining operations and, in most countries, is required by laws and regulations.

The Underground Mine

The underground mine is a factory located in the bedrock inside the earth in which miners work to recover minerals hidden in the rock mass. They drill, charge and blast to access and recover the ore, i.e., rock containing a mix of minerals of which at least one can be processed into a product that can be sold at a profit. The ore is taken to the surface to be refined into a high-grade concentrate.

Working inside the rock mass deep below the surface requires special infrastructures: a network of shafts, tunnels and chambers connecting with the surface and allowing movement of workers, machines and rock within the mine. The shaft is the access to underground where lateral drifts connect the shaft station with production stopes. The internal ramp is an inclined drift which links underground levels at different elevations (i.e., depths). All underground openings need services such as exhaust ventilation and fresh air, electric power, water and compressed air, drains and pumps to collect seeping ground water, and a communication system.

Hoisting plant and systems

The headframe is a tall building which identifies the mine on the surface. It stands directly above the shaft, the mine's main artery through which the miners enter and leave their workplace and through which supplies and equipment are lowered and ore and waste materials are raised to the surface. Shaft and hoist installations vary depending on the need for capacity, depth and so on. Each mine must have at least two shafts to provide an alternate route for escape in case of an emergency.

Hoisting and shaft travelling are regulated by stringent rules. Hoisting equipment (e.g., winder, brakes and rope) is designed with ample margins of safety and is checked at regular intervals. The shaft interior is regularly inspected by people standing on top of the cage, and stop buttons at all stations trigger the emergency brake.

The gates in front of the shaft barricade the openings when the cage is not at the station. When the cage arrives and comes to a full stop, a signal clears the gate for opening. After miners have entered the cage and closed the gate, another signal clears the cage for moving up or down the shaft. Practice varies: the signal commands may be given by a cage tender or, following the instructions posted at each shaft station, the miners may signal shaft destinations for themselves. Miners are generally quite aware of the potential hazards in shaft riding and hoisting and accidents are rare.

Diamond drilling

A mineral deposit inside the rock must be mapped before the start of mining. It is necessary to know where the orebody is located and define its width, length and depth to achieve a three-dimensional vision of the deposit.

Diamond drilling is used to explore a rock mass. Drilling can be done from the surface or from the drift in the underground mine. A drill bit studded with small diamonds cuts a cylindrical core that is captured in the string of tubes that follows the bit. The core is retrieved and analysed to find out what is in the rock. Core samples are inspected and the mineralized portions are split and analysed for metal content. Extensive drilling programmes are required to locate the mineral deposits; holes are drilled at both horizontal and vertical intervals to identify the dimensions of the orebody (see figure 74.9).

Mine development

Mine development involves the excavations needed to establish the infrastructure necessary for stope production and to prepare for the future continuity of operations. Routine elements, all produced by the drill-blast-excavation technique, include horizontal drifts, inclined ramps and vertical or inclined raises.

Shaft sinking

Shaft sinking involves rock excavation advancing downwards and is usually assigned to contractors rather than being done by mine's personnel. It requires experienced workers and special equipment, such as a shaft-sinking headframe, a special hoist with a large bucket hanging in the rope and a cactus-grab shaft mucking device.

The shaft-sinking crew is exposed to a variety of hazards. They work at the bottom of a deep, vertical excavation. People, material and blasted rock must all share the large bucket. People at the shaft bottom have no place to hide from falling objects. Clearly, shaft sinking is not a job for the inexperienced.

Drifting and ramping

A drift is a horizontal access tunnel used for transport of rock and ore. Drift excavation is a routine activity in the development of the mine. In mechanized mines, two-boom, electro-hydraulic drill jumbos are used for face drilling. Typical drift profiles are 16.0 m^2 in section and the face is drilled to a depth of 4.0 m. The holes are charged pneumatically with an explosive, usually bulk ammonium nitrate fuel oil (ANFO), from a special charging truck. Short-delay non-electric (Nonel) detonators are used.

Mucking is done with (load-haul-dump) LHD vehicles (see figure 74.10) with a bucket capacity of about 3.0 m^3. Muck is hauled directly to the ore pass system and transferred to truck for longer hauls. Ramps are passageways connecting one or more levels at grades ranging from 1:7 to 1:10 (a very steep grade compared to normal roads) that provide adequate traction for heavy, self-propelled equipment. The ramps are often driven in

Figure 74.9 • Drill pattern, Garpenberg Mine, a lead-zinc mine in central Sweden.

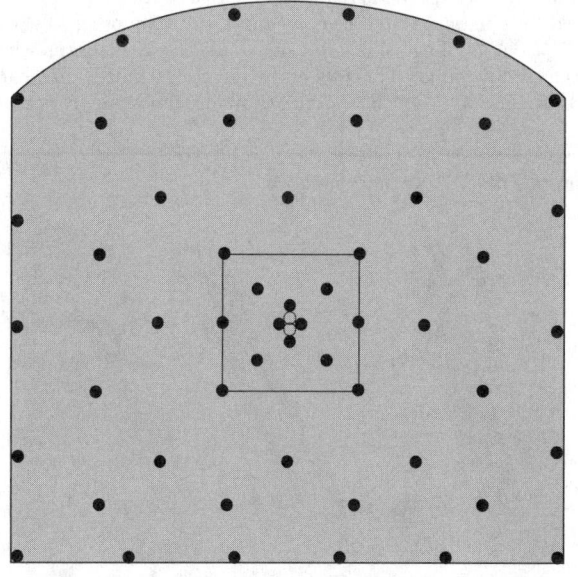

Figure 74.10 • LHD loader.

Atlas Copco

an upward or downward spiral, similar to a spiral staircase. Ramp excavation is a routine in the mine's development schedule and uses the same equipment as drifting.

Raising

A raise is a vertical or steeply-inclined opening that connects different levels in the mine. It may serve as a ladderway access to stopes, as an ore pass or as an airway in the mine's ventilation system. Raising is a difficult and dangerous, but necessary job. Raising methods vary from simple manual drill and blast to mechanical rock excavation with raise boring machines (RBMs) (see figure 74.11).

Manual raising

Manual raising is difficult, dangerous and physically demanding work that challenges the miner's agility, strength and endurance. It is a job to be assigned only to experienced miners in good physical condition. As a rule the raise section is divided into two compartments by a timbered wall. One is kept open for the ladder used for climbing to the face, air pipes, etc. The other fills with rock from blasting which the miner uses as a platform when drilling the round. The timber parting is extended after each round. The work involves ladder climbing, timbering, rock drill-

Figure 74.11 • Raising methods.

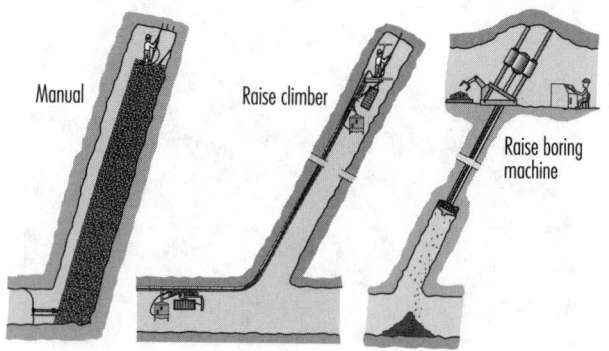

Manual   Raise climber   Raise boring machine

ing and blasting, all done in a cramped, poorly ventilated space. It is all performed by a single miner, as there is no room for a helper. Mines search for alternatives to the hazardous and laborious manual raising methods.

The raise climber

The raise climber is a vehicle that obviates ladder climbing and much of the difficulty of the manual method. This vehicle climbs the raise on a guide rail bolted to the rock and provides a robust working platform when the miner is drilling the round above. Very high raises can be excavated with the raise climber with safety much improved over the manual method. Raise excavation, however, remains a very hazardous job.

The raise boring machine

The RBM is a powerful machine that breaks the rock mechanically (see figure 74.12). It is erected on top of the planned raise and a pilot hole about 300 mm in diameter is drilled to break through at a lower level target. The pilot drill is replaced by a reamer head with the diameter of the intended raise and the RBM is put in reverse, rotating and pulling the reamer head upward to create a full-size circular raise.

Ground control

Ground control is an important concept for people working inside a rock mass. It is particularly important in mechanized mines using

Figure 74.12 • Raise boring machine.

Atlas Copco

rubber-tyred equipment where the drift openings are 25.0 m² in section, in contrast to the mines with rail drifts where they are usually only 10.0 m². The roof at 5.0 m is too high for a miner to use a scaling bar to check for potential rock falls.

Different measures are used to secure the roof in underground openings. In smooth blasting, contour holes are drilled closely together and charged with a low-strength explosive. The blast produces a smooth contour without fracturing the outside rock.

Nevertheless, since there are often cracks in the rock mass which do not show on the surface, rock falls are an ever-present hazard. The risk is reduced by rock bolting, i.e., insertion of steel rods in bore holes and fastening them. The rock bolt holds the rock mass together, prevents cracks from spreading, helps to stabilize the rock mass and makes the underground environment safer.

Methods for Underground Mining

The choice of mining method is influenced by the shape and size of the ore deposit, the value of the contained minerals, the composition, stability and strength of the rock mass and the demands for production output and safe working conditions (which sometimes are in conflict). While mining methods have been evolving since antiquity, this article focuses on those used in semi- to fully-mechanized mines during the late twentieth century. Each mine is unique, but they all share the goals of a safe workplace and a profitable business operation.

Flat room-and-pillar mining

Room-and-pillar mining is applicable to tabular mineralization with horizontal to moderate dip at an angle not exceeding 20° (see figure 74.13). The deposits are often of sedimentary origin and the rock is often in both hanging wall and mineralization in competent (a relative concept here as miners have the option to install rock bolts to reinforce the roof where its stability is in doubt). Room-and-pillar is one of the principal underground coal-mining methods.

Room-and-pillar extracts an orebody by horizontal drilling advancing along a multi-faced front, forming empty rooms behind the producing front. Pillars, sections of rock, are left between the rooms to keep the roof from caving. The usual result is a regular pattern of rooms and pillars, their relative size representing a compromise between maintaining the stability of the rock mass and extracting as much of the ore as possible. This involves careful analysis of the strength of the pillars, the roof strata span capacity and other factors. Rock bolts are commonly used to increase the strength of the rock in the pillars. The mined-out stopes serve as roadways for trucks transporting the ore to the mine's storage bin.

The room-and-pillar stope face is drilled and blasted as in drifting. The stope width and height correspond to the size of the drift, which can be quite large. Large productive drill jumbos are used in normal height mines; compact rigs are used where the ore is less than 3.0 m thick. The thick orebody is mined in steps starting from the top so that the roof can be secured at a height convenient for the miners. The section below is recovered in horizontal slices, by drilling flat holes and blasting against the space above. The ore is loaded onto trucks at the face. Normally, regular front-end loaders and dump trucks are used. For the low-height mine, special mine trucks and LHD vehicles are available.

Room-and-pillar is an efficient mining method. Safety depends on the height of the open rooms and ground control standards. The main risks are accidents caused by falling rock and moving equipment.

Inclined room-and-pillar mining

Inclined room-and-pillar applies to tabular mineralization with an angle or dip from 15° and 30° to the horizontal. This is too steep

Figure 74.13 • Room-and-pillar mining of a flat orebody.

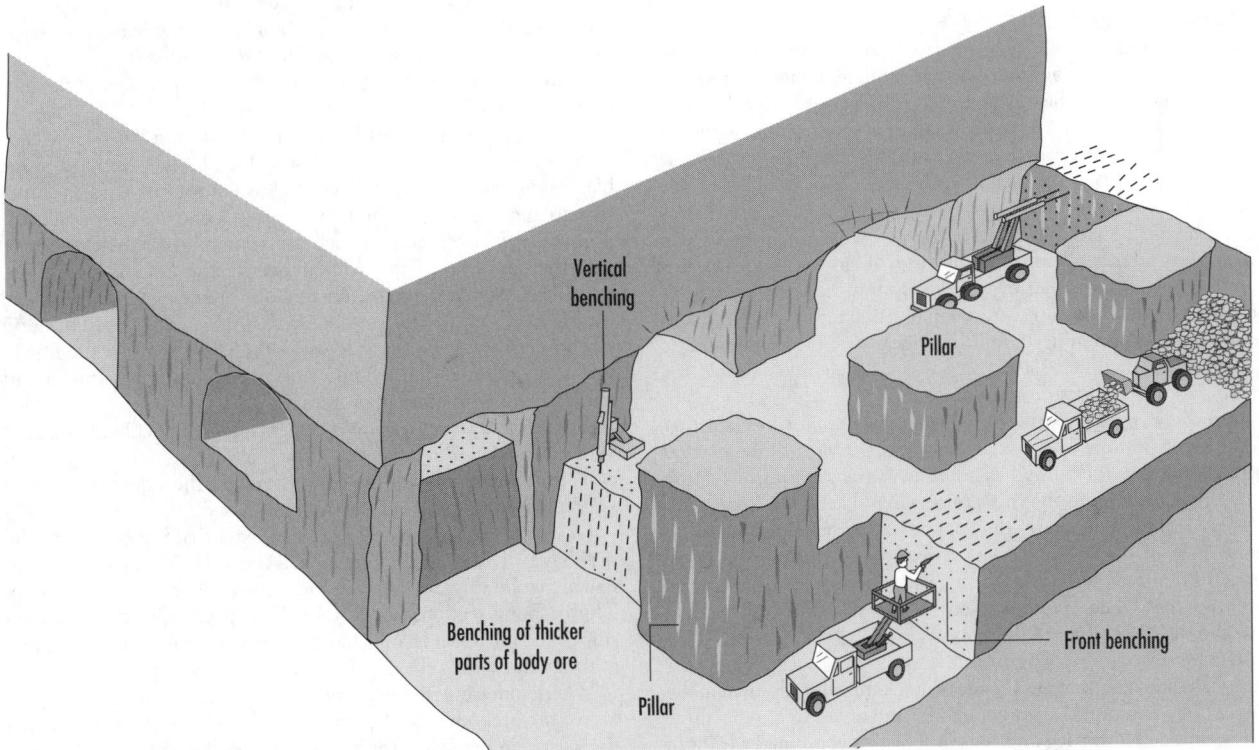

an angle for rubber-tyred vehicles to climb and too flat for a gravity assist rock flow.

The traditional approach to the inclined orebody relies on manual labour. The miners drill blast holes in the stopes with hand-held rock drills. The stope is cleaned with slusher scrapers.

The inclined stope is a difficult place to work. The miners have to climb the steep piles of blasted rock carrying with them their rock drills and the drag slusher pulley and steel wires. In addition to rock falls and accidents, there are the hazards of noise, dust, inadequate ventilation and heat.

Where the inclined ore deposits are adaptable to mechanization, "step-room mining" is used. This is based on converting the "difficult dip" footwall into a "staircase" with steps at an angle convenient for trackless machines. The steps are produced by a diamond pattern of stopes and haulage-ways at the selected angle across the orebody.

Ore extraction starts with horizontal stope drives, branching out from a combined access-haulage drift. The initial stope is horizontal and follows the hanging wall. The next stope starts a short distance further down and follows the same route. This procedure is repeated moving downward to create a series of steps to extract the orebody.

Sections of the mineralization are left to support the hanging wall. This is done by mining two or three adjacent stope drives to the full length and then starting the next stope drive one step down, leaving an elongated pillar between them. Sections of this pillar can later be recovered as cut-outs that are drilled and blasted from the stope below.

Modern trackless equipment adapts well to step-room mining. The stoping can be fully mechanized, using standard mobile equipment. The blasted ore is gathered in the stopes by the LHD vehicles and transferred to mine truck for transport to the shaft/ore pass. If the stope is not high enough for truck loading, the trucks can be filled in special loading bays excavated in the haulage drive.

Shrinkage stoping

Shrinkage stoping may be termed a "classic" mining method, having been perhaps the most popular mining method for most of the past century. It has largely been replaced by mechanized methods but is still used in many small mines around the world. It is applicable to mineral deposits with regular boundaries and steep dip hosted in a competent rock mass. Also, the blasted ore must not be affected by storage in the slopes (e.g., sulphide ores have a tendency to oxidize and decompose when exposed to air). Its most prominent feature is the use of gravity flow for ore handling: ore from stopes drops directly into rail cars via chutes obviating manual loading, traditionally the most common and least liked job in mining. Until the appearance of the pneumatic rocker shovel in the 1950s, there was no machine suitable for loading rock in underground mines.

Shrinkage stoping extracts the ore in horizontal slices, starting at the stope bottoms and advancing upwards. Most of the blasted rock remains in the stope providing a working platform for the miner drilling holes in the roof and serving to keep the stope walls stable. As blasting increases the volume of the rock by about 60%, some 40% of the ore is drawn at the bottom during stoping in order to maintain a work space between the top of the muckpile and the roof. The remaining ore is drawn after blasting has reached the upper limit of the stope.

The necessity of working from the top of the muckpile and the raise-ladder access prevents the use of mechanized equipment in the stope. Only equipment light enough for the miner to handle alone may be used. The air-leg and rock drill, with a combined weight of 45 kg, is the usual tool for drilling the shrinkage stope. Standing on top of the muckpile, the miner picks up the drill/feed, anchors the leg, braces the rock drill/drill steel against the roof and starts drilling; it is not easy work.

Cut-and-fill mining

Cut-and-fill mining is suitable for a steeply dipping mineral deposit contained in a rock mass with good to moderate stability. It removes the ore in horizontal slices starting from a bottom cut and advances upwards, allowing the stope boundaries to be adjusted to follow irregular mineralization. This permits high-grade sections to be mined selectively, leaving low-grade ore in place.

After the stope is mucked clean, the mined out space is backfilled to form a working platform when the next slice is mined and to add stability to the stope walls,

Development for cut-and-fill mining in a trackless environment includes a footwall haulage drive along the orebody at the main level, undercut of the stope provided with drains for the hydraulic backfill, a spiral ramp excavated in the footwall with access turn-outs to the stopes and a raise from the stope to the level above for ventilation and fill transport.

Overhand stoping is used with cut-and-fill, with both dry rock and hydraulic sand as backfill material. Overhand means that the ore is drilled from below by blasting a slice 3.0 m to 4.0 m thick. This allows the complete stope area to be drilled and the blasting of the full stope without interruptions. The "uppers" holes are drilled with simple wagon drills.

Up-hole drilling and blasting leaves a rough rock surface for the roof; after mucking out, its height will be about 7.0 m. Before miners are allowed to enter the area, the roof must be secured by trimming the roof contours with smooth-blasting and subsequent scaling of the loose rock. This is done by miners using hand-held rock drills working from the muckpile.

In *front stoping*, trackless equipment is used for ore production. Sand tailings are used for backfill and distributed in the underground stopes via plastic pipes. The stopes are filled almost completely, creating a surface sufficiently hard to be traversed by rubber-tyred equipment. The stope production is completely mechanized with drifting jumbos and LHD vehicles. The stope face is a 5.0 m vertical wall across the stope with a 0.5 m open slot beneath it. Five-meter-long horizontal holes are drilled in the face and ore is blasted against the open bottom slot.

The tonnage produced by a single blast depends on the face area and does not compare to that yielded by the overhand stope blast. However, the output of trackless equipment is vastly superior to the manual method, while roof control can be accomplished by the drill jumbo which drills smooth-blast holes together with the stope blast. Fitted with an oversize bucket and large tyres, the LHD vehicle, a versatile tool for mucking and transport, travels easily on the fill surface. In a double face stope, the drill jumbo engages it on one side while the LHD handles the muckpile at the other end, providing efficient use of the equipment and enhancing the production output.

Sublevel stoping removes ore in open stopes. Backfilling of stopes with consolidated fill after the mining allows the miners to return at a later time to recover the pillars between the stopes, enabling a very high recovery rate of the mineral deposit.

Development for sublevel stoping is extensive and complex. The orebody is divided into sections with a vertical height of about 100 m in which sublevels are prepared and connected via an inclined ramp. The orebody sections are further divided laterally in alternating stopes and pillars and a mail haulage drive is created in the footwall, at the bottom, with cut-outs for drawpoint loading.

When mined out, the sublevel stope will be a rectangular opening across the orebody. The bottom of the stope is V-shaped to funnel the blasted material into the draw-points. Drilling drifts for the long-hole rig are prepared on the upper sublevels (see figure 74.14).

Figure 74.14 • Sublevel stoping using ring drilling and cross-cut loading.

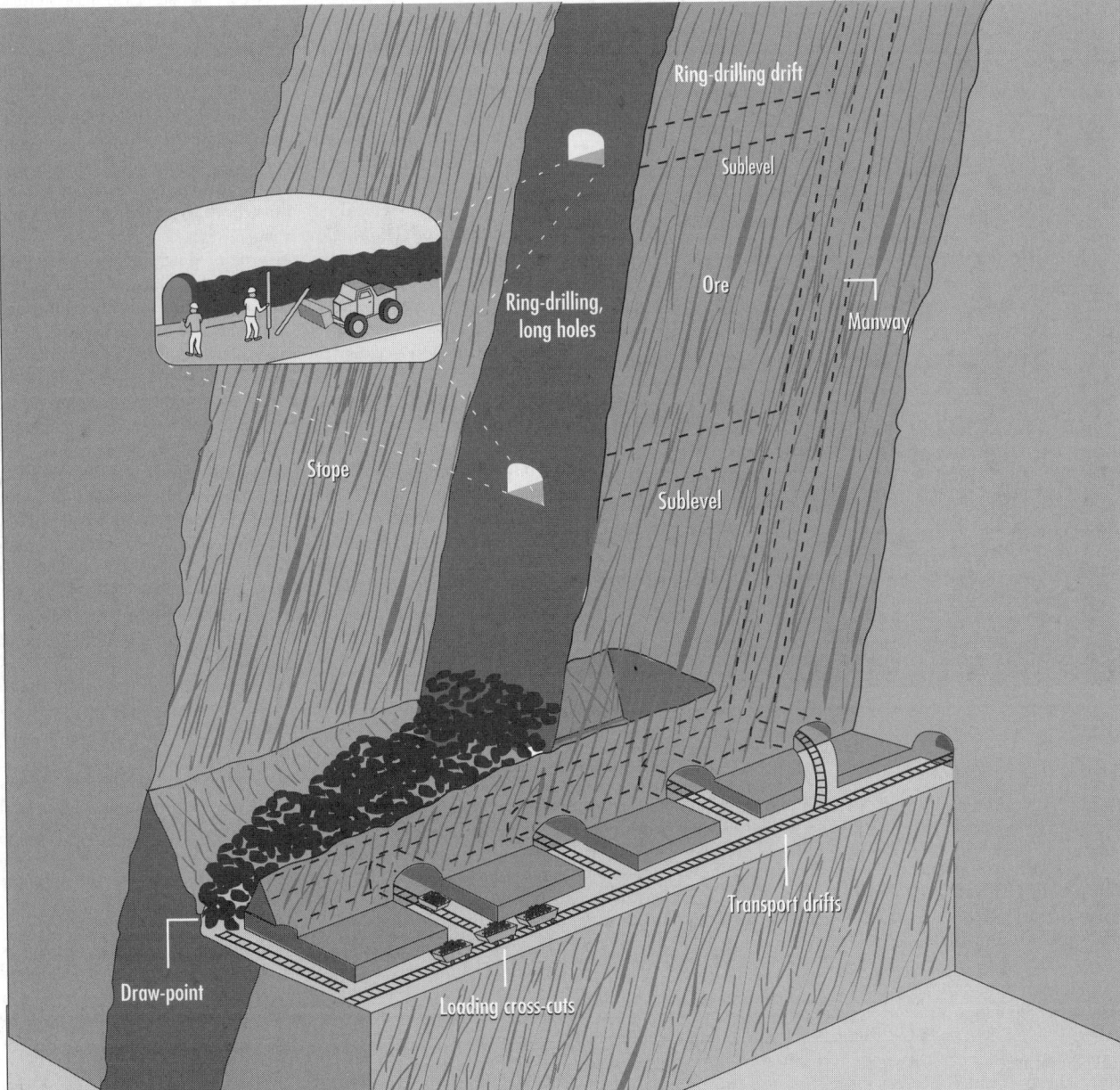

Blasting requires space for the rock to expand in volume. This requires that a slot a few metres wide be prepared before the start of long-hole blasting. This is accomplished by enlarging a raise from the bottom to the top of the stope to a full slot.

After opening the slot, the long-hole rig (see figure 74.15) begins production drilling in sublevel drifts following precisely a detailed plan designed by blasting experts which specifies all the blast holes, the collaring position, depth and direction of the holes. The drill rig continues drilling until all the rings on one level are completed. It is then transferred to the next sublevel to continue drilling. Meanwhile the holes are charged and a blast pattern which covers a large area within the stope breaks up a large volume of ore in one blast. The blasted ore drops to the stope bottom to be recovered by the LHD vehicles mucking in the draw-point beneath the stope. Normally, the long-hole drilling stays ahead of the charging and blasting providing a reserve of ready-to-blast ore, thus making for an efficient production schedule.

Sublevel stoping is a productive mining method. Efficiency is enhanced by the ability to use fully mechanized productive rigs for the long-hole drilling plus the fact that the rig can be used continuously. It is also relatively safe because doing the drilling inside sublevel drifts and mucking through draw-points eliminates exposure to potential rock falls.

Figure 74.15 • Long-hole drill rig.

Atlas Copco

Vertical crater retreat mining

Like sublevel stoping and shrinkage stoping, vertical crater retreat (VCR) mining is applicable to mineralization in steeply dipping strata. However, it uses a different blasting technique breaking the rock with heavy, concentrated charges placed in holes ("craters") with very large diameter (about 165 mm) about 3 m away from a free rock surface. Blasting breaks a cone-shaped opening in the rock mass around the hole and allows the blasted material to remain in the stope during the production phase so that the rock fill can assist in supporting the stope walls. The need for rock stability is less than in sublevel stoping.

The development for VCR mining is similar to that for sublevel stoping except for requiring both over-cut and under-cut excavations. The over-cut is needed in the first stage to accommodate the rig drilling the large-diameter blast holes and for access while charging the holes and blasting. The under-cut excavation provided the free surface necessary for VCR blasting. It may also provide access for a LHD vehicle (operated by remote control with the operator remaining outside the stope) to recover the blasted ore from the draw-points beneath the stope.

The usual VCR blast uses holes in a 4.0 m × 4.0 m pattern directed vertically or steeply inclined with charges carefully placed at calculated distances to free the surface beneath. The charges cooperate to break off a horizontal ore slice about 3.0 m thick. The blasted rock falls into the stope underneath. By controlling the rate of mucking out, the stope remains partly filled so that the rock fill assists in stabilizing the stope walls during the production phase. The last blast breaks the over-cut into the stope, after which the stope is mucked clean and prepared for back filling.

VCR mines often uses a system of primary and secondary stopes to the orebody. Primary stopes are mined in the first stage,

then backfilled with cemented fill. The stope is left for the fill to consolidate. Miners then return and recover the ore in the pillars between the primary stopes, the secondary stopes. This system, in combination with the cemented backfill, results in close to a 100% recovery of the ore reserves.

Sublevel caving

Sublevel caving is applicable to mineral deposits with steep to moderate dip and large extension at depth. The ore must fracture into manageable block with blasting. The hanging wall will cave following the ore extraction and the ground on the surface above the orebody will subside. (It must be barricaded to prevent any individuals from entering the area.)

Sublevel caving is based on gravity flow inside a broken-up rock mass containing both ore and rock. The rock mass is first fractured by drilling and blasting and then mucked out through drift headings underneath the rock mass cave. It qualifies as a safe mining method because the miners always work inside drift-size openings.

Sublevel caving depends on sublevels with regular patterns of drifts prepared inside the orebody at rather close vertical spacing (from 10.0 m to 20 0 m). The drift layout is the same on each sublevel (i.e., parallel drives across the orebody from the footwall transport drive to the hanging wall) but the patterns on each sublevel are slightly off-set so that the drifts on a lower level are located between the drifts on the sublevel above it. A cross section will show a diamond pattern with drifts in regular vertical and horizontal spacing. Thus, development for sublevel caving is extensive. Drift excavation, however, is a straightforward task which can readily be mechanized. Working on multiple drift headings on several sublevels favours high utilization of the equipment.

When the development of the sublevel is completed, the long-hole drill rig moves in to drill a blast holes in a fan-spread pattern in the rock above. When all of the blast holes are ready, the long-hole drill rig is moved to the sublevel below.

The long-hole blast fractures the rock mass above the sublevel drift, initiating a cave that starts at the hanging wall contact and retreats toward the footwall following a straight front across the orebody on the sublevel. A vertical section would show a staircase where each upper sublevel is one step ahead of the sublevel below.

The blast fills the sublevel front with a mix of ore and waste. When the LHD vehicle arrives, the cave contains 100% ore. As loading continues, the proportion of waste rock will gradually increase until the operator decides that the waste dilution is too high and stops loading. As the loader moves to the next drift to continue mucking, the blaster enters to prepare the next ring of holes for blasting.

Mucking out on sublevels is an ideal application for the LHD vehicle. Available in different sizes to meet particular situations, it fills the bucket, travels some 200 m, empties the bucket into the ore pass and returns for another load.

Sublevel caving features a schematic layout with repetitive work procedures (development drifting, long-hole drilling, charging and blasting, loading and transport) that are carried out independently. This allows the procedures to move continuously from one sublevel to another, allowing for the most efficient use of work crews and equipment. In effect the mine is analogous to a departmentalized factory. Sublevel mining, however, being less selective than other methods, does not yield particularly efficient extraction rates. The cave includes some 20 to 40% of waste with a loss of ore that ranges from 15 to 25%.

Block-caving

Block-caving is a large-scale method applicable to mineralization on the order of 100 million tonnes in all directions contained in rock masses amenable to caving (i.e., with internal stresses which, after removal of the supporting elements in the rock mass, assist the fracturing of the mined block). An annual output ranging from 10 to 30 million tonnes is the anticipated yield. These requirements limit block-caving to a few specific mineral deposits. Worldwide, there are block-caving mines exploiting deposits containing copper, iron, molybdenum and diamonds.

Block refers to the mining layout. The orebody is divided into large sections, blocks, each containing a tonnage sufficient for many years of production. The caving is induced by removing the supporting strength of the rock mass directly underneath the block by means of an undercut, a 15 m high section of rock fractured by long-hole drilling and blasting. Stresses created by natural tectonic forces of considerable magnitude, similar to those causing continental movements, create cracks in the rock mass, breaking the blocks, hopefully to pass draw-point openings in the mine. Nature, though, often needs the assistance of miners to handle oversize boulders.

Preparation for block-caving requires long-range planning and extensive initial development involving a complex system of excavations beneath the block. These vary with the site; they generally include undercut, drawbells, grizzlies for control of oversize rock and ore passes that funnel the ore into train loading.

Drawbells are conical openings excavated underneath the undercut which gather ore from a large area and funnel it into the drawpoint at the production level below. Here the ore is recovered in LHD vehicles and transferred to ore passes. Boulders too large for the bucket are blasted in draw-points, while smaller ones are dealt with on the grizzly. Grizzlies, sets of parallel bars for screening coarse material, are commonly used in block-caving mines although, increasingly, hydraulic breakers are being preferred.

Openings in a block-caving mine are subject to high rock pressure. Drifts and other openings, therefore, are excavated with the smallest possible section. Nevertheless, extensive rock bolting and concrete lining is required to keep the openings intact.

Properly applied, block-caving is a low-cost, productive mass mining method. However, the amenability of a rock mass to caving is not always predictable. Also, the comprehensive development that is required results in a long lead-time before the mine starts producing: the delay in earnings can have a negative influence on the financial projections used to justify the investment.

Longwall mining

Longwall mining is applicable to bedded deposits of uniform shape, limited thickness and large horizontal extension (e.g., a coal seam, a potash layer or the reef, the bed of quartz pebbles exploited by gold mines in South Africa). It is one of the main methods for mining coal. It recovers the mineral in slices along a straight line that are repeated to recover materials over a larger area. The space closest to the face in kept open while the hanging wall is allowed to collapse at a safe distance behind the miners and their equipment.

Preparation for longwall mining involves the network of drifts required for access to the mining area and transport of the mined product to the shaft. Since the mineralization is in the form of a sheet that extends over a wide area, the drifts can usually be arranged in a schematic network pattern. The haulage drifts are prepared in the seam itself. The distance between two adjacent haulage drifts determines the length of the longwall face.

Backfilling

Backfilling of mine stopes prevents rock from collapsing. It preserves the inherent stability of the rock mass which promotes safety and allows more complete extraction of the desired ore. Backfilling is traditionally used with cut-and-fill but it is also common with sublevel stoping and VCR mining.

Traditionally, miners have dumped waste rock from development in empty stopes instead of hauling it to the surface. For example, in cut-and-fill, waste rock is distributed over the empty stope by scrapers or bulldozers.

Hydraulic backfilling uses tailings from the mine's dressing plant which are distributed underground through bore holes and plastic tubing. The tailings are first de-slimed, only the coarse fraction being used for filling. The fill is a mix of sand and water, about 65% of which is solid matter. By mixing cement into the last pour, the fill's surface will harden into a smooth roadbed for rubber-tyred equipment.

Backfilling is also used with sublevel stoping and VCR mining, with crushed rock introduced as a complement to sand fill. The crushed and screened rock, produced in a nearby quarry, is delivered underground through special backfill raises where it is loaded on trucks and delivered to the stopes where it is dumped into special fill raises. Primary stopes are backfilled with cemented rock fill produced by spraying a cement-fly ash slurry on the rockfill before it is distributed to the stopes. The cemented rockfill hardens into a solid mass forming an artificial pillar for mining the secondary stope. The cement slurry is generally not required when secondary stopes are backfilled, except for the last pours to establish a firm mucking floor.

Equipment for Underground Mining

Underground mining is becoming increasingly mechanized wherever circumstances permit. The rubber-tyred, diesel-powered, four-wheel traction, articulated steer carrier is common to all mobile underground machines (see figure 74.16).

Face drill jumbo for development drilling

This is an indispensable workhorse in mines that is used for all rock excavation work. It carries one or two booms with hydraulic rock drills. With one worker at the control panel, it will complete a pattern of 60 blast holes 4.0 m deep in a few hours.

Long-hole production drill rig

This rig (see figure 74.15) drills blast holes in a radial spread around the drift which cover a large area of rock and break off large volumes of ore. It is used with sublevel stoping, sublevel caving, block-caving and VCR mining. With a powerful hydraulic

Figure 74.16 • Small-size face rig.

Atlas Copco

rock drill and carousel storage for extension rods, the operator uses remote controls to perform rock drilling from a safe position.

Charging truck

The charging truck is a necessary complement to the drifting jumbo. The carrier mounts a hydraulic service platform, a pressurized ANFO explosive container and a charging hose that permit the operator to fill blast holes all over the face in a very short time. At the same time, Nonel detonators may be inserted for the correct timing of the individual blasts.

LHD vehicle

The versatile load-haul-dump vehicle (see figure 74.10) is used for a variety of services including ore production and materials handling. It is available in a choice of sizes allowing miners to select the model most appropriate for each task and each situation. Unlike the other diesel vehicles used in mines, the LHD vehicle engine is generally run continuously at full power for long periods of time generating large volumes of smoke and exhaust fumes. A ventilation system capable of diluting and exhausting these fumes is essential to compliance with acceptable breathing standards in the loading area.

Underground haulage

The ore recovered in stopes spread along an orebody is transported to an ore dump located close to the hoisting shaft. Special haulage levels are prepared for longer lateral transfer; they commonly feature rail track installations with trains for ore transport. Rail has proved to be an efficient transport system carrying larger volumes for longer distances with electric locomotives that do not contaminate the underground atmosphere like diesel-powered trucks used in trackless mines.

Ore handling

On its route from the stopes to the hoisting shaft, the ore passes several stations with a variety of materials-handling techniques.

The *slusher* uses a scraper bucket to draw ore from the stope to the ore pass. It is equipped with rotating drums, wires and pulleys, arranged to produce a back and forth scraper route. The slusher does not need preparation of the stope flooring and can draw ore from a rough muckpile.

The *LHD vehicle*, diesel powered and travelling on rubber tyres, takes the volume held in its bucket (sizes vary) from the muckpile to the ore pass.

The *ore pass* is a vertical or steeply inclined opening through which rock flows by gravity from upper to lower levels. Ore passes are sometimes arranged in a vertical sequence to collect ore from upper levels to a common delivery point on the haulage level.

The *chute* is the gate located at the bottom of the ore pass. Ore passes normally end in rock close to the haulage drift so that, when the chute is opened, the ore can flow to fill cars on the track beneath it.

Close to the shaft, the ore trains pass a *dump station* where the load may be dropped into a *storage bin*, A *grizzly* at the dump station stops oversized rocks from falling into the bin. These boulders are split by blasting or hydraulic hammers; a *coarse crusher* may be installed below the grizzly for further size control. Under the storage bin is a *measure pocket* which automatically verifies that the load's volume and weight do not exceed the capacities of the skip and the hoist. When an empty *skip*, a container for vertical travel, arrives at the *filling station*, a chute opens in the bottom of the measure pocket filling the skip with a proper load. After the *hoist* lifts the loaded skip to the headframe on the surface, a chute opens to discharge the load into the surface storage bin. Skip hoisting can be automatically operated using closed-circuit television to monitor the process.

UNDERGROUND COAL MINING

Simon Walker

Underground coal production first began with access tunnels, or adits, being mined into seams from their surface outcrops. However, problems caused by inadequate means of transport to bring coal to the surface and by the increasing risk of igniting pockets of methane from candles and other open flame lights limited the depth to which early underground mines could be worked.

Increasing demand for coal during the Industrial Revolution gave the incentive for shaft sinking to access deeper coal reserves, and by the mid-twentieth century by far the greater proportion of world coal production came from underground operations. During the 1970s and 1980s there was widespread development of new surface coal mine capacity, particularly in countries such as the United States, South Africa, Australia and India. In the 1990s, however, renewed interest in underground mining resulted in new mines being developed (in Queensland, Australia, for instance) from the deepest points of former surface mines. In the mid-1990s, underground mining accounted for perhaps 45% of all the hard coal mined worldwide. The actual proportion varied widely, ranging from under 30% in Australia and India to around 95% in China. For economic reasons, lignite and brown coal are rarely mined underground.

An underground coal mine consists essentially of three components: a production area; coal transport to the foot of a shaft or decline; and either hoisting or conveying the coal to the surface. Production also includes the preparatory work that is needed in order to permit access to future production areas of a mine and, in consequence, represents the highest level of personal risk.

Mine Development

The simplest means of accessing a coal seam is to follow it in from its surface outcrop, a still widely practised technique in areas where the overlying topography is steep and the seams are relatively flat-lying. An example is the Appalachian coalfield of southern West Virginia in the United States. The actual mining method used in the seam is immaterial at this point; the important factor is that access can be gained cheaply and with minimal construction effort. Adits are also commonly used in areas of low-technology coal mining, where the coal produced during mining of the adit can be used to offset its development costs.

Other means of access include declines (or ramps) and vertical shafts. The choice usually depends on the depth of the coal seam being worked: the deeper the seam, the more expensive it is to develop a graded ramp along which vehicles or belt conveyors can operate.

Shaft sinking, in which a shaft is mined vertically downwards from the surface, is both costly and time-consuming and requires a longer lead-time between the commencement of construction and the first coal being mined. In cases where the seams are deep-lying, as in most European countries and in China, shafts often have to be sunk through water-bearing rocks overlying the coal seams. In this instance, specialist techniques, such as ground freezing or grouting, have to be used to prevent water from flowing into the shaft, which is then lined with steel rings or cast concrete to provide a long-term seal.

Declines are typically used to access seams that are too deep for open-cast mining, but which are still relatively near-surface. In the Mpumalanga (eastern Transvaal) coalfield in South Africa, for instance, the mineable seams lie at a depth of no more than 150 m; in some areas, they are mined from opencasts, and in others underground mining is necessary, in which case declines are often used to provide access for mining equipment and to install the belt conveyors used to carry the cut coal out of the mine.

Declines differ from adits in that they are usually excavated in rock, not coal (unless the seam dips at a constant rate), and are mined to a constant gradient to optimize vehicle and conveyor access. An innovation since the 1970s has been the use of belt conveyors running in declines to carry deep-mine production, a system that has advantages over traditional shaft hoisting in terms of capacity and reliability.

Mining Methods

Underground coal mining encompasses two principal methods, of which many variations have evolved to address mining conditions in individual operations. Room-and-pillar extraction involves mining tunnels (or roadways) on a regular grid, often leaving substantial pillars for long-term support of the roof. Longwall mining achieves total extraction of large parts of a coal seam, causing the roof rocks to collapse into the mined-out area.

Room-and-pillar mining

Room-and-pillar mining is the oldest underground coal mining system, and the first to use the concept of regular roof support to protect mine workers. The name room-and-pillar mining derives from the pillars of coal that are left behind on a regular grid to provide *in situ* support to the roof. It has been developed into a high-production, mechanized method that, in some countries, accounts for a substantial proportion of the total underground output. For instance, 60% of underground coal production in the United States comes from room-and-pillar mines. In terms of scale, some mines in South Africa have installed capacities exceeding 10 million tonnes per year from multi-production section operations in seams up to 6 m thick. By contrast, many room-and-pillar mines in the United States are small, operating in seam thicknesses as low as 1 m, with the ability to stop and restart production quickly as market conditions dictate.

Room-and-pillar mining is typically used in shallower seams, where the pressure applied by overlying rocks on the support pillars is not excessive. The system has two key advantages over longwall mining: its flexibility and inherent safety. Its major disadvantage is that recovery of the coal resource is only partial, the precise amount depending on factors such as the depth of the seam below surface and its thickness. Recoveries of up to 60% are possible. Ninety per cent recovery is possible if pillars are mined out as a second phase of the extraction process.

The system is also capable of various levels of technical sophistication, ranging from labour-intensive techniques (such as "basket mining" in which most stages of mining, including coal transport, are manual), to highly mechanized techniques. Coal can be excavated from the tunnel face by using explosives or continuous mining machines. Vehicles or mobile belt conveyors provide mechanized coal transport. Roofbolts and metal or timber strapping are used to support the roadway roof and the intersections between roadways where the open span is greater.

A continuous miner, which incorporates a cutting head and coal loading system mounted on crawler tracks, typically weighs from 50 to 100 tonnes, depending on the operating height in which it is designed to work, the installed power and the width of cut required. Some are equipped with on-board rockbolt installation machines that provide roof support simultaneously with coal cutting; in other cases, separate continuous miner and roofbolter machines are used sequentially.

Coal carriers can be supplied with electric power from an umbilical cable or can be battery or diesel-engine powered. The latter provides greater flexibility. Coal is loaded from the rear of the continuous miner into the vehicle, which then carries a pay-load, typically between 5 and 20 tonnes, a short distance to a feed hopper for the main belt conveyor system. A crusher may be included in the hopper feeder to break oversize coal or rock that could block chutes or damage conveyor belts further along the transport system.

An alternative to vehicular transport is the continuous haulage system, a crawler-mounted, flexible sectional conveyor that transports cut coal directly from the continuous miner to the hopper. These offer advantages in terms of personnel safety and productive capacity, and their use is being extended to longwall gateroad development systems for the same reasons.

Roadways are mined to widths of 6.0 m, normally the full height of the seam. Pillar sizes depend on the depth below surface; 15.0 m square pillars on 21.0 m centres would be representative of pillar design for a shallow, low-seam mine.

Longwall mining

Longwall mining is widely perceived to be a twentieth century development; however, the concept is actually believed to have been developed over 200 years earlier. The main advance is that earlier operations were principally manual, while, since the 1950s, the level of mechanization has increased to the stage that a longwall face is now a high-productivity unit which can be operated by a very small crew of workers.

Longwalling has one overriding advantage compared to room-and-pillar mining: it can achieve full extraction of the panel in one pass and recovers a higher overall proportion of the total coal resource. However, the method is relatively inflexible and demands both a large mineable resource and guaranteed sales to be viable, because of the high capital costs involved in developing and equipping a modern longwall face (over US$20 million in some cases).

While in the past individual mines often simultaneously operated several longwall faces (in countries such as Poland, over ten per mine in a number of cases), the current trend is towards consolidation of mining capacity into fewer, heavy-duty units. The advantages of this are reduced labour requirements and the need for less extensive underground infrastructure development and maintenance.

In longwall mining the roof is deliberately collapsed as the seam is mined out; only major access routes underground are protected by support pillars. Roof control is provided on a longwall face by two- or four-leg hydraulic supports which take the immediate load of the overlying roof, permitting its partial distribution to the unmined face and the pillars on either side of the panel, and protect the face equipment and personnel from collapsed roof behind the line of supports. Coal is cut by an electric-powered shearer, usually equipped with two coal-cutting drums, that mines a strip of coal up to 1.1 m thick from the face with each pass. The shearer runs along and loads the cut coal onto an armoured conveyor that snakes forward after each cut by sequential movement of the face supports.

At the face end, the cut coal is transferred to a belt conveyor for transport to the surface. In an advancing face, the belt must be extended regularly as the distance from the face starting point increases, while in retreat-longwalling the opposite applies.

Over the past 40 years, there have been substantial increases in both the length of the longwall face mined and the length of the individual longwall panel (the block of coal through which the face progresses). By way of illustration, in the United States the average longwall face length rose from 150 m in 1980 to 227 m in 1993. In Germany the mid-1990s average was 270 m and face lengths of over 300 m are being planned. In both the United Kingdom and Poland, faces are mined up to 300 m long. Panel lengths are largely determined by geological conditions, such as faults, or by mine boundaries, but are now consistently over

2.5 km in good conditions. The possibility of panels up to 6.7 km long is being discussed in the United States.

Retreat mining is becoming the industry standard, although it involves higher initial capital expenditure in roadway development to the furthest extent of each panel before longwalling can begin. Where possible, roadways are now mined in-seam, using continuous miners, with rockbolt support replacing the steel arches and trusses that were used previously in order to provide positive support to the overlying rocks, rather than passive reaction to rock movements. It is limited in applicability, however, to competent roof rocks.

Safety Precautions

Statistics from the ILO (1994) indicate a wide geographical variation in the rate fatalities occur in coal mining, although these data have to take into account the level of mining sophistication and the number of workers employed on a country-by-country basis. Conditions have improved in many industrialized countries.

Major mining incidents are now relatively infrequent, as engineering standards have improved and fire-resistance has been incorporated into materials such as the conveyor belting and hydraulic fluids used underground. Nonetheless, the potential for incidents capable of causing either personal or structural damage remains. Methane gas and coal dust explosions still occur, despite vastly improved ventilation practices, and roof falls account for the majority of serious accidents on a world-wide basis. Fires, either on equipment or occurring as a result of spontaneous combustion, represent a particular hazard.

Considering the two extremes, labour-intensive and highly mechanized mining, there are also wide differences in both accident rates and the types of incident involved. Workers employed in a small-scale, manual mine are more likely to incur injury through falls of rock or coal from the roadway roof or sidewalls. They also risk greater exposure to dust and flammable gas if ventilation systems are inadequate.

Both room-and-pillar mining and the development of roadways to provide access to longwall panels require support to the roof and sidewall rocks. The type and density of support varies according to the seam thickness, competence of the overlying rocks and the depth of the seam, among other factors. The most hazardous place in any mine is beneath an unsupported roof, and most countries impose strict legislative constraints on the length of roadway that may be developed before support is installed. Pillar recovery in room-and-pillar operations presents specific hazards through the potential for sudden roof collapse and must be scheduled carefully to prevent increased risk to workers.

Modern high-productivity longwall faces require a team of six to eight operators, so the number of people exposed to potential hazards is markedly reduced. Dust generated by the longwall shearer is a major concern. Coal cutting is thus sometimes restricted to one direction along the face to take advantage of the ventilation flow to carry dust away from the shearer operators. The heat generated by increasingly powerful electric machines in the confines of the face also has potentially deleterious effects on face workers, especially as mines become deeper.

The speed at which shearers work along the face is also increasing. Cutting rates of up to 45 m/minute are under active consideration in the late 1990s. The ability of workers physically to keep up with the coal cutter moving repeatedly over a 300 m-long face for a full working shift is doubtful, and increasing shearer speed is thus a major incentive to the wider introduction of automation systems for which miners would act as monitors rather than as hands-on operators.

The recovery of face equipment and its transfer to a new worksite offers unique hazards for workers. Innovative methods have been developed for securing the longwall roof and face coal in order to minimize the risk of rock falls during the transfer operation. However, the individual items of machinery are extremely heavy (over 20 tonnes for a large face support and considerably more for a shearer), and despite the use of custom-designed transporters, there remains the risk of personal crushing or lifting injuries during longwall salvage.

SURFACE MINING METHODS

Thomas A. Hethmon and Kyle B. Dotson

Mine Development

Pit planning and layout

The overall economic goal in surface mining is to remove the least amount of material while gaining the greatest return on investment by processing the most marketable mineral product. The higher the grade of the mineral deposit, the greater the value. To minimize capital investment while accessing the highest valued material within a mineral deposit, a mine plan is developed that precisely details the manner in which the ore body will be extracted and processed. As many ore deposits are not a uniform shape, the mine plan is preceded by extensive exploratory drilling to profile the geology and position of the ore body. The size of the mineral deposit dictates the size and layout of the mine. The layout of a surface mine is dictated by the mineralogy and geology of the area. The shape of most open-pit mines approximates a cone but always reflects the shape of the mineral deposit being developed. Open-pit mines are constructed of a series of concentric ledges or benches that are bisected by mine access and haulage roads angling down from the rim of the pit to the bottom in a spiral or zigzag orientation. Regardless of size, the mine plan includes provisions for pit development, infrastructure, (e.g., storage, offices and maintenance) transportation, equipment, mining ratios and rates. Mining rates and ratios influence the life of the mine which is defined by depletion of the ore body or realization of an economic limit.

Contemporary open-pit mines vary in scale from small privately-operated enterprises processing a few hundred tonnes of ore per day to expanded industrial complexes operated by governments and multinational corporations that mine more than one million tonnes of material per day. The largest operations can involve many square kilometres in area.

Stripping overburden

Overburden is waste rock consisting of consolidated and unconsolidated material that must be removed to expose the underlying ore body. It is desirable to remove as little overburden as possible in order to access the ore of interest, but a larger volume of waste rock is excavated when the mineral deposit is deep. Most removal techniques are cyclical with interruption in the extraction (drilling, blasting and loading) and removal (haulage) phases. This is particularly true for hard rock overburden which must be drilled and blasted first. An exception to this cyclical effect are dredges used in hydraulic surface mining and some types of loose material mining with bucket wheel excavators. The fraction of waste rock to ore excavated is defined as the stripping ratio. Stripping ratios of 2:1 up to 4:1 are not uncommon in large mining operations. Ratios above 6:1 tend to be less economically viable, depending on the commodity. Once removed, overburden can be used for road and tailings construction or may have non-mining commercial value as fill dirt.

Mining equipment selection

The selection of mining equipment is a function of the mine plan. Some of the factors considered in the selection of mine equipment include the topography of the pit and surrounding area, the amount of ore to be mined, the speed and distance the ore must be transported for processing and the estimated mine life, among others. In general, most contemporary surface mining operations rely on mobile drill rigs, hydraulic shovels, front-end loaders, scrapers and haul trucks to extract ore and initiate ore processing. The larger the mine operation, the larger the capacity of equipment required to maintain the mine plan. Equipment is generally the largest available to match the economy of scale of surface mines with consideration for matching the capacities of equipment. For example, a small front-end loader can fill a large haul truck but the match is not efficient. Similarly, a large shovel can load smaller trucks but requires the trucks to decrease their cycle times and does not optimize utilization of the shovel since one shovel bucket may contain enough ore for more than one truck. Safety may be compromised by attempting to load only half of a bucket or if a truck is overloaded. Also, the scale of equipment selected must match the available maintenance facilities. Large equipment is often maintained where it malfunctions due to the logistical difficulties associated with transporting it to established maintenance facilities. When possible, the mine's maintenance facilities are designed to accommodate the scale and quantity of the mine equipment. Therefore, as new larger equipment is introduced into the mine plan, the supporting infrastructure, including the size and quality of haul roads, tools and maintenance facilities, must also be addressed.

Conventional Methods of Surface Mining

Open-pit mining and strip mining are the two major categories of surface mining which account for more than 90% worldwide surface mining production. The primary differences between these mining methods are the location of the ore body and the mode of mechanical extraction. For loose rock mining, the process is essentially continuous with extraction and haulage steps running in series. Solid rock mining requires a discontinuous process of drilling and blasting prior to the loading and hauling stages. *Strip mining* (or open-cast mining) techniques relate to the extraction of ore bodies that are near the surface and relatively flat or tabular in nature and mineral seams. It uses a variety of different types of equipment including shovels, trucks, drag lines, bucket wheel excavators and scrapers. Most strip mines process non-hard rock deposits. Coal is the most common commodity that is strip mined from surface seams. In contrast, *open-pit mining* is employed to remove hard rock ore that is disseminated and/or located in deep seams and is typically limited to extraction by shovel and truck equipment. Many metals are mined by the open-pit technique: gold, silver and copper, to name a few.

Quarrying is a term used to describe a specialized open-pit mining technique wherein solid rock with a high degree of consolidation and density is extracted from localized deposits. Quarried materials are either crushed and broken to produce aggregate or building stone, such as dolomite and limestone, or combined with other chemicals to produce cement and lime. Construction materials are produced from quarries located in close proximity to the site of material use to reduce transportation costs. Dimension stone such as flagstone, granite, limestone, marble, sandstone and slate represent a second class of quarried materials. Dimension stone quarries are found in areas having the desired mineral characteristics which may or may not be geographically remote and require transportation to user markets.

Many ore bodies are too diffuse and irregular, or too small or deep to be mined by strip or open-pit methods and must be extracted by the more surgical approach of underground mining. To determine when open-pit mining is applicable, a number of factors must be considered, including the terrain and elevation of the site and region, its remoteness, climate, infrastructure such as roads, power and water supply, regulatory and environmental requirements, slope stability, overburden disposal and product transportation, among others.

Terrain and elevation: Topography and elevation also play an important role in defining the feasibility and scope of a mining project. In general, the higher the elevation and rougher the terrain, the more difficult mine development and production are likely to be. A higher grade of mineral in an inaccessible mountainous location may be mined less efficiently than a lower grade of ore in a flat location. Mines located at lower elevations generally experience less inclement weather-related problems for exploration, development and production of mines. As such, topography and location affect the mining method as well as economic feasibility.

The decision to develop a mine occurs after exploration has characterized the ore deposit and feasibility studies have defined the options for mineral extraction and processing. Information that is necessary to establish a development plan may include the shape, size and grade of minerals in the ore body, the total volume or tonnage of material including overburden and other factors, such as hydrology and access to a source of process water, availability and source of power, waste rock storage sites, transportation requirements and infrastructure features, including the location of population centres to support the labour force or the need to develop a townsite. Transportation requirements may include roads, highways, pipelines, airports, railroads, waterways and harbours.

For surface mines, large land areas are generally required that may have no existing infrastructure. In such instances roads, utilities and living arrangements must be established first. The pit would be developed in connection with other processing elements such as waste rock storage areas, crushers, concentrators, smelters and refineries, depending on the degree of integration required. Due to the large amount of capital necessary to finance these operations, development may be conducted in phases to take advantage of the earliest possible saleable or leasable mineral to help finance the remainder of the development.

Production and Equipment

Drilling and blasting

Mechanical drilling and blasting are the first steps in extracting ore from most developed open-pit mines and are the most common method used to remove hard rock overburden. While there are many mechanical devices capable of loosening hard rock, explosives are the preferred method as no mechanical device can currently match the fracturing capability of energy contained in explosive charges. A commonly used hard rock explosive is ammonium nitrate. Drilling equipment is selected on the basis of the nature of the ore and the speed and depth of the holes necessary to fracture a specified tonnage of ore per day. For example, in mining a 15-m bench of ore, 60 or more holes will generally be drilled 15 m back from the current muck face depending on the length of the bench to be mined. This must occur with enough lead-time to allow for site preparation for subsequent loading and haulage activities.

Loading

Surface mining is now typically conducted utilizing table shovels, front-end loaders or hydraulic shovels. In open-pit mining loading equipment is matched with haul trucks that can be loaded in three to five cycles or passes of the shovel; however, various factors determine the preference of loading equipment. With sharp rock and/or hard digging and/or wet climates, tracked shovels are preferable. Conversely, rubber-tyred loaders have much lower capital cost and are preferred for loading material that is low volume and easy to dig. Additionally, loaders are very mobile and well-suited for mining scenarios requiring rapid movements from one area to another or for ore blending requirements. Loaders are also frequently used to load, haul and dump material into crushers from blending stock piles deposited near crushers by haul trucks.

Hydraulic shovels and cable shovels have similar advantages and limitations. Hydraulic shovels are not preferred for digging hard rock and cable shovels are generally available in larger sizes. Therefore, large cable shovels with payloads of about 50 cubic metres and greater are the preferred equipment at mines were production exceeds 200,000 tonnes per day. Hydraulic shovels are more versatile on the mine face and allow greater operator control to selectively load the from either the bottom or top half of the mine face. This advantage is helpful where separation of waste from ore can be achieved at the loading zone thereby maximizing the ore grade that is hauled and processed.

Hauling

Haulage in open-pit and strip mines is most commonly accomplished by haul trucks. The role of haul trucks in many surface mines is restricted to cycling between the loading zone and the transfer point such as an in-pit crushing station or conveyance system. Haul trucks are favoured based on their flexibility of operation relative to railroads, which were the preferred haulage method until the 1960s. However, the cost of transporting materials in surface metal and non-metal pits is generally greater than 50% of the total operating cost of the mine. In-pit crushing and conveying through belt conveyor systems has been a primary factor in reducing haulage costs. Technical developments in haul trucks such as diesel engines and electrical drives have lead to much larger capacity vehicles. Several manufactures currently produce 240 tonne capacity trucks with expectation for greater than 310 tonne capacity trucks in the near future. In addition, the use of computerized dispatch systems and global satellite positioning technology allow vehicles to be tracked and scheduled with improved efficiency and productivity.

Haul road systems may use single or dual direction traffic. Traffic may be either left or right lane configuration. Left lane traffic is frequently preferred to improve operator visibility of tyre position on very large trucks. Safety is also improved with left hand traffic by reducing the potential for driver-side collision in the centre of a road. Haul road gradients are typically limited to between 8 and 15% for sustained hauls and optimally are about 7 to 8%. Safety and water drainage requires long gradients to include at least 45-m sections with a maximum gradient of 2% for every 460 m of severe gradient. Road berms (elevated dirt borders) located between roads and adjacent excavations are standard safety features in surface mines. They may also be placed in the middle of the road to separate opposing traffic. Where switch-back haul roads exist, increasing elevation escape lanes may be installed at the end of long steep grades. Road edge barriers such as berms are standard and should be located between all roads and adjacent excavations. High-quality roads enhance maximum productivity by maximizing safe truck speeds, reduced down-time for maintenance and reduced driver fatigue. Haul-truck road maintenance contributes to reduced operating costs through reduced fuel consumption, longer tyre life and reduced repair costs.

Rail haulage, under the best of conditions, is superior to other methods of haulage for transport of ore over long distances outside the mine. However, as a practical matter, rail haulage is no longer widely used in open-pit mining since the advent of electrical and diesel-powered trucks. Rail haulage was replaced to capitalize on the greater versatility and flexibility of haul trucks and in-pit conveyor systems. Railroads requires very gentle grades of 0.5 to a maximum of 3% for up-hill hauls. Capital investment for railroad engines and track requirements is very high and requires a long mine life and large production outputs to justify return on investment.

Ore handling (conveyance)

In-pit crushing and conveying is a methodology that has grown in popularity since first being implemented in the mid-1950s. Location of a semi-mobile crusher in the mine pit with the subsequent transport out of the pit by a conveyor system has resulted in significant production advantages and cost savings over traditional vehicle haulage. High cost haulage road construction and maintenance is reduced and labour costs associated with haul truck operation and truck maintenance and fuel are minimized.

The purpose of the in-pit crusher system is primarily to allow transport of ore by conveyor. In-pit crusher systems may range from permanent facilities to fully mobile units. However, more commonly, crushers are constructed in a modular form to allow some portability within the mine. Crushers might be relocated every one to ten years; it may require hours, days or months to complete the move depending on the size and complexity of the unit and the relocation distance. Conveyors' advantages over haul trucks include instantaneous start up, automatic and continuous operation, and a high degree of reliability with up 90 to 95% availability. They are generally not impaired by inclement weather. Conveyors also have much lower labour requirements relative to haul trucks; operating and maintaining a truck fleet may require ten times as many crew members as an equivalent-capacity conveyor system. Also, conveyors can operate at grades up to 30% while maximum grades for trucks are generally 10%. Using steeper grades lowers the need to remove low-grade overburden material and may reduce the need to establish high cost haulage roads. Conveyors systems are also integrated into bucket wheel shovels in many surface coal operations, which eliminates the need for haulage trucks.

Solution Mining Methods

Solution mining, the most common of two types of aqueous mining, is employed to extract soluble ore where conventional mining methods are less efficient and/or less economical. Also known as leaching or surface leaching, this technique can be a primary mining method, as with gold and silver leach mining, or it can supplement the conventional pyrometallurgical steps of smelting and refining, as in the case of leaching low-grade copper oxide ores. Regardless of the necessity or economic advantage, all surface solution methods share two common characteristics: (1) ore is mined in the usual way and then stockpiled; and, (2) an aqueous solution is applied to the top of the ore stock which reacts chemically with the metal of interest from which the resulting metal salt solution is channelled through the stock pile for collection and processing. The application of surface solution mining is dependent on the volume, the metallurgy of the mineral(s) of interest and the related host rock, and available area and drainage to develop sufficiently large leach dumps to make the operation economically viable.

The development of leach dumps in a surface mine in which solution mining is the primary production method is the same as all open-pit operations with the exception that the ore is destined solely for the dump and not a mill. In mines with both milling and solution methods, ore is segregated into milled and leached portions. For example, most copper sulphide ore is milled and purified to market grade copper by smelting and refining. Copper

Environmental aspects of surface mining

The significant environmental effects of surface mines attract attention wherever the mines are located. Alteration of terrain, destruction of plant life and adverse effects on indigenous animals are inevitable consequences of surface mining. Contamination of surface and underground waters often presents problems, particularly with the use of lixiviants in solution mining and the run-off from hydraulic mining.

Thanks to the increased attention from environmentalists around the world and the use of planes and aerial photography, mining enterprises are no longer free to "dig and run" when the extraction of the desired ore has been complete. Laws and regulations have been promulgated in most of the developed countries and, through the activities of international organizations, are being urged where they do not yet exist. They establish an environmental management programme as an integral element in every mining project and stipulate such requirements as preliminary environmental impact assessments; progressive rehabilitation programmes, including restoration of land contours, reforestation, replanting of indigenous fauna, restocking of indigenous wild life and so on; as well as concurrent and long-term compliance auditing (UNEP 1991, UN 1992, Environmental Protection Agency (Australia) 1996, ICME 1996). It is essential that these be more than statements in the documentation required for the necessary government licenses. The basic principles must be accepted and practised by managers in the field and communicated to workers on all levels.

oxide ore, which is not generally amenable to pyrometallurgical processing, is routed to leach operations. Once the dump is developed, the solution leaches the soluble metal from the surrounding rock at a predictable rate that is controlled by the design parameters of the dump, the nature and volume of the solution applied, and the concentration and mineralogy of the metal in the ore. The solution used to extract the soluble metal is referred to as a *lixiviant*. The most common lixiviants used in this mining sector are dilute solutions of alkaline sodium cyanide for gold, acidic sulphuric acid for copper, aqueous sulphur dioxide for manganese and sulphuric acid-ferric sulphate for uranium ores; however, most leached uranium and soluble salts are collected by *in-situ* mining in which the lixiviant is injected directly into the ore body without prior mechanical extraction. This latter technique enables low-grade ores to be processed without extracting the ore from the mineral deposit.

Health and safety aspects

The occupational health and safety hazards associated with mechanical extraction of the ore in solution mining are essentially similar to those of conventional surface mine operations. An exception to this generalization is the need for non-leaching ore to undergo primary crushing in the surface mine pit before being conveyed to a mill for conventional processing, whereas ore is generally transported by haul truck directly from the extraction site to the leach dump in solution mining. Solution mining workers would therefore have less exposure to primary crushing hazards such as dust, noise and physical hazards. The leading causes of injuries in surface mine environments include materials handling, slips and falls, machinery, hand-tool use, power haulage and electrical source contact. However, unique to solution mining is the potential exposure to the chemical lixiviants during transportation, leach field activities and chemical and electrolytic processing. Acid mist exposures may occur in metal electrowinning tankhouses. Ionizing radiation hazards, which increase propor-

tionally from extraction to concentration, must be addressed in uranium mining.

Hydraulic Mining Methods

In hydraulic mining, or "hydraulicking", high pressure water spray is used to excavate loosely consolidated or unconsolidated material into a slurry for processing. Hydraulic methods are applied primarily to metal and aggregate stone deposits, although coal, sandstone and metal mill tailings are also amenable to this method. The most common and best known application is *placer mining* in which concentrations of metals such as gold, titanium, silver, tin and tungsten are washed from within an alluvial deposit (placer). Water supply and pressure, ground slope gradient for runoff, distance from the mine face to the processing facilities, degree of consolidation of the mineable material and the availability of waste disposal areas are all primary considerations in the development of a hydraulic mining operation. As with other surface mining, the applicability is location specific. Inherent advantages of this method mining include relatively low operating costs and flexibility resulting from the use of simple, rugged and mobile equipment. As a result, many hydraulic operations develop in remote mining areas where infrastructure requirements are not a limitation.

Unlike other types of surface mining, hydraulic techniques rely on water as the medium for both mining and conveyance of the mined material ("sluicing"). High pressure water sprays are delivered by monitors or water cannons to a placer bank or mineral deposit. They disintegrate gravel and unconsolidated material, which washes into collection and processing facilities. Water pressures may vary from a normal gravity flow for very loose fine materials to thousands of kilograms per square centimetre for unconsolidated deposits. Bulldozers and graders or other mobile excavating equipment are sometimes employed to facilitate mining of more compacted materials. Historically, and in modern small-scale operations, the collection of the slurry or runoff is managed with small volume sluice boxes and catches. Commercial-scale operations rely on pumps, containment and settling basins and separation equipment that can process very large volumes of slurry per hour. Depending on the size of the deposit to be mined, the operation of the water monitors may be manual, remotely controlled or computer controlled.

When hydraulic mining occurs underwater it is referred to as dredging. In this method a floating processing station extracts loose deposits such as clay, silt, sand, gravel and any associated minerals using a bucket line, drag line and/or submerged water jets. The mined material is transported hydraulically or mechanically to a washing station which may be part of the dredging rig or physically separate with subsequent processing steps to segregate and complete processing. While dredging is used to extract commercial minerals and aggregate stone, it is best known as a technique used to clear and deepen water channels and floodplains.

Health and safety

Physical hazards in hydraulic mining differ from those in surface mining methods. Due to the minimal application of drilling, explosives, haulage and reduction activities, safety hazards tend to be associated mostly often with high pressure water systems, manual movement of mobile equipment, proximity issues involving power supplies and water, proximity issues associated with collapse of the mine face and maintenance activities. Health hazards primarily involve exposure to noise and dusts and ergonomic hazards related to equipment handling. Dust exposure is generally less of an issue than in traditional surface mining due to the use of water as the mining medium. Maintenance activities such as uncontrolled welding may also contribute to worker exposures.

SURFACE COAL MINING MANAGEMENT

Paul Westcott

The geological characteristics of surface coal mining which distinguish it from other surface mining are the nature of formation and its relatively low value, which often require surface coal mines to move large volumes of overburden over a large area (i.e., it has a high stripping ratio). As a result, surface coal mines have developed specialized equipment and mining techniques. Examples include a dragline strip mine which mines in strips of 30 to 60 m wide, sidecasting material in pits up to 50 km long. Rehabilitation is an integral part of the mining cycle due to the significant disturbance of the involved areas.

Surface coal mines vary from being small (i.e., producing less than 1 million tonnes per annum) to large (above 10 million tonnes per annum). The workforce required depends on the size and type of the mine, the size and amount of equipment and the amount of coal and overburden. There are some typical measurements which indicate the productivity and size of the workforce. These are:

1. Output per miner expressed as tonnes per miner per year; this would range from 5,000 tonnes per miner per year to 40,000 tonnes per miner per year.
2. Total material moved expressed in tonnes per miner per year. This productivity indicator combines the coal and the overburden; productivity of 100,000 tonnes per miner per year would be low with 400,000 tonnes per miner per year being the very productive end of the scale.

Due to the large capital investment involved, many coal mines operate on a seven day continuous shift roster. This involves four crews: three work three shifts of eight hours each with the fourth crew covering rostered time off.

Mine Planning

Mine planning for surface coal mines is a repetitive process which can be summarized in a checklist. The cycle begins with geology and marketing and finishes with an economic evaluation. The level of detail (and cost) of the planning increases as the project goes through different stages of approval and development. Feasibility studies cover the work prior to development. The same checklist is used after production commences to develop annual and five-year plans as well as plans for closing down the mine and rehabilitating the area when all the coal has been extracted.

Significantly, the need for planning is ongoing and the plans need frequent updating to reflect changes in the market, technology, legislation and knowledge of the deposit learned as the mining progresses.

Geological Influences

Geological features have a major influence in the selection of the mining method and equipment used in a particular surface coal mine.

Seam attitude, commonly known as *dip*, represents the angle between the seam being mined and the horizontal plane. The steeper the dip the more difficult it is to mine. The dip also affects the stability of the mine; the limiting dip for dragline operations is around 7°.

The *strength* of coal and waste rock determines what equipment can be used and whether or not the material has to be blasted. Continuous mining equipment, such as bucketwheel excavators commonly used in eastern Europe and Germany, is limited to material of very low strength that does not require

blasting. Typically, however, the overburden is too hard to be dug without some blasting to fragment the rock into smaller sized pieces which can then be excavated by shovels and mechanical equipment.

As the *depth* of coal seams increase, the cost of transporting the waste and coal to the surface or to the dump becomes higher. At some point, it would become more economical to mine by underground methods than by open-cut methods.

Seams as thin as 50 mm can be mined but the recovery of coal becomes more difficult and expensive as *seam thickness* decreases.

Hydrology refers to the amount of water in the coal and overburden. Significant quantities of water affect stability and the pumping requirements add to the cost.

The magnitude of the coal *reserves* and the scale of operation influences what equipment can be used. Small mines require smaller and relatively more expensive equipment, whereas large mines enjoy the economies of scale and lower costs per unit of production.

Environmental characteristics refers to the behaviour of the overburden after it has been mined. Some overburden is termed "acid producing" which means that when exposed to air and water it will produce acid which is detrimental to the environment and requires special treatment.

The combination of the above factors plus others determines which mining method and equipment is appropriate for a particular surface coal mine.

The Mining Cycle

Surface coal mining methodology can be broken into a series of steps.

Removing topsoil and either storing it or replacing it on areas being rehabilitated is an important part of the cycle as the objective is to return the land use to at least as good a condition as it was before mining began. Topsoil is an important component as it contains plant nutrients.

Ground preparation may involve using explosives to fragment the large rocks. In some instances, this is done by bulldozers with rippers which use mechanical force to break the rock into smaller pieces. Some mines where the strength of the rock is low require no ground preparation as the excavator can dig directly from the bank.

Waste removal is the process of mining the rock overlying the coal seam and transporting it to the dump. In a strip mine where the dump is in an adjacent strip, it is a sidecast operation. In some mines, however, the dump may be several kilometres away due to the structure of the seam and available dump space and transport to the dump by trucks or conveyors is necessary.

Coal mining is the process of removing the coal from the exposed face in the mine and transporting it out of the pit. What happens next depends on the location of the coal market and its end use. If fed to an onsite power station, it is pulverised and goes directly to the boiler. If the coal is low grade it may be upgraded by "washing" the coal in a preparation plant. This separates the coal and overburden to yield a higher grade product. Before it is sent to market, this coal usually needs some crushing to get it to a uniform size, and blending to control variations in quality. It may be transported by road, conveyor, train, barge or ship.

Rehabilitation involves shaping the dump to restore the terrain and meet drainage criteria, replacing topsoil and planting vegetation to return it to its original state. Other environmental management considerations include:

- *water management*: diversion of existing water courses and control of mine water by sediment dams and recycling so that contaminated water is not discharged
- *visual planning* : ensuring that the visual impact is minimized
- *flora and fauna*: to restoring trees and vegetation and replace indigenous wild life

- *archaeology*: preservation and/or restoration of culturally significant sites
- *final void*: what to do with the hole after mining has stopped (e.g., it may be filled in or turned into a lake)
- *air blast and vibration*, due to blasting, which need to be managed by specific techniques if buildings are nearby
- *noise and dust*, which need to be managed to avoid creating a nuisance for nearby dwellings and communities.

The impact of surface coal mining on the overall environment can be significant but with appropriate planning and control throughout all phases of the enterprise, it can be managed to meet all requirements.

Mining Methods and Equipment

Three main mining methods are used for surface coal mining: truck and shovel; draglines; and conveyor-based systems, such as bucketwheel excavators and in-pit crushers. Many mines use combinations of these, and there are also specializd techniques such as auger mining and continuous highwall miners. These constitute only a small proportion of total surface coal mining production. The dragline and bucketwheel systems were developed specifically for surface coal mining whereas truck and shovel mining systems are used throughout the mining industry.

The *truck and shovel* mining method involves an excavator, such as an electric rope shovel, a hydraulic excavator or a front-end loader, to load overburden into trucks. The size of the trucks can vary from 35 tonnes up to 220 tonnes. The truck transports the overburden from the mining face to the dumping area where a bulldozer will push and pile the rock to shape the dump for rehabilitation. The truck and shovel method is noted for its flexibility; examples are found in most countries of the world.

Draglines are one of the cheapest methods to mine the overburden, but are limited in their operation by the length of the boom,which is generally 100 m long. The dragline swings on its centre point and can therefore dump the material approximately 100 m from where it is sitting. This geometry requires that the mine be laid out in long narrow strips.

The main limitation of the dragline is that it can only dig to a depth of approximately 60 m; beyond this, another form of supplementary overburden removal such as the truck and shovel fleet is required.

Conveyor-based mining systems use conveyors to transport the overburden instead of trucks. Where the overburden is low strength it can be mined directly from the face by a bucketwheel excavator. It is often called a "continuous" mining method because it feeds the overburden and coal without interruption. Draglines and shovels are cyclical with each bucket load taking 30 to 60 seconds. Harder overburden requires a combination of blasting or an in-pit crusher and shovel loading to feed it onto the conveyor. Conveyor-based surface coal mining systems are most suitable where the overburden has to be transported significant distances or up significant heights.

Conclusion

Surface coal mining involves specialized equipment and mining techniques which allow the removal of large volumes of waste and coal from large areas. Rehabilitation is an integral and important part of the process.

● PROCESSING ORE

Sydney Allison

Almost all the metals and other inorganic materials that have been exploited occur as the compounds that constitute the minerals that make up the earth's crust. The forces and processes that have shaped the earth's surface have concentrated these minerals in widely different amounts. When this concentration is sufficiently great so that the mineral can be economically exploited and recovered, the deposit is referred to as an ore or orebody. However, even then the minerals are not usually available in a form with the purity necessary for immediate processing to the desired end product. In his sixteenth century work on mineral processing Agricola (1950) wrote: "Nature usually creates metals in an impure state, mixed with earth, stones, and solidified juices, it is necessary to separate most of these impurities from the ores as far as can be, before they are smelted."

Valuable minerals must first be separated from those of no commercial value, which are called *gangue*. Ore processing refers to this initial treatment of mined material to produce a mineral concentrate of a sufficiently high grade to be satisfactorily processed further to the pure metal or other end product. The differing characteristics of the minerals making up the ore are exploited to separate them from each other by a variety of physical methods that generally leave the chemical composition of the mineral unchanged. (The processing of coal is specifically discussed in the article "Coal preparation".)

Crushing and Grinding

The particle size of the material arriving at the processing plant will depend on the mining operation employed and on the ore type, but it will be relatively large. *Comminution*, the progressive reduction in the particle size of lumpy ore, is carried out for two reasons: to reduce the material to a more convenient size and to liberate the valuable component from the waste material as a first step towards its effective separation and recovery. In practice, comminution usually consists of the crushing of larger-sized material, followed by the breaking of the material to finer sizes by tumbling it in rotating steel mills.

Crushing

It is not possible to progress from very large lumps to fine material in a single operation or using one machine. Crushing thus is usually a dry operation that typically takes place in stages which are designated as primary, secondary and tertiary.

Primary crushers reduce the ore from anything as large as 1.5 m down to 100 to 200 mm. Machines such as jaw and gyratory crushers apply a fracture force to the large particles, breaking the ore by compression.

In a jaw crusher, ore falls into a wedge-shaped space between a fixed and a moving crushing plate. Material is nipped and squeezed until it breaks and released and nipped again further down as the jaws open and close, until it finally escapes through the gap set at the bottom.

In the gyratory crusher, a long spindle carries a heavy, hard steel conical grinding element that is moved eccentrically by a lower bearing sleeve within the crushing chamber or shell. The relative motion of the crushing faces is produced by the gyration of the eccentrically mounted cone against the outer chamber. Typically this machine is used where a high throughput capacity is required.

Secondary crushing reduces the particle size down to 5 to 20 mm. Cone crushers, rolls and hammer mills are examples of the equipment used. The cone crusher is a modified gyratory crusher with a shorter spindle that is not suspended, but supported in a bearing below the head. A roll crusher consists of two horizontal cylinders rotating towards each other, the rolls drawing the ore into the gap between them and after a single nip discharging the product. The hammer mill is a typical impact crusher mill. Comminution is by the impact of sharp blows applied at high speed by hammers attached to a rotor within the work-space.

Grinding

Grinding, the last stage in comminution, is performed in rotating cylindrical steel vessels known as tumbling mills. Here the mineral particles are reduced to between 10 and 300 μm. A grinding medium, such as steel balls, rods or pebbles (pre-sized lumps of ore much larger than the bulk feed of material), is added to the mill so that the ore is broken down to the desired size. The use of pebbles is termed *autogenous grinding*. Where the ore type is suitable, run-of-mine (ROM) milling may be used. In this form of autogenous milling the entire ore stream from the mine is fed directly to the mill without pre-crushing, the large lumps of ore acting as the grinding medium.

The mill is generally loaded with crushed ore and grinding medium to just under half full. Studies have shown that the breaking produced by milling is a combination of both impact and abrasion. Mill liners are used to protect the mill shell from wear and, by their design, to reduce slip of the grinding media and improve the lifting and impact portion of milling.

There is an optimal size to which ore must be ground for effective separation and recovery of the valuable component. Undergrinding results in incomplete liberation and poor recovery. Overgrinding increases the difficulty of separation, besides using an excess of expensive energy.

Sizing Separation

After crushing and milling, the products are usually separated simply according to their size. The primary purpose is to produce appropriately sized feed material for further treatment. Oversize material is recycled for further reduction.

Screens

Screening is generally applied to fairly coarse material. It may also be used to produce a reasonably uniform feed size for a subsequent operation where this is required. The grizzly is a series of heavy parallel bars set in a frame that screens out very coarse material. The trommel is an inclined rotating cylindrical screen. By use of a number of sections of different sized screens, several sized products can be simultaneously produced. A variety of other screens and screen combinations may be employed.

Classifiers

Classification is the separation of particles according to their settling rate in a fluid. Differences in density, size and shape are effectively utilized. Classifiers are used to separate coarse and fine material, thereby fractionizing a large size distribution. A typical application is to control a closed-circuit grinding operation. While size separation is the primary objective, some separation by mineral type usually occurs due to density differences.

In a spiral classifier, a rake mechanism lifts the coarser sands from a slurry pool to produce a clean de-slimed product.

The hydrocyclone uses centrifugal force to accelerate settling rates and produce efficient separations of fine-sized particles. A slurry suspension is introduced at high velocity tangentially into a conical shaped vessel. Due to the swirling motion, the faster settling, larger and heavier particles move towards the outer wall, where the velocity is lowest, and settle downwards, while the lighter and smaller particles move towards the zone of low pressure along the axis, where they are carried upward.

Concentration Separation

Concentration separation requires particles to be distinguished as being either those of the valuable mineral or as gangue particles and their effective separation into a concentrate and a tailing product. The objective is to achieve maximum recovery of the valuable mineral at a grade that is acceptable for further processing or sale.

Ore sorting

The oldest and simplest method of concentration is the selection of particles visually and their removal by hand. Hand sorting has its modern equivalents in a number of electronic methods. In photometric methods, particle recognition is based on the difference in reflectivity of different minerals. A blast of compressed air is then activated to remove them from a moving belt of material. The differing conductivity of different minerals may be utilized in a similar manner.

Heavy medium separation

Heavy medium or dense medium separation is a process that depends only on the density difference between minerals. It involves introducing the mixture into a liquid with a density lying between that of the two minerals to be separated, the lighter mineral then floats and the heavier sinks. In some processes it is used for the preconcentration of minerals prior to a final grind and is frequently employed as a cleaning step in coal preparation.

Heavy organic fluids such as tetrabromoethane, which has a relative density of 2.96, are used in certain applications, but on a commercial scale suspensions of finely ground solids that behave as simple Newtonian fluids are generally employed. Examples of the material used are magnetite and ferrosilicon. These form low-viscosity, inert and stable "fluids" and are easily removed from suspension magnetically.

Gravity

Natural separating processes such as river systems have produced placer deposits where heavier larger particles have been separated from lighter smaller ones. Gravity techniques mimic these natural processes. Separation is brought about by the movement of the particle in response to the force of gravity and the resistance exerted by the fluid in which separation takes place.

Over the years, many types of gravity separators have been developed, and their continued use testifies to the cost-effectiveness of this type of separation.

In a *jig* a bed of mineral particles is brought into suspension ("fluidized") by a pulsating current of water. As the water drains back between each cycle, the denser particles fall below the less dense and during a period of draining small particles, and particularly smaller denser particles, penetrate between the spaces between the larger particles and settle lower in the bed. As the cycle is repeated, the degree of separation increases.

Shaking tables treat finer material than jigs. The table consists of a flat surface that is inclined slightly from front to back and from one end to the other. Wooden riffles divide the table longitudinally at right angles. Feed enters along the top edge, and the particles are carried downwards by the flow of water. At the same time they are subject to asymmetrical vibrations along the longitudinal or horizontal axis. Denser particles which tend to be trapped behind the riffle are shuffled across the table by the vibrations.

Magnetic separation

All materials are influenced by magnetic fields, although for most the effect is too slight to be detected. However, if one of the mineral components of a mixture has a reasonably strong magnetic susceptibility, this can be used to separate it from the others. Magnetic separators are classified into low- and high-intensity machines, and further into dry- and wet-feed separators.

A drum-type separator consists of a rotating non-magnetic drum containing within its shell stationary magnets of alternating polarity. Magnetic particles are attracted by the magnets, pinned to the drum and conveyed out of the magnetic field. A wet high-intensity separator (WHIMS) of the carousel type consists of a concentric rotating matrix of iron balls that passes through a strong electromagnet. Slurried residues are poured into the matrix where the electromagnet operates, and magnetic particles are attracted to the magnetized matrix while the bulk of the slurry passes through and exits via a base grid. Just past the electromagnet, the field is reversed and a stream of water is used to remove the magnetic fraction.

Electrostatic separation

Electrostatic separation, once commonly used, was displaced to a considerable extent by the advent of flotation (see below). However, it is successfully applied to a small number of minerals, such as rutile, for which other methods prove difficult and where the conductivity of the mineral makes electrostatic separation possible.

The method exploits differences in the electrical conductivity of the different minerals. Dry feed is carried into the field of an ionizing electrode where the particles are charged by ion bombardment. Conducting particles rapidly lose this charge to a grounded rotor and are thrown from the rotor by centrifugal force. Non-conductors lose their charge more slowly, remain clinging to the earth conductor by electrostatic forces, and are carried around to a collection point.

Flotation

Flotation is a process of separation that exploits differences in the physico-chemical surface properties of different minerals.

Chemical reagents called collectors are added to the pulp and react selectively with the surface of the valuable mineral particles. The reaction products formed makes the surface of the mineral hydrophobic or non-wettable, so that it readily attaches to an air bubble.

In each cell of a flotation circuit the pulp is agitated and introduced air is dispersed into the system. The hydrophobic mineral particles attach to the air bubbles and, with a suitable frothing agent present, these form a stable froth at the surface. This continuously overflows the sides of the flotation cell, carrying its mineral load with it.

A flotation plant consist of banks of interconnected cells. A first concentrate produced in rougher bank is cleaned of unwanted gangue components in a cleaner bank, and if necessary recleaned in a third bank of cells. Additional valuable mineral may be scavenged in a fourth bank and recycled to the cleaner banks before the tails are finally discarded.

Dewatering

Following most operations it is necessary to separate the water used in the separation processes from the concentrate produced or from the waste gangue material. In dry environments this is particularly important so that the water may be recycled for re-use.

A settling tank consists of a cylindrical vessel into which pulp is fed at the centre via a feed-well. This is placed below the surface to minimize disturbance of the settled solids. Clarified liquid overflows the sides of the tank into a launder. Radial arms with blades rake the settled solids towards the centre, where they are withdrawn. Flocculants may be added to the suspension to accelerate the settling rate of the solids.

Filtration is the removal of solid particles from the fluid to produce a cake of concentrate that can then be dried and transported. A common form is the continuous vacuum filter, typical of which is the drum filter. A horizontal cylindrical drum rotates in an open tank with the lower section immersed in pulp. The shell of the drum consists of a series of compartments covered by a filter medium. The inner double-walled shell is connected to a valve mechanism on the central shaft that permits either vacuum or pressure to be applied. Vacuum is applied to the section immersed in the pulp, drawing water through the filter and forming a cake of concentrate on the cloth. The vacuum dewaters the cake once out of the slurry. Just before the section re-enters the slurry, pressure is applied to blow off the cake. Disc filters operate on the same principle, but consist of a series of discs attached to the central shaft.

Tailings Disposal

Only a small fraction of the mined ore consists of valuable mineral. The remainder is gangue that after processing forms the tailings that must be disposed of.

The two major considerations in tailings disposal are safety and economics. There are two aspects to safety: the physical considerations surrounding the dump or dam in which the tailings are placed; and pollution by the waste material that may affect human health and cause damage to the environment. Tailings must be disposed of in the most cost-effective manner possible commensurate with safety.

Most commonly the tailings are sized, and the coarse sand fraction is used to construct a dam at a selected site. The fine fraction or slime is then pumped into a pond behind the dam wall.

Where toxic chemicals such as cyanide are present in the waste waters, special preparation of the base of the dam (e.g., by the use of plastic sheeting) may be necessary to prevent the possible contamination of ground waters.

As far as possible, the water recovered from the dam is recycled for further use. This may be of great importance in dry regions and is increasingly becoming required by legislation aimed at preventing the pollution of ground and surface water by chemical pollutants.

Heap and in Situ Leaching

Much of the concentrate produced by ore processing is processed further by hydrometallurical methods. The metal values are leached or dissolved from the ore, and different metals are separated from each other. The solutions obtained are concentrated, and the metal then recovered by steps such as precipitation and electrolytic or chemical deposition.

Many ores are of too low a grade to justify the cost of pre-concentration. Waste material may also still contain a certain amount of metal value. In some instances, such material may be economically processed by a version of a hydrometallurgical process known as heap or dump leaching.

Heap leaching was established at Rio Tinto in Spain more than 300 years ago. Water percolating slowly through heaps of low-grade ore was coloured blue by dissolved copper salts arising from oxidation of the ore. The copper was recovered from solution by precipitation onto scrap iron.

This basic process is utilized for oxide and sulphide heap leaching of low grade and waste material around the world. Once a heap or dump of the material has been created, a suitable solubilizing agent (e.g., an acid solution) is applied by sprinkling or flooding the top of the heap and the solution that seeps to the bottom is recovered.

While heap leaching has long been successfully practised, it was only relatively recently that the important role of certain bacteria in the process was recognized. These bacteria have been identified as the iron-oxidizing species *Thiobacillus ferrooxidans* and the sulphur-oxidizing species *Thiobacillus thiooxidans*. The iron-oxidizing bacteria derive energy from the oxidation of ferrous ions to ferric ions and the sulphur-oxidizing species by the oxidation of sulphide to sulphate. These reactions effectively catalyze the accelerated oxidation of the metal sulphides to the soluble metal sulphates.

In situ leaching, sometimes called solution mining, is effectively a variation of heap leaching. It consists of the pumping of solution into abandoned mines, caved in workings, remote worked-out areas or even entire ore bodies where these are shown to be permeable to solution. The rock formations must lend themselves to contact with the leaching solution and to the necessary availability of oxygen.

● COAL PREPARATION

Anthony D. Walters

Coal preparation is the process whereby the raw run-of-mine coal is turned into a saleable clean coal product of consistent size and quality specified by the consumer. The end use of the coal falls into the following general categories:

- *Electricity generation:* The coal is burned to supply heat to drive turbines which generate electricity.
- *Iron and steel making:* The coal is heated in ovens, in the absence of air, to drive off gases (volatile matter) to produce coke. The coke is used in the blast furnace to make iron and steel. Coal can also be added directly to the blast furnace as in the pulverized coal injection (PCI) process.
- *Industrial:* Coal is used in the metallurgical industry as a reductant, whereby its carbon content is used to remove oxygen (reducing) in a metallurgical process.
- *Heating:* Coal can be used domestically and industrially as a fuel for space heating. It is also used as a fuel in dry kilns for the manufacture of cement.

Crushing and Breaking
Run-of-mine coal from the pit needs to be crushed to an acceptable top size for treatment in the preparation plant. Typical crushing and breaking devices are:

- *Feeder breakers:* A rotation drum fitted with picks that fracture the coal. The coal is delivered by a scraper conveyor and the drum rotates in the same direction as the coal flow. Feeder breakers are commonly used underground, however, there are some in use on surface in the coal preparation circuit.
- *Rotary breakers:* The breaker circuit of an outer fixed shell with an inner rotating drum fitted with perforated plates. Typical rotational speed of the drum is 12–18 rpm. Lifter plates pick up the run-of-mine coal which then falls across the diameter of the drum. The softer coal breaks and passes through the perforations while the harder rock is transported to the exit. The rotary breaker achieves two functions, size reduction and beneficiation by removal of rock.
- *Roll crushers:* Roll crushers can consist of either a single rotating roll and a stationary anvil (plate), or two rolls rotating at the same speed towards one another. The roll faces are usually toothed or corrugated. A common form of crusher is the two stage or quad roll crusher whereby the product from the first twin roll crusher falls into the second twin roll crusher set at a smaller aperture, with the result that a large-scale reduction can be achieved in one machine. A typical application would be crushing run-of-mine material down to 50 mm.

Crushing is sometimes used following the coal cleaning process, when large size coal is crushed to meet market requirements. Roll

crushers or hammer mills are usually used. The hammer mill consists of a set of free swinging hammers rotating on a shaft that strike the coal and throw it against a fixed plate.

Sizing
Coal is sized before and after the beneficiation (cleaning) process. Different cleaning processes are used on different sizes of coal, so that raw coal on entering the coal preparation plant will be screened (sieved) into three or four sizes which then go through to the appropriate cleaning process. The screening process is usually carried out by rectangular vibrating screens with a mesh or punched plate screen deck. At sizes below 6 mm wet screening is used to increase the efficiency of the sizing operation and at sizes below 0.5 mm a static curved screen (sieve bend) is placed before the vibrating screen to improve efficiency.

Following the beneficiation process, the clean coal is sometimes sized by screening into a variety of products for the industrial and domestic coal markets. Sizing of clean coal is rarely used for coal for electricity generating (thermal coal) or for steel making (metallurgical coal).

Storage and Stockpiling
Coal is typically stored and stockpiled at three points in the preparation and handling chain:

1. raw coal storage and stockpiling between the mine and the preparation plant
2. clean coal storage and stockpiling between the preparation plant and the rail or road loadout point
3. clean coal storage at ports which may or may not be controlled by the mine.

Typically raw coal storage occurs after crushing and usually takes the form of open stockpiles (conical, elongated or circular), silos (cylindrical) or bunkers. It is common for seam blending to be carried out at this stage in order to supply a homogenous product to the preparation plant. Blending may be as simple as sequentially depositing different coals onto a conical stockpile to sophisticated operations using stacker conveyors and bucket wheel reclaimers.

Clean coal can be stored in a variety of ways, such as open stockpiles or silos. The clean coal storage system is designed to allow for rapid loading of rail cars or road trucks. Clean coal silos are usually constructed over a rail track allowing unit trains of up to 100 cars to be drawn slowly under the silo and filled to a known weight. In-motion weighing is usually used to maintain a continuous operation.

There are inherent dangers in stockpiled coals. Stockpiles may be unstable. Walking on stockpiles should be forbidden because internal collapses can occur and because reclamation can start without warning. Physically cleaning blockages or hangups in bunkers or silos should be treated with the greatest care as seemingly stable coal can suddenly slip.

Coal Cleaning (Beneficiation)
Raw coal contains material from "pure" coal to rock with a variety of material in between, with relative densities ranging from 1.30 to 2.5. Coal is cleaned by separating the low density material (saleable product) from the high density material (refuse). The exact density of separation depends on the nature of the coal and the clean coal quality specification. It is impractical to separate fine coal on a density basis and as a result 0.5 mm raw coal is separated by processes using the difference in surface properties of coal and rock. The usual method employed is froth flotation.

Density separation
There are two basic methods employed, one being a system using water, where the movement of the raw coal in water results in the

lighter coal having a greater acceleration than the heavier rock. The second method is to immerse the raw coal in a liquid with a density between coal and rock with the result that the coal floats and the rock sinks (dense medium separation).

The systems using water are as follows:

- *Jigs:* In this application raw coal is introduced into a pulsating bath of water. The raw coal is moved across a perforated plate with water pulsating through it. A stratified bed of material is established with the heavier rock at the bottom and the lighter coal at the top. At the discharge end, the refuse is removed from the clean coal. Typical size ranges treated in a jig are 75 mm to 12 mm. There are special application fine coal jigs which use an artificial bed of feldspar rock.
- *Concentrating tables:* A concentrating table consists of a riffled rubber deck carried on a supporting mechanism, connected to a head mechanism that imparts a rapid reciprocating motion in a direction parallel to the riffles. The slide slope of the table can be adjusted. A cross flow of water is provided by means of a launder mounted along the upper side of the deck. The feed enters just ahead of the water supply and is fanned out over the table deck by differential motion and gravitational flow. The raw coal particles are stratified into horizontal zones (or layers). The clean coal overflows the lower side of the table, and the discard is removed at the far side. Tables operate over the size range 5 × 0.5 mm.
- *Spirals:* The treatment of coal fines with spirals utilizes a principle whereby raw fine coal is carried down a spiral path in a stream of water and centrifugal forces direct the lighter coal particles to the outside of the stream and the heavier particles to the inside. A splitter device at the discharge end separates the fine coal from the fine refuse. Spirals are used as a cleaning devise on 2 mm × 0.1 mm size fractions.
- *Water-only cyclones:* The water-borne raw coal is fed tangentially under pressure into a cyclone, resulting in a whirlpool effect and centrifugal forces move the heavier material to the cyclone wall and from there they are transported to the underflow at the apex (or spigot). The lighter particles (coal) remain in the centre of the whirlpool vortex and are removed upwards via a pipe (vortex finder) and report to the overflow. The exact density of separation can be adjusted by varying pressure, vortex finder length and diameter, and apex diameter. The water-only cyclone typically treats material in the 0.5 mm × 0.1 mm size range and is operated in two stages to improve separating efficiency.

The second type of density separation is dense medium. In a heavy liquid (dense medium), particles having a density lower than the liquid (coal) will float and those having a density higher (rock) will sink. The most practical industrial application of a dense medium is a finely ground suspension of magnetite in water. This has many advantages, namely:

- The mixture is benign, as compared to inorganic or organic fluids.
- The density can be rapidly adjusted by varying the magnetite/water ratio.
- The magnetite can be easily recycled by removing it from the product streams with magnetic separators.

There are two classes of dense medium separators, the bath- or vessel-type separator for coarse coal in the range 75 mm × 12 mm and the cyclone-type separator cleaning coal in the range 5 mm × 0.5 mm.

The bath-type separators can be deep or shallow baths where the float material is carried over the lip of the bath and the sink material is extracted from the bottom of the bath by scraper chain or paddle wheel.

The cyclone-type separator enhances the gravitational forces with centrifugal forces. The centrifugal acceleration is about 20 times greater than the gravity acceleration acting upon the particles in the bath separator (this acceleration approaches 200 times greater than the gravity acceleration at the cyclone apex). These large forces account for the high throughput of the cyclone and its ability to treat small coal.

The products from the dense medium separators, namely clean coal and refuse, both pass over drain and rinse screens where the magnetite medium is removed and returned to the separators. The diluted magnetite from the rinsing screens is passed through magnetic separators to recover the magnetite for re-use. The magnetic separators consist of rotating stainless steel cylinders containing fixed ceramic magnets mounted on the stationary drum shaft. The drum is immersed in a stainless steel tank containing the dilute magnetite suspension. As the drum rotates, magnetite adheres to the area near the fixed internal magnets. The magnetite is carried out of the bath and out of the magnetic field and falls from the drum surface via a scraper to a stock tank.

Both nuclear density gauges and nuclear on-stream analysers are used in coal preparation plants. Safety precautions relating to radiation source instruments must be observed.

Froth flotation

Froth flotation is a physio-chemical process that depends upon the selective attachment of air bubbles to coal particle surfaces and the non-attachment of refuse particles. This process involves the use of suitable reagents to establish a hydrophobic (water-repellent) surface on the solids to be floated. Air bubbles are generated within a tank (or cell) and as they rise to the surface the reagent-coated fine coal particles adhere to the bubble, the non-coal refuse remains at the bottom of the cell. The coal bearing froth is removed from the surface by paddles and is then dewatered by filtration or centrifuge. The refuse (or tailings) pass to a discharge box and are usually thickened before being pumped to a tailings impoundment pond.

The reagents used in the froth flotation of coal are generally frothers and collectors. Frothers are used to facilitate the production of a stable froth (i.e., froths that do not break up). They are chemicals that reduce the surface tension of water. The most commonly used frother in coal flotation is methyl isobutyl carbinol (MIBC). The function of a collector is to promote contact between coal particles and air bubbles by forming a thin coating over the particles to be floated, which renders the particle water-repellent. At the same time the collector must be selective, that is, it must not coat the particles that are not to be floated (i.e., the tailings). The most commonly used collector in coal flotation is fuel oil.

Briquetting

The briquetting of coal has a long history. In the late 1800s relatively worthless fine coal or slack was compressed to form a "patent fuel" or briquette. This product was acceptable to both the domestic and industrial markets. In order to form a stable briquette, a binder was necessary. Usually coal tars and pitches were used. The coal briquetting industry for the domestic market has been in decline for some years. However, there have been some advances in technology and applications.

High-moisture low-rank coals may be upgraded by thermal drying and subsequent removal of a portion of the inherent or "locked in" moisture. However, the product from this process is friable and prone to the re-absorbtion of moisture and spontaneous combustion. Briquetting of low-rank coal allows for a stable, transportable product to be made. Briquetting is also used in the anthracite industry, where large-sized products have a significantly higher selling price.

Coal briquetting has also been used in emerging economies where briquettes are used as cooking fuel in rural areas. The process of manufacture usually involves a devolatilizing step whereby excess gas or volatile matter is driven off prior to briquetting in order to produce a "smokeless" domestic fuel.

The briquetting process, therefore, usually has the following steps:

- *Coal drying:* Moisture content is critical because it has an impact on the strength of the briquette. Methods used are direct drying (a flash dryer using hot gas) and indirect drying (a disc dryer using steam heat).
- *Devolatilizing:* This is only applicable to low-rank high-volatile coals. The equipment used is a retort or a beehive type coke oven.
- *Crushing:* The coal is often crushed because a smaller particle size results in a stronger briquette.
- *Binders:* Binders are required to ensure that the briquette has adequate strength to withstand normal handling. The types of binders that have been used are coke oven pitch, petroleum asphalt, ammonium lignosulphorate and starch. The typical addition rate is 5 to 15% by weight. The fine coal and binder are mixed in a pug mill or paddle mixer at an elevated temperature.
- *Briquette manufacture:* The coal-binder mixture is fed to a double roll press with indented surfaces. A variety of briquette shapes can be made depending on the type of roller indentation. The most common form of briquette is the pillow shape. The pressure increases the apparent density of the coal-binder mix by 1.5 to 3 times.
- *Coating and baking:* With some binders (ammonium lignosulphorate and petroleum asphalt) a heat treatment in the range of 300 °C is necessary to harden the briquettes. The heat treatment oven is an enclosed conveyor and heated with hot gases.
- *Cooling/quenching:* The cooling oven is an enclosed conveyor with recirculating air passing to reduce the briquette temperature to an ambient condition. Off-gases are collected, scrubbed and discharged to the atmosphere. Quenching with water is sometimes used to cool the briquettes.

Briquetting of soft brown coal with a high moisture content of 60 to 70% is a somewhat different process than that described above. The brown coals are frequently upgraded by briquetting, which involves crushing, screening and drying the coal to approximately 15% moisture, and extrusion pressing without binder into compacts. Large quantities of coal are treated in this way in Germany, India, Poland and Australia. The dryer used is a steam-heated rotary tube dryer. Following extrusion pressing, the compacted coal is cut and cooled before being transferred to belt conveyors to railcars, road trucks or storage.

Briquetting plants handle large quantities of highly combustible material associated with potentially explosive mixtures of coal dust and air. Dust control, collection and handling as well as good housekeeping are all of considerable importance to safe operation.

Refuse and Tailings Disposal

Waste disposal is an integral part of a modern coal preparation plant. Both coarse refuse and fine tailings in the form of slurry must be transported and disposed of in an environmentally responsible way.

Coarse refuse

Coarse refuse is transported by truck, conveyor belt or aerial ropeway to the solids disposal area, which usually forms the walls of the tailings impoundment. The refuse can also be returned to the open pit.

Innovative cost-effective forms of transporting of coarse waste are now being used, namely, crushing and transportation by pumping in slurry form to an impoundment pond and also by a pneumatic system to underground storage.

It is necessary to select a disposal site which has a minimal amount of exposed surface while at the same time provides for good stability. A structure that is exposed on all sides permits more surface drainage, with a greater tendency for silt formation in nearby water courses, and also a greater probability of spontaneous combustion. To minimize both these effects, greater quantities of cover material, compacting and sealing, are required. The ideal disposal construction is the valley-fill type of operation.

Preparation-plant waste embankments may fail for several reasons:

- weak foundations
- excessively steep slopes of excessive heights
- poor control of water and fine material seepage through the dump
- inadequate water control during extreme rainfall events.

The principal categories of design and construction techniques which can greatly reduce environmental hazards associated with coal-refuse disposal are:

- drainage from within the refuse pile
- diversion of surface drainage
- waste compaction to minimize spontaneous combustion
- waste pile stability.

Tailings

Tailings (fine solid waste in water) are usually transported by pipe line to an impoundment area. However, in some instances tailings impoundment is not environmentally acceptable and alternative treatment is necessary, namely, dewatering of tailings by belt press or high speed centrifuge and then disposal of the dewatered product by belt or truck in the coarse refuse area.

Tailings impoundments (ponds) operate on the principle that the tailings settle out to the bottom and the resulting clarified water is pumped back to the plant for reuse. The pool elevation in the pond is maintained such that storm in-flows are stored and then drawn off by pumping or small decant systems. It may be necessary periodically to remove sediment from smaller impoundments to extend their life. The retaining embankment of the impoundment is usually constructed of coarse refuse. Poor design of the retaining wall and liquefaction of the tailings due to poor drainage can lead to dangerous situations. Stabilizing agents, usually calcium-based chemicals, have been used to produce a cementation effect.

Tailings impoundments normally develop over an extended period of the mine's life, with continually changing conditions. Therefore the stability of the impoundment structure should be carefully and continuously monitored.

GROUND CONTROL IN UNDERGROUND MINES

Luc Beauchamp

The principal objective of ground control is to maintain safe excavations in rock and soil (the terms *strata control* and *slope management* are also used in underground mines and surface mines, respectively). Ground control also finds many applications in civil engineering projects such as tunnels, hydro-electric power plants and nuclear waste repositories. It has been defined as the practical application of rock mechanics to everyday mining. The US National Committee on Rock Mechanics has proposed the following definition: "Rock mechanics is the theoretical and applied science of the mechanical behaviour of rock and rock masses; it is that branch of mechanics concerned with the response of rock and rock masses to the force fields of their physical environment".

Rock masses exhibit extremely complex behaviour, and rock mechanics and ground control have been the subject of considerable fundamental and applied research throughout the world since the 1950s. In many ways ground control is a craft more than a science. Ground control requires an understanding of structural geology, rock properties, groundwater and ground stress regimes and of how these factors interact. Tools include the methods of site investigation and rock testing, measures to minimize damage to the rock mass caused by blasting, the application of design techniques, monitoring and ground support. Several important developments have taken place in rock mechanics and ground control in recent years, including the development of empirical design and computer analysis techniques for mine design, the introduction and wide use of a variety of ground monitoring instruments and the development of specialized ground support tools and techniques. Many mining operations have ground control departments staffed by specialist engineers and technicians.

Underground openings are more difficult to create and maintain than rock or soil slopes, therefore underground mines generally must devote more resources and design efforts to ground control than surface mines and quarries. In traditional underground mining methods, such as shrinkage and cut-and-fill, workers are directly exposed to potentially unstable ground in the ore zone. In bulk mining methods, such as blasthole stoping, workers do not enter the ore zone. There has been a trend away from selective methods to bulk methods in the past decades.

Ground Failure Types

Rock structure and rock stress are important causes of instability in mines.

A particular rock mass consists of intact rock and any number of rock structures or structural discontinuities. Major types of rock structures include bedding planes (division planes which separate the individual strata), folds (bends in rock strata), faults (fractures on which movement has occurred), dykes (tabular intrusions of igneous rock) and joints (breaks of geological origin along which there has been no visible displacement). The following properties of structural discontinuities affect the engineering behaviour of rock masses: orientation, spacing, persistence, roughness, aperture and presence of infilling material. The collection of pertinent structural information by engineers and geologists is an important component of the ground control programme at a mining operation. Sophisticated computer programmes to analyse structural data and the geometry and stability of wedges in surface or underground mines are now available.

Stresses in rock also can cause instability in mines; knowledge of the stress-strain behaviour of rock masses is essential to sound engineering design. Laboratory tests on cylindrical specimens of rock from drill core can provide useful strength and deformability information concerning the intact rock; different rock types behave differently, from the plastic behaviour of salt to the elastic, brittle behaviour of many hard rocks. Jointing will greatly influence the strength and deformability of the entire rock mass.

There are some common types of rock slope failures in surface mines and quarries. The sliding block failure mode occurs where movement takes places along one or more rock structures (plane shear, step path, wedge, step wedge or slab failures); a rotational shear failure can occur in a soil or weak rock mass slope; additional failure modes include toppling of blocks formed by steeply dipping structures and ravelling (e.g., dislodging of blocks by freeze-thaw or

rain). Major slope failures can be catastrophic, although slope instability does not necessarily mean slope failure from an operational standpoint. The stability of individual benches is usually of more immediate concern to the operation, as failure can occur with little warning, with potential loss of life and equipment damage.

In underground mines, instability can result from movement and collapse of rock blocks as a result of structural instability, failure of rock around the opening as a result of high rock stress conditions, a combination of stress-induced rock failure and structural instability and instability caused by rockbursts. Rock structure can influence the choice of an underground mining method and the design of mining layouts because it can control stable excavation spans, support requirements capability and subsidence. Rock at depth is subjected to stresses resulting from the weight of the overlying strata and from stresses of tectonic origin, and horizontal stresses are often greater than the vertical stress. Instruments are available to determine the level of stress in the ground before mining has begun. When a mine opening is excavated, the stress field around this opening changes and possibly exceeds the strength of the rock mass, resulting in instability.

There are also various types of failure which are commonly observed in underground hard rock mines. Under low stress levels, failures are largely structurally controlled, with wedges or blocks falling from the roof or sliding out of the walls of the openings. These wedges or blocks are formed by intersecting structural discontinuities. Unless loose wedges or blocks are supported, failure can continue until natural arching of the opening takes place. In stratified deposits, bed separation and failure can occur along bedding planes. Under high stress levels, failure consists of brittle spalling and slabbing in the case of a massive rock mass with few joints, to a more ductile type of failure for heavily jointed rock masses.

A rockburst may be defined as damage to an excavation that occurs in a sudden or violent manner and is associated with a seismic event. Various rockburst damage mechanisms have been identified, namely expansion or buckling of the rock due to fracturing around the opening, rockfalls induced by seismic shaking and ejection of rock due to energy transfer from a remote seismic source. Outbursts of rock and gas occur catastrophically in some coal, salt and other mines as a result of high rock stresses and large volumes of compressed methane or carbon dioxide. In quarries and surface mines, sudden buckling and heaving of rock floors has also been experienced. Considerable research has taken place in several countries into the causes and possible alleviation of rockbursts. Techniques for minimizing rockbursts include altering the shape, orientation and sequence of extraction, the use of a technique known as destress blasting, stiff mine backfills and the use of specialized support systems. Sophisticated local or mine-wide seismic monitoring systems can assist in the identification and analysis of source mechanisms, although the prediction of rockbursts remains unreliable at the present time.

In the Canadian province of Ontario, nearly one-third of all underground fatal injuries in the highly mechanized mining industry result rom rockfalls and rockbursts; the fatality frequency from rockfalls and rockbursts for the period 1986-1995 was 0.014 per 200,000 hours worked underground. In less mechanized underground mining industries, or where ground support is not widely used, considerably higher injury and fatality frequencies due to falls of ground and rockbursts can be expected. The ground control related safety record for surface mines and quarries is generally better than for underground mines.

Design Methods

The design of underground excavations is the process of making engineering decisions on such matters as the locations, sizes and shapes of excavations and rock pillars, the mining sequence and the application of support systems. In surface mines, an optimum slope angle must be chosen for each section of the pit, along with other design aspects and slope support. Designing a mine is a dynamic process which is updated and refined as more information becomes available through observation and monitoring during the mining. The empirical, observational and analytical design methods are commonly used.

Empirical methods often use a rock mass classification system (several such schemes have been developed, such as the Rock Mass System and the Rock Tunnelling Quality Index), complemented by design recommendations based on a knowledge of accepted practice. Several empirical design techniques have been successfully applied, such as the Stability Graph Method for open stope design.

Observational methods rely on the actual monitoring of ground movement during excavation to detect measurable instability and on the analysis of ground-support interaction. Examples of this approach include the New Austrian Tunnelling Method and the Convergence-Confinement method.

Analytical methods utilize the analysis of stresses and deformations around openings. Some of the earliest stress analysis techniques utilized closed form mathematical solutions or photo elastic models, but their application was limited due to the complex three-dimensional shape of most underground excavations. A number of computer-based numerical methods have been developed recently. These methods provide the means for obtaining approximate solutions to the problems of stresses, displacements and failure in rock surrounding mine openings.

Recent refinements have included the introduction of three-dimensional models, the ability to model structural discontinuities and rock-support interaction and the availability of user-friendly graphical interfaces. In spite of their limitations, numerical models can provide real insights into complex rock behaviour.

The three methodologies described above should be considered as essential parts of a unified approach to the design of underground excavations rather than independent techniques. The design engineer should be prepared to use a range of tools and to re-evaluate the design strategy when required by the quantity and quality of information available.

Drilling and Blasting Controls

A particular concern with rock blasting is its effect on the rock in the immediate vicinity of an excavation. Intense local fracturing and disruption of the integrity of the interlocked, jointed assembly can be produced in the near-field rock by poor blast design or drilling procedures. More extensive damage can be induced by the transmission of blasting energy to the far field, which may trigger instability in mine structures.

Blast results are affected by the rock type, stress regime, structural geology and presence of water. Measures for minimizing blast damage include the proper choice of explosive, the use of perimeter blasting techniques such as pre-split blasting (parallel, closely spaced holes, which will define the excavation perimeter), decoupling charges (the diameter of the explosive is smaller than that of the blasthole), delay timing and buffer holes. The geometry of the drilled holes affects the success of a wall control blast; hole pattern and alignment must be carefully controlled.

Monitoring of blast vibrations is often performed to optimize blasting patterns and to avoid damage to the rock mass. Empirical damage blast damage criteria have been developed. Blast monitoring equipment consists of surface-mounted or down-the-hole transducers, cables leading to an amplifying system and a digital recorder. Blast design has been improved by the development of computer models for the prediction of blast performance, including the fragmentation, muck profile and crack penetration behind blastholes. Input data for these models include the geometry of

the excavation and of the drilled and loaded pattern, detonation characteristics of the explosives and dynamic properties of the rock.

Scaling of Roof and Walls of Excavations

Scaling is the removal of loose slabs of rock from roofs and walls of excavations. It can be performed manually with a steel or aluminium scaling bar or by using a mechanical scaling machine. When scaling manually, the miner checks the soundness of the rock by striking the roof; a drum-like sound usually indicates that the ground is loose and should be barred down. The miner must follow strict rules in order to avoid injury while scaling (e.g., scaling from good ground to unchecked ground, maintaining good footing and a clear area to retreat and ensuring that scaled rock has a proper place on which to fall). Manual scaling requires considerable physical effort, and it can be a high-risk activity. For example, in Ontario, Canada, one third of all injuries caused by falls of rock occur while scaling.

The use of baskets on extendable booms so that miners can manually scale high backs introduces additional safety hazards, such as possible overturning of the scaling platform by falling rocks. Mechanical scaling rigs are now commonplace in many large mining operations. The scaling unit consists of a heavy hydraulic breaker, scraper or impact hammer, mounted on a pivoting arm, which is in turn attached to a mobile chassis.

Ground Support

The main objective of ground support is to help the rock mass support itself. In rock reinforcement, rockbolts are installed within the rock mass. In rock support, such as that provided by steel or timber sets, external support is provided to the rock mass. Ground support techniques have not found wide application in surface mining and quarrying, partly because of the uncertainty of the ultimate pit geometry and partly because of concerns with corrosion. A wide variety of rockbolting systems is available worldwide. Factors to consider when selecting a particular system include ground conditions, planned service life of the excavation, ease of installation, availability and cost.

The mechanically anchored rockbolt consists of an expansion shell (various designs are available to suit different rock types), steel bolt (threaded or with a forged head) and face plate. The expansion shell generally consists of toothed blades of malleable cast iron with a conical wedge threaded at one end of the bolt. When the bolt is rotated inside the hole, the cone is forced into the blades and presses them against the walls of the drillhole. The expansion shell increases its grip on the rock as tension on the bolt increases. Bolts of various lengths are available, along with a range of accessories. Mechanically anchored rockbolts are relatively inexpensive and, therefore, most widely used for short-term support in underground mines.

The grouted dowel consists of a ribbed reinforcing bar that is inserted in a drillhole and bonded to the rock over its full length, providing long-term reinforcement to the rock mass. Several types of cement and polyester resin-grouts are used. The grout can be placed in the drillhole by pumping or by using cartridges, which is quick and convenient. Steel and fibreglass dowels of various diameters are available, and bolts can be untensioned or tensioned.

The friction stabilizer commonly consists of a steel tube slotted along its entire length, which, when driven into a slightly undersized drillhole, compresses and develops friction between the steel tube and the rock. The drillhole diameter must be controlled within close tolerances for this bolt to be effective.

The Swellex rockbolt consists of an involute steel tube which is inserted in a drillhole and expanded by hydraulic pressure using a portable pump. Various types and lengths of Swellex tubes are available.

The grouted cable bolt is frequently installed to control caving and stabilize underground stope roofs and walls. A Portland cement-based grout is generally used, while cable geometries and installation procedures vary. High-capacity reinforcing bars and rock anchors are also found in mines, along with other bolt types, such as tubular groutable mechanically anchored bolts.

Steel straps or mesh, made from either woven or welded wire, is often installed in the roof or walls of the opening to support the rock between bolts.

Mining operations should develop a quality control programme, which can include a variety of field tests, to ensure that ground support is effective. Poor ground support installations can be the result of inadequate design (failure to choose the correct ground support type, length or pattern for the ground conditions), sub-standard ground support materials (as supplied by manufacturer or damaged during handling or because of storage conditions at the mine site), installation deficiencies (defective equipment, poor timing of installation, inadequate preparation of the rock surface, poor training of crews or not following specified procedures), mining-induced effects that were unforeseen at the design stage (stress changes, stress or blast-induced fracturing/spalling, joint relaxation or rockbursting) or mine design changes (changes in excavation geometry or service life longer than originally anticipated).

The behaviour of reinforced or supported rock masses remains incompletely understood. Rules of thumb, empirical design guidelines based on rock mass classification systems and computer programs have been developed. However, the success of a particular design relies heavily on the knowledge and experience of the ground control engineer. A good quality rock mass, with few structural discontinuities and small openings of limited service life, may require little or no support. However, in this case rockbolts may be required at selected locations to stabilize blocks that have been identified as potentially unstable. At many mines, pattern bolting, the systematic installation of rockbolts on a regular grid to stabilize the roof or walls, is often specified for all excavations. In all cases, miners and supervisors must have sufficient experience to recognize areas where additional support may be required.

The oldest and simplest form of support is the timber post; timber props and cribs are sometimes installed when mining through unstable ground. Steel arches and steel sets are high load-carrying capacity elements used to support tunnels or roadways. In underground mines, additional and important ground support is provided by mine backfill, which can consist of waste rock, sand or mill tailings and a cementing agent. Backfill is used to fill voids created by underground mining. Among its many functions, backfill helps prevent large-scale failures, confines and thus provides residual strength to rock pillars, allows transfer of rock stresses, helps reduce surface subsidence, allows for maximum ore recovery and provides a work platform in some mining methods.

A relatively recent innovation in many mines has been the use of *shotcrete*, which is concrete sprayed on a rock face. It can be applied directly to rock with no other form of support, or it can be sprayed over mesh and rockbolts, forming part of an integrated support system. Steel fibres can be added, along with other admixtures and mix designs to impart specific properties. Two different shotcreting processes exist, termed dry mix and wet mix. Shotcrete has found a number of applications in mines, including stabilizing rock faces that would otherwise ravel because of their close jointing. In surface mines, shotcrete has also been used successfully to stabilize progressive ravelling failures. Other recent innovations include the use of polyurethane spray-on liners in underground mines.

In order to function effectively during a rockburst, support systems must possess certain important characteristics, including defor-

mation and energy absorption. Support selection under rockburst conditions is the subject of ongoing research in several countries, and new design recommendations have been developed.

In small underground openings, manual ground support installation is commonly done using a stoper drill. In larger excavations, semi-mechanized equipment (mechanized drilling and manual equipment for rockbolt installation) and fully mechanized equipment (mechanized drilling and rockbolt installation controlled from an operator's panel located under bolted roof) are available. Manual ground support installation is a high-risk activity. For example, in Ontario, Canada, one third of all injuries caused by falls of rock during the period 1986-1995 occurred while installing rockbolts, and 8% of all underground injuries occurred while installing rockbolts.

Other hazards include possible splashes of cement grout or resin in the eyes, allergic reactions from chemical spillage and fatigue. The installation of large numbers of rockbolts is made safer and more efficient by the use of mechanized bolting machines.

Monitoring of Ground Conditions

Monitoring of ground conditions in mines may be carried out for a variety of reasons, including obtaining data needed for mine design, such as rock mass deformability or rock stresses; verifying design data and assumptions, thereby allowing calibration of computer models and adjustment of mining methods to improve stability; assessing the effectiveness of existing ground support and possibly directing the installation of additional support; and warning of potential ground failures.

Monitoring of ground conditions can be done either visually or with the help of specialized instruments. Surface and underground inspections must be done carefully and with the assistance of high-intensity inspection lights if necessary; miners, supervisors, engineers and geologists all have an important role to play in carrying out regular inspections. Visual or audible signs of changing ground conditions in mines include but are not limited to the condition of diamond drill core, contacts between rock types, drum-like ground, the presence of structural features, obvious loading of ground support, floor heaving, new cracks on walls or roof, groundwater and pillar failures. Miners often rely on simple instruments (e.g., wooden wedge in crack) to provide a visual warning that roof movement has occurred.

Planning and implementing a monitoring system involves defining the purpose of the programme and the variables to be monitored, determining the required measurement accuracy, selecting and installing equipment and establishing the frequency of observations and means of data presentation. Monitoring equipment should be installed by experienced personnel. Instrument simplicity, redundancy and reliability are important considerations. The designer should determine what constitutes a threat to safety or stability. This should include the preparation of contingency plans in the event that these warning levels are exceeded.

The components of a monitoring system include a sensor, which responds to changes in the variable being monitored; a transmitting system, which transmits the sensor output to the read-out location, using rods, electrical cables, hydraulic lines or radiotelemetry lines; a read-out unit (e.g., dial gauge, pressure gauge, multimeter or digital display); and a recording/processing unit (e.g., tape recorder, datalogger or microcomputer).

Various modes of instrument operation exist, namely:

- *mechanical:* often provide the simplest, cheapest and most reliable methods of detection, transmission and readout. Mechanical movement detectors use a steel rod or tape, fixed to the rock at one end, and in contact with a dial gauge or electrical system at the other. The main disadvantage of mechanical systems is that they do not lend themselves to remote reading or to continuous recording.

- *optical:* used in conventional, precise and photogrammetric surveying methods of establishing excavation profiles, measuring movements of excavation boundaries and monitoring surface subsidence.
- *hydraulic and pneumatic:* diaphragm transducers that are used for measuring water pressures, support loads and so forth. The quantity measured is a fluid pressure which acts on one side of a flexible diaphragm made of a metal, rubber or plastic.
- *electrical:* the most common instrument mode used in mines, although mechanical systems still find widespread use in displacement monitoring. Electrical systems operate on one of three principles, electric resistance strain gauge, vibrating wire and self-inductance.

Most commonly monitored variables include movement (using surveying methods, surface devices such as crack gauges and tape extensometers, borehole devices such as rod extensometers or inclinometers); rock stresses (absolute stress or stress change from borehole devices); pressure, load and strain on ground support devices (e.g., load cells); seismic events and blast vibrations.

VENTILATION AND COOLING IN UNDERGROUND MINES

M.J. Howes

The main objective of mine ventilation is the provision of sufficient quantities of air to all the working places and travel ways in an underground mine to dilute to an acceptable level those contaminants which cannot be controlled by any other means. Where depth and rock temperatures are such that air temperatures are excessive, mechanical refrigeration systems may be used to supplement the beneficial effects of ventilation.

The Mine Atmosphere

The composition of the gaseous envelope encircling the earth varies by less than 0.01% from place to place and the constitution of "dry" air is usually taken as 78.09% nitrogen, 20.95% oxygen, 0.93% argon and 0.03% carbon dioxide. Water vapour is also present in varying amounts depending on the air temperature and pressure and the availability of free water surfaces. As ventilation air flows through a mine, the concentration of water vapour may change significantly and this variation is the subject of the separate study of psychrometry. To define the state of a water vapour and dry air mixture at a particular point requires the three measurable independent properties of barometric pressure, dry bulb and wet bulb temperatures.

Ventilation Requirements

The contaminants to be controlled by dilution ventilation are primarily gases and dust, although ionizing radiations associated with naturally occurring radon may present problems, especially in uranium mines and where the background uranium concentrations of the host or adjacent rocks are elevated. The amount of air required for dilution control will depend on both the strength of the contaminant source and the effectiveness of other control measures such as water for dust suppression or methane drainage systems in coal mines. The minimum dilution air flow rate is determined by the contaminant requiring the greatest dilution quantity with due cognizance of the possible additive effects of

mixtures and synergism where one contaminant can increase the effect of another. Overriding this value could be a minimum air velocity requirement which is typically 0.25 m/s and increasing as air temperatures also increase.

Diesel-powered equipment ventilation

In mechanized mines using diesel-powered mobile equipment and in the absence of continuous gas monitoring, exhaust gas dilution is used to determine the minimum ventilation air requirements where they operate. The amount of air required normally ranges between 0.03 and 0.06 m^3/s per kW of rated power at the point of operation depending on the type of the engine and whether any exhaust gas conditioning is being used. Continuing developments in both fuel and engine technology are providing lower engine emissions while catalytic converters, wet scrubbers and ceramic filters may further reduce the leaving concentrations of carbon monoxide/aldehydes, oxides of nitrogen and diesel particulates respectively. This helps in meeting increasingly stringent contaminant limits without significantly increasing exhaust dilution rates. The minimum possible dilution limit of 0.02 m^3/s per kW is determined by the carbon dioxide emissions which are proportional to engine power and unaffected by exhaust gas conditioning.

Diesel engines are about one-third efficient at converting the energy available in the fuel to useful power and most of this is then used to overcome friction resulting in a heat output which is about three times the power output. Even when hauling rock up a decline in a truck, the useful work done is only about 10% of energy available in the fuel. Higher diesel engine powers are used in larger mobile equipment which require bigger excavations to operate safely. Allowing for normal vehicle clearances and a typical diesel exhaust gas dilution rate of 0.04 m^3/s per kW, the minimum air velocities where diesels operate average about 0.5 m/s.

Ventilation of different mining methods

Although the setting of general air quantity requirements is not appropriate where detailed mine and ventilation planning information is available or possible, they are supportive of the criteria being used for design. Deviations from normal values generally can be explained and justified, for instance, in mines with heat or radon problems. The general relationship is:

$$\text{Mine quantity} = \alpha t + \beta$$

where t is the annual production rate in million tonnes per annum (Mtpa), α is a variable air quantity factor which is directly related to production rate and β is the constant air quantity required to ventilate the mine infrastructure such as the ore handling system. Typical values of α are given in table 74.1.

Table 74.1 • Design air quantity factors.

Mining method	α (air quantity factor m^3/s/Mtpa)
Block-caving	50
Room-and-pillar (Potash)	75
Sub-level caving	120

Open stoping
  large >.5 Mtpa
  small <.5 Mtpa
	160
	240

Mechanized cut-and-fill	320
Non-mechanized mining	400

The constant air quantity ß is mainly dependent on the ore handling system and, to a certain extent, on the overall mine production rate. For mines where rock is transported through a decline using diesel powered truck haulage or there is no crushing of the mined rock, a suitable value of ß is 50 m³/s. This typically increases to 100 m³/s when using underground crushers and skip hoisting with underground maintenance areas. As the ore handling system become more extensive (i.e., using conveyors or other ore transfer systems), ß can further increase by up to 50%. On very large mines where multiple shaft systems are used, the constant air quantity ß is also a multiple of the number of shaft systems required.

Cooling Requirements

Design thermal conditions

The provision of suitable thermal conditions to minimize the dangers and adverse effects of heat stress may require mechanical cooling in addition to the ventilation necessary to control contaminants. Although the applied heat stress is a complex function of climatic variables and physiological responses to them, in practical mining terms it is the air velocity and wet bulb temperature that have the greatest influence. This is illustrated by the clothing-corrected air cooling powers (W/m²) given in table 74.2. Underground the radiant temperature is taken to be equal to the dry bulb temperature and 10 °C higher than the wet bulb temperature. The barometric pressure and the clothing regime are typical for underground work (i.e., 110 kPa and 0.52 clothing units).

An air velocity of 0.1 m/s reflects the effect of natural convection (i.e., no perceivable airflow at all). An air velocity of 0.25 m/s is the minimum normally allowed in mining and 0.5 m/s would be required where the wet bulb temperature exceeds 25 °C. With respect to achieving thermal equilibrium, the metabolic heat resulting from typical work rates are: rest, 50 W/m²; light work, 115 to 125 W/m², medium work, 150 to 175 W/m²; and hard work, 200 to 300 W/m². Design conditions for a specific mine application would be determined from a detailed optimization study. Generally, optimum wet bulb temperatures are between 27.5 °C and 28.5 °C with the lower temperatures applicable to less mechanized operations. Work performance decreases and the risk of heat-related illness increases significantly when the wet bulb temperature exceeds 30.0 °C, and work should not normally continue when the wet bulb temperature is greater than 32.5 °C.

Mine heat loads

The mine refrigeration load is the mine heat load less the cooling capacity of the ventilation air. The mine heat load includes the effects of auto-compression of the air in the intake airways (the conversion of potential energy to enthalpy as the air flows down into the mine), heat flow into the mine from the surrounding rock, heat removed from the rock broken or any fissure water before they are removed from the intakes or working sections of the mine, and the heat resulting from the operation of any equipment used in the ore breaking and transportation processes. The cooling capacity of the ventilation air depends on both the design thermal environmental conditions in the working places and the actual climatic conditions on surface.

Although the relative contributions of each heat source to the total is site specific, auto-compression is usually the main contributor at between 35 and 50% of the total. As the depth of mining increases, auto-compression can cause the cooling capacity of the air to become negative and the effect of supplying more air is to increase the mine refrigeration load. In this case, the amount of ventilation supplied should be the minimum consistent with meeting contaminant control and increasing amounts of refrigeration are required to provide productive and safe working conditions. The depth of mining at which refrigeration becomes necessary will depend primarily on the surface climatic conditions, the distance the air travels through the intake airways before it is used and the extent to which large equipment (diesel or electric powered) is used.

Primary Ventilation Systems

Networks

Primary ventilation systems or networks are concerned with ensuring the flow of air through interconnected mine openings. The overall ventilation network has junctions where three or more airways meet, branches that are airways between junctions and meshes which are closed paths traversed through the network. Although most mine ventilation networks are ramified with hundreds or even thousands of branches, the number of main intake (branch between surface and the mine workings) and return or exhaust (branch between the workings and surface) airways is usually limited to less than ten.

With large numbers of branches in a network, determining a flow pattern and establishing the overall pressure loss is not straightforward. Although many are in simple series or parallel arrangement which can be solved algebraically and precisely, there will be some compound sections requiring iterative methods with convergence to an acceptable tolerance. Analogue computers have been successfully used for network analysis; however, these have been superseded by less time-consuming digital methods based on the Hardy Cross approximation technique developed to solve water flow networks.

Airway resistance and shock losses

The resistance to airflow of a tunnel or mine opening is a function of its size and surface roughness and the resultant pressure loss depends on this resistance and the square of the air velocity. By adding energy to the system, a pressure can be generated which then overcomes the pressure loss. This may occur naturally where the energy is provided by heat from the rock and other sources (natural ventilation). Although this used to be the main method of providing ventilation, only 2 to 3% of the energy is converted and, during hot summers, the rock may actually cool the intake air resulting in flow reversals. In modern mines a fan is normally used to provide energy to the air stream which then overcomes the pressure loss although the effects of natural ventilation can either assist or retard it depending on the time of year.

When air flows over a surface, the air molecules immediately next to the surface are at a standstill and those adjacent slip over those at rest with a resistance which is dependent on the viscosity of the air. A velocity gradient is formed where the velocity increases with increasing distance from the surface. The boundary layer created as a result of this phenomenon and the laminar sub-layer also formed as the boundary layer develops have a profound effect on the energy required to promote flow. Generally, the roughness of the surface of mine airways is large enough

Table 74.2 • Clothing-corrected air cooling powers (W/m²).

Air velocity (m/s)	Wet bulb temperature (°C)					
	20.0	22.5	25.0	27.5	30.0	32.5
0.1	176	153	128	100	70	37
0.25	238	210	179	145	107	64
0.5	284	254	220	181	137	87
1.0	321	290	254	212	163	104

for the "bumps" to extend through the boundary sub-layer. The airway is then hydraulically rough and the resistance is a function of the relative roughness, i.e., the ratio of the roughness height to the diameter of the airway.

Most airways mined by conventional drill and blast techniques have roughness heights between 100 and 200 mm and even in very "blocky" ground, the average roughness height would not exceed 300 mm. Where airways are driven using boring machines, the roughness height is between 5 and 10 mm and still considered to be hydraulically rough. The roughness of airways can be reduced by lining them, although the justification is more usually ground support rather than a reduction in power required to circulate the ventilation air. For example, a large concrete-lined shaft with a roughness of 1 mm would be transitionally rough and the Reynolds number, which is the ratio of inertial to viscous forces, would also affect the resistance to airflow. In practice, the difficulties in smooth concrete lining such a large shaft from the top down as it is being sunk results in increased roughness and resistances about 50% higher than the smooth values.

With a limited number of intake and return airways between the workings and surface, a large proportion (70 to 90%) of the total mine pressure loss occurs in them. Airway pressure losses also depend on whether there are any discontinuities causing shock losses such as bends, contractions, expansions or any obstructions in the airway. The losses resulting from these discontinuities such as bends into and out of airways, when expressed in terms of the losses which would be produced in an equivalent length of straight airway, can be a significant proportion of the total and need to be assessed carefully, particularly when considering the main intakes and exhausts. The losses in discontinuities depend on the amount of boundary layer separation; this is minimized by avoiding sudden changes in area.

Resistance of airways with obstructions

The effect of an obstruction on pressure losses depends on its drag coefficient and the fill coefficient, which is the ratio of the blockage area of the object and the cross-sectional area of the airway. The losses caused by obstructions can be reduced by minimizing boundary-layer separation and the extent of any turbulent wake by streamlining the object. Drag coefficients are affected by their shape and arrangement in the shaft; comparative values would be: I beam, 2.7; square, 2.0; cylinder, 1.2; elongated hexagon, 0.6; and fully streamlined, 0.4.

Even with small fill coefficients and low drag coefficients, if the obstruction is repeated regularly, such as with the beams separating hoisting compartments in a shaft, the cumulative effect on pressure losses is significant. For example, the resistance of a shaft equipped with semi-streamlined elongated hexagon beams and a fill coefficient of 0.08 would be about four times that of the concrete lined shaft alone. Although the material costs of the more readily available rectangular hollow structural steel sections are more than I beams, the drag coefficients are about one-third and easily justify their application.

Main and booster fans

Both axial and centrifugal fans are used to provide air circulation in mine ventilation systems, with fan efficiencies of over 80% being achievable. The selection between axial flow or centrifugal for main mine fans depends on cost, size, pressure, robustness, efficiency and any performance variation. In mines where a fan failure may result in dangerous methane accumulations, additional fan capacity is installed to ensure continuity of ventilation. Where this is not so critical and with a twin fan installation, about two-thirds of the mine airflow will continue if one fan stops. Vertical axial flow fans installed over the airways have low costs but are limited to about 300 m³/s. For larger air quantities, multiple fans are required and they are connected to the exhaust with ducting and a bend.

To obtain the highest efficiencies at reasonable cost, axial flow fans are used for low pressure (less than 1.0 kPa) applications and centrifugal fans for high pressure (greater than 3.0 kPa) systems. Either selection is suitable for the intermediate pressures. Where robustness is required, such as with exhausts with air velocities above the critical range, and water droplets are carried up and out of the system, a centrifugal fan will provide a more reliable selection. The critical air velocity range is between 7.5 m/s and 12.5 m/s where the water droplets may stay in suspension depending on their size. Within this range, the amount of suspended water can build up and increase the system pressure until the fan stalls. This is the region where some of the air recirculates around the blades and fan operation becomes unstable. Although not desirable for any type of fan, the possibility of a centrifugal fan blade failure is significantly less than an axial blade failure in this region of flow fluctuation.

It is rare that a main fan is required to operate at the same duty point over the life of the mine, and effective methods of varying fan performance are desirable. Although variable speed results in the most efficient operation for both axial and centrifugal fans, the costs, particularly for large fans, is high. The performance of an axial flow fan can be varied by adjusting the blade angle and this can be carried out either when the fan is stopped or, at a significantly higher cost, when it is rotating. By imparting a swirl to the air entering a fan using variable inlet vanes, the performance of a centrifugal fan can be varied while it is running. The efficiency of the centrifugal fan away from its design point falls off more rapidly than that of an axial flow fan and, if a high performance is required over a wide range of operating points and the pressures are suitable, the axial flow fan is selected.

Ventilation systems

The position of the main fan in the overall system is normally on surface at the exhaust airway. The main reasons for this are simplicity where the intake is often a hoisting shaft and the exhaust is a separate single purpose airway and minimization of the heat load by excluding fans from intake airways. Fans can be installed at hoisting shafts either in forcing or exhausting mode by providing a sealed headframe. However, where workers, materials or rock also enter or leave the shaft, there is a potential for air leakage.

Push-pull systems where both intake and exhaust fans are installed are used either to reduce the maximum pressure in the system by sharing or to provide a very small pressure difference between the workings and surface. This is pertinent in mines using caving methods where leakage through the caved area may be undesirable. With large pressure differences, although air leakage through a caved zone is normally small, it may introduce heat, radiation or oxidation problems into the working places.

Underground booster fans, because of space limitations, are almost always axial flow and they are used to boost flow in the deeper or more distant sections of a mine. Their main drawback is the possibility of recirculation between the booster fan exhaust and the intake airways. By only providing a boost to the smaller airflows where they are required, they can result in a lower main fan pressure for the full mine airflow and a consequent reduction in total fan power required.

Secondary Ventilation

Auxiliary systems

Secondary ventilation systems are required where through ventilation is not possible, such as in development headings. Four arrangements are possible, each having its own advantages and disadvantages.

The *forcing system* results in the coolest and freshest air reaching the face and allows cheaper flexible duct to be used. The high velocity of the air issuing from the end of the supply duct creates a jet which entrains additional air and helps sweep the face of contaminants and provide an acceptable face velocity. Its main drawback is that the rest of the heading is ventilated with air that is contaminated with the gases and dust produced by mining operations in the face. This is particularly a problem after blasting, where safe re-entry times are increased.

An *exhausting system* allows all the face contaminants to be removed and maintains the rest of the heading in intake air. The drawbacks are that heat flow from the surrounding rock and moisture evaporation will result in higher face delivery air temperatures; operations in the heading back from the face, such as rock removal using diesel-powered equipment, will contaminate the intake air; there is no air jet produced to sweep the face; and more costly duct which is capable of sustaining a negative pressure is required.

In an *exhaust-overlap system* the problem of clearing the face with an air jet is overcome by installing a smaller fan and duct (the overlap). In addition to the extra cost, a disadvantage is that the overlap needs to be advanced with the face.

In a *reversing system*, the forcing ventilation mode is used, except during blasting and the re-entry period after blasting, when the airflow is reversed. Its main application is in shaft sinking, where re-entry times for deep shafts can be prohibitive if a forcing only system was used. The air reversal can be obtained by either using dampers at the fan inlet and outlet or, by taking advantage of a feature of axial flow fans, where changing the direction of blade rotation results in a flow reversal with about 60% of the normal flow being delivered.

Fans and ducts

The fans used for secondary ventilation are almost exclusively axial flow. To achieve the high pressures necessary to cause the air to flow through long lengths of duct, multiple fans with either contra-rotating or co-rotating impeller arrangements may be used. Air leakage is the greatest problem in auxiliary fan and duct systems, particularly over long distances. Rigid ducts fabricated from galvanized steel or fibreglass, when installed with gaskets, have suitably low leakage and may be used to develop headings up to several kilometres in length.

Flexible ducts are considerably cheaper to purchase and easier to install; however, leakage at the couplings and the ease with which they are ripped by contact with mobile equipment results in much higher air losses. Practical development limits using flexible duct rarely exceed 1.0 km, although they can be extended by using longer duct lengths and ensuring ample clearances between the duct and mobile equipment.

Ventilation Controls

Both through ventilation and auxiliary fan and duct systems are used to provide ventilation air to locations where personnel may work. Ventilation controls are used to direct the air to the working place and to minimize the short circuiting or loss of air between intake and exhaust airways.

A bulkhead is used to stop air flowing through a connecting tunnel. The materials of construction will depend on the pressure difference and whether it will be subject to shock waves from blasting. Flexible curtains attached to the surrounding rock surfaces are suitable for low pressure applications such as separating the intake and return airways in a room-and-pillar panel mined with a continuous miner. Timber and concrete bulkheads are suitable for higher pressure applications and may incorporate a heavy rubber flap which can open to minimize any blast damage.

A ventilation door is needed where pedestrian or vehicular passage is required. The materials of construction, opening mechanism and degree of automation are influenced by the pressure difference and the frequency of opening and closing. For high pressure applications, two or even three doors may be installed to create air locks and reduce leakage and the loss of intake air. To assist in opening air lock doors, they usually contain a small sliding section which is opened first to allow equalization of the pressure on both sides of the door to be opened.

A regulator is used where the amount of air flowing through a tunnel is to be reduced rather than stopped completely and also where access is not required. The regulator is a variable orifice and by changing the area, the air quantity flowing through it can also be changed. A drop board is one of the simplest types where a concrete frame supports channels into which timber boards can be placed (dropped) and the open area varied. Other types, such as butterfly louvres, can be automated and remotely controlled. On the upper levels in some open stoping systems, infrequent access through the regulators may be required and horizontally stiffened, flexible panels can be simply raised or lowered to provide access while minimizing blast damage. Even piles of broken rock have been used to increase the resistance in sections of a level where there is temporarily no mining activity.

Refrigeration and Cooling Systems

The first mine refrigeration system was installed at Morro Velho, Brazil, in 1919. Since that date, the growth in worldwide capacity has been linear at about 3 megawatts of refrigeration (MWR) per year until 1965, when the total capacity reached about 100 MWR. Since 1965 the growth in capacity has been exponential, with a doubling every six or seven years. The development of mine refrigeration has been influenced both by the air conditioning industry and the difficulties of dealing with a dynamic mining system in which the fouling of heat exchanger surfaces may have profound effects on the amount of cooling provided.

Initially, the refrigeration plants were installed on surface and the mine intake air was cooled. As the distance underground from the surface plant increased, the cooling effect was reduced and the refrigeration plants were moved underground closer to the workings. Limitations in underground heat rejection capacity and the simplicity of surface plants has resulted in a move back to the surface location. However, in addition to the intake air being cooled, chilled water is now also supplied underground. This may be used in air-cooling devices adjacent to the working areas or as the service water used in drills and for dust suppression.

Refrigeration plant equipment

Vapour compression refrigeration systems are exclusively used for mines, and the central element of the surface plant is the compressor. Individual plant capacities may vary between 5 MWR and over 100 MWR and generally require multiple compressor systems which are either of the centrifugal or positive displacement screw design. Ammonia is normally the refrigerant selected for a surface plant and a suitable halocarbon is used underground.

The heat required to condense the refrigerant after compression is rejected to the atmosphere and, to minimize the power required to provide the mine cooling, this is kept as low as practical. The wet bulb temperature is always less than or equal to the dry bulb temperature and consequently wet-heat rejection systems are invariably selected. The refrigerant may be condensed in a shell and tube or plate and frame heat exchanger using water and the heat extracted and then rejected to the atmosphere in a cooling tower. Alternatively, the two processes can be combined by using an evaporative condenser where the refrigerant circulates in tubes over which air is drawn and water is sprayed. If the refrigeration plant is installed underground, mine exhaust air is used for heat rejection unless the condenser water is pumped to surface. Operation of the underground plant is limited by the amount of air available and higher underground wet bulb temperatures relative to those on surface.

After passing the condensed refrigerant through an expansion valve, the evaporation of the low temperature liquid and gas mixture is completed in another heat exchanger that cools and provides the chilled water. In turn, this is used both to cool the intake air and as cold service water supplied to the mine. The contact between water, ventilation air and the mine reduces water quality and increases heat exchanger fouling. This increases the resistance to heat flow. Where possible, this effect is minimized by selecting equipment having large water side surface areas that are easy to clean. On surface and underground, spray chambers and cooling towers are used to provide the more effective direct contact heat exchange between the air being cooled and the chilled water. Cooling coils which separate the air and water streams become clogged with dust and diesel particulate and their effectiveness rapidly declines.

Energy recovery systems can be used to offset the costs of pumping the water back out of the mine and pelton wheels are well suited to this application. The use of cold water as service water has helped to ensure that cooling is available wherever there is mining activity; its use has significantly improved the effectiveness of mine cooling systems.

Ice systems and spot coolers

The cooling capacity of 1.0 l/s of chilled water supplied underground is 100 to 120 kWR. On mines where large amounts of refrigeration are required underground at depths greater than 2,500 m, the costs of circulating the chilled water can justify replacing it with ice. When the latent heat of fusion of the ice is taken into account, the cooling capacity of each 1.0 l/s is increased approximately fourfold, thus reducing the mass of water that needs to be pumped from the mine back to surface. The reduction in pump power resulting from the use of ice to transport the coolness offsets the increased refrigeration plant power required to produce the ice and the impracticability of energy recovery.

Development is usually the mining activity with the highest heat loads relative to the amount of air available for ventilation. This often results in worksite temperatures significantly higher than those found with other mining activities in the same mine. Where the application of refrigeration is a borderline issue for a mine, spot coolers specifically targeted to development ventilation can defer its general application. A spot cooler is essentially a miniature underground refrigeration plant where the heat is rejected into the return air from the development and typically provides 250 to 500 kWR of cooling.

Monitoring and Emergencies

Ventilation surveys which include airflow, contaminant and temperature measurements are undertaken on a routine basis to meet both statutory requirements and to provide a continuing measure of the effectiveness of the ventilation control methods used. Where practical, important parameters such as main fan operation are monitored continuously. Some degree of automatic control is possible where a critical contaminant is monitored continuously and, if a pre-set limit is exceeded, corrective action can be prompted.

More detailed surveys of barometric pressure and temperatures are undertaken less frequently and are used to confirm airway resistances and to assist in planning extensions of existing operations. This information can be used to adjust the network simulation resistances and reflect the actual airflow distribution. Refrigeration systems can also be modelled and flow and temperature measurements analysed to determine actual equipment performance and to monitor any changes.

The emergencies that may affect or be affected by the ventilation system are mine fires, sudden gas outbursts and power failures. Fires and outbursts are dealt with elsewhere in this chapter and power failures are only a problem in deep mines where the air temperatures may increase to dangerous levels. It is common to provide a diesel-powered backup fan to ensure a small airflow through the mine under these conditions. Generally, when an emergency such as a fire occurs underground, it is better not to interfere with the ventilation while personnel who are familiar with the normal flow patterns are still underground.

LIGHTING IN UNDERGROUND MINES ●

Don Trotter

Light Sources in Mining

In 1879 a practical incandescent filament lamp was patented. As a result light no longer depended on a fuel source. Many startling breakthroughs have been made in lighting knowledge since Edison's discovery, including some with applications in underground mines. Each has inherent advantages and disadvantages. Table 74.3 lists the light source types and compares some parameters.

Current to energize the light sources may be either alternating (AC) or direct (DC). Fixed light sources almost always use alternating current whereas portable sources such as cap lamps and underground vehicle headlights use a DC battery. Not all light source types are suitable for direct current.

Fixed light sources

Tungsten filament lamps are most common, often with a frosted bulb and a shield to reduce glare. The fluorescent lamp is the second most common light source and is easily distinguishable by its tubular design. Circular and U-shaped designs are compact and have mining applications as mining areas are often in cramped spaces. Tungsten filament and fluorescent sources are used to light such diverse underground openings as shaft stations, conveyors, travelways, lunchrooms, charging stations, fuel bays, repair depots, warehouses, tool rooms and crusher stations.

The trend in mine lighting is to use more efficient light sources. These are the four high-intensity discharge (HID) sources called mercury vapour, metal halide, high-pressure sodium and low-pressure sodium. Each requires a few minutes (one to seven) to come up to full light output. Also, if power to the lamp is lost or turned off, the arc tube must be cooled before the arc can be struck and the lamp relit. (However, in the case of low-pressure sodium (Sox) lamps, restrike is almost instantaneous.) Their spectral energy distributions differ from that of natural light. Mercury vapour lamps produce a bluish white light whereas high-pressure sodium lamps produce a yellowish light. If colour differentiation is important in underground work (e.g., for using colour-coded gas bottles for welding, reading colour-coded signs, electrical wiring hook-ups or sorting ore by colour), care must be taken in the colour rendition properties of the source. Objects will have their surface colours distorted when lit by a low-pressure sodium lamp. Table 74.3 gives colour rendition comparisons.

Table 74.3 • Comparison of mine light sources.

Type of light source	Approximate luminance cd/m² (clear bulb)	Average rated life (h)	DC source	Approximate initial efficacy lm·W⁻¹	Colour rendition
Tungsten filament	10^5 to 10^7	750 to 1,000	Yes	5 to 30	Excellent
Incandescent	2×10^7	5 to 2,000	Yes	28	Excellent
Fluorescent	5×10^4 to 2×10^5	500 to 30,000	Yes	100	Excellent
Mercury vapour	10^5 to 10^6	16,000 to 24,000	Yes with limitations	63	Average
Metal halide	5×10^6	10,000 to 20,000	Yes with limitations	125	Good
High-pressure sodium	10^7	12,000 to 24,000	Not advised	140	Fair
Low-pressure sodium	10^5	10,000 to 18,000	Not advised	183	Poor

cd = candela, DC = direct current; lm = lumens.

Mobile light sources

With working places spread out often both laterally and vertically, and with continual blasting in these working places, permanent installations are often deemed impractical because of the costs of installation and upkeep. In many mines the battery-operated cap lamp is the most important single source of light. Although fluorescent cap lamps are in use, by far the majority of cap lamps use tungsten filament battery-operated cap lamps. Batteries are lead acid or nickel cadmium. A miniature tungsten-halogen lamp bulb is often used for the miner's cap lamp. The small bulb allows the beam to be easily focused. The halogen gas surrounding the filament prevents the tungsten filament material from boiling off, which keeps lamp walls from blackening. The bulb can also be burned hotter and hence brighter.

For mobile vehicle lighting, incandescent lamps are most commonly used. They require no special equipment, are inexpensive and are easy to replace. Parabolic aluminized reflector (PAR) lamps are used as headlights on vehicles.

Standards for Mine Lighting

Countries with a well-established underground mining industry are usually quite specific in their requirements regarding what constitutes a safe mine lighting system. This is particularly true for mines which have methane gas given off from the workings, usually coal mines. Methane gas can ignite and cause an underground explosion with devastating results. Consequently any lights must be designed to be either "intrinsically safe" or "explosion proof". An intrinsically safe light source is one in which the current feeding the light has very little energy so that any short in the circuit would not produce a spark which could ignite the methane gas. For a lamp to be explosion proof, any explosion triggered by the lamp's electrical activity is contained within the device. In addition, the device itself will not become hot enough to cause an explosion. The lamp is more expensive, heavier, with metal parts usually made of castings. Governments usually have test facilities to certify whether lamps can be classified for use in a gassy mine. A low-pressure sodium lamp could not be so certified as the sodium in the lamp could ignite if the lamp were to break and the sodium came in contact with water.

Countries also legislate standards for the amount of light required for various tasks but legislation varies greatly in the amount of light that should be placed in the various working places.

Guidelines for mine lighting are also provided by international bodies concerned with lighting, such as the Illumination Engineering Society (IES) and the Commission internationale de l'éclairage (CIE). The CIE stresses that the quality of light being received by the eye is as important as the quantity and provides formulas to ascertain whether glare may be a factor in visual performance.

Effects of Lighting on Accidents, Production and Health

One would expect that better lighting would reduce accidents, increase production and reduce health hazards, but it is not easy to substantiate this. The direct effect of lighting on underground efficiency and safety is hard to measure because lighting is only one of many variables that affect production and safety. There is well-documented evidence that shows highway accidents decrease with improved illumination. A similar correlation has been noted in factories. The very nature of mining, however, dictates that the work area is constantly changing, so that very few reports relating mine accidents to lighting can be found in the literature and it remains an area of research that has been largely unexplored. Accident investigations show that poor lighting is rarely the primary cause of underground accidents but is often a contributing factor. While lighting conditions play some role in many mine accidents, they have special significance in accidents involving falls of ground, since poor lighting makes it easy to miss dangerous conditions that could otherwise be corrected.

Until the beginning of the twentieth century, miners commonly suffered from the eye disease nystagmus, for which there was no known cure. Nystagmus produced uncontrollable oscillation of the eyeballs, headaches, dizziness and loss of night vision. It was caused by working under very low light levels over long periods of time. Coal miners were particularly susceptible, since very little of the light that strikes the coal is reflected. These miners often had to lie on their sides when working in low coal and this may also have contributed to the disease. With the introduction of the electric cap lamp in mines, miner's nystagmus has disappeared, eliminating the most important health hazard associated with underground lighting.

With recent technological advances in new light sources, the interest in lighting and health has been revived. It is now possible to have lighting levels in mines that would have been extremely difficult to achieve previously. The main concern is glare, but concern has also been expressed about the radiometric energy given off by the lights. Radiometric energy can affect workers either by acting directly on cells on or near the surface of the skin or by triggering certain responses, such as biological rhythms on which physical and mental health depends. An HID light source can still operate even though the glass envelope containing the source is cracked or broken. Workers can then be in danger of receiving doses beyond threshold limit values, particularly since these light sources often cannot be mounted very high.

PERSONAL PROTECTIVE EQUIPMENT IN MINING

Peter W. Pickerill

Head Protection

In most countries miners must be provided with, and must wear, safety caps or hats which are approved in the jurisdiction in which the mine operates. Hats differ from caps in that they have a full brim rather than just a front peak. This has the advantage of shedding water in mines which are very wet. It does, however, preclude the incorporation of side slots for mounting of hearing protection, flashlights and face shields for welding, cutting, grinding, chipping and scaling or other accessories. Hats represent a very small percentage of the head protection worn in mines.

The cap or hat would in most cases be equipped with a lamp bracket and cord holder to permit mounting of a miner's cap lamp.

The traditional miner's cap has a very low profile which significantly reduces the propensity for the miner to bump his or her head in low seam coal mines. However, in mines where head room is adequate the low profile serves no useful purpose. Furthermore, it is achieved by reducing the clearance between the crown of the cap and the wearer's skull so that these types of cap rarely meet the top impact standards for industrial head protection. In jurisdictions where the standards are enforced, the traditional miner's cap is giving way to conventional industrial head protection.

Standards for industrial head protection have changed very little since the 1960s. However, in the 1990s, the boom in recreational head protection, such as hockey helmets, cycle helmets and so on, has highlighted what are perceived to be inadequacies in industrial head protection, most notably lack of lateral impact protection and lack of retention capabilities in the event of an impact. Thus, there has been pressure to upgrade the standards for industrial head protection and in some jurisdictions this has already happened. Safety caps with foam liners and, possibly, ratchet suspensions and/or chin straps are now appearing in the industrial marketplace. They have not been widely accepted by users because of the higher cost and weight and their lesser comfort. However, as the new standards become more widely entrenched in labour legislation the new style of cap is likely to appear in the mining industry.

Cap Lamps

In areas of the mine where permanent lighting is not installed, the miner's cap lamp is essential to permit the miner to move and work effectively and safely. The key requirements for a cap lamp are that it be rugged, easy to operate with gloved hands, provide sufficient light output for the full duration of a work shift (to illumination levels required by local regulation) and that it be as light as possible without sacrificing any of the above performance parameters.

Halogen bulbs have largely replaced the incandescent tungsten filament bulb in recent years. This has resulted in three- or four-fold improvement in illumination levels, making it feasible to meet the minimum standards of illumination required by legislation even at the end of an extended work-shift. Battery technology also plays a major part in lamp performance. The lead acid battery still predominates in most mining applications, although some manufacturers have successfully introduced nickel-cadmium (nicad) batteries, which can achieve the same performance with a lower weight. Reliability, longevity and maintenance issues, however, still favour the lead acid battery and probably account for its continued dominance.

In addition to its primary function of providing lighting, the cap lamp and battery have recently been integrated into mine safety communications systems. Radio receivers and circuitry embedded in the battery cover permit the miners to receive messages, warnings or evacuation instructions through very low frequency (VLF) radio transmission and enable them to be made aware of an incoming message by means of an on/off flashing of the cap lamp. Such systems are still in their infancy but they do have the potential to provide an advance in early warning capability over traditional stench gas systems in those mines where a VLF radio communication system can be engineered and installed.

Eye and Face Protection

Most mining operations around the world have compulsory eye protection programmes which require the miner to wear safety spectacles, goggles, faceshields or a full facepiece respirator, depending on the operations being performed and the combination of hazards to which the miner is exposed. For the majority of mining operations, safety spectacles with side shields provide suitable protection. The dust and dirt in many mining environments, most notably hard-rock mining, can be highly abrasive. This causes scratching and rapid wear of safety glasses with plastic (polycarbonate) lenses. For this reason, many mines still permit the use of glass lenses, even though they do not provide the resistance to impact and shattering offered by polycarbonates, and even though they may not meet the prevailing standard for protective eye wear in the particular jurisdiction. Progress continues to be made in both anti-fog treatments and surface hardening treatments for plastic lenses. Those treatments which change the molecular structure of the lens surface rather than simply applying a film or coating are typically more effective and longer lasting and have the potential to replace glass as the lens material of choice for abrasive mining environments.

Goggles are not worn frequently below ground unless the particular operation poses a danger of chemical splash.

A faceshield may be worn where the miner requires full-face protection from weld spatter, grinding residues or other large flying particles which could be produced by cutting, chipping or scaling. The faceshield may be of a specialized nature, as in welding, or may be clear acrylic or polycarbonate. Although faceshields can be equipped with their own head harness, in mining they will normally be mounted in the accessory slots in the miner's safety cap. Faceshields are designed so that they can be quickly and easily hinged upwards for observation of the work and down over the face for protection when performing the work.

A full facepiece respirator may be worn for face protection when there is also a requirement for respiratory protection against a substance which is irritating to the eyes. Such operations are more often encountered in the above ground mine processing than in the below ground mining operation itself.

Respiratory Protection

The most commonly needed respiratory protection in mining operations is dust protection. Coal dust as well as most other ambient dusts can be effectively filtered using an inexpensive quarter facepiece dust mask. The type which uses an elastomer nose/mouth cover and replaceable filters is effective. The moulded throw-away fibre-cup type respirator is not effective.

Welding, flame cutting, use of solvents, handling of fuels, blasting and other operations can produce air-borne contaminants that require the use of twin cartridge respirators to remove combinations of dust, mists, fumes, organic vapours and acid gases. In these cases, the need for protection for the miner will be indicated by measurement of the contaminants, usually performed locally, using detector tubes or portable instruments. The appropriate respirator is worn until the mine ventilation system has cleared the contaminant or reduced it to levels that are acceptable.

Certain types of particulates encountered in mines, such as asbestos fibres found in asbestos mines, coal fines produced in longwall mining and radionuclides found in uranium mining, may require the use of a positive pressure respirator equipped with a high-efficiency particulate absolute (HEPA) filter. Powered air-purifying respirators (PAPRs) which supply the filtered air to a hood, tight-fitting facepiece or integrated helmet facepiece assembly meet this requirement.

Hearing Protection

Underground vehicles, machinery and power tools generate high ambient noise levels which can create long-term damage to human hearing. Protection is normally provided by ear muff type protectors which are slot-mounted on the miner's cap. Supplementary protection can be provided by wearing closed cell foam ear plugs in conjunction with the ear muffs. Ear plugs, either of the disposable foam cell variety or the reusable elastomeric variety, may be used on their own, either because of preference or because the accessory slot is being used to carry a face shield or other accessory.

Skin Protection

Certain mining operations may cause skin irritation. Work gloves are worn whenever possible in such operations and barrier creams are provided for additional protection, particularly when the gloves cannot be worn.

Foot Protection

The mining work boot may be of either leather or rubber construction, depending on whether the mine is dry or wet. Minimum protective requirements for the boot include a full puncture-proof sole with a composite outer layer to prevent slipping, a steel toe-cap and a metatarsal guard. Although these fundamental requirements have not changed in many years, advances have been made towards meeting them in a boot that is far less cumbersome and far more comfortable than the boots of several years ago. For example, metatarsal guards are now available in moulded fibre, replacing the steel hoops and saddles that were once common. They provide equivalent protection with less weight and less risk of tripping. The lasts (foot forms) have become more anatomically correct and energy absorbing midsoles, full moisture barriers and modern insulating materials have made their way from the sports/recreation footwear market into the mining boot.

Clothing

Ordinary cotton coveralls or treated flame-resistant cotton coveralls are the normal workwear in mines. Strips of reflective material are usually added to make the miner more visible to drivers of moving underground vehicles. Miners working with jumbo drills or other heavy equipment may also wear rain suits over their coveralls to protect against cutting fluid, hydraulic oil and lubricating oils, which can spray or leak from the equipment.

Work gloves are worn for hand protection. A general purpose work glove would be constructed of cotton canvas reinforced with leather. Other types and styles of glove would be used for special job functions.

Belts and Harnesses

In most jurisdictions, the miners belt is no longer considered suitable or approved for fall protection. A webbing or leather belt is still used, however, with or without suspenders and with or without a lumbar support to carry the lamp battery as well as a filter self-rescuer or self-contained (oxygen generating) self-rescuer, if required.

A full body harness with D-ring attachment between the shoulder blades is now the only recommended device for protecting miners against falls. The harness should be worn with a suitable lanyard and shock absorbing device by miners working in shafts, over crushers or near open sump or pits. Additional D-rings may be added to a harness or a miner's belt for work positioning or to restrict movement within safe limits.

Protection from Heat and Cold

In open-pit mines in cold climates, miners will have winter clothing including thermal socks, underwear and gloves, wind resistant pants or over-pants, a lined parka with hood and a winter liner to wear with the safety cap.

In underground mines, heat is more of a problem than cold. Ambient temperatures may be high because of the depth of the mine below ground or because it is located in a hot climate. Protection from heat stress and potential heat stroke can be provided by special garments or undergarments which can accommodate frozen gel packs or which are constructed with a network of cooling tubes to circulate cooling fluids over the surface of the body and then through an external heat exchanger. In situations where the rock itself is hot, heat resistant gloves, socks and boots are worn. Drinking water or, preferably, drinking water with added electrolytes must be available and must be consumed to replace lost body fluids.

Other Protective Equipment

Depending on local regulations and the type of mine, miners may be required to carry a self-rescue device. This is a respiratory protection device which will help the miner to escape from the mine in the event of a mine fire or explosion that renders the atmosphere unbreathable because of carbon monoxide, smoke and other toxic contaminants. The self-rescuer may be a filtration type device with a catalyst for carbon monoxide conversion or it may be a self-contained self-rescuer, i.e., a closed-cycle breathing apparatus which chemically regenerates oxygen from exhaled breath.

Portable instruments (including detector tubes and detector tube pumps) for the detection and measurement of toxic and combustible gases are not carried routinely by all miners, but are used by mine safety officers or other designated personnel in accordance with standard operating procedures to test mine atmospheres periodically or before entry.

Improving the ability to communicate with personnel in underground mining operations is proving to have enormous safety benefits and two-way communication systems, personal pagers and personnel locating devices are finding their way into modern mining operations.

FIRES AND EXPLOSIONS IN MINES

Casey C. Grant

Fires and explosions pose a constant threat to the safety of miners and to the productive capacity of mines. Mine fires and explosions traditionally have ranked among the most devastating industrial disasters.

At the end of the nineteenth century, fires and explosions in mines resulted in loss of life and property damage on a scale unmatched in other industrial sectors. However, clear progress has been achieved in controlling these hazards, as evidenced by the decline in mine fires and explosions reported in recent decades.

This article describes the basic fire and explosion hazards of underground mining and the safeguards needed to minimize them. Fire protection information on surface mines can be found elsewhere in this *Encyclopaedia* and in standards such as those promulgated by organizations such as the National Fire Protection Association in the United States (e.g., NFPA 1996a).

Permanent Service Areas

By their nature, permanent service areas involve certain hazardous activities, and thus special precautions should be taken. Underground maintenance shops and related facilities are a special hazard in an underground mine.

Mobile equipment in maintenance shops is regularly found to be a frequent source of fires. Fires on diesel-powered mining equipment typically arise from leaking high-pressure hydraulic lines which can spray a heated mist of highly combustible liquid onto an ignition source, such as a hot exhaust manifold or turbocharger (Bickel 1987). Fires on this type of equipment can grow quickly.

Much of the mobile equipment used in underground mines contains not only fuel sources (e.g., diesel fuel and hydraulics) but they also contain ignition sources (e.g., diesel engines and electrical equipment). Thus, this equipment presents an appreciable risk for fires. In addition to this equipment, maintenance shops generally contain a variety of other tools, materials and equipment (e.g., degreasing equipment) that are a hazard in any mechanical shop environment.

Welding and cutting operations are a leading cause of fires in mines. This activity can be expected to occur regularly in a maintenance area. Special precautions need to be taken to ensure that these activities do not create a possible ignition source for a fire or explosion. Fire and explosion protection information relating to safe welding practices can be found elsewhere in this *Encyclopaedia* and in other documents (e.g., NFPA 1994a).

Consideration should be given to making the entire shop area a completely enclosed structure of fire resistant construction. This is particularly important for shops intended for use longer than 6 months. If such an arrangement is not possible, then the area should be protected throughout by an automatic fire suppression system. This is especially important for coal mines, where it is critical to minimize any potential fire source.

Another important consideration for all shop areas is that they be vented directly to the air return, thus limiting the spread of products of combustion from any fire. Requirements for these type of facilities are clearly outlined in documents such as NFPA 122, *Standard for Fire Prevention and Control in Underground Metal and Nonmetal Mines*, and NFPA 123, *Standard for Fire Prevention and Control in Underground Bituminous Coal Mines* (NFPA 1995a, 1995b).

Fuel Bays and Fuel Storage Areas

The storage, handling and use of flammable and combustible liquids pose a special fire hazard for all sectors of the mining industry.

In many underground mines, mobile equipment is typically diesel-powered, and a large percentage of the fires involve the fuel used by these machines. In coal mines, these fire hazards are compounded by the presence of coal, coal dust and methane.

The storage of flammable and combustible liquids is an especially important concern because these materials ignite more easily and propagate fire more rapidly than ordinary combustibles. Both flammable and combustible liquids are often stored underground in most non-coal mines in limited quantities. In some mines, the main storage facility for diesel fuel, lubricating oil and grease, and hydraulic fluid is underground. The potential seriousness of a fire in an underground flammable and combustible liquid storage area requires extreme care in the design of the storage areas, plus the implementation and strict enforcement of safe operating procedures.

All aspects of using flammable and combustible liquids present challenging fire protection concerns, including the transfer to underground, storage, dispensing and ultimate use in equipment. The hazards and protection methods for flammable and combustible liquids in underground mines can be found elsewhere in this *Encyclopaedia* and in NFPA standards (e.g., NFPA 1995a, 1995b, 1996b).

Fire Prevention

Safety for fires and explosions in underground mines is based on the general principles of preventing fire and explosion. Normally, this involves using common-sense fire safety techniques, such as preventing smoking, as well as providing built-in fire protection measures to prevent fires from growing, such as portable extinguishers or early fire detection systems.

Fire and explosion prevention practices in mines generally fall into three categories: limiting ignition sources, limiting fuel sources and limiting fuel and ignition source contact.

Limiting ignition sources is perhaps the most basic way of preventing a fire or explosion. Ignition sources that are not essential to the mining process should be banned altogether. For example, smoking and any open fires, especially in underground coal mines, should be prohibited. All automated and mechanized equipment that may be subject to unwanted buildup of heat, such as conveyors, should have slippage and sequence switches and thermal cutouts on electric motors. Explosives present an obvious hazard, but they could also be an ignition source for suspended dust of hazardous gas and should be used in strict conformance with special blasting regulations.

Eliminating electrical ignition sources is essential for preventing explosions. Electrical equipment operating where methane, sulphide dust or other fire hazards may be present should be designed, constructed, tested and installed so that its operation will not cause a mine fire or explosion. Explosion proof enclosures, such as plugs, receptacles and circuit interrupting devices, should be used in hazardous areas. The use of intrinsically safe electrical equipment is described in further detail elsewhere in this *Encyclopaedia* and in documents such as NFPA 70, *National Electrical Code* (NFPA 1996c).

Limiting fuel sources starts with good housekeeping to prevent unsafe accumulations of trash, oily rags, coal dust and other combustible materials.

When available, less hazardous substitutes should be used for certain combustible materials such as hydraulic fluids, conveyor belting, hydraulic hoses and ventilation tubing (Bureau of Mines 1978). The highly toxic products of combustion that may result from the burning of certain materials often necessitates less hazardous materials. As an example, polyurethane foam had previously been widely used in underground mines for ventilation seals, but more recently has been banned in many countries.

For underground coal mine explosions, coal dust and methane are typically the primary fuels involved. Methane may also be present in non-coal mines and is most commonly handled by dilution with ventilation air and exhaustion from the mine (Timmons, Vinson and Kissell 1979). For coal dust, every attempt is made to minimize the generation of dust in the mining processes, but the tiny amount needed for a coal dust explosion is almost unavoidable. A layer of dust on the floor that is only 0.012 mm thick will cause an explosion if suspended in air. Thus, rock dusting using an inert material such as pulverized limestone, dolomite or gypsum (rock dust) will help to prevent coal dust explosions.

Limiting fuel and ignition source contact depends upon preventing contact between the ignition source and the fuel source. For example, when welding and cutting operations cannot be performed in fire-safe enclosures, it is important that areas be wet down and nearby combustibles covered with fire resistant materials or relocated. Fire extinguishers should be readily available and a fire watch posted for as long as necessary to guard against smouldering fires.

Areas with a high loading of combustible materials, such as timber storage areas, explosives magazines, flammable and combustible liquid storage areas and shops, should be designed to minimize possible ignition sources. Mobile equipment should have hydraulic fluid, fuel and lubricant lines re-routed away from hot surfaces, electrical equipment and other possible ignition sources. Spray shields should be installed to deflect sprays of combustible liquid from broken fluid lines away from potential ignition sources.

Fire and explosion prevention requirements for mines are clearly outlined in NFPA documents (e.g., NFPA 1992a, 1995a, 1995b).

Fire Detection and Warning Systems

The elapsed time between the onset of a fire and its detection is critical since fires may grow rapidly in size and intensity. The most rapid and reliable indication of fire is through advanced fire detection and warning systems using sensitive heat, flame, smoke and gas analysers (Griffin 1979).

The detection of gas or smoke is the most cost-effective approach to providing fire detection coverage over a large area or throughout the entire mine (Morrow and Litton 1992). Thermal fire detection systems are commonly installed for unattended equipment, such as over conveyor belts. Faster-acting fire detection devices are considered appropriate for certain high-hazard areas, such as flammable and combustible liquids storage areas, refuelling areas and shops. Optical flame detectors that sense either ultraviolet or infrared radiation emitted by a fire are often used in these areas.

All miners should be warned once a fire has been detected. Telephones and messengers are sometimes used, but miners are often remote from telephones and they are often widely scattered. In coal mines, the most common means of fire warning are shutdown of electric power and subsequent notification by telephone and messengers. This is not an option for non-coal mines, where so little equipment is powered electrically. Stench warning is a common method of emergency communication in non-coal underground mines (Pomroy and Muldoon 1983). Special wireless radio frequency communication systems have also been used successfully in both coal and non-coal mines (Bureau of Mines 1988).

The primary concern during an underground fire is the safety of underground personnel. Early fire detection and warning permit the initiation of an emergency plan in the mine. Such a plan assures that the necessary activities, such as evacuation and fire-fighting will occur. To assure smooth implementation of the emergency plan, miners should be provided with comprehensive training and periodic retraining in emergency procedures. Fire drills, complete with the activation of the mine warning system, should be performed frequently to reinforce the training and to identify weaknesses in the emergency plan.

Further information on fire detection and warning systems can be found elsewhere in this *Encyclopaedia* and in NFPA documents (e.g., NFPA 1995a, 1995b, 1996d).

Fire Suppression

The most common types of fire suppression equipment used in underground mines are portable hand extinguishers, water hoselines, sprinkler systems, rock dust (applied manually or from a rock dusting machine) and foam generators. The most common type of portable hand extinguishers are typically those using multi-purpose dry chemicals.

Fire suppression systems, either manual or automatic, are becoming more common for mobile equipment, combustible liquids storage areas, conveyor belt drives and electrical installations (Grannes, Ackerson and Green 1990). Automatic fire suppression is especially important for unattended, automated or remote control equipment where personnel are not present to detect a fire, to activate a fire suppression system or to initiate fire-fighting operations.

Explosion suppression is a variation of fire suppression. Some European coal mines use this technology in the form of passive or triggered barriers on a limited basis. Passive barriers consist of rows of large tubs containing water or rock dust that are suspended from the roof of a mine entry. In an explosion, the pressure front that precedes the arrival of the flame front triggers the dumping of the contents of the tubs. The dispersed suppressants quench the flame as it passes through the entry protected by the barrier system. Triggered barriers utilize an electrically or pneumatically operated actuation device that is triggered by the heat, flame or pressure of the explosion to release suppressant agents that are stored in pressurized containers (Hertzberg 1982).

Fires that grow to an advanced stage should be fought only by highly trained and specially equipped fire-fighting teams. Where large areas of coal or timber are burning in an underground mine and fire-fighting is complicated by extensive roof falls, ventilation uncertainties and accumulations of explosive gas, special action should be taken. The only practical alternatives may be inerting with nitrogen, carbon dioxide, the combustion products of an inert gas generator, or by flooding with water or sealing part or all of the mine (Ramaswatny and Katiyar 1988).

Further information on fire suppression can be found elsewhere in this *Encyclopaedia* and in various NFPA documents (e.g., NFPA 1994b, 1994c, 1994d, 1995a, 1995b, 1996e, 1996f, 1996g).

Fire Containment

Fire containment is a fundamental control mechanism for any type of industrial facility. Means for confining or limiting an underground mine fire can help ensure a safer mine evacuation and lessen the hazards of fire fighting.

For underground coal mines, oil and grease should be stored in closed, fire-resistant containers, and the storage areas should be of fire-resistant construction. Transformer stations, battery charging stations, air compressors, substations, shops and other installations should be housed in fire-resistant areas or in fireproof structures. Unattended electrical equipment should be mounted on non-combustible surfaces and separated from coal and other combustibles or protected by a fire-suppression system.

Materials for building bulkheads and seals, including wood, cloth, saws, nails, hammers, plaster or cement and rock dust, should be readily available to each working section. In underground non-coal mines, oil, grease and diesel fuel should be stored in tightly sealed containers in fire-resistive areas at safe distances from explosives magazines, electrical installations and shaft stations. Ventilation-control barriers and fire doors are required in certain areas to prevent the spread of fire, smoke and toxic gas (Ng and Lazzara 1990).

Reagent Storage (Mills)

Operations that are used to process the ore produced in a mining operations may result in certain hazardous conditions. Among the concerns are certain types of dust explosions and fires involving conveyor operations.

The heat generated by friction between a conveyor belt and a drive roller or idler is a concern and can be addressed by the use of sequence and slippage switches. These switches can be effectively used along with thermal cutouts on electric motors.

Possible explosions can be prevented by eliminating electrical ignition sources. Electrical equipment operating where methane, sulphide dust or other hazardous environments may be present should be designed, constructed, tested and installed such that its operation will not cause a fire or explosion.

Exothermic oxidation reactions can occur in both coal and metal sulphide ores (Smith and Thompson 1991). When the heat generated by these reactions is not dissipated, the temperature of the rock mass or pile increases. If temperatures become high enough, rapid combustion of coal, sulphide minerals and other combustibles can result (Ninteman 1978). Although spontaneous ignition fires occur relatively infrequently, they are generally quite disruptive to operations and difficult to extinguish.

The processing of coal presents special concerns because by its nature it is a fuel source. Fire and explosion protection information relating to the safe handling of coal can be found elsewhere in this *Encyclopaedia* and in NFPA documents (e.g., NFPA 1992b, 1994e, 1996h).

DETECTION OF GASES

Paul MacKenzie-Wood

All who work in underground mines should have a sound knowledge of mine gases and be aware of the dangers they may present. A general knowledge of gas detection instruments and systems is also necessary. For those assigned to use these instruments, detailed knowledge of their limitations and the gases they measure is essential.

Even without instruments, the human senses may be able to detect the progressive appearance of the chemical and physical phenomena associated with spontaneous combustion. The heating warms the ventilating air and saturates it with both surface and integral moisture driven off by the heating. When this air meets colder air at the ventilation split, condensation occurs resulting in a haze and the appearance of sweating on surfaces in the returns. A characteristic oily or petrol smell is the next indication, followed eventually by smoke and, finally, visible flames.

Carbon monoxide (CO), which is odourless, appears in measurable concentrations some 50 to 60 °C before the characteristic smell of a spontaneous combustion appears. Consequently, most fire detection systems rely on the detection of a rise in carbon monoxide concentration above the normal background for the particular part of the mine.

Sometimes, a heating is first detected by an individual who notices a faint smell for a fleeting instant. Thorough examination of the area may have to be repeated a number of times before a measurable sustained increase in the concentration of carbon monoxide can be detected. Accordingly, vigilance by all those in the mine should never be relaxed and a prearranged intervention process should be implemented as soon as the presence of an indicator has been suspected or detected and reported. Fortunately, thanks to considerable progress in the technology of fire detection and monitoring made since the 1970s (e.g., detector tubes, pocket-sized electronic detectors, and computerized fixed systems), it is no longer necessary to rely on the human senses alone.

Portable Instruments for Gas Detection

The gas detection instrument is designed to detect and monitor the presence of a wide range of gas types and concentrations that could result in a fire, an explosion and a toxic or oxygen-deficient atmosphere as well as to provide early warning of an outbreak of spontaneous combustion. Gases for which they are used include CO, carbon dioxide (CO_2), nitrogen dioxide (NO_2), hydrogen sulphide (H_2S) and sulphur dioxide (SO_2). Different types of instrument are available, but before deciding which to use in a particular situation, the following questions must be answered:

- Why is the detection of a particular gas or gases required?
- What are the properties of these gases?
- Where and in what circumstances do they occur?
- Which gas detecting instrument or device is most suitable for those circumstances?
- How does this instrument work?
- What are its limitations?
- How should the results it provides be interpreted?

Workers must be trained in the correct use of portable gas detectors. Instruments must be maintained according to the manufacturer's specifications.

Universal detector kits

A dectector kit consists of a spring-loaded piston- or bellows-type of pump and a range of replaceable glass indicating tubes that contain chemicals specific for a particular gas. The pump has a capacity of 100 cc and can be operated with one hand. This allows a sample of that size to be drawn through the indicator tube before passing to the bellows. The warning indicator on the graduated scale corresponds to the lowest level of general discolouration, not the deepest point of colour penetration.

The device is easy to use and does not require calibration. However, certain precautions are applicable:

- Indicator tubes (which should be dated) generally have a shelf-life of two years.
- An indicator tube may be re-used ten times provided there has been no discolouration.
- The general accuracy of each determination is usually within ± 20%.
- Hydrogen tubes are not approved for use underground because of the intense heat developed.
- A "pre-tube" filled with activated charcoal is required when estimating low levels of carbon monoxide in the presence of diesel exhausts or the higher hydrocarbons that may be present in afterdamp.
- Exhaust gas should be passed through a cooling device to make sure the temperature is below 40 °C before passing though the indicator tube.
- Oxygen and methane tubes are not approved for use underground because of their inaccuracy.

Catalytic-type methanometers

The catalytic-type methanometer is used in underground mines to measure the concentration of methane in the air. It has a sensor based on the principle of a network of four resistance-matched spiral wires, usually catalytic filaments, arranged in a symmetrical form known as a Wheatstone-bridge. Normally, two filaments are active and the other two are passive. The active filaments or beads are usually coated with a palladium oxide catalyst to cause oxidation of the flammable gas at a lower temperature.

Methane in the atmosphere reaches the sample chamber either by diffusion through a sintered disc or by being drawn in by an aspirator or internal pump. Pressing the operating button of the methanometer closes the circuit and the current flowing through the Wheatstone-bridge oxidizes the methane on the catalytic (active) filaments in the sample chamber. The heat of this reaction raises the temperature of the catalytic filaments, increasing their electrical resistance and electrically unbalancing the bridge. The electric current that flows is proportional to the resistance of the element and, hence, the amount of methane present. This is shown on an output indicator graduated in percentages of methane. The reference elements in the Wheatstone-bridge circuit serve to compensate for variations in environmental conditions such as ambient temperature and barometric pressure.

This instrument has a number of significant limitations:

- Both methane and oxygen must be present to get a response. If the oxygen level in the sample chamber is below 10%, not all the methane reaching the detector will be oxidized and a false low reading will be obtained. For this reason, this instrument should not be used to measure methane levels in afterdamp or in sealed off areas where the oxygen concentration is low. If the chamber contains pure methane, there will be no reading at all. Accordingly, the operating button must be depressed before moving the instrument into a suspected methane layer in order to draw some oxygen-containing air into the chamber. The presence of a layer will be confirmed by a greater than full scale reading followed by a return to scale when the oxygen in consumed.
- The catalytic type of methanometer will respond to flammable gases other than methane, for example, hydrogen and carbon monoxide. Ambiguous reading, therefore, may be obtained in post-fire or explosion gases (afterdamp).
- Instruments with diffusion heads should be sheltered from high air velocities to avoid false readings. This may be accomplished by shielding it with a hand or some other object.
- Instruments with catalytic filaments may fail to respond to methane if the filament comes in contact with the vapours of known poisons when being calibrated or used (e.g., silicones in furniture polish, floor polish and paints, phosphate esters present in hydraulic fluids, and fluorocarbons used as the propellant in aerosol sprays).
- Methanometers based on the Wheatstone-bridge principle may give erroneous readings at variable angles of inclination. Such inaccuracies will be minimized if the instrument is held at an angle of 45° when it is calibrated or used.
- Methanometers may give inaccurate readings at variable ambient temperatures. These inaccuracies will be minimized by calibrating the instrument under temperature conditions similar to those found underground.

Electrochemical cells

Instruments using electrochemical cells are used in underground mines to measure oxygen and carbon monoxide concentrations. Two types are available: the composition cell, which responds only to changes in oxygen concentration, and the partial pressure cell, which responds to changes in the partial pressure of oxygen in the atmosphere and, hence, the number of oxygen molecules per unit of volume.

The composition cell employs a capillary diffusion barrier which slows the diffusion of oxygen through the fuel cell so that the speed at which the oxygen can reach the electrode depends solely on the oxygen content of the sample. This cell is unaffected by variations in altitude (i.e., barometric pressure), temperature and relative humidity. The presence of CO_2 in the mixture, however, upsets the rate of oxygen diffusion and leads to false high readings. For example, the presence of 1% of CO_2 increases the oxygen reading by as much as 0.1%. Although small, this increase may still be significant and not fail-safe. It is particularly important to be aware of this limitation if this instrument is to be used in afterdamp or other atmospheres known to contain CO_2.

The partial pressure cell is based on the same electrochemical principle as the concentration cell but lacks the diffusion barrier. It responds only to the number of oxygen molecules per unit volume, making it pressure dependent. CO_2 in concentrations below 10% have no short-term effect on the reading, but over the long term, the carbon dioxide will destroy the electrolyte and shorten the life of the cell.

The following conditions affect the reliability of oxygen readings produced by partial pressure cells:

- *Altitude and barometric pressure:* The trip from the surface to the bottom of the shaft would increase the oxygen reading by 0.1% for every 40 m travelled. This would also apply to dips, encountered in the underground workings. In addition, the 5 millibar normal daily variations in barometric pressure could alter the oxygen reading by as much as 0.1%. Thunderstorm activity could be accompanied by a 30 millibar drop in pressure that would cause a 0.4% drop in the oxygen reading.
- *Ventilation:* The maximum ventilation change at the fan would be 6-8 inches water gauge or 10 millibar. This would cause a drop of 0.4% in the oxygen reading going from the intake to the return at the fan and a drop of 0.2% in travelling from the furthest face from the pit bottom.
- *Temperature:* Most detectors have an electronic circuit that senses cell temperature and corrects for the temperature effect on the sensor output.
- *Relative humidity:* An increase in relative humidity from dry to saturated at 20 °C would cause approximately a 0.3% decrease in the oxygen reading.

Other electrochemical cells

Electrochemical cells have been developed which are capable of measuring concentrations of CO from 1 ppm to an upper limit of 4,000 ppm. They operate by measuring the electric current between electrodes immersed in an acidic electrolyte. CO is oxidized on the anode to form CO_2 and the reaction releases electrons in direct proportion to the CO concentration.

Electrochemical cells for hydrogen, hydrogen sulphide, nitric oxide, nitrogen dioxide and sulphur dioxide are also available but suffer from cross-sensitivity.

There are no commercially available electrochemical cells for CO_2. The deficiency has been overcome with the development of a portable instrument containing a miniaturized infrared cell that is sensitive to carbon dioxide in concentrations up to 5%.

Non-dispersive infrared detectors

Non-dispersive infrared detectors (NDIRs) can measure all gases that contain such chemical groups as -CO, -CO_2 and -CH_3, which absorb infrared frequencies that are specific to their molecular configuration. These sensors are expensive but they can provide accurate readings for gases such as CO, CO_2 and methane in a changing background of other gases and low oxygen levels and are therefore ideal for monitoring gases behind seals. O_2, N_2 and H_2 do not absorb infrared radiation and cannot be detected by this method.

Other portable systems with detectors based on thermal conduction and refractive index have found limited use in the coal mining industry.

Limitations of portable gas detection instruments

The effectiveness of portable gas detection instruments is limited by a number of factors:

- Calibration is required. This normally involves a daily check on zero and voltage, a weekly span check and a calibration test by an authorized external authority every 6 months.
- Sensors have a finite life. If not dated by the manufacturer, the date of acquisition should be inscribed.
- Sensors can be poisoned.
- Sensors may suffer from cross-sensitivity.
- Overexposure may saturate the sensor causing its slow recovery.

- Inclination may affect the reading.
- Batteries require charging and regular discharging.

Centralized Monitoring Systems

Inspections, ventilation and surveys with hand-held instruments often succeed in detecting and locating a small heating with limited makes of CO before the gas is dispersed by the ventilation system or its level exceeds the statutory limits. These do not suffice, however, where a significant risk of combustion is known to occur, methane levels in the returns exceed 1%, or a potential hazard is suspected. Under these circumstances, continuous monitoring at strategic locations is required. A number of different types of centralized continuous monitoring systems are in use.

Tube bundle systems

The tube bundle system was developed in Germany in the 1960s to detect and monitor the progress of spontaneous combustion. It involves a series of as many as 20 plastic tubes made of nylon or polyethylene 1/4 or 3/8 of an inch in diameter that extend from a bank of analysers on the surface to selected locations underground. The tubes are equipped with filters, drains and flame traps; the analysers are usually infrared for CO, CO_2 and methane and paramagnetic for oxygen. A scavenger pump pulls a sample through each tube simultaneously and a sequential timer directs the sample from each tube through the analysers in turn. The data logger records the concentration of each gas at each location and automatically triggers an alarm when predetermined levels are exceeded.

This system has a number of advantages:

- No explosion-proof instruments are required.
- Maintenance is relatively easy.
- Underground power is not required.
- It covers a wide range of gases.
- Infrared analysers are usually quite stable and reliable; they maintain their specificity in a changing background of fire gases and low oxygen atmospheres (high concentrations of methane and/or carbon dioxide may be cross-sensitive to the carbon monoxide reading in the low ppm range).
- Instruments can be calibrated on the surface, although calibration samples of gases should be sent through the tubes to test the integrity of the collection system and the system for identifying the locations where particular samples originated.

There are also some disadvantages:

- The results are not in real time.
- Leaks are not immediately apparent.
- Condensation may collect in the tubes.
- Defects in the system are not always immediately apparent and may be difficult to identify.
- The tubes may be damaged by blasting or in a fire or an explosion.

Telemetric (electronic) system

The telemetric automatic gas monitoring system has a control module on the surface and intrinsically safe sensor heads strategically located underground which are connected by phone lines or fibre-optic cables. Sensors are available for methane, CO and air velocity. The sensor for CO is similar to the electrochemical sensor used in portable instruments and is subject to the same limitations. The methane sensor works through the catalytic combustion of methane on the active elements of a Wheatstone-bridge circuit which can be poisoned by sulphur compounds, phosphate esters or silicon compounds and will not work when the oxygen concentration is low.

The unique advantages of this system include:

- The results are available in real time (i.e., there is rapid indication of fire or a build-up of methane).
- Long distances between the sensor heads and the control unit are possible without compromising the system.
- Sensor failure is recognized immediately.

There are also some disadvantages:

- A high level of maintenance is required.
- The sensor range for CO is limited (0.4%).
- The variety of sensors is limited; there are none for CO_2 or hydrogen.
- The methane sensor is subject to poisoning.
- *In situ* calibration is required.
- Cross-sensitivity may be a problem.
- There may be a loss of power (e.g., >1.25% for methane).
- Sensor life is limited to 1 to 2 years.
- The system is not suitable for low oxygen atmospheres (e.g., behind seals).

Gas chromatograph

The gas chromatograph is a sophisticated piece of equipment that analyses samples with high degrees of accuracy and that, until recently, could only be fully utilized by chemists or specially qualified and trained personnel. Gas samples from a tube bundle-type of system are injected into the gas chromatograph automatically or they can be manually introduced from bag samples brought out of the mine. A specially packed column is used to separate different gases and a suitable detector, usually thermal conductivity or flame ionization, is used to measure each gas as it elutes from the column. The separation process provides a high degree of specificity.

The gas chromatograph has particular advantages:

- No cross-sensitivity from other gases occurs.
- It is capable of measuring hydrogen.
- It is capable of measuring ethylene and higher hydrocarbons.
- It can accurately measure from very low to very high concentrations of most of the gases that occur or are produced underground by a heating or a fire.
- It is well recognized that modern methods of combating fires and heatings in coal mines may be most effectively implemented on the basis of interpretation of gas analyses from strategic locations in the mine. Accurate, reliable and complete results require a gas chromatograph and interpretation by qualified, experienced and fully trained personnel.

Its disadvantages include:

- The analyses are relatively slow.
- A high level of maintenance is required.
- The hardware and the controls are complex.
- Expert attention is required periodically.
- Calibration must be scheduled frequently.
- High methane concentrations interfere with low level CO measurements.

Choice of system

Tube-bundle systems are preferred for monitoring locations that are not expected to have rapid changes in gas concentrations or, like sealed areas, may have low oxygen environments.

Telemetric systems are preferred in locations such as belt roads or on the face where rapid changes in gas concentrations may have significance.

Gas chromatography does not replace existing monitoring systems but it enhances the range, accuracy and reliability of the analyses. This is particularly important when determination of the risk of explosion is involved or when a heating is reaching an advanced stage.

Sampling considerations

- The siting of sampling points at strategic locations is of major importance. The information from a single sampling point some distance from the source is only suggestive; without confirmation from other locations it may lead to over- or underestimation of the seriousness of the situation. Consequently, sampling points to detect an outbreak of spontaneous combustion must be sited where heatings are most likely to occur. There must be little dilution of flows between the heating and the detectors. Consideration must be given to the possibility of the layering of methane and warm combustion gases which may rise up the dip in a sealed area. Ideally, the sampling sites should be located in panel returns, behind stoppings and seals, and in the main stream of the ventilation circuit. The following considerations are applicable:

  - The sampling site should be set at least 5 m inbye (i.e., toward the face of) a seal because seals "breathe in" when the atmospheric pressure rises.
  - Samples should be taken from boreholes only when they breathe out and when it can be ensured that the borehole is leak free.
  - Samples should be taken more than 50 m downwind from a fire to ensure mixing (Mitchell and Burns 1979).
  - Samples should be taken up the gradient from a fire near the roof because hot gases rise.
  - Samples should be taken inbye a ventilation door to avoid leakage.
  - All sampling points should be clearly shown on maps of schematics of the mine ventilation system. Taking gas samples underground or from surface boreholes for analysis at another location is difficult and error prone. The sample in the bag or container must truly represent the atmosphere at the sampling point.

Plastic bags are now widely used in the industry for taking samples. The plastic minimizes leakage and can keep a sample for 5 days. Hydrogen, if present in the bag, will degrade with a daily loss of about 1.5% of its original concentration. A sample in a football bladder will change concentration in half an hour. Bags are easy to fill and the sample can be squeezed into an analysing instrument or it can be drawn out with a pump.

Metal tubes that are filled under pressure by a pump can store samples for a long time but the size of the sample is limited and leakage is common. Glass is inert to gases but glass containers are fragile and it is difficult to get the sample out without dilution.

In collecting samples, the container should be pre-flushed at least three times to ensure that the previous sample is completely flushed out. Each container should have a tag carrying such information as the date and time of sampling, the exact location, the name of the person collecting the sample and other useful information.

Interpretation of Sampling Data

Interpretation of the results of gas sampling and analysis is a demanding science and should be attempted only by individuals with special training and experience. These data are vital in many emergencies because they provide information on what is happening underground that is needed to plan and implement corrective and preventive actions. During or immediately after an underground heating, fire or explosion, all possible environmental parameters should be monitored in real time to enable those in charge to accurately determine the status of the situation and measure its progress so that they lose no time in initiating any needed rescue activities.

Gas analysis results must meet the following criteria:

- *Accuracy.* Instruments must be correctly calibrated.
- *Reliability.* Cross-sensitivities must be known
- *Completeness.* All gases, including hydrogen and nitrogen, should be measured.
- *Timeliness.* If real time is not possible, trending should be carried out.
- *Validity.* Sample points must be in and around the site of the incident.

The following rules should be followed in interpreting gas analysis results:

- A few sampling points should be carefully selected and marked on the plan. This is better for trending than taking sample from many points.
- If a result deviates from a trend, it should be confirmed by resampling or the calibration of the instrument should be checked before taking action. Variations in outside influences, such as ventilation, barometric pressure and temperature or a diesel engine running in the area, are often the reason for the changing result.
- The gas make or mixture under non-mining conditions should be known and allowed for in the calculations.
- No analysis result should be accepted on faith; results must be valid and verifiable.
- It should be borne in mind that isolated figures do not indicate the progress—trends give a more accurate picture.

Calculating air-free results

Air-free results are obtained by calculating out the atmospheric air in the sample (Mackenzie-Wood and Strang 1990). This allows samples from a similar area to be properly compared after the dilution effect from air leakage has been removed.

The formula is:

$$\text{Air-free result} = \frac{\text{Analysed result}}{100 - 4.776 \, O_2}$$

It is derived as follows:

$$\text{Atmospheric air} = O_2 + N_2$$
$$= O_2 + \frac{79.1 \, O_2}{20.9}$$
$$= 4.776 \, O_2$$

Air-free results are useful when trending of results is required and there has been a risk of air dilution between the sample point and the source, air leakage has occurred in sample lines, or bag samples and seals may have breathed in. For example, if the carbon monoxide concentration from a heating is being trended, then air dilution from an increase in ventilation could be misinterpreted as a decrease in carbon monoxide from the source. The trending of air-free concentrations would give the correct results.

Similar calculations are needed if the sampling area is making methane: the increase in methane concentration would dilute the concentration of other the gases that are present. Hence, an increasing carbon oxide level may actually show up as decreasing.

Methane-free results are calculated as follows:

$$\text{Methane-free result} = \frac{\text{Analysed result}}{100 - CH_4\%}$$

Spontaneous Combustion

Spontaneous combustion is a process whereby a substance can ignite as a result of internal heat which arises spontaneously due to reactions liberating heat faster than it can be lost to the environment. The spontaneous heating of coal is usually slow until the temperature reaches about 70 °C, referred to as the "cross over" temperature. Above this temperature, the reaction usually accelerates. At over 300 °C, the volatiles, also called "coal gas" or "cracked gas", are given off. These gases (hydrogen, methane and carbon monoxide) will ignite spontaneously at temperatures of approximately 650 °C (it has been reported that the presence of free radicals can result in the appearance of flame in the coal at about 400 °C). The processes involved in a classic case of spontaneous combustion are presented in table 74.4 (different coals will produce varying pictures).

Carbon monoxide

CO is actually released some 50 °C before the characteristic smell of combustion is noticed. Most systems designed to detect the onset of spontaneous combustion are based on the detection of carbon monoxide in concentrations above the normal background for a particular area of the mine.

Once a heating has been detected, it must be monitored in order to determine the state of the heating (i.e., its temperature and extent), the rate of accelerations, toxic emissions and explosibility of the atmosphere.

Monitoring a heating

There are a number of indices and parameters available to assist planners to determine the extent, temperature and rate of progression of a heating. These are usually based on changes in the composition of the air passing through a suspected area. Many indicators have been described in the literature over the years and most offer a very limited window of usage and are of minimal value. All are site specific and differ with different coals and conditions. Some of the more popular ones include: carbon monoxide trending; carbon monoxide make (Funkemeyer and Kock 1989); Graham's ratio (Graham 1921) tracer gases (Chamberlain 1970); Morris ratio (Morris 1988); and the carbon monoxide/carbon dioxide ratio. After sealing, indicators may be difficult to use because of the absence of a defined air flow.

No one indicator affords a precise and sure method of measuring the progress of a heating. Decisions must be based on gathering, tabulating, comparing and analysing all information and interpreting it in the light of training and experience.

Table 74.4 • Heating of coal—hierarchy of temperatures.

Temperature at which coal absorbs O_2 to form a complex and produce heat

30 °C	Complex breaks down to produce CO/CO_2
45 °C	True oxidation of coal to produce CO and CO_2
70 °C	Cross-over temperature, heating accelerates
110 °C	Moisture, H_2 and characteristic smell released
150 °C	Desorbed CH_4, unsaturated hydrocarbons released
300 °C	Cracked gases (e.g., H_2, CO, CH_4) released
400 °C	Open flame

Source: Chamberlain et al. 1970.

Explosions

Explosions are the greatest single hazard in coal mining. It has the potential to kill the entire underground workforce, destroy all the equipment and services and prevent any further working of the mine. And, all this can happen in 2 to 3 seconds.

The explosibility of the atmosphere in the mine must be monitored at all times. It is especially urgent when workers are engaged in a rescue operation in a gassy mine.

As in the case of indicators for evaluating a heating, there are a number of techniques for calculating the explosibility of the atmosphere in an underground mine. They include: Coward's triangle (Greuer 1974); Hughes and Raybold's triangle (Hughes and Raybold 1960); Elicott's diagram (Elicott 1981); and Trickett's ratio (Jones and Trickett 1955). Because of the complexity and variability of the conditions and circumstances, there is no single formula that can be relied on as a guarantee that an explosion will not occur at a particular time in a particular mine. One must rely on a high and unremitting level of vigilance, a high index of suspicion and an unhesitating initiation of appropriate action at the slightest indication that an explosion might be imminent. A temporary halt in production is a relatively small premium to pay for assurance that an explosion will not occur.

Conclusion

This article has summarized the detection of gases that might be involved in fires and explosions in underground mines. The other health and safety implications of the gaseous environment in mines (e.g., dust diseases, asphyxia, toxic effects, etc.) are discussed in other articles in this chapter and elsewhere in this *Encyclopaedia*.

EMERGENCY PREPAREDNESS

Gary A. Gibson

Mine emergencies often occur as the result of a lack of systems, or failures in existing systems, to limit, control or prevent circumstances that trigger incidents which, when ineffectively managed, lead to disasters. An emergency may then be defined as an unplanned event that impacts upon the safety or welfare of personnel, or the continuity of operations, which requires an effective and timely response in order to contain, control or mitigate the situation.

All forms of mining operations have particular hazards and risks that may lead to an emergency situation. Hazards in underground coal mining include methane liberation and coal dust generation, high-energy mining systems and coal's propensity to spontaneous combustion. Emergencies can occur in underground metalliferous mining due to strata failure (rock bursts, rock falls, hangingwall and pillar failures), unplanned initiation of explosives and sulphide ore dusts. Surface mining operations involve risks relating to, large-scale high-speed mobile equipment, unplanned initiation of explosives, and slope stability. Hazardous chemical exposure, spill or leak, and tailing dam failure can take place in minerals processing.

Good mining and operational practices have evolved that incorporate relevant measures to control or mitigate these risks. However, mine disasters continue to occur regularly throughout the world, even though formal risk management techniques have been adopted in some countries as a pro-active strategy to improve mine safety and reduce the likelihood and consequence of mine emergencies.

Accident investigations and inquiries continue to identify failures to apply the lessons of the past and failures to apply effective barriers and control measures to known hazards and risks. These failures are often compounded by a lack of adequate measures to intervene, control and manage the emergency situation.

This article outlines an approach to emergency preparedness that can be utilized as a framework to both control and mitigate mining hazards and risks and to develop effective measures to ensure control of the emergency and the continuity of mine operations.

Emergency Preparedness Management System

The emergency preparedness management system proposed comprises an integrated systems approach to the prevention and management of emergencies. It includes:

- organizational intent and commitment (corporate policy, management commitment and leadership)
- risk management (identification, assessment and control of hazards and risks)
- definition of measures to manage an unplanned event, incident or emergency
- definition of emergency organization (strategies, structure, staffing, skills, systems and procedures)
- provision of facilities, equipment, supplies and materials
- training of personnel in the identification, containment and notification of incidents and their roles in the mobilization, deployment and post-incident activities
- evaluation and enhancement of the overall system through regular auditing procedures and trials
- periodic risk and capability reassessment
- critique and evaluation of the response in the event of an emergency, coupled with necessary system enhancement.

Incorporation of emergency preparedness within the ISO 9000 quality management system framework provides a structured approach to contain and control emergency situations in a timely, effective and safe manner.

Organizational Intent and Commitment

Few people will be convinced of the need for emergency preparedness unless a potential danger is recognized and it is seen as directly threatening, highly possible if not probable and likely to occur in a relatively short time span. However, the nature of emergencies is that this recognition generally does not occur prior to the event or is rationalized as non-threatening. The lack of adequate systems, or failures in existing systems, results in an incident or emergency situation.

Commitment to and investment in effective emergency preparedness planning provides an organization with the capability, expertise and systems to provide a safe work environment, meet moral and legal obligations and enhance prospects for business continuity in an emergency. In coal mine fires and explosions, including non-fatal incidents, business continuity losses are often significant due to the extent of damage, the type and nature of control measures employed or even loss of the mine. Investigative processes also impact considerably. Failure to have effective measures in place to manage and control an incident will further compound overall losses.

Development and implementation of an effective emergency preparedness system requires management leadership, commitment and support. Consequently it will be necessary to:

- provide and ensure continuing management leadership, commitment and support
- establish long-term goals and purpose
- guarantee financial support
- guarantee availability of personnel and their access to and involvement in training

- provide appropriate organizational resources to develop, implement and maintain the system.

The necessary leadership and commitment can be demonstrated through the appointment of an experienced, capable and highly respected officer as Emergency Preparedness Coordinator, with the authority to ensure participation and cooperation at all levels and within all units of the organization. Formation of an Emergency Preparedness Planning Committee, under the Coordinator's leadership, will provide the necessary resources to plan, organize and implement an integrated and effective emergency preparedness capability throughout the organization.

Risk Assessment

The risk management process enables the type of risks facing the organization to be identified and analysed to determine the likelihood and the consequence of their occurrence. This framework then enables the risks to be assessed against established criteria to determine if the risks are acceptable or what form of treatment must be applied to reduce those risks (e.g., reducing likelihood of occurrence, reducing consequence of occurrence, transferring all or part of the risks or avoiding the risks). Targeted implementa-

Table 74.5 • Critical elements/sub-elements of emergency preparedness.

Fires	Explosions/implosions	Exposures
• Underground	• Dust	• Heat/cold
• Plant and surface	• Chemicals	• Noise
• Bushfires	• Blasting agents	• Vibration
• Community	• Petroleum	• Radiation
• Vehicle	• Nitrogen	• Chemical
	• Gas line explosion	• Biological
Chemical spills/leaks		
• Oil spills	Civil disturbance	Environmental
• Ruptured gas main	• Strike	• Air pollution
• Containment of spill	• Protest	• Water pollution
• Offsite/onsite	• Bomb threat	• Soil pollution
• Storage capabilities	• Kidnap/extortion	• Waste material (disposal problem)
	• Sabotage	
Injuries	• Other threats	
• Onsite		Cave-in
• Multiple	Power failure	• Underground
• Fatal	• Electrical blackout	• Surface subsidence
• Critical	• Gas shortage	• Highwall failure/slip
	• Water shortage	• Surface excavation failure
Natural disasters	• Communication systems failure	• Structural (building)
• Flooding		
• Cyclone	Water in-rush	Transportation
• Earthquake	• Exploration drill hole	• Automobile accident
• Severe storm	• Bulkheads	• Train accident
• Ruptured dam	• Pillar failure	• Boat/shipping accident
• Mud or land slide	• Unplanned holing of old workings	• Aeroplane accident
	• Tailings	• Hazardous materials in transport accident
Community evacuation	• Ruptured dam	
• Planned	• Fractured ground	Extrication
• Unplanned	• Water main failure	• System/resources
		• Unplanned

Source: Mines Accident Prevention Association Ontario (undated).

tion plans are then developed, implemented and managed to control the identified risks.

This framework can be similarly applied to develop emergency plans that enable effective controls to be implemented, should a contingent situation arise. Identification and analysis of risks enables likely scenarios to be predicted with a high degree of accuracy. Control measures can then be identified to address each of the recognized emergency scenarios, which then form the basis of emergency preparedness strategies.

Scenarios that are likely to be identified may include some or all of those listed in table 74.5 Alternatively national standards, such as the Australian Standard AS/NZS 4360: 1995—Risk Management, may provide a listing of generic sources of risk, other classifications of risk, and the areas of impact of risk that provides a comprehensive structure for hazard analysis in emergency preparedness.

Emergency Control Measures and Strategies

Three levels of response measures should be identified, evaluated and developed within the emergency preparedness system. *Individual or primary response* comprises the actions of individuals upon the identification of hazardous situations or an incident, including:

- notifying appropriate supervisors, controllers or management personnel of the situation, circumstances or incident
- containment (basic fire-fighting, life support or extrication)
- evacuation, escape or refuge.

Secondary response comprises the actions of trained responders upon notification of the incident, including fire teams, search and rescue teams and special casualty access teams (SCAT), all utilizing advanced skills, competencies and equipment.

Tertiary response comprises the deployment of specialized systems, equipment and technologies in situations where primary and secondary response cannot be safely or effectively utilized, including:

- personnel locating devices and seismic event detectors
- large diameter borehole rescue
- inertization, remote sealing or flooding
- surveillance/exploration vehicles and systems (e.g., borehole cameras and atmospheric sampling).

Defining the Emergency Organization

Emergency conditions grow more serious the longer the situation is allowed to proceed. Onsite personnel must be prepared to respond appropriately to emergencies. A multitude of activities must be coordinated and managed to ensure that the situation is rapidly and effectively controlled.

Emergency organization provides a structured framework that defines and integrates the emergency strategies, management structure (or chain of command), personnel resources, roles and responsibilities, equipment and facilities, systems and procedures. It encompasses all phases of an emergency, from the initial identification and containment activities, to notification, mobilization, deployment and recovery (re-establishment of normal operations).

The emergency organization should address a number of key elements, including:

- capability for primary and secondary response to an emergency
- capability to manage and control an emergency
- coordination and communications, including gathering, assessing and evaluating data, decision making and implementation
- the breadth of procedures necessary for effective control, including identification and containment, notification and early reporting, declaration of an emergency, specific operational procedures, fire-fighting, evacuation, extrication and life support, monitoring and review
- identification and assignment of key functional responsibilities
- control, advisory, technical, administration and support services
- transitional arrangements from normal to emergency operations in terms of lines of communication, authority levels, accountability, compliance, liaison and policy
- capability and capacity to maintain emergency operations for an extended period and provide for shift changes
- impact of organizational changes in an emergency situation, including supervision and control of personnel; re-allocation or re-assignment of personnel; motivation, commitment and discipline; role of experts and specialists, external agencies and corporate officers
- contingency provisions to address situations such as those arising after hours or where key organizational members are unavailable or affected by the emergency
- integration and deployment of tertiary response systems, equipment and technologies.

Emergency Facilities, Equipment and Materials

The nature, extent and scope of facilities, equipment and materials required to control and mitigate emergencies will be identi-

Table 74.6 • Emergency facilities, equipment and materials.

Emergency	Response level		
	Primary	Secondary	Tertiary
Fire	Fire extinguishers, hydrants and hoses installed adjacent to high risk areas, such as conveyors, fuelling stations, electrical transformers and sub-stations, and on mobile equipment	Breathing apparatus and protective clothing provided in central areas to enable a "fire team" response with advanced apparatus such as foam generators and multiple hoses	Provision for remote sealing or inertization.
Life support and first aid	Life support, respiration and circulation	First aid, triage, stabilization and extrication	Paramedical, forensic, legal
Evacuation, escape and rescue	Provision of warning or notification systems, secure escapeways, oxygen-based self rescuers, lifelines and communication systems, availability of transportation vehicles	Provision of suitably equipped refuge chambers, trained and equipped mines rescue teams, personnel locating devices	Large diameter borehole rescue systems, inertization, purpose-designed rescue vehicles

fied through application and extension of the risk management process and determination of the emergency control strategies. For example, a high-level risk of fire will necessitate the provision of adequate fire-fighting facilities and equipment. These would be deployed consistently with the risk profile. Similarly, the facilities, equipment and materials necessary to address effectively life support and first aid or evacuation, escape and rescue can be identified as illustrated in table 74.6.

Other facilities and equipment that may be necessary in an emergency include incident management and control facilities, employee and rescue muster areas, site security and access controls, facilities for next of kin and the media, materials and consumables, transport and logistics. These facilities and equipment are provided for prior to an incident. Recent mine emergencies have reinforced the necessity to focus on three specific infrastructure issues, refuge chambers, communications, and atmospheric monitoring.

Refuge chambers

Refuge chambers are being increasingly utilized as a means of enhancing escape and rescue of underground personnel. Some are designed to permit persons to be self-rescuers and communicate with the surface in safety; others have been designed to effect refuge for an extended period so as to permit assisted rescue.

The decision to install refuge chambers is dependent upon the overall escape and rescue system for the mine. The following factors need to be evaluated when considering the need for and design of refuges:

* the likelihood of entrapment
* the time taken for people underground to evacuate through the normal means of egress, which may be excessive in mines with extensive workings or difficult conditions such as low heights or steep grades
* the capability of persons underground to escape unassisted (e.g., pre-existing medical conditions or fitness levels and injuries sustained in the incident)
* the discipline required to maintain and utilize refuge chambers
* the means to assist personnel to locate the refuge chambers in conditions of extremely low visibility and duress
* the required resistance to explosions and fire
* the necessary size and capacity
* the services provided (e.g., ventilation/air purification, cooling, communications, sanitation, and sustenance)
* the potential application of inertization as a control strategy
* the options for final recovery of personnel (e.g., mine rescue teams and large diameter boreholes).

Communications

Communications infrastructure is generally in place in all mines to facilitate management and control of operations as well as contribute to the safety of the mine through calls for support. Unfortunately, the infrastructure is usually not robust enough to survive a significant fire or explosion, disrupting communication when it would be most beneficial. Furthermore conventional systems incorporate handsets which cannot be safely used with most breathing apparatus and are usually deployed in main intake airways adjacent to fixed plant, rather than in escapeways.

The need for post-incident communications should be closely evaluated. While it is preferable that a post-incident communications system is part of the pre-incident system, to enhance maintainability, cost and reliability, a stand-alone emergency communications system may be warranted. Regardless, the communications system should be integrated within the overall escape, rescue and emergency management strategies.

Atmospheric monitoring

Knowledge of conditions in a mine following an incident is essential to enable the most appropriate measures to control a situation to be identified and implemented and to assist escaping workers and protect rescuers. The need for post-incident atmospheric monitoring should be closely evaluated and systems should be provided that meet mine-specific needs, possibly incorporating:

* the location and design of fixed station atmospheric and ventilation sampling points for normal and potentially abnormal atmospheric conditions
* the maintenance of capabilities to analyse, trend and interpret the mine atmosphere, particularly where explosive mixtures may be present post-incident
* modularization of tube-bundle systems around boreholes to minimize sampling delays and improve the system's robustness
* provision of systems to verify integrity of tube-bundle systems post-incident
* utilization of gas chromatography where explosive mixtures are possible after the incident and rescuers may be required to enter the mine.

Emergency Preparedness Skills, Competencies and Training

The skills and competencies required to cope effectively with an emergency can be readily determined by identification of core risks and emergency control measures, development of emergency organization and procedures and identification of necessary facilities and equipment.

Emergency preparedness skills and competencies include not only planning and management of an emergency, but a diverse range of basic skills associated with the primary and secondary response initiatives that should be incorporated in a comprehensive training strategy, including:

* the identification and containment of the incident (e.g., fire-fighting, life support, evacuation and extrication)
* notification (e.g., radio and telephone procedures)
* mobilization and deployment activities (e.g., search and rescue, fire-fighting, casualty management and recovering bodies).

The emergency preparedness system provides a framework for the development of an effective training strategy by identifying the necessity, extent and scope of specific, predictable and reliable workplace outcomes in an emergency situation and the underpinning competencies. The system includes:

* a statement of intent that details why the necessary expertise, skills and competencies are to be developed and provides the organizational commitment and leadership to succeed
* risk management and measures to manage emergencies that identify key content elements (e.g., fires, explosions, hazardous materials, unplanned movements and discharges, sabotage, bomb threats, security breaches, etc.)
* a definition of the emergency organization (strategies, structure, staffing, skills, systems and procedures) that identifies who is to be trained, their role in an emergency and the necessary skills and competencies
* identification of training resources that determines what aids, equipment, facilities and personnel are necessary
* training of personnel in identification and containment, notification, mobilization, deployment and post-incident activities that develops the necessary skills and competency base
* routine testing, evaluation and enhancement of the overall system, coupled with periodic risk and capability reassessment, that completes the learning process and ensures that an effective emergency preparedness system exists.

Table 74.7 • Emergency preparedness training matrix.

Training response level		
Educational primary	**Procedural/secondary**	**Functional/tertiary**
Designed to ensure employees understand the nature of mine emergencies and how specific aspects of the overall emergency plan may involve or affect the individual, including primary response measures.	Skills and competencies to successfully complete specific procedures defined under the emergency response plans and the secondary response measures associated with specific emergency scenarios.	Development of skills and competencies necessary for the management and control of emergencies.
Knowledge and competence elements		
• Knowledge of key indicators of mine incidents	• Knowledge of key indicators of mine incidents	• Knowledge of key indicators of mine emergencies and detailed knowledge of trigger events to initiate emergency response
• Environmental conditions following an incident (e.g., temperature, visibility and gases)	• Ability to detect, monitor and evaluate environmental conditions following an incident (e.g., mine gases, ventilation, smoke)	• Detailed knowledge of mine design, mine ventilation and monitoring systems
• Ability to respond to adverse changes in environmental conditions (e.g., smoke, ventilation disruption)	• Ability to assess and interpret changes to mine ventilation systems (e.g., destruction of stoppings, seals and air crossings, damage to main fans)	• Ability to assess and interpret current information systems at the mine (e.g., ventilation and environmental monitoring data)
• Ability to perform notification and communications required post-incident	• Knowledge of response measures that can be used to manage and mitigate an emergency (e.g., fire-fighting, search and rescue, restoration of ventilation, first aid, triage and extrication)	• Awareness of control measures that can be used to manage and mitigate an emergency
• Knowledge of appropriate emergency response options to environmental conditions	• Knowledge of roles and responsibilities of all mine personnel under the emergency response plans and the capability to perform their nominated role	• Ability to operate and manage emergency response plans and procedures, conducting simulated emergencies
• Awareness of use and limitations of escape apparatus, routes and systems	• Awareness of use and limitations of escape apparatus, routes and systems (e.g., self-rescuers, refuge chambers, breathing apparatus)	• Ability to implement emergency communications and protocols, both internally and externally
• Knowledge of roles and responsibilities of all mine personnel under emergency response plans including specific roles and responsibilities	• Ability to implement internal emergency communications and protocols	• Capability of mine rescue and other emergency services and access support from these services
• Possession of primary response skills and competencies associated with specific emergency scenarios (e.g., basic fire-fighting, life support, escape and refuge	• Awareness of use and limitations of escape and rescue apparatus and systems (e.g., self-rescuers, refuge chambers, breathing apparatus)	• Ability to establish and support critical incident team
• Knowledge about mine rescue and other emergency services	• Capability of mine rescue and other emergency services	• Knowledge of the capability and deployment of tertiary response systems (e.g., locating systems, inertization, remote sealing, large diameter borehole rescue, mobile laboratories)
• Participation in simulated emergencies.	• Initiation of call out and mutual assistance schemes	• Ability to use specialist resources (e.g., paramedical, forensic, legal, critical incident stress debriefing, technologists)
	• Participating in simulated exercises and emergencies	• Crisis management and leadership

Emergency preparedness training can be structured into a number of categories as illustrated in table 74.7.

Audit, Review and Evaluation

Audit and review processes need to be adopted to assess and evaluate the effectiveness of the overall emergency systems, procedures, facilities, maintenance programmes, equipment, training and individual competencies. The conduct of an audit or simulation provides, without exception, opportunities for improvement, constructive criticism and verification of satisfactory performance levels of key activities.

Every organization should test its overall emergency plan at least once per year for each operating shift. Critical elements of the plan, such as emergency power or remote alarm systems, should be tested separately and more frequently.

Two basic forms of auditing are available. *Horizontal auditing* involves the testing of small, specific elements of the overall emergency plan to identify deficiencies. Seemingly minor deficiencies could become critical in the event of an actual emergency. Examples of such elements and related deficiencies are listed in table 74.8. *Vertical auditing* tests multiple elements of a plan simultaneously through simulation of an emergency event. Activities such as activation of the plan, search and rescue procedures, life support, fire-fighting and the logistics related to an emergency response at a remote mine or facility can be audited in this manner.

Simulations may involve personnel from more than one department and perhaps personnel from other companies, mutual aid organizations, or even emergency services such as police and fire departments. Involvement of external emergency service organi-

Table 74.8 • Examples of horizontal auditing of emergency plans.

Element	Deficiency
Indicators of incipient incident or event	Failure to recognize, notify, record and action
Alert/evacuation procedures	Employees unfamiliar with evacuation procedures
Donning of emergency respirators	Employees unfamiliar with respirators
Fire-fighting equipment	Fire extinguishers discharged, sprinkler heads painted over, fire hydrants concealed or buried
Emergency alarms	Alarms ignored
Gas testing instruments	Not regularly maintained, serviced or calibrated

zations provides all parties with an invaluable opportunity to enhance and integrate emergency preparedness operations, procedures and equipment and tailor response capabilities to major risks and hazards at specific sites.

A formal critique should be conducted as soon as possible, preferably immediately following the audit or simulation. Recognition should be extended to those individuals or teams that performed well. Weaknesses must be described as specifically as possible and procedures reviewed to incorporate systemic improvements where necessary. Necessary changes must be implemented and performance must be monitored for improvements.

A sustained programme emphasizing planning, practice, discipline and teamwork are necessary elements of well-balanced simulations and training drills. Experience has proven repeatedly that every drill is a good drill; every drill is beneficial and presents opportunities to demonstrate strengths and expose areas that require improvement.

Periodic Risk and Capability Reassessment

Few risks remain static. Consequently, risks and the capability of control and emergency preparedness measures needs to be monitored and evaluated to ensure that changing circumstances (e.g., people, systems, processes, facilities or equipment) do not alter risk priorities or diminish system capabilities.

Conclusions

Emergencies are often regarded as unforeseen occurrences. However, in this day and age of advanced communication and technology there are few events that can be truly called unforeseen and few misfortunes that have not been already experienced. Newspapers, hazard alerts, accident statistics and technical reports all provide sound historical data and images of what the future may hold for the ill-prepared.

Still, the nature of emergencies changes as industry changes. Relying on techniques and emergency measures adopted from past experience will not always provide the same degree of security for future events.

Risk management provides a comprehensive and structured approach to the understanding of mine hazards and risks and the development of effective emergency response capabilities and systems. The process of risk management must be understood and continuously applied, particularly when deploying mine rescue personnel into a potentially hazardous or explosive environment.

Underpinning competent emergency preparedness is the training of all mine personnel in basic hazard awareness, the early recognition and notification of incipient incidents and trigger events and primary response and escape skills. Expectations-training under conditions of heat, humidity, smoke and low visibility is also essential. Failure to adequately train personnel in these basic skills has often been the difference between an incident and a disaster.

Training provides the mechanism for operationalizing emergency preparedness organization and planning. Integration of emergency preparedness within a quality systems framework coupled with routine auditing and simulation provides the mechanism to improve and enhance emergency preparedness.

The ILO Safety and Health in Mines Convention, 1955 (No. 176), and Recommendation, 1995 (No. 183), provide an overall framework for improving safety and health in mines. The emergency preparedness system proposed provides a methodology for achieving the outcomes identified in the Convention and Recommendation.

Acknowledgement: The assistance of Mr Paul MacKenzie-Wood, Manager Coal Mines Technical Services (Mines Rescue Service NSW, Australia) in the preparation and critique of this article is gratefully acknowledged.

HEALTH HAZARDS OF MINING AND QUARRYING

James L. Weeks

The principal *airborne hazards* in the mining industry include several types of particulates, naturally occurring gases, engine exhaust and some chemical vapours; the principal *physical hazards* are noise, segmental vibration, heat, changes in barometric pressure and ionizing radiation. These occur in varying combinations depending on the mine or quarry, its depth, the composition of the ore and surrounding rock, and the method(s) of mining. Among some groups of miners who live together in isolated locations, there is also risk of transmitting some infectious diseases such as tuberculosis, hepatitis (B and E), and the human-immunodeficiency virus (HIV). Miners' exposure varies with the job, its proximity to the source of hazards and the effectiveness of hazard control methods.

Airborne Particulate Hazards

Free crystalline silica is the most abundant compound in the earth's crust and, consequently, is the most common airborne dust that miners and quarry-workers face. Free silica is silicon dioxide that is not chemically bonded with any other compound as a silicate. The most common form of silica is quartz although it can also appear as trydimite or christobalite. Respirable particles are formed whenever silica-bearing rock is drilled, blasted, crushed or otherwise pulverized into fine particles. The amount of silica in different species of rock varies but is not a reliable indicator of how much respirable silica dust may be found in an air sample. It is not uncommon, for example, to find 30% free silica in a rock but 10% in an air sample, and vice versa. Sandstone can be up to 100% silica, granite up to 40%, slate, 30%, with lesser proportions in other minerals. Exposure can occur in any mining operation, surface or underground, where silica is found in the overburden of a surface mine or the ceiling, floor or ore deposit of an underground mine. Silica can be dispersed by the wind, by vehicular traffic or by earth-moving machinery.

With sufficient exposure, silica can cause silicosis, a typical pneumoconiosis that develops insidiously after years of exposure. Exceptionally high exposure can cause acute or accelerated silicosis within months with significant impairment or death occurring within a few years. Exposure to silica is also associated with an increased risk of tuberculosis, lung cancer and of some autoimmune diseases, including scleroderma, systemic lupus erythematosus and rheumatoid arthritis. Freshly fractured silica dust appears to be more reactive and more hazardous than old or stale dust. This may be a consequence of a relatively higher surface charge on freshly formed particles.

The most common processes that produce respirable silica dust in mining and quarrying are drilling, blasting and cutting silica-containing rock. Most holes drilled for blasting are done with an air powered percussion drill mounted on a tractor crawler. The hole is made with a combination of rotation, impact and thrust of the drill bit. As the hole deepens, steel drill rods are added to connect the drill bit to the power source. Air not only powers the drilling, it also blows the chips and dust out of the hole which, if uncontrolled, injects large amounts of dust into the environment. The hand-held jack-hammer or sinker drill operates on the same principle but on a smaller scale. This device conveys a significant amount of vibration to the operator and with it, the risk of vibration white finger. Vibration white finger has been found among miners in India, Japan, Canada and elsewhere. The track drill and the jack-hammer are also used in construction projects where rock must be drilled or broken to make a highway, to break rock for a foundation, for road repair work and other purposes.

Dust controls for these drills have been developed and are effective. A water mist, sometimes with a detergent, is injected into the blow air which helps the dust particles to coalesce and drop out. Too much water results in a bridge or collar forming between the drill steel and the side of the hole. These often have to be broken in order to remove the bit; too little water is ineffective. Problems with this type of control include reduction in the drilling rate, lack of reliable water supply and displacement of oil resulting in increased wear on lubricated parts.

The other type of dust control on drills is a type of local exhaust ventilation. Reverse air-flow through the drill steel withdraws some of the dust and a collar around the drill bit with ductwork and a fan to remove the dust. These perform better than the wet systems described above: drill bits last longer and the drilling rate is higher. However, these methods are more expensive and require more maintenance.

Other controls that provide protection are cabs with filtered and possibly air-conditioned air supply for drill operators, bulldozer operators and vehicle drivers. The appropriate respirator, correctly fitted, may be used for worker protection as a temporary solution or if all others prove to be ineffective.

Silica exposure also occurs at stone quarries that must cut the stone to specified dimensions. The most common contemporary method of cutting stone is with the use of a channel burner fuelled by diesel fuel and compressed air. This results in some silica particulate. The most significant problem with channel burners is the noise: when the burner is first ignited and when it emerges from a cut, sound level can exceed 120 dBA. Even when it is immersed in a cut, noise is around 115 dBA. An alternative method of cutting stone is to use very high-pressure water.

Often attached to or nearby a stone quarry is a mill where pieces are sculpted into a more finished product. Unless there is very good local exhaust ventilation, exposure to silica can be high because vibrating and rotating hand tools are used to shape the stone into the desired form.

Respirable coal mine dust is a hazard in underground and surface coal mines and in coal-processing facilities. It is a mixed dust, consisting mostly of coal, but can also include silica, clay, limestone and other mineral dusts. The composition of coal mine dust varies with the coal seam, the composition of the surrounding strata and mining methods. Coal mine dust is generated by blasting, drilling, cutting and transporting coal.

More dust is generated with mechanized mining than with manual methods, and some methods of mechanized mining produce more dust than others. Cutting machines that remove coal with rotating drums studded with picks are the principal sources of dust in mechanized mining operations. These include so-called continuous miners and longwall mining machines. Longwall mining machines usually produce larger amounts of dust than do other methods of mining. Dust dispersion can also occur with the movement of shields in longwall mining and with the transfer of coal from a vehicle or conveyor belt to some other means of transport.

Coal mine dust causes coal workers' pneumoconiosis (CWP) and contributes to the occurrence of chronic airways disease such as chronic bronchitis and emphysema. Coal of high rank (e.g., high carbon content such as anthracite) is associated with a higher risk of CWP. There are some rheumatoid-like reactions to coal mine dust as well.

The generation of coal mine dust can be reduced by changes in coal cutting techniques and its dispersion can be controlled with the use of adequate ventilation and water sprays. If the speed of rotation of cutting drums is reduced and the tram speed (the speed with which the drum advances into the coal seam) is increased, dust generation can be reduced without losses in productivity. In longwall mining, dust generation can be reduced by cutting coal in one pass (rather than two) across the face and tramming back without cutting or by a clean-up cut. Dust dispersion on longwall sections can be reduced with homotropal mining (i.e., the chain-conveyor at the face, the cutter head and the air all travelling in the same direction). A novel method of cutting coal, using an eccentric cutter head that continuously cuts perpendicular to the grain of a deposit, seems to generate less dust than the conventional circular cutting head.

Adequate mechanical ventilation flowing first over a mining crew and then to and across the mining face can reduce exposure. Auxiliary local ventilation at the working face, using a fan with ductwork and scrubber, can also reduce exposure by providing local exhaust ventilation.

Water sprays, strategically placed close to the cutterhead and forcing dust away from the miner and towards the face, also assist in reducing exposure. Surfactants provide some benefit in reducing the concentration of coal dust.

Asbestos exposure occurs among asbestos miners and in other mines where asbestos is found in the ore. Among miners throughout the world, exposure to asbestos has elevated the risk of lung cancer and of mesothelioma. It has also elevated the risk of asbestosis (another pneumoconiosis) and of airways disease.

Diesel engine exhaust is a complex mixture of gases, vapours and particulate matter. The most hazardous gases are carbon monoxide, nitrogen oxide, nitrogen dioxide and sulphur dioxide. There are many volatile organic compounds (VOCs), such as aldehydes and unburned hydrocarbons, polycyclic aromatic hydrocarbons (PAHs) and nitro-PAH compounds (N-PAHs). PAH and N-PAH compounds are also adsorbed onto diesel particulate matter. Nitrogen oxides, sulphur dioxide and aldehydes are all acute respiratory irritants. Many of the PAH and N-PAH compounds are carcinogenic.

Diesel particulate matter consists of small diameter (<1 μm in diameter) carbon particles that are condensed from the exhaust fume and often aggregate in air in clumps or strings. These particles are all respirable. Diesel particulate matter and other particles of similar size are carcinogenic in laboratory animals and appear to increase the risk of lung cancer in exposed workers at concentrations above about 0.1 mg/m^3. Miners in underground mines experience exposure to diesel particulate matter at significantly higher levels. The International Agency for Research on Cancer (IARC) considers diesel particulate matter to be a probable carcinogen.

The generation of diesel exhaust can be reduced by engine design and with high-quality, clean and low-sulphur fuel. Derated engines and fuel with a low cetane number and low sulphur content produce less particulate matter. Use of low sulphur fuel reduces the generation of SO_2 and of particulate matter. Filters are effective and feasible and can remove more than 90% of diesel particulate matter from the exhaust stream. Filters are available for engines without scrubbers and for engines with either water or dry scrubbers. Carbon monoxide can be significantly reduced with a catalytic converter. Nitrogen oxides form whenever nitrogen and oxygen are under conditions of high pressure and temperature (i.e., inside the diesel cylinder) and, consequently, they are more difficult to eliminate.

The concentration of dispersed diesel particulate matter can be reduced in an underground mine by adequate mechanical ventilation and restrictions on the use of diesel equipment. Any diesel powered vehicle or other machine will require a minimum amount of ventilation to dilute and remove the exhaust products. The amount of ventilation depends on the size of the engine and its uses. If more than one diesel powered piece of equipment is operating in one air course, ventilation will have to be increased to dilute and remove the exhaust.

Diesel powered equipment may increase the risk of fire or explosion since it emits a hot exhaust, with flame and sparks, and its high surface temperatures may ignite any accumulated coal dust or other combustible material. Surface temperature of diesel engines have to be kept below 305 °F (150 °C) in coal mines in order to prevent the combustion of coal. Flame and sparks from the exhaust can be controlled by a scrubber to prevent ignition of coal dust and of methane.

Gases and Vapours

Table 74.9 lists gases commonly found in mines. The most important naturally occurring gases are *methane* and *hydrogen sulphide* in coal mines and radon in uranium and other mines. Oxygen deficiency is possible in either. Methane is combustible. Most coal mine explosions result from ignitions of methane and are often followed by more violent explosions caused by coal dust that has been suspended by the shock of the original explosion. Throughout the history of coal mining, fires and explosions have been the principal cause of death of thousands of miners. Risk of explosion can be reduced by diluting methane to below its lower explosive limit and by prohibiting potential ignition sources in the face areas, where the concentration is usually the highest. Dusting the mine ribs (wall), floor and ceiling with incombustible limestone (or other silica-free incombustible rock dust) helps to prevent dust explosions; if dust suspended by the shock of a methane

explosion is not combustible, a secondary explosion will not occur.

Radon is a naturally occurring radioactive gas that has been found in uranium mines, tin mines and some other mines. It has not been found in coal mines. The primary hazard associated with radon is its being a source of ionizing radiation, which is discussed below.

Other gaseous hazards include respiratory irritants found in diesel engine exhaust and blasting by-products. *Carbon monoxide* is found not only in engine exhaust but also as a result of mine fires. During mine fires, CO can reach not only lethal concentrations but also can become an explosion hazard.

Nitrogen oxides (NO_x), primarily NO and NO_2, are formed by diesel engines and as a by-product of blasting. In engines, NO_x are formed as an inherent by-product of putting air, 79% of which is nitrogen and 20% of which is oxygen, under conditions of high temperature and pressure, the very conditions necessary to the functioning of a diesel engine. The production of NO_x can be reduced to some extent by keeping the engine as cool as possible and by increasing ventilation to dilute and remove the exhaust.

NO_x is also a blasting by-product. During blasting, miners are removed from an area where blasting will occur. The conventional practice to avoid excessive exposure to nitrogen oxides, dust and other results of blasting is to wait until mine ventilation removes a sufficient amount of blasting by-products from the mine before re-entering the area in an intake airway.

Oxygen deficiency can occur in many ways. Oxygen can be displaced by some other gas, such as methane, or it may be consumed either by combustion or by microbes in an air space with no ventilation.

There is a variety of other airborne hazards to which particular groups of miners are exposed. Exposure to mercury vapour, and thus risk of mercury poisoning, is a hazard among gold miners and millers and among mercury miners. Exposure to arsenic, and risk of lung cancer, occurs among gold miners and lead miners. Exposure to nickel, and thus to risk of lung cancer and skin allergies, occurs among nickel miners.

Some plastics are finding use in mines also. These include *urea-formaldehyde* and *polyurethane foams*, both of which are plastics made in-place. They are used to plug up holes and improve ventilation and to provide a better anchor for roof supports. Formaldehyde and isocyanates, two starting materials for these two foams, are respiratory irritants and both can cause allergic sensitization making it nearly impossible for sensitized miners to work around either ingredient. Formaldehyde is a human carcinogen (IARC Group 1).

Physical Hazards

Noise is ubiquitous in mining. It is generated by powerful machines, fans, blasting and transportation of the ore. The underground mine usually has limited space and thus creates a reverberant field. Noise exposure is greater than if the same sources were in a more open environment.

Exposure to noise can be reduced by using conventional means of noise control on mining machinery. Transmissions can be quieted, engines can be muffled better, and hydraulic machinery can be quieted as well. Chutes can be insulated or lined with sound-absorbing materials. Hearing protectors combined with regular audiometric testing is often necessary to preserve miners' hearing.

Ionizing radiation is a hazard in the mining industry. Radon can be liberated from stone while it is loosened by blasting, but it may also enter a mine through underground streams. It is a gas and therefore it is airborne. Radon and its decay products emit ionizing radiation, some of which have enough energy to produce cancer cells in the lung. As a result, death rates from lung cancer

Table 74.9 • Common names and health effects of hazardous gases occurring in coal mines.

Gas	Common name	Health effects
Methane (CH_4)	Fire damp	Flammable, explosive; simple asphyxiation
Carbon monoxide (CO)	White damp	Chemical asphyxiation
Hydrogen sulphide (H_2S)	Stink damp	Eye, nose, throat irritation; acute respiratory depression
Oxygen deficiency	Black damp	Anoxia
Blasting by-products	After damp	Respiratory irritants
Diesel engine exhaust	Same	Respiratory irritant; lung cancer

among uranium miners are elevated. For miners who smoke, the death rate is very much higher.

Heat is a hazard for both underground and surface miners. In underground mines, the principal source of heat is from the rock itself. The temperature of the rock goes up about 1 °C for every 100 m in depth. Other sources of heat stress include the amount of physical activity workers are doing, the amount of air circulated, the ambient air temperature and humidity and the heat generated by mining equipment, principally diesel powered equipment. Very deep mines (deeper than 1,000 m) can pose significant heat problems, with the temperature of mine ribs about 40 °C. For surface workers, physical activity, the proximity to hot engines, air temperature, humidity and sunlight are the principal sources of heat.

Reduction of heat stress can be accomplished by cooling high temperature machinery, limiting physical activity and providing adequate amounts of potable water, shelter from the sun and adequate ventilation. For surface machinery, air-conditioned cabs can protect the equipment operator. At deep mines in South Africa, for example, underground air-conditioning units are used to provide some relief, and first aid supplies are available to deal with heat stress.

Many mines operate at high altitudes (e.g., greater than 4,600 m), and because of this, miners may experience altitude sickness. This can be aggravated if they travel back and forth between a mine at a high altitude and a more normal atmospheric pressure.

References

Agricola, G. 1950. *De Re Metallica,* translated by HC Hoover and LH Hoover. New York: Dover Publications.

Bickel, KL. 1987. Analysis of diesel-powered mine equipment. In *Proceedings of the Bureau of Mines Technology Transfer Seminar: Diesels in Underground Mines.* Information Circular 9141. Washington, DC: Bureau of Mines.

Bureau of Mines. 1978. *Coal Mine Fire and Explosion Prevention.* Information Circular 8768. Washington, DC: Bureau of Mines.

—. 1988. *Recent Developments in Metal and Nonmetal Fire Protection.* Information Circular 9206. Washington, DC: Bureau of Mines.

Chamberlain, EAC. 1970. The ambient temperature oxidisation of coal in relation to the early detection of spontaneous heating. *Mining Engineer* (October) 130(121):1-6.

Ellicott, CW. 1981. Assessment of the explosibility of gas mixtures and monitoring of sample-time trends. *Proceeding of the Symposium on Ignitions, Explosions and FIres.* Illawara: Australian Institute of Mining and Metallurgy.

Environmental Protection Agency (Australia). 1996. *Best Practice Environmental Management in Mining.* Canberra: Environmental Protection Agency.

Funkemeyer, M and FJ Kock. 1989. Fire prevention in working rider seams prone to spontaneous combustion. *Gluckauf* 9-12.

Graham, JI. 1921. The normal production of carbon monoxide in coal mines. *Transactions of the Institute of Mining Engineers* 60:222-234.

Grannes, SG, MA Ackerson, and GR Green. 1990. *Preventing Automatic Fire Suppression Systems Failure on Underground Mining Belt Conveyers.* Information Circular 9264. Washington, DC: Bureau of Mines.

Greuer, RE. 1974. *Study of Mine Fire Fighting Using Inert Gases.* USBM Contract Report No. S0231075. Washington, DC: Bureau of Mines.

Griffin, RE. 1979. *In-mine Evaluation of Smoke Detectors.* Information Circular 8808. Washington, DC: Bureau of Mines.

Hartman, HL (ed.). 1992. *SME Mining Engineering Handbook,* 2nd edition. Baltimore, MD: Society for Mining, Metallurgy, and Exploration.

Hertzberg, M. 1982. *Inhibition and Extinction of Coal Dust and Methane Explosions.* Report of Investigations 8708. Washington, DC: Bureau of Mines.

Hoek, E, PK Kaiser, and WF Bawden. 1995. *Design of Suppoert for Underground Hard Rock Mines.* Rotterdam: AA Balkema.

Hughes, AJ and WE Raybold. 1960. The rapid determination of the explosibility of mine fire gases. *Mining Engineer* 29:37-53.

International Council on Metals and the Environment (ICME). 1996. *Case Studies Illustrating Environmental Practices in Mining and Metallurgical Processes.* Ottawa: ICME.

International Labour Organization (ILO). 1994. *Recent Developments in the Coalmining Industry.* Geneva: ILO.

Jones, JE and JC Trickett. 1955. Some observations on the examination of gases resulting from explosions in collieries. *Transactions of the Institute of Mining Engineers* 114: 768-790.

Mackenzie-Wood P and J Strang. 1990. Fire gases and their interpretation. *Mining Engineer* 149(345):470-478.

Mines Accident Prevention Association Ontario. n.d. *Emergency Preparedness Guidelines.* Technical Standing Committee Report. North Bay: Mines Accident Prevention Association Ontario.

Mitchell, D and F Burns. 1979. *Interpreting the State of a Mine Fire.* Washington, DC: US Department of Labor.

Morris, RM. 1988. A new fire ratio for determining conditions in sealed areas. *Mining Engineer* 147(317):369-375.

Morrow, GS and CD Litton. 1992. *In-mine Evaluation of Smoke Detectors.* Information Circular 9311. Washington, DC: Bureau of Mines.

National Fire Protection Association (NFPA). 1992a. *Fire Prevention Code.* NFPA 1. Quincy, MA: NFPA.

—. 1992b. *Standard on Pulverized Fuel Systems.* NFPA 8503. Quincy, MA: NFPA.

—. 1994a. *Standard for Fire Prevention in Use of Cutting and Welding Processes.* NFPA 51B. Quincy, MA: NFPA.

—. 1994b. *Standard for Portable Fire Extinguishers.* NFPA 10. Quincy, MA: NFPA.

—. 1994c. *Standard for Medium and High Expansion Foam Systems.* NFPA 11A. Quncy, MA: NFPA.

—. 1994d. *Standard for Dry Chemical Extinguishing Systems.* NFPA 17. Quincy, MA: NFPA.

—. 1994e. *Standard for Coal Preparation Plants.* NFPA 120. Quincy, MA: NFPA.

—. 1995a. *Standard for Fire Prevention and Control in Underground Metal and Nonmetal Mines.* NFPA 122. Quincy, MA: NFPA.

—. 1995b. *Standard for Fire Prevention and Control in Underground Bituminious Coal Mines.* NFPA 123. Quincy, MA: NFPA.

—. 1996a. *Standard on Fire Protection for Self-propelled and Mobile Surface Mining Equipment.* NFPA 121. Quincy, MA: NFPA.

—. 1996b. *Flammable and Combustible Liquids Code.* NFPA 30. Quincy, MA: NFPA.

—. 1996c. *National Electrical Code.* NFPA 70. Quincy, MA: NFPA.

—. 1996d. *National Fire Alarm Code.* NFPA 72. Quincy, MA: NFPA.

—. 1996e. *Standard for the Installation of Sprinkler Systems.* NFPA 13. Quincy, MA: NFPA.

—. 1996f. *Standard for the Installation of Water Spray Systems.* NFPA 15. Quincy, MA: NFPA.

—. 1996g. *Standard on Clean Agent Fire Extinguishing Systems.* NFPA 2001. Quincy, MA: NFPA.

—. 1996h. *Recommended Practice for Fire Protection in Electric Generating Plants and High Voltage DC Converter Stations.* NFPA 850. Quincy, MA: NFPA.

Ng, D and CP Lazzara. 1990. Performance of concrete block and steel panel stoppings in a simulated mine fire. *Fire Technology* 26(1):51-76.

Ninteman, DJ. 1978. *Spontaneous Oxidation and Combustion of Sulfide Ores in Underground Mines.* Information Circular 8775. Washington, DC: Bureau of Mines.

Pomroy, WH and TL Muldoon. 1983. A new stench gas fire warning system. In *Proceedings of the 1983 MAPAO Annual General Meeting and Technical Sessions.* North Bay: Mines Accident Prevention Association Ontario.

Ramaswatny, A and PS Katiyar. 1988. Experiences with liquid nitrogen in combating coal fires underground. *Journal of Mines Metals and Fuels* 36(9):415-424.

Smith, AC and CN Thompson. 1991. Development and application of a method for predicting the spontaneous combustion potential of bituminous coals. Presented at the 24th International Conference of Safety in Mines Research Institutes, Makeevka State Research Institute for Safety in the Coal Industry, Makeevka, Russian Federation.

Timmons, ED, RP Vinson, and FN Kissel. 1979. *Forecasting Methane Hazards in Metal and Nonmetal Mines.* Report of Investigations 8392. Washington, DC: Bureau of Mines.

United Nations (UN) Department of Technical Cooperation for Development and the German Foundation for International Development. 1992. *Mining and the Environment: The Berlin Guidelines.* London: Mining Journal Books.

United Nations Environment Programme (UNEP). 1991. *Environmental Aspects of Selected Non-ferrous Metals (Cu, Ni, Pb, Zn, Au) in Ore Mining.* Paris: UNEP.

Other relevant readings

American Geological Institute. 1992. *Planning for Field Safety.* Alexandria, VA: American Geological Institute.

Banks, DE (ed.). 1993. The mining industry. *Occ Med: State Art Rev* 8(1).

Bieniawski, YT. 1984. *Rock Mechanics Design in Mining and Tunnelling.* Rotterdam: AA Balkema.

Brady, BHG and ET Brown. 1993. *Rock Mechanics for Underground Mining,* 2nd edition. London: Chapman & Hall.

British Columbia and Yukon Chamber of Mines Safety Committee. *Safety Manual: Mineral Exploration in Western Canada.* Vancouver, BC: British Columbia and Yukon Chamber of Mines.

74. MINING AND QUARRYING

Dunnicliff, J and GE Green. 1988. *Geotechnical Instrumentation for Monitoring Field Performance*. New York: John Wiley & Sons.

Franklin, J (ed.). 1990. *Mine Monitoring Manual*. Vol. 42. Etobocoke, ONT: Canadian Institute of Mining and Metallurgy.

Franklin, JA and MB Dusseault. 1989. *Rock Engineering*. New York: McGraw-Hill.

Garcia, MM. 1989. *Mining and Milling: In-plant Practices for Job-related Health Hazards Control, Volume 1: Production Processes*. New York: John Wiley & Sons.

Gilchrist, JD. 1989. *Extraction Metallugry*, 3rd edition. Oxford: Pergamon Press.

Hedley, DGF. 1992. *Rockburst Handbook for Ontario Hardrock Mines*. CANMET Special Report SP92-1E. Ottawa: Supply and Services Canada.

International Agency for Research on Cancer (IARC). 1989. *Diesel and Gasoline Engine Exhausts and Some Nitroarenes*. IARC Monographs on the Evaluation of Carcinogenic Risks to Humans. Vol. 46. Lyon: IARC.

International Labour Organization (ILO). 1990. *Coal Mineworkers' Charter: Collection of Conclusions and Resolutions*. Geneva: ILO.

—. 1991. *Safety and Health in Opencast Mines: A Code of Practice*. Geneva: ILO.

—. 1994. *Productvity and Its Impact on Employment and Labour Relations in the Coalmining Industry*. Geneva: ILO.

—. 1995. *Note on the Proceedings of the 13th Session of the ILO's Coal Mines Committee, 1995*.

Jennings, NS. 1995. *Productivity, Employment and Industrial Relations in Coal Mines: Three Case Studies from China, India and Zimbabwe*. Geneva: ILO.

—. 1995. *Productivity, Employment and Industrial Relations in Coal Mines: Three Case Studies from Australia, United Kingdom, United States*. Geneva: ILO.

—. 1995. *Productivity, Employment and Industrial Relations in Coal Mines: Two Case Studies from the Czech Republic and the Russian Federation*. Geneva: ILO.

Kaiser, PK, DR McCreath, and DD Tannant. 1996. *Canadian Rockburst Support Handbook*. Sudbury, ONT: Geomechanics Research Centre.

Kelly, EG and DJ Spottiswood. 1982. *Introduction to Mineral Processing*. New York: John Wiley & Sons.

Kural, O. (ed.). 1994. *Coal: Resources, Properties, Utilization, Pollution*. Istanbul: Istanbul Technical University.

Keystone, JS (ed.). 1995. *Don't Drink the Water*. Toronto: Canadian Public Health Association.

Laskowski, JS and AD Walters. 1987. *Encyclopedia of Physical Science and Technology*. New York: Academic Press.

Merry, W. 1994. The official Wilderness First Aid Guide. Toronto: McClelland & Stewart.

Osborne, DG. 1988. *Coal Preparation Technology*. London: Graham & Trottman.

Peters, WC. 1987. *Exploration and Mining Geology*, 2nd edition. New York: John Wiley & Sons.

Reedman, JH. 1979. *Techniques in Mineral Exploration*. New York: Applied Science Publishers.

Society for Mining, Metallurgy and Exploration (SME). 1990. *Surface Mining*, 2nd edition, edited by BA Kennedy. Baltimore, MD: SME.

Walker, S. 1996. *Comparative Underground Coal Mining Methods*. London: IEA Coal Research.

Wills, BA. 1979. *Mineral Processing Technology*. Oxford: Pergamon Press.

OIL EXPLORATION AND DRILLING

75

Chapter Editor
Richard S. Kraus

Contents

75. OIL EXPLORATION AND DRILLING

EXPLORATION, DRILLING AND PRODUCTION OF OIL AND NATURAL GAS

Richard S. Kraus

General Profile

Crude oils and natural gases are mixtures of hydrocarbon molecules (organic compounds of carbon and hydrogen atoms) containing from 1 to 60 carbon atoms. The properties of these hydrocarbons depend on the number and arrangement of the carbon and hydrogen atoms in their molecules. The basic hydrocarbon molecule is 1 carbon atom linked with 4 hydrogen atoms (methane). All other variations of petroleum hydrocarbons evolve from this molecule. Hydrocarbons containing up to 4 carbon atoms are usually gases; those with 5 to 19 carbon atoms are usually liquids; and those with 20 or more are solids. In addition to hydrocarbons, crude oils and natural gases contain sulphur, nitrogen and oxygen compounds together with trace quantities of metals and other elements.

Crude oil and natural gas are believed to have been formed over millions of years by the decay of vegetation and marine organisms, compressed under the weight of sedimentation. Because oil and gas are lighter than water, they rose up to fill the voids in these overlying formations. This upward movement stopped when the oil and gas reached dense, overlying, impervious strata or nonporous rock. The oil and gas filled the spaces in porous rock seams and natural underground reservoirs, such as saturated sands, with the lighter gas on top of the heavier oil. These spaces were originally horizontal, but shifting of the earth's crust created pockets, called faults, anticlines, salt domes and stratigraphic traps, where the oil and gas collected in reservoirs.

Shale Oil

Shale oil, or kerogen, is a mixture of solid hydrocarbons and other organic compounds containing nitrogen, oxygen and sulphur. It is extracted, by heating, from a rock called oil shale, yielding from 15 to 50 gallons of oil per ton of rock.

Figure 75.1 • World crude oil production for 1995.

World production (thousand barrels per day) = 57,037

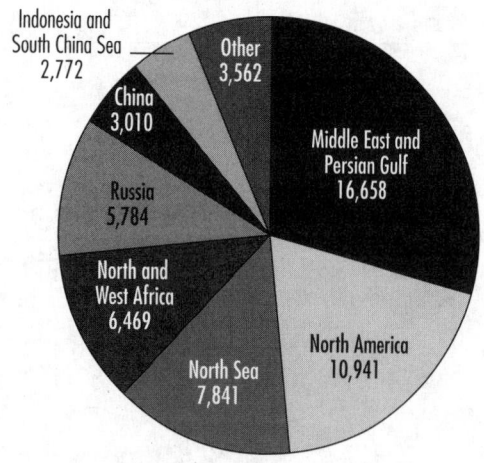

Source: Adapted from Energy Information Administration 1996.

Figure 75.2 • World natural gas plant liquids production for 1995.

World production (thousand barrels per day) = 5,470

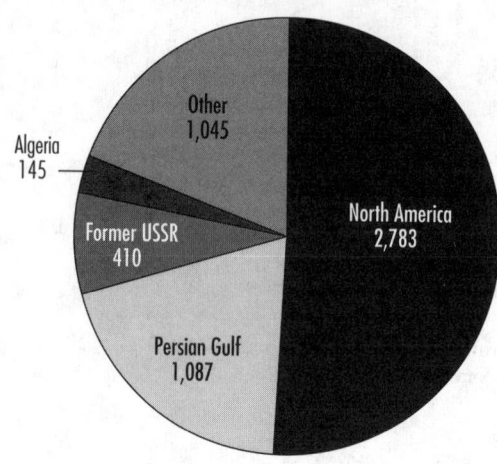

Source: Adapted from Energy Information Administration 1996.

Exploration and production is the common terminology applied to that portion of the petroleum industry which is responsible for exploring for and discovering new crude oil and gas fields, drilling wells and bringing the products to the surface. Historically, crude oil, which had naturally seeped to the surface, was collected for use as medicine, protective coatings and fuel for lamps. Natural gas seepage was recorded as fires burning on the surface of the earth. It was not until 1859 that methods of drilling and obtaining large commercial quantities of crude oil were developed.

Crude oil and natural gas are found throughout the world, beneath both land and water, as follows:

- Western Hemisphere Intercontinental Basin (US Gulf Coast, Mexico, Venezuela)
- Middle East (Arabian Peninsula, Persian Gulf, Black and Caspian Seas)
- Indonesia and South China Sea
- North and West Africa (Sahara and Nigeria)
- North America (Alaska, Newfoundland, California and Mid-continent United States and Canada)
- Far East (Siberia and China)
- North Sea.

Figures 75.1 and 75.2 show world crude oil and natural gas production for 1995.

The names of crude oils often identify both the type of crude and areas where they were originally discovered. For example, the first commercial crude oil, Pennsylvania Crude, is named after its place of origin in the United States. Other examples are Saudi Light and Venezuelan Heavy. Two benchmark crudes used to set world crude prices are Texas Light Sweet and North Sea Brent.

Classification of crude oils

Crude oils are complex mixtures containing many different, individual hydrocarbon compounds; they differ in appearance and composition from one oil field to another, and sometimes are even different from wells relatively near one another. Crude oils range in consistency from watery to tar-like solids, and in colour from clear to black. An "average" crude oil contains about 84%

Table 75.1 • Typical approximate characteristics and properties and gasoline potential of various typical crude oils.*

Crude source and name	Paraffins % vol	Aromatics % vol	Naphthenes % vol	Sulphur % wt	API gravity (approx)	Naphthene yield % vol	Octane number (typical)
Nigerian Light	37	9	54	0.2	36	28	60
Saudi Light	63	19	18	2	34	22	40
Saudi Heavy	60	15	25	2.1	28	23	35
Venezuela Heavy	35	12	53	2.3	30	2	60
Venezuela Light	52	14	34	1.5	24	18	50
USA Midcontinental Sweet	—	—	—	0.4	40	—	—
USA West Texas Sour	46	22	32	1.9	32	33	55
North Sea Brent	50	16	34	0.4	37	31	50

* Representative average numbers.

carbon; 14% hydrogen; 1 to 3% sulphur; and less than 1% of nitrogen, oxygen, metals and salts. See tables 75.1 and 75.2.

Relatively simple crude-oil assays are used to classify crude oils as paraffinic, naphthenic, aromatic or mixed, based on the predominant proportion of similar hydrocarbon molecules. Mixed-base crudes have varying amounts of each type of hydrocarbon. One assay method (US Bureau of Mines) is based on distillation, and another method (UOP "K" factor) is based on gravity and boiling points. More comprehensive crude assays are conducted to determine the value of the crude (i.e., its yield and quality of useful products) and processing parameters. Crude oils are usually grouped according to yield structure, with high-octane gasoline being one of the more desirable products. Refinery crude oil feedstocks usually consist of mixtures of two or more different crude oils.

Crude oils are also defined in terms of API (specific) gravity. For example, heavier crude oils have low API gravities (and high specific gravities). A low-API gravity crude oil may have either a high or low flashpoint, depending on its lightest ends (more volatile constituents). Because of the importance of temperature and pressure in the refining process, crude oils are further classified as to viscosity, pour points and boiling ranges. Other physical and chemical characteristics, such as colour and carbon residue content, are also considered. Crude oils with high carbon, low hydrogen and low API gravity are usually rich in aromatics; while those with low carbon, high hydrogen and high API gravity are usually rich in paraffins.

Crude oils which contain appreciable quantities of hydrogen sulphide or other reactive sulphur compounds are called "sour." Those with less sulphur are called "sweet." Some exceptions to this rule are West Texas crudes (which are always considered "sour" regardless of their H₂S content) and Arabian high-sulphur crudes (which are not considered "sour" because their sulphur compounds are not highly reactive).

Compressed Natural Gas and Liquefied Hydrocarbon Gases

The composition of naturally occurring hydrocarbon gases is similar to crude oils in that they contain a mixture of different hydrocarbon molecules depending on their source. They can be extracted as natural gas (almost free of liquids) from gas fields; petroleum-associated gas which is extracted with oil from gas and oil fields; and gas from gas condensate fields, where some of the liquid components of oil convert into the gaseous state when pressure is high (10 to 70 mPa). When the pressure is decreased (to 4 to 8 mPa) condensate containing heavier hydrocarbons sepa-

Figure 75.3 • Offshore natural gas well set in 87.5 metres of water in the Pitas Point area of the Santa Barbara Channel, Southern California.

American Petroleum Institute

EXPLORATION, DRILLING, PRODUCTION OF OIL & NATURAL GAS

Table 75.2 • Composition of crude oil and natural gas.

Hydrocarbons

Paraffins: The paraffinic saturated chain type hydrocarbon (aliphatic) molecules in crude oil have the formula C_nH_{2n+2}, and can be either straight chains (normal) or branched chains (isomers) of carbon atoms. The lighter, straight chain paraffin molecules are found in gases and paraffin waxes. The branched chain paraffins are usually found in heavier fractions of crude oil and have higher octane numbers than normal paraffins.

Aromatics: Aromatics are unsaturated ring type hydrocarbon (cyclic) compounds. Naphthalenes are fused double ring aromatic compounds. The most complex aromatics, polynuclears (three or more fused aromatic rings), are found in heavier fractions of crude oil.

Naphthenes: Naphthenes are saturated ring type hydrocarbon groupings, with the formula C_nH_{2n}, arranged in the form of closed rings (cyclic), found in all fractions of crude oil except the very lightest. Single ring naphthenes (mono-cycloparaffins) with 5 and 6 carbon atoms predominate, with two ring naphthenes (dicycloparaffins) found in the heavier ends of naphtha.

Non-hydrocarbons

Sulphur and sulphur compounds: Sulphur is present in natural gas and crude oil as hydrogen sulphide (H_2S), as compounds (thiols, mercaptans, sulphides, polysulphides, etc.) or as elemental sulphur. Each gas and crude oil has different amounts and types of sulphur compounds, but as a rule the proportion, stability and complexity of the compounds are greater in heavier crude oil fractions.

Sulphur compounds called mercaptans, which exhibit distinct odours detectable at very low concentrations, are found in gas, petroleum crude oils and distillates. The most common are methyl and ethyl mercaptans. Mercaptans are often added to commercial gas (LNG and LPG) to provide an odour for leak detection.

The potential for exposure to toxic levels of H_2S exists when working in drilling, production, transportation and processing crude oil and natural gas. The combustion of petroleum hydrocarbons containing sulphur produces undesirables such as sulphuric acid and sulphur dioxide.

Oxygen compounds: Oxygen compounds, such as phenols, ketones and carboxylic acids, are found in crude oils in varying amounts.

Nitrogen compounds: Nitrogen is found in lighter fractions of crude oil as basic compounds, and more often in heavier fractions of crude oil as non-basic compounds which may also include trace metals.

Trace metals: Trace amounts, or small quantities of metals, including copper, nickel, iron, arsenic and vanadium, are often found in crude oils in small quantities.

Inorganic salts: Crude oils often contain inorganic salts, such as sodium chloride, magnesium chloride and calcium chloride, suspended in the crude or dissolved in entrained water (brine).

Carbon dioxide: Carbon dioxide may result from the decomposition of bicarbonates present in, or added to crude, or from steam used in the distillation process.

Naphthenic acids: Some crude oils contain naphthenic (organic) acids, which may become corrosive at temperatures above 232 °C when the acid value of the crude is above a certain level.

Normally occurring radioactive materials: Normally occurring radioactive materials (NORMs) are often present in crude oil, in the drilling deposits and in the drilling mud, and can present a hazard from low levels of radioactivity.

rates from the gas by condensation. Gas is extracted from wells reaching up to 4 miles (6.4 km) or more in depth, with seam pressures varying from 3 mPa up to as high as 70 mPa. (See figure 75.3.)

Natural gas contains 90 to 99% hydrocarbons, which consist predominately of methane (the simplest hydrocarbon) together with smaller amounts of ethane, propane and butane. Natural gas also contains traces of nitrogen, water vapour, carbon dioxide, hydrogen sulphide and occasional inert gases such as argon or helium. Natural gases containing more than 50 g/m^3 of hydrocarbons with molecules of three or more carbon atoms (C_3 or higher) are classified as "lean" gases.

Depending how it is used as a fuel, natural gas is either compressed or liquefied. Natural gas from gas and gas condensate fields is processed in the field to meet specific transportation criteria before being compressed and fed into gas pipelines. This preparation includes removal of water with driers (dehydrators, separators and heaters), oil removal using coalescing filters, and the removal of solids by filtration. Hydrogen sulphide and carbon dioxide are also removed from natural gas, so that they do not corrode pipelines and transportation and compression equipment. Propane, butane and pentane, present in natural gas, are also removed before transmission so they will not condense and form liquids in the system. (See the section "Natural gas production and processing operations.")

Natural gas is transported by pipeline from gas fields to liquefication plants, where it is compressed and cooled to approximately –162 °C to produce liquefied natural gas (LNG) (see figure 75.4). The composition of LNG is different from natural gas due to the removal of some impurities and components during the liquefaction process. LNG is primarily used to augment natural gas supplies during peak demand periods and to supply gas in remote areas away from major pipelines. It is regasified by adding nitrogen and air to make it comparable to natural gas before being fed into gas supply lines. LNG is also used as a motor-vehicle fuel as an alternative to gasoline.

Petroleum-associated gases and condensate gases are classified as "rich" gases, because they contain significant amounts of ethane, propane, butane and other saturated hydrocarbons. Petroleum-associated and condensate gases are separated and liquefied to produce liquefied petroleum gas (LPG) by compression, adsorption, absorption and cooling at oil and gas process plants. These gas plants also produce natural gasoline and other hydrocarbon fractions.

Unlike natural gas, petroleum-associated gas and condensate gas, oil processing gases (produced as by-products of refinery processing) contain considerable amounts of hydrogen and unsaturated hydrocarbons (ethylene, propylene and so on). The composition of oil processing gases depends upon each specific process and the crude oils used. For example, gases obtained as a result of thermal cracking usually contain significant amounts of olefins, while those obtained from catalytic cracking contain more isobutanes. Pyrolysis gases contain ethylene and hydrogen. The composition of natural gases and typical oil processing gases is shown in table 75.3.

Combustible natural gas, with a calorific value of 35.7 to 41.9 MJ/m^3 (8,500 to 10,000 $kcal/m^3$), is primarily used as a fuel to produce heat in domestic, agricultural, commercial and industrial applications. The natural gas hydrocarbon also is used as feedstock for petrochemical and chemical processes. Synthesis gas ($CO + H_2$) is processed from methane by oxygenation or water vapour conversion, and used to produce ammonia, alcohol and other organic chemicals. Compressed natural gas (CNG) and liquefied natural gas (LNG) are both used as fuel for internal combustion engines. Oil processing liquefied petroleum gases (LPG) have higher calorific values of 93.7 MJ/m^3 (propane) (22,400 $kcal/m^3$) and 122.9 MJ/m^3 (butane) (29,900 $kcal/m^3$) and are used as fuel in homes, businesses and industry as well as in motor vehicles (NFPA 1991). The unsaturated hydrocarbons (ethylene, propylene and so on) derived from oil processing gases may

Figure 75.4 • World's largest LNG plant at Arzew, Algeria.

American Petroleum Institute

be converted into high-octane gasoline or used as raw materials in the petrochemical and chemical-processing industries.

Properties of Hydrocarbon Gases

According to the US National Fire Protection Association, flammable (combustible) gases are those which burn in the concentrations of oxygen normally present in air. The burning of flammable gases is similar to that of flammable hydrocarbon liquid vapours, as a specific ignition temperature is needed to initiate the burning reaction and each will burn only within a certain defined range of gas-air mixtures. Flammable liquids have a *flashpoint* (the temperature (always below the boiling point) at which they emit sufficient vapours for combustion). There is no apparent flashpoint for flammable gases, as they are normally at temperatures above their boiling points, even when liquefied, and are therefore always at temperatures well in excess of their flashpoints.

The US National Fire Protection Association (1976) defines compressed and liquefied gases, as follows:

- "Compressed gases are those which at all normal atmospheric temperatures inside their containers, exist solely in the gaseous state under pressure."
- "Liquefied gases are those which at normal atmospheric temperatures inside their containers, exist partly in the liquid state

and partly in the gaseous state, and are under pressure as long as any liquid remains in the container."

The major factor which determines the pressure inside the vessel is the temperature of the liquid stored. When exposed to the atmosphere, the liquefied gas very rapidly vaporizes, travelling along the ground or water surface unless dispersed into the air by wind or mechanical air movement. At normal atmospheric temperatures, about one-third of the liquid in the container will vaporize.

Flammable gases are further classified as fuel gas and industrial gas. Fuel gases, including natural gas and liquefied petroleum gases (propane and butane), are burned with air to produce heat in ovens, furnaces, water heaters and boilers. Flammable industrial gases, such as acetylene, are used in processing, welding, cutting and heat treating operations. The differences in properties of liquefied natural gas (LNG) and liquefied petroleum gases (LPG) are shown in table 75.3.

Searching for Oil and Gas

The search for oil and gas requires a knowledge of geography, geology and geophysics. Crude oil is usually found in certain types of geological structures, such as anticlines, fault traps and salt domes, which lie under various terrains and in a wide range of climates. After selecting an area of interest, many different types of geophysical surveys are conducted and measurements performed in order to obtain a precise evaluation of the subsurface formations, including:

- *Magnetometric surveys.* Magnetometers hung from airplanes measure variations in the earth's magnetic field in order to locate sedimentary rock formations which generally have low magnetic properties when compared to other rocks.
- *Aerial photogrammetric surveys.* Photographs taken with special cameras in airplanes, provide three-dimensional views of the earth which are used to determine land formations with potential oil and gas deposits.
- *Gravimetric surveys.* Because large masses of dense rock increase the pull of gravity, gravimeters are used to provide information regarding underlying formations by measuring minute differences in gravity.
- *Seismic surveys.* Seismic studies provide information on the general characteristics of the subsurface structure (see figure 75.5). Measurements are obtained from shock waves generated by setting off explosive charges in small-diameter holes, from the use of vibrating or percussion devices on both land and in water, and from underwater blasts of compressed air. The elapsed time between the beginning of the shock wave and the return of the echo is used to determine the depth of the reflecting substrata. The recent use of super-computers to generate three-dimensional images greatly improves evaluation of seismic test results.

Table 75.3 • Typical approximate composition of natural and oil processing gases (per cent by volume).

Type gas	H_2	CH_4	C_2H_6	C_3H_4	C_3H_8	C_3H_6	C_4H_{10}	C_4H_8	$N_{2+}CO_2$	C_{5+}
Natural gas	n/a	98	0.4	n/a	0.15	n/a	0.05	n/a	1.4	n/a
Petroleum-associated gas	n/a	42	20	n/a	17	n/a	8	n/a	10	3
Oil processing gases Catalytic cracking	5–6	10	3–5	3	16–20	6–11	42–46	5–6	n/a	5–12
Pyrolysis	12	5–7	5–7	16–18	0.5	7–8	0.2	4–5	n/a	2–3

Figure 75.5 • Saudi Arabia, seismic operations.

American Petroleum Institute

- *Radiographic surveys.* Radiography is the use of radio waves to provide information similar to that obtained from seismic surveys.
- *Stratigraphic surveys.* Stratigraphic sampling is the analysis of cores of subsurface rock strata for traces of gas and oil. A cylindrical length of rock, called a core, is cut by a hollow bit and pushed up into a tube (core barrel) attached to the bit. The core barrel is brought to the surface and the core is removed for analysis.

When the surveys and measurements indicate the presence of formations or strata which may contain petroleum, exploratory wells are drilled to determine whether or not oil or gas is actually present and, if so, whether it is available and obtainable in commercially viable quantities.

Offshore Operations

Although the first offshore oil well was drilled in the early 1900s off of the coast of California, the beginning of modern marine drilling was in 1938, with a discovery in the Gulf of Mexico, 1 mile (1.6 km) from the US coastline. After the Second World War, offshore drilling expanded quickly, first in shallow waters adjacent to known land-based production areas, and then to other shallow and deep water areas around the world, and in climates varying from the Arctic to the Persian Gulf. In the beginning, offshore drilling was possible only in water depths of about 91 m; however, modern platforms are now able drill in waters over

3.2 km deep. Offshore oil activities include exploration, drilling, production, processing, underwater construction, maintenance and repair, and the transport of the oil and gas to shore by ship or pipeline.

Offshore platforms

Drilling platforms support drilling rigs, supplies and equipment for offshore or inland water operations, and range from floating or submergible barges and ships, to fixed-in-place platforms on steel legs used in shallow waters, to large, buoyant, reinforced concrete, gravity-type platforms used in deep waters. After the drilling is completed, marine platforms are used to support production equipment. The very largest production platforms have accommodations for over 250 crew members and other support personnel, heliports, processing plants and crude oil and gas condensate storage capability (see figure 75.6).

Typically, with deep water floating platform drilling, the wellhead equipment is lowered to the ocean floor and sealed to the well casing. The use of fibre-optic technology allows a large, central platform to remotely control and operate smaller satellite platforms and sub-sea templates. Production facilities on the large platform process the crude oil, gas and condensate from the satellite facilities, before it is shipped on-shore.

The type of platform used in underwater drilling is often determined by the type of well to be drilled (exploratory or production) and by the depth of the water (see table 75.4).

Types of Wells

Exploratory wells. Following the analysis of geological data and geophysical surveys, exploratory wells are drilled, either on land or offshore. Exploratory wells which are drilled in areas where neither oil nor gas has been previously found are called "wildcats." Those wells which strike oil or gas are called "discovery wells." Other exploratory wells, known as "step-out" or "appraisal" wells, are drilled to determine the limits of a field following discovery, or to search for new oil- and gas-bearing formations next to, or beneath, those already known to contain product. A well which does not find any oil or gas, or finds too little to produce economically, is called a "dry hole".

Figure 75.6 • Drilling vessels; drill ship *Ben Ocean Laneer*.

American Petroleum Institute

Table 75.4 • Platform types for underwater drilling.

Platform type	Depth (m)	Description
Submersible barges and platforms	15–30	Barges or platforms, towed to the site and sunk to rest on the bottom. Lower buoyant column keeps rigs afloat when moved.
Jack-ups (on legs)	30–100	Mobile, self-elevating buoyant platforms whose legs are jacked up for towing. At the site, the legs are lowered to the bottom and then extended to raise the platform above the water level.
Floating platforms	100–3,000+	Large, self-contained, multi-level, reinforced concrete gravity structures, towed to the site, submerged with water ballast to a predetermined depth so the columns and stabilizing devices offset the motion of waves, and anchored in place. The columns often hold the crude oil until it is off-loaded.
		Smaller floating platforms, similarly suspended, which support only the drilling rig and are serviced by a floating tender
Drilling barges	30–300	Self-propelled, floating or semi-submersible barges.
Drill ships	120–3,500+	Highly sophisticated, specially designed, floating or semi-submersible ships.
Fixed on site platforms	0–250	Platforms built on steel supports (jackets) which are sunk and fixed in place, and artificial islands used as platforms.
Sub-sea templates	n/a	Underwater production installations.

Developmental wells. After a discovery, the area of the reservoir is roughly determined with a series of step-out or appraisal wells. Developmental wells are then drilled to produce gas and oil. The number of developmental wells to be drilled is determined by the expected definition of the new field, both in size and in productivity. Because of the uncertainty as to how reservoirs are shaped or confined, some developmental wells may turn out to be dry holes. Occasionally, drilling and producing occurs simultaneously.

Geopressure/geothermal wells. Geopressure/geothermal wells are those which produce extremely high-pressure (7,000 psi) and high-temperature (149 °C) water which may contain hydrocarbons. The water becomes a rapidly expanding cloud of hot steam and vapours upon release to the atmosphere from a leak or rupture.

Stripper wells. Stripper wells are those which produce less than ten barrels of oil a day from a reservoir.

Figure 75.7 • Drilling rig on Ellef Ringnes Island in the Canadian Arctic.

American Petroleum Institute

Multiple completion wells. When multiple producing formations are discovered when drilling a single well, a separate string of pipe may be run into a single well for each individual formation. Oil and gas from each formation is directed into its respective piping and isolated from one another by packers, which seal the annular spaces between the piping string and the casing. These wells are known as multiple completion wells.

Injection wells. Injection wells pump air, water, gas or chemicals into reservoirs of producing fields, either to maintain pressure or move oil toward producing wells by hydraulic force or increased pressure.

Service wells. Service wells include those used for fishing and wire-line operations, packer/plug placement or removal and reworking. Service wells are also drilled for underground disposal of salt water, which is separated from crude oil and gas.

Drilling Methods

Drilling rigs. Basic drilling rigs contain a derrick (tower), a drilling pipe, a large winch to lower and lift out the drilling pipe, a drilling table which rotates the drilling pipe and bit, a mud mixer and pump and an engine to drive the table and winch (see figure 75.7). Small drilling rigs used to drill exploratory or seismic wells may be mounted on trucks for movement from site to site. Larger drilling rigs are either erected onsite or have portable, hinged (jack knife) derricks for easy handling and erection.

Percussion or cable drilling. The oldest drilling technique is percussion or cable drilling. This slow, limited depth method, which is seldom used, involves crushing rock by raising and dropping a heavy chisel bit and stem on the end of a cable. At intervals, the bit is removed and the cuttings are suspended in water and removed by flushing or pumping to the surface. As the hole deepens, it is lined with steel casing to prevent cave-in and protect against contamination of groundwater. Considerable work is required to drill even a shallow well, and upon striking oil or gas, there is no way to control the immediate flow of product to the surface.

75. OIL EXPLORATION AND DRILLING

Rotary drilling. Rotary drilling is the most common method and is used to drill both exploratory and production wells at depths over 5 miles (7,000 m). Lightweight drills, mounted on trucks, are used to drill low-depth seismic wells on land. Medium and heavy rotary mobile and floating drills are used for drilling exploration and production wells. Rotary drilling equipment is mounted on a drilling platform with a 30- to 40-m-high derrick, and includes a rotary table, engine, mud mixer and injector pump, a wire-line drum hoist or winch, and many sections of pipe, each approximately 27 m long. The rotary table turns a square kelly connected to the drilling pipe. The square kelly has a mud swivel on the top which is connected to blowout preventors. The drill pipe rotates at a speed of from 40 to 250 rpm, turning either a drill which has drag bits with fixed chisel-like cutting edges or a drill whose bit has rolling cutters with hardened teeth.

Rotary percussion drilling. Rotary percussion drilling is a combination method whereby a rotary drill uses a circulating hydraulic fluid to operate a hammer-like mechanism, thereby creating a series of rapid percussion blows which allow the drill to simultaneously bore and pound into the earth.

Electro and turbo drilling. Most rotary tables, winches and pumps of heavy drills are usually driven by electric motors or turbines, which allows for increased flexibility in operations and remote-controlled drilling. Electro drill and turbo drill are newer methods which provide more direct power to the drill bit by connecting the drilling motor just above the bit at the bottom of the hole.

Directional drilling. Directional drilling is a rotary drilling technique which directs the drill string along a curved path as the hole deepens. Directional drilling is used to reach deposits which are inaccessible by vertical drilling. It also reduces costs, as a number of wells can be drilled in different directions from a single platform. Extended-reach drilling allows tapping into undersea reservoirs from the shore. Many of these techniques are possible by using computers to direct automatic drilling machines and flexible pipe (coiled tubing), which is raised and lowered without connecting and disconnecting sections.

Other drilling methods. Abrasive drilling uses an abrasive material under pressure (instead of using a drill stem and bit) to cut through the substrata. Other drilling methods include explosive drilling and flame piercing.

Abandonment. When oil and gas reservoirs are no longer productive, the wells are typically plugged with cement to prevent flow or leakage to the surface and to protect the underground strata and water. Equipment is removed and the sites of abandoned wells are cleaned up and returned to normal conditions.

Drilling Operations

Drilling techniques

The drilling platform provides a base for workers to couple and uncouple the sections of drilling pipe which are used to increase the depth of drilling. As the hole deepens, additional lengths of pipe are added and the drilling string is suspended from the derrick. When a drilling bit needs to be changed, the entire drilling string of pipe is pulled out of the hole, and each section is detached and stacked vertically inside the derrick. After the new bit is fitted in place, the process is reversed, and the pipe is returned to the hole to continue drilling. Care is needed to assure that the drilling string pipe does not split apart and drop into the

hole, as it may be difficult and costly to fish out and may even result in the loss of the well. Another potential problem is if drilling tools stick in the hole when drilling stops. For this reason, once drilling begins, it usually continues until the well is completed.

Drilling mud

Drilling mud is a fluid composed of water or oil and clay with chemical additives (e.g., formaldehyde, lime, sodium hydrazide, barite). Caustic soda is often added to control the pH (acidity) of drilling mud and to neutralize potentially hazardous mud additives and completion fluids. Drilling mud is pumped into the well under pressure from the mixing tank on the drilling platform, down the inside of the drilling pipe to the drill bit. It then rises between the outside of the drill pipe and the sides of the hole, returning to the surface, where it is filtered and recirculated.

Drilling mud is used to cool and lubricate the drilling bit, lubricate the pipe and flush the rock cuttings from the drill hole. Drilling mud is also used to control flow from the well by lining the sides of the hole and resisting the pressure of any gas, oil or water which is met by the drill bit. Jets of mud may be applied under pressure at the bottom of the hole to aid in drilling.

Casing and cementation

The casing is a special heavy steel pipe which lines the well hole. It is used to prevent cave-in of the drill hole walls and protect fresh water strata by preventing leakage from the returning flow of mud during drilling operations. The casing also seals off water-permeated sands and high-pressure gas zones. Casing is initially used near the surface and is cemented into place to guide the drill pipe. A cement slurry is pumped down the drilling pipe and forced back up through the gap between the casing and the walls of the well hole. Once the cement sets and the casing is place, drilling continues using a smaller diameter bit.

After the surface casing is placed in the well, blowout preventors (large valves, bags or rams) are attached to the top of the casing, in what is called a stack. Following discovery of oil or gas, casing is set into the bottom of the well to keep dirt, rocks, salt water and other contaminants out of the well hole and to provide a conduit for the crude oil and gas extraction lines.

Completion, Enhanced Recovery and Workover Operations

Completion

Completion describes the process of bringing a well into production after the well has been drilled to the depth where oil or gas is expected to be found. Completion involves a number of operations, including penetration of the casing and cleaning out water and sediment from the pipeline so that flow is unimpeded. Special core bits are used to drill and extract cores up to 50 m long for analysis during the drilling operation to determine when penetration should be performed. The drill pipe and bit are first removed and the final string of casing is cemented into place. A perforating gun, which is a metal tube containing sockets holding either bullets or shaped explosive charges, is then lowered into the well. The charges are discharged by electrical impulse through the casing into reservoir to create openings for the oil and gas to flow into the well and to the surface.

The flow of crude oil and natural gas is controlled by a series of valves, called "Christmas trees", which are placed at the top of the well head. Monitors and controls are installed to automatically or manually operate surface and subsurface safety valves, in the event of a change in pressure, fire or other hazardous condition. Once the oil and gas are produced they are separated, and water and sediment are removed from the crude oil.

Crude oil and gas production and conservation

Producing oil is basically a matter of displacement by either water or gas. At the time of initial drilling, almost all crude oil is under pressure. This natural pressure decreases as oil and gas is removed from the reservoir, during the three phases of a reservoir's life.

- During the first phase, flush production, the flow is governed by the natural pressure in the reservoir which comes from dissolved gas in the oil, gas trapped under pressure above the oil and hydraulic pressure from water trapped under the oil.
- Artificial lift, the second phase, involves pumping pressurized gas into the reservoir when the natural pressure is expended.
- Phase three, stripper or marginal production, occurs when wells only produce intermittently.

Originally there was little understanding of the forces which affected oil and gas production. The study of oil and gas reservoir behaviour began at the beginning of the 20th century, when it was discovered that pumping water into a reservoir increased production. At that time, the industry was recovering between 10 and 20% of reservoir capacity, as compared to recent recovery rates of over 60% before wells become unproductive. The concept of control is that a faster rate of production more quickly dissipates the pressure in the reservoir, thereby reducing the total amount of oil which can be eventually recovered. Two measures used to conserve petroleum reservoirs are unitization and well spacing.

- *Unitization* is the operation of a field as one unit in order to apply secondary recovery methods and maintain pressure, even through a number of different operators may be involved. The total production is allocated on an equitable basis among the operators.
- *Well spacing* is the limiting and proper location of wells so as to achieve maximum production without dissipating a field due to overdrilling.

Methods of Recovering Additional Product

Productivity of oil and gas reservoirs is improved by a variety of recovery methods. One method is either to chemically or physically open passages in the strata to allow oil and gas to move more freely through reservoirs to the well. Water and gas are injected into reservoirs to maintain working pressure by natural displacement. Secondary recovery methods, including displacement by pressure, artificial lift and flooding, improve and restore reservoir pressure. Enhanced recovery is the use of various secondary recovery methods in multiple and different combinations. Enhanced recovery also includes more advanced methods of obtaining additional product from depleted reservoirs, such as thermal recovery, which uses heat instead of water or gas to force more crude oil out of reservoirs.

Acidizing

Acidizing is a method of increasing the output of a well by pumping acid directly into a producing reservoir to open flow channels through the reaction of chemicals and minerals. Hydrochloric (or regular) acid, was first used to dissolve limestone formations. It is still most commonly used; however, various chemicals are now added to the hydrochloric acid to control its reaction and to prevent corrosion and formation of emulsions.

Hydrofluoric acid, formic acid and acetic acid are also used, together with hydrochloric acid, depending on the type of rock or minerals in the reservoir. Hydrofluoric acid is always combined with one of the other three acids, and was originally used to dissolve sandstone. It is often called "mud acid", as it is now used to clean perforations which have been plugged with drilling mud and to restore damaged permeability near the well hole. Formic and acetic acids are used in deep, ultra-hot limestone and dolomite reservoirs and as breakdown acids prior to perforation. Acetic acid is also added to wells as a neutralizing buffer agent to control the pH of well stimulation fluids. Almost all acids have additives, such as inhibitors to prevent reaction with the metal casings and surfactants to prevent formation of sludge and emulsions.

Fracturing

Fracturing describes the method used to increase the flow of oil or gas through a reservoir and into wells by force or pressure. Production may decrease because the reservoir formation is not permeable enough to allow the oil to flow freely toward the well. Fracturing forces open underground channels by pumping a fluid treated with special propping agents (including sand, metal, chemical pellets and shells) into the reservoir under high pressure to open fissures. Nitrogen may be added to the fluid to stimulate expansion. When the pressure is released, the fluid withdraws and the propping agents remain in place, holding the fissures open so that oil can flow more freely.

Massive fracturing (mass frac) involves pumping large amounts of fluid into wells to hydraulically create fissures which are thousands of feet in length. Massive fracturing is typically used to open gas wells where the reservoir formations are so dense that even gas cannot pass through them.

Pressure maintenance

Two common pressure maintenance techniques are the injection of water and gas (air, nitrogen, carbon dioxide and natural gas) into reservoirs where natural pressures are reduced or insufficient for production. Both methods require drilling auxiliary injection wells at designated locations to achieve the best results. The injection of water or gas to maintain the working pressure of the well is called *natural displacement*. The use of pressurized gas to increase the pressure in the reservoir is called *artificial (gas) lift*.

Water flooding

The most commonly used secondary enhanced recovery method is pumping water into an oil reservoir to push product toward producing wells. In *five-spot water flooding*, four injection wells are drilled to form a square with the producing well at the center. The injection is controlled to maintain an even advance of the water front through the reservoir toward the producing well. Some of the water used is salt water, obtained from the crude oil. In *low-tension water flooding*, a surfactant is added to the water to assist the flow of oil through the reservoir by reducing its adhesion to rock.

Miscible flooding

Miscible fluid and miscible polymer flooding are enhanced recovery methods used to improve water injection by reducing the surface tension of crude oil. A fluid miscible (one that can be dissolved in the crude) is injected into a reservoir. This is followed by an injection of another fluid which pushes the crude and miscible fluid mixture toward the producing well. *Miscible polymer flooding* involves the use of a detergent to wash the crude oil from the strata. A gel or thickened water is injected behind the detergent to move the crude toward the producing well.

Fire flooding

Fire flooding, or *in situ* (in place) combustion, is an expensive thermal recovery method wherein large quantities of air or oxygen-containing gas is injected into the reservoir and a portion of the crude oil is ignited. The heat from the fire reduces the viscosity of the heavy crude oil so that it flows more easily. Hot gases,

75. OIL EXPLORATION AND DRILLING

produced by the fire, increase the pressure in the reservoir and create a narrow burning front which pushes the thinner crude from the injection well to the producing well. The heavier crude remains in place, providing additional fuel as the flame front moves slowly forward. The burning process is closely monitored and controlled by regulating the injected air or gas.

Steam injection

Steam injection, or steam flooding, is a thermal recovery method which heats heavy crude oil and lowers its viscosity by injecting super-hot steam into the lowest stratum of relatively shallow reservoir. The steam is injected over a period of 10 to 14 days, and the well is shut for another week or so to allow the steam to thoroughly heat the reservoir. At the same time the increased heat expands reservoir gases, thereby increasing the pressure in the reservoir. The well is then reopened and the heated, less viscous crude flows up into the well. A newer method injects low-heat steam at lower pressure into larger sections of two, three or more zones simultaneously, developing a "steam chest" which squeezes down the oil in each of the zones. This provides a greater flow of oil to the surface, while using less steam.

Natural Gas Production and Processing Operations

There are two types of wells producing natural gas. Wet gas wells produce gas which contains dissolved liquids, and dry gas wells produce gas which cannot be easily liquefied

After natural gas is withdrawn from producing wells, it is sent to gas plants for processing. Gas processing requires a knowledge of how temperature and pressure interact and affect the properties of both fluids and gases. Almost all gas-processing plants handle gases that are mixtures of various hydrocarbon molecules. The purpose of gas processing is to separate these gases into components of similar composition by various processes such as absorption, fractionation and cycling, so they can be transported and used by consumers.

Absorption processes

Absorption involves three processing steps: recovery, removal and separation.

Recovery. Removes undesirable residue gases and some methane by absorption from the natural gas. Absorption takes place in a counterflow vessel, where the well gas enters the bottom of the vessel and flows upward through absorption oil, which is flowing downward. The absorption oil is "lean" as it enters the top of the vessel, and "rich" as it leaves the bottom as it has absorbed the desirable hydrocarbons from the gas. The gas leaving the top of the unit is called "residue gas."

Absorption may also be accomplished by refrigeration. The residue gas is used to pre-cool the inlet gas, which then passes through a gas chiller unit at temperatures from 0 to −40 °C. Lean absorber oil is pumped through an oil chiller, before contacting the cool gas in the absorber unit. Most plants use propane as the refrigerant in the cooler units. Glycol is injected directly into the inlet gas stream to mix with any water in the gas in order to prevent freezing and formation of hydrates. The glycol-water mixture is separated from the hydrocarbon vapour and liquid in the glycol separator, and then reconcentrated by evaporating the water in a regenerator unit.

Removal. The next step in the absorption process is removal, or demethanization. The remaining methane is removed from the rich oil in ethane recovery plants. This is usually a two-phase process, which first rejects at least one-half of the methane from the rich oil by reducing pressure and increasing temperature. The remaining rich oil usually contains enough ethane and propane to

make reabsorption desirable. If not sold, the overhead gas is used as plant fuel or as a pre-saturator, or is recycled to the inlet gas in the main absorber.

Separation. The final step in the absorption process, distillation, uses vapours as a medium to strip the desirable hydrocarbons from the rich absorption oil. Wet stills use steam vapours as the stripping medium. In dry stills, hydrocarbon vapours, obtained from partial vaporization of the hot oil pumped through the still reboiler, are used as the stripping medium. The still controls the final boiling point and molecular weight of the lean oil, and the boiling point of the final hydrocarbon product mix.

Other Processes

Fractionation. Is the separation of the desirable hydrocarbon mixture from absorption plants, into specific, individual, relatively pure products. Fractionation is possible when the two liquids, called top product and bottom product, have different boiling points. The fractionation process has three parts: a tower to separate products, a reboiler to heat the input and a condenser to remove heat. The tower has an abundance of trays so that a lot of vapour and liquid contact occurs. The reboiler temperature determines the composition of the bottom product.

Sulphur recovery. Hydrogen sulphide must be removed from gas before it is shipped for sale. This is accomplished in sulphur recovery plants.

Gas cycling. Gas cycling is neither a means of pressure maintenance nor a secondary method of recovery, but is an enhanced recovery method used to increase production of natural gas liquids from "wet gas" reservoirs. After liquids are removed from the "wet gas" in cycling plants, the remaining "dry gas" is returned to the reservoir through injection wells. As the "dry gas" recirculates through the reservoir it absorbs more liquids. The production, processing and recirculation cycles are repeated until all of the recoverable liquids have been removed from the reservoir and only "dry gas" remains.

Site Development for Producing Oil and Gas Fields

Extensive site development is required to bring a new oil or gas field into production. Site access may be limited or constrained by both climatic and geographic conditions. The requirements include transportation; construction; maintenance, housing and administrative facilities; oil, gas and water separation equipment; crude oil and natural gas transport; water and waste disposal facilities; and many other services, facilities and kinds of equipment. Most of these are not readily available at the site and must be provided by either the drilling or producing company or by outside contractors.

Contractor activities

Contractors are typically used by oil and gas exploration and producing companies to provide some or all of the following supporting services required to drill and develop producing fields:

- Site preparation—brush clearing, road construction, ramps and walkways, bridges, aircraft landing areas, marine harbour, wharfs, docks and landings
- Erection and installation—drilling equipment, power and utilities, tanks and pipeline, housing, maintenance buildings, garages, hangers, service and administration buildings
- Underwater work—installation, inspection, repair and maintenance of underwater equipment and structures

- Maintenance and repair—drilling and production equipment preventive maintenance, vehicles and boats, machinery and buildings
- Contract services—food service; housekeeping; facility and perimeter protection and security; janitorial, recreation and support activity; warehousing and distribution of protective equipment, spare parts and disposable supplies
- Engineering and technical—testing and analyses, computer services, inspections, laboratories, non-destructive analysis, explosives storage and handling, fire protection, permits, environmental, medical and health, industrial hygiene and safety and spill response
- Outside services—telephone, radio and television, sewerage and garbage
- Transportation and material handling equipment—aircraft and helicopter, marine services, heavy-duty construction and materials handling equipment

Utilities

Whether exploration, drilling and producing operations take place on land or offshore, power, light electricity and other support utilities are required, including:

- Power generation—gas, electricity and steam
- Water—fresh water supply, purification and treatment and process water
- Sewerage and drainage—storm water, sanitary treatment and waste (oily) water treatment and disposal
- Communications—telephone, radio and television, computer and satellite communication
- Utilities—light, heat, ventilation and cooling.

Working Conditions, Health and Safety

Work on drilling rigs usually involves a minimum crew of 6 people (primary and secondary *drillers*, three assistant drillers or helpers (*roughnecks*) and a *cathead* person) reporting to a site supervisor or foreman (*tool pusher*) who is responsible for the drilling progression. The primary and secondary drillers have overall responsibility for drilling operations and supervision of the drilling crew during their respective shifts. Drillers should be familiar with the capabilities and limitations of their crews, as work can progress only as fast as the slowest crew member.

Assistant drillers are stationed on the platform to operate equipment, read instruments and perform routine maintenance and repair work. The cathead person is required to climb up near the top of the derrick when drill pipe is being fed into or drawn out of the well hole and assist in moving the sections of pipe into and out of the stack. During drilling, the cathead person also operates the mud pump and provides general assistance to the drilling crew.

Persons who assemble, place, discharge and retrieve perforating guns should be trained, familiar with the hazards of explosives and qualified to handle explosives, primer cord and blasting caps. Other personnel working in and around oil fields include geologists, engineers, mechanics, drivers, maintenance personnel, electricians, pipeline operators and labourers.

Wells are drilled around the clock, on either 8- or 12-hour shifts, and workers require considerable experience, skill and stamina to meet the rigorous physical and mental demands of the job. Overextending a crew may result in a serious accident or injury. Drilling requires close teamwork and coordination in order to accomplish the tasks in a safe and timely fashion. Because of these and other requirements, consideration must be given to the morale and health and safety of workers. Adequate periods of rest and relaxation, nutritious food and appropriate hygiene and living quarters, including air conditioning in hot, humid climates and heating in cold-weather areas, are essential.

The primary occupational hazards associated with exploration and production operations include illnesses from exposure to geographical and climatic elements, stress from travelling long distances over water or harsh terrain and personal injury. Psychological problems may result from the physical isolation of exploratory sites and their remoteness from base camps and the extended work periods required on offshore drilling platforms and at remote onshore sites. Many other hazards particular to offshore operations, such as underwater diving, are covered elsewhere in this *Encyclopaedia*.

Offshore work is dangerous at all times, both when on and off the job. Some workers cannot handle the stress of working offshore at a demanding pace, for extended periods of time, under relative confinement and subject to ever changing environmental conditions. The signs of stress in workers include unusual irritability, other signs of mental distress, excessive drinking or smoking and use of drugs. Problems of insomnia, which may be aggravated by high levels of vibration and noise, have been reported by workers on platforms. Fraternization among workers and frequent shore leave may reduce stress. Seasickness and drowning, as well as exposure to severe weather conditions, are other hazards in offshore work.

Illnesses such as respiratory tract diseases result from exposure to harsh climates, infections or parasitic diseases in areas where these are endemic. Although many of these diseases are still in need of epidemiological study in drilling workers, it is known that oil workers have experienced periarthritis of the shoulder and shoulder blade, humeral epicondylitis, arthrosis of the cervical spine and polyneuritis of the upper limbs. The potential for illnesses as a result of exposure to noise and vibration is also present in drilling operations. The severity and frequency of these drilling-related illnesses appears to be proportional to the length of service and exposure to adverse working conditions (Duck 1983; Ghosh 1983; Montillier 1983).

Injuries while working in drilling and production activities may result from many causes, including slips and falls, pipe handling, lifting pipe and equipment, misuse of tools and mishandling explosives. Burns may be caused by steam, fire, acid or mud containing chemicals such as sodium hydroxide. Dermatitis and skin injuries may result from exposure to crude oil and chemicals.

The possibility exists for acute and chronic exposure to a wide variety of unhealthful materials and chemicals which are present in oil and gas drilling and production. Some chemicals and materials which may be present in potentially hazardous amounts are listed in table 75.2 and include:

- Crude oil, natural gas and hydrogen sulphide gas during drilling and blowouts
- Heavy metals, benzene and other contaminants present in crude
- Asbestos, formaldehyde, hydrochloric acid and other hazardous chemicals and materials
- Normally occurring radioactive materials (NORMs) and equipment with radioactive sources.

Safety

Drilling and production take place in all types of climates and under varying weather conditions, from tropical jungles and deserts to the frozen Arctic, and from dry land to the North Sea. Drilling crews have to work in difficult conditions, subject to noise, vibration, inclement weather, physical hazards and mechanical failures. The platform, rotary table and equipment are usually slippery and vibrate from the engine and drilling operation, requiring workers to make deliberate and careful movements. The hazard exists for slips and falls from heights when climbing the rig and derrick, and there is risk of exposure to crude oil, gas, mud and engine exhaust fumes. The operation of rapidly disconnecting and then reconnecting drill pipe requires training, skill and precision by workers in order to be done safely time after time.

Construction, drilling and production crews working offshore have to contend with the same hazards as crews working on land, and with the additional hazards specific to offshore work. These include the possibility of collapse of the platform at sea and provisions for specialized evacuation procedures and survival equipment in event of an emergency. Another important consideration when working offshore is the requirement for both deep-sea and shallow-water diving to install, maintain and inspect equipment.

Fire and explosion

There is always a risk of blowout when perforating a well, with a gas or vapour cloud release, followed by explosion and fire. Additional potential for fire and explosion exists in gas process operations.

Offshore platform and drilling rig workers should be carefully evaluated after having a thorough physical examination. The selection of offshore crew members with a history or evidence of pulmonary, cardiovascular or neurological diseases, epilepsy, diabetes, psychological disturbances and drug or alcohol addiction requires careful consideration. Because workers will be expected to use respiratory protection equipment and, in particular, those trained and equipped to fight fires, they must be physically and mentally evaluated for capability of carrying out these tasks. The medical examination should include psychological evaluation reflective of the particular job requirements.

Emergency medical services on offshore drilling rigs and production platforms should include provisions for a small dispensary or clinic, staffed by a qualified medical practitioner on board at all times. The type of medical service provided will be determined by the availability, distance and quality of the available onshore services. Evacuation may be by ship or helicopter, or a physician may travel to the platform or provide medical advice by radio to the onboard practitioner, when needed. A medical ship may be stationed where a number of large platforms operate in a small area, such as the North Sea, to be more readily available and quickly provide service to a sick or injured worker.

Persons not actually working on drilling rigs or platforms should also be given pre-employment and periodic medical examinations, particularly if they are employed to work in abnormal climates or under harsh conditions. These examinations should take into consideration the particular physical and psychological demands of the job.

Personal protection

An occupational hygiene monitoring and sampling programme, in conjunction with a medical surveillance programme, should be implemented to evaluate systematically the extent and effect of hazardous exposures to workers. Monitoring for flammable vapours and toxic exposures, such as hydrogen sulphide, should be implemented during exploration, drilling and production operations. Virtually no exposure to H_2S should be permitted, especially on offshore platforms. An effective method of controlling exposure is by using properly weighted drilling mud to keep H_2S from entering the well and by adding chemicals to the mud to neutralize any entrapped H_2S. All workers should be trained to recognize the presence of H_2S and take immediate preventive measures to reduce the possibility of toxic exposure and explosions.

Persons engaged in exploration and production activities should have available and use appropriate personal protective equipment including:

- Head protection (hard hats and weather-proof liners)
- Gloves (oil-resistant, non-slip work gloves, fire insulated or thermal where needed)
- Arm protection (long sleeves or oil-proof gauntlets)
- Foot and leg protection (weather-protected, oil-impervious safety boots with steel toes and non-skid soles)
- Eye and face protection (safety glasses, goggles and face shield for acid handling)
- Skin protection from heat and cold (sun screen ointment and cold-weather face masks)
- Climatized and weather-proof clothing (parkas, rain gear)
- Where required, firefighting gear, flame-resistant clothing and acid-resistant aprons or suits.

Control rooms, living quarters and other spaces on large offshore platforms are usually pressurized to prevent the entry of harmful atmospheres, such as hydrogen sulphide gas, which may be released upon penetration or in an emergency. Respiratory protection may be needed in the event pressure fails, and when there is a possibility of exposure to toxic gases (hydrogen sulphide), asphyxiants (nitrogen, carbon dioxide), acids (hydrogen fluoride) or other atmospheric contaminants when working outside of pressurized areas.

When working around geopressure/geothermal wells, insulated gloves and full heat- and steam-protective suits with supplied breathing air should be considered, as contact with hot steam and vapours can cause burns to skin and lungs.

Safety harnesses and lifelines should be used when on catwalks and gangways, especially on offshore platforms and in inclement weather. When climbing rigs and derricks, harnesses and lifelines with an attached counterweight should be used. Personnel baskets, carrying four or five workers wearing personal flotation devices, are often used to transfer crews between boats and offshore platforms or drilling rigs. Another means of transfer is by "swing ropes." Ropes used to swing from boats to platforms are hung directly above the edge of the boat landings, while those from platforms to boats should hang 3 or 4 feet from the outer edge.

Providing washing facilities for both workers and clothing and following proper hygiene practices are fundamental measures to control dermatitis and other skin diseases. Where needed, emergency eye wash stations and safety showers should be considered.

Safety protection measures

Oil and gas platform safety shutdown systems use various devices and monitors to detect leaks, fires, ruptures and other hazardous conditions, activate alarms and shut down operations in a planned, logical sequence. Where needed due to the nature of the gas or crude, non-destructive testing methods, such as ultrasonic, radiography, magnetic particle, liquid dye penetrant or visual inspections, should be used to determine the extent of corrosion of piping, heater tubes, treaters and vessels used in crude oil, condensate and gas production and processing.

Surface and sub-surface safety shut-in valves protect onshore installations, single wells in shallow water and multi-well offshore deep-water drilling and production platforms, and are automatically (or manually) activated in the event of fire, critical pressure changes, catastrophic failure at the well head or other emergency. They are also used to protect small injection wells and gas lift wells.

Inspection and care of cranes, winches, drums, wire rope and associated appurtenances is an important safety consideration in drilling. Dropping a pipeline string inside a well is a serious incident, which may result in the loss of the well. Injuries, and sometimes fatalities, can occur when personnel are struck by a wire rope which breaks while under tension. Safe operation of the drilling rig is also dependent on a smooth-running, well maintained draw works, with properly adjusted catheads and braking systems. When working on land, keep cranes a safe distance from electric power lines.

Handling of explosives during exploration and drilling operations should be under the control of a specifically qualified person. Some safety precautions to be considered while using a perforating gun include:

- Never strike or drop a loaded gun, or drop piping or other materials on a loaded gun.
- Clear the line of fire and evacuate unnecessary personnel from the drilling rig floor and the floor below as the perforating gun is lowered into and retrieved from the well hole.
- Control work on or around the wellhead while the gun is in the well.
- Restrict use of radios and prohibit arc welding while the gun is attached to the cable to prevent discharge from an inadvertent electric impulse.

Emergency preparedness planning and drills are important to the safety of workers on oil and gas drilling and production rigs and offshore platforms. Each different type of potential emergency (e.g., fire or explosion, flammable or toxic gas release, unusual weather conditions, worker overboard, and the need to abandon a platform) should be evaluated and specific response plans developed. Workers need to be trained in the correct actions to be taken in emergencies, and familiar with the equipment to be used.

Helicopter safety and survival in the event of dropping into water are important considerations for offshore platform operations and emergency preparedness. Pilots and passengers should wear seat-belts and, where required, survival gear during flight. Life vests should be worn at all times, both during flight and when transferring from helicopter to platform or ship. Careful attention to keep bodies and materials beneath the path of the rotor blade is required when entering, leaving or working around a helicopter.

Training of both onshore and offshore workers is essential to a safe operation. Workers should be required to attend regularly scheduled safety meetings, covering both mandatory and other subjects. Statutory regulations have been enacted by government agencies, including the US Occupational Safety and Health Administration, the US Coast Guard for offshore operations, and the equivalents in the United Kingdom, Norway and elsewhere, which regulate the safety and health of exploration and production workers, both onshore and offshore. The International Labour Organization Code of Practice *Safety and Health in the Construction of Fixed Offshore Installations in the Petroleum Industry* (1982) provides guidance in this area. The American Petroleum Institute has a number of standards and recommended practices covering safety and health related to exploration and production activities.

Fire protection and prevention measures

Fire prevention and protection, especially on offshore drilling rigs and production platforms, is an important element in the safety of the workers and continued operations. Workers should be trained and educated to recognize the fire triangle, as discussed in the *Fire* chapter, as it applies to flammable and combustible hydrocarbon liquids, gases and vapours and the potential hazards of fires and explosions. An awareness of fire prevention is essential and includes a knowledge of ignition sources such as welding, open flames, high temperatures, electrical energy, static sparks, explosives, oxidizers and incompatible materials.

Both passive and active fire-protection systems are used onshore and offshore.

- Passive systems include fireproofing, layout and spacing, equipment design, electrical classification and drainage.
- Detectors and sensors are installed which activate alarms, and may also activate automatic protection systems, upon detecting heat, flame, smoke, gas or vapours.
- Active fire protection includes fire water systems, fire water supply, pumps, hydrants, hoses and fixed sprinkler systems; dry chemical automatic systems and manual extinguishers; halon and carbon dioxide systems for confined or enclosed areas such as control rooms, computer rooms and laboratories; and foam water systems.

Employees who are expected to fight fires, from small fires in the incipient stages to large fires in enclosed spaces, such as on offshore platforms, must be properly trained and equipped. Workers assigned as fire brigade leaders and incident commanders need leadership capabilities and additional specialized training in advanced firefighting and fire-control techniques.

Environmental Protection

The major sources of air, water and ground pollution in oil and natural gas production are from oil spills or gas leaks on land or sea, hydrogen sulphide present in oil and gas escaping into the atmosphere, hazardous chemicals present in drilling mud contaminating water or land and combustion products of oil well fires. The potential public health effects of inhalation of smoke particulates from large-scale oil field fires has been of great concern since the oil well fires that occurred in Kuwait during the Persian Gulf War in 1991.

Pollution controls typically include:

- API separators and other waste and water treatment facilities
- Spill control, including booms for spills on water
- Spill containment, dikes and drainage to control oil spills and divert oily water to treatment facilities.

Gas dispersion modelling is conducted to ascertain the probable area which would be affected by a cloud of escaping toxic or flammable gas or vapour. Groundwater table studies are conducted to project the maximum extent of water pollution should oil contamination occur.

Workers should be trained and qualified to provide first aid response to mediate spills and leakage. Contractors who specialize in pollution remediation are usually engaged to manage large spill responses and remediation projects.

References

Duck, BW. 1983. Petroleum, extraction and transport by sea of. In *Encyclopaedia of Occupational Health and Safety*, 3rd edition. Geneva: ILO.

Energy Information Administration. 1996. *International Petroleum Statistics Report: January 1996*. Washington, DC: US Department of Energy

Ghosh, PK. 1983. Offshore oil operations. In *Encyclopaedia of Occupational Health and Safety*, 3rd edition. Geneva: ILO: 1559-1563.

International Labour Organization (ILO). 1982. *Safety and Health in the Construction of Fixed Offshore Installations in the Petroleum Industry*. An ILO Code of Practice. Geneva: ILO.

National Fire Protection Association (NFPA). 1976. *Fire Protection Handbook*, 14th edition. Quincy, MA:NFPA.

—. 1991. *Fire Protection Handbook*, 17th edition. Quincy, MA:NFPA.

Montillier, J. 1983. Drilling, oil and water. In *Encyclopaedia of Occupational Health and Safety*, 3rd edition. Geneva: ILO.

Other relevant readings

American Petroleum Institute. 1980. *Facts about Oil.* Manual 4200-10/80-25m, October 1980. Washington, DC: American Petroleum Institute.

Nabieva, GV. 1976. Occupational disease in oil rig workers. *Gigiene truda i proffesional'nye zabolevanija* 8:22-24.

National Safety Council. 1995. *Petroleum Section Safety and Health Fact Sheet.* Itasca, IL: National Safety Council.

Panov, GE et al. 1977. Ergonomic assessment of work posture on drilling rigs. *Besopasnost' truda v promyslennosti* 3:49.

Salpukas, A. 1995. New ideas for US oil. *New York Times*, 16 November.

76

Chapter Editor
Michael Crane

Contents

GENERAL PROFILE

Michael Crane

In 1993, the worldwide production of electricity was 12.3 trillion kilowatt hours (United Nations 1995). (A kilowatt hour is the amount of electricity needed to light ten 100-watt bulbs for 1 hour.) One can judge the magnitude of this endeavour by considering data from the United States, which alone produced 25% of the total energy. The US electric utility industry, a mix of public and privately owned entities, generated 3.1 trillion kilowatt hours in 1993, using more than 10,000 generating units (US Department of Energy 1995). The portion of this industry that is owned by private investors employs 430,000 people in electric operations and maintenance, with revenues of US$200 billion annually.

Electricity is generated in plants which utilize fossil fuel (petroleum, natural gas or coal) or use nuclear energy or hydropower. In 1990, for example, 75% of France's electrical power came from nuclear power stations. In 1993, 62% of the electricity generated worldwide came from fossil fuels, 19% from hydropower, and 18% from nuclear power. Other reusable sources of energy such as wind, solar, geothermal or biomass account for only a small proportion of world electric production. From generating stations, electricity is then transmitted over interconnected networks or grids to local distribution systems and on through to the consumer.

The workforce that makes all of this possible tends to be primarily male and to possess a high degree of technical skill and knowledge of "the system". The tasks that these workers undertake are quite diverse, having elements in common with the construction, manufacturing, materials handling, transportation and communications industries. The next few articles describe some of these operations in detail. The articles on electric maintenance standards and environmental concerns also highlight major US government regulatory initiatives that affect the electric utility industry.

HYDROELECTRIC POWER GENERATION

Neil McManus

Human beings learned to harness the energy of running water many millennia ago. For more than a century, electricity has been generated using water power. Most people associate the use of water power with the damming of rivers, but hydroelectric energy can also be generated by the harnessing of the tides.

Hydroelectric generation operations span a vast terrain and many climates, ranging from the Arctic permafrost to equatorial rainforest. The geographic location of the generating plant will affect the hazardous conditions that may be present, since occupational hazards such as aggressive insects and animals, or even poisonous plants, will vary from location to location.

A hydrogenerating station generally consists of a *dam* that traps a large quantity of water, a *spillway* that releases surplus water in controlled fashion and a *powerhouse*. *Dykes* and other water containment and control structures may also be part of the hydroelectric power station, although they are not directly involved in generating electricity. The powerhouse contains conducting channels that guide water through turbines that convert the linear flow of the water into a rotating flow. Water will either fall through the blades of the turbine or else flow horizontally through them. The

turbine and generator are connected to each other. Thus, rotation of the turbine causes rotation of the rotor of the generator.

The electric power potential from water flow is the product of the mass of the water, the height through which it falls and gravitational acceleration. The mass is a function of the amount of water that is available and its rate of flow. The design of the power station will determine the height of the water. Most designs draw in water from near the top of the dam and then discharge it at the bottom into an existing downstream riverbed. This optimizes height while maintaining reasonable and controllable flow.

In most modern hydroelectric generating stations, the turbogenerators are oriented vertically. These are the familiar structures that protrude above the main floor in these stations. However, almost all of the structure is located below what is visible at main-floor level. This includes the generator pit, and below that the turbine pit and intake and discharge tube. These structures and the water-guiding channels are entered on occasion.

In stations of older vintage, the turbogenerator is oriented horizontally. The shaft from the turbine protrudes from a wall into the powerhouse, where it connects to the generator. The generator resembles a very large, old-style, open-case electric motor. In testimony to the design and quality of construction of this equipment, some turn-of-the-century facilities still are operating. Some present-day stations incorporate updated versions of the designs of the older stations. In such stations, the water channel completely surrounds the turbogenerator and entry is gained through a tubular casing that passes through the water channel.

A magnetic field is maintained in the windings of the rotor in the generator. The power for this field is provided by banks of lead-acid or caustic-filled nickel cadmium batteries. The motion of the rotor and the magnetic field that is present in its windings induce an electromagnetic field in the windings of the stator. The induced electromagnetic field provides the electrical energy which is supplied to the power grid. Electric voltage is the electrical pressure that arises from the flowing water. In order to maintain the electrical pressure—that is, the voltage—at a constant level requires changing the flow of water across the turbine. This will be done as demand or conditions change.

The flow of electricity can lead to electrical arcing, as for example, in the exciter assembly in the rotor. Electrical arcing can generate ozone, which, even at low levels can adversely affect the rubber in fire hose and other materials.

Hydroelectric power generators produce very high currents and high voltages. Conductors from the generators connect to a unit transformer and from this to a power transformer. The power transformer boosts the voltage and reduces the current for transmission over long distances. Low current minimizes energy loss due to heating during transmission. Some systems use sulphur hexafluoride gas in place of conventional oils as an insulator. Electrical arcing can produce breakdown products which can be significantly more hazardous than sulphur hexafluoride.

The electric circuits include breakers that can rapidly and unpredictably cut out the generator from the power grid. Some units utilize a blast of compressed air to break the connection. When such a unit kicks in, it will produce an extremely high level of impulsive noise.

Administration and Station Operations

Most people are familiar with the administration and station operations aspects of hydro generation, which generally create the public profile of the organization. The power plant administration seeks to ensure that the plant provide reliable service. Administration includes office personnel involved in business and technical

Table 76.1 • Controlling exposures to selected chemical and biological hazards in hydroelectric power generation.

Exposure	Where it can be found	Affected workers	Approaches to control
Abrasive dusts (blasting)	Dust can contain blast material and paint dust. Paint applied prior to 1971 may contain PCBs.	Mechanical maintenance workers	Dust control system Personal protective equipment Respiratory protection Personal hygiene measures Medical surveillance (depends on circumstances)
Asbestos	Asbestos may be present in generator brakes, pipe and electrical insulation, spray-on coatings, asbestos cement and other products; exposure depends on friability and proximity to source.	Electrical maintenance workers, mechanical maintenance workers	Adopt current best practices for work involving asbestos-containing products. Personal protective equipment Respiratory protection Personal hygiene measures Medical surveillance (depends on circumstances)
Battery explosion products	Short circuit across terminals in banks of batteries could cause explosion and fire and exposure to liquid and aerosols of the electrolyte.	Electrical maintenance workers	Shielding of battery terminals and noninsulated conductors Practices and procedures to ensure safe conditions of work around this equipment
Coating decomposition products	Emissions can include: carbon monoxide, inorganic pigments containing lead and other chromates and decomposition products from paint resins. PCBs may have been used as plasticizers prior to 1971. PCBs can form furans and dioxins, when heated.	Mechanical maintenance workers	Local exhaust ventilation Respiratory protection Personal hygiene measures Medical surveillance (depends on composition of the coating)
Chlorine	Chlorine exposure can occur during connection/disconnection of chlorine cylinders in water and wastewater treatment systems.	Operators	Follow chlorine industry guidelines when working with chlorine cylinders Escape respirator
Degreasing solvents	Degreasing of electrical equipment requires solvents with specific properties of inflammability, solvation and rapid evaporation without leaving a residue; solvents meeting these characteristics are volatile and can pose inhalation hazards.	Electrical maintenance workers	Local exhaust ventilation Personal protective equipment Respiratory protection
Diesel exhaust emissions	Emissions primarily include nitrogen dioxide, nitric oxide, carbon monoxide, carbon dioxide, sulphur dioxide and particulates containing polycyclic aromatic hydrocarbons (PAHs) from vehicles or engines operated in the powerhouse.	All workers	Prohibit operation of automobiles and trucks in buildings. Local exhaust system to collect exhaust at source Catalytic converters on exhaust systems
Insect remains	Some insects breed in the fast waters around the station; following mating, the adults die and the carcasses decay and dry; some individuals develop allergic respiratory sensitization to substances in the dust.	All workers	Insects that spend part of their lives in fast-running waters lose habitat as a result of construction of a hydrogenerating station. These organisms may use the water channels of the station as surrogate habitat. Dust from dried remains can cause allergic sensitization.
	Following draining, insect larvae living in the water channels may attempt to lower their bodies into remaining water by production of thread-like ropes; some individuals may develop allergic respiratory sensitivity to dust resulting from drying out of these materials.	Maintenance workers	Control measures include: Lighting that does not attract flying insects Screens on windows, doors and openings in the building envelope Vacuum cleaning to remove carcasses
Oils and lubricants	Oils and hydraulic fluids coat windings of the rotor and stator; decomposition of hydrocarbons in contact with hot surfaces can produce polycyclic aromatic hydrocarbons (PAHs). Exposure can occur by inhalation and skin contact. Skin contact can cause dermatitis.	Electrical maintenance workers, mechanical maintenance workers	Personal protective equipment (depends on circumstances)
Ozone	Ozone generated by arcing in the rotor and other electrical equipment could pose an exposure problem, depending on proximity to the source.	All workers	Maintain electrical equipment to prevent arcing

Continues on next page.

76. POWER GENERATION AND DISTRIBUTION

Table 76.1 • Controlling exposures to selected chemical and biological hazards in hydroelectric power generation.
Continued

Exposure	Where it can be found	Affected workers	Approaches to control
Paint fumes	Paint aerosols contain sprayed paint and diluent; solvent in droplets and vapour can form flammable mixture; resin system can include isocyanates, epoxies, amines, peroxides and other reactive intermediates. Solvent vapours can be present in paint storage and mixing areas, and paint booth; flammable mixtures can develop inside confined spaces during spraying.	Bystanders, painters	Paint spray booth Personal protective equipment Respiratory protection Personal hygiene measures Medical surveillance (depends on circumstances)
Polychlorinated biphenyls (PCBs)	PCBs were used in electrical insulating fluids until the early 1970s; original fluids or residuals may still be present in cables, capacitors, transformers or other equipment; exposure can occur by inhalation or skin contact. Fire or extreme heating during service can convert PCBs into furans and dioxins.	Electrical maintenance workers	Personal protective equipment Respiratory protection Medical surveillance (depends on circumstances)
Sulphur hexafluoride and breakdown products	Electrical arc breakdown of sulphur hexafluoride produces gaseous and solid substances of considerably greater toxicity. Release of large quantities of sulphur hexafluoride into subgrade spaces can create oxygen deficiency by displacing the atmosphere.	Electrical maintenance workers	Local exhaust ventilation Personal protective equipment Respiratory protection Medical surveillance (depends on circumstances)
Welding and brazing fumes	Cadmium, lead, silver in solder	Electrical maintenance workers	Local exhaust ventilation Personal protective equipment Respiratory protection Personal hygiene measures
	Work primarily involves carbon and stainless steels; aluminium welding may occur. Build-up welding is required to repair erosion due to cavitation. Emissions include: shield gases and fluxes, metal fumes, ozone, nitrogen dioxide, visible and ultraviolet energy.	Mechanical maintenance workers	Medical surveillance (depends on composition of base metal and metal in wire or rod)

functions, and management. Station operations personnel include plant managers and supervisors, and process operators.

Hydrogeneration is a process operation but unlike other process operations, such as those in the chemical industry, many hydrogenerating stations have no operating staff. The generating equipment is operated by remote control, sometimes from long distances. Almost all work activity occurs during maintenance, repair, modification and upgrading of plant and equipment. This mode of operation demands effective systems which can transfer control away from energy production to maintenance to prevent unexpected startup.

Hazards and the management structure

Electrical utilities are traditionally managed as "bottom-up" organizations. That is, the organizational structure has traditionally provided a path of upward mobility that begins with entry-level positions and leads to senior management. Relatively few individuals enter the organization laterally. This means that the supervision and the management in a power utility will likely have experienced the same working conditions as the individuals who presently occupy entry-level positions. Such an organizational structure can have implications with respect to potential worker exposure to hazardous agents, especially those which have chronic cumulative effects. For example, consider noise. Employees who currently serve in management positions could themselves have sustained serious hearing loss when they were employed in jobs that had occupational noise exposures. Their hearing loss could go undetected in company audiometric testing programmes, since such programmes generally include only those employees who are currently exposed to high levels of noise at work.

Maintenance of Generating Equipment

Maintenance of generating equipment subdivides into two main types of activity: electrical maintenance and mechanical maintenance. While both types of work may occur simultaneously and side by side, the skills and work needed to perform these are completely different.

Maintenance could necessitate shutting down and dismantling a unit. Water flow at the intake is controlled by headgates. Headgates are steel structures that are lowered into the intake channel to block the flow of water. Blocking the flow permits water to drain from the interior channels. The quiescent water level in the outlet from the turbine (draught tube) is below the level of the scroll case and blades of the turbine runner. This permits access to these structures. The scroll case is a tapered, spiral-shaped structure that directs the flow of water around the turbine runner in a uniform manner. Water passes from the scroll case through guide vanes that direct flow, and movable vanes (wicket gates) that control the volume.

When needed, the generator and turbine can be removed from their normal locations and placed onto the main floor of the powerhouse. Removal may be necessary for repainting or degreasing and repair and replacement of windings, bearings, brakes or hydraulic systems.

Sometimes the blades of the runner, as well as wicket gates, the guide vanes and the water-conducting structures in the scroll case

Table 76.2 • Controlling exposures to selected physical and safety hazards in hydroelectric power generation.

Exposure	Where it can be found	Affected workers	Approaches to control
Awkward working postures	Prolonged work in awkward posture can lead to musculoskeletal injury. Fall hazard exists around pits and openings in structures.	All workers	Equipment designed to reflect ergonomic principles Training in muscle conditioning, lifting and back care Work practices chosen to minimize occurrence of musculoskeletal injury
Confined spaces	The dam, control structures, control gates, water-conducting channels, generator and turbine machinery contain many pits, sumps, tanks and other enclosed and partially enclosed spaces that can become oxygen deficient, can confine hazardous atmospheres, or can contain other hazardous conditions.	All workers	Air testing devices Portable ventilation systems Personal protective equipment Respiratory protection
Drowning	Drowning can occur following a fall into fast-moving water in the forebay (intake zone) or tailrace (discharge zone) or other area. Extremely cold water is present in higher latitudes during spring, fall and winter months.	All workers	Personnel containment barriers Fall-arrest systems Life jackets
Electrocution	Areas in the station contain energized, unshielded conductors; equipment containing shielded conductors can become live following removal of the shielding. Electrocution risk results from deliberate entry into unauthorized areas or from accidental failure of protection systems.	All workers	Establish practices and procedures to ensure safe conditions of work with electrical equipment.
Electromagnetic fields (including radiofrequency)	Generating and other electrical equipment produces DC and 60 Hz (and higher) AC fields; exposure depends on proximity to source and shielding offered by structures. Magnetic fields are especially difficult to attenuate by shielding. Significance of exposure has yet to be established. Radio frequency: Effects on humans not fully established.	All workers	Hazard not established below present limits
Heat	Generators develop considerable heat; generators and heat exchangers may discharge heated air into the powerhouse; powerhouse structure can absorb and radiate solar energy into the building; heat injury can occur during warmer months, depending on climate and level of exertion.	Indoor workers	Deflecting heated air towards the roof, shielding, engineering controls Electrolyte replacement drinks Personal protective equipment
Noise	Steady-state noise from generators and other sources and tasks could exceed regulated limits; air blast breakers produce very high levels of impact noise; these could discharge at any time.	All workers	Apply noise control technology. Personal hearing protection
Shiftwork	Shift operations can produce physiological and psychosocial stresses; psychosocial stresses can be especially serious for the small numbers involved in small and isolated communities where these operations tend to be located.	Operators	Adopt work schedules that reflect current knowledge about circadian rhythms.
Vibration, hand-arm	Vibration produced by powered hand tools and hand-held equipment is transmitted through hand grips.	Electrical maintenance workers, mechanical maintenance workers	Utilize tools meeting current standards for hand-arm vibration. Vibration-absorbing gloves
Vibration, whole-body	Structure-borne vibration originating from the rotational motion of generators and turbulence of water flows is transmitted through floors and walls.	All workers	Monitor and service rotating equipment to minimize vibration.
Visual display units	Effective use of computerized workstations depends on application of visual and office ergonomic principles.	Office workers (management, administrative and technical staff)	Apply office ergonomic principles to selection and utilization of video displays
Weather-related problems	Ultraviolet energy can cause sunburn, skin cancer and cataracts. Cold can cause cold stress and frostbite. Heat can cause heat stress.	Outdoor workers	Work clothing that protects against cold Work clothing that shields against solar radiation Eye protection that provides protection against solar radiation Sunscreens (seek medical advice for prolonged use)

76. POWER GENERATION AND DISTRIBUTION

and draught tube, sustain damage from cavitation. Cavitation occurs when the pressure in the water falls below its vapour pressure. When this happens, gas bubbles form and the turbulence that is caused by these bubbles erodes the materials which the water touches. It may be necessary to repair the damaged materials by welding, or by repairing and recoating the steel and concrete surfaces.

Steel structures may also require repair and recoating if they have become corroded.

Hazards

There are a variety of hazards associated with the generation of hydroelectric power. Some of these hazards are shared by all the employees who work in the industry, while others are restricted to those involved in either electrical or mechanical maintenance activities. Most of the hazards which can arise are summarized in table 76.1 and table 76.2, which also summarize precautions.

Environmental Effects

Hydroelectric generation of power has been promoted as being environmentally friendly. Of course, it does provide tremendous benefit to society through the provision of energy and the stabilization of the flow of water. But such generation of energy does not come without an environmental cost, which has in recent years received more and more public recognition and attention. For example, it is now known that flooding large areas of the earth and of rock by acidic water leads to the leaching of metals from these materials. Bioaccumulation of mercury has been found in fish that have been caught in the water from such flooded areas.

Flooding also changes the turbulence patterns in the water as well as the level of oxygenation. Both of these can have serious ecological effects. For example, salmon runs have disappeared on dammed rivers. This disappearance has occurred, in part, because the fish either cannot locate or traverse a path to the higher water level. In addition, the water has come to resemble a lake more than a river, and the still water of a lake is not compatible with salmon runs.

Flooding also destroys fish habitat and can destroy the breeding areas for insects, upon which fish and other organisms depend for nourishment. In some cases, flooding has destroyed productive agricultural and forest lands. Flooding of large areas has also raised concern about climatic change and other changes in the ecological balance. The holdback of fresh water that had been destined to flow into a body of salt water has also raised concern about changes in salinity.

● FOSSIL FUEL POWER GENERATION

Anthony W. Jackson

The operation of coal-fired electrical generating stations involves a series of steps which may expose workers to traumatic injury and hazardous chemical and physical agents. These hazards may be controlled through a combination of good design, knowledgeable workers and job planning. Good design will ensure that all components meet the necessary codes for integrity and safe operation. It will also ensure that equipment layout allows continuing safe operability and maintainability through easy access. Knowledgeable workers will be aware of hazards in the workplace and will be able to create plans to address the hazards they do encounter. These plans will identify hazards and apply appropriate con-

trols, which may involve a combination of de-energization, physical barriers and personal protective equipment. Analysis of accident experience shows that modern power stations have a safety performance comparable to other heavy mechanical industries. Within the power station staff, most lost-time injuries are suffered by the maintenance staff. Injuries frequently involve sprains and strains to soft tissues of the body, with back strain injuries the most common. Industrial diseases associated with chronic exposure to noise and, occasionally, asbestos are also found.

The operation of a modern powerplant may be considered in a series of steps.

Coal Handling

This includes coal receiving (either by rail or water), storage and recovery for fuelling the turbine generator units. Heavy equipment (tractor-scrapers and bulldozers) is used to create compacted storage piles, which is necessary if spontaneous-combustion fires are to be avoided. Further handling is by conveyors to the powerhouse. Coal dust exposure (leading to possible pneumoconiosis) can be controlled by water spraying of the coal pile and the use of closed control cabs fitted with dust filters. Certain tasks associated with high coal dust levels require respirators with high efficiency particulate absorber (HEPA). Noise levels result in most workers in this work area receiving greater than 85 dBA exposure (leading to hearing loss), which should be controlled through use of ear plugs and muffs, and a hearing conservation programme.

Several conventional safety hazards are found in this area of the plant. Working near water requires careful attention to procedures and also the use of life preservers. Driving heavy equipment on uneven storage piles during the night requires large-scale area lighting, while the lifting and pushing hazards from manual clearing of the conveying coal chutes (which are prone to blockage, particularly when winter is severe) is best controlled through removable chute covers, which provide easy access. Operation and maintenance of extended conveyor systems requires guarding of drive and end pulleys, tensioners and other nip points.

Boiler-Turbine Operation

The operation of a high-pressure boiler-turbine combination should involve a rigorous set of controls to ensure safe operation. These controls include the physical integrity of the equipment and the skill, knowledge and experience of the operating staff. The integrity of the high-pressure components is ensured through a combination of appropriate specifications contained in modern engineering standards, and routine inspections of welded joints using visual and non-destructive imaging techniques (x rays and fluoroscopic methods). In addition, pressure-relief valves, which are regularly tested, ensure that over-pressurizing of the boiler does not occur. The necessary skills and knowledge of the staff may be created through an in-house process of personnel development coupled with government accreditation which extends over several years.

The environment of the powerhouse is a collection of complex engineered systems to carry fuel, combustion air, demineralized boiler water, and cooling water to the boiler. In addition to the high-pressure steam hazards, it contains a variety of other conventional and chemical/physical hazards which must be recognized and controlled. In operation, the most pervasive hazard is noise. Surveys show that all operating and maintenance staff have a time-weighted average exposure of over 85 dBA, which requires the wearing of hearing protection (plugs or muffs) in much of the powerhouse and regular audiometric testing to ensure no deterioration in hearing. Major sources of noise include the coal pulverizers, the turbine-generator unit, and station service air compressors. Dust levels in the powerhouse during operation depend on maintenance attention to the condition of thermal insulation. This is of particular concern as much older insulation contains high levels of asbestos. Careful attention to controls (primarily bonding and containment of damaged insulation) can achieve airborne asbestos concentrations which are undetectable (<0.01 fibre/cc).

The final stage of the operation process which creates potential hazards is ash collection and handling. Usually located outside the powerhouse, ash collection is typically done with large electrostatic precipitators, although there is increasing use of fabric filters in recent years. In both cases the ash is extracted from the flue gas and retained in storage silos. Any subsequent handling processes are inherently dusty despite engineered efforts to control levels. This type of ash (fly ash, as opposed to the bottom ash that has accumulated at the bottom of the boiler) contains a significant fraction (30 to 50%) of respirable material and is therefore a potential concern for possible health effects to exposed workers. Two components of the ash are of potential significance: crystalline silica, associated with silicosis and possibly subsequent lung cancer, and arsenic, associated with skin and lung cancer. In both cases it is necessary to carry out exposure assessments to determine if regulated limits are exceeded and whether specific control programmes are required. These assessments, involving surveys with personal samplers, should include all potentially affected workers, including those who may be exposed during inspections of the dust collection systems and of the grinding and heating surfaces in the boiler, where arsenic is known to deposit. Control programmes, if necessary, should include providing information to the workers about the importance of avoiding ingestion of ash (no eating, drinking or smoking in ash-handling areas), and the need for careful washing after coming in contact with ash. Dust levels encountered in these surveys are usually such that good safety practice indicates a respiratory control programme for exposure to total nuisance dust. The industrial mortality database maintained by the US National Institute for Occupational Safety and Health, for example, contains no entries for deaths attributable to silica or arsenic exposure in the US electrical utility industry.

Maintenance

It is during the maintenance phase that the highest exposure occurs to conventional and chemical/physical agents. Given the complexity of the modern generating station, it is critically important that there be an effective process for isolating equipment so that it cannot be energized while repairs are being carried out. This is typically achieved through a controlled system of locks and tags.

A broad range of conventional hazards are encountered during maintenance. They involve:

- working at heights (fall protection)
- heat stress
- rigging and craning (load security)
- work in confined spaces (atmospheric and conventional hazards)
- excavating (trench collapse)
- working/lifting in cramped environments (sprains and strains).

In all cases, the hazards may be managed by a stepwise process of analysis which identifies hazards and corresponding controls.

A large variety of hazardous commercial products are used and encountered in routine maintenance activities. Asbestos is common, as it has been used widely as thermal insulation and is a component of many commercial products. Control processes should be in place to ensure that all asbestos-containing material is correctly identified by microscopic analysis (on-site capability greatly improves response time). The actual control methods used

for the task depend on the scale of the activity. For large-scale jobs, this will involve constructing enclosures that operate under slightly reduced pressure (to prevent leaks) and ensuring that workers are equipped with respiratory protection following careful procedures to avoid external contamination. In all cases the asbestos-containing material should be completely wetted, and bagged and labelled for disposal. Careful examination is necessary to ensure that all asbestos is removed before proceeding. Workers' exposures should be recorded and periodic chest x rays coupled with pulmonary function testing will determine the onset of any disease. Positive results of these examinations should result in the worker being immediately removed form further exposure. Current practices reflect a high level of concern for asbestos exposures in the electrical utility industry.

For the great majority of other hazardous materials used in the workplace, the quantities involved are small, and the use infrequent, so that the overall impact is insignificant. The most significant class of exposures to hazardous materials are those associated with particular operations rather than particular products.

For example, welding is a common activity that can give rise to a series of possible adverse health outcomes. Exposure to ultraviolet light from the arc causes temporary blindness and severe eye irritation ("arc eye"); inhaled metal oxide fumes may cause "metal fume fever"; and nitrogen oxides and ozone formed at the high temperatures in the arc may cause chemical pneumonia and possible chronic respiratory problems. The controls to be applied include eye shields to protect nearby workers from scattered light, local exhaust ventilation or respiratory protection (through an air-purifying respirator).

A similar common activity is grinding and abrasive blasting, where the concern is for inhalation of the respirable metal oxide and abrasive particles. In this case, the control is usually through choice of abrasive agent (sand has now been abandoned in favour of more benign agents such as vegetable husks) coupled with appropriately high local exhaust ventilation.

The other activity leading to significant exposures is the application of protective coatings to metal surfaces. The coatings may contain a variety of solvents which are released into the working atmosphere. Worker exposures can be controlled either by local exhaust ventilation or, if that is impractical, by respiratory protection.

NUCLEAR POWER GENERATION

W.G. Morison

In all nuclear reactors, energy is produced within the fuel by a chain reaction of fissions of the nuclei of its atoms. The most common nuclear fuel is uranium-235. Each fission splits a fuel atom into two new fission product atoms and also expels from its nucleus neutrons which cause further fissions of the atoms. Most of the energy released by the fission is carried away by the fission products, and in turn is converted into thermal energy in the adjacent fuel atoms as they stop these rapidly moving fission products and absorb their radiation. The neutrons carry away about 3% of the energy of fission.

The reactor core is prevented from getting too hot by a liquid or gaseous coolant, which also produces the steam (either directly or indirectly) to drive the turbine. Neutron-absorbing materials are incorporated into control rods, which can be moved in and out of cavities in the core of the reactor to control the fission reaction rate to that desired by the power station operator. In pressurized water reactors, absorbing materials can be put in the reactor coolant system via soluble absorbers.

Most fission products are unstable, and thus radioactive. They decay, releasing radiation of a type and at a rate characteristic of each fission product element, and a new daughter product which may also be radioactive. This decay sequence continues until it finally results in daughter products which are stable (not radioactive). Other radioactive products are formed in the reactor by absorption of neutrons in the nucleus of the atoms of non-fissile materials, such as uranium-238, and structural materials, such as guides, supports and fuel cladding.

In reactors which have been operating for some time, the decay of the fission products and the creation of new fission products reaches a near equilibrium. At this point, the radiation and resulting energy production from the decay of radioactive products is nearly a tenth of all that produced in the reactor.

It is this large amount of radioactive material that creates the risks which are specific to nuclear power stations. Under operating conditions, most of these radioactive materials behave like solids, but some behave like gases, or become volatile at the high temperature in the reactor. Some of these radioactive materials could be readily absorbed into living organisms, and have significant effects on biological processes. Thus, they are dangerous if released or dispersed into the environment.

Nuclear Station Types and Characteristics

Thermal reactors use materials called *moderators* to slow the fast neutrons produced by fission so that they can be captured more readily by the fissile uranium-235 atoms. Ordinary water is often used as a moderator. Other moderators used are graphite and deuterium, an isotope of hydrogen, which is used in the form of deuterium oxide—heavy water. Ordinary water is mostly hydrogen oxide, and contains a small proportion (0.015%) of heavy water.

Heat is removed from the fuel by a coolant, which directly or indirectly produces steam to drive the turbine, and which also controls the temperature of the reactor core, preventing it from getting too hot and damaging the fuel or structural materials. Coolants in common use in thermal reactors include ordinary water, heavy water and carbon dioxide. Water has good heat transfer characteristics (high specific heat, low viscosity, easily pumped) and is the most common coolant used in nuclear power stations. Cooling a reactor core with pressurized or boiling water allows high core power densities so that large power units can be built into relatively small reactor vessels. However, the reactor coolant system using water must operate at high pressure in order to reach useful steam pressures and temperatures for efficient operation of the steam turbine-generator. The integrity of the reactor cooling system boundary is therefore very important for all water-cooled nuclear power stations, as it is a barrier that protects the safety of the workers, the public and the environment.

The fuel in all water-cooled power reactors, and most other reactors, is ceramic uranium dioxide, clad in metal—stainless steel or a zirconium alloy. The sintered uranium dioxide provides a non-combustible fuel which can operate for extended periods and retain its fission products at high temperatures without significant distortion or failure. The only operating thermal power reactors using other than uranium dioxide fuel, are the Magnox stations (which are carbon dioxide-cooled), and these are gradually being taken out of service as they reach the end of their service life.

Neutron-absorbing materials (such as boron, cadmium, hafnium and gadolinium) used in various forms, such as in steel-clad control rods or in solution in coolants or moderators, can be moved in and out of the reactor core in order to control the

Figure 76.1 • Types of nuclear power stations.

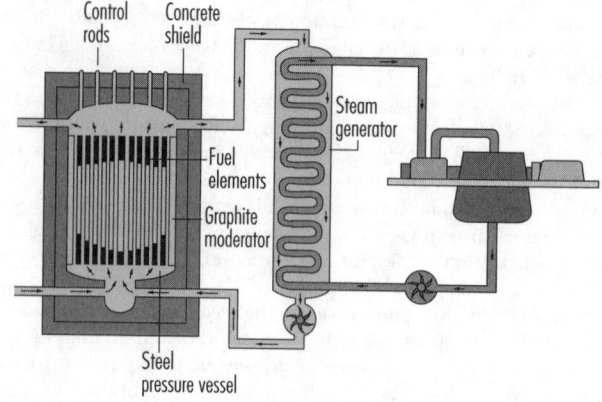

Basic gas-cooled reactor (MAGNOX)

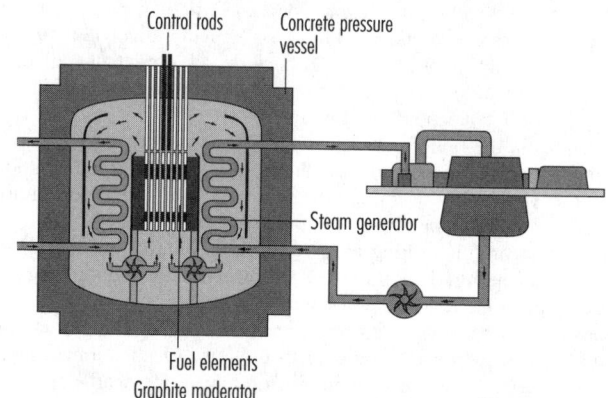

Advanced gas-cooled reactor (AGR)

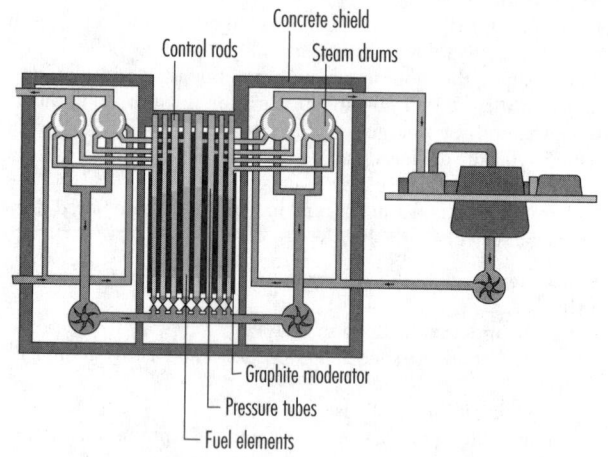

Boiling light water, graphite moderated reactor (RBMK)

Source: Uranium Institute 1988.

fission reaction rate at any designated level. In contrast to fossil fuel power generation, no increase in the quantity of fuel is needed to increase the power level produced in a fission chain reaction.

Table 76.3 • Nuclear power station characteristics (1997).

Reactor type	Fuel	Moderator	Coolant and its approx. pressure (in bars)	Steam generation	No. of operating units	Net output (MWe)
PWR	Enriched uranium dioxide (2% to 5% U-235)	Light water	Light water (160 bars)	Indirect	251	223,717
PHWR (CANDU type)	Unenriched uranium dioxide (0.71% U-235)	Heavy water	Heavy water (90 bars)	Indirect	34	18,927
BWR	Enriched uranium dioxide (2% to 3% U-235)	Light water	Light water boils in core (70 bars)	Direct	93	78,549
GCR (MAGNOX type)	Unenriched uranium metal (0.71% U-235)	Graphite	Carbon dioxide (20 bars)	Indirect	21	3,519
AGR	Enriched uranium dioxide (2.3% U-235)	Graphite	Carbon dioxide (40 bars)	Indirect	14	8,448
LWGR (RBMK type)	Enriched uranium dioxide (2% to 2.5% U-235)	Graphite	Light water boils in core (70 bars)	Direct	18	13,644
FBR	Mixed oxide plutonium	None	Sodium (10 bars)	Indirect	3	928

Once an increase in rate of fission energy production is initiated, it will continue until it is stopped by the insertion into the core of the appropriate quantity of neutron-absorbing materials and moderator. Such a power increase is caused by a surplus of neutrons in the fission chain reaction over that required for just a break-even chain reaction. Therefore, the fission rate and resulting power production can be controlled very sensitively by adding or removing very small amounts of neutron-absorbing materials. If a sudden reduction in power level is required, a relatively large amount of neutron-absorbing material is injected into the core. Each reactor concept has its own reactivity characteristic which determines the designs of control and shutdown neutron-absorbing devices to ensure efficient power control and safe and rapid shutdown when required. However, the same basic control and safety principles apply to all.

The main types of thermal power reactors in service today are illustrated in figure 76.1, and the main characteristics are given in table 76.3. In the simplified illustrations in figure 76.1, concrete shields are shown surrounding the reactors and the primary coolant systems. The shields, which comprise a variety of designs, generally provide both shielding against direct radiation from the reactor and also provide containment of any leaks from reactor cooling or moderator systems, and generally are designed to withstand the significant pressures which could result in the event of a major failure of coolant systems.

In a *pressurized water reactor (PWR)* power station, the reactor primary coolant and moderator are the same—purified ordinary water, which is separated from the secondary feedwater/steam circuit by a metallic boundary in steam generators (sometimes called boilers), through which the heat is transferred by conduction. The steam fed to the turbine-generator is therefore not radioactive, and the steam turbine-generator plant can be operated like a conventional power plant. Because hydrogen in the primary coolant/moderator water absorbs a significant fraction of the neutrons, it is necessary to enrich the fuel's fissile uranium-235 isotope content to between 2% and 5% to sustain a practical chain reaction for long-term power production.

In all operating nuclear power stations with *pressurized heavy water reactors (PHWRs)*, the reactor moderator and primary coolant is heavy water with a very high isotopic deuterium content (>99%). In the *CANDU PHWR*, which constitutes almost all the operating PHWRs, the moderator is separated from the primary coolant and held at relatively low temperature and pressure, which provides a convenient environment to locate monitoring and control instrumentation, and a built-in back-up cooling capability in the event of primary coolant piping failure. The fuel and primary coolant in the CANDU are in horizontal pressure tubes in the reactor core. As in the PWRs, the primary coolant and secondary feedwater/steam circuit are separated by a metallic boundary in steam generators, through which the heat is transferred from the primary heavy water to the ordinary water steam-feedwater system. The steam fed to the turbine generator plant is therefore ordinary water steam, not radioactive (except for small amounts due to leaks), and the turbine-generator plant can be operated like a conventional thermal power plant. The heavy water moderator and coolant absorbs only a very small fraction of the neutrons generated during fission, allowing a practical chain reaction for long-term power production using natural uranium (0.071% uranium-235). Existing PHWRs can operate with slightly enriched uranium-235 fuel, which results in proportionately greater total energy extraction from the fuel.

In a *boiling water reactor (BWR)* nuclear power station, the primary cooling water is partially evaporated in the reactor core itself, and the steam generated there is fed directly to the turbine-generator. The operating pressure in the reactor is lower than that in the PWRs, but the steam pressure fed to the turbine is similar. The steam fed to the turbine is slightly radioactive, requiring some precautions because of the potential low-level contamination of the turbine/feedwater system. However, this has not proven to be an important factor in operation and maintenance of BWRs. In BWRs the control of reactor power is affected by the amount of steam in the core, and this has to be offset by appropriate control of the rate of coolant flow or reactivity insertions as the power level of the reactor is changed.

Magnox reactors, also known as *gas cooled reactors* (GLRs), are fuelled with natural uranium metal clad in magnesium. They are cooled by carbon dioxide at modest pressure, but generate relatively high-temperature steam, which gives good thermal efficiency. They have large cores with low power densities, so that the pressure vessels, which also act as the only containment structures, are also large. The pressure vessels in the early Magnox reactors were steel. In the later Magnox reactors a prestressed concrete vessel contained both the reactor core and the steam-raising heat exchangers.

Advanced gas-cooled reactors (AGRs) use enriched uranium oxide fuel (2.3% U-235). They are cooled by carbon dioxide at higher pressure than the Magnox reactors, and have improved heat transfer and thermal efficiency. The greater core power density in the AGRs compared to the Magnox reactors allows the AGR reactor to be smaller and more powerful. The prestressed concrete pressure vessel, which contains both the reactor core and the steam raising heat exchangers, also acts as the containment structure.

Light water graphite reactors (LWGRs) are a hybrid of different nuclear power systems. The only power stations of this type in operation today are the RBMK reactors located in the former Soviet Union, that is, in Russia, Ukraine and Lithuania. In the RBMK reactors the ordinary water coolant flows upward through vertical coolant channels (tubes) which contain the fuel, and boils within the core. The steam produced in the core is fed directly to the turbine-generator as in a BWR. The graphite moderator which surrounds the coolant channels operates at a temperature sufficiently above that of the coolant so that the heat generated in the graphite by moderating the neutrons is removed by the coolant channels. The RBMK reactors are large and have many coolant channels (>1,500).

Fast breeder reactors (FBRs) require enrichment of fissile material in the range of 20% and can sustain the fission chain reaction primarily by absorbing the fast neutrons produced in the fission process. These reactors do not need a moderator to slow down the neutrons, and can use excess neutrons to breed plutonium-239, a potential fuel for reactors. They can produce more fuel than they consume. While a number of these reactors were built to produce electricity in nine countries around the world, technical and practical difficulties related to the use of liquid metal coolants (sodium) and the very high heat rates has caused interest to wane. There are now only three or four relatively small *liquid metal fast breeder reactors (LMFBRs)* in service as power producers in the world, producing a total of less than 1,000 megawatts of electric power (MWe), and they are being phased out of service gradually. The technology of breeding reactors, however, has been considerably developed and documented for future use if ever required.

Fuel and Fuel Handling

The process that begins with mining uranium-bearing ore and ends with the final disposal of the used fuel and all fuel processing wastes is usually called the *nuclear fuel cycle*. There are many variations in fuel cycles, depending on the type of reactor involved and the design of the heat removal arrangements in the reactor core.

The basic PWR and BWR fuel cycles are nearly identical, varying only in the levels of enrichment and the detailed design of the fuel elements. The steps involved, usually at different locations and facilities, are:

- uranium mining and milling to produce yellowcake (U_3O_8)
- uranium conversion to uranium hexafluoride (UF_6)
- enrichment
- fuel fabrication, which involves uranium conversion to uranium dioxide (UO_2), fuelled pellet production, fuel rod manufacture in lengths equal to the reactor core height, and manufacture of fuel assemblies containing about 200 fuel rods per assembly in a square array

- installation and operation in a nuclear power plant
- either reprocessing or temporary storage
- shipment of used fuel or enrichment waste to a federal/central repository
- eventual disposal, which is still in the development stage.

Precautions are required during these processes to ensure that the amount of enriched fuel at any location is less than that which could result in a significant fission chain reaction, except, of course, in the reactor. This results in material space restrictions in manufacture, shipping and storage.

In contrast, the CANDU reactor uses natural uranium, and has a simple fuel cycle from mining the ore to fuel disposal, which does not include the steps involved to provide enrichment and reprocessing. The fuel for the CANDU is manufactured semi-automatically in half-metre long round bundles of 28 or 37 fuel rods containing UO_2 pellets. There are no space restrictions in manufacturing natural uranium fuel, or in shipping or storing either the new or used fuel. The immobilization and disposal of used CANDU fuel has been under development for 17 years in Canada, and is currently in the concept approval stage.

In all operating power reactors, with the exception of the Magnox type, the basic component of the reactor fuel is the cylindrical fuel pellet, composed of uranium dioxide (UO_2) powder which is compacted and then sintered to attain the required density and ceramic characteristics. These sintered pellets, which are sealed in seamless zirconium alloy or stainless steel tubing to produce *fuel rods or elements*, are chemically inert with respect to their cladding at normal reactor temperatures and pressures. Even if the cladding is damaged or breached and the coolant comes in contact with the UO_2, this ceramic material retains most of the radioactive fission products and resists deterioration caused by the high-temperature water.

The Magnox reactors use natural uranium metal fuel clad in magnesium, and operate successfully at relatively high temperatures, because the coolant, carbon dioxide, does not react with these metals under dry conditions.

The basic objective of the design of the fuel rods in a nuclear reactor is to transfer the fission heat generated in the fuel to the coolant, while maintaining the integrity of the fuel rods even under the most severe transient conditions. For all operating reactors, extensive testing of simulated fuel in heat transfer laboratories has demonstrated that the anticipated maximum in-reactor heat transient condition can be accommodated with adequate safety margins by the specific fuel designed and licensed for the application.

New fuel delivered from the fabrication plant to the power station is not significantly radioactive, and can be handled manually or by manually operated lifting/handling tools, without shielding. A typical *fuel assembly* for a PWR or BWR reactor is a square array of about 200 fuel rods, about 4 m long, weighing about 450 kg. About 200 of these assemblies are required in a large PWR or BWR reactor. The fuel is handled by overhead crane and placed in vertical racks in the dry in the new fuel storage area. To install new fuel in an in-service light-water reactor such as a PWR or BWR, all operations are conducted under a sufficient depth of water to provide shielding for anyone above the reactor. The flanged lid of the reactor vessel must first be removed and some of the used fuel taken out, (usually one-third to one-half reactor core), by overhead crane and fuel-handling elevators. The used fuel is placed in water-filled storage bays. Other used fuel assemblies in the core may be rearranged in position (generally moved toward the centre of the core), to shape the power production in the reactor. New fuel assemblies are then installed in all vacant fuel site positions. It may require from 2 to 6 weeks to refuel a larger reactor, depending on the workforce and the amount of fuel to be replaced.

The CANDU reactor and some gas-cooled reactors are fuelled on-power by remote-operated equipment which removes used fuel and installs new fuel elements or bundles. In the case of the CANDU, the fuel is half-metre-long bundles of fuel rods, approximately 10 cm in diameter and weighing about 24 kg. The fuel is received from the manufacturer in cardboard packing cases and stored in a designated new-fuel storage area, ready to load into the reactor. Fuel is generally loaded into an operating reactor on a daily basis to sustain the reactivity of the reactor. In a large CANDU reactor, 12 bundles per day is a typical refuelling rate. The bundles are loaded by hand onto a new-fuel loading device which in turn loads the bundles into a *fueling machine* which is controlled remotely from the station control room. To load new fuel into a reactor, two remote-operated fuelling machines are manoeuvred by remote control and coupled onto the ends of the horizontal fuel channel to be refuelled. The channel is opened by the fuelling machines at both ends while the cooling system is at operating pressure and temperature, and new fuel is pushed in one end and used fuel is withdrawn from the other end of the channel. When the required number of fuel bundles have been installed, the channel seals are re-installed by the fuelling machine, and the fuelling machines may go on to refuel another channel or to discharge the used fuel into the used-fuel water-filled storage bay.

The used fuel discharged from all operating reactors is very radioactive and requires cooling to prevent overheating, and shielding to prevent direct irradiation of any sensitive living organisms or equipment nearby. The usual procedure is to discharge the used fuel into a water-storage pool with at least 4 m of water coverage over the fuel for shielding. This allows safe observation of the fuel through the water, and access for moving it under water to a more long-term storage location.

One year after discharge from a reactor, the overall radioactivity and heat generation from used fuel will decrease to about 1% of its initial value on discharge, and within 10 years to about 0.1% of its initial value at discharge. After about 5 to 10 years from discharge, the heat production has decreased to the point that it is feasible to remove the fuel from the water pool and store it in the dry form in a container with only natural circulation of air around the fuel container. However, it is still quite radioactive, and shielding of its direct radiation is required for many decades. Prevention of ingestion of the fuel material by living organisms is required for a much longer period.

The actual disposal of used fuel from power reactors is still in the development and approval stages. Disposal of used fuel from power reactors in various geologic structures is being studied intensely in a number of countries, but has not as yet been approved anywhere in the world. The concept of storage deep underground in stable rock structures is now in the approval process in Canada as a safe and practical method of finally disposing of these high-level radioactive wastes. However, it is anticipated that even with concept approval by the year 2000, the actual disposal of used fuel will not take place until about 2025.

In-plant Operations

In all 33 countries with nuclear power programmes, there are regulatory bodies that establish and enforce safety regulations related to the operation of nuclear facilities. However, it is generally the power utility which owns and operates nuclear power facilities that is held responsible and liable for the safe operation of its nuclear power plants. The role of the operator is really a management task of information gathering, planning and decision making, and only occasionally includes a more active control when routine operation is disrupted. The operator is not the primary protective system.

All modern nuclear power plants have highly reliable automatic, very responsive control and safety systems which protect the reactor and other plant components continuously, and which are generally designed to be fail-safe on loss of power. The operator is not expected to duplicate or substitute for these automatic control and protective systems. The operator, however, must be able to shut down the reactor almost instantly if necessary, and should be capable of recognizing and responding to any aspect of plant operation, thus adding to the diversity of protection. The operator needs the ability to understand, diagnose and anticipate the development of the overall situation from a large amount of data provided by the automatic data and information systems.

The operator is expected to:

- understand what the normal conditions are in all systems relevant to the current overall status of the plant
- recognize, with help from the automatic systems or special monitoring devices, when abnormal conditions arise, and their significance
- know how to respond correctly to restore the plant to normal operation, or bring the plant to a safe shutdown condition.

How well the operator can do this depends on the design of the machine as well as the operator's ability and training.

Every nuclear power station must have competent, stable and well-trained operators on duty at all times. Potential nuclear operators undergo a comprehensive training programme, which usually includes classroom and on-the-job training in science, equipment and power systems, radiation protection and operating policies and principles. Training simulators are always used in US utility nuclear plant operation to provide the operator with hands-on experience in plant operations, during upsets and in unusual conditions. The interface between the operator and the power systems is through the control room instrumentation. Well-designed instrumentation systems can improve the understanding and proper response of the operators.

It is usual to appoint the key operating staff for a nuclear power station while it is still under construction, so they can advise from an operating point of view, and can assemble staff who will commission and operate the station. They also prepare a comprehensive set of operating procedures before the station is commissioned and allowed to operate. Design experts and regulatory personnel inspect these procedures for consistency of design intent and operating practices.

The staff are expected to operate the station systematically and rigorously in accordance with the operating procedures and work authorizations. The operating staff continually work to ensure public safety by conducting a comprehensive programme of testing and monitoring the safety systems and protective barriers, and by maintaining the ability to deal with any plant emergency. Where operators may have to take action in response to an alteration in the state of the plant, there are written, systematic procedures to guide them and to provide the detailed information needed to control the plant. Such procedures are reviewed by station and regulatory safety committees.

A well-thought-out operation safety management programme includes:

- detailed knowledge of areas critical to safety
- standards or targets that define acceptable performance
- a programme for monitoring performance, responding to problems and reporting results
- an experience review programme to establish trends, the degree of compliance with standards and the cause of any unacceptable or deteriorating performance

• a means of assessing the impact of proposed changes to hardware or operating procedures and implementing changes consistent with the accepted standard.

In addition to procedures for normal operation, there is an event-reporting system at each nuclear power station to investigate and document any failures and deterioration of equipment, shortcomings in design or construction, and operating errors detected by monitoring systems or regular tests and inspections. The basic cause of each event is determined so that the appropriate corrective or preventive action can be developed. Event reports, including the results of the analysis and recommendations, are reviewed by the station management and by experts in safety and human factors, who are usually based off the station site.

The International Atomic Energy Agency's (IAEA) Incident Reporting System operates around the world to complement the national systems and ensure that information is shared among all participating countries. The World Association of Nuclear Operators (WANO) also provides a detailed information exchange at the operational level.

Nuclear reactors and all their auxiliary and safety-related systems are maintained and tested according to quality assurance requirements at planned intervals, to ensure reliability throughout their service life. In addition to automatic monitoring, there are systematic manual tests and investigations for evidence of impairment or failure of equipment systems. These include regular field surveillance, preventive maintenance, periodic tests and the study of changes in plant conditions.

Very demanding performance targets are set for process and safety systems to keep the risk to the public and station staff acceptably small. For process systems, which are actively operating while electricity is being generated, failure rates are compared to performance targets, which may result in design changes where performance is substandard. Safety systems need a different approach, because they come into operation only if process systems fail. Comprehensive test programmes monitor these systems and their components, and the results are used to determine how much of the time each of them would likely be out of service. The total amount of time the safety systems are calculated to be out of service is compared to a very high performance standard. If a deficiency is detected in a safety system it is put right immediately or the reactor is shut down.

There are also extensive tests and maintenance programmes during periodic scheduled shutdowns. For example, all pressure-bearing vessels, components and their welds are systematically inspected by non-destructive methods according to safety code regulations.

Safety Principles and Related Safety Design Features

There are four aspects of the fission chain reaction which could be dangerous and which cannot be separated from the use of nuclear energy to produce electricity, and therefore require safety measures:

1. Fission results in ionizing radiation, which requires shielding from direct exposure to radiation.
2. Highly radioactive fission products are created, requiring tight enclosures to prevent contamination of the external environment and possible ingestion.
3. The fission chain reaction is a dynamic process requiring continuous control.
4. The heat production cannot be instantly stopped, since radioactive decay continues to produce heat after the fission chain reaction is terminated, requiring long-term cooling.

The safety requirements which these characteristics demand account for the major differences in safety equipment and operating strategy in a nuclear station compared to those in a power-generating station utilizing fossil fuel. How these safety requirements are fulfilled differs for different types of nuclear stations, but the fundamental safety principles are the same in all nuclear stations.

During the licensing procedure, each nuclear installation has to prove that radioactive releases will be less than specified regulatory limits, both during normal operating conditions and in the event of faults or accident conditions. The priority is to prevent failures rather than simply to mitigate their consequences, but the design has to be capable of dealing with failures if, in spite of all precautions, they do occur. This requires the highest degree of quality assurance and control, applied to all equipment, construction functions and operations. Inherent safety characteristics and engineered safety measures are designed to prevent and control accidents and contain and minimize the release of radioactive materials.

In particular, the heat generation and cooling capacity must be matched at all times. During operation, heat is removed from the reactor by a coolant, which is pumped through piping connected to the reactor, and flows over the fuel cladding surface. In the event of loss of power to the pumps or sudden failure of the connecting piping, cooling of the fuel would be interrupted, which could result in a rapid rise in the temperature of the fuel, possible failure of the fuel cladding, and escape of radioactive material from the fuel to the reactor vessel. A rapid shutdown of the fission chain reaction, backed up by possible activation of standby or emergency cooling systems, would prevent fuel damage. These safety measures are provided in all nuclear stations.

Even when the reactor has been shut down, loss of cooling and failure of the standby or emergency cooling capability could result in overheating of the fuel because of the continuing fission product decay heat production in the fuel, as indicated in figure 76.2. While the decay heat is only 1% or 2% of the full-power heat production, if it is not removed, the fuel temperature could reach failure levels within minutes of complete loss of cooling. The principle of nuclear power plant safety design requires that all circumstances that could lead to fuel overheating, damage and release of radioactive materials from the fuel are carefully assessed and prevented by engineered control and protective systems.

To protect a nuclear power station, there are three kinds of safety features: inherent characteristics, passive systems and active

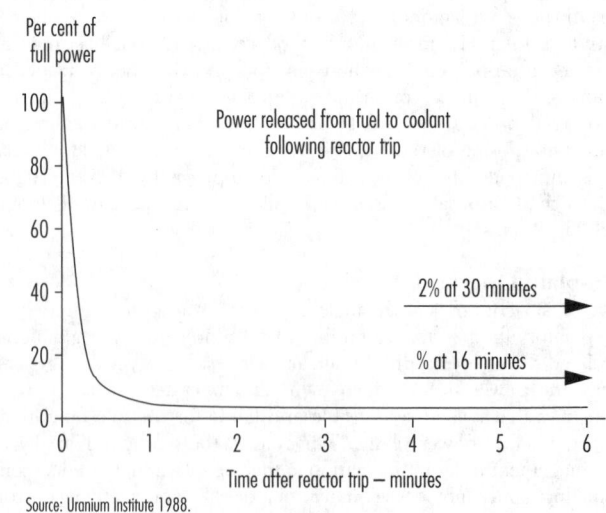

Figure 76.2 • Decay heat after reactor shutdown.

Per cent of full power

Power released from fuel to coolant following reactor trip

2% at 30 minutes

% at 16 minutes

Time after reactor trip — minutes

Source: Uranium Institute 1988.

systems. These are used in various combinations in operating nuclear stations.

Inherent safety characteristics make use of the laws of nature to keep the power plant safe. There are inherent safety characteristics of some nuclear fuels such that, as their temperature rises, the fission chain reaction rate is slowed. There are inherent safety characteristics with some designs of cooling systems whereby the coolant will circulate over the fuel by natural circulation to adequately remove the decay heat without operation of any pumps. There are inherent safety characteristics in most metallic structures that result in yielding or stretching under severe loads rather than bursting or failure.

Passive safety features include the lifting of dead weight (gravity) relief valves by the pressure of the fluid to be relieved, or in the use of stored energy in emergency coolant injection systems, or in some containment vessels which are designed to accommodate the energy from failure of piping systems and subsequent decay heat.

Active safety systems include all systems which require activating signals and a power supply of some form. Active systems can generally control a wider range of circumstances than inherent and passive systems, and can be tested without restrictions during operation of the reactor.

The safety design of nuclear power stations is based on a selected combination of inherent, passive and active systems to meet the regulatory safety requirements of the jurisdiction in which the nuclear station is located. A high degree of automation in safety-related systems is necessary to relieve operations personnel, as much as possible, of the need to take quick decisions and actions under stress. Nuclear power reactor systems are designed to adjust to changes in demanded power output automatically, and generally changes are gradual. It is particularly important that safety-related systems be continuously capable of responding promptly, effectively and reliably when required. To meet this high level of performance these systems must comply with the highest quality assurance criteria and be designed to the well established safety design principles of redundancy, diversity and physical separation.

Redundancy is the provision of more components or subsystems than are needed to just make the system work—for example, providing three or four components where only two are needed to function for the system to perform properly.

Diversity is the provision of two or more systems which are based on different design or functional principles to perform the same safety function.

Physical separation of components or systems which are designed to perform the same safety function, provides protection against local damage which could otherwise impair the performance of the safety systems.

An important illustration of the application of these safety design principles is in the electric power supply in nuclear stations, which is based on more than one connection to the main power system, backed up on site by several automatic-start diesels and/or combustion turbines, and by banks of batteries and motor-generator sets to ensure the reliable supply of electricity to the vital safety-related systems.

The basic preventive measure against release of radioactive materials from a nuclear station is very simple in principle: a series of leak-tight barriers between the radioactive materials and the environment, in order to provide shielding against direct radiation and containment of the radioactive materials. The innermost barrier is the ceramic or metallic fuel itself, which binds most of the radioactive materials within its matrix. The second barrier is the leak-tight, corrosion-resistant cladding. The third barrier is the primary pressure-bearing boundary of the coolant system. Finally, most nuclear power systems are enclosed in a pressure-resistant containment structure which is designed to withstand failure of the largest piping system within and to contain any radioactive materials released into containment.

The basic aim of the nuclear power station safety design is to maintain the integrity of these multiple barriers by a defence-in-depth approach which can be characterized by three levels of safety measures: preventive, protective and mitigative measures.

Preventive measures include: meeting the highest level of quality assurance during design, construction and operation; highly trained operators who undergo periodic retraining; utilizing inherent safety features; providing appropriate design margins; undertaking careful preventive maintenance, continual testing and inspection and correction of deficiencies; constant monitoring; thorough safety assessments and reassessments when required; and evaluation and causal analysis of incidents and faults, making appropriate modifications.

Protective measures include: fast-acting shut-down systems; responsive automatic pressure-relief valves/systems; interlock circuits to protect against false operation; automatic monitoring of vital safety functions; and continuous measurement and control of radiation levels and effluent radioactivity so as not to exceed allowable limits.

Mitigative measures include: emergency reactor cooling systems; highly reliable emergency feedwater systems; diverse and redundant emergency power systems; containment to prevent any radioactive materials leaking from the station, which is designed for a variety of natural and artificial stresses such as earthquakes, high winds, floods or aircraft impingement; and, finally, emergency planning and accident management, which includes radiation monitoring, informing safety authorities and advising the public, control of contamination and distribution of mitigating materials.

Nuclear safety does not only depend on technical and scientific factors; human factors play a very important role. Regulatory control provides an independent verification of all safety aspects of nuclear stations. However, nuclear safety is primarily ensured not by laws and regulations, but by responsible design, operation and utility management, which includes appropriate reviews and approvals by those with knowledge and authority.

The only nuclear station accident to have very serious consequences for the public occurred during a test of cooling capability in an unusual configuration in a RBMK nuclear station at Chernobyl in Ukraine in 1986. In this severe accident the reactor was destroyed and a large amount of radioactive materials escaped to the environment. It was subsequently found that the reactor did not have an adequate shut-down system and that it was unstable at low power. Design weaknesses, human error and lack of proper utility management all contributed to the accident. Modifications have been made to the remaining operating RBMK reactors to eliminate serious design weaknesses, and operating instructions have been improved to ensure there will not be a repeat of this unfortunate accident.

Much has been learned from the RBMK accident and from other less serious nuclear station accidents (such as the Three Mile Island accident in the United States in 1978) and from many minor accidents and incidents over more than 30 years of nuclear power station operation. The goal of the nuclear community is to ensure that no nuclear power station incident endanger the workers, the public or the environment. Close cooperation under such programmes as the IAEA Incident Reporting Systems and WANO, the scrutiny of industry groups and regulatory agencies, and vigilance by nuclear stations owners and operators, make this goal more attainable.

Acknowledgement: The editor thanks Tim Meadler and the Uranium Institute for providing information for table 76.3.

● ## ELECTRIC POWER GENERATION, TRANSMISSION AND DISTRIBUTION SAFETY: A US EXAMPLE

Janet Fox

Generation, Transmission and Distribution

There are three stages of electric power supply; generation, transmission and distribution. Each of these stages involves distinct production processes, work activities and hazards.

Most electricity is generated at 13,200 to 24,000 volts. The hazards of the electrical power generation process include explosions and burns resulting from unexpected equipment failure. Accidents can also occur when proper lockout/tagout procedures are not followed. These procedures are in place to control energy sources. Before performing maintenance on equipment where the unexpected energizing, start up or release of stored energy could occur and cause injury, the equipment must be isolated from the energy source and rendered inoperative. Failure to properly isolate these energy sources (lockout/tagout) can result in serious injury or death.

After electrical power is generated, it is transmitted over distances using transmission lines. Transmission lines are constructed between transmission substations located at electric generating stations. Transmission lines may be supported overhead on towers or they may be underground. They are operated at high voltages. They send out large amounts of electrical power and extend over considerable distances. When electricity comes out of a generating station, the transmission substation located there steps up the voltages to the range of 138,000–765,000 volts. Within the operating area, transmission substations reduce the transmitted voltage to 34,500–138,000 volts. This power is then carried through lines to the distribution systems located in the local service territory. The major hazards present during the transmission process are electrical. Failure to maintain proper approach distances or use appropriate protective equipment (rubber gloves and sleeves) can result in serious injury or death. Falls also are a source of serious accidents and can occur during maintenance work on overhead lines and while working from poles or bucket trucks.

The distribution system connects the transmission system to the customer's equipment. The distribution substation reduces the transmitted electrical voltage to 2,400–19,920 volts. A distribution transformer further reduces the voltage. Hazards related to distribution work also are electrical in nature. However, there is the additional hazard of working in enclosed spaces (manholes and vaults) when dealing with an underground distribution system.

Transmission and distribution substations are installations where the voltage, phase or other characteristics of the electrical energy are changed as part of the final distribution process. Electrocutions represent the primary safety hazard in substations. Such accidents are generally caused by failure to maintain proper approach distances to live electrical equipment and/or failure to use appropriate personal protective equipment, including rubber insulating gloves and sleeves.

Safety Hazards of Generation, Transmission and Distribution

The Electric Power Generation, Transmission and Distribution Standard, also known as the Electric Maintenance Standard Codified at 29 CFR 1910.269, was promulgated by the US Occupational Safety and Health Administration (OSHA) on 31 January 1994. The Standard covers all electric utility workers involved in the operation and maintenance of electric power generation, transmission and distribution equipment and associated equipment. In addition, contract lineworkers, contract line clearance tree trimmers and independent power producers are also covered by the provisions of 1910.269. Other countries and regions have similar regulations.

The hazards that are directly addressed by the OSHA standard are those of an electrical nature which would cause electrocution and injuries resulting from electric shock. The consequences of inadvertent contact with high-voltage electricity are often death or serious injuries such as second- and third-degree burns, amputation of limbs, damage to internal organs and neurological damage.

The standard also addresses fatalities and injuries associated with four other types of accidents—struck by or struck against; falls from ladders, scaffolds, poles or other elevations; caught in or between as a result of the accidental activation of machinery during routine maintenance work; and contact with temperature extremes which can occur when high-pressure steam is inadvertently released during maintenance work on boilers. The Eastern Research Group (ERG), who prepared the Economic Impact Study for the proposed OSHA regulation, reported that "there were more accidents associated with transmission and distribution lines than with substations or power generation installations". ERG reported that in the transmission and distribution line category, line workers, apprentice line workers and working line supervisors experience the most fatal and serious lost-time accidents. Within the substation and power generation category, substation electricians and general utility mechanics experience the most accidents.

Accident Reduction

OSHA has estimated that in the United States an average of 12,976 lost workday injuries occur annually to electric power generation, transmission and distribution employees. They also report that 86 fatalities occur to these workers annually. OSHA estimates that 1,633 lost workday injuries and 61 deaths can be prevented annually through compliance with the provisions of this standard and the other standards referenced in the final rule. OSHA breaks down the reduction in lost-workday injuries and fatalities into two categories. The greatest benefit is expected to be achieved in the electric utilities, which account for approximately 80% of the fatalities. Utility contractors, including electrical contractors and line clearance tree trimmers, and non-utility establishments account for the other 20%. OSHA also expects the greatest reduction in lost workday injuries to be experienced by the electric utilities. The second category of reduction relates to the referencing of existing standards within 1910.269. For example, OSHA expects the employer to provide medical services and first aid as specified in 1910.151.

Excavation operations shall comply with Subpart P of 1926; personal protective equipment shall meet the requirements of Subpart I of 1910; personal fall-arrest equipment shall meet the requirements of Subpart E of Part 1926; and ladders shall comply with Subpart D of 1910. These are a few examples of the many other OSHA standards referenced in the Electric Power Generation, Transmission and Distribution Standard. OSHA believes that these references will foster an increased recognition of the various applicable safety standards and, together with employee training and emphasis on hazard recognition through job briefings, an additional 2 fatalities and 1,310 lost-workday injuries will be prevented annually.

General Provisions

The Electric Power Generation, Transmission, and Distribution Standard provides a comprehensive approach for the control of hazards found in the electric utility industry. This is considered a performance-based standard, where the employer has the opportunity to implement alternative programmes provided he or she can demonstrate that they provide a level of safety equivalent to that specified in the standard. General provisions of the standard include: training requirements, hazardous energy control (lockout/tagout) procedures for power generation, transmission and distribution; enclosed space entry procedures and procedures for working safely in underground installations; requirements for working on or near exposed energized parts; requirements for working on overhead lines; grounding requirements; line clearance tree trimming; procedures for working in substations; and requirements for live-line tools, hand and portable power tools, and ladders and personal protective equipment. The standard is comprehensive and addresses all aspects of the operation and maintenance of power generation, transmission and distribution equipment.

Significant Provisions

Some of the most significant provisions of the Standard include requirements for employees to have emergency aid training, job briefings, and training in safety-related work practices, safety procedures, and emergency procedures including manhole and pole-top rescue. There are also specific clothing requirements for working on energized equipment, and requirements for entry into underground structures, as well as the control of hazardous energy sources. Another significant element of the standard requires employers to certify that employees have been appropriately trained and can demonstrate proficiency in the work practices specified in the standard. A few of these elements are discussed in more detail below.

OSHA requires that employees performing work on or associated with exposed lines or equipment energized at 50 volts or more be trained in first aid and cardiopulmonary resuscitation (CPR). For field work involving two or more employees at a work location, at least two employees shall be trained. For fixed work locations such as a generating station, a sufficient number of employees must be trained to ensure that an employee exposed to electric shock can be reached within 4 minutes.

The lead employee in a work group must conduct *a job briefing* with the employees involved in the work before they start each job. The briefing must cover the hazards associated with the job, work procedures involved, special precautions, energy source controls and personal protective equipment. For repetitive and similar jobs there must be one job briefing before the start of the first job of each day or shift. When significant changes occur, another briefing must be conducted. Reviewing the task at hand requires job planning, and job planning helps to reduce accidents.

OSHA also has required that the employer certify that each employee has received the training required to be qualified and competent. The certification shall be made when the employee demonstrates proficiency in the work practices, and shall be maintained for the duration of an employee's employment. Training alone is inadequate. Proficiency must be demonstrated, generally through testing an employee's knowledge and understanding of the subject at hand. This will help ensure that only qualified workers work on energized equipment.

There are clothing requirements for workers who are exposed to the hazards of flames or electric arcs. The section requires that the employer ensure that each employee who is exposed to the hazards of flames or electric arcs not wear clothing that, when exposed to flames or electric arcs, could increase the extent of injury that would be sustained by the employee. Clothing made from acetate, nylon, polyester or rayon, either alone or in blends, is prohibited unless the employer can demonstrate that the fabric has been treated to withstand the condition that may be encountered. Employees may choose among cotton, wool or flame-retardant clothing, but the employer must determine, based on the exposure, whether or not a natural fibre such as cotton or wool is acceptable. Cotton or wool could ignite under certain circumstances. Although this section of the standard has caused much controversy throughout the industry, prohibiting the use of synthetics is a significant step towards reducing injuries to electrical workers.

HAZARDS

Michael Crane

OSHA in its preamble to the Electric Power Generation, Transmission and Distribution Standard (29 CFR Part 1910.269) states that "overall accident incidence rates for the electric services industry (that is, the electric utility industry, SIC-491) are slightly lower than corresponding rates for the private sector as a whole" and that "except for electrical and fall hazards, electric utility employees face hazards that are similar in nature and degree to those encountered in many other industries" (OSHA 1994). The preamble goes on to cite US Bureau of Labor Statistics (BLS) files identifying the major sources of injury for electric utilities:

- falls
- overexertion
- being "struck by or against an object", leading to sprains and strains, cuts, lacerations and contusions/bruises.

The preamble specifically notes that electric shock does not constitute a major (or frequently reported) injury category. However, labour, industry and OSHA files reveal that electrical accidents are the most frequent type of fatal or serious injuries in the electrical utility industry, followed by motor vehicle accidents, falls and "struck by/crushed."

Many other hazards confront electrical utility workers in performing the varied tasks required by employers. The authors of individual articles in this chapter note many of these in detail; here I will simply mention some of the hazardous exposures.

Musculoskeletal injuries are the most common injuries occurring in this physically active workforce and include:

- vibration white fingers due to jackhammer use
- whiplash due to motor vehicle accidents
- low-back sprain
- head injury
- foot and ankle trauma
- torn medial meniscus.

Electrical workers can work in a wide variety of environments: they climb to the top of rural transmission towers and splice cables in manholes under busy city streets; they swelter on the top floors of the power stations in summer and shiver as they repair overhead distribution lines downed by a blizzard. The physical forces that confront the workers are enormous. A power plant, for example, pushes steam under such pressure that a ruptured pipe may mean scalding and suffocation. Physical hazards in plants in addition to heat include noise, electromagnetic fields (EMF), ionizing radiation in nuclear facilities and asphyxiation in confined spaces. Asbestos exposure has been a major source of morbidity and litigation, and concerns are being raised about other insulating materials. Chemicals such as caustics, corrosives and solvents are widely used. Plants also employ workers in specialized jobs like fire-fighting or scuba diving (to inspect water intake and discharge systems), who are exposed to the unique hazards intrinsic to those tasks.

While modern nuclear power stations have reduced workers' radiation exposure during normal operating periods, substantial exposure may occur during maintenance and refuelling shutdowns. Excellent radiation monitoring capabilities are required to properly protect workers entering radiation areas during these periods. The fact that many contract workers may enter a nuclear plant during a shut-down and then move on to another plant, creates a need for close coordination between regulatory and industry authorities in monitoring the total annual exposure for an individual worker.

The transmission and distribution systems share some of the hazards of the power station, but also are characterized by unique work exposures. The enormous voltages and currents intrinsic to the system predispose to fatal electric shock and severe burns when workers ignore safety procedures or are inadequately protected. As transformers overheat, they may catch fire and explode, releasing oil and possibly PCBs and their breakdown products. Electrical substations share with power stations the potential of exposure to insulation, EMF and confined space hazards. In the distribution system, the cutting, burning and splicing of electrical cable expose workers to lead and other metals both as dusts and fumes. The underground structures which support the system must also be considered potential confined-space hazards. Pentachlorophenol, a pesticide used to preserve wooden utility poles, is an exposure that is somewhat unique to the distribution system.

Finally, meter readers and outdoor workers may be exposed to street violence; fatalities in the course of robbery attempts are not unknown to this workforce.

ENVIRONMENTAL AND PUBLIC HEALTH ISSUES

Alexander C. Pittman, Jr.

All human activity has an environmental impact. The magnitude and consequences of each impact varies, and environmental laws have been created to regulate and minimize these impacts.

Electrical power generation has several major potential and actual environmental hazards, including air emissions and water and soil contamination (table 76.4). Fossil fuel plants have been a particular concern because of their emissions into the air of nitrogen oxides (see "Ozone" below), sulphur oxides and the "acid rain" question, carbon dioxide (see "Global climate change" below) and particulates, which have recently been implicated as contributing to respiratory problems.

The concerns with nuclear plants have been with the long-term storage of nuclear waste, and the possibility of catastrophic accidents involving the release of radioactive contaminants into the air. The 1986 accident at Chernobyl, in Ukraine, is a classic example of what can happen when inadequate precautions are taken with nuclear plants.

With hydroelectric power plants, the main concerns have been leaching of metals and disturbance of both water and land wildlife habitats. This is discussed in the article "Hydroelectric power generation" in this chapter.

Electromagnetic Fields

Research efforts regarding electromagnetic fields (EMF) around the world have been growing since the study by Wertheimer and Leeper was published in 1979. That study suggested an association between childhood cancer and utility wires situated near homes. Studies since that publication have been inconclusive and have not confirmed causality. In fact, these subsequent studies

have pointed to areas where greater understanding and better data are needed to be able to start to draw reasonable conclusions out of these epidemiological studies. Some of the difficulties of performing a good epidemiological study are related to the problems of assessment (i.e., the measurement of exposure, source characterization and levels of magnetic fields in the residences). Even though the most recent study released by the National Research Council of the National Academy of Sciences (1996) determined that there was not enough evidence to consider electric and magnetic fields threatening to human health, the issue will probably remain in the public's eye until the widespread anxiety is alleviated by future studies and research which show no effect.

Global Climate Change

Over the past few years public awareness has increased concerning the impact that humans are having on the global climate. Approximately half of all greenhouse emissions from human activity are thought to be carbon dioxide (CO_2). Much research on this issue on a national and international level has been and continues to be done. Because utility operations make significant contributions to the release of CO_2 to the atmosphere, any rule-making for the control of CO_2 releases has the potential to impact the power generation industry in serious ways. The UN Framework Convention on Climate Change, the US Climate Change Action Plan and the Energy Policy Act of 1992 have created strong driving forces for the power industry to comprehend just how it might have to respond to future legislation.

Presently, some examples of the areas of study taking place are: the modelling of emissions, determining the effects of climate change, determining the costs associated with any climate change management plans, how humans might benefit by reducing greenhouse gas emissions, and predicting climate change.

A major reason for concern about climate change is the possible negative impacts on ecological systems. It is believed that systems that are not managed are the most sensitive and have the highest probability for significant impact on a global scale.

Table 76.4 • Major potential environmental hazards of power generation.

Type of plant	Air	Water*	Soil
Fossil fuel	NO_2	PCBs	Ash
	SO_2	Solvents	Asbestos
	Particulates	Metals	PCBs
	CO	Oil	Solvents
	CO_2	Acids/bases	Metals
	Volatile organic compounds	Hydrocarbons	Oil
			Acids/bases
			Hydrocarbons
Nuclear	Same as above plus radioactive emission		
Hydro	Chiefly leachate from soils to water behind dams		
	Disturbance of wildlife habitat		

* Should include such "local" effects as increases in temperature of the body of water receiving plant discharges and reductions in fish population due to the mechanical effects of feedwater intake systems.

Hazardous Air Pollutants

The US Environmental Protection Administration (EPA) has sent to the US Congress an Interim Report on Utility Hazardous Air Pollutants, which had been required by the 1990 Clean Air Act Amendments. The EPA was to analyse the risks from fossil fuel-fired steam electric generating facilities. EPA concluded that these releases do not constitute a public health hazard. The report delayed conclusions about mercury pending additional studies. A comprehensive Electric Power Research Institute (EPRI) study of fossil-fired power plants indicates that greater than 99.5% of the fossil power plants do not yield cancer risks above the 1 in 1 million threshold (Lamarre 1995). This compares with the risk due to all emission sources, which has been reported to have been as high as 2,700 cases per year.

Ozone

Reduction of ozone levels in air is a major concern in many countries. Nitrogen oxides (NO_x) and volatile organic compounds (VOCs) produce ozone. Because fossil fuel power plants contribute a large component of the world's total NO_x emissions, they can expect tighter control measures as countries tighten environmental standards. This will continue until the inputs for the photochemical grid models that are used for modelling tropospheric ozone transport are more accurately defined.

Site Remediations

Utilities are having to come to terms with the potential costs of manufactured gas plant (MGP) site remediation. The sites were originally created through the production of gas from coal, coke or oil, which resulted in onsite disposal of coal tar and other by-products in large lagoons or ponds, or in the use of offsite for land disposal. Disposal sites of this nature have the potential to contaminate groundwater and soil. Determining the extent of groundwater and soil contamination at these sites and the means to ameliorate it in a cost-effective manner will keep this issue unresolved for some time.

References

Lamarre, L. 1995. Assessing the risks of utility hazardous air pollutants. *EPRI Journal* 20(1):6.

National Research Council of the National Academy of Sciences. 1996. *Possible Health Effects of Exposure to Residential Electric and Magnetic Fields*. Washington, DC: National Academy Press.

United Nations. 1995. *1993 Energy Statistics Yearbook*. New York: United Nations.

Uranium Institute. 1988. *The Safety of Nuclear Power Plants*. London: Uranium Institute.

US Department of Energy. 1995. *Electric Power Annual 1994*. Vol. 1. Washington, DC: US Department of Energy, Energy Information Administration, Office of Coal, Nuclear, Electric and Alternate Fuels.

US Department of Labor, Occupational Safety and Health Administration (OSHA). 1994. 29 CFR Part 1910.269, Electric Power Generation, Transmission and Distribution: Electrical Protective Equipment; Final Rule. *Federal Register,* Vol. 59.

US Environmental Protection Administration (EPA). *Interim Report on Utility Hazardous Air Pollutants*. Washington, DC: EPA.

Wertheimer, N and E Leeper. 1979. Electrical wiring configurations and childhood cancer. *Am J Epidemiol* 109:273-284.

CHEMICAL PROCESSING

77

Chapter Editors
Jeanne Mager Stellman and
Michael McCann

Contents

CHEMICAL INDUSTRY

*L. De Boer**

The business of the chemical industry is to change the chemical structure of natural materials in order to derive products of value to other industries or in daily life. Chemicals are produced from these raw materials-principally minerals, metals and hydrocarbons-in a series of processing steps. Further treatment, such as mixing and blending, is often required to convert them into end-products (e.g., paints, adhesives, medicines and cosmetics). Thus the chemical industry covers a much wider field than what is usually called "chemicals" since it also includes such products as artificial fibres, resins, soaps, paints, photographic films and more.

Chemicals fall into two main classes: *organic* and *inorganic*. Organic chemicals have a basic structure of carbon atoms, combined with hydrogen and other elements. Oil and gas are today the source of 90% of world organic chemical production, having largely replaced coal and vegetable and animal matter, the earlier raw materials. Inorganic chemicals are derived chiefly from mineral sources. Examples are sulphur, which is mined as such or extracted from ores, and chlorine, which is made from common salt.

The products of the chemical industry can be broadly divided into three groups, which correspond to the principal steps in manufacture: *base chemicals* (organic and inorganic) are normally manufactured on a large scale and are normally converted to other chemicals; *intermediates* are derived from base chemicals. Most intermediates require further processing in the chemical industry, but some, such as solvents, are used as they are; *finished chemical products* are made by further chemical processing. Some of these (drugs, cosmetics, soaps) are consumed as such; others, such as fibres, plastics, dyes and pigments, are processed still further.

The main sectors of the chemical industry are as follows:

1. basic inorganics: acids, alkalis and salts, mainly used elsewhere in industry and industrial gases, such as oxygen, nitrogen and acetylene
2. basic organics: feedstocks for plastics, resins, synthetic rubbers, and synthetic fibres; solvents and detergent raw materials; dyestuffs and pigments
3. fertilizers and pesticides (including herbicides, fungicides and insecticides)
4. plastics, resins, synthetic rubbers, cellulosic and synthetic fibres
5. pharmaceuticals (drugs and medicines)
6. paints, varnishes and lacquers
7. soaps, detergents, cleaning preparations, perfumes, cosmetics and other toiletries
8. miscellaneous chemicals, such as polishes, explosives, adhesives, inks, photographic film and chemicals

In the International Standard Industrial Classification of All Economic Activities (ISIC) system, used by the United Nations to classify economic activity into ten major divisions, the chemical industry is classified as Division 35, one of the nine subdivisions of Major Division 3: Manufacturing. Division 35 is further subdivided into industrial chemicals (351), other chemicals (352), petroleum refineries (353), miscellaneous coal and petroleum products, e.g., asphalt (354), rubber products including tyres (355) and plastics processing (356).

In reporting chemical industry statistics each country normally uses its own classification system, and this can be misleading. Thus comparison between countries of total chemical industry

* Adapted from 3rd edition, Encyclopaedia of Occupational Health and Safety.

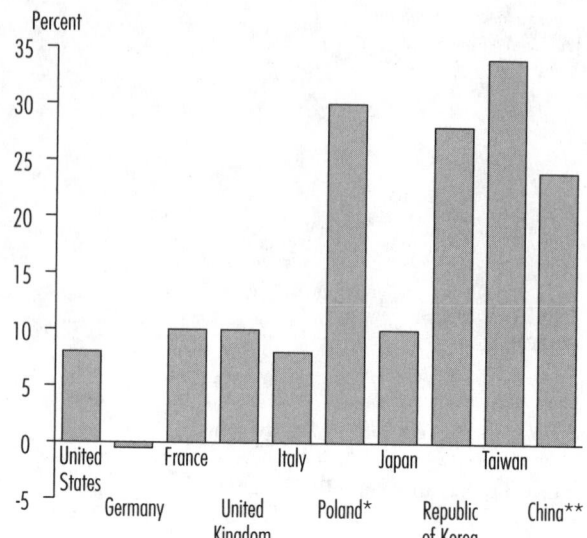

Figure 77.1 • Change in chemical production for selected countries, 1992-95.

* 1993-95

** based on individual products, not composite data

Source: *Chemical and Engineering News* 1996.

performance cannot be based on national sources. However, international bodies like the Organization for Economic Cooperation and Development (OECD) and the United Nations normally supply data on the ISIC basis, though with a delay of about two years.

Trade statistics are published internationally under the Standard International Trade Classification (SITC), which differs from the ISIC system. Trade statistics by individual countries nearly always refer to SITC section 5, which covers about 90% of total chemicals reported in the ISIC system.

The chemical industry has grown much more rapidly in the half century than industry as a whole. Although there was an economic depression in the world's chemical industry in the early 1990s, chemical production increased in the mid-1990s. The biggest area of growth of chemical production has been in Southeast Asia. Figure 77.1 shows the percentage change in chemical production for 1992-95 for selected countries.

Table 77.1 • Chemical industry employment in selected countries (1995).

Country	Employment
United States	1, 045,000
Germany	538,000
France	248,000
United Kingdom	236,000
Italy	191,000
Poland	140,000
Spain	122,000

Source: *Chemical and Engineering News* 1996.

Much of the chemical industry is highly capital-intensive and is also strongly dependent on research and development (e.g., pharmaceuticals). The combined result of these two factors is that the industry employs an abnormally low number of unskilled manual workers for its size, in comparison with manufacturing industry in general. Total employment in the industry rose slightly during the period of rapid growth prior to 1970, but since then the drive for increased productivity has resulted in a decline in employment in the chemical industry in most developed countries. Table 77.1 shows chemical industry employment in the United States and several European countries for 1995.

DEVELOPING A PROCESS SAFETY MANAGEMENT PROGRAMME

Richard S. Kraus

Whenever there are processes that use temperature and pressure to change the molecular structure or create new products from chemicals, the possibility exists for fires, explosions or releases of flammable or toxic liquids, vapours, gases or process chemicals. The control of these undesired events requires a special science called *process safety management*. The terms *process safety* and *process safety management* are most commonly used to describe the protection of employees, the public and the environment from the consequences of undesirable major incidents involving flammable

liquids and highly hazardous materials. According to the United States Chemical Manufacturers' Association (CMA), "process safety is the control of hazards which are caused by maloperation or malfunction of the processes used to convert raw materials into finished products, which may lead to the unplanned release of hazardous material" (CMA 1985).

The process design and technology, changes in the process, materials and changes in materials, operations and maintenance practices and procedures, training, emergency preparedness and other elements affecting the process must all be considered in the systematic identification and evaluation of hazards so as to determine whether or not they have the potential to lead to a catastrophe in the workplace and surrounding community.

Beginning in the early 1980s, a number of serious major incidents occurred in the petroleum and chemical industries involving highly hazardous materials, which resulted in considerable numbers of fatalities and injuries and significant property losses. These incidents provided the impetus for government agencies, labour organizations and industry associations throughout the world to develop and implement codes, regulations, procedures and safe work practices directed toward the elimination or mitigation of these undesirable events, through the application of the principles of process safety management. They are discussed more fully in the *Disasters, natural and technological* chapter and elsewhere in this *Encyclopaedia*.

In response to public concern over the potential hazards of chemicals, governments and regulatory agencies throughout the world initiated programmes which required manufacturers and users to identify hazardous materials in the workplace and inform

Industry and labour process safety involvement

Process safety technology has played an important role in the chemical processing industries so that handling flammable and combustible liquids and gases could proceed without undesirable consequences. During the 1980s, the oil and gas industries, for example, recognized that process safety technology alone, without process safety management, would not prevent catastrophic incidents. With this in mind, a number of industry associations, such as, in the United States, the Center for Chemical Process Safety (CCPS), the American Petroleum Institute (API) and the Chemical Manufacturers' Association (CMA), initiated programmes to develop and provide process safety management guidelines for use by their members. As stated by the CCPS, "The evolution of process safety from a purely technical issue to one that demanded management approaches was essential to continued process safety improvement".

The CCPS was formed in 1985 to promote the improvement of process safety management techniques among those who store, handle, process and use hazardous chemicals and materials. In 1988, the Chemical Manufacturer's Association (CMA) initiated its *Responsible Care®* programme outlining each member company's commitment to environmental, health and safety responsibility in managing chemicals.

In 1990, the API initiated an industry-wide programme entitled, *STEP-Strategies for Today's Environmental Partnership*, with the intention of improving the oil and gas industry's environmental, health and safety performance. One of the seven strategic elements of the STEP programme covers petroleum operating and process safety. The following documents are examples of some of the materials developed as a result of the STEP programme which provide guidance to the oil and gas industry to help prevent the occurrence or minimize the consequences of catastrophic releases of flammable liquids and vapours or hazardous process materials:

- *Management of Process Hazards* (RP 750)
  RP 750 covers the management of hydrocarbon process hazards in design, construction, start-up, operations, inspection, maintenance and facility modifications. It applies specifically to refineries, petrochemical plants and major processing facilities that use, produce, process or store flammable liquids and toxic processing chemicals in quantities above certain hazardous amounts (as defined therein).
- *Management of Hazards Associated with Location of Process Plant Buildings* (RP 752)
  RP 752, co-developed by API and CMA, is intended to help identify process plant buildings of concern, understand the potential hazards related to their location within the process facility and manage the risk of fire, explosion and toxic releases.
- *Management Practices, Self-assessment Process, and Resource Materials* (RP 9000)
  RP 9000 provides resource materials and self assessment methodology to measure progress in implementing process safety management elements.

Examples of other organizations which have developed materials and programmes providing guidance covering chemical process safety management include, but are not limited to, the following:

- Organizations Resource Counselors' (ORC) report, *Process Hazards Management of Substances with Catastrophic Potential*
- National Petroleum Refiners Association (NPRA), *BEST (Building Environmental Stewardship Tools)* programme
- International Labour Organization (ILO), *Code of Practice on the Prevention of Major Accident Hazards*
- International Chamber of Commerce (ICC), *Charter for Sustainable Development*.

employees and consumers of the hazards presented by their manufacture, use, storage and handling. These programmes, which covered emergency preparedness and response, hazard recognition, product knowledge, control of hazardous chemicals and reporting of toxic releases, included hydrocarbon processing.

Process Safety Management Requirements

Process safety management is an integral part of the overall chemical processing facility safety programme. An effective process safety management programme requires the leadership, support and involvement of top management, facility management, supervisors, employees, contractors and contractor employees.

Components to be considered when developing a process safety management programme include:

- *Interdependent continuity of operations, systems and organization*
- *Management of information.* The process safety management programme relies upon providing availability and access to good records and documentation.
- *Control of process quality, deviations and exceptions and alternate methods*
- *Management and supervisory accessibility and communications.* Because process safety management is the basis for all safety efforts within the facility, managerial, supervisory and employee responsibility and accountability should be clearly delineated, communicated and understood in order for the programme to work.
- *Goals and objectives, compliance audits and performance measurement.* Prior to implementation, it is important to establish both long-term and short-term goals and objectives for each of the elements of the process safety management programme.

Elements of the Process Safety Management Programme

All chemical facility process safety management programmes cover the same basic requirements, although the number of programme elements may vary depending on the criteria used. Regardless which government, company or association source document is used as a guide, there are a number of basic requirements which should be included in every chemical process safety management programme:

- process safety information
- employee involvement
- process hazard analysis
- management of change
- operating procedures
- safe work practices and permits
- employee information and training
- contractor personnel
- pre-startup safety reviews
- design quality assurance
- maintenance and mechanical integrity
- emergency response
- periodic safety audits
- process incident investigation
- standards and regulations
- trade secrets.

Process safety information

Process safety information is used by the process industry to define critical processes, materials and equipment. Process safety information includes all available written information concerning process technology, process equipment, raw materials and products and chemical hazards before conducting a process

hazard analysis. Other critical process safety information is documentation relating to capital project reviews and design basis criteria.

Chemical information includes not only the chemical and physical properties, reactivity and corrosive data and thermal and chemical stability of chemicals such as hydrocarbons and highly hazardous materials in the process, but also the hazardous effects of inadvertently mixing different incompatible materials. Chemical information also includes that which may be needed to conduct environmental hazard assessments of toxic and flammable releases and permissible exposure limits.

Process technology information includes block flow diagrams and/or simple process flow diagrams as well as descriptions of the chemistry of each specific process with the safe upper and lower limits for temperatures, pressures, flows, compositions and, where available, process design material and energy balances. The consequences of deviations in the process and materials, including their effect on employee safety and health, are also determined. Whenever processes or materials are changed, the information is updated and re-evaluated in accordance with the facility's management of change system.

Process equipment and mechanical design information includes documentation covering the design codes employed and whether or not equipment complies with recognized engineering practices. A determination is made as to whether existing equipment which was designed and constructed in accordance with codes, standards and practices no longer in general use is maintained, operated, inspected and tested to assure continued safe operation. Information on materials of construction, piping and instrument diagrams, relief system design, electrical classification, ventilation design and safety systems is updated and re-evaluated when changes occur.

Employee involvement

Process safety management programmes should include employee participation in the development and conduct of process safety analyses and other elements of the programme. Access to process safety information, incident investigation reports and process hazard analyses is usually provided to all employees and contractor employees working in the area. Most industrialized nations require that workers be systematically instructed in the identification, nature and safe-handling of all chemicals to which they may be exposed.

Process hazard analysis

After the process safety information is compiled, a thorough and systematic multi-disciplinary process hazard analysis, appropriate to the complexity of the process, is conducted in order to identify, evaluate and control the hazards of the process. Persons performing the process hazard analysis should be knowledgeable and experienced in relevant chemistry, engineering and process operations. Each analysis team normally includes at least one person who is thoroughly familiar with the process being analysed and one person who is competent in the hazard analysis methodology being used.

The priority order used to determine where within the facility to begin conducting process hazard analyses is based on the following criteria:

- extent and nature of the process hazards
- number of potentially affected workers
- operating and incident history of the process
- age of the process.

A number of methods for conducting process safety analyses are used in the chemical industry.

The *"what if?" method* asks a series of questions to review potential hazard scenarios and possible consequences and is most often used when examining proposed modifications or changes to the process, materials, equipment or facility.

The *"checklist" method* is similar to the "what if?" method, except that a previously developed checklist is used which is specific to the operation, materials, process and equipment. This method is useful when conducting pre-startup reviews upon completion of initial construction or following major turnarounds or additions to the process unit. A combination of the "what if?" and "checklist" methods is often used when analysing units that are identical in construction, materials, equipment and process.

The *hazard and operability (HAZOP) study method* is commonly used in the chemical and petroleum industries. It involves a multi-disciplinary team, guided by an experienced leader. The team uses specific guide words, such as "no", "increase", "decrease" and "reverse", which are systematically applied to identify the consequences of deviations from design intent for the processes, equipment and operations being analysed.

Fault tree/event tree analyses are similar, formal deductive techniques used to estimate the quantitative likelihood of an event occurring. Fault tree analysis works backward from a defined incident to identify and display the combination of operational errors and/ or equipment failures which were involved in the incident. Event tree analysis, which is the reverse of fault tree analysis, works forwards from specific events, or sequences of events, in order to pinpoint those that could result in hazards, and thereby calculate the likelihood of an event's sequence occurring.

The *failure mode and effects analysis method* tabulates each process system or unit of equipment with its failure modes, the effect of each potential failure on the system or unit and how critical each failure could be to the integrity of the system. The failure modes are then ranked in importance to determine which is most likely to cause a serious incident.

No matter which method is used, all chemical process hazard analyses consider the following:

- process location, siting and hazards of the process
- identification of any prior incident or near miss with potential catastrophic consequences
- engineering and administrative controls applicable to the hazards
- interrelationships of controls and appropriate application of detection methodology to provide early warnings
- consequences of human factors, facility siting and failure of the controls
- consequences of safety and health effects on workers within areas of potential failure.

Management of change

Chemical process facilities should develop and implement programmes which provide for the revision of process safety information, procedures and practices as changes occur. Such programmes include a system of management authorization and written documentation for changes to materials, chemicals, technology, equipment, procedures, personnel and facilities that affect each process.

Management of change programmes in the chemical industry, for example, include the following areas:

- change of hydrocarbon process technology
- changes in facility, equipment or materials (e.g., catalysts or additives)
- management of change personnel and organizational and personnel changes
- temporary changes, variances and permanent changes

- enhancement of process safety knowledge, including:
  - technical basis for proposed change
  - impact of change on safety, health and environment
  - modifications to operating procedures and safe work practices
  - modifications required to other processes
  - time required for the change
  - authorization requirements for the proposed change
  - updating documentation relating to process information, operating procedures and safety practices
  - required training or education due to change
- management of subtle change (anything which is not replacement in kind)
- non-routine changes.

The management of change system includes informing employees involved in the process and maintenance and contractor personnel whose tasks would be affected by any changes of the changes and providing updated operating procedures, process safety information, safe work practices and training as needed, prior to the startup of the process or affected part of the process.

Operating procedures

Chemical processing facilities must develop and provide operating instructions and detailed procedures to workers. Operating instructions should be regularly reviewed for completeness and accuracy (and updated or amended as changes occur) and cover the process unit's operating limits, including the following three areas:

1. consequences of deviation
2. steps to avoid or correct deviation
3. functions of safety systems related to operating limits.

Workers involved in the process have access to operating instructions covering the following areas:

- initial startup (startup after turnarounds, emergencies and temporary operations)
- normal startup (normal and temporary operations and normal shutdown)
- emergency operations and emergency shutdown
- conditions under which emergency shutdown is required and assignment of shutdown responsibilities to qualified operators
- non-routine work
- operator-process and operator-equipment interface
- administrative controls vs. automated controls.

Safe work practices

Chemical process facilities should implement hot-work and safe work permit and work order programmes to control work conducted in or near process areas. Supervisors, employees and contractor personnel must be familiar with the requirements of the various permit programmes, including permit issuance and expiration and appropriate safety, materials handling and fire protection and prevention measures.

The types of work included in typical chemical facility permit programmes include the following:

- hot work (welding, hot tapping, internal combustion engines, etc.)
- lockout/tagout of electrical, mechanical, pneumatic energy and pressure
- confined-space entry and use of inert gas
- venting, opening and cleaning process vessels, tanks, equipment and lines
- control of entry into process areas by non-assigned personnel.

Chemical facilities should develop and implement safe work practices to control potential hazards during process operations, covering the following areas of concern:

- properties and hazards of materials, catalysts and chemicals used in the process
- engineering, administrative and personal protection controls to prevent exposures
- measures to be taken in event of physical contact or exposure with hazardous chemical
- quality control of raw materials, catalysts and inventory control of hazardous chemicals
- safety and protection system (interlock, suppression, detection, etc.) functions
- special or unique hazards in the workplace.

Employee information and training

Chemical process facilities should use formal process safety training programmes to train and educate incumbent, reassigned and new supervisors and workers. The training provided for chemical process operating and maintenance supervisors and workers should cover the following areas:

- required skills, knowledge and qualifications of process employees
- selection and development of process related training programmes
- measuring and documenting employee performance and effectiveness
- design of process operating and maintenance procedures
- overview of process operations and process hazards
- availability and suitability of materials and spare parts for the processes in which they are to be used
- process start-up, operating, shut-down and emergency procedures
- safety and health hazards related to the process, catalysts and materials
- facility and process area safe work practices and procedures.

Contractor personnel

Contractors are often employed in chemical processing facilities. The facilities must institute procedures to assure that contractor personnel performing maintenance, repair, turnaround, major renovation or specialty work are fully aware of the hazards, materials, processes, operating and safety procedures and equipment in the area. Periodic evaluations of performance are made to assure that contractor personnel are trained, qualified, follow all safety rules and procedures and are informed and aware of the following:

- potential fire, explosion and toxic release hazards related to their work
- plant safety procedures and contractor safe work practices
- emergency plan and contractor personnel actions
- controls for contractor personnel entry, exit and presence in process areas.

Pre-startup safety reviews

Pre-startup process safety reviews are conducted in chemical plants prior to startup of new process facilities and introduction of new hazardous materials or chemicals into facilities, following a major turnaround and where facilities have had significant process modifications.

The pre-startup safety reviews assure the following have been accomplished:

- construction, materials and equipment are verified as in accordance with design criteria

- process systems and hardware, including computer control logic, have been inspected, tested and certified
- alarms and instruments are inspected, tested and certified
- relief and safety devices and signal systems are inspected, tested and certified
- fire protection and prevention systems are inspected, tested and certified
- safety, fire prevention and emergency response procedures are developed, reviewed, in place and are appropriate and adequate
- startup procedures are in place and proper actions have been taken
- a process hazard analysis has been performed and all recommendations addressed, implemented or resolved and actions documented
- all required initial and/ or refresher operator and maintenance personnel training, including emergency response, process hazards and health hazards, is completed
- all operating procedures (normal and upset), operating manuals, equipment procedures and maintenance procedures are completed and in place
- management of change requirements for new processes and modifications to existing processes have been met.

Design Quality Assurances

When new processes or major changes to existing processes are undertaken, a series of process safety design reviews are normally conducted before and during construction (prior to the pre-startup review). The design control review, conducted just before plans and specifications are issued as "final design drawings", covers the following areas:

- plot plan, siting, spacing, electrical classification and drainage
- hazards analysis and process chemistry design
- project management requirements and qualifications
- process equipment and mechanical equipment design and integrity
- piping and instrument drawings
- reliability engineering, alarms, interlocks, reliefs and safety devices
- materials of construction and compatibility.

Another review is normally conducted just prior to the start of construction covering the following:

- demolition and excavation procedures
- control of raw materials
- control of construction personnel and equipment on facility and site
- fabrication, construction and installation procedures and inspection.

One or more reviews are usually conducted during the course of construction or modification to assure the following areas are in accordance with design specifications and facility requirements:

- materials of construction provided and used as specified
- proper assembly and welding techniques, inspections, verifications and certifications
- chemical and occupational health hazards considered during construction
- physical, mechanical and operational safety hazards considered during construction and facility permit and safety practices followed
- interim protective and emergency response systems provided and working.

Maintenance and mechanical integrity

Process facilities have programmes to maintain ongoing integrity of process-related equipment, including periodic inspection, testing, performance maintenance, corrective action and quality assurance. The programmes are intended to assure that mechanical integrity of equipment and materials is reviewed and certified and deficiencies corrected prior to startup, or provisions made for appropriate safety measures.

Mechanical integrity programmes cover the following equipment and systems:

- pressure vessels and storage tanks
- emergency shutdown and fire protection systems
- process safeguards such as relief and vent systems and devices, controls, interlocks, sensors and alarms
- pumps and piping systems (including components such as valves)
- quality assurance, materials of construction and reliability engineering
- maintenance and preventive maintenance programmes.

Mechanical integrity programmes also cover inspection and testing of maintenance materials, spare parts and equipment to assure proper installation and adequacy for the process application involved. The acceptance criteria and frequency of inspections and tests should conform with manufacturers' recommendations, good engineering practices, regulatory requirements, industry practices, facility policies or prior experience.

Emergency Response

Emergency preparedness and response programmes are developed to cover an entire process facility and to provide for hazard identification and assessment of potential process hazards. These programmes include training and educating employees and contractor employees in emergency notification, response and evacuation procedures.

A typical process facility emergency preparedness programme complies with applicable company and regulatory requirements and includes the following:

- distinctive employee and/ or community alarm or notification system
- preferred method of internal reporting of fires, spills, releases and emergencies
- requirements for reporting process-related incidents to appropriate government agencies
- emergency shutdown, evacuation, procedures to account for personnel, emergency escape procedures, vehicle and equipment removal and route assignments
- emergency response and rescue procedures, duties and capabilities including employees, public safety, contractors and mutual aid organizations
- procedures for handling small spills or releases of hazardous chemicals
- procedures for providing and safeguarding emergency power and utilities
- business continuation plans, personnel and equipment sources
- document and record preservation, site security, cleanup, salvage and restoration.

Periodic safety audits

Many process facilities use self-evaluation process safety management audits to measure facility performance and assure compliance with internal and external (regulatory, company and industry) process safety requirements. The two basic principles of conducting self evaluation audits are: gathering all of the relevant documentation covering process safety management requirements at a specific facility and determining the programme's implementation and effectiveness by following up on their application in one or more selected processes. A report of the audit findings and recommendations is developed and facility management maintains documentation which notes how deficiencies had been corrected or mitigated, and if not, reasons why no corrective action had been taken.

Compliance audit programmes in hydrocarbon process facilities cover the following areas:

- establishment of goals, schedule and methods of verification of findings prior to the audit
- determination of the methodology (or format) to be used in conducting the audit, and develop appropriate checklists or audit report forms
- readiness to certify compliance with government, industry and company requirements
- assignment of knowledgeable audit teams (internal and/ or external expertise)
- prompt responses to all findings and recommendations and documentation of actions taken
- maintenance of a copy of at least the most recent compliance audit report on file.

Facility and process unit specific checklists are often developed for use when conducting process safety audits which cover the following items:

- orientation and process safety management programme overview
- preliminary walk-around through the refinery or gas processing facility
- process facility documentation review
- "prior incidents" and near misses (in the process facility or specific unit)
- determination and review of selected process units to be audited
- process unit construction (initial and subsequent modifications)
- process unit chemistry hazards (feedstocks, catalysts, process chemicals, etc.)
- process unit operations
- process unit controls, reliefs and safety systems
- process unit maintenance, repair, testing and inspection
- process unit-related training and employee involvement
- process facility management of change programme, implementation and effectiveness
- process fire protection and emergency notification and response procedures.

Because the objectives and scope of audits can vary, the compliance audit team should include at least one person knowledgeable in the process being audited, one person with applicable regulatory and standards expertise and other persons with the skills and qualifications necessary for conducting the audit. Management may decide to include one or more outside experts on the audit team due to lack of facility personnel or expertise, or because of regulatory requirements.

Process incident investigation

Process facilities have established programmes to thoroughly investigate and analyse process-related incidents and near misses, promptly address and resolve findings and recommendations and review the results with workers and contractors whose jobs are relevant to the incident findings. Incidents (or near misses) are thoroughly investigated as soon as possible by a team which includes at least one person knowledgeable in the process operation involved and others with appropriate knowledge and experience.

Standards and Regulations

Process facilities are subject to two distinct and separate forms of standards and regulations.

1. External codes, standards and regulations applicable to the design, operation and protection of process facilities and employees typically include government regulations and association and industry standards and practices.
2. Internal policies, guidelines and procedures, developed or adopted by the company or facility to complement external requirements and to cover processes which are distinct or unique, are reviewed periodically and changed when necessary, in accordance with the facility's management of change system.

Trade Secrets

Process facility management should provide process information, without regard to possible trade secrets or confidentiality agreements, to persons who are:

- responsible for gathering and compiling process safety information
- conducting process hazard analyses and compliance audits
- developing maintenance, operating and safe work procedures
- involved in incident (near miss) investigations
- responsible for emergency planning and response.

Facilities typically require that persons to whom process information is made available enter into agreements not to disclose the information.

● MAJOR UNIT OPERATIONS AND PROCESSES: AN OVERVIEW

Sydney Lipton

This article presents information on basic process equipment, storage, plant layout and operations considerations in chemical process industries, including major items and concepts that are broadly applicable throughout the chemical industry. However, much of the equipment required in chemical processing is highly

Table 77.2 • Some general site selection factors.

- Population density around the site
- Natural disaster occurrence (earthquake, flood, etc.)
- Prevailing winds and meteorological data
- Availability of power, steam and water
- Safety considerations
- Air, water and waste regulations and their complexity
- Accessibility to raw materials and markets
- Transportation
- Siting permits and complexity of obtaining them
- Interaction requirements in industrial developments
- Labour availability and costs
- Investment incentives

Table 77.3 • Plant siting safety considerations.

- Buffer zone
- Location of other hazardous installations in vicinity
- Inventory of toxic and hazardous materials
- Adequacy of firefighting water supply
- Emergency equipment access
- Availability of emergency response support from adjacent industries and the community
- Weather extremes and prevailing winds
- Location of highways, waterways, railroad and airplane corridors
- Environmental and waste disposal restrictions during emergencies
- Draining and grade slope
- Maintenance and inspection

specialized and cannot be broadly generalized. More detailed information on toxicity and hazardous materials and process safety are reviewed elsewhere in this *Encyclopaedia*.

There are two basic categories of layout in chemical processing industries: plant layout, which covers all process units, utilities, storage areas, loading/unloading areas, buildings, shops and warehousing, and unit or process layout, which covers only equipment placement for a specific process, also termed a process block.

Plant Layout

Siting

Locating or siting an overall plant is based upon a number of general factors, as shown in table 77.2 (CCPS 1993). These factors vary considerably with locations, governments and economic policies. Of these various factors, safety considerations are an extremely important concern, and in some locations they can be the major factor that governs plant siting.

One important aspect of plant safety in siting is defining a buffer zone between a plant with hazardous processes and nearby plants, dwellings, schools, hospitals, highways, waterways and airplane corridors. Some overall safety considerations are presented in table 77.3. The buffer zone is important because distance tends to reduce or mitigate potential exposures from various accidents. The distance necessary to reduce toxic concentrations to acceptable levels through atmospheric interaction and the dispersion of toxic materials from an accidental release can be defined. Moreover, the time lag between a toxic release and public exposure created by a buffer zone can be used to warn the population through pre-planned emergency response programmes. Since plants have various types of facilities containing toxic materials, dispersion analyses should be conducted on the potentially hazardous systems to ensure the buffer zone is adequate in each area surrounding the plant perimeter.

Fire is a potential hazard in process plants and facilities. Large fires can be a source of thermal radiation which can also be mitigated by distance. Elevated flares can also be a source of thermal radiation during an emergency or startup/shutdown operation. A flare is a device that automatically burns exhaust gases or emergency vapour releases at elevated positions or special ground locations. These should be sited away from the plant perimeter (for community protection) and an area at the flare base should be prohibited to workers. If not operated properly, liquid carryover into the flare can result in burning

Table 77.4 • Facilities generally separated in overall plant layouts.

- Process units
- Tank farms
- Loading and unloading facilities
- Flares
- Power, boilers and incinerators
- Cooling towers
- Substations, large electrical switch yards
- Central control houses
- Warehouses
- Analytical laboratories
- Incoming utility metering and block systems
- Fire hoses, fixed monitors, reservoirs and emergency fire pumps
- Waste treatment areas
- Maintenance buildings and areas
- Administrative buildings

liquid droplets. In addition to fire, there can be explosions within equipment or a vapour cloud that produces blast waves. Although distance will reduce the blast intensity somewhat over the buffer zone, the blast will still have an effect on the nearby community.

The potential of accidental releases or fires from existing facilities that may be near the proposed site should also be considered. Potential incidents should be modelled and evaluated to determine the possible effect on the proposed plant layout. Emergency responses to an external event should be evaluated and responses coordinated with other plants and affected communities.

Other considerations

Dow Chemical Company has developed another approach to plant layout based on an acceptable level of Maximum Probable Property Damage (MPPD) and Business Interruption Risk (B1) (Dow Chemical Company 1994a). These considerations are important for both new and existing plants. The Dow Fire and Explosion Index is useful in new plant layouts or in the addition of equipment to existing plants. If risks calculated from the Index are found to be unacceptable, the separation distances should be increased. Alternatively, layout changes may also reduce the risk potential.

Table 77.5 • General considerations in a process unit layout.

- Area definition for future expansion and unit accessibility
- Repair equipment accessibility for frequent maintenance
- Space requirements for individual equipment repair (e.g., area needed for pulling heat exchanger bundle or accessibility for control valve)
- Barriers for high pressure equipment or reactors with explosion potential
- Mechanical and space requirements for loading/unloading solids-filled reactors or towers
- Space for venting dust explosions
- Separation of frequently opened or maintained equipment from high temperature piping, vessels, etc.
- Special buildings or structures and necessary clearance (e.g., a compressor house with an internal bridge crane or external crane)

Overall layout

In an overall plant layout, the prevailing winds are an important consideration. Ignition sources should be located upwind of potential leak sources. Fired heaters, boilers, incinerators and flares are in this category (CCPS 1993). The location of storage tanks downwind of process units and utilities is another recommendation (CCPS 1993). Environmental regulations have led to significantly reduced leakage from tankage (Lipton and Lynch 1994).

Minimum separation distances have been outlined in various publications for process units, equipment and different plant functions (CCPS 1993; Dow Chemical Company 1994a; IRI 1991). General facilities that normally have recommended distance separations in overall plant layouts are shown in table 77.4. Actual distance recommendations should be carefully defined. While fired heaters and process furnaces are not shown in table 77.4, they are an important item and recommended distance separations must be included in a unit process layout.

In addition, roads are necessary for emergency and maintenance vehicle or equipment access and require careful placement between process units and throughout the various sections of the plant. Acceptable clearances for overhead pipe racks and other overhead equipment should be established along with lateral clearances at cross-roads and entrances to all facilities.

The layout requirements can be based on recommended minimum separation distances (CCPS 1993; NFPA 1990; IRI 1991; Mecklenburgh 1985) or determined through a hazard analysis (Dow Chemical Company 1994a).

Process Unit Layout

Table 77.4 presents an overall plant separations layout summary. The process units are contained within the specific block shown in the general layout. The chemical process is generally shown in detail in process and implementation diagrams (P&IDs). A process layout requires considerations beyond specific equipment separation distances, some of which are shown in table 77.5.

The assemblage of equipment in any particular process unit will vary considerably, depending on the process. The toxicity and hazardous characteristics of the streams and materials within the units also vary widely. Despite these differences, minimum distance standards have been developed for many equipment items (CCPS 1993; NFPA 1990; IRI 1991; Mecklenburgh 1985). Procedures for calculating potential leakage and toxic exposures from process equipment that can also affect separation distance are available (Dow Chemical Company 1994b). In addition, dispersion analysis can be applied when leakage estimates have been calculated.

Equipment and separation distance

A matrix technique can be used to calculate the space needed for separating equipment (CCPS 1993; IRI 1991). Calculations based upon specific processing conditions and an equipment hazard evaluation may result in separation distances that differ from a standard matrix guide.

Extensive lists for a matrix can be developed by refinement of individual categories and by the addition of equipment. For example, compressors may be split into several types, such as those handling inert gas, air and hazardous gases. Separation distances for engine-driven compressors may differ from motor- or steam-driven machines. Separation distances in storage facilities that house liquefied gases should be analysed on the basis of whether the gas is inert.

The process battery limits should be carefully defined. They are the boundary lines or plot limits for a process unit (the name derives from the early use of a battery of ovens in processing). Other units, roads, utilities, pipeways, runoff ditches and so on are plotted based upon battery limits. While unit equipment location does not extend to the battery limits, separation distances of equipment from battery limits should be defined.

Control rooms or control houses

In the past each process unit was designed with a control room that provided operational control of the process. With the advent of electronic instrumentation and computer-controlled processing, individual control rooms have been replaced by a central control room that controls a number of process units in many operations. The centralized control room is economically advantageous because of process optimization and increases in efficiency of personnel. Individual process units still exist and, in some specialized units, older control houses which have been supplanted by centralized control rooms may still be used for local process monitoring and for emergency control. Although control room functions and locations are generally determined by process economics, the design of the control room or control house is very important for maintaining emergency control and for worker protection. Some considerations for both central and local control houses include:

- pressurizing the control house to prevent the entrance of toxic and hazardous vapours
- designing the control house for blast and explosion resistance
- establishing a location that is at minimal risk (based upon separation distance and probability of gas releases)
- purifying all inlet air and installing an inlet stack location that minimizes the intake of toxic or hazardous vapours
- sealing all sewer outlets from the control house
- installing a fire suppression system.

Inventory reduction

An important consideration in process and plant layouts is the quantity of toxic and hazardous material in the overall inventory, including the equipment. The consequences of a leak are more severe as the volume of material increases. Consequently, the inventory should be minimized wherever possible. Improved processing that reduces the number and size of pieces of equipment reduces the inventory, lowers the risk and also results in lower investment and improved operating efficiencies.

Some potential inventory reduction considerations are shown in table 77.6. Where a new process facility will be installed, processing should be optimized by taking into consideration some of the objectives shown in table 77.6.

Table 77.6 • Steps for limiting inventory.

- Reducing storage tank inventory reduction through improved process control, operation and just-in-time inventory control
- Eliminating or minimizing onsite tank inventory through process integration
- Using reaction variable analysis and development for reactor volume reduction
- Replacing batch reactors with continuous reactors, which also reduces downstream holdup
- Lowering distillation column holdup through bottoms-volume reductions and tray holdup with either more advanced trays or packings
- Replacing kettle reboilers with thermosyphon reboilers
- Minimizing overhead drum and bottoms surge drum volumes
- Improving pipe layout and sizing to minimize holdup
- Where toxic materials are produced, minimizing the toxic section holdup

---

Figure 77.2 • Typical above-ground storage tanks.

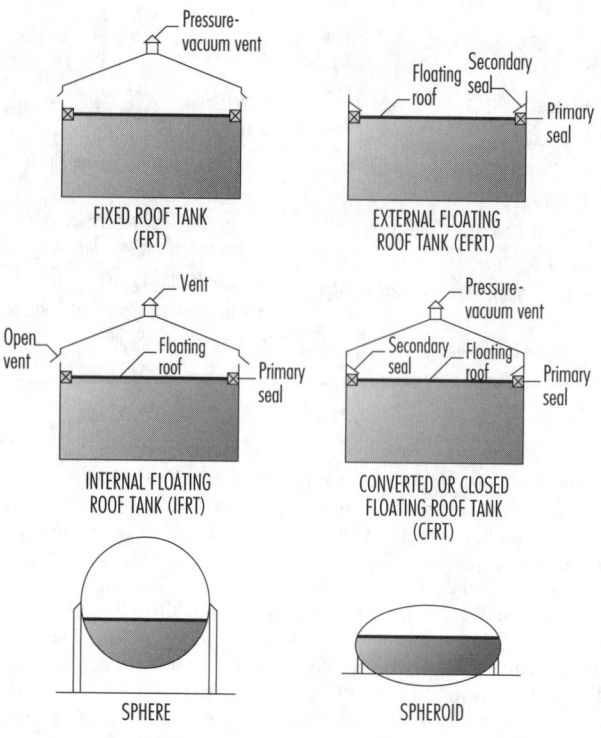

Storage Facilities

The storage facilities in a chemical processing plant can house liquid and solid feed, intermediate chemicals, by-products and process products. Products stored in many facilities serve as intermediates or precursors for other processes. Storage may also be required for diluents, solvents or other process materials. All of these materials are generally stored in above-ground storage tankage (AST). Underground tankage is still used in some locations, but use is generally limited due to access problems and limited capacity. In addition, potential leakage of such underground storage tanks (USTs) presents environmental problems when leaks contaminate ground water. General earth contamination can lead to potential atmospheric exposures with higher vapour-pressure materials leaks. Leaked materials can be a potential exposure problem during ground remediation efforts. UST leakage has resulted in stringent environmental regulations in many countries, such as the requirements for double-walled tanks and underground monitoring.

Typical above-ground storage tanks are shown in figure 77.2. Vertical ASTs are cone or domed roof tanks, floating roof tanks that are covered or non-covered floating roof or external floating roof tanks (EFRTs). Converted or closed roof tanks are EFRTs with covers installed on the tanks that are frequently geodesic type domes. Since EFRTs over time do not maintain a perfectly circular shape, sealing the floating roof is difficult and a covering is installed on the tank. A geodesic dome design eliminates roof trusses needed for cone roof tanks (FRTs). The geodesic dome is more economical than a cone roof and, in addition, the dome reduces losses of materials to the environment.

Normally, the tanks are limited to liquid storage where the liquid vapour pressure does not exceed 77 kPa. Where the pressure exceeds this value, spheroids or spheres are used since both are designed for pressure operation. Spheroids can be quite large but are not installed where the pressure may exceed certain

Table 77.7 • Tank separation and location considerations.

- Separation based on shell to shell distances can be based on references and subject to calculating the thermal radiation distance in the event of fire in an adjacent tank.
- Tanks should be separated from process units.
- A tank location, preferably downwind from other areas, minimizes ignition problems in the event of a tank releasing a significant vapour quantity.
- Storage tanks should have dykes, which are also required by law in most regions.
- Tanks can be grouped for utilization of common dykes and firefighting equipment.
- Dykes should have isolation capability in an emergency.

limits defined by the mechanical design. For most higher vapour-pressure storage applications, spheres are normally the storage container and are equipped with pressure relief valves to prevent over pressuring. A safety concern that has developed with spheres is rollover, which generates excessive vapour and results in relief valve discharges or in more extreme situations such as sphere wall rupture (CCPS 1993). In general, the liquid contents stratify and if warm (less dense) material is loaded into the sphere bottom, the warm material rises to the surface with the cooler, higher density surface material rolled over to the bottom. The warm surface material vaporizes, raising the pressure, which may result in relief valve discharge or sphere overpressuring.

Tank layout

Tankage layout requires careful planning. There are recommendations for tank separation distances and other considerations (CCPS 1988; 1993). In many locations, separation distances are not specified by code, but minimum distances (OSHA 1994) can be a result of various decisions applicable to separation distances and locations. Some of these considerations are presented in table 77.7. In addition, tank service is a factor in tank separation for pressurized, refrigerated and atmospheric tanks (CCPS 1993).

Dykes are required and are nominally sized volumetrically to hold the contents of a tank. Where multiple tanks are within a dyke, the minimum volumetric dyke capacity is equivalent to the capacity of the largest tank (OSHA 1994). The dyke walls can be constructed of earth, steel, concrete or solid masonry. However, the earth dykes should be impenetrable and have a flat top with a minimum width of 0.61 m. In addition, the soil within the dyked area should also have an impenetrable layer to prevent any chemical or oil leakage into the soil.

Tank leakage

A problem that has been developing through the years is tank leakage as a result of corrosion in the tank bottom. Frequently, tanks have water layers in the tank bottom that can contribute to corrosion, and electrolytic corrosion may occur due to contact with the earth. As a result, regulatory requirements have been instituted in various regions to control tank bottom leakage and underground soil and water contamination from contaminants in the water. A variety of design procedures have been developed to control and monitor leakage (Hagen and Rials 1994). In addition, double bottoms have also been installed. In some installations, cathodic protection has been installed to further control metal deterioration (Barletta, Bayle and Kennelley 1995).

Water draw off

Manually discharging water periodically from the tank bottom can result in exposure. Visual observation to determine the interface through open manual draining can result in worker exposure. A closed discharge can be installed with an interface sensor and control valve minimizing potential worker exposures (Lipton and Lynch 1994). A variety of sensors are commercially available for this service.

Overfilling tanks

Frequently, tanks are overfilled, creating potential safety and worker exposure hazards. This can be prevented with redundant or dual-level instruments controlling inlet block valves or feed pumps (Bahner 1996). For many years, overflow lines were installed on chemical tanks, but they terminated a short distance above a drain opening to permit visual observation of the overflow discharge. Moreover, the drain had to be sized for greater than the maximum fill rate to ensure proper drainage. However, such a system is a potential exposure source. This can be eliminated by connecting the overflow line directly to the drain with a flow indicator in the line to show the overflow. Although this will function satisfactorily, this results in overloading the drain system with a very large contaminant volume and potential health and safety problems.

Tank inspection and cleaning

Periodically, tanks are removed from service for inspection and/ or cleaning. These procedures must be carefully controlled to prevent worker exposure and minimize potential safety hazards. Following draining, tanks are frequently flushed with water to remove process liquid traces. Historically, the tanks have then been cleaned manually or mechanically where necessary. When tanks are drained, they are filled with vapour that may be toxic and can be within a combustible range. Water flushing may not significantly affect vapour toxicity, but it may reduce potential combustion problems. With floating roofs, the material below the floating roof can be flushed and drained, but some tanks may still have material in the sump. This bottom material must be removed manually and may present potential exposure concerns. Personnel may be required to wear personal protective equipment (PPE).

Normally, enclosed tanks and any volume below the floating roofs are purged with air until a specified oxygen concentration level is achieved before entry is permitted. However, concentration measurements should be continually obtained to ensure toxic concentration levels are satisfactory and do not change.

Vapour venting and emission control

For fixed roof or converted floating roof tanks (CFRTs), venting to the atmosphere may not be acceptable in many locations. The pressure-vacuum (PV) vent (shown in figure 77.2) on these tanks are removed and the vapours flow through a closed duct to a control device where the contaminants are destroyed or recovered. For both tanks, an inert purge (e.g., nitrogen) can be injected to eliminate the diurnal vacuum effect and maintain a positive pressure for the recovery device. In the CFRT tank, the nitrogen eliminates the diurnal effect and reduces any vapours to the atmosphere through a PV vent. However, vapour emissions are not eliminated. A large number of control devices and techniques are available including combustion, absorbers, condensers and absorption (Moretti and Mukhopadhyay 1993; Carroll and Ruddy 1993; Basta 1994; Pennington 1996; Siegall 1996). Selection of a control system is a function of final emission targets and operating and investment costs.

In floating roof tanks, both external and internal, seals and auxiliary fitting controls effectively minimize vapour losses.

Safety hazards

Flammability is a major concern in tankage and fire-fighting systems are required to aid in control and prevention of expanded fire zones. Firewater systems and installation recommendations are available (CCPS 1993; Dow Chemical Company 1994a; NFPA 1990). Water can be sprayed directly on a fire under certain conditions and is essential in cooling adjacent tankage or equipment to prevent overheating. In addition, foam is an effective fire-fighting agent and permanent foam equipment can be installed on tanks. The installation of foam equipment on mobile fire-fighting equipment should be reviewed with a manufacturer. Environmentally acceptable and low toxicity foams are now available that are effective and comparable to other foams in quickly extinguishing fires.

Processing Equipment

A wide variety of process equipment is required in chemicals processing as a result of the numerous processes, specialized process requirements and variations in products. Consequently, all of the chemical equipment in use today cannot be reviewed; this section will concentrate on the more widely applied equipment found in processing sequences.

Reactors

There are a large number of reactor types in the chemical industry. The basis for reactor selection is a function of a number of variables, beginning with classifying whether the reaction is a batch or continuous reaction. Frequently, batch reactions are converted to continuous operations as experience with the reaction increases and some modifications, such as improved catalysts, become available. Continuous reaction processing is generally more efficient and produces a more consistent product, which is desirable in meeting product quality targets. However, there are still a large number of batch operations.

Reaction

In all reactions, the classifications of a reaction as exothermic or endothermic (producing heat or requiring heat) is necessary in order to define the heating or cooling requirements necessary to control the reaction. In addition, runaway reaction criteria must be established to install instrument sensors and controls that can prevent a reaction from becoming out of control. Prior to full-scale operation of a reactor, emergency procedures must be investigated and developed to ensure the runaway reaction is safely contained. Some of the various potential solutions are emergency control equipment that is automatically activated, injection of a chemical that stops the reaction and vent facilities that can accommodate and contain the reactor contents. Safety valve and vent operation are extremely important requiring well-maintained and functioning equipment at all times. Consequently, multiple interlocked safety valves are frequently installed to ensure that maintenance on one valve will not reduce the required relief capacity.

Should a safety valve or vent discharge due to malfunction, the discharge effluent must be contained in practically all circumstances to minimize potential safety and health hazards. As a result, the method of containing the emergency discharge through piping along with final disposition of the reactor discharge should be carefully analysed. In general, liquid and vapour should be separated with the vapour sent to a flare or recovery and liquid recycled where possible. Solids removal may require some study.

Batch

In reactors involving exothermic reactions, an important consideration is fouling on the walls or internal tubing by the cooling media used to maintain the temperature. Removal of fouled material varies considerably and the method of removal is a function of the fouled material characteristics. Fouled material can be removed with a solvent, a high-pressure jet nozzle stream or, in some cases, manually. In all these procedures, safety and exposure must be carefully controlled. Movement of material in and out of the reactor must not permit the entrance of air, which may result in a flammable vapour mixture. Vacuums should be broken with an inert gas (e.g., nitrogen). Vessel entry for inspection or work can be classified as entry into a confined space and the rules for this procedure should be observed. Vapour and dermal toxicity should be understood and technicians must be knowledgeable about health hazards.

Continuous

Flow-through reactors can be filled with liquid or a vapour and liquid. Some reactions produce slurries in the reactors. Also, there are reactors that contain solid catalysts. The reaction fluid may be liquid, vapour or a combination of vapour and liquid. Solid catalysts, which promote a reaction without participating in it, are normally contained within grids and are termed fixed beds. The fixed-bed reactors may have single or multiple beds and can have exotherinic or endothermic reactions, with most reactions requiring a constant temperature (isothermal) through each bed. This frequently requires the injection of feed streams or a diluent at various locations between beds to control the temperature. With these reaction systems, temperature indication and sensor location through the beds are extremely important to prevent a reaction runaway and product yield or quality changes.

Fixed beds generally lose their activity and must be regenerated or replaced. For regeneration, deposits on the bed may be burned off, dissolved in a solvent or, in some cases, regenerated through the injection of a chemical in an inert fluid into the bed, thereby restoring catalyst activity. Depending on the catalyst, one of these techniques may be applied. Where beds are burned, the reactor is emptied and purged of all process fluids then filled with an inert gas (usually nitrogen), which is heated and recirculated, raising the bed to a specified temperature level. At this point, a very small volume of oxygen is added to the inert stream to initiate a flame front that gradually moves through the bed and controls the temperature rise. Excessive oxygen quantities have a deleterious effect on the catalyst.

Fixed-bed catalyst removal

Removal of fixed-bed catalysts must be carefully controlled. The reactors are drained of process fluid and then the remaining fluid is displaced with a flushing fluid or purged with a vapour until all of the process fluid has been removed. Final purging may require other techniques before the vessel can be purged with an inert gas or air prior to opening the vessel or discharging the catalyst from the vessel under an inert blanket. Should water be used in this process, the water is drained through closed piping to a process sewer. Some catalysts are sensitive to air or oxygen, becoming pyrophoric or toxic. These require special procedures to eliminate air during filling or emptying the vessels. Personal protection along with handling procedures must be carefully defined to minimize potential exposures and protect personnel.

Spent catalyst disposal may require further treating before it is sent to a catalyst manufacturer for recycling or into an environmentally acceptable disposal procedure.

Other catalyst systems

Gas flowing through a loose solid catalyst bed expands the bed and forms a suspension that is similar to a liquid and termed a fluid bed. This type of reaction is used in various processes. Spent catalysts are removed as a gas-solids side stream for regeneration and then returned to the process through an enclosed system. In other reactions, catalyst activity may be very high and, although catalyst is discharged in the product, the concentration is extremely low and does not pose a problem. Where a high concentration of catalyst solids in the product vapour is undesirable, solids carryover must be removed before purification. However, traces of solids will remain. These are removed for disposal in one of the by-product streams, which in turn must be clarified.

In situations where spent catalyst is regenerated through burning, extensive solids recovery facilities are required in fluid-bed systems to meet environmental restrictions. Recovery may consist of various combinations of cyclones, electric precipitators, bag filters) and/ or scrubbers. Where burning occurs in fixed beds, the basic concern is temperature control.

Since fluid-bed catalysts are frequently within the respiratory range, care must be exercised during solids handling to ensure worker protection with either fresh or recovered catalysts.

In some instances a vacuum may be used to remove various components from a fixed bed. In these situations, a steam-driven vacuum jet is frequently the vacuum producer. This produces a steam discharge that frequently contains toxic materials although in very low concentration in the jet stream. However, the discharge of a steam jet should be carefully reviewed to determine contaminant quantities, toxicity and potential dispersion if it is discharged directly to the atmosphere. Should this be unsatisfactory, the jet discharge may require condensing in a sump where all vapours are controlled and the water is sent to the closed sewer system. A rotary vacuum pump will perform in this service. The discharge from a reciprocating vacuum pump may not be permitted to discharge directly to the atmosphere, but can in some instances discharge into a flare line, incinerator or process heater.

Safety

In all reactors, pressure increases are a major concern since the vessel pressure rating must not be exceeded. These pressure increases may be a result of poor process control, malfunction or a runaway reaction. Consequently, pressure relief systems are required to maintain vessel integrity by preventing reactor overpressuring. Relief valve discharges must be carefully designed to maintain adequate relief under all conditions, including relief-valve maintenance. Multiple valves may be required. Should a relief valve be designed to discharge into the atmosphere, the discharge point should be elevated above all nearby structures and a dispersion analysis should be conducted to ensure adequate protection for workers and nearby communities.

If a rupture disk is installed with a safety valve, the discharge should also be enclosed and the final discharge location designated as described above. Since a disk rupture will not reseat, a disk without a safety valve will probably release most of the reactor contents and air may enter the reactor at the end of the release. This requires a careful analysis to ensure that a flammable situation is not created and that highly undesirable reactions do not occur. Moreover, the discharge from a disk may release liquid and the vent system must be designed to contain all liquids with vapour discharged, as described above. Atmospheric emergency releases must be approved by regulatory authorities before installation.

Mixer agitators installed in reactors are sealed. Leaks may be hazardous and if they occur the seal must be repaired which requires a reactor shutdown. The reactor contents may require special handling or precautions and an emergency shutdown procedure should include reaction termination and disposition of the reactor contents. Flammability and exposure control must be carefully reviewed for each step including final disposition of the reactor mix. Since a shutdown can be expensive and involve production loss, magnetic driven mixers and newer seal systems have been introduced to reduce maintenance and reactor shutdowns.

Entrance to all reactors requires compliance with safe confined-space entry procedures.

Fractionation or distillation towers

Distillation is a process whereby chemical substances are separated through methods which take advantage of differences in boiling points. The familiar towers in chemical plants and refineries are distillation towers.

Distillation in various forms is a processing step found in the great majority of chemical processes. Fractionation or distillation can be found in purification, separation, stripping, azeotropic and extractive process steps. These applications now include reactive distillation, where a reaction occurs in a separate section of the distillation tower.

Distillation is conducted with a series of trays in a tower, or it can be conducted in a tower filled with packing. The packings have special configurations that readily permit the passage of vapour and liquid, but provide sufficient surface area for vapour-liquid contact and efficient fractionation.

Operation

Heat is normally supplied to a tower with a reboiler, although the heat content of specific streams may be sufficient to eliminate the reboiler. With reboiler heat, multiple step vapour-liquid separation occurs on the trays and lighter materials ascend through the tower. Vapours from the top tray are fully or partially condensed in the overhead condenser. The condensed liquid is collected in the distillate recovery drum, where part of the liquid is recycled to the tower and the other portion is withdrawn and sent to a specific location. Non-condensed vapours may be recovered elsewhere or sent to a control device which can be a combustor or recovery system.

Pressure

Towers typically operate at pressures higher than atmospheric pressure. However, towers are frequently operated under vacuum to minimize liquid temperatures that may affect product quality or in situations where tower materials become a mechanical and economic concern due to the temperature level that may be difficult to achieve. Also, high temperatures may affect the fluid. In heavy petroleum fractions, very high tower bottoms temperatures frequently result in coking problems.

Vacuums are typically obtained with ejectors or vacuum pumps. In process units, vacuum loadings consist of some light vapour materials, inerts that may have been in the tower feed stream and air from leakage. Normally the vacuum system is installed after a condenser to reduce the organic loading to the vacuum system. The vacuum system is sized based upon the estimated vapour loading, with ejectors handling larger vapour loadings. In certain systems a vacuum machine may be directly connected to a condenser outlet. A typical ejector system operation is a combination of ejectors and direct barometric condensers where the ejector vapours have direct contact with the cooling water. Barometric condensers are very large consumers of water and the steam-water mixture results in high water outlet temperatures that tend to vaporize any organic compound traces in the atmospheric barometric sump, potentially increasing workplace exposures. In addition, a large effluent load is added to the wastewater system.

A large water reduction is achieved along with a substantial reduction in steam consumption in modified vacuum systems. Since the vacuum pump will not handle a large vapour load, a steam ejector is used in the first stage in combination with a surface condenser to reduce the vacuum pump load. In addition, a sump drum is installed for above-ground operation. The simpler system reduces waste-water loading and maintains a closed system that eliminates potential vapour exposures.

Safety

All towers and drums must be protected from overpressure that may result from malfunction, fire (Mowrer 1995) or utility failure. A hazard review is necessary and is required by law in some countries. A general process safety management approach that is applicable to process and plant operation improves safety, minimizes losses and protects worker health (Auger 1995; Murphy 1994; Sutton 1995). Protection is provided by pressure relief valves (PRVs) that discharge to the atmosphere or to a closed system. The PRV is generally mounted at the tower top to relieve the large vapour load, although some installations locate the PRV in other tower locations. The PRV can also be located on the distillate overhead recovery drum as long as valves are not placed between the PRV and the tower top. If block valves are installed in the process lines to the condenser then the PRV must be installed on the tower.

When distillation tower overpressure is relieved, under certain emergency scenarios, the PRV discharge may be exceedingly large. Very high loading in a closed system discharge vent line may be the largest load in the system. Since a PRV discharge can be sudden and the overall relieving time may be quite short (less than 15 minutes), this extremely large vapour load must be carefully analysed (Bewanger and Krecter 1995; Boicourt 1995). Since this short, large peak load is difficult to process in control devices such as absorbers, adsorbers, furnaces and so on, the preferable control device in most situations is a flare for vapour destruction. Normally, a number of PRVs are connected to a flare line header that in turn is connected to a single flare. However, the flare and overall system must be carefully designed to cover a large group of potential contingencies (Boicourt 1995).

Health hazards

For direct relief to the atmosphere, a detailed dispersion analysis of the relief valve discharge vapours should be conducted to ensure that workers are not exposed and that community concentrations are well within allowable concentration guidelines. In controlling dispersion, atmospheric relief valve discharge lines may have to be raised to prevent excessive concentrations on nearby structures. A very tall flare-like stack may be necessary to control dispersion.

Another area of concern is entering a tower for maintenance or mechanical changes during a shutdown. This entails entering a confined space and exposes workers to the associated hazards. The flushing and purging method prior to opening must be

Figure 77.3 • Typical heat exchangers.

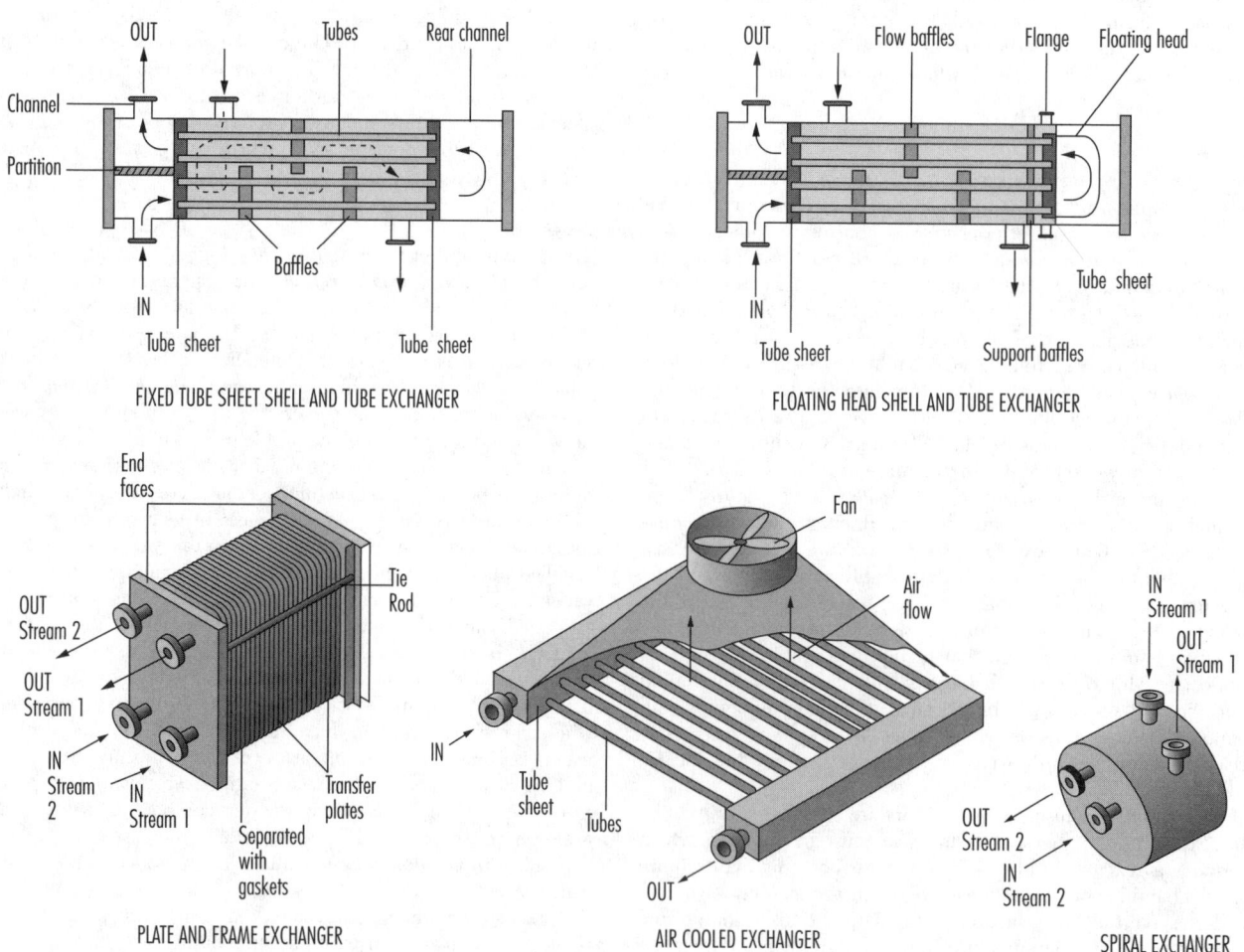

FIXED TUBE SHEET SHELL AND TUBE EXCHANGER

FLOATING HEAD SHELL AND TUBE EXCHANGER

PLATE AND FRAME EXCHANGER

AIR COOLED EXCHANGER

SPIRAL EXCHANGER

carefully conducted to ensure minimal exposures by reducing any toxic concentrations below recommended levels. Before commencing with flushing and purging operations, the tower pressure must be reduced and all piping connections to the tower must be blinded (i.e., flat metal disks must be placed between the tower flanges and the connecting pipe flanges). This step should be carefully managed to ensure minimum exposures. In different processes, the methods of clearing the tower of toxic fluids vary. Frequently, the tower fluid is displaced with a fluid that has very low toxicity characteristics. This displacement fluid is then drained and pumped to a selected location. The remaining liquid film and droplets can be steamed to the atmosphere through a top flange that has a special stand-off blind with an opening between the blind and tower flange. Following steaming, air enters the tower through the special blind opening as the tower cools. A manhole at the tower bottom and one at the tower top are opened permitting the blowing of air through the tower. When the internal tower concentration reaches a predetermined level, the tower can be entered.

Heat exchangers

There are a wide variety of heat exchangers in the chemical process industry. Heat exchangers are mechanical devices for the transfer of heat to or from a process stream. They are selected in accordance with process conditions and exchanger designs. A few of the common exchanger types are shown in figure 77.3. Selection of the optimum exchanger for a process service is somewhat complicated and requires a detailed investigation (Woods 1995). In many situations, certain types are not suitable because of pressure, temperature, solids concentration, viscosity, flow quantity and other factors. Moreover, an individual heat exchanger design can vary considerably; several types of floating head tube and sheet exchangers are available (Green, Maloney and Perry 1984). The floating head is normally selected where the temperatures may cause excessive tube expansion that otherwise could not maintain integrity in a fixed tube sheet exchanger. In the simplified floating head exchanger in figure 77.3, the floating head is contained completely within the exchanger and does not have any connection with the shell cover. In other floating head designs, there may be packing around the floating tubesheet (Green, Maloney and Perry 1984).

Leakage

The packing on floating tubesheets is in contact with the atmosphere and may be a source of leakage and potential exposure. Other exchangers may also have potential leakage sources and should be examined carefully. As a result of their heat transfer characteristics, plate and frame exchangers are often installed in the chemical industry. The plates have various corrugations and configurations. Plates are separated by gaskets that prevent mixing of the streams and provide an external seal. However, the seals limit temperature applications to about 180 °C, although seal improvements may overcome this limitation. Since there are a number of plates, the plates must be compressed properly to ensure proper sealing between them. Consequently, careful mechanical installation is necessary to prevent leakage and potential hazards. Since there are a large number of seals, careful seal monitoring is important to minimize potential exposures.

Air cooled exchangers are attractive economically and have been installed in a wide number of process applications and in various locations within process units. To save space, these exchangers are often installed over pipe runs and are frequently stacked. Since tube material selection is important, a variety of materials is used in the chemical industry. These tubes are connected to the tube sheet. This requires use of compatible materials. Leakage through a tube crack or at the tube sheet is a

concern since the fan will circulate vapours from the leak and dispersion may result in potential exposures. Air dilution may significantly reduce the potential exposure hazard. However, fans are frequently shut down under some weather conditions and in these circumstances leak concentrations can increase thereby increasing potential exposures. Moreover, if leaking tubes are not repaired, the crack may worsen. With toxic liquids that do not readily vaporize, dripping can occur and result in potential dermal exposure.

Shell and tube heat exchangers may develop leaks through any of the various flanges (Green, Maloney and Perry 1984). Since shell and tube heat exchangers vary in size from small to very large surface areas, the diameter of outer flanges is generally much larger than typical pipe flanges. With these large flanges, the gaskets must not only withstand process conditions, but provide a seal under bolt load variations. Various gasket designs are used. Maintaining constant bolt load stresses on all of the flange bolts is difficult, resulting in leakage in many exchangers. The flange leakage can be controlled with flange sealing rings (Lipton and Lynch 1994).

Tube leakage may occur in any of the available exchanger types, with the exception of plate exchangers and a few other specialty exchangers. However, these latter exchangers have other potential problems. Where tubes leak into a cooling water system, the cooling water discharges the contaminant into a cooling tower which can be an exposure source to both workers and a nearby community. Consequently, the cooling water should be monitored.

The dispersion of cooling tower vapours can be widespread as a result of the fans in forced and induced draft cooling towers. In addition, natural convection towers discharge vapours to the atmosphere which then disperse. However, dispersion varies considerably based upon both weather conditions and the discharge elevation. Less volatile toxic materials remain in the cooling water and the cooling tower blowdown stream, which should have sufficient treatment capability to destroy contaminants. The cooling tower and tower basin must be cleaned periodically and contaminants add to the potential hazards in the basin and in the tower fill. Personal protection is necessary for much of this work.

Exchanger cleaning

A problem with tubes in cooling water service is the build-up of material in the tubes resulting from corrosion, biological organisms and solids deposition. As described above, tubes may also leak through cracks, or leakage may occur where tubes are rolled into striations in the tube sheet. When any of these conditions occur, exchanger repair is required and the process fluids must be removed from the exchanger. This requires a completely contained operation, which is necessary to meet environmental, safety and health exposure objectives.

Generally, the process fluid is drained to a receiver and the remaining material is flushed out of the exchanger with a solvent or inert material. The latter material is also sent to a receiver for the contaminated material by draining or pressuring with nitrogen. Where toxic material was in the exchanger, the exchanger should be monitored for any traces of toxic material. If testing results are unsatisfactory, the exchanger can be steamed to vaporize and remove all traces of material. However, the steam vent should be connected to a closed system to prevent vapour escape into the atmosphere. While the closed vent may not be absolutely necessary, at times there may be more contaminant material in the exchanger, requiring closed steam venting at all times to control potential hazards. Following steaming, a vent to the atmosphere admits air. This general procedure is applicable to the exchanger side or sides containing toxic material.

Chemicals then used for cleaning the tubes or the shell side should be circulated in a closed system. Normally, the cleaning solution is recirculated from a tank truck system and the contaminated solution in the system is drained to a truck for disposition.

Pumps

One of the most important process functions is the movement of liquids and in the chemical industry all types of liquid materials are moved with a wide variety of pumps. Canned and magnetic pumps are sealless centrifugal pumps. Magnetic pump drivers are available for installation on other pump types to prevent leakage. Types of pumps used in the chemical process industry are listed in table 77.8.

Sealing

From a health and safety standpoint, sealing and repairing centrifugal pumps are major concerns. Mechanical seals, which constitute the prevalent shaft sealing system, can leak and at times have blown out. However, there have been major advances in seal technology since the 1970s that have resulted in significant leakage reductions and extended pump service life. Some of these improvements are bellows seals, cartridge seals, improved face designs, better face materials and improvements in pump variable monitoring. Moreover, continuing research in seal technology should result in further technology improvements.

Where process fluids are highly toxic, leakless or sealless canned or magnetic pumps are frequently installed. Operating service periods or the mean time between maintenance (MTBM) has improved markedly and generally varies between three and five years. In these pumps, the process fluid is the lubricating fluid for the rotor bearings. Vaporization of the internal fluid adversely affects the bearings and often makes bearing replacement necessary. Liquid conditions in the pumps can be maintained by ensuring the internal pressure in the bearing system is always greater than the liquid vapour pressure at the operating temperature. When repairing a sealless pump, completely draining a relatively low volatility material is important and should be carefully reviewed with the supplier.

In typical centrifugal process pumps, packing has essentially been replaced with mechanical seals. These seals are generally classified as single or dual mechanical seals, with the latter term covering tandem or double mechanical seals. There are other dual seal combinations, but they are not as widely used. In general, tandem or double mechanical seals with liquid buffer fluids between the seals are installed to reduce seal leakage. Pump mechanical seal standards for both centrifugal and rotary pumps covering single and dual mechanical seal specification and installation were issued by the American Petroleum Institute (API 1994). A mechanical seal application guide is now available to aid in the evaluation of seal types (STLE 1994).

To prevent excessive leakage or blow-out from a failed seal, a gland plate is installed following the seal. It may have a gland flush fluid to move the leakage into a closed drain system (API 1994). Since the gland system is not a complete seal, auxiliary seal systems, such as throttle bushings are available. They are installed in the gland that controls excessive leakage to the atmosphere or seal blow-out (Lipton and Lynch 1994). These seals are not designed for continuous operation; after activation they will operate for up to two weeks before failure, thereby providing time for operations to switch pumps or make process adjustments.

A newer mechanical seal system is available that essentially reduces emissions to the nil level. This is a double mechanical seal system with a gas buffer system that replaces the liquid buffer in the standard dual mechanical seal system (Fone 1995; Netzel 1996; Adams, Dingman and Parker 1995). In the liquid buffer

---

Table 77.8 • Pumps in the chemicals process industry.

• Centrifugal	• Diaphragm
• Reciprocating (plunger)	• Axial flow
• Canned	• Screw
• Magnetic	• Moving cavity
• Turbine	• Lobe
• Gear	• Vane

systems, the seal faces are separated by an extremely thin lubricating film of buffer fluid that also cools the seal faces. Although separated slightly, a certain amount of face contact exists which results in seal wear and seal face heating. The gas seals are called non-contact seals since one seal face with curved indentations pumps gas through the seal faces and builds a gas layer or dam that completely separates the seal faces. This lack of contact results in a very long seal life and also reduces the seal friction loss, thereby noticeably decreasing power consumption. Since the seal pumps gas there is a very small flow into the process and to the atmosphere.

Health hazards

A major concern with pumps is draining and flushing to prepare the pump for maintenance or repair. Draining and removal covers both process fluid and buffer fluids. Procedures should require discharge of all fluids into a closed connection drain system. In the pump stuffing box where a throat bushing separates the impeller from the stuffing box, the bushing acts as a weir in holding some liquid in the stuffing box. Weep holes in the bushing or a drain in the stuffing box will permit complete process liquid removal through draining and flushing. For buffer fluids, there should be a method of draining all fluid from the dual seal area. Maintenance requires seal removal and if the seal volume is not completely drained and flushed, the seals are a potential source of exposure during repair.

Dust and powders

Handling of dusts and powders in solids processing equipment is a concern due to the potential for fire or explosion. An explosion within equipment may burst through a wall or enclosure as a result of explosion-generated pressure sending a combined pressure and fire wave into the workplace area. Workers can be at risk, and adjacent equipment can be severely impacted with drastic effects. Dusts or powders suspended in air or in a gas with

---

Table 77.9 • Potential explosion sources in equipment.

Conveying equipment	Storage
• Pneumatic ducts	• Bins
• Mechanical conveyors	• Hoppers
	• Rotary valves
Processing equipment	
• Filter dust collectors	• Grinders
• Fluid bed dryers	• Ball mills
• Transfer line dryers	• Powder mixing
• Screening	• Cyclones

oxygen present and in a confined space are susceptible to explosion when a source of ignition with sufficient energy is present. Some typical explosive equipment environments are shown in table 77.9.

An explosion produces heat and rapid gas expansion (pressure increase) and generally results in deflagration, which is a flame front that moves rapidly but at less than the sound velocity for these conditions. When the flame front velocity is greater than the sound velocity or is at supersonic velocity the condition is termed detonation, which is more destructive than deflagration. Explosion and flame front expansion occur in milliseconds and do not provide sufficient time for standard process responses. Consequently, the potential fire and explosion characteristics of the powder must be defined to determine the potential hazards that may exist in the various processing steps (CCPS 1993; Ebadat 1994; Bartknecht 1989; Cesana and Siwek 1995). This information can then provide a basis for the installation of controls and the prevention of explosions.

Explosion hazard quantification

Since the explosions generally occur in enclosed equipment, various tests are conducted in specially-designed laboratory equipment. While powders may appear similar, published results should not be used since small differences in the powders can have very different explosion characteristics.

A variety of tests conducted on powder can define the explosion hazard and the test series should encompass the following.

The classification test determines whether a powder dust cloud can initiate and propagate flames (Ebadat 1994). Powders that have these characteristics are considered Class A powders. Those powders that do not ignite are termed Class B. The Class A powders then require a further series of tests to evaluate their explosion and hazard potential.

The minimum ignition energy test defines the minimum spark energy necessary for ignition of a powder cloud (Bartknecht 1989).

In explosion severity and analysis Group A powders are then tested as a dust cloud in a sphere where the pressure is measured during a test explosion based on minimum ignition energy. The maximum explosion pressure is defined along with the rate of change in pressure per unit time. From this information, the explosion specific characteristic value (Kst) in bar metres per second is determined and the explosion class is defined (Bartknecht 1989; Garzia and Senecal 1996):

Kst(bar · m/s)	Dust explosion class	Relative strength
1-200	St 1	Somewhat weaker
201-300	St 2	Strong
300+	St 3	Very strong

A large number of powders have been tested and the majority were in the St 1 class (Bartknecht 1989; Garzia and Senecal 1996).

In assessment of non-cloud powders, powders are tested to determine safe operating procedures and conditions.

Explosion prevention tests

Explosion prevention tests can be helpful where explosion suppression systems cannot be installed. They provide some information on desirable operating conditions (Ebadat 1994).

The minimum oxygen test defines the oxygen level below which the dust will not ignite (Fone 1995). Inert gas in the process will prevent ignition if the gas is acceptable.

The minimum dust concentration is determined in order to establish the operating level below which ignition will not occur.

Electrostatic hazard tests

Many explosions are a result of electrostatic ignitions and various tests indicate the potential hazards. Some of the tests cover the minimum ignition energy, powder electric charge characteristics and volume resistivity. From the test results, certain steps can be taken to prevent explosions. Steps include increasing humidity, modifying construction materials, proper grounding, controlling certain aspects of equipment design and preventing sparks (Bartknecht 1989; Cesana and Siwek 1995).

Explosion control

There are basically two methods of controlling explosions or fronts from propagating from one location and another or containing an explosion within a piece of equipment. These two methods are chemical suppressants and isolation valves (Bartknecht 1989; Cesana and Siwek 1995; Garzia and Senecal 1996). Based upon the explosion pressure data from the explosion severity tests, rapid response sensors are available that will trigger a chemical suppressant and/ or rapidly close isolation barrier valves. Suppressants are commercially available, but suppressant injector design is very important.

Explosion vents

In equipment where a potential explosion may occur, explosion vents that rupture at specific pressures are frequently installed. These must be carefully designed and the exhaust path from the equipment must be defined to prevent a worker presence in this path area. Moreover, impingement on equipment in the explosion path should be analysed to ensure equipment safety. A barrier may be required.

Loading and Unloading

Products, intermediates and by-products are loaded into tank trucks and railcars. (In some cases, depending on location of facilities and dockage requirements, tankers and barges are used.) Location of the loading and unloading facilities are important. While the materials loaded and unloaded usually are liquids and gases, solids are also loaded and unloaded at preferred locations based upon the type of solids moved, potential explosion hazard and the degree of transfer difficulty.

Open hatches

In loading tank trucks or railcars through top opening hatches, a very important consideration is minimizing splashing as the container is filled. If the fill pipe is located well above the bottom of the container, filling results in splashing and generation of vapour or mixed liquid-vapour evolvement. Splashing and vapour generation can be minimized by locating the fill pipe outlet well below the liquid level. The fill pipe is normally extended through the container a minimum distance above the container bottom. Since liquid filling also displaces vapour, toxic vapours can be a potential health hazard and also present safety concerns. Consequently, the vapours should be collected. Fill arms are commercially available that have deep fill pipes and extend through a special cover that closes the hatch opening (Lipton and Lynch 1994). In addition, a vapour collection pipe extends a short distance below the special hatch cover. At the upstream end of the arm, the vapour outlet is connected to a recovery device (e.g., an absorber or condenser), or the vapour can be returned to the storage tank as a vapour balance transfer (Lipton and Lynch 1994).

In the tank truck open hatch system, the arm is raised to permit draining into the tank truck and some of the liquid in the arm can be pressured with nitrogen as the arm is withdrawn, but the fill pipes during this operation should remain within the hatch opening. As the fill arm clears the hatch, a bucket should be placed over the outlet to catch arm drippings.

Railcars

Many railcars have closed hatches with deep fill legs very close to the bottom of the container and a separate vapour collection outlet. Through an arm that extends to the closed hatch, liquid is loaded and vapour collected in a fashion similar to the open hatch arm method. In railcar loading systems, following valve shut off at the arm inlet, nitrogen is injected into the container side of the arms to blow the liquid remaining in the arm into the railcar before the fill valve on the railcar is closed (Lipton and Lynch 1994).

Tank trucks

Many tank trucks are filled through the bottom to minimize vapour generation (Lipton and Lynch 1994). The fill lines can be special hoses or manoeuvrable arms. Dry break couplers are placed on the hose or arm ends and on the tank truck bottom connections. When the tank truck is filled and the line is automatically blocked, the arm or hose is disconnected at the drybreak coupling, which automatically closes as the couplings are separated. Newer couplings have been designed to disconnect with almost zero leakage.

In bottom loading, vapour is collected through a top vapour vent and the vapour is conducted through an external line that terminates near the bottom of the container (Lipton and Lynch 1994). This permits worker access to the vapour coupling connections. The collected vapour, which is at a pressure slightly above atmospheric, must be collected and sent to a recovery device (Lipton and Lynch 1994). These devices are selected based upon initial cost, effectiveness, maintenance and operability. Generally, the recovery system is preferable to a flare, which destroys the recovered vapours.

Loading control

In tank trucks, level sensors are permanently installed within the truck body to indicate when the fill level has been reached and signal a remote control block valve that stops flow to the truck. (Lipton and Lynch 1994). There may be more than one sensor in the tank truck as backup to ensure that the truck is not overfilled. Overfilling can result in serious safety and health exposure problems.

Railcars in dedicated chemical service may have level sensors mounted internally in the car. For non-dedicated cars, a flow totalizer controls the amount of liquid sent to the railcar and automatically shuts the remote control block valve at a predetermined setting (Lipton and Lynch 1994). Both container types should be investigated to determine whether liquid remains in the container prior to filling. Many railcars have manual level indicators that can be used for this service. However, where level is shown by opening a small level stick vent to the atmosphere, this procedure should only be performed under properly controlled and approved conditions due to the toxicity of some of the loaded chemicals.

Unloading

Where chemicals have a very high vapour pressure and the railcar or tank truck has a relatively high pressure, the chemical is unloaded under its own vapour pressure. Should the vapour pressure fall to a level that will interfere with the unloading procedure, nitrogen gas can be injected to maintain a satisfactory pressure. Vapour from a tank of the same chemical can also be compressed and injected to raise the pressure.

For toxic chemicals that have a relatively low vapour pressure, such as benzene, the liquid is unloaded under nitrogen pressure, which eliminates pumping and simplifies the system (Lipton and Lynch 1994). Tank trucks and railcars for this service have design pressures capable of handling the pressures and variations encountered. However, lower pressures after unloading a container are maintained until the tank truck or railcar is refilled; the pressure rebuilds during loading. Nitrogen can be added if sufficient pressure has not been attained during loading.

One of the problems in loading and unloading operations is draining and purging lines and equipment in the loading/unloading facilities. Closed drains and particularly low point drains are necessary with nitrogen purges to remove all traces of the toxic chemicals. These materials can be collected in a drum and returned to a receiving or recovery facility (Lipton and Lynch 1994).

EXAMPLES OF CHEMICAL PROCESSING OPERATIONS

CHLORINE AND CAUSTIC PRODUCTION

The Chlorine Institute, Inc.

Electrolysis of salt brines produces chlorine and caustic. Sodium chloride (NaCl) is the primary salt used; it yields caustic soda (NaOH). However, the use of potassium chloride (KCl) produces caustic potash (KOH).

$$2\,NaCl + 2\,H_2O \rightarrow Cl_2\uparrow + 2\,NaOH + H_2\uparrow$$

salt + water → chlorine (gas) + caustic + hydrogen (gas)

Currently the diaphragm cell process is in greatest use for the commercial production of chlorine followed by the mercury cell process and then the membrane cell process. Due to economic, environmental and product quality issues, manufacturers now prefer the membrane cell process for new production facilities.

The Diaphragm Cell Process

A diaphragm cell (see figure 77.4) is fed saturated salt brine into a compartment containing a titanium anode coated with salts of ruthenium and other metals. A plastic cell head collects the hot, wet chlorine gas produced at this anode. Suction by a compressor then draws the chlorine into a collection header for further processing consisting of cooling, drying and compression. Water and unreacted brine percolate through a porous diaphragm separator into the cathode compartment where water reacts at a steel cathode to produce sodium hydroxide (caustic soda) and hydrogen. The diaphragm keeps the chlorine produced at the anode from the sodium hydroxide and hydrogen produced at the cathode. If these products combine, the result is sodium hypochlorite (bleach) or sodium chlorate. Commercial producers of sodium chlorate use cells that do not have separators. The most common diaphragm is a composite of asbestos and a fluorocarbon polymer. Modern diaphragm cell plants do not have the health or environmental problems historically associated with the use of asbestos diaphragms. Some plants do employ non-asbestos diaphragms, which are now commercially available. The diaphragm cell process produces a weak sodium hydroxide solution containing unreacted salt. An additional evaporation process concentrates the caustic and removes most of the salt to make a caustic of commercial quality.

The Mercury Cell Process

A mercury cell actually consists of two electrochemical cells. The reaction in the first cell at the anode is:

$$2\ Cl^- \rightarrow Cl_2 + 2\ e^-$$

chloride → chlorine + electrons

The reaction in the first cell at the cathode is:

$$Na^+ + Hg + e^- \rightarrow Na \cdot Hg$$

sodium ion + mercury + electrons → sodium amalgam

Salt brine flows in an inclined steel trough with rubber-lined sides (see figure 77.4. Mercury, the cathode, flows under the brine. Anodes of coated titanium are suspended in the brine for the production of chlorine, which exits the cell to a collection and processing system. Sodium is electrolyzed in the cell and leaves the first cell amalgamated with the mercury. This amalgam flows into a second electrochemical cell called the decomposer. The decomposer is a cell with graphite as a cathode and the amalgam as the anode. The reaction in the decomposer is:

$$2\ Na \cdot Hg + 2\ H_2O \rightarrow 2\ NaOH + 2\ Hg + H_2 \uparrow$$

The mercury cell process produces commercial (50%) NaOH directly from the cell.

The Membrane Cell Process

The electrochemical reactions in a membrane cell are the same as in the diaphragm cell. A cation-exchange membrane is used in place of the porous diaphragm (see figure 77.4). This membrane prevents the migration of chloride ions into the catholyte, thereby producing essentially salt free 30 to 35% caustic directly from the cell. The elimination of the need to remove salt makes the

evaporation of the caustic to commercial 50% strength simpler, and it requires less investment and energy. Expensive nickel is used as the cathode in the membrane cell due to the stronger caustic.

Safety and Health Hazards

At ordinary temperatures, dry chlorine, either liquid or gas, does not corrode steel. Wet chlorine is highly corrosive because it forms hydrochloric and hypochlorous acids. Precautions should be taken to keep chlorine and chlorine equipment dry. Piping, valves and containers should be closed or capped when not in use to keep out atmospheric moisture. If water is used on a chlorine leak the resulting corrosive conditions will make the leak worse.

The volume of liquid chlorine increases with temperature. Precautions should be taken to avoid hydrostatic rupture of piping, vessels, containers or other equipment filled with liquid chlorine.

Hydrogen is a co-product of all chlorine manufactured by the electrolysis of aqueous brine solutions. Within a known concentration range, mixtures of chlorine and hydrogen are flammable and potentially explosive. The reaction of chlorine and hydrogen can be initiated by direct sunlight, other sources of ultraviolet light, static electricity or sharp impact.

Small quantities of nitrogen trichloride, an unstable and highly explosive compound, can be produced in the manufacturing of chlorine. When liquid chlorine containing nitrogen trichloride is evaporated, the nitrogen trichloride may reach hazardous concentrations in the remaining liquid chlorine.

Chlorine can react, at times explosively, with a number of organic materials such as oil and grease from sources such as air compressors, valves, pumps and oil-diaphragm instrumentation, as well as wood and rags from maintenance work.

As soon as there is any indication of a chlorine release, immediate steps must be taken to correct the condition. Chlorine leaks always get worse if they are not promptly corrected. When a chlorine leak occurs, authorized, trained personnel equipped with respiratory and other appropriate personal protective equipment (PPE) should investigate and take proper action. Personnel should not enter into atmospheres containing concentrations of chlorine in excess of the immediately dangerous to life and health (IDLH) concentration (10 ppm) without appropriate PPE and back-up personnel. Unnecessary personnel should be kept away and the hazard area should be isolated. Persons potentially affected by a chlorine release should be evacuated or sheltered in place as circumstances warrant.

Area chlorine monitors and wind direction indicators can supply timely information (e.g., escape routes) to help determine whether personnel are to be evacuated or sheltered in place.

When evacuation is utilized, potentially exposed persons should move to a point upwind of the leak. Because chlorine is heavier than air, higher elevations are preferable. To escape in the shortest time, persons already in a contaminated area should move crosswind.

When inside a building and sheltering in place is selected, shelter can be achieved by closing all windows, doors and other openings, and turning off air conditioners and air intake systems. Personnel should move to the side of the building furthest from the release.

Care must be taken not to position personnel without an escape route. A safe position may be made hazardous by a change in wind direction. New leaks may occur or the existing leak may get larger.

If fire is present or imminent, chlorine containers and equipment should be moved away from the fire, if possible. If a non-leaking container or equipment cannot be moved, it should be kept cool by applying water. Water should not be used directly on

---

Figure 77.4 • Types of chloralkali cell processes.

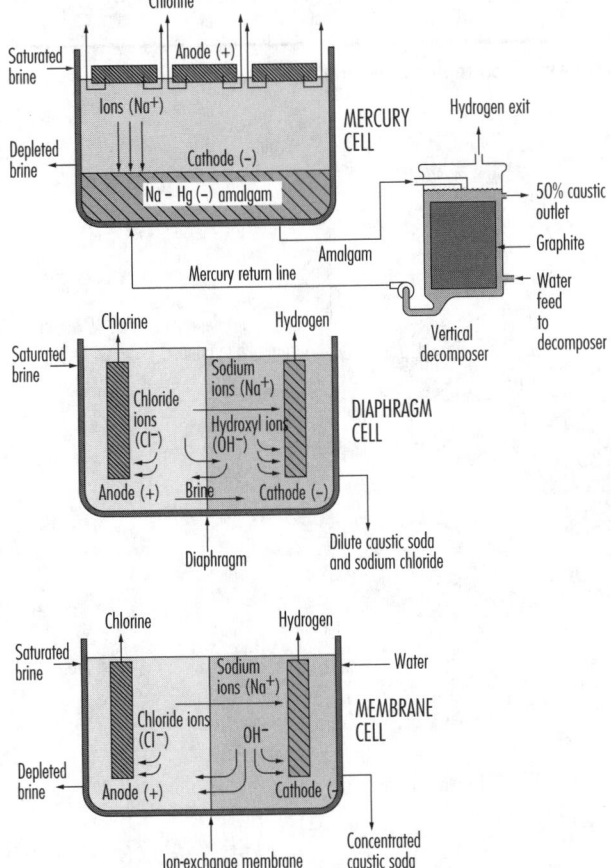

77. CHEMICAL PROCESSING

a chlorine leak. Chlorine and water react forming acids and the leak quickly will get worse. However, where several containers are involved and some are leaking, it may be prudent to use a water spray to help prevent overpressure of the non-leaking containers.

Whenever containers have been exposed to flames, cooling water should be applied until well after the fire is out and the containers are cooled. Containers exposed to fire should be isolated and the supplier should be contacted as soon as possible.

Sodium hydroxide solutions are corrosive, especially when concentrated. Workers at risk for exposure to spills and leaks should wear gloves, face shield and goggles and other protective clothing.

Acknowledgements: Dr. R.G. Smerko is acknowledged for making available the resources of the Chlorine Institute, Inc.

PAINT AND COATING MANUFACTURE

Michael McCann*

Paints and coatings include paints, varnishes, lacquers, stains, printing inks and more. Traditional paints consist of a dispersion of pigment particles in a vehicle consisting of a film-former or binder (usually an oil or resin) and a thinner (usually a volatile solvent). In addition, there can be a wide variety of fillers and other additives. A varnish is a solution of oil and natural resin in an organic solvent. Synthetic resins may also be used. Lacquers are coatings in which the film dries or hardens entirely by evaporation of the solvent.

* Adapted from NIOSH 1984.

Traditional paints were under 70% solids with the remainder being mostly solvents. Air pollution regulations limiting the amount of solvents that can be emitted into the atmosphere have resulted in the development of a wide variety of substitute paints with low or no organic solvents. These include: water-based latex paints; two-part catalysed paints (e.g., epoxy and urethane systems); high solids paints (over 70% solids), including plastisol paints consisting primarily of pigments and plasticizers; radiation-cured paints; and powder coatings.

According to the US National Institute for Occupational Safety and Health (NIOSH 1984), about 60% of paint manufacturers employed fewer than 20 workers, and only about 3% had more than 250 workers. These statistics would be expected to be representative of paint manufacturers worldwide. This indicates a predominance of small shops, most of which would not have in-house health and safety expertise.

Manufacturing Processes

In general, the manufacture of paints and other coatings is a series of unit operations using batch processes. There are few or no chemical reactions; the operations are mostly mechanical. The manufacture involves the assembling of raw materials, mixing, dispersing, thinning and adjusting, filling of containers and warehousing.

Paints

Raw materials used to manufacture paints come as liquids, solids, powders, pastes and slurries. These are manually weighed out and premixed. Agglomerated pigment particles must be reduced to the original pigment size, and the particles must be wet with the binder to ensure dispersion in the liquid matrix. This dispersion process, called grinding, is done with a variety of types of equip-

Figure 77.5 • Flow chart for the manufacture of powder coatings by extrusion melt-mixing method.

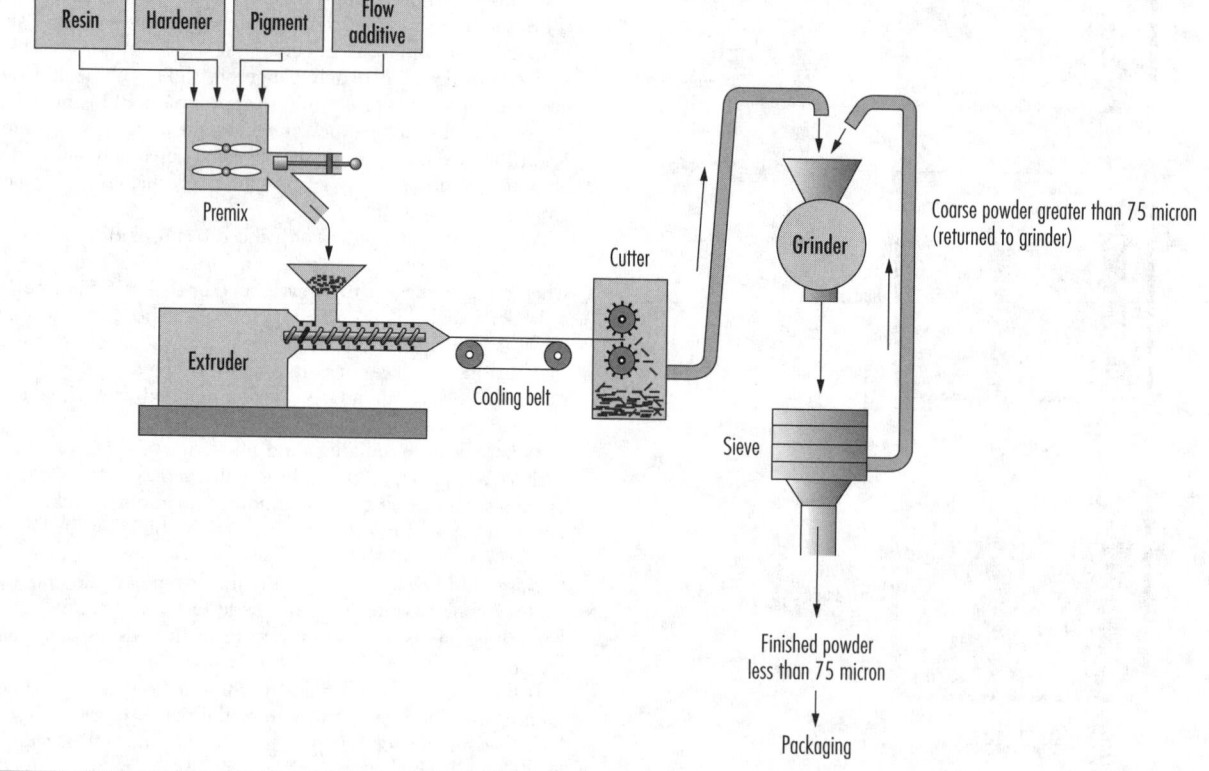

Figure 77.6 • Bag and dust control system.

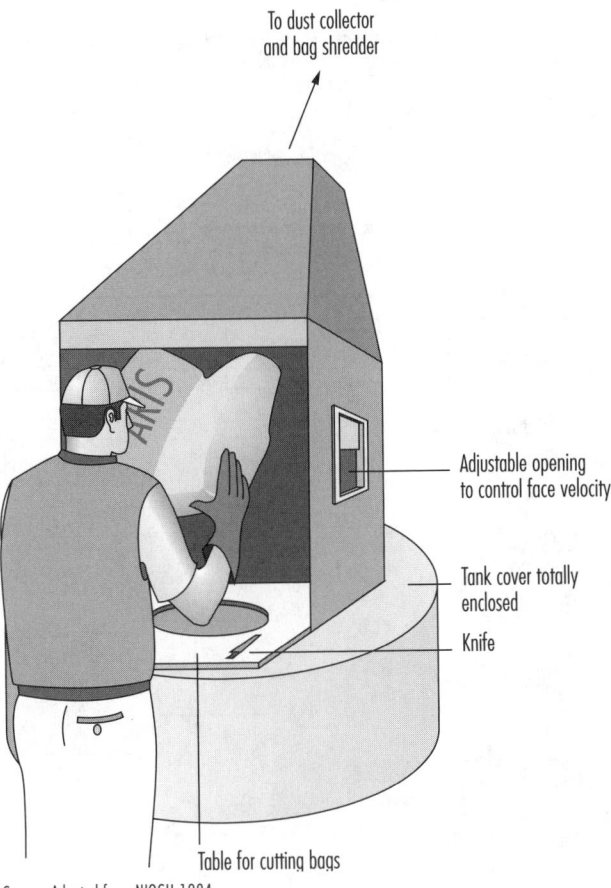

To dust collector
and bag shredder

Adjustable opening
to control face velocity

Tank cover totally
enclosed

Knife

Table for cutting bags

Source: Adapted from NIOSH 1984.

ment, including high-speed shaft-impeller dispersers, dough mixers, ball mills, sand mills, triple roll mills, pug mills and so forth. After an initial run, which might take as long as 48 hours, resin is added to the paste and the grinding process is repeated for a shorter period. The dispersed material is then transferred by gravity to a let-down tank where additional material such as tinting compounds can be added. For water-based paints, the binder is usually added at this stage. The paste is then thinned with resin or solvent, filtered and then transferred again by gravity to the can filling area. The filling can be done manually or mechanically.

After the dispersion process, it may be necessary to clean the tanks and mills before introducing a new batch. This can involve hand and power tools, as well as alkali cleaners and solvents.

Lacquers

Lacquer production usually is carried out in enclosed equipment such as tanks or mixers in order to minimize evaporation of the solvent, which would result in deposits of a dry lacquer film on processing equipment. Otherwise, lacquer production occurs in the same manner as paint production.

Varnishes

The manufacture of oleoresinous varnishes involves cooking the oil and resin to render them more compatible, to develop high molecular weight molecules or polymers and to increase solubility in the solvent. Older plants may use portable, open kettles for the heating. The resin and oil or resin alone are added to the kettle

and then heated to about 316 °C. Natural resins must be heated prior to adding the oils. The materials are poured in over the top of the kettle. During cooking, the kettles are covered with refractory exhaust hoods. After cooking, the kettles are moved to rooms where they are cooled quickly, often by water spray, and then thinner and driers are added.

Modern plants use large closed reactors with capacities of 500 to 8,000 gallons. These reactors are similar to those used in the chemical process industry. They are fitted with agitators, sight-glasses, lines to fill and empty the reactors, condensers, temperature measuring devices, heat sources and so forth.

In both older and modern plants, the thinned resin is filtered as the final step before packaging. This is normally done while the resin is still hot, usually using a filter press.

Powder coatings

Powder coatings are solventless systems based on the melting and fusion of resin and other additive particles onto surfaces of heated objects. The powder coatings may be either thermosetting or thermoplastic, and include such resins as epoxies, polyethylene, polyesters, polyvinyl chloride and acrylics.

The most common method of manufacture involves dry blending of the powdered ingredients and extrusion melt-mixing (see figure 77.5). The dry resin or binder, pigment, filler and additives are weighed and transferred to a premixer. This process is similar to dry blending operations in rubber manufacture. After mixing, the material is placed in an extruder and heated until molten. The molten material is extruded onto a cooling conveyor belt and then transferred to a coarse granulator. The granulated material is passed through a fine grinder and then sieved to achieve the desired particle size. The powder coating is then packaged.

Hazards and Their Prevention

In general, the major hazards associated with the paint and coatings manufacture involve materials handling; toxic, flammable or explosive substances; and physical agents such as electrical shock, noise, heat and cold.

The manual handling of boxes, barrels, containers and so forth which contain the raw materials and finished products are major sources of injury due to improper lifting, slips, falls, dropping containers and so on. Precautions include engineering/ergonomic controls such as materials handling aids (rollers, jacks and platforms) and mechanical equipment (conveyors, hoists and fork-lift trucks), non-skid floors, personal protective equipment (PPE) such as safety shoes and proper training in manual lifting and other materials handling techniques.

Chemical hazards include exposure to toxic dusts such as lead chromate pigment, which can occur during weighing, filling of mixer and mill hoppers, operations of unenclosed equipment, filling of powdered paint containers, cleaning of equipment and from spills of containers. The manufacture of powder coatings can result in high dust exposures. Precautions include substitution of pastes or slurries for powders; local exhaust ventilation (LEV) for opening bags of powders (see figure 77.6) and for processing equipment, enclosure of equipment, spill cleanup procedures and respiratory protection when needed.

A wide variety of volatile solvents are used in paint and coating manufacture, including aliphatic and aromatic hydrocarbons, alcohols, ketones and so forth. The most volatile solvents are usually found in lacquers and varnishes. Exposure to solvent vapours can occur during thinning in solvent-based paint manufacture; while charging reaction vessels (especially older kettle types) in varnish manufacture; during can filling in all solvent-based coatings; and during manual cleaning of process equipment with solvents. Enclosure of equipment such as varnish reactors and lacquer mixers usually involves lower solvent exposures, except in the case of leaks. Precautions include enclosure of process equipment, LEV for thinning and can filling operations and respiratory protection and confined-space procedures for cleaning vessels.

Other health hazards include inhalation and/or skin contact with isocyanates used in manufacturing polyurethane paints and coatings; with acrylates, other monomers and photoinitiators used in the manufacture of radiation-curing coatings; with acrolein and other gaseous emissions from varnish cooking; and with curing agents and other additives in powder coatings. Precautions include enclosure, LEV, gloves and other personal protective clothing and equipment, hazardous material training and good work practices.

Flammable solvents, combustible powders (especially nitrocellulose used in lacquer production) and oils are all fire or explosion risks if ignited by a spark or high temperatures. Sources of ignition can include faulty electrical equipment, smoking, friction, open flames, static electricity and so forth. Oil-soaked rags can be a source of spontaneous combustion. Precautions include bonding and grounding containers while transferring flammable liquids, grounding of equipment such as ball mills containing combustible dusts, ventilation to keep vapour concentrations below the lower explosive limit, covering containers when not in use, removal of sources of ignition, using spark-resistant tools of non-ferrous metals around flammable or combustible materials and good housekeeping practices.

Noise hazards can be associated with the use of ball and pebble mills, high speed dispersers, vibrating screens used for filtering and so forth. Precautions include vibration isolators and other engineering controls, replacing noisy equipment, good equipment maintenance, isolation of noise source and a hearing conservation programme where excessive noise is present.

Other hazards include inadequate machine guarding, a common source of injuries around machinery. Electrical hazards are a particular problem if there is not a proper lockout/tagout programme for equipment maintenance and repair. Burns can result from hot varnish cooking vessels and spattering materials and from hot melt glues used for packages and labels.

PLASTICS INDUSTRY

P.K. Law and T.J. Britton*

The plastics industry is divided into two major sectors, the interrelationship of which can be seen in figure 77.7. The first sector comprises the raw material suppliers who manufacture polymers and moulding compounds from intermediates which they may also have produced themselves. In terms of invested capital this is usually the largest of the two sectors. The second sector is made up of processors who convert the raw materials into saleable items using various processes such as extrusion and injection moulding. Other sectors include machinery manufacturers who supply equipment to the processors and suppliers of special additives for use within the industry.

Polymer Manufacturing

Plastics materials fall broadly into two distinct categories: thermoplastics materials, which can be softened repeatedly by the application of heat and thermosetting materials, which undergo a chemical change when heated and shaped and cannot thereafter be reshaped by the application of heat. Several hundred individual polymers can be made with widely differing properties but as few as 20 types constitute about 90% of total world output.

* Adapted from 3rd edition, *Encyclopaedia of Occupational Health and Safety*.

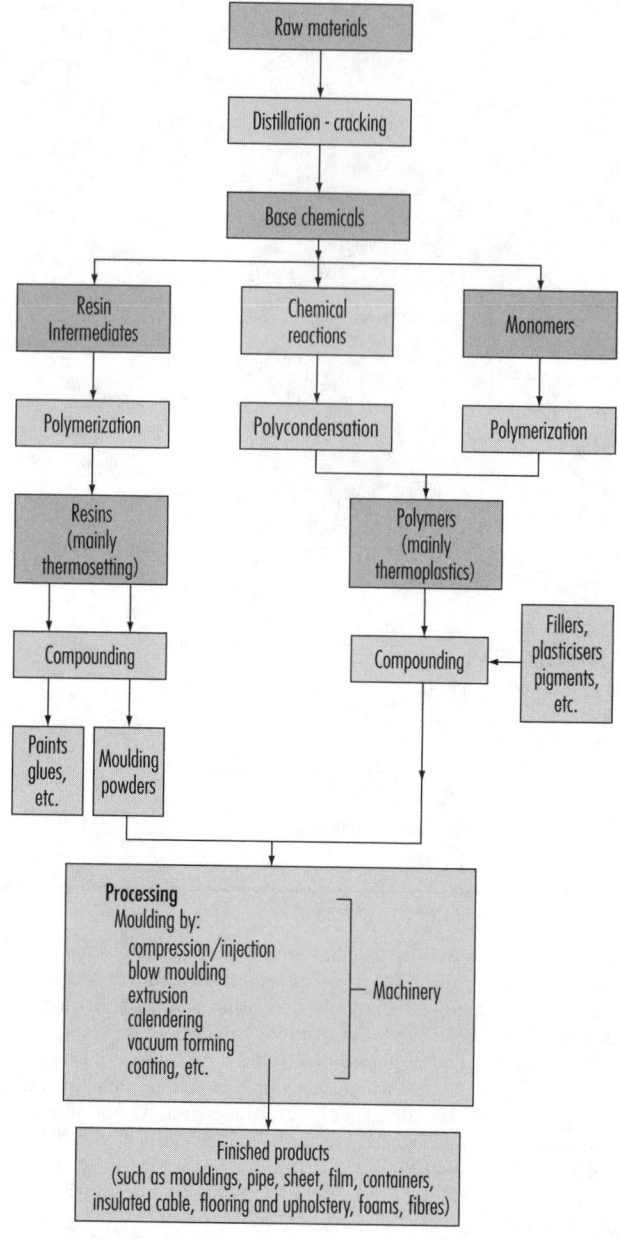

Figure 77.7 • Production sequence in the processing of plastics.

Thermoplastics are the largest group and their production is increasing at a higher rate than the thermosetting. In terms of production quantity the most important thermoplastics are high and low density polyethylene and polypropylene (the polyolefins), polyvinyl chloride (PVC) and polystyrene.

Important thermosetting resins are phenol-formaldehyde and urea-formaldehyde, both in the form of resins and moulding powders. Epoxy resins, unsaturated polyesters and polyurethanes are also significant. A smaller volume of "engineering plastics", for example, polyacetals, polyamides and polycarbonates, have a high value in use in critical applications.

The considerable expansion of the plastics industry in the post Second World War world was greatly facilitated by the broadening of the range of the basic raw materials feeding it; availability and

Figure 77.8 • Schematic diagram illustrating the versatility of production, from petroleum fractions, of raw materials into several types of plastics manufacture.

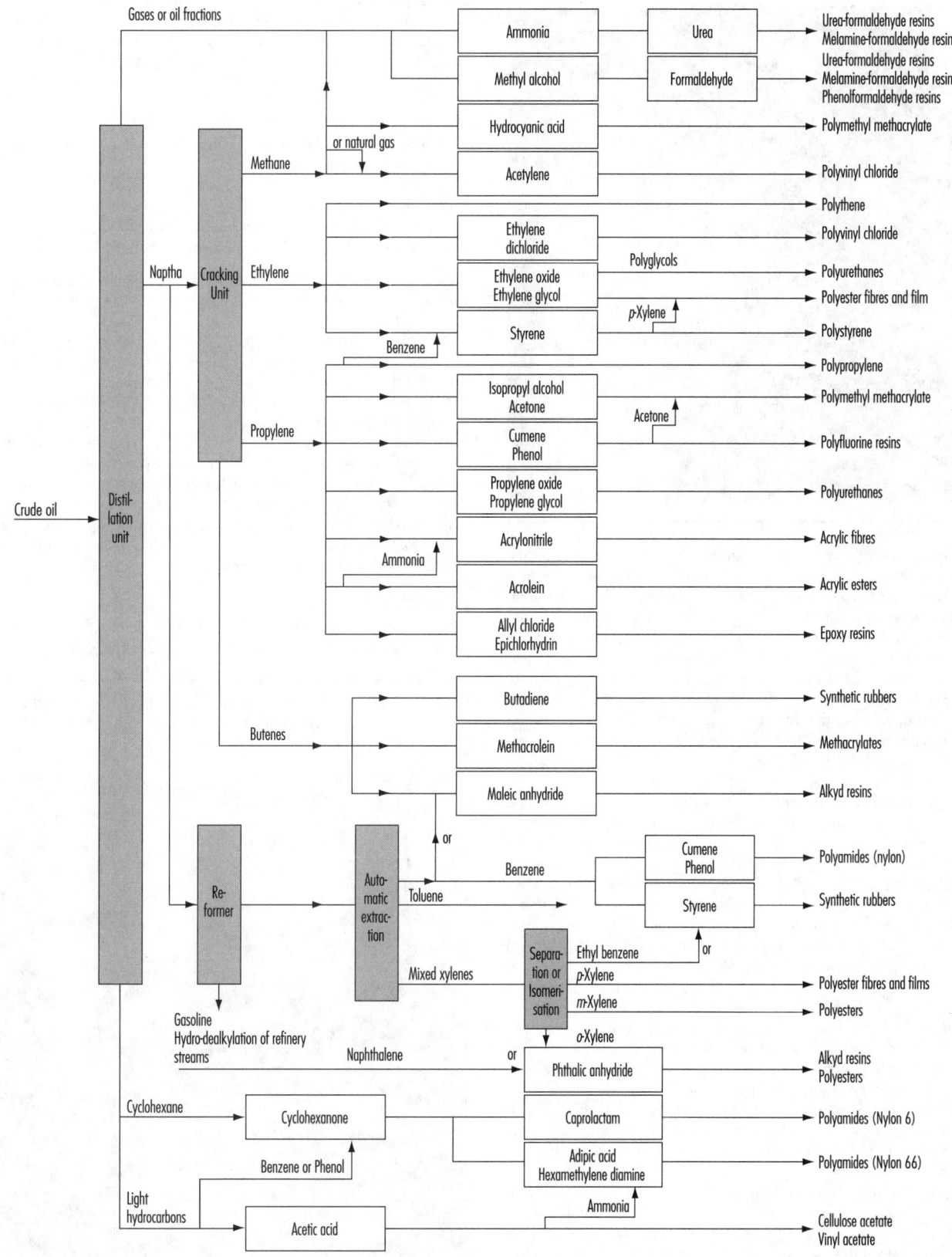

Figure 77.9 • An operator removing a polypropylene bowl from an injection-moulding machine.

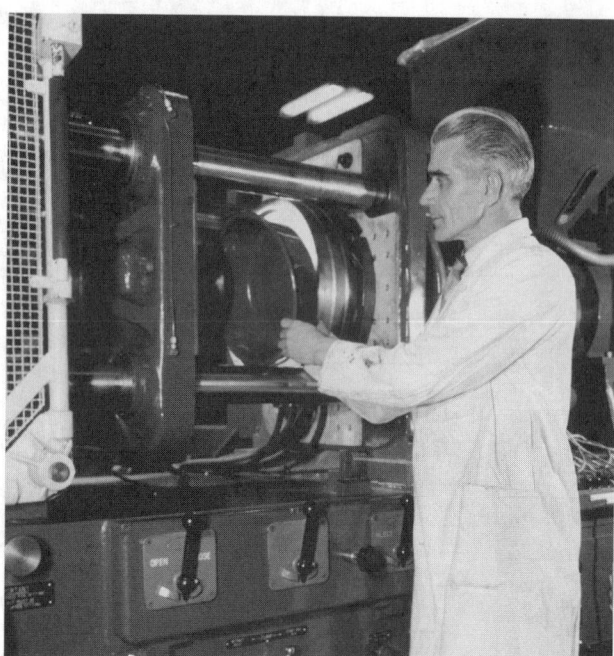

price of raw materials are crucial to any rapidly developing industry. Traditional raw materials could not have provided chemical intermediates in sufficient quantities at an acceptable cost to facilitate the economic commercial production of large-tonnage plastics materials and it was the development of the petrochemicals industry which made growth possible. Petroleum as a raw material is abundantly available, easily transported and handled and was, until the oil crisis of the 1970s, relatively cheap. Therefore, throughout the world, the plastics industry is primarily tied to the use of intermediates obtained from oil cracking and from natural gas. Unconventional feedstocks like biomass and coal have not yet had a major impact on supply to the plastics industry.

The flow chart in figure 77.8 illustrates the versatility of crude petroleum and natural gas feedstocks as starting points for the important thermosetting and thermoplastics materials. Following the first processes of crude oil distillation, naphtha feedstock is either cracked or reformed to provide useful intermediates. Thus the ethylene produced by the cracking process is of immediate use for the manufacture of polyethylene or for utilization in another process which provides a monomer, vinyl chloride—the basis of PVC. Propylene, which also arises during the cracking process, is used via either the cumene route or the isopropyl alcohol route for the manufacture of acetone needed for polymethylmethacrylate; it is also used in the manufacture of propylene oxide for polyester and polyether resins and again may be polymerized directly to polypropylene. Butenes find use in the manufacture of plasticisers and 1,3-butadiene is utilized directly for synthetic rubber manufacture. Aromatic hydrocarbons such as benzene, toluene and xylene are now widely produced from the derivatives of oil distillation operations, instead of being obtained from coal-coking processes; as the flow chart shows, these are intermediates in the manufacture of important plastics materials and auxiliary products such as plasticizers. The aromatic hydrocarbons are also a starting point for many polymers required in the synthetic fibres industry, some of which are discussed elsewhere in this *Encyclopaedia*.

Many widely differing processes contribute to the final production of a finished article made wholly or partly of plastics. Some processes are purely chemical, some involve purely mechanical mixing procedures while others-particularly those towards the lower end of the diagram-involve extensive use of specialized machinery. Some of this machinery resembles that used in rubber, glass, paper and textile industries; the remainder is specific to the plastics industry.

Plastics processing

The plastics processing industry converts bulk polymeric material into finished articles.

Raw materials

The processing section of the plastics industry receives its raw materials for production in the following forms:

- fully compounded polymeric material, in the form of pellets, granules or powder, which is fed directly into the machinery for processing
- uncompounded polymer, in the form of granules or powder, which must be compounded with additives before it is suitable for feeding into to machinery
- polymeric sheet, rod, tube and foil materials which are processed further by the industry
- miscellaneous materials which can be fully polymerized matter in the form of suspensions or emulsions (generally known as latices) or liquids or solids which can polymerise, or substances in an intermediate state between the reactive raw materials and the final polymer. Some of these are liquids and some true solutions of partially polymerised matter in water of controlled acidity (pH) or in organic solvents.

Compounding

The manufacture of compound from polymer entails the mixing of the polymer with additives. Though a great variety of machin-

Figure 77.10 • Plastic extrusion: The ribbon is chopped to make pellets for injection moulding machines.

ery is employed for this purpose, where powders are dealt with, ball mills or high-speed propeller mixers are most common, and where plastic masses are being mixed, kneading machines such as the open rolls or Banbury-type mixers, or extruders themselves are normally employed.

The additives required by the industry are many in number, and range widely in chemical type. Of some 20 classes, the most important are:

- plasticisers—generally esters of low volatility
- antioxidants—organic chemicals to protect against thermal decomposition during processing
- stabilisers—inorganic and organic chemicals to protect against thermal decomposition and against degradation from radiant energy
- lubricants
- fillers—inexpensive matter to confer special properties or to cheapen compositions
- colourants—inorganic or organic matter to colour compounds
- blowing agents—gases or chemicals that emit gases to produce plastic foams.

Conversion processes

All the conversion processes call on the "plastic" phenomenon of polymeric materials and fall into two types. Firstly, those where the polymer is brought by heat to a plastic state in which it is given a mechanical constriction leading to a form which it retains on consolidation and cooling. Secondly, those in which a polymerisable material-which may be partially polymerised-is fully polymerised by the action of heat, or of a catalyst or by both acting together whilst under a mechanical constraint leading to a form which it retains when fully polymerised and cold. Plastics technology has developed to exploit these properties to produce goods with the minimum of human effort and the greatest consistency in physical properties. The following processes are commonly used.

Compression moulding

This consists of heating a plastic material, which can be in the form of granules or powder, in a mould which is held in a press. When the material becomes "plastic" the pressure forces it to conform to the shape of the mould. If the plastic is of the type that hardens on heating, the formed article is removed after a short heating period by opening the press. If the plastic does not harden on heating, cooling must be effected before the press can be opened. Articles made by compression moulding include bottle caps, jar closures, electric plugs and sockets, toilet seats, trays and

Figure 77.11 • Plastic extrusion with local exhaust hood and water bath at extruder head.

Ray Woodcock

Figure 77.12 • Canopy hoods to capture hot emissions from warm-up mills on a calender process.

Ray Woodcock

fancy goods. Compression moulding is also employed to make sheet for subsequent forming in the vacuum forming process or for building into tanks and large containers by welding or by lining existing metal tanks.

Transfer moulding

This is a modification of compression moulding. The thermosetting material is heated in a cavity and then forced by a plunger into the mould, which is physically separate and independently heated from the heating cavity. It is preferred to normal compression moulding when the final article has to carry delicate metallic inserts such as in small electrical switchgear, or when, as in very thick objects, completion of the chemical reaction could not be obtained by normal compression moulding.

Injection moulding

In this process, plastics granules or powders are heated in a cylinder (known as the barrel), which is separate from the mould. The material is heated until it becomes fluid, while it is conveyed through the barrel by a helical screw and then forced into the mould where it cools and hardens. The mould is then opened mechanically and the formed articles are removed (see figure 77.9). This process is one of the most important in the plastics industry. It has been extensively developed and has become capable of making articles of considerable complexity at very low cost.

Though transfer and injection moulding are identical in principle, the machinery employed is very different. Transfer moulding is normally restricted to thermosetting materials and injection moulding to thermoplastics.

Extrusion

This is the process in which a machine softens a plastic and forces it through a die which gives it the shape that it retains on cooling. The products of extrusion are tubes or rods which may have cross sections of almost any configuration (see figure 77.10). Tubes for industrial or domestic purposes are produced in this way, but other articles can be made by subsidiary processes. For example, sachets can be made by cutting tubes and sealing both ends, and bags from thin-walled flexible tubes by cutting and sealing one end.

The process of extrusion has two major types. In one, a flat sheet is produced. This sheet can be converted into useful goods by other processes, such as vacuum forming.

The second is a process in which the extruded tube is formed and when still hot is greatly expanded by a pressure of air maintained inside the tube. This results in a tube which can be several feet in diameter with a very thin wall. On slitting, this tube gives film which is extensively used in the packaging industry for wrapping. Alternatively the tube can be folded flat to give a two-layer sheet which can be used to make simple bags by cutting and sealing. Figure 77.11 provides an example of appropriate local ventilation on an extrusion process.

Calendering

In this process, a plastic is fed to two or more heated rollers and forced into a sheet by passing through a nip between two such rollers and cooling thereafter. Sheet thicker than film is made in this way. Sheet so made is employed in industrial and domestic applications and as the raw material in the manufacture of clothing and inflated goods such as toys (see figure 77.12).

Blow moulding

This process can be regarded as a combination of the process of extrusion and thermo-forming. A tube is extruded downwards into an opened mould; as it reaches the bottom the mould is closed round it and the tube expanded by air pressure. Thus the plastic is forced to the sides of the mould and the top and bottom sealed. On cooling, the article is taken from the mould. This process makes hollow articles of which bottles are the most important.

The compression and impact strength of certain plastic products made by blow moulding can be considerably improved by using stretch-blow moulding techniques. This is achieved by producing a pre-form which is subsequently expanded by air pressure and stretched biaxially. This has led to such an improvement in the burst pressure strength of PVC bottles that they are used for carbonated drinks.

Rotational moulding

This process is used for the production of moulded articles by heating and cooling a hollow form which is rotated to enable gravity to distribute finely divided powder or liquid over the inner surface of that form. Articles produced by this method include footballs, dolls and other similar articles.

Film casting

Apart from the extrusion process, films can be formed by extruding a hot polymer on to a highly polished metal drum, or a solution of polymer can be sprayed on to a moving belt.

An important application of certain plastics is the coating of paper. In this, a film of molten plastic is extruded on to paper under conditions in which the plastic adheres to the paper. Board can be coated in the same way. Paper and board so coated are widely used in packaging, and board of this type is used in box making.

Thermo-forming

Under this heading are grouped a number of processes in which a sheet of a plastic material, more often than not thermoplastic, is heated, generally in an oven, and after clamping at the perimeter is forced to a predesigned shape by pressure which may be from mechanically operated rams or by compressed air or steam. For very large articles the "rubbery" hot sheet is manhandled with tongs over formers. Products so made include external light fittings, advertising and directional road signs, baths and other toilet goods and contact lenses.

Vacuum-forming

There are many processes which come under this general heading, all of which are aspects of thermal forming, but they all have in common that a sheet of plastic is heated in a machine above a cavity, around the edge of which it is clamped, and when pliable it is forced by suction into the cavity, where it takes some specific form and cools. In a subsequent operation, the article is trimmed free from the sheet. These processes produce very cheaply thin-walled containers of all types, as well as display and advertising goods, trays and similar articles, and shock-absorbing materials for packing goods such as fancy cakes, soft fruit and cut meat.

Laminating

In all of the various laminating processes, two or more materials in the form of sheets are compressed to give a consolidated sheet or panel of special properties. At one extreme are found decorative laminates made from phenolic and amino resins, at the other complex films used in packaging having, for example, cellulose, polyethylene and metal foil in their constitution.

Resin technology processes

These include plywood manufacture, furniture manufacture and the construction of large and elaborate articles such as car bodies and boat hulls from glass fibre impregnated with polyester or epoxy resins. In all these processes, a liquid resin is caused to consolidate under the action of heat or of a catalyst and so bind together discrete particles or fibres or mechanically weak films or sheets, resulting in a robust panel of rigid construction. These resins can be applied by hand layup techniques such as brushing and dipping or by spraying.

Small objects such as souvenirs and plastic jewellery can also be made by casting, where the liquid resin and catalyst are mixed together and poured into a mould.

Finishing processes

Included under this heading are a number of processes common to many industries, for example the use of paints and adhesives. There are, however, a number of specific techniques used for the welding of plastics. These include the use of solvents such as chlorinated hydrocarbons, methyl ethyl ketone (MEK) and toluene, which are used for bonding together rigid plastic sheets for general fabrication, advertising display stands and similar work. Radiofrequency (RF) radiation utilizes a combination of mechanical pressure and electromagnetic radiation with frequencies generally in the range of 10 to 100 mHz. This method is commonly used for welding together flexible plastic material in the manufacture of wallets, briefcases and children's push chairs (see the accompanying box). Ultrasonic energies are also used in combination with mechanical pressure for a similar range of work.

Hazards and Their Prevention

Polymer manufacturing

The special hazards of the polymers industry relate closely to those of the petrochemicals industry and depend to a large extent on the substances used. The health hazards of individual raw materials are found elsewhere in this *Encyclopaedia*. The danger of fire and explosion is an important general hazard. Many polymer/resin processes have a fire and explosion risk owing to the nature of the primary raw materials used. If adequate safeguards are not taken there is sometimes a risk during reaction, generally inside partly enclosed buildings, of flammable gases or liquids escaping at temperatures above their flash points. If the pressures involved are very high, provision should be made for

RF dielectric heaters and sealers

Radiofrequency (RF) heaters and sealers are used in many industries to heat, melt or cure dielectric materials, such as plastics, rubber and glue which are electrical and thermal insulators and hard to heat using normal methods. RF heaters are commonly used for sealing polyvinyl chloride (e.g., manufacture of plastic products such as raincoats, seat covers and packaging materials); curing of glues used in woodworking; embossing and drying of textiles, paper, leather and plastics; and curing of many materials containing plastic resins.

RF heaters use RF radiation in the frequency range 10 to 100 MHz with output power from under 1 kW to about 100 kW to produce heat. The material to be heated is placed between two electrodes under pressure, and the RF power is applied for periods ranging from a few seconds to about a minute, depending on the use. RF heaters can produce high stray RF electric and magnetic fields in the surrounding environment, especially if the electrodes are unshielded.

Absorption of RF energy by the human body can cause localized and whole body heating, which can have adverse health effects. The body temperature can rise 1 °C or more, which can cause cardiovascular effects such as increased heart rate and cardiac output. Localized effects include eye cataracts, lowered sperm counts in the male reproductive system and teratogenic effects in the developing foetus.

Indirect hazards include RF burns from direct contact with metal parts of the heater which are painful, deep seated and slow to heal; hand numbness; and neurological effects, including carpal tunnel syndrome and peripheral nervous system effects.

Controls

The two basic types of controls that can be used to reduce hazards from RF heaters are work practices and shielding. Shielding, of course, is preferred, but proper maintenance procedures and other work practices can also reduce exposure. Limiting the amount of time the operator is exposed, an administrative control, has also been used.

Proper maintenance or repair procedures are important because failure to properly reinstall shielding, interlocks, cabinet panels and fasteners can result in excessive RF leakage. In addition, electric power to the heater should be disconnected and locked out or tagged out to protect maintenance personnel.

Operator exposure levels can be reduced by keeping the operator's hands and upper body as far as possible from the RF heater. The operator's control panels for some automated heaters are positioned at a distance from the heater electrodes by using shuttle trays, turning tables or conveyor belts to feed the heater.

The exposure of both operating and non-operating personnel can be reduced by measuring RF levels. Since RF levels decrease with increasing distance from the heater, an "RF hazard area" can be identified around each heater. Workers can be alerted to not occupy these hazard areas when the RF heater is being operated. Where possible, nonconductive physical barriers should be used to keep people at a safe distance.

Ideally, RF heaters should have a box shield around the RF applicator to contain the RF radiation. The shield and all joints should have high conductivity for the interior electrical currents that will flow in the walls. There should be as few openings in the shield as possible, and they should be as small as is practical for operation. The openings should be directed away from the operator. Currents in the shield can be minimized by having separate conductors inside the cabinet to conduct high currents. The heater should be properly grounded, with the ground wire in the same pipe as the power line. The heater should have proper interlocks to prevent exposure to high voltages and high RF emissions.

It is much easier to incorporate this shielding into new designs of RF heaters by the manufacturer. Retrofitting is more difficult. Box enclosures can be effective. Proper grounding can also often be effective in reducing RF emissions. RF measurements have to be carefully taken afterwards to ensure that RF emissions have actually been reduced. The practice of enclosing the heater in a metal screen-encased room can actually increase exposure if the operator is also in that room, although it does reduce exposures outside the room.

Source: ICNIRP in press.

adequate venting to the atmosphere. An excessive build-up of pressure due to unexpectedly fast exothermic reactions may occur and the handling of some additives and preparation of some catalysts may add to the explosion or fire risk. The industry has addressed these problems and particularly on the manufacture of phenolic resins has produced detailed guidance notes on plant design engineering and safe operating procedures.

Plastics processing

The plastics processing industry has injury hazards because of the machinery used, fire hazards because of the combustibility of plastics and their powders and health hazards because of the many chemicals used in the industry.

Injuries

The major area for injuries is in the plastics processing sector of the plastics industry. The majority of the plastics conversion processes depend almost entirely upon the use of machinery. As a result the principal hazards are those associated with the use of such machinery, not only during normal operation but also during cleaning, setting and maintenance of the machines.

Compression, transfer, injection and blow moulding machines all have press platens with a locking force of many tonnes per square centimetre. Adequate guarding should be fitted to prevent amputation or crushing injuries. This is generally achieved by enclosing the dangerous parts and by interlocking any movable guards with the machine controls. An interlocking guard should not allow dangerous movement within the guarded area with the guard open and should bring the dangerous parts to rest or reverse the dangerous motion if the guard is opened during the machine operation.

Where there is a severe risk of injury at machinery such as at the platens of moulding machines, and regular access to the danger area, then a higher standard of interlocking is called for. This may be achieved by a second independent interlocking arrangement at the guard to interrupt the power supply and prevent a dangerous motion when it is open.

For processes involving plastic sheet, a common machinery hazard found is in-running traps between rollers or between rollers and the sheet being processed. These occur at tension rollers and haul-off devices at extrusion plant and calenders. Safeguarding may be achieved by using a suitably located trip device, which immediately brings the rollers to rest or reverses the dangerous motion.

Many of the plastics processing machines operate at high temperatures and severe burns may be sustained if parts of the body come into contact with hot metal or plastics. Where practical, such parts should be protected when the temperature exceeds 50 °C. In addition, blockages which occur on injection moulding machines and extruders can violently free themselves. A safe system of work should be followed when attempting to free frozen plugs of plastic, which should include the use of suitable gloves and face protection.

Most modern machine functions are now controlled by programmed electronic control or computer systems which may also control mechanical take-off devices or are linked with robots. On new machinery there is less need for an operator to approach the danger areas and it follows that safety at machinery should correspondingly improve. There is, however, a greater need for setters and engineers to approach these parts. It is essential therefore that an adequate lockout/tagout programme be instituted before this type of work is carried out, particularly where full protection by the machine safety devices cannot be achieved. In addition adequate back up or emergency systems should be so designed and devised to deal with situations when the programmed control fails for any reason, for example, during the loss of the power supply.

It is important that machines be properly laid out in the workshop with good clear working spaces for each. This assists in maintaining high standards of cleanliness and tidiness. The machines themselves should also be properly maintained and the safety devices should be checked on a routine basis.

Good housekeeping is essential and particular attention should be paid to keeping the floors clean. Without routine cleaning, floors will become badly contaminated from machine oil or spilled plastics granules. Methods of work including safe means of access to areas above floor level should also be considered and provided.

Adequate spacing should also be allowed for the storage of raw materials and finished goods; these areas should be clearly designated.

Plastics are good electrical insulators and, because of this, static charges can build up on machinery on which sheet or film travels. These charges can have a potential high enough to cause a serious accident or act as sources of ignition. Static eliminators should be used to reduce these charges and metal parts properly earthed or grounded.

Increasingly, waste plastics material is being reprocessed using granulators and blending with new stock. Granulators should be totally enclosed to prevent any possibility of reaching the rotors through the discharge and feed openings. The design of the feed openings on large machines should be such as to prevent whole body entry. The rotors operate at high speed and covers should not be removed until they have come to rest. Where interlocking guards are fitted, they should prevent contact with the blades until they have completely stopped.

Fire and explosion hazards

Plastics are combustible materials, although not all polymers support combustion. In finely divided powder form, many can form explosive concentrations in air. Where this is a risk, the powders should be controlled, preferably in an enclosed system, with sufficient relief panels venting at low pressure (about 0.05 bar) to a safe place. Scrupulous cleanliness is essential to prevent accumulations in the workrooms which may become airborne and cause a secondary explosion.

Polymers may be subject to thermal degradation and pyrolysis at temperatures not greatly above normal processing temperatures. Under these circumstances, sufficient pressures may build up in the barrel of an extruder, for example, to eject molten plastic and any solid plug of plastic causing an initial blockage.

Flammable liquids are commonly used in this industry, for example, as paints, adhesives, cleaning agents and in solvent welding. Glass-fibre (polyester) resins also evolve flammable sty-

rene vapours. Stocks of such liquids should be reduced to a minimum in the workroom and stored in a safe place when not in use. Storage areas should include safe places in the open air or a fire resisting store.

Peroxides used in the manufacture of glass reinforced plastics (GRP) resins should be stored separately from flammable liquids and other combustible materials and not subjected to extremes of temperatures since they are explosive when heated.

Health hazards

There are a number of potential health hazards associated with the processing of plastics. The raw plastics are rarely used on their own and appropriate precautions should be taken regarding the additives used in the various formulations. Additives used include lead soaps in PVC and certain organic and cadmium dyestuffs.

There is a significant risk of dermatitis from liquids and powders usually from "reactive chemicals" such as phenol formaldehyde resins (before crosslinking), urethanes and unsaturated polyester resins used in the production of GRP products. Suitable protective clothing should be worn.

It is possible for fumes to be generated from the thermal degradation of polymers during hot processing. Engineering controls can minimize the problem. Particular care, however, must be taken to avoid inhalation of pyrolysis products under adverse conditions, for example, purging of the extruder barrel. Conditions of good LEV may be necessary. Problems have occurred, for example, where operators have been overcome by hydrochloric acid gas and suffered from "polymer fume fever" following overheating of PVC and polytetrafluorethylene (PTFE), respectively. The accompanying box details some chemical decomposition products of plastics.

There is also a danger of inhalation of toxic vapours from certain thermoset resins. Inhalation of isocyanates used with polyurethane resins can lead to chemical pneumonia and severe asthma and, once sensitized, persons should be transferred to alternative work. A similar problem exists with formaldehyde resins. In both these examples, a high standard of LEV is necessary. In the manufacture of GRP articles, significant quantities of styrene vapour is given off and this work must be done in conditions of good general ventilation in the workroom.

There are also certain hazards which are common to a number of industries. These include the use of solvents for dilution or for purposes mentioned previously. Chlorinated hydrocarbons are commonly used for cleaning and bonding and without adequate exhaust ventilation persons may well suffer from narcosis.

Waste disposal of plastics by burning should be done under carefully controlled conditions; for example, PTFE and urethanes should be in an area where the fumes are vented to a safe place.

Very high noise levels are generally obtained during the use of granulators, which may well lead to hearing loss to the operators and persons working nearby. This hazard can be confined by separating this equipment from other working areas. Preferably the noise levels should be reduced at source. This has successfully been achieved by coating the granulator with sound deadening material and fitting baffles at the feed opening. There may also be a hazard to hearing created by audible sound produced from ultrasonic welding machines as a normal accompaniment of the ultrasonic energies. Suitable enclosures can be designed to reduce the received noise levels and can be interlocked to prevent a mechanical hazard. As a minimum standard, persons working in areas of high noise levels should wear suitable hearing protection and there should be a suitable hearing conservation programme, including audiometric testing and training.

Burns are also a hazard. Some additives and catalysts for plastics production and processing can be highly reactive on contact

Table 77.10 • Volatile products of the decomposition of plastics (reference components).*

In many industrial sectors, plastics are subject to thermal stress. Temperatures range from relatively low values in plastics processing (e.g., 150 to 250 °C) to extreme cases, e.g., where painted sheet metal or plastic-coated pipes are welded). The question that constantly arises in such cases is whether toxic concentrations of volatile pyrolysis products occur in work areas.

To answer this question, the substances released first need to be determined and then the concentrations need to be measured. While the second step is in principle feasible, it is usually not possible to determine the relevant pyrolysis products in the field. The *Berufsgenossenschaftliches Institut für Arbeitssicherheit* (BIA) has therefore been examining this problem for years and in the course of many laboratory tests has determined volatile decomposition products for plastics. The test results for the individual types of plastic have been published (Lichtenstein and Quellmalz 1984, 1986a, 1986b, 1986c).

Following is a brief summary of the results to date. This table is intended as an aid for all those faced with the task of measuring hazardous substance concentrations in relevant work areas. The decomposition products listed for the individual plastics may serve as "reference components". It should be remembered, however, that pyrolysis may give rise to highly complex mixtures of substances, their compositions depending on many factors.

The table thus does not claim to be complete where the pyrolysis products listed as reference components are concerned (all determined in laboratory experiments). The occurrence of other substances with potential health risks cannot be ruled out. It is practically impossible to completely record all substances that occur.

Plastic	Abbreviation	Volatile substances
Polyoxymethylene	POM	Formaldehyde
Epoxy resins based on bisphenol A		Phenol
Chloroprene rubber	CR	Chloroprene(2-chlorobuta-1,3-diene), hydrogen chloride
Polystyrene	PS	Styrene
Acrylonitrile-butadiene-styrene-copolymer	ABS	Styrene, 1,3-butadiene, acrylonitrile
Styrene-acrylonitrile copolymer	SAN	Acrylonitrile, styrene
Polycarbonates	PC	Phenol
Polyvinyl chloride	PVC	Hydrogen chloride, plasticisers (frequently phthalic acid esters such as dioctyl phthalate, dibutyl phthalate)
Polyamide 6	PA 6	ε-caprolactam
Polyamide 66	PA 66	Cyclopentanone, hexamethylenediamine
Polyethylene	HDPE, LDPE	Unsaturated aliphatic hydrocarbons, aliphatic aldehydes
Polytetrafluoroethylene	PTFE	Perfluorinated unsaturated hydrocarbons (e.g., tetrafluoroethylene, hexafluoropropene, octafluorobutene)
Polymethyl methacrylate	PMMA	Methyl methacrylate
Polyurethane	PUR	Depending on the type, widely varying decomposition products (e.g., CFCs[1] as foaming agents, ether and glycol ether, diisocyanates, hydrogen cyanide,[2] aromatic amines, chlorinated phosphoric acid esters as flame protection agents)
Polypropylene	PP	Unsaturated and saturated aliphatic hydrocarbons
Polybutyle enterephthalate (polyester)	PBTP	1,3-butadiene, benzene
Polyacrylonitrile	PAN	Acrylonitrile, hydrogen cyanide[2]
Cellulose acetate	CA	Acetic acid

Norbert Lichtenstein

[1] Use is discontinuing.

[2] Could not be detected with the analytical technique used (GC/MS) but is known from the literature.

* Reprinted from BIA 1997, with permission.

with air and water and may readily cause chemical burns. Wherever molten thermoplastics are being handled or transported there is the danger of splashes of hot material and consequent burns and scalds. The severity of these burns may be increased by the tendency of hot thermoplastics, like hot wax, to adhere to the skin.

Organic peroxides are irritants and may cause blindness if splashed in the eye. Suitable eye protection should be worn.

BIOTECHNOLOGY INDUSTRY

Susan B. Lee and Linda B. Wolfe

Evolution and Profile

Biotechnology can be defined as the application of biological systems to technical and industrial processes. It encompasses both traditional and genetically engineered organisms. Traditional biotechnology is the result of classic hybridization, mating or crossing of various organisms to create new organisms that have been used for centuries to produce bread, beer, cheese, soya, saki, vitamins, hybrid plants and antibiotics. More recently, various organisms have also been used to treat waste water, human sewage and industrial toxic wastes.

Modern biotechnology combines the principles of chemistry and biological sciences (molecular and cellular biology, genetics, immunology) with technological disciplines (engineering, computer science) to produce goods and services and for environmental management. Modern biotechnology utilizes restriction enzymes to cut and paste genetic information, DNA, from one organism to another outside living cells. The composite DNA is then reintroduced into host cells to determine whether the desired trait is expressed. The resulting cell is called an engineered clone, a recombinant or a genetically manipulated organism (GMO). The "modern" biotechnology industry was born in 1961-1965 with the breaking of the genetic code and has grown dramatically since the first successful DNA cloning experiments in 1972.

Since the early 1970s, scientists have understood that genetic engineering is an extremely powerful and promising technology, but that there are potentially serious risks to consider. As early as on 1974, scientists called for a worldwide moratorium on specific types of experiments in order to assess the risks and to devise appropriate guidelines for avoiding biological and ecological hazards (Committee on Recombinant DNA Molecules, National Research Council, National Academy of Sciences 1974). Some of the concerns expressed involved the potential "escape of vectors which could initiate an irreversible process, with a potential for creating problems many times greater than those arising from the multitude of genetic recombinations that occur spontaneously in nature". There were concerns that "microorganisms with transplanted genes could prove hazardous to man or other forms of life. Harm could result if the altered host cell has a competitive advantage that would foster its survival in some niche within the ecosystem" (NIH 1976). It was also well understood that laboratory workers would be the "canaries in the coal mine" and some attempt should be made to protect the workers as well as the environment from the unknown and potentially serious hazards.

An international conference at Asilomar, California, was held in February 1975. Its report contained the first consensus guidelines based on biologic and physical containment strategies for controlling potential hazards envisioned from the new technology. Certain experiments were judged to pose such serious potential dangers that the conference recommended against their being conducted at that time (NIH 1976). The following work was originally banned:

- work with DNA from pathogenic organisms and oncogenes
- forming recombinants that incorporate toxin genes
- work which might extend the host range of plant pathogens
- introduction of drug resistance genes into organisms not known to acquire them naturally and where treatment would be compromised
- deliberate release into the environment (Freifelder 1978).

In the United States the first National Institutes of Health Guidelines (NIHG) were published in 1976, replacing the

Asilomar guidelines. These NIHG allowed research to proceed by rating experiments by hazard classes based on the risks associated with host cell, vector systems which transport genes into the cells and gene inserts, thereby allowing or restricting the conduct of the experiments based on risk assessment. The basic premise of the NIHG—to provide for worker protection, and by extension, community safety—remains in place today (NIH 1996). The NIHG are updated regularly and they have evolved to be a widely accepted standard of practice for biotechnology in the US. Compliance is required from institutions receiving federal funding, as well as by many local city or town ordinances. The NIHG provides one basis for regulations in other countries around the world, including Switzerland (SCBS 1995) and Japan (National Institute of Health 1996).

Since 1976, the NIHG have been expanded to incorporate containment and approval considerations for new technologies including large scale production facilities and plant, animal and human somatic gene therapy proposals. Some of the originally banned experiments are now allowed with specific approval from NIH or with specific containment practices.

In 1986 the US Office of Science and Technology Policy (OSTP) published its Coordinated Framework for Biotechnology Regulation. It addressed the underlying policy question of whether existing regulations were adequate to evaluate products derived from the new technologies and whether the review processes for research were sufficient to protect the public and the environment. The US regulatory and research agencies (Environmental Protection Agency (EPA), Food and Drug Administration (FDA), Occupational Safety and Health Administration (OSHA), NIH, US Department of Agriculture (USDA) and National Science Foundation (NSF)) agreed to regulate products, not processes, and that new, special regulations were not necessary to protect workers, the public or the environment. The policy was established to operate regulatory programmes in an integrated and coordinated fashion, minimizing overlap, and, to the extent possible, responsibility for product approval would lie with one agency. The agencies would coordinate efforts by adopting consistent definitions and by using scientific reviews (risk assessments) of comparable scientific rigor (OSHA 1984; OSTP 1986).

The NIHG and Coordinated Framework have provided an appropriate degree of objective scientific discussion and public participation, which has resulted in the growth of US biotechnology into a multibillion dollar industry. Prior to 1970, there were fewer than 100 companies involved in all aspects of modern biotechnology. By 1977, another 125 firms joined the ranks; by 1983 an additional 381 companies brought the level of private capital investment to more than $1 billion. By 1994 the industry had grown to more than 1,230 companies (Massachusetts Biotechnology Council Community Relations Committee 1993), and market capitalization is more than $6 billion.

Employment in US biotechnology companies in 1980 was about 700 people; in 1994 roughly 1,300 companies employed more than 100,000 workers (Massachusetts Biotechnology Council Community Relations Committee 1993). In addition, there is an entire support industry which provides supplies (chemicals, media components, cell lines), equipment, instrumentation and services (cell banking, validation, calibration) necessary to ensure the integrity of the research and production.

Throughout the world there has been a great level of concern and scepticism about the safety of the science and of its products. The Council of the European Communities (Parliament of the European Communities 1987) developed directives to protect workers from the risks associated with exposure to biologicals (Council of the European Communities 1990a) and to place

Table 77.11 • Microorganisms of industrial importance.

Name	Host organism	Uses
Acetobacter aceti	Aerobic bacterium	Ferments fruit
Aspirgillus niger	Asexual fungus	Degrades organic matter Safe use in production of citric acid and enzymes
Aspirgillus oryzae	Asexual fungus	Used in production of miso, soy sauce and sake
Bacillis licheniformis	Bacterium	Industrial chemicals and enzymes
Bacillis subtilis	Bacterium	Chemicals, enzymes, source of single-cell protein for human consumption in Asia
Chinese hampster ovary cells (CHO)*	Mammalian cell culture	Manufacturing of biopharmaceuticals
Clostridium acetobutylicum	Bacterium	Butanol, acetone production
Escherichia coli K-12*	Bacterial strain	Cloning for fermentation, production of pharmaceuticals and biologics
Penicillium roqueforti	Asexual fungus	Blue cheese production
Saccharomyces cerevisiae*	Yeast	Cloning for beer production
Saccharomyces uvarum*	Yeast	Cloning for alcoholic beverages and industrial alcohol production

* Important to modern biotechnology.

environmental controls on experimental and commercial activities including deliberate release. "Release" includes marketing products using GMOs (Council of the European Communities 1990b; Van Houten and Flemming 1993). Standards and guidelines pertaining to biotechnology products within international and multilateral organizations such as World Health Organization (WHO), International Standards Organization (ISO), Commission of the European Community, Food and Agriculture Organization (FAO) and Microbial Strains Data Network have been developed (OSTP 1986).

The modern biotechnology industry can be considered in terms of four major industry sectors, each having laboratory, field and/or clinical research and development (R&D) supporting the actual production of goods and services.

- biomedical-pharmaceuticals, biologics and medical device products
- agricultural-foods, transgenic fish and animals, disease resistant and pest resistant plants
- genetically enhanced industrial products such as citric acid, butanol, acetone, ethanol and detergent enzymes (see table 77.11)
- environmental-waste water treatment, decontamination of industrial wastes.

Biotechnology Workers

Biotechnology begins in the research laboratory and is a multidisciplinary science. Molecular and cellular biologists, immunologists, geneticists, protein and peptide chemists, biochemists and biochemical engineers are most directly exposed to the real and potential hazards of recombinant DNA (rDNA) technology. Other workers who may be exposed less directly to rDNA biohazards include service and support staff such as ventilation and refrigeration technicians, calibration service providers and housekeeping staff. In a recent survey of health and safety practitioners in the industry, it was found that the directly and indirectly exposed workers comprise about 30 to 40% of the total workforce in typical commercial biotechnology companies (Lee and Ryan 1996). Biotechnology research is not limited to "industry"; it is conducted in the academic, medical and government institutions as well.

Biotechnology laboratory workers are exposed to a wide variety of hazardous and toxic chemicals, to recombinant and non-recombinant or "wild type" biological hazards, human bloodborne pathogens and zoonotic illnesses as well as radioactive materials used in labelling experiments. In addition, musculoskeletal disorders and repetitive strain injuries are becoming more widely recognized as potential hazards to research workers due to extensive use of computers and manual micropipettors.

Biotechnology manufacturing operators are also exposed to hazardous chemicals, but not the variety one sees in the research setting. Depending on the product and the process, there may be exposure to radionuclides in manufacturing. At even the lowest biohazard level, biotechnology manufacturing processes are closed systems and potential for exposure to the recombinant cultures is low, except in the case of accidents. In biomedical production facilities, application of current good manufacturing practices complements biosafety guidelines to protect workers on the plant floor. The main hazards to manufacturing workers in good large-scale practice (GLSP) operations involving non-hazardous recombinant organisms include traumatic musculoskeletal injuries (e.g., back strains and pain), thermal burns from steam lines and chemical burns from acids and caustics (phosphoric acid, sodium and potassium hydroxide) used in the process.

Health care workers including clinical laboratory technicians are exposed to gene therapy vectors, excreta and laboratory specimens during the administration of drugs and care of patients enrolled in these experimental procedures. Housekeepers may also be exposed. Worker and environmental protection are two mandatory experimental points to consider in making application to NIH for human gene therapy experiments (NIH 1996).

Agricultural workers may have gross exposure to recombinant products, plants or animals during the application of pesticides, planting, harvesting and processing. Independent of the potential biohazard risk from exposure to genetically altered plants and animals, the traditional physical hazards involving farm equipment and animal husbandry are also present. Engineering controls, PPE, training and medical supervision are used as appropriate to the anticipated risks (Legaspi and Zenz 1994; Pratt and May 1994). PPE including jump suits, respirators, utility gloves, goggles or hoods are important for worker safety during application, growth and harvesting of the genetically modified plants or soil organisms.

Processes and Hazards

In the biotechnology process in the biomedical sector cells or organisms, modified in specific ways to yield desired products, are cultivated in monoculture bioreactors. In mammalian cell culture, the protein product is secreted from the cells into the surrounding nutrient medium, and a variety of chemical separation methods (size or affinity chromatography, electrophoresis) may be used to capture and purify the product. Where *Escherichia coli* host organisms are used in fermentations, the desired product is produced within the cell membrane and the cells must be physically ruptured in order to harvest the product. Endotoxin exposure is a potential hazard of this process. Often antibiotics are added to the production media to enhance production of the desired product or maintain selective pressure on otherwise unstable genetic production elements (plasmids). Allergic sensitivities to these materials are possible. In general, these are aerosol exposure risks.

Leaks and releases of aerosols are anticipated and potential exposure is controlled in several ways. Penetrations into the reactor vessels are necessary for providing nutrients and oxygen, for off-gassing carbon dioxide (CO_2) and for monitoring and controlling the system. Each penetration must be sealed or filtered (0.2 micron) to prevent contamination of the culture. The exhaust gas filtration also protects workers and environment in the work area from aerosols generated during the culture or fermentation. Depending on the biohazard potential of the system, validated biological inactivation of liquid effluents (usually by heat, steam or chemical methods) is standard practice. Other potential hazards in biotech manufacturing are similar to those in other industries: noise, mechanical guarding, steam/heat burns, contact with corrosives and so on.

Enzymes and industrial fermentation are covered elsewhere in this *Encyclopaedia* and involve the processes, hazards and controls that are similar for genetically engineered production systems.

Traditional agriculture depends on strain development that utilizes traditional crossing of related plant species. The great advantage of genetically engineering plants is that the time between generations and the number of crosses needed to obtain the desired trait is greatly reduced. Also the currently unpopular reliance on chemical pesticides and fertilizers (which contribute to runoff pollution) is favouring a technology which will potentially make these applications unnecessary.

Plant biotechnology involves choosing a genetically pliable and/ or financially significant plant species for modifications. Since plant cells have tough, cellulose cell walls, methods used to transfer DNA into plant cells differ from those used for bacteria and mammalian cell lines in the biomedical sector. There are two primary methods used for introducing foreign engineered DNA into plant cells (Watrud, Metz and Fishoff 1996):

- a particle gun shoots DNA into the cell of interest
- a disarmed, nontumorigenic *Agrobacterium tumefaciens* virus introduces gene cassettes into the cell's genetic material.

Wild-type *Agrobacterium tumefaciens* is a natural plant pathogen which causes crown gall tumours in injured plants. These disarmed, engineered vector strains do not cause plant tumour formation.

After transformation by either method, plant cells are diluted, plated and grown on selective tissue culture media for a relatively long (compared to bacterial growth rates) period in plant growth chambers or incubators. Plants regenerated from the treated tissue are transplanted to soil in enclosed growth chambers for further growth. After reaching the appropriate age they are examined for expression of the desired traits and then grown in greenhouses. Several generations of greenhouse experiments are needed to evaluate the genetic stability of the trait of interest and to generate needed seed stock for further study. Environmental impact data is also gathered during this phase of the work and submitted with proposals to regulatory agencies for open field trial release approval.

Controls: The United States Example

The NIHG (NIH 1996) describe a systematic approach to preventing both worker exposure to and environmental release of recombinant organisms. Each institution (e.g., university, hospital or commercial laboratory) is responsible for conducting rDNA research safely and in compliance with the NIHG. This is accomplished through an administrative system which defines responsibilities and requires comprehensive risk assessments by knowledgeable scientists and biosafety officers, implementation of exposure controls, medical surveillance programmes and emergency planning. An Institutional Biosafety Committee (IBC) provides the mechanisms for experiment review and approval within the institution. In some cases, approval of NIH Recombinant Advisory Committee (RAC) itself is required.

The degree of control depends on the severity of the risk and is described in terms of Biosafety Level (BL) designations 1-4; BL1 being the least restrictive and BL4 the most. Containment guidelines are given for research, large scale (greater than 10 litres of culture) R&D, large scale production and animal and plant experiments at both large and small scale.

Appendix G of the NIHG (NIH 1996) describes physical containment at the laboratory scale. BL1 is appropriate for work with agents of no known or of minimal potential hazard to laboratory personnel or the environment. The laboratory is not separated from the general traffic patterns in the building. Work is conducted on the open benchtops. No special containment devices are required or used. Laboratory personnel are trained in laboratory procedures and supervised by a scientist with general training in microbiology or a related science.

BL2 is suitable for work involving agents of moderate potential hazard to personnel and the environment. Access to the laboratory is limited when work is being conducted, workers have specific training in handling pathogenic agents and are directed by competent scientists, and work which creates aerosols is conducted in biological safety cabinets or other containment equipment. This work may require medical surveillance or vaccinations as appropriate and determined by the IBC.

BL3 is applicable when work is conducted with indigenous or exotic agents which may cause serious or potentially lethal disease as a result of exposure by inhalation. Workers have specific training and are supervised by competent scientists who are experienced in working with and handling these hazardous agents. All procedures are done under containment conditions requiring special engineering and PPE.

BL4 is reserved for the most dangerous and exotic agents that pose a high individual and community risk of life-threatening disease. There are only a few BL4 laboratories in the world.

Appendix K addresses physical containment for research or production activities in volumes greater than 10 l (large scale). As in the small-scale guidelines, there is a hierarchy of containment requirements from lowest to highest hazard potential: GLSP to BL3-Large-Scale (BL3-LS).

The NIHG, Appendix P, covers work with plants at bench level, growth chamber and greenhouse scale. As the introduction notes: "The principal purpose of plant containment is to avoid the unintentional transmission of a recombinant DNA-containing plant genome, including nuclear or organelle hereditary material or release of recombinant DNA derived organisms associated with plants. In general these organisms pose no threat to human health or higher animals, unless deliberately modified for that purpose. However, the inadvertent spread of a serious pathogen from a greenhouse to a local agricultural crop or the unintentional introduction and establishment of an organism in a new ecosystem is possible" (NIH 1996). In the United States, the EPA and the USDA's Animal and Plant Health Inspection Service (APHIS) are jointly responsible for risk assessment and for reviewing the data generated prior to giving approval for field release testing (EPA 1996; Foudin and Gay 1995). Issues such as persistence and spread in water, air and soil, by insect and animal species, the presence of other similar crops in the area, environmental stability (frost or heat sensitivity) and competition with native species are evaluated-often first in the greenhouse (Liberman et al. 1996).

Plant containment levels for facilities and practices also range from BL1 to BL4. Typical BL1 experiments involve self-cloning. BL2 may involve transfer of traits from a pathogen to a host plant. BL3 might involve toxin expression or environmentally hazardous agents. Worker protection is achieved in the various levels by PPE and engineering controls such as greenhouses and headhouses with directional airflow and high efficiency particulate air filters (HEPA) to prevent pollen release. Depending on the risk, environmental and community protection from potentially hazardous agents can be achieved by biological controls. Examples are a temperature sensitive trait, drug sensitivity trait or nutritional requirement not present in nature.

As scientific knowledge increased and technology advanced, it was expected that the NIHG would need review and revision. Over the last 20 years, the RAC has met to consider and approve proposals for changes. For example, the NIHG no longer issue blanket prohibitions on deliberate release of genetically engineered organisms; agricultural products field trial releases and human gene therapy experiments are allowed in appropriate circumstances and after suitable risk assessment. One very significant amendment to the NIHG was the creation of the GLSP containment category. It relaxed the containment requirements for "non-pathogenic, non-toxigenic recombinant strains derived from host organisms that have an extended history of safe large scale use, or which have built in environmental limitations that permit optimum growth in the large scale setting but limited survival without adverse consequences in the environment" (NIH 1991). This mechanism has allowed the technology to progress while still considering safety needs.

Controls: The European Community Example

In April 1990 the European Community (EC) enacted two Directives on the contained use and deliberate release into the environment of GMOs. Both Directives require Member States to ensure that all appropriate measures are taken to avoid adverse effects on human health or the environment, in particular by making the user assess all relevant risks in advance. In Germany, the Genetic Technology Act was passed in 1990 partially in response to the EC Directives, but also to respond to a need for legal authority to construct a trial operation recombinant insulin production facility (Reutsch and Broderick 1996). In Switzerland, the regulations are based on the US NIHG, Council directives of the EC and the German law on gene technology. The Swiss require annual registration and updates of experiments to the government. In general, the rDNA standards in Europe are more restrictive than in the US, and this has contributed to many European pharmaceutical firms moving rDNA research from their home countries. However, the Swiss regulations allow a Large Scale Safety Level 4 category, which is not permitted under the NIHG (SCBS 1995).

Products of Biotechnology

Some of the biological and pharmaceutical products which have been successfully made by recombinant DNA biotechnologies include: human insulin; human growth hormone; hepatitis vaccines; alpha-interferon; beta-interferon; gamma-interferon; Granulocyte colony stimulating factor; tissue plasminogen activator; Granulocyte-macrophage colony stimulating factor; IL2; Erythropoietin; Crymax, an insecticide product for the control of caterpillars in vegetable; tree nut and vine crops; Flavr Savr (TM) tomato; Chymogen, an enzyme that makes cheese; ATIII (antithrombin III), derived from transgenic goat milk used to prevent blood clots in surgery; BST and PST (bovine and porcine somatotropin) used to boost milk and meat production.

Health Problems and Disease Patterns

There are five main health hazards from exposure to microorganisms or their products in industrial scale biotechnology:

- infection
- reaction to endotoxin
- allergy to the microorganisms
- allergic reaction to a product
- toxic reaction to a product.

Infection is unlikely since non-pathogens are used in most industrial processes. However, it is possible that microorganisms considered to be harmless such as *Pseudomonas* and *Aspergillus* species may cause infection in immunocompromised individuals (Bennett 1990). Exposure to endotoxin, a component of the lippopolysaccharide layer of the cell wall of all gram negative bacteria, at concentrations greater than about 300 ng/m3 causes transient flu-like symptoms (Balzer 1994). Workers in many industries including traditional agriculture and biotechnology have experienced the effects of endotoxin exposure. Allergic reactions to the microorganism or product also occur in many industries. Occupational asthma has been diagnosed in the biotechnology industry for a wide range of microorganisms and products including *Aspergillus niger*, *Penicillium* spp. and proteases; some companies have noted incidences in greater than 12% of the workforce. Toxic reactions can be as varied as the organisms and products. Exposure to antibiotics has been shown to cause shifts in microbial flora in the gut. Fungi are known to be capable of producing toxins and carcinogens under certain growth conditions (Bennett 1990).

To address concern that exposed workers would be the first to develop any potential adverse health effects from the new technology, medical surveillance of rDNA workers has been a part of the NIHG since their beginning. Institutional Biosafety Committees, in consultation with the occupational health physician, are charged with determining, on a project by project basis, what medical surveillance is appropriate. Depending on the identity of the specific agent, the nature of the biological hazard, the potential routes of exposure and availability of vaccines, the components of the medical surveillance programme might include pre-placement physical, periodic follow-up exams, specific vaccines, specific allergy and illness evaluations, pre-exposure sera and epidemiological surveys.

Bennett (1990) believes it is unlikely that genetically modified microorganisms will pose more of an infection or allergic risk than the original organism, but there could be additional risks from the novel product, or the rDNA. A recent report notes the expression of a brazil-nut allergen in transgenic soybeans may cause unexpected health effects among workers and consumers (Nordlee et al. 1996). Other novel hazards could be the use of animal cell lines containing unknown or undetected oncogenes or viruses potentially harmful to humans.

It is important to note the early fears concerning the creation of genetically dangerous mutant species or super-toxins have not materialized. The WHO found that biotechnology poses no risks that are different from other processing industries (Miller 1983), and, according to Liberman, Ducatman and Fink (1990), "the current consensus is that the potential risks of rDNA were overstated initially and that the hazards associated with this research are similar to those associated with the organism, vector, DNA, solvents and physical apparatus being used". They conclude that engineered organisms are bound to have hazards; however, containment can be defined to minimize exposure.

It is very difficult to identify occupational exposures specific to the biotechnology industry. "Biotechnology" is not a separate industry with a distinguishing Standard Industrial Classification (SIC) code; rather, it is viewed as a process or set of tools used in many industrial applications. Consequently, when accidents and exposures are reported, the data on cases involving biotechnology workers are included among data on all others which occur in the host industry sector (e.g., agriculture, pharmaceutical industry or health care). Furthermore, laboratory incidents and accidents are known to be under reported.

Few illnesses specifically due to genetically altered DNA have been reported; however, they are not unknown. At least one documented local infection and seroconversion was reported when a worker suffered a needle stick contaminated with a recombinant vaccinia vector (Openshaw et al. 1991).

Policy Issues

In the 1980s the first products of biotechnology emerged in the US and Europe. Genetically engineered insulin was approved for use in 1982, as was a genetically engineered vaccine against the pig disease "scours" (Sattelle 1991). Recombinant bovine somatotropin (BST) has been shown to increase a cow's milk production and the weight of beef cattle. Concerns were raised about public health and product safety and whether existing regulations were adequate to address these concerns in all the different areas where products of biotechnology could be marketed. The NIHG provide protection of workers and the environment during research and development stages. Product safety and efficacy is not a NIHG responsibility. In the US, through the Coordinated Framework, potential risks of the products of biotechnology are evaluated by the most appropriate agency (FDA, EPA or USDA).

The debate over safety of genetic engineering and the products of biotechnology continues (Thomas and Myers 1993), especially with respect to agricultural applications and foods for human consumption. Consumers in some areas want produce labelled to identify which are the traditional hybrids and which are derived from biotechnology. Certain manufacturers of dairy products refuse to use milk from cows receiving BST. It is banned in some countries (e.g., Switzerland). The FDA has deemed the products to be safe, but there are also economic and social issues which may not be acceptable to the public. BST may indeed create a competitive disadvantage for smaller farms, most of which are family run. Unlike medical applications where there may be no alternative to genetically engineered treatment, when traditional foods are available and plentiful, the public is in favour of traditional hybridization over recombinant food. However, harsh environments and the current worldwide food shortage may change this attitude.

Newer applications of the technology to human health and inherited diseases have revived the concerns and created new ethical and social issues. The Human Genome Project, which began in the early 1980s, will produce a physical and genetic map of human genetic material. This map will provide researchers with information to compare "healthy or normal" and "diseased" gene expression to better understand, predict and point to cures for the basic genetic defects. Human Genome technologies have produced new diagnostic tests for Huntington's Disease, cystic fibrosis and breast and colon cancers. Somatic human gene therapy is expected to correct or improve treatments for inherited diseases. DNA "fingerprinting" by restriction fragment polymorphism mapping of genetic material is used as forensic evidence in cases of rape, kidnapping and homicide. It can be used to prove (or, technically, disprove) paternity. It can also be used in more controversial areas, such as for assessing chances of developing cancer and heart disease for insurance coverage and preventative treatments or as evidence in war crimes tribunals and as genetic "dogtags" in the military.

Though technically feasible, work on human germ-line experiments (transmissible from generation to generation) have not been considered for approval in the US due to the serious social and ethical considerations. However, public hearings are planned in the US to reopen the discussion of human germ-line therapy and the desirable trait enhancements not associated with diseases.

Finally, in addition to safety, social and ethical issues, legal theories about ownership of genes and DNA and liability for use or misuse are still evolving.

Long-term implications of environmental release of various agents need to be followed. New biological containment and host range issues will come up for work which is carefully and appropriately controlled in the laboratory environment, but for which all environmental possibilities are not known. Developing countries, where adequate scientific expertise and or regulatory agencies may not exist, may find themselves either unwilling or unable to take on the assessment of risk for their particular environment. This could lead to unnecessary restrictions or an imprudent "open-door" policy, either of which could prove damaging to the long-term benefit of the country (Ho 1996).

In addition, caution is important when introducing engineered agricultural agents into novel environments where frost or other natural containment pressures are not present. Will indigenous populations or natural exchangers of genetic information mate with recombinant agents in the wild resulting in transfer of engineered traits? Would these traits prove harmful in other agents? What would be the effect to the treatment administrators? Will immune reactions limit spread? Are engineered live agents capable of crossing species barriers? Do they persist in the environment of deserts, mountains, plain and cities?

Summary

Modern biotechnology in the United States has developed under consensus guidelines and local ordinance since the early 1970s. Careful scrutiny has shown no unexpected, uncontrollable traits expressed by a recombinant organism. It is a useful technology, without which many medical improvements based on natural therapeutic proteins would not have been possible. In many developed countries biotechnology is a major economic force and an entire industry has grown around the biotechnology revolution.

Medical issues for biotechnology workers are related to the specific host, vector and DNA risks and the physical operations performed. So far worker illness has been preventable by engineering, work practice, vaccines and biological containment controls specific to the risk as assessed on a case by case basis. And the administrative structure is in place to do prospective risk assessments for each new experimental protocol. Whether this safety track record continues into the environmental release of viable materials arena is a matter of continued evaluation of the potential environmental risks-persistence, spread, natural exchangers, characteristics of the host cell, host range specificity for transfer agents used, nature of the inserted gene and so on. This is important to consider for all possible environments and species affected in order to minimize surprises that nature often presents.

PYROTECHNICS INDUSTRY

J. Kroeger*

The pyrotechnics industry may be defined as the manufacture of pyrotechnic articles (fireworks) for entertainment, for technical and military use in signalling and illumination, for use as pesticides and for various other purposes. These articles contain pyrotechnic substances made up of powders or paste compositions which are shaped, compacted or compressed as required. When they are ignited, the energy they contain is released to give specific effects, such as illumination, detonation, whistling, screaming, smoke formation, smouldering, propulsion, ignition, priming, shooting and disintegration. The most important pyrotechnic substance is still black powder (gunpowder, consisting of charcoal, sulphur and potassium nitrate), which may be used loose for detonation, compacted for propulsion or shooting, or buffered with wood charcoal as a primer.

Processes

Raw materials used in the manufacture of pyrotechnics must be very pure, free from all mechanical impurities and (above all) free from acid ingredients. This also applies to subsidiary materials such as paper, pasteboard and glue. Table 77.12 lists common raw materials used in pyrotechnics manufacture.

After being dried, ground and sifted, the raw materials are weighed and mixed in a special building. Formerly they were always mixed by hand but in modern plants mechanical mixers are often used. After mixing, the substances should be kept in special storage buildings to avoid accumulations in workrooms. Only the quantities required for the actual processing operations should be taken from these buildings into the workrooms.

The cases for pyrotechnic articles may be of paper, pasteboard, synthetic material or metal. The method of packing varies. For example, for detonation the composition is poured loose into a case and sealed, whereas for propulsion, illumination, screaming or whistling it is poured loose into the case and then compacted or compressed and sealed.

Compacting or compressing formerly was done by blows from a mallet on a wooden "setting-down" tool, but this method is rarely employed in modern facilities; hydraulic presses or rotary lozenge presses are used instead. Hydraulic presses enable the composition to be compressed simultaneously in a number of cases.

Illumination substances are often shaped when wet to form stars, which are then dried and put into cases for rockets, bombs and so on. Substances made by a wet process must be well dried or they may ignite spontaneously.

Since many pyrotechnic substances are difficult to ignite when compressed, the pyrotechnic articles concerned are provided with an intermediate or priming ingredient to ensure ignition; the case is then sealed. The article is ignited from the outside by a quick-match, a fuse, a scraper or sometimes by a percussion cap.

Hazards

The most important hazards in pyrotechnics are clearly fire and explosion. Because of the small number of machines involved,

* Adapted from 3rd edition, *Encyclopaedia of Occupational Health and Safety.*

Table 77.12 • Raw materials used in the manufacture of pyrotechnics.

Products	Raw materials
Explosives	Nitrocellulose (collodion wool), silver fulminate, black powder (potassium nitrate, sulphur and charcoal).
Combustible materials	Acaroid resin, dextrine, gallic acid, gum arabic, wood, charcoal, rosin, lactose, polyvinyl chloride (PVC), shellac, methylcellulose, antimony sulphide, aluminium, magnesium, silicon, zinc, phosphorus, sulphur.
Oxidizing materials	Potassium chlorate, barium chlorate, potassium, perchlorate, barium nitrate, potassium nitrate, sodium nitrate, strontium nitrate, barium peroxide, lead dioxide, chromium oxide.
Flame-tinting materials	Barium carbonate (green), cryolite (yellow), copper, ammonium sulphate (blue), sodium oxalate (yellow), copper carbonate (blue), copper acetate arsenite (blue), strontium carbonate (red), strontium oxalate (red). Dyes are used to produce coloured smoke, and ammonium chloride to produce white smoke.
Inert materials	Glyceryl tristearate, paraffin, diatomaceous earth, lime, chalk.

mechanical hazards are less important; they are similar to those in other industries.

The sensitivity of most pyrotechnic substances is such that in loose form they may easily be ignited by blows, friction, sparks and heat. They present fire and explosion risks and are considered as explosives. Many pyrotechnic substances have the explosive effect of ordinary explosives, and workers are liable to have their clothes or body burned by sheets of flame.

During the processing of toxic substances used in pyrotechnics (e.g., lead and barium compounds and copper acetate arsenite) a health hazard may be present from inhalation of the dust while weighing and mixing.

Safety and Health Measures

Only reliable persons should be employed in the manufacture of pyrotechnic substances. Young persons under 18 years of age should not be employed. Proper instruction and supervision of the workers are necessary.

Before any manufacturing process is undertaken it is important to ascertain the sensitivity of pyrotechnic substances to friction, impact and heat, and also their explosive action. The nature of the manufacturing process and permissible quantities in the workrooms and the storage and drying buildings will depend on these properties.

The following fundamental precautions should be taken in the manufacture of pyrotechnic substances and articles:

- The buildings in the non-hazardous part of the undertaking (offices, workshops, eating areas and so on) should be sited well away from those in the hazardous areas.
- There should be separate manufacturing, processing and storage buildings for the different manufacturing processes in the hazardous areas and these buildings should be situated well apart

- The processing buildings should be divided up into separate workrooms.
- The quantities of pyrotechnic substances in the mixing, processing, storage and drying buildings should be limited.
- The number of workers in the different workrooms should be limited.

The following distances are recommended:

- between buildings in the hazardous areas and those in the non-hazardous areas, at least 30 m
- between the various processing buildings themselves, 15 m
- between mixing, drying and storage buildings and other buildings, 20 to 40 m depending on the construction and the number of workers affected
- between different mixing, drying and storage buildings, 15 to 20 m.

The distances between working premises may be reduced in favourable circumstances and if protective walls are built between them.

Separate buildings should be provided for the following purposes: storing and preparing raw materials, mixing, storing compositions, processing (packing, compacting or compressing), drying, finishing (gluing, lacquering, packing, paraffining, etc.), drying and storing the finished articles, and storing black powder.

The following raw materials should be stored in isolated rooms: chlorates and perchlorates, ammonium perchlorate; nitrates, peroxides and other oxidizing substances; light metals; combustible substances; flammable liquids; red phosphorus; nitrocellulose. Nitrocellulose must be kept wet. Metal powders must be protected against moisture, fatty oils and grease. Oxidizers should be stored separately from other materials.

Building design

For mixing, buildings of the explosion-venting type (three resistant walls, resistant roof and one explosion-vent wall made of plastic sheeting) are the most suitable. A protective wall in front of the explosion-vent wall is advisable. Mixing rooms for substances containing chlorates should not be used for substances containing metals or antimony sulphide.

For drying, buildings with an explosion-vent area and buildings covered with earth and provided with an explosion-vent wall have proved satisfactory. They should be surrounded by an embankment. In drying houses a controlled room temperature of 50 °C is advisable.

In the processing buildings, there should be separate rooms for: filling; compressing or compacting; cutting off, "choking" and closing the cases; lacquering shaped and compressed pyrotechnic substances; priming pyrotechnic substances; storing pyrotechnic substances and intermediate products; packing; and storing packed substances. A row of buildings with explosion-vent areas has been found to be best. The strength of the intermediate walls should be suited to the nature and quantity of the substances handled.

The following are basic rules for buildings in which potentially explosive materials are used or present:

- The buildings should be single-storied and have no basement.
- Roof surfaces should afford sufficient protection against the spread of fire.
- The walls of the rooms must be smooth and washable.

- Floors should have a level, smooth surface without gaps. They should be made of soft material such as xylolith, asphalt free from sand, and synthetic materials. Ordinary wood floors should not be used. The floors of dangerous rooms should be electrically conductive, and the workers in them should wear shoes with electrically conductive soles.
- The doors and windows of all buildings must open outwards. During working hours doors should not be locked.
- The heating of buildings by open fires is not permissible. For heating dangerous buildings, only hot water, low-pressure steam or dust-tight electrical systems should be used. Radiators should be smooth and easy to clean on all sides; radiators with finned pipes should not be used. A temperature of 115 °C is recommended for heating surfaces and pipes.
- Workbenches and shelves should be made of fire-resistant material or hard wood.
- The work, storage and drying rooms and their equipment should be regularly cleaned by wet wiping.
- Workplaces, entrances and ways of escape must be planned in such a way that rooms can be quickly evacuated.
- As far as practicable, workplaces should be separated by protective walls.
- Necessary stocks should be stored safely.
- All buildings should be equipped with lightning conductors.
- Smoking, open flames and the carrying of matches and lighters within the premises must be prohibited.

Equipment

Mechanical presses should have protective screens or walls so that if fire breaks out the workers will not be endangered and the fire cannot spread to neighbouring workplaces. If large quantities of materials are handled, presses should be in isolated rooms and operated from outside. No person should stay in the press room.

Fire-extinguishing appliances should be provided in sufficient quantity, marked conspicuously and checked at regular intervals. They should be suited to the nature of the materials present. Class D fire extinguishers should be used on burning metal powder, not water, foam, dry chemical or carbon dioxide. Showers, woollen blankets and fire-retardant blankets are recommended for extinguishing burning clothing.

Persons who come into contact with pyrotechnic substances or are liable to be endangered by sheets of flame should wear proper fire- and heat-resistant protective clothing. The clothing should be de-dusted daily at a place appointed for the purpose to remove any contaminants.

Measures should be taken in the undertaking to provide first aid in case of accidents.

Materials

Dangerous waste materials with different properties should be collected separately. Waste containers must be emptied daily. Until it is destroyed, collected waste should be kept in a protected place at least 15 m from any building. Defective products and intermediate products should as a rule be treated as waste. They should only be reprocessed if to do so does not create any risks.

When materials injurious to health are processed, direct contact with them should be avoided. Harmful gases, vapours and dusts should be effectively and safely exhausted. If the exhaust systems are inadequate, respiratory protective equipment must be worn. Suitable protective clothing should be provided.

References

Adams, WV, RR Dingman, and JC Parker. 1995. Dual gas sealing technology for pumps. Proceedings 12th International Pump Users Symposium. March, College Station, TX.

American Petroleum Institute (API). 1994. *Shaft Sealing Systems for Centrifugal Pumps.* API Standard 682. Washington, DC: API.

Auger, JE. 1995. Build a proper PSM program from the ground-up. *Chemical Engineering Progress* 91:47-53.

Bahner, M. 1996. Level-measurement tools keep tank contents where they belong. *Environmental Engineering World* 2:27-31.

Balzer, K. 1994. Strategies for developing biosafety programs in biotechnology facilities. Presented at the 3rd National Symposium on Biosafety, 1 March, Atlanta, GA.

Barletta, T, R Bayle, and K Kennelley. 1995. TAPS storage tank bottom: Fitted with improved connection. *Oil & Gas Journal* 93:89-94.

Bartknecht, W. 1989. *Dust Explosions.* New York: Springer-Verlag.

Basta, N. 1994. Technology lifts the VOC cloud. *Chemical Engineering* 101:43-48.

Bennett, AM. 1990. *Health Hazards in Biotechnology.* Salisbury, Wiltshire, UK: Division of Biologics, Public Health Laboratory Service, Centre for Applied Microbiology and Research.

Berufsgenossenschaftlices Institut für Arbeitssicherheit (BIA). 1997. *Measurement of Hazardous Substances: Determination of Exposure to Chemical and Biological Agents.* BIA Working Folder. Bielefeld: Erich Schmidt Verlag.

Bewanger, PC and RA Krecter. 1995. Making safety data "safe". *Chemical Engineering* 102:62-66.

Boicourt, GW. 1995. Emergency relief system (ERS) design: An integrated approach using DIERS methodology. *Process Safety Progress* 14:93-106.

Carroll, LA and EN Ruddy. 1993. Select the best VOC control strategy. *Chemical Engineering Progress* 89:28-35.

Center for Chemical Process Safety (CCPS). 1988. *Guidelines for Safe Storage and Handling of High Toxic Hazard Materials.* New York: American Institute of Chemical Engineers.

—. 1993. *Guidelines for Engineering Design for Process Safety.* New York: American Institute of Chemical Engineers.

Cesana, C and R Siwek. 1995. Ignition behavior of dusts meaning and interpretation. *Process Safety Progress* 14:107-119.

Chemical and Engineering News. 1996. Facts and figures for the chemical industry. *C&EN* (24 June):38-79.

Chemical Manufacturers Association (CMA). 1985. *Process Safety Management (Control of Acute Hazards).* Washington, DC: CMA.

Committee on Recombinant DNA Molecules, Assembly of Life Sciences, National Research Council, National Academy of Sciences. 1974. Letter to the editor. *Science* 185:303.

Council of the European Communities. 1990a. Council Directive of 26 November 1990 on the protection of workers from risks related to exposure to biological agents at work. 90/679/EEC. *Official Journal of the European Communities* 50(374):1-12.

—. 1990b. Council Directive of 23 April 1990 on the deliberate release into the environment of genetically modified organisms. 90/220/EEC. *Official Journal of the European Communities* 50(117): 15-27.

Dow Chemical Company. 1994a. *Dow's Fire & Explosion Index Hazard Classification Guide,* 7th edition. New York: American Institute of Chemical Engineers.

—. 1994b. *Dow's Chemical Exposure Index Guide.* New York: American Institute of Chemical Engineers.

Ebadat, V. 1994. Testing to assess your powder's fire and explosion hazards. *Powder and Bulk Engineering* 14:19-26.

Environmental Protection Agency (EPA). 1996. Proposed guidelines for ecological risk assessment. *Federal Register* 61.

Fone, CJ. 1995. The application of innovation and technology to the containment of shaft seals. Presented at the First European Conference on Controlling Fugitive Emissions from Valves, Pumps, and Flanges, 18-19 October, Antwerp.

Foudin, AS and C Gay. 1995. Introduction of genetically engineered microorganisms into the environment: Review under USDA, APHIS regulatory authority. In *Engineered Organisms in Environmental Settings: Biotechnological and Agricultural Applications,* edited by MA Levin and E Israeli. Boca Raton, FL:CRC Press.

Freifelder, D (ed.). 1978. The controversy. In *Recombinant DNA.* San Francisco, CA: WH Freeman.

Garzia, HW and JA Senecal. 1996. Explosion protection of pipe systems conveying combustible dusts or flammable gases. Presented at the 30th Loss Prevention Symposium, 27 February, New Orleans, LA.

Green, DW, JO Maloney, and RH Perry (eds.). 1984. *Perry's Chemical Engineer's Handbook,* 6th edition. New York: McGraw-Hill.

Hagen, T and R Rials. 1994. Leak-detection method ensures integrity of double bottom storage tanks. *Oil & Gas Journal* (14 November).

Ho, M-W. 1996. Are current transgenic technologies safe? Presented at the Workshop on Capacity Building in Biosafety for Developing Countries, 22-23 May, Stockholm.

Industrial Biotechnology Association. 1990. *Biotechnology in Perspective.* Cambridge, UK: Hobsons Publishing plc.

Industrial Risk Insurers (IRI). 1991. *Plant Layout and Spacing for Oil and Chemical Plants.* IRI Information Manual 2.5.2. Hartford, CT: IRI.

International Commission on Non-Ionizing Radiation Protection (ICNIRP). In press. *Practical Guide for Safety in the Use of RF Dielectric Heaters and Sealers.* Geneva: ILO.

Lee, SB and LP Ryan. 1996. Occupational health and safety in the biotechnology industry: A survey of practicing professionals. *Am Ind Hyg Assoc J* 57:381-386.

Legaspi, JA and C Zenz. 1994. Occupational health aspects of pesticides: Clinical and hygienic principles. In *Occupational Medicine,* 3rd edition, edited by C Zenz, OB Dickerson, and EP Horvath. St. Louis: Mosby-Year Book, Inc.

Lipton, S and JR Lynch. 1994. *Handbook of Health Hazard Control in the Chemical Process Industry.* New York: John Wiley & Sons.

Liberman, DF, AM Ducatman, and R Fink. 1990. Biotechnology: Is there a role for medical surveillance? In *Bioprocessing Safety: Worker and Community Safety and Health Considerations.* Philadelphia, PA: American Society for Testing and Materials.

Liberman, DF, L Wolfe, R Fink, and E Gilman. 1996. Biological safety considerations for environmental release of transgenic organisms and plants. In *Engineered Organisms in Environmental Settings: Biotechnological and Agricultural Applications,* edited by MA Levin and E Israeli. Boca Raton, FL: CRC Press.

Lichtenstein, N and K Quellmalz. 1984. Flüchtige Zersetzungsprodukte von Kunststoffen I: ABS-Polymere. *Staub-Reinhalt* 44(1):472-474.

—. 1986a. Flüchtige Zersetzungsprodukte von Kunststoffen II: Polyethylen. *Staub-Reinhalt* 46(1):11-13.

—. 1986b. Flüchtige Zersetzungsprodukte von Kunststoffen III: Polyamide. *Staub-Reinhalt* 46(1):197-198.

—. 1986c. Flüchtige Zersetzungsprodukte von Kunststoffen IV: Polycarbonate. *Staub-Reinhalt* 46(7/8):348-350.

Massachusetts Biotechnology Council Community Relations Committee. 1993. Unpublished statistics.

Mecklenburgh, JC. 1985. *Process Plant Layout.* New York: John Wiley & Sons.

Miller, H. 1983. Report on the World Health Organization Working Group on Health Implications of Biotechnology. *Recombinant DNA Technical Bulletin* 6:65-66.

Miller, HI, MA Tart and TS Bozzo. 1994. Manufacturing new biotech products: Gains and growing pains. *J Chem Technol Biotechnol* 59:3-7.

Moretti, EC and N Mukhopadhyay. 1993. VOC control: Current practices and future trends. *Chemical Engineering Progress* 89:20-26.

Mowrer, DS. 1995. Use quantitative analysis to manage fire risk. *Hydrocarbon Processing* 74:52-56.

Murphy, MR. 1994. Prepare for EPA's risk management program rule. *Chemical Engineering Progress* 90:77-82.

National Fire Protection Association (NFPA). 1990. *Flammable and Combustible Liquid.* NFPA 30. Quincy, MA: NFPA.

National Institute for Occupational Safety and Health (NIOSH). 1984. *Recommendations for Control of Occupational Safety and Health Hazards. Manufacture of Paint and Allied Coating Products.* DHSS (NIOSH) Publication No. 84-115. Cincinnati, OH: NIOSH.

National Institute of Health (Japan). 1996. Personal communication.

National Institutes of Health (NIH). 1976. Recombinant DNA research. *Federal Register* 41:27902-27905.

—. 1991. Recombinant DNA research actions under the guidelines. *Federal Register* 56:138.

—. 1996. Guidelines for research involving recombinant DNA molecules. *Federal Register* 61:10004.

Netzel, JP. 1996. Seal technology: A control for industrial pollution. Presented at the 45th Society of Tribologists and Lubrication Engineers Annual Meetings. 7-10 May, Denver.

Nordlee, JA, SL Taylor, JA Townsend, LA Thomas, and RK Bush. 1996. Identification of a Brazil-nut allergen in transgenic soybeans. *New Engl J Med* 334 (11):688-692.

Occupational Safety and Health Administration (OSHA). 1984. 50 FR 14468. Washington, DC: OSHA.

—. 1994. CFR 1910.06. Washington, DC:OSHA.

Office of Science and Technology Policy (OSTP). 1986. *Coordinated Framework for Biotechnology Regulation.* FR 23303. Washington, DC: OSTP.

Openshaw, PJ, WH Alwan, AH Cherrie, and FM Record. 1991. Accidental infection of laboratory worker with recombinant vaccinia virus. *Lancet* 338.(8764):459.

Parliament of the European Communities. 1987. Treaty Establishing a Single Council and a Single Commission of the European Communities. *Official Journal of the European Communities* 50(152):2.

Pennington, RL. 1996. VOC and HAP control operations. *Separations and Filtration Systems Magazine* 2:18-24.

Pratt, D and J May. 1994. Agricultural occupational medicine. In *Occupational Medicine,* 3rd edition, edited by C Zenz, OB Dickerson, and EP Horvath. St. Louis: Mosby-Year Book, Inc.

Reutsch, C-J and TR Broderick. 1996. New biotechnology legislation in the European Community and Federal Republic of Germany. *Biotechnology.*

Sattelle, D. 1991. Biotechnology in perspective. *Lancet* 338:9,28.

Scheff, PA and RA Wadden. 1987. *Engineering Design for Control of Workplace Hazards.* New York: McGraw-Hill.

Siegell, JH. 1996. Exploring VOC control options. *Chemical Engineering* 103:92-96.

Society of Tribologists and Lubrication Engineers (STLE). 1994. *Guidelines for Meeting Emission Regulations for Rotating Machinery with Mechanical Seals.* STLE Special Publication SP-30. Park Ridge, IL: STLE.

Sutton, IS. 1995. Integrated management systems improve plant reliability. Hydrocarbon Processing 74:63-66.

Swiss Interdisciplinary Committee for Biosafety in Research and Technology (SCBS). 1995. *Guidelines for Work with Genetically Modified Organisms.* Zurich: SCBS.

Thomas, JA and LA Myers (eds.). 1993. *Biotechnology and Safety Assessment.* New York: Raven Press.

Van Houten, J and DO Flemming. 1993. Comparative analysis of current US and EC biosafety regulations

and their impact on the industry. *Journal of Industrial Microbiology* 11:209-215.

Watrud, LS, SG Metz, and DA Fishoff. 1996. Engineered plants in the environment. In *Engineered Organisms in Environmental Settings: Biotechnological and Agricultural Applications,* edited by M Levin and E Israeli. Boca Raton, FL: CRC Press.

Woods, DR. 1995. *Process Design and Engineering Practice.* Englewood Cliffs, NJ: Prentice Hall.

Other relevant readings

American Petroleum Institute (API). 1990. *Management of Process Hazards.* RP 750. Washington, DC: API.

—. 1992. *Management Practices, Self-assessment Process, and Resource Materials.* RP 9000. Washington, DC: API.

—. 1995. *Management of Hazards Associated with Location of Process Plant Buildings.* RP 752. Washington, DC: API.

Burgess, WA. 1995. *Recognition of Health Hazards in Industry,* 2nd edition. New York: John Wiley & Sons.

Center for Chemical Process Safety (CCPS). 1985. *Guidelines for Hazard Evaluation Procedures.* New York: American Institute of Chemical Engineers.

—. 1989. *Guidelines for Technical Management of Chemical Process Safety.* New York: American Institute of Chemical Engineers.

National Institute for Occupational Safety and Health. 1981. *Control Technology in the Plastics and Resin Industry.* DHHS (NIOSH) Publication No. 81-107. Washington, DC: GPO.

Occupational Safety and Health Administration (OSHA). 1992. *29 CFR Part 1910, Process Safety Management of Highly Hazardous Chemicals, Explosives and Blasting Agents, Final Rule.* Washington, DC: OSHA.

Society of the Plastics Industry and National Safety Council. 1981. *Plastics Industry Safety Handbook.* Boston: Society of the Plastics Industry.

United Nations Economic Commission for Europe (UNECE). 1993. *The Chemical Industry in 1992: Annual Review-Production and Trade Statistics, 1989-1991.* Geneva: UNECE.

OIL AND NATURAL GAS

78

Chapter Editor
Richard S. Kraus

Contents

78. OIL AND NATURAL GAS

• PETROLEUM REFINING PROCESS

Richard S. Kraus

General Profile

Petroleum refining begins with the distillation, or fractionation, of crude oils into separate hydrocarbon groups. The resultant products are directly related to the characteristics of the crude oil being processed. Most of these products of distillation are further converted into more useable products by changing their physical and molecular structures through cracking, reforming and other conversion processes. These products are subsequently subjected to various treatment and separation processes, such as extraction, hydrotreating and sweetening, in order to produce finished products. Whereas the simplest refineries are usually limited to atmospheric and vacuum distillation, integrated refineries incorporate fractionation, conversion, treatment and blending with lubricant, heavy fuels and asphalt manufacturing; they may also include petrochemical processing.

The first refinery, which opened in 1861, produced kerosene by simple atmospheric distillation. Its by-products included tar and naphtha. It was soon discovered that high-quality lubricating oils could be produced by distilling petroleum under vacuum. However, for the next 30 years, kerosene was the product consumers wanted most. The two most significant events which changed this situation were:

- the invention of the electric light, which decreased the demand for kerosene
- the invention of the internal-combustion engine, which created a demand for diesel fuel and gasoline (naphtha).

With the advent of mass production and the First World War, the number of gasoline-powered vehicles increased dramatically, and the demand for gasoline grew accordingly. However, only a certain amount of gasoline could be obtained from crude oil through atmospheric and vacuum distillation processes. The first thermal cracking process was developed in 1913. Thermal cracking subjected heavy fuels to both pressure and intense heat, physically breaking their large molecules into smaller ones, producing additional gasoline and distillate fuels. A sophisticated form of thermal cracking, visbreaking, was developed in the late 1930s to produce more desirable and valuable products.

As higher-compression gasoline engines were developed, there was a demand for higher-octane gasoline with better anti-knock characteristics. The introduction of catalytic cracking and polymerization processes in the mid- to late 1930s met this demand by providing improved gasoline yields and higher octane numbers. Alkylation, another catalytic process, was developed in the early 1940s to produce more high-octane aviation gasoline and petrochemical feedstocks, the starting materials, for explosives and synthetic rubber. Subsequently, catalytic isomerization was developed to convert hydrocarbons to produce increased quantities of alkylation feedstocks.

Table 78.1 • Summary of the history of refining processing.

Year	Process name	Process purpose	Process by-products
1862	Atmospheric distillation	Produce kerosene	Naphtha, tar, etc.
1870	Vacuum distillation	Lubricants (original) Cracking feedstocks (1930s)	Asphalt, residual Coker feedstocks
1913	Thermal cracking	Increase gasoline	Residual, bunker fuel
1916	Sweetening	Reduce sulphur and odour	Sulphur
1930	Thermal reforming	Improve octane number	Residual
1932	Hydrogenation	Remove sulphur	Sulphur
1932	Coking	Produce gasoline base stocks	Coke
1933	Solvent extraction	Improve lubricant viscosity index	Aromatics
1935	Solvent dewaxing	Improve pour point	Waxes
1935	Catalytic polymerization	Improve gasoline yield and octane number	Petrochemical feedstocks
1937	Catalytic cracking	Higher octane gasoline	Petrochemical feedstocks
1939	Visbreaking	Reduce viscosity	Increased distillate, tar
1940	Alkylation	Increase gasoline octane and yield	High-octane aviation gasoline
1940	Isomerization	Produce alkylation feedstock	Naphtha
1942	Fluid catalytic cracking	Increase gasoline yield and octane	Petrochemical feedstocks
1950	Deasphalting	Increase cracking feedstock	Asphalt
1952	Catalytic reforming	Convert low-quality naphtha	Aromatics
1954	Hydrodesulphurization	Remove sulphur	Sulphur
1956	Inhibitor sweetening	Remove mercaptan	Disulphides
1957	Catalytic isomerization	Convert to molecules with high octane number	Alkylation feedstocks
1960	Hydrocracking	Improve quality and reduce sulphur	Alkylation feedstocks
1974	Catalytic dewaxing	Improve pour point	Wax
1975	Residual hydrocracking	Increase gasoline yield from residual	Heavy residuals

Figure 78.1 • Refinery process chart.

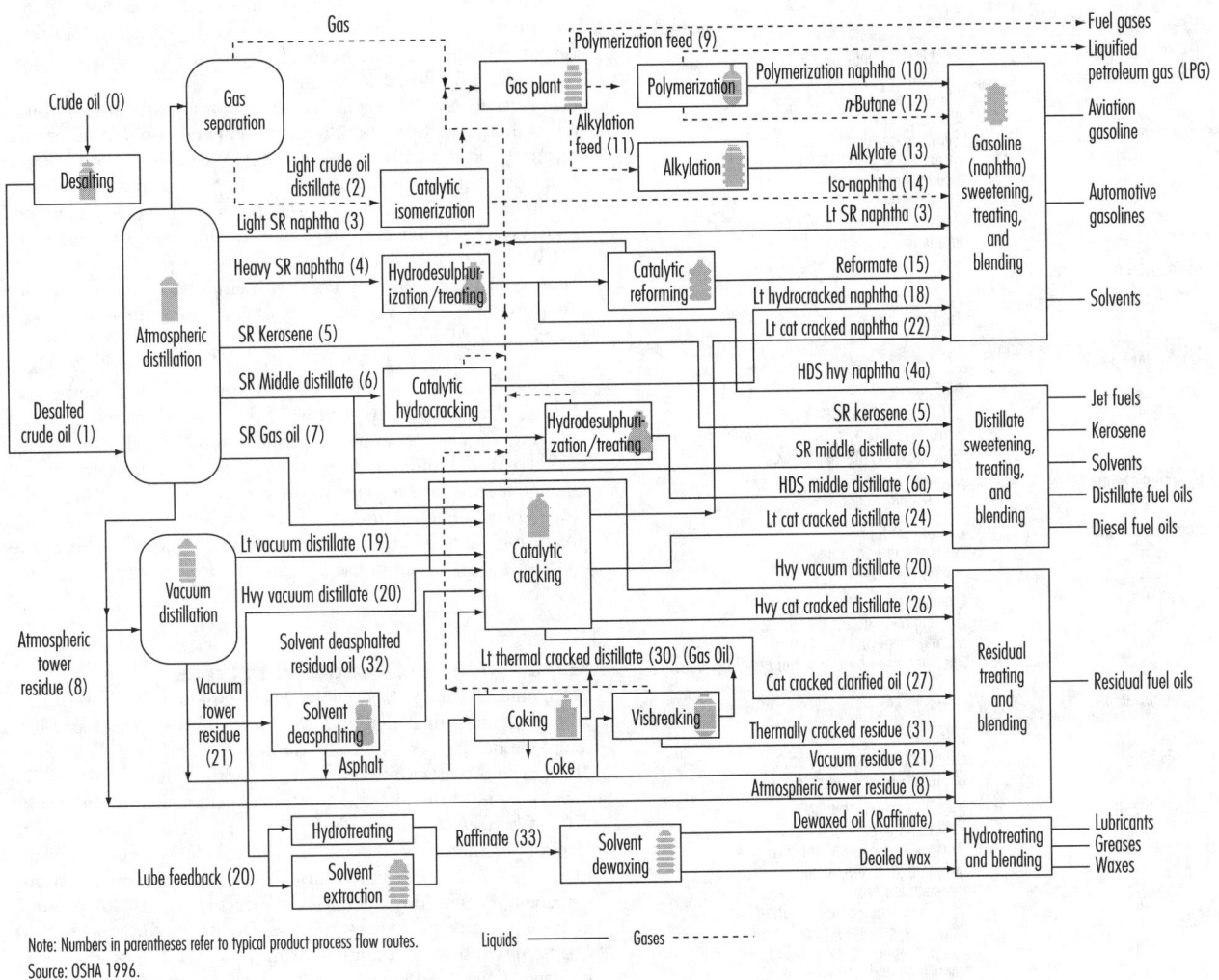

Note: Numbers in parentheses refer to typical product process flow routes.
Source: OSHA 1996.

Following the Second World War, various reforming processes were introduced which improved gasoline quality and yield, and produced higher-quality products. Some of these involved the use of catalysts and/or hydrogen to change molecules and remove sulphur. Improved catalysts, and process methods such as hydrocracking and reforming, were developed throughout the 1960s to increase gasoline yields and improve anti-knock characteristics. These catalytic processes also produced molecules with a double bond (alkenes), forming the basis of the modern petrochemical industry.

The numbers and types of different processes used in modern refineries depend primarily on the nature of the crude feedstock and finished product requirements. Processes are also affected by economic factors including crude costs, product values, availability of utilities and transportation. The chronology of the introduction of various processes is given in table 78.1.

Basic refining processes and operations

Petroleum refining processes and operations can be classified into the following basic areas: separation, conversion, treatment, formulating and blending, auxiliary refining operations and refining non-process operations. See figure 78.1 for a simplified flow chart.

Separation. Crude oil is physically separated by fractionation in atmospheric and vacuum distillation towers, into groups of hydrocarbon molecules with various boiling-point ranges, called "fractions" or "cuts".

Conversion. Conversion processes used to change the size and/or structure of hydrocarbon molecules include:

- decomposition (dividing) by hydro-, thermal and catalytic cracking, coking and visbreaking
- unification (combining) through alkylation and polymerization
- alteration (rearranging) with isomerization and catalytic reforming
- treatment.

Since the beginning of refining, various treatment methods have been used to remove non-hydrocarbons, impurities and other constituents that adversely affect the performance properties of finished products or reduce the efficiency of the conversion processes. Treatment involves both chemical reactions and physical separation, such as dissolving, absorption or precipitation, using a variety and combination of processes. Treatment methods include removing or separating aromatics and naphthenes, as well as removing impurities and undesirable contaminants. Sweeten-

Table 78.2 • Principal products of crude oil refining.

Hydrocarbon gases	Uses
Liquified gases	Cooking and industrial gas
	Motor fuel gas
	Illuminating gas
	Ammonia
	Synthetic fertilizer
	Alcohols
	Solvents and acetone
	Plasticizers
	Resins and fibres for plastics and textiles
	Paints and varnish
Chemical industry feedstock	Rubber products
Carbon black	Printing inks
	Rubber industry
Light distillates	
Light naphthas	Olefins
	Solvents and diluents
	Extraction solvents
	Chemical industry feedstocks
Intermediate naphthas	Aviation and motor gasoline
	Dry-cleaning solvents
Heavy naphthas	Military jet fuel
	Jet fuel and kerosene
	Tractor fuel
Gas oil	Cracking stock
	Heating oil and diesel fuel
	Metallurgical fuel
	Absorber oil—benzene and gasoline recovery
Heavy distillates	
Technical oils	Textile oils
	Medicinal oils and cosmetics
	White oil—food industry
Lubricating oils	Transformer and spindle oils
	Motor and engine oils
	Machine and compressor oils
	Turbine and hydraulic oils
	Transmission oils
	Equipment and cable insulation oils
	Axle, gear and steam engine oils
	Metal treating, cutting and grinding oils
	Quenching and rust inhibitor oils
	Heat transfer oils
	Lubricating greases and compounds
	Printing ink oils
Paraffin wax	Rubber industry
	Pharmaceuticals and cosmetics
	Food and paper industries
	Candles and matches
Residues	
Petrolatum	Petroleum jelly
	Cosmetics
	Rust inhibitors and lubricants
	Cable coating compounds
Residual fuel oil	No. 6 boiler and process fuel oil
Asphalts	Paving asphalt
	Roofing materials
	Asphaltic lubricants
	Insulating and foundation protection
	Waterproof paper products
Refinery by-products	
Coke	Electrodes and fuel
Sulphonates	Emulsifiers
Sulphuric acid	Synthetic fertilizer
Sulphur	Chemicals
Hydrogen	Hydrocarbon reformation

ing compounds and acids are used to desulphurize crude oil before processing, and to treat products during and after processing. Other treatment methods include crude desalting, chemical sweetening, acid treating, clay contacting, hydrodesulphurizing, solvent refining, caustic washing, hydrotreating, drying, solvent extraction and solvent dewaxing.

Formulating and blending is the process of mixing and combining hydrocarbon fractions, additives and other components to produce finished products with specific desired performance properties.

Auxiliary refining operations. Other refinery operations which are required to support hydrocarbon processing include light ends recovery; sour water stripping; solid waste, waste water and process water treatment and cooling; hydrogen production; sulphur recovery; and acid and tail gas treatment. Other process functions are providing catalysts, reagents, steam, air, nitrogen, oxygen, hydrogen and fuel gases.

Refinery non-process facilities. All refineries have a multitude of facilities, functions, equipment and systems which support the hydrocarbon process operations. Typical support operations are heat and power generation; product movement; tank storage; shipping and handling; flares and relief systems; furnaces and heaters; alarms and sensors; and sampling, testing and inspecting. Non-process facilities and systems include firefighting, water and protection systems, noise and pollution controls, laboratories, control rooms, warehouses, maintenance and administrative facilities.

Major Products of Crude Oil Refining

Petroleum refining has evolved continuously in response to changing consumer demand for better and different products. The original process requirement was to produce kerosene as a cheaper and better source of fuel for lighting than whale oil. The development of the internal combustion engine led to the production of benzene, gasoline and diesel fuels. The evolution of the airplane created a need for high-octane aviation gasoline and jet fuel, which is a sophisticated form of the original refinery product, kerosene. Present-day refineries produce a variety of products, including many which are used as feedstocks for cracking processes and lubricant manufacturing, and for the petrochemical industry. These products can be broadly classified as fuels, petrochemical feedstocks, solvents, process oils, lubricants and special products such as wax, asphalt and coke. (See table 78.2.)

A number of chemicals are used in, or formed as a result of, hydrocarbon processing. A brief description of those which are specific and pertinent to refining follows:

Sulphur Dioxide

Flue gas from burning high-sulphur-content fuels usually contains high levels of sulphur dioxide, which usually is removed by water scrubbing.

Caustics

Caustics are added to desalting water to neutralize acids and reduce corrosion. Caustics are also added to desalted crude in order to reduce the amount of corrosive chlorides in the tower overheads. They are used in refinery treating processes to remove contaminants from hydrocarbon streams.

Nitrogen oxides and carbon monoxide

Flue gas contains up to 200 ppm of nitric oxide, which reacts slowly with oxygen to form nitrogen dioxide. Nitric oxide is not removed by water scrubbing, and nitrogen dioxide can dissolve in water to form nitrous and nitric acid. Flue gas normally contains only a slight amount of carbon monoxide, unless combustion is abnormal.

Hydrogen sulphide

Hydrogen sulphide is found naturally in most crude oils and is also formed during processing by the decomposition of unstable sulphur compounds. Hydrogen sulphide is an extremely toxic, colourless, flammable gas which is heavier than air and soluble in water. It has a rotten egg odour which is discernible at concentrations well below its very low exposure limit. This smell cannot be relied upon to provide adequate warning as the senses are almost immediately desensitized upon exposure. Special detectors are required to alert workers to the presence of hydrogen sulphide, and proper respiratory protection should be used in the presence of the gas. Exposure to low levels of hydrogen sulphide will cause irritation, dizziness and headaches, while exposure to levels in excess of the prescribed limits will cause nervous system depression and eventually death.

Sour water

Sour water is process water which contains hydrogen sulphide, ammonia, phenols, hydrocarbons and low-molecular-weight sulphur compounds. Sour water is produced by steam stripping hydrocarbon fractions during distillation, regenerating catalyst, or steam stripping hydrogen sulphide during hydrotreating and hydrofinishing. Sour water is also generated by the addition of water to processes to absorb hydrogen sulphide and ammonia.

Sulphuric acid and hydrofluoric acid

Sulphuric acid and hydrofluoric acid are used as catalysts in alkylation processes. Sulphuric acid is also used in some of the treatment processes.

Solid catalysts

A number of different solid catalysts in many forms and shapes, from pellets to granular beads to dusts, made of various materials and having various compositions, are used in refining processes. Extruded pellet catalysts are used in moving and fixed bed units, while fluid bed processes use fine, spherical particulate catalysts. Catalysts used in processes which remove sulphur are impregnated with cobalt, nickel or molybdenum. Cracking units use acid-function catalysts, such as natural clay, silica alumina and synthetic zeolites. Acid-function catalysts impregnated with platinum or other noble metals are used in isomerization and reforming. Used catalysts require special handling and protection from exposures, as they may contain metals, aromatic oils, carcinogenic polycyclic aromatic compounds or other hazardous materials, and may also be pyrophoric.

Fuels

The principal fuel products are liquefied petroleum gas, gasoline, kerosene, jet fuel, diesel fuel and heating oil and residual fuel oils.

Liquefied petroleum gas (LPG), which consists of mixtures of paraffinic and olefinic hydrocarbons such as propane and butane, is produced for use as a fuel, and is stored and handled as liquids under pressure. LPG has boiling points ranging from about –74 °C to +38 °C, is colourless, and the vapours are heavier than air and extremely flammable. The important qualities from an occupational health and safety perspective of LPGs are vapour pressure and control of contaminants.

Gasoline. The most important refinery product is motor gasoline, a blend of relatively low-boiling hydrocarbon fractions, including reformate, alkylate, aliphatic naphtha (light straight-run naphtha), aromatic naphtha (thermal and catalytic cracked naphtha) and additives. Gasoline blending stocks have boiling points which range from ambient temperatures to about 204 °C, and a flashpoint below –40 °C. The critical qualities for gasoline are octane number (anti-knock), volatility (starting and vapour lock) and vapour pressure (environmental control). Additives are used to enhance gasoline performance and provide protection against oxidation and rust formation. Aviation gasoline is a high-octane product, specially blended to perform well at high altitudes.

Tetra ethyl lead (TEL) and tetra methyl lead (TML) are gasoline additives which improve octane ratings and anti-knock performance. In an effort to reduce lead in automotive exhaust emissions, these additives are no longer in common use, except in aviation gasoline.

Ethyl tertiary butyl ether (ETBE), methyl tertiary butyl ether (MTBE), tertiary amyl methyl ether (TAME) and other oxygenated compounds are used in lieu of TEL and TML to improve unleaded gasoline anti-knock performance and reduce carbon monoxide emissions.

Jet fuel and kerosene. Kerosene is a mixture of paraffins and naphthenes with usually less than 20% aromatics. It has a flashpoint above 38 °C and a boiling range of 160 °C to 288 °C, and is used for lighting, heating, solvents and blending into diesel fuel. Jet fuel is a middle distillate kerosene product whose critical qualities are freezepoint, flashpoint and smokepoint. Commercial jet fuel has a boiling range of about 191 °C to 274 °C, and military jet fuel from 55 °C to 288 °C.

Distillate fuels. Diesel fuels and domestic heating oils are light-coloured mixtures of paraffins, naphthenes and aromatics, and may contain moderate quantities of olefins. Distillate fuels have flashpoints above 60 °C and boiling ranges of about 163 °C to 371 °C, and are often hydrodesulphurized for improved stability. Distillate fuels are combustible and when heated may emit vapours which can form ignitable mixtures with air. The desirable qualities required for distillate fuels include controlled flash- and pourpoints, clean burning, no deposit formation in storage tanks, and a proper diesel fuel cetane rating for good starting and combustion.

Residual fuels. Many ships and commercial and industrial facilities use residual fuels or combinations of residual and distillate fuels, for power, heat and processing. Residual fuels are dark-coloured, highly viscous liquid mixtures of large hydrocarbon molecules, with flashpoints above 121 °C and high boiling points. The critical specifications for residual fuels are viscosity and low sulphur content (for environmental control).

Health and safety considerations

The primary safety hazard of LPG and gasoline is fire. The high volatility and high flammability of the lower-boiling-point products allows vapours to evaporate readily into air and form flammable mixtures which can be easily ignited. This is a recognized hazard that requires specific storage, containment and handling precautions, and safety measures to assure that releases of vapours and sources of ignition are controlled so that fires do not occur. The less volatile fuels, such as kerosene and diesel fuel, should be handled carefully to prevent spills and possible ignition, as their vapours are also combustible when mixed with air in the flammable range. When working in atmospheres containing fuel vapours, concentrations of highly volatile, flammable product vapours in air are often restricted to no more than 10% of the lower flammable limits (LFL), and concentrations of less volatile, combustible product vapours to no more than 20% LFL, depending on applicable company and government regulations, in order to reduce the risk of ignition.

Although gasoline vapour levels in air mixtures are typically maintained below 10% of the LFL for safety purposes, this concentration is considerably above the exposure limits to be observed for health reasons. When inhaled, small amounts of gasoline vapour in air, well below the lower flammable limit, can cause irritation, headaches and dizziness, while inhalation of larger concentrations can cause loss of consciousness and eventually death. Long-term health effects may also be possible.

Gasoline contains benzene, for example, a known carcinogen with allowable exposure limits of only a few parts per million. Therefore, even working in gasoline vapour atmospheres at levels below 10% LFL requires appropriate industrial hygiene precautions, such as respiratory protection or local exhaust ventilation.

In the past, many gasolines contained tetra-ethyl or tetra methyl alky lead anti-knock additives, which are toxic and present serious lead absorption hazards by skin contact or inhalation. Tanks or vessels which contained leaded gasoline at any time during their use must be vented, thoroughly cleaned, tested with a special "lead-in-air" test device and certified to be lead-free to assure that workers can enter without using self-contained or supplied breathing air equipment, even though oxygen levels are normal and the tanks now contain unleaded gasoline or other products.

Gaseous petroleum fractions and the more highly volatile fuel products have a mild anaesthetic effect, generally in inverse ratio to molecular weight. Lower-boiling-point liquid fuels, such as gasoline and kerosene, produce a severe chemical pneumonitis if inhaled, and should not be siphoned by mouth or accidentally ingested. Gases and vapours may also be present in sufficiently high concentrations to displace oxygen (in the air) below normal breathing levels. Maintaining vapour concentrations below the exposure limits and oxygen levels at normal breathing ranges, is usually accomplished by purging or ventilation.

Cracked distillates contain small amounts of carcinogenic polycyclic aromatic hydrocarbons (PAHs); therefore, exposure should be limited. Dermatitis may also develop from exposure to gasoline, kerosene and distillate fuels, as they have a tendency to defat the skin. Prevention is accomplished by use of personal protective equipment, barrier creams or reduced contact and good hygienic practices, such as washing with warm water and soap instead of cleaning hands with gasoline, kerosene or solvents. Some persons have skin sensitivity to the dyes used to colour gasoline and other distillate products.

Residual fuel oils contain traces of metals and may have entrained hydrogen sulphide, which is extremely toxic. Residual fuels which have high cracked stocks boiling above 370 °C contain carcinogenic PAHs. Repeated exposure to residual fuels without appropriate personal protection, should be avoided, especially when opening tanks and vessels, as hydrogen sulphide gas may be emitted.

Petrochemical feedstocks

Many products derived from crude-oil refining, such as ethylene, propylene and butadiene, are olefinic hydrocarbons derived from refinery cracking processes, and are intended for use in the petrochemical industry as feedstocks for the production of plastics, ammonia, synthetic rubber, glycol and so on.

Petroleum solvents

A variety of pure compounds, including benzene, toluene, xylene, hexane and heptane, whose boiling points and hydrocarbon composition are closely controlled, are produced for use as solvents. Solvents may be classified as aromatic or non-aromatic, depending on their composition. Their use as paint thinners, dry-cleaning fluids, degreasers, industrial and pesticide solvents and so on, is generally determined by their flashpoints, which vary from well below −18 °C to above 60 °C.

The hazards associated with solvents are similar to those of fuels in that the lower flashpoint solvents are flammable and their vapours, when mixed with air in the flammable range, are ignitable. Aromatic solvents will usually have more toxicity than non-aromatic solvents.

Process oils

Process oils include the high boiling range, straight run atmospheric or vacuum distillate streams and those which are produced by catalytic or thermal cracking. These complex mixtures, which contain large paraffinic, naphthenic and aromatic hydrocarbon molecules with more than 15 carbon atoms, are used as feedstocks for cracking or lubricant manufacturing. Process oils have fairly high viscosities, boiling points ranging from 260 °C to 538 °C, and flashpoints above 121 °C.

Process oils are irritating to the skin and contain high concentrations of PAHs as well as sulphur, nitrogen and oxygen compounds. Inhalation of vapours and mists should be avoided, and skin exposure should be controlled by the use of personal protection and good hygienic practices.

Lubricants and greases

Lubricating oil base stocks are produced by special refining processes to meet specific consumer requirements. Lubricating base stocks are light- to medium-coloured, low-volatile, medium- to high-viscous mixtures of paraffinic, naphthenic and aromatic oils, with boiling ranges from 371 °C to 538 °C. Additives, such as demulsifiers, anti-oxidants and viscosity improvers, are blended into the lubricating oil base stocks to provide the characteristics required for motor oils, turbine and hydraulic oils, industrial greases, lubricants, gear oils and cutting oils. The most critical quality for lubricating oil base stock is a high viscosity index, providing for less change in viscosity under varying temperatures. This characteristic may be present in the crude oil feed stock or attained through the use of viscosity index improver additives. Detergents are added to keep in suspension any sludge formed during the use of the oil.

Greases are mixtures of lubricating oils and metallic soaps, with the addition of special-purpose materials such as asbestos, graphite, molybdenum, silicones and talc to provide insulation or lubricity. Cutting and metal-process oils are lubricating oils with special additives such as chlorine, sulphur and fatty-acid additives which react under heat to provide lubrication and protection to the cutting tools. Emulsifiers and bacteria prevention agents are added to water-soluble cutting oils.

Although lubricating oils by themselves are non-irritating and have little toxicity, hazards may be presented by the additives. Users should consult supplier material safety data information to determine the hazards of specific additives, lubricants, cutting oils and greases. The primary lubricant hazard is dermatitis, which can usually be controlled by the use of personal protective equipment together with proper hygienic practices. Occasionally workers may develop a sensitivity to cutting oils or lubricants which will require reassignment to a job where contact cannot occur. There are some concerns about carcinogenic exposure to mists from naphthenic-based cutting and light spindle oils, which can be controlled by substitution, engineering controls or personal protection. The hazards of exposure to grease are similar to those of lubricating oil, with the addition of any hazards presented by the grease materials or additives. Most of these hazards are discussed elsewhere in this *Encyclopaedia*.

Special products

Wax is used for protecting food products; in coatings; as an ingredient in other products such as cosmetics and shoe polish and for candles.

Sulphur is produced as a result of petroleum refining. It is stored either as a heated, molten liquid in closed tanks or as a solid in containers or outdoors.

Coke is almost pure carbon, with a variety of uses from electrodes to charcoal briquettes, depending on its physical characteristics, which result from the coking process.

Asphalt, which is primarily used for paving roads and roofing materials, should be inert to most chemicals and weather conditions.

Waxes and asphalts are solid at ambient temperatures, and higher temperatures are needed for storage, handling and transportation, with the resulting hazard of burns. Petroleum wax is so highly refined that it usually does not present any hazards. Skin contact with wax can lead to plugging of pores, which can be controlled by proper hygienic practices. Exposure to hydrogen sulphide when asphalt and molten sulphur tanks are opened can be controlled by the use of appropriate engineering controls or respiratory protection. Sulphur is also readily ignitable at elevated temperatures. Asphalt is discussed elsewhere in the *Encyclopaedia*.

Petroleum Refining Processes

Hydrocarbon refining is the use of chemicals, catalysts, heat and pressure to separate and combine the basic types of hydrocarbon molecules naturally found in crude oil into groups of similar molecules. The refining process also rearranges the structures and bonding patterns of the basic molecules into different, more desirable hydrocarbon molecules and compounds. The type of hydrocarbon (paraffinic, naphthenic or aromatic) rather than the specific chemical compounds present, is the most significant factor in the refining process.

Throughout the refinery, operations procedures, safe work practices and the use of appropriate personal protective clothing and equipment, including approved respiratory protection, is needed for fire, chemical, particulate, heat and noise exposures and during process operations, sampling, inspection, turnaround and maintenance activities. As most refinery processes are continuous and the process streams are contained in enclosed vessels and piping, there is limited potential for exposure. However, the potential for fire exists because even though refinery operations are closed processes, if a leak or release of hydrocarbon liquid, vapour or gas occurs, the heaters, furnaces and heat exchangers throughout the process units are sources of ignition.

Crude oil pretreatment

Desalting

Crude oil often contains water, inorganic salts, suspended solids and water-soluble trace metals. The first step in the refining process is to remove these contaminants by desalting (dehydration) in order to reduce corrosion, plugging and fouling of equipment, and to prevent poisoning the catalysts in processing units.

Chemical desalting, electrostatic separation and filtering are three typical methods of crude-oil desalting. In chemical desalting, water and chemical surfactants (demulsifiers) are added to the crude oil, heated so that salts and other impurities dissolve into the water or attach to the water, and are then held in a tank where they settle out. Electrical desalting applies high-voltage electrostatic charges in order to concentrate suspended water globules in the bottom portion of the settling tank. Surfactants are added only when the crude oil has a large amount of suspended solids. A third, less common process involves filtering heated crude oil using diatomaceous earth as a filtration medium.

In chemical and electrostatic desalting, the crude feedstock is heated to between 66 °C and 177 °C, to reduce viscosity and surface tension for easier mixing and separation of the water. The temperature is limited by the vapour pressure of the crude-oil feedstock. Both methods of desalting are continuous. Caustic or acid may be added to adjust the pH of the water wash, and ammonia added to reduce corrosion. Waste water, together with contaminants, is discharged from the bottom of the settling tank to the waste water treatment facility. The desalted crude oil is continuously drawn from the top of the settling tanks and sent to an atmospheric crude distillation (fractionating) tower. (See figure 78.2)

Inadequate desalting causes fouling of heater tubes and heat exchangers in all refinery process units, restricting product flow and heat transfer, and resulting in failures due to increased pressures and temperatures. Overpressuring the desalting unit will cause failure.

Corrosion, which occurs due to the presence of hydrogen sulphide, hydrogen chloride, naphthenic (organic) acids and other contaminants in the crude oil, also causes equipment failure. Corrosion occurs when neutralized salts (ammonium chlorides and sulphides) are moistened by condensed water. Because desalting is a closed process, there is little potential for exposure to crude oil or process chemicals, unless a leak or release occurs. A fire may occur as a result of a leak in the heaters, allowing a release of low-boiling-point components of crude oil.

There is the possibility of exposure to ammonia, dry chemical demulsifiers, caustics and/or acids during desalting. Where elevated operating temperatures are used when desalting sour crude oils, hydrogen sulphide will be present. Depending on the crude feedstock and the treatment chemicals used, the waste water will contain varying amounts of chlorides, sulphides, bicarbonates, ammonia, hydrocarbons, phenol and suspended solids. If diatomaceous earth is used in filtration, exposures should be minimized or controlled since diatomaceous earth can contain silica with a very fine particle size, making it a potential respiratory hazard.

Figure 78.2 • Desalting (pre-treatment) process.

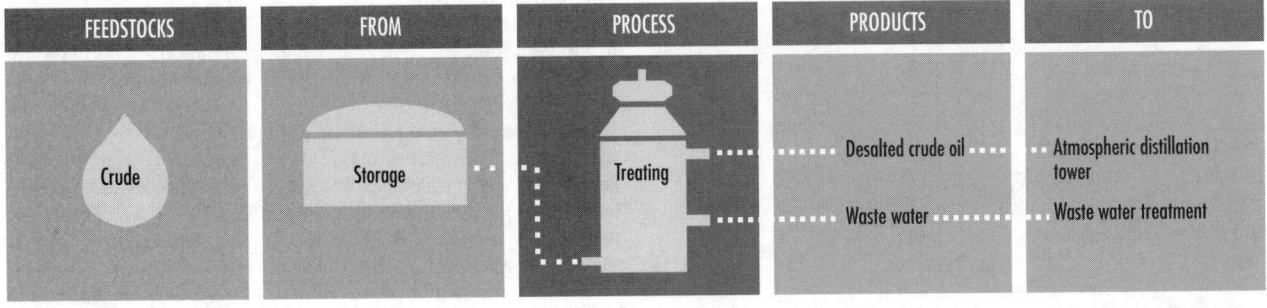

FEEDSTOCKS	FROM	PROCESS	PRODUCTS	TO
Crude	Storage	Treating	Desalted crude oil	Atmospheric distillation tower
			Waste water	Waste water treatment

Source: Adapted from OSHA 1996.

78. OIL AND NATURAL GAS

Figure 78.3 • Atmospheric distillation process.

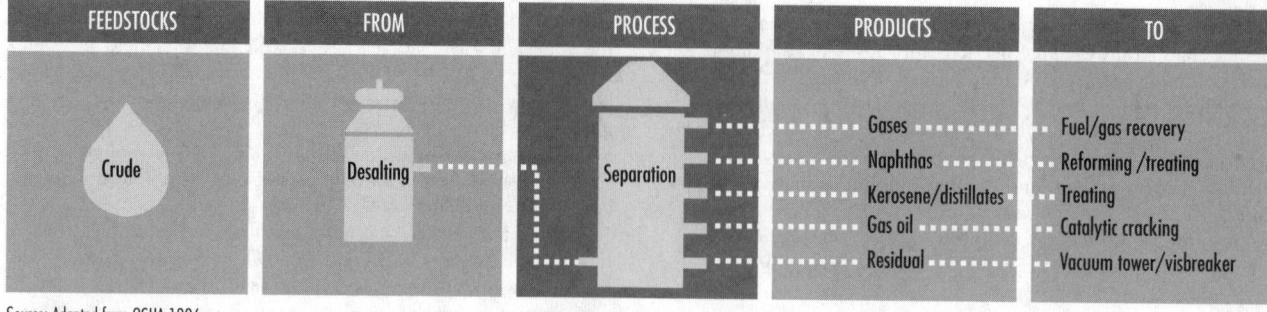

Source: Adapted from OSHA 1996.

Crude oil separation processes

The first step in petroleum refining is the fractionation of crude oil in atmospheric and vacuum distillation towers. Heated crude oil is physically separated into various fractions, or straight-run cuts, differentiated by specific boiling-point ranges and classified, in order of decreasing volatility, as gases, light distillates, middle distillates, gas oils and residuum. Fractionation works because the gradation in temperature from the bottom to the top of the distillation tower causes the higher-boiling-point components to condense first, while the lower-boiling-point fractions rise higher in the tower before they condense. Within the tower, the rising vapours and the descending liquids (reflux) mix at levels where they have compositions in equilibrium with each other. Special trays are located at these levels (or stages) which remove a fraction of the liquid which condenses at each level. In a typical two-stage crude unit, the atmospheric tower, producing light fractions and distillate, is immediately followed by a vacuum tower which processes the atmospheric residuals. After distillation, only a few

hydrocarbons are suitable for use as finished products without further processing.

Atmospheric distillation

In atmospheric distillation towers, the desalted crude feedstock is preheated using recovered process heat. It then flows to a direct-fired crude charge heater, where it is fed into the vertical distillation column just above the bottom at pressures slightly above atmosphere and at temperatures from 343 °C to 371 °C, to avoid undesirable thermal cracking at higher temperatures. The lighter (lower boiling point) fractions diffuse into the upper part of the tower, and are continuously drawn off and directed to other units for further processing, treating, blending and distribution.

Fractions with the lowest boiling points, such as fuel gas and light naphtha, are removed from the top of the tower by an overhead line as vapours. Naphtha, or straight-run gasoline, is taken from the upper section of the tower as an overhead stream. These products are used as petrochemical and reformer feedstocks, gasoline blending stocks, solvents and LPGs.

Intermediate boiling range fractions, including gas oil, heavy naphtha and distillates, are removed from the middle section of the tower as side streams. These are sent to finishing operations for use as kerosene, diesel fuel, fuel oil, jet fuel, catalytic cracker feedstock and blending stocks. Some of these liquid fractions are stripped of their lighter ends, which are returned to the tower as downflowing reflux streams.

The heavier, higher-boiling-point fractions (called residuum, bottoms or topped crude) which condense or remain at the bottom of the tower, are used for fuel oil, bitumen manufacturing or cracking feedstock, or are directed to a heater and into the vacuum distillation tower for further fractionation. (See figures 78.3 and 78.4.)

Vacuum distillation

Vacuum distillation towers provide the reduced pressure required to prevent thermal cracking when distilling the residuum, or topped crude, from the atmospheric tower at higher temperatures. The internal designs of some vacuum towers are different from atmospheric towers in that random packing and demister pads are used instead of trays. Larger diameter towers may also be used to keep velocities lower. A typical first-phase vacuum tower may produce gas oils, lubricating oil base stocks and heavy residual for propane deasphalting. A second-phase tower, operating at a lower vacuum, distills surplus residuum from the atmospheric tower which is not used for lube stock processing, and surplus residuum from the first vacuum tower not used for deasphalting.

Figure 78.4 • Schematic of atmospheric distillation process.

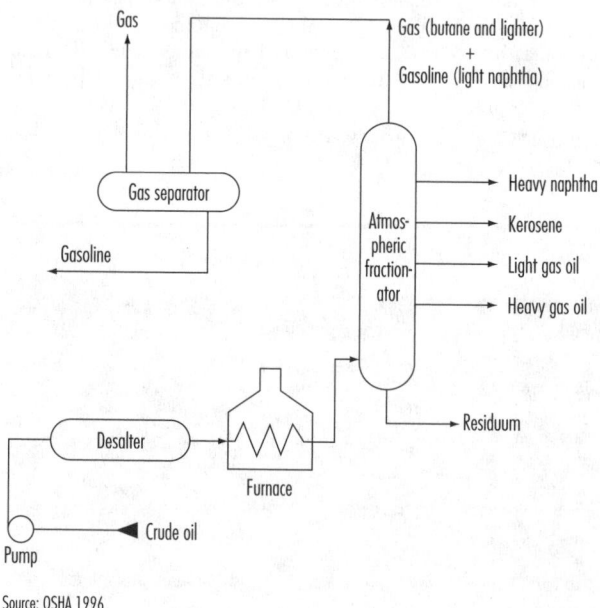

Source: OSHA 1996.

Figure 78.5 • Vacuum distillation process.

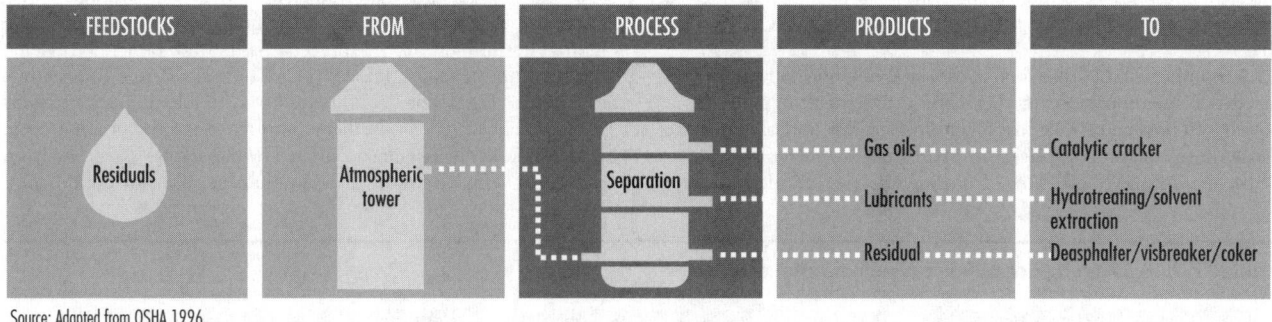

FEEDSTOCKS	FROM	PROCESS	PRODUCTS	TO
Residuals	Atmospheric tower	Separation	Gas oils	Catalytic cracker
			Lubricants	Hydrotreating/solvent extraction
			Residual	Deasphalter/visbreaker/coker

Source: Adapted from OSHA 1996.

Vacuum towers are typically used to separate catalytic cracker feedstocks from surplus residuum. Vacuum tower bottoms may also be sent to a coker, used as lubricant or asphalt stock or desulphurized and blended into low-sulphur fuel oil. (See figures 78.5 and 78.6.)

Distillation columns

Within refineries there are numerous other smaller distillation towers, called columns, designed to separate specific and unique products, which all work on the same principles as atmospheric towers. For example, a depropanizer is a small column designed to separate propane from isobutane and heavier components. Another larger column is used to separate ethyl benzene and xylene. Small "bubbler" towers, called strippers, use steam to remove trace amounts of light products (gasoline) from heavier product streams.

Control temperatures, pressures and reflux must be maintained within operating parameters to prevent thermal cracking from taking place within distillation towers. Relief systems are provided because excursions in pressure, temperature or liquid levels may occur if automatic control devices fail. Operations are monitored in order to prevent crude from entering the reformer charge. Crude feedstocks may contain appreciable amounts of water in suspension which separate during start-up and, along with water remaining in the tower from steam purging, settle in the bottom of the tower. This water may heat to the boiling point and create an instantaneous vaporization explosion upon contact with the oil in the unit.

The preheat exchanger, preheat furnace and bottoms exchanger, atmospheric tower and vacuum furnace, vacuum tower and overhead are susceptible to corrosion from hydrochloric acid (HCl), hydrogen sulphide (H_2S), water, sulphur compounds and organic acids. When processing sour crudes, severe corrosion can occur in both atmospheric and vacuum towers where metal temperatures exceed 232 °C, and in furnace tubing. Wet H_2S will also cause cracks in steel. When processing high-nitrogen crudes, nitrogen oxides, which are corrosive to steel when cooled to low temperatures in the presence of water, form in the flue gases of furnaces.

Chemicals are used to control corrosion by hydrochloric acid produced in distillation units. Ammonia may be injected into the overhead stream prior to initial condensation, and/or an alkaline solution may be carefully injected into the hot crude oil feed. If sufficient wash water is not injected, deposits of ammonium chloride can form, causing serious corrosion.

Atmospheric and vacuum distillation are closed processes, and exposures are minimal. When sour (high sulphur) crudes are processed, there may be potential exposure to hydrogen sulphide in the preheat exchanger and furnace, tower flash zone and overhead system, vacuum furnace and tower, and bottoms exchanger. Crude oils and distillation products all contain high-boiling aromatic compounds, including carcinogenic PAHs. Short-term exposure to high concentrations of naphtha vapour can result in headaches, nausea and dizziness, and long-term exposure can result in loss of consciousness. Benzene is present in aromatic naphthas, and exposure must be limited. The dehexanizer overhead may contain large amounts of normal hexane, which can affect the nervous system. Hydrogen chloride may be present in the preheat exchanger, tower top zones and overheads. Waste water may contain water-soluble sulphides in high concentrations and other water-soluble compounds, such as ammonia, chlorides, phenol and mercaptan, depending upon the crude feedstock and the treatment chemicals.

Figure 78.6 • Schematic of vacuum distillation process.

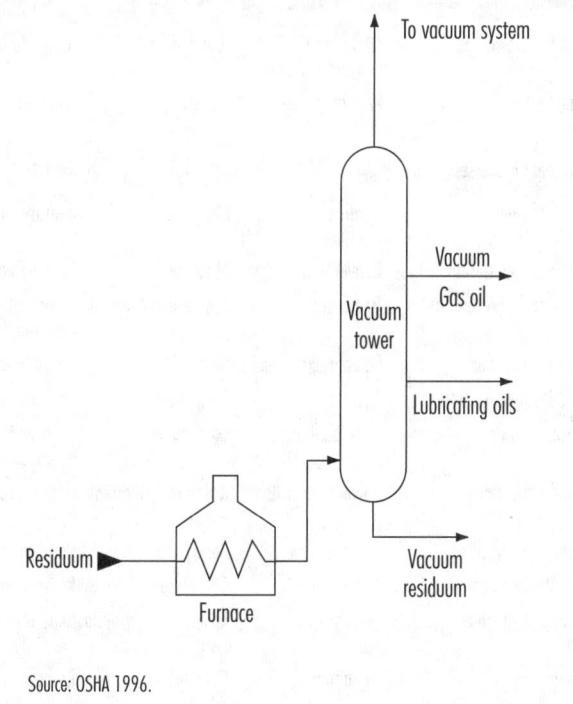

Source: OSHA 1996.

78. OIL AND NATURAL GAS

Crude oil conversion processes

Conversion processes, such as cracking, combining and rearranging, change the size and structure of hydrocarbon molecules in order to convert fractions into more desirable products. (See table 78.3.)

A number of hydrocarbon molecules not normally found in crude oil but important to the refining process are created as a result of conversion. Olefins (alkenes, di-olefins and alkynes) are unsaturated chain- or ring-type hydrocarbon molecules with at least one double bond. They are usually formed by thermal and catalytic cracking and rarely occur naturally in unprocessed crude oil.

Alkenes are straight-chain molecules with the formula C_nH_n containing at least one double bond (unsaturated) linkage in the chain. The simplest alkene molecule is the mono-olefin ethylene, with two carbon atoms, joined by a double bond, and four hydrogen atoms. Di-olefins (containing two double bonds), such as 1,2-butadiene and 1,3-butadiene, and alkynes (containing a triple bond), such as acetylene, occur in C_5 and lighter fractions from cracking. Olefins are more reactive than paraffins or naphthenes,

Table 78.3 • Overview of petroleum refining processes.

Process name	Action	Method	Purpose	Feedstocks	Products
Fractionation processes					
Atmospheric distillation	Separation	Thermal	Separate fractions	Desalted crude oil	Gas, gas oil, distillate, residual
Vacuum distillation	Separation	Thermal	Separate without cracking	Atmospheric tower residual	Gas oil, lube stock, residual
Conversion processes — Decomposition					
Catalytic cracking	Alteration	Catalytic	Upgrade gasoline	Gas oil, coke distillate	Gasoline, petrochemical feedstock
Coking	Polymerization	Thermal	Convert vacuum residuals	Residual, heavy oil, tar	Naphtha, gas oil, coke
Hydrocracking	Hydrogenation	Catalytic	Convert to lighter hydrocarbons	Gas oil, cracked oil, residuals	Lighter, higher quality products
Hydrogen steam reforming	Decomposition	Thermal/catalytic	Produce hydrogen	Desulphurized gas, O_2, steam	Hydrogen, CO, CO_2
Steam cracking	Decomposition	Thermal	Crack large molecules	Atmospheric tower heavy fuel/distillate	Cracked naphtha, coke, residuals
Visbreaking	Decomposition	Thermal	Reduce viscosity	Atmospheric tower residual	Distillate, tar
Conversion processes — Unification					
Alkylation	Combining	Catalytic	Unite olefins and isoparaffins	Tower isobutane/cracker olefin	Iso-octane (alkylate)
Grease compounding	Combining	Thermal	Combine soaps and oils	Lube oil, fatty acid, alkymetal	Lubricating grease
Polymerization	Polymerization	Catalytic	Unite two or more olefins	Cracker olefins	High octane naphtha, petrochemical stocks
Conversion processes — Alteration/rearrangement					
Catalytic reforming	Alteration/dehydrogenation	Catalytic	Upgrade low-octane naphtha	Coker/hydrocracker naphtha	High-octane reformate/aromatic
Isomerization	Rearrangement	Catalytic	Convert straight chain to branch	Butane, pentane, hexane	Isobutane/pentane/hexane
Treatment processes					
Amine treating	Treatment	Absorption	Remove acidic contaminants	Sour gas, hydrocarbons with CO_2 and H_2S	Acid-free gases and liquid hydrocarbons
Desalting (pre-treatment)	Dehydration	Absorption	Remove contaminants	Crude oil	Desalted crude oil
Drying and sweetening	Treatment	Absorption/thermal	Remove H_2O and sulphur compounds	Liquid hydrocarbon, LPG, alkylated feedstock	Sweet and dry hydrocarbons
Furfural extraction	Solvent extraction	Absorption	Upgrade middistillate and lubes	Cycle oils and lube feedstocks	High-quality diesel and lube oil
Hydrodesulphurization	Treatment	Catalytic	Remove sulphur, contaminants	High-sulphur residual/gas oil	Desulphurized olefins
Hydrotreating	Hydrogenation	Catalytic	Remove impurities/saturate hydrocarbons	Residuals, cracked hydrocarbons	Cracker feed, distillate, lube
Phenol extraction	Solvent extraction	Absorption/thermal	Improve lube viscosity index, colour	Lube oil base stocks	High-quality lube oils
Solvent deasphalting	Treatment	Absorption	Remove asphalt	Vacuum tower residual, propane	Heavy lube oil, asphalt
Solvent dewaxing	Treatment	Cool/filter	Remove wax from lube stocks	Vacuum tower lube oils	Dewaxed lube base stock
Solvent extraction	Solvent extraction	Absorption/precipitation	Separate unsaturated aromatics	Gas oil, reformate, distillate	High-octane gasoline
Sweetening	Treatment	Catalytic	Remove H_2S, convert mercaptan	Untreated distillate/gasoline	High-quality distillate/gasoline

Figure 78.7 • Visbreaking process.

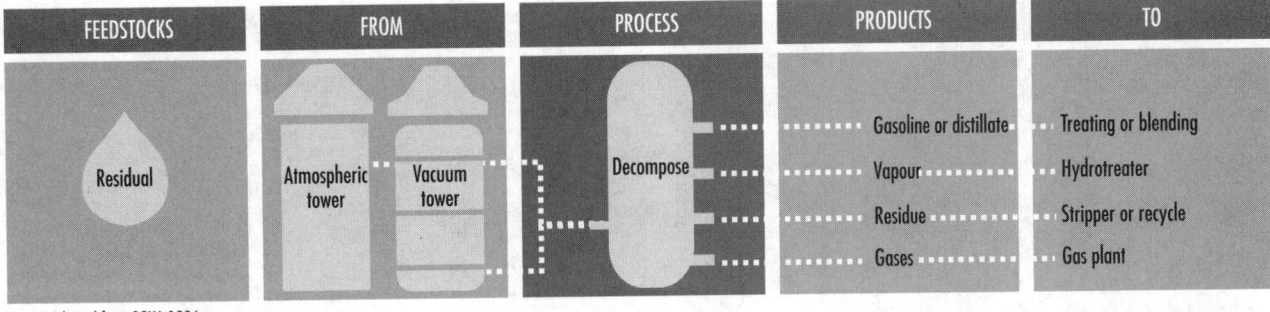

Source: Adapted from OSHA 1996.

and readily combine with other elements such as hydrogen, chlorine and bromine.

Cracking processes

Following distillation, subsequent refinery processes are used to alter the molecular structures of the fractions to create more desirable products. One of these processes, cracking, breaks (or cracks) heavier, higher-boiling-point petroleum fractions into more valuable products such as gaseous hydrocarbons, gasoline blending stocks, gas oil and fuel oil. During the process, some of the molecules combine (polymerize) to form larger molecules. The basic types of cracking are thermal cracking, catalytic cracking and hydro-cracking.

Thermal cracking processes

Thermal cracking processes, developed in 1913, heat distillate fuels and heavy oils under pressure in large drums until they crack (divide) into smaller molecules with better anti-knock characteristics. This early method, which produced large amounts of solid, unwanted coke, has evolved into modern thermal cracking processes including visbreaking, steam cracking and coking.

Visbreaking

Visbreaking is a mild form of thermal cracking which reduces the pour point of waxy residues and significantly lowers the viscosity of feedstock without affecting its boiling-point range. Residual from the atmospheric distillation tower is mildly cracked in a heater at atmospheric pressure. It is then quenched with cool gas oil to control overcracking, and flashed in a distillation tower. The thermally cracked residue tar, which accumulates in the bottom of the fractionation tower, is vacuum flashed in a stripper and the distillate is recycled. (See figure 78.7.)

Steam cracking

Steam cracking produces olefins by thermally cracking large hydrocarbon molecule feedstocks at pressures slightly above atmospheric and at very high temperatures. Residual from steam cracking is blended into heavy fuels. Naphtha produced from steam cracking usually contains benzene, which is extracted prior to hydrotreating.

Coking

Coking is a severe form of thermal cracking used to obtain straight-run gasoline (coker naphtha) and various middle distillate fractions used as catalytic cracking feedstocks. This process so completely reduces hydrogen from the hydrocarbon molecule, that the residue is a form of almost pure carbon called *coke*. The two most common coking processes are delayed coking and continuous (contact or fluid) coking, which, depending upon the reaction mechanism, time, temperature and the crude feedstock, produce three types of coke—sponge, honeycomb and needle coke. (See figure 78.8.)

- *Delayed coking.* In delayed coking, the feedstock is first charged to a fractionator to separate lighter hydrocarbons, and then combined with heavy recycle oil. The heavy feedstock is fed to the coker furnace and heated to high temperatures at low pressures to prevent premature coking in the heater tubes, producing

Figure 78.8 • Coking process.

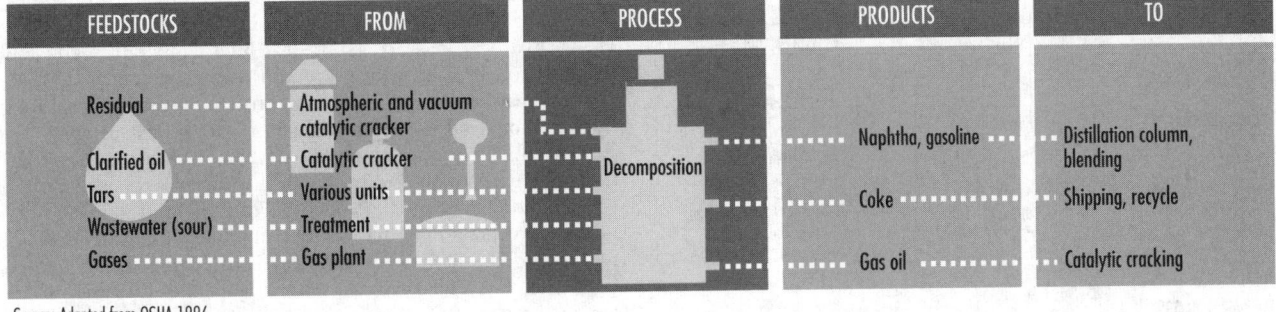

Source: Adapted from OSHA 1996.

Figure 78.9 • Catalytic cracking process.

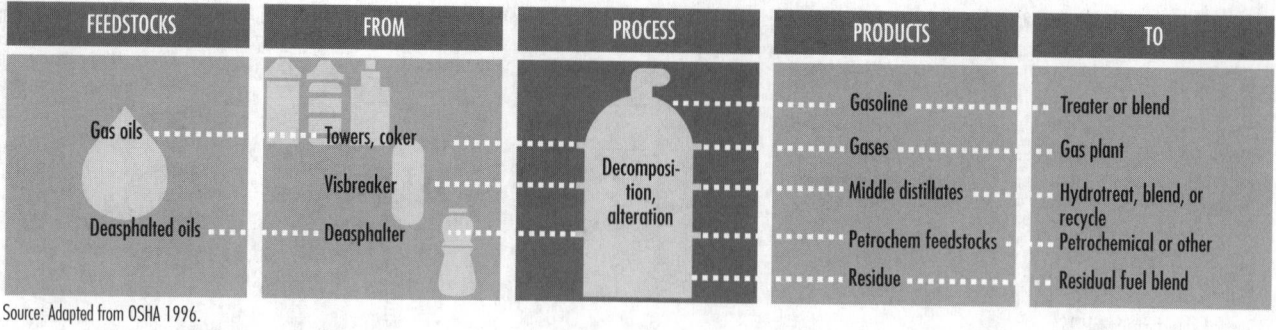

FEEDSTOCKS	FROM	PROCESS	PRODUCTS	TO
Gas oils	Towers, coker	Decomposition, alteration	Gasoline	Treater or blend
	Visbreaker		Gases	Gas plant
			Middle distillates	Hydrotreat, blend, or recycle
Deasphalted oils	Deasphalter		Petrochem feedstocks	Petrochemical or other
			Residue	Residual fuel blend

Source: Adapted from OSHA 1996.

partial vaporization and mild cracking. The liquid/vapour mixture is pumped from the heater to one or more coker drums, where the hot material is held approximately 24 hours (delayed) at low pressures until it cracks into lighter products. After the coke reaches a predetermined level in one drum, the flow is diverted to another drum to maintain continuous operation. Vapour from the drums is returned to the fractionator to separate out gas, naphtha and gas oils, and to recycle heavier hydrocarbons through the furnace. The full drum is steamed to strip out uncracked hydrocarbons, cooled by water injection and decoked mechanically by an auger rising from the bottom of the drum, or hydraulically by fracturing the coke bed with high-pressure water ejected from a rotating cutter.

• *Continuous coking.* Continuous (contact or fluid) coking is a moving bed process which operates at lower pressures and higher temperatures than delayed coking. In continuous coking, thermal cracking occurs by using heat transferred from hot recycled coke particles to feedstock in a radial mixer, called a *reactor*. Gases and vapours are taken from the reactor, quenched to stop further reaction and fractionated. The reacted coke enters a surge drum and is lifted to a feeder and classifier where the larger coke particles are removed. The remaining coke is dropped into the reactor preheater for recycling with feedstock. The process is automatic in that there is a continuous flow of coke and feedstock, and coking occurs both in the reactor and in the surge drum.

Figure 78.10 • Schematic of catalytic cracking process.

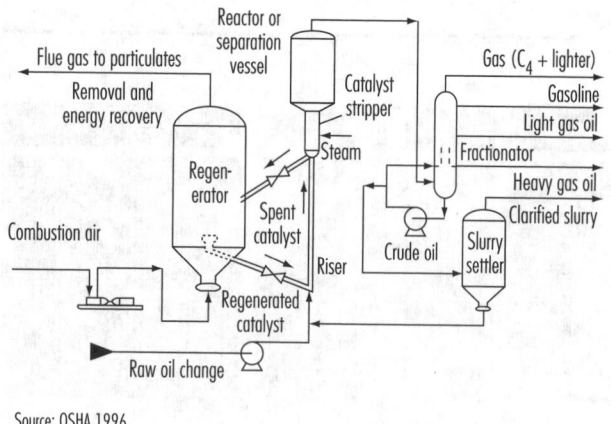

Source: OSHA 1996.

Health and safety considerations

In coking, temperature control should be held within a close range, as high temperatures will produce coke which is too hard to cut out of the drum. Conversely, temperatures which are too low will result in a high asphaltic content slurry. Should coking temperatures get out of control, an exothermic reaction could occur.

In thermal cracking when sour crudes are processed, corrosion can occur where metal temperatures are between 232 °C and 482 °C. It appears that coke forms a protective layer on the metal above 482 °C. However, hydrogen sulphide corrosion occurs when temperatures are not properly controlled above 482 °C. The lower part of the tower, high temperature exchangers, furnace and soaking drums are subject to corrosion. Continuous thermal changes cause coke drum shells to bulge and crack.

Water or steam injection is used to prevent buildup of coke in delayed coker furnace tubes. Water must be completely drained from the coker, so as not to cause an explosion upon recharging with hot coke. In emergencies, alternate means of egress from the working platform on top of coke drums is needed.

Burns may occur when handling hot coke, from steam in the event of a steam line leak, or from hot water, hot coke or hot slurry which may be expelled when opening cokers. The potential exists for exposure to aromatic naphthas containing benzene, hydrogen sulphide and carbon monoxide gases, and to trace amounts of carcinogenic PAHs associated with coking operations. Waste sour water may be highly alkaline, and contain oil, sulphides, ammonia and phenol. When coke is moved as a slurry, oxygen depletion may occur within confined spaces such as storage silos, because wet carbon adsorbs oxygen.

Catalytic cracking processes

Catalytic cracking breaks up complex hydrocarbons into simpler molecules in order to increase the quality and quantity of lighter, more desirable products and decrease the amount of residuals. Heavy hydrocarbons are exposed at high temperature and low pressure to catalysts which promote chemical reactions. This process rearranges the molecular structure, converting heavy hydrocarbon feedstocks into lighter fractions such as kerosene, gasoline, LPG, heating oil and petrochemical feedstocks (see figures 78.9 and 78.10). Selection of a catalyst depends upon a combination of the greatest possible reactivity and the best resistance to attrition. The catalysts used in refinery cracking units are typically solid materials (zeolite, aluminium hydrosilicate, treated bentonite clay, Fuller's earth, bauxite and silica-alumina) which are in the form of powders, beads, pellets or shaped materials called extrudites.

There are three basic functions in all catalytic cracking processes:

- Reaction—feedstock reacts with catalyst and cracks into different hydrocarbons.
- Regeneration—catalyst is reactivated by burning off coke.
- Fractionation—cracked hydrocarbon stream is separated into various products.

Catalytic cracking processes are very flexible and operating parameters can be adjusted to meet changing product demand. The three basic types of catalytic cracking processes are:

- fluid catalytic cracking (FCC)
- moving bed catalytic cracking
- thermofor catalytic cracking (TCC).

Fluid catalytic cracking

Fluid-bed catalytic crackers have a catalyst section (riser, reactor and regenerator) and a fractionating section, both operating together as an integrated processing unit. The FCC uses finely powdered catalyst, suspended in oil vapour or gas, which acts as a fluid. Cracking takes place in the feed pipe (riser) in which the mixture of catalyst and hydrocarbons flow through the reactor.

The FCC process mixes a preheated hydrocarbon charge with hot, regenerated catalyst as it enters the riser leading to the reactor. The charge combines with recycle oil within the riser, is vaporized and is raised to reactor temperature by the hot catalyst. As the mixture travels up the reactor, the charge is cracked at low pressure. This cracking continues until the oil vapours are separated from the catalyst in the reactor cyclones. The resultant product stream enters a column where it is separated into fractions, with some of the heavy oil directed back into the riser as recycle oil.

Spent catalyst is regenerated to remove coke which collects on the catalyst during the process. Spent catalyst flows through the catalyst stripper to the regenerator where it mixes with preheated air, burning off most of the coke deposits. Fresh catalyst is added and worn-out catalyst removed to optimize the cracking process.

Moving bed catalytic cracking

Moving-bed catalytic cracking is similar to fluid catalytic cracking; however, the catalyst is in the form of pellets instead of fine powder. The pellets move continuously by conveyor or pneumatic lift tubes to a storage hopper at the top of the unit, and then flow downward by gravity through the reactor to a regenerator. The regenerator and hopper are isolated from the reactor by steam seals. The cracked product is separated into recycle gas, oil, clarified oil, distillate, naphtha and wet gas.

Thermofor catalytic cracking

In thermofor catalytic cracking, the preheated feedstock flows by gravity through the catalytic reactor bed. Vapours are separated from the catalyst and sent to a fractionating tower. The spent catalyst is regenerated, cooled and recycled, and the flue gas from regeneration is sent to a carbon monoxide boiler for heat recovery.

Health and safety considerations

Regular sampling and testing of feedstock, product and recycle streams should be performed to assure that the cracking process is working as intended and that no contaminants have entered the process stream. Corrosives or deposits in feedstock can foul gas compressors. When processing sour crude, corrosion may be expected where temperatures are below 482 °C. Corrosion takes place where both liquid and vapour phases exist and at areas subject to local cooling, such as nozzles and platform supports.

When processing high-nitrogen feedstocks, exposure to ammonia and cyanide may subject carbon steel equipment in the FCC overhead system to corrosion, cracking or hydrogen blistering, which can be minimized by water wash or by corrosion inhibitors. Water wash may be used to protect overhead condensers in the main column subjected to fouling from ammonium hydrosulphide.

Critical equipment, including pumps, compressors, furnaces and heat exchangers should be inspected. Inspections should include checking for leaks due to erosion or other malfunctions such as catalyst buildup on the expanders, coking in the overhead feeder lines from feedstock residues, and other unusual operating conditions.

Liquid hydrocarbons in the catalyst or entering the heated combustion air stream can cause exothermic reactions. In some processes, caution must be taken to assure that explosive concentrations of catalyst dust are not present during recharge or disposal. When unloading coked catalyst, the possibility of iron sulphide fires exists. Iron sulphide will ignite spontaneously when exposed to air, and therefore needs to be wetted down with water to prevent it from becoming a source of ignition for vapours. Coked catalyst may either be cooled to below 49 °C before dumping from the reactor, or first dumped into containers purged with inert nitrogen and then cooled before further handling.

The possibility of exposure to extremely hot hydrocarbon liquids or vapours is present during process sampling or if a leak or release occurs. In addition, exposure to carcinogenic PAHs, aromatic naphtha containing benzene, sour gas (fuel gas from processes such as catalytic cracking and hydrotreating, which contains hydrogen sulphide and carbon dioxide), hydrogen sulphide and/or carbon monoxide gas may occur during a release of product or vapour. Inadvertent formation of highly toxic nickel carbonyl may occur in cracking processes that use nickel catalysts with resultant potential for hazardous exposures.

Catalyst regeneration involves steam stripping and decoking, which results in potential exposure to fluid waste streams which may contain varying amounts of sour water, hydrocarbon, phenol, ammonia, hydrogen sulphide, mercaptan and other materials, depending upon the feedstocks, crudes and processes. Safe work practices and the use of appropriate personal protective equipment (PPE) are needed when handling spent catalyst, recharging catalyst, or if leaks or releases occur.

Hydrocracking process

Hydrocracking is a two-stage process combining catalytic cracking and hydrogenation, wherein distillate fractions are cracked in the presence of hydrogen and special catalysts to produce more desirable products. Hydrocracking has an advantage over catalytic cracking in that high-sulphur feedstocks can be processed without previous desulphurization. In the process, heavy aromatic feedstock is converted into lighter products under very high pressures and fairly high temperatures. When the feedstock has a high paraffinic content, the hydrogen prevents the formation of PAHs, reduces tar formation and prevents build-up of coke on the catalyst. Hydrocracking produces relatively large amounts of isobutane for alkylation feedstocks and also causes isomerization for pour point control and smoke point control, both of which are important in high-quality jet fuel.

In the first stage, feedstock is mixed with recycled hydrogen, heated and sent to the primary reactor, where a large amount of the feedstock is converted to middle distillates. Sulphur and nitrogen compounds are converted by a catalyst in the primary stage reactor to hydrogen sulphide and ammonia. The residual is heated and sent to a high-pressure separator, where hydrogen-rich gases are removed and recycled. The remaining hydrocar-

Figure 78.11 • Hydrocracking process.

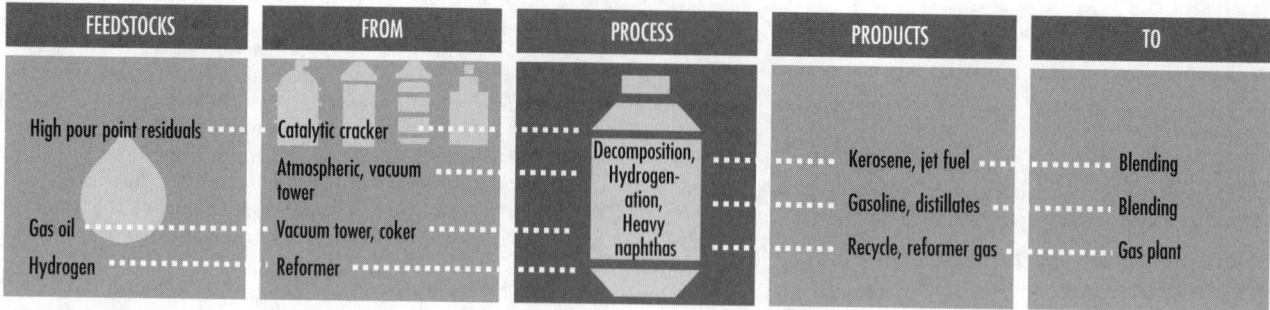

FEEDSTOCKS	FROM	PROCESS	PRODUCTS	TO
High pour point residuals	Catalytic cracker	Decomposition, Hydrogenation, Heavy naphthas	Kerosene, jet fuel	Blending
	Atmospheric, vacuum tower		Gasoline, distillates	Blending
Gas oil	Vacuum tower, coker		Recycle, reformer gas	Gas plant
Hydrogen	Reformer			

Source: Adapted from OSHA 1996.

bons are stripped or purified to remove the hydrogen sulphide, ammonia and light gases, which are collected in an accumulator, where gasoline is separated from sour gas.

The stripped liquid hydrocarbons from the primary reactor are mixed with hydrogen and sent to the second-stage reactor, where they are cracked into high-quality gasoline, jet fuel and distillate blending stocks. These products go through a series of high- and low-pressure separators to remove gases, which are recycled. The liquid hydrocarbons are stabilized, split and stripped, with the light naphtha products from the hydrocracker used to blend gasoline while the heavier naphthas are recycled or sent to a catalytic reformer unit. (See figure 78.11.)

Health and safety considerations
Inspection and testing of safety relief devices are important due to the very high pressures in this process. Proper process control is needed to protect against plugging reactor beds. Because of the operating temperatures and presence of hydrogen, the hydrogen sulphide content of the feedstock must be strictly kept to a minimum in order to reduce the possibility of severe corrosion. Corrosion by wet carbon dioxide in areas of condensation must also be considered. When processing high-nitrogen feedstocks, the ammonia and hydrogen sulphide form ammonium hydrosulphide, which causes serious corrosion at temperatures below the water dew point. Ammonium hydrosulphide is also present in sour water stripping. Because the hydrocracker operates at very high pressures and temperatures, control of both hydrocarbon leaks and hydrogen releases is important to prevent fires.

Because this is a closed process, exposures are minimal under normal operating conditions. There is a potential for exposure to aliphatic naphtha containing benzene, carcinogenic PAHs, hydrocarbon gas and vapour emissions, hydrogen-rich gas and hydrogen sulphide gas as a result of high-pressure leaks. Large quantities of carbon monoxide may be released during catalyst regeneration and changeover. Catalyst steam stripping and regeneration creates waste streams containing sour water and ammonia. Safe work practices and appropriate personal protective equipment are needed when handling spent catalyst. In some processes, care is needed to assure that explosive concentrations of catalytic dust do not form during recharging. Unloading coked catalyst requires special precautions to prevent iron sulphide-induced fires. The coked catalyst should either be cooled to below 49 °C before dumping, or placed in nitrogen-inerted containers until cooled.

Combining processes
Two combining processes, *polymerization* and *alkylation*, are used to join together small hydrogen-deficient molecules, called *olefins*, recovered from thermal and catalytic cracking, in order to create more desirable gasoline blending stocks.

Polymerization
Polymerization is the process of combining two or more unsaturated organic molecules (olefins) to form a single, heavier molecule with the same elements in the same proportion as the original molecule. It converts gaseous olefins, such as ethylene, propylene

Figure 78.12 • Polymerization process.

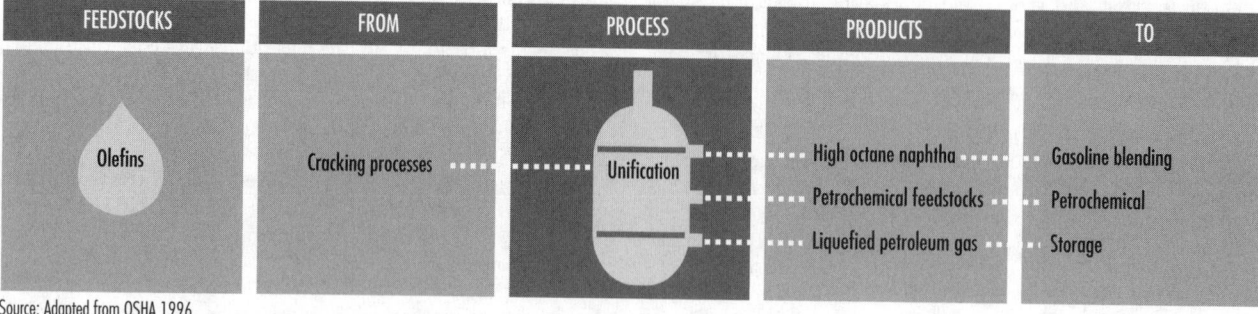

FEEDSTOCKS	FROM	PROCESS	PRODUCTS	TO
Olefins	Cracking processes	Unification	High octane naphtha	Gasoline blending
			Petrochemical feedstocks	Petrochemical
			Liquefied petroleum gas	Storage

Source: Adapted from OSHA 1996.

and butylene converted by thermal and fluid cracking units, into heavier, more complex, higher-octane molecules, including naphtha and petrochemical feedstocks. The olefin feedstock is pretreated to remove sulphur compounds and other undesirables, and then passed over a phosphorus catalyst, usually a solid catalyst or liquid phosphoric acid, where an exothermic polymeric reaction occurs. This requires the use of cooling water and the injection of cold feedstock into the reactor to control temperatures at various pressures. Acid in the liquids is removed by caustic wash, the liquids are fractionated, and the acid catalyst is recycled. The vapour is fractionated to remove butanes and neutralized to remove traces of acid. (See figure 78.12.)

Severe corrosion, leading to equipment failure, will occur should water contact the phosphoric acid, such as during water washing at shutdowns. Corrosion may also occur in piping manifolds, reboilers, exchangers and other locations where acid may settle out. There is a potential for exposure to caustic wash (sodium hydroxide), to phosphoric acid used in the process or washed out during turnarounds, and to catalyst dust. The potential for an uncontrolled exothermic reaction exists should loss of cooling water occur.

Alkylation

Alkylation combines the molecules of olefins produced from catalytic cracking with those of isoparaffins in order to increase the volume and octane of gasoline blends. Olefins will react with isoparaffins in the presence of a highly active catalyst, usually sulphuric acid or hydrofluoric acid (or aluminium chloride) to create a long-branched-chain paraffinic molecule, called *alkylate* (iso-octane), with exceptional anti-knock quality. The alkylate is then separated and fractionated. The relatively low reaction temperatures of 10 °C to 16 °C for sulphuric acid, 27 °C to 0 °C for hydrofluoric acid (HF) and 0 °C for aluminium chloride, are controlled and maintained by refrigeration. (See figure 78.13.)

Sulphuric acid alkylation. In cascade-type sulphuric acid alkylation units, feedstocks, including propylene, butylene, amylene and fresh isobutane, enter the reactor, where they contact the sulphuric acid catalyst. The reactor is divided into zones, with olefins fed through distributors to each zone, and the sulphuric acid and isobutanes flowing over baffles from zone to zone. Reaction heat is removed by evaporation of isobutane. The isobutane gas is removed from the top of the reactor, cooled and recycled, with a portion directed to the depropanizer tower. Residual from the reactor is settled, and the sulphuric acid is removed from the bottom of the vessel and recirculated. Caustic and/or water scrubbers are used to remove small amounts of acid from the process stream, which then goes to a de-isobutanizer tower. The debutanizer isobutane overhead is recycled, and the remaining hydrocarbons are separated in a rerun tower and/or sent to blending.

Hydrofluoric acid alkylation. There are two types of hydrofluoric acid alkylation processes: Phillips and UOP. In the Phillips process, olefin and isobutane feedstock is dried and fed to a combination reactor/settler unit. The hydrocarbon from the settling zone is charged to the main fractionator. The main fractionator overhead goes to a depropanizer. Propane, with trace amounts of hydrofluoric acid (HF), goes to an HF stripper, and is then catalytically defluorinated, treated and sent to storage. Isobutane is withdrawn from the main fractionator and recycled to the reactor/settler, and alkylate from the bottom of the main fractionator is sent to a splitter.

The UOP process uses two reactors with separate settlers. Half of the dried feedstock is charged to the first reactor, along with recycle and make-up isobutane, and then to its settler, where the acid is recycled and the hydrocarbon charged to the second reactor. The other half of the feedstock goes to the second reactor, with the settler acid being recycled and the hydrocarbons charged to the main fractionator. Subsequent processing is similar to Phillips in that the overhead from the main fractionator goes to a depropanizer, isobutane is recycled and alkylate is sent to a splitter.

Health and safety considerations

Sulphuric acid and hydrofluoric acid are dangerous chemicals, and care during delivery and unloading of acid is essential. There is a need to maintain sulphuric acid concentrations of 85 to 95% for good operation and to minimize corrosion. To prevent corrosion from hydrofluoric acid, acid concentrations inside the process unit must be maintained above 65% and moisture below 4%. Some corrosion and fouling in sulphuric acid units occurs from the breakdown of sulphuric acid esters, or where caustic is added for neutralization. These esters can be removed by fresh-acid treating and hot-water washing.

Upsets can be caused by loss of the coolant water needed to maintain process temperatures. Pressure on the cooling water and steam side of exchangers should be kept below the minimum pressure on the acid service side to prevent water contamination. Vents can be routed to soda ash scrubbers to neutralize hydrogen fluoride gas or hydrofluoric acid vapours before release. Curbs, drainage and isolation may be provided for process unit containment so that effluent can be neutralized before release to the sewer system.

Hydrofluoric acid units should be thoroughly drained and chemically cleaned prior to turnarounds and entry, to remove all traces of iron fluoride and hydrofluoric acid. Following shutdown,

Figure 78.13 • Alkylation process.

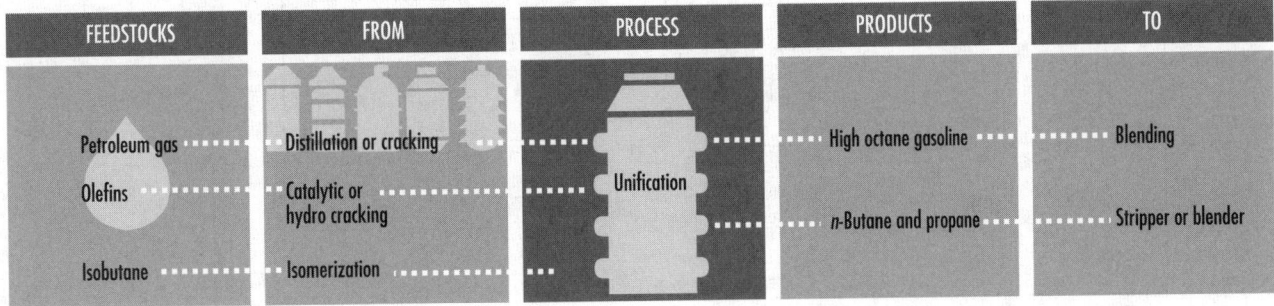

FEEDSTOCKS	FROM	PROCESS	PRODUCTS	TO
Petroleum gas	Distillation or cracking		High octane gasoline	Blending
Olefins	Catalytic or hydro cracking	Unification		
Isobutane	Isomerization		n-Butane and propane	Stripper or blender

Source: Adapted from OSHA 1996.

78. OIL AND NATURAL GAS

Figure 78.14 • Catalytic reforming process.

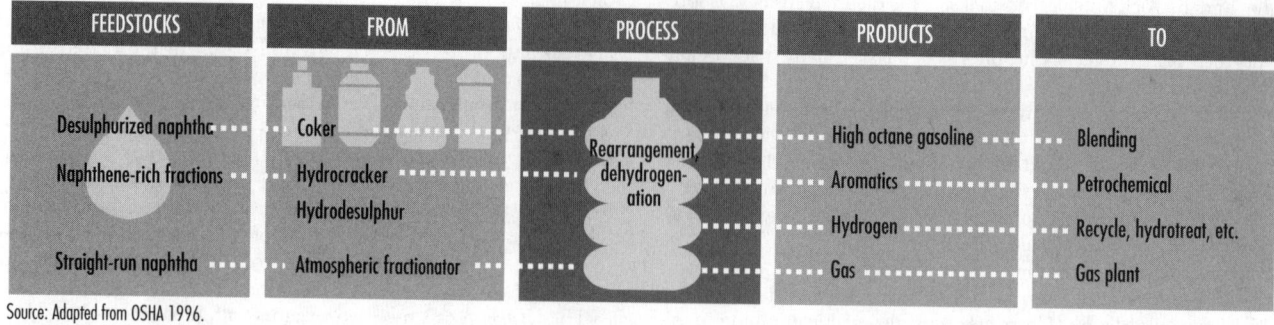

FEEDSTOCKS	FROM	PROCESS	PRODUCTS	TO
Desulphurized naphthc	Coker		High octane gasoline	Blending
Naphthene-rich fractions	Hydrocracker	Rearrangement, dehydrogen-ation	Aromatics	Petrochemical
	Hydrodesulphur		Hydrogen	Recycle, hydrotreat, etc.
Straight-run naphtha	Atmospheric fractionator		Gas	Gas plant

Source: Adapted from OSHA 1996.

where water has been used, the unit should be thoroughly dried before hydrofluoric acid is introduced. Leaks, spills or releases involving hydrofluoric acid, or hydrocarbons containing hydrofluoric acid, are extremely hazardous. Precautions are necessary to assure that equipment and materials which have been in contact with acid are handled carefully and are thoroughly cleaned before they leave the process area or refinery. Immersion wash vats are often provided for neutralization of equipment which has come into contact with hydrofluoric acid.

There is a potential for serious hazardous and toxic exposures should leaks, spills or releases occur. Direct contact with sulphuric or hydrofluoric acid will cause severe skin and eye damage, and inhalation of acid mists or hydrocarbon vapours containing acid will cause severe irritation and damage to the respiratory system. Special precautionary emergency preparedness measures should be used, and protection should be provided that is appropriate to the potential hazard and areas possibly affected. Safe work prac-

tices and appropriate skin and respiratory personal protective equipment are needed where potential exposures to hydrofluoric and sulphuric acids during normal operations exist, such as reading gauges, inspecting and process sampling, as well as during emergency response, maintenance and turnaround activities. Procedures should be in place to assure that protective equipment and clothing worn in sulphuric or hydrofluoric acid activities, including chemical protective suits, head and shoe coverings, gloves, face and eye protection and respiratory protective equipment, are thoroughly cleaned and decontaminated before reissue.

Rearranging processes

Catalytic reforming and *isomerization* are processes which rearrange hydrocarbon molecules to produce products with different characteristics. After cracking, some gasoline streams, although of the correct molecular size, require further processing to improve their performance, because they are deficient in some qualities, such as

Figure 78.15 • C$_4$ isomerization.

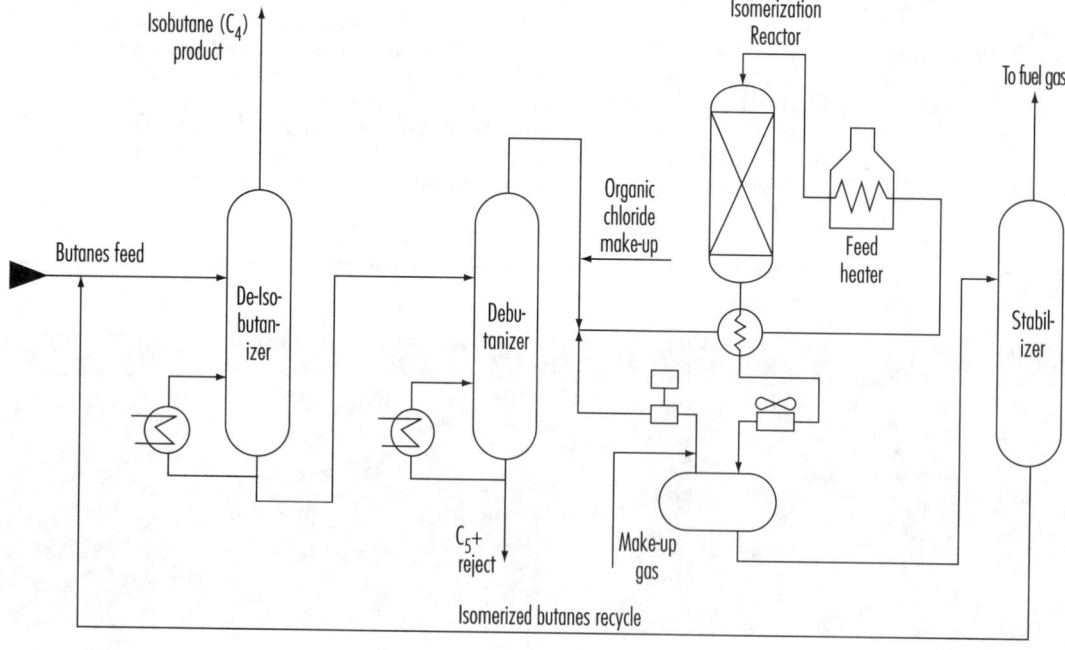

Source: OSHA 1996.

Figure 78.16 • Isomerization process.

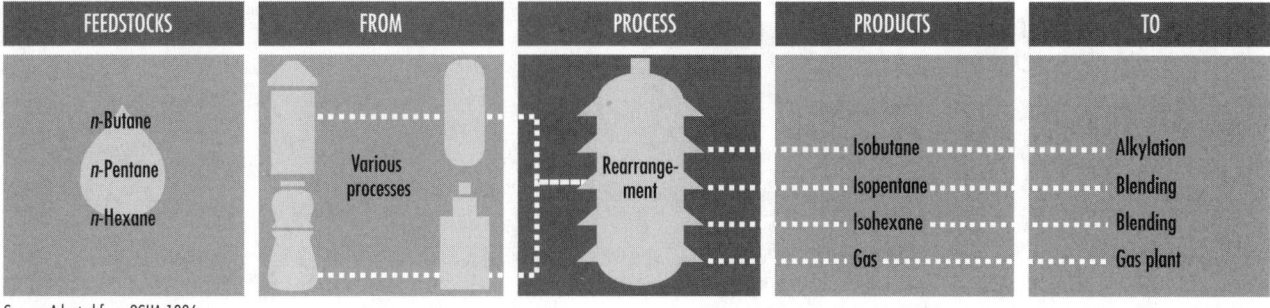

FEEDSTOCKS	FROM	PROCESS	PRODUCTS	TO
n-Butane *n*-Pentane *n*-Hexane	Various processes	Rearrangement	Isobutane Isopentane Isohexane Gas	Alkylation Blending Blending Gas plant

Source: Adapted from OSHA 1996.

octane number or sulphur content. Hydrogen (steam) reforming produces additional hydrogen for use in hydrogenation processing.

Catalytic reforming

Catalytic reforming processes convert low-octane heavy naphthas into aromatic hydrocarbons for petrochemical feedstocks and high-octane gasoline components, called *reformates*, by molecular rearrangement or dehydrogenation. Depending on the feedstock and catalysts, reformates can be produced with very high concentrations of toluene, benzene, xylene and other aromatics useful in gasoline blending and petrochemical processing. Hydrogen, a significant by-product, is separated from the reformate for recycling and use in other processes. The resultant product depends on reactor temperature and pressure, the catalyst used and the hydrogen recycle rate. Some catalytic reformers operate at low pressure and others at high pressure. Some catalytic reforming systems continuously regenerate the catalyst, some facilities regenerate all of the reactors during turnarounds, and others take one reactor at a time off stream for catalyst regeneration.

In catalytic reforming, naphtha feedstock is pretreated with hydrogen to remove contaminants such as chlorine, sulphur and nitrogen compounds, which could poison the catalyst. The product is flashed and fractionated in towers where the remaining contaminants and gases are removed. The desulphurized naphtha feedstock is sent to the catalytic reformer, where it is heated to a vapour and passed through a reactor with a stationary bed of bi-metallic or metallic catalyst containing a small amount of platinum, molybdenum, rhenium or other noble metals. The two primary reactions which occur are production of high-octane aromatics by removing hydrogen from the feedstock molecules, and the conversion of normal paraffins to branched-chain or isoparaffins.

In platforming, another catalytic reforming process, feedstock which has not been hydrodesulphurized is combined with recycle gas and first passed over a less expensive catalyst. Any remaining impurities are converted to hydrogen sulphide and ammonia, and removed before the stream passes over the platinum catalyst. Hydrogen-rich vapour is recirculated to inhibit reactions which may poison the catalyst. The reactor output is separated into liquid reformate, which is sent to a stripping tower, and gas, which is compressed and recycled. (See figure 78.14.)

Operating procedures are needed to control hot spots during start-up. Care must be taken not to break or crush the catalyst when loading the beds, as small fines will plug up the reformer screens. Precautions against dust when regenerating or replacing catalyst are needed. Small emissions of carbon monoxide and hydrogen sulphide may occur during regeneration of catalyst.

Water wash should be considered where stabilizer fouling has occurred in reformers due to the formation of ammonium chloride and iron salts. Ammonium chloride may form in pretreater exchangers and cause corrosion and fouling. Hydrogen chloride, from the hydrogenation of chlorine compounds, may form acids or ammonium chloride salt. The potential exists for exposure to aliphatic and aromatic naphthas, hydrogen-rich process gas, hydrogen sulphide and benzene should a leak or release occur.

Isomerization

Isomerization converts *n*-butane, *n*-pentane and *n*-hexane into their respective iso-paraffins. Some of the normal straight-chain paraffin components of light straight-run naphtha are low in octane. These can be converted to high-octane, branched-chain isomers by rearranging the bonds between atoms, without changing the number or kinds of atoms. Isomerization is similar to catalytic reforming in that the hydrocarbon molecules are rearranged, but unlike catalytic reforming, isomerization just converts normal paraffins to iso-paraffins. Isomerization uses a different catalyst than catalytic reforming.

The two distinct isomerization processes are butane (C_4) and pentane/hexane. (C_5/C_6).

Butane (C_4) isomerization produces feedstock for alkylation. A lower-temperature process uses highly active aluminium chloride or hydrogen chloride catalyst without fired heaters, to isomerize *n*-butane. The treated and preheated feedstock is added to the recycle stream, mixed with HCl and passed through the reactor (see figure 78.15).

Pentane/hexane isomerization is used to increase the octane number by converting *n*-pentane and *n*-hexane. In a typical pentane/hexane isomerization process, dried and desulphurized feedstock is mixed with a small amount of organic chloride and recycled hydrogen, and heated to reactor temperature. It is then passed over supported-metal catalyst in the first reactor, where benzene and olefins are hydrogenated. The feed next goes to the isomerization reactor, where the paraffins are catalytically isomerized to isoparaffins, cooled and passed to a separator. Separator gas and hydrogen, with make-up hydrogen, is recycled. The liquid is neutralized with alkaline materials and sent to a stripper column, where hydrogen chloride is recovered and recycled. (See figure 78.16.)

If the feedstock is not completely dried and desulphurized, the potential exists for acid formation, leading to catalyst poisoning and metal corrosion. Water or steam must not be allowed to enter areas where hydrogen chloride is present. Precautions are needed to prevent HCl from entering sewers and drains. There is a potential for exposure to isopentane and aliphatic naphtha va-

Figure 78.17 • Steam reforming process.

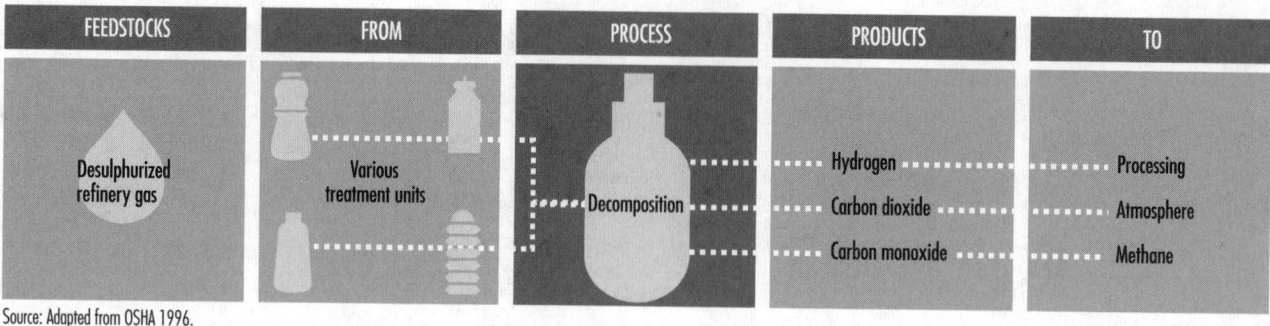

FEEDSTOCKS	FROM	PROCESS	PRODUCTS	TO
Desulphurized refinery gas	Various treatment units	Decomposition	Hydrogen Carbon dioxide Carbon monoxide	Processing Atmosphere Methane

Source: Adapted from OSHA 1996.

pours and liquid, as well as to hydrogen-rich process gas, hydro-chloric acid and hydrogen chloride, and to dust when solid catalyst is used.

Hydrogen production (steam reforming)

High-purity hydrogen (95 to 99%) is needed for hydrodesulphurization, hydrogenation, hydrocracking and petrochemical processes. If not enough hydrogen is produced as by-products of refinery processes to meet the total refinery demand, the manufacture of additional hydrogen is required.

In hydrogen steam reforming, desulphurized gases are mixed with superheated steam and reformed in tubes containing a nickel base catalyst. The reformed gas, which consists of steam, hydrogen, carbon monoxide and carbon dioxide, is cooled and passed through converters where the carbon monoxide reacts with steam to form hydrogen and carbon dioxide. The carbon dioxide is scrubbed with amine solutions and vented to the atmosphere when the solutions are reactivated by heating. Any carbon monoxide remaining in the product stream is converted to methane. (See figure 78.17.)

Inspections and testing must be conducted where the possibility exists for valve failure due to contaminants in the hydrogen. Carryover from caustic scrubbers to prevent corrosion in preheaters must be controlled and chlorides from the feedstock or steam system prevented from entering reformer tubes and contaminating the catalyst. Exposures can result from contamination of condensate by process materials such as caustics and amine compounds, and from excess hydrogen, carbon monoxide and

carbon dioxide. The potential exists for burns from hot gases and superheated steam should a release occur.

Miscellaneous refinery processes

Lubricant base stock and wax processes

Lubricating oils and waxes are refined from various fractions of atmospheric and vacuum distillation. With the invention of vacuum distillation, it was discovered that the waxy residuum made a better lubricant than any of the animal fats that were then in use, which was the beginning of modern hydrocarbon lubricant refining technology, whose primary objective is to remove undesirable products, such as asphalts, sulphonated aromatics and paraffinic and iso-paraffinic waxes from the residual fractions in order to produce high-quality lubricants. This is done by a series of processes including de-asphalting, solvent extraction and separation and treatment processes such as dewaxing and hydrofinishing. (See figure 78.18.)

In extraction processing, reduced crude from the vacuum unit is propane de-asphalted and combined with straight-run lubricating-oil feedstock, preheated and solvent extracted to produce a feedstock called raffinate. In a typical extraction process which uses phenol as the solvent, the feedstock is mixed with phenol in the treating section at temperatures below 204 °C. Phenol is then separated from the raffinate and recycled. The raffinate may then be subjected to another extraction process which uses furfural to separate aromatic compounds from non-aromatic hydrocarbons, producing a lighter-coloured raffinate with improved viscosity index and oxidation and thermal stability.

Figure 78.18 • Lubricating oil and wax manufacturing process.

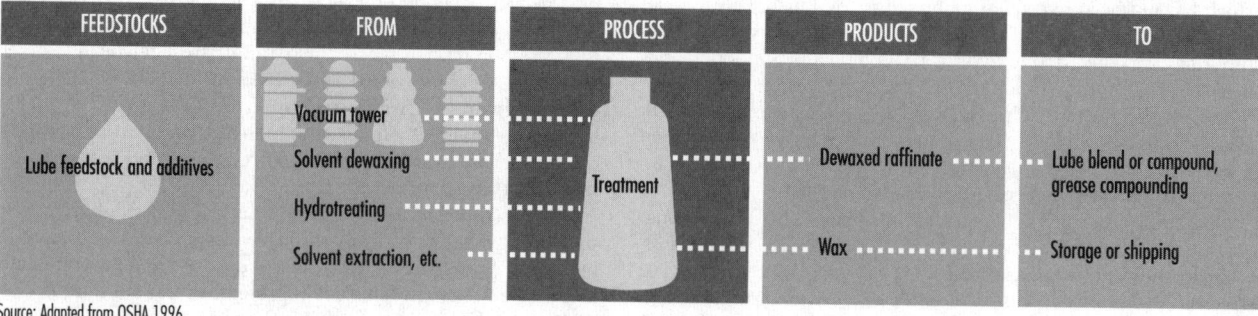

FEEDSTOCKS	FROM	PROCESS	PRODUCTS	TO
Lube feedstock and additives	Vacuum tower Solvent dewaxing Hydrotreating Solvent extraction, etc.	Treatment	Dewaxed raffinate Wax	Lube blend or compound, grease compounding Storage or shipping

Source: Adapted from OSHA 1996.

Dewaxed raffinate may also be subject to further processing to improve the qualities of the base stock. Clay adsorbents are used to remove dark-coloured, unstable molecules from lubricating-oil base stocks. An alternate process, lube hydrofinishing, passes hot dewaxed raffinate and hydrogen through a catalyst that slightly changes the molecular structure, resulting in a lighter-coloured oil with improved characteristics. The treated lube oil base stocks are then mixed and/or compounded with additives to meet the required physical and chemical characteristics of motor oils, industrial lubricants and metal-working oils.

The two distinct types of wax derived from crude oil are paraffin wax, produced from distillate stocks, and microcrystalline wax, manufactured from residual stocks. Raffinate from the extraction unit contains a considerable amount of wax, which can be removed by solvent extraction and crystallization. The raffinate is mixed with a solvent, such as propane, methyl ethyl ketone (MEK) and toluene mixture or methyl isobutyl ketone (MIBK), and precooled in heat exchangers. The crystallization temperature is attained by the evaporation of the propane in the chiller and filter feed tanks. The wax is continuously removed by filters and cold solvent washed to recover retained oil. The solvent is recovered from the dewaxed raffinate by flashing and steam stripping, and recycled.

The wax is heated with hot solvent, chilled, filtered and given a final wash to remove all traces of oil. Before the wax is used, it may be hydro-finished to improve its odour and eliminate all traces of aromatics so the wax can be used in food processing. The dewaxed raffinate, which contains small amounts of paraffins, naphthenes and some aromatics, may be further processed for use as lubricating-oil base stocks.

Control of treater temperature is important to prevent corrosion from phenol. Wax can clog sewer or oil drainage systems and interfere with waste water treatment. The potential exists for exposure to process solvents such as phenol, propane, a methyl ethyl ketone and toluene mixture or methyl isobutyl ketone. Inhalation of hydrocarbon gases and vapours, aromatic naphtha containing benzene, hydrogen sulphide and hydrogen-rich process gas is a hazard.

Asphalt processing

After primary distillation operations, asphalt is a portion of residual matter which requires further processing to impart characteristics required by its final use. Asphalt for roofing materials is produced by air blowing. Residual is heated in a pipe still almost up to its flashpoint and charged to a blowing tower where hot air is injected for a predetermined period of time. The dehydrogenation of the asphalt forms hydrogen sulphide, and the oxidation creates sulphur dioxide. Steam is used to blanket the top of the tower to entrain the contaminants, and is passed through a scrubber to condense the hydrocarbons.

Vacuum distillation is generally used to produce road tar asphalt. The residual is heated and charged to a column where vacuum is applied to prevent cracking.

Condensed steam from the various asphalt processes will contain trace amounts of hydrocarbons. Any disruption of the vacuum can result in the entry of atmospheric air and subsequent fire. In asphalt production, raising the temperature of the vacuum tower bottom to improve efficiency can generate methane by thermal cracking. This creates vapours in asphalt storage tanks which are in the flammable range, but not detectable by flash testing. Air blowing can create some polynuclear aromatics (i.e., PAHs). Condensed steam from the air blowing asphalt process may also contain various contaminants.

Hydrocarbon sweetening and treating processes

Many products, such as thermal naphthas from visbreaking, coking or thermal cracking, and high-sulphur naphthas and distillates from crude-oil distillation, require treating in order to be used in gasoline and fuel oil blends. Distillation products, including kerosene and other distillates, may contain trace amounts of aromatics, and naphthenes and lubricating-oil base stocks may contain wax. These undesirables are removed either at intermediate refining stages or just prior to sending products to blending and storage, by refining processes such as solvent extraction and solvent dewaxing. A variety of intermediate and finished products, including middle distillates, gasoline, kerosene, jet fuel and sour gases need to be dried and sweetened.

Treating is performed either at an intermediate stage in the refining process or just before sending finished products to blending and storage. Treating removes contaminants from oil, such as organic compounds containing sulphur, nitrogen and oxygen, dissolved metals, inorganic salts and soluble salts dissolved in emulsified water. Treating materials include acids, solvents, alkalis and oxidizing and adsorption agents. Acid treatments are used to improve the odour, colour and other properties of lube base stocks, to prevent corrosion and catalyst contamination, and to improve product stability. Hydrogen sulphide which is removed from "dry" sour gas by an absorbing agent (diethanolamine) is flared, used as a fuel or converted to sulphur. The type of treatment and agents depends on the crude feedstock, intermediate processes and end-product specifications.

Solvent treatment processes

Solvent extraction separates aromatics, naphthenes and impurities from product streams by dissolving or precipitation. Solvent ex-

Figure 78.19 • Solvent extraction process.

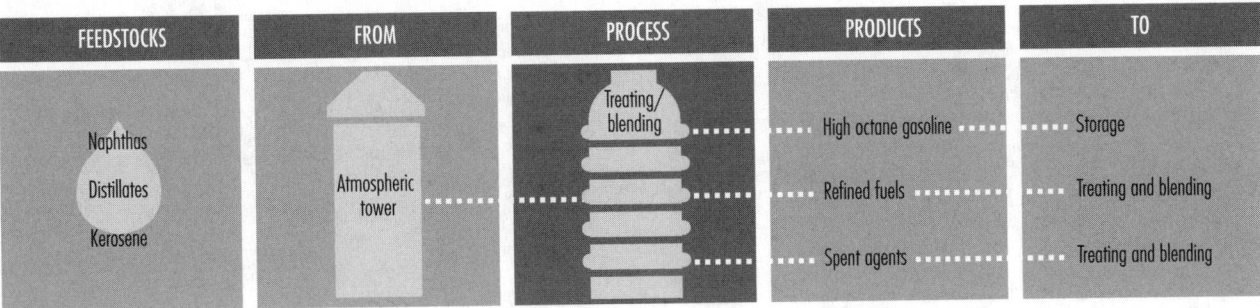

FEEDSTOCKS	FROM	PROCESS	PRODUCTS	TO
Naphthas Distillates Kerosene	Atmospheric tower	Treating/ blending	High octane gasoline	Storage
			Refined fuels	Treating and blending
			Spent agents	Treating and blending

Source: Adapted from OSHA 1996.

78. OIL AND NATURAL GAS

Figure 78.20 • Solvent dewaxing process.

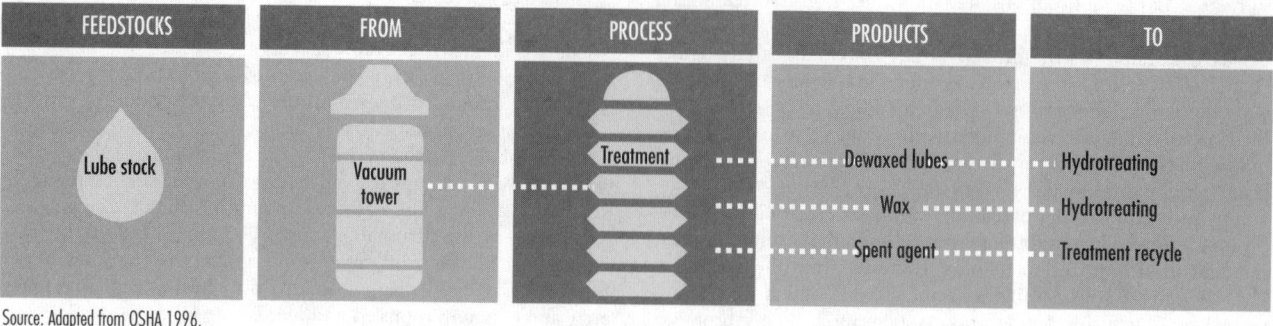

Source: Adapted from OSHA 1996.

traction prevents corrosion, protects catalyst in subsequent processes and improves finished products by removing unsaturated, aromatic hydrocarbons from lubricant and grease base stocks.

The feedstock is dried and subjected to continuous countercurrent solvent treatment. In one process, feedstock is washed with a liquid in which the substances to be removed are more soluble than in the desired resultant product. In another process, selected solvents are added, causing impurities to precipitate out of the product. The solvent is separated from the product stream by heating, evaporation or fractionation, with residual trace amounts subsequently removed from the raffinate by steam stripping or vacuum flashing. Electric precipitation may be used for separation of inorganic compounds. The solvent is then regenerated to be used again in the process.

Typical chemicals used in the extraction process include a wide variety of acids, alkalis and solvents, including phenol and furfural, as well as oxidizing agents and adsorption agents. In the adsorption process, highly porous solid materials collect liquid molecules on their surfaces. The selection of specific processes and chemical agents depends on the nature of the feedstock being treated, the contaminants present and the finished product requirements. (See figure 78.19.)

Solvent dewaxing removes wax from either distillate or residual base stocks, and may be applied at any stage in the refining process. In solvent dewaxing, waxy feedstocks are chilled by heat exchanger and refrigeration, and solvent is added to help develop crystals that are removed by vacuum filtration. The dewaxed oil and solvent are flashed and stripped, and the wax passes through a water settler, solvent fractionator and flash tower. (See figure 78.20.)

Solvent de-asphalting separates heavy oil fractions to produce heavy lubricating oil, catalytic cracking feedstock and asphalt. Feedstock and liquid propane (or hexane) are pumped to an extraction tower at precisely controlled mixtures, temperatures and pressures. Separation occurs in a rotating-disc contactor, based on differences in solubility. The products are then evaporated and steam stripped to recover propane for recycle. Solvent de-asphalting also removes sulphur and nitrogen compounds, metals, carbon residues and paraffins from feedstock. (See figure 78.21.)

Health and safety considerations.
In solvent dewaxing, disruption of the vacuum will create a potential fire hazard by allowing air to enter the unit. The potential exists for exposure to dewaxing solvent vapours, a mixture of MEK and toluene. Although solvent extraction is a closed process, there is potential exposure to carcinogenic PAHs in the process oils and to extraction solvents such as phenol, furfural, glycol, MEK, amines and other process chemicals during handling and operations.

De-asphalting requires exact temperature and pressure control to avoid upset. In addition, moisture, excess solvent or a drop in operating temperature may cause foaming which affects the product temperature control and may create an upset. Contact with hot oil streams will cause skin burns. The potential exists for exposure to hot oil streams containing carcinogenic polycyclic

Figure 78.21 • Solvent de-asphalting process.

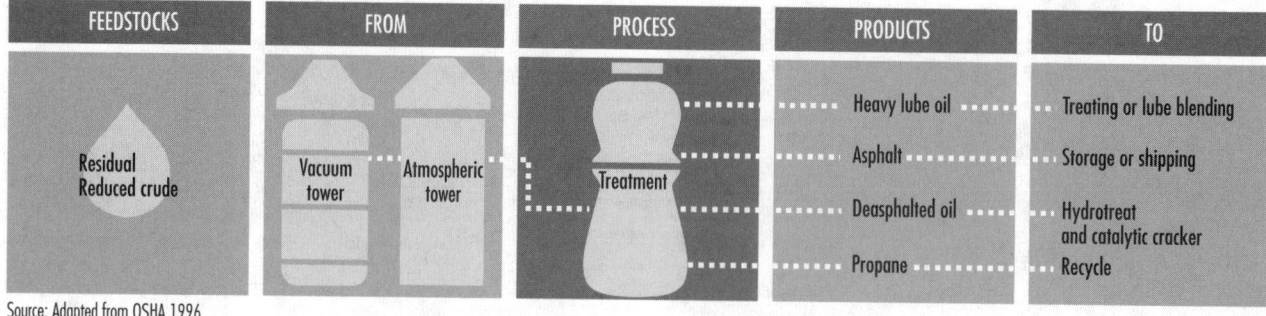

Source: Adapted from OSHA 1996.

Figure 78.22 • Hydrodesulphurization process.

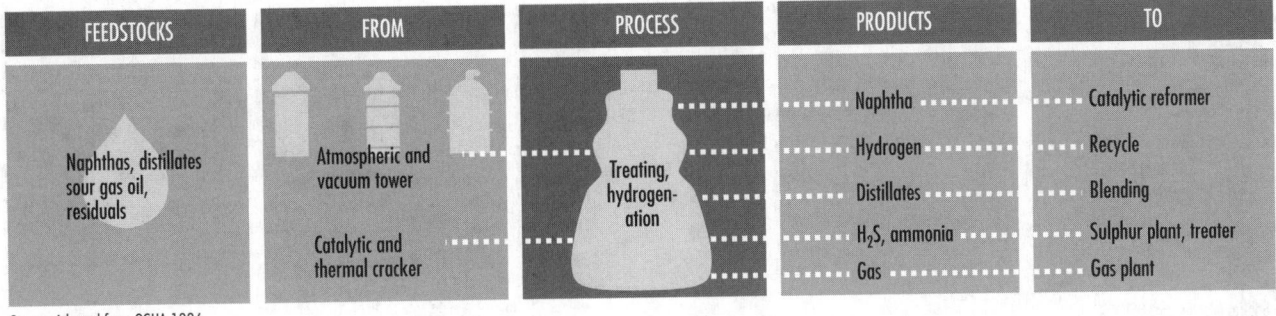

FEEDSTOCKS	FROM	PROCESS	PRODUCTS	TO
Naphthas, distillates sour gas oil, residuals	Atmospheric and vacuum tower / Catalytic and thermal cracker	Treating, hydrogenation	Naphtha / Hydrogen / Distillates / H₂S, ammonia / Gas	Catalytic reformer / Recycle / Blending / Sulphur plant, treater / Gas plant

Source: Adapted from OSHA 1996.

aromatic compounds, liquefied propane and propane vapours, hydrogen sulphide and sulphur dioxide.

Hydrotreating processes

Hydrotreating is used to remove about 90% of contaminants, including nitrogen, sulphur, metals and unsaturated hydrocarbons (olefins), from liquid petroleum fractions such as straight-run gasoline. Hydrotreating is similar to hydrocracking in that both the hydrogen and the catalyst are used to enrich the hydrogen content of the olefin feedstock. However, the degree of saturation is not as great as that achieved in hydrocracking. Typically, hydrotreating is done prior to processes such as catalytic reforming, so that the catalyst is not contaminated by untreated feedstock. Hydrotreating is also used before catalytic cracking to reduce sulphur and improve product yields, and to upgrade middle distillate petroleum fractions into finished kerosene, diesel fuel and heating fuel oils.

Hydrotreating processes differ depending upon the feedstocks and catalysts. Hydrodesulphurization removes sulphur from kerosene, reduces aromatics and gum-forming characteristics, and saturates any olefins. Hydroforming is a dehydrogenation process

used to recover excess hydrogen and produce high-octane gasoline. Hydrotreated products are blended or used as catalytic reforming feedstock.

In *catalytic hydrodesulphurization*, the feedstock is de-aerated, mixed with hydrogen, preheated and charged under high pressure through a fixed-bed catalytic reactor. The hydrogen is separated and recycled and the product stabilized in a stripper column where the light ends are removed.

During this process, sulphur and nitrogen compounds present in the feedstock are converted to hydrogen sulphide (H_2S) and ammonia (NH_3). Residual hydrogen sulphide and ammonia are removed either by steam stripping, by a combination high- and low-pressure separator or by amine wash which recovers hydrogen sulphide in a highly concentrated stream suitable for conversion into elemental sulphur. (See figures 78.22 and 78.23.)

In hydrotreating, the hydrogen sulphide content of the feedstock must be strictly controlled to a minimum to reduce corrosion. Hydrogen chloride may form and condense as hydrochloric acid in the lower-temperature portions of the unit. Ammonium hydrosulphide may form in high-temperature, high-pressure

Figure 78.23 • Schematic of hydrodesulphurization process.

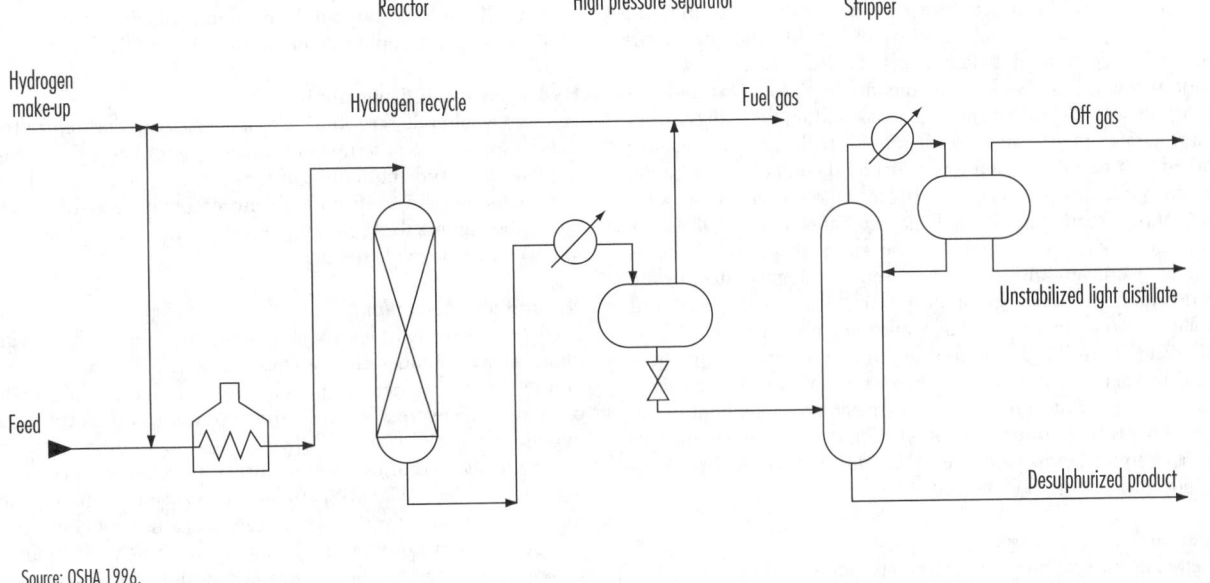

Source: OSHA 1996.

78. OIL AND NATURAL GAS

Figure 78.24 • Sweetening and treating processes.

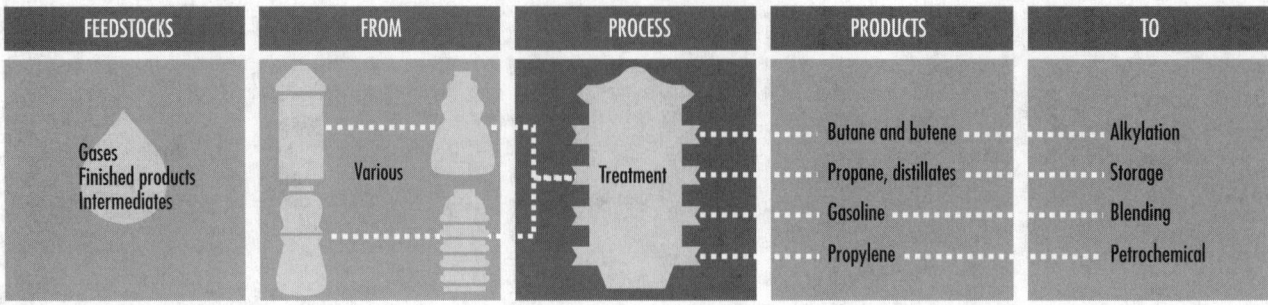

FEEDSTOCKS	FROM	PROCESS	PRODUCTS	TO
Gases Finished products Intermediates	Various	Treatment	Butane and butene Propane, distillates Gasoline Propylene	Alkylation Storage Blending Petrochemical

Source: Adapted from OSHA 1996.

units. In the event of a release, there is a potential for exposure to aromatic naphtha vapours which contain benzene, hydrogen sulphide or hydrogen gas, or to ammonia should a sour water leak or spill occur. Phenol may also be present if high-boiling-point feedstocks are processed.

Excessive contact time and/or temperature will create coking in the unit. Precautions need to be taken when unloading coked catalyst from the unit to prevent iron sulphide fires. The coked catalyst should be cooled to below 49 °C before removal, or dumped into nitrogen-inerted bins where it can be cooled before further handling. Special anti-foam additives may be used to prevent catalyst poisoning from silicone carryover in coker feedstock.

Other sweetening and treating processes

Treatment, drying and sweetening processes are used to remove impurities from blending stocks. (See figure 78.24.)

Sweetening processes use air or oxygen. If excess oxygen enters these processes, it is possible for a fire to occur in the settler due to the generation of static electricity. There is a potential for exposure to hydrogen sulphide, sulphur dioxide, caustic (sodium hydroxide), spent caustic, spent catalyst (Merox), catalyst dust and sweetening agents (sodium carbonate and sodium bicarbonate).

Amine (acid gas treatment) plants

Sour gas (fuel gas from processes such as catalytic cracking and hydrotreating, which contains hydrogen sulphide and carbon dioxide) must be treated before it can be used as refinery fuel. Amine plants remove acid contaminants from sour gas and hydrocarbon streams. In amine plants, gas and liquid hydrocarbon streams containing carbon dioxide and/or hydrogen sulphide are charged to a gas absorption tower or liquid contactor, where the acid contaminants are absorbed by counterflowing amine solutions—monoethanolamine (MEA), diethanolamine (DEA) or methyldiethanolamine (MDEA). The stripped gas or liquid is removed overhead, and the amine is sent to a regenerator. In the regenerator, the acidic components are stripped by heat and reboiling action, and disposed of, while the amine is recycled.

In order to minimize corrosion, proper operating practices should be established, and regenerator bottom and reboiler temperatures need to be controlled. Oxygen should be kept out of the system to prevent amine oxidation. There is potential for exposure to amine compounds (i.e., MEA, DEA, MDEA), hydrogen sulphide and carbon dioxide.

Sweetening and drying

Sweetening (mercaptan removal) treats sulphur compounds (hydrogen sulphide, thiophene and mercaptan) to improve colour, odour and oxidation stability, and reduces concentrations of carbon dioxide in gasoline. Some mercaptans are removed by having the product make contact with water-soluble chemicals (e.g., sulphuric acid) that react with the mercaptans. Caustic liquid (sodium hydroxide), amine compounds (diethanolamine) or fixed-bed catalyst sweetening may be used to convert mercaptans to less objectionable disulphides.

Product drying (water removal) is accomplished by water absorption, with or without adsorption agents. Some processes simultaneously dry and sweeten by adsorption on molecular sieves.

Sulphur recovery

Sulphur recovery removes hydrogen sulphide from sour gases and hydrocarbon streams. The Clause process converts hydrogen sulphide to elemental sulphur through the use of thermal and catalytic reactions. After burning hydrogen sulphide under controlled conditions, knockout pots remove water and hydrocarbons from feed-gas streams, which are then exposed to a catalyst to recover additional sulphur. The sulphur vapour from burning and conversion is condensed and recovered.

Tail gas treatment

Both oxidation and reduction are used to treat tail gas from sulphur recovery units, depending on the composition of the gas and on refinery economics. Oxidation processes burn tail gas to convert all sulphur compounds to sulphur dioxide, and reduction processes convert sulphur compounds to hydrogen sulphide.

Hydrogen sulphide scrubbing

Hydrogen sulphide scrubbing is a primary hydrocarbon feedstock treating process used to prevent catalyst poisoning. Depending on the feedstock and the nature of the contaminants, desulphurization methods will vary from ambient-temperature-activated charcoal absorption to high-temperature catalytic hydrogenation followed by zinc oxide treating.

Sat and unsat gas plants

Feedstocks from various refinery units are sent to gas treating plants, where butanes and butenes are removed for use as alkylation feedstock, heavier components are sent to gasoline blending, propane is recovered for LPG and propylene is removed for use in petrochemicals.

Sat gas plants separate components from refinery gases, including butanes for alkylation, pentanes for gasoline blending, LPGs for fuel and ethane for petrochemicals. There are two different sat gas processes: absorption-fractionation or straight fractionation. In absorption-fractionation, gases and liquids from various units are fed to an absorber/de-ethanizer where C_2 and lighter fractions are separated by lean-oil absorption and removed for use as fuel gas or petrochemical feed. The remaining heavier fractions are stripped and sent to a debutanizer, and the lean oil is recycled back to the absorber/de-ethanizer. C_3/C_4 is separated from pentanes in the debutanizer, scrubbed to remove hydrogen sulphide, and fed to a splitter to separate propane and butane. The absorption stage is eliminated in fractionation plants. Sat gas processes depend on feedstock and product demand.

Corrosion occurs from the presence of hydrogen sulphide, carbon dioxide and other compounds as a result of prior treating. Streams containing ammonia should be dried before processing. Anti-fouling additives are used in absorption oil to protect heat exchangers. Corrosion inhibitors are used to control corrosion in overhead systems. The potential exists for exposure to hydrogen sulphide, carbon dioxide, sodium hydroxide, MEA, DEA and MDEA to be carried over from prior treating.

Unsat gas plants recover light hydrocarbons from wet gas streams from catalytic crackers and delayed coker overhead accumulators or fractionation receivers. In a typical process, wet gases are compressed and treated with amine to remove hydrogen sulphide either before or after entering a fractionating absorber, where they mix into a concurrent flow of debutanized gasoline. The light fractions are separated by heat in a reboiler, with the offgas sent to a sponge absorber and the bottoms sent to a debutanizer. A portion of the debutanized hydrocarbon is recycled, and the balance goes to a splitter for separation. Overhead gases go to a depropanizer for use as alkylation unit feedstock. (See figure 78.25.)

Corrosion can occur from moist hydrogen sulphide and cyanides in unsat gas plants which handle FCC feedstocks. Corrosion from hydrogen sulphide and deposits in the high-pressure sections of gas compressors from ammonium compounds is possible when feedstocks are from the delayed coker or the TCC. The potential exists for exposure to hydrogen sulphide and to amine compounds such as MEA, DEA and MDEA.

Gasoline, distillate fuel and lubricant base stock blending processes

Blending is the physical mixture of a number of different liquid hydrocarbon fractions to produce finished products with specific desired characteristics. Products can be blended in-line through a manifold system or batch blended in tanks and vessels. In-line blending of gasoline, distillates, jet fuel and lubricant base stocks is accomplished by injecting proportionate amounts of each component into the main stream where turbulence promotes thorough mixing.

- Gasolines are blends of reformates, alkylates, straight-run gasoline, thermal and catalytically cracked gasolines, coker gasoline, butane and appropriate additives.
- Fuel oil and diesel fuel are blends of distillates and cycle oils, and jet fuel may be straight-run distillate or blended with naphtha.
- Lubricating oils are blends of refined base stocks
- Asphalt is blended from various residual stocks depending on its intended use.

Additives are often mixed into gasoline and motor fuels during or after blending to provide specific properties not inherent in petroleum hydrocarbons. These additives include octane enhancers, anti-knock agents, anti-oxidants, gum inhibitors, foam inhibitors, rust inhibitors, carburettor (carbon) cleaners, detergents for injector cleaning, diesel odourizers, colour dyes, distillate anti-static, gasoline oxidizers such as methanol, ethanol and methyl tertiary butyl ether, metal deactivators and others.

Batch and in-line blending operations require strict controls to maintain desired product quality. Spills should be cleaned and leaks repaired to avoid slips and falls. Additives in drums and bags need to be handled properly to avoid strain and exposure. The potential for contacting hazardous additives, chemicals, benzene and other materials exists during blending, and appropriate engineering controls, personal protective equipment and proper hygiene are needed to minimize exposures.

Auxiliary Refinery Operations

Auxiliary operations supporting refinery processes include those which provide process heat and cooling; provide pressure relief; control air emissions; collect and treat waste water; provide utilities such as power, steam, air and plant gases; and pump, store, treat and cool process water.

Waste water treatment

Refinery waste water includes condensed steam, stripping water, spent caustic solutions, cooling tower and boiler blowdown, wash water, alkaline and acid waste neutralization water and other process-associated water. Waste water typically contains hydrocarbons, dissolved materials, suspended solids, phenols, ammonia, sulphides and other compounds. Waste water treatment is used for process water, runoff water and sewerage water prior to their discharge. These treatments may require permits, or there must be recycling.

The potential exists for fire should vapours from waste water containing hydrocarbons reach a source of ignition during the treatment process. The potential exists for exposure to the various

Figure 78.25 • Unsat gas plant process.

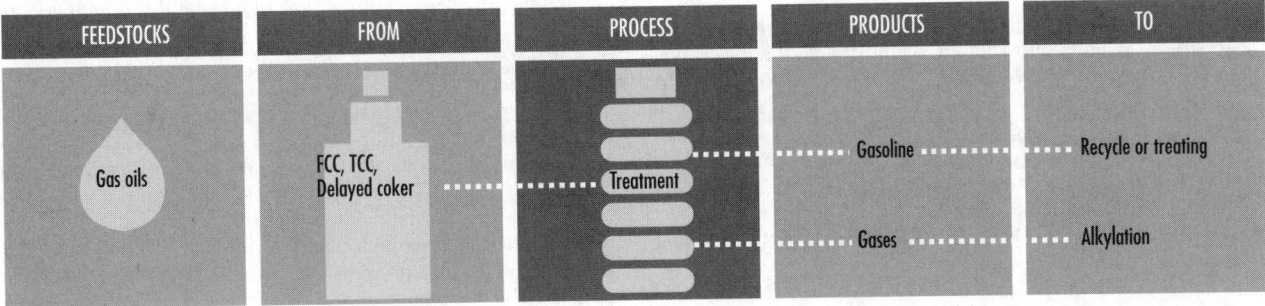

FEEDSTOCKS	FROM	PROCESS	PRODUCTS	TO
Gas oils	FCC, TCC, Delayed coker	Treatment	Gasoline	Recycle or treating
			Gases	Alkylation

Source: Adapted from OSHA 1996.

chemicals and waste products during process sampling, inspection, maintenance and turnarounds.

Pretreatment

Pretreatment is the initial separation of hydrocarbons and solids from waste water. API separators, interceptor plates and settling ponds are used to remove suspended hydrocarbons, oily sludge and solids by gravity separation, skimming and filtration. Acidic waste water is neutralized with ammonia, lime or soda ash. Alkaline waste water is treated with sulphuric acid, hydrochloric acid, carbon dioxide-rich flue gas or sulphur. Some oil-in-water emulsions are first heated to help separate the oil and the water. Gravity separation depends on the different specific gravities of water and immiscible oil globules, which allows free oil to be skimmed off the surface of the waste water.

Sour water stripping

Water containing sulphides, called sour water, is produced in catalytic cracking and hydro-treating processes, and whenever steam is condensed in the presence of gases containing hydrogen sulphide.

Stripping is used on waste water containing sulphides and/or ammonia, and solvent extraction is used to remove phenols from waste water. Waste water which is to be recycled may require cooling to remove heat and/or oxidation by spraying or air stripping to remove any remaining phenols, nitrates and ammonia.

Secondary treatment

Following pretreatment, suspended solids are removed by sedimentation or air flotation. Waste water with low levels of solids is screened or filtered, and flocculation agents may be added to help separation. Materials with high adsorption characteristics are used in fixed-bed filters or added to the waste water to form a slurry which is removed by sedimentation or filtration. Secondary treatment processes biologically degrade and oxidize soluble organic matter by the use of activated sludge, unaerated or aerated lagoons, trickling filter methods or anaerobic treatments. Additional treatment methods are used to remove oils and chemicals from waste water.

Tertiary treatment

Tertiary treatments remove specific pollutants in order to meet regulatory discharge requirements. These treatments include chlorination, ozonation, ion exchange, reverse osmosis, activated carbon adsorption, and others. Compressed oxygen may be diffused into waste water streams to oxidize certain chemicals or to satisfy regulatory oxygen content requirements.

Cooling towers

Cooling towers remove heat from process water by evaporation and latent heat transfer between hot water and air. The two types of towers are counterflow and crossflow.

- In counterflow cooling, hot process water is pumped to the uppermost plenum and allowed to fall through the tower. Numerous slats, or spray nozzles, are located throughout the length of the tower to disperse the water flow and help in cooling. Simultaneously, air enters at the tower bottom, creating a concurrent flow of air against the water. Induced draft towers have the fans at the air outlet. Forced draft towers have the fans or blowers at the air inlet.
- Crossflow towers introduce airflow at right angles to the water flow throughout the structure.

Recirculated cooling water must be treated to remove impurities and any dissolved hydrocarbons. Impurities in cooling water can corrode and foul piping and heat exchangers, scale from dissolved salts can deposit on pipes, and wooden cooling towers can be damaged by micro-organisms.

Cooling tower water can be contaminated by process materials and by-products, including sulphur dioxide, hydrogen sulphide and carbon dioxide, with resultant exposures. There is potential for exposure to water treatment chemicals or to hydrogen sulphide when waste water is treated in conjunction with cooling towers. Because the water is saturated with oxygen from being cooled with air, the chances for corrosion are intensified. One means of corrosion prevention is the addition of a material to the cooling water which forms a protective film on pipes and other metal surfaces.

When cooling water is contaminated by hydrocarbons, flammable vapours can evaporate into the discharge air. If a source of ignition or lightning is present, fires may start. Fire hazards exist when there are relatively dry areas in induced-draft cooling towers of combustible construction. Loss of power to cooling tower fans or water pumps can create serious consequences in process operations.

Steam generation

Steam is produced through heater and boiler operations in central steam generation plants and at various process units, using heat from flue gas or other sources. Steam generation systems include:

- heaters (furnaces), with their burners and a combustion air system
- draft or pressure systems to remove flue gas from the furnace, soot blowers, and compressed air systems which seal openings to prevent flue gas from escaping
- boilers, consisting of a number of tubes which carry the water/steam mixture through the furnace providing for maximum heat transfer (these tubes run between steam distribution drums at the top of the boiler, and water collecting drums at the bottom of the boiler)
- steam drums to collect steam and direct it to the superheater before it enters the steam distribution system.

The most potentially hazardous operation in steam generation is heater start-up. A flammable mixture of gas and air can build up as a result of loss of flame at one or more burners during light-off. Specific start-up procedures are required for each different type of unit, including purging before light-off and emergency procedures in the event of misfire or loss of burner flame. If feedwater runs low and boilers are dry, the tubes will overheat and fail. Excess water will be carried over into the steam distribution system, causing damage to the turbines. Boilers should have continuous or intermittent blowdown systems to remove water from steam drums and to limit build-up of scale on turbine blades and superheater tubes. Care must be taken not to overheat the superheater during start-up and shut down. Alternate fuel sources should be provided in event of loss of fuel gas due to refinery unit shutdown or emergency.

Heater fuel

Any one or any combination of fuels, including refinery gas, natural gas, fuel oil and powdered coal may be used in heaters. Refinery off-gas is collected from process units and combined with natural gas and LPG in a fuel gas balance drum. The balance drum provides constant system pressure, fairly stable BTU (energy) content fuel and automatic separation of suspended liquids in gas vapours, and prevents carryover of large slugs of condensate into the distribution system.

Fuel oil is typically a mix of refinery crude oil and straight-run and cracked residues, blended with other products. The fuel oil system delivers fuel to process unit heaters and steam generators at required temperatures and pressures. The fuel oil is heated to pumping temperature, sucked through a coarse suction strainer, pumped to a temperature-control heater and then through a fine mesh strainer before being burned. Knockout pots, provided at process units, are used to remove liquids from fuel gas before burning.

In one example of process unit heat generation, carbon monoxide (CO) boilers recover heat in catalytic cracking units as carbon monoxide in flue gas is burned to complete combustion. In other processes, waste heat recovery units use heat from the flue gas to make steam.

Steam distribution

Steam typically is generated by heaters and boilers combined into one unit. Steam leaves the boilers at the highest pressure required by the process units or the electrical generator. The steam pressure is then reduced in turbines which drive process pumps and compressors. When refinery steam is also used to drive steam turbine generators to produce electricity, the steam must be produced at much higher pressure than required for process steam. The steam distribution system consists of valves, fittings, piping and connections which are suitable for the pressure of the steam transported. Most steam used in the refinery is condensed to water in heat exchangers and reused as boiler feedwater, or discharged to waste water treatment.

Steam feedwater

Feedwater supply is an important part of steam generation. There must always be as many pounds of water entering the steam generation system as there are pounds of steam leaving it. Water used in steam generation must be free of contaminants, including minerals and dissolved impurities, which can damage the system or affect the operation. Suspended materials such as silt, sewage and oil, which form scale and sludge, are coagulated or filtered out of the water. Dissolved gases, particularly carbon dioxide and oxygen which cause boiler corrosion, are removed by de-aeration and treatment. Dissolved minerals such as metallic salts, calcium and carbonates, which cause scale, corrosion and turbine blade deposits, are treated with lime or soda ash to precipitate them out of the water. Depending on its characteristics, raw boiler feedwater may be treated by clarification, sedimentation, filtration, ion exchange, de-aeration and internal treatment. Recirculated cooling water must also be treated to remove hydrocarbons and other contaminants.

Process heaters, heat exchangers and coolers

Process heaters and heat exchangers preheat feedstocks in distillation towers and in refinery processes to reaction temperatures. The major portion of heat provided to process units comes from fired heaters found on crude and reformer preheater units, coker heaters and large-column reboilers, which are fueled by refinery or natural gas, distillate and residual oils. Heaters are usually designed for specific process operations, and most are either cylindrical vertical or box-type designs. Heat exchangers use either steam or hot hydrocarbon, transferred from some other section of the process, for heat input.

Heat is also removed from some processes by air and water exchangers, fin fans, gas and liquid coolers and overhead condensers, or by transferring the heat to other systems. The basic mechanical vapour compression refrigeration system is designed to serve one or more process units, and includes an evaporator, compressor, condenser, controls and piping. Common coolants are water, alcohol/water mixture or various glycol solutions.

A means of providing adequate draft or steam purging is required to reduce the chance of explosions when lighting fires in heater furnaces. Specific start-up and emergency procedures are required for each type of unit. If fire impinges on fin fans, failure could occur due to overheating. If flammable product escapes from a heat exchanger or cooler due to a leak, a fire could occur.

Care must be taken to assure that all pressure is removed from heater tubes before removing any header or fitting plugs. Consideration should be given to providing for pressure relief in heat exchanger piping systems in the event they are blocked off while full of liquid. If controls fail, variations of temperature and pressure could occur on either side of the heat exchanger. If heat exchanger tubes fail and process pressure is greater than heater pressure, product could enter the heater with downstream consequences. If the pressure is less, the heater stream could enter into the process fluid stream. If loss of circulation occurs in liquid or gas coolers, increased product temperature could affect downstream operations, requiring pressure relief.

Depending on the fuel, process operation and unit design, there is a potential for exposure to hydrogen sulphide, carbon monoxide, hydrocarbons, steam boiler feedwater sludge and water treatment chemicals. Skin contact with boiler blowdown which may contain phenolic compounds should be avoided. Exposure to radiant heat, superheated steam and hot hydrocarbons is possible.

Pressure relief and flare systems

Engineering controls which are incorporated into processes include reducing flammable vapour concentrations by ventilation, dilution and inerting. Pressurization is used to maintain control rooms above atmospheric pressure in order to reduce the possibility of vapours entering. Pressure relief systems are provided to control vapours and liquids which are released by pressure-relieving devices and blowdowns. Pressure relief is an automatic, planned release when operating pressure reaches a predetermined level. Blowdown usually refers to the intentional release of material, such as blowdowns from process unit start-ups, furnace blowdowns, shutdowns and emergencies. Vapour depressuring is the rapid removal of vapours from pressure vessels in case of emergency. This may be accomplished by the use of a rupture disc, usually set at a higher pressure than the relief valve.

Safety relief valves

Safety relief valves, used to control air, steam, gas and hydrocarbon vapour and liquid pressures, open in proportion to the increase in pressure over the normal operating pressure. Safety valves, designed primarily to release high volumes of steam, usually pop open to full capacity. The overpressure needed to open liquid relief valves, where large-volume discharge is not required, increases as the valve lifts due to increased spring resistance. Pilot-operated safety release valves, with up to six times the capacity of normal relief valves, are used where tighter sealing and larger-volume discharges are required. Non-volatile liquids are usually pumped to oil/water separation and recovery systems, and volatile liquids are sent to units operating at a lower pressure.

Flares

A typical closed pressure-release and flare system includes relief valves and lines from process units for collection of discharges, knockout drums to separate vapours and liquids, seals and/or purge gas for flashback protection and a flare and igniter system, which combusts vapours if discharge direct to the atmosphere is not permitted. Steam may be injected into the flare tip to reduce visible smoke.

Liquids should not be allowed to discharge to a vapour disposal system. Flare knockout drums and flares need to be large enough to handle emergency blowdowns, and drums require relief in event of overpressure. Provide pressure relief valves where the potential exists for overpressure in refinery processes, such as due to the following causes:

- loss of cooling water, possibly resulting in a greatly increased pressure drop in condensers, in turn increasing the pressure in the process unit
- rapid vaporization and pressure increase from injection of a lower-boiling-point liquid, including water, into a process vessel operating at higher temperatures
- expansion of vapour and resultant overpressure due to over-heated process steam, malfunctioning heaters or fire
- failure of automatic controls, closed outlets, heat exchanger failure, etc.
- internal explosion, chemical reaction, thermal expansion, accumulated gases, etc.
- loss of reflux, causing a pressure rise in distillation towers.

Because the quantity of reflux affects the volume of vapours leaving the distillation tower, loss of volume causes a pressure drop in condensers and a pressure rise in distillation towers.

Maintenance is important because valves are required to function properly. Common valve operating problems include:

- failure to open at set pressure due to plugging of the valve inlet or outlet or by corrosion, preventing proper operation of the disc holder and guides
- failure to reseat after popping open due to fouling, corrosion or deposits on the seat or moving parts, or by solids in the gas stream cutting the valve disc
- chattering and premature opening, due to operating pressure being too close to the valve set point.

Utilities

Water. Depending on location and community resources, refineries may draw upon public water supplies for drinking and process water or may have to pump and treat their own potable water. Treatment may include a wide range of requirements, from de-salting to filtration, chlorination and testing.

Sewage. Also, depending on availability of community or private offsite treatment plants, refineries may have to provide for the permitting, collection, treatment and discharge of their sanitary waste.

Electric power. Refineries either receive electricity from outside sources or produce their own, using electric generators driven by steam turbines or gas engines. Areas are classified with regard to the type of electrical protection required to prevent a spark from igniting vapours or contain an explosion within electrical equipment. Electrical substations, which are normally located in non-classified areas, away from sources of flammable hydrocarbon vapour or cooling tower water spray, contain transformers, circuit breakers and feed circuit switches. Substations feed power to distribution stations within the process unit areas. Distribution stations can be located in classified areas, provided that electrical classification requirements are met. Distribution stations typically use a liquid-filled transformer provided with an oil-filled or air-break disconnect device.

Normal electrical safety precautions, including dry footing, "high voltage" warning signs and guarding should be implemented to protect against electrocution. Employees should be familiar with refinery electrical safe work procedures. Lockout/tagout and other appropriate safe work practices should be implemented to prevent energizing while work is being performed on high-voltage electrical equipment. Hazardous exposures may occur when working around transformers and switches which contain a dielectric fluid requiring special handling precautions. These subjects are discussed more fully elsewhere in this *Encyclopaedia*.

Turbine, gas and air compressor operations

Air and gas compressors

Refinery exhaust ventilation and air supply systems are designed to capture or dilute gases, fumes, dusts and vapours which may contaminate working spaces or the outside atmosphere. Captured contaminants are reclaimed if feasible, or directed to disposal systems after being cleaned or burned. Air supply systems include compressors, coolers, air receivers, air dryers, controls and distribution piping. Blowers are also used to provide air to certain processes. Plant air is provided for the operation of air-powered tools, catalyst regeneration, process heaters, steam-air decoking, sour water oxidation, gasoline sweetening, asphalt blowing and other uses. Instrument air is provided for use in pneumatic instruments and controls, air motors and purge connections. Plant gas, such as nitrogen, is provided for inerting vessels and other uses. Both reciprocating and centrifugal compressors are used for gas and compressed air.

Air compressors should be located so that the suction does not take in flammable vapours or corrosive gases. There is a potential for fire should a leak occur in gas compressors. Knockout drums are needed to prevent liquid surges from entering gas compressors. If gases are contaminated with solid materials, strainers are needed. Failure of automatic compressor controls will affect processes. If maximum pressure could potentially be greater than compressor or process equipment design pressure, pressure relief should be provided. Guarding is needed for exposed moving parts on compressors. Compressor buildings should be properly electrically classified, and provisions made for proper ventilation.

Where plant air is used as back-up to instrument air, interconnections must be upstream of the instrument air drying system to prevent contamination of instruments with moisture. Alternate sources of instrument air supply, such as use of nitrogen, may be needed in the event of power outages or compressor failure. Apply appropriate safeguards so that gas, plant air and instrument air are not used as the source for breathing or for pressuring potable water systems.

Turbines

Turbines are usually gas or steam powered and are used to drive pumps, compressors, blowers and other refinery process equipment. Steam enters turbines at high temperatures and pressures, expanding across and driving rotating blades while directed by fixed blades.

Steam turbines used for exhaust operating under vacuum need a safety relief valve on the discharge side for protection and to maintain steam in event of vacuum failure. Where maximum operating pressure could be greater than design pressure, steam turbines need relief devices. Consideration should be given to providing governors and overspeed-control devices on turbines.

Pumps, Piping and Valves

Centrifugal and positive displacement (reciprocating) pumps are used to move hydrocarbons, process water, fire water and waste water throughout the refinery. Pumps are driven by electric motors, steam turbines or internal combustion engines.

Process and utility piping systems distribute hydrocarbons, steam, water and other products throughout the facility. They are sized and constructed of materials dependent on the type of service, pressure, temperature and nature of the products. There are vent, drain and sample connections on piping, as well as provisions for blanking. Different types of valves, including gate valves, bypass valves, globe and ball valves, plug valves, block and bleed valves and check valves are used, depending on their operating purpose. These valves can be operated manually or automatically.

Valves and instrumentation which require servicing or other work should be accessible at grade level or from an operating platform. Remote-controlled valves, fire valves and isolation valves may be used to limit the loss of product at pump suction lines in the event of leakage or fire. Operating vent and drain connections may be provided with double block valves, or a block valve and plug or blind flange for protection against releases. Depending on the product and service, backflow prevention from the discharge line may be needed. Provisions may be made for pipeline expansion, movement and temperature changes to avoid rupture. Pumps operated with reduced or no flow can overheat and rupture. The failure of automatic pump controls could cause a deviation in process pressure and temperature. Pressure relief in the discharge piping should be provided where pumps can be overpressured.

Tank storage

Atmospheric storage tanks and pressure storage tanks are used throughout the refinery for storage of crudes, intermediate hydrocarbons (those used for processing) and finished products, both liquids and gases. Tanks are also provided for fire water, process and treatment water, acids, air and hydrogen, additives and other chemicals. The type, construction, capacity and location of tanks depends on their use and the nature, vapour pressure, flashpoints and pour points of the materials stored. Many types of tanks are used in refineries, the simplest being above-ground, cone-roof tanks for storage of combustible (non-volatile) liquids such as diesel fuels, fuel oils and lubricating oils. Open-top and covered (internal) floating-roof tanks, which store flammable (volatile) liquids such as gasoline and crude oil, restrict the amount of space between the top of the product and the tank roof in order to maintain a vapour-rich atmosphere to preclude ignition.

The potential for fire exists if hydrocarbon storage tanks are overfilled or develop leaks which allow liquid and vapours to escape and reach sources of ignition. Refineries should establish manual gauging and product receipt procedures to control overfills or provide automatic overflow control and signaling systems on tanks. Tanks may be equipped with fixed or semi-fixed foam-water fire protection systems. Remote-controlled valves, isolation valves and fire valves may be provided at tanks for pump-out or closure in the event of a fire inside the tank or in the tank dike or storage area. Tank venting, cleaning and confined-space entry programmes are used to control work inside tanks, and hot work permit systems are used to control sources of ignition in and around storage tanks.

Handling, shipping and transportation

Loading gases and liquid hydrocarbons into pipelines, tank cars, tank trucks and marine vessels and barges for transport to terminals and consumers is the final refinery operation. Product characteristics, distribution needs, shipping requirements, fire prevention, and environmental protection and operating criteria are important when designing marine docks, loading racks and pipeline manifolds. Operating procedures need to be established and agreed to by the shipper and receiver, and communications maintained during product transfer. Tank trucks and rail tank cars may be either top or bottom loaded. Loading and unloading liquefied petroleum gas (LPG) requires special considerations over and above those for liquid hydrocarbons. Where required, vapour recovery systems should be provided at loading racks and marine docks.

Safe work practices and appropriate personal protective equipment may be needed when loading or unloading, cleaning up spills or leaks, or when gauging, inspecting, sampling or performing maintenance activities on loading facilities or vapour recovery systems. Delivery should be stopped or diverted in the event of an emergency such as a tank truck or tank car compartment overfill.

A number of different hazardous and toxic chemicals are used in refineries, varying from small amounts of test reagents used in laboratories to large quantities of sulphuric acid and hydrofluoric acids used in alkaline processing. These chemicals need to be received, stored and handled properly. Chemical manufacturers provide material safety information which can be used by refineries to develop safety procedures, engineering controls, personal protection requirements and emergency response procedures for handling chemicals.

The nature of the hazard at loading and unloading facilities depends upon the products being loaded and the products previously transported in the tank car, tank truck or marine vessel. Bonding equalizes the electrical charge between the loading rack and the tank truck or tank car. Grounding prevents the flow of stray currents at truck and rail loading facilities. Insulating flanges are used on marine dock piping connections to prevent static electricity build-up and discharges. Flame arrestors are installed in loading rack and marine vapour recovery lines to prevent flashback. Where switch loading is permitted, safe procedures should be established and followed.

Automatic or manual shutoff systems at supply headers should be provided at top- and bottom-loading racks and marine docks in the event of leaks or overfills. Anti-fall protection, such as hand rails, may be needed for docks and top-loading racks. Drainage and recovery systems may be provided at loading racks for storm drainage, at docks and to handle spills and leaks. Precautions are needed at LPG-loading facilities so as not to overload or overpressurize tank cars and trucks.

Refinery Support Activities and Facilities

A number of different facilities, activities and programmes, each of which has its own specific safety and health requirements, are needed to support refinery processes depending on the refinery's location and available resources.

Administrative activities

A wide variety of administrative support activities, depending on the refining company's philosophy and the availability of community services, are required to assure continued operation of a refinery. The function which controls oil movements into, within and out from the refinery is unique to refineries. The administrative functions can be broken down as follows. The day-to-day operation of the process units is the operations function. Another function is responsible for assuring that arrangements have been made for a continuous supply of crude oil. Other functional activities include medical services (both emergency and continuing health care), food service, engineering services, janitorial services and routine administrative and management functions common to most industries, such as accounting, purchasing, human relations and so on. The refinery training function is responsible for supervisor and employee skills and crafts training including initial, refresher and remedial training, and for employee and contractor orientation and training in emergency response and safe work practices and procedures.

Construction and maintenance

The continued safe operation of refineries depends upon the establishment and implementation of programmes and procedures for regular maintenance and preventive maintenance, and assuring replacement when necessary. Turnarounds, wherein the entire refinery or entire process units will be shut down for total equipment overall and replacement at one time, is a type of preventive maintenance programme unique to the process industry. Mechanical integrity activities, such as inspection, repair, testing and certification of valves and relief devices, which are part of the process safety management programme, are important to the continued safe operation of a refinery, as are maintenance work orders for the continued effectiveness of the refinery "management of change" programme. Work permit programmes control hot work and safe work, such as isolation and lockout, and entry into confined spaces. Maintenance and instrumentation shops have purposes which include:

- delicate and precise work to test, maintain and calibrate refinery process controls, instruments and computers
- welding
- equipment repair and overhaul
- vehicle maintenance
- carpentry and so on.

Construction and maintenance safety and health relies on some of the following programmes.

Isolation

The safe maintenance, repair and replacement of equipment within process units often requires the isolation of tanks, vessels and lines in order to preclude the possibility of flammable liquids or vapours entering an area where hot work is being performed. Isolation is normally attained by disconnecting and closing off all of the piping leading to or from a vessel; blinding or blanking the pipe at a connection near the tank or vessel; or closing a double set of block valves on the piping, if provided, and opening a bleeder valve between the two closed valves.

Lockout/tagout

Lockout and tagout programmes prevent the inadvertent activation of electrical, mechanical, hydraulic or pneumatically energized equipment during repair or maintenance. All electrically powered equipment should have its circuit breaker or main switch locked or tagged out and tested to assure non-operability, prior to starting work. Mechanical hydraulic and pneumatic equipment should be de-energized and have its power source locked or tagged out prior to starting work. Valve closing lines which are being worked on, or which are isolated, should also be locked out or tagged to prevent unauthorized opening.

Metallurgy

Metallurgy is used to assure the continued strength and integrity of lines, vessels, tanks and reactors which are subject to corrosion from the acids, corrosives, sour water, and gases and other chemicals created by and used in processing crude oil. Non-destructive testing methods are employed throughout the refinery to detect excessive corrosion and wear before failure occurs. Proper safety precautions are required to prevent excessive exposures to workers who are handling or are exposed to radioactive testing equipment, dyes and chemicals.

Warehouses

Warehouses store not only the parts, materials and equipment needed for continued refinery operations, but also store packaged chemicals and additives that are used in maintenance, processing and blending. Warehouses may also maintain supplies of required personal protective clothing and equipment including hard hats, gloves, aprons, eye and face protection, respiratory protection, safety and impervious footwear, flame-resistant clothing and acid-protective clothing. Proper storage and separation of flammable and combustible liquids and hazardous chemicals is needed to prevent spills, fires and mixing of incompatible products.

Laboratories

Laboratories are responsible for determining the values and consistency of the crude oils prior to processing, as well as performing the testing required for finished product quality control. Laboratory personnel should be trained to recognize the hazards inherent in the handling and mixing of toxic chemicals and flammable liquids, and provide protection for themselves and others.

Safety and environmental and occupational hygiene

Other important refinery support activities are safety, fire prevention and protection, environmental protection and industrial hygiene. These may be provided as separate functions or integrated into the refinery operations. Safety, emergency preparedness and response, and fire prevention and protection activities are often the responsibility of the same function within a refinery. The safety function participates in process safety management programmes as part of the design review, pre-construction and construction review and pre-start-up review teams. Safety often assists in the contractor qualification process, reviews contractor activities and investigates incidents involving employees and contractors. Safety personnel may be responsible for overseeing permit-required activities such as confined space entry and hot work, and for checking the availability and readiness of portable fire extinguishers, decontamination facilities, safety showers, eye wash stations, fixed detection devices and alarms, and emergency self-contained breathing apparatus placed at strategic locations in event of a toxic gas release.

Safety programmes. The refinery safety function usually has responsibility for the development and administration of various safety and incident prevention programmes, including, but not limited to, the following:

- design construction and pre-start-up safety reviews
- accident, incident and near miss investigation and reporting
- emergency preparedness plans and response programmes
- contractor safety programme
- safe work practices and procedures
- lockout/tagout
- confined and inert space entry
- scaffolding
- electrical safety, equipment grounding and fault protection programme
- machine guarding
- safety signs and notices
- hot work, safe work and entry permit systems.

Fire brigades. Refinery fire brigades and emergency responders may be full-time brigade members; designated refinery employees, such as operators and maintenance personnel who are trained and assigned to respond in addition to their regular duties; or a combination of both. Besides fires, brigades traditionally respond to other refinery incidents such as acid or gas releases, rescue from vessels or tanks, spills and so on. The fire protection function may be responsible for the inspection and testing of fire detectors and signals, and fixed and portable fire protection systems and equipment, including fire trucks, fire pumps, fire water lines, hydrants, hoses and nozzles.

Refinery firefighting differs from normal firefighting because rather than extinguishment, it is often preferable to allow certain fires to continue to burn. In addition, each type of hydrocarbon liquid, gas and vapour has unique fire chemistry characteristics which must be thoroughly understood in order to best control their fires. For example, extinguishment of a hydrocarbon vapour fire without first stopping the vapour release, would only create a continued vapour gas cloud with the probability of re-ignition and explosion. Fires in tanks containing crude oil and heavy residuals need to be handled with specific firefighting techniques to avoid the possibility of an explosion or tank boil-over.

Hydrocarbon fires are often extinguished by stopping the flow of product and allowing the fire to burn out while applying cooling water to protect adjacent equipment, tanks and vessels from heat exposures. Many fixed fire protection systems are designed with this specific purpose. Fighting fires in process units under pressure requires special consideration and training, particularly when catalysts such as hydrofluoric acid are involved. Special firefighting chemicals, such as dry powder and foam-water solutions, may be used to extinguish hydrocarbon fires and control vapour emissions.

Emergency preparedness. Refineries need to develop and implement emergency response plans for a number of different potential situations, including explosions, fires, releases and rescues. The emergency plans should include the use of outside assistance, including contractors, governmental and mutual aid as well as availability of special supplies and equipment, such as firefighting foam and spill containment and adsorption materials.

Gas and vapour testing

Gas, particulate and vapour monitoring, sampling and testing in refineries is conducted to assure that work can be performed safely and processes can be operated without toxic or hazardous exposures, explosions or fires. Atmospheric testing is conducted using a variety of instruments and techniques to measure oxygen content, hydrocarbon vapours and gases, and to determine hazardous and toxic exposure levels. Instruments must be properly calibrated and adjusted prior to use, by qualified persons, to assure dependable and accurate measurements. Depending on the work location, potential hazards and type of work being performed, testing, sampling and monitoring may be conducted prior to the start of work, or at specified intervals during work, or continuously throughout the course of work.

When establishing refinery procedures for sampling and testing flammable, inert and toxic atmospheres, the use of personal protective equipment, including appropriate respiratory protection, should be considered. It should be noted that canister-type respirators are unsuitable for oxygen-deficient atmospheres. Testing requirements should depend upon the degree of hazard which would be present in the event of instrument failure.

Testing of the following substances may be performed using portable equipment or fixed instrumentation:

Oxygen. Combustible gas meters work by burning a minute sample of the atmosphere being tested. In order to obtain an accurate combustible gas reading, a minimum of 10% and a maximum of 25% oxygen must be present in the atmosphere. The amount of oxygen present in the atmosphere is determined by using an oxygen meter prior to, or simultaneously with, using the combustible gas meter. Testing for oxygen is essential when working in confined or enclosed spaces, as entry without respiratory protection (provided that there are no toxic exposures) requires normal breathing-air oxygen concentrations of approximately 21%. Oxygen meters are also used to measure the amount of oxygen present in inerted spaces, to assure that there is not enough present to support combustion during hot work or other operations.

Hydrocarbon vapours and gases. "Hot work" is work which creates a source of ignition, such as welding, cutting, grinding, blast cleaning, operating an internal combustion engine and so on, in an area where the potential for exposure to flammable vapours and gases exists. In order to conduct hot work safely, instruments known as combustible gas meters are used to test the atmosphere for hydrocarbon vapours. Hydrocarbon vapours or gases will burn only when mixed with air (oxygen) in certain proportions and ignited. If there is not enough vapour in the air, the mixture is said to be "too lean to burn", and if there is too much vapour (too little oxygen), the mixture is "too rich to burn". The limiting proportions are called the "upper and lower flammable limits" and are expressed as a percentage of volume of vapour in air.

Each hydrocarbon molecule or mixture has different flammability limits, typically ranging from about 1 to 10% vapour in air. Gasoline vapour, for example, has a lower flammable limit of 1.4% and an upper flammable limit of 7.6 per cent.

Toxic atmospheres. Special instruments are used to measure the levels of toxic and hazardous gases, vapours and particulates which may be present in the atmosphere where people are working. These measurements are used to determine the level and type of protection needed, which may vary from complete ventilation and replacement of the atmosphere to the use of respiratory and personal protective equipment by people working in the area. Examples of hazardous and toxic exposures which may be found in refineries include asbestos, benzene, hydrogen sulphide, chlorine, carbon dioxide, sulphuric and hydrofluoric acids, amines, phenol and others.

Health and safety programmes

The basis for refinery industrial hygiene is an administrative and engineering controls programme covering facility exposures to toxic and hazardous chemicals, laboratory safety and hygiene, ergonomics and medical surveillance.

Regulatory agencies and companies establish exposure limitations for various toxic and hazardous chemicals. The occupational hygiene function conducts monitoring and sampling to measure employee exposure to hazardous and toxic chemicals and substances. Industrial hygienists may develop or recommend engineering controls, preventive work practices, product substitution, personal protective clothing and equipment or alternate measures of protection or reducing exposure.

Medical programmes. Refineries typically require preplacement and periodic medical examinations to determine the employee's ability to initially and subsequently perform the work, and assure that the continued work requirements and exposures will not endanger the employee's health or safety.

Personal protection. Personal protection programmes should cover typical refinery exposures, such as noise, asbestos, insulation, hazardous waste, hydrogen sulphide, benzene and process chemicals including caustics, hydrogen fluoride, sulphuric acid and so on. Industrial hygiene may designate the appropriate personal protective equipment to be used for various exposures, including negative pressure and air-supplied respirators and hearing, eye and skin protection.

Product safety. Product safety awareness covers knowing about the hazards of chemicals and materials to which the potential for exposure exists in the workplace, and what actions to take in the event exposure by ingestion, inhalation or skin contact occurs. Toxicological studies of crude oil, refinery streams, process chemicals, finished products and proposed new products are conducted to determine the potential effects of exposure on both employees and consumers. The data are used to develop health information concerning permissible limits of exposure or acceptable amounts of hazardous materials in products. This information is typically distributed by material safety data sheets (MSDSs) or similar documents, and employees are trained or educated in the hazards of the materials in the workplace.

Environmental Protection

Environmental protection is an important consideration in refinery operations because of regulatory compliance requirements and a need for conservation as oil prices and costs escalate. Oil refineries produce a wide range of air and water emissions that can be hazardous to the environment. Some of these are contaminants in the original crude oil, while others are a result of refinery processes and operations. Air emissions include hydrogen sulphide, sulphur dioxide, nitrogen oxides and carbon monoxide (see table 78.2). Waste water typically contains hydrocarbons, dissolved materials, suspended solids, phenols, ammonia, sulphides, acids, alkalis and other contaminants. There is also the risk of accidental spills and leaks of a wide range of flammable and/or toxic chemicals.

Controls established to contain liquid and vapour releases and reduce operating costs include the following:

- *Energy conservation.* Controls include steam leak control and condensate recovery programmes to conserve energy and increase efficiency.
- *Water pollution.* Controls include waste water treatment in API separators and subsequent treatment facilities, storm water collection, retainment and treatment and spill prevention containment and control programmes.
- *Air pollution.* Since refineries operate continuously, leak detection, particularly at valves and pipe connections, is important. Controls include reducing hydrocarbon vapour emissions and

releases to the atmosphere, refinery valve and fitting tightness programmes, floating roof tank seals and vapour containment programmes, and vapour recovery for loading and unloading facilities and for venting tanks and vessels.

- *Ground pollution.* Preventing oil spillage from polluting soil and contaminating ground water is accomplished by the use of dikes and the providing of drainage to specified, protected containment areas. Contamination from spillage inside dike areas may be prevented by the use of secondary containment measures, such as impervious plastic or clay dike liners.
- *Spill response.* Refineries should develop and implement programmes to respond to spills of crude oil, chemicals and finished products, on both land and water. These programmes may rely on trained employees or outside agencies and contractors to respond to the emergency. The type, amount needed and availability of spill clean-up and restoration supplies and equipment, either on site or on call, should be included in the preparedness plan.

Reference

Occupational Safety and Health Administration (OSHA), 1996. *OSHA Instruction TED 1.15 CH-1.* Washington, DC: OSHA, US Department of Labor.

Other relevant readings

American Petroleum Institute. 1971. *Chemistry and Petroleum for Classroom Use in Chemistry Courses.* Washington, DC: American Petroleum Institute.

—. 1973. *Industrial Hygiene Monitoring Manual for Petroleum Refineries and Selected Petrochemical Operations.* Manual 2700-1/79-1M. Washington, DC: American Petroleum Institue.

—. 1980. *Facts about Oil.* Manual 4200-10/80-25m. Washington, DC: American Petroleum Institute.

—. 1990. RP574, *Inspection of Piping, Tubing, Valves and Fittings.* Washington, DC: American Petroleum Institute.

—. 1990. RP750, *Management of Process Hazard.* Washington, DC: American Petroleum Institute.

—. 1991. RP 573, *Inspection of Fired Boilers and Heaters.* Washington, DC: American Petroleum Institute.

—. 1992. RP 572, *Inspection of Pressure Vessels.* Washington, DC: American Petroleum Institute.

—. 1992. RP576, *Inspection of Pressure Relieving Devices.* Washington, DC: American Petroleum Institute.

—. 1994. RP2001, *Fire Protection in Refineries.* Washington, DC: American Petroleum Institute.

Armistead, GJ. 1950. *Safety in Petroleum Refining and Related Industries.* New York: John G. Simmons & Co., Inc.

Exxon Company. 1987. *Encyclopedia for the User of Petroleum Products.* Houston, TX: Exxon Company, USA, Marketing Technical Services.

International Labour Organization (ILO). 1992. *Labour Inspection in the Oil Refining and Large-Scale Petrochemical Industries.* Geneva: ILO.

Kutler, AA. 1969. Crude distillation. In *Petro/chem Engineering.* New York: John G. Simmonds & Co.

Mobil Oil Corporation. 1972. *Light Products Refining, Fuels Manufacture* (Mobil Technical Bulletin). Fairfax, VA: Mobil Oil Corporation.

—. 1993. *A Mobil Guide to Health Effects of Refinery Streams.* Princeton, NJ: Mobil Oil Corporation.

Nabieva, GV. 1976. CIS 77-1451. Occupational disease in oil rig workers. *Gigiene truda i proffesional'nye zabolevanija* 8:22–24.

Ostrowski, R. 1991. Oil quenching. In *Industrial Fire Hazards Handbook.* Quincy, Ma: National Fire Protection Association.

Parkes, KR. 1992. Mental health in the oil industry: A comparative study of onshore and offshore employees. *Psych Med* 22:997–1009.

Rom, WN, JS Lee, and BF Craft. 1981. Occupational and environmental health problems of the developing oil shale industry: A review. *Am J Ind Med* 2:247–260.

Salpukas, A. 1995. New ideas for U.S. oil. *New York Times,* 16 November.

Skoupy, A and R Ulrich. 1994. Dispersal of chain lubrication oil in one-man chain-saws. *Forsttechnische Information* 11:121–123.

Skyberg, K, A Ronneberg, CC Christensen, CR Naess-Andersen, HE Refsum, and A Borgelsen. 1992. Lung function and radiographic signs of pulmonary fibrosis in oil exposed workers in a cable manufacturing company: A follow up study. *Brit J Ind Med* 49(5):309–315.

Sutherland, VJ and CL Cooper. 1986. *Man and Accidents Offshore: The Costs of Stress among Workers on Oil and Gas Rigs.* London, Belgium: Dietsmann International NV, Lloyd's List.

Vervalin, CH (ed.). 1985. *Fire Protection Manual for Hydrocarbon Processing Plants,* Vol. 1, 3rd ed. Houston, TX: Gulf Publishing Co.

Wagenaar, W, J Groeneweg, PTW Hudson and JT Reason. 1994. Promoting safety in the oil industry. *Ergonomics* 37(12):1999–2013.

Woods, GM. 1984. Oil quenching. In *Industrial Fire Hazards Handbook.* Quincy, MA: National Fire Protection Association.

PHARMACEUTICAL INDUSTRY

79

Chapter Editor
Keith Tait

Contents

PHARMACEUTICAL INDUSTRY

Keith Tait

The pharmaceutical industry is an important component of health care systems throughout the world; it is comprised of many public and private organizations that discover, develop, manufacture and market medicines for human and animal health (Gennaro 1990). The pharmaceutical industry is based primarily upon the scientific research and development (R&D) of medicines that prevent or treat diseases and disorders. Drug substances exhibit a wide range of pharmacological activity and toxicological properties (Hardman, Gilman and Limbird 1996; Reynolds 1989). Modern scientific and technological advances are accelerating the discovery and development of innovative pharmaceuticals with improved therapeutic activity and reduced side effects. Molecular biologists, medicinal chemists and pharmacists are improving the benefits of drugs through increased potency and specificity. These advances create new concerns for protecting the health and safety of workers within the pharmaceutical industry (Agius 1989; Naumann et al. 1996; Sargent and Kirk 1988; Teichman, Fallon and Brandt-Rauf 1988).

Many dynamic scientific, social and economic factors affect the pharmaceutical industry. Some pharmaceutical companies operate in both national and multinational markets. Therefore, their activities are subject to legislation, regulation and policies relating to drug development and approval, manufacturing and quality control, marketing and sales (Spilker 1994). Academic, government and industry scientists, practising physicians and pharmacists, as well as the public, influence the pharmaceutical industry. Health care providers (e.g., physicians, dentists, nurses, pharmacists and veterinarians) in hospitals, clinics, pharmacies and private practice may prescribe drugs or recommend how they should be dispensed. Government regulations and health care policies on pharmaceuticals are influenced by the public, advocacy groups and private interests. These complex factors interact to influence the discovery and development, manufacturing, marketing and sales of drugs.

The pharmaceutical industry is largely driven by scientific discovery and development, in conjunction with toxicological and clinical experience (see figure 79.1). Major differences exist between large organizations which engage in a broad range of drug discovery and development, manufacturing and quality control, marketing and sales and smaller organizations which focus on a specific aspect. Most multinational pharmaceutical companies are involved in all these activities; however, they may specialize in one aspect based upon local market factors. Academic, public and private organizations perform scientific research to discover and develop new drugs. The biotechnology industry is becoming a major contributor to innovative pharmaceutical research (Swarbick and Boylan 1996). Often, collaborative agreements between research organizations and large pharmaceutical companies are formed to explore the potential of new drug substances.

Many countries have specific legal protections for proprietary drugs and manufacturing processes, known as intellectual property rights. In instances when legal protections are limited or do not exist, some companies specialize in manufacturing and marketing generic drugs (Medical Economics Co. 1995). The pharmaceutical industry requires large amounts of capital investment due to the high expenses associated with R&D, regulatory approval, manufacturing, quality assurance and control, marketing and sales (Spilker 1994). Many countries have extensive government regulations affecting the development and approval of drugs for commercial sale. These countries have strict requirements for good manufacturing practices to ensure the integrity of drug manufacturing operations and the quality, safety and efficacy of pharmaceutical products (Gennaro 1990).

International and domestic trade, as well as tax and finance policies and practices, affect how the pharmaceutical industry operates within a country (Swarbick and Boylan 1996). Significant differences exist between developed and developing countries, regarding their needs for pharmaceutical substances. In developing countries, where malnutrition and infectious diseases are prevalent, nutritional supplements, vitamins and anti-infective drugs are most needed. In developed countries, where the diseases associated with ageing and specific ailments are primary health concerns, cardiovascular, central nervous system, gastrointestinal, anti-infective, diabetes and chemotherapy drugs are in the greatest demand.

Human and animal health drugs share similar R&D activities and manufacturing processes; however, they have unique therapeutic benefits and mechanisms for their approval, distribution, marketing and sales (Swarbick and Boylan 1996). Veterinarians

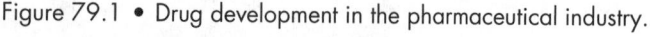

Figure 79.1 • Drug development in the pharmaceutical industry.

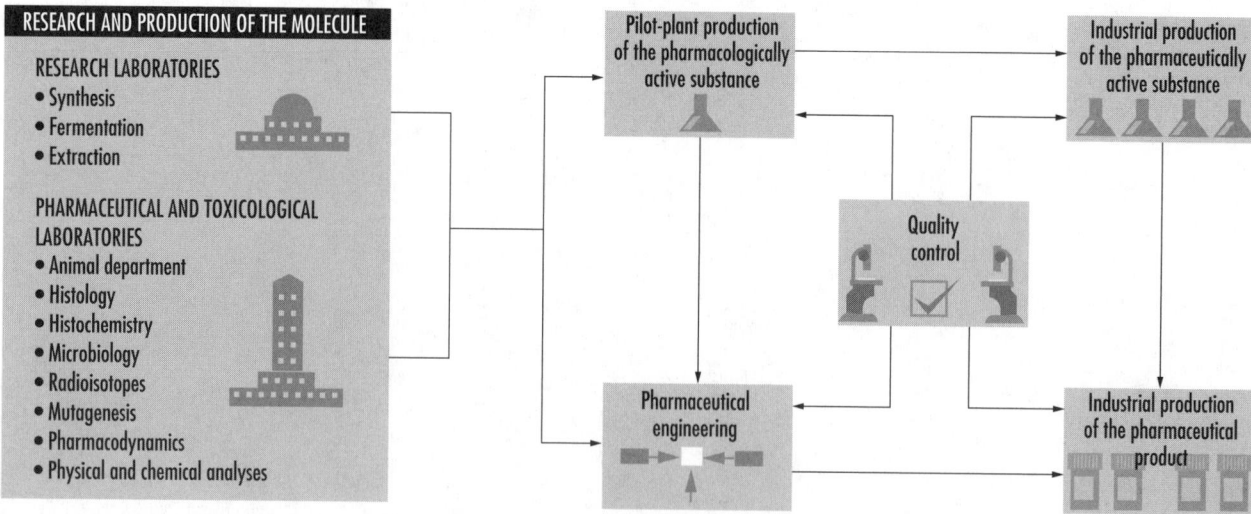

administer drugs to control infectious diseases and parasitic organisms in agricultural and companion animals. Vaccines and anti-infective and antiparasitic drugs are commonly used for this purpose. Nutritional supplements, antibiotics and hormones are widely employed by modern agriculture to promote the growth and health of farm animals. The R&D of pharmaceuticals for human and animal health are often allied, due to concurrent needs to control infectious agents and disease.

Hazardous Industrial Chemicals and Drug-related Substances

Many different biological and chemical agents are discovered, developed and used in the pharmaceutical industry (Hardman, Gilman and Limbird 1996; Reynolds 1989). Some manufacturing processes in the pharmaceutical, biochemical and synthetic organic chemical industries are similar; however, the greater diversity, smaller scale and specific applications in the pharmaceutical industry are unique. Since the primary purpose is to produce medicinal substances with pharmacological activity, many agents in pharmaceutical R&D and manufacturing are hazardous to workers. Proper control measures must be implemented to protect workers from industrial chemicals and drug substances during many R&D, manufacturing and quality control operations (ILO 1983; Naumann et al. 1996; Teichman, Fallon and Brandt-Rauf 1988).

The pharmaceutical industry uses biological agents (e.g., bacteria and viruses) in many special applications, such as vaccine production, fermentation processes, derivation of blood-based products and biotechnology. Biological agents are not addressed by this profile due to their unique pharmaceutical applications, but other references are readily available (Swarbick and Boylan 1996). Chemical agents may be categorized as industrial chemicals and drug-related substances (Gennaro 1990). These may be raw materials, intermediates or finished products. Special situations arise when industrial chemicals or drug substances are employed in laboratory R&D, quality assurance and control assays, engineering and maintenance, or when they are created as by-products or wastes.

Industrial chemicals

Industrial chemicals are used in researching and developing active drug substances and manufacturing bulk substances and finished pharmaceutical products. Organic and inorganic chemicals are raw materials, serving as reactants, reagents, catalysts and solvents. The use of industrial chemicals is determined by the specific manufacturing process and operations. Many of these materials may be hazardous to workers. Since worker exposures to industrial chemicals may be hazardous, occupational exposure limits, such as threshold limit values (TLVs) have been established by government, technical and professional organizations (ACGIH 1995).

Drug-related substances

Pharmacologically active substances may be categorized as natural products and synthetic drugs. Natural products are derived from plant and animal sources, while synthetic drugs are produced by microbiological and chemical technologies. Antibiotics, steroid and peptide hormones, vitamins, enzymes, prostaglandins and pheromones are important natural products. Scientific research is focusing increasingly on synthetic drugs due to recent scientific advances in molecular biology, biochemistry, pharmacology and computer technology. Table 79.1 lists the principal pharmaceutical agents.

Active drug substances and inert materials are combined during pharmaceutical manufacturing to produce dosage forms of medicinal products (e.g., tablets, capsules, liquids, powders,

Definitions

These terms are used frequently in the pharmaceutical industry:

Biologics are bacterial and viral vaccines, antigens, antitoxins and analogous products, serums, plasmas and other blood derivatives for therapeutically protecting or treating humans and animals.

Bulks are active drug substances used to manufacture dosage-form products, process medicated animal feeds or compound prescription medications.

Diagnostic agents assist the diagnosis of diseases and disorders in humans and animals. Diagnostic agents may be inorganic chemicals for examining the gastrointestinal tract, organic chemicals for visualizing the circulatory system and liver and radioactive compounds for measuring the function of organ system.

Drugs are substances with active pharmacological properties in humans and animals. Drugs are compounded with other materials, such as pharmaceutical necessities, to produce a medicinal product.

Ethical pharmaceuticals are biological and chemicals agents for preventing, diagnosing or treating disease and disorders in humans or animals. These products are dispensed by prescription or approval of a medical, pharmacy or veterinary professional.

Excipients are inert ingredients which are combined with drug substances to create a dosage form product. Excipients may affect the rate of absorption, dissolution, metabolism and distribution in humans or animals.

Over-the-counter pharmaceuticals are drug products sold in a retail store or pharmacy which do not require a prescription or the approval of a medical, pharmacy or veterinary professional.

Pharmacy is the art and science of preparing and dispensing drugs for preventing, diagnosing or treating diseases or disorders in humans and animals.

Pharmacokinetics is the study of metabolic processes relating to the absorption, distribution, biotransformation, and elimination of a drug in humans or animals.

Pharmacodynamics is the study of drug action relating to its chemical structure, site of action, and the biochemical and physiological consequences in humans and animals.

creams and ointments) (Gennaro 1990). Drugs may be categorized by their manufacturing process and therapeutic benefits (EPA 1995). Drugs are medicinally administered by strictly prescribed means (e.g., oral, injection, skin) and dosages, whereas workers may be exposed to drug substances by inadvertently breathing airborne dust or vapours or accidentally swallowing contaminated foods or beverages. Occupational exposure limits (OELs) are developed by toxicologists and occupational hygienists to provide guidance on limiting worker exposures to drug substances (Naumann et al. 1996; Sargent and Kirk 1988).

Pharmaceutical necessities (e.g., binders, fillers, flavouring and bulking agents, preservatives and antioxidants) are mixed with active drug substances, providing the desired physical and pharmacological properties in the dosage form products (Gennaro 1990). Many pharmaceutical necessities have no or limited therapeutic value and are relatively non-hazardous to workers during drug development and manufacturing operations. These materials are anti-oxidants and preservatives, colouring, flavouring and diluting agents, emulsifiers and suspending agents, ointment bases, pharmaceutical solvents and excipients.

Pharmaceutical Operations, Related Hazards and Workplace Control Measures

Pharmaceutical manufacturing operations may be categorized as *basic production of bulk drug substances* and *pharmaceutical manufacturing*

Table 79.1 • Major categories of pharmaceutical agents.

Central nervous system	Renal and cardio-vascular system	Gastrointestinal system	Anti-infectives and target organs	Immune system	Chemotherapy	Blood and blood-forming organs	Endocrine system
Analgesics • Acetaminophen • Salicylates **Anaesthetics** • General and local **Anticonvulsants** • Barbituates • Benzodiazepine **Migraine preparations** • Beta adrenergic blocking agents • Serotonin receptor antagonists **Narcotics** • Opiates **Psychotherapeutics** • Antianxiety agents • Antidepressants **Sedatives and hypnotics** • Barbituates • Benzodiazepine	**Antidiabetics** • Biguanides • Glycosidase inhibitors • Insulins • Sulphotryforeas **Cardioprotective agents** • Adrenergic blockers • Stimulants • Angiotensin inhibitors • Antiarrhythmics • Calcium channel blockers • Diuretics • Vasodilators • Vasodepressors	**Gastrointestinal agents** • Antacids • Antiflatulents • Antidiarrhoeals • Antiemetics • Antispasmodics • Laxatives • Prostaglandins	**Systemic anti-infectives** • AIDS therapies • Amebicides • Anthelmintics • Antibiotics • Antifungals • Antimalarials • Sulphonamides • Cephalosporins, penicillins, tetra-cyclines, etc. **Respiratory agents** • Antitussives • Bronchodilators • Decongestants • Expectorants **Skin and mucous membrane agents** • Acne preparations • Allergans • Anti-infectives • Burn preparations • Emollients **Urinary tract agents** • Anti-inflectives • Antispasmodics **Vaginal preparations** • Antifungals	**Analgesics** • Non-steroidal anti-inflammatory agents-(NSAIDs) **Biological response modifiers** • Alpha protein-ase inhibitors • Antitoxins • Immune serums • Toxoids • Vaccines **Antifibrosis therapy** **Immunodilators and immuno-suppressives** **Multiple sclerosis management**	**Antineoplastics** • Adjunct therapy • Alkylating agents • Antibiotics • Antimetabolites • Hormones • Immuno-modulators	**Blood modifiers** • Anticoagulants • Antiplatelet agents • Colony stimulating factors • Haemantinics • Haemostatics • Plasma fractions **Vasodilators** • Cerebral-vasodilators	**Diagnostics** • Adreno cortical steroids • Glucocorticoids • Gondotropins • Hypothalamic dysfunction • Thyroid function test **Hormones** • Adreneal cortical steroid inhibitors • Anabolic steroids • Androgens • Oestrogens • Gonadotropins • Growth hormone • Progesterone • Somatostatin **Prostaglandins**

of dosage form products. Figure 79.2 illustrates the manufacturing process.

Basic production of bulk drug substances may employ three major types of processes: *fermentation, organic chemical synthesis,* and *biological and natural extraction* (Theodore and McGuinn 1992). These manufacturing operations may be discrete batch, continuous or a combination of these processes. Antibiotics, steroids and vitamins are produced by fermentation, whereas many new drug substances are produced by organic synthesis. Historically, most drug substances were derived from natural sources such as plants, animals, fungi and other organisms. Natural medicines are pharmacologically diverse and difficult to produce commercially due to their complex chemistry and limited potency.

Fermentation

Fermentation is a biochemical process employing selected microorganisms and microbiological technologies to produce a chemical product. Batch fermentation processes involve three basic steps: *inoculum* and *seed preparation, fermentation,* and *product recovery* or *isolation* (Theodore and McGuinn 1992). A schematic diagram of a fermentation process is given in figure 79.3. Inoculum preparation begins with a spore sample from a microbial strain. The strain is selectively cultured, purified and grown using a battery of microbiological techniques to produce the desired product. The spores of the microbial strain are activated with water and nutrients in warm conditions. Cells from the culture are grown through a series of agar plates, test tubes and flasks under controlled environmental conditions to create a dense suspension.

The cells are transferred to a *seed tank* for further growth. The seed tank is a small fermentation vessel designed to optimize the growth of the inoculum. The cells from the seed tank are charged to a steam sterilized production *fermentor.* Sterilized nutrients and purified water are added to the vessel to begin the fermentation. During aerobic fermentation, the contents of the fermentor are heated, agitated and aerated by a perforated pipe or *sparger,* maintaining an optimum air flow rate and temperature. After the biochemical reactions are complete, the fermentation broth is filtered to remove the micro-organisms, or *mycelia.* The drug product, which may be present in the filtrate or within the mycelia, is recovered by various steps, such as solvent extraction, precipitation, ion exchange and absorption.

Figure 79.2 • Manufacturing process in the pharmaceutical industry.

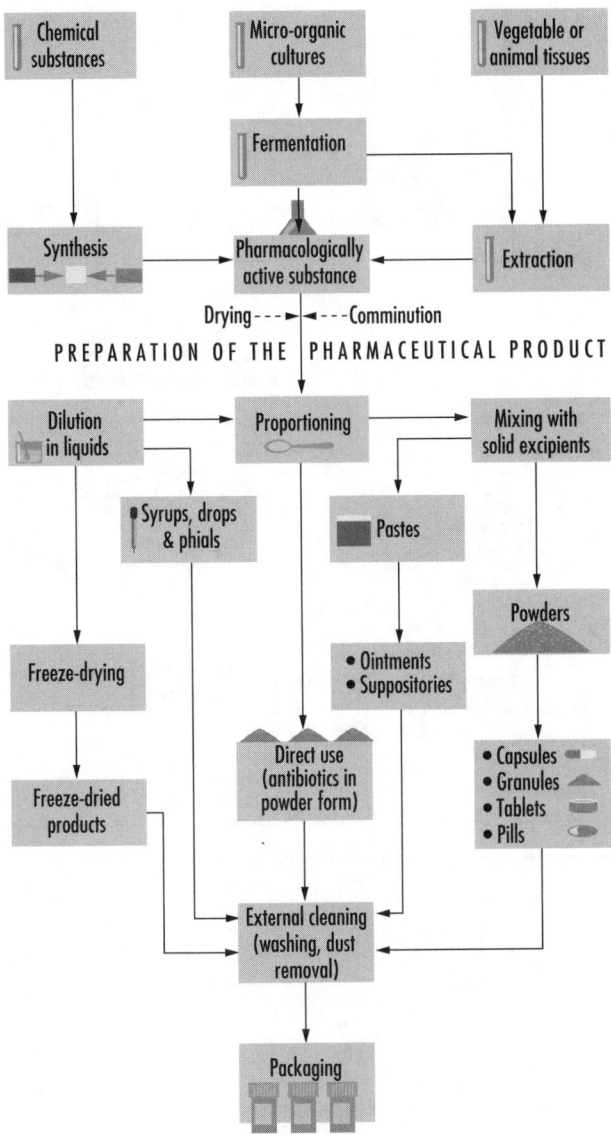

high noise levels. Worker exposures to solvent vapours may occur when recovering or isolating products. Worker exposures to solvents may result from uncontained filtration equipment and fugitive emissions for leaking pumps, valves and manifold stations during extraction and purification steps. Since the isolation and growth of micro-organisms are essential for fermentation, biological hazards are reduced by employing non-pathogenic microbes, maintaining closed process equipment and treating spent broth before its discharge.

Generally, process safety concerns are less important during fermentation than during organic synthesis operations, since fermentation is primarily based upon aqueous chemistry and requires process containment during seed preparation and fermentation. Fire and explosion hazards may arise during solvent extractions; however, the flammability of solvents is reduced by dilution with water in filtration and recovery steps. Safety hazards (i.e., thermal burns and scalding) are posed by the large volumes of pressurized steam and hot water associated with fermentation operations.

Chemical synthesis

Chemical synthesis processes use organic and inorganic chemicals in batch operations to produce drug substances with unique physical and pharmacological properties. Typically, a series of chemical reactions are performed in multi-purpose reactors and the products are isolated by extraction, crystallization and filtration (Kroschwitz 1992). The finished products are usually dried, milled and blended. Organic synthesis plants, process equipment and utilities are comparable in the pharmaceutical and fine chemical industries. A schematic diagram of an organic synthesis process is given in figure 79.4.

Pharmaceutical chemistry is becoming increasingly complex with multi-step processing, where the product from one step becomes a starting material for the next step, until the finished drug product is synthesized. Bulk chemicals which are intermediates of the finished product may be transferred between organic synthesis plants for various technical, financial and legal considerations. Most intermediates and products are produced in a series of batch reactions on a *campaign* basis. Manufacturing processes operate for discrete periods of time, before materials, equipment and utilities are changed to prepare for a new process. Many organic synthesis plants in the pharmaceutical industry are designed to maximize their operating flexibility, due to the diversity and complexity of modern medicinal chemistry. This is achieved by constructing facilities and installing process equipment that can be modified for new manufacturing processes, in addition to their utility requirements.

Multi-purpose reactors are the primary processing equipment in chemical synthesis operations (see figure 79.5). They are reinforced pressure vessels with stainless, glass or metal alloy linings. The nature of chemical reactions and physical properties of materials (e.g., reactive, corrosive, flammable) determine the design, features and construction of reactors. Multi-purpose reactors have external shells and internal coils which are filled with cooling water, steam or chemicals with special heat-transfer properties. The reactor shell is heated or cooled, based upon the requirements of the chemical reactions. Multi-purpose reactors have agitators, baffles and many inlets and outlets connecting them to other process vessels, equipment and bulk chemical supplies. Temperature-, pressure- and weight-sensing instruments are installed to measure and control the chemical process in the reactor. Reactors may be operated at high pressures or low vacuums, depending upon their engineering design and features and the requirements of the process chemistry.

Heat exchangers are connected to reactors to heat or cool the reaction and condense solvent vapours when they are heated above their boiling point, creating a reflux or recycling of the condensed vapours. Air pollution control devices (e.g., scrubbers

Solvents used for extracting the product (table 79.2) generally can be recovered; however, small portions remain in the process wastewater, depending upon their solubility and the design of the process equipment. Precipitation is a method to separate the drug product from the aqueous broth. The drug product is filtered from the broth and extracted from the solid residues. Copper and zinc are common precipitating agents in this process. Ion exchange or adsorption removes the product from the broth by chemical reaction with solid materials, such as resins or activated carbon. The drug product is recovered from the solid phase by a solvent which may be recovered by evaporation.

Worker health and safety

Worker safety hazards may be posed by moving machine parts and equipment; high pressure steam, hot water, heated surfaces and hot workplace environments; corrosive and irritating chemicals; heavy manual handling of materials and equipment; and

Figure 79.3 • Diagram of a fermentation process.

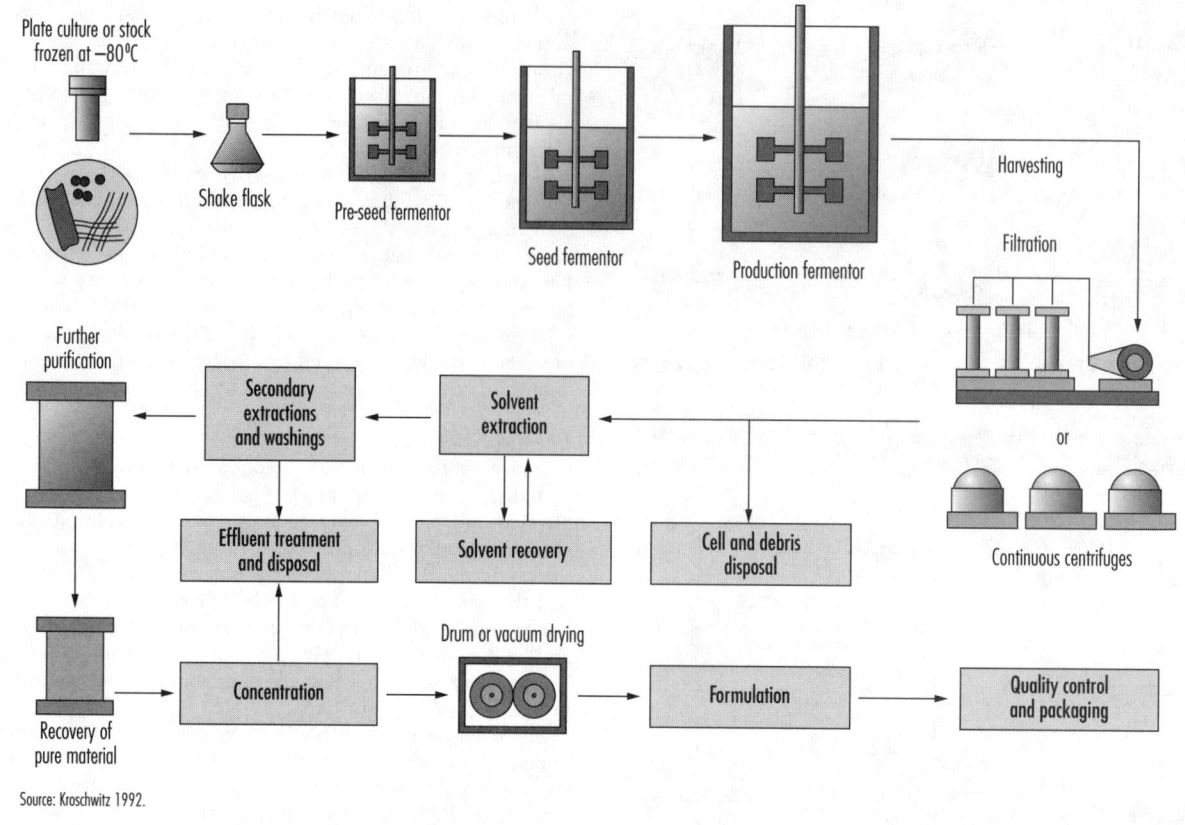

Source: Kroschwitz 1992.

Figure 79.4 • Diagram of an organic synthesis process.

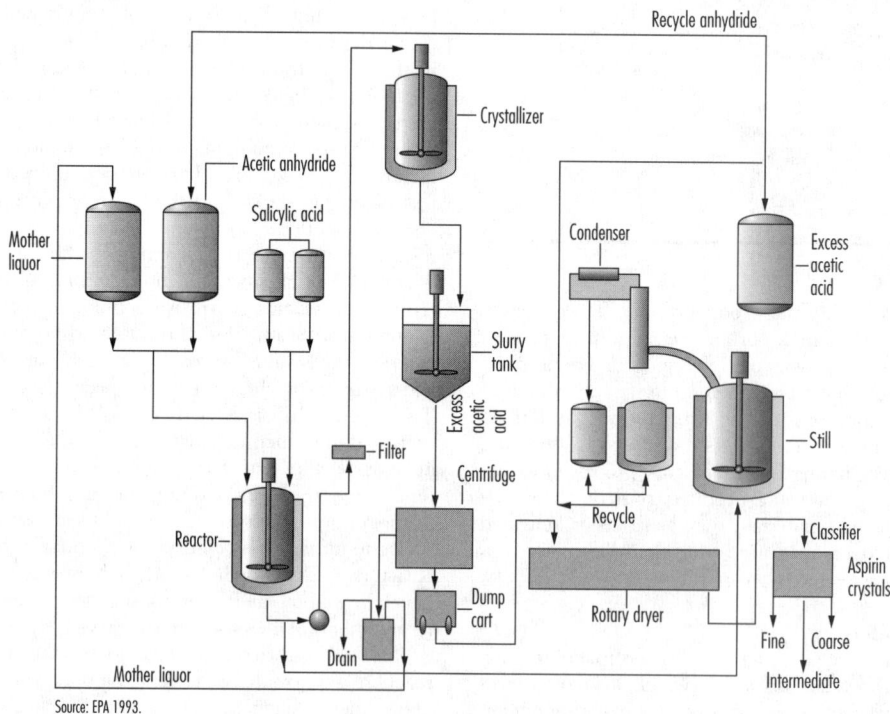

Source: EPA 1993.

Table 79.2 • Solvents used in the pharmaceutical industry.

Solvents	Processes			Solvents	Processes		
Acetone	C	F	B	Formaldehyde	C	F	B
Acetonitrile	C	F	B	Formamide	C		
Ammonia (aqueous)	C	F	B	Furfural	C		
n-Amyl acetate	C	F	B	n-Heptane	C	F	B
Amyl alcohol	C	F	B	n-Hexane	C	F	B
Aniline	C			Isobutyraldehyde	C		
Benzene	C			Isopropanol	C	F	B
2-Butanone (MEK)	C			Isopropyl acetate	C	F	B
n-Butyl acetate	C	F		Isopropyl ether	C		B
n-Butyl alcohol	C	F	B	Methanol	C	F	B
Chlorobenzene	C			Methylamine	C		
Chloroform	C	F	B	Methyl cellosolve	C	F	
Chloromethene	C			Methylene chloride	C	F	B
Cyclohexane	C			Methyl formate	C		
o-Dichlorobenzene (1,2-Dichlorobenzene)	C			Methyl isobutyl ketone (MIBK)	C	F	B
1,2-Dichloroethane	C		B	2-Methylpyridine	C		
Diethylamine	C		B	Petroleum naphtha	C	F	B
Diethyl ether	C		B	Phenol	C	F	B
N,N-Dimethyl acetamide	C			Polyethylene glycol 600	C		
Dimethylamine	C			n-Propanol	C		B
N,N-dimethylaniline	C			Pyridine	C		B
N,N-dimethylformamide	C	F	B	Tetrahydrofuran	C		
Dimethyl sulphoxide	C		B	Toluene	C	F	B
1,4-Dioxane	C		B	Trichlorofluoromethane	C		
Ethanol	C	F	B	Triethylamine	C	F	
Ethyl acetate	C	F	B	Xylenes	C		
Ethylene glycol	C		B				

C = chemical synthesis, F = fermentation, B = biological or natural extraction.
Source: EPA 1995.

and impingers) can be connected to the exhaust vents on process vessels, reducing gas, vapour and dust emissions (EPA 1993). Volatile solvents and toxic chemicals may be released to the workplace or atmosphere, unless they are controlled during the reaction by heat exchangers or air control devices. Some solvents (see table 79.2) and reactants are difficult to condense, absorb or adsorb in air control devices (e.g., methylene chloride and chloroform) due to their chemical and physical properties.

Bulk chemical products are recovered or isolated by separation, purification and filtration operations. Typically, these products are contained in *mother liquors*, as dissolved or suspended solids in a solvent mixture. The mother liquors may be transferred between process vessels or equipment in temporary or permanent pipes or hoses, by pumps, pressurized inert gases, vacuum or gravity. Transferring materials is a concern due to the rates of reaction, critical temperatures or pressures, features of processing equipment and potential for leaks and spills. Special precautions to minimize static electricity are required when processes use or generate flammable gases and liquids. Charging flammable liquids through submerged *dip tubes* and *grounding* and *bonding* con-

ductive materials and maintaining *inert atmospheres* inside process equipment reduce the risk of a fire or explosion (Crowl and Louvar 1990).

Worker health and safety

Many worker health and safety hazards are posed by synthesis operations. They include safety hazards from moving machine parts, pressurized equipment and pipes; heavy manual handling of materials and equipment; steam, hot liquids, heated surfaces and hot workplace environments; confined spaces and hazardous energy sources (e.g., electricity); and high noise levels.

Acute and chronic health risks may result from worker exposures to hazardous chemicals during synthesis operations. Chemicals with acute health effects can damage the eyes and skin, be corrosive or irritating to body tissues, cause sensitization or allergic reactions or be *asphyxiants*, causing suffocation or oxygen deficiency. Chemicals with chronic health effects may cause cancer, or damage the liver, kidneys or lungs or affect the nervous, endocrine, reproductive or other organ systems. Health and safety hazards may be controlled by implementing appropriate control

Figure 79.5 • Diagram of a chemical reactor in organic synthesis.

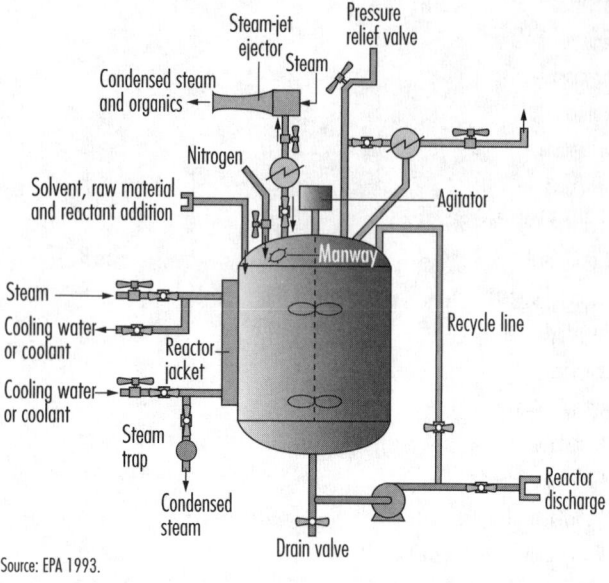

Source: EPA 1993.

Figure 79.6 • Examples of steroidal and non-steroidal oestrogen structure.

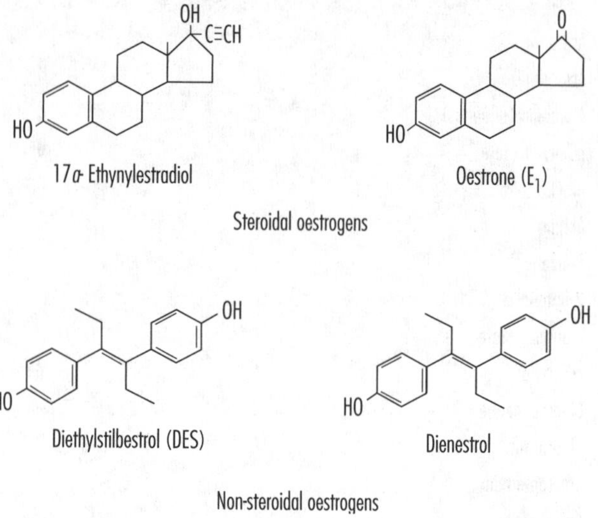

17α- Ethynylestradiol

Oestrone (E₁)

Steroidal oestrogens

Diethylstilbestrol (DES)

Dienestrol

Non-steroidal oestrogens

measures (e.g., process modifications, engineering controls, administrative practices, personal and respiratory protective equipment).

Organic synthesis reactions may create major process safety risks from highly hazardous materials, fire, explosion or uncontrolled chemical reactions which impact the community surrounding the plant. Process safety can be very complex in organic synthesis. It is addressed in several ways: by examining the dynamics of chemical reactions, properties of highly hazardous ma-

terials, design, operation and maintenance of equipment and utilities, training of operating and engineering staff, and emergency preparedness and response of the facility and local community. Technical guidance is available on process hazard analysis and management activities to reduce the risks of chemical synthesis operations (Crowl and Louvar 1990; Kroschwitz 1992).

Biological and natural extraction

Large volumes of natural materials, such as plant and animal matter, may be processed to extract substances which are pharmacologically active (Gennaro 1990; Swarbick and Boylan 1996). In each step of the process, the volumes of materials are reduced by a

Figure 79.7 • Typical oral contraceptive tablet manufacturing process flow.

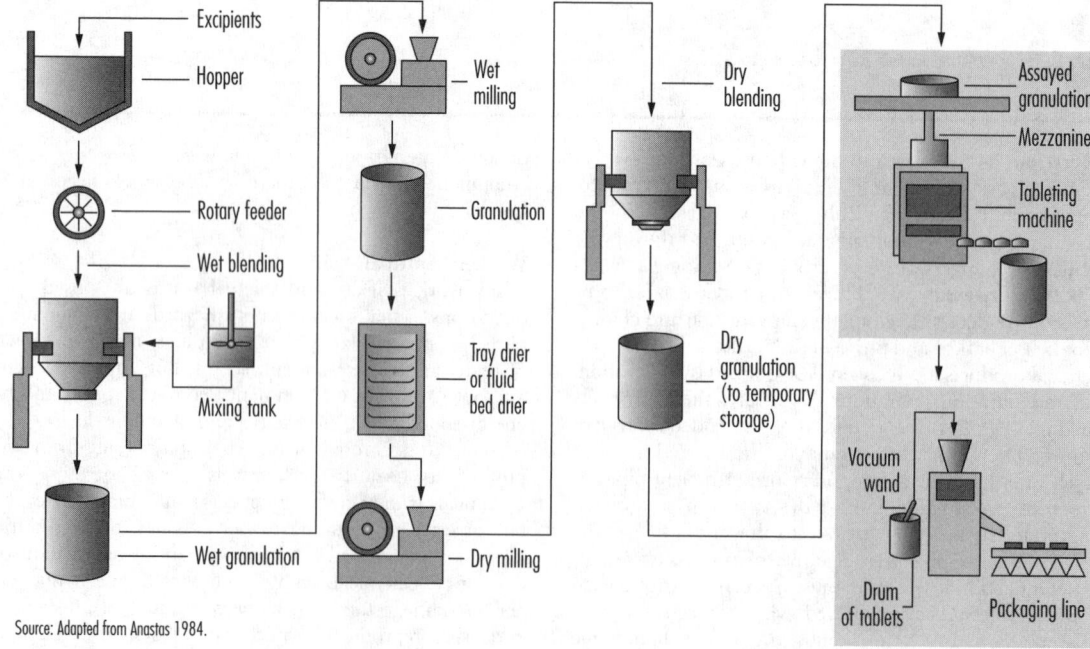

Source: Adapted from Anastas 1984.

Effects of synthetic oestrogens on pharmaceutical workers: A United States example

Background

Oestrogens used in the pharmaceutical industry can generally be classified as natural or synthetic and as steroidal or non-steroidal. All steroidal oestrogens, both natural (e.g., oestrone) and synthetic (e.g., ethynyloestradiol and moestranol) have a typical multi-ring structure, as depicted in figure 79.6. Diethylstilboestrol (DES) and dienoestrol are examples of the non-steroidal oestrogens. The principal uses of oestrogenic compounds are in oral contraceptive tablets and tablets intended for oestrogen replacement therapy. The pure compounds (naturally derived or synthesized) are no longer manufactured in the United States, but are imported.

Manufacturing processes

The following description is a generalized, and composite, description of the manufacturing process used in many US pharmaceutical companies. Specific product processes may not follow the flow exactly as described below; some steps may be absent in some processes, and, in other cases, additional steps may be present that are not described here.

As with most dry-product drugs, pharmaceutical products made from oestrogenic compounds are manufactured in a step-wise batch operation (figure 79.7). The manufacturing steps begin with the assembly and pre-weighing of both active ingredients and excipients (inactive ingredients) in an isolated room under local exhaust ventilation. When needed, the ingredients are moved to a blending room equipped with mechanical blenders. Excipients are usually loaded dry from a hopper above the blender. The active ingredients are almost always dissolved first in an alcohol, and are added manually or are fed through tubing through the side of the blender. The initial blending of the ingredients is done in a wet state. At the end of the wet blending process, the granulation is typically moved to a wet mill, where particles in the mix are reduced to a specific size. The milled granulation is then dried using a fluid bed drier or is tray-dried in ovens designed for the purpose. The dried granulation may or may not undergo the addition of a lubricant before dry-blending and/or dry-milling, depending on the specific product and process. The final granulation, ready to be made into tablets, is then stored in sealed containers. The raw materials and granulation, and sometimes the intermediate products, are typically sampled and assayed by quality-control personnel prior to being moved to the next process step.

When needed, the granulation is moved to a compression room, where it is made into tablets by means of a tablet press. The granulation is typically fed from the storage container (typically a plastic-lined fibre drum or a lined stainless steel container) into the tablet press hopper by gravity or pneumatically by means of a vacuum wand. Formed tablets exit from the machine through tubing at the side, and drop into plastic-lined drums. When filled, the drums are sampled and inspected. After assay by quality-control personnel, the drums are sealed, stored and staged for packaging operations. Some tablets also undergo a coating process, in which layers of edible wax and sometimes sugars are used to seal the tablet.

The tablets are packaged by sealing them in blister packs or bottled, depending on the nature of the product. In this process, the containers of tablets are moved to the packaging area. The tablets may be manually scooped into the packaging machine hopper or fed by means of a vacuum wand. The tablets are then either immediately sealed between layers of aluminium foil and plastic film (blister-packaging) or they are bottled. The blister packs or bottles are then conveyed along a line on which they are inspected and placed in pouches or boxed with appropriate inserts.

Health effects on male and female pharmaceutical workers

Reports of occupational exposures and the effects on males have been relatively few, compared with the considerable literature that exists regarding acute and chronic effects of oestrogens in women as a result of non-occupational exposures. The non-occupational literature is primarily a result of widespread contraceptive and other medical uses of oestrogenic pharmaceuticals (but also environmental pollutants with oestrogenic properties, such as the organochlorines) and focuses particularly on the relationships between that exposure and a variety of human cancers, such as that of the endometrium, cervix and breast in women (Hoover 1980; Houghton and Ritter 1995). In the occupational literature, the hyperoestrogenic syndrome in both male and female workers has been associated with exposures to DES and its derivatives, natural or conjugated oestrogens, hexoestrol and its derivatives and steroidal synthetics such as ethynyloestradiol and moestranol. Shortly after the initiation of commercial production of oestrogens, reports began to surface of their effects, such as gynaecomastia (abnormal enlargement of the breasts in a male) and decreased libido among male workers, and menstrual disorders (increased flow or inter-menstrual spotting) among female workers (Scarff and Smith 1942; Fitzsimons 1944; Klavis 1953; Pagani 1953; Watrous 1947; Watrous and Olsen 1959; Pacynski et al. 1971; Burton and Shumnes 1973; Meyer, Peteet and Harrington 1978; Katzenellenbogen 1956; Dunn 1940; Stoppleman and van Valkenburg 1955; Goldzieher and Goldzieher 1949; Fisk 1950). There have also been a few reports of toxicity syndrome associated with some progoestogenic compounds, including acetoxyprogoesterone (Suciu et al. 1973), and vinyloestrenolone in combination with ethynyloestradiol (Gambini, Farine and Arbosti 1976).

A total of 181 cases of hyperoestrogenism in both males and females (occurring over the period 1940–1978) were recorded and reported by company physicians in 10 pharmaceutical companies (13 plant sites) in the United States (Zaebst, Tanaka and Haring 1980). The 13 plant sites included 9 sites manufacturing primarily oral contraceptives containing various synthetic oestrogens and progoestogens, one firm manufacturing oestrogen replacement pharmaceuticals from natural conjugated oestrogens and one firm manufacturing pharmaceuticals from DES (which had in earlier years also synthesized DES).

Investigators from the US National Institute for Occupational Safety and Health (NIOSH) conducted a pilot industrial hygiene and medical study in 1984 of male and female workers in two plants (Tanaka and Zaebst 1984). Measurable exposures were documented to both moestranol and natural conjugated oestrogens, both inside and outside the respiratory protective equipment used. However, no statistically significant changes in oestrogen-stimulated neurophysins (ESN), corticosteroid-binding globulins (CBG), testosterone, thyroid function, blood-clotting factors, liver function, glucose, blood lipids or gonadotropic hormones were noted in these workers. On physical examination, no adverse physical changes were noted in either male or female workers. However, in the plant using moestranol and norethindrone to manufacture oral contraceptive tablets, serum ethynyloestradiol levels appeared to show possible oestrogen exposure and absorption despite the use of respirators. Inside-respirator air samples obtained at this plant suggested less effective workplace protection factors than expected.

Hyperoestrogenic symptoms in males reported in these studies have included nipple sensitivity (manifested as tingling or tenderness of the nipple) or a feeling of pressure in the breast area and, in some cases, breast hyperplasia and gynaecomastia. Additional subjective symptoms reported by some of the male workers also included decreased libido and/or sexual potency. Findings in females included irregular menstruation, nausea, headaches, breast pain, leucorrhoea (thick, whitish discharge from the vagina or cervical canal) and ankle oedema. There have been no long-term follow-up studies in persons occupationally exposed to oestrogens or progoestogens.

Hazards and control of exposure

One of the most serious hazards in the manufacture of oestrogenic pharmaceuticals is inhalation (and to some extent oral ingestion) of the pure active oestrogenic compound during weighing, assembly and quality-assurance testing. However, substantial inhalation of the dry, blended dust (which contains a low percentage of active ingredient) may also occur to workers during granulation, compression and packaging operations. Skin absorption may also occur, particularly during the wet phases of granulation, since alcohol solutions are used. Quality-control and laboratory personnel are also at risk of exposure while sampling, assaying or otherwise handling pure oestrogenic substances, granulation or tablets. Maintenance personnel can be exposed while cleaning, repairing or inspecting mixers, hoppers, mills, vacuum lines and ventilation systems, or changing filters. NIOSH investigators have conducted an in-depth evaluation of engineering controls which have been used during the manufacturing of oral contraceptive tablets (Anastas 1984). This report provides a detailed review of controls and an evaluation of their effectiveness for granulation, milling, material transfers, powder and tablet feed equipment, and general and local exhaust ventilation systems.

The four main elements of hazard control employed in plants using oestrogenic pharmaceuticals are:

1. *Engineering controls.* These include isolation of processing equipment rooms, control of air flow within a facility from least contaminated areas to most contaminated, local exhaust ventilation at any open transfer points, enclosure of machines, sealed process streams and enclosed powder feed systems. Frequently, implementation of engineering controls, such as general or local exhaust ventilation, is complicated by the fact that good manufacturing regulations (such as those required by the US Food and Drug Administration), which are designed to ensure a safe and effective product, conflict with the best health and safety practices. For example, pressure differentials achieved by general ventilation systems, designed to protect workers outside the hazardous process, conflict with the regulatory requirement to prevent contamination of the product by dust or contaminants external to the process. Because it eliminates direct contact between people and the hazardous contaminants, process or equipment containment is often the best option.

2. *Good work practices.* These include separate clean and contaminated locker rooms separated by showers, changes of clothing, washing or showering before exiting contaminated areas and, where it is feasible and appropriate, systematic rotations of all workers between exposed and non-exposed areas. Appropriate training and education regarding the hazards of oestrogens, and good work practices, are an integral part of an effective worker protection programme. The best engineering controls and per-

sonal protective equipment can be defeated if the operators are not knowledgeable about the hazards and controls, and if they are not properly trained to take advantage of the controls and to use the personal protective equipment provided.

3. *Aggressive environmental and medical monitoring of exposed workers.* In addition to normally administered physicals, routine screening should, at a minimum, include review for symptoms (breast tenderness, libido change and so on), examinations of the breast and axillary nodes and measurement of areolae. The screening frequency will vary, depending on the severity of the exposure hazard. Of course, medical screening and monitoring (e.g., physical exams, health questionnaires or testing of body fluids) should be implemented with the utmost sensitivity to workers' overall welfare, their health and their privacy, since their cooperation and assistance in such a programme are critical to its success. Monitoring of worker exposures to the active oestrogenic or progoestogenic substances should be done regularly and should include not only breathing-zone sampling for air contaminants, but also evaluations of skin contamination and the effectiveness of personal protective equipment.

4. *Use of appropriate personal protective equipment:* Personal protective equipment typically includes disposable or launderable coveralls; separate steroid-area shoes, socks, underclothing and rubber gloves; and effective respirators tailored to the degree of hazard. In the most hazardous areas, air-supplied respiratory protective equipment and impervious (to dusts and/or organic solvents) suits may be required.

Because of the potency of the oestrogenic substances, particularly the synthetic ones such as moestranol and ethynyloestradiol, all of these measures are needed to control exposures adequately. The use of personal protective equipment alone may not provide complete protection. Primary reliance should be placed on controlling exposures at the source, by process containment and by isolation.

Monitoring methods

Both high-performance liquid chromatography and radio-immunoassay procedures have been used to determine oestrogens or progoestogens in environmental samples. Serum samples have been analysed for the exogenous active compound, its metabolite (e.g., ethynyloestradiol is the main metabolite of moestranol), oestrogen-stimulated neurophysins or any of a number of other hormones (e.g., gonadotropic hormones and CBGs) considered appropriate for the specific process and hazard. Airborne monitoring usually includes breathing-zone personal monitoring, but area sampling can be useful in detecting departures from expected values over time. Personal monitoring has the advantages of detecting breakdowns or problems with processing equipment, personal protective equipment or ventilation systems and can provide an earlier warning of exposure. Biological monitoring, on the other hand, can detect exposures which may be missed by environmental monitoring (e.g., skin absorption or ingestion). In general, good practice combines both environmental and biological sampling to protect workers.

Dennis D. Zaebst

series of batch processes, until the final drug product is obtained. Typically, processes are performed in campaigns lasting a few weeks, until the desired quantity of finished product is obtained. Solvents are used to remove insoluble fats and oils, thereby extracting the finished drug substance. The pH (acidity) of the extraction solution and waste products can be adjusted by neutralizing them with strong acids and bases. Metal compounds frequently serve as precipitating agents, and phenol compounds as disinfectants.

Worker health and safety

Some workers may develop allergic and/or skin irritation from handling certain plants. Animal matter may be contaminated with infectious organisms unless appropriate precautions are taken. Workers may be exposed to solvents and corrosive chemicals during biological and natural extraction operations. Fire and explosion risks are posed by storing, handling, processing and recovering flammable liquids. Moving mechanical parts; hot steam, water, surfaces and workplaces; and high noise levels are risks to worker safety.

Process safety issues are often reduced by the large volumes of plant or animal materials, and smaller scale of solvent extraction activities. Fire and explosion hazards, and worker exposures to solvents or corrosive or irritating chemicals may occur during extraction and recovery operations, depending upon the specific chemistry and containment of process equipment.

Pharmaceutical manufacturing of dosage forms

Drug substances are converted into dosage-form products before they are dispensed or administered to humans or animals. Active drug substances are mixed with pharmaceutical necessities, such as binders, fillers, flavouring and bulking agents, preservatives and antioxidants. These ingredients may be dried, milled, blended, compressed and granulated to achieve the desired properties before they are manufactured as a final formulation. Tablets and capsules are very common oral dosage forms; another common form is sterile liquids for injection or ophthalmic application. Figure 79.8 illustrates typical unit operations for manufacturing of pharmaceutical dosage-form products.

Pharmaceutical blends may be compressed by wet granulation, direct compression or slugging to obtain the desired physical properties, before their formulation as a finished drug product. In *wet granulation*, the active ingredients and excipients are wetted with aqueous or solvent solutions to produce course granules with enlarged particle sizes. The granules are dried, mixed with lubricants (e.g., magnesium stearate), *disintegrants* or binders, then compressed into tablets. During *direct compression*, a metal die holds a measured amount of the drug blend while a punch compresses the tablet. Drugs that are not sufficiently stable for wet granulation or cannot be directly compressed are slugged. *Slugging* or *dry granulation* blends and compresses relatively large tablets which are ground and screened to a desired mesh size, then recompressed into the final tablet. Blended and granulated materials may also be produced in capsule form. Hard gelatin capsules are dried, trimmed, filled and joined on capsule-filling machines.

Liquids may be produced as sterile solutions for injection into the body or administration to the eyes; liquids, suspensions and syrups for oral ingestion; and tinctures for application on the skin (Gennaro 1990). Highly controlled environmental conditions, contained process equipment and purified raw materials are required for manufacturing sterile liquids to prevent microbiological and particulate contamination (Cole 1990; Swarbick and Boylan 1996). Facility utilities (e.g., ventilation, steam and water), process equipment and workplace surfaces must be cleaned and maintained to prevent and minimize contamination. Water at high temperatures and pressures is used to destroy and filter bacteria and other contaminants from the sterile water supply when mak-

ing solutions for injection. *Parenteral* liquids are injected by intradermal, intramuscular or intravenous administration into the body. These liquids are sterilized by dry or moist heat under high pressure with bacteria-retaining filters. Although liquid solutions for oral or topical use do not require sterilization, solutions to be administered to the eyes (ophthalmic) must be sterilized. Oral liquids are prepared by mixing the active drug substances with a solvent or preservative to inhibit mold and bacterial growth. Liquid suspensions and emulsions are produced by colloid mills and homogenizers, respectively. Creams and ointments are prepared by blending or compounding active ingredients with petrolatum, heavy greases or emollients before packaging in metal or plastic tubes.

Worker health and safety

Worker health and safety risks during pharmaceutical manufacturing are created by moving machine parts (e.g., exposed gears, belts and shafts) and hazardous energy sources (e.g., electrical, pneumatic, thermal, etc.); manual handling of material and equipment; high-pressure steam, hot water and heated surfaces; flammable and corrosive liquids; and high noise levels. Worker exposures to airborne dusts may occur during dispensing, drying, milling and blending operations. Exposure to pharmaceutical

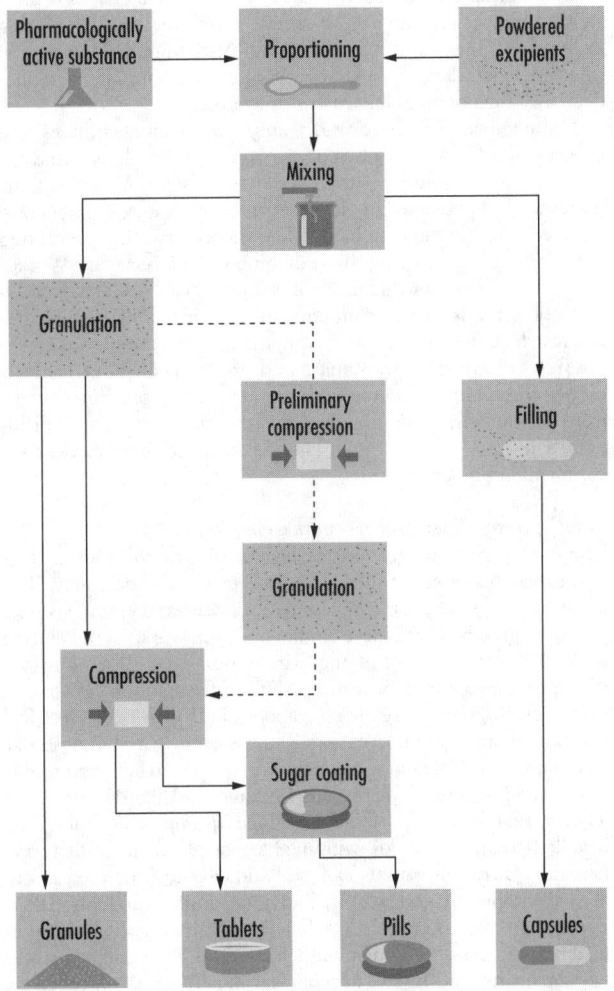

Figure 79.8 • Pharmaceutical manufacturing of dosage-form products.

products is a particular concern when mixtures containing high proportions of active drug substances are handled or processed. Wet granulation, compounding and coating operations may create high worker exposures to solvent vapours.

Process safety issues primarily relate to the risks of fire or explosion during pharmaceutical manufacturing of dosage forms. Many of these operations (e.g., granulation, blending, compounding and drying) use flammable liquids, which may create flammable or explosive atmospheres. Since some pharmaceutical dusts are highly explosive, their physical properties should be examined before they are processed. Fluid bed drying, milling and slugging are a particular concern when they involve potentially explosive materials. Engineering measures and safe work practices reduce the risks of explosive dusts and flammable liquids (e.g., vapour- and dust-tight electrical equipment and utilities, grounding and bonding of equipment, sealed containers with pressure relief and inert atmospheres).

Control measures

Fire and explosion prevention and protection; process containment of hazardous substances, machine hazards and high noise levels; dilution and local exhaust ventilation (LEV); use of respirators (e.g., dust and organic vapour masks and, in some cases, powered air-purifying respirators or air-supplied masks and suits) and personal protective equipment (PPE); and worker training on workplace hazards and safe work practices are workplace control measures applicable during all of the various pharmaceutical manufacturing operations described below. Specific issues involve substituting less hazardous materials whenever possible during drug development and manufacturing. Also, minimizing material transfers, unsealed or open processing and sampling activities decreases the potential for worker exposures.

The engineering design and features of facilities, utilities and process equipment can prevent environmental pollution and reduce worker exposures to hazardous substances. Modern pharmaceutical manufacturing facilities and process equipment are reducing environmental, health and safety risks by preventing pollution and improving the containment of hazards. Worker health and safety and quality control objectives are achieved by improving the isolation, containment and cleanliness of pharmaceutical facilities and process equipment. Preventing worker exposures to hazardous substances and pharmaceutical products is highly compatible with the concurrent need to prevent workers from accidentally contaminating raw materials and finished products. Safe work procedures and good manufacturing practices are complementary activities.

Facility design and process-engineering issues

The engineering design and features of pharmaceutical facilities and process equipment influences worker health and safety. The construction materials, process equipment and housekeeping practices greatly affect the cleanliness of the workplace. Dilution and LEV systems control fugitive vapours and dust emissions during manufacturing operations. Fire and explosion prevention and protection measures (e.g., vapour- and dust-tight electrical equipment and utilities, extinguishing systems, fire and smoke detectors and emergency alarms) are needed when flammable liquids and vapours are present. Storage and handling systems (e.g., storage vessels, portable containers, pumps and piping) are installed to move liquids within pharmaceutical manufacturing facilities. Hazardous solids can be handled and processed in enclosed equipment and vessels, individual bulk containers (IBCs) and sealed drums and bags. The isolation or containment of facilities, process equipment and hazardous materials promotes worker health and safety. Mechanical hazards are controlled by installing barrier guards on moving machine parts.

The process equipment and utilities may be controlled by manual or automatic means. In manual plants, *chemical operators* read instruments and control process equipment and utilities near the process equipment. In automated plants, the process equipment, utilities and control devices are controlled by distributed systems, allowing them to be operated from a remote location such as a control room. Manual operations are often employed when materials are charged or transferred, products are discharged and packaged and when maintenance is performed or nonroutine conditions arise. Written instructions should be prepared, to describe *standard operating procedures* as well as worker health and safety hazards and control measures.

Verification of workplace controls

Workplace control measures are evaluated periodically to protect workers from health and safety hazards and minimize environmental pollution. Many manufacturing processes and pieces of equipment are validated in the pharmaceutical industry to ensure the quality of products (Cole 1990; Gennaro 1990; Swarbrick and Boylan 1996). Similar validation practices may be implemented for workplace control measures to ensure that they are effective and reliable. Periodically, process instructions and safe work practices are revised. Preventive maintenance activities identify when process and engineering equipment may fail, thereby precluding problems. Training and supervision informs and educates workers about environmental, health and safety hazards, reinforcing safe work practices and the use of respirators and personal protective equipment. Inspection programmes examine whether safe workplace conditions and work practices are maintained. This includes inspecting respirators and to ensure they are properly selected, worn and maintained by workers. Audit programmes review the management systems for identifying, evaluating and controlling environmental, health and safety hazards.

Pharmaceutical unit operations

Weighing and dispensing

Weighing and dispensing of solids and liquids is a very common activity throughout the pharmaceutical industry (Gennaro 1990). Usually workers dispense materials by hand-scooping solids and pouring or pumping liquids. Weighing and dispensing are often performed in a warehouse during bulk chemical production or in a pharmacy during pharmaceutical dosage-form manufacturing. Due to the likelihood of spills, leaks and fugitive emissions during weighing and dispensing, proper workplace control measures are necessary to protect workers. Weighing and dispensing should be performed in a partitioned workplace area with good dilution ventilation. The work surfaces in areas where materials are weighed and dispensed should be smooth and sealed, permitting their proper cleaning. LEV with backdraft or sidedraft hoods prevents the release of air contaminants when weighing and dispensing dusty solids or volatile liquids (Cole 1990). Weighing and dispensing highly toxic materials may require additional control measures such as laminar ventilation hoods or isolation devices (e.g., glove boxes or glove bags) (Naumann et al. 1996).

Charging and discharging solids and liquids

Solids and liquids are frequently charged and discharged from containers and process equipment in pharmaceutical manufacturing operations (Gennaro 1990). Charging and discharging of materials are often performed manually by workers; however, other methods are employed (e.g., gravity, mechanical or pneumatic transfer systems). Contained process equipment, transfer systems and engineering controls prevent worker exposures during charging and discharging of highly hazardous materials. Gravity charging from enclosed containers and vacuum, pressure and pumping systems eliminate fugitive emissions during charging and discharging operations. LEV with flanged inlets captures fugitive dusts and vapours which are released at open transfer points.

Liquid separations

Liquids are separated based upon their physical properties (e.g., density, solubility and miscibility) (Kroschwitz 1992). Liquid separations are commonly performed during bulk chemical production and pharmaceutical manufacturing operations. Hazardous liquids should be transferred, processed and separated in closed vessels and piping systems to reduce worker exposures to liquid spills and airborne vapours. Eyewashes and safety showers should be located near operations where hazardous liquids are transferred, processed or separated. Spill control measures and fire and explosion prevention and protection are needed when using flammable liquids.

Transferring liquids

Liquids are often transferred between storage vessels, containers and process equipment during pharmaceutical manufacturing operations. Ideally, facility and manufacturing processes are designed to minimize the need for transferring hazardous materials, thereby decreasing the chance of spills and worker exposures. Liquids may be transferred between process vessels and equipment through *manifold stations*, areas where many pipe flanges are located close together (Kroschwitz 1992). This allows temporary connections to be made between piping systems. Spills, leaks and vapour emissions may occur at manifold stations; therefore proper gaskets and tight seals on hoses and pipes are needed to prevent environmental pollution and workplace releases. Drainage systems with sealed tanks or sumps capture spilled liquids so they can be reclaimed and recovered. Sealed vessels and containers and piping systems are highly desirable when transferring large volumes of liquids. Special precautions should be taken when using inert gases to pressurize transfer lines or process equipment, since this may increase the release of volatile organic compounds (VOCs) and hazardous air pollutants. Recirculation or condensation of exhaust gases and vapours reduces air pollution.

Filtration

Solids and liquids are separated during filtration operations. Filters have different designs and features with varying containment and control of liquids and vapours (Kroschwitz 1992; Perry 1984). When open filters are used for hazardous materials, workers may be exposed to liquids, wet solids, vapours and aerosols during loading and unloading operations. Closed process equipment can be used to filter highly hazardous materials, reducing vapour emissions and preventing worker exposures (see figure 79.9). Filtration should be performed in areas with spill control and good dilution and LEV. Volatile solvent vapours can be exhausted through vents on sealed process equipment and controlled by air emissions devices (e.g., condensers, scrubbers and adsorbers).

Compounding

Solids and liquids are mixed in compounding operations to produce solutions, suspensions, syrups, ointments and pastes. Contained process equipment and transfer systems are recommended when compounding highly hazardous materials (Kroschwitz 1992; Perry 1984). Buffering agents, detergents and germicides that are neutralizing, cleaning and biocidal agents may be hazardous to workers. Eyewashes and safety showers reduce injuries, if workers accidentally contact corrosive or irritating substances. Due to the wet surfaces in compounding areas, workers need to be protected from electrical hazards of equipment and utilities. Thermal hazards are posed by steam and hot water during com-

Figure 79.9 • A sparkler filter.

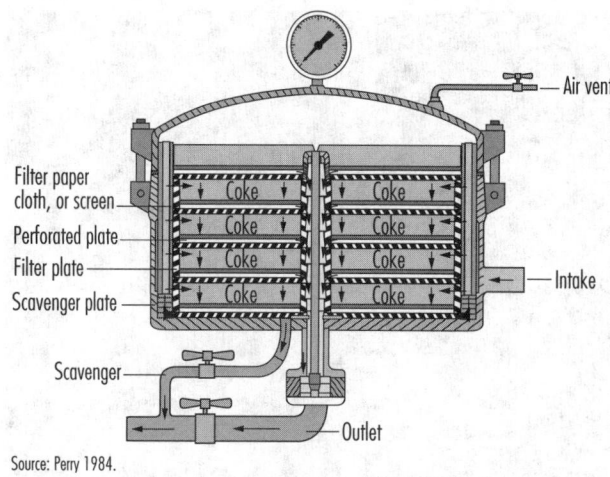

Source: Perry 1984.

pounding and cleaning activities. Worker injuries from burns and falls are prevented by installing insulation on hot surfaces and maintaining dry non-slip floors.

Granulation

Dry and wet solids are granulated to change their physical properties. Granulators have different designs and features with varying containment and control of mechanical hazards and airborne dusts and vapours (Perry 1984; Swarbick and Boylan 1996). Enclosed granulators can be vented to air-control devices, reducing emissions of solvent vapours or dusts to the workplace and atmosphere (see figure 79.10). Material-handling concerns arise when loading and unloading granulators. Mechanical equipment (e.g., elevated platforms, lift tables and pallet jacks) assists workers to perform heavy manual tasks. Eyewashes and safety showers are needed, if workers accidentally contact solvents or irritating dusts.

Figure 79.10 • A high steam granulator.

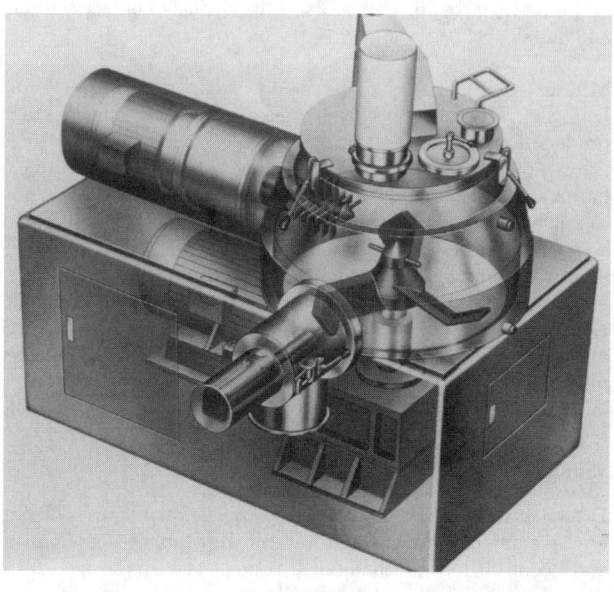

Figure 79.11 • A rotary vacuum dryer.

Glatt Air Techniques, Inc.

Drying

Water- or solvent-wet solids are dried during many pharmaceutical manufacturing operations. Dryers have different designs and features with varying containment and control of vapours and dusts (see figure 79.11). Flammable solvent vapours and explosive airborne dusts may create flammable or explosive atmospheres; explosion relief venting is particularly important on contained dryers. Dilution and LEV reduces the risk of fire or explosion, in addition to controlling worker exposures to solvent vapours when handling wet cakes, or to airborne dusts when unloading dried products. Heavy material handling may be involved when loading or unloading dryer trays, bins or containers (see figure 79.12). Mechanical equipment (e.g., drum jacks, lifts and work platforms) assists these manual tasks. Eyewashes and safety showers should be located nearby, in case workers accidentally contact solvents and dusts.

Milling

Dry solids are milled to change their particle characteristics and produce free-flowing powders. Mills have different designs and features with varying containment and control of mechanical hazards and airborne dusts (Kroschwitz 1992; Perry 1984). Prior to milling materials, their physical properties and hazards should be reviewed or tested. Explosion prevention and protection measures involve installing dust-tight electrical equipment and utilities, grounding and bonding equipment and accessories to eliminate electrostatic sparking, installing safety relief valves on enclosed mills, and constructing blast relief panels in walls. These measures may be necessary due to the explosivity of some drug substances and excipients, high dust levels and energies associated with milling operations.

Blending

Dry solids are blended to produce homogeneous mixtures. Blenders have different designs and features with varying containment and control of mechanical hazards and airborne dusts (Kroschwitz 1992; Perry 1984). Worker exposures to drug sub-

stances, excipients and blends may occur when loading and unloading blending equipment. LEV with flanged inlets reduces fugitive dust emissions during blending. Heavy material handling may be required when charging and discharging solids from blenders. Mechanical equipment (e.g., work platforms, hoists and drum and pallet jacks) reduces the physical demands of heavy material handling.

Compression

Dry solids are compressed or slugged to compact them, changing their particle properties. Compression equipment has different designs and features with varying containment and control of mechanical hazards and airborne dusts (Gennaro 1990; Swarbick and Boylan 1996). Compression equipment may pose serious mechanical hazards if inadequately guarded. High noise levels may also be produced by compression and slugging operations. Enclosing impact sources, isolating vibrating equipment, rotating workers and using hearing-protective devices (e.g., ear muffs and plugs) reduce the impact of noise exposures.

Solid dosage-form manufacturing

Tablets and capsules are the most common oral dosage forms. Compressed or moulded tablets contain mixtures of drug substances and excipients. These tablets may be uncoated or coated with solvent mixtures or aqueous solutions. Capsules are soft or hard gelatin shells. Tablet presses (see figure 79.13), tablet-coating equipment and capsule-filling machines have different designs and features with varying containment and control of mechanical hazards and airborne dusts (Cole 1990). Workers may be exposed to solvent vapours when spray-coating tablets. Modern tablet-coating equipment is highly contained; however, LEV can be installed in older open coating pans to control fugitive solvent vapours. Tablet-coating equipment can be vented to air emission devices to control VOCs from the process (see figure 79.14). Whenever possible, recovered solvents should be reused by the process or aqueous mixtures substituted for solvent mixtures for tablet coating. Modern tablet presses and capsule-filling machines are enclosed by interlocked panels, reducing the hazards of fast-moving parts, high noise levels and dust emissions during their

Figure 79.12 • A vacuum shelf dryer.

Source: EPA 1993.

Figure 79.13 • Tablet press with load hopper and spiral dust pickups for product recovery.

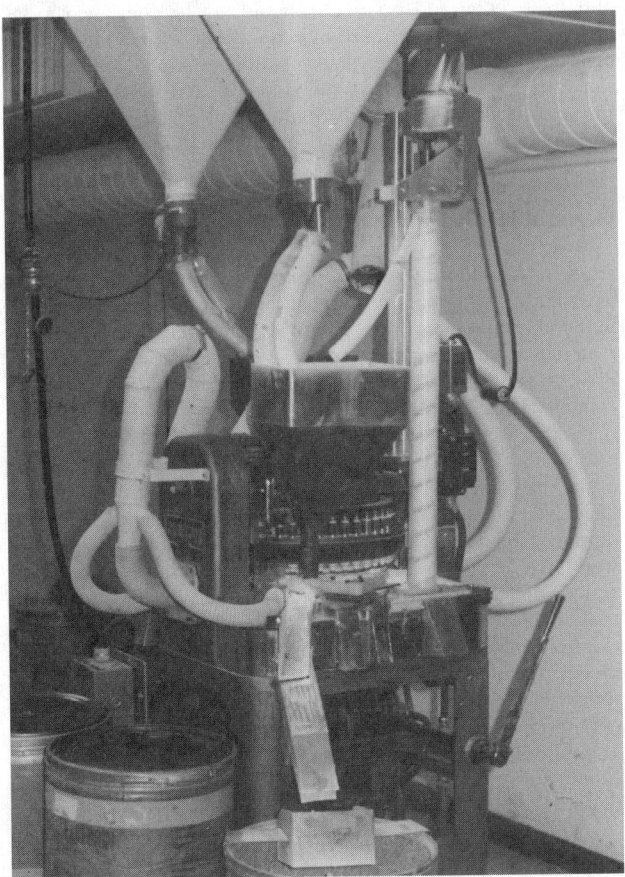

Figure 79.14 • A tablet coating machine.

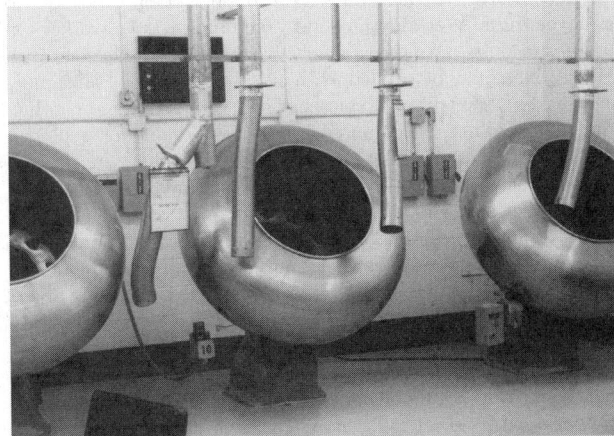

Source: Perry 1984.

practices and appropriate emergency response. Gas sterilization chambers should be fully evacuated under vacuum and purged with air to minimize fugitive workplace emissions before sterilized goods are removed. Gas emissions from sterilization chambers can be vented to air control devices (e.g., carbon adsorption or catalytic converters) to reduce atmospheric emissions. Occupational hygiene monitoring measures worker exposures to chemical germicides and sterilizing gases, helping to assess the adequacy of control measures. Safety hazards involve high-pressure steam and hot water, moving machine parts in washing, filling, capping and packaging equipment, high noise levels and repetitive manual tasks.

Cleaning and maintenance activities
Non-routine tasks may occur when cleaning, repairing and maintaining equipment, utilities and workplaces. Although unique hazards may arise during non-routine tasks, recurring health and safety concerns are encountered. Workplace and equipment surfaces may be contaminated by hazardous materials and drug substances, requiring them to be cleaned before unprotected workers conduct servicing or maintenance work. Cleaning is per-

operation. Hearing-protective devices can reduce worker noise exposures during tablet and capsule operations.

Sterile manufacturing
Sterile products are manufactured in pharmaceutical manufacturing plants with modular design (see figure 79.15), clean workplace and equipment surfaces, and high efficiency particulate air (HEPA) filtered ventilation systems (Cole 1990; Gennaro 1990). The principles and practices of controlling contamination in sterile liquid manufacturing are similar to those in the microelectronics industry. Workers wear protective clothing to prevent them from contaminating products during sterile manufacturing operations. Sterile pharmaceutical technologies to control contamination involve freeze-drying products, using liquid germicides and sterilizing gases, installing laminar flow ventilation, isolating modules with differential air pressures and containing manufacturing and filling equipment.

Chemical hazards are posed by toxic germicides (e.g., formaldehyde and glutaraldehyde) and sterilizing gases (i.e., ethylene oxide). Whenever possible, less hazardous agents should be selected (e.g., alcohols, ammonium compounds). Sterilization of raw materials and equipment may be performed by high-pressure steam or toxic gases (i.e., diluted ethylene oxide gas mixtures) (Swarbick and Boylan 1996). Sterilization vessels can be located in separate areas with remote instrument and control systems, nonrecirculated air and LEV to extract toxic gas emissions. Workers should be trained on standard operating instructions, safe work

Figure 79.15 • Diagram of a sterile liquid manufacturing facility.

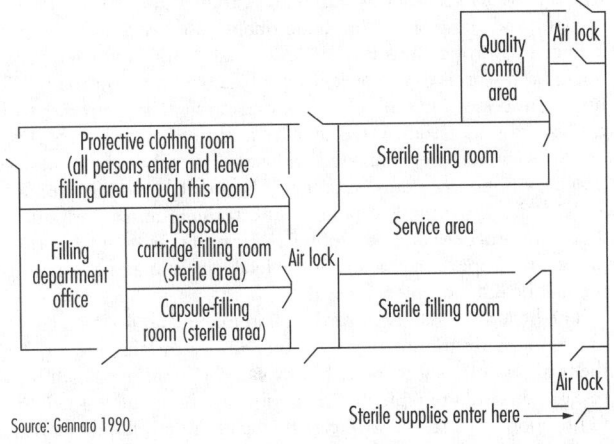

Source: Gennaro 1990.

formed by washing or wiping liquids and sweeping or vacuuming dusts. Dry sweeping and blowing solids with compressed air are not recommended, since they create high worker exposures to airborne dusts. Wet mopping and vacuuming reduce worker exposures to dusts during cleaning activities. Vacuum cleaners with HEPA filters may be needed when cleaning hazardous substances and high-potency drugs. Explosion-proof equipment and conductive materials may be required in vacuum systems for explosive dusts. Eyewashes and safety showers and PPE reduce the effect of workers' accidental contact with corrosive and irritating detergents and cleaning liquids.

Hazardous mechanical, electrical, pneumatic or thermal energy may need to be released or controlled before equipment and utilities are serviced, repaired or maintained. Contract workers may perform special production or engineering tasks in pharmaceutical plants without adequate training on safety precautions. Careful supervision of contract workers is important, so they do not violate safety rules or perform work that creates a fire, explosion or other serious health and safety hazards. Special contractor safety programmes are required when working with highly hazardous materials (e.g., toxic, reactive, flammable or explosive) and processes (e.g., exothermic or high pressure) in bulk pharmaceutical and dosage-form manufacturing facilities.

Packaging

Pharmaceutical packaging operations are performed with a series of integrated machines and repetitive manual tasks (Gennaro 1990; Swarbick and Boylan 1996). Finished dosage-form products may be packaged in many different types of containers (e.g., plastic or glass bottles, foil blister packs, pouches or sachets, tubes and sterile vials). The mechanical equipment fills, caps, labels, cartons and packs the finished products in shipping containers. Worker proximity to packaging equipment necessitates barrier guarding on moving machine parts, accessible control switches and emergency stop cables and employee training on machine hazards and safe work practices. Enclosure and isolation of equipment reduces sound and vibration levels in packaging areas. Use of hearing-protective devices (e.g., ear muffs and plugs) reduces worker exposures to noise. Good industrial design promotes the productivity, comfort and safety of employees, by addressing ergonomic hazards from poor body postures, material handling and highly repetitive tasks.

Laboratory operations

Laboratory operations in the pharmaceutical industry are diverse. They may pose biological, chemical and physical hazards, depending upon the specific agents, operations, equipment and work practices employed. Major distinctions exist between labs which conduct scientific research and product and process development and those which evaluate quality assurance and control activities (Swarbick and Boylan 1996). Lab workers may conduct scientific research to discover drug substances, develop manufacturing processes for bulk chemical and dosage-form products or analyze raw materials, intermediates and finished products. Lab activities should be evaluated individually, although good lab practices apply to many situations (National Research Council 1981). Clearly defined responsibilities, training and information, safe work practices and control measures and emergency response plans are important means for effectively managing environmental, health and safety hazards.

The health and safety hazards of flammable and toxic materials are reduced by minimizing their inventories in labs and storing them in separate cabinets. Lab assays and operations which may release air contaminants can be performed in ventilated exhaust fume hoods to protect workers. Biological safety hoods provide downward and inward laminar flow, preventing the release of

micro-organisms (Gennaro 1990; Swarbick and Boylan 1996). Worker training and information describes the hazards of lab work, safe work practices and proper emergency response to fires and spills. Food and beverages should not be consumed in lab areas. Lab safety is enhanced by requiring supervisors to approve and manage highly hazardous operations. Good lab practices separate, treat and dispose of biological and chemical wastes. Physical hazards (e.g., radiation and electromagnetic energy sources) are often certified and operated, according to specific regulations.

General Health and Safety Hazards

Ergonomics and material handling

The materials shipped, stored, handled, processed and packaged in the pharmaceutical industry range from large quantities of raw materials to small packages containing pharmaceutical products. Raw materials for bulk chemical production are shipped in bulk containers (e.g., tank trucks, rail cars), metal and fibre drums, reinforced paper and plastic bags. Pharmaceutical production uses smaller quantities of raw materials due to the reduced scale of the operations. Material-handling devices (e.g., fork-lift trucks, pallet lifts, vacuum hoists and drum jacks) assist material handling during warehousing and production operations. Heavy manual work may create ergonomic risks when moving materials and equipment if mechanical devices are not available. Good industrial engineering and facility management practices reduce injuries from material handling by improving the design and features of equipment and the workplace and decreasing the size and weight of containers (Cole 1990). Engineering control measures (e.g., ergonomic design of tools, materials and equipment) and administrative practices (e.g., rotating workers, providing worker training) reduce the risks of cumulative trauma injuries during highly repetitive production and packaging operations.

Machine guarding and control of hazardous energy

Unguarded moving machine parts in pharmaceutical manufacturing and packaging equipment create mechanical hazards. Exposed "crush and nip points" in open equipment may seriously injure workers. Mechanical hazards are exacerbated by the large numbers and different designs of equipment, crowded workplace conditions and frequent interactions between workers and equipment. Interlocked guards, control switches, emergency stop devices and operator training are important means of reducing mechanical hazards. Loose hair, long-sleeved clothing, jewellery or other objects may become trapped in equipment. Routine inspection and repair activities identify and control mechanical hazards during production and packaging operations. Hazardous electrical, pneumatic and thermal energy must be released or controlled before working on active equipment and utilities. Workers are protected from sources of hazardous energy by implementing lockout/tagout procedures.

Noise exposures

High sound levels may be generated by manufacturing equipment and utilities (e.g., compressed air, vacuum sources and ventilation systems). Due to the enclosed design of pharmaceutical workplace modules, workers are often located close to machines during manufacturing and packaging operations. Workers observe and interact with production and packaging equipment, thereby increasing their exposure to noise. Engineering methods reduce sound levels by modifying, enclosing and dampening noise sources. Employee rotation and use of hearing-protective devices (e.g., ear muffs and plugs) reduce workers' exposure to high noise levels. Comprehensive hearing conservation programmes identify noise sources, reduce workplace sound levels, and train workers on the hazards of noise exposure and proper use of hearing-protective devices. Noise monitoring and medical surveillance (i.e., audiometry) assess worker exposures to noise and their resulting loss of hearing. This helps to identify noise problems and evaluate the adequacy of corrective measures.

Solvent vapour and potent compound exposures

Special concerns may arise when workers are exposed to toxic solvent vapours and potent drugs as airborne dusts. Worker exposures to solvent vapours and potent compounds may occur during various manufacturing operations, which need to be identified, evaluated and controlled to ensure that workers are protected. Engineering controls are the preferred means of controlling these exposures, due to their inherent effectiveness and reliability (Cole 1990; Naumann et al. 1996). Enclosed process equipment and material handling systems prevent worker exposures, while LEV and PPE supplement these measures. Increased facility and process containment is needed for controlling highly toxic solvents (e.g., benzene, chlorinated hydrocarbons, ketones) and potent compounds. Positive-pressure respirators (e.g., powered-air purifying and supplied-air) and PPE are needed when highly toxic solvents and potent compounds are handled and processed. Special concerns are posed by operations where high levels of solvent vapours (e.g., compounding, granulating and tablet coating) and dusts (e.g., drying, milling and blending) are generated. Locker and shower rooms, decontamination practices and good sanitary practices (e.g., washing and showering) are necessary to prevent or minimize the effects of worker exposures inside and outside the workplace.

Process safety management

Process safety programmes are implemented in the pharmaceutical industry due to the complex chemistry, hazardous materials and operations in bulk chemical manufacturing (Crowl and Louvar 1990). Highly hazardous materials and processes may be employed in multi-step organic synthesis reactions to produce the desired drug substance. The thermodynamics and kinetics of these chemical reactions must be evaluated, since they may involve highly toxic and reactive materials, lachrymators and flammable or explosive compounds. Process safety management involves conducting physical hazard testing of materials and reactions, performing hazard analysis studies to review the process chemistry and engineering practices, examining preventive maintenance and mechanical integrity of the process equipment and utilities, implementing worker training and developing operating instructions and emergency response procedures. Special engineering features for process safety include selecting proper pressure-rated vessels, installing isolation and suppression systems, and providing pressure relief venting with catch tanks. Process safety management practices are similar in the pharmaceutical and chemical industries when manufacturing bulk pharmaceuticals as speciality organic chemicals (Crowl and Louvar 1990; Kroschwitz 1992).

Environmental Issues

The different pharmaceutical manufacturing processes each have their own environmental issues, as discussed below.

Fermentation

Fermentation generates large volumes of solid waste which contains mycelia and spent filter cakes (EPA 1995; Theodore and McGuinn 1992). Filter cakes contain mycelia, filter media and small amounts of nutrients, intermediates and residual products. These solid wastes are typically non-hazardous, yet they may contain solvents and small amounts of residual chemicals depending upon the specific chemistry of the fermentation process. Envi-

ronmental problems may develop if fermentation batches become infected with a viral phage which attacks the micro-organisms in the fermentation process. Although phage infections are rare, they create a significant environmental problem by generating large amounts of waste broth.

Spent fermentation broth contains sugars, starches, proteins, nitrogen, phosphates and other nutrients with high biochemical oxygen demand (BOD), chemical oxygen demand (COD) and total suspended solids (TSS) with pH values ranging from 4 to 8. Fermentation broths can be treated by microbiological wastewater systems, after the effluent is equalized to promote the stable operation of the treatment system. Steam and small amounts of industrial chemicals (e.g., phenols, detergents and disinfectants) maintain the sterility of the equipment and products during fermentation. Large volumes of moist air are exhausted from fermentors, containing carbon dioxide and odours which may be treated before they are emitted to the atmosphere.

Organic synthesis

Wastes from chemical synthesis are complex due to the variety of hazardous materials, reactions and unit operations (Kroschwitz 1992; Theodore and McGuinn 1992). Organic synthesis processes may generate acids, bases, aqueous or solvent liquors, cyanides and metal wastes in liquid or slurry form. Solid wastes may include filter cakes containing inorganic salts, organic by-products and metal complexes. Waste solvents in organic synthesis are usually recovered by distillation and extraction. This allows the solvents to be reused by other processes and reduces the volume of liquid hazardous wastes to be disposed of. Residues from distillation (*still bottoms*) need to be treated before they are disposed. Typical treatment systems include steam stripping to remove solvents, followed by microbiological treatment of other organic substances. Volatile organic and hazardous substance emissions during organic synthesis operations should be controlled by air pollution control devices (e.g., condensers, scrubbers, venturi impingers).

Waste water from synthesis operations may contain aqueous liquors, wash water, discharges from pumps, scrubbers and cooling systems, and fugitive leaks and spills (EPA 1995). This waste water may contain many organic and inorganic substances with different chemical compositions, toxicities and biodegradabilities. Trace amounts of raw materials, solvents and by-products may be present in aqueous mother liquors from crystallizations and wash layers from extractions and equipment cleaning. These waste waters are high in BOD, COD and TSS, with varying acidity or alkalinity and pH values ranging from 1 to 11.

Biological and natural extraction

Spent raw materials and solvents, wash water and spills are the primary sources of solid and liquid wastes (Theodore and McGuinn 1992). Organic and inorganic chemicals may be present as residues in these waste streams. Usually, waste waters have low BOD, COD and TSS, with relatively neutral pH values ranging from 6 to 8.

Pharmaceutical manufacturing of dosage forms

Pharmaceutical manufacturing of dosage-form products generates solid and liquid wastes during cleaning and sterilization, and from leaks and spills and rejected products (Theodore and McGuinn 1992). Drying, milling and blending operations generate atmospheric and fugitive dust emissions. These emissions can be controlled and recycled to the manufacturing of dosage form products; however, quality control practices may prevent this if other residues are present. When solvents are used during wet granulation, compounding and tablet coating, VOCs and hazardous air pollutants may be released to the atmosphere or in the workplace as process or fugitive emissions. Waste waters may contain inorganic salts, sugars, syrups and traces of drug substances. These waste waters usually have low BOD, COD and TSS, with neutral pH values. Some antiparasitic or anti-infective drugs for humans and animals may be toxic to aquatic organisms, requiring special treatment of liquid wastes.

Environmental pollution prevention

Waste minimization and pollution prevention

Good engineering and administrative practices minimize the environmental impact of bulk chemical production and pharmaceutical manufacturing operations. Pollution prevention employs modifying processes and equipment, recycling and recovering materials and maintaining good housekeeping and operating practices (Theodore and McGuinn 1992). These activities enhance the management of environmental issues, as well as worker health and safety.

Process modifications

Processes may be modified to reformulate products by using materials that are less hazardous or persistent or changing manufacturing operations to reduce air emissions, liquid effluents and solid wastes. Reducing the amount and toxicity of wastes is wise, since it improves the efficiency of manufacturing processes and reduces the costs and impacts of waste disposal. Government drug approval regulations may limit the ability of pharmaceutical manufacturers to change hazardous materials, manufacturing processes, equipment and facilities (Spilker 1994). Drug manufacturers must anticipate the environmental, health and safety impacts of selecting hazardous materials and designing manufacturing process at an early stage. It becomes increasingly difficult to make changes during the later stages of drug development and regulatory approval, without considerable loss of time and expense.

It is very desirable to develop manufacturing processes with less hazardous solvents. Ethyl acetate, alcohols and acetone are preferable to highly toxic solvents such as benzene, chloroform and trichloroethylene. Whenever possible, some materials should be avoided due to their physical properties, ecotoxicity or persistence in the environment (e.g., heavy metals, methylene chloride) (Crowl and Louvar 1990). Substituting aqueous washes for solvents during filtrations in bulk chemical production reduces liquid wastes and vapour emissions. Also, substituting aqueous for solvent-based solutions during tablet coating reduces environmental, health and safety concerns. Pollution prevention is promoted by improving and automating process equipment, as well as performing routine calibration, servicing and preventive maintenance. Optimizing organic synthesis reactions increases product yields, often decreasing the generation of wastes. Incorrect or inefficient temperature, pressure and material control systems cause inefficient chemical reactions, creating additional gaseous, liquid and solid wastes.

The following are examples of process modifications in bulk pharmaceutical production (Theodore and McGuinn 1992):

- Minimize the quantities of hazardous materials used and select materials whose wastes can be controlled, recovered and recycled, whenever possible.
- Develop and install systems for recycling raw materials (e.g., solvents), intermediates, wastes and utility materials (e.g., cooling water, heat transfer liquids, lubricants, steam condensate).
- Examine reactants, solvents and catalysts to optimize the efficiency of chemical reactions.
- Modify the design and features of processing equipment to minimize pollution and wastes.

- Improve processes to maximize product yields and desired properties, eliminating additional processing (e.g., re-crystallization, drying and milling).
- Consider using multi-purpose equipment (e.g., reactors, filters and dryers) to reduce pollution and wastes during transfers, cleaning and additional process steps.
- Use appropriate instruments, automated control systems and computer programs to maximize the efficiency of processes and reduce pollution and wastes.

Resource recovery and recycling

Resource recovery uses waste products and reclaims materials during processing by separating waste impurities from desired materials. Solid wastes from fermentation (e.g., mycelia) may be added to animal feeds as a nutritional supplement or as soil conditioners and fertilizers. Inorganic salts may be recovered from chemical liquors produced during organic synthesis operations. Spent solvents are often recycled by separation and distillation. Air emission control devices (e.g., condensers, compression and refrigeration equipment) greatly reduce emissions of volatile organic compounds to the atmosphere (EPA 1993). These devices capture solvent vapours by condensation, enabling the reuse of solvents as raw materials or for cleaning vessels and equipment. Scrubbers neutralize or absorb acid, caustic and soluble gases and vapours, discharging their effluents to waste treatment systems.

Recycled solvents may be reused as media for performing reactions and extractions, and cleaning operations. Different types of solvents should not be mixed, since this reduces their ability to be recycled. Some solvents should be segregated during processing (e.g., chlorinated and non-chlorinated, aliphatic and aromatic, aqueous and flammable solvents). Dissolved and suspended solids are extracted or separated from the solvents, before the solvents are recovered. Laboratory analysis identifies the composition and properties of waste solvents and recycled raw materials. Many new waste prevention and control technologies are being developed for solid, liquid and gaseous wastes.

General housekeeping and operating practices

Written operating procedures, material-handling instructions and waste management practices reduce the generation and improve the treatment of wastes (Theodore and McGuinn 1992). Good operating and housekeeping practices identify specific responsibilities for generating, handling and treating wastes. Training and supervision of operating staff increases their ability to improve and maintain efficient manufacturing and waste management operations. Workers should be trained on the hazards of waste management practices and the proper means of responding to emergency spills, leaks and fugitive emissions. Worker training should address material handling, cleaning or neutralizing wastes and wearing respirators and PPE. Spill and leak detection devices prevent pollution by routinely monitoring production equipment and utilities, identifying and controlling fugitive emissions and leaks. These activities may be successfully integrated with preventive maintenance practices to clean, calibrate, replace and repair equipment that creates pollution.

Written instructions describing normal operating procedures, as well as start-up, shut-down and emergency procedures, prevent pollution and reduce risks to worker health and safety. Careful management of material inventories decreases the excessive purchasing of raw materials and generation of wastes. Computer systems can assist the effective management of plant operations, maintenance practices and material inventories. Automatic weighing, monitoring and alarm systems can be installed to improve the management of materials and equipment (e.g., storage tanks, process equipment and waste treatment systems). Modern instrument and control systems often increase the productivity of operations, reducing pollution and health and safety hazards. Comprehensive pollution prevention programmes examine all wastes generated at a facility and examine the options for elimi-

nating, reducing or treating them. Environmental audits examine the strengths and weaknesses of pollution prevention and waste management programmes, seeking to optimize their performance.

References

American Conference of Governmental Industrial Hygienists (ACGIH). 1995. *Threshold Limit Values (TLVs) for Chemical Substances and Physical Agents and Biological Exposure Indices (BEIs)*. Cincinnati, OH: ACGIH.

Agius, R. 1989. Occupational exposure limits for therapeutic substances. *Ann. Occ. Hyg.* 33: 555-562.

Anastas, MY. 1984. *Engineering and Other Health Hazard Controls in Oral Contraceptive Tablet-Making Operations*. NIOSH, NTIS Pub. No. PB-85-220739. Cincinnati, OH: NIOSH.

Burton, DJ and E Shumnes. 1973. *Health Hazard Evaluation* USDHEW (NIOSH) Report 71-9-50. Cincinnati, OH: NIOSH.

Cole, G. 1990. *Pharmaceutical Production Facilities: Design and Applications*. Chichester, West Sussex: Ellis Horwood Ltd.

Crowl, D and J Louvar. 1990. *Chemical Process Safety: Fundamentals with Applications*. Englewood Cliffs, NJ: Prentice Hall.

Dunn, CW. 1940. Stilbestrol-induced gynecomastia in the male. *JAMA* 115:2263.

Environmental Protection Agency (EPA). 1993. *Control of Volatile Organic Compound Emissions from Batch Processes*. EPA453/R-93-017. Washington, DC: US EPA, Office of Air Quality.

—. 1995. *Development Document for Proposed Effluent Limitations Guidelines and Standards for the Pharmaceutical Manufacturing Point Source Category*. EPA-821-R-95-019. Washington, DC: US EPA, Office of Water.

Fisk, GH. 1950. Oestrogen absorption and toxicity in male workers in a chemical plant. *Can Med Assoc J* 62:285.

Fitzsimons, MP. 1944. Gynecomastia in Stilbestrol Workers. *Brit J Ind Med* 1:235.

Gambini, G, G Farine and G Arbosti. 1976. Estro-progestin syndrome in a worker engaged in the production of a contraceptive drug. *Medicine Lavoro* 67(2): 152-157.

Gennaro, A. 1990. *Remington's Pharmaceutical Sciences*, 18th edition. Easton, PA: Mack Publishing Company.

Goldzieher, MA and JW Goldzieher. 1949. Toxic effects of percutaneously absorbed estrogens. *JAMA* 140:1156.

Hardman, JA Gilman and L Limbird. 1996. *Goodman and Gilman's The Pharmacologic Basis of Therapeutics*. New York: McGraw Hill Co.

Hoover, RH. 1980. Association of exogenous estrogens and cancer in humans. In *Estrogens in the Environment*, edited by JA McLachlan. New York. Elsevier/North-Holland.

Houghton, DL and L Ritter. 1995. Organochlorine residues and risk of breast cancer. *J Am College of Toxic* 14(2):71-89.

International Labour Organization (ILO). 1983. *Encyclopaedia of Occupational Health and Safety*, 3rd edition. Geneva. ILO.

Katzenellenbogen, I. 1956. A dermato-endocrinological syndrome and problems connected with the production and use of stilbestrol. *Harefuah* 50:239.

Klavis, G. 1953. Casuistic report concerning deficiency symptoms of working with stilbestrol. *J of Occup Med And Occup Safety* 4:46-47.

Kroschwitz, J. (ed.). 1992. *Kirk-Othmer Encyclopedia of Chemical Technology*. New York: Wiley Interscience.

Medical Economics Co. 1995. *Physician's Desk Reference*, 49th edition. Montvale, NJ: Medical Economics Co.

Meyer, CR, D Peteet and M. Harrington. 1978. *Health Hazard Evaluation Determination*. USDHEW (NIOSH) HE 77-75-494. Cincinnati, OH: NIOSH.

National Research Council. 1981. *Prudent Practices for Handling Hazardous Chemicals in Laboratories*. Washington, DC: National Academy Press.

Naumann, B, EV Sargent, BS Starkman, WJ Fraser, GT Becker and GD Kirk. 1996. Performance-based exposure control limits for pharmaceutical active ingredients *Am Ind Hyg Assoc J* 57: 33-42. 1996.

Pacynski, A, A Budzynska, S Przylecki and J Robaczynski. 1971. Hyperestrogenism in workers in a pharmaceutical establishment and their children and occupational disease. *Polish Endocrinology* 22:125.

Pagani, C. 1953. Hyperestrinic syndromes of exogenic origin. *Annali di Ostetrica e Gynecologia* 75:1173-1188.

Perry, R. 1984. *Perry's Chemical Engineers' Handbook*. McGraw-Hill Inc. New York, NY. 1984.

Reynolds, J. 1989. *Martindale's: The Extra Pharmacopoeias*, 29th Edition. London: Pharmaceutical Press.

Sargent, E. and G Kirk. 1988. Establishing airborne exposure control limits in the pharmaceutical industry. *Am Ind Hyg Assoc J* 49:309-313.

Scarff, RW and CP Smith. 1942. Proliferative and other lesions of the male breast. *Brit J Surg* 29:393.

Spilker, B. 1994. *Multinational Pharmaceutical Companies: Principles and Practices*, 2nd edition. New York: Raven Press.

Stoppleman, MRH and RA van Valkenburg. 1955. Pigmentation and gynecomastia in children caused by hair lotion containing stilbestrol. *Dutch J Med* 99:2935-2936.

Suciu, I, V Lazar, I Visinescu, A Cocirla, O Zegreanu, A Sin, Z Lorintz, G Resu and A Papp. 1973. Concerning certain neuro-endocrine modifications during the preparation of acetoxyprogesterone. *Arch mal prof méd trav sécur soc.* 34:137-142.

Swarbick, J and J Boylan (eds.). 1996. *Encyclopedia of Pharmaceutical Technology*. New York: Marcel Dekker, Inc.

Tanaka, S and D Zaebst. 1984. *Occupational Exposure to Estrogens: A Report of Two Pilot Medical and Industrial Hygiene Surveys*. Cincinnati, OH: NIOSH.

Teichman, R, F Fallon and P Brandt-Rauf. 1988. Health effects on workers in the pharmaceutical industry: A review. *J Soc Occ Med* 38: 55-57.

Theodore, L and Y McGuinn. 1992. *Pollution Prevention*. New York: Van Nostrand Reinhold.

Watrous, RM. 1947. Health hazards of the pharmaceutical industry. *Brit J Ind Med* 4:111.

Watrous, RM and RT Olsen. 1959. Diethylstilbestrol absorption in industry: A test for early detection as an aid in prevention. *Am Ind Hyg Assoc J* 20:469.

Zaebst, D, S Tanaka and M Haring. 1980. Occupational exposure to estrogens: Problems and approaches. In *Estrogens in the Environment*, edited by JA McLachlan. New York: Elsevier/North-Holland.

RUBBER INDUSTRY

Chapter Editors
Louis S. Beliczky and John Fajen

Contents

GENERAL PROFILE

Louis S. Beliczky and John Fajen

There are two basic types of rubber used in the rubber industry: natural and synthetic. A number of different synthetic rubber polymers are used to make a wide variety of rubber products (see table 80.1). Natural rubber is mostly produced in Southeast Asia, whereas synthetic rubber is mostly produced in the industrialized countries—the United States, Japan, Western Europe and East-ern Europe. Brazil is the only developing country with a signifi-cant synthetic rubber industry.

Tyres and tyre products account for approximately 60% of synthetic rubber use and 75% of natural rubber consumption (Greek 1991), employing about half a million workers worldwide. Important non-tyre uses of rubber include automotive belts and hoses, gloves, condoms and rubber footwear.

In recent years, there has been a globalization of the rubber industry. This labour-intensive industry has grown in developing countries. Table 80.2 shows worldwide natural and synthetic rub-ber consumption for 1993.

Table 80.1 • Some important rubber polymers.

Type of rubber/ Elastomer	Production (1000s of tonnes in 1993)		Properties	Common uses
Natural rubber	Thailand Indonesia Malaysia India	1,501 1,353 923 426	General purpose; not oil-resistant, swollen by solvents; subject to weathering by oxygen, ozone, UV light	Tyres, shock mounts, seals, couplings, bridge and building bearings, footwear, hoses, conveyor belts, moulded products, linings, rolls, gloves, condoms, medical devices, adhesives, carpet backing, thread, foam
Polyisoprene (IR)	US Western Europe Japan	47 15 52	General purpose; synthetic natural rubber, similar properties	See natural rubber above.
Styrene-butadiene (SBR)	US Western Europe Japan	920 1,117 620	General purpose; Second World War natural rubber substitute; poor oil/solvent resistance	Tyres (75%), conveyor belts, sponge, moulded goods, footwear, hoses, roll coverings, adhesives, waterproofing, latex carpet backing, foam products
Polybutadiene (BR)	US Western Europe Japan Eastern Europe	465 297 215 62 (1996)	Poor oil/solvent resistance; subject to weathering; high resilience, abrasion resistance and low temperature flexibility	Tyres, shoes, conveyor belts, transmission belts, toy superballs
Butyl (IIR)	US Western Europe Eastern Europe Japan	130 168 90 83	Low gas permeability; resistant to heat, acid, polar liquids; not resistant to oil, solvents; moderate weathering	Inner tubes, tire curing bladders, caulking and sealants, cable insulation, vibration isolators, pond liners and roofing membranes, high-temperature conveyor belts and hoses
Ethylene-propylene/ Ethylene- Propylene- Diene	US Western Europe Japan	261 201 124	Low-temperature flexibility; resistant to weathering and heat but not oil, solvents; excellent electrical properties	Wire and cable jackets; extruded weather stripping and seals; moulded products; isolation mounts; liner sheeting for grain storage, roofing, ponds, ditches, landfill
Polychloroprene (CR) (neoprene)	US Western Europe Japan	105 102 74	Resistant to oil, flame, heat and weather	Wire and cable jackets, hoses, belts, conveyor belts, footwear, wet suits, coated fabrics and inflatable products, extrusions, adhesives, bridge and rail mounts, sheeting, sponge gaskets, latex foam products
Nitrile (NBR)	US Western Europe Japan Eastern Europe	64 108 70 30	Resistant to oil, solvents, vegetable oil; swollen by polar solvents such as ketones	Sealants, fuel-resistant hose linings and gaskets, roll coverings, conveyor belts, shoe soles, gloves, adhesives, oil-drilling equipment
Silicone (MQ)	US Western Europe Japan	95 107 59 (1990)	Stable at high/low temperatures; resistant to oil, solvents, weathering; physiologically and chemically inert	Wire and cable insulation, seals, adhesives, gaskets, specialty moulded and extruded goods, gas masks and respirators, food and medical tubing, surgical implants
Polysulphide (OT)	US Western Europe Japan	20 0 3	Resistant to oil, solvents, low temperature, weathering; low gas permeability	Roller covering, hose liner, gaskets, moulded goods, sealants, gas meter diaphragms, glass sealants, solid rocket propellant binder
Reclaimed rubber	–	–	Shorter polymer chains; easier processing; less mixing time and power consumption; lower tensile strength and lower cost	Tyres, inner tubes, floor mats, mechanical goods, adhesives, rubberized asphalt

Source: Production figures abstracted from Stanford Research Institute data.

Table 80.2 • Worldwide rubber consumption for 1993.

Region	Synthetic rubber (1000 tonnes)	Natural rubber (1000 tonnes)
North America	2,749	999
Western Europe	2,137	930
Asia and Oceania	1,849	2,043
Latin America	575	260
Central Europe	215	65
Commonwealth of Independent States	1,665	100
Middle East and Africa	124	162
China and Asia*	453	750
Total	9,767	5,309

*Includes China, North Korea and Viet Nam.

Source: International Institute of Synthetic Rubber Producers 1994.

• RUBBER TREE CULTIVATION

Alan Echt

Natural rubber (*cis*-1,4-polyisoprene) is a processed plant product that can be isolated from several hundred species of trees and plants in many areas of the world, including the equatorial regions of Africa, Southeast Asia and South America. The milky sap, or latex, of the commercial rubber tree *Hevea brasiliensis* provides essentially all (more than 99%) of the world's supply of natural rubber. Natural rubber is also produced from *Ficus elastica* and other African plants in production areas such as Côte d'Ivoire, Madagascar, Senegal and Sierra Leone. Natural trans-1,4-polyisoprene is known as gutta-percha, or balata, and comes from trees in South America and Indonesia. This produces a less pure rubber than the *cis* isomer. Another potential source of commercial natural rubber production is the guayule shrub, *Parthenium argentatum*, which grows in hot, arid regions, such as the southwestern United States.

Production of Hevea rubber is divided between plantations larger than 100 acres and small farms, typically less than 10 acres. The productivity of commercial rubber trees has increased regularly since the 1970s. This increased productivity is due primarily to the development and replanting of acreage with faster maturing, higher yielding trees. The use of chemical fertilizers and the control of rubber tree diseases have also contributed to the increased productivity. Strict measures for the control of exposures to herbicides and pesticides during storage, mixing and spraying, the use of appropriate protective clothing and barrier creams, and the provision of change rooms and appropriate medical surveillance can effectively control the hazards associated with the use of agricultural chemicals.

Rubber trees are usually tapped for latex by making a spiral cut through the bark of the tree on alternate days, although the frequency and method of tapping vary. The latex is collected in cups hung on the tree below the cuts. The contents of the cups are transferred to large containers and moved to processing stations. Ammonia is usually added as a preservative. Ammonia disrupts the particles of rubber and produces a two-phase product consisting of 30 to 40% solids. This product is further concentrated to 60% solids, resulting in ammoniated latex concentrate, which contains 1.6% ammonia by weight. A low-ammonia latex concentrate (0.15 to 0.25% ammonia) is also available. The low-ammonia concentrate requires the addition of a secondary preservative to the latex to avoid coagulation and contamination. Secondary preservatives include sodium pentachlorophenate, tetramethylthiuram disulphide, sodium dimethyldithiocarbamate and zinc oxide.

The chief hazards to field workers are exposure to the elements, animal and insect bites and hazards related to the sharp tools used to make incisions in the trees. Injuries that result should be treated promptly to reduce the risk of infection. Preventive and therapeutic measures can reduce the hazards of the climate and pests. The incidences of malaria and gastro-enteric diseases have been reduced on modern plantations through prophylaxis, mosquito control and sanitary measures.

The guayule shrub, a native plant of southern Texas and north central Mexico, contains natural rubber in its stems and roots. The whole shrub must be harvested for the rubber to be extracted.

Guayule rubber is essentially identical to Hevea rubber, except that guayule rubber has less green strength. Guayule rubber is not a viable commercial alternative to Hevea rubber at this time.

Types of Natural Rubber

The types of natural rubber currently produced include ribbed smoked sheets, technically specified rubber, crepes, latex, epoxidized natural rubber and thermoplastic natural rubber. Thailand is the biggest supplier of ribbed smoked sheets, which accounts for about half of world natural rubber production. Technically specified rubber, or block natural rubber, was introduced in Malaysia

Figure 80.1 • Rubber tree tapper coagulating collected latex by first gathering it on a stick and then holding it over a bowl of smoke.

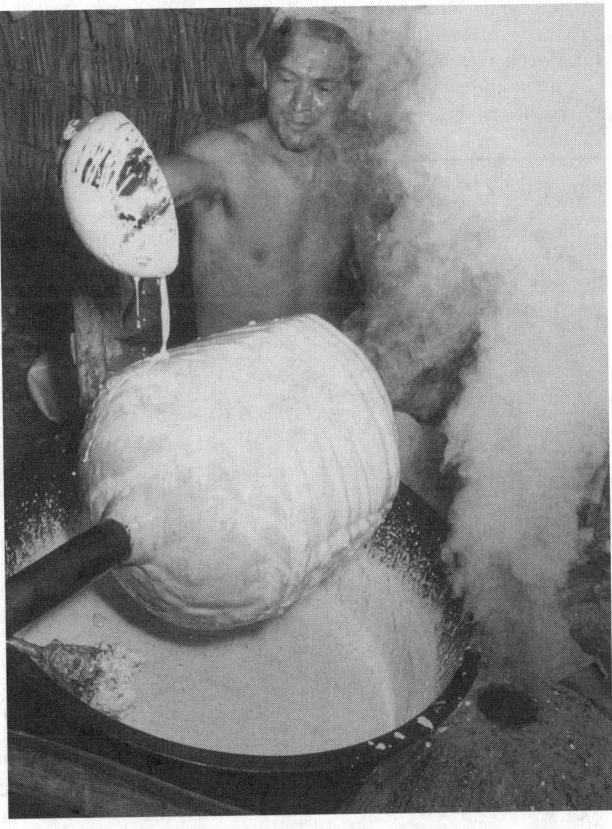

80. RUBBER INDUSTRY

in the mid-1960s, and accounts for about 40 to 45% of natural rubber production. Indonesia, Malaysia and Thailand are the largest suppliers of technically specified rubber. Technically specified rubber derives its name from the fact that its quality is determined by technical specifications, primarily its purity and elasticity, rather than by conventional visual specifications. Crepe rubber now accounts for only a small part of the world natural rubber market. Worldwide consumption of natural rubber latex has recently risen, primarily due to increased demand for latex products as a barrier to the human immunodeficiency virus and other blood-borne pathogens. Latex concentrates are used for the production of adhesives, carpet backing, foam and dipped products. Dipped products include balloons, gloves and condoms. Epoxidized natural rubber is produced by treating natural rubber with peracids. Epoxidized natural rubber is used as a replacement for some synthetic rubbers. Thermoplastic natural rubber results from the partial dynamic vulcanization of blends of polyolefins and natural rubber. It is in the early stages of commercial development.

Production Processes

Latex from rubber trees is either shipped to consumers as a concentrate or processed further into dry rubber (see figures 80.1 and 80.2). For technically specified rubber, one manufacturing process involves coagulating the field latex with acid and passing the coagulated latex through cutting machines and a series of creping rollers. Hammer mills or granulators convert the product to rubber crumbs, which are screened, washed, dried, baled and packed. Another method of technically specified rubber production involves the addition of a crumbling agent before coagulation, followed by crumbling using creping rollers.

Ribbed smoked sheets are produced by passing coagulated latex through a series of rollers to produce thin sheets, which are embossed with a ribbed pattern. The ribbed pattern serves mainly to increase the surface area of the material and aid its drying. The sheets are preserved by placing them in a smokehouse at 60 °C for a week, visually graded, sorted and packed in bales.

Compounding formulas used for natural rubbers are essentially the same as those used for most of the unsaturated synthetic

---

Figure 80.2 • Processing rubber on a plantation in Eastern Cameroon.

rubbers. Accelerators, activators, antioxidants, fillers, softeners and vulcanizing agents may all be required, depending upon what properties are desired in the finished compound.

The hazards arising from the use of mechanized production methods (i.e., rolls and centrifuges) require strict safety controls during installation, use and maintenance, including attention to machine guarding. Appropriate precautions must be used when processing chemicals are used. Attention should be paid to the use of appropriate walking and working surfaces to prevent slips, trips and falls. Employees should receive training in safe work practices. Strict supervision is required to prevent accidents associated with the use of heat as an aid in curing.

TYRE MANUFACTURING

James S. Frederick

Manufacturing Process

Figure 80.3 shows an overview of the tyre manufacturing process.

Compounding and Banbury mixing

A Banbury mixer combines rubber stock, carbon black and other chemical ingredients to create a homogeneous rubber material. Time, heat and raw materials are factors utilized to engineer material composition. The ingredients are generally provided to the plant in pre-weighed packages or are prepared and weighed by the Banbury operator from bulk quantities. Measured ingredients are placed onto a conveyor system, and the Banbury is charged to initiate the mixing process.

Hundreds of components are combined to form rubber utilized for tyre manufacturing. The components include compounds which act as accelerators, anti-oxidants, anti-ozonants, extenders, vulcanizers, pigments, plasticizers, reinforcing agents and resins. Most constituents are unregulated and may not have had extensive toxicological evaluations. Generally speaking, the Banbury operators' occupational exposures to the raw materials have been reduced by improvements in administrative and engineering controls. However, concern remains due to the nature and quantity of components which make up the exposure.

Milling

Shaping of rubber begins in the milling process. At the completion of the Banbury mixing cycle, rubber is placed onto a drop mill. The milling process shapes the rubber into flat, long strips by forcing it through two set rolls rotating in different directions at different speeds.

Mill operators are generally concerned with safety hazards associated with the open operation of the turning rolls. Older mills usually had trip wires or bars which could be pulled by the operator if he or she got caught in the mill (see figure 80.4); modern mills have body bars at about knee level that are automatically triggered if the operator is caught in the mills (see figure 80.5).

Most facilities have extensive emergency rescue procedures in place for workers trapped in mills. Mill operators are exposed to heat and noise as well as components formed by the heating of, or released from, rubber (see a canopy hood over a drop mill in figure 80.6).

Extruding and calendering

The calender operation continues to shape rubber. The calender machine consists of one or more (often four) rolls, through which the rubber sheets are forced (see figure 80.5).

Figure 80.3 • The tyre manufacturing process.

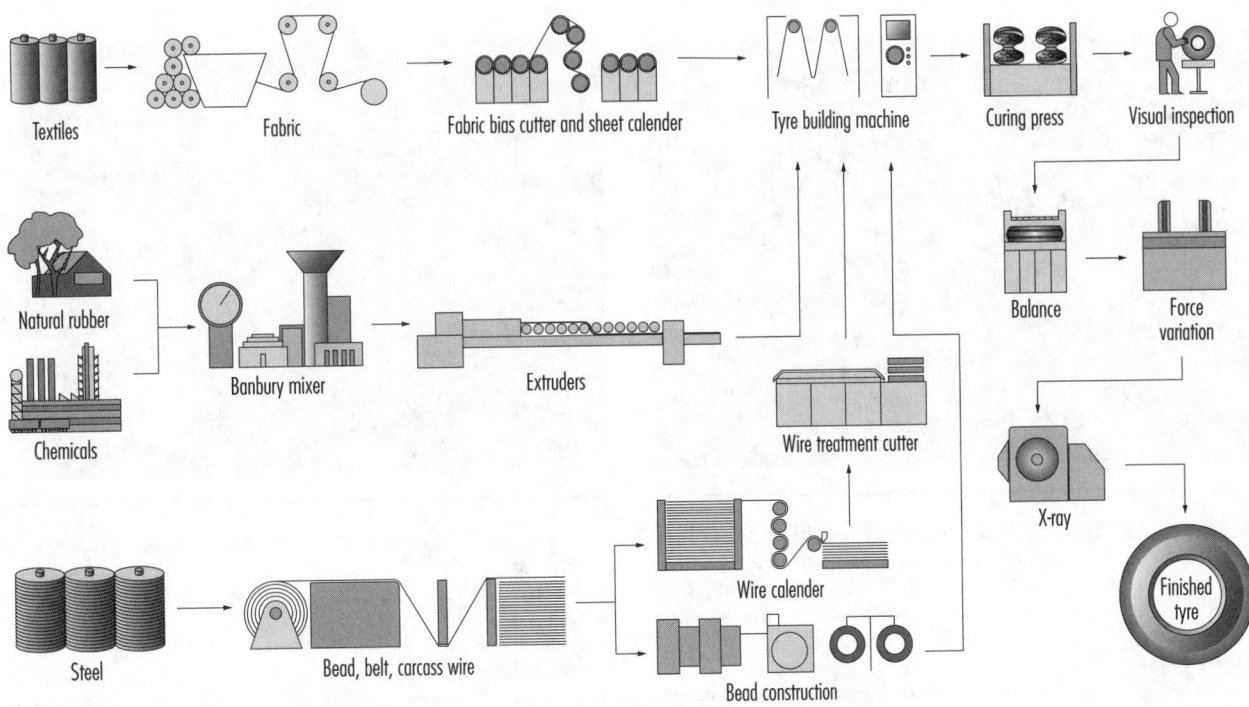

The calender machine has the following functions:

- to prepare compounded rubber as a uniform sheet of definite thickness and width
- to place a thin coat of rubber on a fabric ("coating" or "skimming")
- to force rubber into the interstices of fabric by friction ("frictioning").

The rubber sheets coming off the calender are wound on drums, called "shells," with fabric spacers, called "liners," to prevent sticking.

The extruder is often referred to as a "tuber" because it creates tube-like rubber components. The extruder functions by forcing rubber through dies of appropriate shape. The extruder consists of a screw, barrel or cylinder, head and die. A core or spider is used to form the hollow inside of tubing. The extruder makes the large, flat section of tyre treads.

Extruder and calender operators may be exposed to talc and solvents, which are used in the process. Also, the workers at the end of the extrusion operation are exposed to a highly repetitive task of placing the tread onto multi-tiered carts. This operation is often referred to as booking treads, because the cart looks like a book with the trays being the pages. The configuration of the extruder as well as the weight and quantities of tread to be booked contribute to the ergonomic impact of this operation. Numerous changes have been made to lessen this, and some operations have been automated.

Component assembly and building

Tyre assembly can be a highly automated process. The tyre assembly machine consists of a rotating drum, on which the components are assembled, and feeding devices to supply the tyre builder with the components to assemble (see figure 80.7). The components of a tyre include beads, plies, side walls and treads. After the components are assembled, the tyre is often referred to as a "green tyre".

Tyre builders and other workers in this area of the process are exposed to a number of repetitive motion operations. Components, often in heavy rolls, are placed onto the feeding portions of

Figure 80.4 • Older mill with a trip bar located too high to be effective. The operator, however, has large gloves which would be pulled into the mill before his fingers.

Ray C. Woodcock

Figure 80.5 • Mill for calender line with a body bar guard that shuts down the mill if tripped by workers.

James S. Frederick

Figure 80.7 • Operator assembling a tyre on a single-stage tyre machine.

James S. Frederick

the assembly equipment. This may entail extensive lifting and handling of heavy rolls in a limited space. The nature of assembly also requires the tyre builder to perform a series of similar or identical motions on each assembly. Tyre builders utilize solvents, such as hexane, which allow the tread and plies of rubber to adhere. Exposure to the solvents is an area of concern.

After being assembled, the green tyre is sprayed with a solvent- or water-based material to keep it from adhering to the curing mould. These solvents potentially expose the spray operator, material handler and curing press operator. Nowadays, water-based materials are mostly used.

Curing and Vulcanizing

Curing press operators place green tyres into the curing press or onto press loading equipment. Curing presses in operation in North America exist in a variety of types, ages and degrees of automation (see figure 80.8). The press utilizes steam to heat or cure the green tyre. Rubber curing or vulcanization transforms the tacky and pliable material to a non-tacky, less pliable, long-lasting state.

When rubber is heated in curing or in earlier stages of the process, carcinogenic N-nitrosamines are formed. Any level of N-nitrosamine exposure should be controlled. Attempts should be made to limit N-nitrosamine exposure as much as feasible. In addition, dusts, gases, vapours and fumes contaminate the work environment when rubber is heated, cured or vulcanized.

Inspection and finishing

Following curing, finishing operations and inspection remain to be performed before the tyre is stored or shipped. The finishing operation trims flash or excess rubber from the tyre. This excess rubber remains on the tyre from vents in the curing mould. Additionally, excess layers of rubber may need to be ground from the side walls or raised lettering on the tyre.

One of the major health hazards that workers are exposed to while handling a cured tyre is repetitive motion. The tyre finishing

Figure 80.6 • Drop mill and dryer with canopy hood and trip wires.

James S. Frederick

Figure 80.8 • Passenger and light truck Bag-o-matic McNeal curing press ventilated with a ceiling fan, Akron, Ohio, US.

James S. Frederick

Figure 80.9 • A dust collector of a grinding wheel captures rubber dust.

Ray C. Woodcock

or grinding operations typically expose workers to cured rubber dust or particulate (see figure 80.9). This contributes to respiratory illness in workers in the finishing area. In addition, a potential exists for solvent exposure from the protective paint which is often used to protect the side-wall or tyre lettering.

After finishing, the tyre is ready to be stored in a warehouse or shipped from the plant.

Health and Safety Concerns

Occupational health and safety concerns in tyre manufacturing facilities have always been and continue to be of the utmost importance. Often the impact of serious workplace injuries over-shadows the devastation associated with illnesses which may be linked to workplace exposures. Due to extended latency periods, some diseases do not become apparent until after the worker has left the job. Also, many diseases which may be associated with tyre plant occupational exposures are never diagnosed as being occupation-related. But diseases such as cancer continue to be prevalent among rubber workers in tyre manufacturing facilities.

Many scientific studies have been performed on workers in tyre manufacturing facilities. Some of these studies have identified excess mortality from bladder, stomach, lung, haematopoietic and other cancers. These excess deaths often cannot be attributed to a specific chemical. This is in part due to workplace exposures involving many individual chemicals throughout the duration of exposure and/or combination exposures to several chemicals simultaneously. Also frequent changes occur to the formulation of materials used in a tyre plant. These changes in types and quantities of the rubber compound constituents create additional difficulty in tracking the causal agents.

Another area of concern is respiratory problems or respiratory irritation in tyre plant workers (i.e., chest tightness, shortness of breath, reduction in pulmonary functions and other respiratory symptoms). Emphysema has been shown to be a common reason for early retirement. These problems are often found in curing,

processing (premixing, weighing, mixing and heating of raw ingredients) and final finishing (inspection) areas of the plants. In processing and curing, chemical exposures are often to numerous constituents at relatively low exposure levels. Many of the individual components to which workers are exposed are not regulated by governmental agencies. Almost as many have not been adequately tested for toxicity or carcinogenicity. Also, in the United States, tyre plant workers in these areas are not likely to be required to utilize respiratory protection. No clear cause of respiratory distress has been identified.

Many workers in tyre plants have suffered from contact dermatitis, which has often not been linked to one substance in particular. Some of the chemicals which have been linked to dermatitis are no longer used in the manufacture of tyres in North America; however, many of the replacement chemicals have not been fully evaluated.

Repetitive or cumulative trauma disorders have been identified as an area of concern in tyre manufacturing. Repetitive trauma disorders include tenosynovitis, carpal tunnel syndrome, synovitis, noise-induced hearing loss and other conditions resulting from repetitive motion, vibration or pressure. The tyre manufacturing process inherently contains excessive and multiple occurrences of material and product manipulation for a large portion of production workers. In some countries, many improvements have been and continue to be introduced at the plants to address this issue. Many of the innovative improvements have been initiated by workers or joint labour-management committees. Some of the improvements provide engineering controls to manipulate materials and product (see figure 80.10).

Due in part to workforce restructuring, the average age of workers in many tyre plants continues to increase. Also, more and more tyre manufacturing facilities tend to operate continuously. Many facilities with continuous operations include work shift schedules of 12-hour and/or rotating shifts. Research continues to study the possible relationships between extended work shifts, age and cumulative trauma disorders in tyre manufacturing.

Figure 80.10 • A vacuum lift carries bags to the charging conveyor for a Banbury mixer, eliminating back strain from manual handling.

Ray C. Woodcock

80. RUBBER INDUSTRY

• NON-TYRE INDUSTRIAL PRODUCTS

Ray C. Woodcock

Rubber products are made for countless applications, using processes similar to those described for tyre manufacturing. Non-tyre products, however, use a much greater variety of polymers and chemicals to give them the properties they need (see table 80.1). Compounds are carefully designed to reduce hazards such as dermatitis and nitrosamines in the factory and in products like surgical supplies, respirators and baby bottle nipples that are used in contact with the body. Often processing equipment is on a smaller scale than in tyre making, with more use of mill mixing. Roofing and landfill membranes are made on the largest calenders in the world. Some companies specialize in compounding rubber to the specifications of others who process it into many different kinds of products.

Reinforced products such as drive belts, air brake diaphragms and footwear are built up from calendered rubber, coated fabric or cord on a revolving drum or stationary form. Curing is usually by compression moulding to fix the final shape, sometimes using steam pressure and a bladder or airbag as with a tyre. More synthetic polymers are used in non-tyre products. They are not as sticky as natural rubber, so more solvent is used to clean and make the built-up layers tacky. Milling, calendering and solvents or adhesives are bypassed in some cases by going directly from the mixer to a cross-head extruder to build the product.

Non-reinforced products are formed and cured by transfer or injection moulding, extruded and cured in a hot air oven or formed in a compression mould from a pre-cut slug. Sponge rubber is made by agents in the compound that release gas when heated.

Rubber hose is built by braiding, knitting or spinning reinforcing cord or wire onto an extruded tube supported by air pressure or a solid mandrel, then extruding a cover tube over it. An extruded lead cover or nylon cross-wrap is then put on the hose for compression moulding and removed after curing, or else the hose is put into the pressurized steam vulcanizer bare. Nylon cross-wrap or extruded plastic are increasingly replacing the lead. Automotive curved hose is cut and pushed onto shaped mandrels for curing; in some cases robots are taking over this strenuous manual labour. A process also exists that uses chopped fibre for reinforcement and a movable die in the extruder to shape the hose.

Cements mixed from rubber and solvent are used to coat fabric for a host of products. Toluene, ethyl acetate and cyclohexane are common solvents. Fabric is dipped in thin cement, or rubber can be built up in increments of a few micrometres by applying thicker cement under a knife-edge over a roller. Curing is done on a continuous rotational vulcanizer or in an explosion-protected hot-air oven. Latex processes are being developed for coated fabrics to replace the cements.

Rubber cements are also commonly used as adhesives. Hexane, heptane, naphtha and 1,1,1-trichloroethane are common solvents for these products, but hexane is being replaced because of toxicity.

Latex is a typically very alkaline suspension of natural or synthetic rubber in water. Forms for gloves and balloons are dipped, or the latex compound can be foamed for carpet backing, extruded into an acetic acid coagulant solution and washed to produce thread, or spread on fabric. The product is dried and cured in an oven. Natural rubber latex is widely used in medical gloves and devices. Gloves are powdered with cornstarch, or treated in a chlorine solution to de-tackify the surface. Powder-free gloves are reportedly subject to spontaneous combustion when stored in large quantity in a hot area.

Salt bath vulcanization

Salt bath vulcanization is a liquid curing method (LCM), a common continuous vulcanization (CV) method. CV methods are desirable for producing products such as tubing, hoses and weather stripping. Salt is a good choice for a CV method because it requires relatively short-length curing units—it has good heat exchange properties and can be used at the necessary high temperatures (177 to 260 °C). Also, the salt does not cause surface oxidation, and it is easy to clean off with water. The entire operation involves at least four main processes: the rubber is fed through a cold-feed vented (or vacuum) extruder, conveyed through the salt bath, rinsed and cooled and then cut and processed according to specification. The extrudate is either immersed in or showered by the molten salt, which is a eutectic (easily fusible) blend of nitrate and nitrite salts, such as 53% potassium nitrate, 40% sodium nitrite and 7% sodium nitrate. The salt bath is generally enclosed with access doors on one side and electric heating coils on the other.

A disadvantage of the salt bath LCM is that it has been associated with the formation of nitrosamines, which are suspected human carcinogens. These chemicals are formed when a nitrogen (N) and an oxygen (O) from a "nitrosating" compound bind to the amino group nitrogen (N) of the amine compound. The nitrate and nitrite salts used in the salt bath serve as nitrosating agents and combine with amines in the rubber compound to form nitrosamines. Rubber compounds that are nitrosamine precursors include: sulphenamides, secondary sulphenamides, dithiocarbamates, thiurams and diethylhydroxylamines. Some rubber compounds actually contain a nitrosamine, such as nitrosodiphenylamine (NDPhA), a retarder, or dinitrosopentamethylenetetramine (DNPT), a blowing

agent. These nitrosamines are weakly carcinogenic, but they can "trans-nitrosate", or transfer their nitroso- groups to other amines to form more carcinogenic nitrosamines. Nitrosamines that have been detected at salt bath operations include: nitrosodimethylamine (NDMA), nitrosopiperidine (NPIP), nitrosomorpholine (NMOR), nitrosodiethylamine (NDEA) and nitrosopyrrolidine (NPYR).

In the United States, both the Occupational Safety and Health Administration (OSHA) and the NIOSH consider NDMA to be an occupational carcinogen, but neither has established an exposure limit. In Germany, there are strict regulations for occupational exposures to nitrosamines: in general industry, the total nitrosamine exposure may not exceed $1 \mu g/m^3$. For certain processes, such as rubber vulcanization, total nitrosamine exposures may not exceed $2.5 \mu g/m^3$.

Eliminating the nitrosamine formation from CV operations can be done by either reformulating the rubber compounds or using a CV method other than a salt bath, such as hot air with glass beads or microwave curing. Both changes require research and development to ensure that the final product has all the same desirable properties as the former rubber product. Another option to reduce exposures is local exhaust ventilation. Not only does the salt bath need to be enclosed and properly ventilated, but also other areas along the line, such as places where the product is cut or drilled, need sufficient engineering controls to ensure that worker exposures be kept low.

Beth Donovan Reh

Hazards and Precautions

Rubber processing hazards include exposure to hot surfaces, pressurized steam, solvents, processing aids, curing fumes and noise. Dusting agents include stearates, talc, mica and cornstarch. The organic dusts are explosive. Finishing adds a variety of hazards such as punching, cutting, grinding, printing ink solvents and alkaline or acidic surface treatment washes.

For precautions, see the articles "Engineering controls" and "Safety" in this chapter.

Microwave, electron beam and ultrasonic vulcanization are being developed to generate heat within the rubber instead of transferring it inefficiently from outside to inside. The industry is working hard to eliminate or find safer substitutes for lead, dusting agents and volatile organic solvents and to improve compounds for better and safer properties in processing and use.

● 1,3-BUTADIENE

Ronald L. Melnick

A colourless gas produced as a co-product in the manufacture of ethylene, 1,3-butadiene is used largely as a starting material in the manufacture of synthetic rubber (e.g., styrene-butadiene rubber (SBR) and polybutadiene rubber) and thermoplastic resins.

Health Effects

Animal studies. Inhaled butadiene is carcinogenic at multiple organ sites in rats and mice. In rats exposed to 0, 1,000, or 8,000 ppm butadiene for 2 years, increased tumour incidences and/or dose-response trends were observed in the exocrine pancreas, testis and brain of males and in the mammary gland, thyroid gland, uterus and Zymbal gland of females. Inhalation studies of butadiene in mice were conducted at exposures ranging from 6.25 to 1,250 ppm. Particularly noteworthy in mice were the induction of early malignant lymphomas and uncommon haemangiosarcomas of the heart. Malignant lung tumours were induced at all exposure concentrations. Other sites of tumour induction in mice included the liver, forestomach, Harderian gland, ovary, mammary gland and preputial gland. Non-neoplastic effects of butadiene exposure in mice included bone marrow toxicity, testicular atrophy, ovarian atrophy and developmental toxicity.

Butadiene is genotoxic to bone marrow cells of mice, but not rats, producing increases in sister chromatid exchanges, micronuclei and chromosomal aberrations. Butadiene is also mutagenic to *Salmonella typhimurium* in the presence of metabolic activation systems. The mutagenic activity of butadiene has been attributed to its metabolism to mutagenic (and carcinogenic) epoxide intermediates.

Human studies. Epidemiological studies have consistently found excess mortality from lymphatic and haematopoietic cancers associated with occupational exposure to butadiene. In the butadiene production industry, increases in lymphosarcomas in production workers were concentrated among men who were first employed before 1946. A case-control study of lymphatic and haematopoietic cancers in eight SBR facilities identified a strong association between leukaemia mortality and exposure to butadiene. Important characteristics of the leukaemia cases were that most were hired before 1960, worked in three of the plants and had been employed for at least 10 years in the industry. The International Agency for Research on Cancer (IARC) has classified as 1,3-butadiene probably carcinogenic to humans (IARC 1992).

A recent epidemiological study has provided data that confirm the excess in leukaemia mortality among SBR workers exposed to butadiene (Delzell et al. 1996). The site correspondence between lymphomas induced in mice exposed to butadiene and lymphatic and haematopoietic cancers associated with occupational exposure to butadiene is especially noteworthy. Furthermore, estimates of human cancer risk derived from data of butadiene-induced lymphomas in mice are similar to estimates of leukaemia risk determined from the new epidemiological data.

Industrial Exposure and Control

Surveys of exposure in industries where butadiene is produced and utilized were conducted by the US National Institute for Occupational Safety and Health (NIOSH) in the mid-1980s. Exposures were greater than 10 ppm in 4% of the samples and less than 1 ppm in 81% of the samples. Exposures were not homogeneous within specific job categories, and excursions as high as 370 ppm were measured. Exposures to butadiene were probably much higher during the Second World War, when the synthetic rubber industry was undergoing rapid growth. Limited sampling from rubber tyre and hose manufacture plants were below the limit of detection (0.005 ppm) (Fajen, Lunsford and Roberts 1993).

Exposures to butadiene can be reduced by ensuring that fittings on closed-loop systems are not worn or incorrectly connected. Further measures to control potential exposures include: use of closed-loop systems for cylinder sampling, use of dual mechanical seals to control release from leaking pumps, use of magnetic gauges to monitor rail-car filling operations and use of a laboratory hood for cylinder voiding.

ENGINEERING CONTROLS

Ray C. Woodcock

The manufacture of tyres and other rubber products exposes workers to a large variety of chemicals. These include many different powders, solids, oils and polymers used as compounding ingredients; anti-tack dusts to prevent sticking; mist, fumes and vapours generated by heating and curing rubber compounds; and solvents used for cements and process aids. The health effects related to most of these are not well known, except that they are usually chronic in nature rather than acute at typical exposure levels. Engineering controls are generally aimed at overall reduction of the level of dust, heated rubber emissions or curing fumes to which workers are exposed. Where there is exposure to specific chemicals, solvents or agents (such as noise) that are known to be harmful, control efforts can be targeted more specifically and in many cases the exposure can be eliminated.

Elimination or substitution of harmful materials is perhaps the most effective means of engineering control of hazards in rubber manufacturing. For example, β-naphthylamine contained as an impurity in an anti-oxidant was identified in the 1950s as a cause of bladder cancer and was banned. Benzene was once a common solvent but has been replaced since the 1950s by naphtha, or white gasoline, in which the benzene content has been steadily reduced (from 4-7% to commonly less than 0.1% of the mixture). Heptane has been used as a substitute for hexane and works just as well or better. Lead sheathing is being replaced by other materials for curing hose. Rubber compounds are being designed to reduce dermatitis in handling and the formation of nitrosamines in curing. Talcs used for anti-tack purposes are selected for low asbestos and silica content.

Rubber Compounding

Local exhaust ventilation is used for control of dust, mist and fumes in rubber compound preparation and mixing and in finish-

Figure 80.11 • A canopy hood controls fumes in finishing a tube casting at an industrial rubber plant in Italy.

ing processes involving buffing and grinding of rubber products (see figure 80.11). With good work practices and ventilation designs, dust exposures are usually well under 2 mg/m^3. Effective maintenance of filters, hoods and mechanical equipment is an essential element of engineering control. Specific hood designs are given in the American Conference of Governmental Industrial Hygienists ventilation manual and the Rubber and the Plastics Research Association of Great Britain ventilation handbook (ACGIH 1995).

Compounding chemicals have traditionally been scooped from bins into small bags on a weighing scale, then placed on a conveyor to be poured into the mixer or onto a mill. Dust exposures are controlled by a slotted side-draft hood behind the scale (see figure 80.12). and in some cases by slotted hoods at the edge of the stock bins. Dust control in this process is improved by substituting larger-particle-sized or granular forms for powders, by combining ingredients in a single (often heat-sealed) bag and by feeding compounds automatically from the storage bin to the transfer bag or directly to the mixer. Operator work practices also strongly influence the amount of dust exposure.

The Banbury mixer requires an effective enclosing hood to capture the dust from charging and to collect the fumes and oil mist coming from the heated rubber as it mixes. Well-designed hoods are often disrupted by drafts from pedestal fans used to cool the operator. Powered equipment is available to carry bags from pallets to the charging conveyor.

Mills are provided with canopy hoods to capture emissions of oil mist, vapours and fumes rising from the hot rubber. Unless more enclosed, these hoods are less effective in capturing dust when compounds are mixed on the mill or the mill is dusted with anti-tack powders (see figure 80.13). They are also sensitive to drafts from pedestal fans or misdirected general ventilation make-up air. A push-pull design has been used which places an air curtain in front of the operator directed up into the canopy. Mills are often raised to put the roller nip point out of the operator's reach, and they also have a trip wire or bar in front of the operator to stop the mill in an emergency. Bulky gloves are worn that will be pulled into the nip before the fingers are caught.

Rubber slabs taken off mills and calenders are coated to keep them from sticking together. This is sometimes done by dusting the rubber with powder, but is now more often done by dipping it in a water bath (see figure 80.14). Applying the anti-tack compound this way greatly reduces dust exposure and improves housekeeping.

Figure 80.12 • Slotted local exhaust ventilation at a compound weighing station.

Figure 80.13 • A curtain at the edge of a canopy hood over a mixing mill helps contain dust.

Figure 80.14 • A rubber strip taken from a Banbury batch-off mill goes through a water bath to apply anti-tack compound.

Ray C. Woodcock

Dust and fumes are ducted to bag-house or cartridge-type dust collectors. In large installations, air is sometimes recirculated back into the factory. In that case, leak detection equipment is necessary to be sure contaminants are not recirculated. Odours from some ingredients such as animal glue make air recirculation undesirable. Rubber dust burns easily, so fire and explosion protection for ductwork and dust collectors are important considerations. Sulphur and explosive dusts such as cornstarch also have special fire-protection requirements.

Rubber Processing

Local exhaust hoods are often used at extruder heads to capture mist and vapours from the hot extrusion, which may then be directed into a water bath to cool it and suppress the emissions. Hoods are also used at many other emission points in the factory, such as grinders, dip tanks and laboratory test equipment, where air contaminants can easily be collected at the source.

The numbers and physical configurations of building stations for tyres and other products usually make them unsuitable for local exhaust ventilation. Confinement of solvents to covered containers as much as possible, along with careful work practices and adequate dilution air volume in the work area, are important for keeping exposures low. Gloves or applicator tools are used to minimize skin contact.

Curing presses and vulcanizers release large amounts of hot curing fumes when they are opened. Most of the visible emission is oil mist, but the mixture is also rich in many other organic compounds. Dilution ventilation is the control measure most often used, often in combination with canopy hoods or curtained enclosures over individual vulcanizers or groups of presses. Large volumes of air are required which, if not replaced by adequate make-up air, can disrupt ventilation and hoods in connecting buildings or departments. Operators should be positioned outside the hood or enclosure. If they must be under the hood, downdraft fresh air ventilators can be placed over their work stations. Otherwise, replacement air should be introduced adjacent to the enclo-

sures but not directed into the canopy. The British occupational exposure limit for rubber curing fumes is 0.6 mg/m^3 of cyclohexane soluble material, which is normally feasible with good practice and ventilation design.

Making and applying rubber cement presents special engineering control requirements for solvents. Mixing churns are sealed and vented to a solvent recovery system, while dilution ventilation controls vapour levels in the work area. The highest operator exposures come from reaching into churns to clean them. In applying rubber cement to fabric, a combination of local exhaust ventilation at emission points, covered containers, general ventilation in the workroom and properly directed make-up air controls worker exposure. Drying ovens are exhausted directly, or sometimes air is recirculated in the oven before it is exhausted. Carbon adsorption solvent recovery systems are the most common air-cleaning device. Recovered solvent is returned to the process. Fire-protection standards require that the flammable vapour concentration in the oven be maintained below 25% lower explosion limit (LEL), unless continuous monitoring and automatic controls are provided to ensure that the vapour concentration does not exceed 50% LEL (NFPA 1995).

Automation of processes and equipment often lowers exposure to airborne contaminants and physical agents by placing the operator at a greater distance, by confining the source or by reducing the generation of the hazard. Less physical strain on the body is also an important benefit of automation in processes and material handling.

Noise Control

Significant noise exposures often come from equipment such as braiders and belt grinders, air-exhaust ports, compressed air leaks and steam leaks. Noise-reducing enclosures are effective for braiders and grinders. Very effective silencers are made for air-exhaust ports. In some cases the ports can be ducted to a common header that vents elsewhere. Air noise from leaks can often be reduced by better maintenance, enclosure, design or good work practices to limit the noise cycle.

Work Practices

To prevent dermatitis and rubber allergies, rubber chemicals and fresh rubber batches should not come in contact with the skin. Where engineering controls are insufficient for this, long gauntlet gloves, or gloves and long-sleeved shirts, should be used to keep powders and rubber slabs off the skin. Work clothes should be kept separate from street clothing. Showers are recommended before changing to street clothing to remove residual contaminants from the skin.

Other protective equipment such as hearing protection and respirators may also be necessary at times. However, good practice dictates that priority always be given to substitution or other engineering solutions to reduce hazardous exposures in the workplace.

SAFETY

James R. Townhill

Mill Safety

Mills and calenders are used extensively throughout the rubber industry. Running nip accidents (getting caught in the rotating rolls) are major safety hazards during operation of these machines. In addition, there is a potential for accidents during repair and maintenance of these and other machines used in the rubber industry. This article discusses these safety hazards.

In 1973 in the United States, the National Joint Industrial Council for the Rubber Manufacturing Industry concluded that for in-running nip points, a safety device that depended on action of the operator could not be regarded as an effective method of preventing running nip accidents. This is especially true of mills in the rubber industry. Unfortunately, little has been done to force code changes. Currently there is only one safety device that does not require operator action to activate. The body bar is the only widely accepted automatic device that is an effective means of preventing mill accidents. However, even the body bar has limitations and cannot be used in all cases unless modifications are made to the equipment and work practice.

The problem of mill safety is not a simple one; there are several major issues involved:

- mill height
- the size of the operator
- auxiliary equipment
- the way the mill is worked
- the tack or stickiness of the stock
- stopping distance.

Mill height makes a difference as to where the operator works the mill. For mills less than 1.27 m high, where the height of the operator is greater than 1.68 m, there is a tendency to work too high on the mill or too close to the nip. This allows for a very short reaction time for the automatic safety to stop the mill.

The size of the operator also dictates how close the operator needs to get to the mill face to work the mill. Operators come in many different sizes, and often must operate the same mill. The majority of the time no adjustment is made to the mill safety devices.

Auxiliary equipment such as conveyors or loaders can often conflict with safety cables and ropes. Despite codes to the contrary, often the safety rope or cable is moved to allow for the operation of the auxiliary equipment. This can result in the operator working the mill with the safety cable behind the operator's head.

While the height of the mill and the auxiliary equipment have a part in the way a mill is worked, there are other factors which enter into the picture. If there is no mixing roll below the mixer to distribute the rubber evenly on the mill, the operator will have to physically move the rubber from one side of the mill to the other by hand. The mixing and moving of the rubber exposes the operator to increased risk of strain or sprain injuries in addition to the hazard of the mill nip.

The tack or stickiness of the stock poses an additional hazard. If the rubber sticks to the mill roll and the operator has to pull it off the roll, a body bar becomes a safety hazard. Operators of mills with hot rubber have to wear gloves. Mill operators use knives. Tacky stock can grab a knife, glove or bare hand and pull it toward the running nip of the mill.

Even an automatic safety device will not be effective unless the mill can be stopped before the operator reaches the running nip of the mill. Stopping distances must be checked at least weekly and the brakes tested at the beginning of each shift. Dynamic electrical brakes must be checked on a regular basis. If the zero switch is not adjusted properly, the mill will move back and forth and damage to the mill will result. For some situations, disc brakes are preferred. With electrical brakes a problem can arise if the operator has activated the mill stop button and then tried an emergency mill stop. On some mills the emergency stop will not work after the mill stop button has been activated.

There have been some adjustments made that have improved mill safety. The following steps have greatly reduced exposure to running nip injuries on the mills:

- A body bar should be used on the working face of each mill, but only if the bar is adjustable for the height and reach of the operator.
- Mill brakes can be either mechanical or electrical, but they must be checked each shift and the distance checked weekly. The stopping distances should comply with the American National Standards Institute (ANSI) stopping distance recommendations.
- Where mixer mills have hot, tacky stock, a two-mill system has replaced the single-mill system. This has reduced operator exposure and improved the mixing of the stock.
- Where operators are required to move stock across a mill, a mixing roll should be added to reduce operator exposure.
- Current mill work practices have been reviewed to insure that the operator is not working too close to the running nip on the mill. This includes small lab mills, especially where a sample may require numerous passes through the running nip.
- Mill loaders have been added on mills to load stock. This has eliminated the practice of trying to load a mill using a fork truck, and has eliminated any conflict with the use of a body bar as a safety device.

Currently technology exists to improve mill safety. In Canada, for example, a rubber mill cannot be operated without a body bar on the working face or front of the mill. Countries receiving older equipment from other countries need to adjust the equipment to fit their workforce.

Calender Safety

Calenders have many configurations of machines and auxiliary equipment, making it difficult to be specific on calender safety. For a more in-depth study in calender safety, see National Joint Industrial Council for the Rubber Manufacturing Industry (1959, 1967).

Unfortunately, when a calender or any other piece of equipment has been transferred from one company to another or one country to another, often the accident history is not included. This has resulted in the removal of guards and in dangerous work practices that had been changed because of a prior incident. This has led to history repeating itself, with accidents that have occurred in the past reoccurring. Another problem is language. Machines with the controls and instructions in a different language from the user country makes safe operation more difficult.

Calenders have increased in speed. The braking ability of these machines has not always kept pace with the equipment. This is especially true around the calender rolls. If these rolls cannot be stopped in the recommended stopping distance, an additional method must be used to protect employees. If necessary, the calender should be equipped with a sensing device that will slow the machine when the rolls are approached during operation. This has proven very effective in keeping employees from getting too close to the rolls during the operation of the machine.

Some of the other major areas identified by the National Joint Industrial Council are still a source of injuries today:

- clearing jams and adjusting material
- running nip injuries, especially at wind-ups
- threading up
- communications.

An effective, well understood lockout programme (see below) will do much to reduce or eliminate injuries from the clearing of jams or the adjusting of material while the machine is in operation. Proximity devices that slow the rolls when they are approached may help deter an adjustment attempt.

Running nip injuries remain a problem, especially at wind-ups. Speeds at the wind-up must be adjustable to allow for a slow start-up at the beginning of the roll. Safeties must be available in the event of a problem. A device that slows the roll when it is approached will tend to discourage an attempt to adjust a liner or fabric during the wind-up. Telescoping rolls are a special temptation for even experienced operators.

The problem of threading-up incidents has increased with the speed and complexity of the calender train and the amount of auxiliary equipment. Here the existence of a single line control and good communications are essential. The operator may not be able to see all of the crew. Everyone must be accounted for and communications must be clear and easily understood.

The need for good communications is essential to safe operation when a crew is involved. Critical times are when adjustments are being made or when the machine is started at the beginning of a run or started after a shut-down which had been caused by a problem.

The answer to these problems is a well-trained crew that understands the problems of calender operation, a maintenance system that maintains all safety devices is working condition and a system that audits both.

Machine Lockout

The concept of machine lockout is not new. While lockout has been generally accepted in maintenance programmes, very little has been done to gain acceptance in the operating area. Part of the problem is the recognition of the hazard. A typical lockout standard requires that "if the unexpected movement of equipment or release of energy could cause injury to an employee then that equipment should be locked out". Lockout is not limited to electrical energy, and not all energy can be locked out; some things must be blocked in position, pipes must be disconnected and blanked, stored pressure must be relieved. While the lockout concept is viewed in some industries as a way of life, other industries have not accepted it due to the fear of the cost of locking out.

Central to the concept of lockout is control. Where the person is at risk for injury as the result of movement, the power source(s) must be disabled and the person or persons at risk should have control. All situations requiring lockout are not easy to identify. Even when they are identified, it is not easy to change work practices.

Another key to a lockout programme which is often overlooked is the ease with which a machine or line can be locked out or the power isolated. Older equipment was not designed or installed with lockout in mind. Some machines were installed with a single breaker for several machines. Other machines have multiple power sources, making lockout more complicated. To add to this problem, motor control room breakers are often changed or feed additional equipment, and the documentation of the changes is not always kept current.

The rubber industry has seen general acceptance of lockout in maintenance. While the concept of protecting one's self from the dangers of unexpected movement is not new, the uniform use of lockout is. In the past, maintenance personnel used different means to protect themselves. This protection was not always consistent due to other pressures such as production, and not always effective. For some of the equipment in the industry, the lockout answer is complex and not easily understood.

The tyre press is an example of a piece of equipment for which there is little consensus on the exact time and method for lockout. While the complete lockout of a press for an extensive repair is straightforward, there is no consensus about lockout in such operations as mould and bladder changes, mould cleaning and unjamming equipment.

The tyre machine is another example of difficulty in lockout compliance. Many of the injuries in this area have not been to maintenance personnel, but rather to operators and tyre techni-

cians making adjustments, changing drums, loading or unloading stock or unjamming equipment and to janitorial employees cleaning the equipment.

It is difficult to have a successful lockout programme if the lockout is time consuming and difficult. Where possible, the means to disconnect should be available at the equipment, which helps with ease of identification and can eliminate or reduce the possibility of someone being in the danger zone when the energy is returned to the equipment. Even with changes that make identification easier, no lockout can ever be considered complete unless a test is made to be sure the correct power isolation devices were used. In the case of work with electrical wiring, a test should be made after the disconnect is pulled to ensure that all power has been disconnected.

An effective lockout programme must include the following:

- The equipment should be designed to facilitate a lockout for all energy sources.
- Lockout sources must be identified correctly.
- Work practices requiring lockout must be identified.
- All employees affected by lockout should have some training in lockout.
- Employees who are required to lockout should be trained and advised that lockout is expected and that anything less is unacceptable under any circumstances.
- The programme needs to be audited on a regular basis to make sure that it is effective.

EPIDEMIOLOGICAL STUDIES

Robert Harris

In the 1920s and 1930s, reports from the United Kingdom showed that rubber workers had higher death rates than did the general population, and that the excess deaths were from cancers. Thousands of different materials are used in manufacturing rubber products and which if any of these might be associated with the excess deaths in the industry was not known. Continued concern for the health of rubber workers led to joint company-union occupational health research programmes within the US rubber industry at Harvard University and at the University of North Carolina. The research programmes continued through the decade of the 1970s, after which they were supplanted by jointly sponsored company-union health surveillance and health maintenance programmes based, at least in part, on findings of the research effort.

Work in the Harvard research programme focused generally on mortality in the rubber industry (Monson and Nakano 1976a, 1976b; Delzell and Monson 1981a, 1981b; Monson and Fine 1978) and on respiratory morbidity among rubber workers (Fine and Peters 1976a, 1976b, 1976c; Fine et al. 1976). An overview of the Harvard research has been published (Peters et al. 1976).

The University of North Carolina group engaged in a combination of epidemiological and environmental research. The early efforts were primarily descriptive studies of rubber workers' mortality experience and investigations of conditions of work (McMichael, Spirtas and Kupper 1974; McMichael et al. 1975; Andjelkovich, Taulbee and Symons 1976; Gamble and Spirtas 1976; Williams et al. 1980; Van Ert et al. 1980). The major focus, however, was in analytic studies on associations between work-related exposures and disease (McMichael et al. 1976a; McMichael et al. 1976b; McMichael, Andjelkovich and Tyroler 1976; Lednar et al. 1977; Blum et al. 1979; Goldsmith, Smith and McMichael 1980; Wolf et al. 1981; Checkoway et al. 1981; Symons et al.

1982; Delzell, Andjelkovich and Tyroler 1982; Arp, Wolf and Checkoway 1983; Checkoway et al. 1984; Andjelkovich et al. 1988). Noteworthy were findings regarding associations between exposures to hydrocarbon solvent vapours and cancers (McMichael et al. 1975; McMichael et al. 1976b; Wolf et al. 1981; Arp, Wolf and Checkoway 1983; Checkoway et al. 1984) and associations between exposures to airborne particulate materials and pulmonary disability (McMichael, Andjelkovich and Tyroler 1976; Lednar et al. 1977).

At the University of North Carolina, the initial analytic studies of leukaemia among rubber workers showed excess cases among workers who had a history of working in jobs in which solvents were used (McMichael et al. 1975). Exposure to benzene, a common solvent in the rubber industry many years ago, and a recognized cause of leukaemia, was immediately suspected. More detailed analyses, however, showed that the excess leukaemias were generally lymphocytic, while exposures to benzene had commonly been associated with the myeloblastic type (Wolf et al. 1981). It was surmised that some agent other than benzene could be involved. A very painstaking review of records of solvent use and solvent sources of supply for one large company showed that use of coal-based solvents, including both benzene and xylene, had a much stronger association with lymphocytic leukaemia than did use of petroleum-based solvents (Arp, Wolf and Checkoway 1983). Coal-based solvents are generally contaminated with polynuclear aromatic hydrocarbons, including compounds which have been shown to cause lymphocytic leukaemia in experimental animals. Further analyses in this study showed an even stronger association of lymphocytic leukaemia with exposures to carbon disulphide and carbon tetrachloride than with exposures to benzene (Checkoway et al. 1984). Exposures to benzene are hazardous, and exposures to benzene in workplaces should be eliminated or minimized to the extent possible. A conclusion, however, that eliminating benzene from use in rubber processes will eliminate future excesses of leukaemia, particularly of lymphocytic leukaemia, among rubber workers may be incorrect.

Special studies at the University of North Carolina of rubber workers who had taken disability retirement showed that disabling pulmonary disease, such as emphysema, was more likely to have occurred among people with a history of work in curing, curing preparation, finishing and inspection than among workers in other jobs (Lednar et al. 1977). All of these work areas involve exposures to dusts and fumes which can be inhaled. In these studies it was found that a history of smoking generally more than doubled the risk of pulmonary disability retirement, even in the dusty jobs which themselves were associated with disability.

Epidemiological studies were under way in the European and Asian rubber industries (Fox, Lindars and Owen 1974; Fox and Collier 1976; Nutt 1976; Parkes et al. 1982; Sorahan et al. 1986; Sorahan et al. 1989; Kilpikari et al. 1982; Kilpikari 1982; Bernardinelli, Marco and Tinelli 1987; Negri et al. 1989; Norseth, Anderson and Giltvedt 1983; Szeszenia-Daborowaska et al. 1991; Solionova and Smulevich 1991; Gustavsson, Hogstedt and Holmberg 1986; Wang et al. 1984; Zhang et al. 1989) at about the same time and continued after those of Harvard and the University of North Carolina in the United States. Findings of excess cancers at various sites were commonly reported. Several studies showed an excess of lung cancer (Fox, Lindars and Owen 1974; Fox and Collier 1976; Sorahan et al. 1989; Szeszenia-Daborowaska et al. 1991; Solionova and Smulevich 1991; Gustavsson, Hogstedt and Holmberg 1986; Wang et al. 1984), associated, in some cases, with a history of work in curing. This finding was duplicated in some studies in the United States (Monson and Nakano 1976a; Monson and Fine 1978) but not in others (Delzell, Andjelkovich and Tyroler 1982; Andjelkovich et al. 1988).

The mortality experience among a cohort of workers in the German rubber industry has been reported (Weiland et al. 1996). Mortality from all causes and from all cancers was significantly elevated in the cohort. Statistically significant excesses in mortality from lung cancer and from pleural cancer were identified. The excess of mortality from leukaemia among German rubber workers barely failed to reach statistical significance.

A case-control study of lymphatic and haematopoietic cancers in eight styrene-butadiene rubber (SBR) facilities identified a strong association between leukaemia mortality and exposure to butadiene. The IARC has concluded that 1,3-butadiene is probably carcinogenic to humans (IARC 1992). A more recent epidemiological study has provided data that confirm the excess in leukaemia mortality among SBR workers exposed to butadiene (Delzell et al. 1996).

Over the years, epidemiological studies among rubber workers have led to the identification of workplace hazards and to improvements in their control. The area of occupational epidemiological research in greatest need of improvement at this time is assessment of past exposures of study subjects. Progress is being made in both research techniques and in databases in this area. Although questions regarding causal associations remain, continued epidemiological progress will surely lead to continued improvements in control of exposures in the rubber industry and, consequently, to continued improvement in the health of rubber workers.

Acknowledgement: I would like to recognize the pioneering efforts of Peter Bommarito, former president of the United Rubber Workers Union, who was primarily responsible for causing research to be done in the US rubber industry in the 1970s and 1980s on the health of rubber workers.

RUBBER CONTACT DERMATITIS AND LATEX ALLERGY

James S. Taylor and Yung Hian Leow

Contact Dermatitis

Adverse skin reactions have been reported frequently among workers who have direct contact with rubber and with the hundreds of chemicals used in the rubber industry. These reactions include irritant contact dermatitis, allergic contact dermatitis, contact urticaria (hives), aggravation of pre-existing skin diseases and other less common skin disorders such as oil folliculitis, xerosis (dry skin), miliaria (heat rash) and depigmentation from certain phenol derivatives.

Irritant contact dermatitis is the most frequent reaction and is caused by either acute exposure to strong chemicals or by cumulative exposure to weaker irritants such as those found in wet work and in repeated use of solvents. Allergic contact dermatitis is a delayed type of allergic reaction from the accelerators, vulcanizers, anti-oxidants and anti-ozonants which are added during rubber manufacture. These chemicals are often present in the final product and may cause contact dermatitis in both the end-product user as well as in rubber workers, especially Banbury, calender and extruder operators and assemblers.

Some workers acquire contact dermatitis through exposure in work which does not permit the use of chemical-protective clothing (CPC). Other workers also develop allergy to CPC itself, most commonly from rubber gloves. A valid positive patch test to the suspected allergen is the key medical test which is used to differentiate allergic contact dermatitis from irritant contact dermatitis. It is important to remember that allergic contact dermatitis may coexist with irritant contact dermatitis as well as with other skin disorders.

Dermatitis may be prevented by automated mixing and pre-blending of chemicals, provision of exhaust ventilation, substitution of known contact allergens with alternative chemicals and improved materials handling to reduce skin contact.

Natural Rubber Latex (NRL) Allergy

NRL allergy is an immunoglobulin E–mediated, immediate, Type I allergic reaction, most always due to NRL proteins present in medical and non-medical latex devices. The spectrum of clinical signs ranges from contact urticaria, generalized urticaria, allergic rhinitis (inflammation of nasal mucosa), allergic conjunctivitis, angio-oedema (severe swelling) and asthma (wheezing) to anaphylaxis (severe, life-threatening allergic reaction). Highest risk individuals are patients with spina bifida, health care workers and other workers with significant NRL exposure. Predisposing factors are hand eczema, allergic rhinitis, allergic conjunctivitis or asthma in individuals who frequently wear gloves, mucosal exposure to NRL and multiple surgical procedures. Fifteen deaths following NRL exposure during barium enema examinations have been reported to the US Food and Drug Administration. Thus the route of exposure to NRL proteins is important and includes direct contact with intact or inflamed skin and mucosal exposure, including inhalation, to NRL-containing glove powder, especially in medical facilities and in operating rooms. As a result, NRL allergy is a major worldwide medical, occupational health, public health and regulatory problem, with the number of cases having increased dramatically since the mid-1980s.

Diagnosis of NRL allergy is strongly suggested if there is a history of angio-oedema of the lips when inflating balloons and/or itching, burning, urticaria or anaphylaxis when donning gloves, undergoing surgical, medical and dental procedures or following exposure to condoms or other NRL devices. Diagnosis is confirmed by either a positive wear or use test with NRL gloves, a valid positive intracutaneous prick test to NRL or a positive RAST (radioallergosorbent test) blood test for latex allergy. Severe allergic reactions have occurred from prick and wear tests; epinephrine and resuscitation equipment free of NRL should be available during these procedures.

NRL allergy may be associated with allergic reactions to fruit, especially bananas, chestnuts and avocados. Hyposensitization to NRL is not yet possible, and NRL avoidance and substitution is imperative. Prevention and control of NRL allergy includes latex avoidance in health care settings for affected workers and patients. Substitute synthetic non-NRL gloves should be available, and in many cases low-allergen NRL gloves should be worn by co-workers to accommodate those with NRL allergy, in order to minimize symptoms and to decrease induction of NRL allergy. Continued cooperation among government, industry and health care professionals is necessary to control latex allergy, as discussed in the *Health care facilities* chapter.

● ERGONOMICS

William S. Marras

Ergonomics is the science of assessing the relationship between workers and their work environment. This science includes not only an assessment of musculoskeletal risk due to the design of the work, but also includes a consideration of the cognitive processes involved in work that may lead to human errors.

Jobs in the rubber and tyre industry have been identified with an increased risk of particular types of musculoskeletal disorders.

In particular, back injuries appear to be prominent. A sample of materials-handling jobs in the tyre and rubber industry has indicated that the high-risk jobs result in low-back disorder injury rates that are approximately 50% higher than that of general industry. An assessment of jobs indicates that these problems typically arise from jobs requiring the manual transport of rubber products. These jobs include rubber processing (Banbury) operations, tyre builders, tyre finishers and tyre transporters both in the factory and warehouse environment. Wrist problems such as carpal tunnel syndrome and tenosynovitis also appear to be prominent in tyre construction. An examination of tyre manufacturing operations suggests that shoulder problems would be expected. However, as expected, injury records tend to under-report the risk of shoulder injuries due to a lack of sensitivity to the problem. Finally, there appear to be some cognitive processing issues involved in the tyre industry. These are apparent in the inspection tasks and are often exacerbated by poor lighting.

There are several workplace-related risk factors believed to be responsible for these musculoskeletal problems in the tyre and rubber industry. Risk factors consist of static, awkward postures in the back, shoulders and wrists, rapid motions in the wrist and back, and large weights handled, as well as large forces applied to the trunk while handling large pieces of rubber during tyre building. A study of factors associated with low-back disorder risk indicates that greater weight is handled by workers in the tyre building industry than in other fields and these loads are handled at greater than average distances from the body. Furthermore, these forces and weights are often imposed on the body during asymmetric motions of the trunk, such as bending. The duration of the force applications in this type of work is also problematic. Often in a tyre-building operation, lengthy applications of force are required which diminish the worker's available force over time. Finally, tyre and rubber workplaces are often warm and exposed to dirt and dust. The heat within the workplace will tend to increase the caloric demands of the job, thus increasing the energy demands. Resin and dust within the workplace increase the likelihood that workers will be wearing gloves while performing their tasks. This glove use will increase the required tension in the forearm muscles that control the fingers. In addition, when workers wear gloves they will increase their grip force since they cannot perceive when an object is about to slip out of their hands. Solutions to these ergonomic-related problems include the simple rearrangement of the workplace (e.g., raising or lowering of the work or moving the workstations in order to eliminate large twisting or lateral bending motions of the trunk; the latter can often be accomplished by reorienting origins and destinations of lifting tasks from 180° twists to 90° turns). Often more significant changes are needed. These may range from incorporating adjustable workstations such as scissors jacks or lift tables, to incorporating lifting assistance devices such as lifts and cranes, to fully automating the workstation. There is obviously a large cost associated with some of these solutions to the problem. Therefore the key to proper ergonomic design is to make only the changes that are necessary and to determine the effect of the change in terms of the change in musculoskeletal risk. Fortunately, new methods for quantifying the extent of the risk associated with a given design of the workplace are becoming available. For example, a risk model has been reported that assesses the risk of occupationally related low-back disorder given the demands of the job (Marras et al. 1993; 1995). Models have also been developed that assess the loading of the spine due to dynamic trunk activities (Marras and Sommerich 1991; Granata and Marras 1993). Thus, models are becoming available for the assessment of workplace designs in the industry that are capable of addressing the issue of how much exposure to a workplace is too much.

ENVIRONMENTAL AND PUBLIC HEALTH ISSUES

Thomas Rhodarmer

All rubber products start out as a "rubber compound". Rubber compounds start with a rubber polymer, either natural or one of the many synthetic polymers, fillers, plasticizers, anti-oxidants, process aids, activators, accelerators and curatives. Many of the chemical ingredients are classified as hazardous or toxic chemicals, and some may be listed as carcinogens. Handling and processing of these chemicals create both environmental and safety concerns.

Hazardous Waste

Ventilation systems and dust collectors are necessary for workers handling and weighing the rubber chemicals and for workers mixing and processing the uncured rubber compound. Personal protection equipment may also be necessary for these workers. The material collected in the dust collectors must be tested to determine whether it is a hazardous waste. It would be a hazardous waste if it is reactive, corrosive, flammable or contains chemicals that are listed hazardous as wastes.

Hazardous waste must be listed on a manifest and sent for disposal at a hazardous wastesite. Non-hazardous waste can go to local sanitary landfills or may have to go to an industrial landfill, depending on applicable environmental regulations.

Air Pollution

Some rubber products require a rubber cement application in the manufacturing process. Rubber cements are made by mixing the uncured rubber compound with a solvent. The solvents used in this process are usually classified as volatile organic compounds (VOCs). Processes that use VOCs must have some type of emission-control equipment. This equipment can be a solvent recovery system or a thermal oxidizer. A thermal oxidizer is an incineration system that destroys the VOCs by combustion and usually requires a fuel supplement such as natural gas. Without emission control equipment the VOCs can cause health concerns in the factory and in the community. If the VOCs are photochemically reactive, they will affect the ozone layer.

When rubber parts are cured and the curing vessel is opened, curing fumes rush out of the vessel and from the rubber part. These fumes will be in the form of smoke, steam or both. Curing fumes can carry unreacted chemicals, plasticizers, mould lubes and other materials out into the atmosphere. Emission controls are needed.

Ground and Water Pollution

Storage and handling of VOCs must be done with extreme caution. In past years, VOCs were stored in underground storage tanks, which in some cases resulted in leaks or spills. Leaks and/or spills around underground storage tanks generally result in soil and groundwater contamination, which triggers expensive soil and groundwater remediation. The best storage choice is above-ground tanks with good secondary containment for spill prevention.

Waste Rubber

Every manufacturing process has process and finished goods scrap. Some of the process scrap can be reprocessed in the intended product or other product processes. However, once the rubber is cured or vulcanized, it can no longer be reprocessed. All cured process and finished goods scrap becomes waste material.

Disposal of scrap or waste rubber products has become a worldwide problem.

Every household and business in the world uses some type of rubber product. Most rubber products are classified as non-hazardous materials and therefore would be non-hazardous waste. However, rubber products such as tyres, hose and other tubular products create an environmental problem as related to disposal after their useful life.

Tyres and tubular products cannot be buried in a landfill because the void areas trap air, which causes the products to rise to the surface over time. Shredding the rubber products eliminates this problem; however, shredding requires special equipment and is very expensive.

Smoldering tyre fires can generate large amounts of irritating smoke that can contain a wide variety of toxic chemicals and particulates.

Incineration of Scrap Rubber

One of the options for disposing of scrap rubber products and process scrap rubber from the manufacturing processes is incineration. Incineration might initially seem to be the best solution for disposal of the numerous "worn out" rubber products that exist in the world today. Some rubber-manufacturing companies have looked at incineration as a means of disposing of scrap rubber parts as well as cured and uncured rubber-process scrap. In theory, the rubber could be burned to generate steam that could be used back in the factory.

Unfortunately, it is not that simple. The incinerator must be designed so as to handle air emissions and would most likely require scrubbers to remove such contaminants as chlorine. Chlorine emissions generally would come from burning products and scrap that contain chloroprene polymers. The scrubbers generate an acidic discharge that may have to be neutralized prior to discharge.

Almost all rubber compounds contain some type of fillers, either carbon blacks, clays, calcium carbonates or hydrated silica compounds. When these rubber compounds are burned, they generate ash equivalent to the filler loading in the rubber compound. The ash is collected either by wet scrubbers or dry scrubbers. Both methods must be analysed for heavy metals prior to disposal. Wet scrubbers most likely will produce a wastewater that contains 10 to 50 ppm zinc. This much zinc being discharged into a sewage system will create problems at the treatment plant. If this occurs, then a treatment system for the removal of zinc must be installed. This treatment system then generates a zinc-containing sludge that must be shipped out for disposal.

Dry scrubbers generate an ash that must be collected for disposal. Both wet and dry ash is difficult to handle, and disposal can be a problem since most landfills do not accept this type of waste. Both wet and dry ash can be very alkaline if the rubber compounds being burned are heavily loaded with calcium carbonate.

Finally, the amount of steam generated is not enough to supply the full amount necessary to operate a rubber-manufacturing facility. The scrap rubber supply is inconsistent, and efforts are currently underway to reduce scrap, which would reduce the fuel supply. The maintenance cost of an incinerator designed to burn rubber scrap and rubber products is also very high.

When all of these costs are taken into consideration, incineration of scrap rubber may be the least cost-effective method of disposal.

Conclusion

Perhaps the best solution to environmental and health concerns associated with manufacturing rubber products would be good engineering control for producing and compounding powdered chemicals used in rubber compounds, and recycling programmes for all uncured and cured rubber process scrap and products. The powdered chemicals collected in dust-collector systems could be added back to rubber compounds with the appropriate engineering controls, which would eliminate the landfilling of these chemicals.

Controlling the environmental and health issues in the rubber industry can be done, but it will not come easy or be free. The cost associated with controlling environmental and health problems must be added back to the cost of rubber products.

References

American Conference of Governmental Industrial Hygienists (ACGIH). 1995. *Industrial Ventilation: A Manual of Recommended Practice,* 22nd ed. Cincinnati: OH: ACGIH.

Andjelkovich, D, JD Taulbee, and MJ Symons. 1976. Mortality experience in a cohort of rubber workers, 1964–1973. *J Occup Med* 18:386–394.

Andjelkovich, D, H Abdelghany, RM Mathew, and S Blum. 1988. Lung cancer case-control study in a rubber manufacturing plant. *Am J Ind Med* 14:559–574.

Arp, EW, PH Wolf, and H Checkoway. 1983. Lymphocytic leukemia and exposures to benzene and other solvents in the rubber industry. *J Occup Med* 25:598–602.

Bernardinelli, L, RD Marco, and C Tinelli. 1987. Cancer mortality in an Italian rubber factory. *Br J Ind Med* 44:187–191.

Blum, S, EW Arp, AH Smith, and HA Tyroler. 1979. Stomach cancer among rubber workers: An epidemiologic investigation. In *Dusts and Disease.* Park Forest, IL: SÖEH, Pathotox Publishers.

Checkoway, H, AH Smith, AJ McMichael, FS Jones, RR Monson, and HA Tyroler. 1981. A case-control study of bladder cancer in the U.S. tire industry. *Br J Ind Med* 38:240–246.

Checkoway, H, T Wilcosky, P Wolf, and H Tyroler. 1984. An evaluation of the associations of leukemia and rubber industry solvent exposures. *Am J Ind Med* 5:239–249.

Delzell, E and RR Monson. 1981a. Mortality among rubber workers. III. Cause-specific mortality 1940–1978. *J Occup Med* 23:677–684.

—. 1981b. Mortality among rubber workers. IV. General mortality patterns. *J Occup Med* 23:850–856.

Delzell, E, D Andjelkovich, and HA Tyroler. 1982. A case-control study of employment experience and lung cancer among rubber workers. *Am J Ind Med* 3:393–404.

Delzell, E, N Sathiakumar, M Hovinga, M Macaluso, J Julian, R Larson, P Cole, and DCF Muir. 1996. A follow-up study of synthetic rubber workers. *Toxicology* 113:182–189.

Fajen, J, RA Lunsford, and DR Roberts. 1993. Industrial exposure to 1,3-butadiene in monomer, polymer and end-user industries. In *Butadiene and Styrene: Assessment of Health Hazards,* edited by M Sorsa, K Peltonen, H Vainio and K Hemminki. Lyon: IARC Scientific Publications.

Fine, LJ and JM Peters. 1976a. Respiratory morbidity in rubber workers. I. Prevalence of respiratory symptoms and disease in curing workers. *Arch Environ Health* 31:5–9.

—. 1976b. Respiratory morbidity in rubber workers. II. Pulmonary function in curing workers. *Arch Environ Health* 31:10–14.

—. 1976c. Studies of respiratory morbidity in rubber workers. III. Respiratory morbidity in processing workers. *Arch Environ Health* 31:136–140.

Fine, LJ, JM Peters, WA Burgess, and LJ DiBerardinis. 1976. Studies of respiratory morbidity in rubber workers. IV. Respiratory morbidity in talc workers. *Arch Environ Health* 31:195–200.

Fox, AJ and PF Collier. 1976. A survey of occupational cancer in the rubber and cablemaking industries: Analysis of deaths occurring in 1972–74. *Br J Ind Med* 33:249–264.

Fox, AJ, DC Lindars, and R Owen. 1974. A survey of occupational cancer in the rubber and cablemaking industries: Results of a five-year analysis, 1967–71. *Br J Ind Med* 31:140–151.

Gamble, JF and R Spirtas. 1976. Job classification and utilization of complete work histories in occupational epidemiology. *J Occup Med* 18:399–404.

Goldsmith, D, AH Smith, and AJ McMichael. 1980. A case-control study of prostate cancer within a cohort of rubber and tire workers. *J Occup Med* 22:533–541.

Granata, KP and WS Marras. 1993. An EMG-assisted model of loads on the lumbar spine during asymmetric trunk extensions. *J Biomech* 26:1429–1438.

Greek, BF. 1991. Rubber demand is expected to grow after 1991. *C & EN* (13 May): 37-54.

Gustavsson, P, C Hogstedt, and B Holmberg. 1986. Mortality and incidence of cancer among Swedish rubber workers. *Scand J Work Environ Health* 12:538–544.

International Agency for Research on Cancer (IARC). 1992. 1,3-Butadiene. In *IARC Monographs on the Evaluation of Carcinogenic Risks to Humans: Occupational Exposures to Mists and Vapours from Strong Inorganic Acids and Other Industrial Chemicals.* Lyon: IARC.

International Institute of Synthetic Rubber Producers. 1994. *Worldwide Rubber Statistics.* Houston, TX: International Institute of Synthetic Rubber Producers.

Kilpikari, I. 1982. Mortality among male rubber workers in Finland. *Arch Environ Health* 37:295–299.

Kilpikari, I, E Pukkala, M Lehtonen, and M Hakama. 1982. Cancer incidence among Finnish rubber workers. *Int Arch Occup Environ Health* 51:65–71.

Lednar, WM, HA Tyroler, AJ McMichael, and CM Shy. 1977. The occupational determinants of chronic disabling pulmonary disease in rubber workers. *J Occup Med* 19:263–268.

Marras, WS and CM Sommerich. 1991. A three dimensional motion model of loads on the lumbar spine, Part I: Model structure. *Hum Factors* 33:123–137.

Marras, WS, SA Lavender, S Leurgans, S Rajulu, WG Allread, F Fathallah, and SA Ferguson. 1993. The role of dynamic three dimensional trunk motion in occupationally-related low back disorders: The effects of workplace factors, trunk position and trunk motion characteristics on injury. *Spine* 18:617–628.

Marras, WS, SA Lavender, S Leurgans, F Fathallah, WG Allread, SA Ferguson, and S Rajulu. 1995. Biomechanical risk factors for occupationally related low back disorder risk. *Ergonomics* 35:377–410.

McMichael, AJ, DA Andjelkovich, and HA Tyroler. 1976. Cancer mortality among rubber workers: An epidemiologic study. *Ann NY Acad Sci* 271:125–137.

McMichael, AJ, R Spirtas, and LL Kupper. 1974. An epidemiologic study of mortality within a cohort of rubber workers, 1964–72. *J Occup Med* 16:458–464.

McMichael, AJ, R Spirtas, LL Kupper, and JF Gamble. 1975. Solvent exposures and leukemia among rubber workers: An epidemiologic study. *J Occup Med* 17:234–239.

McMichael, AJ, R Spirtas, JF Gamble, and PM Tousey. 1976a. Mortality among rubber workers: Relationship to specific jobs. *J Occup Med* 18:178–185.

McMichael, AJ, WS Gerber, JF Gamble, and WM Lednar. 1976b. Chronic respiratory symptoms and job type within the rubber industry. *J Occup Med* 18:611–617.

Monson, RR and KK Nakano. 1976a. Mortality among rubber workers. I. White male union employees in Akron, Ohio. *Am J Epidemiol* 103:284–296.

—. 1976b. Mortality among rubber workers. II. Other employees. *Am J Epidemiol* 103:297–303.

Monson, RR and LJ Fine. 1978. Cancer mortality and morbidity among rubber workers. *J Natl Cancer Inst* 61:1047–1053.

National Fire Protection Association (NFPA). 1995. *Standard for Ovens and Furnaces.* NFPA 86. Quincy, MA: NFPA.

National Joint Industrial Council for the Rubber Manufacturing Industry. 1959. *Running Nip Accidents.* London: National Joint Industrial Council for the Rubber Manufacturing Industry.

—.1967. *Safe Working of Calenders.* London: National Joint Industrial Council for the Rubber Manufacturing Industry.

Negri, E, G Piolatto, E Pira, A Decarli, J Kaldor, and C LaVecchia. 1989. Cancer mortality in a northern Italian cohort of rubber workers. *Br J Ind Med* 46:624–628.

Norseth, T, A Anderson, and J Giltvedt. 1983. Cancer incidence in the rubber industry in Norway. *Scand J Work Environ Health* 9:69–71.

Nutt, A. 1976. Measurement of some potentially hazardous materials in the atmosphere of rubber factories. *Environ Health Persp* 17:117–123.

Parkes, HG, CA Veys, JAH Waterhouse, and A Peters. 1982. Cancer mortality in the British rubber industry. *Br J Ind Med* 39:209–220.

Peters, JM, RR Monson, WA Burgess, and LJ Fine. 1976. Occupational disease in the rubber industry. *Environ Health Persp* 17:31–34.

Solionova, LG and VB Smulevich. 1991. Mortality and cancer incidence in a cohort of rubber workers in Moscow. *Scand J Work Environ Health* 19:96–101.

Sorahan, R, HG Parkes, CA Veys, and JAH Waterhouse. 1986. Cancer mortality in the British rubber industry 1946–80. *Br J Ind Med* 43:363–373.

Sorahan, R, HG Parkes, CA Veys, JAH Waterhouse, JK Straughan, and A Nutt. 1989. Mortality in the British rubber industry 1946–85. *Br J Ind Med* 46:1–11.

Szeszenia-Daborowaska, N, U Wilezynska, T Kaczmarek, and W Szymezak. 1991. Cancer mortality among male workers in the Polish rubber industry. *Polish Journal of Occupational Medicine and Environmental Health* 4:149–157.

Van Ert, MD, EW Arp, RL Harris, MJ Symons, and TM Williams. 1980. Worker exposures to chemical agents in the manufacture of rubber tires: Solvent vapor studies. *Am Ind Hyg Assoc J* 41:212–219.

Wang, HW, XJ You, YH Qu, WF Wang, DA Wang, YM Long, and JA Ni. 1984. Investigation of cancer epidemiology and study of carcinogenic agents in the Shanghai rubber industry. *Cancer Res* 44:3101–3105.

Weiland, SK, KA Mundt, U Keil, B Kraemer, T Birk, M Person, AM Bucher, K Straif, J Schumann, and L Chambless. 1996. Cancer mortality among workers in the German rubber industry. *Occup Environ Med* 53:289–298.

Williams, TM, RL Harris, EW Arp, MJ Symons, and MD Van Ert. 1980. Worker exposure to chemical agents in the manufacture of rubber tires and tubes: Particulates. *Am Ind Hyg Assoc J* 41:204–211.

Wolf, PH, D Andjelkovich, A Smith, and H Tyroler. 1981. A case-control study of leukemia in the U.S. rubber industry. *J Occup Med* 23:103–108.

Zhang, ZF, SZ Yu, WX Li, and BCK Choi. 1989. Smoking, occupational exposure to rubber and lung cancer. *Br J Ind Med* 46:12–15.

Other relevant readings

Auchter, JF, R Mulach, and S Mori. 1992. *CEH Marketing Research Report: Natural Rubber.* Menlo Park, CA: SRI International.

Bhowmick, AK, MM Hall, and HA Benarey (eds.). 1994. *Rubber Products Manufacturing Technology.* New York: Marcel Dekker, Inc.

British Rubber Manufacturers' Association (BRMA). 1990. *Toxicity and Safe Handling of Rubber Chemicals: Code of Practice*, 3rd edition. Birmingham: BRMA.

Burgess, WA. 1995. Rubber products. In *Recognition of Health Hazards in Industry*, 3rd ed. New York: John Wiley & Sons.

Dunlop Co. Ltd. 1983. Rubber cultivation. In *Encyclopaedia of Occupational Health and Safety*, 3rd ed., Vol. 2. Geneva: ILO.

Feinman, SE. 1987. Sensitivity to rubber chemicals. *Journal of Toxicology—Cutaneous and Ocular Toxicology* 6:117–153.

Fenoglio, S, G Meo, and A Bonzanino. 1968. *Manufacturing Risks in the Rubber Industry and Their Prevention I: Some Technical Aspects.* Turin, Italy: University of Turin, Institute of General Clinical Medicine and Medical Therapy.

Fink JN. 1995. Latex allergy. *Immunology and Allergy Clinics of North America* 15:1–175.

International Federation of Chemical, Energy and General Workers' Unions (ICEF). 1990. *Change and Concentration in the World Rubber Industry.* Brussels: ICEF.

McKinnery, WN, Jr and WA Heitbrink. 1984. *Control of Air Contaminants in Tire Manufacturing.* Research Report DHHS (NIOSH) #84-111. Cincinnati, OH: NIOSH.

Morton, M (ed.). 1987. *Rubber Technology*, 3rd edition. New York: Van Nostrand Reinhold.

Reisch, MS. 1993. Rubber: Slow growth ahead. *C & EN* (10 May): 24–33.

Slater, JE. 1994. Latex allergy. *J Allergy Clin Immunol* 94:139–149.

Symons, MJ, DA Andjelkovich, R Spirtas, and DR Herman. 1982. Brain and central nervous system cancer mortality in U.S. rubber workers. *Ann NY Acad Sci* 381:146–159.

Taylor, JS and P Praditsuwan. 1996. Latex allergy: Review of 44 cases including outcome and frequent association with allergic hand eczema. *Archives of Dermatology* 132:265–271.

Taylor, JS. 1986. Rubber. In *Contact Dermatitis*, 3rd ed, edited by AA Fisher. Philadelphia: Lea & Febiger.

UK Health and Safety Commission (HSC). 1994. *Control of Fume at Extruders, Calendars and Vulcanising Operations.* London: HSC Rubber Industry Advisory Committee/Health and Safety Executive.

—. 1996. Dust and Fume Control in Rubber Mixing and Milling. London: HSC Rubber Industry Advisory Committee/Health and Safety Executive.

ELECTRICAL APPLIANCES AND EQUIPMENT

81

Chapter Editor
N. A. Smith

Contents

81. ELECTRICAL APPLIANCES AND EQUIPMENT

GENERAL PROFILE

N. A. Smith

Overview of the Sector

Electrical equipment includes a wide-ranging field of devices. It would be impossible to include information on all items of equipment, and this chapter will therefore be limited to coverage of products of some of the major industries. Numerous processes are involved in the manufacture of such equipment. This chapter discusses the hazards likely to be encountered by persons working in the manufacture of batteries, electric cables, electric lamps and general domestic electrical equipment. It concentrates upon electrical equipment; electronic equipment is discussed in detail in the chapter *Microelectronics and semiconductors*.

Evolution of the Industry

The pioneering discovery of electromagnetic induction was instrumental in the development of today's vast electrical industry. The discovery of the electrochemical effect led to the development of batteries as a means of supplying electrical equipment from portable power sources using direct current systems. As devices which relied upon power from mains were invented, a system of transmission and distribution of electricity was required, which led to the introduction of flexible electrical conductors (cables).

The early forms of artificial lighting (i.e., carbon arc and gas lighting) were superseded by the filament lamp (originally with a carbon filament, exhibited by Joseph Swan in England in January 1879). The filament lamp was to enjoy an unprecedented monopoly in domestic, commercial and industrial applications prior to the outbreak of the Second World War, at which stage the fluorescent lamp was introduced. Other forms of discharge lighting, all of which depend upon the passage of an electric current through a gas or vapour, have subsequently been developed and have a variety of applications in commerce and industry.

Other electrical appliances in many fields (e.g., audio-visual, heating, cooking and refrigeration) are constantly being developed, and the range of such devices is increasing. This is typified by the introduction of satellite television and the microwave cooker.

While the availability and accessibility of raw materials had a significant effect upon the development of the industries, the locations of the industries were not necessarily determined by the locations of the raw material sources. The raw materials are often processed by a third party before being used in the assembly of electrical appliances and equipment.

Characteristics of the Workforce

The skills and expertise possessed by those who work in the industry now are different from those possessed by the workforce in earlier years. Equipment used in the production and manufacture of batteries, cables, lamps and domestic electrical appliances is highly automated.

In many instances those who are currently involved in the industry require specialized training in order to carry out their work. Teamwork is a significant factor in the industry, since many processes involve production line systems, where the work of individuals depends upon the work of others.

An ever-increasing number of manufacturing processes involved in the production of electrical appliances rely on some form of computerization. It is necessary, therefore, for the workforce to be familiar with computer techniques. This may not present any problems to the younger workforce, but older workers may not have had any previous computer experience, and it is likely that they will need to be re-trained.

Economic Importance of the Industry

Some countries benefit more than others from the electrical appliances and equipment industry. The industry has economic importance for those countries from which raw materials are obtained and those in which the end products are assembled and/or constructed. Assembly and construction take place in many different countries.

Raw materials do not have infinite availability. Discarded equipment should be re-used wherever possible. However, the costs involved in recovering those parts of discarded equipment which may be re-used may ultimately be prohibitive.

LEAD-ACID BATTERY MANUFACTURE ●

Barry P. Kelley

The first practical design of a lead-acid battery was developed by Gaston Planté in 1860, and production has continued to grow steadily since. Automotive batteries represent the major use of lead-acid technology, followed by industrial batteries (stand-by power and traction). More than half the worldwide production of lead goes into batteries.

The low cost and ease of manufacture of lead-acid batteries in relation to other electrochemical couples should ensure a continuing demand for this system in the future.

The lead-acid battery has a positive electrode of lead peroxide (PbO_2) and a negative electrode of high surface area spongy lead (Pb). The electrolyte is a sulphuric acid solution with specific gravity in the range 1.21 to 1.30 (28 to 39% by weight). On discharge, both electrodes convert to lead sulphate, as shown below:

$$PbO_2 + Pb + 2H_2SO_4 \underset{\text{charge}}{\overset{\text{discharge}}{\rightleftharpoons}} 2PbSO_4 + 2H_2O$$

Manufacturing Process

The manufacturing process, which is shown in the process flow chart (figure 81.1), is described below:

Oxide manufacture: Lead oxide is manufactured from pigs of lead (masses of lead from smelting furnaces) by one of two methods—a Barton Pot or a milling process. In the Barton Pot process, air is blown over molten lead to produce a fine stream of lead droplets. The droplets react with oxygen in the air to form the oxide, which consists of a core of lead with a lead oxide (PbO) coating.

In the milling process, solid lead (which may range in size from small balls to complete pigs) is fed into a rotating mill. The tumbling action of the lead generates heat and the surface of the lead oxidizes. As the particles roll around in the drum, the surface layers of oxide are removed to expose more clean lead for oxidation. The airstream carries the powder to a bag filter, where it is collected.

Grid production: Grids are produced mainly by casting (both automatic and manual) or, particularly for automotive batteries, expansion from wrought or cast lead alloy.

Pasting: Battery paste is made by mixing the oxide with water, sulphuric acid and a range of proprietary additives. The paste is pressed by machine or hand into the grid lattice, and the plates are usually flash-dried in a high-temperature oven.

Pasted plates are cured by storing them in ovens under carefully controlled conditions of temperature, humidity and time. Free lead in the paste converts to lead oxide.

Formation, plate cutting and assembly: Battery plates undergo an electrical formation process in one of two ways. In tank formation, plates are loaded into large baths of dilute sulphuric acid and a

Figure 81.1 • Lead-acid battery manufacturing process.

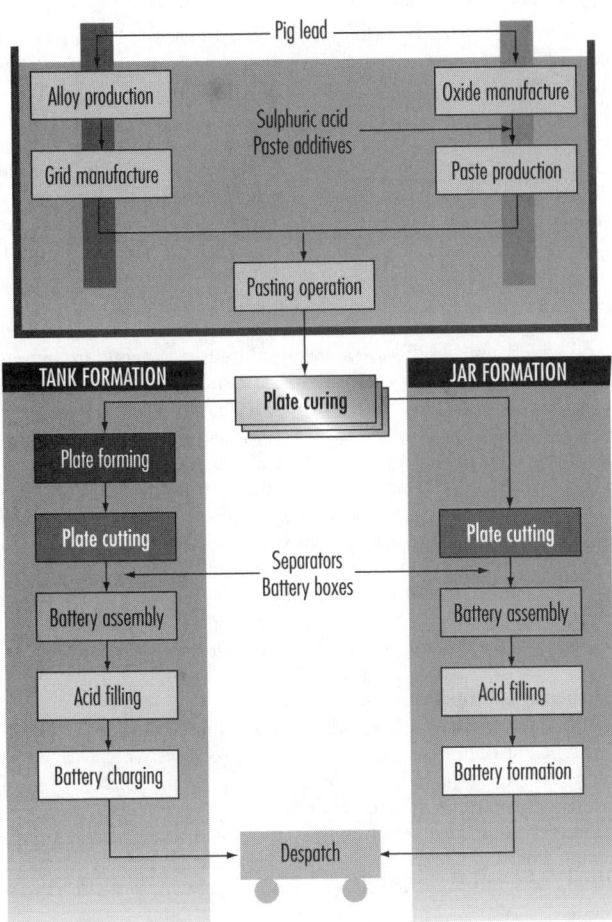

Pasting areas have traditionally resulted in high lead exposures. The manufacturing method often results in splashes of lead slurry getting onto machinery, the floor, aprons and boots. These splashes dry out and produce airborne lead dust. Control is achieved by keeping the floor permanently wetted and frequently sponging down aprons.

Lead exposures in other departments (forming, plate cutting and assembly) occur through handling dry, dusty plates. Exposures are minimized by LEV together with appropriate use of personal protective equipment.

Many countries have legislation in place to limit the degree of occupational exposure, and numerical standards exist for lead-in-air and blood lead levels.

An occupational health professional is normally employed to take blood samples from exposed workers. The frequency of blood testing can range from annual for low-risk workers to quarterly for those in high-risk departments (e.g., pasting). If a worker's blood lead level exceeds the statutory limit, then the worker should be removed from any work exposure to lead until the blood lead falls to a level deemed acceptable by the medical adviser.

Air sampling for lead is complementary to blood lead testing. Personal, rather than static, sampling is the preferred method. A large number of lead-in-air samples is usually required because of the inherent variability in results. Use of the correct statistical procedures in analysing the data can give information on sources of lead and can provide a basis for making improvements to engineering design. Regular air sampling can be used to assess the continuing effectiveness of control systems.

The allowable lead-in-air concentrations and blood lead concentrations vary from country to country, and presently range from 0.05 to 0.20 mg/m³ and 50 to 80 mg/dl respectively. There is a continuing downward trend in these limits.

In addition to the normal engineering controls, other measures are necessary to minimize lead exposures. There should be no eating, smoking, drinking or gum chewing in any production area.

Suitable washing and changing facilities should be provided to enable work clothing to be kept in a separate area from personal clothing and footwear. Washing/shower facilities should be located between the clean and dirty areas.

Sulphuric acid

During the formation process the active material on the plates is converted to PbO_2 at the positive and Pb at the negative electrode. As the plates become fully charged, the formation current begins to dissociate the water in the electrolyte into hydrogen and oxygen:

Positive: $H_2O \rightarrow 2H^+ + \frac{1}{2}O_2 + 2e^-$

Negative: $\dfrac{2H^+ + 2e^- \rightarrow H_2}{H_2O \rightarrow H_2 + \frac{1}{2}O_2}$

Gassing generates sulphuric acid mist. Tooth erosion was, at one time, a common feature among workers in formation areas. Battery companies have traditionally employed the services of a dentist, and many continue to do so.

Recent studies (IARC 1992) have suggested a possible link between exposures to inorganic acid mists (including sulphuric acid) and cancer of the larynx. Research continues in this area.

The occupational exposure standard in the UK for sulphuric acid mist is 1 mg/m³. Exposures can be kept below this level with LEV in place over the formation circuits.

Skin exposure to the corrosive sulphuric acid liquid is also of concern. Precautions include personal protection equipment, eyewash fountains and emergency showers.

direct current is passed to form the positive and negative plates. After drying, the plates are cut and assembled, with separators between them, into battery boxes. Plates of like polarity are connected by welding together the plate lugs.

In jar formation, the plates are electrically formed after being assembled into battery boxes.

Occupational Health Hazards and Controls

Lead

Lead is the major health hazard associated with battery manufacture. The principal exposure route is through inhalation, but ingestion can also pose a problem if insufficient attention is paid to personal hygiene. Exposure can occur at all stages of production.

Lead oxide manufacture is potentially very hazardous. Exposures are controlled by automating the process, thus removing the workers from the hazard. In many factories the process is operated by one person.

In grid casting, exposures to lead fumes are minimized by the use of local exhaust ventilation (LEV) together with thermostatic control of lead pots (lead fume emissions increase markedly above 500 °C). Lead-bearing dross, which forms on top of the molten lead, can also cause problems. The dross contains a large amount of very fine dust, and great care has to be exercised when disposing of it.

81. ELECTRICAL APPLIANCES AND EQUIPMENT

Talc

Talc is used in certain hand-casting operations as a mould release agent. Long-term exposure to talc dust can cause pneumoconiosis, and it is important that the dust be controlled by suitable ventilation and process control measures.

Man-made mineral fibres (MMFs)

Separators are used in lead-acid batteries to electrically insulate the positive from the negative plates. Various types of material have been used over the years (e.g., rubber, cellulose, polyvinyl chloride (PVC), polyethylene), but, increasingly, glass fibre separators are being used. These separators are manufactured from MMFs.

An increased risk of lung cancer amongst workers was demonstrated in the early days of the mineral wool industry (HSE 1990). However, this may have been caused by other carcinogenic materials in use at the time. It is prudent nevertheless to ensure that any exposure to MMFs is kept to a minimum by either total enclosure or LEV.

Stibine and arsine

Antimony and arsenic are commonly used in lead alloys, and stibine (SbH_3) or arsine (AsH_3) can be produced under certain circumstances:

- when a cell is given excessive overcharge
- when dross from a lead calcium alloy is mixed with dross from a lead antimony or lead arsenic alloy. The two drosses can react chemically to form calcium stibide or calcium arsenide which, on subsequent wetting, can generate SbH_3 or AsH_3.

Stibine and arsine are both highly toxic gases which act by destroying red blood cells. Strict process controls during battery manufacture should prevent any risk of exposure to these gases.

Physical hazards

A variety of physical hazards also exists in battery manufacturing (e.g., noise, molten metal and acid splashes, electrical hazards and manual handling), but the risks from these can be reduced by appropriate engineering and process controls.

Environmental Issues

The effect of lead on the health of children has been extensively studied. It is therefore very important that environmental releases of lead be kept to a minimum. For battery factories, the most polluting air emissions should be filtered. All process waste (usually an acidic lead-bearing slurry) should be processed at an effluent treatment plant to neutralize the acid and settle out the lead from the suspension.

Future Developments

It is likely that there will be increasing restrictions on the use of lead in the future. In an occupational sense this will result in increasing automation of processes so that the worker is removed from the hazard.

● BATTERIES

N. A. Smith

The term *battery* refers to a collection of individual *cells*, which can generate electricity though chemical reactions. Cells are categorized as either *primary* or *secondary*. In primary cells, the chemical reactions that produce the electron flow are not reversible, and therefore the cells are not easily recharged. Conversely, secondary cells must be charged prior to their use, which is achieved by passing an electrical current through the cell. Secondary cells have the advantage that they can often be repeatedly recharged and discharged through use.

The classic primary battery in everyday use is the Leclanché dry cell, so called because the electrolyte is a paste, not a liquid. The Leclanché cell is typified by the cylindrical batteries used in flashlights, portable radios, calculators, electric toys and the like. In recent years, alkaline batteries, such as the zinc-manganese dioxide cell, have become more prevalent for this type of use. Miniature or "button" batteries have found use in hearing aids, computers, watches, cameras and other electronic equipment. The silver oxide-zinc cell, mercury cell, the zinc-air cell, and the lithium-manganese dioxide cell are some examples. See figure 81.2 for a cutaway view of a typical alkaline miniature battery.

The classic secondary or storage battery is the lead-acid battery, widely used in the transportation industry. Secondary batteries are also used in power plants and industry. Rechargeable, battery-operated tools, toothbrushes, flashlights and the like are a new market for secondary cells. Nickel-cadmium secondary cells are becoming more popular, especially in pocket cells for emergency lighting, diesel starting and stationary and traction applications, where the reliability, long life, frequent rechargeability and low-temperature performance outweigh their extra cost.

Rechargeable batteries under development for use in electric vehicles utilize lithium-ferrous sulphide, zinc-chlorine and sodium-sulphur.

Table 81.1 gives the composition of some common batteries.

Manufacturing Processes

While there are clear differences in the manufacture of the different types of batteries, there are several processes which are common: weighing, grinding, mixing, compressing and drying of constituent ingredients. In modern battery plants many of these processes are enclosed and highly automated, using sealed equipment. Therefore, exposure to the various ingredients can occur during weighing and loading and during cleaning of the equipment.

In older battery plants, many of the grinding, mixing and other operations are done manually, or the transfer of ingredients from one step of the process to another is done manually. In these instances, the risk of inhalation of dusts or skin contact with

Figure 81.2 • Cutaway view of alkaline miniature battery.

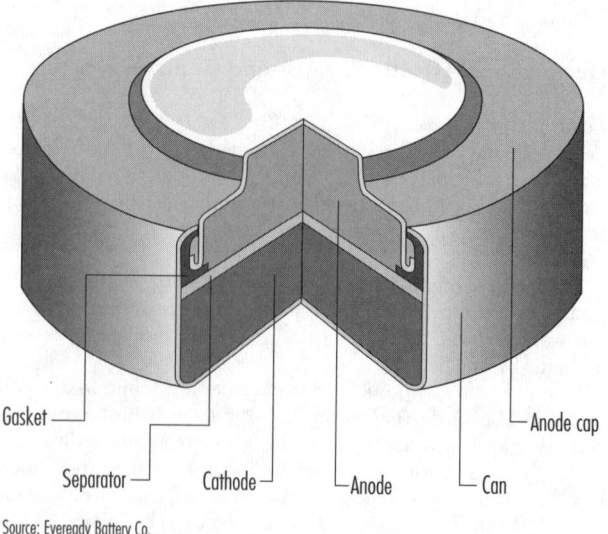

Gasket — Separator — Cathode — Anode — Can — Anode cap

Source: Eveready Battery Co.

Table 81.1 • Composition of common batteries.

Type of battery	Negative electrode	Positive electrode	Electrolyte
Primary cells			
Leclanché dry cell	Zinc	Manganese dioxide	Water, zinc chloride, ammonium chloride
Alkaline	Zinc	Manganese dioxide	Potassium hydroxide
Mercury (Ruben's cell)	Zinc	Mercuric oxide	Potassium hydroxide, zinc oxide, water
Silver	Zinc	Silver oxide	Potassium hydroxide, zinc oxide, water
Lithium	Lithium	Manganese dioxide	Lithium chlorate, $LiCF_3SO_3$
Lithium	Lithium	Sulphur dioxide	Sulphur dioxide, acetonitrile, lithium bromide
		Thionyl chloride	Lithium aluminium chloride
Zinc in air	Zinc	Oxygen	Zinc oxide, potassium hydroxide
Secondary cells			
Lead-acid	Lead	Lead dioxide	Dilute sulphuric acid
Nickel-iron (Edison battery)	Iron	Nickel oxide	Potassium hydroxide
Nickel-cadmium	Cadmium hydroxide	Nickel hydroxide	Potassium hydroxide, possibly lithium hydroxide
Silver-zinc	Zinc powder	Silver oxide	Potassium hydroxide

corrosive substances is high. Precautions for dust-producing operations include total enclosure and mechanized handling and weighing of powders, local exhaust ventilation, daily wet mopping and/or vacuuming and wearing of respirators and other personal protective equipment during maintenance operations.

Noise is also a hazard, since compressing machines and wrapping machines are noisy. Noise control methods and hearing conservation programmes are essential.

The electrolytes in many batteries contain corrosive potassium hydroxide. Enclosure and skin and eye protection are indicated precautions. Exposures can also occur to the particulates of toxic metals such as cadmium oxide, mercury, mercuric oxide, nickel and nickel compounds, and lithium and lithium compounds, which are used as anodes or cathodes in particular types of batteries. The lead-acid storage battery, sometimes referred to as the accumulator, can involve considerable lead exposure hazards and is discussed separately in the article "Lead-acid battery manufacture".

Lithium metal is highly reactive, thus lithium batteries must be assembled in a dry atmosphere in order to avoid the lithium reacting with water vapour. Sulphur dioxide and thionyl chloride, used in some lithium batteries, are respiratory hazards. Hydrogen gas, used in nickel-hydrogen batteries, is a fire and explosion hazard. These, as well as materials in newly developed batteries, will require special precautions.

Leclanché Cells

Leclanché dry-cell batteries are produced as shown in figure 81.3. The positive electrode or cathode mixture comprises 60 to 70% manganese dioxide, the remainder being made up of graphite, acetylene black, ammonium salts, zinc chloride and water. Dry, finely ground manganese dioxide, graphite and acetylene black are weighed and fed into a grinder-mixer; electrolyte containing water, zinc chloride and ammonium chloride is added, and the prepared mixture is pressed on a hand-fed tableting or agglomerating press. In certain cases, the mixture is dried in an oven, sifted and remoistened before tableting. The tablets are inspected and wrapped on hand-fed machines after being allowed to harden for a few days. The agglomerates are then placed in trays and soaked in electrolyte, and are now ready for assembly.

The anode is the zinc case, which is prepared from zinc blanks on a hot press (or zinc sheets are folded and welded to the case). An organic gelatinous paste consisting of maize and flour starches soaked in electrolyte is mixed in large vats. The ingredients are usually poured in from sacks without weighing. The mixture is then purified with zinc chips and manganese dioxide. Mercuric chloride is added to the electrolyte to form an amalgam with the interior of the zinc container. This paste will form the conducting medium or electrolyte.

Cells are assembled by automatic pouring of the required amount of gelatinous paste into the zinc cases to form an inner sleeve lining on the zinc container. In some cases, the cases receive a chromate finish by the pouring in and emptying of a mixture of chromic and hydrochloric acid before adding the gelatinous paste. The cathode agglomerate is then placed in position in the centre of the case. A carbon rod is placed centrally in the cathode to act as the current collector.

The zinc cell is then sealed with molten wax or paraffin and heated with a flame to give a better seal. The cells are then welded together to form the battery. The reaction of the battery is:

$$2\,MnO_2 + 2\,NH_4Cl + Zn \rightarrow ZnCl_2 + H_2O_2 + Mn_2O_3$$

Workers may be exposed to manganese dioxide during weighing, mixer loading, grinding, cleaning the oven, sifting, hand pressing and wrapping, depending on the degree of automation, sealed enclosure and local exhaust ventilation. In manual pressing and wet wrapping, there may be exposure to the wet mixture, which can dry to produce inhalable dust; dermatitis may occur from exposure to the slightly corrosive electrolyte. Personal hygiene measures, gloves and respiratory protection for cleaning and maintenance operations, showering facilities and separate lockers for work and street clothes can reduce these risks. As mentioned above, noise hazards can result from the wrapping and tableting press.

Mixing is automatic during manufacture of the gelatinous paste, and the only exposure is during addition of the materials. During addition of mercuric chloride to the gelatinous paste, there is the risk of inhalation and skin absorption and possible mercury poisoning. LEV or personal protective equipment is necessary.

Figure 81.3 • Flow chart of Leclanché cell battery production.

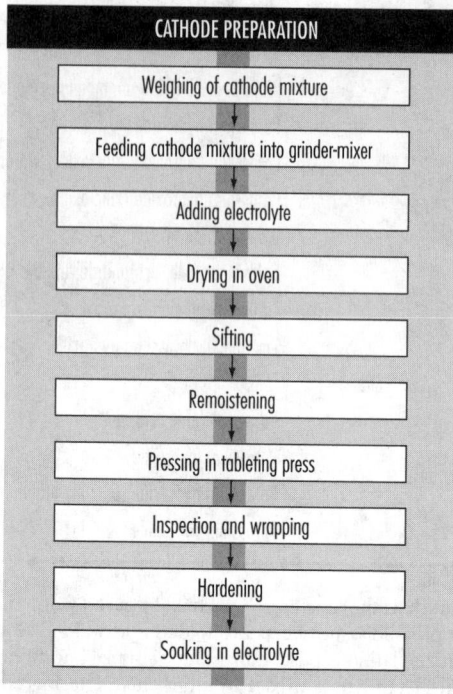

CATHODE PREPARATION

Weighing of cathode mixture

Feeding cathode mixture into grinder-mixer

Adding electrolyte

Drying in oven

Sifting

Remoistening

Pressing in tableting press

Inspection and wrapping

Hardening

Soaking in electrolyte

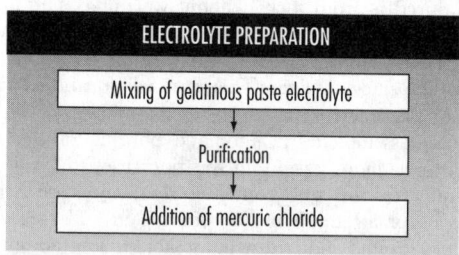

ELECTROLYTE PREPARATION

Mixing of gelatinous paste electrolyte

Purification

Addition of mercuric chloride

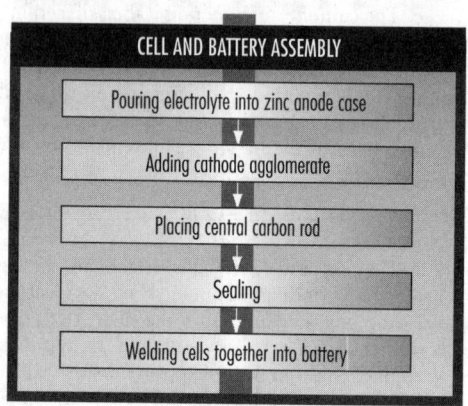

CELL AND BATTERY ASSEMBLY

Pouring electrolyte into zinc anode case

Adding cathode agglomerate

Placing central carbon rod

Sealing

Welding cells together into battery

Exposure to spills of chromic acid and hydrochloric acid during chromating and exposure to welding fumes and fumes from heating the sealing compound are also possible. Mechanization of the chromating process, use of gloves and LEV for heat sealing and welding are suitable precautions.

Nickel-Cadmium Batteries

The most common method today of making nickel-cadmium electrodes is by depositing the active electrode material directly into a porous sintered nickel substrate, or plate. (See figure 81.4.) The plate is prepared by pressing a paste of sintered grade nickel powder (often made by decomposition of nickel carbonyl) into the open grid of nickel-plated perforated sheet steel (or nickel gauze or nickel-plated steel gauze) and then sintering or drying in an oven. These plates may then be cut, weighed and coined (compressed) for particular purposes or rolled into a spiral for household-type cells.

The sintered plaque is then impregnated with nickel nitrate solution for the positive electrode or cadmium nitrate for the negative electrode. These plaques are rinsed and dried, immersed in sodium hydroxide to form nickel hydroxide or cadmium hydroxide and washed and dried again. Usually the next step is to immerse the positive and negative electrodes in a large temporary cell containing 20 to 30% sodium hydroxide. Charge-discharge cycles are run to remove impurities and the electrodes are removed, washed and dried.

An alternative way of making cadmium electrodes is to prepare a paste of cadmium oxide mixed with graphite, iron oxide and paraffin, which is milled and finally compacted between rollers to form the active material. This is then pressed into a moving perforated steel strip that is dried, sometimes compressed, and cut into plates. Lugs may be attached at this stage.

The next steps involve cell and battery assembly. For large batteries, the individual electrodes are then assembled into electrode groups with plates of opposite polarity interleaved with plastic separators. These electrode groups may be bolted or welded together and placed in a nickel-plated steel casing. More recently, plastic battery casings have been introduced. The cells are filled with an electrolyte solution of potassium hydroxide, which may also contain lithium hydroxide. The cells are then assembled into batteries and bolted together. Plastic cells may be cemented or taped together. Each cell is connected with a lead connector to the adjacent cell, leaving a positive and negative terminal at the ends of the battery.

For cylindrical batteries, the impregnated plates are assembled into electrode groups by winding the positive and negative electrodes, separated by an inert material, into a tight cylinder. The electrode cylinder is then placed in a nickel-plated metal case, potassium hydroxide electrolyte is added and the cell is sealed by welding.

The chemical reaction involved in the charging and discharging of nickel-cadmium batteries is:

$$2Ni(OH)_2 + Cd(OH)_2 \xrightarrow[\text{discharging}]{\text{charging}} Cd^{\circ} + 2HO_2O + 2NiOOH$$

The major potential exposure to cadmium occurs from handling of cadmium nitrate and its solution while making paste from cadmium oxide powder and handling the dried active powders. Exposure can also occur during reclamation of cadmium from scrap plates. Enclosure and automated weighing and mixing can reduce these hazards during the early steps.

Similar measures can control exposures to nickel compounds. The production of sintered nickel from nickel carbonyl, although done in sealed machinery, involves potential exposure to extremely toxic nickel carbonyl and carbon monoxide. The process requires continuous monitoring for gas leaks.

The handling of caustic potassium or lithium hydroxide requires suitable ventilation and personal protection. Welding generates fumes and requires LEV.

Health Effects and Disease Patterns

The most serious health hazards in traditional battery making are lead, cadmium, mercury and manganese dioxide exposures. Lead hazards are discussed elsewhere in this chapter and *Encyclopaedia*.

Figure 81.4 • Flow chart of nickel-cadmium battery production using sintered nickel.

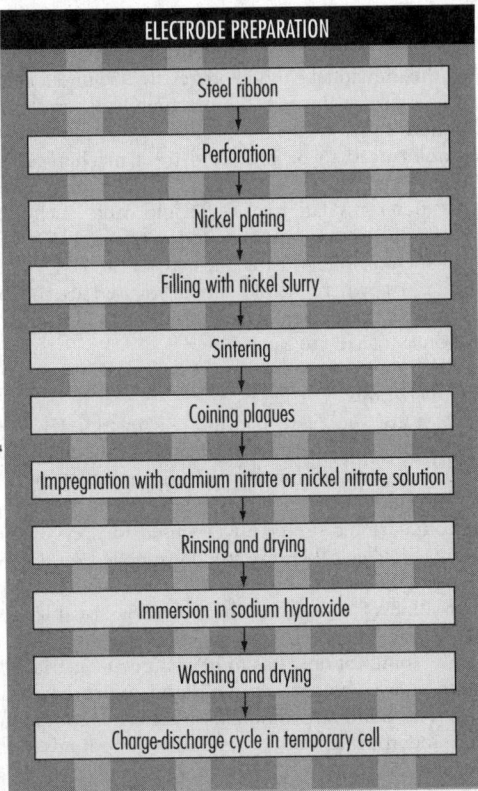

ELECTRODE PREPARATION

Steel ribbon

↓

Perforation

↓

Nickel plating

↓

Filling with nickel slurry

↓

Sintering

↓

Coining plaques

↓

Impregnation with cadmium nitrate or nickel nitrate solution

↓

Rinsing and drying

↓

Immersion in sodium hydroxide

↓

Washing and drying

↓

Charge-discharge cycle in temporary cell

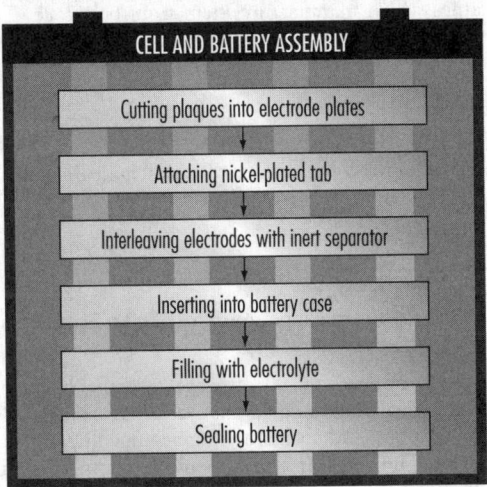

CELL AND BATTERY ASSEMBLY

Cutting plaques into electrode plates

↓

Attaching nickel-plated tab

↓

Interleaving electrodes with inert separator

↓

Inserting into battery case

↓

Filling with electrolyte

↓

Sealing battery

Cadmium can cause kidney disease and is carcinogenic. Cadmium exposure was found to be widespread in US nickel-cadmium battery plants, and many workers have had to be medically removed under the Occupational Safety and Health Administration's Cadmium Standard provisions due to high cadmium levels in blood and urine (McDiarmid et al. 1996). Mercury affects the kidneys and nervous system. Excessive exposure to mercury vapour has been shown in studies of several mercury battery plants (Telesca 1983). Manganese dioxide exposures have been shown to be high in powder mixing and handling in alkaline dry cell manufacturing (Wallis, Menke and Chelton 1993). This can result in

neurofunctional deficits in battery workers (Roels et al. 1992). Manganese dusts can, if absorbed in excessive quantities, lead to disorders of the central nervous system similar to Parkinson's syndrome. Other metals of concern include nickel, lithium, silver and cobalt.

Skin burns can result from exposure to zinc chloride, potassium hydroxide, sodium hydroxide and lithium hydroxide solutions used in the electrolytes of batteries.

ELECTRIC CABLE MANUFACTURE

David A. O'Malley

Cables come in a variety of sizes for different uses, from supertension power cables which carry electrical power at more than 100 kilovolts, down to telecommunication cables. The latter in the past utilized copper conductors, but these have been superseded by fibre optic cables, which carry more information in a much smaller cable. In between there are the general cables used for house wiring purposes, other flexible cables and power cables at voltages below those of the supertension cables. In addition, there are more specialized cables such as mineral insulated cables (used where their inherent protection from burning in a fire is crucial—for example, in a factory, in a hotel or on board a ship), enamelled wires (used as electrical windings for motors), tinsel wire (used in the curly connection of a telephone handset), cooker cables (which historically used asbestos insulation but now use other materials) and so on.

Materials and Processes

Conductors

The most common material used as the conductor in cables has always been copper, due to its electrical conductivity. Copper has to be refined to high purity before it can be made into a conductor. The refining of copper from ore or scrap is a two-stage process:

1. fire refining in a large furnace to remove unwanted impurities and cast a copper anode
2. electrolytic refining in an electrical cell containing sulphuric acid, from which very pure copper is deposited on to the cathode.

In modern plants, copper cathodes are melted in a shaft furnace and continuously cast and rolled into copper rod. This rod is drawn down to the required size on a wire-drawing machine by pulling the copper through a series of precise dies. Historically, the wire-drawing operation was conducted in one central location, with many machines producing wires of different sizes. More recently, smaller autonomous factories have their own, smaller wire-drawing operation. For some specialist applications the copper conductor is plated with a metal coating, such as tin, silver or zinc.

Aluminium conductors are used in overhead power cables where the lighter weight more than compensates for the inferior conductivity compared to copper. Aluminium conductors are made by squeezing a heated billet of aluminium through a die using an extrusion press.

More specialized metallic conductors utilize special alloys for a particular application. A cadmium-copper alloy has been used for overhead catenaries (the overhead conductor used on a railway) and for the tinsel wire used in a telephone handset. The cadmium

81. ELECTRICAL APPLIANCES AND EQUIPMENT

increases the tensile strength compared to pure copper, and is used so that the catenary does not sag between supports. Beryllium-copper alloy is also used in certain applications.

Optical fibres, consisting of a continuous filament of high optical quality glass to transmit telecommunications, were developed in the early 1980s. This required a totally new manufacturing technology. Silicon tetrachloride is burnt inside a lathe to deposit silicon dioxide on a blank. The silicon dioxide is converted to glass by heating in a chlorine atmosphere; then it is drawn to size, and a protective coating is applied.

Insulation

Many insulation materials have been used on different types of cables. The most common types are plastic materials, such as PVC, polyethylene, polytetrafluoroethylene (PTFE) and polyamides. In each case, the plastic is formulated to meet a technical specification, and is applied to the outside of the conductor using an extrusion machine. In some instances, materials may be added to the plastic compound for a particular application. Some power cables, for example, incorporate a silane compound for cross-linking the plastic. In cases where the cable is going to be buried in the ground, a pesticide is added to prevent termites from eating the insulation.

Some flexible cables, particularly those in underground mines, use rubber insulation. Hundreds of different rubber compounds are needed to meet different specifications, and a specialist rubber compounding facility is required. The rubber is extruded on to the conductor. It must also be vulcanized by passing through either a bath of hot nitrite salt or a pressurized liquid. To prevent adjacent rubber-insulated conductors from sticking together, they are drawn through talc powder.

The conductor inside a cable may be wrapped with an insulator such as paper (which may have been soaked in a mineral or a synthetic oil) or mica. An outer sheath is then applied, typically by plastic extrusion.

Two methods of manufacturing mineral insulated (MI) cables have been developed. In the first, a copper tube has a number of solid copper conductors inserted into it, and the space between is packed with a magnesium oxide powder. The whole assembly is then drawn down through a series of dies to the required size. The other technique involves continuous welding of a copper spiral around conductors separated by powder. In use, the outer copper sheath of an MI cable is the earth connection, and the inner conductors carry the current. Although no outer layer is needed, some customers specify a PVC sheath for aesthetic reasons. This is counter-productive, since the main advantage of MI cable is that it does not burn, and a PVC sheath negates this advantage somewhat.

In recent years the behaviour of cables in fires has received increasing attention for two reasons:

1. Most rubbers and plastics, the traditional insulation materials, emit copious quantities of smoke and toxic gases in a fire, and in a number of high-profile fire incidents this has been the main cause of death.
2. Once a cable has burnt through, the conductors touch and fuse the circuit, and so electrical power is lost. This has led to the development of low smoke and fire (LSF) compounds, both for plastic and rubber materials. It should be realized, however, that the best performance in a fire will always be obtained from an MI cable.

A number of specialized materials are used for certain cables. Supertension cables are oil-filled both for insulation and cooling properties. Other cables use a hydrocarbon grease known as MIND, petroleum jelly or a lead sheath. Enamelled wires are typically made by coating them with a polyurethane enamel dissolved in cresol.

Cablemaking

In many cables the individual, insulated conductors are twisted together to form a particular configuration. A number of reels containing the individual conductors revolve around a central axis as the cable is drawn through the machine, in operations known as *stranding* and *lay-up*.

Some cables need to be protected from mechanical damage. This is often done by *braiding*, where a material is interwoven around the outer insulation of a flexible cable such that each strand crosses each other one over and over again in a spiral. An example of such a braided cable (at least in the UK) is that used on electric irons, where textile thread is used as the braiding material. In other cases steel wire is used for the braiding, where the operation is referred to as *armouring*.

Ancillary operations

Larger cables are supplied on drums of up to a few metres in diameter. Traditionally, drums are wooden, but steel ones have been used. A wooden drum is made by nailing together sawn timber using either a machine or a pneumatic nailing gun. A copper-chrome-arsenic preservative is used to prevent the wood from rotting. Smaller cables are usually supplied on a cardboard reel.

The operation of connecting the two ends of cables together, known as *jointing*, may well have to be carried out in a remote location. The joint not only has to have a good electrical connection, but must also be able to withstand future environmental conditions. The jointing compounds used are commonly acrylic resins and incorporate both isocyanate compounds and silica powder.

Cable connectors are commonly made out of brass on automatic lathes which manufacture them from bar stock. The machines are cooled and lubricated using a water-oil emulsion. Cable clips are made by plastic injection machines.

Hazards and their Prevention

The most widespread health hazard throughout the cable industry is noise. The noisiest operations are:

- wire-drawing
- braiding
- the copper fire refinery
- continuous casting of copper rods
- cable drum manufacture.

Noise levels in excess of 90 dBA are common in these areas. For wire-drawing and braiding the overall noise level depends upon the number and location of machines and the acoustic environment. The machine layout should be planned to minimize noise exposures. Carefully designed acoustic enclosures are the most effective means of controlling the noise, but are expensive. For the copper fire refinery and continuous casting of copper rods the main sources of noise are the burners, which should be designed for low noise emission. In the case of cable drum manufacture the pneumatically operated nail guns are the principal source of noise, which can be reduced by lowering the air-line pressure and installing exhaust silencers. The industry's norm in most of the above cases, however, is to issue hearing protection to workers in the areas affected, but such protection will be more uncomfortable than usual due to the hot environments in the copper fire refinery and continuous casting of copper rods. Regular audiometry should also be conducted to monitor each individual's hearing.

Many of the safety hazards and their prevention are the same as those in many other manufacturing industries. However, special hazards are presented by some cablemaking machines, in that they have numerous reels of conductors rotating around two axes at the same time. It is essential to ensure that machine guards are interlocked to prevent the machine from operating unless the guards are in position to prevent access to running nips and other rotating parts, such as large cable drums. During the initial threading of the machine, when it may well be necessary to permit the operator access inside the machine guard, the machine should be capable of moving only a few centimetres at a time. Interlock arrangements can be achieved by having a unique key which either opens the guard or has to be inserted into the control console to allow it to operate.

An assessment of the risk from flying particles—for example, if a wire breaks and whips out—should be made.

Guards should preferably be designed to physically prevent such particles from reaching the operator. Where this is not possible, suitable eye protection must be issued and worn. Wire-drawing operations are often designated as areas where eye protection must be used.

Conductors

In any hot metal process, such as a copper fire refinery or casting copper rods, water must be prevented from coming into contact with molten metal to prevent an explosion. Loading the furnace can result in the escape of metal oxide fumes into the workplace. This should be controlled using effective local exhaust ventilation over the charging door. Similarly the launders down which the molten metal passes from the furnace to the casting machine and the casting machine itself need to be adequately controlled.

The principal hazard in the electrolytic refinery is the sulphuric acid mist evolved from each cell. Airborne concentrations must be kept below 1 mg/m^3 by suitable ventilation to prevent irritation.

When casting copper rods, an additional hazard can be presented by the use of insulation boards or blankets to conserve heat around the casting wheel. Ceramic materials may have replaced asbestos in such applications, but ceramic fibres themselves must be handled with great care to prevent exposures. Such materials become more friable (i.e., easily broken up) after use when they have been affected by heat, and exposures to airborne respirable fibres have resulted from handling them.

An unusual hazard is presented in the manufacture of aluminium power cables. A suspension of graphite in a heavy oil is applied to the ram of the extrusion press to prevent the aluminium billet from sticking to the ram. As the ram is hot, some of this material is burnt off and rises into the roof space. Provided that there is no overhead crane operator in the vicinity and that roof fans are fitted and working, there should be no risk to the health of workers.

Making either cadmium-copper alloy or beryllium-copper alloy can present high risks to the employees involved. Since cadmium boils well below the melting point of copper, freshly generated cadmium oxide fumes will be generated in great quantities whenever cadmium is added to molten copper (which it must be to make the alloy). The process can be carried out safely only with very careful design of the local exhaust ventilation. Similarly the manufacture of beryllium-copper alloy requires great attention to detail, since beryllium is the most toxic of all the toxic metals and has the most stringent of exposure limits.

The manufacture of optical fibres is a highly specialized, high-technology operation. The chemicals used have their own special hazards, and control of the working environment requires the design, installation and maintenance of complex LEV and process ventilation systems. These systems must be controlled by computer-monitored control dampers. The main chemical hazards are from chlorine, hydrogen chloride and ozone. In addition, the solvents used to clean the dies must be handled in extracted fume cabinets, and skin contact with the acrylate-based resins used to coat the fibres must be avoided.

Insulation

Both plastic compounding and rubber compounding operations present particular hazards which must be adequately controlled (see the chapter *Rubber industry*). Although the cable industry may use different compounds than other industries, the control techniques are the same.

When they are heated, plastic compounds will give off a complex mixture of thermal degradation products, the composition of which will depend upon the original plastic compound and the temperature to which it is subjected. At the normal processing temperature of plastic extruders, airborne contaminants are usually a relatively small problem, but it is prudent to install ventilation over the gap between the extruder head and the water trough used to cool the product down, mainly to control exposure to the phthalate plasticizers commonly used in PVC. The phase of the operation which may well warrant further investigation is during a changeover. The operator has to stand over the extruder head to remove the still-hot plastic compound, and then run the new compound through (and on to the floor) until only the new colour is coming through and the cable is centralized in the extruder head. It can be difficult to design effective LEV during this phase when the operator is so close to the extruder head.

Polytetrafluoroethylene (PTFE) has its own special hazard. It can cause polymer fume fever, which has symptoms resembling those of influenza. The condition is a temporary one, but should be prevented by adequately controlling exposures to the heated compound.

The use of rubber in making cables has presented a lower level of risk than other uses of rubber, such as in the tyre industry. In both industries the use of an antioxidant (Nonox S) containing β-naphthylamine, up to its withdrawal in 1949, resulted in cases of bladder cancer up to 30 years later in those who had been exposed prior to the withdrawal date, but none in those employed after 1949 only. The cable industry, however, has not experienced the increased incidence of other cancers, particularly of lung and stomach, seen in the tyre industry. The reason is almost certainly that in cable manufacture the extrusion and vulcanizing machines are enclosed, and employee exposures to rubber fumes and rubber dust were generally much lower than in the tyre industry. One exposure of potential concern in rubber cable factories is the use of talc. It is important to ensure that only the non-fibrous form of talc (i.e., one which does not contain any fibrous tremolite) is used and that the talc is applied in an enclosed box with local exhaust ventilation.

Many cables are printed with identification markings. Where modern video jet printers are used the risk to health is almost certainly negligible due to the very small quantities of solvent utilized. Other printing techniques, however, can result in significant solvent exposures, either during normal production, or more usually during cleaning operations. Suitable exhaust systems should therefore be used to control such exposures.

The main hazards from making MI cables are dust exposure, noise and vibration. The first two of these are controlled by standard techniques described elsewhere. Vibration exposure occurred in the past during *swaging*, when a point was formed at the end of the assembled tube by manual insertion into a machine with rotating hammers, so that the point could be inserted into the drawing machine. More recently this type of swaging machine has been replaced with pneumatic ones, and this has eliminated both the vibration and the noise generated by the older method.

Lead exposure during lead sheathing should be controlled by using adequate LEV and by prohibiting eating, drinking and cigarette smoking in areas liable to be contaminated with lead. Regular biological monitoring should be undertaken by analysing blood samples for lead content at a qualified laboratory.

The cresol used in the manufacture of enamelled wires is corrosive and has a distinctive odour at very low concentrations. Some of the polyurethane is thermally degraded in the enamelling ovens to release toluene di-isocyanate (TDI), a potent respiratory sensitizer. Good LEV is needed around the ovens with catalytic afterburners to ensure that the TDI does not pollute the surrounding area.

Ancillary operations

Jointing operations present hazards to two distinct groups of workers—those that make them and those that use them. Manufacture involves the handling of a fibrogenic dust (silica), a respiratory sensitizer (isocyanate) and a skin sensitizer (acrylic resin). Effective LEV must be used to adequately control employee exposures, and suitable gloves must be worn to prevent skin contact with the resin. The main hazard to users of the compounds is from skin sensitization to the resin. This can be difficult to control since the jointer may not be able to avoid skin contact altogether, and will often be in a remote location away from a source of water for cleaning purposes. A waterless hand cleanser is therefore essential.

Environmental hazards and their prevention

In the main, cable manufacture does not result in significant emissions outside the factory. There are three exceptions to this rule. The first is that exposure to the vapours of solvents used for printing and other purposes are controlled by the use of LEV systems which discharge the vapours to the atmosphere. Such emissions of volatile organic compounds (VOCs) are one of the components necessary to form photochemical smog, and so are coming under increasing pressure from regulatory authorities in a number of countries. The second exception is the potential release of TDI from enamelled wire manufacture. The third exception is that in a number of instances the manufacture of the raw materials used in cables can result in environmental emissions if control measures are not taken. Metal particulate emissions from a copper fire refinery, and from the manufacture of either cadmium-copper or beryllium-copper alloys, should each be ducted to suitable bag filter systems. Similarly any particulate emissions from rubber compounding should be ducted to a bag filter unit. Emissions of particulates, hydrogen chloride and chlorine from the manufacture of optical fibres should be ducted to a bag filter system followed by a caustic soda scrubber.

● ELECTRIC LAMP AND TUBE MANUFACTURE

Albert M. Zielinski

Lamps consist of two basic types: filament (or incandescent) lamps and discharge lamps. The basic components of both lamp types include glass, various metal wire pieces, a fill gas and usually a base. Depending on the lamp manufacturer, these materials are either made in-house or may be obtained from an outside supplier. The typical lamp manufacturer will make its own glass bulbs, but may purchase other parts and glasses from speciality manufacturers or other lamp companies.

Depending on the lamp type, a variety of glasses may be used. Incandescent and fluorescent lamps typically use a soda-lime

glass. Higher temperature lamps will use a borosilicate glass, while high-pressure discharge lamps will use either quartz or ceramic for the arc tube and borosilicate glass for the outer envelope. Leaded glass (containing approximately 20 to 30% lead) is typically used for sealing the ends of the lamp bulbs.

The wires used as supports or connectors in lamp construction may be made from a variety of materials including steel, nickel, copper, magnesium and iron, while the filaments are made from tungsten or tungsten-thorium alloy. One critical requirement for the support wire is that it must match the expansion characteristics of the glass where the wire penetrates the glass to conduct the electrical current for the lamp. Frequently, multi-part lead wires are used in this application.

Bases (or caps) are typically made from either brass or aluminium, brass being the preferred material when outdoor use is required.

Filament or Incandescent Lamps

Filament or incandescent lamps are the oldest lamp type still being manufactured. They take their name from the way these lamps produce their light: through the heating of a wire filament to a temperature high enough to cause it to glow. While it is possible to manufacture an incandescent lamp with almost any type of filament (early lamps used carbon), today most such lamps use a filament made of tungsten metal.

Tungsten lamps. The common household version of these lamps consists of a glass bulb enclosing a tungsten wire filament. Electricity is conducted to the filament by wires which support the filament and extend through the glass mount which is sealed to the bulb. The wires are then connected to the metal base, with one wire soldered at the centre eyelet of the base, the other connecting to the threaded shell. The supporting wires are of special composition, so that they have the same expansion characteristics as the glass, preventing leaks when the lamps become hot during use. The glass bulb is typically made from lime glass, while the glass mount is leaded glass. Sulphur dioxide is frequently used in preparing the mount. The sulphur dioxide acts as a lubricant during high-speed lamp assembly. Depending on the design of the lamp, the bulb may enclose a vacuum or may use a fill gas of argon or some other non-reactive gas.

Lamps of this design are sold using clear glass bulbs, frosted bulbs and bulbs coated with a variety of materials. Frosted bulbs and ones coated with a white material (frequently clay or amorphous silica) are used to reduce the glare from the filament found with clear bulbs. The bulbs are also coated with a variety of other decorative coatings, including coloured ceramics and lacquers on the outside of the bulbs and other colours, such as yellow or pink, on the inside of the bulb.

While the typical household shape is the most common, incandescent lamps can be made in many bulb shapes, including tubular, globes and reflector, as well as in many sizes and wattages, from subminiature through to large stage/studio lamps.

Tungsten-halogen lamps. One problem in the design of the standard tungsten filament lamp is that the tungsten evaporates during use and condenses on the cooler glass wall, darkening it and reducing the light transmission. Adding a halogen, such as hydrogen bromide or methyl bromide, to the fill gas eliminates this problem. The halogen reacts with the tungsten, preventing it from condensing on the glass wall. When the lamp cools, the tungsten will re-deposit back on the filament. Since this reaction works best at higher lamp pressures, tungsten-halogen lamps typically contain gas at several atmospheres pressure. Typically the halogen is added as a part of the lamp fill gas, usually at concentrations of 2% or less.

Tungsten-halogen lamps may also use bulbs made from quartz instead of glass. Quartz bulbs can withstand higher pressures than those made from glass. The quartz bulbs present a potential hazard, however, since the quartz is transparent to ultraviolet light. Although the tungsten filament produces relatively little ultraviolet, prolonged exposure at close range can produce reddening of the skin and cause eye irritation. Filtering the light through a cover glass will greatly reduce the amount of ultraviolet, as well as provide protection from the hot quartz in the event the lamp ruptures during use.

Hazards and Precautions

Overall, the greatest hazards in lamp production, regardless of product type, are due to the hazards of automated equipment and the handling of glass bulbs and lamps and other material. Cuts from the glass and reaching into the operating equipment are the most common causes of accidents; material-handling issues, such as repetitive motion or back injuries, are of particular concern.

Lead solder is frequently used on the lamps. For lamps used in higher temperature applications, solders containing cadmium may be used. In automated lamp assembly operations, exposure to both of these solders is minimal. Where hand soldering is done, as in repair or semi-automated operations, the exposures to lead or cadmium should be monitored.

Potential exposures to hazardous materials during lamp manufacturing have consistently decreased since the middle of the 20th century. In incandescent lamp manufacturing, large numbers of the lamps formerly were etched with hydrofluoric acid or bifluoride salt solutions to produce a frosted lamp. This has largely been replaced by the use of a low-toxicity clay coating. While not completely replaced, the use of hydrofluoric acid has been greatly reduced. This change has reduced the risk of burns to the skin and lung irritation due to the acid. The ceramic coloured coatings used on the outside of some lamp products formerly contained heavy metal pigments such as lead, cadmium, cobalt and others, as well as using a lead silicate glass frit as part of the composition. During recent years, many of the heavy metal pigments have been replaced by less toxic colourants. In cases where the heavy metals are still used, a lower toxicity form may be used (e.g., chromium III instead of chromium VI).

Coiled tungsten filaments continue to be made by wrapping the tungsten around a molybdenum or a steel mandrel wire. Once the coil has been formed and sintered, the mandrels are dissolved using either hydrochloric acid (for the steel) or a mixture of nitric and sulphuric acid for the molybdenum. Due to the potential acid exposures, this work is routinely done in hood systems or, more recently, in totally enclosed dissolvers (especially where the nitric/sulphuric mix is involved).

The fill gasses used in tungsten-halogen lamps are added to the lamps in totally enclosed systems with little loss or exposure. Hydrogen bromide use presents its own problems due to its corrosive nature. LEV must be provided, and corrosion-resistant piping must be used for the gas delivery systems. Thoriated tungsten wire (usually 1 to 2% thorium) is still used in some lamp types. However, there is little risk from the thorium in the wire form.

Sulphur dioxide must be carefully controlled. LEV should be used wherever the material is added to the process. Leak detectors may also be useful in storage areas. Use of smaller 75-kg gas cylinders is preferred over larger 1,000-kg containers due to the potential consequences of a catastrophic release.

Skin irritation can be a potential hazard from either the soldering fluxes or from the resins used in the basing cement. Some basing cement systems use paraformaldehyde instead of natural resins, resulting in potential formaldehyde exposure during curing of the basing cement.

All lamps use a chemical "gettering" system, in which a material is coated on the filament prior to assembly. The purpose of the getter is to react with and scavenge any residual moisture or oxygen in the lamp after the lamp is sealed. Typical getters include phosphorus nitride and mixtures of aluminium and zirconium metal powders. While the phosphorus nitride getter is fairly benign in use, handling aluminium and zirconium metal powders can be a flammability hazard. The getters are applied wet in an organic solvent, but if the material is spilled, the dry metal powders can be ignited by friction. Metal fires must be extinguished with special Class D fire extinguishers and cannot be fought with water, foam or other usual materials. A third type of getter includes use of phosphine or silane. These materials can be included in the gas fill of the lamp at low concentration or can be added at high concentration and "flashed" in the lamp prior to the final gas fill. Both these materials are highly toxic; if used at high concentration, totally enclosed systems with leakage detectors and alarms should be used at the site.

Discharge Lamps and Tubes

Discharge lamps, both low- and high-pressure models, are more efficient on a light per watt basis than incandescent lamps. Fluorescent lamps have been used for many years in commercial buildings and have been finding increased use in the home. Recently, compact versions of the fluorescent lamp have been developed specifically as replacements for the incandescent lamp.

High-pressure discharge lamps have long been used for large area and street lighting. Lower-wattage versions of these products are also being developed.

Fluorescent lamps

Fluorescent lamps are named for the fluorescent powder used to coat the inside of the glass tube. This powder absorbs ultraviolet light produced by the mercury vapour used in the lamp, and converts and re-emits it as visible light.

The glass used in this lamp is similar to that used in incandescent lamps, using lime glass for the tube and leaded glass for the mounts on each end. Two different families of phosphors are in use currently. Halophosphates, based on either calcium or strontium chloro-fluoro-phosphate, are the older phosphors, coming into wide use in the early 1950s when they replaced phosphors based on beryllium silicate. The second phosphor family includes phosphors made from rare earths, typically including yttrium, lanthanum and others. These rare-earth phosphors typically have a narrow emission spectrum, and a mixture of these are used—generally a red, a blue and a green phosphor.

The phosphors are mixed with a binder system, suspended in either an organic mix or a water/ammonia mixture and coated on the inside of the glass tube. The organic suspension uses butyl acetate, butyl acetate/naphtha or xylene. Due to environmental regulations, water-based suspensions are replacing those that are organic based. Once the coating is applied, it is dried onto the tube, and the tube is heated to a high temperature to remove the binder.

One mount is attached to each end of the lamp. Mercury is now introduced into the lamp. This can be done in a variety of ways. Although in some areas the mercury is added manually, the predominant way is automatically, with the lamp mounted either vertically or horizontally. On vertical machines, the mount stem on one end of the lamp is closed. Then mercury is dropped into the lamp from above, the lamp is filled with argon at low pressure, and the top mount stem is sealed, completely sealing the lamp. On horizontal machines, the mercury is introduced from one side, while the lamp is exhausted from the other side. Argon is again added to the proper pressure, and both ends of the lamp are sealed. Once sealed, the caps or bases are added to the ends, and the wire leads are then either soldered or welded to the electrical contacts.

Two other possible ways of introducing mercury vapour can be used. In one system, the mercury is contained on a mercury-impregnated strip, which releases the mercury when the lamp is first started. In the other system, liquid mercury is used, but it is contained within a glass capsule which is attached to the mount. The capsule is ruptured after the lamp has been sealed and exhausted, thereby releasing the mercury.

Compact fluorescent lamps are smaller versions of the standard fluorescent lamp, sometimes including the ballast electronics as an integral component of the lamp. Compact fluorescents generally will use a mixture of rare-earth phosphors. Some compact lamps will incorporate a glow starter containing small amounts of radio-active materials to aid in starting the lamp. These glow starters typically use krypton-85, hydrogen-3, promethium-147 or natural thorium to provide what is called a dark current, which helps the lamp start quicker. This is desirable from a consumer standpoint, where the customer wants the lamp to start immediately, without flickering.

Hazards and precautions

Fluorescent lamp manufacturing has seen a considerable number of changes. Early use of a beryllium-containing phosphor was discontinued in 1949, eliminating a significant respiratory hazard during phosphor production and use. In many operations, water-based phosphor suspensions have replaced organic suspensions in the coating of the fluorescent lamps, reducing exposure to the workers as well as reducing the emission of VOCs to the environment. Water-based suspensions do involve some minimal exposure to ammonia, particularly during mixing of the suspensions.

Mercury remains the material of greatest concern during fluorescent lamp making. While the exposures are relatively low except around the exhaust machines, there is potential for significant exposure to workers stationed around the exhaust machine, to mechanics working on these machines and during clean-up operations. Personal protective equipment, such as coveralls and gloves to avoid or limit exposure and, where needed, respiratory protection, should be used, especially during maintenance activities and clean-up. A biological monitoring programme, including mercury urinalysis, should be established for fluorescent lamp manufacturing sites.

The two phosphor systems currently in production utilize materials considered to have relatively low toxicity. While some of the additives to the parent phosphors (such as barium, lead and manganese) have exposure limits established by various governmental agencies, these components are usually present in relatively low percentages in the compositions.

Phenol-formaldehyde resins are used as electrical insulators in the end caps of the lamps. The cement typically includes natural and synthetic resins, which may include skin irritants such as hexamethylene-tetramine. Automated mixing and handling equipment limits the potential for skin contact to these materials, thereby limiting the potential for skin irritation.

High-pressure mercury lamps

High-pressure mercury lamps include two similar types: those using just mercury and those using a mixture of mercury and a variety of metal halides. The basic design of the lamps is similar. Both types use a quartz arc tube which will contain the mercury or mercury/halide mixture. This arc tube is then enclosed in a hard, borosilicate glass outer jacket, and a metal base is added to provide for electrical contacts. The outer jacket can be clear or coated with either a diffusing material or a phosphor to modify the colour of the light.

Mercury lamps contain only mercury and argon in the quartz arc tube of the lamp. The mercury, under high pressure, generates light with a high blue and ultraviolet content. The quartz arc tube is completely transparent to UV light, and in the event that the outer jacket is broken or removed, is a powerful UV light source that can produce skin and eye burns in those exposed. Though the typical mercury lamp design will continue to operate if the outer jacket is removed, manufacturers also offer some models in a fused design which will stop operating if the jacket is broken. During normal use, the borosilicate glass of the outer jacket absorbs a high percentage of the UV light, so that the intact lamp does not pose a hazard.

Because of the high blue content of the mercury lamp spectrum, the inside of the outer jacket is frequently coated with a phosphor such as yttrium vanadate phosphate or similar red-enhancing phosphor.

Metal halide lamps also contain mercury and argon in the arc tube, but add metal halides (typically a mixture of sodium and scandium, possibly with others). The addition of the metal halides enhances the red light output of the lamp, producing a lamp which has a more balanced light spectrum.

Hazards and precautions

Other than mercury, potentially hazardous materials used in high-pressure mercury lamp production include the coating materials used on the outer envelopes and the halide additives used in the metal halide lamps. One coating material is a simple diffuser, the same as that used in incandescent lamps. Another is a colour-correcting phosphor, yttrium vanadate or yttrium vanadate phosphate. While similar to vanadium pentoxide, the vanadate is considered to be less toxic. Exposure to the halide materials is normally not significant, since the halides react in moist air and must be kept dry and under an inert atmosphere during handling and use. Similarly, although the sodium is a highly reactive metal, it too needs to be handled under an inert atmosphere to avoid oxidizing the metal.

Sodium Lamps

Two types of sodium lamps are currently produced. Low-pressure lamps contain only metallic sodium as the light emitting source and produce a highly yellow light. High-pressure sodium lamps use mercury and sodium to generate a whiter light.

Low-pressure sodium lamps have one glass tube, which contains the metallic sodium, enclosed within a second glass tube.

High-pressure sodium lamps contain a mixture of mercury and sodium within a high-purity ceramic alumina arc tube. Other than the composition of the arc tube, the construction of the high-pressure sodium lamp is essentially the same as the mercury and metal halide lamps.

Hazards and precautions

There are few unique hazards during manufacturing of high- or low-pressure sodium lamps. In both lamp types, the sodium must be kept dry. Pure metallic sodium will violently react with water, producing hydrogen gas and enough heat to cause ignition. Metallic sodium left out in air will react with the moisture in the air, producing an oxide coating on the metal. To avoid this, the sodium is usually handled in a glove box, under a dry nitrogen or argon atmosphere. For sites manufacturing high-pressure sodium lamps, additional precautions are needed to handle the mercury, similar to those sites manufacturing high-pressure mercury lamps.

Environmental and Public Health Issues

Waste disposal and/or recycling of mercury-containing lamps is an issue that has received a high degree of attention in many areas of the world over the last several years. While at best a "break even" operation from a cost viewpoint, technology currently exists to reclaim the mercury from fluorescent and high-pressure discharge lamps. Recycling of lamp materials at the present time is more accurately described as reclamation, since the lamp materials are rarely reprocessed and used in making new lamps. Typically, the metal parts are sent to scrap metal dealers. The recovered glass may be used to make fibreglass or glass blocks or used as aggregate in cement or asphalt paving. Recycling may be the lower-cost alternative, depending on location and availability of recycling and hazardous or special waste disposal options.

The ballasts used in fluorescent lamp installations previously contained capacitors which used PCBs as the dielectric. While manufacture of PCB-containing ballasts has been discontinued, many of the older ballasts may still be in use due to their long life expectancy. Disposal of the PCB-containing ballasts may be regulated and may require disposal as a special or hazardous waste.

Glass manufacturing, particularly borosilicate glasses, can be a significant source of NO_x emission to the atmosphere. Recently, pure oxygen instead of air has been used with gas burners as a means of reducing the NO_x emissions.

DOMESTIC ELECTRICAL APPLIANCE MANUFACTURE

N. A. Smith and W. Klost*

The domestic electrical appliance industry is responsible for the manufacture of a wide-ranging variety of equipment including appliances designed for audio-visual, cooking, heating, food preparation and storage (refrigeration) uses. The production and manufacture of such appliances involve many highly-automated processes which can have associated health hazards and disease patterns.

Manufacturing Processes

Materials used in the manufacture of domestic electrical appliances can be categorized into:

1. metals which are used typically for electric conductors in cables and appliance structure and/or framework
2. dielectrics or insulating materials used for prevention of accidental contact with live electrical equipment
3. paints and finishes
4. chemicals.

Examples of the materials included in the four categories referred to are shown in table 81.2.

The materials used in the domestic electrical appliance industry must satisfy exacting requirements, including the ability to withstand the handling likely to be encountered in normal operation, the ability to withstand metal fatigue and the ability to be unaffected by any other processes or treatment which could render the appliance dangerous to use either immediately or after a prolonged period of time.

The materials used in the industry will often be received at the appliance assembly stage having already undergone several manufacturing processes, each of which is likely to have its own hazards and health problems. Details of these hazards and problems are considered under the appropriate chapters elsewhere in this *Encyclopaedia*.

The manufacturing processes will vary from product to product, but in general will follow the production flow shown in figure 81.5. This chart also shows the hazards associated with the different processes.

* Adapted from 3rd edition, *Encyclopaedia of Occupational Health and Safety.*

Health and Safety Issues

Fire and explosion

Many of the solvents, paints and insulating oils used in the industry are flammable substances. These materials should be stored in suitable cool, dry premises, preferably in a fireproof building separate from the production facility. Containers should be clearly labelled and different substances well separated or stored apart as required by their flashpoints and their class of risk. In the case of insulating materials and plastics, it is important to obtain information on the combustibility or fire characteristics of each new substance used. Powdered zirconium, which is now used in significant quantities in the industry, is also a fire hazard.

The quantities of flammable substances issued from storerooms should be kept to the minimum required for production. When flammable liquids are being decanted, charges of static electricity may form, and consequently all containers should be grounded. Fire-extinguishing appliances must be provided and the personnel of the storeplace instructed in their use.

Painting of components is usually carried out in specially built paint booths, which must have adequate exhaust and ventilation equipment that, when used with personal protective equipment (PPE), will create a safe working environment.

During welding, special fire precautions should be taken.

Accidents

Reception, storage and dispatch of raw materials, components and finished products can give rise to accidents involving trips and falls, falling objects, fork trucks and so forth. Manual materials handling can also create ergonomic problems which can be alleviated by automation whenever possible.

Since numerous different processes are employed in the industry, the accident hazards will vary from shop to shop in the plant. During component production there will be machine hazards in the use of machine tools, power presses, plastics injection-moulding machines and so on, and efficient machinery guarding is essential. During electroplating, precautions must be taken against splashes of corrosive chemicals. During component assembly, the constant movement of components from one process to another means that the danger of accidents due to in-plant transport and mechanical handling equipment is high.

Quality testing does not give rise to any special safety problems. However, performance testing requires special precautions since the tests are often carried out on semi-finished or uninsulated appliances. During electrical testing, all live components, conductors, terminals and measuring instruments should be protected to prevent accidental contact. The workplace should be screened off, entrance of unauthorized persons prohibited and warning notices

Table 81.2 • Examples of materials used in the manufacture of domestic electrical appliances.

Metals	Dielectrics	Paints/finishes	Chemicals
Steel	Inorganic materials (e.g., mica)	Paints	Acids
Aluminium	Plastics (e.g., PVC)	Lacquers	Alkalis
Lead	Rubber	Varnishes	Solvents
Cadmium	Silico-organic materials	Corrosion-resistant treatments	
Mercury	Other polymers (e.g., nylon)		

Note: Lead and mercury are decreasingly common in domestic electrical appliance manufacturing.

Figure 81.5 • Typical manufacturing process sequence and hazards likely to be encountered in the processes.

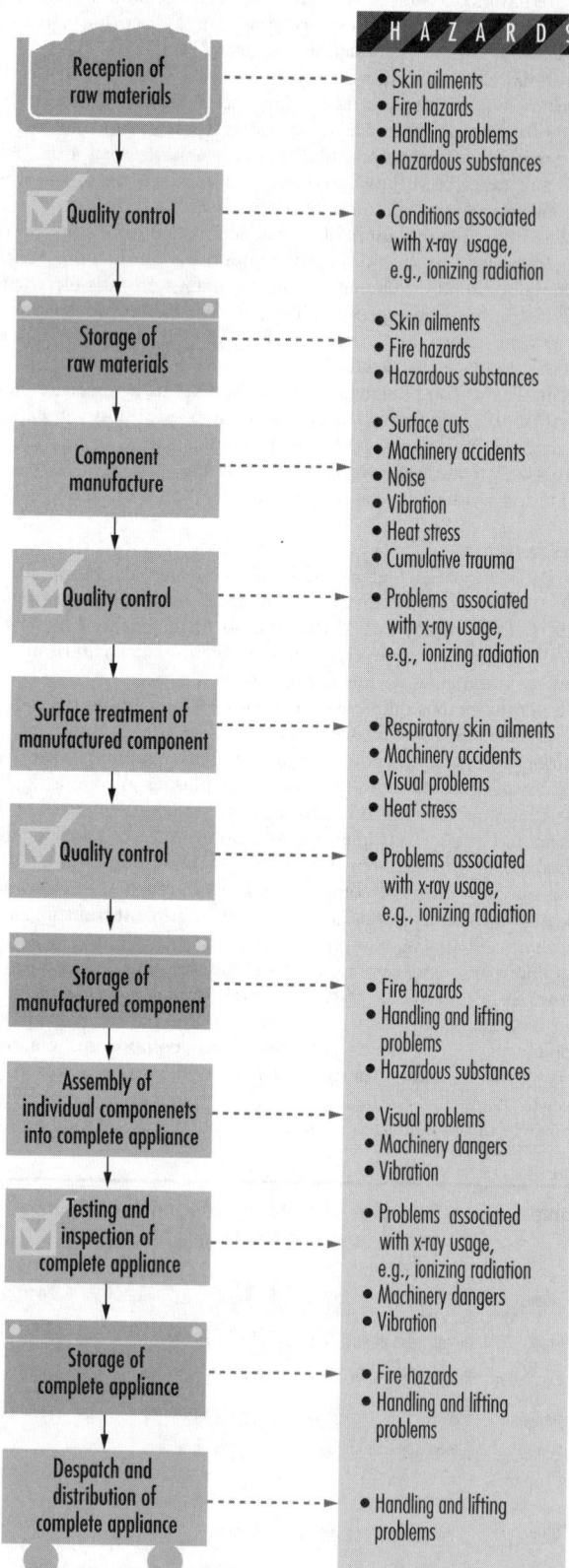

posted. In electrical testing areas, the provision of emergency switches is particularly advisable, and the switches should be in a prominent position so that in an emergency all equipment can be immediately de-energized.

For testing appliances that emit x rays or contain radioactive substances, there are radiation protection regulations. A competent supervisor should be made responsible for observance of the regulations.

There are special risks in the use of compressed gases, welding equipment, lasers, impregnation plant, spray-painting equipment, annealing and tempering ovens and high-voltage electrical installations.

During all repair and maintenance activities, adequate lockout/tagout programmes are essential.

Health Hazards

Occupational diseases associated with the manufacture of domestic electrical equipment are relatively low in number and not normally considered to be severe. Such problems that do exist are typified by:

- the development of skin conditions due to the use of solvents, cutting oils, hardeners used with epoxy resin and polychlorinated biphenyls (PCBs)
- the onset of silicosis due to the inhalation of silica in sandblasting (although sand is being increasingly replaced by less toxic blasting agents such as corundum, steel grit or shot)
- health problems due to inhalation of solvent vapours in painting and degreasing, and lead poisoning from use of lead pigments, enamels, etc.
- varying levels of noise produced during the processes.

Wherever possible, highly toxic solvents and chlorinated compounds should be replaced by less dangerous substances; under no circumstances should benzene or carbon tetrachloride be employed as solvents. Lead poisoning may be overcome by substitution of safer materials or techniques and the strict application of safe working procedures, personal hygiene and medical supervision. Where there is a danger of exposure to hazardous concentrations of atmospheric contaminants, the workplace air should be regularly monitored, and appropriate measures such as the installation of an exhaust system taken where necessary. The noise hazard may be reduced by enclosure of noise sources, the use of sound-absorbent materials in workrooms or the use of personal hearing protection.

Safety engineers and industrial physicians should be called upon at the design and planning stage of new plants or operations, and the hazards of processes or machines should be eliminated before processes are started up. This should be followed up by regular inspection of machines, tools, plant, transport equipment, firefighting appliances, workshops and test areas and so on.

Worker participation in the safety effort is essential, and supervisors should ensure that personal protective equipment is available and worn where necessary. Particular attention should be paid to the safety training of new workers, since these account for a relatively high proportion of accidents.

Workers should receive a pre-placement medical examination and, where there is the possibility of hazardous exposure, periodic examination as necessary.

Many processes in the production of individual components will involve the rejection of waste material (e.g., "swarf" from sheet or bar metal), and the disposal of such materials must be in accordance with safety requirements. Furthermore, if such process waste cannot be returned to the producer or manufacturer for recycling, then its subsequent disposal must be by approved processes in order to avoid environmental pollution.

• ENVIRONMENTAL AND PUBLIC HEALTH ISSUES

N. A. Smith

The main environmental problems associated with electrical appliance and equipment manufacture involve pollution and treatment of materials discarded during the manufacturing processes, together with the recycling, where possible, of the complete product when it has reached the end of its life.

Batteries

The exhaust of air contaminated with acid, alkali, lead, cadmium and other potentially harmful materials into the atmosphere and the pollution of water from the manufacturing of batteries should be prevented as far as possible, and where this is not possible it should be monitored to ensure compliance with relevant legislation.

The use of batteries can generate public health concerns. Leaking lead-acid or alkaline batteries can result in burns from the electrolyte. Recharging large lead-acid batteries can produce hydrogen gas, a fire and explosion hazard in enclosed areas. Release of thionyl chloride or sulphur dioxide from large lithium batteries can involve exposure to sulphur dioxide, hydrochloric acid mist, burning lithium and so on, and has caused at least one fatality (Ducatman, Ducatman and Barnes 1988). This could also be a hazard during manufacture of these batteries.

Battery manufacturers have become aware of increasing environmental concern from the disposal of batteries containing toxic heavy metals by putting them in landfills or incinerating them with other garbage. Leakage of toxic metals from waste dumps or alternatively escaping from the chimneys of waste incinerators can result in water and air contamination. The manufacturers therefore recognized the need to reduce the mercury content of batteries, in particular, within the limits allowable by modern technology. The campaign for mercury elimination commenced in advance of the legislation introduced in the European Union, the EC Battery Directive.

Recycling is another way to deal with environmental pollution. Nickel-cadmium batteries can be recycled relatively easily. The recovery of cadmium is very efficient and it is re-used in the construction of nickel-cadmium batteries. The nickel will subsequently be used in the steel industry. The initial economics suggested that the recycling of nickel-cadmium batteries was not cost effective, but advances in technology are expected to improve the situation. Mercuric oxide cells, which are covered by the EC Battery Directive, have been used primarily in hearing aids, and are being replaced typically with lithium or zinc-air batteries. Silver oxide cells are recycled, especially by the jewellery industry, due to the value of the silver content.

When recycling harmful materials, care has to be taken similar to that exercised during the manufacturing processes. During the recycling of silver batteries, for example, workers may be exposed to mercury vapour and silver oxide.

The repair and recycling of lead-acid batteries can result not only in lead poisoning among the workers, and sometimes their families, but also in extensive lead contamination of the environment (Matte et al. 1989). In many countries, particularly in the Caribbean and Latin America, lead car battery plates are burned to produce lead oxide for pottery glazes.

Electric Cable Manufacture

Electric cable manufacture has three major sources of pollution: solvent vapours, potential release of toluene di-isocyanate from enamelled wire manufacture and environmental emissions during the manufacture of materials used in cables. All of these require appropriate environmental controls.

Electric Lamp and Tube Manufacture

The major environmental concerns here are the waste disposal and/or recycling of mercury-containing lamps and the disposal of PCBs from the ballasts of fluorescent lamps. Glass manufacturing can also be a significant source of emission of nitrogen oxides into the atmosphere.

Domestic Electric Appliances

Since the electric appliance industry is to a large extent an assembly industry, environmental issues are minimal, with the major exception being paints and solvents used as surface coatings. Standard pollution control measures should be instituted in accordance with environmental regulations.

The recycling of electrical appliances involves separation of the recovered equipment into different materials such as copper and mild steel which can be reused, which is discussed elsewhere in this *Encyclopaedia*.

References

Ducatman, AM, BS Ducatman and JA Barnes. 1988. Lithium battery hazard: Old-fashioned planning implications of new technology. *J Occup Med* 30:309–311.

Health and Safety Executive (HSE). 1990. *Man-made Mineral Fibres*. Executive Guidance Note EH46. London: HSE.

International Agency for Research on Cancer (IARC). 1992. *Monographs on the Evaluation of Carcinogenic Risks to Humans*, Vol. 54. Lyon: IARC.

Matte TD, JP Figueroa, G Burr, JP Flesch, RH Keenlyside and EL Baker. 1989. Lead exposure among lead-acid battery workers in Jamaica. *Amer J Ind Med* 16:167–177.

McDiarmid, MA, CS Freeman, EA Grossman and J Martonik. 1996. Biological monitoring results for cadmium exposed workers. *Amer Ind Hyg Assoc J* 57:1019–1023.

Roels, HA, JP Ghyselen, E Ceulemans and RR Lauwerys. 1992. Assessment of the permissible exposure level to manganese in workers exposed to manganese dioxide dust. *Brit J Ind Med* 49:25–34.

Telesca, DR. 1983. *A Survey of Health Hazard Control Systems for Mercury Use and Processing*. Report No. CT-109-4. Cincinnati, OH: NIOSH.

Wallis, G, R Menke and C Chelton. 1993. Workplace field testing of a disposable negative pressure half-mask dust respirator (3M 8710). *Amer Ind Hyg Assoc J* 54:576-583.

81. ELECTRICAL APPLIANCES AND EQUIPMENT

METAL PROCESSING AND METAL WORKING INDUSTRY

82

Chapter Editor
Michael McCann

Contents

General profile

The metal smelting and refining industry processes metal ores and scrap metal to obtain pure metals. The metal working industries process metals in order to manufacture machine components, machinery, instruments and tools which are needed by other industries as well as by the other different sectors of the economy. Various types of metals and alloys are used as starting materials, including rolled stock (bars, strips, light sections, sheets or tubes) and drawn stock (bars, light sections, tubes or wire). Basic metal processing techniques include:

- smelting and refining of metal ores and scrap
- casting molten metals into a given shape (foundry)

- hammering or pressing metals into the shape of a die (hot or cold forging)
- welding and cutting sheet metal
- sintering (compressing and heating materials in powder form, including one or more metals)
- shaping metals on a lathe.

A wide variety of techniques are used to finish metals, including grinding and polishing, abrasive blasting and many surface finishing and coating techniques (electroplating, galvanizing, heat treatment, anodizing, powder coating and so forth).

SMELTING AND REFINING OPERATIONS

● SMELTING AND REFINING

Pekka Roto*

In the production and refining of metals, valuable components are separated from worthless material in a series of different physical and chemical reactions. The end-product is metal containing controlled amounts of impurities. Primary smelting and refining produces metals directly from ore concentrates, while secondary smelting and refining produces metals from scrap and process waste. Scrap includes bits and pieces of metal parts, bars, turnings, sheets and wire that are off-specification or worn-out but are capable of being recycled (see the article "Metal reclamation" in this chapter).

Overview of Processes

Two metal recovery technologies are generally used to produce refined metals, *pyrometallurgical* and *hydrometallurgical*. Pyrometallurgical processes use heat to separate desired metals from other materials. These processes use differences between oxidation potentials, melting points, vapour pressures, densities and/or miscibility of the ore components when melted. Hydrometallurgical technologies differ from pyrometallurgical processes in that the desired metals are separated from other materials using techniques that capitalize on differences between constituent solubilities and/or electrochemical properties while in aqueous solutions.

Pyrometallurgy

During pyrometallic processing, an ore, after being *beneficiated* (concentrated by crushing, grinding, floating and drying), is sintered or roasted (calcined) with other materials such as baghouse dust and flux. The concentrate is then smelted, or melted, in a blast furnace in order to fuse the desired metals into an impure molten bullion. This bullion then undergoes a third pyrometallic process to refine the metal to the desired level of purity. Each time the ore or bullion is heated, waste materials are created. Dust from ventilation and process gases may be captured in a baghouse and are either disposed of or returned to the process, depending upon the residual metal content. Sulphur in the gas is also captured, and when concentrations are above 4% it can be turned into sulphuric acid. Depending upon the origin of the ore and its residual metals content, various metals such as gold and silver may also be produced as by-products.

* Adapted from the 3rd edition, *Encyclopaedia of Occupational Health and Safety*.

Roasting is an important pyrometallurgical process. Sulphating roasting is used in the production of cobalt and zinc. Its purpose is to separate the metals so that they can be transformed into a water-soluble form for further hydrometallurgical processing.

The smelting of sulphidic ores produces a partially oxidized metal concentrate (matte). In smelting, the worthless material, usually iron, forms a slag with fluxing material and is converted into the oxide. The valuable metals acquire the metallic form at the converting stage, which takes place in converting furnaces. This method is used in copper and nickel production. Iron, ferrochromium, lead, magnesium and ferrous compounds are produced by reduction of the ore with charcoal and a flux (limestone), the smelting process usually taking place in an electric furnace. (See also the *Iron and steel industry* chapter.) Fused salt electrolysis, used in aluminium production, is another example of a pyrometallurgical process.

The high temperature required for the pyrometallurgical treatment of metals is obtained by burning fossil fuels or by using the exothermic reaction of the ore itself (e.g., in the flash smelting process). The flash smelting process is an example of an energy-saving pyrometallurgical process in which iron and sulphur of the ore concentrate are oxidized. The exothermic reaction coupled with a heat recovery system saves a lot of energy for smelting. The high sulphur recovery of the process is also beneficial for environmental protection. Most of the recently built copper and nickel smelters use this process.

Hydrometallurgy

Examples of hydrometallurgical processes are leaching, precipitation, electrolytic reduction, ion exchange, membrane separation and solvent extraction. The first stage of hydrometallurgical processes is the leaching of valuable metals from less valuable material, for example, with sulphuric acid. Leaching is often preceded by pre-treatment (e.g., sulphating roasting). The leaching process often requires high pressure, the addition of oxygen or high temperatures. Leaching may also be carried out with electricity. From the leaching solution the desired metal or its compound is recovered by precipitation or reduction using different methods. Reduction is carried out, for example, in cobalt and nickel production with gas.

Electrolysis of metals in aqueous solutions is also considered to be a hydrometallurgical process. In the process of electrolysis the metallic ion is reduced to the metal. The metal is in a weak acid solution from which it precipitates on cathodes under the influence of an electrical current. Most non-ferrous metals can also be refined by electrolysis.

Often metallurgical processes are a combination of pyro- and hydrometallurgical processes, depending on the ore concentrate to be treated and the type of metal to be refined. An example is nickel production.

Hazards and Their Prevention

Prevention of health risks and accidents in the metallurgical industry is primarily an educational and technical question. Medical examinations are secondary and have only a complementary role in the prevention of health risks. A harmonious exchange of information and collaboration between the planning, line, safety and occupational health departments within the company give the most efficient result in the prevention of health risks.

The best and least costly preventive measures are those taken at the planning stage of a new plant or process. In planning of new production facilities, the following aspects should be taken into account as a minimum:

- The potential sources of air contaminants should be enclosed and isolated.
- The design and placement of the process equipment should allow easy access for maintenance purposes.
- Areas in which a sudden and unexpected hazard may occur should be monitored continuously. Adequate warning notices should be included. For example, areas in which arsine or hydrogen cyanide exposure might be possible should be under continuous monitoring.
- Addition and handling of poisonous process chemicals should be planned so that manual handling can be avoided.
- Personal occupational hygiene sampling devices should be used in order to evaluate the real exposure of the individual worker, whenever possible. Regular fixed monitoring of gases, dusts and noise gives an overview of exposure but has only a complementary role in the evaluation of exposure dose.
- In space planning, the requirements of future changes or extensions of the process should be taken into account so that the occupational hygiene standards of the plant will not worsen.
- There should be a continuous system of training and education for safety and health personnel, as well as for foremen and workers. New workers in particular should be thoroughly informed about potential health risks and how to prevent them in their own working environments. In addition, training should be done whenever a new process is introduced.
- Work practices are important. For example, poor personal hygiene by eating and smoking in the worksite may considerably increase personal exposure.
- The management should have a health and safety monitoring system which produces adequate data for technical and economic decision making.

The following are some of the specific hazards and precautions that are found in smelting and refining.

Injuries

The smelting and refining industry has a higher rate of injuries than most other industries. Sources of these injuries include: splattering and spills of molten metal and slag resulting in burns; gas explosions and explosions from contact of molten metal with water; collisions with moving locomotives, wagons, travelling cranes and other mobile equipment; falls of heavy objects; falls from a height (e.g., while accessing a crane cab); and slipping and tripping injuries from obstruction of floors and passageways.

Precautions include: adequate training, appropriate personal protective equipment (PPE) (e.g., hard hats, safety shoes, work gloves and protective clothing); good storage, housekeeping and equipment maintenance; traffic rules for moving equipment (in-cluding defined routes and an effective signal and warning system); and a fall protection programme.

Heat

Heat stress illnesses such as heat stroke are a common hazard, primarily due to infrared radiation from furnaces and molten metal. This is especially a problem when strenuous work must be done in hot environments.

Prevention of heat illnesses can involve water screens or air curtains in front of furnaces, spot cooling, enclosed air-conditioned booths, heat-protective clothing and air-cooled suits, allowing sufficient time for acclimatization, work breaks in cool areas and an adequate supply of beverages for frequent drinking.

Chemical hazards

Exposure to a wide variety of hazardous dusts, fumes, gases and other chemicals can occur during smelting and refining operations. Crushing and grinding ore in particular can result in high exposures to silica and toxic metal dusts (e.g., containing lead, arsenic and cadmium). There can also be dust exposures during furnace maintenance operations. During smelting operations, metal fumes can be a major problem.

Dust and fume emissions can be controlled by enclosure, automation of processes, local and dilution exhaust ventilation, wetting down of materials, reduced handling of materials and other process changes. Where these are not adequate, respiratory protection would be needed.

Many smelting operations involve the production of large amounts of sulphur dioxide from sulphide ores and carbon monoxide from combustion processes. Dilution and local exhaust ventilation (LEV) are essential.

Sulphuric acid is produced as a by-product of smelting operations and is used in electrolytic refining and leaching of metals. Exposure can occur both to the liquid and to sulphuric acid mists. Skin and eye protection and LEV is needed.

The smelting and refining of some metals can have special hazards. Examples include nickel carbonyl in nickel refining, fluorides in aluminium smelting, arsenic in copper and lead smelting and refining, and mercury and cyanide exposures during gold refining. These processes require their own special precautions.

Other hazards

Glare and infrared radiation from furnaces and molten metal can cause eye damage including cataracts. Proper goggles and face shields should be worn. High levels of infrared radiation may also cause skin burns unless protective clothing is worn.

High noise levels from crushing and grinding ore, gas discharge blowers and high-power electric furnaces can cause hearing loss. If the source of the noise cannot be enclosed or isolated, then hearing protectors should be worn. A hearing conservation program including audiometric testing and training should be instituted.

Electrical hazards can occur during electrolytic processes. Precautions include proper electrical maintenance with lockout/tagout procedures; insulated gloves, clothing and tools; and ground fault circuit interrupters where needed.

Manual lifting and handling of materials can cause back and upper extremity injuries. Mechanical lifting aids and proper training in lifting methods can reduce this problem.

Pollution and Environmental Protection

Emissions of irritant and corrosive gases like sulphur dioxide, hydrogen sulphide and hydrogen chloride may contribute to air pollution and cause corrosion of metals and concrete within the plant and in the surrounding environment. The tolerance of vegetation to sulphur dioxide varies depending on the type of forest and soil. In general, evergreen trees tolerate lower concentrations of sulphur dioxide than deciduous ones. Particulate emissions may contain non-specific particulates, fluorides, lead, arsenic, cadmium and many other toxic metals. Wastewater effluent may contain a variety of toxic metals, sulphuric acid and other impurities. Solid wastes can be contaminated with arsenic, lead, iron sulphides, silica and other pollutants.

Smelter management should include evaluation and control of emissions from the plant. This is specialized work which should be carried out only by personnel thoroughly familiar with the chemical properties and toxicities of the materials discharged from the plant processes. The physical state of the material, the temperature at which it leaves the process, other materials in the gas stream and other factors must all be considered when planning measures to control air pollution. It is also desirable to maintain a weather station, to keep meteorological records and to be prepared to reduce output when weather conditions are unfavourable for dispersal of stack effluents. Field trips are necessary to observe the effect of air pollution on residential and farming areas.

Sulphur dioxide, one of the major contaminants, is recovered as sulphuric acid when present in sufficient quantity. Otherwise, to meet emission standards, sulphur dioxide and other hazardous gaseous wastes are controlled by scrubbing. Particulate emissions are commonly controlled by fabric filters and electrostatic precipitators.

Large amounts of water are used in flotation processes such as copper concentration. Most of this water is recycled back into the process. Tailings from the flotation process are pumped as slurry into sedimentation ponds. Water is recycled in the process. Metal-containing process water and rainwater are cleaned in water-treatment plants before discharging or recycling.

Solid-phase wastes include slags from smelting, blowdown slurries from sulphur dioxide conversion to sulphuric acid and sludges from surface impoundments (e.g., sedimentation ponds). Some slags can be reconcentrated and returned to smelters for reprocessing or recovery of other metals present. Many of these solid-phase wastes are hazardous wastes that must be stored according to environmental regulations.

COPPER, LEAD AND ZINC SMELTING AND REFINING*

Copper

Copper is mined in both open pits and underground mines, depending upon the ore grade and the nature of the ore deposit. Copper ore typically contains less that 1% copper in the form of sulphide minerals. Once the ore is delivered above the ground, it is crushed and ground to a powdery fineness and then concentrated for further processing. In the concentration process, ground ore is slurried with water, chemical reagents are added and air is blown through the slurry. The air bubbles attach themselves to the copper minerals and are then skimmed off the top of the flotation cells. The concentrate contains between 20 and 30% copper. The tailings, or gangue minerals, from the ore fall to the bottom of the cells and are removed, dewatered by thickeners and transported as a slurry to a tailings pond for disposal. All water used in this operation, from dewatering thickeners and the tailings pond, is recovered and recycled back into the process.

* Adapted from EPA 1995.

Copper can be produced either pyrometallurgically or hydrometallurgically depending upon the ore-type used as a charge. The ore concentrates, which contain copper sulphide and iron sulphide minerals, are treated by pyrometallurgical processes to yield high purity copper products. Oxide ores, which contain copper oxide minerals that may occur in other parts of the mine, together with other oxidized waste materials, are treated by hydrometallurgical processes to yield high purity copper products.

Copper conversion from the ore to metal is accomplished by smelting. During smelting the concentrates are dried and fed into one of several different types of furnaces. There the sulphide minerals are partially oxidized and melted to yield a layer of matte, a mixed copper-iron sulphide and slag, an upper layer of waste.

The matte is further processed by converting. The slag is tapped from the furnace and stored or discarded in slag piles onsite. A small amount of slag is sold for railroad ballast and for sand blasting grit. A third product of the smelting process is sulphur dioxide, a gas which is collected, purified and made into sulphuric acid for sale or for use in hydrometallurgical leaching operations.

Following smelting, the copper matte is fed into a converter. During this process the copper matte is poured into a horizontal cylindrical vessel (approximately 10×4 m) fitted with a row of pipes. The pipes, known as tuyères, project into the cylinder and are used to introduce air into the converter. Lime and silica are added to the copper matte to react with the iron oxide produced in the process to form slag. Scrap copper may also be added to the converter. The furnace is rotated so that the tuyères are submerged, and air is blown into the molten matte causing the remainder of the iron sulphide to react with oxygen to form iron oxide and sulphur dioxide. Then the converter is rotated to pour off the iron silicate slag.

Once all of the iron is removed, the converter is rotated back and given a second blow of air during which the remainder of the sulphur is oxidized and removed from the copper sulphide. The converter is then rotated to pour off the molten copper, which at this point is called blister copper (so named because if allowed to solidify at this point, it will have a bumpy surface due to the presence of gaseous oxygen and sulphur). Sulphur dioxide from the converters is collected and fed into the gas purification system together with that from the smelting furnace and made into sulphuric acid. Due to its residual copper content, slag is recycled back to the smelting furnace.

Blister copper, containing a minimum of 98.5% copper, is refined to high purity copper in two steps. The first step is fire refining, in which the molten blister copper is poured into a cylindrical furnace, similar in appearance to a converter, where first air and then natural gas or propane are blown through the melt to remove the last of the sulphur and any residual oxygen from the copper. The molten copper is then poured into a casting wheel to form anodes pure enough for electrorefining.

In electrorefining, the copper anodes are loaded into electrolytic cells and interspaced with copper starting sheets, or cathodes, in a bath of copper sulphate solution. When a direct current is passed through the cell the copper is dissolved from the anode, transported through the electrolyte and re-deposited on the cathode starting sheets. When the cathodes have built-up to sufficient thickness they are removed from the electrolytic cell and a new set of starting sheets is put in their place. Solid impurities in the anodes fall to the bottom of the cell as a sludge where they are ultimately collected and processed for the recovery of precious metals such as gold and silver. This material is known as anode slime.

The cathodes removed from the electrolytic cell are the primary product of the copper producer and contain 99.99+% cop-

Table 82.1 • Process materials inputs and pollution outputs for copper smelting and refining.

Process	Material input	Air emissions	Process wastes	Other wastes
Copper concentration	Copper ore, water, chemical reagents, thickeners		Flotation wastewaters	Tailings containing waste minerals such as limestone and quartz
Copper leaching	Copper concentrate, sulphuric acid		Uncontrolled leachate	Heap leach waste
Copper smelting	Copper concentrate, siliceous flux	Sulphur dioxide, particulate matter containing arsenic, antimony, cadmium, lead, mercury and zinc		Acid plant blowdown slurry/sludge, slag containing iron sulphides, silica
Copper conversion	Copper matte, scrap copper, siliceous flux	Sulphur dioxide, particulate matter containing arsenic, antimony, cadmium, lead, mercury and zinc		Acid plant blowdown slurry/sludge, slag containing iron sulphides, silica
Electrolytic copper refining	Blister copper, sulphuric acid			Slimes containing impurities such as gold, silver, antimony, arsenic, bismuth, iron, lead, nickel, selenium, sulphur and zinc

per. These may be sold to wire-rod mills as cathodes or processed further to a product called rod. In manufacturing rod, cathodes are melted in a shaft furnace and the molten copper is poured onto a casting wheel to form a bar suitable for rolling into a 3/8 inch diameter continuous rod. This rod product is shipped to wire mills where it is extruded into various sizes of copper wire.

In the hydrometallurgical process, the oxidized ores and waste materials are leached with sulphuric acid from the smelting process. Leaching is performed *in situ*, or in specially prepared piles by distributing acid across the top and allowing it to percolate down through the material where it is collected. The ground under the leach pads is lined with an acid-proof, impermeable plastic material to prevent leach liquor from contaminating groundwater. Once the copper-rich solutions are collected they can be processed by either of two processes—the cementation process or the solvent extraction/electrowinning process (SXEW). In the cementation process (which is rarely used today), the copper in the acidic solution is deposited on the surface of scrap iron in exchange for the iron. When sufficient copper has been cemented out, the copper-rich iron is put into the smelter together with the ore concentrates for copper recovery via the pyrometallurgical route.

In the SXEW process, the pregnant leach solution (PLS) is concentrated by solvent extraction, which extracts copper but not impurity metals (iron and other impurities). The copper-laden organic solution is then separated from the leachate in a settling tank. Sulphuric acid is added to the pregnant organic mixture, which strips the copper into an electrolytic solution. The leachate, containing the iron and other impurities, is returned to the leaching operation where its acid is used for further leaching. The copper-rich strip solution is passed into an electrolytic cell known as an electrowinning cell. An electrowinning cell differs from an electrorefining cell in that it uses a permanent, insoluble anode. The copper in solution is then plated onto a starting sheet cathode in much the same manner as it is on the cathode in an electrorefining cell. The copper-depleted electrolyte is returned to the solvent extraction process where it is used to strip more copper from the organic solution. The cathodes produced from the electrowinning process are then sold or made into rods in the same manner as those produced from the electrorefining process.

Electrowinning cells are used also for the preparation of starting sheets for both the electrorefining and electrowinning processes by plating the copper onto either stainless steel or titanium cathodes and then stripping off the plated copper.

Hazards and their prevention

The major hazards are exposure to ore dusts during ore processing and smelting, metal fumes (including copper, lead and arsenic) during smelting, sulphur dioxide and carbon monoxide during most smelting operations, noise from crushing and grinding operations and from furnaces, heat stress from the furnaces and sulphuric acid and electrical hazards during electrolytic processes.

Precautions include: LEV for dusts during transfer operations; local exhaust and dilution ventilation for sulphur dioxide and carbon monoxide; a noise control and hearing protection programme; protective clothing and shields, rest breaks and fluids for heat stress; and LEV, PPE and electrical precautions for electrolytic processes. Respiratory protection is commonly worn to protect against dusts, fumes and sulphur dioxide.

Table 82.1 lists environmental pollutants for various steps in copper smelting and refining.

Lead

The primary lead production process consists of four steps: sintering, smelting, drossing and pyrometallurgical refining. To begin, a feedstock comprising mainly of lead concentrate in the form of lead sulphide is fed into a sintering machine. Other raw materials may be added including iron, silica, limestone flux, coke, soda, ash, pyrite, zinc, caustic and particulates gathered from pollution control devices. In the sintering machine the lead feedstock is subjected to blasts of hot air which burn off the sulphur, creating sulphur dioxide. The lead oxide material existing after this process contains about 9% of its weight in carbon. The sinter is then fed along with coke, various recycled and cleanup materials, limestone and other fluxing agents into a blast furnace for reducing, where the carbon acts as a fuel and smelts or melts the lead material. The molten lead flows to the bottom of the furnace where four layers form: "speiss" (the lightest material, basically arsenic and antimony); "matte" (copper sulphide and other metal sulphides); blast furnace slag (primarily silicates); and lead bullion (98% lead, by weight). All layers are then drained off. The speiss and matte are sold to copper smelters for recovery of copper and precious metals. The blast furnace slag which contains zinc, iron, silica and lime is stored in piles and partially recycled. Sulphur oxide emissions are generated in blast furnaces from small quantities of residual lead sulphide and lead sulphates in the sinter feed.

Rough lead bullion from the blast furnace usually requires preliminary treatment in kettles before undergoing refining opera-

Table 82.2 • Process materials inputs and pollution outputs for lead smelting and refining.

Process	Material input	Air emissions	Process wastes	Other wastes
Lead sintering	Lead ore, iron, silica, limestone flux, coke, soda, ash, pyrite, zinc, caustic, baghouse dust	Sulphur dioxide, particulate matter containing cadmium and lead		
Lead smelting	Lead sinter, coke	Sulphur dioxide, particulate matter containing cadmium and lead	Plant washdown wastewater, slag granulation water	Slag containing impurities such as zinc, iron, silica and lime, surface impoundment solids
Lead drossing	Lead bullion, soda ash, sulphur, baghouse dust, coke			Slag containing such impurities as copper, surface impoundment solids
Lead refining	Lead drossing bullion			

tions. During drossing, the bullion is agitated in a drossing kettle and cooled to just above its freezing point (370 to 425 °C). A dross, which is composed of lead oxide, along with copper, antimony and other elements, floats to the top and solidifies above the molten lead.

The dross is removed and fed into a dross furnace for recovery of the non-lead useful metals. To enhance copper recovery, drossed lead bullion is treated by adding sulphur-bearing materials, zinc, and/or aluminium, lowering the copper content to approximately 0.01%.

During the fourth step, the lead bullion is refined using pyrometallurgical methods to remove any remaining non-lead saleable materials (e.g., gold, silver, bismuth, zinc, and metal oxides such as antimony, arsenic, tin and copper oxide). The lead is refined in a cast iron kettle by five stages. Antimony, tin and arsenic are removed first. Then zinc is added and gold and silver are removed in the zinc slag. Next, the lead is refined by vacuum removal (distillation) of zinc. Refining continues with the addition of calcium and magnesium. These two materials combine with bismuth to form an insoluble compound that is skimmed from the kettle. In the final step caustic soda and/or nitrates may be added to the lead to remove any remaining traces of metal impurities. The refined lead will have a purity of 99.90 to 99.99% and may be mixed with other metals to form alloys or it may be directly cast into shapes.

Hazards and their prevention

The major hazards are exposure to ore dusts during ore processing and smelting, metal fumes (including lead, arsenic and antimony) during smelting, sulphur dioxide and carbon monoxide during most smelting operations, noise from grinding and crushing operations and from furnaces, and heat stress from the furnaces.

Precautions include: LEV for dusts during transfer operations; local exhaust and dilution ventilation for sulphur dioxide and carbon monoxide; a noise control and hearing protection programme; and protective clothing and shields, rest breaks and fluids for heat stress. Respiratory protection is commonly worn to protect against dusts, fumes and sulphur dioxide. Biological monitoring for lead is essential.

Table 82.2 lists environmental pollutants for various steps in lead smelting and refining.

Zinc

Zinc concentrate is produced by separating the ore, which may contain as little as 2% zinc, from waste rock by crushing and

flotation, a process normally performed at the mining site. The zinc concentrate is then reduced to zinc metal in one of two ways: either pyrometallurgically by distillation (retorting in a furnace) or hydrometallurgically by electrowinning. The latter accounts for approximately 80% of total zinc refining.

Four processing stages are generally used in hydrometallurgic zinc refining: calcining, leaching, purification and electrowinning. Calcining, or roasting, is a high-temperature process (700 to 1000 °C) that converts zinc sulphide concentrate to an impure zinc oxide called calcine. Roaster types include multiple-hearth, suspension or fluidized-bed. In general, calcining begins with the mixing of zinc-containing materials with coal. This mixture is then heated, or roasted, to vaporize the zinc oxide which is then moved out of the reaction chamber with the resulting gas stream. The gas stream is directed to the baghouse (filter) area where the zinc oxide is captured in baghouse dust.

All of the calcining processes generate sulphur dioxide, which is controlled and converted to sulphuric acid as a marketable process by-product.

Electrolytic processing of desulphurized calcine consists of three basic steps: leaching, purification and electrolysis. Leaching refers to the dissolving of the captured calcine in a solution of sulphuric acid to form a zinc sulphate solution. The calcine may be leached once or twice. In the double-leach method, the calcine is dissolved in a slightly acidic solution to remove the sulphates. The calcine is then leached a second time in a stronger solution which dissolves the zinc. This second leaching step is actually the beginning of the third step of purification because many of the iron impurities drop out of the solution as well as the zinc.

After leaching, the solution is purified in two or more stages by adding zinc dust. The solution is purified as the dust forces deleterious elements to precipitate so that they can be filtered out. Purification is usually conducted in large agitation tanks. The process takes place at temperatures ranging from 40 to 85 °C and pressures ranging from atmospheric to 2.4 atmospheres. The elements recovered during purification include copper as a cake and cadmium as a metal. After purification the solution is ready for the final step, electrowinning.

Zinc electrowinning takes place in an electrolytic cell and involves running an electric current from a lead-silver alloy anode through the aqueous zinc solution. This process charges the suspended zinc and forces it to deposit onto an aluminium cathode which is immersed in the solution. Every 24 to 48 hours, each cell is shut down, the zinc-coated cathodes removed and rinsed, and the zinc mechanically stripped from the aluminium plates. The zinc concentrate is then melted and cast into ingots and is often as high as 99.995% pure.

Table 82.3 • Process materials inputs and pollution outputs for zinc smelting and refining.

Process	Material input	Air emissions	Process wastes	Other wastes
Zinc calcining	Zinc ore, coke	Sulphur dioxide, particulate matter containing zinc and lead		Acid plant blowdown slurry
Zinc leaching	Zinc calcine, sulphuric acid, limestone, spent electrolyte		Wastewaters containing sulphuric acid	
Zinc purification	Zinc-acid solution, zinc dust		Wastewaters containing sulphuric acid, iron	Copper cake, cadmium
Zinc electrowinning	Zinc in a sulphuric acid/aqueous solution, lead-silver alloy anodes, aluminium cathodes, barium carbonate or strontium, colloidal additives		Dilute sulphuric acid	Electrolytic cell slimes/sludges

Electrolytic zinc smelters contain as many as several hundred cells. A portion of the electrical energy is converted into heat, which increases the temperature of the electrolyte. Electrolytic cells operate at temperature ranges from 30 to 35 °C at atmospheric pressure. During electrowinning a portion of the electrolyte passes through cooling towers to decrease its temperature and to evaporate the water it collects during the process.

Hazards and their prevention

The major hazards are exposure to ore dusts during ore processing and smelting, metal fumes (including zinc and lead) during refining and roasting, sulphur dioxide and carbon monoxide during most smelting operations, noise from crushing and grinding operations and from furnaces, heat stress from the furnaces and sulphuric acid and electrical hazards during electrolytic processes.

Precautions include: LEV for dusts during transfer operations; local exhaust and dilution ventilation for sulphur dioxide and carbon monoxide; a noise control and hearing protection programme; protective clothing and shields, rest breaks and fluids for heat stress; and LEV, PPE, and electrical precautions for electrolytic processes. Respiratory protection is commonly worn to protect against dusts, fumes and sulphur dioxide.

Table 82.3 lists environmental pollutants for various steps in zinc smelting and refining.

● ALUMINIUM SMELTING AND REFINING

Bertram D. Dinman

Process Overview

Bauxite is extracted by open-pit mining. The richer ores are used as mined. The lower grade ores may be beneficiated by crushing and washing to remove clay and silica waste. The production of the metal comprises two basic steps:

1. *Refining.* Production of alumina from bauxite by the Bayer process in which bauxite is digested at high temperature and pressure in a strong solution of caustic soda. The resulting hydrate is crystallized and calcined to the oxide in a kiln or fluid bed calciner.
2. *Reduction.* Reduction of alumina to virgin aluminium metal employing the Hall-Heroult electrolytic process using carbon electrodes and cryolite flux.

Experimental development suggests that in the future aluminium may be reduced to the metal by direct reduction from the ore.

There are presently two major types of Hall-Heroult electrolytic cells in use. The so-called "pre-bake" process utilizes electrodes manufactured as noted below. In such smelters exposure to polycyclic hydrocarbons normally occurs in the electrode manufacturing facilities, especially during mixing mills and forming presses. Smelters utilizing the Soderberg-type cell do not require facilities for the manufacture of baked carbon anodes. Rather, the mixture of coke and pitch binder is put into hoppers whose lower ends are immersed in the molten cryolite-alumina bath mixture. As the mixture of pitch and coke is heated by the molten metal-cryolite bath within the cell, this mixture bakes into a hard graphitic mass *in situ*. Metal rods are inserted into the anodic mass as conductors for a direct current electric flow. These rods must be replaced periodically; in extracting these, considerable amounts of coal tar pitch volatiles are evolved into the cell room environment. To this exposure is added those pitch volatiles generated as the baking of the pitch-coke mass proceeds.

Within the last decade the industry has tended to either not replace or to modify existent Soderberg type reduction facilities as a consequence of the demonstrated carcinogenic hazard they present. In addition, with the increasing automation of reduction cell operations—particularly the changing of anodes, tasks are more commonly performed from enclosed mechanical cranes. Consequently worker exposures and the risk of developing those disorders associated with aluminium smelting are gradually decreasing in modern facilities. By contrast, in those economies wherein adequate capital investment is not readily available, the persistence of older, manually operated reduction processes will continue to present the risks of those occupational disorders (see below) previously associated with aluminium reduction plants. Indeed, this tendency will tend to become more aggravated in such older, unimproved operations, especially as they age.

Carbon electrode manufacture

The electrodes required by pre-bake electrolytic reduction to pure metal are normally made by a facility associated with this type of aluminium smelting plant. The anodes and cathodes are most frequently made from a mixture of ground petroleum-derived coke and pitch. Coke first is ground in ball mills, then conveyed and mixed mechanically with the pitch and finally cast into blocks in a moulding presses. These anode or cathode blocks are next heated in a gas-fired furnace for several days until they form hard graphitic masses with essentially all volatiles having been driven off. Finally they are attached to anode rods or saw-grooved to receive the cathode bars.

82. METAL PROCESSING AND METAL WORKING INDUSTRY

Table 82.4 • Process materials inputs and pollution outputs for aluminium smelting and refining.

Process	Material input	Air emissions	Process wastes	Other wastes
Bauxite refining	Bauxite, sodium hydroxide	Particulates, caustic/water vapour		Residue containing silicon, iron, titanium, calcium oxides and caustic
Alumina clarification and precipitation	Alumina slurry, starch, water		Wastewater containing starch, sand and caustic	
Alumina calcination	Aluminium hydrate	Particulates and water vapour		
Primary electrolytic aluminium smelting	Alumina, carbon anodes, electrolytic cells, cryolite	Fluoride — both gaseous and particulates, carbon dioxide, sulphur dioxide, carbon monoxide, C_2F_6, CF_4 and perfluorinated carbons (PFC)		Spent potliners

It should be noted that the pitch used to form such electrodes represents a distillate which is derived from coal or petroleum tar. In the conversion of this tar to pitch by heating, the final pitch product has boiled off essentially all of its low-boiling point inorganics, e.g., SO_2, as well as aliphatic compounds and one- and two ring aromatic compounds. Thus, such pitch should not present the same hazards in its use as coal or petroleum tars since these classes of compounds ought not to be present. There are some indications that the carcinogenic potential of such pitch products may not be as great as the more complex mixture of tars and other volatiles associated with the incomplete combustion of coal.

Hazards and Their Prevention

The hazards and preventive measures for aluminium smelting and refining processes are basically the same as those found in smelting and refining in general; however, the individual processes present certain specific hazards.

Mining

Although sporadic references to "bauxite lung" occur in the literature, there is little convincing evidence that such an entity exists. However, the possibility of the presence of crystalline silica in bauxite ores should be considered.

Bayer process

The extensive use of caustic soda in the Bayer process presents frequent risks of chemical burns of the skin and eyes. Descaling of tanks by pneumatic hammers is responsible for severe noise exposure. The potential hazards associated with the inhalation of excessive doses of aluminium oxide produced in this process are discussed below.

All workers involved in the Bayer process should be well informed of the hazards associated with handling caustic soda. In all sites at risk, eyewash fountains and basins with running water and deluge showers should be provided, with notices explaining their use. PPE (e.g., goggles, gloves, aprons and boots) should be supplied. Showers and double locker accommodations (one locker for work clothing, the other for personal clothing) should be provided and all employees encouraged to wash thoroughly at the end of the shift. All workers handling molten metal should be supplied with visors, respirators, gauntlets, aprons, armlets and spats to protect them against burns, dust and fumes. Workers employed on the Gadeau low-temperature process should be supplied with special gloves and suits to protect them from hydrochloric acid fumes given off when the cells start up; wool has proved to have a good resistance to these fumes. Respirators with charcoal cartridges or alumina-impregnated masks give adequate protection against pitch and fluorine fumes; efficient dust masks are necessary for protection against carbon dust. Workers with more severe dust and fume exposure, particularly in Soderberg operations, should be provided with air-supplied respiratory protective equipment. As mechanized potroom work is remotely performed from enclosed cabins, these protective measures will become less necessary.

Electrolytic reduction

Electrolytic reduction exposes workers to the potential for skin burns and accidents due to molten metal splashes, heat stress disorders, noise, electrical hazards, cryolite and hydrofluoric acid fumes. Electrolytic reduction cells may emit large quantities of dusts of fluoride and alumina.

In carbon-electrode manufacturing shops, exhaust ventilation equipment with bag filters should be installed; enclosure of pitch and carbon grinding equipment further effectively minimizes exposures to heated pitches and carbon dusts. Regular checks on atmospheric dust concentrations should be made with a suitable sampling device. Periodic x-ray examinations should be carried out on workers exposed to dust, and these should be followed up by clinical examinations when necessary.

In order to reduce the risk of handling pitch, transport of this material should be mechanized as far as possible (e.g., heated road tankers can be used to transport liquid pitch to the works where it is pumped automatically into heated pitch tanks). Regular skin examinations to detect erythema, epitheliomata or dermatitis are also prudent, and extra protection can be provided by alginate-base barrier creams.

Workers doing hot work should be instructed prior to the onset of hot weather to increase fluid intake and heavily salt their food. They and their supervisors should also be trained to recognise incipient heat-induced disorders in themselves and their co-workers. All those working here should be trained to take the proper measure necessary to prevent the occurrence or progression of the heat disorders.

Workers exposed to high noise levels should be supplied with hearing protection equipment such as earplugs which allow the passage of low-frequency noise (to allow perception of orders) but reduce the transmission of intense, high-frequency noise. Moreover, workers should undergo regular audiometric examination to detect hearing loss. Finally, personnel should also be trained to give cardiopulmonary resuscitation to victims of electric shock accidents.

The potential for molten metal splashes and severe burns are widespread at many sites in reduction plants and associated operations. In addition to protective clothing (e.g., gauntlets, aprons, spats and face visors) the wearing of synthetic apparel should be prohibited, since the heat of molten metal causes such heated fibers to melt and adhere to the skin, further intensifying skin burns.

Individuals using cardiac pacemakers should be excluded from reduction operations because of the risk of magnetic field induced dysrhythmias.

Other Health Effects

The hazards to workers, the general population and the environment resulting from the emission of fluoride-containing gases, smokes and dusts due to the use of cryolite flux have been widely reported (see table 82.4). In children living in the vicinity of poorly controlled aluminium smelters, variable degrees of mottling of permanent teeth have been reported if exposure occurred during the developmental phase of permanent teeth growth. Among smelter workers prior to 1950, or where inadequate control of fluoride effluents continued, variable degrees of bony fluorosis have been seen. The first stage of this condition consists of a simple increase in bone density, particularly marked in the vertebral bodies and pelvis. As fluoride is further absorbed into bone, calcification of the ligaments of the pelvis is next seen. Finally, in the event of extreme and protracted exposure to fluoride, calcification of the paraspinal and other ligamentous structures as well as joints are noted. While this last stage has been seen in its severe form in cryolite processing plants, such advanced stages have rarely if ever been seen in aluminium smelter workers. Apparently the less severe x-ray changes in bony and ligamentous structures are not associated with alterations of the architectural or metabolic function of bone. By proper work practices and adequate ventilatory control, workers in such reduction operations can be readily prevented from developing any of the foregoing x-ray changes, despite 25 to 40 years of such work. Finally, mechanization of potroom operations should minimize if not totally eliminate any fluoride associated hazards.

Since the early 1980s an asthma-like condition has been definitively demonstrated among workers in aluminium reduction potrooms. This aberration, referred to as occupational asthma associated with aluminium smelting (OAAAS), is characterized by variable airflow resistance, bronchial hyperresponsiveness, or both, and is not precipitated by stimuli outside the workplace. Its clinical symptoms consist of wheezing, chest tightness and breathlessness and non-productive cough which are usually delayed some several hours following work exposures. The latent period between commencement of work exposure and the onset of OAAAS is highly variable, ranging from 1 week to 10 years, depending upon the intensity and character of the exposure. The condition usually is ameliorated with removal from the workplace following vacations and so on, but will become more frequent and severe with continued work exposures. While the occurrence of this condition has been correlated with potroom concentrations of fluoride, it is not clear that the aetiology of the disorder arises specifically from exposure to this chemical agent. Given the complex mixture of dusts and fumes (e.g., particulate and gaseous fluorides, sulphur dioxide, plus low concentrations of the oxides of vanadium, nickel and chromium) it is more likely that such fluorides measurements represent a surrogate for this complex mixture of fumes, gases and particulates found in potrooms.

It presently appears that this condition is one of an increasingly important group of occupational diseases: occupational asthma. The causal process which results in this disorder is determined with difficulty in an individual case. Signs and symptoms of OAAAS may result from: pre-existing allergy-based asthma, non-specific bronchial hyperresponsiveness, the reactive airway dysfunction syndrome (RADS), or true occupational asthma. Diagnosis of this condition is presently problematic, requiring a compatible history, the presence of variable airflow limitation, or

in its absence, production of pharmacologically induced bronchial hyperresponsivity. But if the latter is not demonstrable, this diagnosis is unlikely. (However, this phenomenon can eventually disappear after the disorder subsides with removal from work exposures.)

Since this disorder tends to become progressively more severe with continued exposure, affected individuals most usually need be removed from continued work exposures. While individuals with pre-existent atopic asthma should initially be restricted from aluminium reduction cell rooms, the absence of atopy cannot predict whether this condition will occur subsequent to work exposures.

There are presently reports suggesting that aluminium may be associated with neurotoxicity among workers engaged in smelting and welding this metal. It has been clearly shown that aluminium is absorbed via the lungs and excreted in the urine at levels greater than normal, particularly in reduction cell room workers. However, much of the literature regarding neurological effects in such workers derives from the presumption that aluminium absorption results in human neurotoxicity. Accordingly, until such associations are more reproducibly demonstrable, the connection between aluminium and occupational neurotoxicity must be considered speculative at this time.

Because of the occasional need to expend in excess of 300 kcal/h in the course of changing anodes or performing other strenuous work in the presence of molten cryolite and aluminium, heat disorders may be seen during periods of hot weather. Such episodes are most likely to occur when the weather initially changes from the moderate to hot, humid conditions of summer. In addition, work practices which result in accelerated anode changing or employment over two successive work shifts during hot weather will also predispose workers to such heat disorders. Workers inadequately heat acclimatized or physically conditioned, whose salt intake is inadequate or who have intercurrent or recent illness are particularly prone to development of heat exhaustion and/or heat cramps while performing such arduous tasks. Heat stroke has occurred but rarely among aluminium smelter workers except among those with known predisposing health alterations (e.g., alcoholism, ageing).

Exposure to the polycyclic aromatics associated with breathing of pitch fume and particulates have been demonstrated to place Soderberg-type reduction cell personnel in particular at an excessive risk of developing urinary bladder cancer; the excess cancer risk is less well-established. Workers in carbon electrode plants where mixtures of heated coke and tar are heated are assumed to also be at such risk. However, after electrodes have been baked for several days at about 1,200 °C, polycyclic aromatic compounds are practically totally combusted or volatilized and are no longer associated with such anodes or cathodes. Hence the reduction cells utilizing prebaked electrodes have not been as clearly shown to present an undue risk of development of these malignant disorders. Other neoplasia (e.g., non-granulocytic leukaemia and brain cancers) have been suggested to occur in aluminium reduction operations; at present such evidence is fragmentary and inconsistent.

In the vicinity of the electrolytic cells, the use of pneumatic crust breakers in the potrooms produce noise levels of the order of 100 dBA. The electrolytic reduction cells are run in series from a low-voltage high-amperage current supply and, consequently, cases of electric shock are not usually severe. However, in the power house at the point where the high-voltage supply joins the series-connection network of the potroom, severe electrical shock accidents may occur particularly as the electrical supply is an alternating, high voltage current.

Because health concerns have been raised regarding exposures associated with electromagnetic power fields, the exposure of workers in this industry has been brought into question. It must be recognized that the power supplied to electrolytic reduction cells is direct current; accordingly, the electromagnetic fields generated in the potrooms are mainly of the static or standing field type. Such fields, in contrast to low frequency electromagnetic fields, are even less readily shown to exert consistent or reproducible biological effects, either experimentally or clinically. In addition, the flux levels of the magnetic fields measured in present day cell rooms are commonly found to be within presently proposed, tentative threshold limit values for static magnetic fields, sub-radio frequency and static electric fields. Exposure to ultra-low frequency electromagnetic fields also occur in reduction plants, especially at the far-ends of these rooms adjacent to rectifier rooms. However, the flux levels found in the nearby potrooms are minimal, well below present standards. Finally, coherent or reproducible epidemiological evidence of adverse health effects due to electromagnetic fields in aluminium reduction plants have not been convincingly demonstrated.

Electrode manufacture

Workers in contact with pitch fumes may develop erythema; exposure to sunlight induces photosensitization with increased irritation. Cases of localized skin tumours have occurred among carbon electrode workers where inadequate personal hygiene was practised; after excision and change of job no further spread or recurrence is usually noted. During electrode manufacture, considerable quantities of carbon and pitch dust can be generated. Where such dust exposures have been severe and inadequately controlled, there have been occasional reports that carbon electrode makers may develop simple pneumoconiosis with focal emphysema, complicated by the development of massive fibrotic lesions. Both the simple and complicated pneumoconioses are indistinguishable from the corresponding condition of coalworkers' pneumoconiosis. The grinding of coke in ball mills produces noise levels of up to 100 dBA.

Editor's note: The aluminium production industry has been classified as a Group 1 known cause of human cancers by the International Agency for Research on Cancer (IARC). A variety of exposures have been associated with other diseases (e.g., "potroom asthma") which are described elsewhere in this *Encyclopaedia*.

• GOLD SMELTING AND REFINING

I.D. Gadaskina and L.A. Ryzik*

Gold mining is carried out on a small scale by individual prospectors (e.g., in China and Brazil) and on a large scale in underground mines (e.g., in South Africa) and in open pit mining (e.g., in the United States).

The simplest method of gold mining is panning, which involves filling a circular dish with gold-bearing sand or gravel, holding it under a stream of water and swirling it. The lighter sand and gravel are gradually washed off, leaving the gold particles near the centre of the pan. More advanced hydraulic gold mining consists of directing a powerful stream of water against the gold-bearing gravel or sand. This crumbles the material and washes it away through special sluices in which the gold settles, while the lighter gravel is floated off. For river mining, elevator dredges are used, consisting of flat-bottomed boats which use a chain of small buckets to scoop up material from the river bottom and empty it into a screening container (trommel). The material is rotated in the

* Adapted from 3rd edition, *Encyclopaedia of Occupational Health and Safety*.

trommel as water is directed on it. The gold-bearing sand sinks through perforations in the trommel and drops onto shaking tables for further concentration.

There are two main methods for the extraction of gold from ore. These are the processes of *amalgamation* and *cyanidation*. The process of amalgamation is based on the ability of gold to alloy with metallic mercury to form amalgams of varying consistencies, from solid to liquid. The gold can be fairly easily removed from the amalgam by distilling off the mercury. In internal amalgamation, the gold is separated inside the crushing apparatus at the same time as the ore is crushed. The amalgam removed from the apparatus is washed free of any admixtures by water in special bowls. Then the remaining mercury is pressed out of the amalgam. In external amalgamation, the gold is separated outside the crushing apparatus, in amalgamators or sluices (an inclined table covered with copper sheets). Before the amalgam is removed, fresh mercury is added. The purified and washed amalgam is then pressed. In both processes the mercury is removed from the amalgam by distillation. The amalgamation process is rare today, except in small scale mining, because of environmental concerns.

Extraction of gold by means of cyanidation is based on the ability of gold to form a stable water-soluble double salt $KAu(CN)_2$ when combined with potassium cyanide in association with oxygen. The pulp resulting from the crushing of gold ore consists of larger crystalline particles, known as sands, and smaller amorphous particles, known as silt. The sand, being heavier, is deposited at the bottom of the apparatus and allows solutions (including silt) to pass through. The gold extraction process consists of feeding finely ground ore into a leaching tub and filtering a solution of potassium or sodium cyanide through it. The silt is separated from the gold cyanide solutions by adding thickeners and by vacuum filtration. Heap leaching, in which the cyanide solution is poured over a levelled heap of coarsely crushed ore, is becoming more popular, especially with low grade ores and mine tailings. In both instances, the gold is recovered from the gold cyanide solution by adding aluminium or zinc dust. In a separate operation, concentrated acid is added in a digest reactor to dissolve the zinc or aluminium, leaving behind the solid gold.

Under the influence of carbonic acid, water and air, as well as the acids present in the ore, the cyanide solutions decompose and give off hydrogen cyanide gas. In order to prevent this, alkali is added (lime or caustic soda). Hydrogen cyanide is also produced when the acid is added to dissolve the aluminium or zinc.

Another cyanidation technique involves the use of activated charcoal to remove the gold. Thickeners are added to the gold cyanide solution before slurrying with activated charcoal in order to keep the charcoal in suspension. The gold-containing charcoal is removed by screening, and the gold extracted using concentrated alkaline cyanide in alcoholic solution. The gold is then recovered by electrolysis. The charcoal can be reactivated by roasting, and the cyanide can be recovered and reused.

Both amalgamation and cyanidation produce metal that contains a considerable quantity of impurities, the pure gold content rarely exceeding 900 per mil fineness, unless it is further electrolytically refined in order to produce a degree of fineness of up to 999.8 per mil and more.

Gold is also recovered as a by-product from the smelting of copper, lead and other metals (see the article "Copper, lead and zinc smelting and refining" in this chapter).

Hazards and Their Prevention

Gold ore occurring in great depths is extracted by underground mining. This necessitates measures to prevent the formation and spread of dust in mine workings. The separation of gold from arsenical ores gives rise to arsenic exposure of mine workers and to pollution of air and soil with arsenic-containing dust.

In the mercury extraction of gold, workers may be exposed to high airborne mercury concentrations when mercury is placed in or removed from the sluices, when the amalgam is purified or pressed and when the mercury is distilled off; mercury poisoning has been reported amongst amalgamation and distilling workers. The risk of mercury exposure in amalgamation has become a serious problem in several countries in the Far East and South America.

In amalgamation processes the mercury must be placed on the sluices and the amalgam removed in such a manner as to ensure that the mercury does not come in contact with the skin of the hands (by using shovels with long handles, protective clothing impervious to mercury and so on). The processing of the amalgam and the removal or pressing of mercury must also be as fully mechanized as possible, with no possibility of the hands being touched by mercury; the processing of amalgam and the distilling off of mercury must be carried out in separate isolated premises in which the walls, ceilings, floors, apparatus and work surfaces are covered with material which will not absorb mercury or its vapours; all surfaces must be regularly cleaned so as to remove all mercury deposits. All premises intended for operations involving the use of mercury must be equipped with general and local exhaust ventilation. These ventilation systems must be particularly efficient in premises where mercury is distilled off. Stocks of mercury must be kept in hermetically sealed metal containers under a special exhaust hood; workers must be provided with the PPE necessary for work with mercury; and the air must be monitored systematically in premises used for amalgamation and distilling. There should also be medical monitoring.

Contamination of the air by hydrogen cyanide in cyanidation plants is dependent on air temperature, ventilation, the volume of material being processed, the concentration of the cyanide solutions in use, the quality of the reagents and the number of open installations. Medical examination of workers in gold-extracting factories has revealed symptoms of chronic hydrogen cyanide poisoning, in addition to a high frequency of allergic dermatitis, eczema and pyoderma (an acute inflammatory skin disease with pus formation).

Proper organization of the preparation of cyanide solutions is particularly important. If the opening of drums containing cyanide salts and the feeding of these salts into dissolving tubs is not mechanized, there can be substantial contamination by cyanide dust and hydrogen cyanide gas. Cyanide solutions should be fed in through closed systems by automatic proportioning pumps. In gold cyanidation plants, the correct degree of alkalinity must be maintained in all cyanidation apparatus; in addition, cyanidation apparatus must be hermetically sealed and equipped with LEV backed up by adequate general ventilation and leak monitoring. All cyanidation apparatus and the walls, floors, open areas and stairs of the premises must be covered with non-porous materials and regularly cleaned with weak alkaline solutions.

The use of acids to break down zinc in the processing of gold slime may give off hydrogen cyanide and arsine. These operations must therefore be performed in specially equipped and separated premises, with the use of local exhaust hoods.

Smoking should be prohibited and workers should be provided with separate facilities for eating and drinking. First-aid equipment should be available and should contain material for immediately removing any cyanide solution that comes in contact with workers' bodies and antidotes for cyanide poisoning. Workers must be supplied with personal protective clothing impervious to cyanide compounds.

Environmental Effects

There is evidence of exposure to metallic mercury vapour and methylation of mercury in nature, particularly where the gold is processed. In one study of water, settlements and fish from gold mining areas of Brazil, the mercury concentrations in edible parts of locally consumed fish surpassed by almost 6 times the Brazilian advisory level for human consumption (Palheta and Taylor 1995). In a contaminated area of Venezuela, gold prospectors have been using mercury to separate gold from auriferous sand and rock powders for many years. The high level of mercury in the surface soil and rubber sediments of the contaminated area constitutes a serious occupational and public health risk.

Cyanide contamination of wastewater is also a great concern. Cyanide solutions should be treated before being released or should be recovered and reused. Emissions of hydrogen cyanide gas, for example, in the digest reactor, are treated with a scrubber before being exhausted out the stack.

METAL PROCESSING AND METAL WORKING

FOUNDRIES

Franklin E. Mirer

Founding, or metal casting, involves the pouring of molten metal into the hollow inside of a heat-resistant mould which is the outside or negative shape of the pattern of the desired metal object. The mould may contain a core to determine the dimensions of any internal cavity in the final casting. Foundry work comprises:

- making a pattern of the desired article
- making the mould and cores and assembling the mould
- melting and refining the metal
- pouring the metal into the mould
- cooling the metal casting
- removing the mould and core from the metal casting
- removing extra metal from the finished casting.

The basic principles of foundry technology have changed little in thousands of years. However, processes have become more mechanized and automatic. Wooden patterns have been replaced by metal and plastic, new substances have been developed for producing cores and moulds, and a wide range of alloys are used. The most prominent foundry process is sand moulding of iron.

Iron, steel, brass and *bronze* are traditional cast metals. The largest sector of the foundry industry produces grey and ductile iron castings. Gray iron foundries use iron or pig iron (new ingots) to make standard iron castings. Ductile iron foundries add magnesium, cerium or other additives (often called *ladle additives*) to the ladles of molten metal before pouring to make nodular or malleable iron castings. The different additives have little impact on workplace exposures. Steel and malleable iron make up the balance of the ferrous foundry industrial sector. The major customers of the largest ferrous foundries are the auto, construction and agricultural implement industries. Iron foundry employment has decreased as engine blocks become smaller and can be poured in a single mould, and as aluminium is substituted for cast iron. Non-ferrous foundries, especially aluminium foundry and die-cast operations, have heavy employment. Brass foundries, both free standing and those producing for the plumbing equipment industry, are a shrinking sector which, however, remains important

Table 82.5 • Types of foundry furnaces.

Furnace	Description
Cupola furnace	A cupola furnace is a tall, vertical furnace, open at the top with hinged doors at the bottom. It is charged from the top with alternate layers of coke, limestone and metal; the molten metal is removed at the bottom. Special hazards include carbon monoxide and heat.
Electric arc furnace	The furnace is charged with ingots, scrap, alloy metals and fluxing agents. An arc is produced between three electrodes and the metal charge, melting the metal. A slag with fluxes covers the surface of the molten metal to prevent oxidation, to refine the metal and protect the furnace roof from excessive heat. When ready, the electrodes are raised and the furnace tilted to pour the molten metal into the receiving ladle. Special hazards include metal fumes and noise.
Induction furnace	An induction furnace melts the metal by passing a high electric current through copper coils on the outside of the furnace, inducing an electric current in the outer edge of the metal charge that heats the metal because of the high electrical resistance of the metal charge. Melting progresses from the outside of the charge to the inside. Special hazards include metal fumes.
Crucible furnace	The crucible or container holding the metal charge is heated by a gas or oil burner. When ready, the crucible is lifted out of the furnace and tilted for pouring into moulds. Special hazards include carbon monoxide, metal fumes, noise and heat.
Rotary furnace	A long, inclined rotating cylindrical furnace that is charged from the top and fired from the lower end.
Channel furnace	A type of induction furnace.
Reverberatory furnace	This horizontal furnace consists of a fireplace at one end, separated from the metal charge by a low partition wall called the fire-bridge, and a stack or chimney at the other end. The metal is kept from contact with the solid fuel. Both the fireplace and metal charge are covered by an arched roof. The flame in its path from the fireplace to the stack is reflected downwards or reverberated on the metal beneath, melting it.

from an occupational health perspective. In recent years, titanium, chromium, nickel and magnesium, and even more toxic metals such as beryllium, cadmium and thorium, are used in foundry products.

Although the metal founding industry may be assumed to start by remelting solid material in the form of metal ingots or pigs, the iron and steel industry in the large units may be so integrated that the division is less obvious. For instance, the merchant blast furnace may turn all its output into pig iron, but in an integrated plant some iron may be used to produce castings, thus taking part in the foundry process, and the blast furnace iron may be taken molten to be turned into steel, where the same thing can occur. There is in fact a separate section of the steel trade known for this reason as *ingot moulding*. In the normal iron foundry, the remelting of pig iron is also a refining process. In the non-ferrous foundries the process of melting may require the addition of metals and other substances, and thus constitutes an alloying process.

Moulds made from silica sand bound with clay predominate in the iron foundry sector. Cores traditionally produced by baking silica sand bound with vegetable oils or natural sugars have been

substantially replaced. Modern founding technology has developed new techniques to produce moulds and cores.

In general, the health and safety hazards of foundries can be classified by type of metal cast, moulding process, size of casting and degree of mechanization.

Process Overview

On the basis of the designer's drawings, a pattern conforming to the external shape of the finished metal casting is constructed. In the same way, a corebox is made that will produce suitable cores to dictate the internal configuration of the final article. Sand casting is the most widely used method, but other techniques are available. These include: permanent mould casting, using moulds of iron or steel; die casting, in which the molten metal, often a light alloy, is forced into a metal mould under pressures of 70 to 7,000 kgf/cm^2; and investment casting, where a wax pattern is made of each casting to be produced and is covered with refractory which will form the mould into which the metal is poured. The "lost foam" process uses polystyrene foam patterns in sand to make aluminium castings.

Metals or alloys are melted and prepared in a furnace which may be of the cupola, rotary, reverberatory, crucible, electric arc, channel or coreless induction type (see table 82.5.) Relevant metallurgical or chemical analyses are performed. Molten metal is poured into the assembled mould either via a ladle or directly from the furnace. When the metal has cooled, the mould and core material are removed (shakeout, stripping or knockout) and the casting is cleaned and dressed (despruing, shot-blasting or hydroblasting and other abrasive techniques). Certain castings may require welding, heat treatment or painting before the finished article will meet the specifications of the buyer.

Hazards such as the danger arising from the presence of hot metal are common to most foundries, irrespective of the particular casting process employed. Hazards may also be specific to a particular foundry process. For example, the use of magnesium presents flare risks not encountered in other metal founding industries. This article emphasizes iron foundries, which contain most of the typical foundry hazards.

The mechanized or production foundry employs the same basic methods as the conventional iron foundry. When moulding is done, for example, by machine and castings are cleaned by shot blasting or hydroblasting, the machine usually has built-in dust control devices, and the dust hazard is reduced. However, sand is frequently moved from place to place on an open-belt conveyor, and transfer points and sand spillage may be sources of considerable quantities of airborne dust; in view of the high production rates, the airborne dust burden may be even higher than in the conventional foundry. A review of air sampling data in the middle 1970s showed higher dust levels in large American production foundries than in small foundries sampled during the same period. Installation of exhaust hoods over transfer points on belt conveyors, combined with scrupulous housekeeping, should be normal practice. Conveying by pneumatic systems is sometimes economically possible and results in a virtually dust-free conveying system.

Iron Foundries

For simplicity, an iron foundry can be presumed to comprise the following six sections:

1. metal melting and pouring
2. pattern-making
3. moulding
4. coremaking
5. shakeout/knockout
6. casting cleaning.

In many foundries, almost any of these processes may be carried out simultaneously or consecutively in the same workshop area.

In a typical production foundry, iron moves from melting to pouring, cooling, shakeout, cleaning and shipping as a finished casting. Sand is cycled from sand mix, moulding, shakeout and back to sand mixing. Sand is added to the system from core making, which starts with new sand.

Melting and pouring

The iron founding industry relies heavily on the cupola furnace for metal melting and refining. The cupola is a tall, vertical furnace, open at the top with hinged doors at the bottom, lined with refractory and charged with coke, scrap iron and limestone. Air is blown through the charge from openings (tuyers) at the bottom; combustion of coke heats, melts and purifies the iron. Charge materials are fed into the top of the cupola by crane during operation and must be stored close at hand, usually in compounds or bins in the yard adjacent to the charging machinery. Tidiness and efficient supervision of the stacks of raw materials are essential to minimize the risk of injury from slippages of heavy objects. Cranes with large electromagnets or heavy weights are often used to reduce the scrap metal to manageable sizes for charging into the cupola and for filling the charging hoppers themselves. The crane cab should be well protected and the operators properly trained.

Employees handling raw materials should wear hand leathers and protective boots. Careless charging can overfill the hopper and can cause dangerous spillage. If the charging process is found to be too noisy, the noise of metal-on-metal impact can be reduced by fitting rubber noise-dampening liners to storage skips and bins. The charging platform is necessarily above ground level and can present a hazard unless it is level and has a non-slip surface and strong rails around it and any floor openings.

Cupolas generate large quantities of carbon monoxide, which may leak from the charging doors and be blown back by local eddy currents. Carbon monoxide is invisible, odourless and can quickly produce toxic ambient levels. Employees working on the charging platform or surrounding catwalks should be well trained in order to recognize the symptoms of carbon monoxide poisoning. Both continuous and spot monitoring of exposure levels are needed. Self-contained breathing apparatus and resuscitation equipment should be maintained in readiness, and operators should be instructed in their use. When emergency work is carried out, a confined-space entry system of contaminant monitoring should be developed and enforced. All work should be supervised.

Cupolas are usually sited in pairs or groups, so that while one is being repaired the others operate. The period of use must be based on experience with durability of refractories and on engineering recommendations. Procedures must be worked out in advance for tapping out iron and for shutting down when hot spots develop or if the water cooling system is disabled. Cupola repair necessarily involves the presence of employees inside the cupola shell itself to mend or renew refractory linings. These assignments should be considered confined-space entries and appropriate precautions taken. Precautions should also be taken to prevent the discharge of material through the charging doors at such times. To protect the workers from falling objects, they should wear safety helmets and, if working at a height, safety harnesses.

Workers tapping cupolas (transferring molten metal from the cupola well to a holding furnace or ladle) must observe rigorous personal protection measures. Goggles and protective clothing are essential. The eye protectors should resist both high velocity impact and molten metal. Extreme caution should be exercised in order to prevent remaining molten slag (the unwanted debris removed from the melt with the aid of the limestone additives) and metal from coming into contact with water, which will cause a steam explosion. Tappers and supervisors must ensure that any person not involved in the operation of the cupola remains outside the danger area, which is delineated by a radius of about 4 m from the cupola spout. Delineation of a non-authorized no-entry zone is a statutory requirement under the British Iron and Steel Foundries Regulations of 1953.

When the cupola run is at an end, the cupola bottom is dropped to remove the unwanted slag and other material still inside the shell before employees can carry out the routine refractory maintenance. Dropping the cupola bottom is a skilled and dangerous operation requiring trained supervision. A refractory floor or layer of dry sand on which to drop the debris is essential. If a problem occurs, such as jammed cupola bottom doors, great caution must be exercised to avoid risks of burns to workers from the hot metal and slag.

Visible white-hot metal is a danger to workers' eyes due to the emission of infrared and ultraviolet radiation, extensive exposure to which can cause cataracts.

The ladle must be dried before filling with molten metal, to prevent steam explosions; a satisfactory period of flame heating must be established.

Employees in metal and pouring sections of the foundry should be provided with hard hats, tinted eye protection and face shields, aluminized clothing such as aprons, gaiters or spats (lower-leg and foot coverings) and boots. Use of protective equipment should be mandatory, and there should be adequate instruction in its use and maintenance. High standards of housekeeping and exclusion of water to the highest degree possible are needed in all areas where molten metal is being manipulated.

Where large ladles are slung from cranes or overhead conveyors, positive ladle-control devices should be employed to ensure that spillage of metal cannot occur if the operator releases his or her hold. Hooks holding molten metal ladles must be periodically tested for metal fatigue to prevent failure.

In production foundries, the assembled mould moves along a mechanical conveyor to a ventilated pouring station. Pouring may be from a manually controlled ladle with mechanical assist, an indexing ladle controlled from a cab, or it can be automatic. Typically, the pouring station is provided with a compensating hood with a direct air supply. The poured mould proceeds along the conveyor through an exhausted cooling tunnel until shakeout. In smaller, job shop foundries, moulds may be poured on a foundry floor and allowed to burn off there. In this situation, the ladle should be equipped with a mobile exhaust hood.

Tapping and transport of molten iron and charging of electric furnaces creates exposure to iron oxide and other metal oxide fumes. Pouring into the mould ignites and pyrolyses organic materials, generating large amounts of carbon monoxide, smoke, carcinogenic polynuclear aromatic hydrocarbons (PAHs) and pyrolysis products from core materials which may be carcinogenic and also respiratory sensitizers. Moulds containing large polyurethane bound cold box cores release a dense, irritating smoke containing isocyanates and amines. The primary hazard control for mould burn off is a locally exhausted pouring station and cooling tunnel.

In foundries with roof fans for exhausting pouring operations, high metal fume concentrations may be found in the upper regions where crane cabs are located. If the cabs have an operator, the cabs should be enclosed and provided with filtered, conditioned air.

Pattern making

Pattern making is a highly skilled trade translating the two-dimensional design plans to a three-dimensional object. Traditional wooden patterns are made in standard workshops containing hand tools and electric cutting and planing equipment. Here, all reasonably practicable measures should be taken to reduce the noise to the greatest extent possible, and suitable ear protectors must be provided. It is important that the employees are aware of the advantages of using such protection.

Power-driven wood cutting and finishing machines are obvious sources of danger, and often suitable guards cannot be fitted without preventing the machine from functioning at all. Employees must be well versed in normal operating procedure and should also be instructed in the hazards inherent in the work.

Wood sawing can create dust exposure. Efficient ventilation systems should be fitted to eliminate wood dust from the pattern shop atmosphere. In certain industries using hard woods, nasal cancer has been observed. This has not been studied in the founding industry.

Casting in permanent metal moulds, as in die-casting, has been an important development in the foundry industry. In this case, pattern making is largely replaced by engineering methods and is really a die manufacture operation. Most of the pattern-making hazards and the risks from sand are eliminated, but are replaced by the risk inherent in the use of some sort of refractory material to coat the die or mould. In modern die-foundry work, increasing use is made of sand cores, in which case the dust hazards of the sand foundry are still present.

Moulding

The most common moulding process in the iron founding industry uses the traditional "green sand" mould made from silica sand, coal dust, clay and organic binders. Other methods of mould production are adapted from coremaking: thermosetting, cold self-setting and gas-hardened. These methods and their hazards will be discussed under coremaking. Permanent moulds or the lost foam process may also be used, especially in the aluminium foundry industry.

In production foundries, sand mix, moulding, mould assembly, pouring and shakeout are integrated and mechanized. Sand from shakeout is recycled back to the sand mix operation, where water and other additives are added and the sand is mixed in mullers to maintain the desired physical properties.

For ease of assembly, patterns (and their moulds) are made in two parts. In manual mould-making, the moulds are enclosed in metal or wooden frames called *flasks*. The bottom half of the pattern is placed in the bottom flask (the *drag*), and first fine sand and then heavy sand are poured around the pattern. The sand is compacted in the mould by a jolt-squeeze, sand slinger or pressure process. The top flask (the *cope*) is prepared similarly. Wooden spacers are placed in the cope to form the sprue and riser channels, which are the pathway for the molten metal to flow into the mould cavity. The patterns are removed, the core inserted, and then the two halves of the mould assembled and fastened together, ready for pouring. In production foundries, the cope and drag flasks are prepared on a mechanical conveyor, cores are placed in the drag flask, and the mould assembled by mechanical means.

Silica dust is a potential problem wherever sand is handled. Moulding sand is usually either damp or mixed with liquid resin, and is therefore less likely to be a significant source of respirable dust. A parting agent such as talc is sometimes added to promote the ready removal of the pattern from the mould. Respirable talc causes talcosis, a type of pneumoconiosis. Parting agents are more widespread where hand moulding is employed; in the larger, more automatic processes they are rarely seen. Chemicals are sometimes sprayed onto the mould surface, suspended or dissolved in isopropyl alcohol, which is then burned off to leave the compound, usually a type of graphite, coating the mould in order

to achieve a casting with a finer surface finish. This involves an immediate fire risk, and all employees involved in applying these coatings should be provided with fire-retardant protective clothing and hand protection, as organic solvents can also cause dermatitis. Coatings should be applied in a ventilated booth to prevent the organic vapours from escaping into the workplace. Strict precautions should also be observed to ensure that the isopropyl alcohol is stored and used with safety. It should be transferred to a small vessel for immediate use, and the larger storage vessels should be kept well away from the burning-off process.

Manual mould making can involve the manipulation of large and cumbersome objects. The moulds themselves are heavy, as are the moulding boxes or flasks. They are often lifted, moved and stacked by hand. Back injuries are common, and power assists are needed so employees do not need to lift objects too heavy to be carried safely.

Standardized designs are available for enclosures of mixers, conveyors and pouring and shakeout stations with appropriate exhaust volumes and capture and transport velocities. Adherence to such designs and strict preventive maintenance of control systems will attain compliance with international recognized limits for dust exposure.

Coremaking

Cores inserted into the mould determine the internal configuration of a hollow casting, such as the water jacket of an engine block. The core must withstand the casting process but at the same time must not be so strong as to resist removal from the casting during the knocking-out stage.

Prior to the 1960s, core mixtures comprised sand and binders, such as linseed oil, molasses or dextrin (oil sand). The sand was packed in a core box with a cavity in the shape of the core, and then dried in an oven. Core ovens evolve harmful pyrolysis products and require a suitable, well maintained chimney system. Normally, convection currents within the oven will be sufficient to ensure satisfactory removal of fumes from the workplace, although they contribute enormously to air pollution After removal from the oven, the finished oil sand cores can still give rise to a small amount of smoke, but the hazard is minor; in some cases, however, small amounts of acrolein in the fumes may be a considerable nuisance. Cores may be treated with a "flare-off coating" to improve the surface finish of the casting, which calls for the same precautions as in the case of moulds.

Hot box or shell moulding and coremaking are thermosetting processes used in iron foundries. New sand may be mixed with resin at the foundry, or resin-coated sand may be shipped in bags for addition to the coremaking machine. Resin sand is injected into a metal pattern (the core box). The pattern is then heated—by direct natural gas fires in the hot box process or by other means for shell cores and moulding. Hot boxes typically use a furfuryl alcohol (furan), urea- or phenol-formaldehyde thermosetting resin. Shell moulding uses a urea- or phenol-formaldehyde resin. After a short curing time, the core hardens considerably and can be pushed clear of the pattern plate by ejector pins. Hot box and shell coremaking generate substantial exposure to formaldehyde, which is a probable carcinogen, and other contaminants, depending on the system. Control measures for formaldehyde include direct air supply at the operator station, local exhaust at the corebox, enclosure and local exhaust at the core storage station and low-formaldehyde-emission resins. Satisfactory control is difficult to achieve. Medical surveillance for respiratory conditions should be provided to coremaking workers. Phenol- or urea-formaldehyde resin contact with the skin or eyes must be prevented because the resins are irritants or sensitizers and can cause dermatitis. Copious washing with water will help to avoid the problem.

Cold-setting (no-bake) hardening systems presently in use include: acid-catalyzed urea- and phenol-formaldehyde resins with and without furfuryl alcohol; alkyd and phenolic isocyanates; Fascold; self-set silicates; Inoset; cement sand and fluid or castable sand. Cold-setting hardeners do not require external heating to set. The isocyanates employed in binders are normally based on methylene diphenyl isocyanate (MDI), which, if inhaled, can act as a respiratory irritant or sensitizer, causing asthma. Gloves and protective goggles are advisable when handling or using these compounds. The isocyanates themselves should be carefully stored in sealed containers in dry conditions at a temperature between 10 and 30 °C. Empty storage vessels should be filled and soaked for 24 hours with a 5% sodium carbonate solution in order to neutralize any residual chemical left in the drum. Most general housekeeping principles should be strictly applied to resin moulding processes, but the greatest caution of all should be exercised when handling the catalysts used as setting agents. The catalysts for the phenol and oil isocyanate resins are usually aromatic amines based on pyridine compounds, which are liquids with a pungent smell. They can cause severe skin irritation and renal and hepatic damage and can also affect the central nervous system. These compounds are supplied either as separate additives (three-part binder) or are ready mixed with the oil materials, and LEV should be provided at the mixing, moulding, casting and knockout stages. For certain other no-bake processes the catalysts used are phosphoric or various sulphonic acids, which are also toxic; accidents during transport or use should be adequately guarded against.

Gas-hardened coremaking comprises the carbon dioxide (CO_2)-silicate and the Isocure (or "Ashland") processes. Many variations of the CO_2-silicate process have been developed since the 1950s. This process has generally been used for the production of medium to large moulds and cores. The core sand is a mixture of sodium silicate and silica sand, usually modified by adding such substances as molasses as breakdown agents. After the core box is filled, the core is cured by passing carbon dioxide through the core mixture. This forms sodium carbonate and silica gel, which acts as a binder.

Sodium silicate is an alkaline substance, and can be harmful if it comes into contact with the skin or eyes or is ingested. It is advisable to provide an emergency shower close to areas where large quantities of sodium silicate are handled and gloves should always be worn. A readily available eye-wash fountain should be located in any foundry area where sodium silicate is used. The CO_2 can be supplied as a solid, liquid or gas. Where it is supplied in cylinders or pressure tanks, a great many housekeeping precautions should be taken, such as cylinder storage, valve maintenance, handling and so on. There is also the risk from the gas itself, since it can lower the oxygen concentration in the air in enclosed spaces.

The Isocure process is used for cores and moulds. This is a gas-setting system in which a resin, frequently phenol-formaldehyde, is mixed with a di-isocyanate (e.g., MDI) and sand. This is injected into the core box and then gassed with an amine, usually either triethylamine or dimethylethylamine, to cause the crosslinking, setting reaction. The amines, often sold in drums, are highly volatile liquids with a strong smell of ammonia. There is a very real risk of fire or explosion, and extreme care should be taken, especially where the material is stored in bulk. The characteristic effect of these amines is to cause halo vision and corneal swelling, although they also affect the central nervous system, where they can cause convulsions, paralysis and, occasionally, death. Should some of the amine come into contact with the eyes or skin, first-aid measures should include washing with copious quantities

of water for at least 15 minutes and immediate medical attention. In the Isocure process, the amine is applied as a vapour in a nitrogen carrier, with excess amine scrubbed through an acid tower. Leakage from the corebox is the principle cause of high exposure, although offgassing of amine from manufactured cores is also significant. Great care should be taken at all times when handling this material, and suitable exhaust ventilation equipment should be installed to remove vapours from the working areas.

Shakeout, casting extraction and core knockout

After the molten metal has cooled, the rough casting must be removed from the mould. This is a noisy process, typically exposing operators well above 90 dBA over an 8 hour working day. Hearing protectors should be provided if it is not practicable to reduce the noise output. The main bulk of the mould is separated from the casting usually by jarring impact. Frequently the moulding box, mould and casting are dropped onto a vibrating grid to dislodge the sand (shakeout). The sand then drops through the grid into a hopper or onto a conveyor where it can be subjected to magnetic separators and recycled for milling, treatment and re-use, or merely dumped. Sometimes hydroblasting can be used instead of a grid, creating less dust. The core is removed here, also sometimes using high-pressure water streams.

The casting is then removed and transferred to the next stage of the knockout operation. Often small castings can be removed from the flask by a "punch-out" process before shakeout, which produces less dust. The sand gives rise to hazardous silica dust levels because it has been in contact with molten metal and is therefore very dry. The metal and sand remain very hot. Eye protection is needed. Walking and working surfaces must be kept free of scrap, which is a tripping hazard, and of dust, which can be resuspended to pose an inhalation hazard.

Relatively few studies have been carried out to determine what effect, if any, the new core binders have on the health of the de-coring operator in particular. The furanes, furfuryl alcohol and phosphoric acid, urea- and phenol-formaldehyde resins, sodium silicate and carbon dioxide, no-bakes, modified linseed oil and MDI, all undergo some type of thermal decomposition when exposed to the temperatures of the molten metals.

No studies have yet been conducted on the effect of the resin-coated silica particle on the development of pneumoconiosis. It is not known whether these coatings will have an inhibiting or accelerating effect on lung-tissue lesions. It is feared that the reaction products of phosphoric acid may liberate phosphine. Animal experiments and some selected studies have shown that the effect of the silica dust on lung tissue is greatly accelerated when silica has been treated with a mineral acid. Urea- and phenol-formaldehyde resins can release free phenols, aldehydes and carbon monoxide. The sugars added to increase collapsibility produce significant amounts of carbon monoxide. No-bakes will release isocyanates (e.g., MDI) and carbon monoxide.

Fettling (cleaning)

Casting cleaning, or fettling, is carried out following shakeout and core knockout. The various processes involved are variously designated in different places but can be broadly classified as follows:

- *Dressing* covers stripping, roughing or mucking-off, removal of adherent moulding sand, core sand, runners, risers, flash and other readily disposable matter with hand tools or portable pneumatic tools.
- *Fettling* covers removal of burnt-on moulding sand, rough edges, surplus metal, such as blisters, stumps of gates, scabs or other unwanted blemishes, and the hand cleaning of the casting

using hand chisels, pneumatic tools and wire brushes. Welding techniques, such as oxyacetylene-flame cutting, electric arc, arc-air, powder washing and the plasma torch, may be employed for burning off headers, for casting repair and for cutting and washing.

Sprue removal is the first dressing operation. As much as half of the metal cast in the mould is not part of the final casting. The mould must include reservoirs, cavities, feeders and sprue in order that it be filled with metal to complete the cast object. The sprue usually can be removed during the knockout stage, but sometimes this must be carried out as a separate stage of the fettling or dressing operation. Sprue removal is done by hand, usually by knocking the casting with a hammer. To reduce noise, the metal hammers can be replaced by rubber-covered ones and the conveyors lined with the same noise-damping rubber. Hot metal fragments are thrown off and pose an eye hazard. Eye protection must be used. Detached sprues should normally be returned to the charging region of the melting plant and should not be permitted to accumulate at the despruing section of the foundry. After despruing (but sometimes before) most castings are shot blasted or tumbled to remove mould materials and perhaps to improve the surface finish. Tumbling barrels generate high noise levels. Enclosures may be necessary, which can also require LEV.

Dressing methods in steel, iron and non-ferrous foundries are very similar, but special difficulties exist in the dressing and fettling of steel castings owing to greater amounts of burnt-on fused sand compared to iron and non-ferrous castings. Fused sand on large steel castings may contain cristobalite, which is more toxic than the quartz found in virgin sand.

Airless shot blasting or tumbling of castings before chipping and grinding is needed to prevent overexposure to silica dust. The casting must be free of visible dust, although a silica hazard may still be generated by grinding if silica is burnt into the apparently clean metal surface of the casting. The shot is centrifugally propelled at the casting, and no operator is required inside the unit. The blast cabinet must be exhausted so no visible dust escapes. Only when there is a breakdown or deterioration of the shot-blast cabinet and/or the fan and collector is there a dust problem.

Water or water and sand or pressure shot blasting may be used to remove adherent sand by subjecting the casting to a high-pressure stream of either water or iron or steel shot. Sand blasting has been banned in several countries (e.g., the United Kingdom) because of the silicosis risk as the sand particles become finer and finer and the respirable fraction thus continually increases. The water or shot is discharged through a gun and can clearly present a risk to personnel if not handled correctly. Blasting should always be carried out in an isolated, enclosed space. All blasting enclosures should be inspected at regular intervals to ensure that the dust extraction system is functioning and that there are no leaks through which shot or water could escape into the foundry. Blasters' helmets should be approved and carefully maintained. It is advisable to post a notice on the door to the booth, warning employees that blasting is under way and that unauthorized entry is prohibited. In certain circumstances delay bolts linked to the blast drive motor can be fitted to the doors, making it impossible to open the doors until blasting has ceased.

A variety of grinding tools are used to smooth the rough casting. Abrasive wheels may be mounted on floor-standing or pedestal machines or in portable or swing-frame grinders. Pedestal grinders are used for smaller castings that can be easily handled; portable grinders, surface disc wheels, cup wheels and cone wheels are used for a number of purposes, including smoothing of internal surfaces of castings; swing-frame grinders are used primarily on large castings that require a great deal of metal removal.

Other Foundries

Steel founding

Production in the steel foundry (as distinct from a basic steel mill) is similar to that in the iron foundry; however, the metal temperatures are much higher. This means that eye protection with coloured lenses is essential and that the silica in the mould is converted by heat to tridymite or crystobalite, two forms of crystalline silica which are particularly dangerous to the lungs. Sand often becomes burnt on to the casting and has to be removed by mechanical means, which give rise to dangerous dust; consequently, effective dust exhaust systems and respiratory protection are essential.

Light-alloy founding

The light-alloy foundry uses mainly aluminium and magnesium alloys. These often contain small amounts of metals which may give off toxic fumes under certain circumstances. The fumes should be analysed to determine their constituents where the alloy might contain such components.

In aluminium and magnesium foundries, melting is commonly done in crucible furnaces. Exhaust vents around the top of the pot for removing fumes are advisable. In oil-fired furnaces, incomplete combustion due to faulty burners may result in products such as carbon monoxide being released into the air. Furnace fumes may contain complex hydrocarbons, some of which may be carcinogenic. During furnace and flue cleaning there is the hazard of exposure to vanadium pentoxide concentrated in furnace soot from oil deposits.

Fluorspar is commonly used as a flux in aluminium melting, and significant quantities of fluoride dust may be released to the environment. In certain cases barium chloride has been used as a flux for magnesium alloys; this is a significantly toxic substance and, consequently, considerable care is required in its use. Light alloys may occasionally be degassed by passing sulphur dioxide or chlorine (or proprietary compounds that decompose to produce chlorine) through the molten metal; exhaust ventilation and respiratory protective equipment are required for this operation. In order to reduce the cooling rate of the hot metal in the mould, a mixture of substances (usually aluminium and iron oxide) which react highly exothermically is placed on the mould riser. This "thermite" mixture gives off dense fumes which have been found to be innocuous in practice. When the fumes are brown in colour, alarm may be caused due to suspicion of the presence of nitrogen oxides; however, this suspicion is unfounded. The finely divided aluminium produced during the dressing of aluminium and magnesium castings constitutes a severe fire hazard, and wet methods should be used for dust collection.

Magnesium casting entails considerable potential fire and explosion hazard. Molten magnesium will ignite unless a protective barrier is maintained between it and the atmosphere; molten sulphur is widely employed for this purpose. Foundry workers applying the sulphur powder to the melting pot by hand may develop dermatitis and should be provided with gloves made of fireproof fabric. The sulphur in contact with the metal is constantly burning, so considerable quantities of sulphur dioxide are given off. Exhaust ventilation should be installed. Workers should be informed of the danger of a pot or ladle of molten magnesium catching fire, which may give rise to a dense cloud of finely divided magnesium oxide. Protective clothing of fireproof materials should be worn by all magnesium foundry workers. Clothing coated with magnesium dust should not be stored in lockers without humidity control, since spontaneous combustion may occur. The magnesium dust should be removed from the clothing. French chalk is used extensively in mould dressing in magnesium foundries; the dust should be controlled to prevent talcosis. Penetrating oils and dusting powders are employed in the inspection of light-alloy castings for the detection of cracks. Dyes have been introduced to improve the effectiveness of these techniques. Certain red dyes have been found to be absorbed and excreted in sweat, thus causing soiling of personal clothing; although this condition is a nuisance, no effects on health have been observed.

Brass and bronze foundries

Toxic metal fumes and dust from typical alloys are a special hazard of brass and bronze foundries. Exposures to lead above safe limits in both melting, pouring and finishing operations are common, especially where alloys have a high lead composition. The lead hazard in furnace cleaning and dross disposal is particularly acute. Overexposure to lead is frequent in melting and pouring and can also occur in grinding. Zinc and copper fumes (the constituents of bronze) are the most common causes of metal fume fever, although the condition has also been observed in foundry workers using magnesium, aluminium, antimony and so on. Some high-duty alloys contain cadmium, which can cause chemical pneumonia from acute exposure and kidney damage and lung cancer from chronic exposure.

Permanent-mould process

Casting in permanent metal moulds, as in die-casting, has been an important development in the foundry. In this case, pattern making is largely replaced by engineering methods and is really a die-sinking operation. Most of the pattern making hazards are thereby removed and the risks from sand are also eliminated but are replaced by a degree of risk inherent in the use of some sort of refractory material to coat the die or mould. In modern die-foundry work, increasing use is made of sand cores, in which case the dust hazards of the sand foundry are still present.

Die casting

Aluminium is a common metal in die casting. Automotive hardware such as chrome trim is typically zinc die cast, followed by copper, nickel and chrome plating. The hazard of metal fume fever from zinc fumes should be constantly controlled, as must be chromic acid mist.

Pressure die-casting machines present all the hazards common to hydraulic power presses. In addition, the worker may be exposed to the mist of oils used as die lubricants and must be protected against the inhalation of these mists and the danger of oil-saturated clothing. The fire-resistant hydraulic fluids used in the presses may contain toxic organophosphorus compounds, and particular care should be taken during maintenance work on hydraulic systems.

Precision founding

Precision foundries rely on the investment or lost-wax casting process, in which patterns are made by injection moulding wax into a die; these patterns are coated with a fine refractory powder which serves as a mould-facing material, and the wax is then melted out prior to casting or by the introduction of the casting metal itself.

Wax removal presents a definite fire hazard, and decomposition of the wax produces acrolein and other hazardous decomposition products. Wax-burnout kilns must be adequately ventilated. Trichloroethylene has been used to remove the last traces of wax; this solvent may collect in pockets in the mould or be absorbed by the refractory material and vaporize or decompose during pouring. The inclusion of asbestos investment

casting refractory materials should be eliminated due to the hazards of asbestos.

Health Problems and Disease Patterns

Foundries stand out among industrial processes because of a higher fatality rate arising from molten metal spills and explosions, cupola maintenance including bottom drop and carbon monoxide hazards during relining. Foundries report a higher incidence of foreign body, contusion and burn injuries and a lower proportion of musculoskeletal injuries than other facilities. They also have the highest noise exposure levels.

A study of several dozen fatal injuries in foundries revealed the following causes: crushing between mould conveyor cars and building structures during maintenance and trouble-shooting, crushing while cleaning mullers which were remotely activated, molten metal burns after crane failure, mould cracking, overflowing transfer ladle, steam eruption in undried ladle, falls from cranes and work platforms, electrocution from welding equipment, crushing from material-handling vehicles, burns from cupola bottom drop, high-oxygen atmosphere during cupola repair and carbon monoxide overexposure during cupola repair.

Abrasive wheels

The bursting or breaking of abrasive wheels may cause fatal or very serious injuries: gaps between the wheel and the rest at pedestal grinders may catch and crush the hand or forearm. Unprotected eyes are at risk at all stages. Slips and falls, especially when carrying heavy loads, may be caused by badly maintained or obstructed floors. Injuries to the feet may be caused by falling objects or dropped loads. Sprains and strains may result from overexertion in lifting and carrying. Badly maintained hoisting appliances may fail and cause materials to fall on workers. Electric shock may result from badly maintained or unearthed (ungrounded) electrical equipment, especially portable tools.

All dangerous parts of machinery, especially abrasive wheels, should have adequate guarding, with automatic lockout if the guard is removed during processing. Dangerous gaps between the wheel and the rest at pedestal grinders should be eliminated, and close attention should be paid to all precautions in the care and maintenance of abrasive wheels and in regulation of their speed (particular care is required with portable wheels). Strict maintenance of all electrical equipment and proper grounding arrangements should be enforced. Workers should be instructed in correct lifting and carrying techniques and should know how to attach loads to crane hooks and other hoisting appliances. Suitable PPE, such as eye and face shields and foot and leg protection, should also be provided. Provision should be made for prompt first aid, even for minor injuries, and for competent medical care when needed.

Dust

Dust diseases are prominent among foundry workers. Silica exposures are often close to or exceed prescribed exposure limits, even in well-controlled cleaning operations in modern production foundries and where castings are free of visible dust. Exposures many times above the limit occur where castings are dusty or cabinets leak. Overexposures are likely where visible dust escapes venting in shakeout, sand preparation or refractory repair.

Silicosis is the predominant health hazard in the steel fettling shop; a mixed pneumoconiosis is more prevalent in iron fettling (Landrigan et al. 1986). In the foundry, the prevalence increases with length of exposure and higher dust levels. There is some evidence that conditions in steel foundries are more likely to cause silicosis than those in iron foundries because of the higher levels of free silica present. Attempts to set an exposure level at which silicosis will not occur have been inconclusive; the threshold is probably less than 100 micrograms/m^3 and perhaps as low as half that amount.

In most countries, the occurrence of new cases of silicosis is declining, in part because of changes in technology, a move away from silica sand in foundries and a shift away from silica brick and towards basic furnace linings in steel melting. A major reason is the fact that automation has resulted in the employment of fewer workers in steel production and foundries. Exposure to respirable silica dust remains stubbornly high in many foundries, however, and in countries where processes are labour intensive, silicosis remains a major problem.

Silico-tuberculosis has long been reported in foundry workers. Where the prevalence of silicosis has declined, there has been a parallel falling off in reported cases of tuberculosis, although that disease has not been completely eradicated. In countries where dust levels have remained high, dusty processes are labour intensive and the prevalence of tuberculosis in the general population is elevated, tuberculosis remains an important cause of death amongst foundry workers.

Many workers suffering from pneumoconiosis also have chronic bronchitis, often associated with emphysema; it has long been thought by many investigators that, in some cases at least, occupational exposures may have played a part. Cancer of the lung, lobar pneumonia, bronchopneumonia and coronary thrombosis have also been reported to be associated with pneumoconiosis in foundry workers.

A recent review of mortality studies of foundry workers, including the American auto industry, showed increased deaths from lung cancer in 14 of 15 studies. Because high lung cancer rates are found among cleaning room workers where the primary hazard is silica, it is likely that mixed exposures are also found.

Studies of the carcinogens in the foundry environment have concentrated on polycyclic aromatic hydrocarbons formed in the thermal breakdown of sand additives and binders. It has been suggested that metals such as chromium and nickel, and dusts such as silica and asbestos, may also be responsible for some of the excess mortality. Differences in moulding and core-making chemistry, sand type and the composition of iron and steel alloys may be responsible for different levels of risk in different foundries (IARC 1984).

Increased mortality from non-malignant respiratory disease was found in 8 of 11 studies. Silicosis deaths were recorded as well. Clinical studies found x-ray changes characteristic of pneumoconiosis, lung function deficits characteristic of obstruction, and increased respiratory symptoms among workers in modern "clean" production foundries. These resulted from exposures after the 1960s and strongly suggest that the health risks prevalent in the older foundries have not yet been eliminated.

Prevention of lung disorders is essentially a matter of dust and fume control; the generally applicable solution is providing good general ventilation coupled with efficient LEV. Low-volume, high-velocity systems are most suitable for some operations, particularly portable grinding wheels and pneumatic tools.

Hand or pneumatic chisels used to remove burnt-on sand produce much finely divided dust. Brushing off excess materials with revolving wire brushes or hand brushes also produces much dust; LEV is required.

Dust control measures are readily adaptable to floor-standing and swing-frame grinders. Portable grinding on small castings can be carried out on exhaust-ventilated benches, or ventilation may be applied to the tools themselves. Brushing can also be carried out on a ventilated bench. Dust control on large castings presents a problem, but considerable progress has been made with low-volume, high-velocity ventilation systems. Instruction and training

in their use is needed to overcome the objections of workers who find these systems cumbersome and complain that their view of the working area is impaired.

Dressing and fettling of very large castings where local ventilation is impracticable should be done in a separate, isolated area and at a time when few other workers are present. Suitable PPE that is regularly cleaned and repaired, should be provided for each worker, along with instruction in its proper use.

Since the 1950s, a variety of synthetic resin systems have been introduced into foundries to bind sand in cores and moulds. These generally comprise a base material and a catalyst or hardener which starts the polymerization. Many of these reactive chemicals are sensitizers (e.g., isocyanates, furfuryl alcohol, amines and formaldehyde) and have now been implicated in cases of occupational asthma among foundry workers. In one study, 12 out of 78 foundry workers exposed to Pepset (cold-box) resins had asthmatic symptoms, and of these, six had a marked decline in airflow rates in a challenge test using methyl di-isocyanate (Johnson et al. 1985).

Welding

Welding in fettling shops exposes workers to metal fumes with the consequent hazard of toxicity and metal fever, depending on the composition of the metals involved. Welding on cast iron requires a nickel rod and creates exposure to nickel fumes. The plasma torch produces a considerable amount of metal fumes, ozone, nitrogen oxide and ultraviolet radiation, and generates high levels of noise.

An exhaust-ventilated bench can be provided for welding small castings. Controlling exposures during welding or burning operations on large castings is difficult. A successful approach involves creating a central station for these operations and providing LEV through a flexible duct positioned at the point of welding. This requires training the worker to move the duct from one location to another. Good general ventilation and, when necessary, the use of PPE will aid in reducing the overall dust and fume exposures.

Noise and vibration

The highest levels of noise in the foundry are usually found in knockout and cleaning operations; they are higher in mechanized than in manual foundries. The ventilation system itself may generate exposures close to 90 dBA.

Noise levels in the fettling of steel castings may be in the range of 115 to 120 dBA, while those actually encountered in the fettling of cast iron are in the 105 to 115 dBA range. The British Steel Casting Research Association established that the sources of noise during fettling include:

- the fettling tool exhaust
- the impact of the hammer or wheel on the casting
- resonance of the casting and vibration against its support
- transmission of vibration from the casting support to surrounding structures
- reflection of direct noise by the hood controlling air flow through the ventilation system.

Noise control strategies vary with the size of the casting, the type of metal, the work area available, the use of portable tools and other related factors. Certain basic measures are available to reduce noise exposure of individuals and co-workers, including isolation in time and space, complete enclosures, partial sound-absorbing partitions, execution of work on sound-absorbing surfaces, baffles, panels and hoods made from sound-absorbing or other acoustical materials. The guidelines for safe daily exposure limits should be observed and, as a last resort, personal protective devices may be used.

A fettling bench developed by the British Steel Casting Research Association reduces the noise in chipping by about 4 to 5 dBA. This bench incorporates an exhaust system to remove dust. This improvement is encouraging and leads to hope that, with further development, even greater noise reductions will become possible.

Hand-arm vibration syndrome

Portable vibrating tools may cause Raynaud's phenomenon (hand-arm vibration syndrome—HAVS). This is more prevalent in steel fettlers than in iron fettlers and more frequent among those using rotating tools. The critical vibratory rate for the onset of this phenomenon is between 2,000 and 3,000 revolutions per minute and in the range of 40 to 125 Hz.

HAVS is now thought to involve effects on a number of other tissues in the forearm apart from peripheral nerves and blood vessels. It is associated with carpal tunnel syndrome and degenerative changes in the joints. A recent study of steelworks chippers and grinders showed they were twice as likely to develop Dupuytren's contracture than a comparison group (Thomas and Clarke 1992).

Vibration transmitted to the hands of the worker can be considerably reduced by: selection of tools designed to reduce the harmful ranges of frequency and amplitude; direction of the exhaust port away from the hand; use of multiple layers of gloves or an insulating glove; and shortening of exposure time by changes in work operations, tools and rest periods.

Eye problems

Some of the dusts and chemicals encountered in foundries (e.g., isocyanates, formaldehyde and tertiary amines, such as dimethlyethylamine, triethylamine and so on) are irritants and have been responsible for visual symptoms among exposed workers. These include itchy, watery eyes, hazy or blurred vision or so called "blue-grey vision". On the basis of the occurrence of these effects, reducing time-weighted average exposures below 3 ppm has been recommended.

Other problems

Formaldehyde exposures at or above the US exposure limit are found in well-controlled hot-box core-making operations. Exposures many times above the limit may be found where hazard control is poor.

Asbestos has been used widely in the foundry industry and, until recently, it was often used in protective clothing for heat-exposed workers. Its effects have been found in x-ray surveys of foundry workers, both among production workers and maintenance workers who have been exposed to asbestos; a cross-sectional survey found the characteristic pleural involvement in 20 out of 900 steel workers (Kronenberg et al. 1991).

Periodic examinations

Preplacement and periodic medical examinations, including a survey of symptoms, chest x rays, pulmonary function tests and audiograms, should be provided for all foundry workers with appropriate follow-up if questionable or abnormal findings are detected. The compounding effects of tobacco smoke on the risk of respiratory problems among foundry workers mandate inclusion of advice on smoking cessation in a programme of health education and promotion.

Conclusion

Foundries have been an essential industrial operation for centuries. Despite continuing advances in technology, they present workers with a panoply of hazards to safety and health. Because hazards continue to exist even in the most modern plants

with exemplary prevention and control programmes, protecting the health and well-being of workers remains an ongoing challenge to management and to the workers and their representatives. This remains difficult both in industry downturns (when concerns for worker health and safety tend to give way to economic stringencies) and in boom times (when the demand for increased output may lead to potentially dangerous short cuts in the processes). Education and training in hazard control, therefore, remain a constant necessity.

FORGING AND STAMPING

Robert M. Park

Process Overview

Forming metal parts by application of high compressive and tensile forces is common throughout industrial manufacturing. In stamping operations, metal, most often in the form of sheets, strips or coils, is formed into specific shapes at ambient temperatures by shearing, pressing and stretching between dies, usually in a series of one or more discrete impact steps. Cold-rolled steel is the starting material in many stamping operations creating sheet metal parts in the automotive and appliance and other industries. Approximately 15% of workers in the automotive industry work in stamping operations or plants.

In forging, compressive force is applied to pre-formed blocks (blanks) of metal, usually heated to high temperatures, also in one or more discrete pressing steps. The shape of the final piece is determined by the shape of the cavities in the metal die or dies used. With open impression dies, as in drop hammer forging, the blank is compressed between one die attached to the bottom anvil and the vertical ram. With closed impression dies, as in press forging, the blank is compressed between the bottom die and an upper die attached to the ram.

Figure 82.1 • Press forging.

Drop hammer forges use a steam or air cylinder to raise the hammer, which is then dropped by gravity or is driven by steam or air. The number and force of the hammer blows are manually controlled by the operator. The operator often holds the cold end of the stock while operating the drop hammer. Drop hammer forging once comprised about two-thirds of all forging done in the United States, but is less common today.

Press forges use a mechanical or hydraulic ram to shape the piece with a single, slow, controlled stroke (see figure 82.1). Press forging is usually controlled automatically. It can be done hot or at normal temperatures (cold-forging, extruding). A variation on normal forging is rolling, where continuous applications of force are used and the operator turns the part.

Die lubricants are sprayed or otherwise applied to die faces and blank surfaces before and between hammer or press strokes.

High-strength machine parts such as shafts, ring gears, bolts and vehicle suspension components are common steel forging products. High-strength aircraft components such as wing spars, turbine disks and landing gear are forged from aluminium, titanium or nickel and steel alloys. Approximately 3% of automotive workers are in forging operations or plants.

Working Conditions

Many hazards common in heavy industry are present in stamping and forging operations. These include repetitive strain injuries (RSIs) from repeated handling and processing of parts and operation of machine controls such as palm buttons. Heavy parts place workers at risk for back and shoulder problems as well as upper extremity musculoskeletal disorders. Press operators in automotive stamping plants have rates of RSIs that are comparable to those of assembly plant workers in high-risk jobs. High-impulse vibration and noise are present in most stamping and some forging (e.g., steam or air hammer) operations, causing hearing loss and possible cardiovascular illness; these are among the highest-noise industrial environments (over 100 dBA). As in other forms of automation-driven systems, worker energy loads can be high, depending on the parts handled and machine cycling rates.

Catastrophic injuries resulting from unanticipated machine movements are common in stamping and forging. These can be due to: (1) mechanical failure of machine control systems, such as clutch mechanisms in situations where workers are routinely expected to be within the machine operating envelope (an unacceptable process design); (2) deficiencies in machine design or performance that invite unprogrammed worker interventions such as moving jammed or misaligned parts; or (3) improper, high-risk maintenance procedures performed without adequate lockout of the entire machine network involved, including parts transfer automation and the functions of other connected machines. Most automated machine networks are not configured for quick, efficient and effective lockout or safe trouble-shooting.

Mists from machine lubricating oils generated during normal operation are another generic health hazard in stamping and forging press operations powered by compressed air, potentially putting workers at risk for respiratory, dermatological and digestive diseases.

Health and Safety Problems

Stamping

Stamping operations have high risk of severe laceration due to the required handling of parts with sharp edges. Possibly worse is the handling of the scrap resulting from cut-off perimeters and punched out sections of parts. Scrap is typically collected by gravity-fed chutes and conveyors. Clearing occasional jams is a high-risk activity.

Chemical hazards specific to stamping typically arise from two main sources: drawing compounds (i.e., die lubricants) in actual press operations and welding emissions from assembly of the stamped parts. Drawing compounds (DCs) are required for most stamping. The material is sprayed or rolled onto sheet metal and further mists are generated by the stamping event itself. Like other metalworking fluids, drawing compounds may be straight oils or oil emulsions (soluble oils). Components include petroleum oil fractions, special lubricity agents (e.g., animal and vegetable fatty acid derivatives, chlorinated oils and waxes), alkanolamines, petroleum sulphonates, borates, cellulose-derived thickeners, corrosion inhibitors and biocides. Air concentrations of mist in stamping operations may reach those of typical machining operations, although these levels tend to be lower on average (0.05 to 2.0 mg/m^3). However, visible fog and accumulated oil film on building surfaces are often present, and skin contact may be higher due to extensive handling of parts. Exposures most likely to present hazards are chlorinated oils (possible cancer, liver disease, skin disorders), rosin or tall oil fatty acid derivatives (sensitizers), petroleum fractions (digestive cancers) and, possibly, formaldehyde (from biocides) and nitrosamines (from alkanolamines and sodium nitrite, either as DC ingredients or in surface coatings on incoming steel). Elevated digestive cancer has been observed in two automotive stamping plants. Microbiological blooms in systems that apply DCs by rolling it onto sheet metal from an open reservoir can pose risks to workers for respiratory and dermatological problems analogous to those in machining operations.

Welding of stamped parts is often performed in stamping plants, usually without intermediate washing. This produces emissions that include metal fumes and pyrolysis and combustion products from drawing compound and other surface residues. Typical (primarily resistance) welding operations in stamping plants generate total particulate air concentrations in the range 0.05 to 4.0 mg/m^3. Metal content (as fumes and oxides) usually makes up less than half of that particulate matter, indicating that up to 2.0 mg/m^3 is poorly characterized chemical debris. The result is haze visible in many stamping plant welding areas. The presence of chlorinated derivatives and other organic ingredients raises serious concerns over the composition of welding smoke in these settings and strongly argues for ventilation controls. Application of other materials prior to welding (such as primer, paint and epoxy-like adhesives), some of which are then welded over, adds further concern. Welding production repair activities, usually done manually, often pose higher exposures to these same air contaminants. Excess rates of lung cancer have been observed among welders in an automotive stamping plant.

Forging

Like stamping, forging operations can pose high laceration risks when workers handle forged parts or trim the flash or unwanted edges off parts. High impact forging can also eject fragments, scale or tools, causing injury. In some forging activities, the worker grasps the working piece with tongs during the pressing or impact steps, increasing the risk for musculoskeletal injuries. In forging, unlike stamping, furnaces for heating parts (for forging and annealing) as well as bins of hot forgings are usually nearby. These create potential for high heat stress conditions. Additional factors in heat stress are the worker's metabolic load during manual handling of materials and, in some cases, heat from combustion products of oil-based die lubricants.

Die lubrication is required in most forging and has the added feature that the lubricant comes in contact with high-temperature parts. This causes immediate pyrolysis and aerosolization not only in the dies but also subsequently from smoking parts in cooling bins. Forging die lubricant ingredients can include graphite slurries, polymeric thickeners, sulphonate emulsifiers, petroleum fractions, sodium nitrate, sodium nitrite, sodium carbonate, sodium silicate, silicone oils and biocides. These are applied as sprays or, in some applications, by swab. Furnaces used for heating metal to be forged are usually fired by oil or gas, or they are induction furnaces. Emissions can result from fuel-fired furnaces with inadequate draft and from non-ventilated induction furnaces when incoming metal stock has surface contaminants, such as oil or corrosion inhibitors, or if, prior to forging, it was lubricated for shearing or sawing (as in the case of bar stock). In the US, total particulate air concentrations in forging operations typically range from 0.1 to 5.0 mg/m^3 and vary widely within forging operations due to thermal convection currents. An elevated lung cancer rate was observed among forging and heat treatment workers from two ball-bearing manufacturing plants.

Health and Safety Practices

Few studies have evaluated actual health effects in workers with stamping or forging exposures. Comprehensive characterization of the toxicity potential of most routine operations, including identification and measurement of priority toxic agents, has not been done. Evaluating the long-term health effects of die lubrication technology developed in the 1960s and 1970s has only recently become feasible. As a result, regulation of these exposures defaults to generic dust or total particulate standards such as 5.0 mg/m^3 in the US. While probably adequate in some circumstances, this standard is not demonstrably adequate for many stamping and forging applications.

Some reduction in die lubricant mist concentrations is possible with careful management of the application procedure in both stamping and forging. Roll application in stamping is preferred when feasible, and using minimal air pressure in sprays is beneficial. Possible elimination of priority hazardous ingredients should be investigated. Enclosures with negative pressure and mist collectors can be highly effective but may be incompatible with parts handling. Filtering air released from high-pressure air systems in presses would reduce press oil mist (and noise). Skin contact in stamping operations can be reduced with automation and good personal protective wear, providing protection against both laceration and liquid saturation. For stamping plant welding, washing parts prior to welding is highly desirable, and partial enclosures with LEV would reduce smoke levels substantially.

Controls to reduce heat stress in stamping and hot forging include minimizing the amount of manual material handling in high-heat areas, shielding of furnaces to reduce radiation of heat, minimizing the height of furnace doors and slots and using cooling fans. The location of cooling fans should be an integral part of the design of air movement to control mist exposures and heat stress; otherwise, cooling may be obtained only at the expense of higher exposures.

Mechanization of material handling, switching from hammer to press forging when possible and adjusting the work rate to ergonomically practical levels can reduce the number of musculoskeletal injuries.

Noise levels can be reduced through a combination of switching from hammer to press forges when possible, well-designed enclosures and quieting of furnace blowers, air clutches, air leads and parts handling. A hearing conservation programme should be instituted.

PPE needed includes head protection, foot protection, goggles, hearing protectors (around are as with excessive noise), heat- and oil-proof aprons and leggings (with heavy use of oil-based die lubricants) and infrared eye and face protection (around furnaces).

Environmental Health Hazards

The environmental hazards arising from stamping plants, relatively minor compared to those from some other types of plants,

Figure 82.2 • Gas welding with a torch and rod of filler metal. The welder is protected by a leather apron, gauntlets and goggles.

include disposal of waste drawing compound and washing solutions and the exhausting of welding smoke without adequate cleaning. Some forging plants historically have caused acute degradation of local air quality with forging smoke and scale dust. However, with appropriate air cleaning capacity, this need not occur. Disposition of stamping scrap and forging scale containing die lubricants is another potential issue.

WELDING AND THERMAL CUTTING

Philip A. Platcow and G.S. Lyndon*

Process Overview

Welding is a generic term referring to the union of pieces of metal at joint faces rendered plastic or liquid by heat or pressure, or both. The three common direct sources of heat are:

1. flame produced by the combustion of fuel gas with air or oxygen
2. electrical arc, struck between an electrode and a workpiece or between two electrodes
3. electrical resistance offered to passage of current between two or more workpieces.

Other sources of heat for welding are discussed below (see table 82.6).

* This article is a revision of the 3rd edition of the *Encyclopaedia of Occupational Health and Safety* article "Welding and thermal cutting" by G.S. Lyndon.

Table 82.6 • Description and hazards of welding processes.

Welding Process	Description	Hazards
Gas welding and cutting		
Welding	The torch melts the metal surface and filler rod, causing a joint to be formed.	Metal fumes, nitrogen dioxide, carbon monoxide, noise, burns, infrared radiation, fire, explosions
Brazing	The two metal surfaces are bonded without melting the metal. The melting temperature of the filler metal is above 450 °C. Heating is done by flame heating, resistance heating and induction heating.	Metal fumes (especially cadmium), fluorides, fire, explosion, burns
Soldering	Similar to brazing, except the melting temperature of the filler metal is below 450 °C. Heating is also done using a soldering iron.	Fluxes, lead fumes, burns
Metal cutting and flame gouging	In one variation, the metal is heated by a flame, and a jet of pure oxygen is directed onto the point of cutting and moved along the line to be cut. In flame gouging, a strip of surface metal is removed but the metal is not cut through.	Metal fumes, nitrogen dioxide, carbon monoxide, noise, burns, infrared radiation, fire, explosions
Gas pressure welding	The parts are heated by gas jets while under pressure, and become forged together.	Metal fumes, nitrogen dioxide, carbon monoxide, noise, burns, infrared radiation, fire, explosions
Flux-shielded arc welding		
Shielded metal arc welding (SMAC); "stick" arc welding; manual metal arc welding (MMA); open arc welding	Uses a consumable electrode consisting of a metal core surrounded by a flux coating	Metal fumes, fluorides (especially with low-hydrogen electrodes), infrared and ultraviolet radiation, burns, electrical, fire; also noise, ozone, nitrogen dioxide
Submerged arc welding (SAW)	A blanket of granulated flux is deposited on the workpiece, followed by a consumable bare metal wire electrode. The arc melts the flux to produce a protective molten shield in the welding zone.	Fluorides, fire, burns, infrared radiation, electrical; also metal fumes, noise, ultraviolet radiation, ozone, and nitrogen dioxide
Gas-shielded arc welding		
Metal inert gas (MIG); gas metal arc welding (GMAC)	The electrode is normally a bare consumable wire of similar composition to the weld metal and is fed continuously to the arc.	Ultraviolet radiation, metal fumes, ozone, carbon monoxide (with CO_2 gas), nitrogen dioxide, fire, burns, infrared radiation, electrical, fluorides, noise
Tungsten inert gas (TIG); gas tungsten arc welding (GTAW); heliarc	The tungsten electrode is non-consumable, and filler metal is introduced as a consumable into the arc manually.	Ultraviolet radiation, metal fumes, ozone, nitrogen dioxide, fire, burns, infrared radiation, electrical, noise, fluorides, carbon monoxide
Plasma arc welding (PAW) and plasma arc spraying; tungsten arc cutting	Similar to TIG welding, except that the arc and stream of inert gases pass through a small orifice before reaching the workpiece, creating a "plasma" of highly ionized gas which can achieve temperatures of over 33,400 °C. This is also used for metallizing.	Metal fumes, ozone, nitrogen dioxide, ultraviolet and infrared radiation, noise; fire, burns, electrical, fluorides, carbon monoxide, possible x rays
Flux core arc welding (FCAW); metal active gas welding (MAG)	Uses a flux-cored consumable electrode; may have carbon dioxide shield (MAG)	Ultraviolet radiation, metal fumes, ozone, carbon monoxide (with CO_2 gas), nitrogen dioxide, fire, burns, infrared radiation, electrical, fluorides, noise
Electric resistance welding		
Resistance welding (spot, seam, projection or butt welding)	A high current at low voltage flows through the two components from electrodes. The heat generated at the interface between the components brings them to welding temperatures. During the passage of the current, pressure by the electrodes produces a forge weld. No flux or filler metal is used.	Ozone, noise (sometimes), machinery hazards, fire, burns, electrical, metal fumes
Electro-slag welding	Used for vertical butt welding. The workpieces are set vertically, with a gap between them, and copper plates or shoes are placed on one or both sides of the joint to form a bath. An arc is established under a flux layer between one or more continuously fed electrode wires and a metal plate. A pool of molten metal is formed, protected by molten flux or slag, which is kept molten by resistance to the current passing between the electrode and the workpieces. This resistance-generated heat melts the sides of the joint and the electrode wire, filling the joint and making a weld. As welding progresses, the molten metal and slag are retained in position by shifting the copper plates.	Burns, fire, infrared radiation, electrical, metal fumes

Continues on next page.

Table 82.6 • Description and hazards of welding processes.
Continued

Welding Process	Description	Hazards
Flash welding	The two metal parts to be welded are connected to a low-voltage, high-current source. When the ends of the components are brought into contact, a large current flows, causing "flashing" to occur and bringing the ends of the components to welding temperatures. A forge weld is obtained by pressure.	Electrical, burns, fire, metal fumes
Other welding processes		
Electron beam welding	A workpiece in an vacuum chamber is bombarded by a beam of electrons from an electron gun at high voltages. The energy of the electrons is transformed into heat upon striking the workpiece, thus melting the metal and fusing the workpiece.	X rays at high voltages, electrical, burns, metal dusts, confined spaces
Arcair cutting	An arc is struck between the end of a carbon electrode (in a manual electrode holder with its own supply of compressed air) and the workpiece. The molten metal produced is blown away by jets of compressed air.	Metal fumes, carbon monoxide, nitrogen dioxide, ozone, fire, burns, infrared radiation, electrical
Friction welding	A purely mechanical welding technique in which one component remains stationary while the other is rotated against it under pressure. Heat is generated by friction, and at forging temperature the rotation ceases. A forging pressure then effects the weld.	Heat, burns, machinery hazards
Laser welding and drilling	Laser beams can be used in industrial applications requiring exceptionally high precision, such as miniature assemblies and micro techniques in the electronics industry or spinnerets for the artificial fibre industry. The laser beam melts and joins the workpieces.	Electrical, laser radiation, ultraviolet radiation, fire, burns, metal fumes, decomposition products of workpiece coatings
Stud welding	An arc is struck between a metal stud (acting as the electrode) held in a stud welding gun and the metal plate to be joined, and raises the temperature of the ends of the components to melting point. The gun forces the stud against the plate and welds it. Shielding is provided by a ceramic ferrule surrounding the stud.	Metal fumes, infrared and ultraviolet radiation, burns, electrical, fire, noise, ozone, nitrogen dioxide
Thermite welding	A mixture of aluminium powder and a metal oxide powder (iron, copper, etc.) is ignited in a crucible, producing molten metal with the evolution of intense heat. The crucible is tapped and the molten metal flows into the cavity to be welded (which is surrounded by a sand mould). This is often used to repair castings or forgings.	Fire, explosion, infrared radiation, burns

In *gas welding and cutting*, oxygen or air and a fuel gas are fed to a blowpipe (torch) in which they are mixed prior to combustion at the nozzle. The blowpipe is usually hand held (see figure 82.2). The heat melts the metal faces of the parts to be joined, causing them to flow together. A filler metal or alloy is frequently added. The alloy often has a lower melting point than the parts to be joined. In this case, the two pieces are generally not brought to fusion temperature (brazing, soldering). Chemical fluxes may be used to prevent oxidation and facilitate the joining.

In arc welding, the arc is struck between an electrode and the workpieces. The electrode can be connected to either an alternating current (AC) or direct current (DC) electric supply. The temperature of this operation is about 4,000°C when the workpieces fuse together. Usually it is necessary to add molten metal to the joint either by melting the electrode itself (consumable electrode processes) or by melting a separate filler rod which is not carrying current (non-consumable electrode processes).

Most conventional arc welding is done manually by means of a covered (coated) consumable electrode in a hand-held electrode holder. Welding is also accomplished by many semi or fully automatic electric welding processes such as resistance welding or continuous electrode feed.

During the welding process, the welding area must be shielded from the atmosphere in order to prevent oxidation and contamination. There are two types of protection: flux coatings and inert gas shielding. In *flux-shielded arc welding*, the consumable electrode consists of a metal core surrounded by a flux coating material, which is usually a complex mixture of mineral and other components. The flux melts as welding progresses, covering the molten metal with slag and enveloping the welding area with a protective atmosphere of gases (e.g., carbon dioxide) generated by the heated flux. After welding, the slag must be removed, often by chipping.

In *gas-shielded arc welding*, a blanket of inert gas seals off the atmosphere and prevents oxidation and contamination during the welding process. Argon, helium, nitrogen or carbon dioxide are commonly used as the inert gases. The gas selected depends upon the nature of the materials to be welded. The two most popular types of gas-shielded arc welding are metal- and tungsten inert gas (MIG and TIG).

Resistance welding involves using the electrical resistance to the passage of a high current at low voltage through components to be welded to generate heat for melting the metal. The heat generated at the interface between the components brings them to welding temperatures.

Hazards and Their Prevention

All welding involves hazards of fire, burns, radiant heat (infrared radiation) and inhalation of metal fumes and other contaminants. Other hazards associated with specific welding processes include electrical hazards, noise, ultraviolet radiation, ozone, nitrogen dioxide, carbon monoxide, fluorides, compressed gas cylinders and explosions. See table 82.6 for additional detail.

Much welding is not done in shops where conditions can generally be controlled, but in the field in the construction or repair of large structures and machinery (e.g., frameworks of buildings, bridges and towers, ships, railroad engines and cars, heavy equipment and so on). The welder may have to carry all his or her equipment to the site, set it up and work in confined spaces or on scaffolds. Physical strain, inordinate fatigue and musculoskeletal injuries may follow being required to reach, kneel or work in other uncomfortable and awkward positions. Heat stress may result from working in warm weather and the occlusive effects of the personal protective equipment, even without the heat generated by the welding process.

Compressed gas cylinders

In high-pressure gas welding installations, oxygen and the fuel gas (acetylene, hydrogen, town gas, propane) are supplied to the torch from cylinders. The gases are stored in these cylinders at high pressure. The special fire and explosion hazards and precautions for the safe use and storage of the fuel gases are also discussed elsewhere in this *Encyclopaedia*. The following precautions should be observed:

- Only pressure regulators designed for the gas in use should be fitted to cylinders. For example, an acetylene regulator should not be used with coal gas or hydrogen (although it may be used with propane).
- Blowpipes must be kept in good order and cleaned at regular intervals. A hardwood stick or soft brass wire should be used for cleaning the tips. They should be connected to regulators with special canvas-reinforced hoses placed in such a way that they are unlikely to be damaged.
- Oxygen and acetylene cylinders must be stored separately and only on fire-resistant premises devoid of flammable material and must be so located that they may be readily removed in case of fire. Local building and fire protection codes must be consulted.
- The colour coding in force or recommended for identification of cylinders and accessories should be scrupulously observed. In many countries, the internationally accepted colour codes used for the transport of dangerous materials are applied in this field. The case for enforcement of uniform international standards in this respect is strengthened by safety considerations bound up with the increasing international migration of industrial workers.

Acetylene generators

In the low-pressure gas welding process, acetylene is generally produced in generators by reaction of calcium carbide and water. The gas is then piped to the welding or cutting torch into which oxygen is fed.

Stationary generating plants should be installed either in the open air or in a well-ventilated building away from the main workshops. The ventilation of the generator house should be such as to prevent the formation of an explosive or toxic atmosphere. Adequate lighting should be provided; switches, other electrical gear and electrical lamps should either be located outside the building or be explosion-proof. Smoking, flames, torches, welding plant or flammable materials must be excluded from the house or from the vicinity of an open-air generator. Many of these precautions also apply to portable generators. Portable generators should be used, cleaned and recharged only in the open air or in a well-ventilated shop, away from any flammable material.

Calcium carbide is supplied in sealed drums. The material should be stored and kept dry, on a platform raised above the floor level. Stores must be situated under cover, and if they adjoin another building the party wall must be fireproof. The storeroom should be suitably ventilated through the roof. Drums should be opened only immediately before the generator is charged. A special opener should be provided and used; a hammer and chisel should never be used to open drums. It is dangerous to leave calcium carbide drums exposed to any source of water.

Before a generator is dismantled, all calcium carbide must be removed and the plant filled with water. The water should remain in the plant for at least half an hour to ensure that every part is free from gas. The dismantling and servicing should be carried out only by the manufacturer of the equipment or by a specialist. When a generator is being recharged or cleaned, none of the old charge must be used again.

Pieces of calcium carbide wedged in the feed mechanism or adhering to parts of the plant should be carefully removed, using non-sparking tools made of bronze or another suitable non-ferrous alloy.

All concerned should be fully conversant with the manufacturer's instructions, which should be conspicuously displayed. The following precautions should also be observed:

- A properly designed back-pressure valve must be fitted between the generator and each blowpipe to prevent backfire or reverse flow of gas. The valve should be regularly inspected after backfire, and the water level checked daily.
- Only blowpipes of the injector type designed for low-pressure operation should be used. For heating and cutting, town gas or hydrogen at low pressure are sometimes employed. In these cases, a non-return valve should be placed between each blowpipe and the supply main or pipeline.
- An explosion may be caused by "flash-back", which results from dipping the nozzle-tip into the molten metal pool, mud or paint, or from any other stoppage. Particles of slag or metal that become attached to the tip should be removed. The tip should also be cooled frequently.
- Local building and fire codes should be consulted.

Fire and explosion prevention

In locating welding operations, consideration should be given to surrounding walls, floors, nearby objects and waste material. The following procedures should be followed:

- All combustible material must be removed or adequately protected by sheet metal or other suitable materials; tarpaulins should never be used.
- Wood structures should be discouraged or similarly protected. Wood floors should be avoided.
- Precautionary measures should be taken in the case of openings or cracks in walls and floors; flammable material in adjoining rooms or on the floor below should be removed to a safe position. Local building and fire codes should be consulted.
- Suitable fire-extinguishing apparatus should always be at hand. In the case of low-pressure plant using an acetylene generator, buckets of dry sand should also be kept available; fire extinguishers of dry powder or carbon dioxide types are satisfactory. Water must never be used.
- Fire brigades may be necessary. A responsible person should be assigned to keep the site under observation for at least half an hour after completion of the work, in order to deal with any outbreak of fire.
- Since explosions can occur when acetylene gas is present in air in any proportion between 2 and 80%, adequate ventilation

and monitoring are required to ensure freedom from gas leaks. Only soapy water should be used to search for gas leaks.

- Oxygen must be carefully controlled. For example, it should never be released into the air in a confined space; many metals, clothing and other materials become actively combustible in the presence of oxygen. In gas cutting, any oxygen which may not be consumed will be released into the atmosphere; gas cutting should never be undertaken in a confined space without proper ventilation arrangements.
- Alloys rich in magnesium or other combustible metals should be kept away from welding flames or arcs.
- Welding of containers can be extremely hazardous. If the previous contents are unknown, a vessel should always be treated as if it had contained a flammable substance. Explosions may be prevented either by removing any flammable material or by making it non-explosive and non-flammable.
- The mixture of aluminium and iron oxide used in thermite welding is stable under normal conditions. However, in view of the ease with which aluminium powder will ignite, and the quasi-explosive nature of the reaction, appropriate precautions should be taken in handling and storage (avoidance of exposure to high heat and possible ignition sources).
- A written hot-work permit programme is required for welding in some jurisdictions. This programme outlines the precautions and procedures to be followed during welding, cutting, burning and so on. This programme should include the specific operations conducted along with the safety precautions to be implemented. It must be plant specific and may include an internal permit system that must be completed with each individual operation.

Protection from heat and burn hazards

Burns of the eyes and exposed parts of the body may occur due to contact with hot metal and spattering of incandescent metal particles or molten metal. In arc welding, a high-frequency spark used to initiate the arc can cause small, deep burns if concentrated at a point on the skin. Intense infrared and visible radiation from a gas welding or cutting flame and incandescent metal in the weld pool can cause discomfort to the operator and persons in the vicinity of the operation. Each operation should be considered in advance, and necessary precautions designed and implemented. Goggles made specifically for gas welding and cutting should be worn to protect the eyes from heat and light radiated from the work. Protective covers over filter glass should be cleaned as required and replaced when scratched or damaged. Where molten metal or hot particles are emitted, the protective clothing being worn should deflect spatter. The type and thickness of fire-resistant clothing worn should be chosen according to the degree of hazard. In cutting and arc welding operations, leather shoe coverings or other suitable spats should be worn to prevent hot particles from falling into boots or shoes. For protecting the hands and forearms against heat, spatter, slag and so on, the leather gauntlet type of glove with canvas or leather cuffs is sufficient. Other types of protective clothing include leather aprons, jackets, sleeves, leggings and head covering. In overhead welding, a protective cape and cap are necessary. All protective clothing should be free from oil or grease, and seams should be inside, so as not to trap globules of molten metal. Clothing should not have pockets or cuffs that could trap sparks, and it should be worn so sleeves overlap gloves, leggings overlap shoes and so on. Protective clothing should be inspected for burst seams or holes through which molten metal or slag may enter. Heavy articles left hot on completion of welding should always be marked "hot" as a warning to other workers. With resistance welding, the heat produced may not be visible, and burns can result from handling of hot

assemblies. Particles of hot or molten metal should not fly out of spot, seam or projection welds if conditions are correct, but non-flammable screens should be used and precautions taken. Screens also protect passers-by from eye burns. Loose parts should not be left in the throat of the machine because they are liable to be projected with some velocity.

Electrical safety

Although no-load voltages in manual arc welding are relatively low (about 80 V or less), welding currents are high, and transformer primary circuits present the usual hazards of equipment operated at power supply line voltage. The risk of electric shock should therefore not be ignored, especially in cramped spaces or in insecure positions.

Before welding commences, the grounding installation on arc welding equipment should always be checked. Cables and connections should be sound and of adequate capacity. A proper grounding clamp or bolted terminal should always be used. Where two or more welding machines are grounded to the same structure, or where other portable electric tools are also in use, grounding should be supervised by a competent person. The working position should be dry, secure and free from dangerous obstructions. A well-arranged, well-lighted, properly ventilated and tidy workplace is important. For work in confined spaces or dangerous positions, additional electrical protection (no-load, low-voltage devices) can be installed in the welding circuit, ensuring that only extremely low-voltage current is available at the electrode holder when welding is not taking place. (See discussion of confined spaces below.) Electrode holders in which the electrodes are held by a spring grip or screw thread are recommended. Discomfort due to heating can be reduced by effective heat insulation on that part of the electrode holder which is held in the hand. Jaws and connections of electrode holders should be cleaned and tightened periodically to prevent overheating. Provision should be made to accommodate the electrode holder safely when not in use by means of an insulated hook or a fully insulated holder. The cable connection should be designed so that continued flexing of the cable will not cause wear and failure of the insulation. Dragging of cables and plastic gas supply tubes (gas-shielded processes) across hot plates or welds must be avoided. The electrode lead should not come in contact with the job or any other earthed object (ground). Rubber tubes and rubber-covered cables must not be used anywhere near the high-frequency discharge, because the ozone produced will rot the rubber. Plastic tubes and polyvinyl chloride (PVC) covered cables should be used for all supplies from the transformer to the electrode holder. Vulcanized or tough rubber-sheathed cables are satisfactory on the primary side. Dirt and metallic or other conducting dust can cause a breakdown in the high-frequency discharge unit. To avoid this condition, the unit should be cleaned regularly by blowing-out with compressed air. Hearing protection should be worn when using compressed air for more than a few seconds. For electron-beam welding, the safety of the equipment used must be checked prior to each operation. To protect against electric shock, a system of interlocks must be fitted to the various cabinets. A reliable system of grounding of all units and control cabinets is necessary. For plasma welding equipment used for cutting heavy thicknesses, the voltages may be as high as 400 V and danger should be anticipated. The technique of firing the arc by a high-frequency pulse exposes the operator to the dangers of an unpleasant shock and a painful, penetrating high-frequency burn.

Ultraviolet radiation

The brilliant light emitted by an electric arc contains a high proportion of ultraviolet radiation. Even momentary exposure to bursts of arc flash, including stray flashes from other workers' arcs, may produce a painful conjunctivitis (photo-ophthalmia) known as "arc eye" or "eye flash". If any person is exposed to arc flash, immediate medical attention must be sought. Excessive exposure to ultraviolet radiation may also cause overheating and burning of the skin (sunburn effect). Precautions include:

- A shield or helmet fitted with correct grade of filter should be used (see the article "Eye and face protection" elsewhere in this *Encyclopaedia*). For the gas-shielded arc welding processes and carbon-arc cutting, flat handshields provide insufficient protection from reflected radiation; helmets should be used. Filtered goggles or eyeglasses with sideshields should be worn under the helmet to avoid exposure when the helmet is lifted up for inspection of the work. Helmets will also provide protection from spatter and hot slag. Helmets and handshields are provided with a filter glass and a protective cover glass on the outside. This should be regularly inspected, cleaned and replaced when scratched or damaged.
- The face, nape of the neck and other exposed parts of the body should be properly protected, especially when working close to other welders.
- Assistants should wear suitable goggles at a minimum and other PPE as the risk requires.
- All arc welding operations should be screened to protect other persons working nearby. Where the work is carried out at fixed benches or in welding shops, permanent screens should be erected where possible; otherwise, temporary screens should be used. All screens should be opaque, of sturdy construction and of a flame-resistant material.
- The use of black paints for the inside of welding booths has become an accepted practice, but the paint should produce a matte finish. Adequate ambient lighting should be provided to prevent eye strain leading to headaches and accidents.
- Welding booths and portable screens should be checked regularly to ensure that there is no damage which might result in the arc affecting persons working nearby.

Chemical hazards

Airborne contaminants from welding and flame cutting, including fumes and gases, arise from a variety of sources:

- the metal being welded, the metal in the filler rod or constituents of various types of steel such as nickel or chromium)
- any metallic coating on the article being welded or on the filler rod (e.g., zinc and cadmium from plating, zinc from galvanizing and copper as a thin coating on continuous mild steel filler rods)
- any paint, grease, debris and the like on the article being welded (e.g., carbon monoxide, carbon dioxide, smoke and other irritant breakdown products)
- flux coating on the filler rod (e.g., inorganic fluoride)
- the action of heat or ultraviolet light on the surrounding air (e.g., nitrogen dioxide, ozone) or on chlorinated hydrocarbons (e.g., phosgene)
- inert gas used as a shield (e.g., carbon dioxide, helium, argon).

Fumes and gases should be removed at the source by LEV. This can be provided by partial enclosure of the process or by the installation of hoods which supply sufficiently high air velocity across the weld position so as to ensure capture of the fumes.

Special attention should be paid to ventilation in the welding of non-ferrous metals and certain alloy steels, as well as to protection from the hazard of ozone, carbon monoxide and nitrogen dioxide which may be formed. Portable as well as fixed ventilation systems are readily available. In general, the exhausted air should

not be recirculated. It should be recirculated only if there are not hazardous levels of ozone or other toxic gases and the exhaust air is filtered through a high-efficiency filter.

With electron-beam welding and if materials being welded are of a toxic nature (e.g., beryllium, plutonium and so on), care must be taken to protect the operator from any dust cloud when opening the chamber.

When there is a risk to health from toxic fumes (e.g., lead) and LEV is not practicable—for example, when lead-painted structures are being demolished by flame cutting—the use of respiratory protective equipment is necessary. In such circumstances, an approved, high-efficiency full-facepiece respirator or a high-efficiency positive pressure powered air-purified respirator (PAPR) should be worn. A high standard of maintenance of the motor and the battery is necessary, especially with the original high-efficiency positive pressure power respirator. The use of positive pressure compressed air line respirators should be encouraged where a suitable supply of breathing-quality compressed air is available. Whenever respiratory protective equipment is to be worn, the safety of the workplace should be reviewed to determine whether extra precautions are necessary, bearing in mind the restricted vision, entanglement possibilities and so on of persons wearing respiratory protective equipment.

Metal fume fever

Metal fume fever is commonly seen in workers exposed to the fumes of zinc in the galvanizing or tinning process, in brass founding, in the welding of galvanized metal and in metallizing or metal spraying, as well as from exposure to other metals such as copper, manganese and iron. It occurs in new workers and those returning to work after a weekend or holiday hiatus. It is an acute condition that occurs several hours after the initial inhalation of particles of a metal or its oxides. It starts with a bad taste in the mouth followed by dryness and irritation of the respiratory mucosa resulting in cough and occasionally dyspnoea and "tightness" of the chest. These may be accompanied by nausea and headache and, some 10 to 12 hours after the exposure, chills and fever which may be quite severe. These last several hours and are followed by sweating, sleep and often by polyuria and diarrhoea. There is no particular treatment, and recovery is usually complete in about 24 hours with no residua. It can be prevented by keeping exposure to the offending metallic fumes well within the recommended levels through the use of efficient LEV.

Confined spaces

For entry into confined spaces, there may be a risk of the atmosphere being explosive, toxic, oxygen deficient or combinations of the above. Any such confined space must be certified by a responsible person as safe for entry and for work with an arc or flame. A confined-space entry programme, including an entry permit system, may be required and is highly recommended for work that must be carried out in spaces that are typically not constructed for continuous occupancy. Examples include, but are not limited to, manholes, vaults, ship holds and the like. Ventilation of confined spaces is crucial, since gas welding not only produces airborne contaminants but also uses up oxygen. Gas-shielded arc welding processes can decrease the oxygen content of the air. (See figure 82.3.)

Noise

Noise is a hazard in several welding processes, including plasma welding, some types of resistance welding machines and gas welding. In plasma welding, the plasma jet is ejected at very high speeds, producing intense noise (up to 90 dBA), particularly in the

Figure 82.3 • Welding in an enclosed space.

S.F. Gilman

higher frequency bands. The use of compressed air to blow off dust also creates high noise levels. To prevent hearing damage, ear plugs or muffs must be worn and a hearing conservation programme should be instituted, including audiometric (hearing capacity) examinations and employee training.

Ionizing radiation

In welding shops where welds are inspected radiographically with x-ray or gamma-ray equipment, the customary warning notices and instructions must be strictly observed. Workers must be kept at a safe distance from such equipment. Radioactive sources must be handled only with the required special tools and subject to special precautions.

Local and governmental regulations must be followed. See the chapter *Radiation, ionizing* elsewhere in this *Encyclopaedia*.

Sufficient shielding must be provided with electron-beam welding to prevent x rays from penetrating the walls and windows of the chamber. Any parts of the machine providing shields against x-ray radiation should be interlocked so that the machine cannot be energized unless they are in position. Machines should be checked at the time of installation for leaks of x-ray radiation, and regularly thereafter.

Other hazards

Resistance welding machines have at least one electrode, which moves with considerable force. If a machine is operated while a finger or hand is lying between the electrodes, severe crushing will result. Where possible, a suitable means of guarding must be devised to safeguard the operator. Cuts and lacerations can be minimized by first deburring components and by wearing protective gloves or gauntlets.

Lockout/tagout procedures should be used when machinery with electrical, mechanical or other energy sources is being maintained or repaired.

When slag is being removed from welds by chipping and so on, the eyes should be protected by goggles or other means.

LATHES

*Toni Retsch**

The important part lathes play in metalworking shops is best illustrated by the fact that 90 to 95% of the swarf (metal shavings) produced in the valves and fittings industry originates from lathes. About one-tenth of the accidents reported in this industry are due to lathes; this corresponds to one-third of all machine accidents. According to a study of the relative accident frequency per machine unit carried out in a plant manufacturing small precision parts and electrical equipment, lathes rank fifth after woodworking machines, metal-cutting saws, power presses and drilling machines. The need for protective measures on lathes is therefore beyond doubt.

Turning is a machine process in which the diameter of material is reduced by a tool with a special cutting edge. The cutting movement is produced by rotating the workpiece, and the feed and traverse movements are produced by the tool. By varying these three basic movements, and also by choosing the appropriate tool cutting-edge geometry and material, it is possible to influence the rate of stock removal, surface quality, shape of the chip formed and tool wear.

Structure of Lathes

A typical lathe consists of:

- a bed or base with machined slideways for the saddle and tailstock
- a headstock mounted on the bed, with the spindle and chuck
- a feed gearbox attached to the front of the bed for transmitting the feed movement as a function of the cutting speed through the leadscrew or feed shaft and apron to the saddle
- a saddle (or carriage) carrying the cross slide which performs the traverse movement
- a toolpost mounted on the cross slide (see figure 82.4).

This basic model of a lathe can be infinitely varied, from the universal machine to the special automatic lathe designed for one type of work only.

The most important types of lathe are as follows:

- *Centre lathe.* This is the most frequently used turning machine. It corresponds to the basic model with horizontal turning axis. The work is held between centres, by a faceplate or in a chuck.
- *Multiple-tool lathe.* This enables several tools to be engaged at the same time.
- *Turret lathe, capstan lathe.* Machines of this type enable a workpiece to be machined by several tools which are engaged one after the other. The tools are held in the turret, which rotates for bringing them into cutting position. The turrets are generally of the disc or crown type, but there are also drum-type turret lathes.
- *Copy-turning lathes.* The desired shape is transmitted by tracer control from a template to the work.
- *Automatic lathe.* The various operations, including the change of the work, are automated. There are bar automatics and chucking automatics.
- *Vertical lathe (boring and turning mill).* The work turns about a vertical axis; it is clamped to a horizontal revolving table. This type of machine is generally used for machining large castings and forgings.

* Adapted from the 3rd edition, *Encyclopaedia of Occupational Health and Safety*.

82. METAL PROCESSING AND METAL WORKING INDUSTRY

Figure 82.4 • Lathes, cutting-off machines, threading machines.

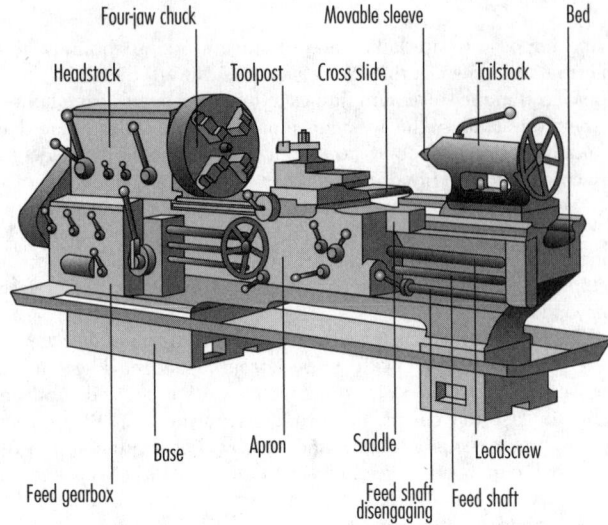

Four-jaw chuck
Movable sleeve
Bed
Headstock
Toolpost
Cross slide
Tailstock
Base
Apron
Saddle
Leadscrew
Feed gearbox
Feed shaft disengaging
Feed shaft

- *NC and CNC lathes.* All the aforementioned machines can be equipped with a numerical control (NC) or computer-assisted numerical control (CNC) system. The result is a semi-automated or fully automated machine which can be used rather universally, thanks to the great versatility and easy programmability of the control system.

The future development of the lathe will probably concentrate on control systems. Contact controls will be increasingly replaced by electronic control systems. As regards the latter, there is a trend in evolution from interpolation-programmed to memory-programmed controls. It is foreseeable in the long run that the use of increasingly efficient process computers will tend to optimize the machining process.

Accidents

Lathe accidents are generally caused by:

- disregard for safety regulations when the machines are installed in workshops (e.g., not enough space between machines, no power disconnect switch for each machine)
- missing guards or the absence of auxiliary devices (severe injuries have been caused to workers who tried to brake the spindle of their lathes by pressing one of their hands against unguarded belt pulleys and to operators who inadvertently engaged unguarded clutch levers or pedals; injuries due to flying chips because of the absence of hinged or sliding covers have also occurred)
- inadequately located control elements (e.g., a turner's hand can be pierced by the tailstock centre if the pedal controlling the chuck is mistaken for the one controlling the hydraulic circuit of the tailstock centre movement)
- adverse conditions of work (i.e., shortcomings from the point of view of occupational physiology)
- lack of PPE or wearing unsuitable work clothing (severe and even fatal injuries have been caused to lathe operators who wore loose clothes or had long, free-hanging hair)
- insufficient instruction of personnel (an apprentice was fatally injured when he filed a short shaft which was fixed between centres and rotated by a cranked carrier on the spindle nose

and a straight one on the shaft; the lathe carrier seized his left-hand sleeve, which was wrapped around the workpiece, dragging the apprentice violently into the lathe)
- poor work organization leading to the use of unsuitable equipment (e.g., a long bar was machined on a conventional production lathe; it was too long for this lathe, and it projected more than 1 m beyond the headstock; moreover, the chuck aperture was too large for the bar and was made up by inserting wooden wedges; when the lathe spindle started rotating, the free bar end bent by 45° and struck the operator's head; the operator died during the following night)
- defective machine elements (e.g., a loose carrier pin in a clutch may cause the lathe spindle to start rotating while the operator is adjusting a workpiece in the chuck).

Accident Prevention

The prevention of lathe accidents starts at the design stage. Designers should give special attention to control and transmission elements.

Control elements

Each lathe must be equipped with a power disconnect (or isolating) switch so that maintenance and repair work may be carried out safely. This switch must disconnect the current on all poles, reliably cut the pneumatic and hydraulic power and vent the circuits. On large machines, the disconnect switch should be so designed that it can be padlocked in its out position—a safety measure against accidental reconnection.

The layout of the machine controls should be such that the operator can easily distinguish and reach them, and that their manipulation presents no hazard. This means that controls must never be arranged at points which can be reached only by passing the hand over the working zone of the machine or where they may be hit by flying chips.

Switches which monitor guards and interlock them with the machine drive should be chosen and installed in such a way that they positively open the circuit as soon as the guard is shifted from its protecting position.

Emergency stop devices must cause the immediate standstill of the dangerous movement. They must be designed and located in such a way that they can be easily operated by the threatened worker. Emergency stop buttons must be easily reached and should be in red.

The actuating elements of control gear which may trip a dangerous machine movement must be guarded so as to exclude any inadvertent operation. For instance, the clutch engaging levers on the headstock and apron should be provided with safety locking devices or screens. A push-button can be made safe by lodging it in a recess or by shrouding it with a protective collar.

Hand-operated controls should be designed and located in such a way that the hand movement corresponds to the controlled machine movement.

Controls should be identified with easily readable and understandable markings. To avoid misunderstandings and linguistic difficulties, it is advisable to use symbols.

Transmission elements

All moving transmission elements (belts, pulleys, gears) must be covered with guards. An important contribution to the prevention of lathe accidents can be made by the persons responsible for the installation of the machine. Lathes should be so installed that the operators tending them do not hinder or endanger each other. The operators should not turn their backs towards passageways. Protective screens should be installed where neighbouring workplaces or passageways are within the range of flying chips.

Passageways must be clearly marked. Enough space should be left for materials-handling equipment, for stacking workpieces and for tool boxes. Bar-stock guides must not protrude into the passageways.

The floor on which the operator stands must be insulated against cold. Care should be taken that the insulation forms no stumbling obstacle, and the flooring should not become slippery even when covered with a film of oil.

Conduit and pipework should be installed in such a way that they do not become obstacles. Temporary installations should be avoided.

Safety engineering measures on the shop floor should be directed in particular at the following points:

- work-holding fixtures (faceplates, chucks, collets) should be dynamically balanced before use
- the maximum permissible speed of a chuck should be indicated on the chuck by the manufacturer and respected by the lathe operator
- when scroll chucks are used, it should be ensured that the jaws cannot be slung out when the lathe is started
- chucks of this type should be designed in such a manner that the key cannot be taken off before the jaws have been secured. The chuck keys in general should be so designed that it is impossible to leave them in the chuck.

It is important to provide for auxiliary lifting equipment to facilitate mounting and removing of heavy chucks and faceplates. To prevent chucks from running off the spindle when the lathe is suddenly braked, they must be securely fixed. This can be achieved by putting a retaining nut with left-hand thread on the spindle nose, by using a "Camlock" quick-action coupling, by fitting the chuck with a locking key or by securing it with a two-part locking ring.

When powered work-holding fixtures are used, such as hydraulically operated chucks, collets and tailstock centres, measures must be taken which make it impossible for the hands to be introduced into the danger zone of closing fixtures. This can be achieved by limiting the travel of the clamping element to 6 mm, by choosing the location of deadman's controls so as to exclude the introduction of the hands into the danger zone or by providing a moving guard which has to be closed before the clamping movement can be started.

If starting the lathe while the chuck jaws are open presents a danger, the machine should be equipped with a device which prevents the spindle rotation being started before the jaws are closed. The absence of power must not cause the opening or closure of a powered work-holding fixture.

If the gripping force of a power chuck diminishes, the spindle rotation must be stopped, and it must be impossible to start the spindle. Reversing the gripping direction from inside to outside (or vice versa) while the spindle rotates must not cause the chuck to be dislodged from the spindle. Removal of holding fixtures from the spindle should be possible only when the spindle has ceased rotating.

When machining bar stock, the portion projecting beyond the lathe must be enclosed by bar-stock guides. Bar feed weights must be guarded by hinged covers extending to the floor.

Carriers

To prevent serious accidents—in particular, when filing work in a lathe—unprotected carriers must not be used. A centring safety carrier should be used, or a protective collar should be fitted to a conventional carrier. It is also possible to use self-locking carriers or to provide the carrier disc with a protective cover.

Working zone of the lathe

Universal-lathe chucks should be guarded by hinged covers. If possible, protective covers should be interlocked with spindle drive circuits. Vertical boring and turning mills should be fenced with bars or plates to prevent injury from revolving parts. To enable the operator to watch the machining process safely, platforms with railings must be provided. In certain cases, TV cameras can be installed so that the operator may monitor the tool edge and tool in-feed.

The working zones of automatic lathes, NC and CNC lathes should be completely enclosed. Enclosures of fully automatic machines should only have openings through which the stock to be machined is introduced, the turned part ejected and the swarf removed from the working zone. These openings must not constitute a hazard when work passes through them, and it must be impossible to reach through them into the danger zone.

The working zones of semi-automatic, NC and CNC lathes must be enclosed during the machining process. The enclosures are generally sliding covers with limit switches and interlocking circuit.

Operations requiring access to the working zone, such as change of work or tools, gauging and so on, must not be carried out before the lathe has been safely stopped. Zeroing a variable-speed drive is not considered a safe standstill. Machines with such drives must have locked protective covers that cannot be unlocked before the machine is safely stopped (e.g., by cutting the spindle-motor power supply).

If special tool-setting operations are required, an inching control is to be provided which enables certain machine movements to be tripped while the protective cover is open. In such cases, the operator can be protected by special circuit designs (e.g., by permitting only one movement to be tripped at a time). This can be achieved by using two-hand controls.

Turning swarf

Long turning chips are dangerous because they may get entangled with arms and legs and cause serious injury. Continuous and ravelled chips can be avoided by choosing appropriate cutting speeds, feeds and chip thicknesses or by using lathe tools with chip breakers of the gullet or step type. Swarf hooks with handle and buckle should be used for removing chips.

Ergonomics

Every machine should be so designed that it enables a maximal output to be obtained with a minimum of stress on the operator. This can be achieved by adapting the machine to the worker.

Ergonomic factors must be taken into account when designing the human-machine interface of a lathe. Rational workplace design also includes providing for auxiliary handling equipment, such as loading and unloading attachments.

All controls must be located within the physiological sphere or reach of both hands. The controls must be clearly laid out and should be logical to operate. Pedal-operated controls should be avoided in machines tended by standing operators.

Experience has shown that good work is performed when the workplace is designed for both standing and sitting postures. If the operator has to work standing up, he or she should be given the possibility of changing posture. Flexible seats are in many cases a welcome relief for strained feet and legs.

Measures should be taken to create optimal thermal comfort, taking into account the air temperature, relative humidity, air movement and radiant heat. The workshop should be adequately ventilated. There should be local exhaust devices to eliminate gaseous emanations. When machining bar stock, sound-absorbent-lined guide tubes should be used.

The workplace should preferably be provided with uniform lighting, affording an adequate level of illumination.

Work Clothing and Personal Protection

Overalls should be close fitting and buttoned or zipped to the neck. They should be without breast pockets, and the sleeves must be tightly buttoned at the wrists. Belts should not be worn. No finger rings and bracelets should be worn when working on lathes. Wearing of safety spectacles should be obligatory. When heavy workpieces are machined, safety shoes with steel toe caps must be worn. Protective gloves must be worn whenever swarf is being collected.

Training

The lathe operator's safety depends to a large extent on working methods. It is therefore important that he or she should receive thorough theoretical and practical training to acquire skills and develop a behaviour affording the best possible safeguards. Correct posture, correct movements, correct choice and handling of tools should become routine to such an extent that the operator works correctly even if his or her concentration is temporarily relaxed.

Important points in a training programme are an upright posture, the proper mounting and removal of the chuck and the accurate and secure fixing of workpieces. Correct holding of files and scrapers and safe working with abrasive cloth must be intensively practised.

Workers must be well informed about the hazards of injury which may be caused when gauging work, checking adjustments and cleaning lathes.

Maintenance

Lathes must be regularly maintained and lubricated. Faults must be corrected immediately. If safety is at stake in the event of a fault, the machine should be put out of operation until corrective action has been taken.

Repair and maintenance work must be carried out only after the machine has been isolated from the power supply.

● GRINDING AND POLISHING

K. Welinder*

Grinding generally involves the use of a bonded abrasive to wear away parts of a workpiece. The aim is to give the work a certain shape, correct its dimensions, increase the smoothness of a surface or improve the sharpness of cutting edges. Examples include removal of sprues and rough edges from a foundry casting, removal of surface scale from metals before forging or welding and deburring of parts in sheet metal and machine shops. Polishing is used to remove surface imperfections such as tool marks. Buffing does not remove metal, but uses a soft abrasive blended in a wax or grease base to produce a high-lustre surface.

Grinding is the most comprehensive and diversified of all machining methods and is employed on many materials—predominantly iron and steel but also other metals, wood, plastics, stone, glass, pottery and so on. The term covers other methods of producing very smooth and glossy surfaces, such as polishing, honing, whetting and lapping.

The tools used are wheels of varying dimensions, grinding segments, grinding points, sharpening stones, files, polishing

* Adapted from the 3rd edition, Encyclopaedia of Occupational Health and Safety.

wheels, belts, discs and so on. In grinding wheels and the like, the abrasive material is held together by bonding agents to form a rigid, generally porous body. In the case of abrasive belts, the bonding agent holds the abrasive secured to a flexible base material. Buffing wheels are made from cotton or other textile disks sewn together.

The natural abrasives—natural corundum or emery (aluminium oxides), diamond, sandstone, flint and garnet—have been largely superseded by artificial abrasives including aluminium oxide (fused alumina), silicon carbide (carborundum) and synthetic diamonds. A number of fine-grained materials such as chalk, pumice, tripoli, tin putty and iron oxide are also used, especially for polishing and buffing.

Aluminium oxide is most widely used in grinding wheels, followed by silicon carbide. Natural and artificial diamonds are used for important special applications. Aluminium oxide, silicon carbide, emery, garnet and flint are used in grinding and polishing belts.

Both organic and inorganic bonding agents are used in grinding wheels. The main type of inorganic bonds are vitrified silicate and magnesite. Notable among organic bonding agents are phenol- or urea- formaldehyde resin, rubber and shellac. The vitrified bonding agents and phenolic resin are completely dominating within their respective groups. Diamond grinding wheels can also be metal bonded. The various bonding agents give the wheels different grinding properties, as well as different properties with regard to safety.

Abrasive and polishing belts and discs are composed of a flexible base of paper or fabric to which the abrasive is bonded by means of a natural or synthetic adhesive.

Different machines are used for different types of operations, such as surface grinding, cylindrical (including centreless) grinding, internal grinding, rough grinding and cutting. The two main types are: those where either the grinder or the work is moved by hand and machines with mechanical feeds and chucks. Common equipment types include: surface-type grinders; pedestal-type grinders, polishers and buffers; disk grinders and polishers; internal grinders; abrasive cut-off machines; belt polishers; portable grinders, polishers and buffers; and multiple polishers and buffers.

Hazards and Their Prevention

Bursting

The major injury risk in the use of grinding wheels is that the wheel may burst during grinding. Normally, grinding wheels operate at high speeds. There is a trend towards ever-increasing speeds. Most industrialized nations have regulations limiting the maximum speeds at which the various types of grinding wheels may be run.

The fundamental protective measure is to make the grinding wheel as strong as possible; the nature of the bonding agent is most important. Wheels with organic bonds, in particular phenolic resin, are tougher than those with inorganic bonds and more resistant to impacts. High peripheral speeds may be permissible for wheels with organic bonds.

Very high-speed wheels, in particular, often incorporate various types of reinforcement. For example, certain cup wheels are fitted with steel hubs to increase their strength. During rotation the major stress develops around the centre hole. To strengthen the wheel, the section around the centre hole, which takes no part in the grinding, can thus be made of an especially strong material which is not suitable for grinding. Large wheels with a centre section reinforced in this way are used particularly by the steel works for grinding slabs, billets and the like at speeds up to 80 m/s.

The most common method of reinforcing grinding wheels, however, is to include glass fibre fabric in their construction. Thin wheels, such as those used for cutting, may incorporate glass fibre fabric at the centre or at each side, while thicker wheels have a number of fabric layers depending on the thickness of the wheel.

With the exception of some grinding wheels of small dimensions, either all wheels or a statistical sampling of them must be given speed tests by the manufacturer. In tests the wheels are run over a certain period at a speed exceeding that permitted in grinding. Test regulations vary from country to country, but usually the wheel has to be tested at a speed 50% above the working speed. In some countries, regulations require special testing of wheels that are to operate at higher speeds than normal at a central testing institute. The institute may also cut specimens from the wheel and investigate their physical properties. Cutting wheels are subjected to certain impact tests, bending tests and so on. The manufacturer is also obliged to ensure that the grinding wheel is well balanced prior to delivery.

The bursting of a grinding wheel may cause fatal or very serious injuries to anyone in the vicinity and heavy damage to plant or premises. In spite of all precautions taken by the manufacturers, occasional wheel bursts or breaks may still occur unless proper care is exercised in their use. Precautionary measures include:

- *Handling and storing.* A wheel may become damaged or cracked during transit or handling. Moisture may attack the bonding agent in phenolic resin wheels, ultimately reducing their strength. Vitrified wheels may be sensitive to repeated temperature variations. Irregularly absorbed moisture may throw the wheel out of balance. Consequently, it is most important that wheels are carefully handled at all stages and kept in an orderly manner in a dry and protected place.

Figure 82.5 • A well guarded, vitrified abrasive wheel mounted in a surface grinder and operating at a peripheral speed of 33 m/s.

- *Checking for cracks.* A new wheel should be checked to ensure that it is undamaged and dry, most simply by tapping with a wooden mallet. A faultless vitrified wheel will give a clear ring, an organic bonded wheel a less ringing tone; but either can be differentiated from the cracked sound of a defective wheel. In case of doubt, the wheel should not be used and the supplier should be consulted.
- *Testing.* Before the new wheel is put into service, it should be tested at full speed with due precautions being observed. After wet grinding, the wheel should be run idle to eject the water; otherwise the water may collect at the bottom of the wheel and cause imbalance, which may result in bursting when the wheel is next used.
- *Mounting.* Accidents and breakages occur when grinding wheels are mounted on unsuitable apparatus—for example, on spindle ends of buffing machines. The spindle should be of adequate diameter but not so large as to expand the centre hole of the wheel; flanges should be not less than one-third the diameter of the wheel and made of mild steel or of similar material.
- *Speed.* In no circumstances should the maximum permissible operating speed specified by the makers be exceeded. A notice indicating the spindle speed should be fitted to all grinding machines, and the wheel should be marked with the maximum permissible peripheral speed and the corresponding number of revolutions for a new wheel. Special precautions are necessary with variable speed grinding machines and to ensure the fitting of wheels of appropriate permissible speeds in portable grinders.
- *Work rest.* Wherever practicable, rigidly mounted work rests of adequate dimensions should be provided. They should be adjustable and kept as close as possible to the wheel to prevent a trap in which the work might be forced against the wheel and break it or, more probable, catch and injure the operator's hand.
- *Guarding.* Abrasive wheels should be provided with guards strong enough to contain the parts of a bursting wheel (see figure 82.5). Some countries have detailed regulations regarding the design of the guards and the materials to be used. In general, cast iron and cast aluminium are to be avoided. The grinding opening should be as small as possible, and an adjustable nose piece may be necessary. Exceptionally, where the nature of the work precludes the use of a guard, special protective flanges or safety chucks may be used. The spindles and tapered ends of double-ended polishing machines can cause entanglement accidents unless they are effectively guarded.

Eye injuries

Dust, abrasives, grains and splinters are a common hazard to the eyes in all dry-grinding operations. Effective eye protection by goggles or spectacles and fixed eye shields at the machine are essential; fixed eye shields are particularly useful when wheels are in intermittent use—for example, for tool grinding.

Fire

Grinding of magnesium alloys carries a high fire risk unless strict precautions are taken against accidental ignition and in the removal and drenching of dust. High standards of cleanliness and maintenance are required in all exhaust ducting to prevent risk of fire and also to keep ventilation working efficiently. Textile dust released from buffing operations is a fire hazard requiring good housekeeping and LEV.

Vibration

Portable and pedestal grinders carry a risk of hand-arm vibration syndrome (HAVS), also known as "white finger" from its most noticeable sign. Recommendations include limiting intensity and duration of exposure, redesigning tools, protective equipment and monitoring exposure and health.

Health hazards

Although modern grinding wheels do not themselves create the serious silicosis hazard associated in the past with sandstone wheels, highly dangerous silica dust may still be given off from the materials being ground—for example, sand castings. Certain resin-bonded wheels may contain fillers which create a dangerous dust. In addition, formaldehyde-based resins can emit formaldehyde during grinding. In any event, the volume of dust produced by grinding makes efficient LEV essential. It is more difficult to provide local exhaust for portable wheels, although some success in this direction has been achieved by use of low-volume, high-velocity capture systems. Prolonged work should be avoided and respiratory protective equipment provided if necessary. Exhaust ventilation is also required for most belt sanding, finishing, polishing and similar operations. With buffing in particular, combustible textile dust is a serious concern.

Protective clothing and good sanitary and washing facilities with showers should be provided, and medical supervision is desirable, especially for metal grinders.

INDUSTRIAL LUBRICANTS, METAL WORKING FLUIDS AND AUTOMOTIVE OILS

Richard S. Kraus

The industrial revolution could not have occurred without the development of refined petroleum-based industrial oils, lubricants, cutting oils and greases. Prior to the discovery in the 1860s that a superior lubricant could be produced by distilling crude oil in a vacuum, industry depended on naturally occurring oils and animal fats such as lard and whale sperm oil for lubricating moving parts. These oils and animal products were especially susceptible to melting, oxidation and breakdown from exposure to heat and moisture produced by the steam engines which powered almost all industrial equipment at that time. The evolution of petroleum-based refined products has continued from the first lubricant, which was used to tan leather, to modern synthetic oils and greases with longer service life, superior lubricating qualities and better resistance to change under varying temperatures and climatic conditions.

Industrial Lubricants

All moving parts on machinery and equipment require lubrication. Although lubrication may be provided by dry materials such as Teflon or graphite, which are used in parts such as small electrical motor bearings, oils and greases are the most commonly used lubricants. As the complexity of the machinery increases, the requirements for lubricants and metal process oils become more stringent. Lubricating oils now range from clear, very thin oils used to lubricate delicate instruments, to thick, tar-like oils used on large gears such as those which turn steel mills. Oils with very specific requirements are used both in the hydraulic systems and to lubricate large computer-operated machine tools such as those used in the aerospace industry to produce parts with extremely close tolerances. Synthetic oils, fluids and greases, and blends of synthetic and petroleum-based oils, are used where extended lubricant life is desired, such as sealed-for-life electric motors, where the increased time between oil changes offsets the difference in

cost; where extended temperature and pressure ranges exist, such as in aerospace applications; or where it is difficult and expensive to re-apply the lubricant.

Industrial Oils

Industrial oils such as spindle and lubricating oils, gear lubricants, hydraulic and turbine oils and transmission fluids are designed to meet specific physical and chemical requirements and to operate without discernible change for extended periods under varying conditions. Lubricants for aerospace use must meet entirely new conditions, including cleanliness, durability, resistance to cosmic radiation and the ability to operate in extremely cold and hot temperatures, without gravity and in a vacuum.

Transmissions, turbines and hydraulic systems contain fluids which transfer force or power, reservoirs to hold the fluids, pumps to move the fluids from one place to another and auxiliary equipment such as valves, piping, coolers and filters. Hydraulic systems, transmissions and turbines require fluids with specific viscosities and chemical stability to operate smoothly and provide the controlled transfer of power. The characteristics of good hydraulic and turbine oils include a high viscosity index, thermal stability, long life in circulating systems, deposit resistance, high lubricity, anti-foam capabilities, rust protection and good demulsibility.

Gear lubricants are designed to form strong, tenacious films which provide lubrication between gears under extreme pressure. The characteristics of gear oils include good chemical stability, demulsibility and resistance to viscosity increase and deposit formation. Spindle oils are thin, extremely clean and clear oils with lubricity additives. The most important characteristics for way oils—used to lubricate two flat sliding surfaces where there is high pressure and slow speed—are lubricity and tackiness to resist squeezing out and resistance to extreme pressure.

Cylinder and compressor oils combine the characteristics of both industrial and automotive oils. They should resist accumulation of deposits, act as a heat transfer agent (internal combustion engine cylinders), provide lubrication for cylinders and pistons, provide a seal to resist blow-back pressure, have chemical and thermal stability (especially vacuum pump oil), have a high viscosity index and resist water wash (steam-operated cylinders) and detergency.

Automotive Engine Oils

Manufacturers of internal combustion engines and organizations, such as the Society of Automotive Engineers (SAE) in the United States and Canada, have established specific performance criteria for automotive engine oils. Automotive gasoline and diesel engine oils are subjected to a series of performance tests to determine their chemical and thermal stability, corrosion resistance, viscosity, wear protection, lubricity, detergency and high and low temperature performance. They are then classified according to a code system which allows consumers to determine their suitability for heavy-duty use and for different temperatures and viscosity ranges.

Oils for automotive engines, transmissions and gear cases are designed with high viscosity indexes to resist changes in viscosity with temperature changes. Automotive engine oils are especially formulated to resist breakdown under heat as they lubricate internal combustion engines. Internal combustion engine oils must not be too thick to lubricate the internal moving parts when an engine starts up in cold weather, and they must not thin out as the engine heats up when operating. They should resist carbon build-up on valves, rings and cylinders and the formation of corrosive acids or deposits from moisture. Automotive engine oils contain detergents designed to hold carbon and metallic wear particles in suspension so that they can be filtered out as the oil circulates and not accumulate on internal engine parts and cause damage.

Cutting Fluids

The three types of cutting fluids used in industry are mineral oils, soluble oils and synthetic fluids. Cutting oils are typically a blend of high-quality, high-stability mineral oils of various viscosities together with additives to provide specific characteristics depending on the type of material being machined and the work performed. Soluble water-in-oil cutting fluids are mineral oils (or synthetic oils) which contain emulsifiers and special additives including defoamants, rust inhibitors, detergents, bactericides and germicides. They are diluted with water in varying ratios before being used. Synthetic cutting fluids are solutions of non-petroleum-based fluids, additives and water, rather than emulsions, some of which are fire resistant for machining specific metals. Semi-synthetic fluids contain 10 to 15% mineral oil. Some special fluids have both lubricating oil and cutting fluid characteristics due to the tendency of fluids to leak and intermix in certain machine tools such as multi-spindle, automatic screw machines.

The desired characteristics of cutting fluids depend on the composition of the metal being worked on, the cutting tool being used and the type of cutting, planing or shaping operation performed. Cutting fluids improve and enhance the metal working process by cooling and lubrication (i.e., protecting the edge of the cutting tool). For example, when working on a soft metal which creates a lot of heat, cooling is the most important criterion. Improved cooling is provided by using a light oil (such as kerosene) or water-based cutting fluid. Control of the built-up edge on cutting tools is provided by anti-weld or anti-wear additives such as sulphur, chlorine or phosphorus compounds. Lubricity, which is important when working on steel to overcome the abrasiveness of iron sulphide, is provided by synthetic and animal fats or sulphurized sperm oil additives.

Other Metal Working and Process Oils

Grinding fluids are designed to provide cooling and prevent metal build-up on grinding wheels. Their characteristics include thermal and chemical stability, rust protection (soluble fluids), preventing gummy deposits upon evaporation and a safe flashpoint for the work performed.

Quench oils, which require high stability, are used in metal treating to control the change of the molecular structure of steel as it cools. Quenching in lighter oil is used to case harden small, inexpensive steel parts. A slower quench rate is used to produce machine tool steels which are fairly hard on the outside with lower internal stress. A gapped or multi-phase quenching oil is used to treat high carbon and alloy steels.

Roll oils are specially formulated mineral or soluble oils which lubricate and provide a smooth finish to metal, particularly aluminium, copper and brass, as it goes through hot and cold rolling mills. Release oils are used to coat dies and moulds to facilitate the release of the formed metal parts. Tanning oils are still used in the felt and leather-making industry. Transformer oils are specially formulated dielectric fluids used in transformers and large electric breakers and switches.

Heat transfer oils are used in open or closed systems and may last up to 15 years in service. The primary characteristics are good thermal stability as systems operate at temperatures from 150 to 315 °C, oxidation stability and high flashpoint. Heat transfer oils are normally too viscous to be pumped at ambient temperatures and must be heated to provide fluidity.

Petroleum solvents are used to clean parts by spraying, dripping or dipping. The solvents remove oil and emulsify dirt and metal particles. Rust preventive oils may be either solvent or water based. They are applied to stainless steel coils, bearings and other parts by dipping or spraying, and leave polarized or wax films on the metal surfaces for fingerprint and rust protection and water displacement.

Greases

Greases are mixtures of fluids, thickeners and additives used to lubricate parts and equipment which cannot be made oil-tight, which are hard to reach or where leaking or splashed liquid lubricants might contaminate products or create a hazard. They have a wide range of applications and performance requirements, from lubricating jet engine bearings at sub-zero temperatures to hot rolling mill gears, and resisting acid or water washout, as well as the continuous friction created by railroad car wheel roller bearings.

Grease is made by the blending of metallic soaps (salts of long-chained fatty acids) into a lubricating oil medium at temperatures of 205 to 315 °C. Synthetic greases may use di-esters, silicone or phosphoric esters and polyalkyl glycols as fluids. The characteristics of the grease depend to a great extent upon the particular fluid, metallic element (e.g., calcium, sodium, aluminium, lithium and so on) in the soap and the additives used to improve performance and stability and to reduce friction. These additives include extreme-pressure additives which coat the metal with a thin layer of non-corrosive metallic sulphur compounds, lead naphthenate or zinc dithiophosphate, rust inhibitors, antioxidants, fatty acids for added lubricity, tackiness additives, colour dyes for identification and water inhibitors. Some greases may contain graphite or molybdenum fillers which coat the metallic parts and provide lubrication after the grease has run out or decomposed.

Industrial Lubricants, Grease and Automotive Engine Oil Additives

In addition to using high-quality lubricant base stocks with chemical and thermal stability and high viscosity indexes, additives are needed to enhance the fluid and provide specific characteristics required in industrial lubricants, cutting fluids, greases and automotive engine oils. The most commonly used additives include but are not limited to the following:

- *Anti-oxidants.* Oxidation inhibitors, such as 2,6-ditertiary butyl, paracresol and phenyl naphthylamine, reduce the rate of deterioration of oil by breaking up the long-chain molecules which form when exposed to oxygen. Oxidation inhibitors are used to coat metals such as copper, zinc and lead to prevent contact with the oil so they will not act as catalysts, speeding up oxidation and forming acids which attack other metals.
- *Foam inhibitors.* Defoamants, such as silicones and polyorganic silioxanes, are used in hydraulic oils, gear oils, transmission fluids and turbine oils to reduce surface film tension and remove air entrapped in the oil by pumps and compressors, in order to maintain constant hydraulic pressure and prevent cavitation.
- *Corrosion inhibitors.* Anti-rust additives, such as lead naphthenate and sodium sulphonate, are used to prevent rust from forming on metallic parts and systems where circulating oil has been contaminated with water or by moist air which entered system reservoirs as they cooled down when the equipment or machinery was not in use.
- *Anti-wear additives.* Anti-wear additives, such as tricresylphosphate, form polar compounds which are attracted to metal surfaces and provide a physical layer of additional protection in the event that the oil film is not sufficient.
- *Viscosity index improvers.* Viscosity index improvers help oils resist the effects of temperature changes. Unfortunately, their effectiveness diminishes with extended use. Synthetic oils are designed with very high viscosity indexes, allowing them to maintain their structure over wider temperature ranges and for much longer periods of time than mineral oils with viscosity index improver additives.

- *Demulsifiers.* Water inhibitors and special compounds separate water out of oil and prevent gum formation; they contain waxy oils which provide added lubricity. They are used where equipment is subject to water wash or where a large amount of moisture is present, such as in steam cylinders, air compressors and gear cases contaminated by soluble cutting fluids.
- *Colour dyes.* Dyes are used to assist users to identify different oils used for specific purposes, such as transmission fluids and gear oils, in order to prevent misapplication.
- *Extreme pressure additives.* Extreme pressure additives, such as non-corrosive sulphurized fatty compounds, zinc dithiophosphate and lead naphthenate, are used in automotive, gear and transmission oils to form coatings which protect metal surfaces when the protective oil film thins or is squeezed out and cannot prevent metal to metal contact.
- *Detergents.* Metal sulphonate and metal phenate detergents are used to hold dirt, carbon and metallic wear particles in suspension in hydraulic oils, gear oils, engine oils and transmission fluids. These contaminants are typically removed when the oil passes through a filter to prevent their being recirculated through the system where they could cause damage.
- *Tackiness additives.* Adhesive or tackiness additives are used to enable oils to adhere to and resist leakage from bearing assemblies, gear cases, large open gears on mills and construction equipment, and overhead machinery. Their tackiness diminishes with extended service.
- *Emulsifiers.* Fatty acids and fatty oils are used as emulsifiers in soluble oils to help form solutions with water.
- *Lubricity additives.* Fat, lard, tallow, sperm and vegetable oils are used to provide a higher degree of oiliness in cutting oils and some gear oils.
- *Bactericides.* Bactericides and germicides, such as phenol and pine oil, are added to soluble cutting oils to prolong the life of the fluid, maintain stability, reduce odours and prevent dermatitis.

Manufacturing Industrial Lubricants and Automotive Oils

Industrial lubricants and oils, grease, cutting fluids and automotive engine oils are manufactured in blending and packaging facilities, also called "lube plants" or "blending plants". These facilities may be located either in or adjacent to refineries which produce lubricant base stocks, or they may be some distance away and receive the base stocks by marine tankers or barges, railroad tank cars or tank trucks. Blending and packaging plants blend and compound additives into lubricating oil base stocks to manufacture a wide range of finished products, which are then shipped in bulk or in containers.

The blending and compounding processes used to manufacture lubricants, fluids and greases depend on the age and sophistication of the facility, the equipment available, the types and formulation of the additives used and the variety and volume of products produced. Blending may require only physical mixing of base stocks and additive packages in a kettle using mixers, paddles or air agitation, or auxiliary heat from electric or steam coils may be needed to help dissolve and blend in the additives. Other industrial fluids and lubricants are produced automatically by mixing base stocks and pre-blended additive and oil slurries through manifold systems. Grease may be either batch produced or continuously compounded. Lube plants may compound their own additives from chemicals or purchase pre-packaged additives from specialty companies; a single plant may use both methods. When lube plants manufacture their own additives and additive packages, there may be a need for high temperatures and pressures in addition to chemical reactions and physical agitation to compound the chemicals and materials.

After production, fluids and lubricants may be held in the blending kettles or placed in holding tanks to ensure that the additives remain in suspension or solution, to allow time for testing to determine whether the product meets quality specifications and certification requirements, and to allow process temperatures to return to ambient levels before products are packaged and shipped. When testing is completed, finished products are released for bulk shipment or packaging into containers.

Finished products are shipped in bulk in railroad tank cars or in tank trucks directly to consumers, distributors or outside packaging plants. Finished products also are shipped to consumers and distributors in railroad box cars or package delivery trucks in a variety of containers, as follows:

- Metal, plastic and combination metal/plastic or plastic/fibre intermediate bulk containers, which range in size from 227 l to approximately 2,840 l, are shipped as individual units on built-in or separate pallets, stacked 1 or 2 high.
- Metal, fibre or plastic drums with a capacity of 208 l, 114 l or 180 kg are typically shipped 4 to a pallet.
- Metal or plastic drums with a capacity of 60 l or 54 kg, and 19 l or 16 kg metal or plastic pails, are stacked on pallets and banded or stretch wrapped to maintain stability.
- Metal or plastic containers with a capacity of 8 l or 4 l, 1 l plastic, metal and fibre bottles and cans and 2 kg grease cartridges are packaged in cartons which are stacked on pallets and banded or stretch wrapped for shipment.

Some blending and packaging plants may ship pallets of mixed products and mixed sizes of containers and packages directly to small consumers. For example, a single-pallet shipment to a service station could include 1 drum of transmission fluid, 2 kegs of grease, 8 cases of automotive engine oil and 4 pails of gear lubricant.

Product Quality

Lubricant product quality is important to keep machines and equipment operating properly and to produce quality parts and materials. Blending and packaging plants manufacture finished petroleum products to strict specifications and quality requirements. Users should maintain the level of quality by establishing safe practices for the handling, storage, dispensing and transfer of lubricants from their original containers or tanks to the dispensing equipment and to the point of application on the machine or equipment to be lubricated or the system to be filled. Some industrial facilities have installed centralized dispensing, lubrication and hydraulic systems which minimize contamination and exposure. Industrial oils, lubricants, cutting oils and grease will deteriorate from water or moisture contamination, exposure to excessively high or low temperatures, inadvertent mixing with other products and long-term storage which allows additive dropout or chemical changes to occur.

Health and Safety

Because they are used and handled by consumers, finished industrial and automotive products must be relatively free of hazards. There is a potential for hazardous exposures when blending and compounding products, when handling additives, when using cutting fluids and when operating oil mist lubrication systems.

The chapter *Oil and natural gas refineries* in this *Encyclopaedia* gives information regarding potential hazards associated with auxiliary facilities at blending and packaging plants such as boiler rooms, laboratories, offices, oil-water separators and waste treatment facilities, marine docks, tank storage, warehouse operations, railroad tank car and tank truck loading racks and railroad box car and package truck loading and unloading facilities.

Safety

Manufacturing additives and slurries, batch compounding, batch blending and in-line blending operations require strict controls to maintain desired product quality and, along with the use of PPE, to minimize exposure to potentially hazardous chemicals and materials as well as contact with hot surfaces and steam. Additive drums and containers should be stored safely and kept tightly sealed until ready for use. Additives in drums and bags need to be handled properly to avoid muscular strain. Hazardous chemicals should be properly stored, and incompatible chemicals should not be stored where they can mix with one another. Precautions to be taken when operating filling and packaging machinery include using gloves and avoiding catching fingers in devices which crimp covers on kegs and pails. Machine guards and protective systems should not be removed, disconnected or by-passed to expedite work. Intermediate bulk containers and drums should be inspected before filling to make sure they are clean and suitable.

A confined-space permit system should be established for entry into storage tanks and blending kettles for cleaning, inspection, maintenance or repair. A lockout/tagout procedure should be established and implemented before working on packaging machinery, blending kettles with mixers, conveyors, palletizers and other equipment with moving parts.

Leaking drums and containers should be removed from the storage area and spills cleaned up to prevent slips and falls. Recycling, burning and disposal of waste, spilled and used lubricants, automotive engine oils and cutting fluids should be in accordance with government regulations and company procedures. Workers should use appropriate PPE when cleaning spills and handling used or waste products. Drained motor oil, cutting fluids or industrial lubricants which may be contaminated with gasoline and flammable solvents should be stored in a safe place away from sources of ignition, until proper disposal.

Fire protection

While the potential for fire is less in industrial and automotive lubricant blending and compounding than in refining processes, care must be taken when manufacturing metal working oils and greases due to the use of high blending and compounding temperatures and lower flashpoint products. Special precautions should be taken to prevent fires when products are dispensed or containers filled at temperatures above their flashpoints. When transferring flammable liquids from one container to another, proper bonding and grounding techniques should be applied to prevent static build-up and electrostatic discharge. Electrical motors and portable equipment should be properly classified for the hazards present in the area in which they are installed or used.

The potential for fire exists if a leaking product or vapour release in the lube blending and grease processing or storage areas reaches a source of ignition. The establishment and implementation of a hot-work permit system should be considered to prevent fires in blending and packaging facilities. Storage tanks installed inside buildings should be constructed, vented and protected in accordance with government requirements and company policy. Products stored on racks and in piles should not block fire protection systems, fire doors or exit routes.

Storage of finished products, both in bulk and in containers and packages, should be in accordance with recognized practices and fire prevention regulations. For example, flammable liquids and additives which are in solutions of flammable liquids may be stored in outside buildings or separate, specially designed inside or attached storage rooms. Many additives are stored in warm rooms (38 to 65 °C) or in hot rooms (over 65 °C) in order to keep the ingredients in suspension, to reduce the viscosity of thicker products or to provide for easier blending or compounding. These storage rooms should comply with electrical classification, drainage, ventilation and explosion venting requirements, especially when flammable liquids or combustible liquids are stored and dispensed at temperatures above their flashpoints.

Health

When blending, sampling and compounding, personal and respiratory protective equipment should be considered to prevent exposures to heat, steam, dusts, mists, vapours, fumes, metallic salts, chemicals and additives. Safe work practices, good hygiene and appropriate personal protection may be needed for exposure to oil mists, fumes and vapours, additives, noise and heat when conducting inspection and maintenance activities while sampling and handling hydrocarbons and additives during the production and packaging and when cleaning up spills and releases:

- Work shoes with oil- or slip-resistant soles should be worn for general work, and approved protective toe safety shoes with oil- or slip-resistant soles should be worn where hazards of foot injuries from rolling or falling objects or equipment exist.
- Safety goggles and respiratory protection may be needed for hazardous exposures to chemicals, dust or steam.
- Impervious gloves, aprons, footwear, face shields and chemical goggles should be worn when handling hazardous chemicals, additives and caustic solutions and when cleaning up spills.
- Head protection may be needed when working in pits or areas where the potential exists for injury to the head.
- Ready access to appropriate cleaning and drying facilities to handle splashes and spills should be provided.

Oil is a common cause of dermatitis, which can be controlled through the use of PPE and good personal hygiene practices. Direct skin contact with any formulated greases or lubricants should be avoided. Lighter oils such as kerosene, solvents and spindle oils defat the skin and cause rashes. Thicker products, such as gear oils and greases, block the pores of the skin, leading to folliculitis.

Health hazards due to microbial contamination of oil may be summarized as follows:

- Pre-existing skin conditions may be aggravated.
- Lubricant aerosols of respirable size may cause respiratory illness.
- Organisms may change the composition of the product so that it becomes directly injurious.
- Harmful bacteria from animals, birds or humans may be introduced.

Contact dermatitis may occur when employees are exposed to cutting fluids during production, work or maintenance and when they wipe oil-covered hands with rags embedded with minute metal particles. The metal causes small lacerations in the skin which may become infected. Water-based cutting fluids on skin and clothing may contain bacteria and cause infections, and the emulsifiers may dissolve fats from the skin. Oil folliculitis is caused by prolonged exposure to oil-based cutting fluids, such as from wearing oil-soaked clothing. Employees should remove and launder clothing that is soaked with oil before wearing it again. Dermatitis may also be caused by using soaps, detergents or solvents to clean the skin. Dermatitis is best controlled by good hygiene practices and minimizing exposure. Medical advice should be sought when dermatitis persists.

In the extensive review conducted as a basis for its criteria document, the US National Institute for Occupational Safety and Health (NIOSH) found an association between exposure to metal working fluids and the risk of developing cancer at several organ sites, including the stomach, pancreas, larynx and rectum (NIOSH 1996). The specific formulations responsible for the elevated cancer risks remain to be determined.

Occupational exposure to oil mists and aerosols is associated with a variety of non-malignant respiratory effects, including lipoid pneumonia, asthma, acute airways irritation, chronic bronchitis and impaired pulmonary function (NIOSH 1996).

Metal working fluids are readily contaminated by bacteria and fungi. They may affect the skin or, when inhaled as contaminated aerosols, they may have systemic effects.

Refinery processes such as hydrofinishing and acid treatment are used to remove aromatics from industrial lubricants, and the use of naphthenic base stocks has been restricted in order to minimize carcinogenicity. Additives introduced in blending and compounding may also create a potential risk to health. Exposures to chlorinated compounds and leaded compounds, such as those used in some gear lubricants and greases, cause irritation of the skin and may be potentially hazardous. Tri-orthocresyl phosphate has caused outbreaks of nerve palsies when lubricating oil was accidentally used for cooking. Synthetic oils consist mainly of sodium nitrite and triethanolamine and additives. Commercial triethanolamine contains diethanolamine, which can react with sodium nitrite to form a relatively weak carcinogen, N-nitrosodiethanolamine, which may create a hazard. Semi-synthetic lubricants present the hazards of both products, as well as the additives in their formulations.

Product safety information is important to employees of both manufacturers and users of lubricants, oils and greases. Manufacturers should have material safety data sheets (MSDSs) or other product information available for all of the additives and base stocks used in blending and compounding. Many companies have conducted epidemiological and toxicological testing to determine the degree of hazards associated with any acute and chronic health effects of their products. This information should be available to workers and users through warning labels and product safety information.

● SURFACE TREATMENT OF METALS

J.G. Jones, J.R. Bevan, J.A. Catton,
A. Zober, N. Fish, K.M. Morse,
G. Thomas, M.A. El Kadeem
and Philip A. Platcow*

There is a wide variety of techniques for finishing the surfaces of metal products so that they resist corrosion, fit better and look better (see table 82.7). Some products are treated by a sequence of several of these techniques. This article will briefly describe some of those most commonly used.

Before any of these techniques can be applied, the products must be thoroughly cleaned. A number of methods of cleaning are used, individually or in sequence. They include mechanical grinding, brushing and polishing (which produce metallic or oxidic dust—aluminium dust may be explosive), vapour degreasing, washing with organic grease solvents, "pickling" in concentrated acid or alkaline solutions and electrolytic degreasing. The last involves immersion in baths containing cyanide and concentrated alkali in which electrolytically formed hydrogen or oxygen remove the grease, resulting in "blank" metal surfaces that are free from oxides and grease. The cleaning is followed by adequate rinsing and drying of the product.

Proper design of the equipment and effective LEV will reduce some of the risk. Workers exposed to the hazard of splashes must be provided with protective goggles or eye shields and protective

gloves, aprons and clothing. Showers and eyewash fountains should be nearby and in good working order, and splashes and spills should be washed away promptly. With electrolytic equipment, the gloves and shoes must be non-conducting, and other standard electrical precautions, such as the installation of ground fault circuit interrupters and lockout/tagout procedures should be followed.

Treatment Processes

Electrolytic polishing
Electrolytic polishing is used to produce a surface of improved appearance and reflectivity, to remove excess metal to accurately fit the required dimensions and to prepare the surface for inspection for imperfections. The process involves preferential anodic dissolution of high spots on the surface after vapour degreasing and hot alkaline cleaning. Acids are frequently used as the electrolyte solutions; accordingly, adequate rinsing is required afterwards.

Electroplating
Electroplating is a chemical or electrochemical process for applying a metallic layer to the product—for example, nickel to protect against corrosion, hard chromium to improve the surface properties or silver and gold to beautify it. Occasionally, non-metallic materials are used. The product, wired as the cathode, and an anode of the metal to be deposited are immersed in an electrolyte solution (which can be acidic, alkaline or alkaline with cyanide salts and complexes) and connected externally to a source of direct current. The positively charged cations of the metallic anode migrate to the cathode, where they are reduced to the metal and deposited as a thin layer (see figure 82.6). The process is continued until the new coating reaches the desired thickness, and the product is then washed, dried and polished.

$$\text{Anode: } Cu \rightarrow Cu^{+2} + 2e^-; \text{ Cathode: } Cu^{2+} + 2e^- \rightarrow Cu$$

In *electroforming*, a process closely related to electroplating, objects moulded of, for example, plaster or plastic are made

Figure 82.6 • Schematic representation of electroplating.

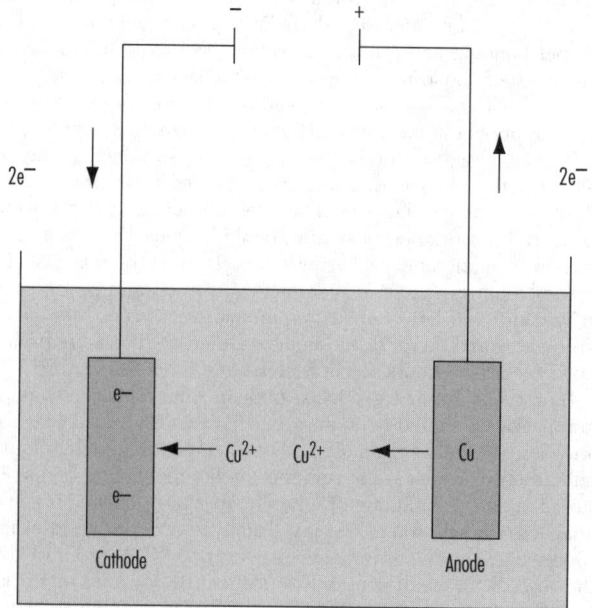

* Adapted from 3rd edition, *Encyclopaedia of Occupational Health and Safety*.

Table 82.7 • Summary of the hazards associated with the different metal treatment methods.

Metal treatment method	Hazards	Precautions
Electrolytic polishing	Burns and irritation from caustic and corrosive chemicals	Use appropriate personal protective equipment. Install effective exhaust ventilation.
Electroplating	Exposure to potentially cancer causing chromium and nickel; exposure to cyanides; burns and irritation from caustic and corrosive chemicals; electric shock; the process can be wet, causing slip and fall hazards; potential explosive dust generation; ergonomic hazards	Use appropriate personal protective equipment. Install effective exhaust ventilation, often slotted, push-pull system. Clean up spills immediately. Install non-skid flooring. Use effective design of work procedures and stations to avoid ergonomic stress.
Enamels and glazing	Physical hazards from grinders, conveyers, mills; burn hazard from high temperature liquids and equipment; exposure to dusts that may cause lung disease	Install proper machine guards, including interlocks. Use appropriate personal protective equipment. Install effective exhaust ventilation to avoid dust exposure. HEPA-filtered equipment may be necessary.
Etching	Exposure to hydrofluoric acid; burns and irritation from caustic and corrosive chemicals; burn hazard from high temperature liquids and equipment	Implement a programme to avoid exposure to hydrofluoric acid. Use appropriate personal protective equipment. Install effective exhaust ventilation.
Galvanizing	Burn hazard from high temperature liquids, metals, and equipment; burns and irritation from caustic and corrosive chemicals; metal fume fever; potential lead exposure	Use appropriate personal protective equipment. Install effective exhaust ventilation. Implement a lead exposure reduction/monitoring programme.
Heat treatment	Burn hazard from high temperature liquids, metals and equipment; burns and irritation from caustic and corrosive chemicals; possible explosive atmospheres of hydrogen; potential exposure to carbon monoxide; potential exposure to cyanides; fire hazard from oil quenching	Use appropriate personal protective equipment. Install effective exhaust ventilation. Display signs warning of high temperature equipment and surfaces. Install systems to monitor the concentration of carbon monoxide. Install adequate fire-suppression systems.
Metallizing	Burn hazard from high temperature metals and equipment; possible explosive atmospheres of dust, acetylene; zinc metal fume fever	Install adequate fire suppression systems. Properly separate chemicals and gases. Use appropriate personal protective equipment. Install effective exhaust ventilation.
Phosphating	Burns and irritation from caustic and corrosive chemicals	Use appropriate personal protective equipment. Install effective exhaust ventilation.
Plastics coating	Exposure to chemical sensitizers	Seek alternatives to sensitizers. Use appropriate personal protective equipment. Install effective exhaust ventilation.
Priming	Exposure to various solvents which are potentially toxic and flammable, exposure to chemical sensitizers, exposure to potentially carcinogenic chromium	Seek alternatives to sensitizers. Use appropriate personal protective equipment. Install effective exhaust ventilation. Properly separate chemicals/gases.

conductive by the application of graphite and then are connected as the cathode so that the metal is deposited on them.

In *anodization*, a process that has become increasingly important in recent years, products of aluminium (titanium and other metals are also used) are connected as the anode and immersed in dilute sulphuric acid. However, instead of the formation of positive aluminium ions and migrating for deposition on the cathode, they are oxidized by the oxygen atoms arising at the anode and become bound to it as an oxide layer. This oxide layer is partially dissolved by the sulphuric acid solution, making the surface layer porous. Subsequently, coloured or light-sensitive materials can be deposited in these pores, as in the fabrication of nameplates, for example.

Enamels and glazes

Vitreous enamel or porcelain enamel is used to give a high heat-, stain- and corrosion-resistant covering to metals, usually iron or steel, in a wide range of fabricated products including bath tubs, gas and electric cookers, kitchen ware, storage tanks and containers, and electrical equipment. In addition, enamels are used in the decoration of ceramics, glass, jewellery and decorative ornaments. The specialized use of enamel powders in the production of such ornamental ware as Cloisonné and Limoges has been known for centuries. Glazes are applied to pottery ware of all kinds.

The materials used in the manufacture of vitreous enamels and glazes include:

- refractories, such as quartz, feldspar and clay
- fluxes, such as borax (sodium borate decahydrate), soda ash (anhydrous sodium carbonate), sodium nitrate, fluorspar, cryolite, barium carbonate, magnesium carbonate, lead monoxide, lead tetroxide and zinc oxide
- colours, such as oxides of antimony, cadmium, cobalt, iron, nickel, manganese, selenium, vanadium, uranium and titanium
- opacifiers, such as oxides of antimony, titanium, tin and zirconium, and sodium antimoninate
- electrolytes, such as borax, soda ash, magnesium carbonate and sulphate, sodium nitrite and sodium aluminate
- flocculating agents, such as clay, gums, ammonium alginate, bentonite and colloidal silica.

The first step in all types of vitreous enamelling or glazing is the making of the frit, the enamel powder. This involves preparation of the raw materials, smelting and frit handing.

After careful cleaning of the metal products (e.g., shot blasting, pickling, degreasing), the enamel may be applied by a number of procedures:

- In the wet process, the object is dipped into the aqueous enamel slip, withdrawn and allowed to drain or, in "slushing", the enamel slip is thicker and must be shaken from the object.
- In the dry process, the ground-coated object is heated to the enamelling temperature and then dry enamel powder is dusted through sieves onto it. The enamel sinters into place and, when

the object is returned to the furnace, it melts down to a smooth surface.

- Spray application is being used increasingly, usually in a mechanized operation. It requires a cabinet under exhaust ventilation.
- Decorative enamels are usually applied by hand, using brushes or similar tools.
- Glazes for porcelain and pottery articles are usually applied by dipping or spraying. Although some dipping operations are being mechanized, pieces are usually dipped by hand in the domestic porcelain industry. The object is held in the hand, dipped into a large tub of glaze, the glaze is removed by a flick of the wrist and the object is placed in a dryer. An enclosed hood or cabinet with efficient exhaust ventilation should be provided when the glaze is sprayed.

The prepared objects are then "fired" in a furnace or kiln, which usually is gas fuelled.

Etching

Chemical etching produces a satin or matte finish. Most frequently, it is used as a pre-treatment prior to anodizing, lacquering, conversion coating, buffing or chemical brightening. It is most frequently applied to aluminium and stainless steel, but is also used for many other metals.

Aluminium is usually etched in alkaline solutions containing various mixtures of sodium hydroxide, potassium hydroxide, trisodium phosphate and sodium carbonate, together with other ingredients to prevent sludge formation. One of the most common processes uses sodium hydroxide at a concentration of 10 to 40 g/l maintained at a temperature of 50 to 85 °C with an immersion time as long as 10 minutes.

The alkaline etching is usually preceded and followed by treatment in various mixtures of hydrochloric, hydrofluoric, nitric, phosphoric, chromic or sulphuric acid. A typical acid treatment involves immersions of 15 to 60 seconds in a mixture of 3 parts by volume of nitric acid and 1 part by volume of hydrofluoric acid that is maintained at a temperature of 20 °C.

Galvanizing

Galvanizing applies a zinc coating to a variety of steel products to protect against corrosion. The product must be clean and oxide-free for the coating to adhere properly. This usually involves a number of cleaning, rinsing, drying or annealing processes before the product enters the galvanizing bath. In "hot dip" galvanizing, the product is passed through a bath of molten zinc; "cold" galvanizing is essentially electroplating, as described above.

Manufactured products are usually galvanized in a batch process, while the continuous strip method is used for steel strip, sheet or wire. Flux may be employed to maintain satisfactory cleaning of both the product and the zinc bath and to facilitate drying. A prefluxing step may be followed by an ammonium chloride flux cover on the surface of the zinc bath, or the latter may be used alone. In galvanizing pipe, the pipe is immersed in a hot solution of zinc ammonium chloride after cleaning and before the pipe enters the molten zinc bath. The fluxes decompose to form irritating hydrogen chloride and ammonia gas, requiring LEV.

The various types of continuous hot-dip galvanizing differ essentially in how the product is cleaned and whether the cleaning is done on-line:

- cleaning by flame oxidation of the surface oils with subsequent reduction in the furnace and annealing done in-line
- electrolytic cleaning done prior to in-line annealing
- cleaning by acid pickling and alkali cleaning, using a flux prior to the preheat furnace and annealing in a furnace before galvanizing

- cleaning by acid pickling and alkali cleaning, eliminating the flux and preheating in a reducing gas (e.g., hydrogen) prior to galvanizing.

The continuous galvanizing line for light-gauge strip steel omits pickling and the use of flux; it uses alkaline cleaning and maintains the clean surface of the strip by heating it in a chamber or furnace with a reducing atmosphere of hydrogen until it passes below the surface of the molten zinc bath.

Continuous galvanizing of wire requires annealing steps, usually with a molten lead pan in front of the cleaning and galvanizing tanks; air or water cooling; pickling in hot, dilute hydrochloric acid; rinsing; application of a flux; drying; and then galvanizing in the molten zinc bath.

A dross, an alloy of iron and zinc, settles to the bottom of the molten zinc bath and must be removed periodically. Various types of materials are floated on the surface of the zinc bath to prevent oxidation of the molten zinc. Frequent skimming is needed at the points of entry and exit of the wire or strip being galvanized.

Heat treatment

Heat treatment, the heating and cooling of a metal which remains in the solid state, is usually an integral part of the processing of metal products. It almost always involves a change in the crystalline structure of the metal which results in a modification of its properties (e.g., annealing to make the metal more malleable, heating and slow cooling to reduce hardness, heating and quenching to increase hardness, low-temperature heating to minimize internal stresses).

Annealing

Annealing is a "softening" heat treatment widely used to allow further cold working of the metal, improve machinability, stress-relieve the product before it is used and so on. It involves heating the metal to a specific temperature, holding it at that temperature for a specific length of time and allowing it to cool at a particular rate. A number of annealing techniques are used:

- *Blue annealing*, in which a layer of blue oxide is produced on the surface of iron-based alloys
- *Bright annealing*, which is carried out in a controlled atmosphere to minimize surface oxidation
- *Close annealing* or *box annealing*, a method in which both ferrous and non-ferrous metals are heated in a sealed metal container with or without a packing material and then slowly cooled
- *Full annealing*, usually carried out in a protective atmosphere, aimed at obtaining the maximum softness economically feasible
- *Malleablizing*, a special kind of anneal given to iron castings to make them malleable by transforming the combined carbon in the iron to fine carbon (i.e., graphite)
- *Partial annealing*, a low-temperature process to remove internal stresses induced in the metal by cold working
- *Sub-critical* or *spheroidizing annealing*, which produces improved machinability by allowing the iron carbide in the crystalline structure to acquire a spheroid shape.

Age-hardening

Age-hardening is a heat treatment often used on aluminium-copper alloys in which the natural hardening that takes place in the alloy is accelerated by heating to about 180 °C for about 1 hour.

Homogenizing

Homogenizing, usually applied to ingots or powdered metal compacts, is designed to remove or greatly reduce segregation. It is achieved by heating to a temperature about 20 °C below the metal's melting point for about 2 hours or more and then quenching.

Normalizing

A process similar to full annealing, ensures the uniformity of the mechanical properties to be obtained and also produces greater toughness and resistance to mechanical loading.

Patenting

Patenting is a special type of annealing process that is usually applied to materials of small cross-section which are intended to be drawn (e.g., 0.6% carbon steel wire). The metal is heated in an ordinary furnace to above the transformation range and then passes from the furnace directly into, for example, a lead bath held at a temperature of about 170 °C.

Quench-hardening and tempering

An increase in hardness can be produced in an iron-based alloy by heating to above the transformation range and rapidly cooling to room temperature by quenching in oil, water or air. The article is often too highly stressed to be put into service and, in order to increase its toughness, it is tempered by reheating to a temperature below the transformation range and allowing it to cool at the desired rate.

Martempering and austempering are similar processes except that the article is quenched, for example, in a salt or lead bath held at a temperature of 400 °C.

Surface- and case-hardening

This is another heat-treatment process applied most frequently to iron-based alloys, which allows the surface of the object to remain hard while its core remains relatively ductile. It has a number of variations:

- *Flame hardening* involves hardening the surfaces of the object (e.g., gear teeth, bearings, slideways) by heating with a high-temperature gas torch and then quenching in oil, water or another suitable medium.
- *Electrical induction hardening* is similar to flame hardening except that the heating is produced by eddy currents induced in the surface layers.
- *Carburizing* increases the carbon content of the surface of an iron-based alloy by heating the object in a solid, liquid or gaseous carbonaceous medium (e.g., solid charcoal and barium carbonate, liquid sodium cyanide and sodium carbonate, gaseous carbon monoxide, methane and so on) at a temperature of about 900 °C.
- *Nitriding* increases the nitrogen content of the surface of a special low-alloy cast iron or steel object by heating it in a nitrogenous medium, usually ammonia gas, at about 500 to 600 °C.
- *Cyaniding* is a method of case-hardening in which the surface of a low-carbon steel object is enriched in both carbon and nitrogen simultaneously. It usually involves heating the object for 1 hour in a bath of molten 30% sodium cyanide at 870 °C, and then quenching in oil or water.
- *Carbo-nitriding* is a gaseous process for the simultaneous absorption of carbon and nitrogen into the surface layer of steel by heating it to 800 to 875 °C in an atmosphere of a carburizing gas (see above) and a nitriding gas (e.g., 2 to 5% anhydrous ammonia).

Metallizing

Metallizing, or metal spraying, is a technique for applying a protective metallic coating to a mechanically roughened surface by spraying it with molten droplets of metal. It is also used to build up worn or corroded surfaces and for salvaging badly-machined component parts. The process is widely known as Schooping, after the Dr. Schoop who invented it.

It uses the Schooping gun, a hand-held, pistol-shaped spray gun through which the metal in wire form is fed into a fuel gas/oxygen blowpipe flame which melts it and, using compressed air, sprays it onto the object. The heat source is a mixture of oxygen and either acetylene, propane or compressed natural gas. The coiled wire is usually straightened before being fed into the gun. Any metal that can be made into a wire may be used; the gun can also accept the metal in powder form.

Vacuum metallizing is a process in which the object is placed in a vacuum jar into which the coating metal is sprayed.

Phosphating

Phosphating is used mainly on mild and galvanized steel and aluminium to augment the adhesion and corrosion resistance of paint, wax and oil finishes. It is also used to form a layer which acts as a parting film in the deep drawing of sheet metal and improves its wear resistance. It essentially consists of allowing the metal surface to react with a solution of one or more phosphates of iron, zinc, manganese, sodium or ammonium. Sodium and ammonium phosphate solutions are used for combined cleaning and phosphating. The need to phosphate multi-metal objects and the desire to increase line speeds in automated operations have led to reducing reaction times by the addition of accelerators such as fluorides, chlorates, molybdates and nickel compounds to the phosphating solutions. To reduce crystal size and, consequently, increase the flexibility of zinc phosphate coatings, crystal refining agents such as tertiary zinc phosphate or titanium phosphate are added to the pre-treatment rinse. The phosphating sequence typically includes the following steps:

- hot caustic cleaning
- brushing and rinsing
- further hot caustic cleaning
- conditioning water rinse
- spraying or dipping in hot solutions of acid phosphates
- cold water rinse
- warm chromic acid rinse
- another cold water rinse
- drying.

Priming

Organic paint primers are applied to metal surfaces to promote the adhesion of subsequently applied paints and to retard corrosion at the paint-metal interface. The primers usually contain resins, pigments and solvents and may be applied to the prepared metal surfaces by brush, spray, immersion, roller coating or electrophoresis.

The solvents may be any combination of aliphatic and aromatic hydrocarbons, ketones, esters, alcohols and ethers. The most commonly used resins are polyvinyl butynol, phenolic resins, drying oil alkyds, epoxidized oils, epoxyesters, ethyl silicates and chlorinated rubbers. In complex primers, cross-linking agents such as tetraethylene pentamine, pentaethylene hexamine, isocyanates and urea formaldehyde are used. Inorganic pigments used in primer formulations include lead, barium, chromium, zinc and calcium compounds.

Plastic coating

Plastic coatings are applied to metals in liquid form, as powders which are subsequently cured or sintered by heating, or in the form of fabricated sheets which are laminated to the metal surface with an adhesive. The most commonly used plastics include poly-

82. METAL PROCESSING AND METAL WORKING INDUSTRY

ethylene, polyamides (nylons) and PVC. The latter may include plasticizers based on monomeric and polymeric esters and stabilizers such as lead carbonate, fatty acid salts of barium and cadmium, dibutyltin dilaurate, alkyltin mercaptides and zinc phosphate. Although generally of low toxicity and non-irritating, some of the plasticizers are skin sensitizers.

Hazards and Their Prevention

As might be deduced from the complexity of the processes outlined above, there is a large variety of safety and health hazards associated with the surface treatment of metals. Many are regularly encountered in manufacturing operations; others are presented by the uniqueness of the techniques and materials employed. Some are potentially life threatening. By and large, however, they can be prevented or controlled.

Workplace design

The workplace should be designed to allow the delivery of raw materials and supplies and the removal of the finished products without interfering with the ongoing processing. Since many of the chemicals are flammable or prone to react when mixed, proper separation in storage and in transit is essential. Many of the metal finishing operations involve liquids, and when leaks, spills or splashes of acids or alkalis occur they must be washed away promptly. Accordingly, adequately drained, slip-resistant floors must be provided. Housekeeping must be diligent to keep the work areas and other spaces clean and free from accumulations of materials. Systems for disposal of solid and liquid wastes and effluents from furnaces and exhaust ventilation must be designed with environmental concerns in mind.

Work stations and work assignments should use ergonomic principles to minimize strains, sprains, excessive fatigue and RSIs. Machine guards must have automatic lockout so the machine is de-energized if the guard is removed. Splash guards are essential. Because of the danger of splashes of hot acid and alkali solutions, eyewash fountains and whole-body showers must be installed within easy reach. Signs should be posted to warn other production and maintenance personnel of such dangers as chemical baths and hot surfaces.

Chemical assessment

All chemicals should be evaluated for potential toxicity and physical hazards, and less hazardous materials should be substituted where possible. However, since the less toxic material may be more flammable, the hazard of fire and explosion must also be considered. In addition, the chemical compatibility of materials must be considered. For example, mixing of nitrate and cyanide salts by accident could cause an explosion due to the strong oxidizing properties of nitrates.

Ventilation

Most of the metal coating processes require LEV that is strategically placed to draw the vapours or other contaminants away from the worker. Some systems push fresh air across the tank to "push" airborne contaminants to the exhaust side of the system. Fresh air intakes must be located away from exhaust vents so that potentially toxic gases are not recirculated.

Personal protective equipment

Processes should be engineered to prevent potentially toxic exposures, but since they cannot always be totally avoided, employees will have to be provided with appropriate PPE (e.g., goggles with or without face shields as appropriate, gloves, aprons or coveralls and shoes). Because many of the exposures involve hot corrosive or caustic solutions, the protective items should be insulated and chemical-resistant. If there is possible exposure to elec-

tricity, PPE should be non-conductive. PPE must be available in adequate quantity to allow contaminated, wet items to be cleaned and dried before re-using them. Insulated gloves and other protective clothing should be available where there is the risk of thermal burns from hot metal, furnaces and so on.

An important adjunct is the availability of wash-up facilities and clean lockers and dressing rooms, so that workers' clothing remains uncontaminated and workers do not carry toxic materials back into their homes.

Employee training and supervision

Employee education and training are essential both when new to the job or when there have been changes in the equipment or the process. MSDSs must be provided for each of the chemical products which explain the chemical and physical hazards, in languages and at educational levels that ensure they will be understood by the workers. Competence testing and periodic re-training will assure that workers have retained the needed information. Close supervision is advisable to make sure that the proper procedures are being followed.

Selected hazards

Certain hazards are unique to the metal coating industry and deserve special consideration.

Alkaline and acid solutions

The heated alkaline and acid solutions used in cleaning and treatment of metals are particularly corrosive and caustic. They are irritating to the skin and mucous membranes and are especially dangerous when splashed into the eye. Eyewash fountains and emergency showers are essential. Proper protective clothing and goggles will guard against the inevitable splashes; when a splash reaches the skin, the area should be immediately and copiously rinsed with cool, clean water for at least 15 minutes; medical attention may be necessary, particularly when the eye is involved.

Care should be exercised when utilizing chlorinated hydrocarbons as phosgene may result from a reaction of the chlorinated hydrocarbon, acids and metals. Nitric and hydrofluoric acid are particularly dangerous when their gases are inhaled, because it may take 4 hours or more before the effects on the lungs become apparent. Bronchitis, pneumonitis and even potentially fatal pulmonary oedema may appear belatedly in a worker who apparently had no initial effect from the exposure. Prompt prophylactic medical treatment and, often, hospitalization are advisable for workers who have been exposed. Skin contact with hydrofluoric acid can cause severe burns without pain for several hours. Prompt medical attention is essential.

Dust

Metallic and oxidic dusts are a particular problem in grinding and polishing operations, and are most effectively removed by LEV as they are created. Ductwork should be designed to be smooth and air velocity should be sufficient to keep the particulates from settling out of the air stream. Aluminium and magnesium dust may be explosive and should be collected in a wet trap. Lead has become less of a problem with the decline of its use in ceramics and porcelain glazes, but it remains the ubiquitous occupational hazard and must always be guarded against. Beryllium and its compounds have received interest recently due to the possibility of carcinogenicity and chronic beryllium disease.

Certain operations present a risk of silicosis and pneumoconiosis: the calcining, crushing and drying of flint, quartz or stone; the sieving, mixing and weighing out of these substances in the dry state; and the charging of furnaces with such materials. They also represent a danger when they are used in a wet process and are splashed about the workplace and on workers' clothing, to become dusts again when they dry out. LEV and rigorous cleanliness and personal hygiene are important preventive measures.

Organic solvents

Solvents and other organic chemicals used in degreasing and in certain processes are dangerous when inhaled. In the acute phase, their narcotic effects may lead to respiratory paralysis and death. In chronic exposure, toxicity of the central nervous system and liver and kidney damage are most frequent. Protection is provided by LEV with a safety zone of at least 80 to 100 cm between the source and the breathing area of the worker. Bench ventilation must also be installed to remove residual vapours from the finished workpieces. Defatting of the skin by organic solvents may be a precursor of dermatitis. Many solvents are also flammable.

Cyanide

Baths containing cyanides are frequently used in electrolytic degreasing, electroplating and cyaniding. Reaction with acid will form the volatile, potentially lethal hydrogen cyanide (prussic acid). The lethal concentration in air is 300 to 500 ppm. Fatal exposures may also result from skin absorption or ingestion of cyanides. Optimum cleanliness is essential for workers using cyanide. Food should not be eaten before washing, and should never be in the work area. Hands and clothing must be carefully cleaned following a potential cyanide exposure.

First aid measures for cyanide poisoning include transport into the open air, removal of contaminated clothing, copious washing of the exposed areas with water, oxygen therapy and inhalation of amyl nitrite. LEV and skin protection are essential.

Chromium and nickel

Chromic and nickel compounds used in galvanic baths in electroplating may be hazardous. Chromium compounds can cause burns, ulceration and eczema of the skin and mucosa and a characteristic perforation of the nasal septum. Bronchial asthma may occur. Nickel salts can cause obstinate allergic or toxic-irritative skin injury. There is evidence that both chromium and nickel compounds may be carcinogenic. LEV and skin protection are essential.

Furnaces and ovens

Special precautions are needed when working with the furnaces employed, for example, in the heat treatment of metals where components are handled at high temperatures and the materials used in the process may either be toxic or explosive or both. The gaseous media (atmospheres) in the furnace may react with the metal charge (oxidizing or reducing atmospheres) or they may be neutral and protective. Most of the latter contain up to 50% hydrogen and 20% carbon monoxide, which, in addition to being combustible, form highly explosive mixtures with air at elevated temperatures. The ignition temperature varies from 450 to 750 °C, but a local spark may cause ignition even at lower temperatures. The danger of explosion is greater when the furnace is being started up or shut down. Since a cooling furnace tends to suck in air (a particular danger when the fuel or power supply is interrupted), a supply of inert gas (e.g., nitrogen or carbon dioxide) should be available for purging when the furnace is shut down as well as when a protective atmosphere is introduced into a hot furnace.

Carbon monoxide is perhaps the greatest hazard from furnaces and ovens. Since it is colourless and odourless, it frequently reaches toxic levels before the worker becomes aware of it. Headache is one of the earliest symptoms of toxicity, and, therefore, a worker developing a headache on the job should immediately be removed into fresh air. Danger zones include recessed pockets in which the carbon monoxide may collect; it should be remembered that brickwork is porous and may retain the gas during normal purging and emit it when the purging is completed.

Lead furnaces may be dangerous since lead tends to vaporize quite rapidly at temperatures above 870 °C. Accordingly, an effective fume extraction system is required. A pot breakage or failure may also be hazardous; a sufficiently large well or pit should be provided to capture the molten metal if this occurs.

Fire and explosion

Many of the compounds used in metal coating are flammable and, under certain circumstances, explosive. For the most part, the furnaces and drying ovens are gas fired, and special precautions such as flame-failure devices at burners, low-pressure cut-off valves in the supply lines and explosion relief panels in the structure of the stoves should be installed. In electrolytic operations, hydrogen formed in the process may collect at the surface of the bath and, if not exhausted, may reach explosive concentrations. Furnaces should be properly ventilated and burners protected from being clogged by dripping material.

Oil quenching is also a fire hazard, especially if the metal charge is not completely immersed. Quenching oils should have a high flashpoint, and their temperature should not exceed 27 °C.

Compressed oxygen and fuel gas cylinders used in metallizing are fire and explosion hazards if not stored and operated properly. See the article "Welding and thermal cutting" in this chapter for detailed precautions.

As required by local ordinances, firefighting equipment, including alarms, should be provided and maintained in working order, and the workers drilled in using it properly.

Heat

The use of furnaces, open flames, ovens, heated solutions and molten metals inevitably presents the risk of excessive heat exposure, which is compounded in hot, humid climates and, particularly, by occlusive protective garments and gear. Complete air conditioning of a plant may not be economically feasible, but supplying cooled air in local ventilation systems is helpful. Rest breaks in cool surroundings and adequate fluid intake (fluids taken at the work station should be free of toxic contaminants) will help to avert heat toxicity. Workers and supervisors should be trained in the recognition of heat stress symptoms.

Conclusion

Surface treatment of metals involves a multiplicity of processes entailing a broad range of potentially toxic exposures, most of which can be prevented or controlled by the diligent application of well-recognized preventive measures.

METAL RECLAMATION

Melvin E. Cassady and Richard D. Ringenwald, Jr.

Metal reclamation is the process by which metals are produced from scrap. These reclaimed metals are not distinguishable from the metals produced from primary processing of an ore of the metal. However, the process is slightly different and the exposure could be different. The engineering controls are basically the same. Metal reclamation is very important to the world economy because of the depletion of raw materials and the pollution of the environment created by scrap materials.

Aluminium, copper, lead and zinc comprise 95% of the production in the secondary non-ferrous metal industry. Magnesium, mercury, nickel, precious metals, cadmium, selenium, cobalt, tin and titanium are also reclaimed. (Iron and steel are discussed in the chapter *Iron and steel industry*. See also the article "Copper, lead and zinc smelting and refining" in this chapter.)

Control Strategies

Emission/exposure control principles

Metal reclamation involves exposures to dust, fumes, solvents, noise, heat, acid mists and other potential hazardous materials and risks. Some process and/or material handling modifications may be feasible to eliminate or reduce the generation of emissions: minimizing handling, lowering pot temperatures, decreasing dross formation and surface generation of dust, and modifying plant layout to reduce material handling or re-entrainment of settled dust.

Exposure can be reduced in some cases if machines are selected to perform high-exposure tasks so that employees may be removed from the area. This can also reduce ergonomic hazards due to materials handling.

To prevent cross contamination of clean areas in the plant, it is desirable to isolate processes generating significant emissions. A physical barrier will contain emissions and reduce their spread. Thus, fewer people are exposed, and the number of emission sources contributing to exposure in any one area will be reduced. This simplifies exposure evaluations and makes the identification and control of major sources easier. Reclaim operations are often isolated from other plant operations.

Occasionally, it is possible to enclose or isolate a specific emission source. Because enclosures are seldom air tight, a negative draught exhaust system is often applied to the enclosure. One of the most common ways to control emissions is to provide local exhaust ventilation at the point of emission generation. Capturing emissions at their source reduces the potential for emissions to disperse into the air. It also prevents secondary employee exposure created by the re-entrainment of settled contaminants.

The capture velocity of an exhaust hood must be great enough to prevent fumes or dust from escaping the air flow into the hood. The air flow should have enough velocity to carry fume and dust particles into the hood and to overcome the disrupting effects of cross drafts and other random air movements. The velocity required to accomplish this will vary from application to application. The use of recirculation heaters or personal cooling fans which can overcome local exhaust ventilation should be restricted.

All exhaust or dilution ventilation systems also require replacement air (known also as "make-up" air systems). If the replacement air system is well designed and integrated into natural and comfort ventilation systems, more effective control of exposures can be expected. For example, replacement air outlets should be placed so clean air flows from the outlet across the employees, towards the emission source and to the exhaust. This technique is often used with supplied-air islands and places the employee between clean incoming air and the emission source.

Clean areas are intended to be controlled through direct emission controls and housekeeping. These areas exhibit low ambient contaminant levels. Employees in contaminated areas can be protected by supplied-air service cabs, islands, stand-by pulpits and control rooms, supplemented by personal respiratory protection.

The average daily exposure of workers can be reduced by providing clean areas such as breakrooms and lunchrooms that are supplied with fresh filtered air. By spending time in a relatively contaminant-free area, the employees' time-weighted average exposure to contaminants can be reduced. Another popular application of this principle is the supplied-air island, where fresh filtered air is supplied to the breathing zone of the employee at the workstation.

Sufficient space for hoods, duct work, control rooms, maintenance activities, cleaning and equipment storage should be provided.

Wheeled-vehicles are significant sources of secondary emissions. Where wheeled-vehicle transport is used, emissions can be reduced by paving all surfaces, keeping surfaces free of accumulated dusty materials, reducing vehicle travel distances and speed, and by re-directing vehicle exhaust and cooling fan discharge. Appropriate paving material such as concrete should be selected after considering factors such as load, use and care of surface. Coatings may be applied to some surfaces to facilitate wash down of roadways.

All exhaust, dilution and make-up air ventilation systems must be properly maintained in order to effectively control air contaminants. In addition to maintaining general ventilation systems, process equipment must be maintained to eliminate spillage of material and fugitive emissions.

Work practice programme implementation

Although standards emphasize engineering controls as a means of achieving compliance, work practice controls are essential to a successful control programme. Engineering controls can be defeated by poor work habits, inadequate maintenance and poor housekeeping or personal hygiene. Employees who operate the same equipment on different shifts can have significantly different airborne exposures because of differences in these factors between shifts.

Work practice programmes, although often neglected, represent good managerial practice as well as good common sense; they are cost effective but require a responsible and cooperative attitude on the part of employees and line supervisors. The attitude of senior management toward safety and health is reflected in the attitude of line supervisors. Likewise, if supervisors do not enforce these programmes, employees attitudes may suffer. Fostering good health and safety attitudes can be accomplished through:

- a cooperative atmosphere in which employees participate in the programmes
- formal training and educational programmes
- emphasizing the plant safety and health programme. Motivating employees and obtaining their trust is necessary in order to have an effective programme.

Work practice programmes cannot be simply "installed". Just as with a ventilation system, they must be maintained and continually checked to insure that they are functioning properly. These programmes are the responsibility of management and employees. Programmes should be established to teach, encourage and supervise "good" (i.e., low exposure) practices.

Personal protective equipment

Safety glasses with side shields, coveralls, safety shoes and work gloves should be routinely worn for all jobs. Those engaged in casting and melting, or in casting alloys, should wear aprons and hand protection made of leather or other suitable materials to protect against the splatter of molten metal.

In operations where engineering controls are not adequate to control dust or fume emissions, appropriate respiratory protection should be worn. If noise levels are excessive, and cannot be engineered out or noise sources cannot be isolated, hearing protection should be worn. There should also be a hearing conservation programme, including audiometric testing and training.

Processes

Aluminium

The secondary aluminium industry utilizes aluminium-bearing scrap to produce metallic aluminium and aluminium alloys. The processes used in this industry include scrap pre-treatment, re-melting, alloying and casting. The raw material used by the secondary aluminium industry includes new and old scrap, sweated pig and some primary aluminium. New scrap consists of clippings, forging and other solids purchased from the aircraft industry, fabricators and other manufacturing plants. Borings and turnings are by-product of the machining of castings, rods and forging by the aircraft and automobile industry. Drosses, skimmings and slags are obtained from primary reduction plants, secondary smelting plants and foundries. Old scrap includes automobile parts, household items and airplane parts. The steps involved are as follows:

- *Inspection and sorting.* Purchased aluminium scrap undergoes inspection. Clean scrap requiring no pre-treatment is transported to storage or is charged directly into the smelting furnace. The aluminium that needs pre-treatment is manually sorted. Free iron, stainless steel, zinc, brass and oversized materials are removed.
- *Crushing and screening.* Old scrap, especially casting and sheet contaminated with iron, are inputs to this process. Sorted scrap is conveyed to a crusher or hammer mill where the material is shredded and crushed, and the iron is torn away from the aluminium. The crushed material is passed over vibrating screens to remove dirt and fines.
- *Baling.* Specially designed baling equipment is used to compact bulky aluminium scrap such as scrap sheet, castings and clippings.

- *Shredding/classifying.* Pure aluminium cable with steel reinforcement or insulation is cut with alligator-type shears, then granulated or further reduced in hammer mills to separate the iron core and plastic coating from the aluminium.
- *Burning/drying.* Borings and turning are pre-treated in order to remove cutting oils, greases, moisture and free iron. The scrap is crushed in a hammer mill or ring crusher, the moisture and organics are volatilized in a gas- or oil-fired rotary dryer, the dried chips are screened to remove aluminium fines, the remaining material is magnetically treated for iron removal, and the clean, dried borings are sorted in tote boxes.
- *Hot-dross processing.* Aluminium can be removed from the hot dross discharged from the refining furnace by batch fluxing with a salt-cryolite mixture. This process is carried out in a mechanically rotated, refractory-lined barrel. The metal is tapped periodically through a hole in its base.
- *Dry milling.* In the dry-milling process, cold aluminium-laden dross and other residues are processed by milling, screening and concentrating to obtain a product containing a minimum aluminium content of 60 to 70%. Ball mills, rod mills or hammer mills can be used to reduce the oxides and non-metallics to fine powders. Separation of dirt and other non-recoverables from the metal is achieved by screening, air classification and/or magnetic separation.
- *Roasting.* Aluminium foil backed with paper, gutta-percha or insulation is an input in this process. In the roasting process, carboneous materials associated with aluminium foils are charged and then separated from the metal product.
- *Aluminium sweating.* Sweating is a pyrometallurgical process which is used to recover aluminium from high-iron-content scrap. High-iron aluminium scrap, castings and dross are inputs in this process. Open-flame reverberatory furnaces with sloping hearths are generally employed. Separation is accom-

Table 82.8 • Engineering/administrative controls for aluminium, by operation.

Process equipment	Exposure	Engineering/administrative controls
Sorting	Torch desoldering — metal fumes such as lead and cadmium	Local exhaust ventilation during desoldering; PPE — respiratory protection when desoldering
Crushing/screening	Non-specific dusts and aerosol, oil mists, metal particulates, and noise	Local exhaust ventilation and general area ventilation, isolation of noise source; PPE — hearing protection
Baling	No known exposure	No controls
Burning/drying	Non-specific particulate matter which may include metals, soot, and condensed heavy organics. Gases and vapours containing fluorides, sulphur dioxide, chlorides, carbon monoxide, hydrocarbons and aldehydes	Local exhaust ventilation, general area ventilation, heat stress work/rest regimen, fluids, isolation of noise source; PPE — hearing protection
Hot-dross processing	Some fumes	Local exhaust ventilation, general area ventilation
Dry milling	Dust	Local exhaust ventilation, general area ventilation
Roasting	Dust	Local exhaust ventilation, general area ventilation, heat stress work/rest regimen, fluids, isolation of noise source; PPE — hearing protection
Sweating	Metal fumes and particulates, non-specific gases and vapours, heat and noise	Local exhaust ventilation, general area ventilation, heat stress work/rest regimen, fluids, isolation of noise source; PPE — hearing protection and respiratory protection
Reverberatory (chlorine) smelting-refining	Products of combustion, chlorine, hydrogen chlorides, metal chlorides, aluminium chlorides, heat and noise	Local exhaust ventilation, general area ventilation, heat stress work/rest regimen, fluids, isolation of noise source; PPE — hearing protection and respiratory protection
Reverberatory (fluorine) smelting-refining	Products of combustion, fluorine, hydrogen flluorides, metal fluorides, aluminium fluorides, heat and noise	Local exhaust ventilation, general area ventilation, heat stress work/rest regimen, fluids, isolation of noise source; PPE — hearing protection and respiratory protection

plished as aluminium and other low-melting constituents melt and trickle down the hearth, through a grate and into air-cooled moulds, collecting pots or holding wells. The product is termed "sweated pig". The higher-melting materials including iron, brass and oxidation products formed during the sweating process are periodically tapped from the furnace.

- *Reverberatory (chlorine) smelting-refining*. Reverberatory furnaces are used to convert clean sorted scrap, sweated pigs or, in some cases, untreated scrap into specification alloys. The scrap is charged to the furnace by mechanical means. Materials are added for processing by batch or continuous feed. After the scrap is charged a flux is added to prevent contact with and subsequent oxidation of the melt by air (cover flux). Solvent fluxes are added which react with non-metallics, such as residues from burned coatings and dirt, to form insolubles which float to the surface as slag. Alloying agents are then added, depending on the specifications. *Demagging* is the process which reduces the magnesium content of the molten charge. When demagging with chlorine gas, chlorine is injected through carbon tubes or lances and reacts with magnesium and aluminium as it bubbles. In the skimming step impure semi-solid fluxes are skimmed off the surface of the melt.
- *Reverberatory (fluorine) smelting-refining*. This process is similar to the reverberatory (chlorine) smelting-refining process except that aluminium fluoride rather than chlorine is employed.

Table 82.8 lists exposure and controls for aluminium reclamation operations.

Copper reclamation

The secondary copper industry utilizes copper-bearing scrap to produce metallic copper and copper based alloys. The raw materials used can be classified as new scrap produced in the fabrication of finished products or old scrap from obsolete worn out or salvaged articles. Old scrap sources include wire, plumbing fixtures, electrical equipment, automobiles and domestic appliances. Other materials with copper value include slags, drosses, foundry ashes and sweepings from smelters. The following steps are involved:

- *Stripping and sorting*. Scrap is sorted on the bases of its copper content and cleanliness. Clean scrap may be manually separated for charging directly to a melting and alloying furnace. Ferrous components can be separated magnetically. Insulation and lead cable coverings are stripped by hand or by specially designed equipment.
- *Briquetting and crushing*. Clean wire, thin plate, wire screen, borings, turnings and chips are compacted for easier handling. The equipment used includes hydraulic baling presses, hammer mills and ball mills.
- *Shredding*. The separation of copper wire from insulation is accomplished by reducing the size of the mixture. The shredded material is then sorted by air or hydraulic classification with magnetic separation of any ferrous materials.
- *Grinding and gravity separation*. This process accomplishes the same function as shredding but uses an aqueous separation medium and different input materials such as slags, drosses, skimmings, foundry ashes, sweepings and baghouse dust.
- *Drying*. Borings, turnings and chips containing volatile organic impurities such as cutting fluids, oils and greases are removed.
- *Insulation burning*. This process separates insulation and other coatings from copper wire by burning these materials in furnaces. The wire scrap is charged in batches to a primary ignition chamber or afterburner. Volatile combustion products are then passed through a secondary combustion chamber or

baghouse for collection. Non-specific particulate matter is generated which may include smoke, clay and metal oxides. Gases and vapours may contain oxides of nitrogen, sulphur dioxide, chlorides, carbon monoxide, hydrocarbons and aldehydes

- *Sweating*. The removal of low vapour-melting components from scrap is accomplished by heating the scrap to a controlled temperature which is just above the melting point of the metals to be sweated out. The primary metal, copper, is generally not the melted component.
- *Ammonium carbonate leaching*. Copper can be recovered from relatively clean scrap by leaching and dissolution in a basic ammonium carbonate solution. Cupric ions in an ammonia solution will react with metallic copper to produce cuprous ions, which can be reoxidized to the cupric state by air oxidation. After the crude solution is separated from the leach residue, the copper oxide is recovered by steam distillation.
- *Steam distillation*. Boiling the leached material from the carbonate leaching process precipitates the copper oxide. The copper oxide is then dried.
- *Hydrothermal hydrogen reduction*. Ammonium carbonate solution containing copper ions is heated under pressure in hydrogen, precipitating the copper as a powder. The copper is filtered, washed, dried and sintered under a hydrogen atmosphere. The powder is ground and screened.
- Sulphuric acid leaching. Scrap copper is dissolved in hot sulphuric acid to form a copper sulphate solution for feed to the electrowinning process. After digestion, the undissolved residue is filtered off.
- *Converter smelting*. Molten black copper is charged to converter, which is a pear-shaped or cylindrical steel shell lined refractory brick. Air is blown into the molten charges through nozzles called *tuyères*. The air oxidizes copper sulphide and other metals. A flux containing silica is added to react with the iron oxides to form an iron silicate slag. This slag is skimmed from the furnace, usually by tipping the furnace and then there is a secondary blow and skim. The copper from this process is called blister copper. The blister copper is generally further refined in a fire refining furnace.
- *Fire refining*. The blister copper from the converter is fire refined in a cylindrical tilting furnace, a vessel like a reverberatory furnace. The blister copper is charged to the refining vessel in an oxidizing atmosphere. The impurities are skimmed from the surface and a reducing atmosphere is created by the addition of green logs or natural gas. The resulting molten metal is then cast. If the copper is to be electrolytically refined, the refined copper will be cast as an anode.
- *Electrolytic refining*. The anodes from the fire refining process are placed in a tank containing sulphuric acid and a direct current. The copper from the anode is ionized and the copper ions are deposited on a pure copper starter sheet. As the anodes dissolve in the electrolyte the impurities settle to the bottom of the cell as a slime. This slime can be additionally processed to recover other metal values. The cathode copper produced is melted and cast into a variety of shapes.

Table 82.9 lists exposures and controls for copper reclamation operations.

Lead reclamation

Raw materials purchased by secondary lead smelters may require processing prior to being charged into a smelting furnace. This section discusses the most common raw materials which are purchased by secondary lead smelters and feasible engineering controls and work practices to limit employee exposure to lead from raw materials processing operations. It should be noted that lead

Table 82.9 • Engineering/administrative controls for copper, by operation.

Process equipment	Exposures	Engineering/administrative controls
Stripping and sorting	Air contaminants from material handling and desoldering or scrap cutting	Local exhaust ventilation, general area ventilation
Briquetting and crushing	Non-specific dusts and aerosol, oil mists, metal particulates and noise	Local exhaust ventilation and general area ventilation, isolation of noise source; PPE — hearing protection and respiratory protection
Shredding	Non-specific dusts, wire insulation material, metal particulates and noise	Local exhaust ventilation and general area ventilation, isolation of noise source; PPE — hearing protection and respiratory protection
Grinding and gravity separation	Non-specific dusts, metal particulates from fluxes, slags and drosses, and noise	Local exhaust ventilation and general area ventilation, isolation of noise source; PPE — hearing protection and respiratory protection
Drying	Non-specific particulate matter, which may include metals, soot and condensed heavy organics. Gases and vapours containing fluorides, sulphur dioxide, chlorides, carbon monoxide, hydrocarbons and aldehydes	Local exhaust ventilation, general area ventilation, work/rest regimen, fluids, isolation of noise source; PPE — hearing protection and respiratory protection
Insulation burning	Non-specific particulate matter which may include smoke, clay and metal oxides. Gases and vapours containing oxides of nitrogen, sulphur dioxide, chlorides, carbon monoxide, hydrocarbons and aldehydes	Local exhaust ventilation, general area ventilation, work/rest regimen, fluids, isolation of noise source; PPE — respiratory protection
Sweating	Metal fumes and particulates, non-specific gases, vapours and particulates	Local exhaust ventilation, general area ventilation, work/rest regimen, fluids, isolation of noise source; PPE — hearing protection and respiratory protection
Ammonium carbonate leaching	Ammonia	Local exhaust ventilation, general area ventilation; PPE — respiratory protection
Steam distillation	Ammonia	Local exhaust ventilation, general area ventilation; PPE — glasses with side shields
Hydrothermal hydrogen reduction	Ammonia	Local exhaust ventilation, general area ventilation; PPE — respiratory protection
Sulphuric acid leaching	Sulphuric acid mists	Local exhaust ventilation, general area ventilation
Converter smelting	Volatile metals, noise	Local exhaust ventilation, general area ventilation; PPE — respiratory protection and hearing protection
Electric crucible smelting	Particulate, sulphur and nitrogen oxides, soot, carbon monoxide, noise	Local exhaust ventilation, general area ventilation; PPE — hearing protection
Fire refining	Sulphur oxides, hydrocarbons, particulates	Local exhaust ventilation, general area ventilation; PPE — hearing protection
Electrolytic refining	Sulphuric acid and metals from sludge	Local exhaust ventilation, general area ventilation

dust can generally be found throughout lead reclamation facilities and that any vehicular air is likely to stir up lead dust which can then be inhaled or adhere to shoes, clothing, skin and hair.

Automotive batteries
The most common raw material at a secondary lead smelter is junk automotive batteries. Approximately 50% of the weight of a junk automotive battery will be reclaimed as metallic lead in the smelting and refining process. Approximately 90% of the automotive batteries manufactured today utilize a polypropylene box or case. The polypropylene cases are reclaimed by almost all secondary lead smelters due to the high economic value of this material. Most of these processes can generate metal fumes, in particular lead and antimony.

In *automotive battery breaking* there is a potential for forming arsine or stibine due to the presence of arsenic or antimony used as hardening agents in grid metal and the potential for having nascent hydrogen present.

The four most common processes for breaking automotive batteries are:

1. high speed saw
2. slow speed saw
3. shear
4. whole battery crushing (Saturn crusher or shredder or hammer mill).

The first three of these processes involve cutting the top off of the battery, then dumping the groups, or lead-bearing material. The fourth process involves crushing the entire battery in a hammer mill and separating the components by gravity separation.

Automotive battery separation takes place after automotive batteries have been broken in order that the lead-bearing material can be separated from the case material. Removing the case may generate acid mists. The most widely used techniques for accomplishing this task are:

• The *manual* technique. This is used by the vast majority of secondary lead smelters and remains the most widely used technique in small to mid-sized smelters. After the battery passes through the saw or shear, an employee manually dumps the groups or lead-bearing material into a pile and places the

Table 82.10 • Engineering/administrative controls for lead, by operation.

Process equipment	Exposures	Engineering/administrative controls
Vehicles	Lead dust from roads and splashing water containing lead	Water washdown and keeping areas wetted down. Operator training, prudent work practices and good housekeeping are key elements in minimizing lead emissions when operating mobile equipment. Enclose equipment and provide a positive pressure filtered air system.
Conveyors	Lead dust	It is also preferable to equip belt conveyor systems with self-cleaning tail pulleys or belt wipes if they are used to transport furnace feed materials or flue dusts.
Battery decasing	Lead dust, acid mists	Local exhaust ventilation, general area ventilation
Charge preparation	Lead dust	Local exhaust ventilation, general area ventilation
Blast furnace	Metal fumes and particulates (lead, antimony), heat and noise, carbon monoxide	Local exhaust ventilation, general area ventilation, work/rest regimen, fluids, isolation of noise source; PPE — respiratory protection and hearing protection
Reverberatory furnace	Metal fumes and particulates (lead, antimony), heat and noise	Local exhaust ventilation, general area ventilation, work/rest regimen, fluids, isolation of noise source; PPE — respiratory protection and hearing protection
Refining	Lead particulates and possibly alloying metals and fluxing agents, noise	Local exhaust ventilation, general area ventilation; PPE — hearing protection
Casting	Lead particulates and possibly alloying metals	Local exhaust ventilation, general area ventilation

case and top of the battery into another pile or conveyance system.

- A *tumbler* device. Batteries are placed into a tumbler device after the tops have been sawed/sheared off to separate the groups from the cases. Ribs inside the tumbler dump the groups as it slowly rotates. Groups fall through the slots in the tumbler while the cases are conveyed to the far end and are collected as they exit. Plastic and rubber battery cases and tops are further processed after being separated from the lead bearing material.
- A *sink/float process*. The sink/float process typically is combined with the hammer mill or crushing process for battery breaking. Battery pieces, both lead bearing and cases, are placed in a series of tanks filled with water. Lead bearing material sinks to the bottom of the tanks and is removed by screw conveyor or drag chain while the case material floats and is skimmed off the tank surface.

Industrial batteries which were used to power mobile electric equipment or for other industrial uses are purchased periodically for raw material by most secondary smelters. Many of these batteries have steel cases which require removal by cutting the case open with a cutting torch or a hand-held gas powered saw.

Other purchased lead-bearing scrap

Secondary lead smelters purchase a variety of other scrap materials as raw materials for the smelting process. These materials include battery manufacturing plant scrap, drosses from lead refining, scrap metallic lead such as linotype and cable covering, and tetraethyl lead residues. These types of materials may be charged directly into smelting furnaces or mixed with other charge materials.

Raw material handling and transport

An essential part of the secondary lead smelting process is the handling, transportation and storage of raw material. Materials are transported by fork-lifts, front-end loaders or mechanical conveyors (screw, bucket elevator or belt). The primary method of material transporting in the secondary lead industry is mobile equipment.

Some common mechanical conveyance methods which are used by secondary lead smelters include: belt conveying systems that can be used to transport furnace feed material from storage areas to the furnace charring area; screw conveyors for transport-

ing flue dust from the baghouse to an agglomeration furnace or a storage area or bucket elevators and drag chains/lines.

Smelting

The smelting operation at a secondary lead smelter involves the reduction of lead-bearing scrap into metallic lead in a blast furnace or reverberatory.

Blast furnaces are charged with lead-bearing material, coke (fuel) limestone and iron (flux). These materials are fed into the furnace at the top of the furnace shaft or through a charge door in the side of the shaft neat the top of the furnace. Some environmental hazards associated with blast furnace operations are metal fumes and particulates (especially lead and antimony), heat, noise and carbon monoxide. A variety of charge material conveying mechanisms are used in the secondary lead industry. The skip hoist is probably the most common. Other devices in use include vibratory hoppers, belt conveyors and bucket elevators.

Blast furnace tapping operations involve removing the molten lead and slag from the furnace into moulds or ladles. Some smelters tap metal directly into a holding kettle which keeps the metal molten for refining. The remaining smelters cast the furnace metal into blocks and allow the blocks to solidify.

Blast air for the combustion process enters the blast furnace through tuyères which occasionally begin to fill with accretions and must be physically punched, usually with a steel rod, to keep them from being obstructed. The conventional method to accomplish this task is to remove the cover of the tuyères and insert the steel rod. After the accretions have been punched, the cover is replaced.

Reverberatory furnaces are charged with lead-bearing raw material by a furnace charging mechanism. Reverberatory furnaces in the secondary lead industry typically have a sprung arch or hanging arch constructed of refractory brick. Many of the contaminants and physical hazards associated with reverberatory furnaces are similar to those of blast furnaces. Such mechanisms can be a hydraulic ram, a screw conveyor or other devices similar to those described for blast furnaces.

Reverberatory furnace tapping operations are very similar to blast-furnace tapping operations.

Refining

Lead refining in secondary lead smelters is conducted in indirect fired kettles or pots. Metal from the smelting furnaces is typically

Table 82.11 • Engineering/administrative controls for zinc, by operation.

Process equipment	Exposures	Engineering/administrative controls
Reverberatory sweating	Particulates containing zinc, aluminium, copper, iron, lead, cadmium, manganese and chromium, contaminants from fluxing agents, sulphur oxides, chlorides and fluorides	Local exhaust ventilation, general area ventilation, heat stress—work/rest regimen, fluids
Rotary sweating	Particulates containing zinc, aluminium, copper, iron, lead, cadmium, manganese and chromium, contaminants from fluxing agents, sulphur oxides, chlorides and fluorides	Local exhaust ventilation, general area ventilation, work/rest regimen, fluids
Muffle sweating and kettle (pot) sweating	Particulates containing zinc, aluminium, copper, iron, lead, cadmium, manganese and chromium, contaminants from fluxing agents, sulphur oxides, chlorides and fluorides	Local exhaust ventilation, general area ventilation, work/rest regimen, fluids
Crushing/screening	Zinc oxide, minor amounts of heavy metals, chlorides	Local exhaust ventilation, general area ventilation
Sodium carbonate leaching	Zinc oxide, sodium carbonate, zinc carbonate, zinc hydroxide, hydrogen chloride, zinc chloride	Local exhaust ventilation, general area ventilation
Kettle (pot) melting crucible, reverberatory, electric induction melting	Zinc oxide fumes, ammonia, ammonia chloride, hydrogen chloride, zinc chloride	Local exhaust ventilation, general area ventilation, work/rest regimen, fluids
Alloying	Particulates containing zinc, alloying metals, chlorides; non-specific gases and vapours; heat	Local exhaust ventilation, general area ventilation, work/rest regimen, fluids
Retort distillation, retort distillation/oxidation and muffle distillation	Zinc oxide fumes, other metal particulates, oxides of sulphur	Local exhaust ventilation, general area ventilation, work/rest regimen, fluids
Graphite rod resistor distillation	Zinc oxide fumes, other metal particulates, oxides of sulphur	Local exhaust ventilation, general area ventilation, work/rest regimen, fluids

melted in the kettle, then the content of trace elements is adjusted to produce the desired alloy. Common products are soft (pure) lead and various alloys of hard (antimony) lead.

Virtually all secondary lead refining operations employ manual methods for adding alloying materials to the kettles and employ manual drossing methods. Dross is swept to the rim of the kettle and removed by shovel or large spoon into a container.

Table 82.10 lists exposures and controls for lead reclamation operations.

Zinc reclamation

The secondary zinc industry utilizes new clippings, skimmings and ashes, die-cast skimmings, galvanizers' dross, flue dust and chemical residue as sources of zinc. Most of the new scrap processed is zinc- and copper-based alloys from galvanizing and die-casting pots. Included in the old scrap category are old zinc engravers' plates, die castings, and rod and die scrap. The processes are as follows:

- *Reverberatory sweating.* Sweating furnaces are used to separate zinc from other metals by controlling the furnace temperature. Scrap die-cast products, such as automobile grilles and licence plate frames, and zinc skins or residues are starting materials for the process. The scrap is charged to the furnace, flux is added and the contents melted. The high-melting residue is removed and the molten zinc flows out of the furnace directly to subsequent processes, such as melting, refining or alloying, or to collecting vessels. Metal contaminants include zinc, aluminium, copper, iron, lead, cadmium, manganese and chromium. Other contaminants are fluxing agents, sulphur oxides, chlorides and fluorides.
- *Rotary sweating.* In this process zinc scrap, die-cast products, residues and skimmings are charged to a direct-fired furnace and melted. The melt is skimmed, and zinc metal is collected in kettles situated outside the furnace. Unmeltable material, the slag, is then removed prior to recharging. The metal from this

process is sent to distillation or alloying process. Contaminants are similar to those of reverberatory sweating.
- *Muffle sweating and kettle (pot) sweating.* In these processes zinc scrap, die-vapour-cast products, residues and skimmings are charged to the muffle furnace, the material sweated and the sweated zinc is sent to refining or alloying processes. The residue is removed by a shaker screen which separates the dross from the slag. Contaminants are similar to those of reverberatory sweating.
- *Crushing/screening.* Zinc residues are pulverized or crushed to break down physical bonds between metallic zinc and contaminant fluxes. The reduced material is then separated in a screening or pneumatic classification step. Crushing can produce zinc oxide and minor amounts of heavy metals and chlorides.
- *Sodium carbonate leaching.* Residues are chemically treated to leach out and convert zinc to zinc oxide. The scrap is first crushed and washed. In this step, the zinc is leached out of the material. The aqueous portion is treated with sodium carbonate, causing zinc to precipitate. The precipitate is dried and calcined to yield crude zinc oxide. The zinc oxide is then reduced to zinc metal. Various zinc salt contaminants can be produced.
- *Kettle (pot), crucible, reverberatory, electric induction melting.* The scrap is charged to the furnace and fluxes are added. The bath is agitated to form a dross that can be skimmed from the surface. After the furnace has been skimmed the zinc metal is poured into ladles or moulds. Zinc oxide fumes, ammonia and ammonium chloride, hydrogen chloride and zinc chloride can be produced.
- *Alloying.* The function of this process is to produce zinc alloys from pre-treated scrap zinc metal by adding to it in a refining kettle fluxes and alloying agents either in the solidified or molten form. The contents are then mixed, the dross skimmed, and the metal is cast into various shapes. Particulates containing zinc, alloying metals, chlorides, non-specific gases and vapours, as well as heat, are potential exposures.

Table 82.12 • Engineering/administrative controls for magnesium, by operation.

Process equipment	Exposures	Engineering/administrative controls
Scrap sorting	Dust	Water washdown
Open pot melting	Fumes and dust, a high potential for fires	Local exhaust ventilation and general area ventilation and work practices
Casting	Dust and fumes, heat and a high potential for fires	Local exhaust ventilation, general area ventilation, work/rest regimen, fluids

- *Muffle distillation.* The muffle distillation process is used to reclaim zinc from alloys and to manufacture pure zinc ingots. The process is semi-continuous which involves charging molten zinc from a melting pot or sweating furnace to the muffle section and vaporizing the zinc and condensing the vaporized zinc and tapping from the condenser to moulds. The residue is removed periodically from the muffle.

- *Retort distillation/oxidation and muffle distillation/oxidation.* The product of the retort distillation/oxidation and muffle distillation/oxidation processes is zinc oxide. The process is similar to retort distillation through the vaporization step, but, in this process, the condenser is bypassed and combustion air is added. The vapour is discharged through an orifice into an air stream. Spontaneous combustion occurs inside a refractory vapour-lined chamber. The product is carried by the combustion gases and excess air into a baghouse where the product is collected. Excess air is present to insure complete oxidation and to cool the product. Each of these distillation processes can lead to zinc oxide fume exposures, as well as other metal particulate and oxides of sulphur exposure.

Table 82.11 lists exposures and controls for zinc reclamation operations.

Magnesium reclamation

Old scrap is obtained from sources such as scrap automobile and aircraft parts and old and obsolete lithographic plates, as well as some sludges from primary magnesium smelters. New scrap consists of clippings, turnings, borings, skimmings, slags, drosses and defective articles from sheet mills and fabrication plants. The greatest danger in handling magnesium is that of fire. Small fragments of the metal can readily be ignited by a spark or flame.

- *Hand sorting.* This process is used to separate magnesium and magnesium-alloy fractions from other metals present in the scrap. The scrap is spread out manually, sorted on the basis of weight.

- *Open pot melting.* This process is used to separate magnesium from contaminants in the sorted scrap. Scrap is added to a crucible, heated and a flux consisting of a mixture of calcium, sodium and potassium chlorides is added. The molten magnesium is then cast into ingots.

Table 82.12 lists exposures and controls for magnesium reclamation operations.

Mercury reclamation

The major sources for mercury are dental amalgams, scrap mercury batteries, sludges from electrolytic processes that use mercury as a catalyst, mercury from dismantled chlor-alkali plants and mercury-containing instruments. Mercury vapour can contaminate each of these processes.

- *Crushing.* The crushing process is used to release residual mercury from metal, plastic and glass containers. After the containers are crushed, the contaminated liquid mercury is sent to the filtering process.

- *Filtration.* Insoluble impurities such as dirt are removed by passing the mercury-vapour bearing scrap through a filter media. The filtered mercury is fed to the oxygenation process and the solids which do not pass through the filters are sent to retort distillation.

- *Vacuum distillation.* Vacuum distillation is employed to refine contaminated mercury when the vapour pressures of the impurities are substantially lower than that of mercury. Mercury charge is vaporized in a heating pot and the vapours are condensed using a water-cooled condenser. Purified mercury is collected and sent to the bottling operation. The residue remaining in the heating pot is sent to the retorting process to recover the trace amounts of mercury that were not recovered in the vacuum distillation process.

- *Solution purification.* This process removes metallic and organic contaminants by washing the raw liquid mercury with a dilute acid. The steps involved are: leaching the raw liquid mercury with dilute nitric acid to separate metallic impurities; agitating the acid-mercury with compressed air to provide good mixing; decanting to separate the mercury from the acid; washing with water to remove the residual acid; and filtering the mercury in a medium such as activated carbon or silica gel to remove the last traces of moisture. In addition to mercury vapour there can be exposure to solvents, organic chemicals and acid mists.

- *Oxygenation.* This process refines the filtered mercury by removing metallic impurities by oxidation with sparging air. The

Table 82.13 • Engineering/administrative controls for mercury, by operation.

Process equipment	Exposures	Engineering/administrative controls
Crushing	Volatile mercury	Local exhaust; PPE—respiratory protection
Filtration	Volatile mercury	Local exhaust ventilation; PPE—respiratory protection
Vacuum distillation	Volatile mercury	Local exhaust ventilation; PPE—respiratory protection
Solution purification	Volatile mercury, solvents, organics and acid mists	Local exhaust ventilation, general area ventilation; PPE—respiratory protection
Oxidation	Volatile mercury	Local exhaust ventilation; PPE—respiratory protection
Retorting	Volatile mercury	Local exhaust ventilation; PPE—respiratory protection

Table 82.14 • Engineering/administrative controls for nickel, by operation.

Process equipment	Exposures	Engineering/administrative controls
Sorting	Dust	Local exhaust and solvent substitution
Degreasing	Solvent	Local exhaust ventilation and solvent substitution and/or recovery, general area ventilation
Smelting	Fumes, dust, noise, heat	Local exhaust ventilation, work/rest regimen, fluids; PPE—respiratory protection and hearing protection
Refining	Fumes, dust, heat, noise	Local exhaust ventilation, general area ventilation, work/rest regimen, fluids; PPE—respiratory protection and hearing protection
Casting	Heat, metal fumes	Local exhaust ventilation, general area ventilation, work/rest regimen, fluids

oxidation process involves two steps, sparging and filtering. In the sparging step, contaminated mercury is agitated with air in a closed vessel to oxidize the metallic contaminants. After sparging, the mercury is filtered in a charcoal bed to remove the solid metal oxides.

• *Retorting.* The retorting process is used to produce pure mercury by volatilizing the mercury found in solid mercury-bearing scrap. The steps involved in retorting are: heating the scrap with an external heat source in a closed still pot or stack of trays to vaporize the mercury; condensing the mercury vapour in water-cooled condensers; collecting the condensed mercury in a collecting vessel.

Table 82.13 lists exposures and controls for mercury reclamation operations.

Nickel reclamation

The principal raw materials for nickel reclamation are nickel-, copper- and aluminium-vapour based alloys, which can be found as old or new scrap. Old scrap comprises alloys that are salvaged from machinery and airplane parts, while new scrap refers to sheet scrap, turnings and solids which are by-products of the manufacture of alloy products. The following steps are involved in nickel reclamation:

• *Sorting.* The scrap is inspected and manually separated from the non-metallic and non-nickel materials. Sorting produces dust exposures.
• *Degreasing.* Nickel scrap is degreased by using trichloroethylene. The mixture is filtrated or centrifuged to separate the nickel scrap. The spent solvent solution of trichloroethylene and grease goes through a solvent recovery system. There can be solvent exposure during degreasing.
• *Smelting (electric arc or rotary reverberatory) furnace.* Scrap is charged to an electric arc furnace and a reducing agent added, usually lime. The charge is melted and is either cast into ingots or sent

directly to a reactor for additional refining. Fumes, dust, noise and heat exposures are possible.

• *Reactor refining.* The molten metal is introduced into a reactor where cold-base scrap and pig nickel are added, followed by lime and silica. Alloying materials such as manganese, columbium or titanium are then added to produce the desired alloy composition. Fumes, dust, noise and heat exposures are possible.
• *Ingot casting.* This process involves casting the molten metal from the smelting furnace or the refining reactor into ingots. The metal is poured into moulds and allowed to cool. The ingots are removed from the moulds. Heat and metal fume exposures are possible.

Exposures and control measures for nickel reclamation operations are listed in table 82.14.

Precious metals reclamation

The raw materials for the precious metal industry consist of both old and new scrap. Old scrap includes electronic components from obsolete military and civilian equipment and scrap from the dental industry. New scrap is generated during the fabrication and manufacturing of precious metal products. The products are the elemental metals such as gold, silver, platinum and palladium. Precious metal processing includes the following steps:

• *Hand sorting and shredding.* Precious metal-bearing scrap is hand sorted and crushed and shredded in a hammer mill. Hammer mills are noisy.
• *Incineration process.* Sorted scrap is incinerated to remove paper, plastic and organic liquid contaminants. Organic chemicals, combustion gases and dust exposures are possible.
• *Blast-furnace smelting.* Treated scrap is charged to a blast furnace, along with coke, flux and recycled slag metal oxides. The charge is melted and slagged, producing black copper which contains the precious metals. The hard slag that is formed

Table 82.15 • Engineering/administrative controls for precious metals, by operation.

Process equipment	Exposures	Engineering/administrative controls
Sorting and shredding	Hammermill is a potential noise hazard	Noise control material; PPE—hearing protection
Incineration	Organics, combustion gases and dust	Local exhaust ventilation and general area ventilation
Blast furnace smelting	Dust, noise	Local exhaust ventilation; PPE—hearing protection and respiratory protection
Electrolytic refining	Acid mists	Local exhaust ventilation, general area ventilation
Chemical refining	Acid	Local exhaust ventilation, general area ventilation; PPE—acid-resistant clothing, chemical goggles and face shield

82. METAL PROCESSING AND METAL WORKING INDUSTRY

Table 82.16 • Engineering/administrative controls for cadmium, by operation.

Process equipment	Exposures	Engineering/administrative controls
Scrap degreasing	Solvents and cadmium dust	Local exhaust and solvent substitution
Alloy smelting/refining	Products of oil and gas combustion, zinc fumes, cadmium dust and fumes	Local exhaust ventilation and general area ventilation; PPE—respiratory protection
Retort distillation	Cadmium fumes	Local exhaust ventilation; PPE—respiratory protection
Melting/dezincing	Cadmium fumes and dust, zinc fumes and dust, zinc chloride, chlorine, hydrogen chloride, heat stress	Local exhaust ventilation, general area ventilation, work/rest regimen, fluids; PPE—respiratory protection
Casting	Cadmium dust and fumes, heat	Local exhaust ventilation, general area ventilation, work/rest regimen, fluids; PPE—respiratory protection

contains most of the slag impurities. Dust and noise may be present.

- *Converter smelting.* This process is designed to further purify the black copper by blowing air through the melt in a converter. Slag-containing metal contaminants are removed and recycled to the blast furnace. The copper bullion containing the precious metals is cast into moulds.
- *Electrolytic refining.* Copper bullion serves as the anode of an electrolytic cell. Pure copper thus plates out on the cathode while the precious metals fall to the bottom of the cell and are collected as slimes. The electrolyte used is copper sulphate. Acid mist exposures are possible.
- *Chemical refining.* The precious metal slime from the electrolytic refining process is chemically treated to recover the individual metals. Cyanide-based processes are used to recover gold and silver, which can also be recovered by dissolving them in *aqua regia* solution and/or nitric acid, followed by precipitation with ferrous sulphate or sodium chloride to recover the gold and silver, respectively. The platinum-group metals can be recovered by dissolving them in molten lead, which is then treated with nitric acid and leaves a residue from which the platinum-group metals can be selectively precipitated. The precious metal precipitates are then either melted or ignited in order to collect the gold and silver as grains and the platinum metals as sponge. There can be acid exposures.

Exposures and controls are listed, by operation, in table 82.15 (see also "Gold smelting and refining" in this chapter).

Cadmium reclamation
Old cadmium-bearing scrap includes cadmium-plated parts from junked vehicles and boats, household appliances, hardware and fasteners, cadmium batteries, cadmium contacts from switches

and relays and other used cadmium alloys. New scrap is normally cadmium vapour bearing rejects and contaminated by-products from industries which handle the metals. The reclamation processes are:

- *Pre-treatment.* The scrap pre-treatment step involves the vapour degreasing of alloy scrap. Solvent vapours generated by heating recycled solvents are circulated through a vessel containing scrap alloys. The solvent and stripped grease are then condensed and separated with the solvent being recycled. There can be exposure to cadmium dust and solvents.
- *Smelting/refining.* In the smelting/refining operation, pre-treated alloy scrap or elemental cadmium scrap is processed to remove any impurities and produce cadmium alloy or elemental cadmium. Products of oil and gas combustion exposures and zinc and cadmium dust may be present.
- *Retort distillation.* Degreased scrap alloy is charged to a retort and heated to produce cadmium vapours which are subsequently collected in a condenser. The molten metal is then ready for casting. Cadmium dust exposures are possible.
- *Melting/dezincing.* Cadmium metal is charged to a melting pot and heated to the molten stage. If zinc is present in the metal, fluxes and chlorinating agents are added to remove the zinc. Among potential exposures are cadmium fumes and dust, zinc fumes and dust, zinc chloride, chlorine, hydrogen chloride and heat.
- *Casting.* The casting operation forms the desired product line from the purified cadmium alloy or cadmium metal produced in the previous step. Casting can produce cadmium dust and fumes and heat.

Exposures in cadmium reclamation processes and the necessary controls are summarized in table 82.16.

Table 82.17 • Engineering/administrative controls for selenium, by operation.

Process equipment	Exposures	Engineering/administrative controls
Scrap pretreatment	Dust	Local exhaust
Retort smelting	Combustion gases and dust, noise	Local exhaust ventilation and general area ventilation; PPE—hearing protection; control of burner noise
Refining	SO_2, acid mist	Local exhaust ventilation; PPE—chemical goggles
Distillation	Dust and combustion products	Local exhaust ventilation, general area ventilation
Quenching	Metal dust	Local exhaust ventilation, general area ventilation
Casting	Selenium fumes	Local exhaust ventilation, general area ventilation

Table 82.18 • Engineering/administrative controls for cobalt, by operation.

Process equipment	Exposures	Engineering/administrative controls
Hand sorting	Dust	Water washdown
Degreasing	Solvents	Solvent recovery, local exhaust and solvent substitution
Blasting	Dust—toxicity dependent upon the grit used	Local exhaust ventilation; PPE for physical hazard and respiratory protection depending on grit used
Pickling and chemical treatment process	Acid mists	Local exhaust ventilation, general area ventilation; PPE—respiratory protection
Vacuum melting	Heavy metals	Local exhaust ventilation, general area ventilation
Casting	Heat	Local exhaust ventilation, general area ventilation, work/rest regimen, fluids

Selenium reclamation

Raw materials for this segment are used xerographic copying cylinders and scrap generated during the manufacture of selenium rectifiers. Selenium dusts may be present throughout. Distillation and retort smelting can produce combustion gases and dust. Retort smelting is noisy. Sulphur dioxide mist and acid mist are present in refining. Metal dusts can be produced from casting operations (see table 82.17). The reclamation processes are as follows:

- *Scrap pre-treatment.* This process separates selenium by mechanical processes such as the hammer mill or shot blasting.
- *Retort smelting.* This process purifies and concentrates pretreated scrap in a retort distillation operation by melting the scrap and separating selenium from the impurities by distillation.
- *Refining.* This process achieves a purification of scrap selenium based on leaching with a suitable solvent such as aqueous sodium sulphite. Insoluble impurities are removed by filtration and the filtrate is treated to precipitate selenium.
- *Distillation.* This process produces a high vapour purity selenium. The selenium is melted, distilled and the selenium vapours are condensed and transferred as molten selenium to a product formation operation.

- *Quenching.* This process is used to produce purified selenium shot and powder. The selenium melt is used in producing a shot. The shot is then dried. The steps required to produce powder are the same, except that selenium vapour, rather than molten selenium, is the material which is quenched.
- *Casting.* This process is used to produce selenium ingots or other shapes from the molten selenium. These shapes are produced by pouring molten selenium into moulds of the proper size and shape and cooling and solidifying the melt.

Cobalt reclamation

The sources of cobalt scrap are super alloy grindings and turnings, and obsolete or worn engine parts and turbine blades. The processes of reclamation are:

- *Hand sorting.* Raw scrap is hand sorted to identify and separate the cobalt-base, nickel-base and non-processable components. This is a dusty operation.
- *Degreasing.* Sorted dirty scrap is charged to a degreasing unit where vapours of perchloroethylene are circulated. This solvent removes the grease and oil on the scrap. The solvent-oil-grease vapour mixture is then condensed and the solvent is recovered. Solvent exposures are possible.

Table 82.19 • Engineering/administrative controls for tin, by operation.

Process equipment	Exposures	Engineering/administrative controls
Dealuminization	Sodium hydroxide	Local exhaust; PPE—chemical goggles and/or face shield
Batch mixing	Dust	Local exhaust ventilation and general area ventilation
Chemical detinning	Caustic	Local exhaust ventilation; PPE—chemical goggles and/or face shield
Dross smelting	Dust and heat	Local exhaust ventilation, general area ventilation, work/rest regimen, fluids
Dust leaching and filtration	Dust	Local exhaust ventilation, general area ventilation
Settling and leaf filtration	None identified	None identified
Evapocentrifugation	None identified	None identified
Electrolytic refining	Acid mist	Local exhaust ventilation and general area ventilation; PPE—chemical goggles and/or face shield
Acidification and filtration	Acid mists	Local exhaust ventilation and general area ventilation; PPE—chemical goggles and/or face shield
Fire refining	Heat	Work/rest regimen, PPE
Smelting	Combustion gases, fumes and dust, heat	Local exhaust ventilation and general area ventilation, work/rest regimen, PPE
Calcining	Dust, fumes, heat	Local exhaust ventilation and general area ventilation work/rest regimen, PPE
Kettle refining	Dust, fumes, heat	Local exhaust ventilation and general area ventilation, work/rest regimen, PPE

Table 82.20 • Engineering/administrative controls for titanium, by operation.

Process equipment	Exposures	Engineering/administrative controls
Solvent degreasing	Solvent	Local exhaust and solvent recovery
Pickling	Acids	Face shields, aprons, long sleeves, safety glasses or goggles
Electrorefining	None known	None known
Smelting	Volatile metals, noise	Local exhaust ventilation and control of noise from burners; PPE — hearing protection
Casting	Heat	PPE

- *Blasting.* Degreased scrap is blasted with grit to remove dirt, oxides and rust. Dusts can be present, depending on the grit used.
- *Pickling and chemical treatment process.* Scrap from the blasting operation is treated with acids to remove residual rust and oxide contaminants. Acid mists are a possible exposure.
- *Vacuum melting.* Cleaned scrap is charged to a vacuum furnace and melted by electric arc or induction furnace. There can be exposure to heavy metals.
- *casting.* Molten alloy is cast into ingots. Heat stress is possible.

See table 82.18 for a summary of exposures and controls for cobalt reclamation.

Tin reclamation

The major sources of raw materials are tin-plated steel trimmings, rejects from tin-can manufacturing companies, rejected plating coils from the steel industry, tin drosses and sludges, solder drosses and sludges, used bronze and bronze rejects and metal type scrap. Tin dust and acid mists can be found in many of the processes.

- *Dealuminization.* In this process hot sodium hydroxide is used to leach aluminium from tin-can scrap by contacting the scrap with hot sodium hydroxide, separating the sodium aluminate solution from the scrap residue, pumping the sodium aluminate to a refining operation to recover soluble tin and recovering the dealuminized tin scrap for feed.
- *Batch mixing.* This process is a mechanical operation which prepares a feed suitable for charging to the smelting furnace by mixing drosses and sludges with a significant tin content.
- *Chemical detinning.* This process extracts the tin in scrap. A hot solution of sodium hydroxide and sodium nitrite or nitrate is added to dealuminized or raw scrap. Draining and pumping the solution to a refining/casting process are performed when the detinning reaction is complete. The detinned scrap is then washed.
- *Dross smelting.* This process is used to partially purify drosses and produce crude furnace metal by melting the charge, tapping the crude furnace metal and tapping the mattes and slags
- *Dust leaching and filtration.* This process removes the zinc and chlorine values from flue dust by leaching with sulphuric acid to remove zinc and chlorine, filtering the resulting mixture to separate the acid and dissolved zinc and chlorine from the leached dust, drying the leached dust in a dryer and conveying the tin and lead rich dust back to the batch mixing process.
- *Settling and leaf filtration.* This process purifies the sodium stannate solution produced in the chemical detinning process. Im-

purities such as silver, mercury, copper, cadmium, some iron, cobalt and nickel are precipitated as sulphides.

- *Evapocentrifugation.* The sodium stannate is concentrated from the purified solution by evaporation, crystallization of sodium stannate and recovery of sodium stannate is by centrifugation.
- *Electrolytic refining.* This process produces cathodic-pure tin from the purified sodium stannate solution by passing the sodium stannate solution through electrolytic cells, removing the cathodes after the tin has been deposited and stripping the tin from the cathodes.
- *Acidification and filtration.* This process produces a hydrated tin oxide from the purified sodium stannate solution. This hydrated oxide can either be processed to produce the anhydrous oxide or smelted to produce elemental tin. The hydrated oxide is neutralized with sulphuric acid to form the hydrated tin oxide and filtered to separate the hydrate as filter cake.
- *Fire refining.* This process produces purified tin from the cathodic tin by melting the charge, removing the impurities as slag and dross, pouring the molten metal and casting the metallic tin.
- *Smelting.* This process is used to produce tin when electrolytic refining is not feasible. This is accomplished by reducing the hydrated tin oxide with a reducing agent, melting the tin metal formed, skimming the dross, pouring the molten tin and casting the molten tin.
- *Calcining.* This process converts the hydrated tin oxides to anhydrous stannic oxide by calcining the hydrate and removing and packaging the stannic oxides.
- *Kettle refining.* This process is used to purify crude furnace metal by charging a preheated kettle with it, drying the dross to remove the impurities as slag and matte, fluxing with sulphur to remove copper as matte, fluxing with aluminium to remove antimony and casting molten metal into desired shapes.

See table 82.19 for a summary of exposures and controls for tin reclamation.

Titanium reclamation

The two primary sources of titanium scrap are the home and titanium consumers. Home scrap which is generated by the milling and manufacturing of titanium products includes trim sheets, plank sheet, cuttings, turnings and borings. Consumer scrap consists of recycled titanium products. The reclamation operations include:

- *Degreasing.* In this process sized scrap is treated with vapourized organic solvent (e.g., trichloroethylene). Contaminant grease and oil are stripped from the scrap by the solvent vapour. The solvent is recirculated until it can no longer has an ability to degrease. Spent solvent can then be regenerated. The scrap can also be degreased by steam and detergent.
- *Pickling.* The acid-pickling process removes oxide scale from the degreasing operation by leaching with a solution of hydrochloric and hydrofluoric acids. The acid treatment scrap is washed with water and dried.
- *Electrorefining.* Electrorefining is a titanium scrap pre-treatment process which electro-refines scrap in a fused salt.
- *Smelting.* Pre-treated titanium scrap and alloying agents are melted in a electric-arc vacuum furnace to form a titanium alloy. The input materials include pre-treated titanium scrap and alloying materials such as aluminium, vanadium, molybdenum, tin, zirconium, palladium, columbium and chromium.
- *Casting.* Molten titanium is poured into moulds. The titanium solidifies into a bar called an ingot.

Controls for exposures in titanium reclamation procedures are listed in table 82.20.

ENVIRONMENTAL ISSUES IN METAL FINISHING AND INDUSTRIAL COATINGS

Stewart Forbes

Metal Finishing

The surface treatment of metals increases their durability and improves their appearance. A single product may undergo more than one surface treatment—for example, an auto body panel may be phosphated, primed and painted. This article deals with the processes used for surface treatment of metals and the methods used to reduce their environmental impact.

Operating a metal finishing business requires cooperation between company management, employees, government and the community to effectively minimize the environmental effect of the operations. Society is concerned with the amount and the long-term effects of pollution entering the air, water and land environment. *Effective environmental management* is established through detailed knowledge of all elements, chemicals, metals, processes and outputs.

Pollution prevention planning shifts the environmental management philosophy from reacting to problems to anticipating solutions focusing on chemical substitution, process change and internal recycling, using the following planning sequence:

1. Initiate pollution prevention across all aspects of the business.
2. Identify waste streams.
3. Set priorities for action.
4. Establish root cause of the waste.
5. Identify and implement changes that reduce or eliminate the waste.
6. Measure the results.

Continuous improvement is achieved by setting new priorities for action and repeating the sequence of actions.

Detailed process documentation will identify the waste streams and allow priorities to be set for waste reduction opportunities. Informed decisions about potential changes will encourage:

- easy and practical operational improvements
- process changes involving customers and suppliers
- changes to less harmful activities where possible
- reuse and recycling where change is not practical
- using landfilling of hazardous wastes only as a last resort.

Major processes and standard operating processes

Cleaning is required because all metal finishing processes require that parts to be finished be free from organic and inorganic soils, including oils, scale, buffing and polishing compounds. The three basic types of cleaners in use are solvents, vapour degreasers and alkaline detergents.

Solvents and vapour degreasing cleaning methods have been almost totally replaced by alkaline materials where the subsequent processes are wet. Solvents and vapour degreasers are still in use where parts must be clean and dry with no further wet processing. Solvents such as terpenes are in some instances replacing volatile solvents. Less toxic materials such as 1,1,1-trichloroethane have been substituted for more hazardous materials in vapour degreasing (although this solvent is being phased out as an ozone depleter).

Alkaline cleaning cycles usually include a soak immersion followed by an anodic electroclean, followed by a weak acid immersion. Non-etching, non-silicated cleaners are typically used to clean aluminium. The acids are typically sulphuric, hydrochloric and nitric.

Anodizing, an electrochemical process to thicken the oxide film on the metal surface (frequently applied to aluminium), treats the parts with dilute chromic or sulphuric acid solutions.

Conversion coating is used to provide a base for subsequent painting or to passivate for protection against oxidation. With chromating, parts are immersed in a hexavalent chrome solution with active organic and inorganic agents. For phosphating, parts are immersed in dilute phosphoric acid with other agents. Passivating is accomplished through immersion in nitric acid or nitric acid with sodium dichromate.

Electroless plating involves a deposition of metal without electricity. Copper or nickel electroless deposition is used in the manufacture of printed circuit boards.

Electroplating involves the deposition of a thin coat of metal (zinc, nickel, copper, chromium, cadmium, tin, brass, bronze, lead,

Figure 82.7 • Inputs and outputs for a typical electroplating line.

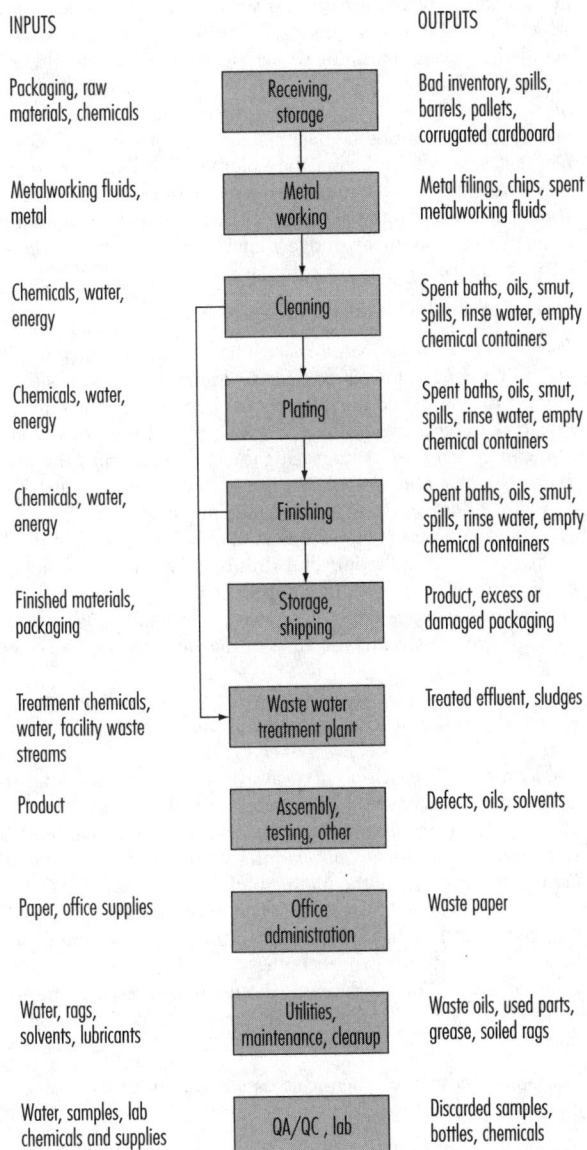

INPUTS		OUTPUTS
Packaging, raw materials, chemicals	Receiving, storage	Bad inventory, spills, barrels, pallets, corrugated cardboard
Metalworking fluids, metal	Metal working	Metal filings, chips, spent metalworking fluids
Chemicals, water, energy	Cleaning	Spent baths, oils, smut, spills, rinse water, empty chemical containers
Chemicals, water, energy	Plating	Spent baths, oils, smut, spills, rinse water, empty chemical containers
Chemicals, water, energy	Finishing	Spent baths, oils, smut, spills, rinse water, empty chemical containers
Finished materials, packaging	Storage, shipping	Product, excess or damaged packaging
Treatment chemicals, water, facility waste streams	Waste water treatment plant	Treated effluent, sludges
Product	Assembly, testing, other	Defects, oils, solvents
Paper, office supplies	Office administration	Waste paper
Water, rags, solvents, lubricants	Utilities, maintenance, cleanup	Waste oils, used parts, grease, soiled rags
Water, samples, lab chemicals and supplies	QA/QC, lab	Discarded samples, bottles, chemicals

tin-lead, gold, silver and other metals such as platinum) on a substrate (ferrous or non-ferrous). Process baths include metals in solution in acid, alkaline neutral and alkaline cyanide formulations (see figure 82.7).

Chemical milling and etching are controlled dissolution immersion processes using chemical reagents and etchants. Aluminium is typically etched in caustic prior to anodizing or chemically brightened in a solution which could contain nitric, phosphoric and sulphuric acids.

Hot-dip coatings involve the application of metal to a workpiece by immersion in molten metal (zinc or tin galvanizing of steel).

Good management practices

Important safety, health and environmental improvements can be achieved through process improvements, such as:

- using counter-current rinsing and conductivity controls
- increasing drainage time
- using more or better wetting agents
- keeping process temperatures as high as possible to lower viscosity, thus increasing drag-out recovery (i.e., recovery of solution left on metal)
- using air agitation in rinsing to increase rinsing efficiency
- using plastic balls in plating tanks to reduce misting
- using improved filtration on plating tanks to reduce the frequency of purification treatment
- placing a curb around all process areas to contain spills
- using separate treatments for recoverable metals such as nickel
- installing recovery systems such as ion exchange, atmospheric evaporation, vacuum evaporation, electrolytic recovery, reverse osmosis and electrodialysis
- complementing drag-out recovery systems with reductions in drag-in of contaminants and improved cleaning systems
- using modern inventory controls to reduce waste and workplace hazards
- applying standard procedures (i.e., written procedures, regular operating reviews and sound operating logs) to provide the basis for a sound environmental management structure.

Environmental planning for specific wastes

Specific waste streams, usually spent plating solutions, can be reduced by:

- *Filtration.* Cartridge or diatomaceous earth filters can be used to remove the accumulation of solids, which reduce the efficiency of the process.
- *Carbon treatment* can be used to remove organic contaminants (most commonly applied in nickel plating, copper electroplating and zinc and cadmium plating).
- *Purified water.* The natural contaminants in water make-up and rinses (e.g., calcium, iron, magnesium, manganese, chlorine and carbonates) can be removed by using deionization, distillation or reverse osmosis. Improving rinse water efficiency reduces the volume of bath sludges requiring treatment.
- *Cyanide bath carbonate freezing.* Lowering the bath temperature to −3 °C crystallizes the carbonates formed in cyanide bath by the breakdown of cyanide, excessive anode current densities and the adsorption of carbon dioxide from the air and facilitates their removal.
- *Precipitation.* Removal of metal contaminants entering the bath as impurities in anodes can be achieved through precipitation with barium cyanide, barium hydroxide, calcium hydroxide, calcium sulphate or calcium cyanide.
- *Hexavalent chrome alternatives.* Hexavalent chromium can be replaced with trivalent chromium plating solutions for decorative plating. Chrome conversion coatings for paint pretreatments

can sometimes be replaced by non-chrome conversion coatings or no-rinse chrome chemistries.

- *Non-chelated process chemistries.* Instead of chelators being added to process baths to control the concentration of free ions in the solution, non-chelated process chemistries can be used so that it may not be necessary to keep metals in solution. These metals can be allowed to precipitate and can be removed by continuous filtration.
- *Non-cyanide process chemicals.* Waste streams containing free cyanide are typically treated using hypochlorite or chlorine to accomplish oxidation, and complex cyanides are commonly precipitated using ferrous sulphate. Using non-cyanide process chemistries both eliminates a treatment step and reduces the sludge volume.
- *Solvent degreasing.* Hot alkaline cleaning baths can be used in place of solvent degreasing of workpieces before processing. The effectiveness of alkaline cleaners can be enhanced by applying electrocurrent or ultrasonics. The benefits of avoiding solvent vapours and sludges often outweigh any additional operating costs.
- *Alkaline cleaners.* Having to discard alkaline cleaners when the accumulation of oil, grease and soils from use reaches a level which impairs the cleaning efficiency of the bath can be avoided by using skimming devices to remove free-floating oils, settling devices or cartridge filters to remove particulates and oil-water coalescers and by using microfiltration or ultrafiltration to remove emulsified oils.
- *Drag-out reduction.* Reducing the volume of drag-out from process baths serves to reduce the amount of valuable process chemicals that contaminates the rinse water, which in turn reduces the amount of sludge that is generated by a conventional metal precipitation treatment process.

Several methods of reducing drag-out include:

- *Process bath operating concentration.* The chemical concentration should be kept as low as possible to minimize the viscosity (for quicker draining) and the quantity of chemicals (in the film).
- *Process bath operating temperature.* The viscosity of the process solution can be reduced by increasing the bath temperature.
- *Wetting agents.* The surface tension of the solution can be reduced by adding wetting agents to the process bath.
- *Workpiece positioning.* The workpiece should be positioned on the rack so that the adhering film drains freely and does not get trapped in grooves or cavities.
- *Withdrawal or drainage time.* The faster a workpiece is removed from the process bath, the thicker the film on the workpiece surface.
- *Air knives.* Blowing air at the workpiece as the workpiece rack is raised above the process tank can improve drainage and drying.
- *Spray rinses.* These can be used above heated baths so that the rinse flow rate equals the evaporation rate of the tank.
- *Plating baths.* Carbonates and organic contaminants should be removed to prevent accumulation of contamination that increases the viscosity of the plating bath.
- *Drainage boards.* The spaces between process tanks should be covered with drainage boards to capture process solutions and to return them to the process bath.
- *Drag-out tanks.* The workpieces should be placed in drag-out tanks ("static rinse" tanks) before the standard rinsing operation.

Drag-out recovery of chemicals uses a variety of technologies. These include:

- *Evaporation.* Atmospheric evaporators are most common, and vacuum evaporators offer energy savings.

- *Ion exchange* is used for chemical recovery of rinse water.
- *Electrowinning*. This is an electrolytic process whereby the dissolved metals in the solution are reduced and deposited on the cathode. The deposited metal is then recovered.
- *Electrodialysis*. This utilizes ion-permeable membranes and applied current in order to separate ionic species from the solution.
- *Reverse osmosis*. This utilizes a semi-permeable membrane to produce purified water and a concentrated ionic solution. High pressure is used to force the water through the membrane, while most dissolved salts are retained by the membrane.

Rinse water

Most of the hazardous waste produced in a metal finishing facility comes from waste water generated by the rinsing operations that follow cleaning and plating. By increasing rinse efficiency, a facility can significantly reduce waste water flow.

Two basic strategies improve rinsing efficiency. First, turbulence can be generated between the workpiece and the rinse water through spray rinses and rinse water agitation. Movement of the rack or forced water or air are used. Second, the contact time between the workpiece and the rinse water can be increased. Multiple rinse tanks set countercurrent in series will reduce the amount of rinse water used.

Industrial Coatings

The term *coatings* includes paints, varnishes, lacquers, enamels and shellacs, putties, wood fillers and sealers, paint and varnish removers, paint brush cleaners and allied paint products. Liquid coatings contain pigments and additives dispersed in a liquid binder and solvent mixture. Pigments are inorganic or organic compounds that provide coating colour and opacity and influence coating flow and durability. Pigments often contain heavy metals such as cadmium, lead, zinc, chromium and cobalt. The binder increases coating adhesiveness, cohesiveness and consistency and is the primary component that remains on the surface when coating is completed. Binders include a variety of oils, resins, rubbers and polymers. Additives such as fillers and extenders may be added to coatings to reduce manufacturing costs and increase coating durability.

The types of organic solvents used in coatings include aliphatic hydrocarbons, aromatic hydrocarbons, esters, ketones, glycol ethers and alcohols. Solvents disperse or dissolve the binders and decrease the coating viscosity and thickness. Solvents used in coatings formulations are hazardous because many are human carcinogens and are flammable or explosive. Most solvents contained in a coating evaporate when the coating cures, which generates volatile organic compound (VOC) emissions. VOC emissions are becoming increasingly regulated because of the negative effects on human health and the environment. Environmental concerns associated with conventional ingredients, coating application technologies and coating wastes are a driving force for developing pollution prevention alternatives.

Most coatings are used on architectural, industrial or special products. Architectural coatings are used in buildings and building products and for decorative and protective services such as varnishes to protect wood. Industrial facilities incorporate coating operations in various production processes. The automotive, metal can, farm machinery, coil coating, wood and metal furniture and fixtures, and household appliance industries are the major industrial coatings consumers.

Design of a coating formulation depends on the purpose of the coating application. Coatings provide aesthetics, and corrosion and surface protection. Cost, function, product safety, environmental safety, transfer efficiency and drying and curing speed determine formulations.

Coating processes

There are five operations comprising most coating processes: raw materials handling and preparation, surface preparation, coating, equipment cleaning and waste management.

Raw material handling and preparation

Raw material handling and preparation involves inventory storage, mixing operations, thinning and adjusting of coatings and raw material transfer through the facility. Monitoring and handling procedures and practices are needed to minimize the generation of wastes from spoilage, off specification and improper preparation that can result from excessive thinning and consequent wastage. Transfer, whether manual or through a piped system, must be scheduled to avoid spoilage.

Surface preparation

The type of surface preparation technique used depends on the surface being coated—previous preparation, amount of soil, grease, the coating to be applied and the surface finish required. Common preparation operations include degreasing, precoating or phosphating and coating removal. For metal finishing purposes, degreasing involves solvent wiping, cold cleaning or vapour degreasing with halogenated solvents, aqueous alkaline cleaning, semi-aqueous cleaning or aliphatic hydrocarbon cleaning to remove organic soil, dirt, oil and grease. Acid pickling, abrasive cleaning or flame cleaning are used to remove mill scale and rust.

The most common preparation operation for metal surfaces, other than cleaning, is phosphate coating, used to promote adhesion of organic coatings onto metal surfaces and retard corrosion. Phosphate coatings are applied by immersing or spraying metal surfaces with zinc, iron or manganese phosphate solution. Phosphating is a surface finishing process similar to electroplating, consisting of a series of process chemical and rinse baths in which parts are immersed to achieve the desired surface preparation. See the article "Surface treatment of metals" in this chapter.

Coating removal, chemical or mechanical, is conducted on surfaces that require recoating, repair or inspection. The most common chemical coating removal method is solvent stripping. These solutions usually contain phenol, methylene chloride and an organic acid to dissolve the coating from the coated surface. A final water wash to remove the chemicals can generate large quantities of wastewater. Abrasive blasting is the common mechanical process, a dry operation that uses compressed air to propel a blasting medium against the surface to remove the coating.

Surface preparation operations affect the quantity of waste from the specific preparation process. If the surface preparation is inadequate, resulting in poor coating, then removal of the coating and recoating adds to waste generation.

Coating

The coating operation involves transferring the coating to the surface and curing the coating on the surface. Most coating technologies fall into 1 of 5 basic categories: dip coating, roll coating, flow coating, spray coating, and the most common technique, air-atomized spray coating using solvent-based coatings.

Air-atomized spray coatings are usually conducted in a controlled environment because of solvent emissions and overspray. Overspray control devices are fabric filters or water walls, generating either used filters or wastewater from air scrubbing systems.

Curing is performed to convert the coating binder into a hard, tough, adherent surface. Curing mechanisms include: drying, baking or exposure to an electron beam or infrared or ultraviolet light. Curing generates significant VOCs from solvent-based coatings and poses a potential for explosion if the solvent concentrations rise above the lower explosive limit. Consequently, curing operations are equipped with air pollution control devices to prevent VOC emissions and for safety control to prevent explosions.

Environmental and health concerns, increased regulations affecting conventional coating formulations, high solvent costs and expensive hazardous waste disposal have created a demand for alternative coating formulations that contain less hazardous constituents and generate less waste when applied. Alternative coating formulations include:

- *High-solid coatings,* containing twice the amount of pigment and resin in the same volume of solvent as conventional coatings. Application lowers VOC emissions between 62 and 85% compared to conventional low-solid solvent-based coatings because the solvent content is reduced.
- *Water-based coatings* using water and an organic solvent mixture as the carrier with water used as the base. Compared to solvent-based coatings, water-based coatings generate between 80 and 95% less VOC emissions and spent solvents than conventional low-solid solvent-based coatings.
- *Powder coatings* containing no organic solvent, consisting of finely pulverized pigment and resin particles. They are either thermoplastic (high molecular weight resin for thick coatings) or thermosetting (low molecular weight compounds that form a thin layer before chemically cross-linking) powders.

Equipment cleaning

Equipment cleaning is a necessary, routine maintenance operation in coating processes. This creates significant amounts of hazardous waste, particularly if halogenated solvents are used for cleaning. Equipment cleaning for solvent-based coatings has traditionally been conducted manually with organic solvents to remove coatings from process equipment. Piping requires flushing with solvent in batches until clean. Coating equipment must be cleaned between product changes and after process shutdowns. The procedures and practices used will determine the level of waste generated from these activities.

Waste management

Several waste streams are generated by coating processes. Solid waste includes empty coating containers, coating sludge from overspray and equipment cleaning, spent filters and abrasive materials, dry coating and cleaning rags.

Liquid wastes include waste water from surface preparation, overspray control or equipment cleaning, off-specification or excess coating or surface preparation materials, overspray, spills and spent cleaning solutions. Onsite closed-loop recycling is becoming more popular for spent solvents as disposal costs rise. Water-based liquids are usually treated onsite prior to discharge to publicly owned treatment systems.

VOC emissions are generated by all conventional coating processes that use solvent-based coatings, requiring control devices such as carbon adsorption units, condensers or thermal catalytic oxidizers.

References

Buonicore, AJ and WT Davis (eds.). 1992. *Air Pollution Engineering Manual.* New York: Van Nostrand Reinhold/Air and Waste Management Association.

Environmental Protection Agency (EPA). 1995. *Profile of the Nonferrous Metals Industry.* EPA/310-R-95-010. Washington, DC: EPA.

International Association for Research on Cancer (IARC). 1984. *Monographs on the Evaluation of Carcinogenic Risks to Humans.* Vol. 34. Lyon: IARC.

Johnson A, CY Moira, L MacLean, E Atkins, A Dybunico, F Cheng, and D Enarson. 1985. Respiratory abnormalities amongst workers in iron and steel industry. *Brit J Ind Med* 42:94–100.

Kronenberg RS, JC Levin, RF Dodson, JGN Garcia, and DE Griffith. 1991. Asbestos-related disease in employees of a steel mill and a glass bottle manufacturing plant. *Ann NY Acad Sci* 643:397–403.

Landrigan, PJ, MG Cherniack, FA Lewis, LR Catlett, and RW Hornung. 1986. Silicosis in a grey iron foundry. The persistence of an ancient disease. *Scand J Work Environ Health* 12:32–39.

National Institute for Occupational Safety and Health (NIOSH). 1996. *Criteria for a Recommended Standard: Occupational Exposures to Metalworking Fluids.* Cincinnatti, OH: NIOSH.

Palheta, D and A Taylor. 1995. Mercury in environmental and biological samples from a gold mining area in the Amazon Region of Brazil. *Science of the Total Environment* 168:63-69.

Thomas, PR and D Clarke. 1992 Vibration white finger and Dupuytren's contracture: Are they related? *Occup Med* 42(3):155–158.

Other relevant readings

American Conference of Government Industrial Hygienists (ACGIH) Committee on Industrial Ventilation. 1992. *Industrial Ventilation: A Manual of Recommended Practice,* 22nd ed. Cincinnati, OH: ACGIH.

American National Standards Institute (ANSI). 1976. *Safety Requirements for the Construction, Care, and Use of Lathes.* ANSI B11.6-1976. New York: ANSI.

—. 1988a. *The Use, Care, and Protection of Abrasive Wheels.* ANSI B7.1-1988. New York: ANSI.

—.1988b. *Safety in Welding and Cutting.* ANSI Z49.1-1988. New York: ANSI.

American Petroleum Institute (API). 1971. *Chemistry and Petroleum for Classroom Use in Chemistry Courses.* Washington, DC: API.

—. 1980. *Facts about Oil.* Manual 4200. Washington, DC: API.

—. 1984. *Safe Operation of Inland Bulk Plants.* Publication 2008. Washington, DC: API.

Antoni, H. 1978. Massnahmen zu höherer Sicherheit beim Spannen mit Backenfuttern [Measures to increase safety in gripping with jaw chucks]. *Zeitschrift für industrielle Fertigung* 10:611–615.

Burgess, WA. 1995. *Recognition of Health Hazards in Industry,* 2nd edition. New York: John Wiley & Sons.

Exxon Company. 1987. *Encyclopedia for the User of Petroleum Products.* Houston, TX: Exxon Company, USA, Marketing Technical Services.

Goldsmith, AH, KW Vorpahl, KA French, PT Jordan, and NB Jurinski. 1976. Health hazards from oil, soot and metals at a hot forging operation. *Am Ind Hyg Assoc J* 37:217–226.

Gulf Publishing Company. 1964. *Petroleum Marketing and Transportation, 1964.* Houston TX: Gulf Publishing Company.

Harten, GA. 1976. Een nieuwe, ergonomisch verbeterde draaibank [A new, ergonomically improved lathe]. *Tijdschrift voor sociale geneeskunde* (Amstelveen) 54(17):575–578.

Kusiak, RA, J Springer, AC Ritchie, and J Muller. 1991. Carcinoma of the lung in Ontario gold miners: Possible aetiological factors. *Brit J Ind Med* 48(12):808-817.

Mobil Oil Corporation. 1990. *Handling, Storing and Dispensing Industrial Lubricants.* Mobil Technical Bulletin. Fairfax, VA: Mobil Oil Corporation.

National Institute for Occupational Safety and Health (NIOSH). 1975. *Ventilation Requirements for Grinding, Buffing and Polishing Operations.* NIOSH Publ. No. 75-105. Cincinnati, OH: NIOSH.

National Safety Council. 1995. *Petroleum Section Safety and Health Fact Sheets, 1988-95.* Itasca, IL: National Safety Council.

Occupational Safety and Health Administration (OSHA). 1979. *Prudent Practices for Controlling Lead Exposure in the Secondary Lead Smelting Industry: A Guide for Employers and Employees.* Washington, DC: OSHA.

—. 1982. *Cooperative Assessment Program Manual for the Secondary Lead Smelting Industry.* Washington, DC: OSHA.

—. 1984. *Cooperative Assessment Program Manual for the Battery Manufacturing Industry.* Washington, DC: OSHA.

Ontario Metal Finishing Industry Pollution Prevention Project. 1995. *Metal Finishing Pollution Prevention Guide.* Ottawa: Environment Canada, Water Technology International, Sheridan Environmental Technology Institute.

Simonato, L, JJ Moulin, B Javeland, G Ferro, P Wild, R Winkelmann, and R Saracci. 1994. A retrospective mortality study of workers exposed to arsenic in a gold mine and refinery in France. *Am J Ind Med* 25:652-633.

MICROELECTRONICS AND SEMICONDUCTORS

83

Chapter Editor
Michael E. Williams

Contents

GENERAL PROFILE

Michael E. Williams

The diversity of processes and products within the microelectronics and semiconductor industry is immense. The focus of the occupational health and safety discussion in this chapter centres on semiconductor integrated circuit (IC) production (both in silicon-based products and valence III-V compounds), printed wiring board (PWB) production, printed circuit board (PCB) assembly and computer assembly.

The industry is composed of numerous major segments. The Electronics Industry Association uses the following delineation in reporting data on pertinent trends, sales and employment within the industry:

- electronic components
- consumer electronics
- telecommunications
- defence communications
- computers and peripheral equipment
- industrial electronics
- medical electronics.

Electronic components include electron tubes (e.g., receiving, special-purpose and television tubes), solid-state products (e.g., transistors, diodes, ICs, light-emitting diodes (LEDs) and liquid-crystal displays (LCDs)) and passive and other components (e.g., capacitors, resistors, coils, transformers and switches).

Consumer electronics include television sets and other home and portable audio and video products, as well as information equipment such as personal computers, facsimile transmission machines and telephone answering devices. Electronic gaming hardware and software, home security systems, blank audio and video cassettes and floppy disks, electronic accessories and total primary batteries also fall under the consumer electronics heading.

In addition to general purpose and specialized computers, computers and peripheral equipment includes auxiliary storage equipment, input/output equipment (e.g., keyboards, mice, optical scanning devices and printers), terminals and so on. While telecommunications, defence communications and industrial and medical electronics utilize some of the same technology these segments also involve specialized equipment.

The emergence of the microelectronics industry has had a profound impact on the evolution and structure of the world's economy. The pace of change within industrialized nations of the world has been greatly influenced by advances within this industry, specifically in the evolution of the integrated circuit. This pace of change is graphically represented in the timeline of the number of transistors per integrated circuit chip (see figure 83.1).

The economic importance of worldwide semiconductor sales is significant. Figure 83.2 is a projection by the Semiconductor Industry Association for worldwide and regional semiconductor sales for 1993 to 1998.

The semiconductor IC and computer/electronics assembly industries are unique compared to most other industrial categories in the relative composition of their production workforces. The semiconductor fabrication area has a high percentage of female operators that run the process equipment. The operator-related tasks typically do not require heavy lifting or excess physical strength. Also, many of the job tasks involve fine motor skills and attention to detail. Male workers predominate in the maintenance-related tasks, engineering functions and management. A similar composition is found in the computer/electronics assembly portion of this industry segment. Another unusual feature of this industry is the concentration of manufacturing in the

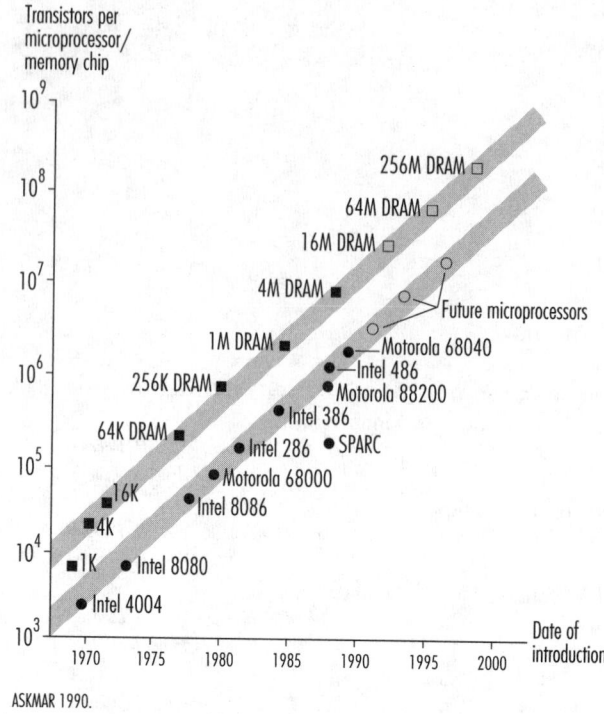

Figure 83.1 • Timeline of the number of transistors per integrated circuit chip (1970 to 2000).

ASKMAR 1990.

Asia/Pacific area of the world. This is especially true in the *final assembly* or *back-end* processes in the semiconductor industry. This processing involves the positioning and placement of the fabricated integrated circuit chip (technically known as a die) on a chip carrier and lead frame. This processing requires precise positioning of the chip, typically through a microscope, and very fine motor skills. Again, female workers predominate this part of the process, with the majority of worldwide production being concentrated in the Pacific Rim, with high concentrations in Taiwan, Malaysia, Thailand, Indonesia and the Philippines, and growing numbers in China and Vietnam.

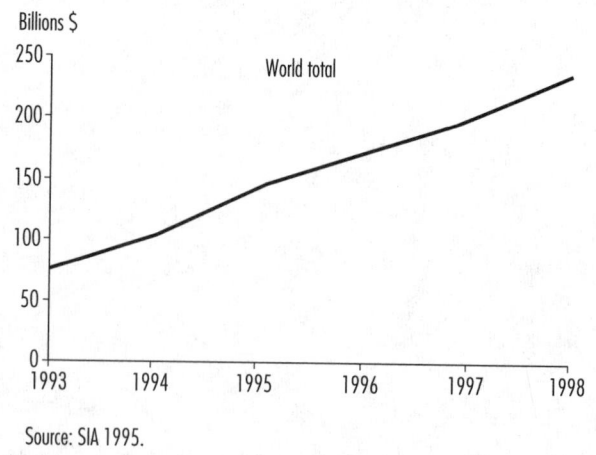

Figure 83.2 • Worldwide semiconductor sales forecast, 1993 to 1998.

Source: SIA 1995.

Figure 83.3 • Operators working in a state-of-the-art cleanroom in a semiconductor fabrication area.

Asyst Technology, Inc.

The semiconductor IC fabrication areas have various unusual properties and characteristics unique to this industry. Namely, the IC processing involves extremely tight particulate control regimens and requirements. A typical modern IC fabrication area may be rated as a Class 1 or less cleanroom. As a method of comparison, an outdoor environment would be greater than Class 500,000; a typical room in a house approximately Class 100,000; and a semiconductor back-end assembly area approximately Class 10,000. To attain this level of particulate control involves actually putting the fabrication worker in totally enclosed *bunny suits* that have air supply and filtration systems to control the levels of particulates generated by the workers in the fabrication area. The human occupants of the fabrication areas are considered very potent generators of fine particulates from their exhaled air, shedding of skin and hair, and from their clothing and shoes. This requirement for wearing confining clothing and isolating work routines has contributed to employees feeling like they are working in a "non-hospitable" work environment. See figure 83.3. Also, in the photolithographic area, the processing involves exposing the wafer to a photoactive solution, and then patterning an image on the wafer surface using ultraviolet light. To alleviate unwanted ultraviolet (UV) light from this processing area, special yellow lights are used (they lack the UV wavelength component normally found in indoor lighting). These yellow lights help to make the workers feel they are in a different work environment and can possibly have a disorienting affect on some individuals.

SILICON SEMICONDUCTOR MANUFACTURING

David G. Baldwin, James R. Rubin and Afsaneh Gerami

Process Overview

The description of silicon semiconductor device processing, either discrete devices (a semiconductor containing only one active device, such as a transistor) or ICs (interconnected arrays of active and passive elements within a single semiconductor substrate capable of performing at least one electronic circuit function), involves numerous highly technical and specific operations. The intent of this description is to provide a basic framework and explanation of the primary component steps utilized in fabricating a silicon semiconductor device and the associated environmental, health and safety (EHS) issues.

The fabrication of an IC involves a sequence of processes that may be repeated many times before a circuit is complete. The most popular ICs use 6 or more masks to complete patterning processes, with 10 to 24 masks being typical. The manufacture of a microcircuit begins with an ultra-high purity silicon wafer 4 to 12 inches in diameter. Perfectly pure silicon is almost an insulator, but certain impurities, called *dopants,* added in amounts of from 10 to 100 parts per million, make silicon conduct electricity.

An integrated circuit can consist of millions of transistors (also diodes, resistors and capacitors) made of doped silicon, all connected by the appropriate pattern of conductors to create the computer logic, memory or other type of circuit. Hundreds of microcircuits can be made on one wafer.

Six major fabrication processing steps are universal to all silicon semiconductor devices: oxidation, lithography, etching, doping, chemical vapour deposition and metallization. These are followed by assembly, testing, marking, packing and shipping.

Oxidation

Generally, the first step in semiconductor device processing involves the oxidation of the exterior surface of the wafer to grow a thin layer (about one micron) of silicon dioxide (SiO_2). This primarily protects the surface from impurities and serves as a mask for the subsequent diffusion process. This ability to grow a chemically stable protective wafer of silicon dioxide on silicon makes silicon wafers the most widely used semiconductor substrate.

Oxidation, commonly called thermal oxidation, is a batch process which takes place in a high-temperature diffusion furnace. The protective silicon dioxide layer is grown in atmospheres containing either oxygen (O_2) (dry oxidation) or oxygen combined with water vapour (H_2O) (wet oxidation). The temperatures in the furnace range from 800 to 1,300 °C. Chlorine compounds in the form of hydrogen chloride (HCl) may also be added to help control unwanted impurities.

The tendency in newer fabrication facilities is towards vertical oxidation furnaces. Vertical furnaces better address the need for greater contamination control, larger wafer size and more uniform processing. They allow a smaller equipment footprint that conserves precious cleanroom floor space.

Dry oxidation

Silicon wafers to be oxidized are first cleaned, using a detergent and water solution, and solvent rinsed with xylene, isopropyl alcohol or other solvents. The cleaned wafers are dried, loaded into a quartz wafer holder called a *boat* and loaded into the operator end (*load end*) of the quartz diffusion furnace tube or cell. The inlet end of the tube (*source end*) supplies high-purity oxygen or oxygen/nitrogen mixture. The "dry" oxygen flow is controlled into the quartz tube and assures that an excess of oxygen is available for the growth of silicon dioxide on the silicon wafer surface. The basic chemical reaction is:

$$Si + O_2 \rightarrow SiO_2$$

Wet oxidation

Four methods of introducing water vapour are commonly used when water is the oxidizing agent—pyrophoric, high-pressure, bubbler and flash. The basic chemical reactions are:

$$Pyrophoric \text{ and high pressure: } Si + 2O_2 + 2\,H_2 \rightarrow SiO_2 + 2H_2O$$

$$Flash \text{ and bubbler: } Si + 2H_2O \rightarrow SiO_2 + 2H_2$$

Pyrophoric oxidation involves the introduction and combustion of a hydrogen/oxygen gas mixture. Such systems are generally called *burnt hydrogen* or *torch* systems. Water vapour is produced when proper amounts of hydrogen and oxygen are introduced at the inlet end of the tube and allowed to react. The mixture must be controlled precisely to guarantee proper combustion and prevent the accumulation of explosive hydrogen gas.

High-pressure oxidation (HiPox) is technically called a water pyrosynthesis system and generates water vapour through the reaction of ultra-pure hydrogen and oxygen. The steam is then pumped into a high-pressure chamber and pressurized to 10 atmospheres, which accelerates the wet oxidation process. De-ionized water may also be used as a steam source.

In *bubbler oxidation* de-ionized water is placed in a container called a *bubbler* and maintained at a constant temperature below its boiling point of 100 °C through the use of a heating mantle. Nitrogen or oxygen gas enters the inlet side of the bubbler, becomes saturated with water vapour as it rises through the water, and exits through the outlet into the diffusion furnace. Bubbler systems appear to be the most widely used method of oxidation.

In *flash oxidation* de-ionized water is dripped continuously into the heated bottom surface of a quartz container and the water evaporates rapidly once it hits the hot surface. Nitrogen or oxygen carrier gas flows over the evaporating water and carries the water vapour into the diffusion furnace.

Lithography

Lithography, also known as photolithography or simply masking, is a method of accurately forming patterns on the oxidized wafer. The microelectronic circuit is built up layer by layer, each layer receiving a pattern from a mask prescribed in circuit design.

The printing trades developed the true antecedents of today's semiconductor device microfabrication processes. These developments relate to the manufacture of printing plates, usually of metal, on which removal of material through chemical etching produces a surface relief pattern. This same basic technique is used in producing *master masks* used in the fabrication of each layer of processing of a device.

Circuit designers digitize the basic circuitry of each layer. This computerized schematic allows quick generation of the mask circuitry and facilitates any changes that may be needed. This technique is known as computer-aided design (CAD). Utilizing powerful computer algorithms, these on-line design systems permit the designer to lay out and modify the circuitry directly on video display screens with interactive graphic capabilities.

The final drawing, or mask, for each layer of circuitry is created by a computer-driven photoplotter, or pattern generator. These photoplotted drawings are then reduced to the actual size of the circuit, a master mask produced on glass with chrome relief, and reproduced on a work plate which serves for either contact or projection printing on the wafer.

These masks delineate the pattern of the conducting and insulating areas which are transferred to the wafer through photolithography. Most companies do not produce their own masks, but utilize those furnished by a mask producer.

Cleaning

The need for a particulate- and contamination-free exterior wafer surface requires frequent cleaning. The major categories are:

- de-ionized water and detergent scrubbing
- solvent: isopropyl alcohol (IPA), acetone, ethanol, terpenes
- acid: hydrofluoric (HF), sulphuric (H_2SO_4) and hydrogen peroxide (H_2O_2), hydrochloric (HCl), nitric (HNO_3) and mixtures
- caustic: ammonium hydroxide (NH_4OH).

Resist application

Wafers are coated with a resist material of solvent-based polymer and rapidly rotated on a *spinner*, which spreads a thin uniform layer. The solvents then evaporate, leaving a polymeric film.

Figure 83.4 • Photolithographic "yellow room" equipment in a state-of-the-art cleanroom.

ASYST Technology, Inc.

All resist materials depend on (primarily ultraviolet) radiation-induced changes in the solubility of a synthetic organic polymer in a selected developer rinse. Resist materials are classified as either negative or positive resists, depending on whether the solubility in the developer decreases (negative) or increases (positive) upon exposure to radiation. Table 83.1 identifies the component makeup of various photoresist systems.

Since most photoresists are ultraviolet (UV) light sensitive, the processing area is lit with special yellow lights lacking sensitive UV wavelengths (see figure 83.4).

Negative and positive UV resists are primarily in use in the industry. E-beam and x-ray resists, however, are gaining in market share because of their higher resolutions. Health concerns in lithography are primarily caused by potential reproductive hazards associated with selected positive resists (e.g., ethylene glycol monoethyl ether acetate as a carrier) that are currently being phased out by the industry. Occasional odours from the negative resists (e.g., xylene) also result in employee concerns. Because of these concerns, a great deal of time is spent by semiconductor industry industrial hygienists sampling photoresist operations. While this is useful in characterizing these operations, routine exposures during spinner and developer operations are typically less than 5% of the airborne standards for occupational exposure for the solvents used in the process (Scarpace et al. 1989).

A 1 hour exposure to ethylene glycol monoethyl ether acetate of 6.3 ppm was found during the operation of a spinner system. This exposure was primarily caused by poor work practices during the maintenance operation (Baldwin, Rubin and Horowitz 1993).

Table 83.1 • Photoresist systems.

Ultraviolet			
Near (350–450 nm)	Negative	PB	Azide base aliphatic rubber (isoprene)
		S	n-Butyl acetate, xylene, n-methyl-2-pyrrolidone, ethyl benzene
		D	Xylene, aliphatic hydrocarbons, n-butyl acetate, Stoddard solvent (petroleum distillates)
	Positive	PB	Ortho-diazoketone
		S	Propylene glycol monomethyl ether acetate, ethyl lactate, methyl methoxy propionate, ethyl ethoxy propionate, n-butyl acetate, xylene, chlorotoluene
		D	Sodium hydroxide, silicates, potassium hydroxide
Deep (200–250 nm)	Primarily positive resists		
Electron-beam (about 100 nm)			
	Negative	PB	Copolymer-ethyl acrylate and glycidyl methacrylate (COP)
		S	n/a
		D	n/a
	Positive	PB	Polymethylmethacrylate, polyfluoralkylmethacrylate, polyalkylaldehyde, poly-cyano ethylacrylate
		S	Propylene glycol monomethyl ether acetate
		D	Alkaline or IPA, ethyl acetate, or methyl isobutyl ketone (MIBK)
X ray (0.5–5 nm)			
	Negative	PB	Copolymer-ethyl acrylate and glycidyl methacrylate (COP)
		S	n/a
		D	n/a
	Positive	PB	Polymethylmethacrylate, ortho-diazoketone, poly (hexa-fluorobutylmethacrylate), poly (butene-1-sulphone)
		S	Propylene glycol monomethyl ether acetate
		D	n/a

PB = polymer base; S = solvent; D = developer.

Drying and pre-baking
After the resist has been applied, the wafers are moved on a track or manually moved from the spinner to a temperature-controlled oven with a nitrogen atmosphere. A moderate temperature (70 to 90 °C) causes the photoresist to cure (soft bake) and the remaining solvents to evaporate.

To ensure adhesion of the resist layer to the wafer, a primer, hexamethyldisilizane (HMDS), is applied to the wafer. The primer ties up molecular water on the surface of the wafer. HMDS is applied either directly in an immersion or spin-on process or through a vapour prime that offers process and cost advantages over the other methods.

Mask aligning and exposure
The mask and wafer are brought close together using a precise piece of optical/mechanical equipment, and the image on the mask is aligned to any pattern already existing in the wafer beneath the layer of photoresist. For the first mask, no alignment is necessary. In older technologies, alignment for successive layers is made possible by the use of a biscope (dual lens microscope) and precision controls for positioning the wafer with respect to the mask. In newer technologies alignment is done automatically using reference points on the wafers.

Once the alignment is done, a high-intensity ultraviolet mercury vapour or arc lamp source shines through the mask, exposing the resist in places not protected by opaque regions of the mask.

The various methods of wafer alignment and exposure include UV flood exposure (contact or proximity), UV exposure through projection lens for reduction (projection), UV step and repeat reduction exposure (projection), x-ray flood (proximity) and electron beam scan exposure (direct writing). The primary method in use involves UV exposure from mercury vapour and arc lamps through proximity or projection aligners. The UV resists are either designed to react to a broad spectrum of UV wavelengths, or they are formulated to react preferentially to one or more of the main spectrum lines emitted from the lamp (e.g., g-line at 435 nm, h-line at 405 nm and i-line at 365 nm).

The predominant wavelengths of UV light currently used in photomasking are 365 nm or above, but UV lamp spectra also contain significant energy in the wavelength region of health concern, the actinic region below 315 nm. Normally, the intensity of the UV radiation escaping from the equipment is less than both what is present from sunlight in the actinic region and the standards set for occupational exposure to UV.

Occasionally during maintenance, the alignment of the UV lamp requires that it be energized outside the equipment cabinet or without normal protective filters. Exposure levels during this operation can exceed occupational exposure limits, but standard cleanroom attire (e.g., smocks, vinyl gloves, face masks and polycarbonate safety glasses with UV inhibitor) is usually adequate to attenuate the UV light to below exposure limits (Baldwin and Stewart 1989).

While the predominant wavelengths for ultraviolet lamps used in photolithography are 365 nm or above, the quest for smaller features in advanced ICs is leading to the use of exposure sources with smaller wavelengths, such as deep UV and x rays. One new technology for this purpose is the use of krypton-fluoride excimer lasers used in steppers. These steppers use a wavelength of 248 nm with high laser power outputs. However, enclosures for these systems contain the beam during normal operation.

As with other equipment containing high-power laser systems used in semiconductor manufacturing, the main concern is when interlocks for the system must be defeated during beam alignment. High-powered lasers are also one of the most significant electrical hazards in the semiconductor industry. Even after power is off, a significant shock potential exists within the tool. Controls and safety design considerations for these systems are covered by Escher, Weathers and Labonville (1993).

One advanced-technology exposure source used in lithography is x rays. Emission levels from x-ray lithography sources may result in dose rates approaching 50 millisieverts (5 rems) per year in the centre of the equipment. Restricting access to areas inside the shielded wall is recommended to minimize exposure (Rooney and Leavey 1989).

Developing

During the development step the unpolymerized areas of the resist are dissolved and removed. Solvent-based developer is applied to the resist-covered wafer surface by either immersion, spraying or atomization. Developer solutions are identified in table 83.1. A solvent rinse (n-butyl acetate, isopropyl alcohol, acetone, etc.) is usually applied following the developer to remove any residual material. The resist remaining after developing protect the individual layers during subsequent processing.

Baking

After aligning, exposing and developing the resist, the wafers then move to another temperature-controlled oven with a nitrogen atmosphere. The higher-temperature oven (120 to 135 °C) causes

Table 83.2 • Photoresist strippers.

Wet chemical
Acid
Sulphuric (H_2SO_4) and chromic (CrO_3)
Sulphuric (H_2SO_4) and ammonium persulphate (($NH_4)_2S_2O_8$)
Sulphuric (H_2SO_4) and hydrogen peroxide (H_2O_2)
Organics
Phenols, sulphuric acids, trichlorobenzene, perchloroethylene
Glycol ethers, ethanolamine, triethanolamine
Sodium hydroxide and silicates (positive resist)
Dry chemical
Plasma ashing (stripping)
RF (radio frequency) power source—13.56 MHz or 2,450 MHz frequency
Oxygen (O_2) source gas
Vacuum pump systems
—Oil lubricated with liquid nitrogen trap (old technology)
—Lubricated with inert perfluoropolyether fluids (newer technology)
—Dry pump (newest technology)

the photoresist to cure and fully polymerize on the wafer surface (hard bake).

Photoresist stripping

The developed wafer is then selectively etched using wet or dry chemicals (see "Etching" below). The remaining photoresist must be stripped from the wafer prior to further processing. This is done either by using wet chemical solutions in temperature-controlled baths or through the use of a plasma asher or dry chemical. Table 83.2 identifies both wet and dry chemical constituents. A discussion of dry chemical plasma etching—using the same equipment and principles of operation as plasma ashing—follows.

Etching

Etching removes layers of silicon dioxide (SiO_2), metals and polysilicon, as well as resists, according to the desired patterns delineated by the resist. The two major categories of etching are wet and dry chemical. Wet etching is predominantly used and involves solutions containing the etchants (usually an acid mixture) at the desired strengths, which react with the materials to be removed. Dry etching involves the use of reactive gases under vacuum in a highly energized chamber, which also removes the desired layers not protected by resist.

Wet chemical

The wet chemical etching solutions are housed in temperature-controlled etch baths made of polypropylene (poly-pro), flame-resistant polypropylene (FRPP) or polyvinyl chloride (PVC). The baths generally are equipped with either ring-type plenum exhaust ventilation or slotted exhaust at the rear of the wet chemical etch station. Vertical laminar flow hoods supply uniformly filtered particulate-free air to the top surface of the etch baths. Common wet etchant chemical solutions are presented in table 83.3, in relation to the surface layer being etched.

Vertically mounted flow supply hoods, when used in conjunction with splash shields and exhaust ventilation, can create areas of air turbulence within the wet chemical etch station. As a result, a decrease is possible in the effectiveness of the local exhaust ventilation in capturing and routing fugitive air contaminants from the etch baths in use.

The main concern with wet etching is the possibility of skin contact with the concentrated acids. While all the acids used in etching can cause acid burns, exposure to hydrofluoric acid (HF) is of particular concern. The lag time between skin contact and pain (up to 24 hours for solutions less than 20% HF and 1 to 8 hours for 20 to 50% solutions) can result in delayed treatment and more severe burns than expected (Hathaway et al. 1991).

Historically acid burns have been a particular problem within the industry. However, the incidence of skin contact with acids have been reduced in recent years. Some of this reduction was caused by product-related improvements in the etch process, such as the shift to dry etching, the use of more robotics and the installation of chemical dispense systems. The reduction in the rate of acid burns may also be attributed to better handling techniques, greater use of personal protective equipment, better designed wet decks and better training—all of which require continued attention if the rate is to decline further (Baldwin and Williams 1996).

Dry chemical

Dry chemical etching is an area of growing interest and usage due to its ability to better control the etching process and reduce contamination levels. Dry chemical processing effectively etches desired layers through the use of chemically reactive gases or through physical bombardment.

Table 83.3 • Wet chemical etchants.

Material to etch	Etchants
Silicon	
Polycrystalline silicon (Si)	Hydrofluoric, nitric, acetic acids and iodine Potassium hydroxide Ethylene diamine/catechol Ammonium fluoride, glacial acetic and nitric acids
Silicon dioxide (SiO$_2$)	Buffered oxide etch (BOE) - Hydrofluoric and ammonium fluoride BOE, ethylene glycol, monomethyl ether Hydrofluoric and nitric (P-etch)
Silicon nitride (Si$_3$N$_4$)	Phosphoric and hydrofluoric acids
CVD Oxide or Pad Etch	Ammonium fluoride, acetic and hydrofluoric acids
Metals	
Aluminium (Al)	Phosphoric, nitric, acetic and hydrochloric acids Sodium hydroxide, potassium hydroxide
Chromium–Nickel (Cr/Ni)	Ceric ammonium nitrate and nitric acid Hydrochloric and nitric acids (aqua regia)
Gold (Au)	Hydrochloric and nitric acids (aqua regia) Potassium iodide (KI) Potassium cyanide (KCN) and hydrogen peroxide (H$_2$O$_2$) Ferric chloride (FeCl$_3$) and hydrochloric acid
Silver (Ag)	Ferric nitrate (FeNO$_3$) and ethylene glycol Nitric acid

Compound	Formula	Standard concentration (%)
Acetic acid	CH$_3$COOH	36
Ammonium fluoride	NH$_4$F	40
Glacial acetic acid	CH$_3$COOH	99.5
Hydrochloric acid	HCl	36
Hydrofluoric acid	HF	49
Nitric acid	HNO$_3$	67
Phosphoric acid	H$_3$PO$_4$	85
Potassium hydroxide	KOH	50 or 10
Sodium hydroxide	NaOH	50 or 10
Sulphuric acid	H$_2$SO$_4$	96

Chemically reactive plasma etching systems have been developed which can effectively etch silicon, silicon dioxide, silicon nitride, aluminium, tantalum, tantalum compounds, chromium, tungsten, gold and glass. Two kinds of plasma etching reactor systems are in use—the barrel, or cylindrical, and the parallel plate, or planar. Both operate on the same principles and primarily vary in configuration only.

A plasma is similar to a gas except that some of the atoms or molecules of the plasma are ionized and may contain a substantial number of free radicals. The typical reactor consists of a vacuum reactor chamber containing the wafer, usually made of aluminium, glass or quartz; a radio-frequency (RF) energy source—usually at 450 kHz, 13.56 MHz or 40.5 MHz and a control module to control processing time, composition of reactant gas, flow rate of gas and RF power level. In addition, an oil-lubricated (older technology) or dry (newer technology) roughing

pump vacuum source is in line with the reactor chamber. Wafers are loaded into the reactor, either individually or in cassettes, a pump evacuates the chamber and the reagent gas (usually carbon tetrafluoride) is introduced. Ionization of the gas forms the etching plasma, which reacts with the wafers to form volatile products which are pumped away. The introduction of fresh reactant gas into the chamber maintains etching activity. Table 83.4 identifies the materials and plasma gases in use for etching various layers.

Another method that currently is being developed for etching is microwave downstream. It uses a high-power-density microwave discharge to produce metastable atoms with long lifetimes that etch material almost as if it were immersed in acid.

Physical etching processes are similar to sandblasting in that argon gas atoms are used to physically bombard the layer to be etched. A vacuum pump system is used to remove dislocated material. Reactive ion etching involves a combination of chemical and physical dry etching.

The sputtering process is one of ion impact and energy transfer. Sputter etching incorporates a sputtering system, where the wafer to be etched is attached to a negative electrode or target in a glow-discharge circuit. Material sputters from the wafer by bombardment with positive ions, usually argon, and results in the dislocation of the surface atoms. Power is provided by an RF source at 450 kHz frequency. An in-line vacuum system is used for pressure control and reactant removal.

Ion-beam etching and milling is a gentle etching process which uses a beam of low-energy ions. The ion-beam system consists of a source to generate the ion beam, a work chamber in which the etching or milling occurs, fixturing with a target plate for holding the wafers in the ion beam, a vacuum pump system, supporting electronics and instruments. The ion beam is extracted from an ionized gas (argon or argon/oxygen) or plasma, which is created by the electrical discharge. The discharge is obtained by applying a voltage between an electron-emitting hot-filament cathode and an anode cylinder located in the outer diameter of the discharge region.

Ion-beam milling is done in the low-energy range of ion bombardment, where only surface interactions occur. These ions,

Table 83.4 • Plasma etching gases and etched materials.

Material	Gas
Silicon	
Polysilicon (polySi) and Silicon	CF + O$_2$, CCl$_4$ or CF$_3$Cl, CF$_4$ and HCl
Silicon dioxide (SiO$_2$)	C$_2$F$_6$, C$_3$F$_8$, CF$_4$, SiF$_4$, C$_5$F$_{12}$, CHF$_3$, CCl$_2$F$_2$, SF$_6$, HF
Silicon nitride (Si$_3$N$_4$)	CF$_4$ + Ar, CF$_4$ + O$_2$, CF$_4$ + H$_2$
Metals	
Aluminium (Al)	CCl$_4$ or BCl$_3$ + He or Ar
Chromium (Cr)	CCl$_4$
Chromium oxide (CrO$_3$)	Cl$_2$ + Ar or CCl$_4$ + Ar
Gallium arsenide (GaAs)	CCl$_2$F$_2$
Vanadium (V)	CF$_4$
Titanium (Ti)	CF$_4$
Tantulum (Ta)	CF$_4$
Molybdenum (Mo)	CF$_4$
Tungsten (W)	CF$_4$

83. MICROELECTRONICS AND SEMICONDUCTORS

usually in the 500 to 1,000 eV range, strike a target and *sputter off* surface atoms by breaking the forces bonding the atom to its neighbour. Ion-beam etching is done in a slightly higher energy range, which involves a more dramatic dislocation of surface atoms.

Reactive ion etching (RIE) is a combination of physical sputtering and chemical reactive species etching at low pressures. RIE uses ion bombardment to achieve directional etching and also a chemically reactive gas, carbon tetrafluoride (CF_4) or carbon tetrachloride (CCl_4), to maintain good etched layer selectivity. A wafer is placed in a chamber with an atmosphere of chemically reactive gas compound at a low pressure of about 0.1 torr (1.3×10^{-4} atmosphere). An electrical discharge creates a plasma of reactive "free radicals" (ions) with an energy of a few hundred electron volts. The ions strike the wafer surface vertically, where they react to form volatile species that are removed by a low-pressure in-line vacuum system.

Dry etchers sometimes have a cleaning cycle that is used to remove deposits that accumulate on the inside of the reaction chambers. Parent compounds used for the cleaning cycle plasmas include nitrogen trifluoride (NF_3), hexafluoroethane (C_2F_6) and octafluoropropane (C_3F_8).

These three gases used in the cleaning process, and many of the gases used in etching, are a cornerstone to an environmental issue facing the semiconductor industry which surfaced in the mid-1990s. Several of the highly fluorinated gases were identified as having significant global warming (or greenhouse effect) potential. (These gases are also referred to as PFCs, perfluorinated compounds.) The long atmospheric lifetime, high global warming potential and significant increased usage of PFCs like NF_3, C_2F_6, C_3F_8, CF_4, trifluoromethane (CHF_3) and sulphur hexafluoride (SF_6) had the semiconductor industry focus on ways to reduce their emissions.

Atmospheric emissions of PFCs from the semiconductor industry have been due to poor tool efficiency (many tools consumed only 10 to 40% of the gas used) and inadequate air emission abatement equipment. Wet scrubbers are not effective in removing PFCs, and tests on many combustion units found poor destruction efficiencies for some gases, especially CF_4. Many of these combustion units broke down C_2F_6 and C_3F_8 into CF_4. Also, the high cost of ownership for these abatement tools, their power demand, their release of other global warming gases and their combustion by-products of hazardous air pollutants indicated combustion abatement was not a suitable method for controlling PFC emissions.

Making process tools more efficient, identifying and developing more environmentally friendly alternatives to these dry etchant gases and recovery/recycling of the exhaust gases have been the environmental emphases associated with dry etchers.

The major occupational hygiene emphasis for dry etchers has been on potential exposures to maintenance personnel working on the reaction chambers, pumps and other associated equipment that may contain reaction product residues. The complexity of plasma metal etchers and the difficulty in characterizing the odours associated with their maintenance has made them the subject of many investigations.

The reaction products formed in plasma metal etchers are a complex mixture of chlorinated and fluorinated compounds. The maintenance of metal etchers often involves short-duration operations that generate strong odours. Hexachloroethane was found to be the major cause of odour in one type of aluminium etcher (Helb et al. 1983). In another, cyanogen chloride was the main problem: exposure levels were 11 times the 0.3 ppm occupational exposure limit (Baldwin 1985). In still other types of etchers, hydrogen chloride is associated with the odour; maximum exposure measured was 68 ppm (Baldwin, Rubin and Horowitz

1993). For additional information on the subject see Mueller and Kunesh (1989).

The complexity of the chemistries present in metal etcher exhausts has led researchers to develop experimental methods for investigating the toxicity of these mixtures (Bauer et al. 1992a). Application of these methods in rodent studies indicates certain of these chemical mixtures are suspected mutagens (Bauer et al. 1992b) and suspected reproductive toxins (Schmidt et al. 1995).

Because dry etchers operate as closed systems, chemical exposure to the operators of the equipment typically does not occur while the system is closed. One rare exception to this is when the purge cycle for older batch etchers is not long enough to adequately remove the etchant gases. Brief but irritating exposures to fluorine compounds that are below the detection limit for typical industrial hygiene monitoring procedures have been reported when the doors to these etchers are opened. Normally this can be corrected by simply increasing the length of the purge cycle prior to opening the etch chamber door.

The primary concern for operator exposure to RF energy comes during plasma etching and ashing (Cohen 1986; Jones 1988). Typically, the leakage of RF energy can be caused by:

- misaligned doors
- cracks and holes in the cabinets
- metal tables and electrical cables acting as antennae due to improper grounding of the etcher
- no attenuating screen in the viewing window of the etcher (Jones 1988; Horowitz 1992).

RF exposure can also occur during the maintenance of etchers, particularly if the equipment cabinet has been removed. An exposure of 12.9 mW/cm^2 was found at the top of an older model plasma etcher with the cover removed for maintenance (Horowitz 1992). The actual RF radiation leakage in the area where the operator stands was typically less than 4.9 mW/cm^2.

Doping

The formation of an electrical junction or boundary between p and n regions in a single crystal silicon wafer is the essential element for the functioning of all semiconductor devices. Junctions permit current to flow in one direction much more easily than in the other. They provide the basis for diode and transistor effects in all semiconductors. In an integrated circuit, a controlled number of elemental impurities or dopants, must be introduced into selected etched regions of the silicon substrate, or wafer. This can be done either by diffusion or ion implantation techniques. Regardless of the technique used, the same types or dopants are used for the production of semiconductor junctions. Table 83.5 identifies the main components used for doping, their physical state, electrical type (p or n) and the primary junction technique in use—diffusion or ion implantation.

Routine chemical exposures to operators of both diffusion furnaces and ion implanters are low—typically less that the detection limit of standard occupational hygiene sampling procedures. Chemical concerns with the process centre on the possibility of toxic gas releases.

As early as the 1970s, progressive semiconductor manufacturers began installing the first continuous gas-monitoring systems for flammable and toxic gases. The main focus of this monitoring was to detect accidental releases of the most toxic dopant gases with odour thresholds above their occupational exposure limits (e.g., arsine and diborane).

Most industrial hygiene air monitors in the semiconductor industry are used for flammable and toxic gas leak detection. However, some facilities are also using continuous monitoring systems to:

Table 83.5 • Junction formation dopants for diffusion and ion implantation.

Element	Compound	Formula	State	Technique
n-type				
Antimony	Antimony trioxide	Sb_2O_3	Solid	Diffusion
	Antimony trichloride	$SbCl_3$	Liquid	Diffusion
Arsenic	Arsenic trioxide	As_2O_3	Solid	Diffusion
	Arsenic trioxide	As_2O_3	Liquid	Diffusion — spin on
	Arsine	AsH_3	Gas	Diffusion and ion implantation
	Arsenic pentafluoride	AsF_5	Gas	Ion implantation
Phosphorus	Phosphorus pentoxide	P_2O_5	Solid	Diffusion
	Phosphorus pentoxide	P_2O_5	Liquid	Diffusion — spin on
	Phosphorus tribromide	PBr_3	Liquid	Diffusion
	Phosphorus trichloride	PCl_3	Liquid	Diffusion
	Phosphorus oxychloride	$POCl_3$	Liquid	Diffusion
	Phosphine	PH_3	Gas	Ion implantation
	Phosphorus pentafluoride	PF_5	Gas	Ion implantation
p-type				
Boron	Boron nitride	BN	Solid	Diffusion
	Boron tribromide	BBr_3	Liquid	Diffusion
	Boron trioxide	B_2O_3	Solid	Diffusion
	Boron trioxide	B_2O_3	Liquid	Diffusion — spin on
	Triethylborate	$B(COC_2H_5)_3$	Liquid	Diffusion — spin on
	Silicon tetrabromide	$SiBr_4$	Liquid	Diffusion
	Boron trichloride	BCl_3	Liquid	Diffusion ion implantation
	Boron trifluoride	BF_3	Gas	Ion implantation
	Diborane	B_2H_6	Gas	Ion implantation

- analyse exhaust duct (stack) emissions
- quantify ambient air concentrations of volatile chemicals
- identify and quantify odours in the fab areas.

The technologies most used in the semiconductor industry for this type of monitoring are colorimetric gas detection (e.g., MDA continuous gas detector), electrochemical sensors (e.g., sensydyne monitors) and Fourier transform infrared (e.g., Telos ACM) (Baldwin and Williams 1996).

Diffusion

Diffusion is a term used to describe the movement of dopants away from regions of high concentration at the source end of the diffusion furnace to regions of lower concentration within the silicon wafer. Diffusion is the most established method of junction formation.

This technique involves subjecting a wafer to a heated atmosphere within the diffusion furnace. The furnace contains the desired dopants in a vapour form and results in creating regions of doped electrical activity, either *p* or *n*. The most commonly used dopants are boron for p-type; and phosphorus (P), arsenic (As) or antimony (Sb) for n-type (see table 83.5).

Typically, wafers are stacked in a quartz carrier or boat and placed in the diffusion furnace. The diffusion furnace contains a long quartz tube and a mechanism for accurate temperature control. Temperature control is extremely important, as the rates of diffusion of the various silicon dopants are primarily a function of temperature. The temperatures in use range from 900 to 1,300 °C, depending on the specific dopant and process.

The heating of the silicon wafer to a high temperature allows the impurity atoms to diffuse slowly through the crystal structure. Impurities move more slowly through silicon dioxide than through the silicon itself, enabling the thin oxide pattern to serve as a mask and thereby permitting the dopant to enter silicon only where it is unprotected. After enough impurities have accumulated, the wafers are removed from the furnace and diffusion effectively ceases.

For maximum control, most diffusions are performed in two steps—*predeposition* and *drive in*. The predeposit, or diffusion with constant source, is the first step and takes place in a furnace in which the temperature is selected to achieve the best control of impurity amounts. The temperature determines the solubility of the dopant. After a comparatively short predeposit treatment, the wafer is physically moved to a second furnace, usually at a higher temperature, where a second heat treatment drives in the dopant to the desired depth of diffusion in the silicon wafer lattice.

The dopant sources used in the predeposit step are in three distinct chemical states: gas, liquid and solid. Table 83.5 identifies the various types of diffusion source dopants and their physical states.

Gases are generally supplied from compressed gas cylinders with pressure controls or regulators, shut-off valves and various purging attachments and are dispensed through small-diameter metal tubing.

Liquids are dispensed normally from bubblers, which saturate a carrier gas stream, usually nitrogen, with the liquid dopant vapours, as is described in the section on wet oxidation. Another form of liquid dispensing is through the use of the *spin-on* dopant apparatus. This entails putting a solid dopant in solution with a liquid solvent carrier, then dripping the solution on the wafer and spinning, in a manner similar to the application of photoresists.

Solid sources may be in the shape of a boron nitride wafer, which is sandwiched between two silicon wafers to be doped and then placed in a diffusion furnace. Also, the solid dopants, in powder or bead form, may be placed in a *quartz bomb* enclosure (arsenic trioxide), manually dumped in the source end of a diffusion tube or loaded in a separate source furnace in line with the main diffusion furnace.

In the absence of proper controls, arsenic exposures above 0.01 mg/m^3 were reported during the cleaning of a deposition furnace (Wade et al. 1981) and during the cleaning of source housing chambers for solid-source ion implanters (McCarthy 1985; Baldwin, King and Scarpace 1988). These exposures occurred when no precautions were taken to limit the amount of dust in the air. However, when residues were kept wet during cleaning, exposures were reduced to far below the airborne exposure limit.

In the older diffusion technologies safety hazards exist during the removal, cleaning and installation of furnace tubes. The hazards include potential cuts from broken quartz ware and acid burns during the manual cleaning. In newer technologies these hazards are lessened by *in situ* tube cleaning that eliminates much of the manual handling.

Diffusion furnace operators experience the highest routine cleanroom exposure to extremely low-frequency electromagnetic fields (e.g., 50 to 60 hertz) in semiconductor manufacturing. Average exposures greater than 0.5 microteslas (5 milligauss) were reported during actual operation of the furnaces (Crawford et al. 1993). This study also noted that cleanroom personnel working in the vicinity of diffusion furnaces had average measured exposures that were noticeably higher than those of other cleanroom workers. This finding was consistent with point measurements reported by Rosenthal and Abdollahzadeh (1991), who found that diffusion furnaces produced proximity readings (5 cm or 2 inches away) as high as 10 to 15 microteslas, with the surrounding fields falling off more gradually with distance than other cleanroom equipment studied; even at 6 feet away from diffusion furnaces, the reported flux densities were 1.2 to 2 microteslas (Crawford et al. 1993). These emission levels are well below current health-based exposure limits set by the World Health Organization and those set by individual countries.

Ion implantation

Ion implantation is the newer method of introducing impurities elements at room temperature into silicon wafers for junction formation. Ionized dopant atoms (i.e., atoms stripped of one or more of their electrons) are accelerated to a high energy by passing them through a potential difference of tens of thousands of volts. At the end of their path, they strike the wafer and are embedded at various depths, depending on their mass and energy. As in conventional diffusion, a patterned oxide layer or a photoresist pattern selectively masks the wafer from the ions.

A typical ion implantation system consists of an ion source (gaseous dopant source, usually in small lecture bottles), analysis equipment, accelerator, focusing lens, neutral beam trap, scanner process chamber and a vacuum system (normally three separate sets of in-line roughing and oil-diffusion pumps). The stream of electrons is generated from a hot filament by resistance, an arc discharge or cold cathode electron beam.

Generally, after wafers are implanted, a high temperature annealing step (900 to 1,000 °C) is performed by a laser beam anneal or pulsed annealing with an electron-beam source. The annealing process helps repair the damage to the exterior surface of the implanted wafer caused by the bombardment of dopant ions.

With the advent of a safe delivery system for arsine, phosphine and boron trifluoride gas cylinders used in ion implanters, the potential for catastrophic release of these gases has been greatly reduced. These small gas cylinders are filled with a compound to which the arsine, phosphine and boron trifluoride are adsorbed. The gases are pulled out of the cylinders by use of a vacuum.

Ion implanters are one of the most significant electrical hazards in the semiconductor industry. Even after power is off, a significant shock potential exists within the tool and must be dissipated prior to working inside the implanter. A careful review of maintenance operations and the electrical hazards is warranted for all newly installed equipment, but especially for ion implanters.

Exposures to hydrides (probably a mixture of arsine and phosphine) as high as 60 ppb have been found during ion implanter cryo-pump maintenance (Baldwin, Rubin and Horowitz 1993). Also, high concentrations of both arsine and phosphine can off-gas from contaminated implanter parts that are removed during preventive maintenance (Flipp, Hunsaker and Herring 1992).

Portable vacuum cleaners with high-efficiency particulate attenuator (HEPA) filters are used to clean arsenic-contaminated work surfaces in ion implantation areas. Exposures above $1,000 \text{ μg/m}^3$ were measured when HEPA vacuums were improperly cleaned. HEPA vacuums, when discharging to the workspace, can also efficiently distribute the distinctive, hydride-like odour associated with ion implanter beam line cleaning (Baldwin, Rubin and Horowitz 1993).

While a concern, there have been no published reports of significant dopant gas exposures during oil changes of vacuum pumps used with dopants—possibly because this is usually done as a closed system. The lack of reported exposure may also be a result of low levels of off-gassing of hydrides from the used oil.

The result of a field study where 700 ml of used roughing pump oil from an ion implanter which used both arsine and phosphine was heated only showed detectable concentrations of airborne hydrides in the pump head space when the pump oil exceeded 70 °C (Baldwin, King and Scarpace 1988). Since normal operating temperatures for mechanical roughing pumps are 60 to 80 °C, this study did not indicate the potential for a significant exposure.

During ion implantation, x rays are formed incidental to the operation. Most implanters are designed with sufficient cabinet shielding (which includes lead sheeting strategically placed around the ion source housing and adjacent access doors) to maintain employee exposure below 2.5 microsieverts (0.25 millirems) per hour (Maletskos and Hanley 1983). However, an older model of implanters was found to have x-ray leakage above 20 microsieverts per hour (μSv/hr) at the unit's surface (Baldwin, King and Scarpace 1988). These levels were reduced to less than 2.5 μSv/hr after additional lead shielding was installed. Another older model of ion implanter was found to have x-ray leakage around an access door (up to 15 μSv/hr) and at a viewport (up to 3 μSv/hr). Additional lead shielding was added to attenuate possible exposures (Baldwin, Rubin and Horowitz 1993).

In addition to x-ray exposures from ion implanters, the possibility of neutron formation has been postulated if the implanter is operated above 8 million electron volts (MeV) or deuterium gas is

Table 83.6 • Major categories of silicon vapour-phase epitaxy.

Parameters	
Pressure	Atmospheric
Temperature	900–1300 °C
Silicon sources	Silane (SiH_4), silicon tetrachloride ($SiCl_4$), trichlorosilane ($SiHCl_3$), and dichlorosilane (SiH_2Cl_2)
Dopant gases	Arsine (AsH_3), phosphine (PH_3), diborane (B_2H_6)
Dopant gas concentration	≈100 ppm
Etchant gas	Hydrogen chloride (HCl)
Etchant gas concentration	≈1–4%
Carrier gases	Hydrogen (H_2), nitrogen (N_2)
Heating source	Radio frequency (RF) or infrared (IR)

Vapour-phase epitaxy types	Chemical reactions
Hydrogen reduction of silicon tetrachloride (1,150–1,300 °C)	$SiCl_4 + 2H_2 \rightarrow Si + 4HCl$
Pyrolytic decomposition of silane (1,000–1,100 °C)	$SiH_4 \rightarrow Si + 2H_2$
Hydrogen reduction of trichlorosilane	$SiHCl_3 + H_2 \rightarrow Si + 3HCl$
Reduction of dichlorosilane	$SiH_2Cl_2 \rightarrow Si + 2HCl$

used as an ion source (Rogers 1994). However, typically implanters are designed to operate at well below 8 MeV, and deuterium is not commonly used in the industry (Baldwin and Williams 1996).

Chemical vapour deposition

Chemical vapour deposition (CVD) involves the layering of additional material on the silicon wafer surface. CVD units normally operate as a closed system resulting in little or no chemical exposure to the operators. However, brief hydrogen chloride exposure above 5 ppm can occur when certain CVD prescrubbers are cleaned (Baldwin and Stewart 1989). Two broad categories of deposition are in common use—epitaxial and the more general category of non-epitaxial CVD.

Epitaxial chemical vapour deposition

Epitaxial growth is rigidly controlled deposition of a thin single crystal film of a material which maintains the same crystal structure as the existing substrate wafer layer. It serves as a matrix for fabricating semiconductor components in subsequent diffusion processes. Most epitaxial films are grown on substrates of the same material, such as silicon on silicon, in a process referred to as homoepitaxy. Growing layers of different materials on a substrate, such as silicon on sapphire, is called heteroepitaxy IC device processing.

Three primary techniques are used to grow epitaxial layers: vapour phase, liquid phase and molecular beam. Liquid-phase and molecular-beam epitaxy are primarily used in the processing of III-V (e.g., GaAs) devices. These are discussed in the article "III-V semiconductor manufacturing".

Vapour-phase epitaxy is used to grow a film by the CVD of molecules at a temperature of 900 to 1,300 °C. Vapours containing the silicon and controlled amounts of p- or n-type dopants in a carrier gas (usually hydrogen) are passed over heated wafers to deposit doped layers of silicon. The process is generally performed at atmospheric pressure.

Table 83.6 identifies the four major types of vapour-phase epitaxy, parameters and the chemical reactions taking place. The deposition sequence normally followed in an epitaxial process involves:

- *substrate cleaning*—physical scrubbing, solvent degreasing, acid cleaning (sulphuric, nitric and hydrochloric, and hydrofluoric is a common sequence) and drying operation
- *wafer loading*
- *heat up*—nitrogen purging and heating to approximately 500 °C, then hydrogen gas is used and RF generators inductively heat wafers
- *hydrogen chloride (HCl) etch*—usually 1 to 4% concentration of HCl is dispensed to the reactor chamber
- *deposition*—silicon source and dopant gases are metered in and deposited on wafer surface
- *cool down*—hydrogen gas switched to nitrogen again at 500 °C
- *unloading.*

Non-epitaxial chemical vapour deposition

Whereas epitaxial growth is a highly specific form of CVD where the deposited layer has the same crystalline structure orientation as the substrate layer, non-epitaxial CVD is the formation of a stable compound on a heated substrate by the thermal reaction or decomposition of gaseous compounds.

CVD can be used to deposit many materials, but in silicon semiconductor processing the materials generally encountered, in addition to epitaxial silicon, are:

- polycrystalline silicon (poly Si)
- silicon dioxide (SiO_2—both doped and undoped; p-doped glass)
- silicon nitride (Si_3N_4).

Each of these materials may be deposited in a variety of ways, and each has many applications.

Table 83.7 identifies the three major categories of CVD using operating temperature as a mechanism of differentiation.

The following components are found in nearly all the types of CVD equipment:

- reaction chamber
- gas control section
- time and sequence control
- heat source for substrates
- effluent handling.

Basically, the CVD process entails supplying controlled amounts of silicon or nitride source gases, in conjunction with nitrogen and/or hydrogen carrier gases, and a dopant gas if desired, for chemical reaction within the reactor chamber. Heat is applied to provide the necessary energy for the chemical reaction in addition to controlling the surface temperatures of the reactor and wafers. After the reaction is complete, the unreacted source gas plus the carrier gas are exhausted through the effluent handling system and vented to the atmosphere.

Passivation is a functional type of CVD. It involves the growth of a protective oxide layer on the surface of the silicon wafer, generally as the last fabrication step prior to non-fabrication processing. The layer provides electrical stability by isolating the integrated circuit's surface from electrical and chemical conditions in the environment.

Metallization

After the devices have been fabricated in the silicon substrate, they must be connected together to perform circuit functions.

83. MICROELECTRONICS AND SEMICONDUCTORS

Table 83.7 • Major categories of silicon chemical vapour deposition (CVD).

Parameters	
Pressure	Atmospheric (APCVD) or low pressure (LPCVD)
Temperature	500–1,100 °C
Silicon and nitride sources	Silane (SiH_4), silicon tetrachloride ($SiCl_4$), ammonia (NH_3), nitrous oxide (N_2O)
Dopant sources	Arsine (AsH_3), phosphine (PH_3), diborane (B_2H_6)
Carrier gases	Nitrogen (N_2), hydrogen (H_2)
Heating source	Cold wall system — radio frequency (RF) or infrared (IR)
	Hot wall system — thermal resistance

CVD type	Reaction	Carrier gas	Temperature
Medium temperature ($\approx$ 600–1,100 °C)			
Silicon nitride (Si_3N_4)	$3SiH_4 + 4NH_3 \rightarrow Si_3N_4 + 12H_2$	H_2	900–1,100 °C
Polysilicon (poly Si)	$SiH_4 + Heat \rightarrow Si + 2H_2$	H_2	850–1,000 °C
		N_2	600–700 °C
Silicon dioxide (SiO_2)	$SiH_4 + 4CO_2 \rightarrow SiO_2 + 4CO + 2H_2O$	N_2	500–900 °C
	$2H_2 + SiCl_4 + CO_2 \rightarrow SiO_2 + 4HCl$ *	H_2	800–1,000 °C
	$SiH_4 + CO \rightarrow SiO_2 + 2H_2$ *	H_2	600–900 °C
Low temperature ($\approx$ <600 °C) Silox, Pyrox, Vapox and Nitrox**			
Silicon dioxide (SiO_2) or p-doped SiO_2			
Silox	$SiH_4 + 2O_2 + Dopant \rightarrow SiO_2 + 2H_2O$	N_2	200–500 °C
Pyrox	$SiH_4 + 2O_2 + Dopant \rightarrow SiO_2 + 2H_2O$	N_2	<600 °C
Vapox	$SiH_4 + 2O_2 + Dopant \rightarrow SiO_2 + 2H_2O$	N_2	<600 °C
Silicon nitride (Si_3N_4)			
Nitrox	$3SiH_4 + 4NH_3 \ (or\ N_2O^*) \rightarrow Si_3N_4 + 12H_2$	N_2	600–700 °C
Low temperature plasma enhanced (passivation) (<600 °C)			
Utilizing radio-frequency (RF) or reactive sputtering			
Silicon dioxide (SiO_2)	$SiH_4 + 2O_2 \rightarrow SiO_2 + 2H_2O$		
Silicon nitride (Si_3N_4)	$3SiH_4 + 4NH_3 \ (or\ N_2O^*) \rightarrow Si_3N_4 + 12H_2$		

* Note: Reactions are not stoichiometrically balanced.

**Generic, proprietary or trademark names for CVD reactor systems

This process is known as metallization. Metallization provides a means of wiring or interconnecting the uppermost layers of integrated circuits by depositing complex patterns of conductive materials, which route electrical energy within the circuits.

The broad process of metallization is differentiated according to the size and thickness of the layers of metals and other materials being deposited. These are:

- *thin film*—approximate film thickness of one micron or less
- *thick film*—approximate film thickness of 10 microns or greater
- *plating*—film thicknesses are variable from thin to thick, but generally thick films.

The most common metals used for silicon semiconductor metallization are: aluminium, nickel, chromium or an alloy called nichrome, gold, germanium, copper, silver, titanium, tungsten, platinum and tantalum.

Thin or thick films may also be evaporated or deposited on various ceramic or glass substrates. Some examples of these substrates are: alumina (96% Al_2O_3), beryllia (99% BeO), borosilicate glass, pyroceram and quartz (SiO_2).

Thin film

Thin film metallization is often applied through the use of a high-vacuum or partial-vacuum deposition or evaporation technique. The major types of high-vacuum evaporation are electron beam, flash and resistive, while partial-vacuum deposition is primarily done by sputtering.

To perform any type of thin film vacuum metallization, a system usually consists of the following basic components:

- a chamber that can be evacuated to provide a sufficient vacuum for deposition
- a vacuum pump (or pumps) to reduce ambient gases in the chamber
- instrumentation for monitoring the vacuum level and other parameters
- a method of depositing or evaporating the layers of metallizing material.

Electron-beam evaporation, frequently called *E beam*, uses a focused beam of electrons to heat the metallization material. A high-intensity beam of electrons is generated in a manner similar to that used in a television picture tube. A stream of electrons is accelerated through an electrical field of typically 5 to 10 kV and focused on the material to be evaporated. The focused beam of electrons melts the material contained in a water-cooled block with a large depression called a hearth. The melted material then vaporizes within the vacuum chamber and condenses on the cool wafers as well as on the entire chamber surface. Then standard photoresist, exposure, development and wet or dry etch operations are performed to delineate the intricate metallized circuitry.

Flash evaporation is another technique for the deposition of thin metallized films. This method is primarily used when a mixture of two materials (alloys) are to be simultaneously evaporated. Some examples of two component films are: nickel/chromium (Nichrome), chromium/silicon monoxide (SiO) and aluminium/silicon.

In flash evaporation, a ceramic bar is heated by thermal resistance and a continuously fed spool of wire, stream of pellets or vibrationally dispensed powder is brought in contact with the hot filament or bar. The vaporized metals then coat the interior chamber and wafer surfaces.

Resistive evaporation (also known as filament evaporation) is the simplest and least expensive form of deposition. The evaporation is accomplished by gradually increasing the current flowing through the filament to first melt the loops of material to be evaporated, thereby wetting the filament. Once the filament is wetted, the current through the filament is increased until evaporation occurs. The primary advantage of resistive evaporation is the wide variety of materials that can be evaporated.

Maintenance work is sometimes done on the inside surface of E-beam evaporator deposition chambers called bell jars. When the maintenance technicians have their heads inside the bell jars, significant exposures can occur. Removing the metal residues that deposit on the inside surface of bell jars may result in such exposures. For example, technician exposures far above the airborne exposure limit for silver were measured during residue removal from an evaporator used to deposit silver (Baldwin and Stewart 1989).

Cleaning bell jar residues with organic cleaning solvents can also result in high solvent exposure. Technician exposures to methanol above 250 ppm have occurred during this type of cleaning. This exposure can be eliminated by using water as the cleaning solvent instead of methanol (Baldwin and Stewart 1989).

The *sputtering deposition* process takes place in a low-pressure or partial-vacuum gas atmosphere, using either direct electric current (DC, or cathode sputtering) or RF voltages as a high-energy source. In sputtering, ions of argon inert gas are introduced into a vacuum chamber after a satisfactory vacuum level has been reached through the use of a roughing pump. An electric field is formed by applying a high voltage, typically 5,000 V, between two oppositely charged plates. This high-energy discharge ionizes the argon gas atoms and causes them to move and accelerate to one of the plates in the chamber called the target. When the argon ions strike the target made of the material to be deposited, they dislodge, or sputter, these atoms or molecules. The dislodged atoms of the metallization material are then deposited in a thin film on the silicon substrates which face the target.

RF leakage from the sides and backs on many older sputter units was found to exceed the occupational exposure limit (Baldwin and Stewart 1989). Most of the leakage was attributable to cracks in the cabinets caused by repeated removal of the maintenance panels. In newer models by the same manufacturer, panels with wire mesh along the seams prevent significant leakage. The older sputterers can be retrofitted with wire mesh or,

alternatively, copper tape can be used to cover the seams to reduce the leakage.

Thick film

The structure and dimension of most thick films are not compatible with the metallization of silicon integrated circuits, primarily due to size constraints. Thick films are used mostly for metallization of hybrid electronic structures, such as in the manufacture of LCDs.

The silk-screening process is the dominant method of thick film application. Thick film materials typically used are palladium, silver, titanium dioxide and glass, gold-platinum and glass, gold-glass and silver-glass.

Resistive thick films are normally deposited and patterned on a ceramic substrate using silk-screening techniques. *Cermet* is a form of resistive thick film composed of a suspension of conductive metal particles in a ceramic matrix with an organic resin as filler. Typical cermet structures are composed of chromium, silver or lead oxide in a silicon monoxide or dioxide matrix.

Plating

Two basic types of plating techniques are used in forming metallic films on semiconductor substrates: electroplating and electroless plating.

In *electroplating*, the substrate to be plated is placed at the cathode, or negatively charged terminal, of the plating tank and immersed in an electrolytic solution. An electrode made of the metal to be plated serves as the anode, or positively charged terminal. When a direct current is passed through the solution, the positively charged metal ions, which dissolve into the solution from the anode, migrate and plate on the cathode (substrate). This method of plating is used for forming conductive films of gold or copper.

In *electroless plating*, the simultaneous reduction and oxidation of the metal to be plated is used in forming a free metal atom or molecule. Since this method does not require electrical conduction during the plating process, it can be used with insulating-type substrates. Nickel, copper and gold are the most common metals deposited in this manner.

Alloying/annealing

After the metallized interconnections have been deposited and etched, a final step of alloying and annealing may be performed. The alloying consists of placing the metallized substrates, usually with aluminium, in a low-temperature diffusion furnace to assure a low-resistance contact between the aluminium metal and silicon substrate. Finally, either during the alloy step or directly following it, the wafers are often exposed to a gas mixture containing hydrogen in a diffusion furnace at 400 to 500 °C. The annealing step is designed to optimize and stabilize the characteristics of the device by combining the hydrogen with uncommitted atoms at or near the silicon-silicon dioxide interface.

Backlapping and backside metallization

There is also an optional metallization processing step called backlapping. The backside of the wafer may be lapped or ground down using a wet abrasive solution and pressure. A metal such as gold may be deposited on the back side of the wafer by sputtering. This makes attachment of the separated die to the package easier in the final assembly.

Assembly and testing

Non-fabrication processing, which includes external packaging, attachments, encapsulation, assembly and testing, is normally performed in separate production facilities and many times is done in Southeast Asian countries, where these labour-intensive jobs are

83. MICROELECTRONICS AND SEMICONDUCTORS

less expensive to perform. In addition, ventilation requirements for process and particulate control are generally different (non-cleanroom) in the non-fabrication processing areas. These final steps in the manufacturing process involve operations that include soldering, degreasing, testing with chemicals and radiation sources, and trimming and marking with lasers.

Soldering during semiconductor manufacturing normally does not result in high lead exposures. To prevent thermal damage to the integrated circuit, the solder temperature is kept below the temperature where significant molten lead fume formation can occur (430 °C). However, cleaning solder equipment by scraping or brushing of the lead-containing residues can result in lead exposures above 50 µg/m^3 (Baldwin and Stewart 1989). Also, lead exposures of 200 µg/m^3 have occurred when improper dross removal techniques are used during wave solder operations (Baldwin and Williams 1996).

One growing concern with solder operations is respiratory irritation and asthma due to exposure to the pyrolysis products of the solder fluxes, particularly during hand soldering or touch-up operations, where historically local exhaust ventilation has not been commonly used (unlike wave solder operations, which for the last few decades have typically been enclosed in exhausted cabinets) (Goh and Ng 1987). See the article "Printed circuit board and computer assembly" for more details.

Since colophony in the solder flux is a sensitizer, all exposures should be reduced to as low as possible, regardless of air sampling results. New soldering installations particularly should include local exhaust ventilation when soldering is to be performed for extended periods of time (e.g., greater than 2 hours).

Fumes from hand soldering will rise vertically on thermal currents, entering the employee's breathing zone as the person leans over the point of soldering. Control usually is achieved by means of effective high velocity and low volume local exhaust ventilation at the solder tip.

Devices that return filtered air to the workplace may, if the filtration efficiency is inadequate, cause secondary pollution which can affect people in the workroom other than those soldering. Filtered air should not be returned to the workroom unless the amount of soldering is small and the room has good general dilution ventilation.

Wafer sort and test

After wafer fabrication is completed, each intrinsically finished wafer undergoes a wafer sort process where integrated circuitry on each specific die is electrically tested with computer-controlled probes. An individual wafer may contain from one hundred to many hundreds of separate dies or chips which must be tested. After the test results are finished, the dies are physically marked with an automatically dispensed one-component epoxy resin. Red and blue are used to identify and sort dies which do not meet the desired electrical specifications.

Die separation

With the devices or circuits on the wafer tested, marked and sorted, the individual dies on the wafer must be physically separated. A number of methods have been designed for separating the individual dies—diamond scribing, laser scribing and diamond wheel sawing.

Diamond scribing is the oldest method in use and involves drawing a precisely shaped diamond-imbedded tip across the wafer along the scribe line or "street" separating the individual dies on the wafer surface. The imperfection in the crystal structure caused by scribing allows the wafer to be bent and fractured along this line.

Laser scribing is a relatively recent die separation technique. A laser beam is generated by a pulsed, high-powered neodymium-

yttrium laser. The beam generates a groove in the silicon wafer along the scribe lines. The groove serves as the line along which the wafer breaks.

A widely used method of die separation is wet sawing—cutting substrates along the street with a high-speed circular diamond saw. Sawing can either partially cut (scribe) or completely cut (dice) through the silicon substrate. A wet slurry of material removed from the street is generated by sawing.

Die attach and bonding

The individual die or chip must be attached to a carrier package and metal lead-frame. Carriers are typically made of an insulating material, either ceramic or plastic. Ceramic carrier materials are usually made of alumina (Al_2O_3), but can possibly consist of beryllia (BeO) or steatite (MgO-SiO$_2$). Plastic carrier materials are either of the thermoplastic or thermosetting resin type.

The attachment of the individual die is generally accomplished by one of three distinct types of attachment: eutectic, preform and epoxy. Eutectic die attachment involves using an eutectic brazing alloy, such as gold-silicon. In this method, a layer of gold metal is predeposited on the backside of the die. By heating the package above the eutectic temperature (370 °C for gold-silicon) and placing the die on it, a bond is formed between the die and package.

Preform bonding involves the use of a small piece of special composition material that will adhere to both the die and the package. A preform is placed on the die-attach area of a package and allowed to melt. The die is then scrubbed across the region until the die is attached, and then the package is cooled.

Epoxy bonding involves the use of an epoxy glue to attach the die to the package. A drop of epoxy is dispensed on the package and the die placed on top of it. The package may need to be baked at an elevated temperature to cure the epoxy properly.

Once the die is physically attached to the package, electrical connections must be provided between the integrated circuit and package leads. This is accomplished by using either thermocompression, ultrasonic or thermosonic bonding techniques to attach gold or aluminium wires between the contact areas on the silicon chip and the package leads.

Thermocompression bonding is often used with gold wire and involves heating the package to approximately 300 °C and forming the bond between the wire and bonding pads using both heat and pressure. Two major types of thermocompression bonding are in use—*ball bonding* and *wedge bonding*. Ball bonding, which is used only with gold wire, feeds the wire through a capillary tube, compresses it, and then a hydrogen flame melts the wire. In addition, this forms a new ball on the end of the wire for the next bonding cycle. Wedge bonding involves a wedge-shaped bonding tool and a microscope used for positioning the silicon chip and package accurately over the bonding pad. The process is performed in an inert atmosphere.

Ultrasonic bonding uses a pulse of ultrasonic, high-frequency energy to provide a scrubbing action that forms a bond between the wire and the bonding pad. Ultrasonic bonding is primarily used with aluminium wire and is often preferred to thermocompression bonding, since it does not require the circuit chip to be heated during the bonding operation.

Thermosonic bonding is a recent technological change in gold wire bonding. It involves the use of a combination of ultrasonic and heat energies and requires less heat than thermocompression bonding.

Encapsulation

The primary purpose of encapsulation is to put an integrated circuit into a package which meets the electrical, thermal, chemical and physical requirements associated with the application of the integrated circuit.

The most widely used package types are the radial-lead type, the flat pack and the dual-in-line (DIP) package. The radial-lead type of packages are mostly made of Kovar, an alloy of iron, nickel and cobalt, with hard glass seals and Kovar leads. Flat packs use metal-lead frames, usually made of an aluminium alloy combined with ceramic, glass and metal components. Dual-in-line packages are generally the most common and often use ceramic or moulded plastics.

Moulded plastic semiconductor packages are primarily produced by two separate processes—*transfer moulding* and *injection moulding.* Transfer moulding is the predominant plastic encapsulation method. In this method, the chips are mounted on un-trimmed lead frames and then batch loaded into moulds. Powdered or pellet forms of thermosetting plastic moulding compounds are melted in a heated pot and then forced (transferred) under pressure into the loaded moulds. The powdered or pellet form plastic moulding compound systems can be used on epoxy, silicone or silicone/epoxy resins. The system usually consists of a mixture of:

- *thermosetting resins*—epoxy, silicone or silicone/epoxy
- *hardeners*—epoxy novolacs and epoxy anhydrides
- *fillers*—silica-fused or crystalline silicon dioxide (SiO_2) and alumina (Al_2O_3), generally 50-70% by weight
- *fire retardant*—antimony trioxide (Sb_2O_3) generally 1-5% by weight.

Injection moulding uses either a thermoplastic or thermosetting moulding compound which is heated to its melting point in a cylinder at a controlled temperature and forced under pressure through a nozzle into the mould. The resin solidifies rapidly, the mould is opened and the encapsulation package ejected. A wide variety of plastic compounds are used in injection moulding, with epoxy and polyphenylene sulphide (PPS) resins being the newest entries in semiconductor encapsulating.

The final packaging of the silicon semiconductor device is classified according to its resistance to leakage or ability to isolate the integrated circuit from its environment. These are differentiated as being hermetically (airtight) or non-hermetically sealed.

Leak testing and burn in

Leak testing is a procedure developed to test the actual sealing ability or hermetism of the packaged device. Two common forms of leak testing are in use: helium leak detection and radioactive tracer leak detection.

In helium leak detection, the completed packages are placed in an atmosphere of helium pressure for a period of time. Helium is able to penetrate through imperfections into the package. After removal from the helium pressurization chamber, the package is transferred to a mass-spectrometer chamber and tested for helium leaking out of imperfections in the package.

Radioactive tracer gas, usually krypton-85 (Kr-85), is substituted for helium in the second method, and the radioactive gas leaking out of the package is measured. Under normal conditions, personnel exposure from this process is less than 5 millisieverts (500 millirems) per year (Baldwin and Stewart 1989). Controls for these systems usually include:

- isolation in rooms with access limited only to necessary personnel
- posted radiation warning signs on the doors to the rooms containing Kr-85
- continuous radiation monitors with alarms and auto shut-down/isolation
- dedicated exhaust system and negative pressure room
- monitoring exposures with personal dosimetry (e.g., radiation film badges)

- regular maintenance of alarms and interlocks
- regular checks for radioactive material leakage
- safety training for operators and technicians
- ensuring radiation exposures are kept as low as reasonably achievable (ALARA).

Also, materials that come in contact with Kr-85 (e.g., exposed ICs, used pump oil, valves and O-rings) are surveyed to ensure they do not emit excessive levels of radiation because of residual gas in them before they are removed from the controlled area. Leach-Marshal (1991) provides detailed information on exposures and controls from Kr-85 fine-leak detection systems.

Burn in is a temperature and electrical stressing operation to determine the reliability of the final packaged device. Devices are placed in a temperature-controlled oven for an extended period of time using either ambient atmosphere or an inert atmosphere of nitrogen. Temperatures range from 125 °C to 200 °C (150 °C is an average), and time periods from a few hours to 1,000 hours (48 hours is an average).

Final test

For a final characterization of the packaged silicon semiconductor device's performance, a final electrical test is performed. Because of the large number and the complexity of the tests required, a computer performs and evaluates the testing of numerous parameters important to the eventual functioning of the device.

Mark and pack

Physical identification of the final packaged device is accomplished by the use of a variety of marking systems. The two major categories of component marking are contact and non-contact printing. Contact printing typically incorporates a rotary offset technique using solvent-based inks. Non-contact printing, which transfers markings without physical contact, involves ink-jet head or toner printing using solvent-based inks or laser marking.

The solvents used as a carrier for the printing inks and as a pre-cleaner are typically composed of a mixture of alcohols (ethanol) and esters (ethyl acetate). Most of the component marking systems, other than laser marking, use inks which require an additional step for setting, or curing. These curing methods are air curing, heat curing (thermal or infrared) and ultraviolet curing. Ultraviolet-curing inks contain no solvents.

Laser marking systems utilize either a high-powered carbon dioxide (CO_2) laser, or a high-powered neodymium:yttrium laser. These lasers are typically embedded in the equipment and have interlocked cabinets that enclose the beam path and the point where the beam contacts the target. This eliminates the laser beam hazard during normal operations, but there is a concern when the safety interlocks are defeated. The most common operation where it is necessary to remove the beam enclosures and defeat the interlocks is alignment of the laser beam.

During these maintenance operations, ideally the room containing the laser should be evacuated, except for necessary maintenance technicians, with the doors to the room locked and posted with appropriate laser safety signs. However, high-powered lasers used in semiconductor manufacturing are often located in large, open manufacturing areas, making it impractical to relocate non-maintenance personnel during maintenance. For these situations, a temporary control area is typically established. Normally these control areas consist of laser curtains or welding screens capable of withstanding direct contact with the laser beam. Entrance to the temporary control area is usually through a maze entry that is posted with a warning sign whenever the interlocks for the laser are defeated. Other safety precautions during beam alignment are similar to those required for the operation of an open-beamed high-powered laser (e.g., training, eye protection, written procedures and so on).

High-powered lasers are also one of the most significant electrical hazards in the semiconductor industry. Even after power is off, a significant shock potential exists within the tool and must be dissipated prior to working inside the cabinet.

Along with the beam hazard and electrical hazard, care should also be taken in performing maintenance on laser marking systems because of the potential for chemical contamination from the fire retardant antimony trioxide and beryllium (ceramic packages containing this compound will be labelled). Fumes can be created during the marking with the high-powered lasers and create residues on the equipment surfaces and fume extraction filters.

Degreasers have been used in the past to clean semiconductors before they are marked with identification codes. Solvent exposure above the applicable occupational airborne exposure limit can easily occur if an operator's head is placed below the cooling coils that cause the vapours to recondense, as can happen when an operator attempts to retrieve dropped parts or when a technician cleans residue from the bottom of the unit (Baldwin and Stewart 1989). The use of degreasers has been greatly reduced in the semiconductor industry due to restrictions on the use of ozone-depleting substances such as chlorofluorocarbons and chlorinated solvents.

Failure analysis and quality assurance

Failure analysis and quality analysis laboratories typically perform various operations used to ensure the reliability of the devices. Some of the operations performed in these laboratories present the potential for employee exposure. These include:

- *marking tests* utilizing various solvent and corrosive mixtures in heated beakers on hotplates. Local exhaust ventilation (LEV) in the form of a metal hood with adequate face velocities is needed to control fugitive emissions. Monoethanolamine solutions can result in exposures in excess of its airborne exposure limit (Baldwin and Williams 1996).
- *bubble/leak testing* utilizing high molecular weight fluorocarbons (tradename Fluorinerts)
- *x-ray packaging units*.

Cobalt-60 (up to 26,000 curies) is used in irradiators for testing the ability of ICs to withstand exposure to gamma radiation in military and space applications. Under normal conditions, personnel exposures from this operation are less than 5 millisieverts (500 millirems) per year (Baldwin and Stewart 1989). Controls for this somewhat specialized operation are similar to those utilized for Kr-85 fine-leak systems (e.g., isolated room, continuous radiation monitors, personnel exposure monitoring and so on).

Small "specific licence" alpha sources (e.g., micro- and millicuries of Americium-241) are used in the failure analysis process. These sources are covered by a thin protective coating called a window that allows alpha particles to be emitted from the source to test the integrated circuit's ability to operate when bombarded by alpha particles. Typically the sources are periodically checked (e.g., semi-annually) for leakage of radioactive material that can occur if the protective window is damaged. Any detectable leakage usually triggers removal of the source and its shipment back to the manufacturer.

Cabinet x-ray systems are used to check the thickness of metal coatings and to identify defects (e.g., air bubbles in mould compound packages). While not a significant source of leakage, these units are typically checked on a periodic basis (e.g., annually) with a hand-held survey meter for x-ray leakage and inspected to ensure that door interlocks operate properly.

Shipping

Shipping is the endpoint of most silicon semiconductor device manufacturers' involvement. Merchant semiconductor manufacturers sell their product to other end-product producers, while captive manufacturers use the devices for their own end products.

Health Study

Each process step uses a particular set of chemistries and tools that result in specific EHS concerns. In addition to concerns associated with specific process steps in silicon semiconductor device processing, an epidemiological study investigated health effects among employees of the semiconductor industry (Schenker et al. 1992). See also the discussion in the article "Health effects and disease patterns".

The main conclusion of the study was that work in semiconductor fabrication facilities is associated with an increased rate of spontaneous abortion (SAB). In the historical component of the study, the number of pregnancies studied in fabrication and non-fabrication employees were approximately equal (447 and 444 respectively), but there were more spontaneous abortions in fabrication (n = 67) than non-fabrication (n = 46). When adjusted for various factors that could cause bias (age, ethnicity, smoking, stress, socio-economic status and pregnancy history) the relative risk (RR) for fabrication verses non-fabrication was 1.43 (95% confidence interval = 0.95-2.09).

The researchers linked the increased SAB rate with exposure to certain ethylene-based glycol ethers (EGE) used in semiconductor manufacturing. The specific glycol ethers that were involved in the study and are suspected of causing adverse reproductive effects are:

- 2-methoxyethanol (CAS 109-86-4)
- 2-methoxyethyl acetate (CAS 110-49-6)
- 2-ethoxyethyl acetate (CAS 111-15-9).

While not part of the study, two other glycol ethers used in the industry, 2-ethoxyethanol (CAS 110-80-5) and diethylene glycol dimethyl ether (CAS 111-96-6) have similar toxic effects and have been banned by some semiconductor manufacturers.

In addition to an increased SAB rate associated with exposure to certain glycol ethers, the study also concluded:

- An inconsistent association existed for fluoride exposure (in etching) and SAB.
- Self-reported stress was a strong independent risk factor for SAB among women working in the fabrication areas.
- It took longer for women working in the fabrication area to get pregnant compared to women in non-fabrication areas.
- An increase in respiratory symptoms (eye, nose and throat irritation and wheezing) was present for fabrication workers compared to non-fabrication workers.
- Musculoskeletal symptoms of the distal upper extremity, such as hand, wrist, elbow and forearm pain, were associated with fabrication room work.
- Dermatitis and hair loss (alopecia) were reported more frequently among fabrication workers than non-fabrication workers.

Equipment Review

The complexity of semiconductor manufacturing equipment, coupled with continuous advancements in the manufacturing processes, makes the pre-installation review of new process equipment important for minimizing EHS risks. Two equipment review processes help ensure that new semiconductor process equipment will have appropriate EHS controls: CE marking and

Semiconductor Equipment and Materials International (SEMI) standards.

CE marking is a manufacturer's declaration that the equipment so marked conforms to the requirements of all applicable Directives of the European Union (EU). For semiconductor manufacturing equipment, the Machinery Directive (MD), Electromagnetic Compatibility (EMC) Directive and Low Voltage Directive (LVD) are considered those directives most applicable.

In the case of the EMC Directive, the services of a competent body (organization officially authorized by an EU member state) need to be retained to define testing requirements and approve findings of the examination. The MD and LVD may be assessed by either the manufacturer or a notified body (organization officially authorized by an EU member state). Regardless of the path chosen (self assessment or third party) it is the importer of record who is responsible for the imported product being CE marked. They may use the third party or self assessment information as the basis for their belief that the equipment meets the requirements for the applicable directives, but, ultimately, they will prepare the declaration of conformity and affix the CE marking themselves.

Semiconductor Equipment and Materials International is an international trade association that represents semiconductor and flat panel display equipment and materials suppliers. Among its activities is the development of voluntary technical standards that are agreements between suppliers and customers aimed at improving product quality and reliability at a reasonable price and steady supply.

Two SEMI standards that specifically apply to EHS concerns for new equipment are SEMI S2 and SEMI S8. SEMI S2-93, *Safety Guidelines for Semiconductor Manufacturing Equipment*, is intended as a minimum set of performance-based EHS considerations for equipment used in semiconductor manufacturing. SEMI S8-95, *Supplier Ergonomic Success Criteria User's Guide*, expands on the ergonomics section in SEMI S2.

Many semiconductor manufacturers require that new equipment be certified by a third party as meeting the requirements of SEMI S2. Guidelines for interpreting SEMI S2-93 and SEMI S8-95 are contained in a publication by the industry consortium SEMATECH (SEMATECH 1996). Additional information on SEMI is available on the worldwide web (http://www.semi.org).

Chemical Handling

Liquid dispensing

With automated chemical-dispensing systems becoming the rule, not the exception, the number of chemical burns to employees has decreased. However, proper safeguards need to be installed in these automated chemical-dispensing systems. These include:

- leak detection and automatic shut-off at the bulk supply source and at junction boxes
- double containment of lines if the chemical is considered a hazardous material
- high-level sensors at endpoints (bath or tool vessel)
- timed pump shut-off (allows only a specific quantity to be pumped to a location before it automatically shuts off).

Gas dispensing

Gas distribution safety has improved significantly over the years with the advent of new types of cylinder valves, restricted flow orifices incorporated into the cylinder, automated gas purge panels, high flow rate detection and shut-off and more sophisticated leak detection equipment. Because of its pyrophoric property and its wide use as a feed stock, silane gas represents the most significant explosion hazard within the industry. However, silane gas incidents have become more predictable with new research con-

ducted by Factory Mutual and SEMATECH. With proper reduced-flow orifices (RFOs), delivery pressures and ventilation rates, most explosive incidents have been eliminated (SEMATECH 1995).

Several safety incidents have occurred in recent years due to an uncontrolled mixing of incompatible gases. Because of these incidents, semiconductor manufacturers often review gas line installations and tool gas boxes to ensure that improper mixing and/or back flow of gases cannot occur.

Chemical issues typically generate the greatest concerns in semiconductor manufacturing. However, most injuries and deaths within the industry result from non-chemical hazards.

Electrical Safety

There are numerous electrical hazards associated with equipment used in this industry. Safety interlocks play an important role in electrical safety, but these interlocks are often overridden by maintenance technicians. A significant amount of maintenance work is typically performed while equipment is still energized or only partially de-energized. The most significant electrical hazards are associated with ion implanters and laser power supplies. Even after power is off, a significant shock potential exists within the tool and must be dissipated prior to working inside the tool. The SEMI S2 review process in the United States and the CE mark in Europe have helped improve electrical safety for new equipment, but maintenance operations are not always adequately considered. A careful review of maintenance operations and the electrical hazards is needed for all newly installed equipment.

Second on the electrical hazard list is the set of equipment that generates RF energy during etching, sputtering and chamber cleaning processes. Proper shielding and grounding are needed to minimize the risk of RF burns.

These electrical hazards and the many tools not being powered down during maintenance operations require the maintenance technicians to employ other means to protect themselves, such as lockout/tagout procedures. Electrical hazards are not the only energy sources which are addressed with lockout/tagout. Other energy sources include pressurized lines, many containing hazardous gas or liquids, and pneumatic controls. Disconnections for controlling these energy sources need to be in a readily available location—within the *fab* (fabrication) or chase area where the employee will be working, rather than in inconvenient locations such as subfabs.

Ergonomics

The interface between the employee and the tool continues to cause injuries. Muscle strain and sprains are fairly common within the semiconductor industry, especially with the maintenance technician. The access to pumps, chamber covers and so on often is not well designed during manufacturing of the tool and during the placement of the tool in the fab. Pumps should be on wheels or placed in pull-out drawers or trays. Lifting devices need to be incorporated for many operations.

Simple wafer handling causes ergonomic hazards, especially in older facilities. Newer facilities typically have larger wafers and thus require more automated handling systems. Many of these wafer-handling systems are considered robotic devices, and the safety concerns with these systems must be accounted for when they are designed and installed (ANSI 1986).

Fire Safety

In addition to silane gas, which has already been addressed, hydrogen gas has the potential for being a significant fire hazard. However, it is better understood and the industry has not seen many major issues associated with hydrogen.

The most serious fire hazard now is associated with *wet decks* or etching baths. The typical plastic materials of construction (polyvinyl chloride, polypropylene and flame-resistant polypropylene) all have been involved in fab fires. The ignition source may be an etch or plating bath heater, the electrical controls mounted directly to the plastic or an adjacent tool. If a fire occurs with one of these plastic tools, particle contamination and corrosive combustion products spread throughout the fab. The economic loss is high due to the down time in the fab while the area and equipment are brought back to cleanroom standards. Often some expensive equipment cannot be adequately decontaminated, and new equipment must be purchased. Therefore, adequate fire prevention and fire protection are both critical.

Fire prevention can be addressed with different non-combustible building materials. Stainless steel is the preferred material of construction for these wet decks, but often the process will not "accept" a metal tool. Plastics with less fire/smoke potential exist, but have not yet been adequately tested to determine if they will be compatible with semiconductor manufacturing processes.

For fire protection, these tools must be protected by unobstructed sprinkler protection. The placement of HEPA filters above wet benches often blocks sprinkler heads. If this occurs, additional sprinkler heads are installed below the filters. Many companies also require that a fire detection and suppression system be installed inside the plenum cavities on these tools, where many fires start.

● LIQUID CRYSTAL DISPLAYS

David G. Baldwin, James R. Rubin and Afsaneh Gerami

Liquid crystal displays (LCDs) have been commercially available since the 1970s. They are commonly used in watches, calculators, radios and other products requiring indicators and three or four alphanumeric characters. Recent improvements in the liquid crystal materials allow large displays to be manufactured. While LCDs are only a small portion of the semiconductor industry, their importance has grown with their use in flat-panel displays for portable computers, very light laptop computers and dedicated word processors. The importance of LCDs is expected to continue to grow as they eventually replace the last vacuum tube commonly used in electronics—the cathode ray tube (CRT) (O'Mara 1993).

The manufacture of LCDs is a very specialized process. Industrial hygiene monitoring results indicate very low airborne contaminant levels for the various solvent exposures monitored (Wade et al. 1981). In general, the types and quantities of toxic, corrosive and flammable solid, liquid and gaseous chemicals and hazardous physical agents in use are limited in comparison with other types of semiconductor manufacturing.

Liquid crystal materials are rod-like molecules exemplified by the cyanobiphenyl molecules shown in figure 83.5. These molecules possess the property of rotating the direction of polarized light passing through. Although the molecules are transparent to visible light, a container of the liquid material appears milky or translucent instead of transparent. This occurs because the long axis of the molecules are aligned at random angles, so the light is scattered randomly. A liquid crystal display cell is arranged so that the molecules follow a specific alignment. This alignment can be changed with an external electric field, allowing the polarization of incoming light to be changed.

In the manufacture of flat panel displays, two glass substrates are processed separately, then joined together. The front substrate

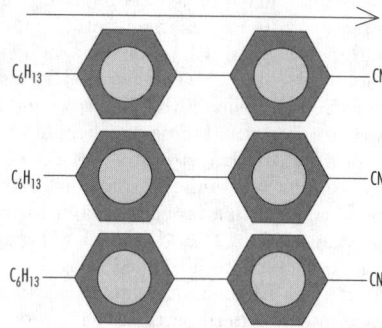

Figure 83.5 • Basic liquid crystal polymer molecules.

is patterned to create a colour filter array. The rear glass substrate is patterned to form thin film transistors and the metal interconnect lines. These two plates are mated in the assembly process and, if necessary, sliced and separated into individual displays. Liquid crystal material is injected into a gap between the two glass plates. The displays are inspected and tested and a polarizer film is applied to each glass plate.

Numerous individual processes are required to manufacture flat panel displays. They require specialized equipment, materials and processes. Certain key processes are outlined below.

Glass Substrate Preparation

The glass substrate is an essential and expensive component of the display. Very tight control of the optical and mechanical properties of the material is required at every stage of the process, especially when heating is involved.

Glass fabrication

Two processes are used to make very thin glass with very precise dimensions and reproducible mechanical properties. The fusion process, developed by Corning, utilizes a glass feed rod that melts in a wedge-shaped trough and flows up and over the sides of the trough. Flowing down both sides of the trough, the molten glass joins into a single sheet at the bottom of the trough and can be drawn downward as a uniform sheet. The thickness of the sheet is controlled by the speed of drawing down the glass. Widths of up to almost 1 m can be obtained.

Other manufacturers of glass with the appropriate dimensions for LCD substrates use the float method of manufacturing. In this method, the molten glass is allowed to flow out onto a bed of molten tin. The glass does not dissolve or react with the metallic tin, but floats on the surface. This allows gravity to smooth the surface and allow both sides to become parallel. (See the chapter *Glass, ceramics and related materials.*)

A variety of substrate sizes are available extending to 450×550 mm and larger. Typical glass thickness for flat panel displays is 1.1 mm. Thinner glass is used for some smaller displays, such as pagers, telephones, games and so on.

Cutting, bevelling and polishing

Glass substrates are trimmed to size after the fusion or float process, typically to about 1 m on a side. Various mechanical operations follow the forming process, depending on the ultimate application of the material.

Since glass is brittle and easily chipped or cracked at the edges, these are typically bevelled, chamfered or otherwise treated to reduce chipping during handling. Thermal stresses at edge cracks accumulate during substrate processing and lead to breakage. Glass breakage is a significant problem during production. Be-

Table 83.8 • Cleaning of flat panel displays.

Physical cleaning	Dry cleaning	Chemical cleaning
Brush scrubbing	Ultraviolet ozone	Organic solvent*
Jet spray	Plasma (oxide)	Neutral detergent
Ultrasonic	Plasma (non-oxide)	
Megasonic	Laser	Pure water

* Common organic solvents used in the chemical cleaning include: acetone, methanol, ethanol, n-propanol, xylene isomers, trichloroethylene, tetrachloroethylene.

sides the possibility of employee cuts and lacerations, it represents a yield loss, and glass fragments might remain in equipment, causing particulate contamination or scratching of other substrates.

Increased substrate size results in increased difficulties for glass polishing. Large substrates are mounted to carriers using wax or other adhesive and polished using a slurry of abrasive material. This polishing process must be followed by a thorough chemical cleaning to remove any remaining wax or other organic residue, as well as the metallic contaminants contained in the abrasive or polishing medium.

Cleaning

Cleaning processes are used for bare glass substrates and for substrates covered with organic films, such as colour filters, polyimide orientation films and so on. Also, substrates with semiconductor, insulator and metal films require cleaning at certain points within the fabrication process. As a minimum, cleaning is required prior to each masking step in colour filter or thin film transistor fabrication.

Most flat panel cleaning employs a combination of physical and chemical methods, with selective use of dry methods. After chemical etching or cleaning, substrates are usually dried using isopropyl alcohol. (See table 83.8.)

Colour Filter Formation

Colour filter formation on the front glass substrate includes some of the glass finishing and preparation steps common to both the front and rear panels, including the bevelling and lapping processes. Operations such as patterning, coating and curing are performed repeatedly on the substrate. Many points of similarity with silicon wafer processing exist. Glass substrates are normally handled in track systems for cleaning and coating.

Colour filter patterning

Various materials and application methods are used to create colour filters for various flat panel display types. Either a dyestuff or a pigment can be used, and either one can be deposited and patterned in several ways. In one approach, gelatin is deposited and dyed in successive photolithographic operations, using proximity printing equipment and standard photoresists. In another, pigments dispersed in photoresist are employed. Other methods for forming colour filters include electrodeposition, etching and printing.

ITO Deposition

After colour filter formation, the final step is the sputter deposition of a transparent electrode material. This is indium-tin oxide (ITO), which is actually a mixture of the oxides In_2O_3 and SnO_2. This material is the only one suitable for the transparent conductor application for LCDs. A thin ITO film is required on both sides of the display. Typically, ITO films are made using vacuum evaporation and sputtering.

Thin films of ITO are easy to etch with wet chemicals such as hydrochloric acid, but, as the pitch of the electrodes becomes smaller and features become finer, dry etching may be necessary to prevent undercutting of the lines due to overetching.

Thin Film Transistor Formation

Thin film transistor formation is very similar to the fabrication of an integrated circuit.

Thin film deposition

The substrates begin the fabrication process with a thin film application step. Thin films are deposited by CVD or physical vapour deposition (PVD). Plasma-enhanced CVD, also known as glow discharge, is used for amorphous silicon, silicon nitride and silicon dioxide.

Device patterning

Once the thin film has been deposited, a photoresist is applied and imaged to allow etching of the thin film to the appropriate dimensions. A sequence of thin films is deposited and etched, as with integrated circuit fabrication.

Orientation Film Application and Rubbing

On both the upper and bottom substrate, a thin polymer film is deposited for orientation of the liquid crystal molecules at the glass surface. This orientation film, perhaps 0.1 μm thick, may be a polyimide or other "hard" polymer material. After deposition and baking, it is rubbed with fabric in a specific direction, leaving barely detectable grooves in the surface. Rubbing can be done with a once through cloth on a belt, fed from a roller on one side, passing under a roller which contacts the substrate, onto a roller on the other side. The substrate moves underneath the cloth in the same direction as the cloth. Other methods include a travelling brush that moves across the substrate. The nap of the rubbing material is important. The grooves serve to aid the liquid crystal molecules to align at the substrate surface and to assume the proper tilt angle.

The orientation film can be deposited by spin coating or by printing. The printing method is more efficient in material usage; 70 to 80% of the polyimide is transferred from the printing roll to the substrate surface.

Assembly

Once the substrate rubbing step is completed, an automated assembly line sequence is begun, which consists of:

- adhesive application (required for sealing the panels)
- spacer application
- location and optical alignment of one plate with respect to the other
- exposure (heat or UV) to cure the adhesive and bond the two glass plates together.

Automated transport of both top and bottom plates occurs through the line. One plate receives the adhesive, and the second plate is introduced at the spacer applicator station.

Liquid Crystal Injection

In the case where more than one display has been constructed on the substrate, the displays are now separated by slicing. At this point, the liquid crystal material can be introduced into the gap between the substrates, making use of a hole left in the seal material. This entrance hole is then sealed and prepared for final inspection. Liquid crystal materials are often delivered as two or three component systems which are mixed at injection. Injection systems provide mixing and purging of the cell to avoid trapping bubbles during the filling process.

83. MICROELECTRONICS AND SEMICONDUCTORS

Inspection and Test

Inspection and functional testing are performed after assembly and liquid crystal injection. Most defects are related to particles (including point and line defects) and cell gap problems.

Polarizer Attachment

The final manufacturing step for the liquid crystal display itself is the application of the polarizer to the outside of each glass plate. Polarizer films are composite films which contain the pressure-sensitive adhesive layer needed to attach the polarizer to the glass. They are applied by automated machines which dispense the material from rolls or pre-cut sheets. The machines are variants of labelling machines developed for other industries. The polarizing film is attached to both sides of the display.

In some cases, a compensation film is applied prior to the polarizer. Compensation films are polymer films (e.g., polycarbonate and polymethyl methacrylate) that are stretched in one direction. This stretching changes the optical properties of the film.

A completed display will ordinarily have driver integrated circuits mounted on or near one of the glass substrates, usually the thin film transistor side.

Hazards

Glass breakage is a significant hazard in LCD manufacturing. Cuts and lacerations can occur. Exposure to chemicals used for cleaning is another concern.

• III-V SEMICONDUCTOR MANUFACTURING

David G. Baldwin, Afsaneh Gerami and James R. Rubin

Silicon has historically dominated IC technology development as the primary semiconductor material. The principal focus in recent years on a silicon alternative has concentrated on III-V compounds, such as gallium arsenide (GaAs), as a substrate material. As a semiconductor material, GaAs exhibits increased capabilities over silicon, such as electron mobility 5 to 6 times that of silicon. This characteristic, coupled with the potential semi-insulating properties of GaAs, leads to increased performance in both speed and power consumption.

GaAs has a zinc blende-structure consisting of two interpenetrating face-centred cubic sublattices which relate to the growth of high quality ingot material. The technology involved in the growth of GaAs is considerably more complicated than that employed for silicon, as a more complicated two-phase equilibrium and a highly volatile component, arsenic (As), is involved. Precise control of the As vapour pressure in the ingot growth system is required to maintain exact stoichiometry of the GaAs compound during the growth process. Two primary categories of III-V semiconductor display and device production have economically feasible processing procedures—LED displays and microwave IC devices.

LEDs are fabricated from single-crystal GaAs in which p-n junctions are formed by the addition of suitable doping agents—typically tellurium, zinc or silicon. Epitaxial layers of ternary and quaternary III-V materials such as gallium arsenide phosphide (GaAsP) are grown on the substrate and result in an emission band of specific wavelengths in the visible spectrum for displays or in the infrared spectrum for emitters or detectors. For example, red light with a peak at about 650 nm comes from the direct recombination of the p-n electrons and holes. Green-emitting diodes are generally composed of gallium phosphide (GaP). The generalized LED processing steps are covered in this article.

Microwave IC devices are a specialized form of integrated circuit; they are used as high-frequency amplifiers (2 to 18 GHz) for radar, telecommunications and telemetry, as well as for octave and multi-octave amplifiers for use in electronic warfare systems. Microwave IC device manufacturers typically purchase single-crystal GaAs substrate, either with or without an epitaxial layer, from outside vendors (as do silicon device manufacturers). The major processing steps include liquid-phase epitaxial deposition, fabrication and non-fabrication processing similar to silicon device manufacturing. Processing steps which warrant description additional to that for LED processing are also discussed in this article.

Wafer Manufacturing

Similar to the silicon ingot growth process, elemental forms of gallium and arsenic, plus small quantities of dopant material—silicon, tellurium or zinc—are reacted at elevated temperatures to form ingots of doped single-crystal GaAs. Three generalized methods of ingot production are utilized:

- horizontal or vertical Bridgeman
- horizontal or vertical gradient freeze
- high- or low-pressure liquid encapsulated Czochralski (LEC).

The bulk polycrystalline GaAs compound is normally formed by the reaction of As vapour with Ga metal at elevated temperatures in sealed quartz ampoules. Typically, an As reservoir located at one end of the ampoule is heated to 618 °C. This generates approximately 1 atmosphere of As vapour pressure in the ampoule, a prerequisite for obtaining stoichiometric GaAs. The As vapour reacts with the Ga metal maintained at 1,238 °C and located at the other end of the ampoule in a quartz or pyrolytic boron nitride (PBN) boat. After the arsenic has been completely reacted, a polycrystalline charge is formed. This is used for single-crystal growth by programmed cooling (gradient freeze) or by physically moving either the ampoule or furnace to provide proper temperature gradients for growth (Bridgeman). This indirect approach (arsenic transport) for compounding and growth of GaAs is used because of the high vapour pressure of arsenic at the melting point of GaAs, about 20 atmospheres at 812 °C and 60 atmospheres at 1,238 °C, respectively.

Another approach to the commercial production of bulk single-crystal GaAs is the LEC technique. A Czochralski crystal puller is loaded with chunk GaAs in a crucible with an outer graphite susceptor. The bulk GaAs is then melted at temperatures close to 1,238 °C, and the crystal is pulled in a pressurized atmosphere which could vary by manufacturer typically from a few atmospheres up to 100 atmospheres. The melt is completely encapsulated by a viscous glass, B_2O_3, which prevents melt dissociation as the As vapour pressure is matched or exceeded by the pressure of an inert gas (typically argon, or nitrogen) applied in the puller chamber. Alternatively, monocrystalline GaAs can be synthesized *in situ* by injecting the As into the molten Ga or combining As and Ga directly at high pressure.

GaAs wafer manufacturing represents the semiconductor manufacturing process with the greatest potential for significant, routine chemical exposures. While GaAs wafer manufacturing is done only by a small percentage of semiconductor manufacturers, particular emphasis is needed in this area. The large amounts of As used in the process, the numerous steps in the process and the low airborne exposure limit for arsenic make it difficult to control exposures. Articles by Harrison (1986); Lenihan, Sheehy and Jones (1989); McIntyre and Sherin (1989) and Sheehy and Jones (1993) provide additional information on the hazards and controls for this process.

Polycrystalline ingot synthesis

Ampoule load and seal

Elemental As (99.9999%) in chunk form is weighed and loaded into a quartz boat in an exhausted glove box. Pure liquid Ga (99.9999%) and the dopant material are also weighed and loaded into a quartz or pyrolytic boron nitride (PBN) boat(s) in the same manner. The boats are loaded into a long cylindrical quartz ampoule. (In the Bridgman and gradient freeze techniques, a seed crystal with the desired crystallographic orientation is also introduced, whereas in the two-stage LEC technique, where only poly GaAs is needed at this stage, a polycrystalline GaAs is synthesized without the seed crystal.)

The quartz ampoules are placed in a low-temperature furnace and heated while the ampoule is purged with hydrogen (H_2), in a process known as hydrogen reduction reaction, to remove oxides. After purging with an inert gas such as argon, the quartz ampoules are attached to a vacuum pump assembly, evacuated, and the ampoule ends are heated and sealed with a hydrogen/oxygen torch. This creates a charged and sealed quartz ampoule ready for furnace growth. Hydrogen purging and the hydrogen/oxygen torch system is a potential fire/explosion hazard if proper safety devices and equipment are not in use (Wade et al. 1981).

Because the arsenic is being heated, this assembly is maintained under exhaust ventilation. Arsenic oxide deposits can form in the exhaust duct supporting this assembly. Care must be taken to prevent exposure and contamination should the ducts be disturbed in any way.

Storage and handling of arsenic chunks is a concern. For security, often the arsenic is kept under locked storage and with a tight inventory control. Typically the arsenic is also kept in a fire-rated storage cabinet to prevent its involvement in event of a fire.

Furnace growth

The Bridgeman and the gradient freeze methods of single-crystal ingot growth both utilize charged and sealed quartz ampoules in a high-temperature furnace enclosure which is vented to a wet scrubber system. The primary exposure hazards during furnace growth relate to the potential for the quartz ampoule to implode or explode during ingot growth. This situation occurs on a rather sporadic and infrequent basis, and is the result of one of the following:

- the partial pressure of the As vapour which results from the high temperatures used in the growth process
- devitrification of the quartz ampoule glass, which creates hairline cracks and the attendant potential for de-pressurization of the ampoule
- lack of accurate high-temperature control devices on the heating source—usually resistance type—with the resultant over-pressurization of the quartz ampoule
- thermocouple malfunction or failure, resulting in over-pressurization of the quartz ampoule
- excess As or too little Ga in the ampoule tube, resulting in extremely high As pressure, which can cause catastrophic de-pressurization of the ampoule.

The horizontal Bridgeman system consists of a multizone furnace in which the sealed quartz ampoule has separate temperature zones—the arsenic "cold" finger end at 618°C and the quartz gallium/dopant/seed crystal boat containing the melt at 1,238 °C. The basic principle in the horizontal Bridgeman system involves traversing two heated zones (one above the melting point of GaAs, and one below the melting point) over a boat of GaAs to provide the precisely controlled freezing of molten GaAs. The seed crystal, maintained at all times in the freeze zone, provides

the initial crystal starting structure, defining the direction and orientation of the crystalline structure within the boat. The quartz boat and ampoule of Ga and As are suspended within the heater chamber by a set of silicon carbide liners called support tubes, which are positioned within the resistance heater assembly to mechanically move the full distance of the ampoule. Additionally, the furnace assembly rests on a table which must be tilted during growth to provide the proper interface of the synthesized GaAs melt with the seed crystal.

In the gradient freeze method, a multizone high temperature furnace utilizing resistance heating is kept at 1,200 to 1,300 °C (1,237 °C is the melt/freeze point of GaAs). The total ingot growth process duration is typically 3 days and comprises the following steps:

- furnace firing to temperature
- GaAs synthesis
- seeding the melt
- cool down/crystal growth.

The quartz ampoule is also tilted during the growth process by the use of a scissors-type manual jack.

Ampoule breakout

After the single-crystal GaAs ingot is grown within the sealed quartz ampoule, the ampoule must be opened and the quartz boat containing the ingot plus seed crystal removed. This is accomplished by one of the following methods:

- cutting off the sealed end of the ampoules with a wet circular saw
- heating and cracking the ampoule with a hydrogen/oxygen torch
- breaking the bagged ampoule with a hammer while under exhaust to control the airborne arsenic.

The quartz ampoules are recycled by wet etching the condensed arsenic on the interior surface with aqua regia (HCl,HNO_3) or sulphuric acid/hydrogen peroxide (H_2SO_4/H_2O_2).

Ingot beadblasting/cleaning

In order to see polycrystalline defects and remove exterior oxides and contaminants, the single-crystal GaAs ingot must be beadblasted. The beadblasting is done in an exhausted glove-box unit utilizing either silicon carbide or calcined alumina blasting media. Wet cleaning is done in chemical baths provided with local exhaust ventilation and utilizing *aqua regia* or alcohol rinses (isopropyl alcohol and/or methanol).

Monocrystalline ingot growth

The polycrystalline GaAs ingot retrieved from the ampoule is broken into chunks, weighed and placed into a quartz or PBN crucible, and a boron oxide disc is placed on top of it. The crucible is then placed into a crystal grower (puller) pressurized in an inert gas, and heated to 1,238 °C. At this temperature, the GaAs melts, with the lighter boron oxide becoming a liquid encapsulant to prevent the arsenic from dissociating from the melt. A seed crystal is introduced into the melt below the liquid cap and while counter-rotating, is slowly withdrawn from the melt, thereby solidifying as it leaves the "hot-zone". This process takes approximately 24 hours, depending on the charge size and crystal diameter.

Once the growth cycle is completed, the grower is opened to retrieve the monocrystalline ingot and for cleaning. Some amount of arsenic escapes from the melt even with the liquid cap in place.

There can be significant exposure to airborne arsenic during this step of the process. To control this exposure, the grower is cooled to below 100 °C, which results in the deposition of fine arsenic particulate on the interior surface of the grower. This cooling helps minimize the amount of arsenic that becomes airborne.

Heavy deposits of arsenic-containing residues are left on the inside of the crystal grower. Removal of the residues during routine preventive maintenance can result in significant airborne concentrations of arsenic (Lenihan, Sheehy and Jones 1989; Baldwin and Stewart 1989; McIntyre and Sherin 1989). Controls used during this maintenance operation often include scavenger exhaust ventilation, disposable clothing and respirators.

When the ingot is removed, the grower is dismantled. A HEPA vacuum is utilized to pick up arsenic particulates on all parts of the grower. After vacuuming, the stainless steel parts are wiped with an ammonium hydroxide/hydrogen peroxide mixture to remove any residual arsenic, and the grower is assembled.

Wafer processing

X-ray diffraction
The crystalline orientation of the GaAs ingot is determined by the use of an x-ray diffraction unit, as in silicon ingot processing. A low-powered laser can be used to determine the crystalline orientation in a production setting; however, x-ray diffraction is more accurate and is the preferred method.

When x-ray diffraction is used, often the x-ray beam is totally enclosed in a protective cabinet that is periodically checked for radiation leakage. Under certain circumstances, it is not practical to fully contain the x-ray beam in an interlocked enclosure. In this instance operators may be required to wear radiation finger badges, and controls similar to those used for high-powered lasers are used (e.g., enclosed room with limited access, operator training, enclosing the beam as much as practical, etc.) (Baldwin and Williams 1996).

Ingot cropping, grinding and slicing
The ends or tails of the single-crystal ingot are removed, using a water-lubricated single-bladed diamond saw, with various coolants added to the water. The monocrystalline ingot is then placed on a lathe which shapes it into a cylindrical ingot of uniform diameter. This is the grinding process, which is also a wet process.

After cropping and grinding, GaAs ingots are epoxy or wax mounted to a graphite beam and sawed into individual wafers through the use of automatically operated inside diameter (ID) diamond-blade saws. This wet operation is done with the use of lubricants and generates a GaAs slurry, which is collected, centrifuged and treated with calcium fluoride to precipitate out the arsenic. The supernatant is tested to ensure that it does not contain excess arsenic, and the sludge is pressed into a cake and disposed of as hazardous waste. Some manufacturers send the collected slurry from the ingot cropping, grinding and slicing processes for Ga reclaim.

Arsine and phosphine may be formed from the reaction of GaAs and indium phosphide with moisture in the air, other arsenides and phosphides or when mixed with acids during the processing of gallium arsenide and indium phosphide; 92 ppb arsine and 176 ppb phosphine have been measured 2 inches away from the slicing blades used to cut GaAs and indium phosphide ingots (Mosovsky et al. 1992, Rainer et al. 1993).

Wafer washing
After GaAs wafers are dismounted from the graphite beam, they are cleaned by sequential dipping in wet chemical baths containing solutions of sulphuric acid/hydrogen peroxide or acetic acid and alcohols.

Edge profiling
Edge profiling is also a wet process performed on sliced wafers to form an edge around the wafer, which makes it less prone to breakage. Because only a thin cut is made on the surface of the wafer, only a small amount of slurry is generated.

Lapping and polishing
Wafers are wax mounted on a lapping or grinding plate, using a hotplate, and are lapped on a machine exerting a set rotational speed and pressure. A lapping solution is fed onto the lapping surface (a slurry of aluminium oxide, glycerine and water). After a brief lapping period, when the desired thickness is achieved, the wafers are rinsed and mounted on a mechanical polishing machine. Polishing is performed using a sodium bicarbonate, 5% chlorine, water (or sodium hypochlorite) and colloidal silica slurry. The wafers are then dismounted on a hotplate, the wax is removed using solvents and the wafers are cleaned.

Epitaxy
The single-crystal GaAs wafers are used as substrates for the growth of very thin layers of the same or other III-V compounds having the desired electronic or optical properties. This must be done in such a way as to continue, in the grown layer, the crystal structure of the substrate. Such crystal growth, in which the substrate determines the crystallinity and orientation of the grown layer, is called epitaxy, and a variety of epitaxial growth techniques are used in III-V display and device production. The most common techniques are:

- liquid-phase epitaxy (LPE)
- molecular-beam epitaxy (MBE)
- vapour-phase epitaxy (VPE)
- metallorganic chemical-vapour deposition (MOCVD)—also known as organometallic vapour-phase epitaxy (OMVPE).

Liquid-phase epitaxy
In LPE a layer of doped III-V material is grown directly on the surface of the GaAs substrate using a graphite holder that contains separate chambers for the material to be deposited on the wafers. Weighed quantities of deposition materials are added to the upper chamber of the holder, while the wafers are placed in a lower chamber. The assembly is placed within a quartz reaction tube under a hydrogen atmosphere. The tube is heated to melt the deposition materials, and when the melt equilibrates, the upper section of the holder is slid so that the melt is positioned over the wafer. The furnace temperature is then lowered to form the epitaxial layer.

LPE is primarily used in microwave IC epitaxy and for manufacturing LEDs of certain wavelengths. The major concern with this LPE process is the use of highly flammable hydrogen gas in the system, which is mitigated by good engineering controls and early warning systems.

Molecular-beam epitaxy
Vacuum epitaxy in the form of MBE has developed as a particularly versatile technique. MBE of GaAs consists of an ultrahigh-vacuum system containing sources for atomic or molecular beams of Ga and As and a heated substrate wafer. The molecular-beam sources are usually containers for liquid Ga or solid As. The sources have an orifice that faces the substrate wafer. When the effusion oven (or container) is heated, atoms of Ga or molecules of As effuse from the orifice. For GaAs, growth usually takes place with a substrate temperature above 450 °C.

High exposures to arsine can occur during the maintenance of solid-source MBE systems. Room air concentrations of 0.08 ppm were detected in one study when the chamber of the MBE unit was opened for maintenance. The authors hypothesized that transient arsine generation may be caused by a reaction of very fine particulate arsenic with water vapour, with aluminium acting as a catalyst (Asom et al. 1991).

Vapour phase epitaxy

Degreased and polished wafers undergo an etch and clean step prior to epitaxy. This involves a sequential wet-chemical dipping operation utilizing sulphuric acid, hydrogen peroxide and water in a 5:1:1 ratio; a de-ionized water rinse; and an isopropyl alcohol clean/dry. A visual inspection is also performed.

Two major techniques of VPE are in use, based on two different chemistries:

- the III-halogens ($GaCl_3$) and V-halogens ($AsCl_3$) or V-hydrogen (AsH_3 and PH_3)
- the III metal-organics and V-hydrogen, such as $Ga(CH_3)_3$ and AsH_3—OMVPE.

The thermochemistries of these techniques are very different. The halogen reactions are usually "hot" to "cold" ones, in which the III-halogen is generated in a hot zone by reaction of the III element with HCl, and then diffuses to the cold zone, where it reacts with the V species to form III-V material. The metalorganic chemistry is a "hot wall" process in which the III metalorganic compound "cracks" or pyrolyzes away the organic group and the remaining III and hydride V react to form III-V.

In VPE, GaAs substrate is placed in a heated chamber under a hydrogen atmosphere. The chamber is heated by either RF or resistance heating. HCl is bubbled through a Ga boat, forming gallium chloride, which then reacts with the AsH_3 and PH_3 near the surface of the wafers to form GaAsP, which is deposited as the epitaxial layer on the substrate. There are a number of dopants that can be added (depending on the product and the recipe). These include low concentrations of tellurides, selenides and sulphides.

A common technique used for VPE in LED processing is the III-halogen and V-hydrogen (hydride) system. It involves a two-cycle process—initially growing the epitaxial layer of GaAsP on the GaAs substrate and, lastly, an etch cycle to clean the graphite/quartz reactor chamber of impurities. During the epitaxial growth cycle, the pre-cleaned GaAs wafers are loaded onto a carousel located inside a quartz reactor chamber containing a reservoir of elemental liquid gallium through which anhydrous HCl gas is metered, forming $GaCl_3$. The hydride/hydrogen gas mixtures (e.g., 7% AsH_3/H_2 and 10% PH_3/H_2) are also metered into the reactor chamber with the addition of ppm concentrations of organometallic dopants of tellurium and selenium. The chemical species in the hot zone, the upper part of the reaction chamber, react, and, in the cold zone, the lower part of the chamber, form the desired layer of GaAsP on the wafer substrate as well as on the interior of the reactor chamber.

Effluents from the reactor are routed to a hydrogen torch system (combustion chamber or burnbox) for pyrolysis and are vented to a wet scrubber system. Alternatively, the reactor effluents can be bubbled through a liquid medium to trap most of the particulates. The safety challenge is reliance on the reactors themselves to "crack" the gases. The efficiency of these reactors is approximately 98 to 99.5%; therefore, some unreacted gases may be coming off of the bubbler when they are taken out by the operators. There is off-gassing of various arsenic- and phosphorus-containing compounds from these bubblers, requiring that they be quickly transported to a vented sink for maintenance, where they are purged and cleaned, in order to keep personnel exposure low. The occupational hygiene challenge of this process is profiling the exhaust effluent, since most of the out-gassed compounds from various parts of the reactor, especially the bub-

bler, are unstable in air and the available conventional collection media and analytical techniques are not discriminatory towards the different species.

Another concern is prescrubbers for VPE reactors. They can contain high concentrations of arsine and phosphine. Exposures above occupational exposure limits can occur if these prescrubbers are indiscriminately opened (Baldwin and Stewart 1989).

The etch cycle is performed at the end of the growth cycle and on new reactor parts to clean the interior surface of impurities. Undiluted HCl gas is metered into the chamber for periods of approximately 30 minutes, and the reactor is heated to over 1,200 °C. The effluents are vented to the wet scrubber system for neutralization.

At the end of both the growth and etch cycles, an extended N_2 purge is used to flush the reactor chamber of toxic/flammable and corrosive gases.

Reactor cleaning

After each growth cycle, the VPE reactors must be opened, the wafers removed, and both the upper and the lower portion of the reactor physically cleaned. The cleaning process is performed by the operator.

The quartz prescrubber from the reactors is physically moved out of the reactor and placed in an exhausted sink where it is purged with N_2, rinsed with water and then submerged in *aqua regia*. This is followed by another water rinse prior to drying the part. The intention of the N_2 purge is to simply displace the oxygen due to the presence of unstable, pyrophoric phosphorus. Some residues containing various arsenicals and phosphorus-containing by-products are left on these parts even after the purge and water rinse. The reaction between these residues and the strong oxidizer/acid mixture could potentially generate significant amounts of AsH_3 and some PH_3. There is also exposure potential with other maintenance procedures in the area.

The bottom part of the quartz reaction chamber and the bottom plate (base plate) are scraped clean using a metal tool, and the particulate material (mixture of GaAs, GaAsP, arsenic oxides, phosphorus oxides and entrapped hydride gases) is collected in a metal container positioned below the vertical reactor. A high-efficiency vacuum is used for the final clean-up.

Another operation with potential for chemical exposure is cleaning the reactor's trap. The trap cleaning is done by scraping the graphite parts from the upper chamber, which have a crust of all the previously mentioned by-products plus arsenic chloride. The scraping procedure generates dust and is performed in a ventilated sink to minimize exposure to the operators. The process exhaust line, which contains all the by-products plus moisture that forms a liquid waste, is opened and drained into a metal container. The HEPA vacuum is used to clean off any dust particles that may have escaped during the transfer of the graphite parts and from the raising and lowering of the bell jar, which knocks off any loose particles.

Metallorganic chemical-vapour deposition

MOCVD is widely used in the preparation of III-V devices. In addition to the hydride gases used as source materials in other CVD systems (e.g., arsine and phosphine), less toxic liquid alternatives (e.g., tertiary butyl arsine and tertiary butyl phosphine) are also used in MOCVD systems, along with other toxics such as cadmium alkyls and mercury (Content 1989; Rhoades, Sands and Mattera 1989; Roychowdhury 1991).

While VPE refers to a compound material deposition process, MOCVD refers to the parent chemistry sources used in the system. Two chemistries are used: halides and metallorganic. The VPE process described above is a halide process. A group III halide (gallium) is formed in the hot zone and the III-V compound is deposited in the cold zone. In the metallorganic process for GaAs, trimethylgallium is metered into the reaction chamber along with arsine, or a less toxic liquid alternative such as tertiary butyl arsine, to form gallium arsenide. An example of a typical MOCVD reaction is:

$$(CH_3)_3Ga + AsH_3 \rightarrow GaAs + 3CH_4$$

There are other chemistries used in MOCVD processing of LEDs. Organometallics used as the group III elements include trimethyl gallium (TMGa), triethyl gallium (TEGa), TM indium, TE indium and TM aluminium. Hydride gases are also used in the process: 100% AsH_3 and 100% PH_3. The dopants used in the process are: dimethyl zinc (DMZ), bis-cyclopentadienyl magnesium and hydrogen selenide (H_2Se). These materials are reacted within the reaction chamber under a low-pressure H_2 atmosphere. The reaction produces epitaxial layers of AlGaAs, AlInGaP, InAsP and GaInP. This technique has been traditionally used in the manufacturing of semiconductor lasers and optical communication devices such as transmitters and receivers for fibre optics. The AlInGaP process is used to produce very bright LEDs.

Similar to the VPE process, MOCVD reactor and part cleaning presents challenges for both the process as well as the occupational hygienist, especially if large amounts of concentrated PH_3 is used in the process. The "cracking" efficiency of these reactors is not as great as that of the VPE reactors. There is a significant amount of phosphorus generated, which is a fire hazard. The cleaning procedure involves the use of dilute hydrogen peroxide/ammonium hydroxide on various parts from these reactors, which is an explosion hazard if, due to operator error, a concentrated solution is used in the presence of a metal catalyst.

Device Fabrication

The GaAs wafer with an epitaxially grown layer of GaAsP on the upper surface proceeds to the device fabrication processing sequence.

Nitride deposition

A high-temperature CVD of silicon nitride (Si_3N_4) is performed, using a standard diffusion furnace. The gaseous sources are silane (SiH_4) and ammonia (NH_3) with a nitrogen carrier gas.

Photolithographic process

The standard photoresist, aligning/exposure, developing and stripping process is utilized as in silicon device processing (see the section on lithography in the article "Silicon semiconductor manufacturing").

Wet etching

Various mixtures of wet-chemical acid solutions are used in plastic baths in locally exhausted etch stations, some provided with vertically mounted laminar HEPA filtered supply systems. The primary acids in use are sulphuric (H_2SO_4), hydrofluoric (HF), hydrochloric (HCl) and phosphoric (H_3PO_4). As in silicon processing, hydrogen peroxide (H_2O_2) is used with sulphuric acid, and ammonium hydroxide (NH_4OH) provides a caustic etch. A cyanide solution (sodium or potassium) is also used for etching aluminium. However, cyanide etching is slowly being phased out as other etchants are developed for this process. As an alternative to wet etching, a plasma etching and ashing process is used. The reactor configurations and reactant gases are very similar to those utilized in silicon device processing.

Diffusion

A closed ampoule zinc diarsenide solid source diffusion is performed in a vacuum diffusion furnace at 720 °C, utilizing a N_2

carrier gas. Arsenic and zinc arsenide are used as dopants. They are weighed in a glove box in the same manner as in bulk substrate.

Metallization

An initial aluminium evaporation is performed utilizing an E-beam evaporator. After backlapping, a last step gold evaporation is performed utilizing a filament evaporator.

Alloying

A final alloying step is performed in a low-temperature diffusion furnace, utilizing a nitrogen inert atmosphere.

Backlapping

Backlapping is done to remove deposited materials (GaAsP, Si_3N_4 and so on) from the backside of the wafer. The wafers are wax mounted to a lapper plate and wet lapped with a colloidal silica slurry. Then the wax is removed by wet stripping the wafers in an organic stripper in a locally exhausted wet chemical etch station. Another alternative to wet lapping is dry lapping, which utilizes aluminium oxide "sand".

There are a number of resists and resist strippers used, typically containing sulphonic acid (dodecyl benzene sulphonic acid), lactic acid, aromatic hydrocarbon, naphthalene and catechol. Some resist strippers contain butyl ethanoate, acetic acid and butyl ester. There are both negative and positive resists and resist strippers used, depending on the product.

Final test

As in silicon device processing, the completed LED circuits are computer tested and marked (see "Silicon semiconductor manufacturing"). Final inspection is performed and then the wafers are electrically tested to mark defective dies. A wet saw is then used to separate the individual dies, which are then sent for assembly.

PRINTED CIRCUIT BOARD AND COMPUTER ASSEMBLY

Michael E. Williams

Printed Wiring Boards

Printed wiring boards (PWBs) are the interconnective electrical framework and physical structure that hold together the various electronic components of a printed circuit board. The major categories of PWBs are single-sided, double-sided, multilayer and flexible. The complexity and spacing requirements of ever increasingly dense and smaller boards have required that both sides of the board be covered with underlying circuits. Single-sided boards met early calculator and simple consumer electronic devices requirements, but portable notebook computers, personal digital assistants and personal music systems have required double-sided and multilayer PWBs. The processing of the patterning of PWBs is essentially a photolithographic process that involves selectively depositing and removing layers of materials on a dielectric substrate that acts as the electrical "wiring" that is etched or deposited on the printed wiring board.

Multilayer boards contain two or more pieces of dielectric material with circuitry that are stacked up and bonded together. Electrical connections are established from one side to the other, and to the inner layer circuitry, by drilled holes which are subsequently plated through with copper. The dielectric substrate most commonly used is fibreglass sheets (epoxy/fibreglass laminate). Other materials are glass (with polyimide, Teflon or triazine resins) and paper covered with phenolic resin. In the United

Table 83.9 • PWB process: Environmental, health and safety issues.

Primary process steps	Health and safety issues	Environmental issues
Material prep Purchase specific laminate, entry material and backup board in pre-cut size Computer aided processing layout	Computer aided design — VDU and ergonomics hazards	None
Stack and pin Copper-clad panels are stacked with entry material and backup board; holes drilled and dowel pinned.	Noise during drilling; drilling particulate containing copper, lead, gold and epoxy/fibreglass	Waste particulate (copper, lead, gold and epoxy/fibreglass) — recycled or reclaimed
Drilling Numerically controlled (N/C) drilling machines	Noise during drilling; drilling particulate containing copper, lead, gold and epoxy/fibreglass	Waste particulate (copper, lead, gold and epoxy/fibreglass) — recycled or reclaimed
Deburr Drilled panels pass through brushes or abrasive wheel	Noise during deburr; particulate containing copper, lead, gold and epoxy/fibreglass	Waste particulate (copper, lead, gold and epoxy/fiberglass) — recycled or reclaimed
Electroless copper plating Adding thin copper layer to through holes (multistep process)	Inhalation and dermal exposure to cleaners, conditioners, etchants, catalysts — H_2SO_4, H_2O_2, glycol ethers, $KMnO_4$, NH_4HF_2, palladium, $SnCl_2$, $CuSO_4$, formaldehyde, NaOH	Water effluents — acids, copper, caustics, fluorides; air emissions — acid gases, formaldehyde
Imaging Dry film resist — UV sensitive photopolymer Screen printed resist — light sensitive emulsion Liquid resist — photosensitive liquid resists	Inhalation and dermal exposure to resists; developers; and strippers — rubber-based resists with solvents; Na_3PO_4 and K_2CO_3; cupric chloride (Cl_2 gas), monoethanol amine (MEA)	Air emissions — solvents (VOCs), acid gases, MEA; waste — liquids
Pattern plating Cleaning Copper plating Tin or tin/lead plating Rack stripping	Inhalation and dermal hazards from cleaning; copper plating or tin/tin and lead plating and rack stripping — H_3PO_4, H_2SO_4; H_2SO_4 and $CuSO_4$; fluoboric acid and Sn/Pb; concentrated HNO_3	Air emissions — acid gases; water effluents — acids, fluorides, metals (copper, lead and tin)
Strip, etch, strip Resist strip Alkaline etch Copper strip	Inhalation and dermal hazards from resist strip; alkaline etch or copper strip — monoethanol amine (MEA); NH_4OH; NH_4Cl/NH_4OH or NH_4HF_2	Air emissions — MEA, ammonia, fluorides; water effluents — ammonia, fluorides, metals (copper, lead and tin), resist compounds
Solder mask Epoxy inks — screen printing Dry films — laminated to PWB Liquid photo imageable epoxy ink	Inhalation and dermal hazards from precleaning; epoxy inks and solvent carriers; developers — H_2SO_4; epichlorhydrin + bisphenol A, glycol ethers (PGMEA based); gamma-butyrolactone. UV light from curing process	Air emissions — acid gases, glycol ethers (VOCs); waste — solvents, epoxy inks
Solder coating Solder levelling	Inhalation and dermal hazards from flux, decomposition products and lead/tin solder residues — dilute glycol ethers + <1% HCl and <1% HBr; aldehydes, HCl, CO; lead and tin	Air emissions — glycol ethers (VOC), acid gases, aldehydes, CO; waste — lead/tin solder, flux
Gold and nickel plating	Inhalation and dermal hazards from acids, metals and cyanides — H_2SO_4, HNO_3, $NiSO_4$, potassium gold cyanide	Air emissions — acid gases, cyanides; water emissions — acids, cyanides, metals; waste — cyanides, metals
Component legend Screen print Oven cure	Inhalation and dermal hazards from epoxy based inks and solvent carriers — glycol ether-based solvents, epichlorhydrin + bisphenol A	Air emissions — glycol ethers (VOCs) waste — inks and solvents (small quantities)

Cl_2 = chlorine gas; CO = carboon monoxide; $CuSO_4$ = copper sulphate; H_2O_2 = hydrogen peroxide; H_2SO_4 = sulphuric acid; H_3PO_4 = phosphoric acid; HBR = hydrobromic acid; HCl = hydrochloric acid; HNO_3 = nitric acid; K_2CO_3 = potassium carbonate; $KMnO_4$ = potassium permanganate; NA_3PO_4 = sodium phosphate; NH_4Cl = ammonium chloride; NH_4OH = ammonium hydroxide; $NiSO_4$ = nickel sulphate; Pb = lead; Sn = tin; $SnCl_2$ = stannous chloride; UV = ultraviolet; VOCs = volatile organic compounds.

83. MICROELECTRONICS AND SEMICONDUCTORS

States, laminated boards are categorized based on their fire-extinguishing properties; drilling, punching and machining properties; properties of moisture absorption; chemical and heat resistance; and mechanical strength (Sober 1995). The FR-4 (epoxy resin and glass cloth substrate) is widely used for high-technology applications.

The actual PWB process involves numerous steps and a wide variety of chemical agents. Table 83.9 illustrates a typical multi-layer process and the EHS issues associated with this process. The primary differences between a single-sided and double-sided board is that the single-sided starts with raw material clad only on one side with copper, and omits the electroless copper plating step. The standard double-sided board has a solder mask over bare copper and is plated through the holes; the board has gold-coated contacts and a component legend. The majority of PWBs are multilayer boards, which are double-sided with internal layers that have been fabricated and sandwiched inside the laminate package and then processed almost identically to a double-layer board.

Printed Circuit Board Assembly

Printed circuit board (PCB) assembly involves the hard attachment of electronic components to the PWB through the use of lead/tin solder (in a wave solder machine or applied as a paste and then reflowed in a low-temperature furnace) or epoxy resins (cured in a low-temperature furnace). The underlying PWB (single-sided, double-sided, multilayer or flexible) will determine the densities of components that can be attached. Numerous process and reliability issues form the basis for the selection of the PCB assembly processes that will be utilized. The major technological processes are: total surface mounting technology (SMT), mixed technology (includes both SMT and plated through hole (PTH)) and underside attachment. Typically in modern electronics/computer assembly facilities, the mixed technology is utilized, with some components being surface mounted and other connectors/components being soldered on using through-hole technology or solder reflowing. A "typical" mixed technology process is discussed below, wherein a surface mount process involving adhesive attach, wave soldering and reflow soldering is utilized. With mixed technology, it is sometimes possible to reflow surface mount components (SMCs) on the top side of a double-sided board and wave solder the SMCs on the underside. Such a process is particularly useful when the surface mount and through-hole technologies must be mixed on a single board, which is the norm in current electronics manufacturing. The first step is to mount the SMCs to the top side of the board, using the solder reflow process. Next, the through-hole components are inserted. The board is then inverted, and the underside SMCs are mounted adhesively to the board. Wave soldering of both through-hole components and underside SMCs is the final step.

The major technical mixed technology process steps include:

- pre- and post-cleaning
- solder paste and adhesive application (screen print and placement (SMT and PTH))
- component insertion
- adhesive cure and solder reflow
- fluxing (PTH)
- wave soldering (PTH)
- inspection and touch-up
- testing
- reworking and repairing
- support operations—stencil cleaning.

A brief discussion of the important environmental, health and safety implications for each process step is provided below.

Pre- and post-cleaning

Commercial PWBs are typically purchased from a PWB supplier and have been pre-cleaned with de-ionized (DI) water solution to remove all surface contaminants. Prior to the concerns regarding stratospheric ozone layer depletion, an ozone depleting substance, such as a chlorofluorocarbon (CFC), would be used as a final clean, or even pre-clean by the electronic device manufacturer. At the end of the PCB assembly process, the use of a chlorofluorocarbon "vapour degreasing" operation to remove residues from the flux/wave soldering operation was typical. Again due to concerns about ozone depletion and tight regulatory controls on the production of CFCs, process changes were made that allowed the complete PWB assemblies to by-pass cleaning or use only a DI water cleaning.

Solder paste and adhesive application (stencil print and placement) and component insertion

The application of lead/tin solder paste to the PWB surface allows the surface mount component to be attached to the PWB and is key to the SMT process. The solder material acts as a mechanical linkage for electrical and thermal conduction and as a coating for surface protection and enhanced solderability. The solder paste is made up of approximately 70 to 90% non-volatile matter (on a weight per weight or weight per volume basis):

- lead/tin solder
- a blend of modified resins (rosin acids or mildly activated rosin)
- activators (in the case of "no clean" products, mixtures of amine hydrohalides and acids or just carboxylic acids).

Solvents (volatile matter) make-up the remainder of the product (typically an alcohol and glycol ether mixture that is a proprietary blend).

The solder paste is printed through a stencil, which is an exact pattern of the surface design that is to be added to the PWB surface. The solder paste is pushed through the apertures in the stencil onto the pad sites on the PWB by means of a squeegee that slowly traverses the stencil. The stencil is then lifted away, leaving the paste deposits on the appropriate pads on the board. The components are then inserted on the PWB. The primary EHS hazards relate to the housekeeping and personal hygiene of the operators that apply the solder paste to the stencil surface, clean the squeegee and clean the stencils. The concentration of lead in the solder and the tendency of the dried solder paste to adhere to the skin and equipment/facility work surfaces requires the use of protective gloves, good clean-up of work surfaces, safe disposal of contaminated clean-up materials (and environmental handling) and strict personal hygiene by the operators (e.g., handwashing with soap prior to eating, drinking or applying cosmetics). Airborne exposure levels are typically below the detection limit for lead, and if good housekeeping/personal hygiene is used, blood lead readings are at background levels.

The adhesive application involves the automated dispensing of small quantities of an epoxy resin (typically a bisphenol A-epichlorhydrin mixture) onto the PWB surface and then "picking and placing" the component and inserting it through the epoxy resin onto the PWB. The EHS hazards primarily relate to the mechanical safety hazards of the "pick and place" units, due to their automated mechanical assemblies, component shuttles on the rear of the units and potential for serious injury if appropriate guarding, light curtains and hardware interlocks are not present.

Adhesive cure and solder reflow

The components that were attached by stencil printing or adhesive application are then carried on a fixed-height mechanical conveyor to an in-line reflow furnace that "sets off" the solder by reflowing the solder paste at approximately 200 to 400 °C. The components that were attached by the epoxy adhesive are also run through a furnace that is downline of the solder reflow and is typically run at 130 to 160 °C. The solvent components of the solder paste and epoxy resin are driven off during the furnace process, but the lead/tin component is not volatilized. A spider-web type residue will build up in the exhaust duct of the reflow furnace, and a metal mesh filter can be used to prevent this. PWBs can occasionally get caught in the conveyor system and will overheat in the furnace, causing objectionable odours.

Fluxing

To form a reliable solder joint at the PWB surface and the component lead, both must be free of oxidation and must remain so even at the elevated temperatures used in soldering. Also, the molten solder alloy must wet the surfaces of the metals to be joined. This means the solder flux must react with and remove metal oxides from the surfaces to be joined and prevent the re-oxidation of the cleaned surfaces. It also requires that the residues be either non-corrosive or easily removable. Fluxes for soldering electronic equipment fall into three broad categories, commonly known as rosin-based fluxes, organic or water-soluble fluxes and solvent-removable synthetic fluxes. Newer, low-solids "no clean" or non-volatile organic compound (NVOC) fluxes fall into the middle category.

Rosin-based fluxes

The rosin-based fluxes are the most commonly used fluxes in the electronics industry, either as *spray flux* or *foam flux*. The fluxer may be contained either internal to the wave soldering equipment or as a stand-alone unit positioned at the infeed to the unit. As a base, rosin-based fluxes have natural rosin, or colophony, the translucent, amber-coloured rosin obtained after turpentine has been distilled from the oleoresin and canal resin of pine trees. The resin is collected, heated and distilled, which removes any solid particles, resulting in a purified form of the natural product. It is a homogeneous material with a single melting point. Colophony is a mixture of approximately 90% resin acid, which is mostly abietic acid (a non-water soluble, organic acid) with 10% neutral materials such as stilbene derivatives and various hydrocarbons. Figure 83.6 provides the chemical structures for abietic and pimaric acids.

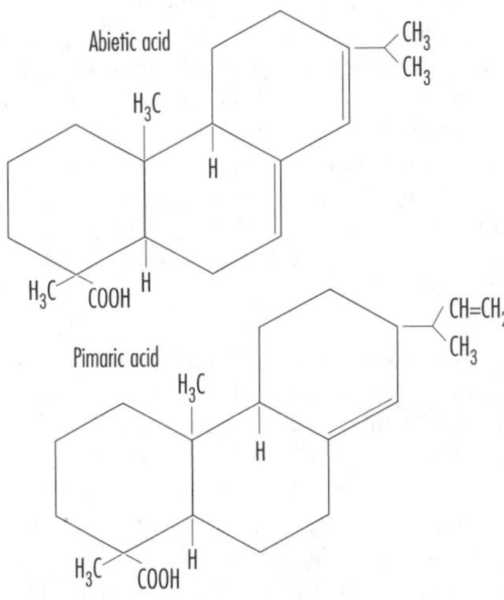

The active constituent is abietic acid, which at soldering temperature is chemically active and attacks the copper oxide on the PWB surface, forming copper abiet. Rosin-based fluxes have three components: the solvent or vehicle, the rosin and the activator. The solvent simply acts as a vehicle for the flux. To be effective the rosin must be applied to the board in a liquid state. This is accomplished by dissolving the rosin and activator in a solvent system, typically isopropyl alcohol (IPA) or multicomponent mixtures of alcohols (IPA, methanol or ethanol). Then the flux is either foamed onto the bottom surface of the PCB through the addition of air or nitrogen, or sprayed in a "low-solids" mixture which has a higher solvent content. These solvent components have different evaporation rates, and a thinner must be added to the flux mixture to maintain a constituent flux composition. The primary categories of rosin-based fluxes are: rosin mildly active (RMA), which are the typical fluxes in use, to which a mild activator is added; and rosin active (RA), to which a more aggressive activator has been added.

The primary EHS hazard of all the rosin-based fluxes is the alcohol solvent base. Safety hazards relate to flammability in storage and use, classification and handling as a hazardous waste, air emissions and treatment systems required to remove the VOCs and industrial hygiene issues related to inhalation and skin (dermal) exposure. Each of these items requires a different control strategy, employee education and training and permits/regulatory

Figure 83.6 • Abietic and pimaric acids.

compliance (Association of the Electronics, Telecommunications and Business Equipment Industries 1991).

During the wave soldering process, the flux is heated to 183 to 399 °C; airborne products generated include *aliphatic aldehydes*, such as formaldehyde. Many fluxes also contain an *organic amine hydrochloride activator*, which helps clean the area being soldered and releases hydrochloric acid when heated. Other gaseous components include benzene, toluene, styrene, phenol, chlorophenol and isopropyl alcohol. In addition to the gaseous components of heated flux, a significant amount of particulates are created, ranging in size from 0.01 micron to 1.0 micron, known as *colophony fumes*. These particulate materials have been found to be respiratory irritants and also respiratory sensitizers in sensitive individuals (Hausen, Krohn and Budianto 1990). In the United Kingdom, airborne exposure standards require that colophony fume levels be controlled to the lowest levels attainable (Health and Safety Commission 1992). Additionally, the American Conference of Governmental Industrial Hygienists (ACGIH) has established a separate threshold limit value for the pyrolysis products of rosin core solder of 0.1 mg/m^3, measured as formaldehyde (ACGIH 1994). The Lead Industries Association, Inc. identifies acetone, methyl alcohol, aliphatic aldehydes (measured as formaldehyde), carbon dioxide, carbon monoxide, methane, ethane, abietic acid and related diterpene acids as typical decomposition products of rosin core soldering (Lead Industries Association 1990).

Organic fluxes

Organic fluxes, sometimes called intermediate fluxes or water-soluble fluxes, are composites that are more active than the rosin-based fluxes and less corrosive than acid fluxes used in the metal-working industries. The general active compounds of this class of fluxes fall into three groups:

- acids (e.g., stearic, glutamic, lactic, citric)
- halogens (e.g., hydrochlorides, bromides, hydrazine)
- amides and amines (e.g., urea, triethanolamine).

These materials and other parts of the formulation, such as surfactants to assist in reducing the solder surface tension, are dissolved in polyethylene glycol, organic solvents, water or usually a mixture of several of these. Organic fluxes must be considered corrosive, but can be cleaned off easily, with no more than hot water.

83. MICROELECTRONICS AND SEMICONDUCTORS

Synthetic activated (AS) fluxes

Whereas rosin-based fluxes are solid materials dissolved in a solvent, AS fluxes are usually totally liquid formulas (solvent + flux). The solvent carrier is driven off during the preheating phase of wave soldering, leaving a wet and oily residue on the PWB surface, which must be cleaned off immediately following soldering. The primary attribute of AS fluxes is their ability to be removed by the use of a suitable solvent, typically fluorocarbon based. With restrictions on the use of ozone-depleting substances such as fluorocarbons (Freon TF, Freon TMS and so on), the required use of these cleaning materials has severely restricted the use of this class of fluxes.

Low-solids "no clean" or non-VOC fluxes

The need for the elimination of the post-soldering cleaning of corrosive or tacky flux residues with fluorocarbon solvents has lead to the widespread usage of a new class of fluxes. These fluxes are similar in activity to the RMA fluxes and have a solids content of approximately 15%. The solids content is a measure of viscosity and equals the ratio of flux to solvent. The lower the solids contents, the higher the percentage of solvent. The higher the solids content, the more active the flux, and the more potential for needing a post-soldering cleaning step. Low-solids flux (LSF) is commonly used in the electronics industry and typically does not require the post-cleaning step. From an environmental air-emission perspective, the LSF eliminated the need for fluorocarbon vapour degreasing of wave soldered boards, but with their higher solvent content, they increased the quantity of alcohol-based solvents evaporated, resulting in higher VOC levels. VOC air-emission levels are tightly controlled in the United States, and in many locations worldwide. This situation was addressed by the introduction of "no clean" fluxes, which are water based (rather than solvent based) but contain similar activators and fluxing rosins. The primary active ingredients are dicarboxylic acid based (2 to 3%), typically glutaric, succinic and adipic acids. *Surfactants* and *corrosion inhibitors* (approximately 1%) are also included, resulting in a pH (acidity) of 3.0 to 3.5. These fluxes virtually eliminate VOC air emissions and other EHS hazards associated with using solvent-based fluxes. The decomposition products noted in rosin-based fluxes are still applicable, and the mild pH does require that the flux-handling equipment be acid resistant. Some anecdotal evidence points to potential dermal or respiratory problems from the dried, mildly acidic dicarboxylic acids and corrosion inhibitors that may become a residue on board carriers, carts and internal surfaces of wave soldering equipment utilizing these compounds. Also, the water component of these fluxes may not get adequately evaporated prior to hitting the molten solder pot, which can lead to splattering of the hot solder.

Figure 83.7 • Wave solder unit schematic.

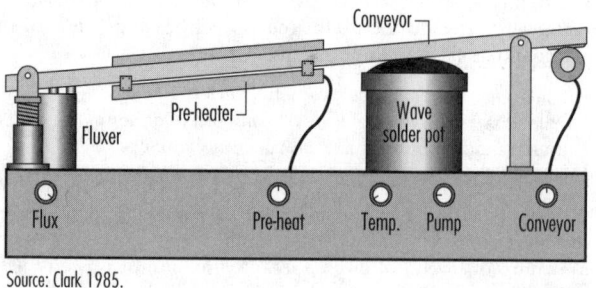

Source: Clark 1985.

Wave soldering

The addition of flux to the bottom surface of the PWB can be accomplished either by a fluxer located internal to the wave soldering unit or a stand-alone unit at the entry to the wave soldering unit. Figure 83.7 provides a schematic representation of a standard wave soldering unit with the fluxer located internally. Either configuration is used to foam or spray the flux onto the PWB.

Preheating

The flux carriers must be evaporated prior to soldering. This is accomplished by using high-temperature preheaters to drive off the liquid components. Two basic types of preheaters are in use: radiant (hot rod) and volumetric (hot air). The radiant heaters are common in the United States and present the potential for ignition of excess flux or solvent or the decomposition of a PWB should it become immobilized under the preheater. Local exhaust ventilation is provided on the fluxer/preheater side of the wave soldering unit to capture and exhaust the solvent/flux materials evaporated during these operations.

Soldering

The solder alloy (typically 63% tin to 37% lead) is contained in a large reservoir called the *solder pot*, and is heated electrically to maintain the solder in a molten state. The heaters include a powerful bulk heater to do the initial melt and a smaller regulated heat supply to control the temperature thermostatically.

Successful board-level soldering requires that the design of the solder pot and recirculation pump systems continually provide a consistent "wave" of fresh solder. With soldering, the pure solder becomes contaminated with oxidized lead/tin compounds, metallic impurities and flux decomposition products. This *dross* forms on the surface of the molten solder, and the more dross formed, the more of a tendency for additional formation. Dross is harmful to the soldering process and the solder wave. If enough forms in the pot, it can get pulled into the recirculation pump and cause impeller abrasion. Wave solder operators are required to de-dross the wave on a routine basis. This process involves the operator straining the solidified dross from the molten solder and collecting the residues for reclaim/recycling. The process of de-drossing involves the operator physically opening up the rear access door (typically a gulf-wing configuration) adjacent to the solder pot and manually scooping out the hot dross. During this process, visible emissions are liberated from the pot which are highly irritating to the eyes, nose and throat of the operator. The operator is required to wear thermal gloves, an apron, safety glasses and a face shield and respiratory protection (for lead/tin particulate, corrosive gases (HCl) and aliphatic aldehyde (formaldehyde)). Local exhaust ventilation is provided from the interior of the wave soldering unit, but the solder pot is mechanically withdrawn from the main cabinet to allow the operator direct access to both sides of the hot pot. Once withdrawn, the local exhaust duct that is mounted in the cabinet becomes ineffective for removing the liberated materials. The primary health and safety hazards are: thermal burns from hot solder, respiratory exposure to materials noted above, back injuries from handling heavy solder ingots and dross drums and exposure to lead/tin solder residues/fine particulate during maintenance activities.

During the actual soldering process, the access doors are closed and the interior of the wave soldering unit is under a negative pressure due to the local exhaust ventilation provided on the flux and solder pot sides of the wave. This ventilation and the operating temperatures of the solder pot (typically 302 to 316 °C, which is just above the melting point of solder), result in the minimal formation of lead fumes. The primary exposure to lead/tin particulate comes during the de-drossing and equipment maintenance activities, from the agitation of the dross in the pot, transfer to the reclaim vessel and clean-up of solder residues. Fine lead/tin particulate is formed during the de-drossing operation and can be released into the workroom and breathing zone of the wave solder operator. Various engineering control strategies have been devised to minimize these potential lead particulate exposures, including the incorporation of local exhaust ventilation to the reclaim vessel (see figure 83.8), use of HEPA vacuums for residue clean-up and flexible exhaust ducts with articulating arms to position ventilation at the hot pot during de-drossing. The use of brooms or brushes for sweeping up solder residues must be prohibited. Stringent housekeeping and personal hygiene practices must also be required. During wave solder equipment maintenance operations (which are done on a weekly, monthly, quarterly and annual basis), various components of the hot pot are either cleaned within the equipment or removed and cleaned in a locally exhausted hood. These cleaning operations may involve physically scraping or mechanically cleaning (using an electric drill and wire brush attachment) the solder pump and baffles. High levels of lead particulate are generated during the mechanical cleaning process, and the process should be performed in a locally exhausted enclosure.

Inspection, touch-up and testing

Visual inspection and touch-up functions are conducted after wave soldering and involve the use of magnifying lenses/task lights for fine inspection and touch-up of imperfections. The touch-up function may involve the use of a *stick-solder* hand-held soldering iron and rosin core solder or brushing on a small amount of liquid flux and lead/tin wire solder. The visual fumes from the stick soldering involve breakdown products from the flux. Small quantities of lead/tin solder bead that did not adhere to the solder joint may present a housekeeping and personal hygiene issue. Either a fan adjacent to the workstation for general dilution ventilation away from the operator's breathing zone or a more sophisticated fume exhaust system that captures the breakdown products at the tip of the soldering iron or adjacent to the operation should be provided. The fumes are then routed to an air scrubber exhaust system that incorporates HEPA filtration for particulates and activated carbon gas adsorption for the aliphatic aldehydes and hydrochloric acid gases. The effectiveness of these soldering exhaust systems is highly dependent on capture velocities, proximity to the point of fume generation and lack of cross drafts at the work surface. The electrical testing of the completed PCB requires specialized test equipment and software.

Reworking and repairing

Based on the results of the board testing, defective boards are evaluated for specific component failures and replaced. This reworking of the boards may involve stick soldering. If primary components on the PCB such as the microprocessor need replacement, a *rework solder pot* is used for immersing that portion of the board housing the defective component or joint in a small solder pot, removing the component and then inserting a new functional component back onto the board. If the component is smaller or more easily removed, an *air vac* system that uses hot air for heating the solder joint and vacuum for removing the solder is employed. The rework solder pot is housed within a locally exhausted enclosure that provides sufficient exhaust velocity to capture the flux decomposition products formed when the liquid solder is brushed on the board and solder contact made. This pot also forms dross and requires de-drossing equipment and procedures (on a much smaller scale). The air vac system does not require being housed within an enclosure, but the lead/tin solder removed must be handled as a hazardous waste and reclaimed/recycled.

Figure 83.8 • Dross cart with vacuum cover.

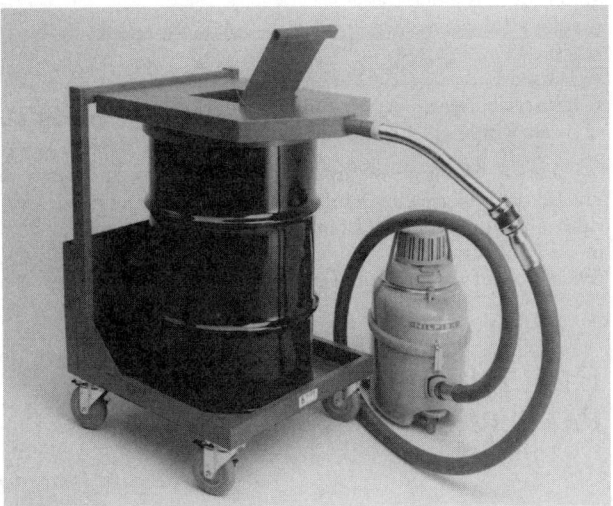

Source: Bliss Industries 1996.

Support operations—stencil cleaning

The first step in the PCB assembly process involved the use of a stencil for providing the pattern of bonding locations for the lead/tin solder paste to be squeegeed through. Typically, the stencil's openings start to become clogged and the lead/tin solder paste residues must be removed on a per shift basis. A pre-cleaning is usually performed at the screen printer to capture gross contamination on the board, by wiping the board surface with a dilute alcohol mixture and disposable wipes. To completely remove the remaining residues a wet-cleaning process is required. In a system similar to a large dishwasher, hot water (57 °C) and a chemical solution of dilute aliphatic amines (monoethanol amine) is used to chemically remove the solder paste from the stencil. Significant quantities of lead/tin solder are washed off the board and either deposited in the wash chamber or in solution in the water effluent. This effluent requires filtration or chemical removal of lead and pH adjustment for the corrosive aliphatic amines (using hydrochloric acid). Newer closed system stencil cleaners utilize the same wash solution until it is spent. The solution is transferred to a distillation unit, and the volatiles are distilled off until a semi-liquid residue is formed. This residue is then handled as a lead/tin-contaminated hazardous waste.

Computer Assembly Process

Once the final PCB is assembled, it is transferred to the systems assembly operation for incorporation into the final computer product. This operation is typically very labour intensive, with the component parts to be assembled supplied to the individual workstations on staging carts along the mechanized assembly line. The major health and safety hazards relate to materials movement and staging (fork-lifts, manual lifting), ergonomic implications of the assembly process (range of motion, insertion force required to "set" components, installation of screws and connectors) and final packaging, shrink wrapping and shipping. A typical computer assembly process involves:

- chassis/case preparation
- PCB (mother and daughter board) insertion
- primary component (floppy drive, hard drive, power supply, CD-ROM drive) insertion
- display assembly (portables only)

- mouse and keyboard insertion (portables only)
- cabling, connectors and speakers
- top cover assembly
- software downloading
- test
- rework
- battery charging (portables only) and packaging
- shrink wrapping and shipping.

The only chemicals that may be used in the assembly process involve the final cleaning of the computer case or monitor. Typically, a dilute solution of isopropyl alcohol and water or a commercial mixture of cleaners (e.g., Simple Green—a dilute butyl cellosolve and water solution) is used.

HEALTH EFFECTS AND DISEASE PATTERNS

Donald V. Lassiter

As an emerging industry, semiconductor manufacturing often has been viewed as the epitome of the high-technology workplace. Because of stringent manufacturing requirements associated with producing multiple layers of micron dimensional electronic circuitry on silicon wafers, the cleanroom environment has become synonymous with the workplace for this industry. Since certain of the hydride gases used in semiconductor manufacturing (e.g., arsine, phosphine) were recognized early as highly toxic chemicals, inhalation exposure control technology has always been an important component of wafer fabrication. Semiconductor workers are further isolated from the production process by wearing special clothing covering the whole body (e.g., gowns), hair covers, shoe covers and, frequently, facial masks (or even air-supplied breathing devices). From a practical standpoint, employer concerns for product purity have resulted, also, in worker exposure protection.

In addition to personal protective clothing, highly sophisticated systems of ventilation and chemical/gas air monitoring are used throughout the semiconductor industry to detect leaks of toxic chemical solvent vapours, acids and hydride gases at parts per million (ppm) or less. Although, from the historic viewpoint, the industry has experienced frequent worker evacuations from wafer fabrication rooms, based on real or suspected leaks of gases or solvents, such evacuation episodes have become rare events because of the lessons learned in design of ventilation systems, toxic gas/chemical handling and increasingly sophisticated air-monitoring systems with continuous air sampling. However, the increasing monetary value of individual silicon wafers (together with increasing wafer diameters), which can contain scores of individual microprocessors or memory devices, can place mental stress on workers who must manually manipulate containers of these wafers during manufacturing processes. Evidence of such stress was obtained during a study of semiconductor workers (Hammond et al. 1995; Hines et al. 1995; McCurdy et al. 1995).

The semiconductor industry had its beginnings in the United States, which has the highest number of semiconductor industry workers (approximately 225,000 in 1994) of any country (BLS 1995). However, obtaining valid international employment estimates for this industry is difficult because of the inclusion of semiconductor workers with "electrical/electronic equipment manufacturing" workers in most nations' statistics. Because of the highly stringent engineering controls required for semiconductor device manufacturing, it is most probable that semiconductor workplaces (i.e., cleanrooms) are comparable, in most respects, throughout the world. This understanding, coupled with US gov-

ernment requirements for recording all significant work-related injuries and illnesses among US workers, makes the work injury and illness experience of US semiconductor workers a highly relevant issue on both a national and international scale. Simply stated, at this time there are few international sources of relevant information and data concerning semiconductor worker safety and health experience, other than those from the Annual Survey of Occupational Injuries and Illnesses by the US Bureau of Labor Statistics (BLS).

In the United States, which has collected work injury and illness data on all industries since 1972, the frequency of work-related injuries and illnesses among semiconductor workers has been among the lowest of all manufacturing industries. However, concerns have been voiced that more subtle health effects may be present among semiconductor workers (LaDou 1986), although such effects have not been documented.

Several symposia have been held concerning control technology assessment in the semiconductor industry, with several of the symposia papers dealing with environmental and worker safety and health issues (ACGIH 1989, 1993).

A limited quantity of work injury and illness data for the international semiconductor manufacturing community was derived via a special survey performed in 1995, involving cases reported for the years 1993 and 1994. These survey data are summarized below.

Work Injuries and Illness among Semiconductor Workers

With respect to international statistical data associated with work injuries and illnesses among semiconductor workers, the only comparable data appear to be those derived from a survey of multi-national semiconductor manufacturing operations performed in 1995 (Lassiter 1996). The data collected in this survey involved the international operations of US-based semiconductor manufacturers for the years 1993-94. Some of the data from the survey included operations other than semiconductor manufacturing (e.g., computer and disk drive manufacturing), although all participating companies were involved in the electronics industry. The results of this survey are presented in figures 83.9 and 83.10, which include data from the Asia-Pacific region, Europe, Latin America and the United States. Each case involved a work-related injury or illness which required medical treatment or work loss or restriction. All incidence rates in the figures have been calculated as numbers of cases (or lost workdays) per 200,000 worker-hours per year. If total worker-hours was not available, average annual employment estimates were used. The 200,000 worker-hours denominator is equal to 100 full-time equivalent workers per year (assuming 2,000 work hours per worker per year).

Figure 83.9 depicts work injury and illness incidence rates for the various world regions in the 1993-94 survey. Individual country rates have not been included to ensure confidentiality of those participating companies which were the sole sources of data for certain countries. Hence, for certain countries in the survey, data were reported for only a single facility. In several instances, companies combined all international data into a single statistic. These latter data are listed in figures 83.9 and 83.10 as "Combined".

The annual incidence of work injuries and illnesses among all workers in the international survey was 3.3 cases per 100 employees (200,000 worker-hours) in 1993 and 2.7 in 1994. There were 12,615 cases reported for 1993 and 12,368 for 1994. The great majority of cases (12,130 in 1993) were derived from US companies. These cases were associated with approximately 387,000 workers in 1993 and 458,000 in 1994.

Figure 83.10 presents incidence rates for lost workday cases involving days away from work. The 1993 and 1994 incidence

Figure 83.9 • Distribution of incidence rates for work injuries and illnesses by world sector, 1993 and 1994.

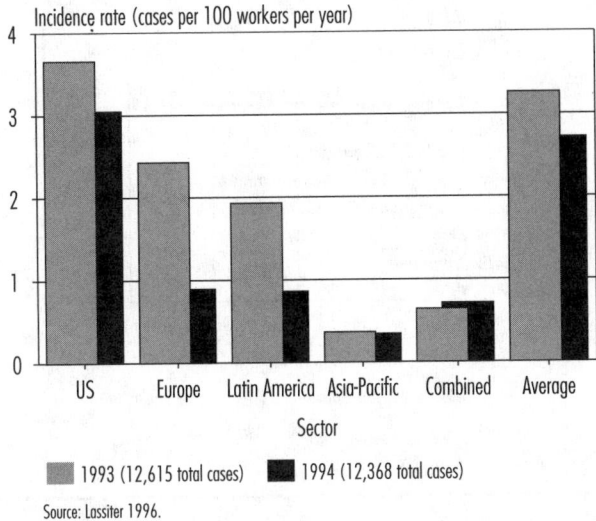

1993 (12,615 total cases) 1994 (12,368 total cases)

Source: Lassiter 1996.

Figure 83.10 • Distribution of incidence rates for work injuries and illnesses with days away from work by world sector 1993 and 1994.

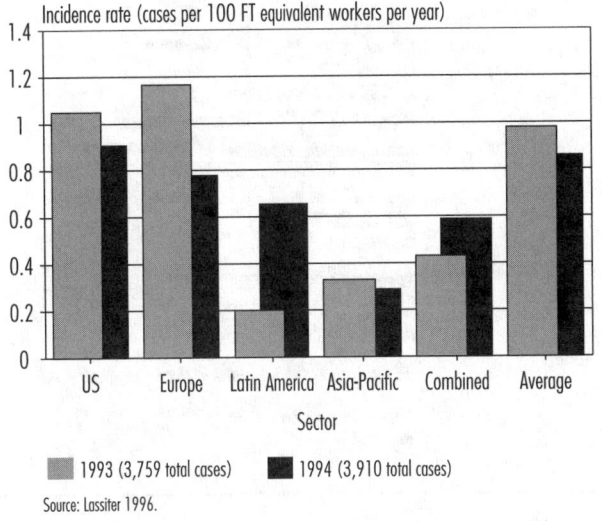

1993 (3,759 total cases) 1994 (3,910 total cases)

Source: Lassiter 1996.

rates were based on approximately 4,000 lost workday cases for each of the 2 years in the international survey. The international/regional range in incidence rates for this statistic was the most narrow of those measured. The incidence of lost workday cases may represent the most comparable international statistics with respect to worker safety and health experience. The incidence rate for lost workdays (days away from work) was approximately 15.4 days away from work per 100 workers for each of the 2 years.

The only detailed data known to exist concerning case characteristics of semiconductor worker injuries and illnesses are those compiled annually in the US by the BLS, involving cases with lost workdays. The cases discussed here were identified by the BLS in their annual survey for the year 1993. Data obtained from these cases appear in figures 83.11 to 83.14. Each figure compares the lost workday case experience for the private sector, all manufacturing and semiconductor manufacturing.

Figure 83.11 compares the lost workday case experience of US semiconductor workers in 1993 with the private sector and with all manufacturing with respect to type of event or exposure. The incidence rates for most categories in this figure were much less for semiconductor industry workers than for the private sector or all manufacturing. Cases involving overexertions among semiconductor workers were less than half the rate for all workers in the manufacturing sector. The harmful exposure category (primarily associated with exposures to chemical substances) was equivalent among all three groups.

Comparative distributions of lost workday cases according to source of injury or illness are presented in figure 83.12. Lost workday case incidence rates for semiconductor workers were less than those for the private sector and all manufacturing in all source categories except for cases associated with exposures to chemical substances.

Figure 83.13 compares lost workday case incidence rates associated with nature of injury or illness among the three groups. The rates for semiconductor workers were less than half of the rates for both the private sector and for all manufacturing in 1993. The incidence of chemical burns was slightly higher for semiconductor workers, but was very low for all three comparison groups. The incidence of carpal tunnel syndrome (CTS) among

US semiconductor workers was less than half the rate for all manufacturing.

In figure 83.14, the distribution and incidence of cases involving days away from work is illustrated according to part of body affected. Although the incidence of cases involving body systems was low for all comparison groups, the rate for semiconductor workers was slightly elevated. All other body parts affected were much lower for semiconductor workers than for the other two comparison groups.

Epidemiological Studies of Semiconductor Workers
Concern for possible reproductive health consequences associated with employment in the semiconductor surfaced in 1983 when a female employee at the Digital Equipment Corporation's semiconductor facility in Hudson, Massachusetts, indicated that she

Figure 83.11 • Comparative incidence of lost workday cases[1] by type of event or exposure, 1993.

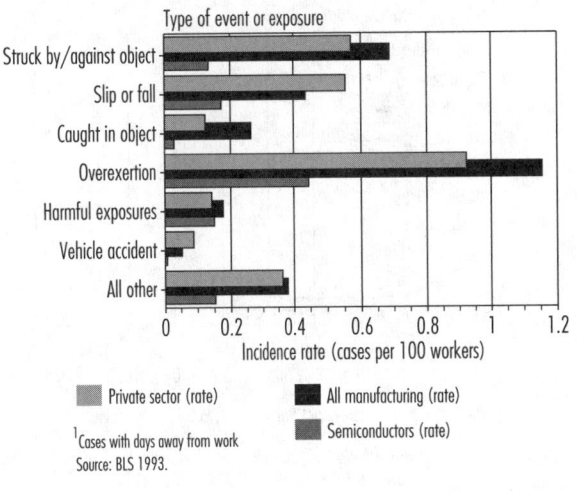

Private sector (rate) All manufacturing (rate) Semiconductors (rate)

[1]Cases with days away from work
Source: BLS 1993.

83. MICROELECTRONICS AND SEMICONDUCTORS

Figure 83.12 • Comparative incidence of lost workday cases[1] by source of injury or illness, 1993.

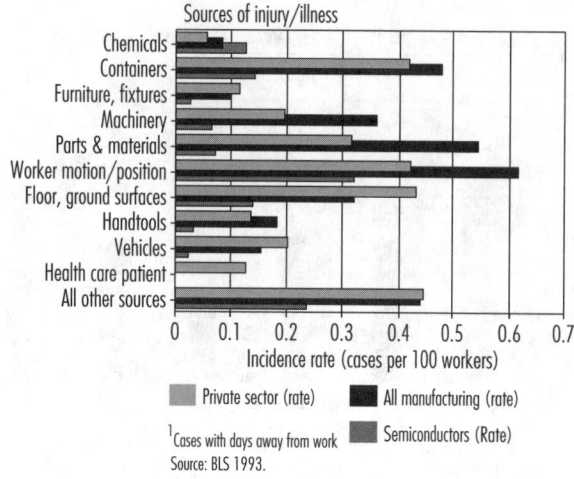

Sources of injury/illness

■ Private sector (rate)   ■ All manufacturing (rate)
■ Semiconductors (Rate)
[1] Cases with days away from work
Source: BLS 1993.

Figure 83.14 • Comparative incidence of lost workday cases by part of body affected, 1993.

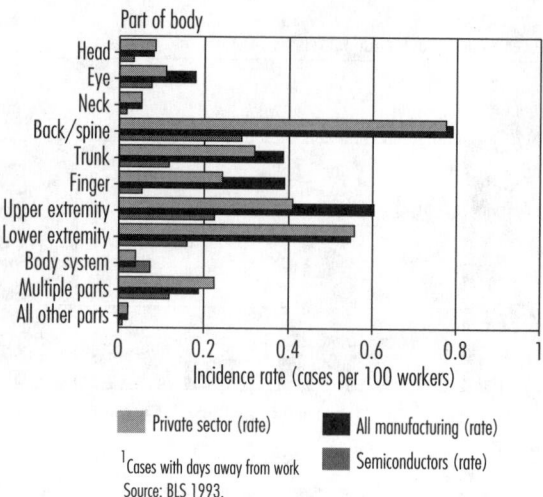

Part of body

■ Private sector (rate)   ■ All manufacturing (rate)
■ Semiconductors (rate)
[1] Cases with days away from work
Source: BLS 1993.

believed that an excess of miscarriages had occurred among employees in the facility's cleanrooms. This allegation, coupled with an absence of internal data at the facility, led to an epidemiological study by the University of Massachusetts School of Public Health in Amherst (UMass). The study was begun in May of 1984 and completed in 1985 (Pastides et al. 1988).

An elevated risk of miscarriage was observed in both the photolithographic area and the diffusion area when compared to non-exposed workers in other areas of the facility. A relative risk of 1.75 was considered to be not statistically significant (p <0.05), although a 2.18 relative risk observed among workers in diffusion areas was significant. Publication of the UMass study led to concern throughout the semiconductor industry that a larger study was warranted to validate the observed findings and to determine their extent and possible causation.

The Semiconductor Industry Association (SIA) of the United States sponsored a larger study performed by the University of

Figure 83.13 • Comparative incidence of lost workday cases[1] by nature of injury or illness, 1993.

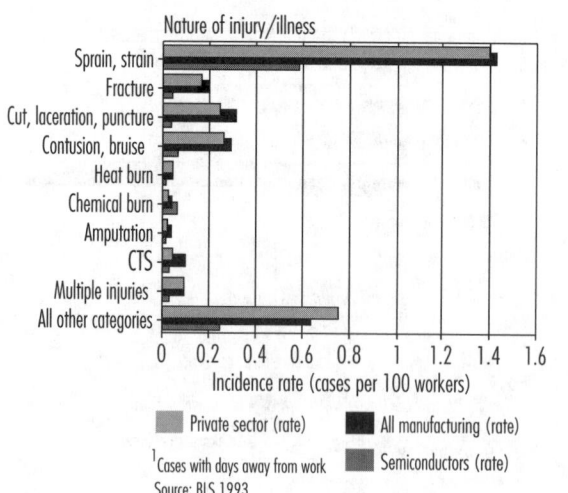

Nature of injury/illness

■ Private sector (rate)   ■ All manufacturing (rate)
■ Semiconductors (rate)
[1] Cases with days away from work
Source: BLS 1993.

California at Davis (UC Davis) beginning in 1989. The UC Davis study was designed to test the hypothesis that semiconductor manufacturing was associated with an increased risk of miscarriage for female wafer fabrication employees. The study's population was selected from among 14 companies which represented 42 production sites in 17 states. The highest number of sites (representing almost half of the employees in the study) was in California.

The UC Davis study consisted of three different components: a cross-sectional component (McCurdy et al. 1995; Pocekay et al. 1995); an historical cohort component (Schenker et al. 1995); and a prospective component (Eskenazi et al. 1995). Central to each of these studies was an exposure assessment (Hines et al. 1995; Hammond et al. 1995). The exposure assessment component assigned employees to a relative exposure group (i.e., high exposure, low exposure and so on).

In the historical component of the study, it was determined that the relative risk of fabrication workers, compared with non-fabrication workers, was 1.45 (i.e., 45% excess risk of miscarriage). The highest risk group identified in the historical component of the study were women who worked in photolithography or etching operations. Women performing etching operations experienced a relative risk of 2.15 (RR=2.15). In addition, a dose-response relationship was observed among women who worked with any photoresist or developer with respect to increased risk of miscarriage. These data supported a dose-response association for ethylene glycol ethers (EGE) but not for propylene glycol ethers (PGE).

Although an increased risk of miscarriage was observed among female wafer fabrication workers in the prospective component of the UC Davis study, the results were not statistically significant (p less than 0.05). A small number of pregnancies significantly reduced the power of the prospective component of the study. Analysis by exposure to chemical agent indicated an increased risk for those women who worked with ethylene glycol monoethyl ether, but was based on only 3 pregnancies. One important finding was the general support for, and not contradiction of, the findings of the historical component.

The cross-sectional component of the study noted an increase in upper respiratory symptoms primarily in the diffusion furnace and thin film groups of workers. An interesting finding was the apparent protective effects of various engineering controls related to ergonomics (e.g., footrests and the use of an adjustable chair to reduce back injuries).

Air measurements made in the wafer fabs found most solvent exposures were less than 1% of the permissible exposure limits (PEL) established by the US government.

A separate epidemiological study (Correa et al. 1996) was performed by the Johns Hopkins University (JHU), involving a group of IBM Corporation semiconductor employees in 1989. The overall miscarriage rate observed in the JHU study involving female cleanroom workers was 16.6%. The relative risk for miscarriage among female cleanroom workers with the highest potential exposure to ethylene glycol ethers was 2.8 (95% C.I. = 1.4-5.6).

Discussion of Reproductive Epidemiological Studies Involving Semiconductor Workers

The epidemiological studies were remarkable in the scope and similarity of results. These studies all produced similar findings. Each study documented an excess risk of spontaneous abortion (miscarriage) for female semiconductor wafer fabrication workers. Two of the studies (JHU and UC Davis) may indicate a causal association with exposures to ethylene-based glycol ethers. The UMass study found that the photo group (those exposed to glycol ether) had less risk than the diffusion group, which had no documented glycol ether exposure. While these studies indicate an increased risk of spontaneous abortions among wafer fabrication workers, the cause of such excess risk is unclear. The JHU study failed to document a significant role for glycol ethers, and the UC Davis study only marginally linked glycol ethers (through modelling of exposures and self-reported work practices) to reproductive effects. Little if any monitoring was performed in either study to determine exposures to glycol ethers. Following completion of these studies the semiconductor industry began switching from ethylene series glycol ethers to substitutes such as ethyl lactate and propylene series glycol ethers.

Conclusion

Based on the best available data concerning the annual incidence of work-related injuries and illnesses, semiconductor workers are at less risk than workers in other manufacturing sectors or throughout the private sector (including many non-manufacturing industries). On an international basis, it appears that work injury and illness statistical data associated with lost workday cases may be a fairly reliable indicator of the worldwide safety and health experience of semiconductor workers. The industry has sponsored several independent epidemiological studies in an attempt to find answers to questions of reproductive health consequences related to employment in the industry. Although a definitive association between observed miscarriages and exposures to ethylene-based glycol ethers was not established, the industry has begun to use alternative photoresist solvents.

● ENVIRONMENTAL AND PUBLIC HEALTH ISSUES

Corky Chew

Industry Overview

The electronics industry, compared to other industries, has been viewed as "clean" in terms of its environmental impact. None the less, the chemicals used in the manufacture of electronic parts and components, and the waste generated, create significant environment issues that must be addressed on a global scale due to the size of the electronics industry. The wastes and by-products derived from the manufacture of printed wiring boards (PWBs), printed circuit boards (PCBs) and semiconductors are areas of interest that the electronic industry has vigorously pursued in terms of pollution prevention, treatment technology and recycling/reclamation techniques.

To a large degree, the incentive to control the environmental footprint of electronic processes has migrated from an environmental impetus to a financial domain. Due to the costs and liabilities associated with hazardous waste and emissions, the electronics industry has aggressively implemented and developed environmental controls that have greatly reduced the impact of its by-products and waste. In addition, the electronics industry has taken a proactive approach to incorporate environmental goals, tools and techniques into its environmentally conscious businesses. Examples of this proactive approach are the phase-out of CFCs and perfluorinated compounds and the development of "environmentally friendly" alternatives, as well as the emerging "design for the environment" approach to product development.

The manufacture of PWBs, PCBs and semiconductors requires the use of a variety of chemicals, specialized manufacturing techniques and equipment. Due to the hazards associated with these manufacturing processes, the proper management of chemical by-products, wastes and emissions is essential to assure the safety of the industry's employees and the protection of the environment in the communities in which they reside.

Tables 83.10, 83.11 and 83.12 present an outline of the key by-products and wastes that are generated in the manufacturing of PWBs, PCBs and semiconductors. In addition, the tables present the main types of environmental impact and the generally accepted means of mitigation and control of the waste stream. Primarily, the wastes that are generated affect industrial wastewater or the air, or become a solid waste.

The following are generally accepted means of mitigating emissions in the PWB, PCB and semiconductor industries. The controls of choice will vary according to engineering capabilities, regulatory agency requirements and the specific constituents/concentrations of the waste stream.

Wastewater Control

Chemical precipitation

Chemical precipitation is generally used in the removal of particulate or soluble metals from wastewater effluents. Since metals do not naturally degrade and are toxic at low concentrations, their removal from industrial wastewater is essential. Metals can be removed from wastewater by chemical means since they are not very soluble in water; their solubilities depend upon the pH, metal concentration, type of metal and the presence of other ions. Typically, the waste stream requires pH adjustment to the proper level to precipitate out the metal. The addition of chemicals to wastewater in an effort to alter the physical state of dissolved and suspended solids is required. Lime, caustic and sulphide precipitation agents are commonly used. The precipitating agents facilitate the removal of dissolved and suspended metals by coagulation, sedimentation or entrapment within a precipitate.

A result of chemical precipitation of wastewater is the accumulation of sludge. Therefore, dewatering processes have been developed to reduce the weight of the sludge by means of centrifuges, filter presses, filters or drying beds. The resultant dewatered sludge can then be sent off for incineration or landfill.

pH neutralization

pH (the hydrogen-ion concentration or acidity) is an important quality parameter in industrial wastewater. Due to the adverse effects of pH extremes in natural waters and on sewage treatment

Table 83.10 • PWB waste generation and controls.

Process steps	Hazardous waste/materials	Environmental impact	Controls[1]
Material preparation	None	None	None
Stack and pin	Heavy/precious metals	Solid waste[2]	Recycle/reclaim
	Epoxy/fibreglass	Solid waste[2]	Recycle/reclaim
Drilling	Heavy/precious metals	Solid waste[2]	Recycle/reclaim
	Epoxy/fibreglass	Solid waste[2]	Recycle/reclaim
Deburr	Heavy/precious metals	Solid waste[2]	Recycle/reclaim
	Epoxy/fibreglass	Solid waste[2]	Recycle/reclaim
Electroless copper plating	Metals	Wastewater	Chemical precipitation
	Corrosives/caustics	Wastewater/ air	pH neutralization/ air scrubbing (absorption)
	Fluorides	Wastewater	Chemical neutralization
Imaging	Solvents	Air	Adsorption, condensation or incineration
	Corrosives	Air	Air scrubbing (absorption)
	Solvents	Solid waste[2]	Recycle/reclaim/ incineration
Pattern plating	Corrosives	Wastewater/ air	pH neutralization/ air scrubbing (absorption)
	Metals	Wastewater	Chemical precipitation
	Fluorides	Wastewater	Chemical precipitation
Strip, etch, strip	Ammonia	Air	Air scrubbing (adsorption)
	Metals	Wastewater	Chemical precipitation
	Solvents	Solid waste[2]	Recycle/reclaim/ incineration
Solder mask	Corrosives	Air	Air scrubbing (adsorption)
	Solvents	Air	Adsorption, condensation, or incineration
	Solvents/epoxy inks	Solid waste[2]	Recycle/reclaim/ incineration
Solder coating	Solvents	Air	Adsorption, condensation or incineration
	Corrosives	Air	Air scrubbing (adsorption)
	Lead/tin solder, flux	Solid waste[2]	Recycle/reclaim
Gold plating	Corrosives	Air	Air scrubbing (adsorption)
	Corrosives	Wastewater	pH neutralization
	Metals	Wastewater	Chemical precipitation
	Metals	Solid waste[2]	Recycle/reclaim
Component legend	Solvents	Air	Adsorption condensation or incineration
	Solvents/inks	Solid waste[2]	Recycle/reclaim/ incineration

1. Use of mitigation controls depends upon discharge limits in the specific location.
2. A solid waste is any discarded material regardless of its state.

Table 83.11 • PCB waste generation and controls.

Process steps	Hazardous waste/materials	Environmental impact	Controls
Cleaning	Metals (lead)	Wastewater	pH neutralization, chemical precipitation, recycle lead
Solder paste	Solder paste (lead/tin)	Solid waste	Recycle/reclaim
Adhesive application	Epoxy glues	Solid waste	Incineration
Component insertion			Plastic tapes, reels and tubes are recycled/reused
Adhesive cure and solder reflow			
Fluxing	Solvent (IPA flux)	Solid waste	Recycle
Wave soldering	Metal (solder dross)	Solid waste	Recycle/reclaim
Inspection and touch-up	Metal (lead wire clippings)	Solid waste	Recycle/reclaim
Testing	Scrapped populated boards	Solid waste	Recycle/reclaim (boards smelted for precious metal recovery)
Reworking and repairing	Metal (solder dross)	Solid waste	Recycle/reclaim
Support operations — stencil cleaning	Metal (lead/tin/solder paste)	Solid waste	Recycle/ incineration

operations, the pH of industrial wastewater must be adjusted prior to discharge from the manufacturing facility. Treatment occurs in a series of tanks that are monitored for the hydrogen-ion concentration of the wastewater effluent. Typically, hydrochloric or sulphuric acid is used as neutralizing corrosives, and sodium hydroxide is used as a neutralizing caustic. The neutralizing agent is metered into the wastewater effluent to adjust the pH of the discharge to its desired level.

Adjustment of pH is often required prior to the application of other wastewater treatment processes. Such processes include chemical precipitation, oxidation/reduction, activated carbon sorption, stripping and ion exchange.

Solid Waste Control

Materials are a solid waste if they are abandoned or discarded by being disposed of; burned or incinerated; or accumulated, stored or treated before or in lieu of being abandoned (US Code of Federal Regulation 40, Section 261.2). Hazardous waste generally exhibits one or more of the following characteristics: ignitability, corrosivity, reactivity, toxicity. Depending upon the characteristic of the hazardous material/waste, various means are used to control the substance. Incineration is a common treatment alternative for solvent and metal wastes generated during PWB, PCB and semiconductor manufacturing.

Incineration

Incineration (afterburner) or thermal destruction has become a popular option in handling ignitable and toxic wastes. In many

Table 83.12 • Semiconductor manufacturing waste generation and controls.

Process steps	Hazardous waste/materials	Environmental impact	Controls
Lithography/ etching	Solvents	Solid waste	Recycle/reclaim/ incineration
	Metals	Wastewater	Chemical precipitation
	Corrosives/Caustics	Wastewater	pH neutralization
	Corrosives	Air	Air scrubbing (absorption)
	Sulphuric acid	Solid waste	Recycle/reprocess
	Fluorides	Wastewater	Chemical precipitation
Oxidation	Solvents	Solid waste	Recycle/reclaim/ incineration
	Corrosives	Wastewater	pH neutralization
Doping	Poison gas (arsine, phosphine, diborane, boron trifluoride, boron trichloride, etc.)	Air	Substitution with liquid sources/incineration (afterburner)
	Metals (arsenic, phosphorus, boron)	Solid waste	Recycle/reclaim
Chemical vapour deposition	Metals	Solid waste	Incineration
	Corrosives	Wastewater	pH neutralization
Metallization	Solvents	Solid waste	Incineration
	Metals	Solid waste	Recycle/reclaim
Assembly and testing	Solvents	Solid waste	Recycle/reclaim/ incineration
	Metals	Solid waste	Recycle/reclaim
Cleaning	Corrosives	Wastewater	pH neutralization
	Fluorides	Wastewater	Chemical precipitation

Table 83.13 • Matrix of priority needs.

Priority need (decreasing order of priority)	Approach	Selected tasks
More efficient use, regeneration and recycling of hazardous wet chemistries	Extend life of electrolytic and electroless plating baths. Develop chemistries and processes to allow recycling or in-house regeneration. Eliminate formaldehyde from materials and chemistries. Promote onsite recycling and reclamation/regeneration.	Research to extend baths. Research in-line purification/ regeneration. Research alternative chemistries. Modify government regulations to promote recycling. Educate line production on drag-in/drag-out problems.
Reduce solid waste generated by scrap PWBs, leads and components in the waste stream.	Develop and promote recycling of scrap PWBs, leads and components. Develop new process-control and performance tools. Improve the solderability of PWBs.	Develop infrastructure to handle recycled material. Establish enhanced process-control and evaluation tools usable by small and medium-sized businesses. Deliver consistently clean, solderable boards.
Establish better supplier relationships to enhance the development and acceptance of environmentally friendly materials.	Promote supplier, manufacturer, customer partnerships to implement environmental materials.	Develop a model hazardous materials management system for small and medium-sized PWB companies.
Minimize the impact of hazardous materials use in PWB fabrication.	Reduce lead solder use when possible and/or reduce the lead content of the solder. Develop alternatives to solder plating as an etch resist.	Change specifications to accept solder mask over bare copper. Validate quality of lead plating alternatives.
Use additive processes that are competitive with existing processes.	Develop simplified, cost-effective additive material and process technologies. Seek alternative sources and approaches for additive process capital equipment needs.	Collaborate on projects to establish novel additive dielectrics and metallization technologies and processes.
Eliminate hole smear in PWB fabrication.	Develop no-smear resins or drilling systems.	Investigate alternative laminate and pre-preg materials. Develop the use of laser and other alternatives to drilling systems.
Reduce water consumption and discharge.	Develop water use optimization and recycle system. Reduce the number of cleaning steps in PWB manufacture. Eliminate parts handling and preparation to reduce recleaning.	Modify specifications to reduce cleaning requirements. Investigate alternative parts-handling methods. Change or eliminate chemistries that require cleaning.

Source: MCC 1994.

instances, ignitable wastes (solvents) are used as a fuel source (fuel blending) for thermal and catalytic incinerators. Proper incineration of solvents and toxic wastes provides complete oxidation of the fuel and converts combustible material to carbon dioxide, water and ash, thereby leaving no liabilities associated with residual hazardous waste. The common types of incineration are thermal and catalytic incinerators. The selection of the type of incineration method is dependent upon the combustion temperature, fuel characteristics and residence time. Thermal incinerators operate at high temperatures and are widely used with halogenated compounds. Types of thermal incinerators include rotary kiln, liquid injection, fixed-hearth, fluidized bed and other advanced design incinerators.

Catalytic incinerators oxidize combustible materials (e.g., VOCs) by injecting a heated gas stream through a catalyst bed. The catalyst bed maximizes surface area, and by injecting a heated gas stream into the catalyst bed combustion can occur at a lower temperature than thermal incineration.

Air Emissions

Incineration is also used in control of air emissions. Absorption and adsorption are used as well.

Absorption

Air absorption is typically used in the scrubbing of corrosive air emissions, by passing the contaminant through and dissolving it in a non-volatile liquid (e.g., water). The effluent from the absorption process is typically discharged to a wastewater treatment system, where it undergoes pH adjustment.

Adsorption

Adsorption is the adherence (by means of physical or chemical forces) of a gas molecule to the surface of another substance, called an adsorbent. Typically, adsorption is used to extract solvents from an air emission source. Activated carbon, activated alumina or silica gel are commonly used adsorbents.

Recycling

Recyclable materials are used, reused or reclaimed as ingredients in an industrial process to make a product. Recycling of materials and waste provides environmental and economic means of effectively addressing specific types of waste streams, such as metals and solvents. Materials and wastes can be recycled in-house, or secondary markets may accept recyclable materials. The selection of recycling as an alternative for wastes must be evaluated against financial considerations, the regulatory framework and available technology to recycle the materials.

Future Direction

As the demand for pollution prevention increases and industry seeks cost-effective means to address chemical use and waste, the electronics industry must evaluate new techniques and technologies to improve the methods for hazardous-materials handling and waste generation. The end-of-pipe approach has been replaced by design for the environment techniques, where environmental issues are addressed over the full life cycle of a product, including: material conservation; efficient manufacturing operations; the use of more environmentally friendly materials; recycling, regeneration and reclamation of waste products; and a host of other techniques that will assure a smaller environmental impact for the electronics manufacturing industry. One example is the large amount of water that is used in the many rinsing and other processing steps in the microelectronics industry. In water-poor areas, this is forcing the industry to find alternatives. However, it is essential to make sure that the alternative (e.g., solvents) does not create additional environmental problems.

As an example of future directions in the PWB and PCB process, table 83.13 presents various alternatives for creating more environmentally sound practices and preventing pollution. Priority needs and approaches have been identified.

References

American Conference of Governmental Industrial Hygienists (ACGIH). 1989. *Hazard Assessment and Control Technology in Semiconductor Manufacturing.* Chelsea, MI: Lewis Publishers.

—. 1993. *Hazard Assessment and Control Technology in Semiconductor Manufacturing II.* Cincinnati, OH: ACGIH.

—. 1994. *Documentation of Threshold Limit Value, Rosin Core Solder Thermal Decomposition Products, as Resin Acids-Colophony.* Cincinnati, OH: ACGIH.

American National Standards Institute (ANSI). 1986. *Safety Standard for Industrial Robots and Industrial Robot Systems.* ANSI/RIA R15.06-1986. New York: ANSI.

ASKMAR. 1990. *Computer Industry: Critical Trends for the 1990's.* Saratoga, CA: Electronic Trend Publications.

Asom, MT, J Mosovsky, RE Leibenguth, JL Zilko, and G Cadet. 1991. Transient arsine generation during opening of solid source MBE chambers. *J Cryst Growth* 112(2-3):597–599.

Association of the Electronics, Telecommunications and Business Equipment Industries (EEA). 1991. *Guidelines on the Use of Colophony (Rosin) Solder Fluxes in the Electronics Industry.* London: Leichester House EEA.

Baldwin, DG. 1985. Chemical exposure from carbon tetrachloride plasma aluminum etchers. *Extended Abstracts, Electrochem Soc* 85(2):449–450.

Baldwin, DG and JH Stewart. 1989. Chemical and radiation hazards in semiconductor manufacturing. *Solid State Technology* 32(8):131–135.

Baldwin, DG and ME Williams. 1996. Industrial hygiene. In *Semiconductor Safety Handbook,* edited by JD Bolmen. Park Ridge, NJ: Noyes.

Baldwin, DG, BW King, and LP Scarpace. 1988. Ion implanters: Chemical and radiation safety. *Solid State Technology* 31(1):99–105.

Baldwin, DG, JR Rubin, and MR Horowitz. 1993. Industrial hygiene exposures in semiconductor manufacturing. *SSA Journal* 7(1):19–21.

Bauer, S, I Wolff, N Werner, and P Hoffman. 1992a. Health hazards in the semiconductor industry, a review. *Pol J Occup Med* 5(4):299–314.

Bauer, S, N Werner, I Wolff, B Damme, B Oemus, and P Hoffman. 1992b. Toxicological investigations in the semiconductor industry: II. Studies on the subacute inhalation toxicity and genotoxicity of gaseous waste products from the aluminum plasma etching process. *Toxicol Ind Health* 8(6):431–444.

Bliss Industries. 1996. *Solder Dross Particulate Capture System Literature.* Fremont, CA: Bliss Industries.

Bureau of Labor Statistics (BLS). 1993. *Annual Survey of Occupational Injuries and Illnesses.* Washington, DC: BLS, US Department of Labor.

—. 1995. *Employment and Wages Annual Averages, 1994. Bulletin.* 2467. Washington, DC: BLS, US Department of Labor.

Clark, RH. 1985. *Handbook of Printed Circuit Manufacturing.* New York: Van Nostrand Reinhold Company.

Cohen, R. 1986. Radiofrequency and microwave radiation in microelectronics industry. In *State of the Art Reviews—Occupational Medicine: The Microelectronics Industry,* edited by J LaDou. Philadelphia, PA: Hanley & Belfus, Inc.

Coombs, CF. 1988. *Printed Circuits Handbook,* 3rd ed. New York: McGraw-Hill Book Company.

Content, RM. 1989. Control methods for metal and metalloids in III-V materials vapor-phase epitaxy. *In Hazard Assessment and Control Technology in Semiconductor Manufacturing,* edited by the American Conference of Governmental Industrial Hygienists. Chelsea, MI: Lewis Publishers.

Correa A, RH Gray, R Cohen, N Rothman, F Shah, H Seacat, and M Corn. 1996. Ethylene glycol ethers and risks of spontaneous abortion and subfertility. *Am J Epidemiol* 143(7):707–717.

Crawford, WW, D Green, WR Knolle, HM Marcos, JA Mosovsky, RC Petersen, PA Testagrossa, and GH Zeman. 1993. Magnetic field exposure in semiconductor cleanrooms. In *Hazard Assessment and Control Technology in Semiconductor Manufacturing II.* Cincinnati, OH: ACGIH.

Escher, G, J Weathers, and B Labonville. 1993. Safety design considerations in deep-UV excimer laser photolithography. In *Hazard Assessment and Control Technology in Semiconductor Manufacturing II.* Cincinnati, OH: American Conference of Governmental Industrial Hygienists.

Eskenazi B, EB Gold, B Lasley, SJ Samuels, SK Hammond, S Wright, MO Razor, CJ Hines, and MB Schenker. 1995. Prospective monitoring of early fetal loss and clinical spontaneous abortion among female semiconductor workers. *Am J Indust Med* 28(6):833–846.

Flipp, N, H Hunsaker, and P Herring. 1992. Investigation of hydride emissions during the maintenance of ion implantation equipment. Presented at the June 1992 American Industrial Hygiene Conference, Boston—Paper 379 (unpublished).

Goh, CL and SK Ng. 1987. Airborne contact dermatitis to colophony in soldering flux. *Contact Dermatitis* 17(2):89–93.

Hammond SK, CJ Hines MF Hallock, SR Woskie, SAbdollahzadeh, CR Iden, E Anson, F Ramsey, and MB Schenker. 1995. Tiered exposure assessment strategy in the Semiconductor Health Study. *Am J Indust Med* 28(6):661–680.

Harrison, RJ. 1986. Gallium arsenide. In *State of the Art Reviews—Occupational Medicine: The Microelectronics Industry,* edited by J LaDou Philadelphia, PA: Hanley & Belfus, Inc.

Hathaway, GL, NH Proctor, JP Hughes, and ML Fischman. 1991. *Chemical Hazards of the Workplace,* 3rd ed. New York: Van Nostrand Reinhold.

Hausen, BM, K Krohn, and E Budianto. 1990. Contact allergy due to colophony (VII). Sensitizing studies with oxidation products of abietic acid and related acids. *Contact Dermat* 23(5):352–358.

Health and Safety Commission. 1992. *Approved Code of Practice—Control of Respiratory Sensitizers.* London: Health and Safety Executive.

Helb, GK, RE Caffrey, ET Eckroth, QT Jarrett, CL Fraust, and JA Fulton. 1983. Plasma processing: Some safety, health and engineering considerations. *Solid State Technology* 24(8):185–194.

Hines, CJ, S Selvin, SJ Samuels, SK Hammond, SR Woskie, MF Hallock, and MB Schenker. 1995. Hierarchical cluster analysis for exposure assessment of workers in the Semiconductor Health Study. *Am J Indust Med* 28(6):713–722.

Horowitz, MR. 1992. Nonionizing radiation issues in a semiconductor R and D facility. Presented at the June 1992 American Industrial Hygiene Conference, Boston—Paper 122 (unpublished).

Jones, JH. 1988. Exposure and control assessment of semiconductor manufacturing. *AIP Conf. Proc. (Photovoltaic Safety)* 166:44–53.

LaDou, J (ed.). 1986. *State of the Art Reviews—Occupational Medicine: The Microelectronics Industry.* Philadelphia, PA: Hanley and Belfus, Inc.

Lassiter, DV. 1996. Work injury and illness surveillance on an international basis. Proceedings of the Third International ESH Conference, Monterey, CA.

Leach-Marshall, JM. 1991. Analysis of radiation detected from exposed process elements from the krypton-85 fine leak testing system. *SSA Journal* 5(2):48–60.

Lead Industries Association. 1990. *Safety in Soldering, Health Guidelines for Solderers and Soldering.* New York: Lead Industries Association, Inc.

Lenihan, KL, JK Sheehy, and JH Jones. 1989. Assessment of exposures in gallium arsenide processing: A case study. In *Hazard Assessment and Control Technology in Semiconductor Manufacturing,* edited by the American Conference of Governmental Industrial Hygienists. Chelsea, MI: Lewis Publishers.

Maletskos, CJ and PR Hanley. 1983. Radiation protection considerations of ion implantation systems. *IEEE Trans on Nuclear Science* NS-30:1592–1596.

McCarthy, CM. 1985. *Worker Exposure during Maintenance of Ion Implanters in the Semiconductor Industry.* Masters thesis, University of Utah, Salt Lake City, UT, 1984. Summarized in *Extended Abstracts, Electrochem Soc* 85(2):448.

McCurdy SA, C Pocekay, KS Hammond, SR Woskie, SJ Samuels, and MB Schenker. 1995. A cross-sectional survey of respiratory and general health outcomes among semiconductor industry workers. *Am J Indust Med* 28(6):847–860.

McIntyre, AJ and BJ Sherin. 1989. Gallium arsenide: hazards, assessment, and control. *Solid State Technology* 32(9):119–126.

Microelectronics and Computer Technology Corporation (MCC). 1994. *Electronics Industry Environmental Roadmap.* Austin, TX: MCC.

—. 1996. *Electronics Industry Environmental Roadmap.* Austin, TX: MCC.

Mosovsky, JA, D Rainer, T Moses and WE Quinn. 1992. Transient hydride generation during III-semiconductor processing. *Appl Occup Environ Hyg* 7(6):375–384.

Mueller, MR and RF Kunesh. 1989. Safety and health implications of dry chemical etchers. In *Hazard Assessment and Control Technology in Semiconductor Manufacturing,* edited by the American Conference of Governmental Industrial Hygienists. Chelsea, MI: Lewis Publishers.

O'Mara, WC. 1993. *Liquid Crystal Flat Panel Displays.* New York: Van Nostrand Reinhold.

PACE Inc. 1994. *Fume Extraction Handbook.* Laurel, MD: PACE Inc.

Pastides, H, EJ Calabrese, DW Hosmer, Jr, and DR Harris. 1988. Spontaneous abortion and general illness symptoms among semiconductor manufacturers. *J Occup Med* 30:543–551.

Pocekay D, SA McCurdy, SJ Samuels, and MB Schenker. 1995. A cross-sectional study of musculoskeletal symptoms and risk factors in semiconductor workers. *Am J Indust Med* 28(6):861–871.

Rainer, D, WE Quinn, JA Mosovsky, and MT Asom. 1993. III-V transient hydride generation, *Solid State Technology* 36(6):35–40.

Rhoades, BJ, DG Sands, and VD Mattera. 1989. Safety and environmental control systems used in chemical vapor deposition (CVD) reactors at AT&T-Microelectronics-Reading. *Appl Ind Hyg* 4(5):105–109.

Rogers, JW. 1994. Radiation safety in semiconductors. Presented at the April 1994 Semiconductor Safety Association Conference, Scottsdale, AZ (unpublished).

Rooney, FP and J Leavey. 1989. Safety and health considerations of an x-ray lithography source. In *Hazard Assessment and Control Technology in Semiconductor Manufacturing,* edited by the American Conference of Governmental Industrial Hygienists. Chelsea, MI: Lewis Publishers.

Rosenthal, FS and S Abdollahzadeh. 1991. Assessment of extremely low frequency (ELF) electric and magnetic fields in microelectronics fabrication rooms. *Appl Occup Environ Hyg* 6(9):777–784.

Roychowdhury, M. 1991. Safety, industrial hygiene, and environmental considerations for MOCVD reactor systems. *Solid State Technology* 34(1):36–38.

Scarpace, L, M Williams, D Baldwin, J Stewart, and D Lassiter. 1989. Results of industrial hygiene sampling in semiconductor manufacturing operations. In *Hazard Assessment and Control Technology in Semiconductor Manufacturing*, edited by the American Conference of Governmental Industrial Hygienists. Chelsea, MI: Lewis Publishers.

Schenker MB, EB Gold, JJ Beaumont, B Eskenazi, SK Hammond, BL Lasley, SA McCurdy, SJ Samuels, CL Saiki, and SH Swan. 1995. Association of spontaneous abortion and other reproductive effects with work in the semiconductor industry. *Am J Indust Med* 28(6):639–659.

Schenker, M, J Beaumont, B Eskenazi, E Gold, K Hammond, B Lasley, S McCurdy, S Samuels, and S Swan. 1992. *Final Report to the Semiconductor Industry Association—Epidemiologic Study of Reproductive and Other Health Effects among Workers Employed in the Manufacture of Semiconductors*. Davis, CA: University of California.

Schmidt, R, H Scheufler, S Bauer, L Wolff, M Pelzing, and R Herzschuh. 1995. Toxicological investigations in the semiconductor industry: III: Studies on prenatal toxicity caused by waste products from aluminum plasma etching processes. *Toxicol Ind Health* 11(1):49–61.

SEMATECH. 1995. *Silane Safety Transfer Document, 96013067 A-ENG*. Austin, TX: SEMATECH.

—. 1996. *Interpritive Guide for SEMI S2-93 and SEMI S8-95*. Austin, TX: SEMATECH.

Semiconductor Industry Association (SIA). 1995. *World Semiconductor Sales Forecast Data*. San Jose, CA: SIA.

Sheehy, JW and JH Jones. 1993. Assessment of arsenic exposures and controls in gallium arsenide production. *Am Ind Hyg Assoc J* 54(2):61–69.

Sober, DJ. 1995. *Selecting Laminates Using "Fitness for Use" Criteria, Surface Mount Technology (SMT)*. Libertyville, IL: IHS Publishing Group.

Wade, R, M Williams, T Mitchell, J Wong, and B Tusé. 1981. *Semiconductor industry study*. San Francisco, CA: California Department of Industrial Relations, Division of Occupational Safety and Health.

Other relevant readings

Carlson, V. 1995. *Step-by-Step SMT—Design for Test—Part 2, Surface Mount Technology (SMT)*. Libertyville, IL: IHS Publishing Group.

Corbitt, RA. 1990. *Standard Handbook of Environmental Engineering*. New York: McGraw-Hill Publishing Company.

Crawford, TJ. 1995. *Step-by-Step SMT—Cleaning—Part 8, Surface Mount Technology (SMT)*. Libertyville, IL: IHS Publishing Group.

Electronic Industries Association (EIA). 1995. *Electronic Market Data Book—Statistical Yearbook of the Electronics Industries*. Arlington, VA: EIA.

Environmental Protection Agency (EPA). 1995. *Profile of the Electronics and Computer Industry*. Washington, DC: US EPA, Office of Compliance Sector Notebook Project.

Flatt, M. 1992. *Printed Circuit Board Basics: An introduction to the PCB Industry*. San Francisco, CA: Miller Freeman Inc.

Gilleo, K. 1995. *Step-by-Step SMT—Adhesives/epoxies and Dispensing—Part 5, Surface Mount Technology (SMT)*. Libertyville, IL: IHS Publishing Group.

Ginsberg, G. 1989. *Surface Mount and Related Technologies*. New York: Marcel Dekker, Inc.

Gray RH, M Corn, R Cohen, A Correa, R Hakim, W Hou, F Shah, and H Zauer. 1993. *Final Report: The Johns Hopkins University Retrospective and Prospective Studies of Reproductive Health Among IBM Employees in Semiconductor Manufacturing*. Baltimore, MD: Johns Hopkins University.

Howes, MJ and DV Morgan (eds.). 1985. *Gallium Arsenide Materials, Devices and Circuits*. New York: Wiley.

Hutchins, CL. 1996. *Step-by-Step SMT—Rework and repair—Part 10, Surface Mount Technology (SMT)*. Libertyville, IL: IHS Publishing Group.

Hwang, JS. 1995. *Step-by-Step SMT—Solder Materials—Part 3, Surface Mount Technology (SMT)*. Libertyville, IL: IHS Publishing Group.

Hwang, JS. 1996. *Surface Mount Technology: 1980's vs. 1990's, Surface Mount Technology (SMT)*. Libertyville, IL: IHS Publishing Group.

ITM, Inc. 1995. *Step-by-Step SMT—Printing—Part 4, Surface Mount Technology (SMT)*. Libertyville, IL: IHS Publishing Group.

Kear, FW. 1987. *Printed Circuit Assembly Manufacturing*. New York: Marcel Dekker, Inc.

Leow, YH, SK Ng, and CL Goh. 1995. Allergic contact dermatitis from epoxy resin in Singapore. *Contact Dermat* 33(5):355–356.

Manahan, SE. 1994. *Environmental Chemistry*, 6th edition. Boca Raton, FL: Lewis Publishers.

Manzione, LT. 1990. *Plastic Packaging of Microelectronic Devices*. New York: Van Nostrand Reinhold.

Meridith S. 1993. Reported incidence of occupational asthma in the United Kingdom, 1989-90. *J Epidemiol Community Health* 47(6):459–463.

Moreau, WM. 1988. *Semiconductor Lithography—Principles, Practices, and Materials*. New York: Plenum.

O'Mara, WC. 1993. *Liquid Crystal Flat Panel Displays*. New York: Van Nostrand Reinhold.

PACE Inc. 1994. *Environmental Health and Safety Hazards of Soldering*. Laurel, MD: PACE Inc.

Parker, SP (ed.). 1988. *Encyclopedia of Electronics and Computers*, 2nd edition. New York: McGraw-Hill.

Prasad, R. 1995. *Step-by-Step SMT—Component Placement—Part 6, Surface Mount Technology (SMT)*. Libertyville, IL: IHS Publishing Group.

Rooks, S and B Bolliger. 1995. *Step-by-Step SMT—Test/inspection—Part 9, Surface Mount Technology (SMT)*. Libertyville, IL: IHS Publishing Group.

Ryssel, H and I Ruge. 1993. *Ion Implantation*. New York: Wiley.

Salmon, ER. 1987. *Encapsulation of Electronic Devices and Components*. New York: Marcel Dekker.

Semiconductor Industry Association (SIA). 1994. *The National Technology Roadmap for Semiconductors*. San Jose, CA: SIA.

—. 1995. *Semiconductor Industry Comparative Annual Injury and Illness Rates*. San Jose, CA: SIA.

—. 1995. *Semiconductor Industry Roadmap*. San Jose, CA: SIA.

Sherman, A. 1987. *Chemical Vapor Deposition for Microelectronics—Principles, Technology, and Applications*. Park Ridge, NJ: Noyes.

Tolliver, DL. 1988. *Handbook of Contamination Control in Microelectronics: Principles, Applications, and Technology*. Park Ridge: NJ: Noyes.

Ungers, LJ, JH Jones, AJ McIntyre, and CR McHenry. 1985. Release of arsenic from semiconductor wafers. *Am Indust Hyg J* 46(8):416–420.

Van Zant, P. 1990. *Microchip fabrication—A Practical Guide to Semiconductor Processing*, 2nd ed. New York: McGraw-Hill.

Warwick, M and P Hedges. 1996. Changes in reduced residue solder pastes, surface mount technology (SMT). In *SMT's Guide to Soldering*. Libertyville, IL: IHS Publishing Group.

Williams, ME and DG Baldwin. 1995. *Semiconductor Industrial Hygiene Handbook*. Park Ridge, NJ: Noyes.

Willis, R. 1995. *Step-by-Step SMT—Soldering—Part 7, Surface Mount Technology (SMT)*. Libertyville, IL: IHS Publishing Group.

GLASS, POTTERY AND RELATED MATERIALS

84

Chapter Editor
Joel Bender and Jonathan P. Hellerstein

Contents

GLASS, CERAMICS AND RELATED MATERIALS

Jonathan P. Hellerstein, Joel Bender,
John G. Hadley and Charles M. Hohman

This chapter covers the following product sectors:

- glass
- synthetic vitreous fibres
- pottery
- ceramic tile
- industrial ceramics
- brick and tile
- refractories
- synthetic gems
- optical fibres.

Interestingly, not only do most of these sectors have roots in antiquity, but they also share a number of common general processes. For example, all are fundamentally based on the use of naturally occurring raw materials in powder or fine particulate form which are transformed by heat into the desired products. Therefore, despite the range of processes and products encompassed in this group, these common processes allow a common overview of potential health hazards associated with these industries. Since the various manufacturing sectors are composed of both small, fragmented segments (e.g., brick manufacturing) and large, technically sophisticated manufacturing plants employing thousands of workers, each sector is described separately.

Common Processes and Hazards

There are common safety and health hazards encountered in manufacturing of products in these business sectors. The hazards and control measures are discussed in other sections of the *Encyclopaedia*. Process-specific hazards are discussed in the individual sections of this chapter.

Batch raw material processes

Most of the industrial manufacturing processes receive dry solid raw materials in bulk form or individual bags. Bulk solid raw materials are unloaded from hopper rail cars or over-the-road trucks into bins, hoppers or mixers by gravity, pneumatic transfer lines, screw conveyors, bucket conveyors or other mechanical transfer. Pallets of bagged raw materials (20 to 50 kg) or large bulk fabric bag containers (0.5 to 1.0 tonnes) are unloaded from truck trailers or rail boxcars by powered industrial lift trucks, cranes or hoists. Individual bags or raw materials are removed from pallets manually or with powered lift assists. Bagged raw materials are typically charged into a bag dumping station or directly into storage hoppers or scale hoppers.

Potential safety and health hazards associated with the solid raw material unloading, handling and transfer processes include:

- *noise exposures* in the 85 to 100 dBA range. Pneumatic vibrators, compressors, valve actuators, mixing drive motors, blowers, and dust collectors are some major noise sources.
- *exposures to respirable airborne particulate* from the transfer and mixing of granular solid raw materials. Exposures depend on composition of raw materials but may commonly include silica (SiO_2), clay, alumina, limestone, alkaline dusts, metal oxides, heavy metals and nuisance particulate.
- *ergonomic hazards* associated with manual lifting or handling of raw material bags, vibrators, or transfer lines and system maintenance activities

- *physical hazards* from manoeuvring rail cars or trucks, powered-industrial truck traffic, work at elevated heights, confined-space entries and contact with electrical, pneumatic or mechanical energy sources—e.g., nip points, rotating parts, drive gears, shafts, belts and pulleys.

Firing or melting processes

Manufacturing products in these business sectors involves drying, melting or firing processes in kilns or furnaces. The heat for these processes is generated by combustion of propane, natural gas (methane) or fuel oil, electric arc melting, microwave, dielectric drying and/or resistance heating with electricity. Potential hazards presented from firing or melting processes include:

- *exposures to combustion products* such as carbon monoxide, nitrogen oxides (NO_x) and sulphur dioxide
- *fumes and particulates* from airborne raw materials (e.g., silica, metals, alkaline dusts) or by-products (e.g., hydrogen fluoride, cristobalite, heavy metal fumes)
- *fire or explosion* associated with fuel systems used for process heat or fuel for lift trucks; potential fire or explosion hazards associated with flammable fuel storage tanks, piping distribution systems and vaporizers. Back-up or stand-by fuel systems infrequently used for natural gas curtailments can present similar fire or explosion concerns.
- *infrared radiation exposure* from molten material, which can increase risk of heat cataracts or skin burns
- *radiant energy and heat stress*. The working environment around furnaces or kilns can be extremely hot. Significant heat stress problems can occur when emergency repair work or routine maintenance is performed near or above firing or melting processes. Severe thermal burns can result from direct skin contact with hot surfaces or molten materials (see figure 84.1).

Figure 84.1 • Quality-control technician taking glass samples from furnace and wearing personal heat protective equipment and IR shielding glasses.

Libbey-Owens-Ford

- *electrical energy hazards.* Direct contact with high-voltage electric energy used for resistance heating to supplement fuel-fired processes presents an electrocution hazard and possible health concerns about exposure to electromagnetic fields (EMF). Strong magnetic and electric fields can potentially interfere with pacemakers and other implanted medical devices.
- *noise exposures* above 85 to 90 dBA from combustion blowers, batch hoppers or mixers, feed processes and conveyors.

Material handling in production, fabrication, packaging and warehousing

Material-handling, fabrication and packaging processes differ to a large extent in this business sector, as do the size, shape and weights of products. The high density of materials in this sector or bulky configurations present common material-handling hazards. Manual lifting and material handling in production, fabrication, packaging and warehousing in this industry accounts for many disabling injuries. (See "Injury and illness profile" section below.) Injury reduction efforts are focusing on reducing manual lifting and material handling. For example, innovative packaging designs, robotics for stacking and palletizing finished products, and automatic guided transport vehicles for warehousing are starting to be used in select parts of this business sector to eliminate manual material handling and associated injuries. Use of conveyors, manned lift assists (e.g., vacuum hoists) and scissors platforms for handling and palletizing products are currently common material-handling practices (see figure 84.2).

The use of robotics to eliminate manual material handling is playing a major role in prevention of ergonomic injuries. Robotics has reduced ergonomic stresses and severe laceration injuries that have been historically associated with material handling (e.g., flat glass) in the production workforce (see figure 84.3). However, increased utilization of robotics and process automation introduces moving machinery and electric power hazards, which transforms the types of hazards and also transfers risks to other workers (from production to maintenance workers). Proper designs of electronic controls and logic sequencing, machine guards, total energy lockout practices and establishing safe operating and maintenance procedures are fundamental ways to control injuries to maintenance and production workers.

Figure 84.2 • Vacuum lift assist being used to handle 20 to 35 kg packages of textile glass.

Figure 84.3 • Robotics used in plate-glass handling reduces ergonomic and laceration hazards.

Libbey-Owens-Ford

Rebuilds and reconstruction activities

Numerous potential health and safety hazards are encountered during periodic major rebuilds or cold repairs to furnaces or kilns. A wide range of hazards associated with construction activities may be encountered. Examples include: ergonomic hazards with material handling (e.g., refractory bricks); airborne exposures to silica, asbestos, refractory ceramic fibres or particulate matter

Figure 84.4 • Confined-space entry during furnace rebuild at fibreglass plant. Water misting reduces airborne particulates during furnace demolition.

Owens Corning

84. GLASS, POTTERY AND RELATED MATERIALS

containing heavy metal, during demolition, or by-products of cutting and welding; heat stress; work at elevated heights; slip, trip or fall hazards; confined-space hazards (see figure 84.4); and contact with hazardous energy sources.

Glass

General profile

Glass was formed naturally from common elements in the earth's crust long before anyone ever thought of experimenting with its composition, moulding its shape or putting it to the myriad of uses that it enjoys today. Obsidian, for instance, is a naturally occurring combination of oxides fused by intense volcanic heat and vitrified (made into a glass) by rapid air cooling. Its opaque, black colour comes from the relatively high amounts of iron oxide it contains. Its chemical durability and hardness compare favourably with many commercial glasses.

Glass technology has evolved for 6,000 years, and some modern principles date back to ancient times. The origin of the first synthetic glasses is lost in antiquity and legend. *Faience* was made by the Egyptians, who molded figurines from sand (SiO_2), the most popular glass-forming oxide. It was coated with natron, the residue left by the flooding Nile river, which was composed principally of calcium carbonate ($CaCO_3$), soda ash (Na_2CO_3), salt (NaCl) and copper oxide (CuO). Heating below 1,000 °C produced a glassy coating by the diffusion of the fluxes, CaO and Na_2O into the sand and their subsequent solid-state reaction with the sand. The copper oxide gave the article an appealing blue colour.

According to the definition given by Morey: "Glass is an inorganic substance in a condition which is continuous with, and analogous to, the liquid state of that substance, but which, as the result of a reversible change in viscosity during cooling, has attained so high a degree of viscosity as to be, for all practical purposes, rigid." ASTM defines glass as "an inorganic product of fusion that has cooled to a rigid condition without crystallizing." Both organic and inorganic materials may form glasses if their structure is non-crystalline—that is, if they lack long-range order.

A most important development in glass technology was the use of a blow pipe (see figure 84.5), which was first used in approximately 100 years BC. From then onwards, there was a rapid development in the technique of manufacturing glass.

Figure 84.5 • The blow pipe.

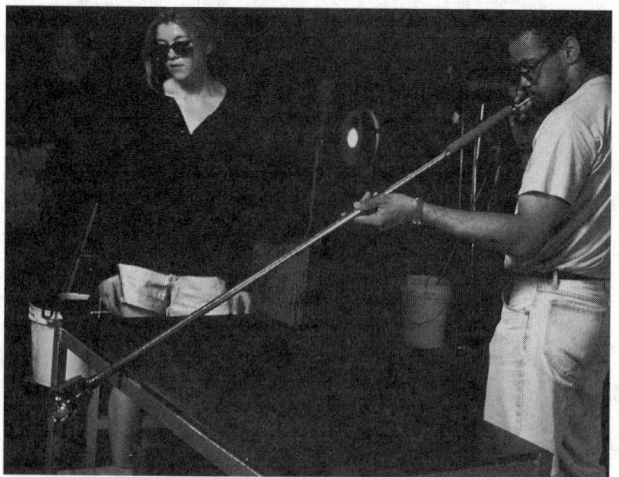

Urban Glass

The first glass was coloured because of the presence of various impurities such as oxides of iron and chromium. Virtually colourless glass was first made some 1,500 years ago.

At that time glass manufacturing was developing in Rome, and from there it moved to many other countries in Europe. Many glass works were built in Venice, and an important development took place there. In the 13th century, many of the glass plants were moved from Venice to a nearby island, Murano. Murano is still a centre for the production of hand-made glass in Italy.

By the 16th century, glass was made all over Europe. Now Bohemian glass from the Czech Republic is well known for its beauty and glass plants in the United Kingdom and Ireland produce high-quality lead crystal glass tableware. Sweden is another country that is home to artistic glass crystalware production.

In North America the first manufacturing establishment of any sort was a glass factory. English settlers started to produce glass at the beginning of the 17th century at Jamestown, Virginia.

Today glass is manufactured in most countries all over the world. Many products of glass are made in fully automatic processing lines. Although glass is one of the oldest materials, its properties are unique and not yet fully understood.

The glass industry today is made up of several major market segments, which include the flat glass market, the consumer houseware market, the glass containers market, the optical glass industry and the scientific glassware market segment. The optical and scientific glass markets tend to be very ordered and are dominated by one or two suppliers in most countries. These markets are also much lower in volume than the consumer-based markets. Each of these markets has developed over the years by innovations in specific glass technology or manufacturing advancements. The container industry, for example, was driven by the development of high-speed bottle-making machines developed in the early 1900s. The flat glass industry was significantly advanced by the development of the float glass process in the early 1960s. Both of these segments are multi-billion-dollar businesses worldwide today.

Glass housewares fall into four general categories:

1. tableware (including dinnerware, cups and mugs)
2. drinkware
3. bakeware (or ovenware)
4. top-of-stove cookware.

While worldwide estimates are difficult to obtain, the market for glass housewares is undoubtedly on the order of US$1 billion in the United States alone. Depending upon the specific category, a variety of other materials compete for market share, including ceramics, metals and plastics.

Manufacturing processes

Glass is an inorganic product of fusion which has cooled to a rigid condition without crystallizing. Glass is typically hard and brittle and has a conchoidal fracture. Glass may be manufactured to be coloured, translucent or opaque by varying the dissolved amorphous or crystalline materials that are present.

When glass is cooled from the hot molten state, it gradually increases in viscosity without crystallization over a wide temperature range, until it assumes its characteristic hard, brittle form. Cooling is controlled to prevent crystallization, or high strain.

While any compound which has these physical properties is theoretically a glass, most commercial glasses fall into three main types and have a wide range of chemical compositions.

1. *Soda-lime-silica glasses* are the most important glasses in terms of quantity produced and variety of use, including almost all flat glass, containers, low-cost mass-produced domestic glassware and electric light bulbs.

2. *Lead-potash-silica glasses* contain a varying but often high proportion of lead oxide. Optical glass manufacture makes use of the high refractive index of this type of glass; hand-blown domestic and decorative glassware makes use of its ease of cutting and polishing; electrical and electronic applications takes advantage of its high electrical resistivity and radiation protection.

3. *Borosilicate glasses* have a low thermal expansion and are resistant to thermal shock, which makes them ideal for domestic oven and laboratory glassware and for glass fibre for plastic reinforcements.

A commercial glass batch consists of a mixture of several ingredients. However, the largest fraction of the batch is made up of from 4 to 6 ingredients, chosen from such materials as sand, limestone, dolomite, soda ash, borax, boric acid, feldspathic materials, lead and barium compounds. The remainder of the batch consists of several additional ingredients, chosen from a group of some 15 to 20 materials commonly referred to as minor ingredients. These latter additions are added with a view to providing some specific function or quality, such as colour, which is to be realized during the glass preparation process.

Figure 84.6 illustrates the basic principles of glass manufacture. The raw materials are weighed, mixed and, after the addition of broken glass (cullet), taken to the furnace for melting. Small pots of up to 2 tonnes capacity are still used for the melting of glass for hand-blown crystalware and special glasses required in small quantity. Several pots are heated together in a combustion chamber.

In most modern manufacture, melting takes place in large regenerative, recuperative or electric furnaces built of refractory material and heated by oil, natural gas or electricity. Electric boosting and cold top electric melting were commercialized and became extensively utilized globally in the late 1960s and 1970s. The driving force behind cold top electric melting was emission control, while electric boosting was generally used in order to improve glass quality and to increase throughput.

The most significant economic factors concerning the use of electricity for glass furnace melting are related to fossil fuel costs, the availability of various fuels, electricity costs, capital costs for equipment and so on. However, in many instances the prime reason for the use of electric melting or boosting is environmental control. Various locations worldwide either already have or are expected soon to have environmental regulations that strictly restrict the discharge of various oxides or particulate matter in general. Thus, manufacturers in many locations face the possibility of either having to reduce glass melting throughputs, install baghouses or precipitators in order to handle waste flue gases or modify the melting

Figure 84.6 • The processes and materials involved in the manufacture of glass.

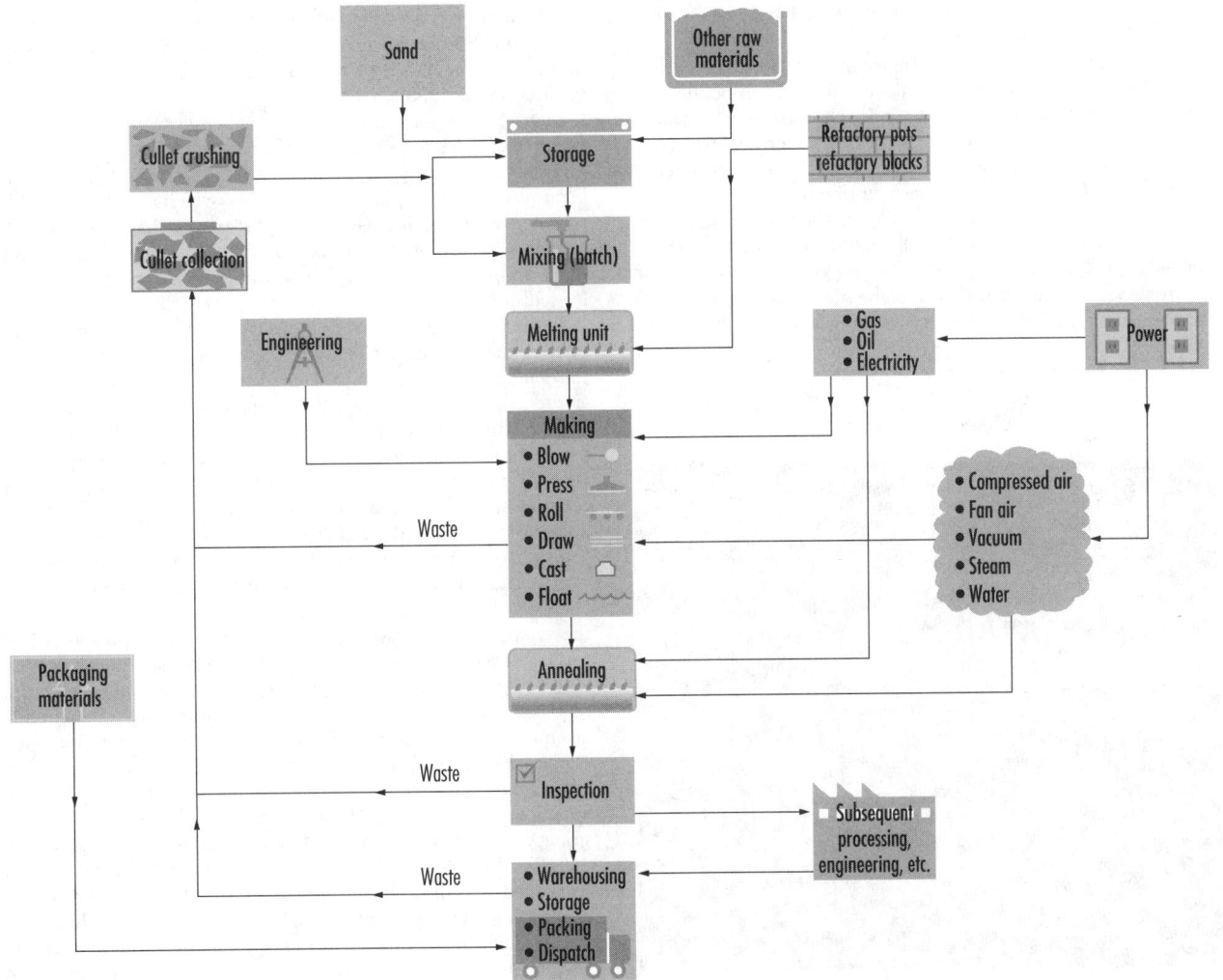

84. GLASS, POTTERY AND RELATED MATERIALS

Figure 84.7 • Continuous float process.

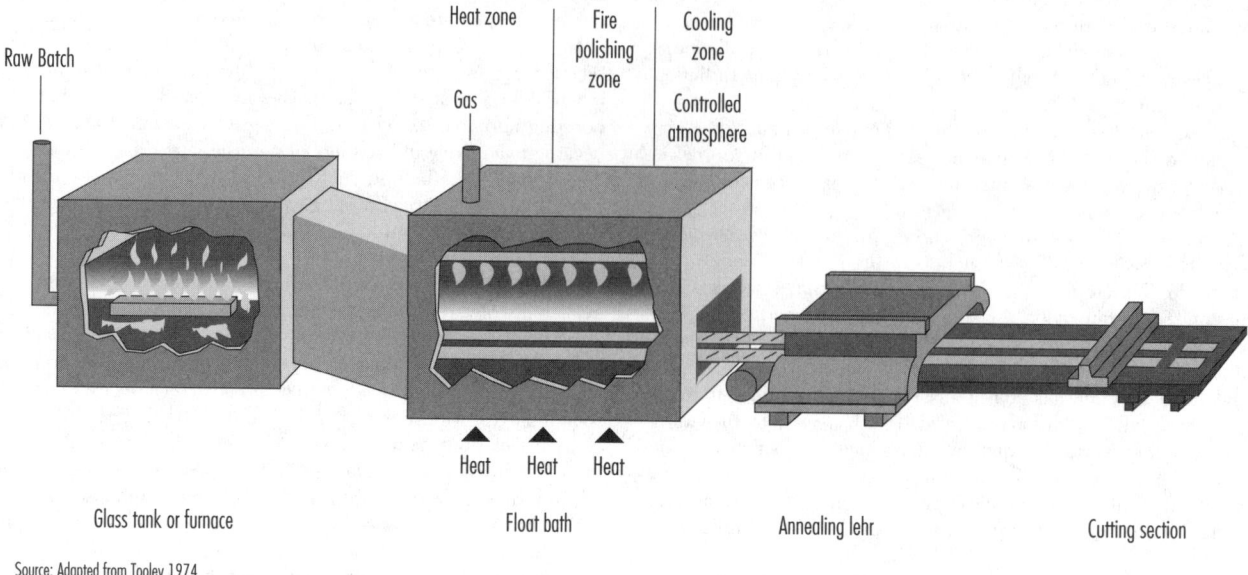

Source: Adapted from Tooley 1974.

process and include electric melting or boost. The alternatives to such modification may in some cases be plant shutdowns.

The hottest part of the furnace (superstructure) may be at 1,600 to 2,800 °C. Controlled cooling reduces the glass temperature to 1,000 to 1,200 °C at the point where the glass leaves the furnace. In addition, all types of glass are subjected to further controlled cooling (annealing) in a special oven or lehr. Subsequent processing will depend on the type of manufacturing process.

Automatic blowing is used on machines for bottle and lamp bulb production in addition to traditional hand-blown glass. Simple shapes, such as in insulators, glass bricks, lens blanks and so on, are pressed rather than blown. Some manufacturing processes use a combination of mechanical blowing and pressing. Wired

Figure 84.8 • Ribbon of float glass exiting from lehr after being annealed.

and figured glass is rolled. Sheet glass is drawn from the furnace by a vertical process which gives it a fire-finished surface. Owing to the combined effects of drawing and gravity, some minor distortion is inevitable.

Plate glass passes through water-cooled rollers onto an annealing lehr. It is free from distortion. Surface damage can be removed by grinding and polishing after fabrication. This process has largely been replaced by the float glass process, which was introduced in recent years (see figure 84.7). The float process has made possible the manufacture of a glass that combines the advantages of both sheet and plate. Float glass has a fire-finished surface and is free from distortion.

In the float process, a continuous ribbon of glass moves out of a melting furnace and floats along the surface of a bath of molten tin. The glass conforms to the perfect surface of the molten tin. On its passage over the tin, the temperature is reduced until the glass is sufficiently hard to be fed onto the rollers of the annealing lehr without marking its under surface. An inert atmosphere in the bath prevents oxidation of the tin. The glass, after annealing, requires no further treatment and can be further processed by automatic cutting and packing (see figure 84.8).

The trend in new residential and commercial architecture toward the inclusion of more glazing area, and the need to reduce energy consumption, has put increased emphasis on improving the energy efficiency of windows. Thin films deposited at the surface of the glass provide low emissivity or solar control properties. The commercialization of such commodity-coated products requires a low cost, large area deposition technology. As a result, an increasing number of float glass manufacturing lines are equipped with sophisticated on-line coating processes.

In commonly used chemical vapour deposition (CVD) processes, a complex gas mixture is brought into contact with the hot substrate, where it pyrolytically reacts to form a coating at the surface of the glass. In general, the coating equipment consists of thermally controlled structures which are suspended over the width of the glass ribbon. They may be located in the tin bath, the lehr gap or the lehr. The function of the coaters is to uniformly deliver the precursor gases over the ribbon width in a temperature-controlled fashion and to safely extract the exhaust gas by-products from the deposition region. For multiple coating stacks, multiple coaters are used in series along the glass ribbon.

For the treatment of the exhaust gas by-products generated by such large-scale processes, wet scrubbing techniques with a conventional filter press are normally sufficient. When the effluent gases are not easily reacted or wetted by aqueous solutions, incineration is the primary option.

Some optical glasses are chemically strengthened by processes which involve immersing the glass for several hours in high-temperature baths containing molten salts of, typically, lithium nitrate and potassium nitrate.

Safety glass is of two major types:

1. *Toughened glass* is made by pre-stressing by heating and then rapidly cooling pieces of flat glass of desired shape and size in special ovens.
2. *Laminated glass* is formed by bonding a sheet of plastic (usually polyvinyl butyral) between two thin sheets of flat glass.

Synthetic Vitreous Fibres

General profile

Synthetic vitreous fibres are produced from a wide variety of materials. They are amorphous silicates manufactured from glass, rock, slag or other minerals. The fibres produced are both continuous and discontinuous fibres. In general, the continuous fibres are glass fibres drawn through nozzles and used to reinforce other materials, such as plastics, to produce composite materials with unique properties. The discontinuous fibres (generally known as wools) are used for many purposes, most commonly for thermal and acoustical insulation. Synthetic vitreous fibres, for purposes of this discussion, have been divided into continuous glass fibres, with the insulation wools made of glass, rock or slag fibres, and refractory ceramic fibres, which are generally aluminium silicates.

The possibility of drawing heat-softened glass into fine fibres was known to glass makers in antiquity and is actually older than the technique of glass blowing. Many early Egyptian vessels were made by winding coarse glass fibres onto a suitably shaped mandrel of clay, then heating the assembly until the glass fibres flowed into one another and, after cooling, removing the clay core. Even after the advent of glass blowing in the 1st century AD, the glass fibre technique was still employed. Venetian glassmakers in the 16th and 17th centuries used it for decorating glassware. In this case, bundles of opaque white fibres were wound onto the surface of a plain transparent blown glass vessel (e.g., a goblet) and then fused into it by heating.

Despite the long history of generally decorative or artistic uses of glass fibres, widespread use did not arise again until the 20th century. Initial commercial US production of glass fibres occurred in the 1930s, while in Europe the initial use occurred some years earlier. Rock and slag wools were produced several years earlier than that.

The manufacture and use of synthetic vitreous fibres is a global multi-billion-dollar industry since these useful materials have become an important component of modern society. Their uses as insulations have resulted in tremendous reduction in energy requirements for heating and cooling buildings, and this energy savings has resulted in significant reduction in global pollution associated with energy production. The number of applications of continuous glass filaments as reinforcements for a plethora of products, from sporting goods to computer chips to aerospace applications, has been estimated to be in excess of 30,000. The development and widespread commercialization of refractory ceramic fibres occurred in the 1970s, and these fibres continue to play an important role in protecting workers and equipment in a variety of high-temperature manufacturing processes.

Manufacturing processes

Continuous glass filaments

Glass filaments are formed by drawing the molten glass through precious-metal bushings into fine filaments of nearly uniform diameter. Due to the physical requirements for the fibres when used as reinforcements, their diameters are relatively large compared to those in the insulation wools. Almost all continuous glass filaments have diameters of 5 to 15 μm or greater. These large diameters, coupled with the narrow range of diameters produced during the manufacture, eliminate any potential chronic respiratory effects, as the fibres are too large to be inhaled into the lower respiratory tract.

Continuous glass fibres are made by the rapid attenuation of drops of molten glass exuding through nozzles under gravity and suspended from them. The dynamic balance between the forces of surface tension and mechanical attenuation results in the drop of glass taking on the shape of a meniscus held at the annular opening of the nozzle and tapering to the diameter of the fibre being drawn. For fibre drawing to be successful, the glass has to be within a narrow range of viscosities (i.e., between 500 and 1,000 poise). At lower viscosities, the glass is too fluid and falls away from the nozzles as drops; in this case surface tension dominates. At higher viscosities, the tension in the fibre during attenuation is too high. The rate of flow of glass through the nozzle can also become too low to maintain a meniscus.

The function of the bushing is to provide a plate containing several hundred nozzles at a uniform temperature and to condition the glass to this uniform temperature so that the fibres drawn are of uniform diameter. Figure 84.9 shows a schematic diagram of the principal features of a direct-melt bushing attached to a forehearth from which it takes a supply of molten glass very near the temperature at which the glass will pass through the nozzles; in this case, therefore, the basic function of the bushing is also its sole function.

In the case of a bushing operating from marbles, a second function is required—namely, to first melt the marbles before conditioning the glass to the correct fibre-drawing temperature. A typical marble bushing is shown in figure 84.10. The broken line within the bushing is a perforated plate which retains the unmelted marbles.

Figure 84.9 • Schematic of direct-melt bushing.

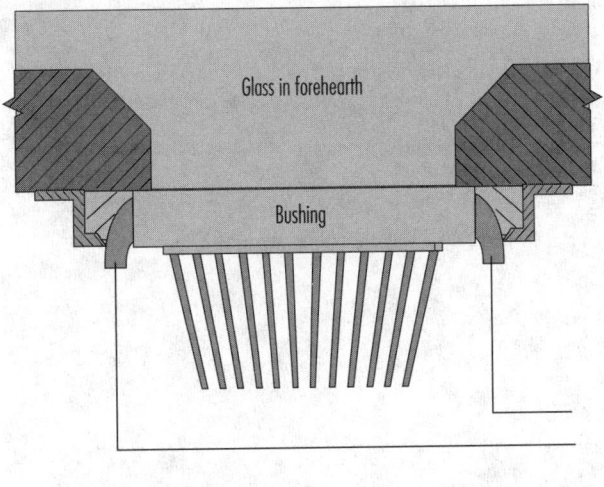

Glass in forehearth

Bushing

Source: Adapted from Tooley 1974.

84. GLASS, POTTERY AND RELATED MATERIALS

Figure 84.10 • Schematic of a marble bushing.

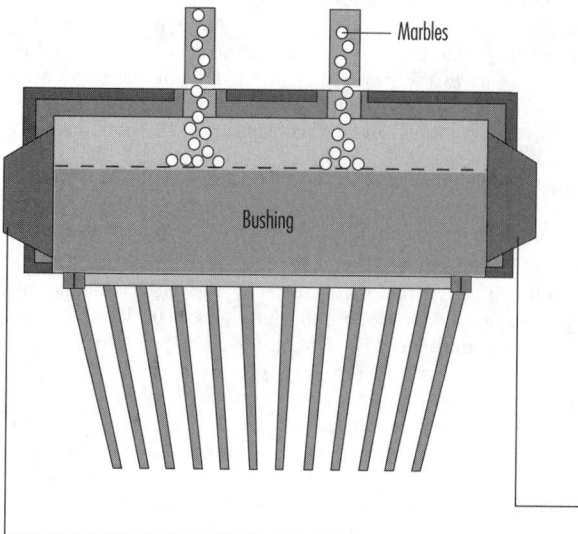

Source: Adapted from Tooley 1974.

Figure 84.11 • Textile glass filaments being pulled through bushing. Filaments are gathered into strands and wound into packages for processing.

The design of bushings is largely empirical. For reasons of resistance to attack by molten glass and stability at the temperatures needed for fibre drawing, bushings are made from platinum alloys; both 10% rhodium-platinum and 20% rhodium-platinum are used, the latter being more resistant to distortion at elevated temperatures.

Before the individual fibres being drawn from a bushing are gathered and consolidated into a strand, or a multiplicity of strands, they are coated with a fibre size. These fibre sizes are basically of two types:

1. starch-oil sizes usually applied to fibres intended for weaving into fine fabrics or similar operations
2. keying agent plus film-former sizes applied to fibres intended for the direct reinforcement of plastics and rubber.

After the fibre is formed, a protective coating of organic sizing is applied at an applicator and the continuous filaments are gathered into a multifilament strand (see figure 84.11) before being wrapped on a winding tube. Applicators function by allowing the fan of fibres, when about 25 to 45 mm wide and on their way to the gathering shoe below the applicator, to pass over a moving surface covered with a film of fibre size.

There are basically two types of applications:

1. roller applicators, made of rubber, ceramic or graphite, in which the fibre runs over the surface of the roller coated with a film of fibre size
2. belt applicators, in which at one end the belt passes over a driven roller which dips the belt into the fibre size and at the other end passes over a fixed hard chrome steel bar at which position the fibres touch the belt to pick up the size.

The protective coating and the fibre-gathering process can vary depending on the types of textile or reinforcement fibre being produced. The basic objective is to coat the fibres with size, gather them into a strand and locate them on a removable tube on the collet with the minimum necessary tension.

Figure 84.12 shows the process of continuous glass manufacturing.

Insulation wool manufacturing

In contrast to continuous filaments, the fibres of the insulation wools and refractory ceramic fibres are made in very high energy processes in which molten material is dropped into either spinning discs or a series of rotating wheels. These methods result in the production of fibres with a range of diameters much wider than seen with continuous filaments. Thus, all of the insulation wools and ceramic fibres contain a fraction of the fibres with diameters of less than 3.0 μm; these could become respirable if fractured into relatively short lengths (less than 200 to 250 μm). Extensive data are available on exposures to respirable synthetic vitreous fibres in the workplace.

Several processes are used to manufacture *glass wool*, including the steam blowing process and flame blown process; but the most popular is the rotary forming process developed in the mid-1950s. The rotary processes have largely replaced direct blowing processes for the commercial production of glass-fibre insulation products. These rotary processes all employ a hollow drum, or spinner, mounted with its axis vertical. The vertical wall of the spinner is perforated with several thousand holes uniformly distributed around the circumference. Molten glass is allowed to fall at a controlled rate into the centre of the spinner, from where some suitable distributor forces it to the inside of the vertical perforated wall. From that position, centrifugal force drives the glass radially outwards in the form of discrete glass filaments issuing from every perforation. Further attenuation of these primary filaments is achieved by a suitable blowing fluid emerging from a nozzle or nozzles arranged around and concentric with the spinner. The net result is the production of fibres with a mean fibre diameter of 6 to 7 mm. The blowing fluid acts in a downwards direction and so, as well as providing the final attenuation, it also deflects the fibres towards a collecting surface situated below the spinner. On the way to this collecting surface, the fibres are sprayed with a suitable binder before being uniformly distributed across the collecting surface (see figure 84.13).

In a rotary process, glass wool fibres are made by allowing molten glass to run through a series of small openings which are situated in a revolving spinner and then attenuating the primary filament by air or steam blowing.

Mineral wool, however, cannot be produced on the rotary spinner process and historically has been produced in process with a series of horizontal spinning mandrels. The mineral wool process consists of a set of rotors (mandrels) mounted in a cascade formation and rotating very rapidly (see figure 84.14). A stream of molten stone is continuously transferred to one of the upper rotors and from this rotor distributed on the second and so on. The melt is uniformly spread on the outside surface of all the rotors. From the rotors, droplets are thrown out by centrifugal force. The droplets are attached to the rotor surface by elongated necks which, under further elongation and simultaneous cooling, develop into fibres. The elongation is, of course, followed by a decrease in diameter which, in turn, causes an accelerated cooling. Thus, there is a lower limit for the diameter among fibres produced in this process. A normal distribution of fibre diameters around the mean value is, therefore, not expected.

Refractory ceramic fibres
Ceramic fibres are primarily produced by blowing and spinning with methods similar to those described for the insulation wools. In the steam blowing process, raw materials such as alumina and silica are fused in an electric furnace, and the molten material is drawn off and blown with either pressurized steam or other hot gas. The fibres produced are then collected on a screen.

Similar to the spinning process for rock and slag fibres, those for ceramic fibres produce a high proportion of long silky fibres. In this method, a stream of molten material is dropped onto rapidly spinning discs and thrown off tangentially to form fibres.

Figure 84.12 • Continuous filament glass manufacturing.

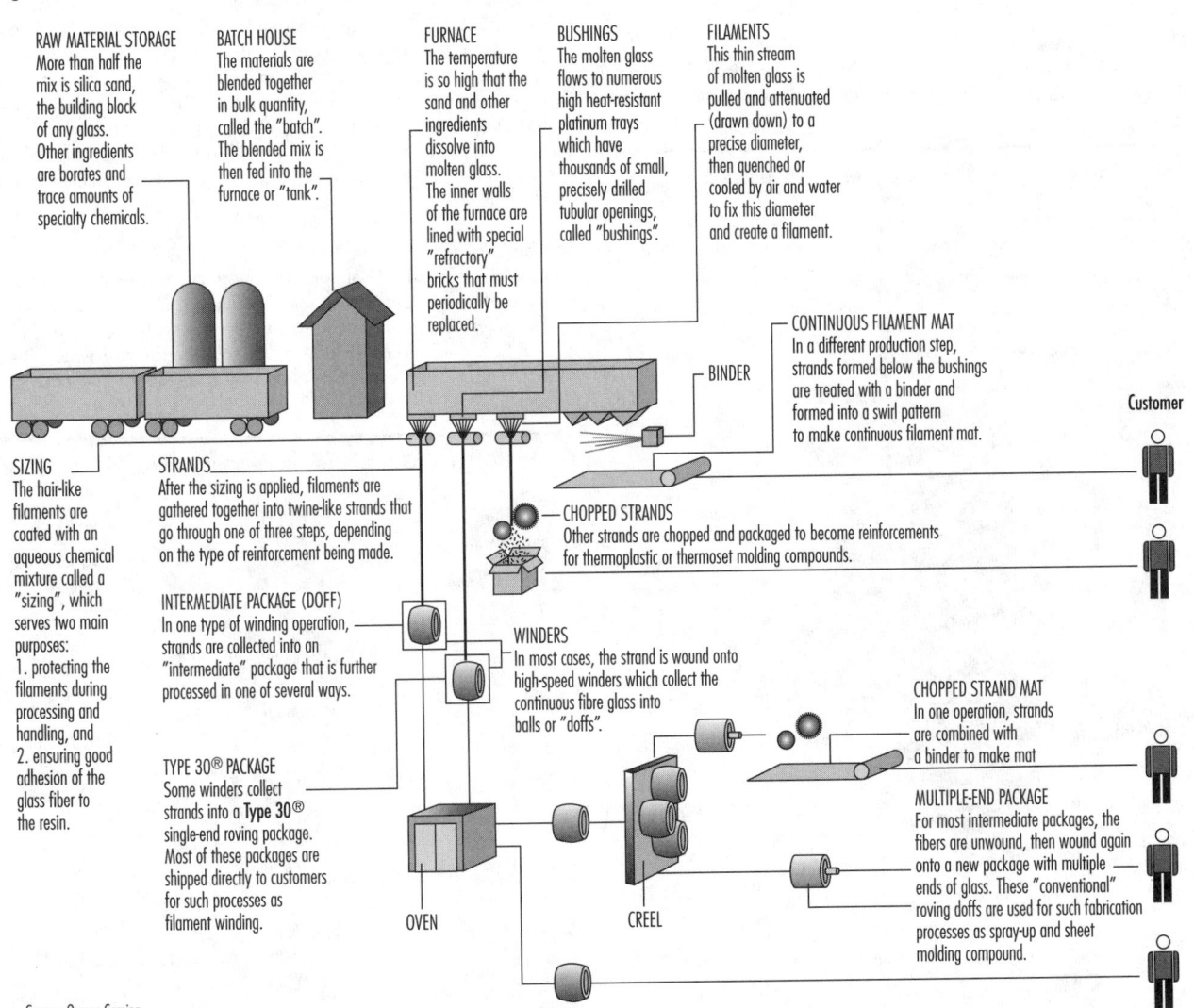

RAW MATERIAL STORAGE
More than half the mix is silica sand, the building block of any glass. Other ingredients are borates and trace amounts of specialty chemicals.

BATCH HOUSE
The materials are blended together in bulk quantity, called the "batch". The blended mix is then fed into the furnace or "tank".

FURNACE
The temperature is so high that the sand and other ingredients dissolve into molten glass. The inner walls of the furnace are lined with special "refractory" bricks that must periodically be replaced.

BUSHINGS
The molten glass flows to numerous high heat-resistant platinum trays which have thousands of small, precisely drilled tubular openings, called "bushings".

FILAMENTS
This thin stream of molten glass is pulled and attenuated (drawn down) to a precise diameter, then quenched or cooled by air and water to fix this diameter and create a filament.

CONTINUOUS FILAMENT MAT
In a different production step, strands formed below the bushings are treated with a binder and formed into a swirl pattern to make continuous filament mat.

BINDER

Customer

SIZING
The hair-like filaments are coated with an aqueous chemical mixture called a "sizing", which serves two main purposes:
1. protecting the filaments during processing and handling, and
2. ensuring good adhesion of the glass fiber to the resin.

STRANDS
After the sizing is applied, filaments are gathered together into twine-like strands that go through one of three steps, depending on the type of reinforcement being made.

CHOPPED STRANDS
Other strands are chopped and packaged to become reinforcements for thermoplastic or thermoset molding compounds.

INTERMEDIATE PACKAGE (DOFF)
In one type of winding operation, strands are collected into an "intermediate" package that is further processed in one of several ways.

WINDERS
In most cases, the strand is wound onto high-speed winders which collect the continuous fibre glass into balls or "doffs".

CHOPPED STRAND MAT
In one operation, strands are combined with a binder to make mat

TYPE 30® PACKAGE
Some winders collect strands into a **Type 30®** single-end roving package. Most of these packages are shipped directly to customers for such processes as filament winding.

OVEN

CREEL

MULTIPLE-END PACKAGE
For most intermediate packages, the fibers are unwound, then wound again onto a new package with multiple ends of glass. These "conventional" roving doffs are used for such fabrication processes as spray-up and sheet molding compound.

Source: Owens Corning.

84. GLASS, POTTERY AND RELATED MATERIALS

Figure 84.13 • The rotary process for making glass wool fibres.

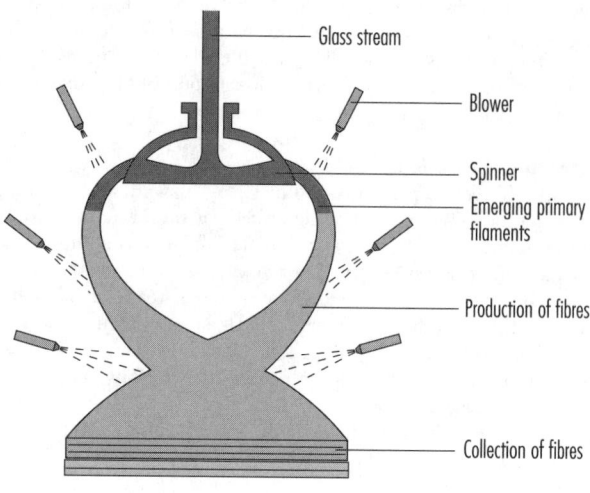

Pottery Industry

General profile

The making of pottery is one of the oldest of human crafts. Over the centuries different styles and techniques have developed in

Figure 84.14 • Mineral wool process (rock and slag).

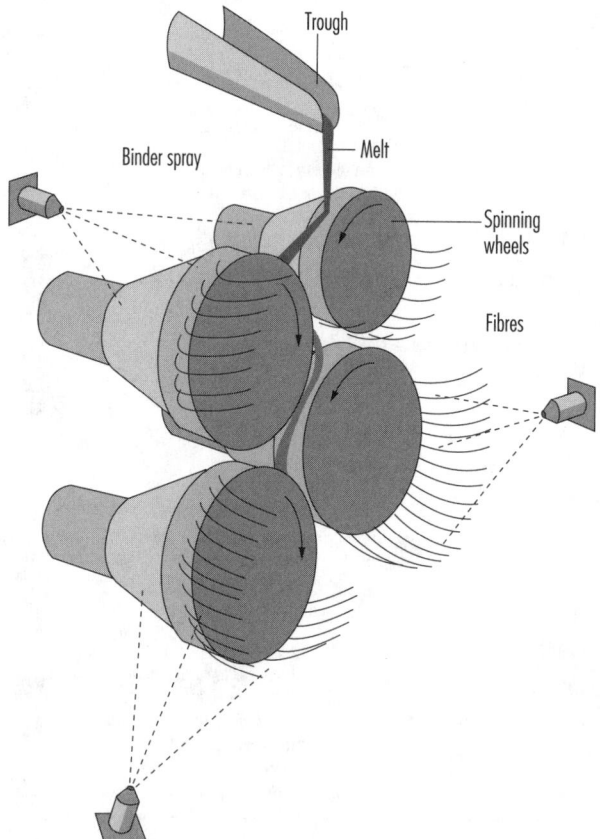

Figure 84.15 • Single and multi-mode optical fibres.

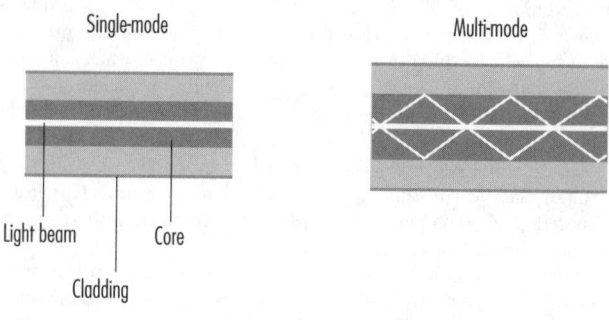

different parts of the world. In the 18th century, a flourishing industry in many parts of Europe was strongly influenced by the import of fine and highly decorated ware from the Far East. Japan had learned the ceramic art from China about 400 years earlier. With the Industrial Revolution and the general change in conditions in Western Europe, production grew rapidly. At present, almost every country manufactures some ware for domestic use, and pottery is an important export from some countries. Production is now on a factory scale in many parts of the world. While the basic principles of manufacture have not changed, there has been considerable progress in the way in which manufacturing is carried out. This is particularly so in the forming or shaping of ware, in its firing and in the decoration techniques used. The increasing use of microprocessors and robots results in the introduction of high levels of automation in production areas. However, there also still exist everywhere many small-scale craft potteries.

Methods of forming

The earliest method of making pottery involved the hand method of building. Coils of clay are wound around, one on top of the other, and stuck together by pressing with the hands. The clay is first made into a soft state by working it with water. The object is then shaped and moulded by hand, once the coils are adhered.

Figure 84.16 • Optic fibre manufacturing flow chart.

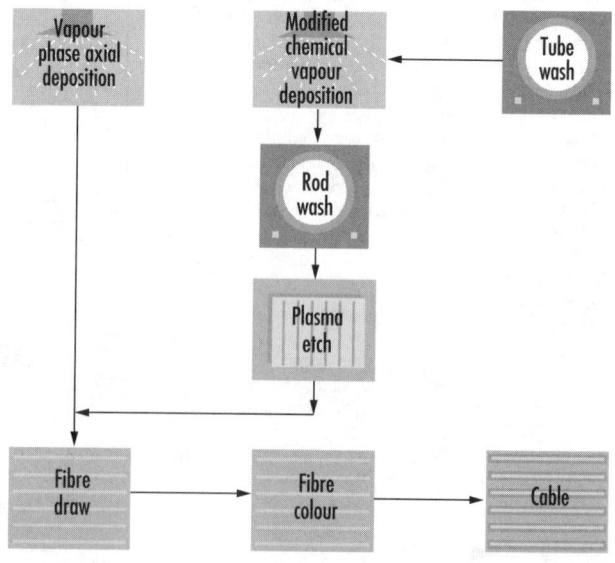

Optical fibres

Optical fibres are hair-thin strands of glass designed to transmit light rays along their axis. *Light-emitting diodes (LEDs)* or *laser diodes* convert electrical signals into the optical signals that are transmitted through an inner cylindrical core of the optical fibre cable. The lower refractive properties of the external cladding allows light signals to be propagated by internal reflection along the inner cylindrical core. Optical fibres are designed and manufactured to propagate either as a single light beam or as multiple light beams simultaneously transmitted along the core. (See figure 84.15.)

Single-mode fibre is primarily used for telephony, cable television applications and campus backbones. Multi-mode fibre is commonly used for data communications and in premise networks.

Optical fibre manufacturing

Special materials and processes are required to manufacture optical fibres that meet the basic design criteria: (1) a core with a high refractive index and cladding with a low refractive index, (2) a low signal attenuation or power loss, and (3) a low dispersion or broadening of the light beam.

High-purity silica glass with other glass materials (i.e., heavy-metal fluoride glasses, chalcogenide glasses) are the primary materials currently used to manufacture optical fibres. Polycrystalline materials, single-crystal materials, hollow waveguides and polymeric plastic materials are also used. Raw materials must be relatively pure with very low concentrations of transition metals and hydroxyl-forming groups (below the parts per billion level). Processing methods must shield the forming glass from impurities in the manufacturing environment.

Optical fibres are manufactured by using a non-conventional vapour phase preparation of a glass preform which is then drawn into fibre. Volatile silica compounds are converted to SiO_2 by flame hydrolysis, chemical vapour deposition (CVD) or high-temperature oxidation. Other dopants are then added to the glass to change the glass properties. Variations in the process of vapour deposition start with the same material but differ in the method used to convert this material to silica.

One of the following vapour phase deposition methods is used to manufacture silica-based optical fibres: (1) modified chemical vapour deposition (MCVD), (2) plasma chemical vapour deposition (PCVD), (3) outside vapour deposition (OVD), and (4) vapour phase axial deposition (VAD) (see figure 84.16). Silicon tetrachloride ($SiCl_4$), germanium tetrachloride ($GeCl_4$) or other volatile liquid halides convert to gas when heated slightly due to their high vapour pressures. Gaseous halide is delivered to a reaction zone and converted to glass particles (see also the chapter *Microelectronics and semiconductors*.)

MCVD and PCVD processes. A high-quality fused silica tube is attached to a glass working lathe fitted with a hydrogen/oxygen torch that traverses its length. A halide material supply is attached to one end of the glass tube and a scrubber to the opposite end to remove excess halide material. The surface of the glass tube is first cleaned by fire polishing as the torch traverses the tube's length. Various reagents are added in the vapour system depending on the product being manufactured. A chemical reaction occurs as the halides pass through the section of the tube being heated. The halides convert to silica "soot" particles that deposit on the inner glass tube wall downstream from the torch. Deposited particles are sintered into the glass layer. The PCVD process is similar to MCVD except that the halides are supplied by a bubbler system, and microwaves are used instead of a torch to convert the halide material to glass.

OVD and VAD processes. In the first stage of the fibre manufacturing process, the *core* and *cladding* glasses are vapour deposited around a rotating target rod to form a "soot" preform. The core material is deposited first, followed by the cladding. The entire preform must be extremely pure, since both the core and cladding are vapour deposited. Fibre geometry is determined during the laydown phase of manufacturing. After the target rod is removed, the preform is placed in a furnace, where it is consolidated into a solid, clear glass and the centre hole is closed. Gas is passed through the preform to remove residual moisture which adversely affects the attenuation of the fibre (loss of optical signal as light transmits along the fibre axis). Preforms are then washed with hydrofluoric acid to ensure the purity of the glass and to remove contaminants.

The consolidated glass preform is placed in a draw tower to form a continuous strand of glass fibre. First the preform is loaded into the top of a draw furnace. Next, the tip of the preform is heated and a piece of molten glass begins to fall. As this piece is drawn (pulled), it passes through an inline diameter monitor to assure the fibre meets an exact specified diameter (usually measured in microns.) The fibre's cladding diameter must conform with exact specifications in order to keep signal loss at connections low. The outer cladding diameter is used as a guide to align fibre cores during end use. The cores must line up so light transfer occurs efficiently.

Acrylate polymer or other coatings are applied and cured with ultraviolet lamps. The coatings are intended to protect the optical fibre from the environment during end use. The optical fibres are tested to assure conformance with manufacturing standards for strength, attenuation and geometry. Specific lengths of fibre are wound onto reels per customer specifications.

A number of potential hazards are encountered during optical fibre manufacturing. These include: (1) exposure to hydrofluoric acid (when cleaning glass preforms), (2) radiant energy and heat stress associated with working environments near lathes and vapour deposition processes, (3) direct contact with hot surfaces or molten material (glass preforms), (4) exposure to acrylate polymer coatings (skin sensitizers), (5) skin punctures and lacerations during fibre handling and (6) a variety of physical hazards previously described.

George R. Osborne

The potter's wheel has become a tool for creating pottery. With this method of forming, a pile of clay is placed on a revolving circular plate and is shaped by the wet hands of the potter. The water keeps the potter's hands from sticking to the clay and keeps the clay moist and workable. Handles, spouts and other protrusions from the spinning clay are placed on just before the object is fired.

Casting is often used today when pottery of a high quality is desired and when the walls of the vessel are to be very thin. A mixture of clay and water, called slip, is poured into a plaster-of-Paris mould. The plaster absorbs the water, causing a thin coat of clay to be deposited all around the inside of the mould. When the deposit of clay is thick enough to form the walls of the vase, the rest of the slip is poured out, leaving the wet piece of ware on the inside of the form. As this dries it shrinks somewhat and can be removed from the mould. Usually the moulds are so constructed that they can be taken apart.

When the piece becomes thoroughly dry, it is smoothed and prepared for the firing process. It is placed in a fire-clay box called a *sagger*, which protects the piece from the flames and gases that are emitted during the process, just as an oven would protect a loaf of bread that is being baked. The saggers are placed one on

84. GLASS, POTTERY AND RELATED MATERIALS

top of another in a *kiln*. The kiln is a large structure that is built of fire brick and is surrounded by flues so that the flames of the fire may totally surround the dishes yet never actually come in contact with them. Smoke would discolour the pieces if they were not protected in such a manner.

Most pieces are fired at least twice. The first time through the kiln is called the *bisque* firing, and the piece of pottery is called a *biscuit* or *bisque piece*. After firing, the biscuit ware is glazed. A glaze is a glassy, glossy coating that makes the pottery more attractive and serviceable. Glazes contain silica, a flux to lower the melting temperature (lead, barium and so on) and metal oxides as colourants. When the glaze is applied to the pottery and is completely dry, it is again placed back into the kiln and is fired at such a high temperature that the glaze melts and covers the entire surface of the pottery.

Kinds of pottery

- *Stoneware* is a pottery made from either light or dark clay. It is glazed on the unburned body either before setting in the kiln or by means of salt during the burning process and is burned to a dense, hard condition.
- *Porcelain* is a white, vitrified ware. It is translucent. In porcelain, the body and glaze are brought to completion and maturity at one and the same burning, which takes place at a very high temperature.
- *China* is a ware similar to porcelain. The body and glaze are brought to completion and maturity at the same firing, at extremely high temperatures.
- *Bone china* is a variety of china in which burned bone is used as an ingredient, constituting about 40% of the mass.
- *Earthenware* has a white or nearly white body. It is produced by two firings, like china, but its body remains porous. The glaze is similar to that of china but is made of a cheaper material.
- *Faience* is a fine glazed earthenware used for ornamental and decorative purposes. Usually there is no attempt to produce a white body, and the glazes are frequently coloured.

Manufacturing processes

The physical properties of pottery vary according to the composition of the body and conditions of firing. The body for any particular use is selected mainly for its physical properties, but white bodies are most usually chosen for tableware.

Industrial products (e.g., refractories, electrical insulators, catalyst carriers and so on) have a wide range of properties according to their eventual use.

Raw materials. The basic ingredients in a pottery body are shown in table 84.1, which also indicates typical proportions in sample body types.

Nepheline-syenite is sometimes used as flux, and alumina can replace some or all of the quartz filler in some porcelain-type bodies. Cristobalite (calcined sand) is used as a filler in some pottery bodies, particularly in the wall tile industry.

The body composition is determined partly by the required properties of the end product and partly by the production method. A plastic base is essential for ware that is shaped while moist, but not for non-plastic forming processes, such as dust pressing. The plastic base is not essential, although clay is still the principal ingredient in most ceramic products, including those prepared by dust pressing.

Industrial ceramics are not shown in table 84.1, as their composition ranges from all ball clay or fireclay, without additional flux or filler, to almost all alumina, with a minimal amount of clay and no added flux.

During firing, the flux melts to a glass to bind the ingredients together. As the amount of flux increases, the temperature of vitrification is lowered. Fillers influence the mechanical strength of the clayware before and during firing; in making tableware, quartz (as sand or calcined flint) is traditionally used, except that bone ash is used in making bone china. The use of alumina or other non-siliceous fillers, which are already employed in the manufacture of industrial ceramics, is being extended to the making of other ware, including domestic products.

Processing. The basic processes in the production of pottery include:

- preparation of the body ingredients
- forming and shaping
- biscuit firing
- application of glaze
- glost firing
- decoration.

The preparatory processes of calcining, crushing and grinding of flint or stone may be done in a separate establishment, but it is usual for all subsequent processes to be carried on in the same factory. In the slip house, the body ingredients are blended in water; plastic clay is then produced by filtering and plugging; the casting slip is then prepared by blunging to a creamy consistency. Dust for pressing is prepared by drying and grinding.

Traditional classifications of shaping processes are shown in table 84.2. In casting, a water suspension of the body is poured into an absorbent mould and the cast is removed after partial drying. Plastic clay shaping by throwing is now rare in industrial production; mechanical spreading over or in a plaster mould (jiggering and jolly) with separation from the mould after drying is almost universal in making tableware. Pressing of plastic clay or extrusion is mainly restricted to industrial ceramics. Dust-pressed articles are produced by compacting pre-dried body-dust by hand or mechanical pressing.

Table 84.1 • Typical body constituents (%).

Body	Plastic Base			Flux		Filler		
	Ball Clay	Kaolin	Stoneware clay	Stone	Feldspar	Quartz	Bone ash	Other
Earthenware	25	25		15		35		
Stoneware	30–40		25–35		20–25			20–30 (grog)
China	20–25	20–25			15–25	25–30		
Porcelain		40–50			20–30	15–25		
Bone China		20–25		25–30			45–50	

Table 84.2 • Manufacturing processes.

Products	Usual processes
Tables	Plastic clay shaping; casting
Sanitary ware	Casting
Tiles	Dust pressing (wall or vitrified floor tiles), plastic clay pressing (floor quarries)
Industrial ware	Dust pressing, plastic clay pressing

After shaping, the ware may be dried and finished by fettling, towing or sponging. Then it is ready for biscuit firing.

After biscuit firing, glaze is applied by dipping or spraying; dipping may be by hand or mechanized. The glazed ware is then fired again. Sometimes, as with sanitary whiteware, glaze is applied to the dried clay article and there is only one firing.

Decoration may be applied either under or over glaze and may be by hand painting, machine printing or transfer; over-glaze decoration involves a third firing; and sometimes separate firings for different colours are necessary.

In the final stages, the ware is sorted and packed for shipping. Figure 84.17 identifies the various paths followed by various types of pottery and ceramics during their fabrication.

Ceramic Tile

General profile

Ceramic is a term once thought to refer only to the art or technique of producing articles of pottery. The etymology of the term shows that it derives from the Greek *keramos*, meaning "a potter" or "a pottery". However, the Greek word is related to an older Sanskrit root, meaning "to burn"; as used by the Greeks themselves, its primary meaning was simply "burnt stuff" or "burnt earth". The fundamental concept contained in the term was that of a product obtained through the action of fire upon earthy materials.

A traditional ceramic, in the context of this article, refers to the products commonly used as building materials or within the home and industry. Although there is a tendency to equate traditional ceramics with low technology, advanced manufacturing technologies are often used in this industry. Stiff competition among producers has caused the technology to become more efficient and cost effective by utilizing complex tooling and machinery, coupled with computer-assisted process control.

The oldest ceramic products originated from clay-bearing materials. Early potters found the plastic nature of clay to be useful in forming shapes. Because of its tendency to exhibit a large amount of shrinkage, clay bodies were modified by adding coarse sand and stone, which reduced shrinkage and cracking. In modern clay-based bodies, the typical non-clay additions are silica flour and alkali minerals that are added as fluxes. In traditional ceramic formulations, clay acts as a plasticizer and binder for other constituents.

Development of the industry

The production of dried and fired clay tiles has very ancient origins dating back to Middle Eastern populations. The tile whiteware industry developed significantly in Europe, and by the beginning of the 20th century floor and wall tile production achieved industrial scale. Further development in this field occurred after the Second World War. Europe (Italy and Spain, in particular), Latin America and the Far East are now the most important areas of industrial tile production.

Figure 84.17 • Flow chart by type of ceramic.

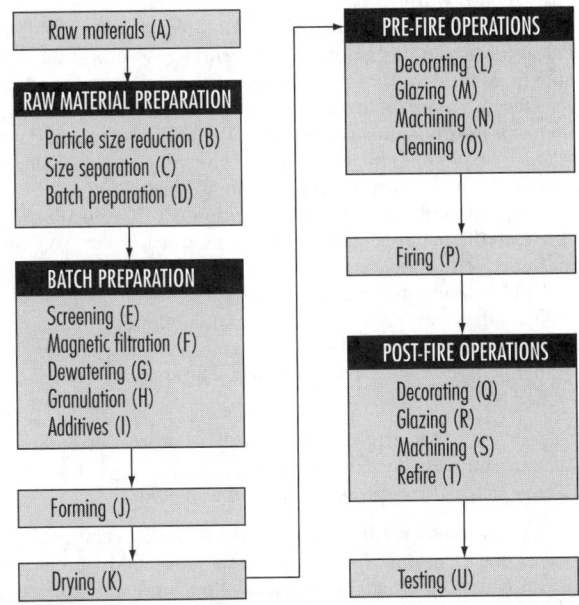

Source: Haber and Smith 1987.

The floor and wall tile sector of the whiteware industry has seen a great deal of development since the mid-1980s with the introduction of new technologies, automation and integration of production flow into the manufacturing process. Subsequently, productivity and efficiency increased, while energy consumption and costs have been reduced. Tile manufacturing is now continuous in both wet and dry tile production, and many plants today have nearly 100% automation. The major innovations in the tile industry during the last decade include wet grinding, spray drying, high-pressure dry pressing, roller drying and fast-firing technologies.

The value of the US ceramic tile market supply (US factory shipments plus imports) increased an estimated 9.2% compounded annually between 1992 and 1994. Dollar sales were estimated to have reached US$1.3 billion in 1994. At the same time, volume sales rose 11.9% compounded annually to 1.3 billion square feet. This compares with a market growth rate of 7.6% based on dollar sales, and 6.9% based on volume sales between 1982 and 1992.

Classifications of ceramic tiles

Redware and whiteware

Many types of ceramic tile are available on the market. They differ according to the condition of the surface, colour of the body (white or red), manufacturing technology, raw materials and end use. The difference between "red" and "white" tiles lies in the amount of iron minerals contained in the body. By reacting with the other body components, they can give more or less colouration and modify the behaviour of the body during firing.

A complete and exhaustive classification is very difficult owing to the extreme heterogeneity of the tile products, their processing and subsequent characteristics. In this chapter, European (EN) and ASTM standards are considered.

EN standards exclusively classify ceramic tiles as a function of water absorption (which directly correlates to the porosity) and shaping method (extrusion or pressing). The shaping methods are classified as:

- *shaping process A* (extruded floor tiles). This process includes split tiles and individually extruded tiles.
- *shaping process B* (dry-pressed floor and wall tiles).

European Standard EN 87, approved in November 1981, specifies that "Ceramic wall and floor tiles are building materials that are generally designed for use as floor and wall coverings, both indoors and outdoors, regardless of shape and sizes".

The American National Standards Institute (ANSI) specification for ceramics tile (ANSI A 137.1) contains the following definitions:

- *Ceramic mosaic tile* is formed by either the dust-pressed or plastic method, usually 6.4 to 9.5 mm (1/4 to 1/8 in.) thick, and has a facial area of less than 39 cm^2 (6 in^2). Ceramic mosaic tiles may be either porcelain or natural clay composition, and they may be either plain or with an abrasive mixture throughout.
- *Decorative wall tile* is glazed tile with a thin body that is usually non-vitreous and suitable for interior decorative residential wall use where breaking strength is not a requirement.
- *Paver tile* is glazed or unglazed porcelain or natural clay tile formed by the dust-pressed method having 39 cm^2 (6 in^2) or more facial area.
- *Porcelain tile* is ceramic mosaic tile or paver tile that is generally made by the dust-pressed method with the resulting tile composition that is dense, impervious, fine-grained and smooth, with a sharply formed face.
- *Quarry tile* is glazed or unglazed tile, made by the extrusion process from natural clay or shale, usually having 39 cm^2 (6 in^2) or more facial area.
- *Wall tile* is glazed tile with a body that is suitable for interior use and usually non-vitreous and is not required to withstand excessive impact or be subject to freezing and thawing conditions.
- *Individual tile whiteware grades* include unglazed tiles (ceramic mosaic tile, quarry tile, paver tile) and glazed tiles (glazed wall tile, glazed ceramic mosaic tile, glazed quarry tile, glazed paver tile) (ANSI 1988).

The tiles are manufactured by standard ceramic processes. Ceramic wall and floor tiles are prepared from a mixture of ball clays, sand, fluxes, colouring agents and other mineral raw materials, and they undergo processing such as milling, screening, blending and wetting. They are shaped by a pressing, extrusion, casting or other process, normally at room temperature, and are subsequently dried and finally fired at high temperature. Tiles may be glazed, unglazed or engobed. Glazes are glasslike, impervious coatings, and engobes are matte, clay-based coatings that may also be porous. Glazed wall and floor tiles are produced either by single- or two-stage firing.

Traditional ceramic bodies are formed into shapes using many different techniques. The specific forming process is dictated by numerous factors, including material characteristics, size and shape of the part, part specifications, production yield and accepted practices within the geographic region.

Clay-based bodies are heterogeneous mixtures of one or more clays and one or more nonclay powders. Before attaining a final shape, these powders undergo a sequence of unit operations, firing and post-fire operations (see figure 84.17).

For most traditional bodies, forming techniques can be classified as soft plastic forming, stiff plastic forming, pressing and casting.

Applied pressure is employed to rearrange and redistribute the raw materials into a better-packed configuration. The rheological behaviour of clay-based bodies results from clay mineral interaction with water, which imparts plasticity to the batch. In non-clay bodies, this same type of behaviour can be achieved by adding plasticizers.

Industrial Ceramics

General profile

Ceramics differ from other engineering materials (metals, plastics, wood products, textiles) in a number of individual properties. Perhaps the most distinctive difference to a designer or potential user of ceramic ware is the unique shape and size of each individual ceramic piece. Ceramics are not readily shaped or worked after firing, except by very costly grinding; consequently, they normally must be used as is. Except for some simple tile, rod and tube shapes of limited sizes, ceramics cannot be marketed by the foot or by the yard, nor cut to fit on the job.

All the useful properties, including shape and size, must be provided in advance, beginning with the very early stages of ceramic processing. The structural integrity of each piece must be preserved through a variety of thermal and mechanical stress exposures during processing and until the piece is finally installed and in service. If a ceramic should fail in service as a result of a variety of causes (brittle fracture on impact, thermal shock, dielectric breakdown, abrasion or melting slag corrosion), it is not likely to be repairable, and usually must be replaced.

Significant advances have been made in fundamental understanding and technological control of the properties of ceramics, and of their utilization in many new, demanding, highly technical applications. The industry in general, and the technical and electronic ceramic portions of it in particular, have devised production and control techniques for mass producing complex shapes in bodies having carefully controlled electrical, magnetic and/or mechanical properties while maintaining dimensional tolerances that are good enough to permit relatively easy assembly with other components.

Many ceramics are produced in large volume as standard items. Refractory bricks and shapes, crucibles, muffles, furnace tubes, insulators, thermocouple protection tubes, capacitor dielectrics, hermetic seals and fibre boards are routinely stocked by a number of ceramic producers in a variety of compositions and sizes. It is usually quicker and cheaper to use stock items whenever possible. When stock items will not meet the need, most manufacturers are prepared to custom produce items. The more stringent the requirements for a given property of the ceramic, or the more restrictive the requirements for specific combinations of properties, sizes and shapes, the more limited are the accepted compositional, microstructural and configurational parameters for the ceramic. Hence the cost and difficulty of manufacture are greater. Most ceramic manufacturers have experienced staff engineers and designers who are well qualified to work with potential customers on details of ceramic ware design.

Markets

The major market for state-of-the-art ceramics has been and will continue to be in electronics, but vigorous worldwide research and development programmes are continuously searching for new applications and identifying ways of improving ceramic properties such that new markets can be accessed.

Advanced ceramics are produced in Japan, the United States and Western Europe. The raw materials used in the industry are traded on an international basis, principally as powders, but there is also a significant amount of in-house processing.

The major applications of industrial ceramics are:

- *Oxides.* The main oxide materials in use today are alumina in spark plugs, substrates and wear applications; zirconia (ZrO_2) in oxygen sensors, as a component in lead-zirconium-titanate (PZT) piezoelectrics, wear applications and thermal barrier coatings; titanates in barium titanate capacitors and PZT piezoelectrics; and ferrites in permanent magnets, magnetic recording heads, memory devices, temperature sensors and electric motor parts.
- *Carbides and nitrides.* Carbides (mainly silicon carbide and boron carbide) are used in wear applications, while nitrides (mainly silicon nitride and Sialon) are used in wear applications and cutting tools. Aluminium nitride, with its high thermal conductivity, is the primary contending material for part of the electronics substrate market currently dominated by alumina.
- *Mixed oxide ceramics.* Ceramics research and development efforts are focused on a number of new applications for ceramics that all have enormous potential. Three significant applications are: (1) ceramic superconductors, (2) ceramics for solid oxide fuel cells and (3) ceramic components for heat engines.

Ceramic superconductors are based on a number of mixed oxide systems that include yttrium, barium, copper, strontium and copper ($YBa_2Cu_3O_{7-8}$, $Bi_2Sr_2CaCu_2O_8$, $Bi_2Sr_2Ca_2Cu_3O_{10}$) stabilized with lead oxide. Solid oxide fuel-cell ceramics are based on ionic conductors in which high-purity stabilized zirconia is currently the material of choice. Ceramic heat-engine components under investigation are composed of silicon carbide, Sialons and zirconia, either as single-phase ceramics, ceramic-ceramic composites or metal-matrix composites (MMCs).

Manufacturing processes

Manufacturing technology development

Processing innovations. Research and development activity is generating new technologies for the production of ceramic materials. Precursor-derived ceramics were estimated to have a market value of US$2 million in 1989, the major part of which was in CVD (86% of the total market value). Other segments of this growing market include chemical vapour infiltration (CVI), sol-gel and polymer pyrolysis. Products that are being successfully produced by these means include continuous ceramic fibres, composites, membranes and ultra-high-purity/high-activity powders.

The processes used to convert these raw materials to finished products include additional powder processing (e.g., milling and spray drying) prior to forming green shapes that are then fired under controlled conditions. The forming processes include die pressing, isostatic pressing, slip casting, tape casting, extrusion, injection moulding, hot pressing, hot isostatic pressing (HIP), CVD and so on.

Chemical additives to aid ceramic processing. Each step in the manufacturing process requires careful control so that end-product properties are obtained at maximum production efficiency and key effect chemicals are used to optimize powder treatment and green forming. The effect chemicals include milling aids, flocculants and binders, lubricants to effect product release during pressing and minimize wear of die parts, and plasticizers to aid extrusion and injection moulding. A list of such chemicals is shown in table 84.3. While these materials play an important economic role in production, they are burnt out during firing and play no part in the final product chemistry. The burn out process has to be carefully controlled to avoid residual carbon in the finished products, and process research and development is continuously investigating ways of minimizing the levels of effect chemicals used.

In addition to spawning ceramic products and ceramic manufacturing technologies for new applications, the influence of the advanced ceramics industry on the traditional ceramics industry should not be overlooked. It is expected that many high-technology materials and processes will find application in the traditional ceramics industry as the latter strives to reduce manufacturing costs, to improve quality and to give better value in service to the end user.

Raw materials

There are certain key materials that are either used directly by the ceramics industry or that represent the starting point for the production of added-value materials:

- silica
- clay
- alumina
- magnesia
- titania
- iron oxide
- zircon/zirconia.

Table 84.3 • Selected chemical additives used to optimize powder treatment and green forming of ceramics.

Material	Application or function
Polyvinyl alcohol	Binder for advanced ceramics
Polyethylene glycol	Binder for advanced ceramics
Sodium polyacrylate	Deflocculant for slip casting
Tertiary amide polymer	Binder for dry pressing
Starch blended with dry colloidal aluminosilicate	Binder for vacuum forming
Cationic alumina plus organic flocculant	Binder for vacuum forming
Pre-gelled, cationic corn starch	Flocculant for colloidal silica and alumina binder
High-purity sodium carboxymethyl-cellulose	Binder
Inorganic colloidal magnesium aluminium silicate	Suspending agent
Medium-viscosity sodium carboxy-methylcellulose added to Veegum	Suspending agent, viscosity stabilizer
Ammonium polyelectrolyte	Dispersing agent for casting slips for electronic ceramics
Sodium polyelectrolyte	Dispersing agent binder for spray-dried bodies
Microcrystalline cellulose and sodium carboxymethylcellulose	Thickening agent
Polysilazane	Processing aid, binder and precursor for advanced ceramics

84. GLASS, POTTERY AND RELATED MATERIALS

This discussion will focus on the properties of silica, alumina and zircon/zirconia.

Silica, in addition to its use in refractories and whitewares, is also the starting point in the manufacture of elemental silicon, silicon carbide and silicon tetrachloride. Silicon, in turn, is the starting point for silicon nitride, and silicon tetrachloride is the precursor for a wide range of silicon organics that can be pyrolyzed under controlled conditions to high-quality silicon carbide and silicon nitride.

Silicon nitride and its Sialon derivatives, as well as silicon carbide, despite their tendency to oxidize, have the potential to meet many of the property targets set by the heat-engine market. A feature of silica and the ceramic materials that are derived from silica is that all the elements are readily available in the earth's crust. In this respect, these materials offer the potential of ease of supply in all parts of the world. In practice, however, there is a significant energy input required to produce silicon and silicon carbide. Consequently, manufacture of these materials is by and large limited to countries with cheap and readily available electric power.

Alumina is found throughout the earth's crust as a component in aluminosilicate minerals. Economics dictate that alumina be extracted from bauxite using the Bayer process. Bauxite is widespread in the equatorial belt in different states of purity, and is divided into two classifications: refractory grade ore and metallurgical ore.

Refractory grade bauxite is supplied by China and Guyana as a high-temperature calcine of the naturally occurring mineral: diaspore ($Al_2O_3 \cdot H_2O$) in China and gibbsite ($Al_2O_3 \cdot 3H_2O$) in Guyana. During calcination, a complex phase assemblence of corundum (Al_2O_3), mullite, silica glass and minor levels of aluminium titanate is formed. The consumption of refractory grade bauxite exceeds 700,000 tonnes per year on a worldwide basis.

Metallurgical grade bauxite is mined in Australia, Jamaica and West Africa, and has variable alumina levels in conjunction with major impurities such as iron oxide and silica. The alumina in the metallurgical ores is extracted from the ore when dissolved by sodium hydroxide, yielding a sodium aluminate solution that is separated from the iron oxide and silica, which are rejected as a waste product in the form of red mud. Essentially, pure aluminium hydroxide is precipitated from the sodium aluminate and then calcined to a number of grades of alumina.

The high-purity aluminas used in the ceramics industry and derived by the Bayer process are classified as tabular alumina, fused alumina or speciality calcined alumina.

Tabular alumina is produced by high-temperature (~2,000 °C or 3,630 °F) calcination of low-temperature calcined alumina in large, oil-fired rotary kilns. Fused alumina is produced by the electric melting of calcined alumina. Tabular and fused alumina are sold to the refractory industry in crushed and graded form for use in a wide range of high-quality products, such as in continuous casting refractories (e.g., single-edge-notched or SEN/slide gates), monolithic refractories for application in blast furnaces and the petrochemical industry.

Speciality calcined alumina powders are the major raw materials used in the advanced ceramics industry for both electronic and engineering applications. The powders are produced in a wide range of grades according to exacting specifications of chemistry, particle size and crystal type, to suit a wide range of end-product applications.

There is an established international trade in high-quality aluminas. Many of the ceramic manufacturers have in-house milling and spray drying facilities. There is clearly a limitation to the growth in the supply of spray-dried systems and a continuing need to supply aluminas which match the customer plants so that use of the latter can be optimized at an acceptable price. Alumina is a

significant ceramic material that is available at a high degree of purity. The dominant position of alumina as a ceramic raw material arises because it has desirable properties at a relatively low cost. This cost effectiveness is attributable to the commodity nature of the business arising from the large demand for alumina by the aluminium industry.

Zircon and zirconia. The primary source of zirconia is the mineral zircon ($ZrO_2 \cdot SiO_2$), which exists in beach sands principally in Australia, South Africa and the United States. Zircon extracted from beach sands contains ~2% hafnium oxide and traces of Al_2O_3 (0.5%), Fe_2O_3 (0.1%) and TiO_2 (0.1%). In addition, all zircons contain traces of uranium and thorium. Zircon is processed by fine grinding to produce a range of milled products of defined particle size. These products have found use in investment casting, foundries, refractory products and as an opacifier in glazes for whitewares.

Zircon is also the principal source of zirconia. Zircon can be chlorinated in the presence of carbon to give zirconium and silicon tetrachlorides that are then separated by distillation. The zirconium tetrachloride produced can be used to prepare zirconia directly or as a feedstock for other zirconium chemicals. Sintering with alkali or alkaline earth oxides is also used to decompose zircon. Silica is leached from the decomposition products with water, leaving zirconium hydroxide to be further purified by acid dissolution and reprecipitation. Zirconia is then obtained by calcining the hydroxide. Zircon is also converted to zirconia and silica in a plasma at 1,800 °C (3,270 °F) with rapid cooling to prevent reassociation. The free silica is removed by dissolution in sodium hydroxide. Fused zirconia is produced in electric arc furnaces from either baddeleyite or zircon/carbon feedstocks. In the latter process the silica component of zircon is carbothermally reduced to silicon monoxide, which volatilizes prior to the fusion of the residual zirconia.

Summary

The industrial ceramic industry is very diverse and there is much in-house processing. Many of the final manufacturing operations are in foundry-type atmospheres. The material-handling systems in these operations convey fine raw materials where dust can be an issue. Materials are then raised to very high temperatures and melted or fused into shapes needed for the final parts. Therefore, many of the safety issues which exist in any high-temperature industry also exist in the industrial ceramics industry.

Brick and Tile

General profile

Bricks and tiles made from clay have been used as building material since the earliest times in many parts of the world. When properly made and fired they are more durable than some stones, resistant to weather and great changes of temperature and moisture. The brick is a rectangle of standard size, varying slightly from region to region but essentially convenient for handling with one hand by a bricklayer; roofing tiles are thin slabs, either flat or curved; clay tiles may also be used for floors.

The brick industry is very fragmented. There are many small suppliers located all over the world. Brick manufacturing tends to involve local suppliers and local markets due to the cost of shipping of the finished product. In 1994, there were 218 brick manufacturing plants in the United States, and in 1992 the number of producers of structural clay products in the UK was listed at 182, for example. Brick manufacturers generally are located near the clay deposits to reduce raw material shipping cost.

In the United States, bricks are used primarily in residential construction as either a load-bearing material or as a facade material. Since the brick industry is so closely coupled to the housing indus-

Figure 84.18 • The manufacture of bricks and tiles.

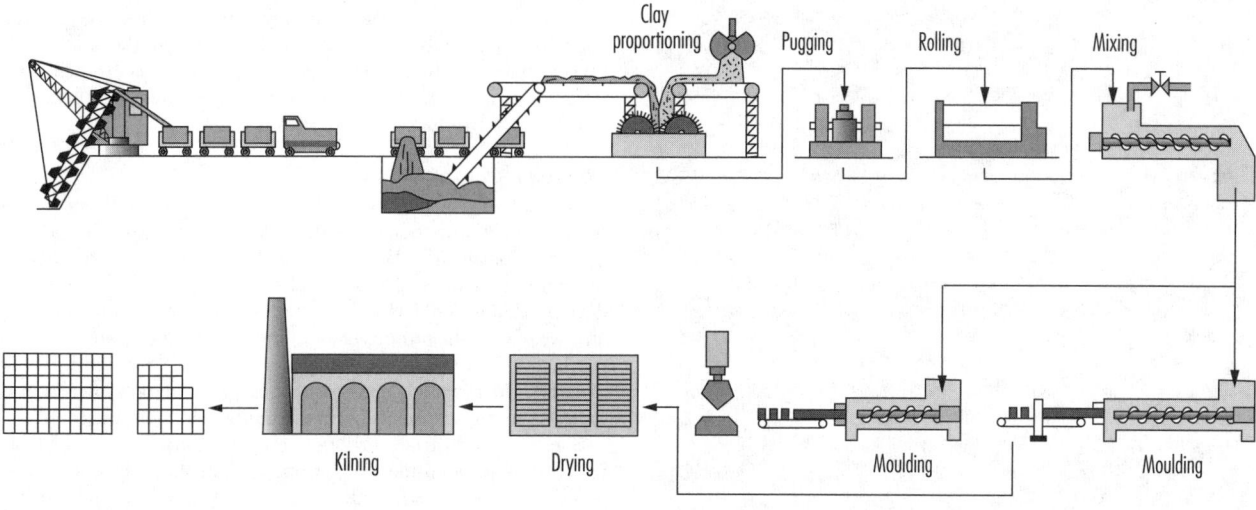

try, manufacturing activity is highly dependent on the residential construction industry and almost totally dependent on the combined residential and non-residential construction industry.

Manufacturing processes

Materials and processing

The basic material is clay of various kinds with mixtures of loams, shales and sand, according to local supply and needs, to give the required properties of texture, plasticity, regularity and shrinkage, and colour.

Extraction of clay is now often fully mechanized; manufacture usually takes place alongside the extraction hole, but in large works the clay is sometimes conveyed in skids on ropeways. The subsequent processing of the clay varies according to its constitution and the end-product, but in general includes crushing, grinding, screening and mixing. See figure 84.18 for a typical brick-manufacturing operation.

Clay for wire-cut bricks is broken up by rollers; water is added in a mixer; the mixture is rolled again and then fed through a horizontal pugmill. The plastic clay extruded is then cut to size on a wire-cutting table. Semi-dry and stiff plastic material is produced by rolling and screening and is then fed to mechanical presses. Some bricks are still hand moulded.

Where plastic material is used, the bricks have to be dried either by sun and air, or more frequently in regulated kilns, before firing; bricks made from semi-dry or stiff plastic may be fired immediately. Firing may take place in ring kilns, often hand fed, or in tunnel kilns, mechanically fed. The fuels used will vary according to local availability. A finishing glaze is applied to some decorative bricks.

Refractories

General profile

Refractory materials are traditionally thought of as non-metallics that resist degradation by corrosive gases, liquids or solids at elevated temperatures. These materials must withstand thermal shock caused by rapid heating or cooling, failure attributable to thermal stresses, mechanical fatigue due to other material contacting the refractory itself and chemical attack activated by the high-temperature environment. These materials are required for

the manufacture of most ceramic products and are specifically needed in ovens, dryers, furnaces and high-temperature-bearing engine parts.

Refractories remained almost exclusively mineral-based until well into the 20th century. Yet technologists who were skilled in mineralogy were paying attention. Metallurgists had been experimenting with acid and basic slagging practices since the Middle Ages and had catalogued some of the benefits of each. Refractory artisans had correspondingly experimented with ganister, with other nearly pure silica minerals and with magnesite, a predominantly $MgCO_3$ mineral which was calcined to MgO. When the Bessemer steel-making converter was invented in 1856, combining working temperatures of over 1,600 °C with corrosive acid slagging, "acid" silica refractories were all but ready. When the Siemens open hearth furnace followed in 1857 at even higher temperatures, and steel making went over in both cases to corrosive basic slagging, "basic" magnesite linings were soon introduced. Basic refractories made from dolomite (MgO-CaO) were developed during the First World War, when the European magnesite supply was cut off from the Allies. Later, with the development of other mineral resources worldwide, magnesite reasserted itself.

Meanwhile, bonded carbon bricks were produced in the United Kingdom starting in 1863 and eventually found their way into the iron-smelting blast furnace as its working temperatures climbed still higher. They also went quickly into the Hall-Héroult cells for the production of aluminium (1886).

Lime had been made for some 5,000 years using clay and then firebrick kilns. Portland cement manufacturing first called for an innovative refractory when rotary kilns were introduced after 1877. The first resistant linings were made of cement-bonded cement clinker. Later on more durable commercial refractories returned to this industry.

Recuperative and regenerative furnaces, originating in the new-born manufacture of steel in the 1850s, were introduced into nonferrous metallurgy and glassmaking in the late 19th century. Fireclay refractories had to be superseded there, too. Magnesite linings were used in copper converters from 1909, and in the first modern glass tanks about 10 years later. Electric arc furnaces were first tried for steel making in 1853 and became common after 1990. A roughly 100-tonne unit installed in the United States in 1927 employed a magnesite lining.

Properties of refractory materials

The properties that characterize quality refractory materials depend on the nature of the application. The most important aspect of the materials is referred to as "refractoriness". This term refers to the point at which the specimen begins to soften (or melt). Typically, refractories do not have a specific melting point; the phase transition proceeds over a range of temperatures in a phenomenon called softening. This characteristic is often quantified with a pyrometic cone equivalent (PCE), which is a measure of heat content measured by the slumping of a cone during thermal cycling.

A related, and often more useful property, is the temperature of failure under load. Refractories often fail under load at temperatures much less than the temperature that corresponds to the PCE. In obtaining a value for this parameter, the refractory is subjected to a known load and is subsequently heated. The temperature at which sagging or general deformation occurs is reported. This is of great interest because the value is used to predict mechanical properties during use of the refractory. The load-bearing ability of refractory materials is directly proportional to the amount of viscosity of the glass present.

Another factor that is essential to understanding the performance of a refractory is the dimensional stability. Throughout industrial use, refractory materials are subjected to heating/cooling cycles, which cause the refractory units to either expand or contract. Large changes in the dimensions will reduce stability and may ultimately lead to failure of the refractory-based structure.

A related phenomenon commonly observed with refractory materials is spalling. Spalling is generally considered fracture, splitting or flaking of the refractory, resulting in the exposure of the inner mass of the material. Spalling is usually brought about by temperature gradients within the material, compression in the structure due to large-volume charges and variations of the thermal expansion coefficient within the brick. Every effort is made in refractory manufacture to avoid spalling because it reduces the effectiveness of the refractory.

Refractories have application across a wide variety of industrial applications ranging from extensive use in the iron and steel industry to low volume usages in the cement and public utilities industries. Basically, refractories are used in any industry where high temperatures are used to heat and dry or incinerate material. Table 84.4 provides a current breakdown by industry of refractory usage within the United States.

As shown in table 84.4, the steel industry is the area where over 50% of the refractory produced in the U.S. is utilized. Therefore, the needs of the steel industry to a great extent have driven the refractory developments which have occurred.

Table 84.4 • Refractory usage by industry in the United States.

Industry	Percentage of total US sales
Iron and steel	51.6
Nonferrous metals	7.5
Cement	4.9
Glass	5.1
Ceramics	9.7
Chemical and petroleum	2.1
Public utilities	0.9
Export	7.4
All other and unspecified	10.8

Three-phase arc furnaces were in place before 1950; it was only then that serious demands arose for more sophisticated refractories. In the same time frame, oxygen blowing was introduced into Bessemer and open-hearth furnaces in the 1940s. The basic oxygen furnace (BOF) literally took over steel making in the late 1950s. Oxygen blowing, by its sheer economic importance, impelled the refractories industry for the first time to introduce synthetic materials into its products on a significant scale.

Modern refractories

Ceramics had grown substantially from craft to applied science. The American Ceramic Society had been founded in 1899, the British Ceramic Society in 1901. Oxide phase diagrams began to appear in the literature in the 1920s. The techniques of petrography were well developed, and the detailed mechanisms of refractory degradation and wear were beginning to be understood. American refractory producers had become largely reorganized, consolidated and capable of performing their own research. The tools of refractory synthesis and instruments of investigation were both burgeoning.

Synthetic industrial carbons were, of course, not new. Coke was first made commercially from coal in the 1860s, and from petroleum shortly thereafter. Synthetic graphite and silicon carbide appeared almost simultaneously at the turn of the century, following Acheson's invention of the self-resistance-heated electric furnace in 1896. These products, having properties quite unlike those of oxides, rapidly stimulated their own uses and markets.

Synthetic alumina, Al_2O_3, had been available since the Bayer process started feeding aluminium production about 1888. Synthetic magnesia (MgO) was first made from seawater in the United Kingdom in 1937 and in the United States in 1942, stimulated by wartime needs for magnesium. Zirconia had become available, also spurred by the military. Lime had been a major commodity for ages. A host of other chemicals were on hand for consideration as refractory components or as minor additives and bonding agents. The only important component of oxide refractories that for the most part has resisted replacement by synthetics is silica (SiO_2) High-purity silica rocks and sands abound and are used in this industry as well as in glass formulation.

The use of synthetics in refractory manufacture has been enormously helpful; but mineral raw materials have by no means been displaced. Synthetics cost more, and that cost has to be justified. Some synthetic materials create severe problems in refractory processing, and new ways must be found to overcome these. Optimum results have often been achieved by combinations of synthetic and mineral raw materials, along with creative inputs into their processing.

Mixtures of clay with carbon had been used to line crucibles and ladles since iron was first poured; and silica bricks containing carbon were made in France in the 1860s. Since 1960 both the techniques and the compositions have changed dramatically. The use of carbon-bearing oxide refractories has mushroomed, starting with MgO+C. The first real impetus may have been provided by the BOF; but today there is hardly any advanced oxide refractory type that cannot be had either with or without added carbon or a carbon precursor for superior performance in specific applications.

Arc-fused refractory grain or aggregate had been made since the early 1900s, and fused-cast refractory bricks of several compositions followed in the twenties and thirties, notably of mullite, alumina, magnesia-alumina-silica and alumina-zirconia-silica. More often than not, these products were made entirely from mineral raw materials.

In fact, all-mineral-based refractories remain today an important component of the product menu. They are on the whole cheaper, they often perform admirably and there are still many applications of lesser demand as well as those of critical demand for the highest levels of refractoriness and corrosion resistance.

Refractory industry

Refractories will be found in use in many industries for lining boilers, kilns and furnaces of all kinds, but the largest percentage are used in manufacture of metals. In the steel industry, a typical blast or open-hearth furnace may use many different types of refractories, some made from silica, some from chrome and/or magnesite and others of fire clay.

Much smaller quantities are also used in the following industries: gas, coke and by-products; power-generating plants; chemicals; bake ovens and stoves; cement and lime; ceramics; glass; enamels and glazes; locomotives and ships; nuclear reactors; oil refineries; refuse disposal (incinerators).

Manufacturing processes

The type of refractory that is used in any particular application depends on the critical requirements of the process. For example, processes that demand resistance to gaseous or liquid corrosion require low porosity, high physical strength and abrasion resistance. Conditions that demand low thermal conductivity may require entirely different refractories. Indeed, combinations of several refractories are generally employed. There is no well-established line of demarcation between those materials that are and those that are not refractory, although the ability to withstand temperatures above 1,100 °C without softening has been cited as a practical requirement of industrial refractory materials.

The technical goals of manufacture of a given refractory are embodied in its properties and performance in an intended application. The tools of manufacture consist of choices among raw materials and among processing methods and parameters. The requirements of manufacture have to do with the features of phase composition and microstructure—collectively called material character—that are developed through processing and are themselves responsible for product properties and behaviour.

Raw materials

In the past, refractory raw materials were selected from a variety of available deposits and used as mined minerals. Selective mining yielded materials of the desired properties, and only in cases of expensive raw materials, such as magnesite, was a beneficiation process required. Today, however, high-purity natural raw materials are increasingly in demand as are synthetically prepared refractory grain made from combinations of high-purity and beneficiated raw materials. The material produced upon firing raw as-mined minerals or synthetic blends is called grain, clinker, co-clinker or grog.

Refractories are usually classified into four types: aluminosilicate, silica (or acid), basic and miscellaneous.

The materials generally used in the four types of refractories include:

1. *Aluminosilicate refractories.* Fireclays consist mainly of the mineral kaolinite [CAS 1318-74-7] ($Al_2O_3 \, 2SiO_2 \, 2H_2O$) with small amounts of other clay minerals, quartzite, iron oxide, titania and alkali impurities. Clays can be used in the raw state or after being calcined. Raw clays may be coarsely sized or finely ground for incorporation in a refractory mix. Some high-purity kaolins are slurried, classified, dried and air floated to achieve a consistent, high quality. The classified clays also may be blended and extruded or pelletized and then calcined to produce burned synthetic kaolinitic grog, or coarsely crushed raw kaolinite may be burned to produce

grog. Upon calcination or burning, kaolinite decomposes to mullite and a siliceous glass incorporating mineral impurities associated with the clay deposit (e.g., quartzite, iron oxide, titania and alkalis) and is consolidated into dense, hard granular grog at high temperatures.

2. *Silica or acid refractories* use mainly silica in the form of crushed and ground quartzite (ganister) (92 to 98%), to which a suitable bonding substance, such as lime (CaO), is added. Silica bricks are generally heated twice because they expand when heated (fireclay bricks shrink), and it is desirable that the expansion be completed before the wall or lining is built.

3. *Basic refractories* use dolomite, magnesite (MgO), chrome oxide, iron and aluminium.

4. *Miscellaneous refractories.* Of the great variety of materials now in use, the more common ones are carbides such as silicon carbide, graphite, alumina, beryllia, thoria, uranium oxide, asbestos and zirconium oxide.

Several revolutions in the industry have occured. Included in these revolutions are further mechanized methods of handling tonnage solids, increased capabilities and automation of processing equipment and techniques for the rapid acquisition and analysis of in-process control data. These advances have transformed refractory manufacturing practice.

Figure 84.19 illustrates how different kinds of refractories are made. The figure is drawn in "decision tree" style with the diverging branches keyed by numbers for identification. There are various paths, each making a particular type of refractory product.

These generic flow diagrams represent thousands of specific processes, differentiated, for example, by their raw materials lists, the manner of preparation and the sizing and batching (meaning quantity weighed out) of each, the sequence and manner of mixing and so on. Omissions are allowed—for example, some unformed refractories are dry-mixed and never wetted until installation.

Refractories or products may be preformed (shaped) or formed and installed on site, but in general are supplied in the following shapes:

Brick. The standard dimensions of a refractory brick are 23 cm long by 11.4 cm wide and 6.4 cm thick (straight brick). Bricks may be extruded or dry-pressed on mechanical or hydraulic presses. Formed shapes may be burned before use or, in the case of pitch, resin or chemically bonded brick (cured).

Fusion-cast shapes. Refractory compositions are arc-melted and cast into shapes (e.g., glass-tank flux blocks as large as $0.33 \times 0.66 \times 1.33$ m). After casting and annealing, the blocks are accurately ground to ensure a precise fit.

Cast and hand-moulded refractories. Large shapes, such as burner blocks and flux blocks, and intricate shapes, such as glass feeder parts, saggers and the like, are produced by either slip or hydraulic cement casting or hand-moulding techniques. Because these techniques are labour intensive, they are reserved for articles that cannot be satisfactorily formed in other ways.

Insulating refractories. Insulating refractories in the form of brick are much lighter than conventional brick of the same composition by virtue of the brick porosity.

Castables and gunning mixes. Castables consist of refractory grains to which a hydraulic binder is added. Upon mixing with water, the hydraulic agent reacts and binds the mass together. Gunning mixes are designed to be sprayed through a nozzle under water and air pressure. The mixture may be slurried before being shot through the gun, or mixed with water at the nozzle.

Plastic refractories and ramming mixes. Plastic refractories are mixtures of refractory grains and plastic clays or plasticizers with water. Ramming mixes may or may not contain clay and are generally used with forms. The amount of water used with these products varies but is held to a minimum.

84. GLASS, POTTERY AND RELATED MATERIALS

Occupational Hazards and Precautions

Table 84.5 provides information on many of the potential hazards found in this industrial sector.

Safety and Health Problems and Disease Patterns

This section provides an overview of industry-wide documented or suspected safety and health problems. International data on injuries and illnesses in this business sector were not located in literature searches and searches on the Internet (in 1997). Information compiled by the US Department of Labor, Occupational Safety and Health Administration (OSHA) and Bureau of Labor Statistics (BLS), was used to identify common hazards in the workplace and to describe characteristics of injuries and illnesses. These data should be representative of the situation worldwide.

Hazards detected during inspections

Regulatory compliance inspections of companies in the stone, clay, glass and concrete products manufacturing (Standard Industrial Classification (SIC) Code 32, equivalent to ISIC Code 36) reveal some of the common hazards in this sector. Regulatory compliance citations issued by OSHA indicate that common health and safety issues can be grouped as follows:

Figure 84.19 • Consolidated refractory manufacturing flow diagram.

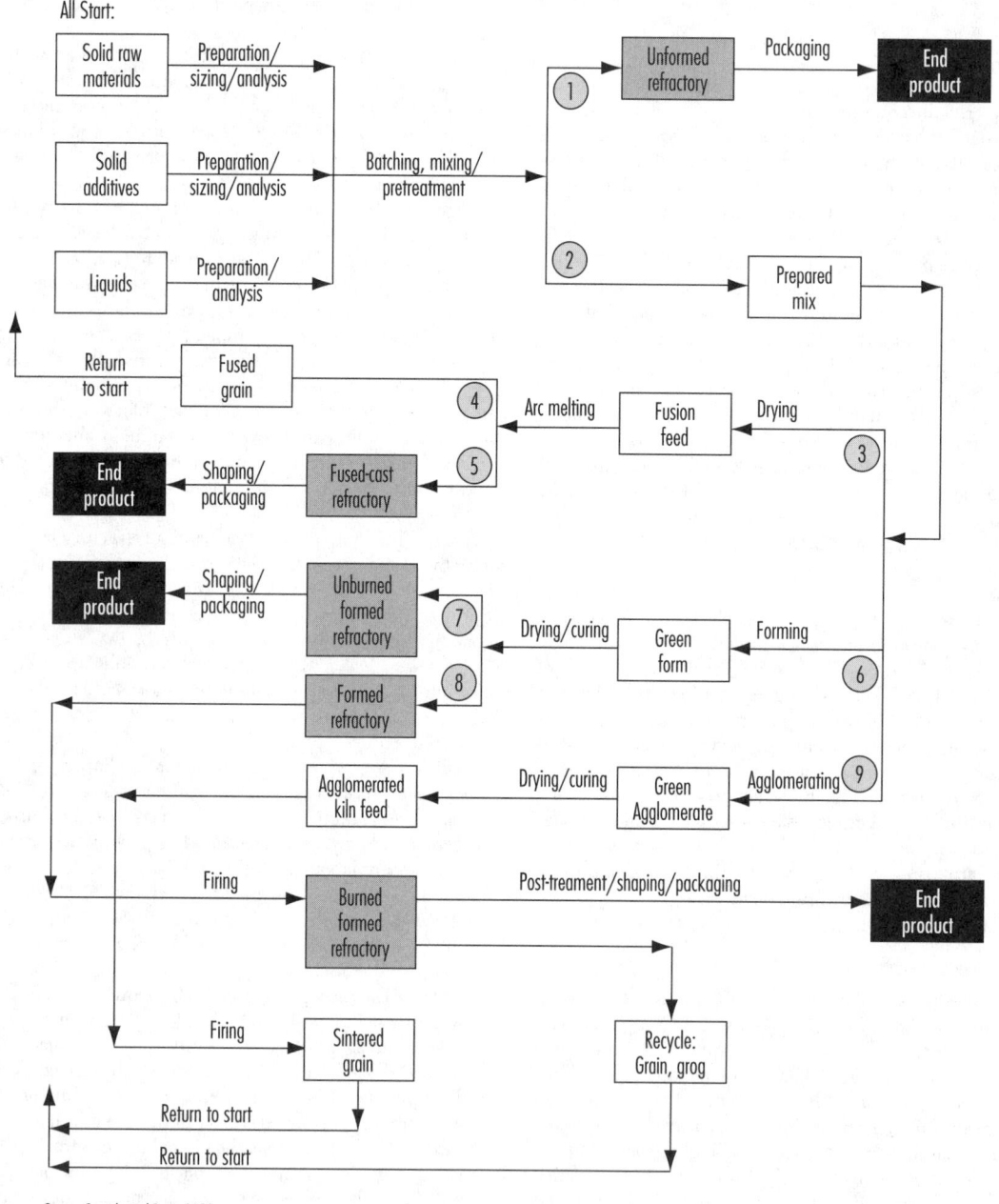

Source: Carniglia and Barria 1992.

Table 84.5 • Potential health and safety hazards found during manufacturing of glass, ceramic and related materials.

Hazards	Uses or sources of exposure to hazard	Potential effects (physical hazards or health effects)	Precautions or control strategies
Ergonomic stressors; biomechanical hazards	Overexertion from manual material-handling practices and excessive force, poor posture, high frequency/duration of tasks involving lifting, pushing or pulling	Strains, sprains and run in skeletal muscular damage to back, upper and lower extremities Excessive physical and mental fatigue can cause errors leading to secondary incidents	• Physical demands assessments of suspect job tasks • Job design/structure • Use of material-handling devices including lift assists, powered vehicles • Process automation or semi automation • Education on proper techniques and practices
Physical hazards	Caught in or struck by or against fixed or mobile equipment Slips, trips and falls on walking and working surfaces, hoses and other equipment, tools or materials	Abrasions, cuts, contusions, lacerations, punctures, fractures, amputations	• Safe work procedures • Good housekeeping practice • Equipment design and layout • Job design and structure • Material-handing equipment • Anti-slip surfaces
Noise	Pneumatic vibrators, compressors, valve actuators, mixing drive motors, blowers and dust collectors, conveyors, powered industrial trucks, mechanized process and packaging equipment, etc.	Occupational hearing loss, communication difficulty and stress	• Isolation, enclosure, dampening, reflective barriers or sound absorption materials • Innovative design of machine guarding to reduce noise • Specifying lower-noise motors or equipment (e.g., dampened vibrators) • Mufflers on pneumatic discharge points • Use of hearing protection and a hearing conservation programme
Radiant heat, high-temperature work environments	Heating or melting processes during maintenance or emergency response activities	Physiological strain, heat stress or thermal burns	• Shielding, screens, barriers, reflective surfaces, insulation • Water-cooled equipment jacketing • Air-conditioned control rooms or enclosures • Heat-protective clothing and gloves, water-cooled undersuits • Acclimatization to hot working environments, intake of water and electrolyte beverages, controlled work-rest regimens, other proactive heat stress management practices
Inhalation of airborne particulate matter from raw materials including crystalline silica, clay, lime, iron oxide, nuisance dusts	Handling raw materials and during production Exposures during routine maintenance activities, demolition and during construction activities or rebuilds Exposures can occur from non-ventilated equipment or from leaks or poor seals at transfer points, chutes, conveyors, elevators, screens, sieves, mixing equipment, grinding or crushing machines, storage bins, valves, piping, drying or curing ovens, shaping operations, etc. Raw materials are extremely abrasive, causing deterioration of transfer or storage system components in manufacturing processes. Failure to maintain baghouses, scrubbers or dust collectors and use of compressed air for clean-up activities increases risk of overexposures Intense heating processes may lead to exposure to the most hazardous forms of silica (cristobalite or tridymite)	Range from irritation (nuisance particulate) to chemical burns (burnt lime or other alkaline raw materials) to chronic effects such as decreased pulmonary function, lung disease, pneumoconiosis silicosis, tuberculosis	• Local or process equipment exhaust ventilation with baghouses, scrubbers or other dust collectors • Good design and maintenance of materials handling, manufacturing process, transfer and unloading equipment • Proper material handling, work practices, waste reduction and disposal • Isolation of operators in pressurized control rooms or booths and automation of transfer to minimize time in dusty areas • Respiratory protection, protective clothing, gloves and other personal protective equipment (PPE) • Active leak detection and repairs, predictive and preventive maintenance on equipment including dust collectors, valves • Routine housekeeping practices with proper vacuum system or wet/damp methods • Prohibition of compressed air for clean-up • Periodic medical screening, surveillance and early intervention based on exposure

Continues on next page.

84. GLASS, POTTERY AND RELATED MATERIALS

Table 84.5 • Potential health and safety hazards found during manufacturing of glass, ceramic and related materials.
Continued

Hazards	Uses or sources of exposure to hazard	Potential effects (physical hazards or health effects)	Precautions or control strategies
Lacerations, abrasions, or foreign bodies; contact with sharp glass, pottery or ceramics fragments or objects	Flying glass, ceramics or other fragments may cause penetrating wounds and serious eye injury. A special risk exists when toughened glass "explodes" during manufacture Direct contact with glass or other filaments, especially in forming or winding in continuous filament production operations and coating Drawing operations in optical fibre manufacturing	Puncture wounds, lacerations or abrasion of skin and soft tissues (tendons, ligaments, nerves, muscle), and foreign bodies in the eye Risks of serious secondary infections or dermal exposures to corrosive or toxic materials	• Use of cut-resistant protective gloves • Knitted wire, metal chain or other suitable gloves in handling flat glass • Mechanization and automation reduces hazards in producing and handling flat glass. Risk is shifted to maintenance workers • Establishing work practices on safe handling • First aid to prevent infection
Lacerations from hand-tools	Razor knives, finger knives, cullet knives or other sharp hand tools are commonly used in production, packaging and warehousing areas or during maintenance activities	Cuts to finger(s) or hand(s) and to lower extremities (legs)	• Knives with retractable blades • Substitution of other tools (shears or scissors) • Storage sheaths • Routine blade replacement and sharpening • First aid to prevent infection
Heavy metals particulates or fumes (lead, cadmium, chromium, arsenic, copper, nickel, cobalt, manganese or tin)	As raw materials or impurities in glazes, product formulas, pigments, colouring agents, films or coatings Maintenance and construction activities involving soldering, cutting, welding and applying/removal of protective coatings Grinding, cutting, welding, drilling, or shaping fabricated metal parts, structural members or machinery (e.g., refractory blocks or high-temperature alloys) that are components of manufacturing processes	Heavy metal toxicity	• Engineering controls including local exhaust and enclosures on process machinery or equipment • HEPA-ventilated portable power tools • Use of ventilated booths for spray painting or coating activities • Good work practices to reduce airborne particulates, including wet methods • Housekeeping practices, HEPA vacuuming, wet clean-up, water blasting • Personal hygiene, segregated laundering of contaminated work clothes • Respiratory protection and protective clothing • Medical surveillance and biological monitoring
Formaldehyde via inhalation or direct contact	Component of binders and sizes in vitreous fibre industry Potential exposures during mixing of binders or sizes, and during production	Sensory irritation, and irritation of respiratory tract Probable human carcinogen	• Process exhaust and general ventilation • Automated dispensing and mixing • Maintainance of curing ovens, screens or filters, and combustion dynamics • Active leak detection and control programme on curing ovens • Face shield with eye protection, gloves and chemical protective clothing for direct contact • Respiratory protection as needed
Bases (sodium hydroxide) or acids (hydrochloric acid, sulphuric acid, hydrofluoric acid)	Process water, boiler water or wastewater treatment and pH control Acid cleaning or etching processes with hydrofluoric acid	Corrosive to skin or eyes Respiratory tract and mucous membrane irritant Hydrofluoric acid causes severe shin burns that can go undetected for hours	• Process isolation • Safe handling practices • PPE use — respiratory protection, rubber gloves, faceshield with eye protection, rubber apron, protective clothing, eyewash/safety shower • Exhaust ventilation to control acid vapours or aerosols
Epoxies, acrylates and urethanes (may contain solvents such as xylene, toluene, etc.)	Ingredients in resins, sizes, binders and coatings used in production Maintenance products	Potential sensitizers to skin or respiratory tract Some epoxies contain unreacted epichlorohydrin, a suspect carcinogen Some urethanes contain unreacted toluene diisocyanate, a suspected carcinogen Amine curatives used in some systems — irritants or corrosives Flammability hazard	• Safe handling practices • Avoidance of spray applications (roller/brush apply) • Ventilation • Medical screening of users to avoid exposing sensitized workers • PPE use — impervious gloves, long sleeves • Barrier creams • Proper storage

Continues on next page.

Table 84.5 • Potential health and safety hazards found during manufacturing of glass, ceramic and related materials.
Continued

Hazards	Uses or sources of exposure to hazard	Potential effects (physical hazards or health effects)	Precautions or control strategies
Styrene	Polyester resins containing styrene, size ingredients	Irritant to eyes, skin, respiratory tract; effects on central nervous system (CNS) and target organs Possible carcinogen Flammability hazard	• Safe handling practices • Avoidance of spray applications (roller/brush apply) Ventilation • PPE use—chemically resistant gloves, long sleeves, barrier creams • Respirators in some cases
Silanes	Adhesion promoters added to sizes, binders or coatings. Can hydrolyze to release ethanol, methanol, butanol or other alcohols	Irritant to eyes, skin and respiratory system; potential CNS effects. Splashes in eye can cause permanent damage Flammability hazard	• Safe handling practices • PPE—gloves, and eye protection • Ventilation
Latex	Size or binder mixing areas, coatings and some maintenance products	Irritant to skin and eyes. Some may contain formaldehyde or other biocides and/or solvents	• PPE—gloves, eye protection • Respirators in some cases
Catalysts and accelerators	Added to resins or binders for curing in production and/or for some maintenance products	Irritants or corrosives to skin or eyes. Some are highly reactive and temperature sensitive	• Safe handling precautions • PPE, gloves, eye protection • Proper storage—temperature and segregation
Hydrocarbon solvents and/or chlorinated solvents	Maintenance shops and parts-cleaning operations	Various—irritation, chemical dermatitis, CNS effects. Non-chlorinated solvents may be flammable Chlorinated solvent can decompose if burned or heated	• Substitution of less hazardous cleaning agents (water-based detergents) • Substitute cleaning methods—high-pressure water cleaning, strippable coatings, etc. • Ventilation of parts washing stations • PPE use—gloves, eye/face protection, respirators as needed
Propane, natural gas, gasoline, fuel oil	Fuels for process heat Fuels for powered industrial trucks	Fire and explosion hazards Exposure to carbon monoxide or other products of incomplete combustion	• Proper design and inspections of storage and distribution system, and combustion process controls • Process hazard analysis reviews and periodic integrity testing • Safe unloading, filling and handling practices • Hot-work procedures • Routine testing and control of combustion processes and exhaust discharges
Inhalation of bioaerosols	Aerosols containing bacteria, moulds or fungus generated from spraying process or cooling water in humidification processes, cooling towers, ventilation systems, wet clean-up activities	Waterborne illness with systemic non-specific flu-like symptoms, fatigue Potential for dermatitis	• Process design and mist reduction • Process and cooling water treatment with biocides • Routine cleaning and sanitization • Elimination or reduction of nutrient source in water system • Respiratory protection • Personal protective clothing, gloves and good personal hygiene
Fibrous glass, mineral wool fibre, refractory ceramic fibres	In manufacturing processes including fibre formation, heat curing, cutting or cubing, winding, packaging and fabrication In use of fibrous materials as a component of furnaces, ducts and process equipment	Non-respirable fibres can cause mechanical irritation to skin or eyes Respirable fibres can cause irritation to eyes, skin and respiratory tract. Durable fibres have caused fibrosis and tumours in animal studies	• General ventilation and local exhaust ventilation on process equipment • Cutting methods • Good housekeeping practices (vacuuming vs. compressed air clean-up methods) • Personal protective clothing (long sleeves) and frequent washing • Personal hygiene • Respirators as needed • Demolition or removal practices including dampening for after service removals

84. GLASS, POTTERY AND RELATED MATERIALS

Synthetic gems

Synthetic gems are chemically and structurally identical to stones found in nature. Imitation gems, in contrast, are stones that are made to appear similar to a particular gem. There are a few basic processes that produce a variety of gem stones. Synthetic gems include garnet, spinel, emerald, sapphire and diamond. Most of these stones are produced for use in jewellery. Diamonds are used as abrasives, while rubies and garnets are used in lasers.

The first synthetic gem used in jewellery was emerald. The process employed in its manufacture is proprietary and kept secret, but probably involves a flux-growth method in which silicates of alumina and beryllium with additions of chromium for colour are melted together. Emeralds crystallize out of the flux. It may take a year to produce stones by this process.

The Verneuil or flame-fusion process is used in the production of sapphire and ruby. It requires large amounts of hydrogen and oxygen, therefore consuming great amounts of energy. This process involves heating a seed crystal with an oxyhydrogen flame until the surface is liquid. Powered raw material such as Al_2O_3 for sapphire is added carefully. As the raw material becomes molten, the seed crystal is slowly withdrawn from the flame, causing the liquid furthest from the flame to solidify. The end closest to the flame is still liquid and ready for more raw material. The end result is the formation of a rod-like crystal. Sundry colours are created by adding small amounts of various metal ions to the raw materials. Ruby is created by replacing 0.1% of its aluminium ions with chromium atoms.

Spinel, a colourless synthetic germ ($MgAl_2O_4$), is made by the Verneuil process. Along with sapphire, spinel is used by industry to provide a wide range of colours for use as birth stones and in class rings. The colour produced by adding the same metal ions will be different in spinel than it will be in sapphire.

Synthetic diamonds are used in industry because of their hardness. Applications for diamonds include cutting, polishing, grinding and drilling. Some of the common uses are cutting and grinding of granite for use in building construction, well drilling and grinding non-ferrous alloys. In addition, processes are being developed that will deposit diamond on surfaces to provide clear, hard, scratch-resistant surfaces.

Diamonds are formed when elemental carbon or graphite is subjected to pressure and heat over time. To create a diamond on the factory floor involves combining graphite and metal catalysts and pressing them together in high heat (up to 1,500 °C). The size and quality of the diamonds are controlled by adjusting the time, pressure and/or heat. Large tungsten carbide dies are used to achieve the high pressures needed to form diamonds in a reasonable period of time. These dies measure up to 2 m across and 20 cm thick, resembling a large doughnut. The mixture of graphite and catalyst is placed in a ceramic gasket, and tapered pistons squeeze from above and below. After a specified time, the gasket containing diamonds is removed from the press. The gaskets are broken away and the diamond-bearing graphite is subjected to a series of agents designed to digest away all material except for the diamonds. The reactants employed are strong agents that are potential sources of significant burns and respiratory injury. Gem-quality diamonds may be produced in the same manner, but the long press times required make this process prohibitively expensive.

Hazards resulting from the manufacture of diamonds include potential exposure to the highly reactive acids and caustic agents in great volumes, noise, dust from forming and breaking of ceramic gaskets, and metal dust exposure. Another potential hazard is created by the failure of the massive carbide dies. After a variable number of uses, the dies fail, posing a trauma hazard if the dies are not isolated. Ergonomic issues arise when the diamonds manufactured are classified and graded. Their small size makes this a tedious and repetitive job.

Basil Dolphin

Figure 84.20 • Machine guarding protects operators from rotating shafts, belts or drive chains.

Owens Corning

- *hazard communication* of physical and health hazards of chemical substances in the workplace
- *control of hazardous energy*—lockout and tagout procedures to control activities around machinery or equipment where unexpected energization or release of stored energy could cause injury. Hazardous energy includes electrical, mechanical, hydraulic, pneumatic, chemical, thermal radiation and other sources.
- *electrical safety*, including electrical equipment or system design, wiring methods, safe work practices and training
- *permit required confined-space entry*—identification, evaluation and safe entry procedures
- *personal protective equipment*—assessments, selection and use of eye, face, hand, foot and head protection
- *guarding machines, equipment and tools* to protect operators and adjacent workers from hazards at point of operation, ingoing nip points, and from rotating parts, flying chips or sparks; includes fixed machinery, portable machinery and portable power tools, and adjustment of guards and work rests on abrasive wheel machinery (grinders) (see figure 84.20)
- *respiratory protection*—selection, use, maintenance, training, medical clearance and fit testing of respirators
- *occupational noise exposure*—control of exposures by engineering, administrative or hearing protection and implementation of hearing conservation programmes
- *fire prevention and emergency preparedness and response*, including fire extinguishers, escape routes, plans and flammable/combustible materials storage or use

- *walking and working surfaces*, including guarding floor and wall openings and holes; housekeeping; and keeping aisles and passageways free from conditions that present slip, trip or fall hazards (see figure 84.21)
- *powered industrial trucks*—design, maintenance, use and other safety requirements for fork-lift trucks, platform trucks, tractors, motorized hand trucks or other specialized industrial trucks powered by electric motors or internal combustion motors
- *fixed and portable ladders, stairways and scaffolds*—design, inspection or maintenance and safe use
- *fall protection*—use of fall restraints and arrest equipment for elevated work
- *cutting and welding*—safe use and procedures for oxygen/acetylene or fuel gas or arc cutting or welding equipment
- *material-handling equipment*—including overhead and gantry cranes, hoists, chains and slings
- *control of exposure to toxic or hazardous substances*, including air contaminants or specifically regulated chemicals (e.g., silica, lead, asbestos, formaldehyde, cadmium or arsenic).

Injury and Illness Profile

Injury illness incidence rates

Based on records from the US Department of Labor, manufacturers of stone, clay and glass products (SIC 32) have a total "recordable" incidence rate of nonfatal occupational injuries and illnesses of 13.2 cases per 100 full-time workers per year. This incidence rate is higher than corresponding rates for all manufacturing (12.2) and all private industry (8.4). About 51% of the "recordable injury" cases in the stone, clay and glass product manufacturing sector do not result in lost work days (time away from work).

The "total lost workday case" incidence rates based on the number of disabling injuries or illnesses resulting in a worker missing days of work per 100 full-time workers are also available from the US Department of Labor. The total lost workday incidence rate includes cases where workdays are lost and the worker is not capable of performing the full scope of the job (restricted or light duty). Stone, clay and glass products manufacturers have a total lost

workday incidence rate of 6.5 cases per 100 workers per year. This is higher than the corresponding rates for all manufacturing (5.5) and for all private industry (3.8). About 93% of the lost workday cases in the stone, clay and glass product manufacturing sector results from injuries rather than occupational illnesses.

Table 84.6 presents more detailed information on incidence rates for injuries and illnesses (combined) or injuries (alone) for various types of manufacturing processes within the stone, clay, and glass product manufacturing sector (SIC Code 32). Incidence rates and demographics may not be representative of global information, but it is the most complete information available.

Demographics of injuries and illness cases

Workers aged 25 to 44 years accounted for about 59% of the 23,203 lost-time injury or illness cases in the U.S. stone, clay and glass product manufacturing sector. The next highest affected group was workers aged 45 to 54 years, who had 18% of the lost-time injury or illness cases (see figure 84.22).

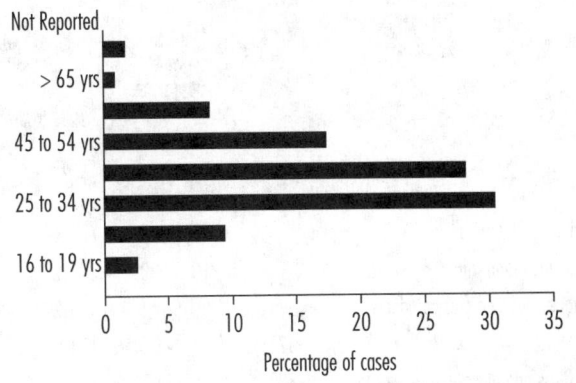

Figure 84.22 • Percentage of lost-time injuries and illnesses by age, US, SIC Code 32, 1994.

Figure 84.21 • Walking and working surfaces should be free from trip and slip hazards.

Owens Corning

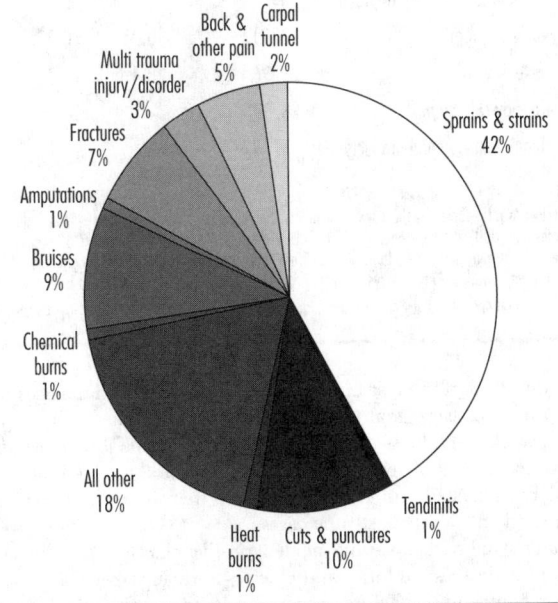

Figure 84.23 • Nature of occupational injuries and illnesses lost workday cases, US, SIC Code 32, 1994.

84. GLASS, POTTERY AND RELATED MATERIALS

Table 84.6 • Nonfatal occupational injury and illness incidence rates[1] per 100 full-time workers for US companies in SIC Code 32, private industry and manufacturing, 1994.

Industry	SIC Code[2]	1994 annual average employment[3] (thousands)	Injuries and illnesses				Injuries			
				Lost workday cases				Lost workday cases		
			Total cases	Total[4]	With days away from work	Cases without lost workdays	Total cases	Total[5]	With days away from work[5]	Cases without lost workdays
Private industry, all		95,449.3	8.4	3.8	2.8	4.6	7.7	3.5	2.6	4.2
Manufacturing, all		18,303.0	12.2	5.5	3.2	6.8	10.4	4.7	2.9	5.7
Stone, clay and glass products	32	532.5	13.2	6.5	4.3	6.7	12.3	6.1	4.1	6.2
Flat glass	321	15.0	21.3	6.6	3.1	14.7	17.3	5.2	2.6	12.1
Glass and glassware, pressed or blown	322	76.8	12.5	6.0	3.0	6.5	11.3	5.5	2.8	5.8
Glass containers	3221	33.1	14.1	6.9	3.4	7.2	13.2	6.5	3.2	6.7
Pressed and blown glass, nec	3229	43.7	11.3	5.4	2.8	5.9	9.8	4.8	2.4	5.1
Products of purchased glass	323	60.7	14.1	6.1	3.1	8.0	12.7	5.4	2.9	7.4
Structural clay products	325	32.4	14.1	7.7	4.2	6.5	13.1	7.2	4.0	5.9
Brick and structural clay tile	3251	–	15.5	8.4	5.1	7.1	14.8	7.9	5.0	6.9
Clay refractories	3255	–	16.0	9.3	4.7	6.8	15.6	9.3	4.7	6.4
Pottery and related products	326	40.8	13.6	6.8	3.8	6.8	12.2	6.1	3.5	6.1
Vitreous plumbing fixtures	3261	–	17.8	10.0	3.8	7.8	16.1	9.0	3.5	7.1
Vitreous china table and kitchenware	3262	–	12.8	6.3	4.4	6.5	11.0	5.6	3.8	5.5
Porcelain electrical supplies	3264	–	11.3	5.8	3.7	5.6	9.8	5.0	3.4	4.8
Pottery products, nec	3269	–	12.6	5.6	3.7	7.1	11.6	5.0	3.5	6.6
Concrete, gypsum and plaster products	327	198.3	13.4	7.0	5.6	6.4	13.0	6.9	5.5	6.2
Concrete block and brick	3271	17.1	14.5	7.8	6.8	6.8	14.0	7.7	6.7	6.2
Concrete products, nec	3272	65.6	17.7	9.8	7.0	7.9	17.1	9.5	6.8	7.6
Ready-mixed concrete	3273	98.8	11.6	6.0	5.3	5.6	11.5	6.0	5.3	5.5
Misc. nonmetallic mineral products	329	76.7	10.7	5.4	3.3	5.3	9.8	5.0	3.2	4.9
Abrasive products	3291	20.0	10.2	3.9	2.5	6.3	9.5	3.7	2.4	5.8
Mineral wool	3296	23.4	11.0	6.1	3.0	4.9	10.0	5.6	2.7	4.3
Nonclay refractories	3297	–	10.6	5.8	4.5	4.8	10.2	5.7	4.3	4.6
Nonmetallic mineral products, nec	3299	–	13.1	8.2	5.8	4.9	11.4	7.0	5.5	4.3

nec = not elsewhere classified. – = data not available.

[1] The incidence rates represent the number of injuries and illnesses per 100 full-time workers and were calculated as the number of injuries and illnesses divided by hours worked by all employees in the calendar year times 200,000 (the base equivalent for 100 workers at 40 hours per week for 52 weeks per year). [2] *Standard Industrial Classification Manual*, 1987 edition. [3] Employment is expressed as an annual average and was derived primarily from the BLS State Current Employment Statistics programme. [4] Total cases includes cases involving restricted work activity only, in addition to days away from work cases with or without restricted work activity. [5] Days away from work cases include those which result from days away from work, with or without restricted work activity.

Source: Based on national survey of work-related injuries and illnesses in private industry by the US Department of Labor, BLS.

About 85% of the lost-time injury cases injuries and illnesses in SIC Code 32 were males. In 24% of the lost-time cases (both sexes), workers had less than 1 year of service in the job. Workers with 1 to 5 years of service in the job accounted for 32% of the cases. Experienced employees with more than 5 years of service comprised 35% of the lost-time cases.

Nature. Analysis of lost-time incident profiles characterizes the nature of the disabling injuries and illnesses and helps explain causative or contributing factors. Strains and sprains are the leading nature of injury and illness in the stone, clay and glass product manufacturing sector. As shown in figure 84.23, strains and sprains make up about 42% of all lost-time cases. Cuts and punctures (10%) were the second most common nature of disabling injury or illness. Other major nature of injury categories were bruises (9%), fractures (7%) and back/other pain (5%). Heat burns, chemical burns and amputations were less common (1% or less).

Events or exposures. Figure 84.24 shows that overexertion while lifting leads all other disabling injury events or exposures. Over exertion while lifting was a causative factor in about 17% of the disabling cases; repetitive motion was the exposure in an additional 5% of the disabling cases. Struck by an object was the next most common event, which led to 16% of the cases. Struck against an object events caused 10% of the cases. Other important events were caught in an object (9%), falls on same level (9%), falls to lower level (6%), and slips/trips without a fall (6%). Exposure to harmful substances or environment was a causative factor in only 5% of the cases.

Body part. The body part most frequently affected was the back (24% of the cases) (see figure 84.25). Injuries to the upper extremities (finger, hand, wrist and arm combined) occurred in 23% of the cases, with injury to the finger in 7% of the cases. Lower-extremity injuries was similar (22% of cases), with the knee affected in 9% of the cases.

Sources. The most common sources of disabling injury or illness cases were: parts and materials (20%); worker position or motion (16%); floors, walkways or ground surfaces (15%); containers (10%); machinery (9%); vehicles (9%); handtools (4%); furniture and fixtures (2%); and chemicals and chemical products (2%) (see figure 84.26).

Disease prevention and control

Cumulative trauma associated with repetitive motion, overexertion and excessive forces is a common finding in this manufacturing sector. Robotic devices are available in some instances, but manual handling practices still dominate. Compressors, blowers, spinners, pneumatic vibrators and packaging equipment can create noise exceeding 90 to 95 dBA. Hearing protection and a sound hearing conservation programme will prevent permanent changes in hearing.

This industry consumes large quantities of crystalline silica. Exposures must be limited during handling, maintenance and cleaning. Good housekeeping with a proper vacuum system or wet cleaning methods will reduce potential exposures. Periodic screening should be conducted utilizing pulmonary function tests and chest films if excessive exposure to silica has occurred. Exposures to heavy metals found as raw materials, glazing or pig-

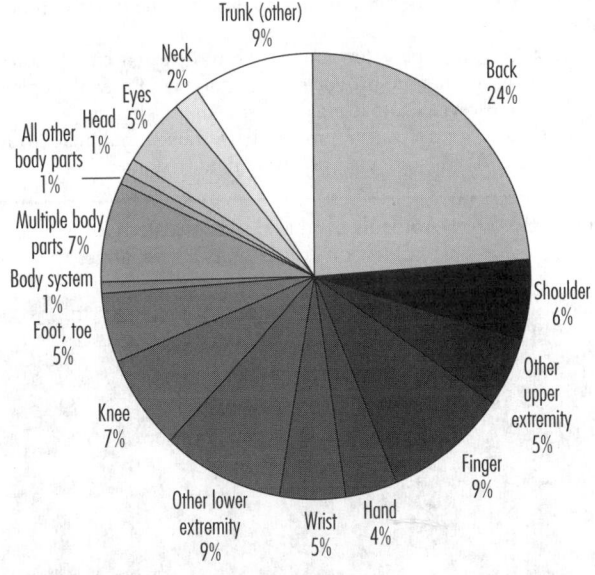

Figure 84.25 • Body part affected in lost workday injury or illness cases, US, SIC Code 32, 1994.

ments should also be minimized. Using substitutes for heavy metals found in glazes will also eliminate health concerns regarding leaching of metals into food or beverages. Good housekeeping practices and respiratory protection are used to prevent adverse effects. Medical surveillance that includes biological monitoring may be necessary.

The use of binders containing formaldehyde, epoxies and silanes is common in the manufacture of vitreous fibres. Steps must be taken to minimize skin and respiratory irritation. Formaldehyde is regulated as a carcinogen in many countries. Respirable

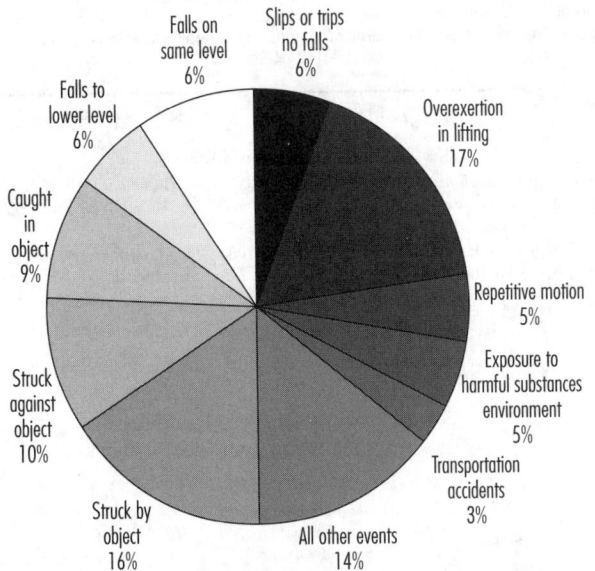

Figure 84.24 • Event or exposure in occupational injuries and illnesses lost workday cases, US, SIC Code 32, 1995.

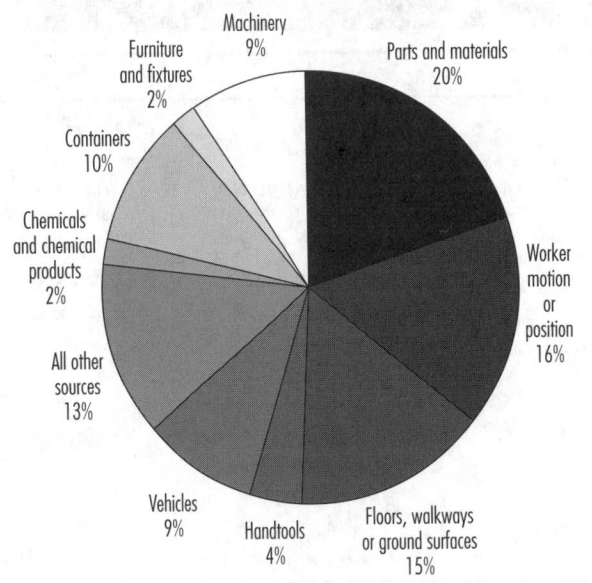

Figure 84.26 • Sources of occupational injuries and illnesses lost workday cases, US, SIC Code 32, 1994.

84. GLASS, POTTERY AND RELATED MATERIALS

fibres are produced during manufacturing, fabrication, cutting and installation of glass, rock, slag, and refractory ceramic fibre products. Although exposures to airborne fibres have generally been quite low (less than 1 fibre per cubic centimetre) for most of these materials, loose fill blowing applications tend to be much higher.

Rock, slag, and glass are among the most extensively studied commercial insulation products in use today. Epidemiological studies have revealed that cigarette smoking is having a major impact on lung cancer mortality among manufacturing employees. Well-conducted cross-sectional studies have not

Figure 84.27 • Aerosols of reused waste water that is not treated can cause waterborne illness.

shown that the fibres produce excess lung mortality or morbidity. Recent chronic inhalation studies in rats have shown that the durability of vitreous fibres is a critical determinant of the biological potential of these fibres. Composition, which determines the durability of these fibres, may vary considerably. To avoid public health concerns, a European Commission Technical Committee has recently proposed that the bio-persistence of vitreous fibres be tested using short-term inhalation. An insulation wool composition which has been thoroughly tested at maximum tolerated dose by chronic inhalation in rats and found not to produce irreversible disease is suggested as a reference fibre.

Environmental and Public Health Issues

The primary air pollutant emitted during the manufacture of glass, ceramics, pottery and brick is particulate matter. Maximum achievable control technology consisting of baghouses and wet electrostatic precipitators is available to reduce emissions when necessary. Hazardous air pollutants generated during binder mixing, application and curing processes are coming under scrutiny. These substances include styrene, silanes and epoxies used on continuous glass filament, and formaldehyde, methanol and phenol utilized during rock, slag and glass production. Formaldehyde is the hazardous air pollutant that is driving the control standards for the latter manufacturing lines. Heavy metal hazardous air pollutants such as chromium are driving glass melting furnace standards while NO_x and SO_x remain issues in some countries. Fluoride and boron emissions are of concern in continuous glass filament production. Boron may also become an environmental concern if highly soluble vitreous glass wool fibres are required in some countries.

Due to the high discharge volume of air and the nature of forming and glass melting, the industry evaporates considerable quantities of water. Many facilities, as, for example, in the United States, have zero discharge of wastewater. Recycled wastewater that contains organic material can create biological hazards in the workplace if treatment is not implemented to prevent biological growth (see figure 84.27). Waste generated by this industrial sector includes heavy metals, corrosives, some binders and spent solvents. The glass fibre industry has become a major point for recycling glass bottles and plate glass. For example, current glass wool products contain 30 to 60% recycled glass. Spent refractories are also reclaimed and beneficially reused.

Acknowledgements: Special thanks to Dan Dimas, CSP, Libbey-Owens-Ford, for providing photographs, and to Michel Soubeyrand, Libbey-Owens-Ford, for providing information on chemical vapour deposition for the section on glass.

References

American National Standards Institute (ANSI). 1988. *Ceramic Tile.* ANSI A 137.1-1988. New York: ANSI.

Carniglia, and SC Barna. 1992. *Handbook of Industrial Refractories Technology: Principles, Types, Properties and Applications.* Park Ridge, NJ: Noyes Publications.

Haber, RA and PA Smith. 1987. *Overview of Traditional Ceramics.* New Brunswick, NJ: Ceramic Casting Program, Rutgers, State University of New Jersey.

Persson, HR. 1983. *Glass Technology Manufacturing and Properties.* Seoul: Cheong Moon Gak Publishing Company.

Tooley, FV (ed.). 1974. *The Handbook of Glass Manufacture.* Vols. I and II. New York: Books for Industry, Inc.

Other relevant readings

Kroschwitz, JI and M Howe-Grant (eds.). 1991. *Encyclopedia of Chemical Technology,* 4th ed. New York: Wiley & Sons.

Lowenstein, KL. 1983. *The Manufacturing Technology of Continuous Glass Fibres.* Amsterdam, New York: Elsevier Science Publishers.

PRINTING, PHOTOGRAPHY AND REPRODUCTION INDUSTRY

Chapter Editor
David Richardson

Contents

• PRINTING AND PUBLICATION

Gordon C. Miller

Overview of the Printing Processes

The invention of printing dates back to China in the 11th century. In the latter part of the 15th century, Johannes Gutenburg first introduced moveable type and invented the printing press, thus creating the process of printing that is now common around the world. Since then, the printing process has expanded dramatically beyond simply printing of words on paper to printing of words and other forms of graphic arts on paper and other materials (substrates). In the 20th century, the packaging of all types of consumer products has taken printing to yet another level. Printing, packaging and publications, along with the closely associated field of coating and laminating, are found in everyday products and processes used in the home, at leisure and at work.

The art of placing words and pictures on paper or other substrates is moving in directions not anticipated even a few years ago. A very wide spectrum of technologies, ranging from the older and more traditional styles of printing to the newest technologies involving computers and related processes has evolved. This includes everything from the older technology of lead-based type in flat-bed presses to today's modern web-fed, direct-to-plate presses (see figure 85.1). In some operations, these varying technologies are literally found side by side.

There are four general types of printing and there are many safety, health and environmental hazards associated with these technologies.

1. *Letterpress or relief printing.* This process, used for many years in printing and publication, involves the creation of images, often letters or pictures, that are raised above a background or non-printing area. Ink is applied to the raised area, which is then placed into contact with the paper or other substrate which accepts the image.

    There are several ways to create the relief image, such as assembly of individual letters by using moveable type, or by using the once common linotype machine or machine-created type. These processes are appropriate for simpler, shorter run printing tasks. For longer-running tasks, printing

General profile

The printing, commercial photography and reproduction industries are important worldwide in terms of their economic significance. The printing industry is very diverse in technologies and in size of enterprises. However, regardless of size as measured by production volume, the different printing technologies described in this chapter are the most common. In terms of production volume, there are a limited number of large-scale operations, but many small ones. From the economic perspective, the printing industry is one of the largest industries and generates annual revenues of at least US$500 billion worldwide. Similarly, the commercial photography industry is diverse, with a limited number of large-volume and many small-volume operations. Photofinishing volume is about equally divided between the large and small-volume operations. The commercial photographic market generates annual revenues of approximately US$60 billion worldwide, with photofinishing operations comprising approximately 40% of this total. The reproduction industry, which consists of smaller-volume operations with combined annual revenues of about US$27 billion, generates close to 2 trillion copies annually. In addition, reproduction and duplication services on an even smaller scale are provided onsite at most organizations and companies.

Health, environmental and safety issues in these industries are evolving in response to substitutions with potentially less hazardous materials, new industrial hygiene control strategies, and the advent of new technologies, such as the introduction of digital technologies, electronic imaging and computers. Many historically important health and safety issues (e.g., solvents in the printing industry or formaldehyde as a stabilizer in photoprocessing solutions) will not be issues in the future due to material substitution or other risk management strategies. Nevertheless, new health, environmental and safety issues will arise that will have to be addressed by health and safety professionals. This suggests the continued importance of health and environmental monitoring as part of an effective risk management strategy in the printing, commercial photography and reproduction industries.

David Richardson

plates, often made of metal or plastic or rubber-type materials, are more appropriate. Using rubber or similar plates is often called flexography or flexographic printing.

Inks typical of this process can be either solvent or water based. Some newer inks, based on ultraviolet (UV) curing and other chemico-physical systems, are being developed and implemented in this printing system.

2. *Intaglio or gravure printing.* In intaglio or gravure printing processes, the image to be printed is recessed into the face of an engraved plate or cylinder. The plate or cylinder is bathed in ink. Excess ink is then removed from the non-engraved parts of the plate by use of a *doctor blade*. The plate or cylinder is then brought into contact with the paper or other substrate to which the ink transfers the image. This system of printing is very typical of long-run printed products, such as magazines and packaging materials.

    Inks typically are solvent based, with toluene being the most common solvent in intaglio or gravure inks. Use of inks based on soybean oil and water is under way with some success. However, not all applications can utilize this newer technology.

3. *Planographic or lithography printing.* Dissimilar materials form the basis for planographic or lithographic printing. By using dissimilar materials, areas can be developed that are water re-

Figure 85.1 • The finishing end of a printing process where the web material, after printing, is cut and formed into the print product.

ceptive or water repelling (i.e., receptive to solvent ink). The solvent ink-receptive area will carry the image, while the water-receptive area will become the background or un-printed area. Thus, ink adheres only in specific areas for transfer to the paper or other substrate. In many instances, this step will involve transfer to an intermediate surface, known as the *blanket*, which will later be placed against the paper or other substrate. This transfer process is called offset printing, which is widely used for many printing, publication and packaging applications.

It should be noted that not all offset printing involves lithography. Depending upon the exact needs of the printing process, other printing methods may utilize elements of offset printing.

Inks used in planographic or lithographic printing are usually solvent based (i.e., not water based), but some inks that are not solvent based are rapidly being developed.

4. *Porous or screen printing*. Porous or screen printing uses a stencil placed over a fine mesh screen. The ink is applied to the open screen areas and pressed (squeegeed) over the stencil and open mesh area. The ink will transfer through the screen to the paper or other substrate under the screen. Screen printing is often used for simpler, low volume printing tasks, where this process may have a cost advantage. Typical use of this printing process is for textiles, posters, displays and wallpaper.

Inks for screen printing are either solvent or water based, depending largely on the substrate to be printed. Since the coating used in screen printing is often thicker, inks are typically more viscous than those used in other printing methods.

Preparation of Print-Ready Material

Preparing material for printing involves assembling the various materials, including text, photographs, artwork, illustrations and designs, that are the subject of reproduction into the printed material. All materials must be completely finalized because changes cannot be made after print plates are created. In order to correct errors, the process must be redone. Principles of graphic arts are applied at this point to insure proper aesthetics of the printed product.

The health and safety aspects of the graphic arts step of the printing process are generally regarded as less hazardous than the other aspects of printing. The generation of artwork may involve considerable physical strain, as well as health risks from the pigments, rubber cement, spray adhesives and other materials used. Much of this is being replaced by computerized graphics which is also discussed in the article "Commercial art" in the *Entertainment and the arts* chapter. The potential hazards of working with visual display units and computers are discussed elsewhere in this *Encyclopaedia*. Ergonomically sound workstations can alleviate the hazards.

Platemaking

The printing plates or cylinders that are typical of contemporary printing processes must be created for either process photography or computer-generated make-up. Often, the platemaking starts with a camera system that is used to create an image, which subsequently may be transferred by photochemical methods to the plate. Colours must be separated, and aspects of the print quality such as halftone imagery must be developed in this process. The photography used for platemaking is very sophisticated when compared to the typical home-use of a camera. Exceptionally fine sharpness, colour separation and register are needed to allow for the production of quality printed materials. With the introduction of the computer, much of the manual assembly and image development work has been eliminated.

The potential hazards seen in this part of the printing process are similar to those typical of the photographic industry and are discussed elsewhere in this chapter. Controlling potential chemical exposures is important during platemaking.

After the image is created, photomechanical processes are used to create the printing plate. The typical photomechanical processes for making plates can be grouped into the following:

Manual methods. Hand tools, engravers and knives can be used to create relief in the plate, or crayons can be used to create water-repelling areas on a lithography plate. (This is generally a method used in small production, or for special printing tasks.)

Mechanical methods. Lathes, ruling machines and similar types of mechanical equipment are used to create relief, or other equipment can be used to produce water-repelling areas on lithography plates.

Electrochemical methods. Electrochemical methods are used to deposit metals onto plates or cylinders.

Electronic methods. Electronic engravers are used to create relief on plates or cylinders.

Electrostatic methods. Xerographic or similar methods are used to create either relief or water-repelling image components on plates or cylinders.

Photomechanical methods. Photographic images can be transferred to the plates through light-sensitive coatings on the plate or cylinder.

Photomechanical platemaking is the most common process today. In many instances, two or more systems may be used to create the plate or cylinder.

The health and safety implications of making printing plates are extensive owing to the various methods used to create the plate. Mechanical methods, less used today than in the past, were the source of typical mechanical safety issues, including hazards arising from the use of hand tools and the larger mechanical equipment often seen in the machine shop. Risks related to hand safety and guarding are typical in platemaking using mechanical methods. Such platemaking often involves the use of oils and cleaners that may be flammable or toxic.

Older methods are often still in use in many facilities right alongside newer equipment and hazards can be spread. If the plate consists of movable type, a linotype machine, once very common in most printshops, would make type by casting lead into the shape of letters. The lead is melted and kept in a lead pot. With the lead pot present, many of the hazards associated with lead come directly into the printshop. Lead, which is discussed elsewhere in this *Encyclopaedia*, can enter the body through inhalation of lead compounds and by skin contamination with lead and lead-containing type which can then lead to lead ingestion. The result is possible chronic low-grade lead poisoning, with resultant nervous system dysfunction, kidney dysfunction and other toxicity.

Other methods of platemaking use chemical systems typical of plating or chemical etching to create an image on the plate or cylinder. This involves many different chemicals, including acids and heavy metals (zinc, chromium, copper and aluminium), along with organic chemical-based resin systems that make up some of the upper layers of the plate itself. Some systems now use petroleum-based solvents in the chemical processes of making plates. The potential health hazards from such chemicals must be considered in the safety effort undertaken for such a facility. Ventilation and personal protective equipment that are appropriate for chemicals used are very important. Additionally, the potential environmental effects of corrosives and heavy metals need to be taken into account as part of the safety effort for the chemistry of platemaking. Storage and mixing of these chemical systems also presents health risks which can be significant if a spill occurs.

Engraving systems, used in some instances to transfer the image to the plate or cylinder, also may present potential hazards. Standard systems of engraving will generate some metal contamination that can be a problem for those working with these systems. The newer systems utilize laser equipment to carve the image into the plate material. While this allows the elimination of some steps in the platemaking process, the presence of the laser may present a hazard to the eyes and skin. The laser may also be used to soften materials, such as plastics, rather than to heat them to vapourization, thus creating additional vapour- and fume-related problems for the workplace.

In most instances, the platemaking process is a relatively small portion of the total production operations of the printing facility, which automatically limits the risk present, since few people work in the platemaking area and smaller quantities of materials are typical of these types of operations. As technology progresses, fewer steps will be needed to translate the image to the plate, thus presenting fewer opportunities for hazards to have an impact on employees and the environment.

Ink Manufacture

Depending upon the technologies utilized, a variety of inks and coatings are used. Inks are typically made up of a carrier and pigment or dyes and resins that go to form the image.

The carrier allows the pigments and other components to remain in solution until the ink is dried. Typical printing ink carriers include alcohols, esters (acetates), ketones or water. Gravure inks often include large amounts of toluene. Newer inks may contain epoxidized soybean oil and other chemicals that are less hazardous because they are not volatile.

Another component of typical inks is the resin binder. The resin bender is used, after the solvent has dried, to hold the pigment to the substrate. Organic resins, some natural and others synthetic, such as acrylic resins, are routinely used in inks.

The pigment provides the colour. Pigment bases can come from a variety of chemicals including heavy metals and organic materials.

UV-cured inks are based on acrylates and do not contain carriers. They are not involved in the curing/drying process. These inks tend to be simply a resin and pigment system. The acrylates are potential skin and respiratory sensitizers.

There are many health and safety hazards associated with ink manufacture. Since ink make-up often includes flammable solvents, fire protection is important at any facility where ink manufacture is undertaken. Sprinkler systems and portable extinguishing equipment must be present and in full and complete operating condition. Since employees must know how to use the equipment, training is needed. Electrical systems should be instrinsically safe or involve purging or explosion proofing. Control of static is critical since many solvents can generate a static charge when run through a plastic hose or through the air. Humidity control, grounding and bonding are strongly recommended for static control.

Mixing equipment, from small mixers to large batch tanks, can impose many mechanical safety hazards. Mixer blades and systems must be guarded or otherwise protected during operation and while in make-ready and clean-up modes. Machine guards are needed and must be in place; when they are removed for maintenance-related activities, lockout/tagout programmes are essential.

Owing to the quantities of materials present, the handling of material may also present hazards. While it is recommended that all materials that are conveniently piped directly to the area of use be handled in such a manner, many ink components must be manually moved to the mixing area in bags, drums or other containers. This involves using not only mechanical equipment such as lift trucks and hoists, but also manual handling by the employee doing the mixing. Back strains and similar stresses are common in these operations. Training on correct lifting practices is an important aspect of preventive measures, as well as selecting mechanical lifting processes that require less direct human involvement.

With this much handling, spills and chemical handling incidents can occur. Systems should be in place to deal with such emergency situations. Also, care in storage to prevent spillage and possible mixing of incompatible materials is needed.

The specific chemicals and large amounts stored can lead to issues related to possible employee health exposures. Each component, whether carrier, resin or pigment, should be evaluated both individually and within the context of the ink system. The safety effort should include: industrial hygiene evaluation and sampling to determine whether exposures are judged acceptable; adequate ventilation for removal of toxic materials; and the use of appropriate personal protective equipment should be considered. Since spills and other opportunities for overexposure are present, emergency systems should be in place to render first aid. Safety showers, eye washes, first aid kits and medical surveillance are all recommended, otherwise injury to skin, eyes, respiratory system and other body systems may occur. Inputs can range from simple dermatitis resulting from skin exposure to solvents, to more permanent organ damage due to exposure to heavy-metal pigments, such as lead chromate, that are found in some ink formulations. The spectrum of possible toxicity is large because of the many materials that are used in various ink and coating manufacture. With newer technologies such as UV-curable inks, the hazard may change from standard solvent hazards to sensitization from repeated contact with skin. Care must be taken to fully understand the potential risks of the chemicals used in ink and coating manufacture. This is best done prior to formulation.

Since many inks contain materials that are potentially harmful if they find their way into the environment, controls on the ink-making process may be necessary. Additionally, residual materials including clean-up materials and wastes must be handled carefully, to minimize their impact on the environment.

With the strong worldwide emphasis on a better environment, more "earth friendly" inks are being introduced, which use water as the solvent and less toxic resins and pigments. This should help reduce the hazards related to ink manufacturing.

Printing

Printing involves taking the plate, placing an ink onto the plate, and transferring the ink to the substrate. In offset processes, the image is transferred from a plate wrapped around a cylinder to an intermediate rubber cylinder (blanket) before being transferred to the desired substrate. Substrates are not always limited to paper, although paper is one of the most common substrates. Many fancy labels are printed on vacuum-metallized polyester film, using conventional printing techniques. Laminated plastics may be fed into the printing press in sheets or as part of a continuous web that is later cut to specification to make packaging.

Since printing often involves colour, several printed layers may be placed onto the substrate and then dried prior to the addition of the next layer. All of this must be done very precisely in order to keep all the colours in register. This requires multiple printing stations and sophisticated controls to maintain proper speed and tension through the press.

The hazards associated with operating a printing press are similar to those involved in ink manufacturing. The fire hazard is critical. As with ink manufacturing, sprinkler systems and other means of fire protection are needed. Other systems may be mounted directly to the press. These serve as added controls in addition to the portable extinguishers which should be available. Electrical systems should meet the purged, explosion-proof or intrinsically safe requirements. Static electricity control is also important, especially with solvents like isopropyl alcohol and with web presses. Added to the handling of flammable liquids that can generate static while moving through plastic hoses or the air, most plastic films or webs will also generate very substantial static charges when they move over a metal roll. Humidity control, grounding and bonding are necessary for removing static, along with web-focused static elimination techniques.

Manual handling of printing equipment, substrate materials and related inks is another safety concern. Storage issues similar to those in ink manufacture are present. Minimizing manual handling of equipment, substrate materials and inks is recommended. Where this is not possible, routine and focused education is needed for those employed in the printing room.

Added to the safety issues in the printing room are the mechanical safety issues involving rapidly moving/rotating equipment along with a substrate moving along at speeds in excess of 1,500 feet per minute. Guarding systems and alarms are needed to help insure employee safety. Lockout and tagout systems are also needed during repair/maintenance functions.

With the amount of rotating equipment and the speeds that are common in many printing operations, noise is often a significant issue, especially when multiple presses are present, as in newspaper printing. If noise levels are not acceptable, a hearing conservation programme should be implemented that includes engineering controls.

Although inks are often dried into the air around the press, drying tunnels are recommended to reduce exposure to volatile solvents.

Also, in some higher-speed printing operations, ink misting may occur. Both solvent drying and possible ink misting present a risk of inhalation of possibly toxic chemicals. Further, routine management of the printing operation, filling of tanks and trays, cleaning of rolls and idlers, and related tasks may involve contact with inks and cleaning solvents.

As with ink manufacturing, a well constructed industrial hygiene sampling effort, along with adequate ventilation and personal protective equipment, is recommended. Since these presses, some of which are very large, need to be routinely cleaned, chemical solvents are often used, leading to further chemical contact. Handling procedures can reduce exposures but not entirely remove them, depending on the size of the printing operations. As noted previously, even new inks and coatings that represent better technology still may have hazards. For example, UV-curable inks are potential sensitizers when in contact with the skin, and there is potential exposure to hazardous levels of UV radiation.

Emissions from printing operations, along with clean-up solutions and waste inks, are potential issues of environmental concern. Air pollution abatement systems may be needed to capture and either destroy or reclaim solvents evaporated from inks after printing. Careful management of the wastes generated to minimize the impact on the environment is important. Waste handling systems are recommended where solvents or other components can be recycled. Newer technology using better solvents for clean-up are coming from current research efforts. This may reduce emissions and possible exposures. An active review of current clean-up technology is recommended to see if alternatives to solvent cleaning, such as using water-based solutions or vegetable oils, are available that will meet the requirements found in specific printing operations. However, water-based cleaning solutions that are contaminated with solvent-based inks may still require careful management both inside the printing operation and upon disposal.

Finishing

Once printed, the substrate typically needs some additional finishing prior to being prepared for final use. Some materials can be sent directly from the press to packaging equipment which will form the package and fill in the contents or will apply an adhesive and place the label onto the container. In other instances, a large amount of cutting or slitting to size is needed for final assembly of the book or other printed material.

The health and safety issues related to finishing are mostly mechanical safety issues. Since much of the finishing involves cutting to size, cuts and lacerations to the fingers, hands and wrist/arm are typical. Guarding is important and must be used as part of every task. Small knives and blades used by employees also need to be used carefully and stored and disposed of properly to prevent inadvertent cuts and lacerations. Larger systems also need the same level of attention in guarding and training to prevent accidents.

The material handling aspect of finishing is significant. This applies to the material to be finished as well as the final packaged printed product. Where mechanical equipment such as lift trucks, hoists and conveyors can be used, they are recommended. Where manual lifting and handling must occur, education on proper lifting should be undertaken.

Recent evaluation of this component of the printing process indicates that possible ergonomic stress is placed on the human body. Each task—cutting, sorting, packaging—should be reviewed to determine possible ergonomic implications. If ergonomic problems are found, changes in the workplace may be needed to reduce this possible stressor to acceptable levels. Often some form of automation can help, but there still remain in most printing operations many manual handling tasks that may create ergonomic stress. Job rotation can help reduce this problem.

Printing in the Future

There will always be a need to print words on a substrate. But the future of printing will involve more direct transfer of information from computer to press, as well as electronic printing, where words and images are impressed onto electromagnetic media and other substrates. While such electronic print can be viewed and read only through an electronic device, more and more printed text and literature will move from the printed substrate to the electronic substrate format. This will lessen many of the mechanical safety and health issues related to printing, but will increase the number of ergonomic health risks in the printing industry.

REPRODUCTION AND DUPLICATING SERVICES

Robert W. Kilpper

The modern office may contain several types of reproduction machines. They range from the ubiquitous dry-process photocopier to the rather special-purpose blueprint machine, the fax and mimeograph machines, as well as other types of duplicators. Within this article, the different devices will be grouped according to broad technology classes. Since dry-process photocopiers are so widespread, they will receive the greatest attention.

Photocopiers and Laser Printers

Processing operations

Most steps in *conventional electrophotography* (xerography) are directly analogous to those in photography. In the exposure step, the printed page or photograph to be copied is illuminated by a flash of bright light, and the reflected image is focused by a lens onto an electrically charged, light-sensitive photoreceptor, which loses its charge wherever the light hits its surface. The light will have hit in the same pattern as on the surface being copied. Next, developer, generally composed of large carrier beads with small, electrostatically charged particles adhering to them, is transported to the photoreceptor by a cascading or magnetic conveying process. The charged, latent image on the photoreceptor is developed when the finely divided powder (known as toner, dry imager or dry ink) is electrostatically attracted, separates out of the developer and remains on the image. Finally, the toner that has adhered to the imaged areas is electrostatically transferred (printed) to a sheet of plain paper and permanently fused to it (fixed) by the application of heat, or heat and pressure. Residual toner is removed from the photoreceptor by a cleaning process and deposited into a waste toner sump. The photoreceptor is then prepared for the next imaging cycle. Since the imaged paper removes only toner from the developer, the carrier that supplied it to the image is recirculated back into the developer housing and mixed with fresh toner that is metered into the system from a replaceable toner supply bottle or cartridge.

Many machines apply both pressure and heat to the toner-on-paper image during a fusing process. The heat is supplied by a fusing roll, which contacts the toned surface. Depending on the characteristics of the toner and fuser materials, some toner may stick to the fuser surface rather than to the paper, resulting in a deletion of part of the image on the copy. In order to prevent this, a fuser lubricant, commonly a silicone-based fluid, is applied to the surface of the fuser roll.

In *laser printing*, the image is first converted to an electronic format; that is, it is digitized into a series of very small dots (pixels) by a document scanner, or a digital image may be created directly in a computer. The digitized image is then written onto the photoreceptor in the laser printer by a laser beam. The remaining steps are essentially those of conventional xerography, wherein the image on the photoreceptor is transformed to paper or other surfaces.

Some photocopiers use a process known as *liquid development*. This differs from the conventional, dry process in that the developer is generally a liquid hydrocarbon carrier in which finely divided toner particles are dispersed. Development and transfer are generally analogous to the conventional processes, except that the developer is washed over the photoreceptor and the wet copy is dried by the evaporation of residual liquid upon the application of heat or both heat and pressure.

Materials

The consumables associated with photocopying are toners, developers, fuser lubricants and paper. Although not generally considered as consumables, photoreceptors, fuser and pressure rolls and various other parts routinely wear out and need replacement, especially in high-volume machines. These parts are generally not considered to be customer replaceable, and require special knowledge for their removal and the adjustment. Many new machines incorporate customer replaceable units (CRUs), which contain the photoreceptor and developer in a self-contained unit which the customer can replace. In these machines, the fuser rolls and so on either last the life of the machine or require separate repair. In a move toward reduced service costs and greater customer convenience, some companies are moving towards increased customer reparability, where repair can be made with no mechanical or electrical hazard risk to the customer and will, at most, require a telephone call to a support centre for assistance.

Toners produce the image on the finished copy. Dry toners are fine powders composed of plastics, colourants and small quantities of functional additives. A polymer (plastic) is usually the major component of a dry toner; styrene-acrylic, styrene-butadiene and polyester polymers are common examples. In black toners, different carbon blacks or pigments are used as the colourant, while in colour copying, various dyes or pigments are employed. During the toner manufacturing process, the carbon black or colourant and the polymer are melt mixed and most of the colourant becomes encapsulated by the polymer. Dry toners may also contain internal and/or external additives which help determine the toner's static charging and/or flow characteristics.

Wet-process toners are similar to dry toners in that they consist of pigments and additives inside a polymer coating. The difference is that those components are purchased as a dispersion in an isoparaffinic hydrocarbon carrier.

Developers are usually mixtures of toner and carrier. Carriers literally carry toner to the surface of the photoreceptor and are frequently made of materials based on special grades of sand, glass, steel or ferrite types of substances. They may be coated with a small amount of polymer to achieve the desired behaviour in a specific application. Carrier/toner mixtures are known as two-component developers. Single-component developers do not use a separate carrier. Rather, they incorporate a compound like iron oxide into the toner and utilize a magnetic device for applying the developer to the photoreceptor.

Fuser lubricants are most often silicone-based fluids which are applied to fuser rolls to prevent toner offset from the developed image to the roll. While many are simple polydimethylsiloxanes (PDMSs), others contain a functional component to enhance their adhesion to the fuser roll. Some fuser lubricants are poured from a bottle into a sump, from which they are pumped and ultimately applied to the fuser roll. In other machines the lubricant may be applied via a saturated fabric web which wipes part of the roll's surface, while in some smaller machines and printers, an oil-impregnated wick makes the application.

Most, if not all, modern photocopiers are made to perform well with various weights of ordinary, untreated bond paper. Special carbonless forms are made for some high-speed machines, and non-fusing transfer papers are produced for imaging in photocopiers and then applying the image to a T-shirt or other fabric with the application of heat and pressure in a press. Large engineering/architectural drawing copiers often produce their copies on a translucent velum.

Potential hazards and their prevention

Responsible manufacturers have worked hard to minimize the risk from any unique hazards in the photocopying process. However, material safety data sheets (MSDSs) should be obtained for any consumables or service chemicals used with a particular machine.

Perhaps the only unique material to which one may be significantly exposed in the photocopying process is *toner*. Modern, dry toners should not present a skin or eye hazard to any but perhaps the most sensitive individuals, and recently designed equipment utilizes toner cartridges and CRUs that minimize contact with bulk toner. Liquid toners, as well, should not be directly irritating to the skin. However, their isoparaffinic hydrocarbon carriers are solvents and can defat the skin, leading to dryness and cracking upon repeated exposure. These solvents may also be mildly irritating to the eyes.

Well-designed equipment will not present a *bright light* hazard, even if the platen is flashed with no original on it, and some illumination systems are interlocked with the platen cover to prevent any operator exposure to the light source. All laser printers are classified as Class I laser products, meaning that, under normal conditions of operation, the *laser radiation* (beam) is inaccessible, being contained within the printing process, and does not present a biological hazard. Additionally, the laser device should not require maintenance, and in the highly unusual event that access to the beam is required, the manufacturer must provide safe working procedures to be followed by a properly trained service technician.

Finally, properly manufactured hardware will not have sharp edges, pinch points or exposed shock hazards in areas where operators might place their hands.

Skin and eye hazards

In addition to dry toners not presenting a significant skin or eye hazard, one would expect the same with silicon oil–based *fuser lubricants*. Polydimethylsiloxanes (PDMSs) have been subjected to extensive toxicological evaluations and have generally been found to be benign. While some low-viscosity PDMSs may be eye irritants, those used as fuser lubricants usually are not, nor are they skin irritants. Regardless of actual irritation, any of these materials will be nuisances either on the skin or in the eyes. Affected skin may be washed with soap and water, and eyes should be flooded with water for several minutes.

Individuals frequently working with *liquid toners*, especially under potential splash conditions, may want to wear protective goggles, safety glasses with side shields, or a face shield if needed. Rubber or vinyl-coated gloves should prevent the dry skin problems mentioned above.

Papers are generally benign as well. However, there have been cases of significant skin irritation when proper care was not taken during processing. Poor manufacturing processes can also cause odour problems when the paper is heated in the fuser of a dry-process copier. Occasionally, the vellum in an engineering copier has not been properly processed and creates a hydrocarbon solvent odour problem.

In addition to the isoparaffinic base of liquid toners, numerous *solvents* are routinely used in machine upkeep. Included are platen and cover cleaners and film removers, which, typically, are alcohols or alcohol/water solutions containing small amounts of surfactants. Such solutions are eye irritants, but do not directly irritate the skin. However, like the liquid toner dispersants, their solvent action can defat skin and lead to eventual skin-cracking problems. Rubber or vinyl-coated gloves and goggles or safety glasses with side shields should be sufficient to preclude problems.

Inhalation hazards

Ozone is usually the greatest concern of those in the general vicinity of photocopiers. The next most readily identified concerns would be toner, including paper dust, and volatile organic compounds (VOCs). Some situations also give rise to odour complaints.

Ozone is primarily generated by corona discharge from the devices (corotrons/scorotrons) which charge the photoreceptor in preparation for exposure and cleaning. At concentrations most apt to be encountered in photocopying, it can be identified by its pleasant, clover-like odour. Its low odour threshold (0.0076 to 0.036 ppm) gives it good "warning properties", in that its presence can be detected before it reaches harmful concentrations. As it reaches concentrations which might produce headaches, eye irritation and breathing difficulty, its odour becomes strong and pungent. One should not expect ozone problems from well-maintained machines in properly ventilated areas. However, ozone may be detected when operators work in the machine's exhaust stream, especially in the case of long copy runs. Odours that are identified as ozone by inexperienced operators are usually found to have arisen from other sources.

Toner has long been considered to be a nuisance particulate, or "particulate not otherwise classified" (PNOC). Studies performed by Xerox Corporation in the 1980s indicated that inhaled toner elicits the pulmonary responses one would expect from exposure

to such insoluble particulate materials. They also demonstrated a lack of carcinogenic hazard at exposure concentrations well above those expected to be found in the office environment.

Paper dust consists of paper fibre fragments and sizers and fillers such as clay, titanium dioxide and calcium carbonate. All of these materials are considered to be PNOCs. No reasons for concern have been found for the paper dust exposures expected to occur in the office environment.

The emission of VOCs by photocopiers is a byproduct of their use in plastic toners and parts, rubbers and organic lubricants. Even so, exposures to individual organic chemicals in the environment of an operating photocopier are usually orders of magnitude below any occupational exposure limits.

Odour problems with modern photocopiers are most often an indication of inadequate ventilation. Treated papers, such as carbonless forms or image transfer papers, and occasionally vellums used in engineering copiers, may produce hydrocarbon solvent odours, but exposures will be well below any occupational exposure limits if ventilation is adequate for normal copying. Modern photocopiers are complex electro-mechanical devices which have some parts (fusers) operating at elevated temperatures. In addition to odours that are present during normal operation, odours also occur when a part fails under a heat load and the smoke and emissions from hot plastic and/or rubber are released. Obviously, one should not remain in the presence of such exposures. Common to nearly all odour problems are complaints of nausea and some sort of eye or mucous membrane irritation. These complaints are usually simply indications of exposure to an unknown, and probably unpleasant, odour, and are not necessarily signs of significant acute toxicity. In such cases, the exposed individual should seek fresh air, which nearly always leads to a rapid recovery. Even exposures to smoke and vapours from overheated parts are usually of such short duration that there is no need for concern. Even so, it is only prudent to seek medical advice if symptoms persist or exacerbate.

Installation considerations

As discussed above, copiers produce heat, ozone and VOCs. While the siting and ventilation recommendations should be obtained from the manufacturer and should be followed, it is reasonable to expect that, for all but possibly the largest machines, location in a room having reasonable air circulation, more than two air changes per hour and adequate space around the machine for servicing will be sufficient to prevent ozone and odour issues. Naturally, this recommendation also assumes that all American Society of Heating, Refrigeration and Air Conditioning Engineers (ASHRAE) recommendations for room occupants are also met. If more than one photocopier is added to a room, care should be taken to provide added ventilation and cooling capability. Large, high-volume machines may require special heat-control considerations.

Supplies do not require special considerations beyond those for the keeping of any flammable solvents and avoiding excessive heat. Paper should be kept in its box to the extent practical and the wrapper should not be opened until the paper is needed.

Facsimile (Fax) Machines

Processing operations. In facsimile reproduction, the document is scanned by a light source and the image is converted to an electronic form compatible with telephone communications. At the receiver, electro-optical systems decode and print the transmitted image via direct thermal, thermal transfer, xerographic or ink-jet processes.

Machines using the thermal processes have a linear print array like a printed circuit board, over which the copy paper is stepped during the printing process. There are about 200 contacts per inch across the width of the paper, which are rapidly heated when activated by an electric current. When hot, a contact either causes the contact spot on a treated copy paper to turn black (direct thermal) or the coating on a typewriter ribbon–like donor roll to deposit a black dot onto the copy paper (thermal transfer).

Fax machines which operate by the xerographic process use the telephone-transmitted signal to activate a laser beam and they then function the same as a laser printer. In a similar fashion, ink-jet machines function the same as ink-jet printers.

Materials. Paper, either treated or plain, donor rolls, toner and ink are the major materials used in faxing. Direct thermal papers are treated with leuco dyes, which turn from white to black when heated. Donor rolls contain a mixture of carbon black in a wax and polymer base, coated onto a film substrate. The mixture is sufficiently firm that it does not transfer to the skin when rubbed, but when heated it will transfer to the copy paper. Toners and inks are discussed in the photocopying and ink-jet printing sections.

Potential hazards and their prevention. No unique hazards have been associated with fax machines. There have been odour complaints with some early direct thermal machines; however, as with many odours in the office environment, the problem is more indicative of a low odour threshold, and possibly inadequate ventilation, than a health problem. Thermal transfer machines usually are odour free, and no hazards have been identified with the donor rolls. Xerographic fax machines have the same potential problems as dry photocopiers; however, their low speed normally precludes any inhalation concerns.

Blueprinting (Diazo)

Processing operations. Modern references to "blueprints" or "blueprint machines" generally mean diazo copies or copiers. These copiers are most often used with large architectural or engineering drawings made on a film, vellum or translucent paper base. Diazo-treated papers are acidic and contain a coupler which yields a colour change upon reaction with the diazo compound; however, the reaction is prevented by the acidity of the paper. The sheet to be copied is placed in contact with the treated paper and exposed to intense ultraviolet (UV) light from a fluorescent or mercury vapour source. The UV light breaks the diazo bond on the areas of the copy paper not protected from exposure by the image on the master, eliminating the possibility of subsequent reaction with the coupler. The master is then removed from contact with the treated paper, which is then exposed to an ammonia atmosphere. The alkalinity of the ammonia developer neutralizes the acidity of the paper, permitting the diazo/coupler colour-change reaction to produce a copy of the image on the parts of the paper which were protected from the UV by the image on the master.

Materials. Water and ammonia are the only diazo-process materials in addition to the treated paper.

Potential hazards and their prevention. The obvious concern around diazo-process copiers is the exposure to ammonia, which can cause eye and mucous membrane irritation. Modern machines usually control emissions, and hence exposures are usually considerably less than 10 ppm. However, older equipment may require careful and frequent maintenance and possible local exhaust ventilation. Care should be taken when servicing a machine to avoid spills and prevent eye contact. Manufacturers' recommendations regarding protective equipment should be fol-

lowed. One should also be aware that improperly manufactured paper also has the potential for causing skin problems.

Digital Duplicators and Mimeographs

Processing operations. Digital duplicators and mimeographs share the same basic process in that a master stencil is "burned" or "cut" and placed onto an ink-containing drum, from which ink flows through the master onto the copy paper.

Materials. Stencils, inks and papers are the supplies used by these machines. The scanned image is digitally burned onto the mylar master of a digital duplicator, while it is electro-cut into a mimeograph's paper stencil. A further difference is that digital duplicator inks are water based, though containing some petroleum solvent, while mimeograph inks are based on either a naphthenic distillate or a glycol ether/alcohol mixture.

Potential hazards and their prevention. The primary hazards associated with digital duplicators and mimeographs are due to their inks, although there is a potential hot wax vapour exposure associated with burning the image onto the digital duplicator's stencil and an ozone exposure during the electro-cutting of stencils. Both types of ink have the potential for eye and skin irritation, while mimeograph ink's higher petroleum distillate content has a greater potential for causing dermatitis. The use of protective gloves while working with the inks, and adequate ventilation while making copies, should protect against skin and inhalation hazards.

Spirit Duplicators

Processing operations. Spirit duplicators use a reverse-image stencil which is coated with an alcohol-soluble dye. In processing, the copy paper is lightly coated with a methanol-based duplicating fluid, which removes a small amount of dye upon coming in contact with the stencil, resulting in image transfer to the copy paper. The copies may emit methanol for some time after duplication.

Materials. Paper, stencils and duplicating fluid are the main supplies for this equipment.

Potential hazards and their prevention. Spirit duplicating fluids are usually methanol based, and hence are toxic if absorbed through the skin, inhaled or ingested; they are also flammable. Ventilation should be adequate to ensure operator exposures are below current occupational exposure limits and should include providing a ventilated area for drying. Some more recent duplicating fluids used are ethyl alcohol or propylene glycol based, which avoid the toxicity and flammability concerns of methanol. Manufacturers' recommendations should be followed regarding the use of protective equipment when handling all duplicating fluids.

HEALTH ISSUES AND DISEASE PATTERNS

Barry R. Friedlander

Interpreting the human health data in the printing, commercial photographic processing and reproduction industry is no simple matter, since the processes are complex and are continually evolving—sometimes dramatically. While the use of automation has substantially reduced manual work exposures in modernized versions of all three of the disciplines, work volume per employee has increased substantially. Furthermore, dermal exposure represents an important route of exposure for these industries, yet is less well characterized by available industrial hygiene data. Case reporting of the less serious, reversible effects (e.g., headaches, nose and eye irritation) is incomplete and under-reported in the published literature. Despite these challenges and limitations, epidemiological studies, health surveys and case reports provide a substantial amount of information regarding the health status of workers in these industries.

Printing Activities

Agents and exposures

Today there are five categories of printing processes: flexography, gravure, letterpress, lithography and screen printing. The type of exposure that can occur from each process is related to the types of printing inks that are used and to the likelihood of inhalation (mists, solvent fumes and so on) and penetrable skin contact from the process and cleaning activities employed. It should be noted that the inks are composed of organic or inorganic pigments, oil or solvent vehicles (i.e., carriers), and additives applied for special printing purposes. Table 85.1 outlines some characteristics of different printing processes.

Mortality and chronic risks

Several epidemiological and case-report studies exist on printers. Exposure characterizations are not quantified in much of the older literature. However, respirable-size carbon black particles with potentially carcinogenic polycyclic aromatic hydrocarbons (benzo(a)pyrene) bound to the surface have been reported in rotary letterpress printing machine rooms of newspaper production. Animal studies find the benzo(a)pyrene tightly bound to the surface of the carbon black particle and not easily released to lung or other tissues. This lack of "bioavailability" makes it more difficult to determine whether cancer risks are feasible. Several, but not all, cohort (i.e., populations followed through time) epidemiological studies have found suggestions of increased lung cancer rates in printers (table 85.2). A more detailed assessment of over 100 lung cancer cases and 300 controls (case-control type

Table 85.1 • Some potential exposures in the printing industry.

Process	Type of ink	Solvent	Potential exposures
Flexography and gravure	Liquid inks (low viscosity)	Volatiles water	Organic solvents: xylene, benzene
Letterpress and lithography	Paste inks (high viscosity)	Oils — vegetable mineral	Ink mist: hydrocarbon solvents; isopropanol; polycyclic aromatic hydrocarbons (PAHs)
Screen printing	Semipaste	Volatiles	Organic solvents: xylene, cyclohexanone, butyl acetate

study) from a group of over 9,000 printing workers in Manchester, England (Leon, Thomas and Hutchings 1994) found that the duration of work in a machine room was related to lung cancer occurrence in rotary letterpress workers. Since smoking patterns of the workers are not known, direct consideration of the role of occupation in the study is unknown. However, it is suggestive that rotary letterpress work may have presented a lung cancer risk in previous decades. In some areas of the world, however, older technologies, such as rotary letterpress work, may still exist and thus afford opportunities for preventive assessments, as well as installation of appropriate controls where needed.

Another group of workers that has been substantially studied are lithographers. Modern lithographers' exposure to organic solvents (turpentine, toluene and so on), pigments, dyes, hydroquinone, chromates and cyanates has been markedly reduced in recent decades due to the use of computer technologies, automated processes and changes in materials. The International Agency for Research on Cancer (IARC) recently concluded that occupational exposures in printing process are possibly carcinogenic to humans (IARC 1996). At the same time, it may be important to point out that IARC's conclusion is based on historical exposures which, in most cases, should be significantly different today. Reports of malignant melanoma have suggested risks about twice the expected rate (Dubrow 1986). While some postulate that skin contact with hydroquinone could be related to

Table 85.2 • Cohort studies of printing trade mortality risks.

Population studied	Number of workers	Mortality risks* (95% C.I.) Follow-up period	Country	All causes	All cancers	Lung cancer
Newspaper pressmen	1,361	(1949–65) – 1978	USA	1.0 (0.8–1.0)	1.0 (0.8–1.2)	1.5 (0.9–2.3)
Newspaper pressmen	700	(1940–55) – 1975	Italy	1.1 (0.9–1.2)	1.2 (0.9–1.6)	1.5 (0.8–2.5)
Typographers	1,309	1961–1984	USA	0.7 (0.7–0.8)	0.8 (0.7–1.0)	0.9 (0.6–1.2)
Printers (NGA)	4,702	(1943–63) – 1983	UK	0.8 (0.7–0.8)	0.7 (0.6–0.8)	0.6 (0.5–0.7)
Printers (NATSOPA)	4,530	(1943–63) – 1983	UK	0.9 (0.9–1.0)	1.0 (0.9–1.1)	0.9 (0.8–1.1)
Rotogravure	1,020	(1925–85) – 1986	Sweden	1.0 (0.9–1.2)	1.4 (1.0–1.9)	1.4 (0.7–2.5)
Paperboard printers	2,050	(1957–88) – 1988	USA	1.0 (0.9–1.2)	0.6 (0.3–0.9)	0.5 (0.2–1.2)

* Standardized Mortality Ratios (SMR) = number of observed deaths divided by number of expected deaths, adjusted for age effects over the time periods in question. An SMR of 1 indicates no difference between observed and expected. Note: 95% confidence intervals are provided for the SMRs.

NGA = National Graphical Association, UK

NATSOPA = National Society of Operative Printers, Graphical and Media Personnel, UK.

Sources: Paganini-Hill et al. 1980; Bertazzi and Zoccheti 1980; Michaels, Zoloth and Stern 1991; Leon 1994; Svensson et al. 1990; Sinks et al. 1992.

melanoma (Nielson, Henriksen and Olsen 1996), it has not been confirmed in a hydroquinone manufacturing plant where significant exposure to hydroquinone was reported (Pifer et al. 1995). However, practices which minimize skin contact with solvents, particularly in plate cleaning, should be emphasized.

Photographic Processing Activities

Exposures and agents

Photographic processing of black-and-white or colour film or paper can be done either manually or by essentially fully automated larger-scale processes. The selection of the process, chemicals, working conditions (including ventilation, hygiene and personal protective equipment) and workload can all influence the types of exposures and potential health issues of the occupational environment. The types of jobs (i.e., processor-related tasks) having the greatest potential for exposure to key photographic chemicals, such as formaldehyde, ammonia, hydroquinone, acetic acid and colour developers, are noted in table 85.3. The typical photographic processing and handling work flow is depicted in figure 85.2.

In more recently designed high-volume processing units, some of the steps in the workflow have been combined and automated, making inhalation and skin contact less likely. Formaldehyde, an agent that has been used for decades as a colour image stabilizer, is diminishing in concentration in photographic product. Depending on the specific process and site environmental conditions, its air concentration may range from non-detectable levels in the operator's breathing zone up to about 0.2 ppm at machine dryer vents. Exposures can also occur during equipment cleaning, making or replenishing stabilizer fluid and unloading processors, as well as in spill situations.

It should be noted that while chemical exposures have been the primary focus of most health studies of photographic processors, other work environmental aspects, such as reduced light, materials handling and the postural demands of the job, are also of preventive health interest.

Mortality risks

The only published mortality surveillance of photographic processors suggests no increased risks of death for the occupation (Friedlander, Hearne and Newman 1982). The study covered nine processing laboratories in the United States, and was updated to cover 15 more years of follow-up (Pifer 1995). It should be noted that this is a study of over 2,000 employees who were actively working at the beginning of 1964, with over 70% of them having had at least 15 years of employment in their profession at that time. The group was followed for 31 years, through 1994. Many exposures relevant earlier in the careers of these employees, such as carbon tetrachloride, n-butylamine, and isopropylamine, were discontinued in the laboratories over thirty years ago. However, many of the key exposures in modern laboratories (i.e., acetic acid, formaldehyde and sulphur dioxide) were also present in previous decades, albeit at much higher concentrations. During the 31-year follow-up time period, the standardized mortality ratio was only 78% of that expected (SMR 0.78), with 677 deaths in the 2,061 workers. No individual causes of death were significantly increased. The 464 processors in the study also had reduced mortality, whether compared to the general population (SMR 0.73) or to other hourly workers (SMR 0.83) and had no significant increases in any cause of death. Based on available epidemiological information, it does not appear that photographic processing presents an increased mortality risk, even at the higher concentrations of exposure likely to have been present in the 1950s and 1960s.

Table 85.3 • Tasks in photographic processing with chemical exposure potential.

Work area	Tasks with exposure potential
Chemical mixing	Mix chemicals into solution. Clean equipment. Maintain work area.
Analytical laboratory	Handle samples. Analyse and replenish solutions. Quality control assessment.
Film/print processing	Process film and print using developers, hardeners, bleaches.
Film/print take-off	Remove processed film and prints for drying.

Pulmonary disease

The literature has very few reports of pulmonary disorders for photographic processors. Two articles, (Kipen and Lerman 1986; Hodgson and Parkinson 1986) describe a total of four potential pulmonary responses to processing workplace exposures; however, neither had quantitative environmental exposure data to assess the measured pulmonary findings. No increases in longer-term illness absence for pulmonary disorders was identified in the only epidemiological review of the subject (Friedlander, Hearne

Figure 85.2 • Outline of photographic processing operations.

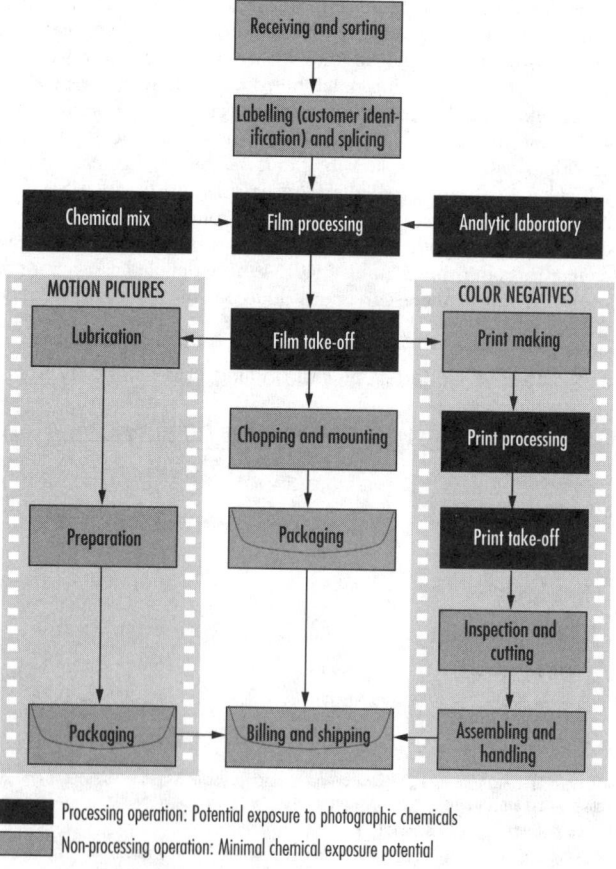

Processing operation: Potential exposure to photographic chemicals

Non-processing operation: Minimal chemical exposure potential

Source: Adapted from Friedlander, Hearne and Newman 1982.

and Newman 1982); however, it is important to note that illness-absences of eight consecutive days were required in order to be captured in that study. It appears that respiratory symptoms can be aggravated or initiated in sensitive individuals by exposure to higher concentrations of acetic acid, sulphur dioxide and other agents in photographic processing, should ventilation be poorly controlled or errors occur during mixing, resulting in the release of undesired concentrations of these agents. However, work-related pulmonary cases have only rarely been reported in this occupation (Hodgson and Parkinson 1986).

Acute and subchronic effects

Contact irritative and allergic dermatitis has been reported in photographic processors for decades, starting with the initial use of colour chemicals in the late 1930s. Many of these cases occurred in the first few months of a processor's exposure. The use of protective gloves and improved handling processes have substantially reduced photographic dermatitis. Eyesplashes with some photochemicals can present risks of corneal injury. Training on eyewash procedures (flushing eyes with cool water for at least 15 minutes followed by medical attention) and the use of protective eyewear is particularly important for photoprocessors, many of whom may work in isolation and/or in diminished light environments.

Some ergonomics concerns exist regarding the operation of rapid-turnaround, high-volume photographic processing units. The mounting and dismounting of large rolls of photographic paper can present a risk of upper back, shoulder and neck disorders. The rolls can weigh 13.6 to 22.7 kg (30 to 50 pounds), and may be awkward to handle, depending partly on access to the machine, which can be compromised in compact work sites.

Injuries and strains to the staff can be prevented by proper staff training, by provision of adequate access to the rolls and by considerations of human factors in the general design of the processing area.

Prevention and methods of early detection of effects

Protection from dermatitis, respiratory irritation, acute injury and ergonomic disorders starts with the recognition that such disorders can occur. With proper worker information (including labels, material safety data sheets, protective equipment and health protection training programmes), periodic health/safety reviews of the worksetting and informed supervision, prevention can be strongly emphasized. In addition, the early identification of disorders can be facilitated by having a medical resource for worker health reporting, coupled with targeted voluntary periodic health assessments, focusing on respiratory and upper extremity symptoms in questionnaires and direct observation of exposed skin areas for signs of work-related dermatitis.

Because formaldehyde is a potential respiratory sensitizer, a strong irritant and a possible carcinogen, it is important that each workplace be assessed to determine where formaldehyde is used (chemical inventory and material safety data sheet reviews), to assess air concentrations (if indicated by materials used), to identify where leaks or spills could occur and to estimate the quantity that could be spilled and the concentration generated in worst-case scenarios. An emergency response plan should be developed, conspicuously posted, communicated and periodically practised. A health and safety specialist should be consulted in the development of such an emergency plan.

Reproduction Activities

Agents and exposures

Modern photocopying machines emit very low levels of ultraviolet radiation through the glass cover (plenum), generate some noise and may emit low concentrations of ozone during the processing activity. These machines use a toner, primarily carbon black (for black-and-white printers), to produce a dark print on the paper or transparent film. Thus, potential routine exposures of health interest for photocopy operators can include ultraviolet radiation, noise, ozone and possibly toner. In older machines, toner could be an issue during replacement, although modern self-contained cartridges have substantially reduced potential respiratory and skin exposure.

The degree of ultraviolet radiation exposure that occurs through the copier machine platen glass is very low. The duration of a photocopier flash is approximately 250 microseconds, with continual copying making about 4,200 flashes per hour—a value that can vary depending upon the copier. With the glass platen in place, the emitted wavelength ranges from 380 to about 396 nm. UVB does not typically result from copier flashes. UVA measurements maximally recorded at the glass paten average about 1.65 microjoule/cm^2 per flash. Thus, the maximum 8-hour near-UV spectral exposure from a continuously run photocopier making about 33,000 copies per day is approximately 0.05 joules/cm^2 at the glass surface. This value is only a fraction of the threshold limit value recommended by the American Conference of Governmental Industrial Hygienists (ACGIH) and appears to present no measurable health risk, even in such exaggerated exposure conditions.

It should be noted that certain workers may be at higher risk for UV exposures, including those with photosensitive conditions, people using photosensitizing agents/medicines and people with impaired ocular pupils (aphakics). Such people are usually advised to minimize their UV exposures as a general precautionary measure.

Acute effects. The literature does not reveal many acute effects meaningfully related to photocopying. Older, insufficiently maintained units could emit detectable ozone concentrations if run in poorly vented settings. While eye and upper respiratory irritation symptoms have been reported from workers in such environments, the minimum manufacturer specifications for space and ventilation, coupled with newer copier technology, have essentially eliminated ozone as an emission issue.

Mortality risks. No studies were found that described mortality or chronic health risks from long-term photocopying.

Prevention and early detection

By simply following manufacturers' recommended use, photocopying activity should not present a workplace risk. Individuals experiencing an aggravation of symptoms related to intense use of photocopiers should seek health and safety advice.

OVERVIEW OF ENVIRONMENTAL ISSUES

Daniel R. English

Major Environmental Issues

Solvents

Organic solvents are used for a number of applications in the printing industry. Major uses include cleaning solvents for presses and other equipment, solubilizing agents in inks, and additives in fountain solutions. In addition to general concerns about volatile organic compound (VOC) emissions, some potential solvent components may be persistent in the environment or have high ozone-depleting potential.

Silver

During black-and-white and colour photographic processing, silver is released into some of the processing solutions. It is important to understand the environmental toxicology of silver so that these solutions can be properly handled and disposed of. While free silver ion is highly toxic to aquatic life, its toxicity is much lower in a complexed form as in photoprocessing effluent. Silver chloride, silver thiosulphate and silver sulphide, which are forms of silver commonly observed in photoprocessing, are over four orders of magnitude less toxic than silver nitrate. Silver has a high affinity for organic material, mud, clay and other matter found in natural environments, and this lessens its potential impact in aquatic systems. Given the extremely low level of free silver ion found in photoprocessing effluents or in natural waters, control technology appropriate to complexed silver is sufficiently protective of the environment.

Other photoprocessing effluent characteristics

The composition of photographic effluent varies, depending on the processes being run: black-and-white, colour reversal, colour negative/positive or some combination of these. Water comprises 90 to 99% of the effluent volume, with the majority of the remainder being inorganic salts that function as buffers and fixing (silver halide–solubilizing) agents, iron chelates, such as FeEthylene diamine tetra-acetic acid, and organic molecules that serve as developing agents and anti-oxidants. Iron and silver are the significant metals present.

Solid waste

Every component of the printing, photography and reproduction industries generates solid waste. This can consist of packaging waste such as cardboard and plastics, consumables such as toner cartridges or waste material from operations such as scrap paper or film. Increasing pressure on industrial generators of solid waste has led businesses to examine carefully options to lower solid waste through reduction, reuse or recycling.

Equipment

Equipment plays an obvious role in determining the environmental impact of the processes used in the printing, photography and reproduction industries. Beyond this, scrutiny is increasing on other aspects of equipment. One example is energy efficiency, which relates back to the environmental impact of the energy generation. Another example is "takeback legislation", which requires the manufacturers to receive equipment back for proper disposal after its useful commercial life.

Control Technologies

The effectiveness of a given control methodology can be quite dependent on the specific operating processes of a facility, the size of that facility and the necessary level of control.

Solvent control technologies

Solvent use can be reduced in several ways. More volatile components, such as isopropyl alcohol, can be replaced with compounds having lower vapour pressure. In some situations, solvent-based inks and washes can be replaced with water-based materials. Many printing applications need improvements in water-based options to compete effectively with solvent-based materials. High-solids ink technology can also result in reduction of organic solvent use.

Solvent emissions can be lowered by reducing the temperature of dampening or fountain solutions. In limited applications, solvents can be captured on adsorptive materials such as activated carbon, and reused. In other instances, windows of operation are too strict to allow captured solvents to be reused directly, but they may be recaptured for recycling offsite. Solvent emissions may be concentrated in condenser systems. These systems consist of heat exchangers followed by a filter or electrostatic precipitator. The condensate passes through an oil-water separator before ultimate disposal.

In larger operations, incinerators (sometimes called afterburners) can be used to destroy emitted solvents. Platinum or other precious metal materials may be used to catalyze the thermal process. Non-catalyzed systems must operate at higher temperatures but are not sensitive to processes that can poison catalysts. Heat recovery is generally necessary to make non-catalyzed systems cost effective.

Silver recovery technologies

The level of silver recovery from photoeffluent is controlled by the economics of recovery and/or by solution discharge regulations. Major silver recovery techniques include electrolysis, precipitation, metallic replacement and ion exchange.

In electrolytic recovery, current is passed through the silver-bearing solution and silver metal is plated on the cathode, usually a stainless steel plate. The silver flake is harvested by flexing, chipping or scraping and sent to a refiner for reuse. Attempting to lower the residual solution silver level significantly below 200 mg/l is inefficient and can result in formation of undesired silver sulphide or noxious sulphurous byproducts. Packed-bed cells are capable of reducing silver to lower levels but are more complex and expensive than cells with two-dimensional electrodes.

Silver may be recovered from solution by precipitation with some material that forms an insoluble silver salt. The most common precipitating agents are trisodium trimercaptotriazine (TMT) and various sulphide salts. If a sulphide salt is used, care must be taken to avoid generation of highly toxic hydrogen sulphide. TMT is an inherently safer alternative recently introduced to the photoprocessing industry. Precipitation has a recovery efficiency of greater than 99%.

Metallic replacement cartridges (MRCs) allow the flow of the silver-bearing solution over a filamentous deposit of iron metal. Silver ion is reduced to silver metal as iron is oxidized to ionic soluble species. The metallic silver sludge settles to the bottom of the cartridge. MRCs are not appropriate in areas where iron in the effluent is a concern. This method has a recovery efficiency of greater than 95%.

In ion exchange, anionic silver thiosulphate complexes exchange with other anions on a resin bed. When the capacity of the resin bed is exhausted, additional capacity is regenerated by stripping the silver with a concentrated thiosulphate solution or converting the silver to silver sulphide under acidic conditions. Under well-controlled conditions, this technique can lower silver below 1 mg/l. However, ion-exchange can be used only on solutions dilute in silver and thiosulphate. The column is extremely sensitive to stripping if the thiosulphate concentration of the influent is too high. Also, the technique is very labour- and equipment-intensive, making it expensive in practice.

Other photoeffluent control technologies

The most cost-efficient method to handle photographic effluent is via biological treatment at a secondary waste treatment plant (often referred to as a publicly owned treatment works, or POTW). Several constituents or parameters of photographic effluent may be regulated by sewer discharge permits. In addition to silver, other common regulated parameters include pH, chemical oxygen demand, biological oxygen demand and total dissolved solids. Multiple studies have demonstrated that photoprocessing wastes (including the small amount of silver remaining after reasonable silver recovery) following biological treatment are not expected to have an adverse effect on the receiving waters.

Other technologies have been applied to photoprocessing wastes. Haul-away for treatment in incinerators, cement kilns or other ultimate disposal is practised in some regions of the world. Some laboratories reduce the volume of solution to be hauled away through evaporation or distillation. Other oxidative techniques such as ozonation, electrolysis, chemical oxidation and wet air oxidation have been applied to photoprocessing effluents.

Another major source of reduced environmental burden is through source reduction. The level of silver coated per square metre in sensitized goods is steadily decreasing as new generations of products enter the marketplace. As the silver levels in media decrease, the amount of chemicals necessary to process a given area of film or paper has also decreased. Regeneration and reuse of solution overflows have also resulted in less environmental burden per image. For example, the amount of colour developing agent required to process a square metre of colour paper in 1996 is less than 20% of that required in 1980.

Solid-waste minimization

The desire to minimize solid waste is encouraging efforts to recycle and reuse materials rather than dispose of them in landfills. Recycling programmes exist for toner cartridges, film cassettes, single-use cameras and so on. Recycling and reuse of packaging is becoming more prevalent as well. More packaging and equipment parts are being labelled appropriately to allow more efficient material recycling programmes.

Life cycle analysis design for the environment

All of the issues discussed above have resulted in increasing consideration of the entire life cycle of a product, from procuring of natural resources to creating the products, to dealing with end-of-life issues for these products. Two related analytic tools, life cycle analysis and design for the environment, are being used to incorporate environmental issues into the decision-making process in product design, development and sales. Life cycle analysis takes into consideration all of the inputs and material flows for a product or process and attempts to quantitatively measure the impact on the environment of different options. Design for the environment brings into consideration various aspects of product design such as recyclability, reworkability and so on to minimize the impact on the environment of the production or disposal of the equipment in question.

● COMMERCIAL PHOTOGRAPHIC LABORATORIES

David Richardson

Materials and Processing Operations

Black-and-white processing

In black-and-white photographic processing, exposed film or paper is removed from a light-tight container in a darkroom and sequentially immersed in water solutions of developer, stop bath and fixer. After a water washing, the film or paper is dried and ready for use. The developer reduces the light-exposed silver halide to metallic silver. The stop bath is a weakly acidic solution that neutralizes the alkaline developer and stops further reduction of the silver halide. The fixer solution forms a soluble complex with the unexposed silver halide, which is subsequently removed from the emulsion in the washing process together with various water-soluble salts, buffers and halide ions.

Colour processing

Colour processing is more complex than black-and-white processing, with additional steps required for processing most types of colour film, transparencies and paper. In short, instead of one silver halide layer, as in black-and-white films, there are three superimposed silver negatives; that is, a silver negative is produced for each of three sensitized layers. On contact with the colour developer, the exposed silver halide is converted to metallic silver while the oxidized developer reacts with a specific coupler in each layer to form the dye image.

Another difference in colour processing is the use of a bleach to remove the unwanted metallic silver from the emulsion by converting metallic silver to silver halide by means of an oxidizing agent. Subsequently, the silver halide is converted to a soluble silver complex, which is then removed by washing as in the case of black-and-white processing. In addition, colour processing procedures and materials vary depending on whether a colour transparency is being formed or whether colour negatives and colour prints are being processed.

General processing design

The essential steps in photoprocessing thus consist of passing the exposed film or paper through a series of processing tanks either by hand or in machine processors. Although the individual processes may be different, there are similarities in the types of procedures and equipment used in photoprocessing. For example, there will be a storage area for chemicals and raw materials and facilities for handling and sorting incoming exposed photographic materials. Facilities and equipment are necessary for measuring, weighing and mixing processing chemicals, and for supplying these solutions to the various processing tanks. In addition, a variety of pumping and metering devices are used to deliver processing solutions to tanks. A professional or photofinishing laboratory will typically utilize larger, more automated equipment that will process either film or paper. To produce a consistent product, the processors are temperature controlled and, in most cases, are replenished with fresh chemicals as sensitized product is run through the processor.

Larger operations may have quality-control laboratories for chemical determinations and measurement of photographic quality of materials being produced. Although the use of packaged chemical formulations may eliminate the need for measuring, weighing and maintaining a quality-control laboratory, many large photoprocessing facilities prefer to mix their own processing solutions from bulk quantities of the constituent chemicals.

Following the processing and drying of materials, protective lacquers or coatings may be applied to the finished product, and film-cleaning operations may take place. Finally, materials are inspected, packaged and prepared for shipment to the customer.

Potential Hazards and their Prevention

Unique darkroom hazards

The potential hazards in commercial photographic processing are similar to those in other types of chemical operations; however, a unique feature is the requirement that certain portions of the processing operations be conducted in darkness. Consequently, the processing operator must have a good understanding of the equipment and its potential hazards, and of precautionary measures in case of accidents. Safelights or infrared goggles are available and can be used to provide sufficient illumination for operator safety. All mechanical elements and live electrical parts must be enclosed and projecting machine parts must be covered. Safety locks should be installed to ensure that light does not enter the darkroom and should be designed so that they allow free passage of personnel.

Skin and eye hazards

Because of the wide variety of formulae used by various suppliers and different methods of packaging and mixing photoprocessing chemicals, only a few generalizations can be made regarding the types of chemical hazards present. A variety of strong acids and caustic materials may be encountered, especially in storage and mixing areas. Many photoprocessing chemicals are skin and eye irritants and, in some cases, may cause skin or eye burns following direct contact. The most frequent health issue in photoprocessing is the potential for contact dermatitis, which most commonly arises from skin contact with alkaline developer solutions. The dermatitis may be due to irritation caused by alkaline or acidic solutions, or, in some cases, to skin allergy.

Colour developers are aqueous solutions that usually contain derivatives of p-phenylenediamine, whereas black-and-white developers usually contain p-methyl-aminophenolsulphate (also known as Metol or KODAK ELON Developing Agent) and/or hydroquinone. Colour developers are more potent skin sensitizers and irritants than black-and-white developers and may also cause lichenoid reactions. In addition, other skin sensitizers such as formaldehyde, hydroxylamine sulphate and S-[2-(dimethyl-amino)-ethyl]-isothiouronium dihydrochloride are found in some photoprocessing solutions. The development of skin allergy is more likely to occur after repeated and prolonged contact with processing solutions. Persons with pre-existing skin diseases or skin irritation are often more susceptible to the effects of chemicals on the skin.

Avoiding skin contact is an important goal in photoprocessing areas. Neoprene gloves are recommended for reducing skin contact, especially in the mixing areas, where more concentrated solutions are encountered. Alternatively, nitrile gloves may be used when prolonged contact with photochemicals is not required. Gloves should be of sufficient thickness to prevent tears and leaks, and should be inspected and cleaned frequently, preferably by thorough washing of the outer and inner surfaces with a non-alkaline hand cleaner. It is particularly important that maintenance personnel be provided with protective gloves during repair or cleaning of the tanks and rack assemblies, and so on, since these may become coated with deposits of chemicals. Barrier creams are not appropriate for use with photochemicals because they are not impervious to all photochemicals and may contaminate processing solutions. A protective apron or lab coat should be worn in the darkroom, and frequent laundering of work clothing is desirable. For all reusable protective clothing, users should look for signs of permeation or degradation after each use and replace clothing as appropriate. Protective goggles and a face shield also should be used, especially in areas where concentrated photochemicals are handled.

If photoprocessing chemicals contact the skin, the affected area should be flushed quickly with copious amounts of water. Because materials such as developers are alkaline, washing with a non-alkaline hand cleaner (pH of 5.0 to 5.5) reduces the potential to develop dermatitis. Clothing should be changed immediately if there is any contamination with chemicals, and spills or splashes should be immediately cleaned up. Hand-washing facilities and provisions for rinsing the eyes are particularly important in the mixing and processing areas. Emergency shower facilities should also be available.

Inhalation hazards

In addition to potential skin and eye hazards, gases or vapours emitted from some photoprocessing solutions may present an inhalation hazard, as well as contribute to unpleasant odours, especially in poorly ventilated areas. Some colour processing solutions may release vapours such as acetic acid, triethanolamine and benzyl alcohol, or gases such as ammonia, formaldehyde and

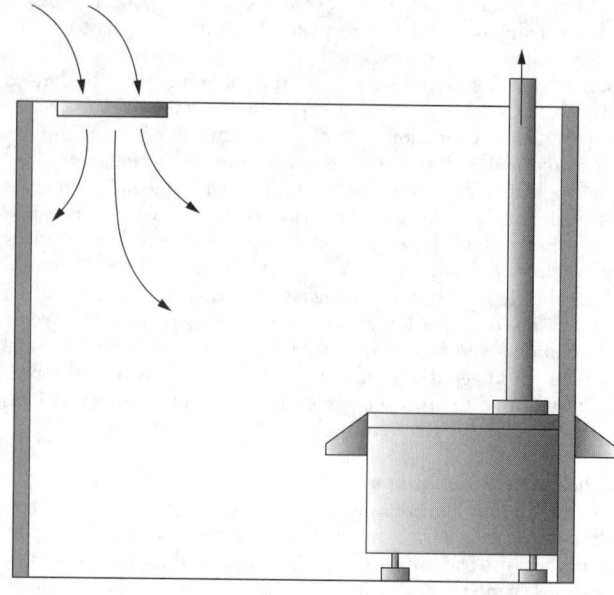

Figure 85.3 • Enclosed-machine ventilation.

sulphur dioxide. These gases or vapours may be irritating to the respiratory tract and eyes, or, in some cases, may cause other health-related effects. The potential health-related effects of these gases or vapours is concentration dependent and is usually observed only at concentrations that exceed occupational exposure limits. However, because of a wide variation in individual susceptibility, some individuals—for example, persons with pre-existing medical conditions such as asthma—may experience effects at concentrations below occupational exposure limits.

Some photochemicals may be detectable by odour because of the chemical's low odour threshold. Although the odour of a chemical is not necessarily indicative of a health hazard, strong odours or odours that are increasing in intensity may indicate that the ventilation system is inadequate and should be reviewed.

Appropriate photoprocessing ventilation incorporates both general dilution and local exhaust to exchange air at an acceptable rate per hour. Good ventilation offers the added benefit of making the working environment more comfortable. The amount of ventilation required varies according to room conditions, processing output, specific processors and processing chemicals. A ventilation engineer may be consulted to ensure optimum operation of room and local exhaust ventilation systems. High-temperature processing and nitrogen-burst agitation of tank solutions may increase the release of some chemicals to the ambient air. Processor speed, solution temperatures and solution agitation should be set at minimum suitable performance levels to reduce the potential release of gases or vapours from processing tanks.

General room ventilation—for example, 4.25 m³/min supply and 4.8 m³/min exhaust (equivalent to 10 air changes per hour in a 3 × 3 × 3–metre room), with a minimum outside air replenishment rate of 0.15 m³/min per m² floor area—is usually adequate for photographers who undertake basic photoprocessing. An exhaust rate higher than a supply rate produces a negative pressure in the room and reduces the opportunity for gases or vapours to escape to adjoining areas. The exhaust air should be discharged outside the building to avoid redistributing potential air contaminants within the building. If the processor tanks are enclosed and have an exhaust (see figure 85.3), the minimum air supply and exhaust rate can probably be reduced.

Figure 85.4 • Open-tank with "push-pull" ventilation.

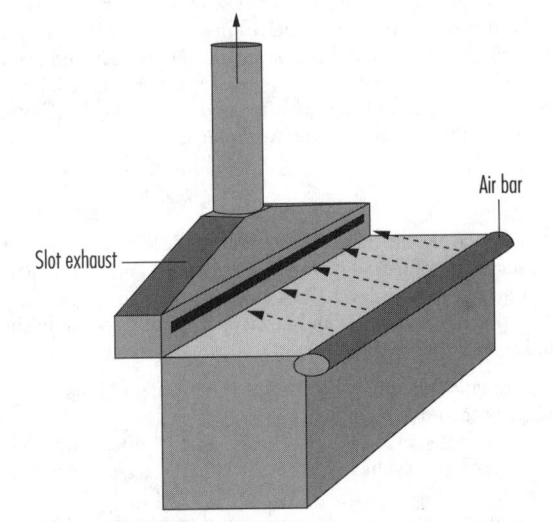

Some operations (e.g., toning, film cleaning, mixing operations and special processing procedures) may require supplementary local exhaust ventilation or respiratory protection. Local exhaust is important because it reduces the concentration of airborne contaminants that might otherwise be recirculated by the general dilution ventilation system.

A lateral slot-type ventilation system for extracting vapours or gases at the surface of a tank may be used for some tanks. When designed and operated correctly, lateral slot-type exhausts draw clean air across the tank and remove contaminated air from the operator's breathing zone and the surface of the processing tanks.

Figure 85.5 • Overhead canopy exhaust (not recommended).

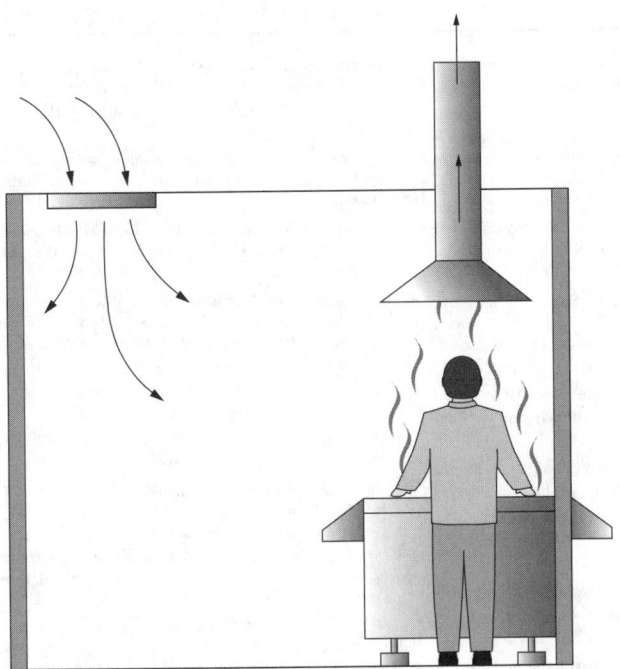

Push-pull lateral slot-type exhausts are the most effective systems (see figure 85.4).

A hooded or canopy exhaust system (see figure 85.5) is not recommended because operators often lean over tanks with their heads under the hood. In this position, the hood draws vapours or gases into the operator's breathing zone.

Split-tank covers with local exhaust attached to the stationary portion on mixing tanks may be used to supplement general room ventilation in mixing areas. Tank covers (tight-fitting covers or floating lids) should be used to prevent the release of potential air contaminants from storage and other tanks. A flexible exhaust may be attached to tank covers to facilitate the removal of volatile chemicals (see figure 85.6). As appropriate, automixers, which allow individual parts of multicomponent products to be added directly to and subsequently mixed in processors, should be used because they decrease the potential for operator exposure to photochemicals.

When mixing dry chemicals, the containers should be emptied gently to minimize chemical dust from becoming airborne. Tables, benches, shelves and ledges should be wiped with a water-dampened cloth frequently to keep residual chemical dust from accumulating and later becoming airborne.

Facility and operations design

Surfaces that may be contaminated with chemicals should be constructed to permit flushing with water. Adequate provisions should be made for floor drains, particularly in storage, mixing and processing areas. Because of the potential for leaks or spills, arrangements should be made for containment, neutralization and proper disposal of photochemicals. Since floors may be wet at times, flooring around potentially wet areas should be covered with non-skid tape or paint for safety purposes. Consideration should also be given to potential electrical hazards. For electrical devices used in or near water, ground-fault circuit interrupters and appropriate grounding should be used.

As a general rule, photochemicals should be stored in a cool (at temperatures no lower than 4.4 °C), dry (relative humidity

Figure 85.6 • Chemical mixing tank exhaust with partial cover.

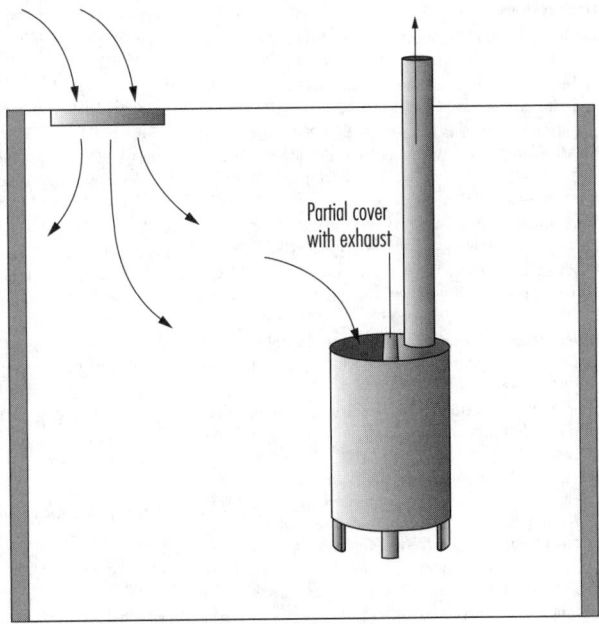

between 35 and 50%), well-ventilated area, where they can be easily inventoried and retrieved. Chemical inventories should be actively managed so that the quantities of hazardous chemicals stored can be minimized and so that materials are not stored beyond their expiration dates. All containers should be properly labelled.

Chemicals should be stored to minimize the likelihood of container breakage during storage and retrieval. Chemical containers should not be stored where they can fall over, above eye level or where personnel have to stretch to reach them. Most hazardous materials should be stored at a low level and on a firm base in order to avoid possible breakage and spilling on the skin or eyes. Chemicals that, if accidentally mixed, might lead to fire, explosion or toxic chemical release should be segregated. For example, strong acids, strong bases, reducers, oxidizers and organic chemicals should be stored separately.

Flammable and combustible liquids should be stored in approved containers and storage cabinets. Storage areas should be kept cool, and smoking, open flames, heaters or anything else that might cause accidental ignition should be prohibited. During transfer operations, it should be ensured that containers are properly bonded and grounded. The design and operation of storage and handling areas for flammable and combustible materials should comply with applicable fire and electrical codes.

Whenever possible, solvents and liquids should be dispensed by metering pumps rather than by pouring. Pipetting of concentrated solutions and establishing siphons by mouth should not be permitted. The use of pre-weighed or pre-measured preparations may simplify operations and reduce the opportunities for accidents. Careful maintenance of all pumps and lines is necessary to avoid leakage.

Good personal hygiene should always be practiced in photoprocessing areas. Chemicals should never be placed in beverage or food containers or vice versa; only containers intended for chemicals should be used. Food or drink should never be brought into areas where chemicals are used, and chemicals should not be stored in refrigerators used for food. After handling chemicals, hands should be washed thoroughly, especially before eating or drinking.

Training and education

All personnel, including maintenance and housekeeping, should be trained in safety procedures relevant to their job tasks. An education programme for all personnel is essential in promoting safe work practices and preventing accidents. The educational programme should be carried out before personnel are allowed to work, at regular intervals thereafter and whenever new potential hazards are introduced into the workplace.

Summary

The key to working safely with photoprocessing chemicals is to understand the potential hazards of exposure and to manage the risk to an acceptable level. Risk management strategies for controlling potential occupational hazards in photoprocessing should include:

- providing personnel with training on potential hazards and safety procedures in the workplace,
- encouraging personnel to read and understand hazard communication vehicles (e.g., safety data sheets and product labels),
- maintaining workplace cleanliness and good personal hygiene,
- making certain that processors and other equipment are installed, operated and maintained to manufacturers' specifications,
- substituting with less hazardous or less odorous chemicals, where possible,
- using engineering controls (e.g., general and local exhaust ventilation systems) where applicable,
- using protective equipment (e.g., protective gloves, goggles or face shield) when necessary,
- establishing procedures to ensure prompt medical attention for anyone with evidence of injury, and
- consideration of environmental exposure monitoring and health monitoring of employees as a verification of effective risk management strategies.

Additional information on black-and-white processing is discussed in the *Entertainment and the arts* chapter.

References

Bertazzi, PA and CA Zoccheti. 1980. Mortality study of newspaper printing workers. *Am J Ind Med* 1:85-97.

Dubrow, R. 1986. Malignant melanoma in the printing industry. *Am J Ind Med* 10:119-126.

Friedlander, BR, FT Hearne and BJ Newman. 1982. Mortality, cancer incidence, and sickness-absence in photographic processors: An epidemiologic study. *J Occup Med* 24:605-613.

Hodgson, MJ and DK Parkinson. 1986. Respiratory disease in a photographer. *Am J Ind Med* 9:349-54.

International Agency for Research on Cancer (IARC). 1996. *Printing Processes and Printing Inks, Carbon Black and Some Nitro Compounds.* Vol 65. Lyon: IARC.

Kipen, H and Y Lerman. 1986. Respiratory abnormalities among photographic developers: A report of three cases. *Am J Ind Med* 9:341-47.

Leon, DA. 1994. Mortality in the British printing industry: A historical cohort study of trade union members in Manchester. *Occ and Envir Med* 51:79-86.

Leon, DA, P Thomas, and S Hutchings. 1994. Lung cancer among newspaper printers exposed to ink mist: A study of trade union members in Manchester, England. *Occup and Env Med* 51:87-94.

Michaels, D, SR Zoloth, and FB Stern. 1991. Does low-level lead exposure increase risk of death? A mortality study of newspaper printers. *Int J Epidemiol* 20:978-983.

Nielson, H, L Henriksen, and JH Olsen. 1996. Malignant melanoma among lithographers. *Scand J Work Environ Health* 22:108-11.

Paganini-Hill, A, E Glazer, BE Henderson, and RK Ross. 1980. Cause-specific mortality among newspaper web pressmen. *J Occup Med* 22:542-44.

Pifer, JW. 1995. *Mortality Update of the 1964 U.S. Kodak Processing Laboratories Cohort through 1994.* Kodak Report EP 95-11. Rochester, NY: Eastman Kodak Company.

Pifer, JW, FT Hearne, FA Swanson, and JL O'Donoghue. 1995. Mortality study of employees engaged in the manufacture and use of hydroquinone. *Arch Occup Environ Health* 67:267-80.

Sinks, T, B Lushniak, BJ Haussler et al. 1992. Renal cell disease among paperboard printing workers. *Epidemiology* 3:483-89.

Svensson, BG, G Nise, V Englander et al. 1990. Deaths and tumours among rotogravure printers exposed to toluene. *Br J Ind Med* 47:372-79.

Other relevant readings

Bober, TW, TJ Dagon, and HE Fowler. 1992. *Handbook of Industrial Waste Treatment.* New York: Marcel Dekker.

Cunningham, HW. 1992. *Air Pollution Engineering Manual.* New York: Van Nostrand Reinhold.

Eastman Kodak Company. 1989. *The Prevention of Contact Dermatitis in Photographic Work.* Kodak publication No. J-4S. Rochester, NY: Eastman Kodak Company.

—. 1993. *Safe Handling of Photographic Chemicals.* Kodak publication No. J-4 Rochester, NY: Eastman Kodak Company.

Gosselin, RE, RP Smith, and HD Hodge. 1984. *Clinical Toxicology of Commercial Products.* Baltimore: Williams and Wilkins.

Health and Safety Executive (HSE). 1986. *Chemicals in the Printing Industry: The Provision of Health and Safety Information by Manufacturers, Importers and Suppliers of Chemical Products to the Printing Industry.* London: HSE.

—. 1995. *Chemical Safety in the Printing Industry.* London: HSE.

Hollins, R. 1994. *Practical Printers Handbook.* Sutton Coldfield, UK: Comprint Services.

Kanerva, L, T Estlander, R Jolanki, and ML Sysilampi. 1995. Allergy caused by acrylate compounds—history, research and prevention. From research to prevention. *Managing Occupational and Environmental Health Hazards, People and Work.* Research Reports 4. Proceedings of the International Symposium, 20-23 March. Helsinki, Finland.

Press Standards Board of Finance. 1994. *Newspaper and Magazine Publishing in the UK: Code of Practice.* London: Press Standards Board of Finance Ltd.

WOODWORKING

86

Chapter Editor
Jon Parish

Contents

GENERAL PROFILE

Debra Osinsky

Traditionally, furniture factories have been located in Europe and North America. With the increased cost of labour in industrialized countries, more furniture production, which is labour intensive, has shifted to Far Eastern countries. It is likely that this movement will continue unless more automated equipment can be developed.

Most furniture manufacturers are small enterprises. For example, in the United States, approximately 86% of the factories in the wood furniture industry have fewer than 50 employees (EPA 1995); this is representative of the situation internationally.

The woodworking industry in the United States is responsible for manufacturing household, office, store, public building and restaurant furniture and fixtures. The woodworking industry falls under the US Bureau of the Census Standard Industrial Classification (SIC) Code 25 (equivalent to International SIC Code 33) and includes: wood household furniture, such as beds, tables, chairs and bookshelves; wood television and radio cabinets; wood office furniture, such as cabinets, chairs and desks; and wood office and store fixtures and partitions, such as bar fixtures, counters, lockers and shelves.

Because production lines for assembling furniture are costly, most manufacturers do not supply an exceptionally large range of items. Manufacturers may specialize in the product manufactured, the product group or the production process (EPA 1995).

WOODWORKING PROCESSES

Jon K. Parish

For the purposes of this article, the processes of the woodworking industry will be considered to start with the reception of converted timber from the sawmill and continue until the shipping of a finished wood article or product. Earlier stages in the handling of wood are dealt with in the chapters *Forestry* and *Lumber industry*.

The woodworking industry produces furniture and a variety of building materials, ranging from plywood floors to shingles. This article covers the main stages in the processing of wood for the production of wooden products, which are machine working of natural wood or manufactured panels, assembly of machined parts and surface finishing (e.g., painting, staining, lacquering, veneering and so on). Figure 86.1 is a flow diagram for wood furniture manufacturing, which covers nearly the whole range of these processes.

Drying. Some furniture manufacturing facilities may purchase dried lumber, but others perform drying onsite using a drying kiln or oven, fired by a boiler. Usually wood waste is the fuel.

Machining. Once the lumber is dried, it is sawed and otherwise machined into the shape of the final furniture part, such as a table leg. In a normal plant, the wood stock moves from rough planer, to cutoff saw, to rip saw, to finish planer, to moulder, to lathe, to table saw, to band saw, to router, to shaper, to drill and mortiser, to carver and then to a variety of sanders.

Wood can be hand carved/worked with a variety of hand tools, including chisels, rasps, files, hand saws, sandpaper and the like.

In many instances, the design of furniture pieces requires bending of certain wooden parts. This occurs after the planing process, and usually involves the application of pressure in conjunction with a softening agent, such as water, and increased atmospheric pressure. After bending into the desired shape, the piece is dried to remove excess moisture.

Assembly. Wood furniture can either be finished and then assembled, or the reverse. Furniture made of irregularly shaped components is usually assembled and then finished.

The assembly process usually involves the use of adhesives (either synthetic or natural) in conjunction with other joining methods, such as nailing, followed by the application of veneers. Purchased veneers are trimmed to correct size and patterns, and bonded to purchased chipboard.

After assembly, the furniture part is examined to ensure a smooth surface for finishing.

Pre-finishing. After initial sanding, an even smoother surface is attained by spraying, sponging or dipping the furniture part with water to cause the wood fibres to swell and "raise". After the surface has dried, a solution of glue or resin is applied and allowed to dry. The raised fibres are then sanded down to form a smooth surface.

If the wood contains rosin, which can interfere with the effectiveness of certain finishes, it may be derosinated by applying a mixture of acetone and ammonia. The wood is then bleached by spraying, sponging or dipping the wood into a bleaching agent such as hydrogen peroxide.

Surface finishing. Surface finishing may involve the use of a large variety of coatings. These coatings are applied after the product is assembled or in a flat line operation before assembly. Coatings could normally include fillers, stains, glazes, sealers, lacquers, paints, varnishes and other finishes. The coatings may be applied by spray, brush, pad, dip, roller or flow-coating machine.

Coatings can be either solvent based or water based. Paints may contain a wide variety of pigments, depending on the desired colour.

Hazards and Precautions

Machining safety

Woodworking manufacturing has many of the hazards to safety and health that are common to general industry, with a much larger proportion of extremely hazardous equipment and operations than most. Consequently, safety requires constant attention to safe work habits by employees, vigilant supervision, and maintenance of a safe work environment by employers.

Although in many instances woodworking machinery and equipment may be purchased without the necessary guards and other safety devices, it is management's responsibility to provide adequate safeguards before such machinery and equipment is used. See also the articles "Routing machines" and "Wood planing machines".

Sawing machines. Employees should be made aware of the safe operating practices necessary for the proper use of various woodworking saws (see figures 86.2 and 86.3). Specific guidelines are as follows:

1. When feeding a table saw, hands must be kept out of the line of the cut. No guard can prevent a person's hand from following the stock into the saw. When ripping with the fence gauge near the saw, a push stick or suitable jig must be used to complete the cut. See figure 86.4.
2. The saw blade must be positioned so as to minimize its protrusion above the stock; the lower the blade, the less chance for kickbacks. It is good practice to stand out of the line of the stock being ripped. A heavy leather apron or other guard for the abdomen is recommended.
3. Freehand sawing is always dangerous. The stock must always be held against a gauge or fence. See figure 86.3.
4. The saw must be appropriate for the job. For instance, it is an unsafe practice to rip with a table saw not equipped with a non-kickback device. Kickback aprons are recommended.

Figure 86.1 • Flow diagram for wood furniture manufacturing.

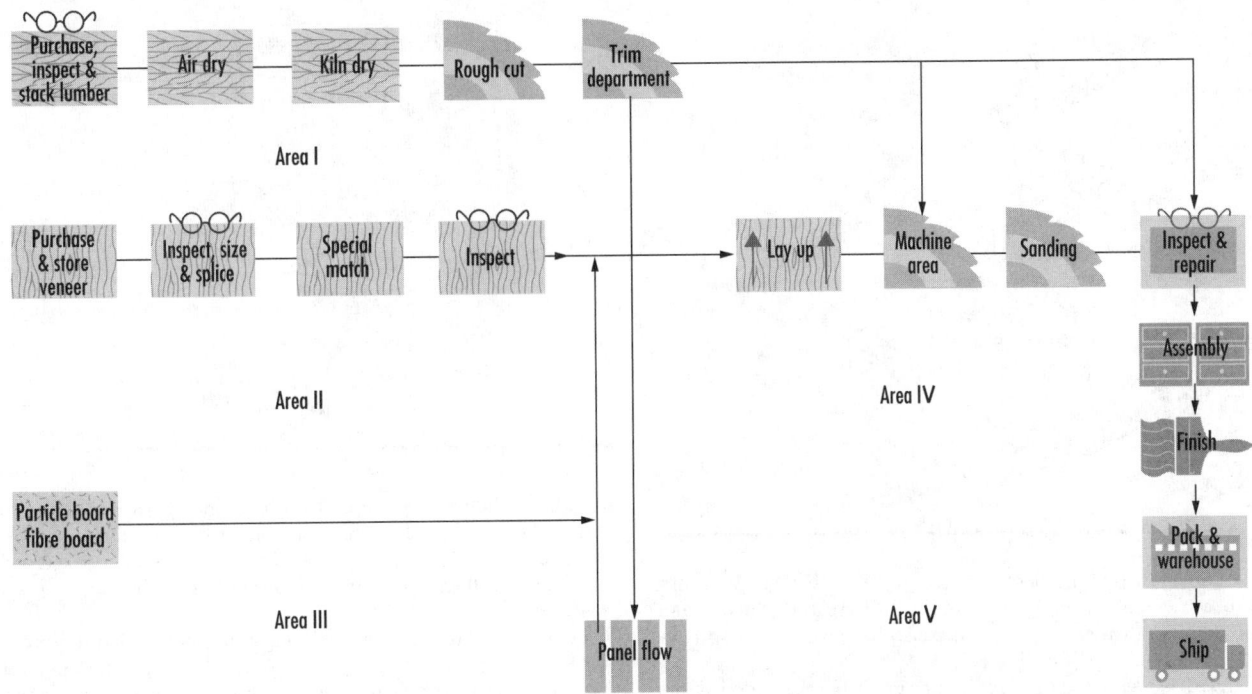

5. The dangerous practice of removing a hood guard because of narrow clearance on the gauge side can be avoided by clamping a filler board to the table between the gauge and the saw and using it to guide the stock. Employees must never be permitted to bypass guards. Combs, featherboards (see figure 86.5) or suitable jigs must be provided where standard guards cannot be used.

6. Crosscutting long boards on a table saw should be avoided because the operator is required to use considerable hand pressure near the saw blade. Also, boards extending beyond the table may be struck by people or trucks. Long stock should be crosscut on a swing pull saw or radial arm saw with adequate supporting bench.

7. Work that should be done on special power-feed machines should not be done on general-purpose hand-fed machines.

8. To set a gauge of a table saw without taking off the guards, a permanent mark should designate the line of cut on the table top.

9. It is considered safe practice to bring equipment to a complete stop before adjusting blades or fences, and to disconnect the power source when changing blades.

10. A brush or stick should be used to clean sawdust and scrap from a saw.

Figure 86.2 • Band saw.

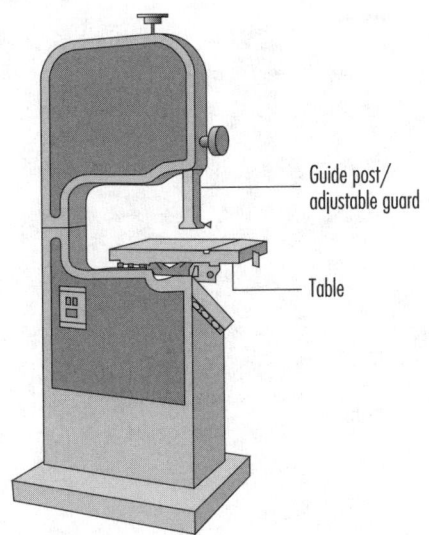

Guide post/ adjustable guard

Table

Figure 86.3 • Table saw.

Saw blade guard   Fence

Table

Figure 86.4 • Push sticks.

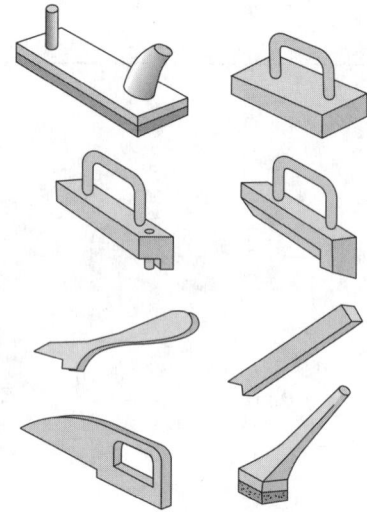

A table saw is also called a variety saw because it can perform a wide variety of sawing functions. For this reason the operator should have a variety of guards, because no one guard can protect from every function. See figure 86.3.

Cutting machines. Cutting machines can also be hazardous if not adequately guarded and always used with respect and alertness. Cutting tools should be kept well sharpened and correctly balanced on their spindles.

The router shown in figure 86.6 has a brush guard. Other routers may have a ring guard, a round guard that encircles the router bit. The purpose of guards is to keep the hands away from the cutting bit. Computer numerical controlled (CNC) routers may have several bits and are high production machines. On CNC machines the operator's hands are kept further from the bit area. However, another problem is the high amount of wood dust. See also the article "Routing machines".

Guarding on a jointer or surface planing machine is mainly to keep the operator's hands away from the revolving knives. The "mutton chop"-type guard allows only the portion of the knives which are cutting the stock to be exposed (see figure 86.7). The exposed portion of the knives behind the fence should also be guarded.

The shaper is a potentially very dangerous machine (see figure 86.8). If the shaper knives become separated from the above and below collars on the arbor, they can be thrown with great force. Also, stock must often be held close to the knives. This holding must be done with a fixture instead of by the operator's hands. Featherboards can be used to hold the stock down against the table. Ring or saucer guards should be used whenever possible. A saucer guard is a round, flat, plastic disk that is mounted horizontally on the arbor above the shaper knives.

Figure 86.5 • Featherboards and combs.

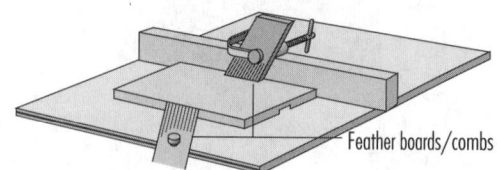

Feather boards/combs

Figure 86.6 • Router.

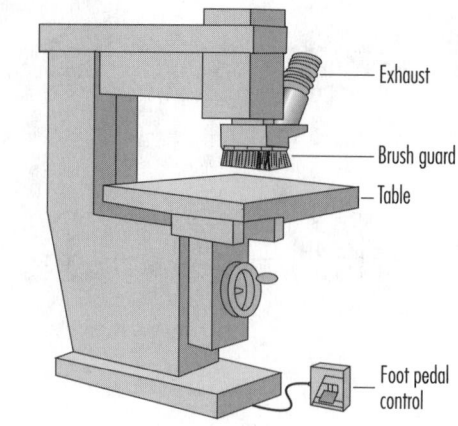

Exhaust

Brush guard

Table

Foot pedal control

A lathe should be guarded by a hood guard because there is a danger of the stock being thrown from the machine. See figure 86.9. It is good practice for the hood to be interlocked with the motor so the lathe cannot be run unless the hood guard is in place.

A ripsaw should have anti-kickback fingers installed to prevent the stock from reversing its direction and striking the operator. See figure 86.10. Also, the operator should wear a padded apron to lessen the impact if a kickback does occur.

Because the radial arm saw blade can be tilted sideways, a guard must be used which will not lie into the blade. See figure 86.11.

Sanding machines. Machined stock pieces are sanded down using belt, jitterbug, disc, drum or orbital sanders. Nip points are created in sanding belts. See figure 86.12. Often these nip points can be guarded with a hood which will also be part of a dust exhaust system.

Figure 86.7 • Jointer.

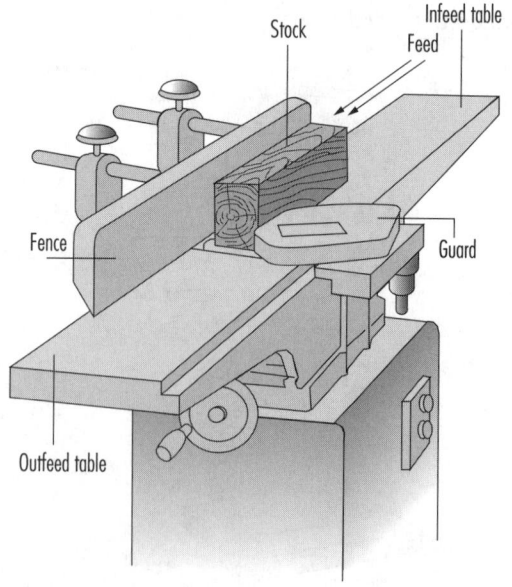

Stock

Infeed table

Feed

Fence

Guard

Outfeed table

Figure 86.8 • Shaper.

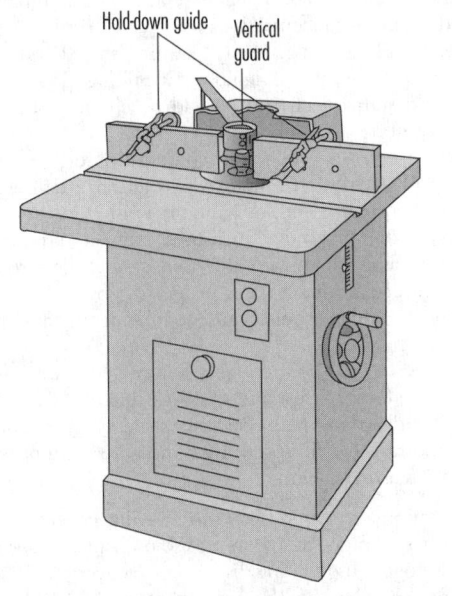

Figure 86.10 • Ripsaw.

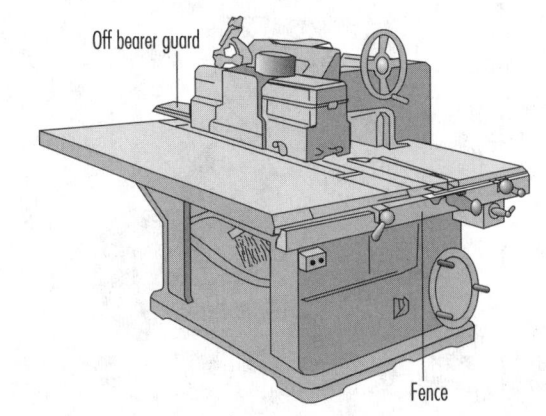

Machine guarding. Figure 86.13 illustrates that the opening between a guard and the point of contact must be decreased as the distance decreases.

Miscellaneous machine safety concerns. Care must be taken that the use of stock-clamping/holding devices do not create additional hazards.

Most woodworking machines create the necessity of the operator (and helper) wearing eye protection.

It is common practice for employees to blow dust off of themselves with compressed air. They should be cautioned to keep air pressure below 30 psi and to avoid blowing into eyes or open cuts.

Wood dust hazards

Machines that produce wood dust should be equipped with dust-collecting systems. If the exhaust system is inadequate to dispose of the wood dust, the operator may need to wear a dust respirator. The International Agency for Research on Cancer (IARC) has now determined that "there is sufficient evidence in humans for the carcinogenicity of wood dust", and that

"Wood dust is carcinogenic to humans (Group 1)". Other studies indicate that wood dust may prove an irritant to the mucous membranes of the eyes, nose and throat. Some toxic woods are more actively pathogenic and may produce allergic reactions and occasionally pulmonary disorders and systemic poisoning. See table 86.1 on page 86.13.

Increased use of high-production CNC machinery such as routers, tenoners and lathes creates more wood dust and will require new dust-collection technology.

Dust control. Most dust in a woodworking production shop is removed by local exhaust systems. However, often there is a considerable accumulation of very fine dust that has settled on rafters and other structural members, especially in areas where sanding is done. This is a hazardous situation, with great potential for fire and explosion. A flash fire over dust-covered surfaces may be followed by explosions of increasing force. In order to minimize this probability, it would be wise to use a checklist. See sample checklist in box.

Assembly hazards

A wide range of adhesives is used in the bonding of veneers to manufactured panels, depending on the characteristics required of the final product. Apart from casein glue, natural adhesives are less widely employed and the greatest use is made of synthetic

Figure 86.9 • Lathe.

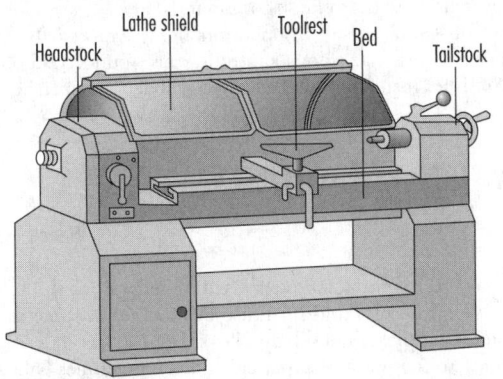

Figure 86.11 • Radial arm saw.

Because the radial arm saw blade can be tilted sideways, a guard must be used which will not lie into the blade.

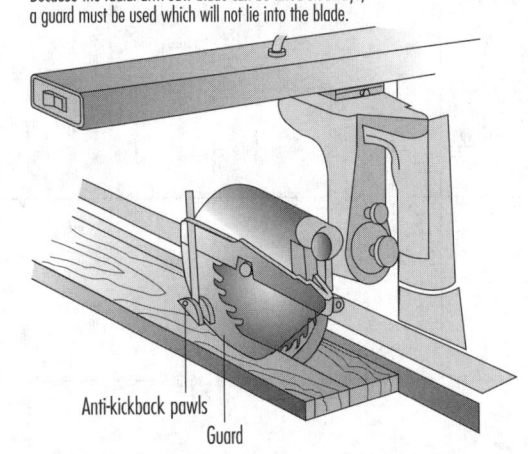

Figure 86.12 • Sander.

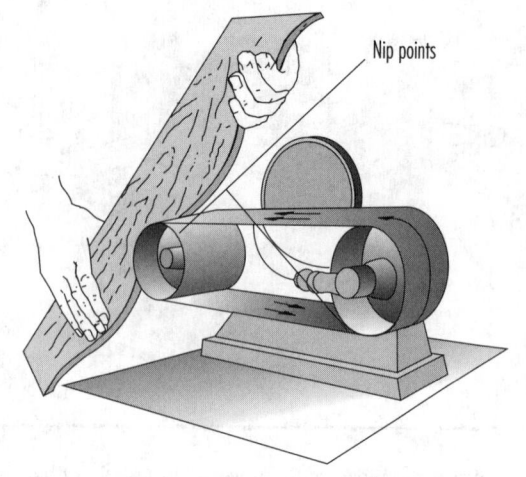

Nip points

adhesives such as urea-formaldehyde. Synthetic adhesives may pose a hazard of skin disease or systemic intoxication, especially those which release free formaldehyde or organic solvents into the atmosphere. Adhesives should be handled in well ventilated premises and sources of vapour emission should be equipped with exhaust ventilation. Employees should be provided with gloves, protective creams, respirators and eye protection when necessary.

The moving parts, especially blades, of veneer slicing, jointing and clipping machines should be fully guarded. Two-hand controls may be necessary.

Finishing hazards

Surface finishing. Solvents used for carrying the sprayed pigments or for thinning can include a wide variety of volatile organic com-

Figure 86.13 • Distance between guard and point of operation.

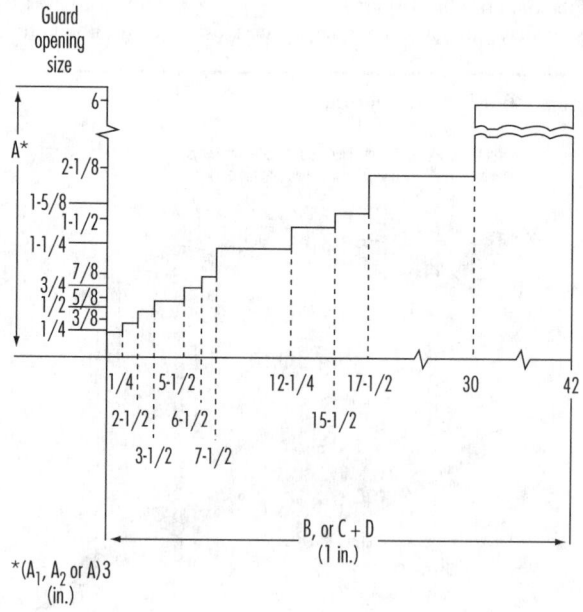

Guard opening size

A*

6-

2-1/8-

1-5/8-
1-1/2-

1-1/4-

7/8-
3/4-
1/2- 5/8-
1/4- 3/8-

1/4   5-1/2   12-1/4   17-1/2   30   42

2-1/2 6-1/2   15-1/2

3-1/2 7-1/2

B, or C + D
(1 in.)

*(A$_1$, A$_2$ or A)3
(in.)

pounds (VOCs) which may reach toxic and explosive concentrations in the air. In addition, many pigments are toxic by inhalation of spray mist (e.g., lead, manganese and cadmium pigments). Wherever dangerous concentrations of vapour or mist can occur, use exhaust ventilation (e.g., spray painting in a booth) or use water sprays. All sources of ignition, including fires, electrical equipment and static electricity, should be eliminated *before* any operations begin.

An active hazardous material communication programme should be in place to alert employees to all hazards created by toxic, reactive, corrosive and/or ignitable finish, glue and solvent chemicals and the protective measures that should be taken. Eating where these chemicals are used should be prohibited. Proper storage of flammables and proper disposal of soiled rags and steel wool which could cause spontaneous ignition are imperative.

Fire prevention. In view of the highly flammable nature of wood (especially in the form of dust and shavings) and of the other items found in a woodworking plant (such as solvents, glues and coatings), the importance of fire prevention measures cannot be overemphasized. Measures include:

- installing automatic wood-dust and shaving collection equipment on saws, planers, moulders and so on, which transport the waste to storage silos pending disposal or recovery
- prohibiting smoking at the workplace and eliminating all sources of ignition (e.g., open flames)
- ensuring regular clean-up procedures of deposited dust and shavings
- adequate maintenance of machines to prevent occurrences such as the overheating of bearings
- installation of fire barriers, sprinkler systems, fire extinguishers, fire hoses and a crew trained to use this equipment
- proper storage of flammables
- explosion-proof electrical equipment where needed.

Environmental and Public Health Concerns

The production of finished products from wood can be done without long-range environmental damage. The harvesting of trees can be done in such a manner that new growth can replace what is cut. Major deforestation such as has been the case in rain forests can be discouraged. Waste products from the machining of wood (i.e., sawdust, wood chips) can be used in chipcore or as fuel.

While there are solid waste and process wastewater implications for the woodworking industry, the major concerns are the air emissions resulting from the use of waste wood as fuel and from solvent-intensive finishing operations. Wood-fired boilers are commonly used in drying operations, while many of the finishing materials are applied by spray. In both instances, engineering controls are required to reduce air-borne particulates and recover and/or incinerate the volatile compounds.

Controls should result in operators being exposed to less toxic chemicals as less hazardous substitutes are found. Use of water-based finishes instead of solvent-based will decrease fire hazards.

ROUTING MACHINES

Beat Wegmüller

Stationary routing machines are used in general for the manufacture of wood articles and furniture elements, but sometimes also for machining plastics and light alloys. Important types of routing machines are copy routers, pattern millers, machines with mobile router heads and automatic copying machines. The automatic

Sample checklist

Housekeeping

1. A daily housekeeping programme is essential.
2. Dust accumulations of 1/8″ depth in any area indicate a need for cleaning. It should be noted that any accumulation of dust may lead to a fire. The finer the dust, the greater the hazards.
3. Clean wood dust frequently.
   a. Wipe down daily around hot surfaces.
   b. Major blow down or vacuum when possible of all areas, including rafters, at least twice per year.
   c. When concentrations are high, work small areas at a time.
   d. Low humidity increases the potential for hazards and should be taken in consideration during blow downs.
4. Schedule blow downs or clean ups while equipment is down, such as Friday afternoons and weekends.

Electrical maintenance

1. Inspect/clean all motors regularly to avoid dust build-up.
2. Ensure all electrical boxes and panels meet the applicable electrical code requirements for their classified location.
3. Listen for unusual sounds, note unusual smells and watch for visual dust accumulations on machines and motors. Check motors and other electricals often to detect overheating.
4. Ensure that maintenance or operating personnel are lubricating bearings to motors, conveyors, chains and sprockets on a timely basis.
5. Ensure that electrical panels and boxes are kept closed and maintained to prevent dust accumulations, including keeping all knockout holes plugged.

Fire prevention

1. Actively prohibit smoking in unauthorized locations.
2. Adopt procedures for hot-work permits and ensure that procedures are followed.
3. Do not allow operator-controlled machines to operate unattended.

4. Install a device at the mouth of the dust collecting system to prevent sanding belts and other spark producing items from entering the system and causing a fire.
5. Trap metal in wood hogs by installing magnets in the conveyor system and metal detectors in the hog. Policies and procedures should be implemented to prevent metal and other foreign objects from reaching the hogs.
6. Conduct weekly and monthly inspections of fire protective systems including fire extinguishers, fire hoses, alarms and sprinkler control valves.
7. Ensure that boiler rooms and heating equipment are free of dust accumulations, that written boiler start-up procedures are being followed and that properly classified equipment is used.
8. Recognize the correct procedure in fighting dust fires.
9. Request a detailed inspection by the local fire marshal or insurance carrier.
10. Encourage mock drills/visits by the local fire department.
11. Install spark detection and extinguishing systems in dust collection systems and check periodically to ensure that they are working.
12. Review evacuation plans, emergency lighting, fire drills periodically for each work shift.

Miscellaneous

1. Contact insurance carrier for assistance in hazard identifications associated with safety, health and fire prevention.
2. Contact appropriate government safety agencies for additional assistance.
3. Employees should enter dust silos only when confined space procedures are followed.
4. All operators should ensure that dust collecting systems are working properly and report any malfunctions to management immediately.
5. Check for objects obstructing the ducts to the dust system.
6. It is recommended that all supervisors, safety committee members and other employees be made aware of the contents of this voluntary checklist to achieve maximum implementation.

copying machines are generally used for machining several workpieces simultaneously.

A common feature of all routing machines is that the tool is located above the workpiece support, which is normally a table. The tool-spindle axis is nearly always vertical, but on some machines the router head, and thus also the tool-spindle axis, may be tilted. The machining head is lowered for machining and returns automatically to its initial (rest) position. On older machines the machining head is lowered manually by operating a mechanical foot-pedal or hand lever. On modern machines the head is generally lowered by a pneumatic or hydraulic system. Figure 86.14 shows various accessories (hold-down shoes, guides and so on) and the Swiss National Accident Insurance Organization (SUVA) safety guard.

The tool-spindle is driven either by a belt drive or directly by a high-frequency motor, which is often of the two-speed type. The tool-spindle speeds generally range from 6,000 to 24,000 rpm. They are lower in pattern millers, where the lowest speed may be 250 rpm. Pattern millers are often equipped with a gearbox for the selection of different speeds.

The cutting diameter of the routing tool varies from 3 to 50 mm. However, on special pattern millers the cutting diameter of the tool may be as large as 300 mm.

Tooling

On routing machines single-edged spoon bits, double-edged panel cutters or solid-shaped cutters mainly are used. Like any tool they must be designed and made of such materials that will withstand the forces and loads to be expected during operation. Machines should be used and maintained in compliance with the manufacturer's instructions.

The routing tools should be:

- clearly and permanently marked with the permissible speed, e.g., less than 20,000 rpm
- of a type tested by an approved body
- of round form design with a minimal radial cutting edge projection to reduce the danger of kickback.

Guarding of the tool

On routing machines where the tool is moving and the workpiece remains fixed, access to the rotating tool should be prevented by an adjustable guard (hand protector). It should be supplemented by a movable guard which can be lowered on to the workpiece surface. The lower end of this movable guard may be a brush.

On routing machines where the workpiece is held and/or fed by hand, it is highly recommended to use a safety device exerting vertical pressure on the workpiece. The SUVA has designed such a guard. This safety device has been successfully used since the end of the 1940s and is still the most complete guard of its kind. Its main features are:

- prevention of unintentional contact with the rotating tool both in its rest position and in its working position
- fast and easy changeover from one size of hold-down shoe to another. Several sizes of hold-down shoes are available to fit tools with different cutting diameters.
- manually adjustable amount of pressure exerted on the workpiece by the hold-down shoe
- automatic return of the hold-down shoe to its upper position when the router head rises to its rest position. The guarding device can be adjusted so that the hold-down shoe may be lifted only when the lower edge of the tool is above the level of the lower edge of the hold-down shoe; this is to prevent any unintentional contact with the tool from below (see figure 86.15. Serious injuries to the back of the hand, where the tendons are protected only by the skin, are thus avoided.
- possibility of connection of a chip extraction system to the guarding device.

This guarding device also enables workpieces to be routed along a guide with the aid of a horizontal pressure pad.

Hazards

Routing machines have been found to be less dangerous than vertical spindle moulding machines. One reason for this is the smaller diameter of most routing tools. However, the tools on routing machines are easily accessible and thus present a constant hazard for the hands and arms of the operator. Therefore, copy routers, where the workpiece is generally fed by hand, are by far the most dangerous routing machines.

Causes of accidents

The main causes of router accidents are:

- unintentional contact of the hand or arm with the rotating tool in its rest position (1) when removing chips and dust from the table by hand rather than using a wooden stick, (2) when the workpiece or the jig is not correctly handled or (3) when the sleeve of the operator's clothing becomes entangled in the rotating tool
- unintentional contact of the hand with the routing tool as a result of kickback of the workpiece held by hand.

Kickback may happen because of:

- an unsafe working practice
- faults in the workpiece (knots, etc.)
- workpieces being fed into the tool too abruptly or from the wrong direction
- blunt cutter edges
- inadequate cutting speed
- incorrect fixing of the workpiece to the jig
- workpiece breakage
- ejection of the tool or parts of the tool due to bad tool design, excessive hardness of the tool material, faults in the material of the tool, overspeed of the tool or poor clamping of the tool in the tool holder.

In the event of ejection of a tool or workpiece, not only the operator but also other persons working in the area may be injured by ejected parts.

Figure 86.14 • SUVA safety device with routing tool in working position.

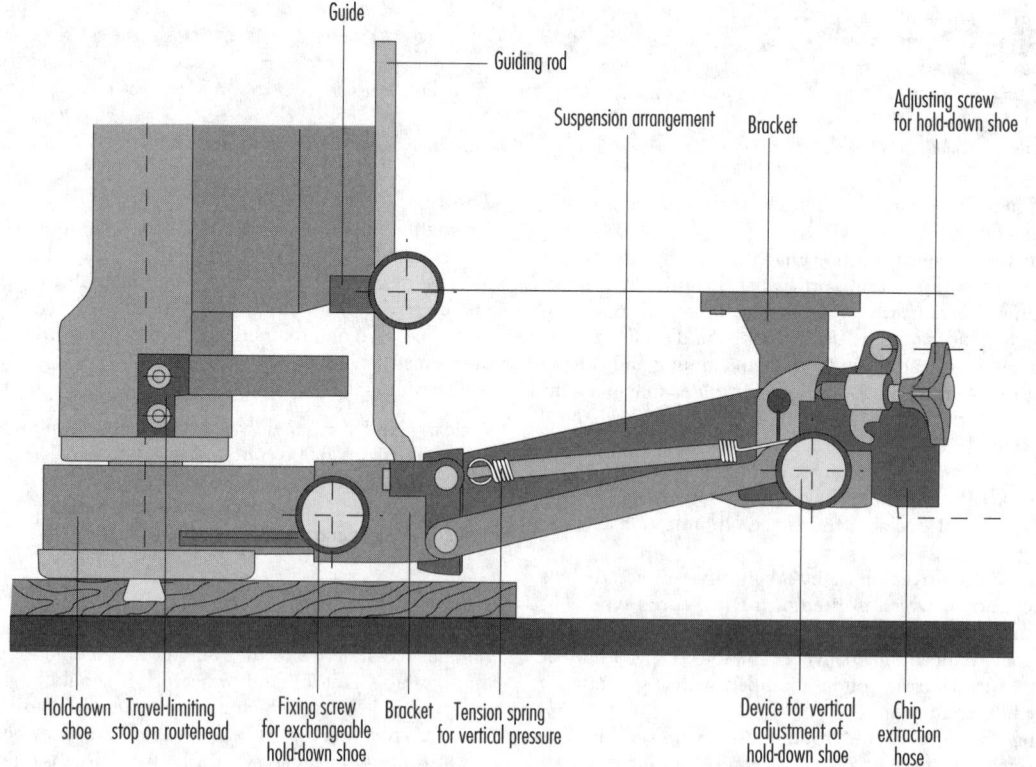

Figure 86.15 • Safety device according to figure 86.14 with routing tool in initial position (rest position).

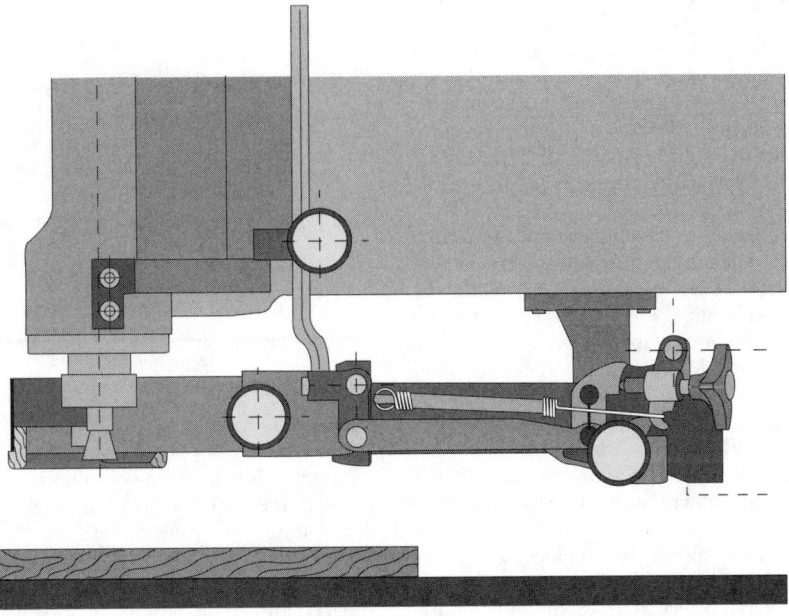

Measures to prevent accidents

Measures to prevent accidents should be directed at:

- the design and construction of the machine
- the tooling
- guarding the tool in its rest position (figure 86.15) and as far as possible in the working position (figure 86.14), in particular when the workpiece is held and fed by hand.

Design and Construction of the Machine

Routing machines must be designed to be safe to operate. It should be ensured that:

- the machine is sufficiently rigid
- the electrical equipment conforms to safety regulations
- actuators used to initiate a start function or movement of a machine element are constructed and mounted so as to minimize inadvertent operation
- access to moving machine parts, such as belt drives, hydraulic or pneumatically moved router heads or travelling tables on machines with automatic feeds, are prevented by adequate guarding
- the actual revolutions per minute of the tool are clearly visible to the operator
- the safety devices and chip extraction systems are easy to install
- the noise level of the machine is reduced as far as possible.

Furthermore, it is advisable to equip the tool drive of the routing machine with an automatic brake that activates when the machine is stopped. The braking time should not exceed 10 seconds.

• WOOD PLANING MACHINES

Beat Wegmüller

The development of stationary planing machines can be traced back to the beginning of the 19th century. On the first machines of this type, the workpiece was clamped to a carriage and fed below a horizontal shaft fitted with blades extending over the full working width. In 1850 a planing machine was built in Germany on which the workpiece was fed over a cutterblock located between two tables used to position and to support the workpiece. Apart from technical improvements this basic design has been maintained to this day. Such a machine is called a surface planing machine or a jointer (see figure 86.7).

More recently, machines were designed to plane the upper surface of a workpiece to a predetermined thickness by means of a horizontally rotating cutterblock. The distance between the cutting circle diameter and the surface of the table supporting the workpiece is adjustable. Such machines are called one-side-thickness planing machines.

These two basic machine types were eventually combined into a machine which could be used for both surface and thickness planing. This development ended in planing machines for two-, three- and four-sided working in one pass.

From the point of view of occupational safety and health, it is strongly recommended that measures be taken for the extraction of wood dust and chips from the planing machine (e.g., by connecting the planing machine to a dust extraction system). Dust originating from hardwood (oak, beech) and tropical wood is considered a particular health hazard and must be extracted. Measures to reduce the noise level of planing machines should also be taken. An automatic brake for the cutterblock is compulsory in many countries.

Surface Planing Machines

A surface planing machine has rigid main frame that supports the infeed and the outfeed table. The cutterblock is located between the two tables and mounted on ball bearings. The main frame should be ergonomically designed (i.e., it should enable the operator to work comfortably).

Hand-operated control devices should be installed in such a way that the operator is not placed in a hazardous situation when operating them, and the possibility of inadvertent operation should be minimized.

The side of the main frame facing the operator's position must be free of projecting parts such as handwheels, levers and so on. The table to the left of the cutterblock (outfeed table) is normally set at the same height as the cutting circle of the cutterblock. The table to the right of the cutterblock (infeed table) is set lower than the outfeed table to obtain the desired depth of cut. Contact between the table lips and the cutterblock should not be possible over the full setting range of the tables. However, the clearance between the table lips and the cutting circle of the cutterblock shall be as small as possible to provide for good support of the workpiece to be planed.

The major operations on a surface planing machine are flatting and edging. The position of the hands on the workpiece is important from an operational and safety viewpoint. When flatting, the workpiece should be fed with one hand, with the other hand holding it down initially on the infeed table. As soon as there is a sufficient portion of timber on the outfeed table, the latter hand can pass safely over the bridge-guard to apply pressure on the outfeed table and will be followed by the feeding hand to complete the feeding operation. When edging, the hands should not pass over the cutterblock while in contact with the timber. Their prime function is to exert horizontal pressure on the workpiece to maintain it square to the fence.

The noise produced by the rotating cutterblock often may exceed the level considered harmful to the ear. Measures to reduce the noise level are therefore necessary. Some of the noise reduction measures which have proved successful on surface planers are the following:

- use of a "quiet" cutterblock (e.g., a round form with minimum blade projection, helical blade instead of straight blade, segmental rotating tools with offset cutting)
- slotted or drilled table lips (the configuration and the dimensions of the apertures in the table lips must be selected so that no accident hazards arise; e.g., slots shall be no more than 6 mm wide and the diameter of the holes shall not exceed 6 mm)
- aerodynamic design of the chip deflectors below the table lips
- reduction of the cutterblock speed to below 1,000 rpm, provided the surface quality of the workpiece is still satisfactory.

Noise reduction up to 12 dBA when idling and 10 dBA under load can be achieved.

Cutterblocks should have a circular cross-section, and the chip clearance grooves and slots should be as small as possible. The blades and inserts shall be properly secured, preferably by form lock fixing.

The cutterblock rotates generally at speeds between 4,500 and 6,000 rpm. The diameters of conventional cutterblocks vary from 56 to 160 mm, and their lengths (working widths) from 200 to 900 mm. By analogy with the kinematics of conventional milling, the surface of the workpiece planed with a cutterblock is composed of cycloid arcs. The surface quality of the work therefore depends on the speed and diameter of the cutterblock, the number of cutting blades and the feed rate of the workpiece.

Equipping surface planing machines with an automatic brake for the cutterblock is recommended. The brake should be activated when the machine is stopped, and the braking time should not exceed 10 seconds.

Access to the cutterblock at the rear of the fence should be prevented by a guard attached either to the fence or the fence support. The cutterblock in front of the fence should be guarded by an adjustable bridge-type guard fixed to the machine (e.g., to the main frame on the outfeed table side) (see figure 86.16). Access to the transmission elements should be prevented by a fixed guard.

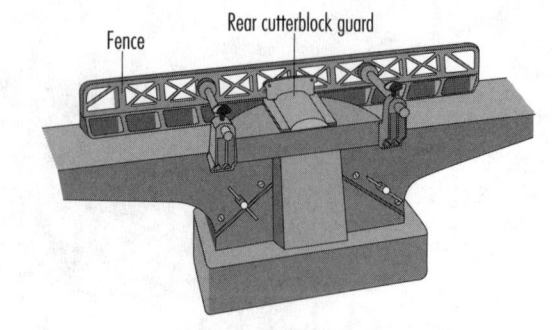

Figure 86.16 • Fence and rear cutterblock guard.

Hazards

As the cutterblock rotates opposite to the direction in which the workpiece is fed, the hazard of kickback exists. If the workpiece is ejected, the operator's hand or fingers may come in contact with the rotating cutterblock unless adequate guarding has been provided. It also frequently happens that the hand comes in contact with the cutterblock while feeding the workpiece with stretched fingers instead of pushing it forward with closed fist. Cutting blades not properly secured may be ejected by centrifugal force and may cause severe injury and/or material damage.

Guarding systems for surface planing machines

In many countries legislation covering the use of surface planing machines requires that the cutterblock be covered by an adjustable guarding system in order to prevent accidental contact of the operator's hand with the rotating cutterblock.

In 1938, the SUVA introduced a planer guard which efficiently met all practical requirements. Over the years this guard has proved useful not only as a guarding system but also as an aid for most operations. It is well accepted by the woodworking trade in Switzerland, and almost all industrial surface planing machines are equipped with it. The design features of this guard have been introduced into the draft European standard for surface planing machines. The main features of this guard are the following:

- strong and rigid
- not easily deflected to expose cutterblock
- always stays parallel to the cutterblock axis regardless of its horizontal or vertical adjustment
- easily adjustable horizontally and vertically without the use of a tool.

However, accidents still happen. These accidents are mainly caused by failure to adjust the guard properly. Therefore, SUVA engineers have developed a bridge-type guard which covers the cutterblock in front of the fence automatically, and constantly exerts a defined pressure against the workpiece or the fence. This guard has been available since 1992.

The main design features of this new guard, called "Suvamatic", are the following:

- *complete guarding of the cutterblock.* The full planing width is safeguarded by one single bridge-type guard. It can be folded down using a hinged locking system. This prevents the guard from projecting too far over the face of the machine.
- *practical workpiece guiding system.* The workpiece guiding system consists of a pressure pad and a guide for the workpiece. Both

are fitted to the tip of the guard. The latter can be tilted to guide the workpiece both for flatting and edging.

- *pressure application to assist work.* For edging, the guard exerts pressure in direction of the fence. After edging, it automatically covers the full length of the cutterblock in front of the fence.
- *automatic lifting and lowering of the guard.* For flatting, the guard is lifted by the workpiece guide. After flatting, it lowers itself automatically to cover the cutterblock.
- *guard can be locked in position for batch jobs.* For batch jobs, the guard can be locked in vertical position to just accommodate the thickness of the workpiece. The guard will return automatically to this preset position after being pressed down.
- *will fit all machines.* The guard can be fitted to all surface planing machines and combined surface and thickness planing machines.

One-Side Thickness Planing Machines

The main frame of a one-side thickness planing machine houses the cutterblock, thickness planing table and feed elements.

Once the workpiece has been flattened and edged on a surface planing machine, it is planed to the desired thickness on the thickness planing machine. Unlike that of a surface planing machine, the cutterblock of a thickness planing machine is located above the planing table and the workpiece is no longer fed by hand but mechanically by feed rollers. The feed rollers are driven either by a separate motor (approximately 1 kW) or via a speed-reduction gearbox receiving its power from the cutterblock motor. With a separate drive the feed rate remains constant, but if the power is transmitted from the cutterblock motor the feed rate varies according to the cutterblock speed. Feed rates between 4 and 35 m/min are common.

Two spring-mounted feed rollers rest on the upper surface of the workpiece. The feed roller in front of the cutterblock is grooved for better grip on the workpiece; the feed roller at the outfeed end of the cutterblock is smooth. An infeed and an outfeed pressure bar located next to the cutterblock press the workpiece down onto the table, thereby ensuring a clean and even cut. The design and arrangement of the feed rollers and pressure bars should be such that contact with the rotating cutterblock is impossible.

Sectional feed rollers and pressure bars allow for the simultaneous working of two or more workpieces of slightly different thickness. From the point of view of accident prevention, sectional feed rollers and pressure bars are essential. The width of the individual feed roller or pressure bar section should not exceed 50 mm.

Two idle rollers are arranged in the table. They are designed to facilitate the passage of the workpiece over the table.

The surface of the table must be a plane free from slots or holes. Accidents involving an operator's fingers being squeezed between openings and the workpiece have occurred. Vertical adjustment of the table may be manual or power assisted. A mechanical end-stop should prevent any contact of the table with the cutterblock or feed rollers. It must be ensured that the vertical adjustment mechanism hold the table in a stable position.

In order to prevent the feeding of oversize workpieces, a device (e.g., a fixed rod or fixed bar) is located on the infeed side of the machine, thereby limiting the maximum workpiece height. A maximum height of 250 mm between the surface of the table in its lowest position and the above-mentioned safety device is rarely exceeded. The usual working width varies between 315 and 800 mm (for special machines this width might go up to 1,300 mm).

The cutterblock diameter generally varies from 80 to 160 mm. Normally four blades are fitted to the cutterblock. The cutterblock rotates at speeds between 4,000 and 6,000 rpm, and its input power varies from 4 to 20 kW. The maximum depth of cut is 10 to 12 mm.

To minimize the danger of kickback, one-side thickness planing machines should be fitted with an anti-kickback device covering the full working width of the machine. This anti-kickback device generally consists of several grooved elements arranged on a rod. The individual element is between 8 and 15 mm wide, and it falls under its own weight to the rest position. The lowest point of the individual grooved element in its rest position should be 3 mm below the cutting circle of the cutterblock. The grooved elements should be made of a material (preferably steel) with a resilience strength of 15 J/cm^2 and a surface hardness of 100 HB.

The following noise-reduction measures have proved to be successful on one-side thickness planing machines:

- use of a "quiet" cutterblock (like that suggested for surface planing machines)
- aerodynamic design of the pressure bars and the chip extraction hood
- reduction of the cutterblock speed
- partial or complete enclosure of the machine (tunnel-like design of the infeed and outfeed opening with sound-absorbing material on the surface facing the source of noise)

Noise reduction of up to 20 dBA may be achieved by a well designed complete enclosure.

Hazards

The major cause of accidents on one-side thickness planing machines is kickback of the workpiece. Kickback may happen because of:

- poor maintenance of the anti-kickback device (the individual elements may not fall free under their own weight but stick together because of dust accumulation; the grooves in the elements may be covered with resin, be blunt or be incorrectly reground)
- poor maintenance of the sectional feed rollers and pressure bars (e.g., resin-covered or rusty sections)
- insufficient spring load on feed rollers and pressure bars when several pieces of non-uniform thickness are fed at the same time.

Typical causes of other accidents are:

- contact of the hand with the rotating cutterblock when removing chips and dust from the table by hand rather than with a wooden stick or rake
- ejection of cutterblock blades due to incorrect fixing.

Combined Surface Planing and Thicknessing Machines

The design and operation of combined machines (see figure 86.17) are similar to those of the individual machines described above. The same can be said in regards to the feed rates, motor power, table and roller adjustments. For thickness planing the surface planing tables are either pulled away, folded down or lifted up sideways, exposing the cutterblock, which is covered by a chip extraction hood to prevent access Combined machines are mainly used in small workshops with few workers, or where space is limited (i.e., in cases where the installation of two individual machines is impossible or unprofitable).

The changeover from one operation to the other is often time-consuming and may be annoying if only a few pieces have to be machined. Moreover, usually only one person at a time can use the machine. However, since 1992 machines have been introduced to the market where simultaneous operation (surface and thickness planing at the same time) is possible.

The hazards of combined machines are to a large extent identical to the hazards listed for the individual machines.

86. WOODWORKING

Figure 86.17 • Combined surface and thickness planer.

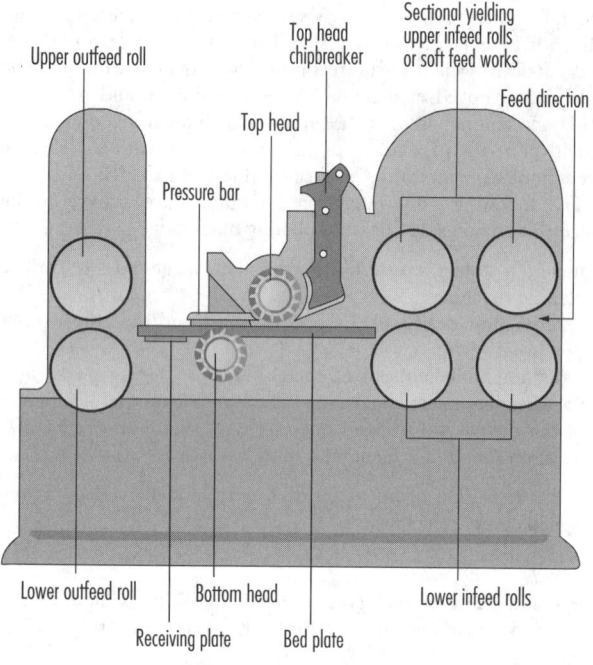

and amputations resulting from improperly used or inadequately guarded woodworking machinery (Ma, Wang and Chou 1991); sprains and strains from injudicious lifting or working in an awkward position (Nestor, Bobick and Pizatella 1990); repetitive motion injuries involving the hand or shoulder; and eye injuries. Many if not most of these can be prevented by proper training, the judicious application of machine guards and restraints and the use of personal protective equipment such as gloves and safety glasses. When they occur, prompt removal of splinters and prevention of infection by expeditious cleansing and first aid treatment of wounds will minimize disability.

HEALTH EFFECTS AND DISEASE PATTERNS

Leon J. Warshaw

The health and safety problems in the forestry and lumber industries are covered elsewhere in this *Encyclopaedia*. This article will deal with wood as it arrives from the mill and is used in carpentry and the making of furniture and other articles. These activities are predominantly performed in small enterprises. Many workers in these industries are individual contractors and, therefore, often are not listed as employees, and large numbers of individuals are exposed in do-it-yourself projects and in-home workshops. This means that many of the workers involved are inadequately trained and are supervised poorly or not at all, while proper safeguards and protective equipment are often lacking.

Ahman and colleagues (1995a, 1995b, 1996) call attention to the exposure of teachers of industrial arts and woodworking in Sweden. In contrast to unexposed controls, these teachers had notable (but mainly reversible) nasal effects and complaints that increased with the number of classes from the beginning of the week and receded over the weekends, even though the dust concentrations were below the Swedish threshold limit of 2 mg/m³. In several establishments in the Netherlands, dust levels regularly exceeded that limit, and during sanding operations in a furniture factory, almost all exposures were over the local threshold limit of 5 mg/m³ (Scheeper, Kromhout and Boleij 1995).

Accidental Injuries

The most common health problem in the wood and woodworking industries is accidental injuries. These are more frequent among younger, inexperienced workers, and, for the most part, they are relatively minor. On occasion, however, they may involve long-term impairment or loss of an extremity. They include: splinters, which may become infected, and lacerations, gouges

Wood Dust

Wood dust exposure occurs whenever wood is sawed, chipped, planed, routed or sanded. The effects vary with the intensity and duration of the exposure and the size of the particles. Particles in the eyes may cause irritation, and wood dust gathering in skin folds may be aggravated by perspiration and chemicals and lead to irritation and infection. These effects may be reduced by vacuum removal of the dust, protective masks and clothing and good personal hygiene practices.

Nasopharyngeal and respiratory passages

Wood dust in the nasal passages may diminish mucociliary clearance and impair olfactory sensitivity (Andersen, Solgaard and Andersen 1976; Ahman et al. 1996). These may lead to irritation, frequent sneezing, nosebleeds and infection of the sinuses (Imbus 1994).

Exposures in a furniture factory (Whitehead, Ashikaga and Vacek 1981) and in sawmill workers (Hessel et al. 1995) were shown to be accompanied by decreases in both 1-second forced expiratory volume (FEV_1) and forced vital capacity (FVC), adjusted for age, height and smoking. These were accompanied by significant increases in shortness of breath and wheeze with chest tightness and the occurrence of bronchitis and asthma. There is, however, no convincing evidence of other non-cancer lung disease due to wood dust exposures (Imbus 1994). In a 6-year prospective follow-up study of approximately 350,000 males in the United States, the 11,541 individuals who reported having been employed in wood-related occupations had a lower relative risk of mortality due to non-malignant respiratory disease than those who did not report exposure to wood dust (Demers et al. 1996).

Allergy and Asthma

Some woods, notably teak, mansonia and radiata pine, contain chemicals that are irritants (see table 86.1 for an extended list of wood species, their geographic origins, and their health effects). Some species may cause allergic contact dermatitis (e.g., Douglas fir, western red cedar, poplar, rosewood, teak, African mahogany and other "exotic" woods). Western red cedar, rosewood, mahogany and other exotic woods have been shown to cause asthma (Imbus 1994).

Cancer

An unusually high incidence of nasal cancer has been described among woodworkers in Australia, Canada, Denmark, Finland, France, Italy, the Netherlands, the United Kingdom and the United States (Imbus 1994). A recent pooled re-analysis of 12 case-control cohort studies conducted in seven countries confirmed a high risk of nasopharyngeal cancer among woodworkers (Demers et al. 1995). The cause of these excesses of nasal cancer is not known, but, according to recent reports from the United Kingdom and the United States, the risk of nasal cancer among furniture workers has declined since the Second World War, presumably reflecting changes in the manufacturing process

(Imbus 1994). No excess risk of sino-nasal cancer was found among the 45,399 men exposed to wood dust included among the 362,823 men enrolled in the American Cancer Society's 6-year Cancer Prevention Study, but, the researchers note, the number of cases was small. They did, however, find an especially high increase in lung cancer mortality among woodworkers who also reported exposure to asbestos or formaldehyde, and suggested that exposure to these known carcinogens was responsible for the observed increased risk (Stellman et al., in press).

Chemical Exposures

Wood may contain biological contaminants. Moulds and fungi, which often grow on the bark of trees, may cause allergic reactions. Inhalation of fungal spores found on maple, redwood and cork trees has been shown to cause maple bark disease, sequoiosis and suberosis (Imbus 1994).

Wood often contains exogenous chemicals applied in the course of its processing. These include adhesives, solvents, resin binders, insecticides and fungicides, waterproofing compounds, paints and pigments, lacquers and varnishes. Many of these are volatile and may be emitted when the wood is treated, heated or incinerated; they are also conveyed as elements in wood dust. The most important of these include: toluene, methanol, xylene, methyl ethyl ketone, n-butyl alcohol, 1, 1,1-trichlorethane and dichloromethane (EPA 1995), many of which are known or suspected carcinogens.

Conclusion

Health hazards of the wood and woodworking industries may be controlled by installation of engineering controls (e.g., proper placement and guarding of power machinery, ventilation systems to control wood dust and chemical emissions) and personal protective equipment (e.g., gloves, safety glasses, respirators), coupled with periodic inspections to ensure that these are properly maintained and used. Perhaps most important is appropriate education and training of the workers and their supervisors.

Table 86.1 • Poisonous, allergenic and biologically active wood varieties.

Scientific names	Selected commercial names	Family	Health impairment
Abies alba Mill (A. pectinata D.C.)	Silver fir	Pinaceae	Dermatitis; conjunctivitis-rhinitis; asthma
Acacia spp. A. harpophylla F. Muell. A. melanoxylon R. Br. A. seyal Del. A. shirley Maiden	Australian blackwood	Mimosaceae	Dermatitis; conjunctivitis-rhinitis; asthma; toxic effects
Acer spp. A. platanoides L.	Maple	Aceraceae	Dermatitis
Afrormosia elata Harms. (Pericopsis elata Van Meeuwen)	Afrormosia, kokrodua, asamala, obang, oleo pardo, bohele, mohole	Papilionaceae	Dermatitis; conjunctivitis-rhinitis; asthma
Afzelia africana Smith A. bijuga A. Chev. (Intsia bijuga A. Cunn.) A. palembanica Bak. (Intsia palembanica Bak.)	Doussié, afzelia, aligua, apa, chanfuta, lingue merbau, intsia, hintsy	Caesalpinaceae	Dermatitis; conjunctivitis-rhinitis; asthma
Agonandra brasiliensis Miers	Pao, marfim, granadillo	Olacaceae	Dermatitis
Ailanthus altissima Mill	Chinese sumac	Simaroubaceae	Dermatitis
Albizzia falcata Backer A. ferruginea Benth. A. lebbek Benth. A. toona F.M. Bail	latandza Kokko, siris	Mimosaceae	Dermatitis; conjunctivitis-rhinitis; asthma; toxic effects
Alnus spp. A. glutinosa Gaertn.	Common alder, Black alder	Betulaceae	Dermatitis; conjunctivitis-rhinitis; asthma
Amyris spp. A. balsamifera L. A. toxifera Willd.	Venezuelan or West Indian sandalwood	Rutaceae	Dermatitis; toxic effects
Anacardium occidentale L. A. excelsum Skels.	Cashew	Anacardiaceae	Dermatitis
Andira araroba Aguiar. (Vataireopsis araroba Ducke) A. coriacea Pulle A. inermis H.B.K.	Red cabbage tree Partridge wood	Papilionaceae	Dermatitis; conjunctivitis-rhinitis; asthma
Aningeria spp. A. robusta Aubr. and Pell.	Aningeria	Sapotaceae	Conjunctivitis-rhinitis; asthma
A. altissima Aubr. and Pell. Antiaris africana Engl. A. welwitschi Engl.	Antiaris, ako, chen chen	Moraceae	Toxic effects
Apuleia molaris spruce (A. leiocarpa MacBride) (A. ferrea Mart.)	Redwood	Caesalpinaceae	Dermatitis; toxic effects
Araucaria angustifolia O. Ktze A. brasiliana A. Rich.	Parana pine, araucaria	Araucariaceae	Toxic effects

Continues on next page.

Table 86.1 • Poisonous, allergenic and biologically active wood varieties.
Continued

Scientific names	Selected commercial names	Family	Health impairment
Aspidosperma spp. A. peroba Fr. All. A. vargasii A. DC.	Red peroba Pau marfim, pau amarello, pequia marfim, guatambu, amarilla, pequia	Apocynaceae	Dermatitis; conjunctivitis-rhinitis; asthma; toxic effects
Astrocaryum spp.	Palm	Palmaceae	Dermatitis; toxic effects
Aucoumea klaineana Pierre	Gabon mahogany	Burseraceae	Dermatitis; conjunctivitis-rhinitis; asthma; allergic extrinsic alveolitis
Autranella congolensis A. Chev. (Mimusops congolensis De Wild.)	Mukulungu, autracon, elang, bouanga, kulungu	Sapotaceae	Dermatitis
Bactris spp. (Astrocaryum spp.)	Palm	Palmaceae	Dermatitis; toxic effects
Balfourodendron riedelianum Engl.	Guatambu, gutambu blanco	Rutaceae	Dermatitis
Batesia floribunda Benth.	Acapu rana	Caesalpinaceae	Toxic effects
Berberis vulgaris L.	Barberry	Berberidaceae	Toxic effects
Betula spp. B. alba L. (B. pendula Roth.)	Birch	Betulaceae	Dermatitis
Blepharocarva involucrigera F. Muell.	Rosebutternut	Anacardiaceae	Dermatitis; conjunctivitis-rhinitis; asthma;
Bombax brevicuspe Sprague B. chevalieri Pell	Kondroti, alone	Bombacaceae	Dermatitis
Bowdichia spp. B. nitida Benth. B. guianensis Ducke (Diplotropis guianensis Benth.) (Diplotropis purpurea Amsh.)	Black sucupira	Papilionaceae	Dermatitis
Brachylaena hutchinsii Hutch.	Muhuhu	Compositae	Dermatitis
Breonia spp.	Molompangady	Rubiaceae	Dermatitis
Brosimum spp. B. guianense Hub. (Piratinera guianensis Aubl.)	Snakewood, letterwood, tigerwood	Moraceae	Dermatitis; conjunctivitis-rhinitis; asthma; toxic effects
Brya ebenus DC. (Amerimnum ebenus Sw.) Brya buxifolia Urb.	Brown ebony, green ebony, Jamaican ebony, tropical American ebony	Papilionaceae	Dermatitis
Buxus sempervirens L. B. macowani Oliv.	European boxwood, East London b., Cape b.	Buxaceae	Dermatitis; conjunctivitis-rhinitis; asthma; toxic effects
Caesalpinia echinata Lam. (Guilandina echinata Spreng.)	Brasilwood	Caesalpinaceae	Dermatitis; toxic effects
Callitris columellaris F. Muell.	White cypress pine	Cupressaceae	Dermatitis; conjunctivitis-rhinitis; asthma
Calophyllum spp. C. brasiliense Camb.	Santa maria, jacareuba, kurahura, galba	Guttiferae	Dermatitis; toxic effects
Campsiandra laurifolia Benth.	Acapu rana	Caesalpinaceae	Toxic effects
Carpinus betulus	Hornbeam	Betulaceae	Dermatitis
Cassia siamea Lamk.	Tagayasan, muong ten, djohar	Caesalpinaceae	Dermatitis; conjunctivitis-rhinitis; asthma
Castanea dentata Borkh C. sativa Mill. C. pumila Mill.	Chestnut, sweet chestnut	Fagaceae	Dermatitis; conjunctivitis-rhinitis; asthma
Castanospermum australe A. Cunn.	Black bean, Australian or Moreton Bay chestnut	Papilionaceae	Dermatitis
Cedrela spp. (Toona spp.)	Red cedar, Australian cedar	Meliaceae	Dermatitis; conjunctivitis-rhinitis; asthma
Cedrus deodara (Roxb. ex. Lamb.) G. Don (C. libani Barrel. lc)	Deodar	Pinaceae	Dermatitis; conjunctivitis-rhinitis; asthma
Celtis brieyi De Wild. C. cinnamomea Ldl.	Diania Gurenda	Ulmaceae	Dermatitis
Chlorophora excelsa Benth. and Hook I. C. regia A. Chev. C. tinctoria (L.) Daub.	Iroko, gelbholz, yellowood, kambala, mvule, odum, moule, African teak, abang, tatajuba, fustic, mora	Moraceae	Dermatitis; conjunctivitis-rhinitis; asthma; allergic extrinsic alveolitis

Continues on next page.

Table 86.1 • Poisonous, allergenic and biologically active wood varieties.
Continued

Scientific names	Selected commercial names	Family	Health impairment
Chloroxylon spp. *C. swietenia* A.DC.	Ceylon satinwood	Rutaceae	Dermatitis; toxic effects
Chrysophyllum spp.	Najara	Sapotaceae	Dermatitis
Cinnamomum camphora Nees and Ebeim	Asian camphorwood, cinnamon	Lauraceae	Toxic effects
Cryptocarya pleurosperma White and Francis	Poison walnut	Lauraceae	Dermatitis; conjunctivitis-rhinitis; asthma; toxic effects
Dacrycarpus dacryoides (A. Rich.) de Laub.	New Zealand white pine	Podocarpaceae	Dermatitis; conjunctivitis-rhinitis; asthma
Dacrydium cupressinum Soland	Sempilor, rimu	Podocarpaceae	conjunctivitis-rhinitis; asthma
Dactylocladus stenostachys Oliv.	Jong kong, merebong, medang tabak	Melastomaceae	Toxic effects

Dalbergia spp.
  D. amerimnon Benth.
  D. granadillo Pitt.
  D. hypoleuca Standl.
  D. latifolia Roxb.
  D. melanoxylon Guill. and Perr.
  D. nigra Fr. All.
 	
  D. oliveri Gamble
  D. retusa Hemsl.
  D. sissoo Roxb.
  D. stevensonii Standl.
	Ebony
	
	Red foxwood
	
	Indian rosewood, Bombay blackwood,
	  African blackwood, pallisander,
	  riopalissandro, Brasilian rosewood,
	  jacaranda
	Burma rosewood
	Red foxwood
	Nagaed wood, Honduras rosewood
		Papilionaceae	Dermatitis; conjunctivitis-rhinitis; asthma;
			  toxic effects

Dialium spp. *D. dinklangeri* Harms.	Eyoum, eyum	Caesalpinaceae	Dermatitis; conjunctivitis-rhinitis; asthma

Diospyros spp.
  D. celebica Bakh.
  D. crassiflora Hiern
  D. ebenum Koenig
	Ebony, African ebony
	
	  Macassar ebony, African ebony,
	  Ceylon ebony
		Ebenaceae	Dermatitis; conjunctivitis-rhinitis; asthma;
			  toxic effects

Dipterocarpus spp. *D. alatus* Roxb.	Keruing, gurjum, yang, keruing	Dipterocarpaceae	Dermatitis
Distemonanthus benthamianus Baill.	Movingui, ayan, anyaran, Nigerian satinwood	Caesalpinaceae	Dermatitis

Dysoxylum spp.
  D. fraseranum Benth.
  D. muelleri Benth.
	Mahogany, stavewood, red bean
	
	  Rose mahogany
		Meliaceae	Dermatitis; conjunctivitis-rhinitis; asthma;
			  toxic effects

Echirospermum balthazarii Fr. All. (*Plathymenia reticulata* Benth.)	Vinhatico	Mimosaceae	Dermatitis; conjunctivitis-rhinitis; asthma

Entandophragma spp.
  E. angolense C.D.C.
  E. candollei Harms.
  E. cylindricum Sprague
  E. utile Sprague
	Tiama
	  Kosipo, omo
	  Sapelli, sapele, aboudikro
	  Sipo, utile, assié,
	  kalungi, mufumbi
		Meliaceae	Dermatitis; allergic extrinsic alveolitis

Erythrophloeum guineense G. Don
  E. ivorense A. Chev.
	Tali, missanda, eloun, massanda, sasswood,
	  erun, redwater tree
		Caesalpinaceae	Dermatitis; conjunctivitis-rhinitis; asthma;
			  toxic effects

Esenbeckia leiocarpa Engl.	Guaranta	Rutaceae	Dermatitis

Eucalyptus spp.
  E. delegatensis R.T. Back
  E. hemiphloia F. Muell.
  E. leucoxylon Maiden
  E. maculata Hook.
  E. marginata Donn ex Sm.
  E. microtheca F. Muell.
  E. obliqua L. Herit.
  E. regnans F. Muell.
  E. saligna Sm.
	
	Alpine ash
	Grey box
	Yellow gum
	Spotted gum
	
	Mountain ash
		Myrtaceae	Dermatitis; conjunctivitis-rhinitis; asthma

Euxylophora paraensis Hub.	Boxwood	Rutaceae	Dermatitis; conjunctivitis-rhinitis; asthma

Continues on next page.

86. WOODWORKING

Table 86.1 • Poisonous, allergenic and biologically active wood varieties.
Continued

Scientific names	Selected commercial names	Family	Health impairment
Excoecaria africana M. Arg. (*Spirostachys africana* Sand) *E. agallocha* L.	African sandalwood, tabootie, geor, aloewood, blind-your-eye	Euphorbiaceae	Dermatitis; conjunctivitis-rhinitis; asthma; toxic effects
Fagara spp. *F. flava* Krug and Urb. (*Zanthoxylum flavum* Vahl.) *F. heitzii* Aubr. and Pell. *F. macrophylla* Engl.	Yellow sanders, West Indian satinwood, atlaswood, olon, bongo, mbanza	Rutaceae	Dermatitis; conjunctivitis-rhinitis; asthma; toxic effects
Fagus spp. (*Nothofagus* spp.) *F. sylvatica* L.	Beech	Fagaceae	Dermatitis; conjunctivitis-rhinitis; asthma
Fitzroya cupressoides (Molina) Johnston (*F. patagonica* Hook. f.)	Alerce	Cupressaceae	Dermatitis
Flindersia australis R. Br. *F. brayleyana* F. Muell. *F. pimenteliana* F. Muell.	Australian teak, Queensland maple, maple Silkwood, Australian maple	Rutaceae	Dermatitis
Fraxinus spp. *F. excelsior* L.	Ash	Oleaceae	Dermatitis
Gluta spp. *G. rhengas* L. (*Melanorrhoea* spp.) *M. curtisii* Pierre *M. laccifera wallichii* Hook.	Rengas, gluta Renga wood Rhengas	Anacardiaceae	Dermatitis; toxic effects
Gonioma kamassi E. Mey.	Knysna boxwood, kamassi	Apocynaceae	Dermatitis; conjunctivitis-rhinitis; asthma; toxic effects
Gonystylus bancanus Baill.	Ramin, melawis, akenia	Gonystylaceae	Dermatitis; conjunctivitis-rhinitis; asthma; allergic extrinsic alveolitis
Gossweilerodendron balsamiferum (Verm.) Harms.	Nigerian cedar	Caesalpinaceae	Dermatitis; conjunctivitis-rhinitis; asthma
Grevillea robusta A. Cunn.	Silky oak	Proteaceae	Dermatitis
Guaiacum officinale L.	Gaiac, lignum vitae	Zygophyllaceae	Dermatitis; conjunctivitis-rhinitis; asthma
Guarea spp. *G. cedrata* Pell. *G. laurentii* De Wild. *G. thompsonii* Sprague	Bossé Nigerian pearwood, cedar mahogany Scented guarea Black guarea	Meliaceae	Dermatitis; conjunctivitis-rhinitis; asthma; toxic effects
Halfordia scleroxyla F. Muell. *H. papuana* Lauterb.	Saffron-heart	Polygonaceae	Dermatitis; allergic extrinsic alveolitis
Hernandia spp. *H. sonora* L. (*H. guianensis* Aubl.)	Mirobolan, topolite	Hernandiaceae	Dermatitis
Hippomane mancinella L.	Beach apple	Euphorbiaceae	Dermatitis; conjunctivitis-rhinitis; asthma; toxic effects
Illipe latifolia F. Muell. *I. longifolia* F. Muell. (*Bassia latifolia* Roxb.) (*B. longifolia* Roxb.)	Moak, edel teak	Sapotaceae	Dermatitis
Jacaranda spp. *J. brasiliana* Pers. Syn. (*Bignonia brasiliana* Lam.) *J. coerulea* (I.) Gris.	Jacaranda Caroba, boxwood	Bignoniaceae	Dermatitis
Juglans spp. *J. nigra* L. *J. regia* L.	Walnut	Juglandaceae	Dermatitis; conjunctivitis-rhinitis; asthma
Juniperus sabina L. *J. phoenicea* L. *J. virginiana* L.	 Virginian pencil cedar, Eastern red cedar	Cupressaceae	Dermatitis; conjunctivitis-rhinitis; asthma; toxic effects
Khaya antotheca C. DC. *K. ivorensis* A. Chev. *K. senegalensis* A. Juss.	Ogwango, African mahogany, krala Dry-zone mahogany	Meliaceae	Dermatitis; allergic extrinsic alveolitis

Continues on next page.

Table 86.1 • Poisonous, allergenic and biologically active wood varieties.
Continued

Scientific names	Selected commercial names	Family	Health impairment
Laburnum anagyroides Medic. (*Cytisus laburnum* L.) *L. vulgare* Gris	Laburnum	Papilionaceae	Dermatitis; conjunctivitis-rhinitis; asthma; toxic effects
Larix spp. *L. decidua* Mill. *L. europea* D.C.	Larch European larch	Pinaceae	Dermatitis; conjunctivitis-rhinitis; asthma
Liquidambar styracifolia L.	Amberbaum, satin-nussbaum	Hamamelidaceae	Dermatitis
Liriodendron tulipifera L.	American whitewood, tulip tree	Magnoliaceae	Dermatitis
Lovoa trichilioides Harms. (*L. klaineana* Pierre)	Dibetou, African walnut, apopo, tigerwood, side	Meliaceae	Dermatitis; conjunctivitis-rhinitis; asthma; toxic effects
Lucuma spp. (*Pouteria* spp.) *L. procera*	Guapeva, abiurana Massaranduba	Sapotaceae	Dermatitis; conjunctivitis-rhinitis; asthma
Maba ebenus Wight.	Makassar-ebenholz	Ebenaceae	Dermatitis
Machaerium pedicellatum Vog. *M. scleroxylon* Tul. *M. violaceum* Vog.	Kingswood	Papilionaceae	Dermatitis
Mansonia altissima A. Chev.	Nigerian walnut	Sterculiaceae	Dermatitis; conjunctivitis-rhinitis; asthma; toxic effects
Melanoxylon brauna Schott	Brauna, grauna	Caesalpinaceae	Dermatitis
Microberlinia brazzavillensis A. Chev. *M. bisulcata* A. Chev.	African zebrawood	Caesalpinaceae	Dermatitis; conjunctivitis-rhinitis; asthma; toxic effects
Millettia laurentii De Wild. *M. stuhlmannii* Taub.	Wenge Panga-panga	Papilionaceae	Dermatitis; conjunctivitis-rhinitis; asthma; toxic effects
Mimusops spp. (*Manilkara* spp.) *Mimusops* spp. (*Dumoria* spp.) (*Tieghemella* spp.) *M. congolensis* De Wild. (*Autranella congolensis* A. Chev.) *M. djave* Engl. (*Baillonella toxisperma* Pierre) *M. heckelii* Hutch. et Dalz. (*Tieghemella heckelii* Pierre) (*Dumoria heckelii* A. Chev.)	Muirapiranga Makoré Mukulungu, autracon Moabi Cherry mahogany	Sapotaceae	Dermatitis; conjunctivitis-rhinitis; asthma; allergic extrinsic alveolitis; toxic effects
Mitragyna ciliata Aubr. and Pell. *M. stipulosa* O. Ktze	Vuku, African poplar Abura	Rubiaceae	Dermatitis; conjunctivitis-rhinitis; asthma; toxic effects
Nauclea diderrichii Merrill (*Sarcocephalus diderrichii* De Wild.) *Nauclea trillessi* Merrill	Bilinga, opepe, kussia, badi, West African boxwood	Rubiaceae	Dermatitis; conjunctivitis-rhinitis; asthma; toxic effects
Nesogordonia papaverifera R. Capuron	Kotibé, danta, epro, otutu, ovové, aborbora	Tiliaceae	Toxic effects
Ocotea spp. *O. bullata* E. Mey *O. porosa* L. Barr. (*Phoebe porosa* Mez.) *O. rodiaei* Mez. (*Nectandra rodiaei* Schomb.) *O. rubra* Mez. *O. usambarensis* Engl.	Stinkwood Laurel, Brazilian walnut Greenheart Louro vermelho East African camphorwood	Lauraceae	Dermatitis; conjunctivitis-rhinitis; asthma; toxic effects
Paratecoma spp. *P. alba* *P. peroba* Kuhlm.	Brazilian white peroba Peroba white. p.	Bignoniaceae	Dermatitis; conjunctivitis-rhinitis; asthma; toxic effects
Parinarium spp. *P. guianense* (*Parinari* spp.) (*Brosimum* spp.) *P. variegatum*	Guyana-satinholz Antillen-satinholz	Rosaceae	Dermatitis
Peltogyne spp. *P. densiflora* Spruce	Blue wood, purpleheart	Caesalpinaceae	Toxic effects
Phyllanthus ferdinandi F.v.M.	Lignum vitae, chow way, tow war	Euphorbiaceae	Dermatitis; conjunctivitis-rhinitis; asthma

Continues on next page.

Table 86.1 • Poisonous, allergenic and biologically active wood varieties.
Continued

Scientific names	Selected commercial names	Family	Health impairment
Picea spp. P. abies Karst. P. excelsa Link. P. mariana B.S.P. P. polita Carr.	European spruce, whitewood Black spruce	Pinaceae	Dermatitis; conjunctivitis-rhinitis; asthma; allergic extrinsic alveolitis
Pinus spp. P. radiata D. Don	Pine	Pinaceae	Dermatitis; conjunctivitis-rhinitis; asthma
Piptadenia africana Hook f. Piptadeniastrum africanum Brenan	Dabema, dahoma, ekhimi agobin, mpewere, bukundu	Mimosaceae	Dermatitis; conjunctivitis-rhinitis; asthma
Platanus spp.	Plane	Platanaceae	Dermatitis
Pometia spp. P. pinnata Forst.	Taun Kasai	Sapindaceae	Dermatitis; conjunctivitis-rhinitis; asthma
Populus spp.	Poplar	Salicaceae	Dermatitis; conjunctivitis-rhinitis; asthma
Prosopis juliflora D.C.	Cashaw	Mimosaceae	Dermatitis
Prunus spp. P. serotina Ehrl.	Cherry Blackcherry	Rosaceae	Dermatitis; conjunctivitis-rhinitis; asthma
Pseudomorus brunoniana Bureau	White handlewood	Moraceae	Dermatitis; toxic effects
Pseudotsuga douglasii Carr. (P. menziesii Franco)	Douglas fir, red fir, Douglas spruce	Pinaceae	Dermatitis; conjunctivitis-rhinitis; asthma
Pterocarpus spp. P. angolensis D.C. P. indicus Willd. P. santalinus L.f. (Vatairea guianensis Aubl.)	African padauk, New Guinea rosewood, red sandalwood, red sanders, quassia wood	Papilionaceae	Dermatitis; conjunctivitis-rhinitis; asthma; toxic effects
Pycnanthus angolensis Warb. (P. kombo Warb.)	Ilomba	Myristicaceae	Toxic effects
Quercus spp.	Oak	Fagaceae	Dermatitis; conjunctivitis-rhinitis; asthma
Raputia alba Engl. R. magnifica Engl.	Arapoca branca, arapoca	Rutaceae	Dermatitis
Rauwolfia pentaphylla Stapf. O.	Peroba	Apocynaceae	Dermatitis; conjunctivitis-rhinitis; asthma; toxic effects
Sandoricum spp. S. indicum Cav.	Sentul, katon, kra-ton, ketjapi, thitto	Meliaceae	Dermatitis; conjunctivitis-rhinitis; asthma; toxic effects
Schinopsis lorentzii Engl. S. balansae Engl.	Quebracho colorado, red q., San Juan, pau mulato	Anacardiaceae	Dermatitis; toxic effects
Semercarpus australiensis Engl. S. anacardium L.	Marking nut	Anacardiaceae	Dermatitis; toxic effects
Sequoia sempervirens Endl.	Sequoia, California redwood	Taxodiaceae	Dermatitis; conjunctivitis-rhinitis; asthma; toxic effects
Shorea spp.	Alan, almon, red balau, white heavy, red lauan, white L., yellow L., mayapis, meranti bakau, dark red M., light red M., red M., white M., yellow M., red seraya, white seraya	Dipterocarpaceae	Dermatitis
S. assamica Dyer	Yellow lauan, white meranti		
Staudtia stipitata Warb. (S. gabonensis Warb.)	Niové	Myristicaceae	Dermatitis
Swietenia spp. S. macrophylla King S. mahogany Jacq.	Mahogany, Honduras mahogany, Tabasco m., baywood, American mahogany, Cuban mahogany	Meliaceae	Dermatitis; conjunctivitis-rhinitis; asthma; allergic extrinsic alveolitis; toxic effects
Swintonia spicifera Hook. S. floribunda Griff.	Merpauh	Anacardiaceae	Dermatitis
Tabebuia spp. T. ipe Standl. (T. avellanedae Lor. ex Gris.) T. guayacan Hensl. (T. lapacho K. Schum)	Araguan, ipé preto, lapacho	Bignoniaceae	Dermatitis; conjunctivitis-rhinitis; asthma; toxic effects

Continues on next page.

86. WOODWORKING

Table 86.1 • Poisonous, allergenic and biologically active wood varieties.
Continued

Scientific names	Selected commercial names	Family	Health impairment
Taxus baccata L.	Yew	Taxaceae	Dermatitis; conjunctivitis-rhinitis; asthma; allergic extrinsic alveolitis; toxic effects

Tecoma spp.
  T. araliacea D.C.
  T. lapacho
	Green heart
	  Lapacho
		Bignoniaceae	Dermatitis; conjunctivitis-rhinitis; asthma; toxic effects

Tectona grandis L.	Teak, djati, kyun, teck	Verbenaceae	Dermatitis; conjunctivitis-rhinitis; asthma; allergic extrinsic alveolitis

Terminalia alata Roth.
  T. superba Engl. and Diels.
	Indian laurel
	  limba, afara, ofram, fraké, korina, akom
		Combretaceae	Dermatitis; conjunctivitis-rhinitis; asthma

Thuja occidentalis L.
  T. plicata D. Don
  T. standishii Carr.
	White cedar
	  Western red cedar
		Cupressaceae	Dermatitis; conjunctivitis-rhinitis; asthma; toxic effects

Tieghemella africana A. Chev. (*Dumoria* spp.) *T. heckelii* Pierre	Makoré, douka, okola, ukola, makoré, abacu, baku, African cherry	Sapotaceae	Dermatitis; conjunctivitis-rhinitis; asthma; toxic effects
Triplochiton scleroxylon K. Schum	Obeche, samba, wawa, abachi, African whitewood, arere	Sterculiaceae	Dermatitis; conjunctivitis-rhinitis; asthma
Tsuga heterophylla Sarg.	Tsuga, Western hemlock	Pinaceae	Dermatitis
Turraeanthus africana Pell.	Avodiré Lusamba	Meliaceae	Dermatitis; allergic extrinsic alveolitis
Ulmus spp.	Elm	Ulmaceae	Dermatitis

Vitex ciliata Pell.
  V. congolensis De Wild. and Th. Dur
  V. pachyphylla Bak.
	Difundu
	  Evino
		Verbenaceae	Dermatitis

Xylia dolabriformis Benth. *X. xylocarpa* Taub.	Pyinkado	Mimosaceae	Conjunctivitis-rhinitis; asthma
Zollernia paraensis Huber	Santo wood	Caesalpinaceae	Dermatitis; toxic effects

Source: Istituto del Legno, Florence, Italy.

References

Ahman, M, E Soderman, I Cynkier, and B Kolmodin-Hedman. 1995a. Work-related respiratory problems in industrial arts teachers. *Int Arch Occup Environ Health* 67:111–118.

Ahman, M, M Holmstrom, and H Ingelman-Sundberg. 1995b. Inflammatory markers in nasal lavage fluid from industrial arts teachers. *Am J Ind Med* 28:541–550.

Ahman, M, M Holmstrom, I Cynkier, and E Soderman. 1996. Work-related impairment of nasal function in Swedish woodwork teachers. *Occup Environ Med* 53:112–117.

Andersen, HC, J Solgaard, and I Andersen. 1976. Nasal cancer and nasal mucus-transport rates in woodworkers. *Acta Otolaryngol* 82:263–265.

Demers, PA, M Kogevinas, P Boffetta, A Leclerc, D Luce, M Guerin, G Battista, S Belli, U Bolm-Audorf, LA Brinton et al. 1995. Wood dust and sino-nasal cancer: Pooled reanalysis of twelve case-control studies. *Am J Ind Med* 28:151–166.

Demers, PA, SD Stellman, D Colin, and P Boffetta. 1996. Non-malignant respiratory disease mortality among wood workers participating in the American Cancer Society Cancer Prevention Study-2 (CPS-II). Presented at the 25th meeting of the International Congress on Occupational Health, Stockholm, 15–20 September.

Environmental Protection Agency (EPA). 1995. *EPA Office of Compliance Sector Notebook Project: Profile of the Wood Furniture and Fixtures Industry*. Washington, DC: EPA.

Hessel, PA, FA Herbert, LS Melenka, K Yoshida, D Michaelchuk, and M Nakaza. 1995. Lung health in sawmill workers exposed to pine and spruce. *Chest* 108:642–646.

Imbus, H. 1994. Wooddust. In *Physical and Biological Hazards in the Workplace*, edited by PH Wald and GM Stave. New York: Van Nostrand Reinhold.

Ma, W-S A, M-JJ Wang, and FS Chou. 1991. Evaluating the mechanical injury problem in the wood-bamboo furniture manufacturing industry. *Int J Ind Erg* 7:347–355.

Nestor, DE, TG Bobick, and TJ Pizatella. 1990. Ergonomic evaluation of a cabinet manufacturing facility. In *Proceedings of the Human Factors Society, 34th Annual Meeting*. Santa Monica, CA: Human Factors Society.

Scheeper, B, H Kromhout, and JS Boleij. 1995. Wood dust exposure during wood-working processes. *Ann Occup Hyg* 39:141–154.

Stellman, SD, PA Demers, D Colin, and P Boffetta. In press. Cancer mortality and wood dust exposure among CPS-II participants. *Am J Ind Med*.

Whitehead, LW, T Ashikaga, and P Vacek. 1981. Pulmonary function status of workers exposed to hardwood or pine dust. *Am Ind Hyg Assoc* 42:1780–1786.

87

Chapter Editors
Robin Herbert and Rebecca Plattus

Contents

87. CLOTHING AND FINISHED TEXTILE PRODUCTS

● MAJOR SECTORS AND PROCESSES

Rebecca Plattus and Robin Herbert

Overall Processes

In general, the processes involved in the production of clothing and other finished textile products have changed little since the inception of the industry. Although the organization of the production process has changed, and continues to change, and some technological advances have upgraded machinery, many of the safety and health hazards in this industry remain the same as those facing the earliest apparel workers.

The major health and safety concerns in the apparel industry are related to general conditions of the work environment. Poorly designed workstations, tools and equipment, combined with piece-rate compensation systems and the progressive bundle system of production, pose serious risks of musculoskeletal injury and stress-related conditions. Garment shops are often housed in buildings that are poorly maintained and inadequately ventilated, cooled, heated and lit. Overcrowding, together with improper storage of flammable materials, frequently creates serious fire hazards. Poor sanitation and lack of proper housekeeping measures contribute to these conditions.

Figure 87.1 • A sequin-manufacturing facility.

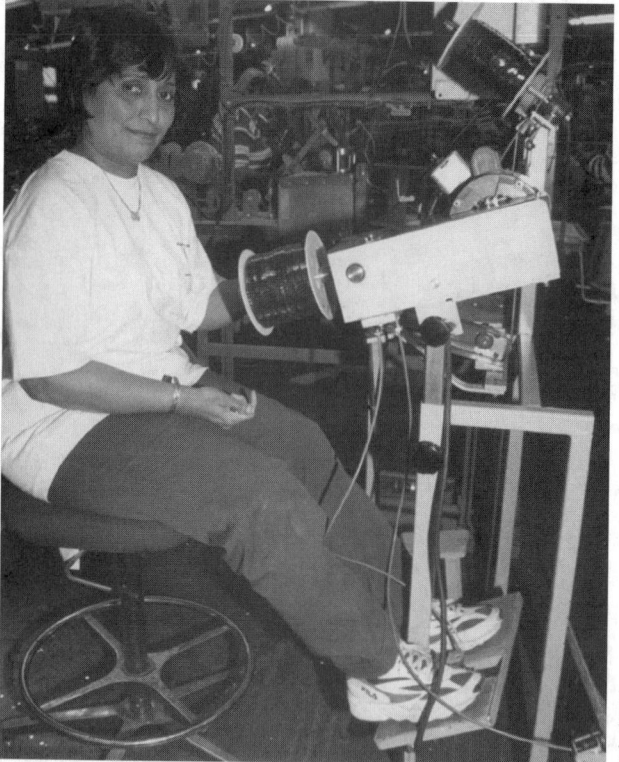

In this facility a comprehensive ergonomics programme was initiated to prevent work-related musculo-skeletal disorders. Prior to this intervention, garment workers were required to repetitively turn a manual, waist-height crank with the right hand while simultaneously holding threaded sequins with the left hand. After introduction of an ergonomics programme that featured education, engineering control changes (including an adjustable chair and an adjustable and automated foot pedal) and work enlargement, there was an improvement in neutral joint postures and a decrease in musculoskeletal symptomatology.

Major advances have been made in the design and production of well-designed, ergonomic sewing workstations that include adjustable sewing tables and chairs and take into consideration proper positioning of equipment and tools. These workstations are widely available and are in use in some facilities, mostly large manufacturing establishments. However, only the largest, best-capitalized facilities are able to afford these amenities. Ergonomic redesign is also possible in other clothing manufacturing operations (see figure 87.1). The majority of apparel production, however, still takes place in small, ill-equipped contracting operations where, in general, little attention is paid to workplace design, working conditions and health and safety hazards.

Product design and sample-making. The design of clothing and other textile products is overseen by apparel manufacturers, retailers or "jobbers", with the design process performed by skilled designers. Apparel jobbers, manufacturers or retailers are frequently responsible only for the design, sample production and marketing of the product. While the jobber or manufacturer takes responsibility for specifying all details of the garment's production, purchases the fabric and trims items to be used, the actual large-scale production work is typically performed by independent contracting shops.

Sample-making, in which small numbers of sample garments are made to be used to market the product and to be sent to contracting shops as examples of the finished product, also takes place on the jobber's premises. Samples are produced by highly skilled sewing machine operators, sample-makers, who sew the entire garment.

Pattern-making and cutting. Garment design must be broken down into pattern parts for cutting and sewing. Traditionally, cardboard patterns are made up for each piece of the garment; these patterns are graded by the sizes to be made. From these patterns, paper-cutting markers are created, which are used by the garment cutter to cut out the pattern pieces. In more modern plants, cutting markers are made up and graded for size on a computer screen, then printed on a computerized plotter.

In the cutting phase, fabric is first spread into multiple piles on a cutting table, the length and width of which is determined by production demands. This is most often performed by an automatic or semi-automatic spreading machine which unrolls the bolts of fabric along the length of the table. Plaid or print fabrics may be laid out by hand and pinned to assure that plaids for prints will match. Markers are then laid down on the fabric to be cut.

Fabric for apparel production is usually cut using hand-held band saw cutting tools (see figure 87.2). Small parts may be cut using a die press. Advanced cutting technology includes robotic cutting, which automatically follows patterns made on a computer.

There are several hazards associated with fabric cutting. Although the blade on the cutting tool is guarded, this guard must be correctly set in order to afford the necessary protection to the hand positioning the material. Guards should always be used and correctly positioned. As an additional protection it is recommended that cutting machine operators wear a protective glove, preferably of metal mesh. Besides posing the risk of accidental cuts, cutting fabric also presents ergonomic risks. Supporting and manoeuvering a cutting machine, while stretching across the cutting table, can present a risk of neck, upper-extremity and back disorders. Finally, many cutters have a tendency to work with the cutting machine at ear level, often exposing themselves to excessive noise with the attendant risk of noise-induced hearing loss.

Handling rolls of fabric, which can weigh up to 32 kg and must be lifted above the head onto a rack for spreading, also poses an ergonomic hazard. Proper material-handling equipment can eliminate or reduce these risks.

Figure 87.2 • A clothing factory in the Philippines.

Sewing machine operation. Typically, cut fabric pieces are sewn together on sewing machines operated by hand. The traditional "progressive bundle system", in which bundles of cut pieces progress from one sewing machine operator to the next, with each operator performing a different single operation, continues to prevail in the industry, despite significant changes in work organization in many shops. This type of work organization breaks the production process down into many different operations, each consisting of a very short cycle repeated hundreds of times by one operator during the course of a workday. This system, combined with piece-rate pay compensation that rewards speed above all else and affords workers very little control over the production process, creates a potentially very stressful work environment.

The majority of the sewing machine workstations currently in use are designed without the comfort, health or convenience of the sewing machine operator in mind (see figure 87.3). Because sewing machine operators generally work in a seated position at poorly designed workstations, performing the same operation during the entire course of the workday, the risk of developing musculoskeletal disorders is high. The poor postures resulting from the conditions described above, combined with highly repetitive, time-pressured work, has resulted in high rates of work-related musculoskeletal disorders (WRMDs) among sewing machine operators and other workers in the industry.

Advances in sewing workstation design, such as adjustable chairs and worktables, create the potential for reduction of some of the risks associated with sewing machine operation. However, while these workstations and chairs are widely available, their price often places them out of reach of all but the most profitable enterprises. Additionally, even with better-designed workstations, the risk factor of repetition remains.

Changes in the organization of work and the introduction of teamwork, in the form of modular or flexible manufacturing, offer an alternative to the traditional, Taylorist production process and may serve to alleviate some of the health risks involved in the traditional system. In a teamwork system sewing machine operators work in a group to produce an entire garment, often shifting frequently between machines and jobs.

In one of the most popular team systems, workers work standing up, rather than seated, and move frequently from machine to machine. Cross-training for a variety of jobs enhances workers'

skills, and workers are given more control over production. Changes from an individual piece-rate system of pay to hourly pay or to a group incentive system, as well as increased emphasis on monitoring quality throughout the production process, may help to eliminate some factors that put workers at risk of developing WRMDs.

Some newer manufacturing systems, while technologically advanced, may actually contribute to increased risk of WRMD. So-called unit production systems, for example, are designed to mechanically convey cut goods on an overhead conveyor from worker to worker, thus speeding up the progress of the goods and eliminating much of the material handling previously performed by the sewing machine operators or by floor workers. While these systems often increase production by speeding up the line, they eliminate the already small rest time that was afforded to the operator between cycles, resulting in increased fatigue and repetition.

When instituting any alternative production system, care should be taken to evaluate risk factors and design the new system with ergonomics in mind. For example, when workers will be trained to do a variety of jobs, jobs should be combined to stress differing parts of the body and not overtax any one muscle or joint. Care should be taken to ensure that equipment and machinery can be adapted to fit all the workers in the team.

Whenever any new equipment is purchased, it should be easily adjustable by the workers themselves, and training should be provided on how to make adjustments. This is particularly important in the apparel industry, where mechanics are often not readily available to adjust equipment to properly fit workers.

Recent studies have raised concerns about sewing machine operators' exposure to high levels of electromagnetic fields (EMFs) generated by sewing machine motors. These studies have indi-

Figure 87.3 • Woman using a sewing machine without a needle guard.

87. CLOTHING AND FINISHED TEXTILE PRODUCTS

cated that there may be an association between increased levels of Alzheimer's disease (Sobel et al. 1995) and other chronic diseases found among sewing machine operators and the operators' exposure to high levels of EMFs.

Finishing and pressing. Once sewn, the completed garment is ironed by pressers and checked for loose threads, stains and other defects by finishers. Finishers perform a variety of hand work, including clipping loose threads, hand sewing, turning and hand pressing. Ergonomic hazards are a problem for workers who finish, ticket, pack and distribute apparel. They often perform highly repetitive tasks, frequently involving working with the hands and arms in awkward and unhealthy postures. Seating and workstations for these workers are rarely adjustable or designed for comfort or health. Finishing workers, including pressers, often work standing and in static positions, despite the fact that many of the jobs could be equipped with chairs, stools or sit-stand chairs, and workers could alternate between standing and sitting. Table tops could be adjusted to the proper height for the operator and could be tilted to enable the operator to work in a more comfortable position. Padded table edges and properly designed and sized tools could eliminate some stresses on hands, wrists and arms.

Pressing the sewn product is performed either using a hand iron or a buck press. Sewn products may also be steamed using a hand steamer or a steam tunnel. Presses and irons may present risks of burns, as well as ergonomic hazards. While most presses are designed with two-handed controls, eliminating the possibility of getting the hand stuck in the press, some old machines still exist which do not have these safety features. Working a pressing machine also presents the risks of shoulder, neck and back injury caused by frequent overhead reaching and by constant standing and operating the foot pedals. While the job can be made safer by a more highly automated machine and by proper positioning of the worker at the machine, the current machinery makes it difficult to eliminate the high stress.

Ticketers, who use ticketing guns to place tags on finished garments, are at risk of hand and wrist injury from this highly repetitive operation. Automatic, as opposed to manual, ticketing guns can help decrease the force needed to perform the operation, greatly reducing stress and strain on the fingers and hands.

Distribution. Workers in apparel distribution centres are exposed to all the hazards of other warehouse workers. Manual material handling accounts for many of the injuries in warehouse operations. Particular hazards include lifting and overhead work. Designing the distribution workplace with the proper handling of materials in mind, such as placement of conveyors and worktables at appropriate heights, can help prevent many injuries. Mechanical material-handling equipment, such as fork-lifts and hoists, can help prevent injuries caused by having to perform awkward or heavy lifts.

Chemical exposure. Workers at every stage of apparel production may be exposed to the chemicals used in fabric finishing; the most common of these is formaldehyde. Used to make fabric permanent press and colour-fast, formaldehyde is released into the air from fabric in the form of a gas. Workers may also have skin exposure to formaldehyde as they handle the fabric. The amount of formaldehyde released from fabric depends on a variety of factors, including the amount used in finishing, the finishing process used and the ambient heat and humidity. Exposure to formaldehyde can be prevented by allowing the fabric to off-gas in a well-ventilated area before it is handled and by providing good ventilation in the work areas, particularly where fabric is exposed to high heat and humidity (e.g., in pressing operations). Workers who experience skin problems from handling formaldehyde-treated fabric can wear gloves or protective cream. Finally, textile manufacturers should be encouraged to develop safer alternative fabric treatments.

Special Processes

Pleating. The pleating process is used to place creases or pleats into fabric or garments. This process uses high temperatures and high humidity to put folds into various types of fabric. Pleaters are exposed to these conditions of high heat and humidity, which may cause the release of greater quantities of substances used to finish the fabric than may otherwise be released under conditions of normal temperature and humidity. Stiffening agents may be added to fabrics that are to be pleated to facilitate the fabric's ability to hold the crease. Steam boxes and steam chambers expose the pleated fabric to steam under pressure.

Rubberizing/waterproofing. To create a rubberized or waterproof finish, fabrics may be coated with a waterproof substance. These various coatings, which may be a type of rubber, are often thinned with solvents, including those that pose serious health risks to exposed workers. These coatings may include benzene or dimethylformamide, as well as other solvents. Workers are exposed to these chemicals when they are mixed or poured, often by hand, or in large vats in poorly ventilated areas. Workers can also be exposed as they pour the mixtures on the fabric to coat it. Hazardous exposures should be minimized by substitution of less toxic substances and by providing adequate ventilation at the point of use. In addition, mixing and pouring operations should be contained and automated, where possible.

Computer use. Computers are increasingly used in the apparel industry, from computer-aided design/computer-aided manufacturing (CAD/CAM) systems in the design, marking and cutting processes to the tracking of goods in the warehousing and shipping operations. Hazards associated with computer usage are discussed elsewhere in this *Encyclopaedia*.

Buttons, buckles and other adornments. Buttons, buckles and other fasteners on apparel or sewn products are most often manufactured in facilities separate from those that produce apparel. Buttons may be manufactured from a variety of materials, and the material used will determine the production process. Most commonly, buttons and buckles are made from moulded plastic or metals, including lead. During the production process, the heated raw materials are poured into moulds and then cooled. Workers may be exposed to toxic chemicals or metals during this moulding process. After cooling, workers may be exposed to the dust generated when the products are polished or ground. These exposures can be prevented by providing adequate ventilation during this finishing process or by containment of these operations. Other adornments, such as sequins, beads and so on, are produced from plastics and metals, either stamped or moulded, and may expose the production workers to the hazards of their components.

Sewn plastic products and plastic accessories. Various items such as shower curtains, tablecloths and protective raingear are made of sewn, or joined, plastics. Where goods are sewn from sheet plastic, the hazards are similar to those of other sewn items. However, working with large stores of plastic material creates a unique fire safety hazard, since the heating and burning of plastic creates a release of toxic materials that can be very dangerous. Extreme care should be taken in the area of fire prevention and protection where large amounts of plastic materials are used or stored.

In addition to being sewn, plastics can also be joined together by heat or electromagnetic radiation. When plastics are heated they release their components and they may expose workers to these toxics. When electromagnetic radiation is used to join or seal plastics, care must be taken not to expose workers to dangerous levels of this radiation.

Work Organization

The piece-rate system, where workers are paid according to the number of units they produce, is one which is still widely used in the production of apparel and sewn products. The continued use of the piece-work system of compensation poses both stress-related and musculoskeletal health risks to workers in the apparel industry. As discussed above, alternative compensation systems, as well as alternative production systems, may make apparel production a more attractive, less stressful and less hazardous option for workers entering the workforce.

A teamwork system, which gives workers more control over the production process, as well as the opportunity to work with others, may be less stressful than the traditional progressive bundle system. However, these team systems may also cause additional stress if they are set up so that workers are responsible for enforcing work rules against their co-workers. Some types of group compensation systems which penalize an entire team for the slowness or absenteeism of any of its members may create tension and stress within the group.

Home work is the system of sending out work to be done in the home of a worker. It is very common in the apparel industry. Work may be sent home with a factory worker at the end of the workday to be done in the evening or the weekend; or, work may be sent directly into the worker's home, bypassing the factory altogether.

The home-work system is often synonymous with exploitation of workers. Home work cannot easily be regulated by agencies that enforce labour standards, including laws governing child labour, health and safety, minimum wage and so on. In many instances home workers are paid substandard wages and forced to furnish, at their own expense, equipment and tools needed for production. Children in the home may be drawn into doing home work, regardless of their age or ability to work safely, or at a detriment to their schooling or leisure time. Health and safety hazards may abound in homeworking situations, including exposure to dangerous chemicals, fire and electrical hazards. Industrial machinery may present hazards to small children in the home.

● ACCIDENTS IN CLOTHING MANUFACTURE

*A.S. Bettenson**

Small enterprises in unsuitable domestic premises used for clothing manufacture often present a serious fire hazard. In any workroom, large or small, there is much combustible material, and combustible waste will accumulate unless very strict control is exercised. Some of the materials used are particularly flammable (e.g., foam resins used for lining and padding and fine particulate coir). Adequate means of escape, adequate fire extinguishers and training in procedures in case of fire are necessary. Maintenance and good housekeeping not only assist in preventing fires and limiting their spread, but are essential where goods are transported mechanically.

In general, the accident frequency and severity rates are low, but the trade produces a multiplicity of minor injuries that can be prevented from becoming more serious by immediate first aid. Band knives can cause serious wounds unless effectively protected; only that part of the knife necessarily exposed for cutting should be left unguarded; the circular knives of portable cutting machines should be similarly protected. If power presses are used, adequate machinery guarding, preferably fixed, is necessary to keep hands out of the danger area. The sewing machine presents two main hazards—the driving mechanisms and the needle. In many

places, long lines of machines are still driven by underbench shafting. It is essential that this shafting be effectively guarded by enclosure or close railing; many entanglement accidents have occurred when workers stooped under benches to retrieve materials or to replace belts. Several different types of needle guard, which keep fingers out of the area of risk, are available.

The use of garment presses involves a serious risk of crushing and burning. Two-handed controls are widely used but are not entirely satisfactory: they may be subject to misuse (e.g., operation by the knee). They should always be set to make this impossible and to prevent operation by one hand. Guards which prevent the pressure head from closing on the buck if anything (most importantly, the hand) comes within the area are to be used. All presses, with their steam and pneumatic supplies, require frequent inspection.

All portable electrical power tools require careful maintenance of the earthing arrangements.

Recent developments in plastics welding (to replace seaming and so on) and in the making of foam backs usually involve the use of an electric press, sometimes operated by treadle, sometimes by compressed air. There is a risk of physical trapping between the electrodes and also of electrical burns from high-frequency current. The only sure safety measure is to enclose the dangerous parts so that the electrode cannot operate when the hand is in the danger area: double-handed control has not proved satisfactory. Seaming machines must incorporate built-in safety designs.

HEALTH EFFECTS AND ENVIRONMENTAL ISSUES

Robin Herbert and Rebecca Plattus

Health Problems and Disease Patterns

Garment production workers are at risk for the development of WRMDs; occupational asthma; contact and irritative dermatitis; eye, nose and throat irritative symptoms; lung, nasopharyngeal and bladder cancers; and noise-induced hearing loss. Additionally, as some processes in this industry involve exposure to heated plastic fumes, metal dust and fumes (especially lead), leather dust, wool dust and hazardous solvents such as dimethyl formamide, the illnesses associated with these exposures may also be seen among garment workers. Electromagnetic field exposures generated by sewing machine motors are an area of increasing concern. Associations have been reported between maternal employment in apparel production and adverse reproductive outcomes.

Table 87.1 summarizes the spectrum of occupational diseases which may be seen in the clothing and finished textile industry.

Musculoskeletal disorders. Garment production involves the performance of monotonous, highly repetitive and high-speed tasks, often requiring non-neutral and awkward joint postures. These exposures place garment workers at risk of developing WRMDs of the neck, upper extremities, back and lower extremities (Andersen and Gaardboe 1993; Schibye et al. 1995). It is not uncommon for garment workers to develop multiple WRMDs, often with both soft-tissue disorders, such as tendinitis, and concomitant nerve entrapment syndromes, such as carpal tunnel syndrome (Punnett et al. 1985; Schibye et al. 1995).

Sewing machine operators and hand sewers (sample-makers and finishers) perform work which requires repetitive hand and wrist movements, typically performed with non-neutral postures of the fingers, wrist, elbows, shoulders and neck. Therefore, they are at risk for developing carpal tunnel syndrome, ganglion cysts, forearm tendinitis, epicondylitis, shoulder disorders including bicipital and rotator cuff tendinitis, rotator cuff tears and neck

Table 87.1 • Examples of occupational diseases which may be seen in garment workers.

Condition	Exposure
Musculoskeletal disorders	
Carpal tunnel syndrome, forearm tendinitis, DeQuervains tendinitis, epicondylitis, bicipital tendinitis, rotator cuff tears and tendinitis, trapezius spasm, cervical radiculopathy, low-back syndrome, sciatica, disc herniation, osteoarthritis of the knees	Force Repetition Lifting Non-neutral postures Prolonged sitting
Asthma	Formaldehyde Other fabric treatments Heated plastics Dust
Cancer	
Bladder cancer	Dyes
Lung, nasopharyngeal cancer	Formaldehyde
Hearing loss	Noise
Skin	
Contact and irritative dermatitis	Formaldehyde, textile dyes
Lead poisoning	Lead

disorders. Additionally, sewing machine operation typically requires prolonged sitting (often in seats without backrests and in workstations that necessitate leaning forward from the waist), intermittent lifting and repetitive use of foot pedals. Thus, sewing machine operators may develop WRMDs of the low back and lower extremities.

Cutters, whose work requires lifting and carrying of fabric rolls as well as operation of hand-held or computer-operated cutting machines, are also at risk for development of musculoskeletal disorders of the neck, shoulder, elbow, forearm/wrist and low back. Pressers are at risk for developing tendinitis and related disorders of the shoulder, elbow and forearm, and may also be at risk for developing related nerve entrapment disorders.

In addition to ergonomic/biomechanical factors, rapid piece-rate production systems and work organizational factors described more fully in the previous section may contribute to musculoskeletal disorders among workers in the clothing industry. In one study of garment workers, duration of employment in piece-work was found to be associated with an increased prevalence of severe disability (Brisson et al. 1989). Consequently, prevention of work-related musculoskeletal disorders may require both workplace ergonomic modifications and attention to work organization issues, including piece-work.

Chemical hazards. Resin-treated fabrics used in permanent press clothing may release formaldehyde. Exposures are greatest during cutting, because off-gassing is greatest when fabric bolts are first unrolled; during pressing, as heating promotes the liberation of formaldehyde from residual amounts of resins; in production areas in which large quantities of fabric are being used; and in warehouse and retail areas. Many garment shops are poorly ventilated and afford poor control of ambient temperatures. With increased temperature, off-gassing is greater; with poor ventilation, increasing ambient concentrations of formaldehyde can accumulate. Formaldehyde is a well-recognized acute irritant of the eyes, nose, throat and upper and lower airways. Formaldehyde may be a cause of occupational asthma due to either irritative

effects or allergic sensitization (Friedman-Jimenez 1994; Ng et al. 1994). Formaldehyde exposure has been associated in a number of studies with the development of lung and nasopharyngeal cancers (Alderson 1986). Additionally, formaldehyde exposure can result in both allergic contact and irritative dermatitis. Garment workers may develop a chronic, eczema-like dermatitis of the hands and arms which is likely related to sensitization to formaldehyde. The irritative and other non-allergic health effects of formaldehyde can be minimized by the implementation of proper ventilation systems and product substitution where feasible. Allergic sensitization, however, can occur at lower levels of exposure. Once a garment worker has developed allergic sensitization, removal from exposure may be necessary.

Workers in the finished textile industry may sustain exposure to organic solvents. Solvents such as perchlorethylene, trichlorethylene and 1,1,1-trichlorethane are frequently used in finishing departments for stain removal. Health effects due to such exposures may include central nervous system depression, peripheral neuropathy, dermatitis and, less commonly, liver toxicity. Dimethyl formamide (DMF) is a particularly hazardous solvent which has been employed to waterproof fabric. Its use in one such setting resulted in an outbreak of occupational hepatitis among exposed garment workers (Redlich et al. 1988). DMF use should be avoided both due to its hepatotoxicity and because it has been found to be associated with testicular cancer in two distinct occupational settings. Similarly, benzene may still be used in some clothing industry settings. Its use should be scrupulously avoided.

Physical hazards; electromagnetic fields. Recent reports have indicated that operation of a sewing machine may result in high exposures to electromagnetic fields (EMFs). The health effects of EMFs are not yet well understood and are the subject of current debate. However, one case-control study, which utilized three separate data sets from two countries (United States and Finland), found a strong association in all three data sets between occupational EMF exposure and Alzheimer's disease among sewing machine operators and others classified as having sustained medium and high EMF exposures (Sobel et al. 1995). A case-control study of maternal occupation and acute lymphoblastic leukaemia (ALL) in Spain found an increased risk of ALL in offspring of mothers working at home during pregnancy, with most performing sewing machine operation. Although the authors of the study initially speculated that maternal exposure to organic dust and synthetic fibres might be responsible for the observed increase, the possibility of EMF exposure as a possible aetiological agent was raised (Infante-Rivard et al. 1991). (See the chapter *Radiation, non-ionizing* for further discussion.)

Other occupational illnesses and hazards. Garment workers have been shown in a number of studies to be at increased risk for the development of asthma (Friedman-Jimenez et al. 1994; Ng et al. 1994). In addition to potentially increased risk of lung and nasopharyngeal cancer due to formaldehyde exposure, garment workers have been found to have an increased risk of bladder cancer (Alderson 1986). Lead poisoning has been observed among clothing workers involved in production of metallic buttons. Warehouse and distribution workers may be at risk of developing the illnesses associated with exposure to diesel exhaust.

Worldwide, the high proportion of women and children employed in the garment industry, combined with the predominance of sub-contracting and industrial home work, has created an ideal field for exploitation. Sexual harassment, including non-consensual sexual activity with its attendant health problems, is a serious problem in the clothing industry worldwide. Child workers are particularly vulnerable to the health effects of toxic exposures and to the effects of poor workplace ergonomics due to their developing bodies. Working children are also highly vulnerable to workplace accidents. Lastly, two recent studies have found associations between work in the apparel industry during pregnancy and adverse reproductive outcomes, suggesting the need for further investigation in this area (Eskenazi et al. 1993; Decouflé et al. 1993).

Public Health and Environmental Issues

The apparel and other finished textile products industry is, generally, an industry which yields relatively little environmental contamination via discharges into air, soil or water. However, off-gassing of formaldehyde can persist at the retail level in this industry, creating the potential for development of formaldehyde-related allergic, irritative and respiratory symptomatology among both sales people and customers. Additionally, some of the special processes utilized in the garment industry, such as rubberizing

and production of lead-based adornments, can pose more serious threats of environmental contamination.

In recent years, growing concerns about the potential adverse health effects associated with exposure to formaldehyde and other fabric treatments has lead to development of a "green" industry. Apparel and other finished textile products are typically sewn from natural rather than synthetic fibre-based materials. Additionally, these natural products are generally not treated with crease-resistant and other finishing agents.

The crowded, often squalid, conditions in the garment industry create ideal conditions for transmission of infectious diseases. In particular, tuberculosis has been a recurrent public health issue among workers in the garment industry.

References

Alderson, M. 1986. *Occupational Cancer*. London: Butterworths.

Anderson, JH and O Gaardboe 1993. Musculoskeletal disorders of the neck and upper limb among sewing machine operators: A clinical investigation. *Am J Ind Med* 24:689–700.

Brisson, CB, A Vinet, N Vezina, and S Gingras. 1989. Effect of duration of employment in piecework on severe disability among female garment workers. *Scand J Work Environ Health* 15:329–334.

Decouflé, P, CC Murphy, CD Drews, and M Yeargin-Allsopp. 1993. Mental retardation in ten-year-old children in relation to their mothers' occupations during pregnancy. *Am J Ind Med* 24:567–586.

Eskenazi, B, S Guendelman, EP Elkin, and M Jasis. 1993. A preliminary study of reproductive outcomes of female maquiladora workers in Tijuana, Mexico. *Am J Ind Med* 24:667–676.

Friedman-Jimenez, G. 1994. Adult onset asthma in women garment workers from the Bellevue Asthma Clinic. PA855. *Am J Resp Crit Care Med* 4:149.

Infante-Rivard, C, D Mur, B Armstrong, C Alvarez-Dardet, and F Bolumar. 1991. Acute lymphoblastic leukemia among Spanish children and mothers' occupation: A case-control study. *J Epidemiol Community Health* 45:11-15.

Ng, TP, CY Hong, LG Goh, ML Wang, KT Koh, and SL Ling. 1994. Risks of asthma associated with occupations in a community-based case control study. *Am J Ind Med* 25:709–718.

Punnett, L, JM Robins, DH Wegman, and WM Keyserling. 1985. Soft tissue disorders in the upper limbs of female garment workers. *Scand J Work Environ Health* 11:417–425.

Redlich, CA, WS Beckett, J Sparer, KW Barwick, CA Reily, H Miller, SL Sigal, SL Shalat, and MR Cullen. 1988. Liver disease associated with occupational exposure to the solvent dimethyl formamide. *Ann Intern Med* 108:680-686.

Schibye, B, T Skor, D Ekner, JU Christiansen, and G Sjogaard. 1995. Musculoskeletal symptoms among sewing machine operators. *Scand J Work Environ Health* 21:427–434.

Sobel, E, Z Davanipour, R Sulkava, T Erkinjuntti, J Wikström, VW Henderson, G Buckwalter, JD Bowman, and PJ Lee. 1995. Occupations with exposure to electromagnetic fields: A possible risk factor for Alzheimer's disease. *Am J Epidemiol* 142:515–524.

Other relevant readings

Courcel, M. 1979. Prevention of accidents in the use of sewing machines in clothing industry (La prevention des accidents dus aux machines a coudre). *Prevention et securite du travail (Lille)* 122:25–29.

Solinger, J. 1961. *Apparel Manufacturing Analysis*. New York: Textile Book Publishers.

LEATHER, FUR AND FOOTWEAR

88

Chapter Editor
Michael McCann

Contents

GENERAL PROFILE

Debra Osinsky

Animal furs and leather from tanned animal hides and skins have been used to make clothing for thousands of years. Fur and leather remain important industries today. Fur is used to produce a variety of outer garments, such as coats, jackets, hats, gloves and boots, and it provides trim for other types of garments as well. Leather is used to make garments and can be employed in the manufacture of other products, including leather upholstery for automobiles and furniture, and a wide variety of leather goods, such as watch straps, purses and suitcases. Footwear is another traditional leather product.

Fur-producing animals include aquatic species such as beaver, otter, muskrat and seal; northern land species such as fox, wolf, mink, weasel, bear, marten and raccoon; and tropical species such as leopard, ocelot and cheetah. In addition, the young of certain animals such as cattle, horse, pig and goat may be processed to produce furs. Although most fur-bearing animals are trapped, mink in particular is produced on fur farms.

Production

The major sources of leather are cattle, pigs, lambs and sheep. As of 1990, the United States was the largest producer of bovine hides and skins. Other significant producers include Argentina, Australia, Brazil, China, France, Germany (former Federal Republic) and India. Australia, China, India, Islamic Republic of Iran, New Zealand, the Russian Federation, Turkey and the United Kingdom are major producers of sheepskins. Goatskins are largely produced in China, India and Pakistan. The major producers of pigskin are China, Eastern Europe and the former USSR.

An analysis prepared by Landell Mills Commodities Studies (LMC) for the International Labour Organization (ILO) shows that the international market for hides is increasingly dominated by a few large producing countries in North America, Western Europe and Oceania, which allow free exportation of hides in any form. The tanning industry in the United States has been shrinking steadily since 1981, while most surviving tanneries in northern Europe have diversified in order to reduce dependence on the footwear-leather market. Worldwide footwear production has continued to shift primarily to Southeast Asia (ILO 1992).

Several factors influence the overall demand for leather throughout the world: the level, rate of growth and distribution of income; the price of leather compared to alternative materials; and changes in consumers' preference for leather over alternative materials for a variety of products.

The fastest growing end-use sector in the leather industry has been leather upholstery, which accounted for about one-third of the world's high-quality bovine leather production in 1990. Over one-third of all upholstery leather is destined for the vehicle industry and, according to LMC forecasts, the prospects for this subsector are fairly bright. The proportion of cars with leather upholstery has increased substantially through the 1990s.

The demand for leather garments is determined primarily by income and fashion, while fashion particularly influences the changing demand for specific types of leather. For example, a strong demand for the softer, more supple sheepskin leather in fashion garments motivated the production of the fashionable garment nappa from sheepskins and cattle hides.

The major producers of mink pelts in 1996 were Canada, the Russian Federation, the Scandinavian countries and the United States.

Between 1980 and 1989, leather employment increased in China, Hungary, India, Indonesia, the Republic of Korea, Uruguay and Venezuela and decreased in Australia, Colombia, Kenya, the Philippines, Poland and the United States. Leather employment also fell in Denmark, Finland, Norway and Sweden. In Botswana leather employment declined sharply in 1984, then experienced a steep increase, doubling the 1980 level by 1988.

There are several issues which will affect future production and employment in the leather, footwear and fur industries. New technology, the relocation of footwear production to developing countries and environmental regulations in the tanning industry will continue to affect the skills and the health and safety of workers in these industries.

TANNING AND LEATHER FINISHING

Dean B. Baker*

Tanning is the chemical process that converts animal hides and skins into leather. The term *hide* is used for the skin of large animals (e.g., cows or horses), while *skin* is used for that of small animals (e.g., sheep). Hides and skins are mostly by-products of slaughterhouses, although they may also come from animals that have died naturally or been hunted or trapped. Tanning industries are usually located near stock-raising regions; however, hides and skins may be preserved and transported prior to tanning, so the industry is widespread.

The tanning process consists in strengthening the hide's protein structure by creating a bond between the peptide chains. The hide is composed of three layers: epidermis, dermis and subcutaneous layer. The dermis consists of about 30 to 35% protein, which is mostly collagen, with the remainder being water and fat. The dermis is used to make leather after the other layers have been removed using chemical and mechanical means. The tanning process uses acids, alkalis, salts, enzymes and tanning agents to dissolve fats and non-fibrous proteins and chemically bond the collagen fibres together.

Tanning has been practised since prehistoric times. The oldest system of tanning relies on the chemical action of vegetable material containing tannin (tannic acid). Extracts are taken from the parts of plants that are rich in tannin and processed into tanning liquors. The hides are soaked in pits or vats of increasingly strong liquors until they are tanned, which may take weeks or months. This process is used in countries with low levels of technology. This process is also used in developed countries to produce firmer, thicker leather for shoe soles, bags, cases and straps, although process changes have been introduced to shorten the time needed for tanning. Chemical tanning using mineral salts such as chromium sulphate was introduced during the late 19th century and has become the primary process to produce softer, thinner leather for goods such as handbags, gloves, garments, upholstery and shoe uppers. Tanning may also be accomplished using fish oils or synthetic tannins.

There is great variation in the scale and types of tanning facilities. Some tanneries are highly mechanized and use closed automatic systems and many chemicals, whereas others still use largely manual work and natural tanning substances with techniques essentially unchanged over the centuries (see figure 88.1). The type of product required (e.g., heavy-duty leather or fine flexible leathers) influences the choice of tanning agents and the finishing required.

---

* Some text was revised from the article authored by V.P. Gupta in the 3rd edition of this *Encyclopaedia*.

Figure 88.1 • Manual working methods in an Afghanistan tannery.

Process Description

Leather production can be divided into three stages: preparation of the hide for tanning, which includes processes such as the removal of hair and adherent flesh; the tanning process; and the finishing process. Finishing includes mechanical processes to shape and smooth the leather and chemical treatments to colour, lubricate, soften and apply a surface finish to the leather (see figure 88.2). All of these processes may take place in one facility, although it is common for leather finishing to be conducted at locations different from tanning in order to take advantage of transportation costs and local markets. The implication is that it affects the likelihood of cross-contamination among the processes.

Curing and shipment. Because raw hides and skins decay rapidly, they are preserved and disinfected prior to shipment to the tannery. The hide or skin is flayed from the carcass and then preserved by curing. Curing can be accomplished by a variety of means. Curing by drying is suitable in regions where hot and dry climatic conditions prevail. Drying consists of stretching the hides on frames or spreading them on the ground in the sun. Dry-salting, another method of curing hides, consists of rubbing the fleshy side of the hide with salt. Brine curing, or brining, consists of submerging the hides in a solution of sodium chloride to which naphthalene may have been added. Brining is the most common form of preservation in developed countries.

Prior to shipment, hides are generally treated with DDT, zinc chloride, mercury chloride, chlorophenols or other agents for disinfection. These substances may represent hazards both at the site of curing and on receipt at the tannery.

Preparation. The cured hides and skins are prepared for tanning by several operations, collectively referred to as *beamhouse* operations. First the hides are sorted, trimmed and then washed in vats or drums. Disinfectants such as bleaching powder, chlorine and sodium acid fluoride in the water prevent putrefaction of hides. Chemicals such as caustic soda, sodium sulphide and surfactants are added to the water to accelerate soaking of dry-salted or dried hides.

The soaked hides and skins are then limed by immersing in milk of lime to loosen the epidermis and hair roots and to remove other unwanted soluble proteins and fats. In another method, a depilatory paste of lime, sulphide and salt is applied to the flesh side of the skins in order to save hair and wool. The limed hides are unhaired to remove the loosened hairs and defleshed. Epider-

mal debris and fine hair roots are mechanically removed by the scudding operation.

These operations are followed by deliming and bating with buffering salts, such as ammonium sulphate or ammonium chloride, and the action of proteolytic enzymes neutralizes the high alkalinity of limed hides. In pickling, hides are placed in an acid environment consisting of sodium chloride and sulphuric acid. The acid is necessary because chrome-tanning agents are not soluble under alkaline conditions. Vegetable-tanned hides do not need to be pickled.

Many of the beamhouse operations are carried out by processing the hides in solutions using large pits, vats or drums. Solutions are piped or poured into the containers and later emptied through pipes or into open drainage channels in the work area. The chemicals may be added to the containers by pipes or manually by workers. Good ventilation and personal protective equipment are needed to prevent respiratory and dermal exposure.

Tanyard. Various substances may be used for tanning, but the main distinction is between vegetable and chrome tanning. Vegetable tanning may be carried out either in pits or in rotating drums. Rapid tanning, in which high concentrations of tannins are used, is carried out in rotating drums. The chrome-tanning process most often used is the *one-bath* method, in which the hides are milled in a colloidal solution of chromium (III) sulphate until tanning is complete. A *two-bath* chrome-tanning process was used in the past, but this process involved potential exposure to hexavalent chromium salts and required more manual handling of the hides. The two-bath process is now considered obsolete and is rarely used.

Once tanned, the hide is further processed to shape and condition the leather. The hide is removed from the solution and excess water is removed by wringing. Chrome leather must be neutralized after being tanned. Splitting is the longitudinal division of wet or dry leather that is too thick, for articles such as shoe uppers and leather goods. Roll machines with cutting blades are used to further reduce the leather to the thickness required. A large amount of dust may be released when the leather is split or shaved while dry.

Re-tanning, colouring and fat-liquoring. After tanning, most leathers except sole leathers undergo colouring (dyeing). Generally, colouring is performed in a batch mode; and re-tanning, colouring and fat liquoring operations are all performed in sequence in the same drum with intermediate steps of washing and drying. Three major types of dyes are used: acid, basic and direct. Blends of dyes are used in order to obtain the exact shade desired, so the composition is not always known except by the supplier. The purpose of fat-liquoring is to lubricate leather to give it strength and flexibility. Oils, natural fats, their transformation products, mineral oils and several synthetic fats are used.

Finishing. After drying, vegetable tanned leather is subjected to mechanical operations (setting and rolling) and given a final polish. The finishing process for chrome leather includes a series of mechanical operations and, normally, the application of a covering layer to the leather surface. Staking is a mechanical beating operation used to make the leather soft. To improve the final appearance, the grain side of the leather is buffed using a sanding drum. This process generates a tremendous amount of dust.

A final surface finish is applied, which may contain solvents, plasticizers, binders and pigments. These solutions are applied by pads, flow coating or spraying. Some tanneries employ hand labour to apply the finish using pads, but this is usually carried out by machines. In flow coating, the solution is pumped into a reservoir above the conveyor carrying the leather and flows down onto it. In most cases, painted or sprayed leathers are not dried in ovens, but on trays on shelves. This practice provides a wide evaporating surface and contributes to air pollution.

Figure 88.2 • Typical processes for leather tanning and finishing.

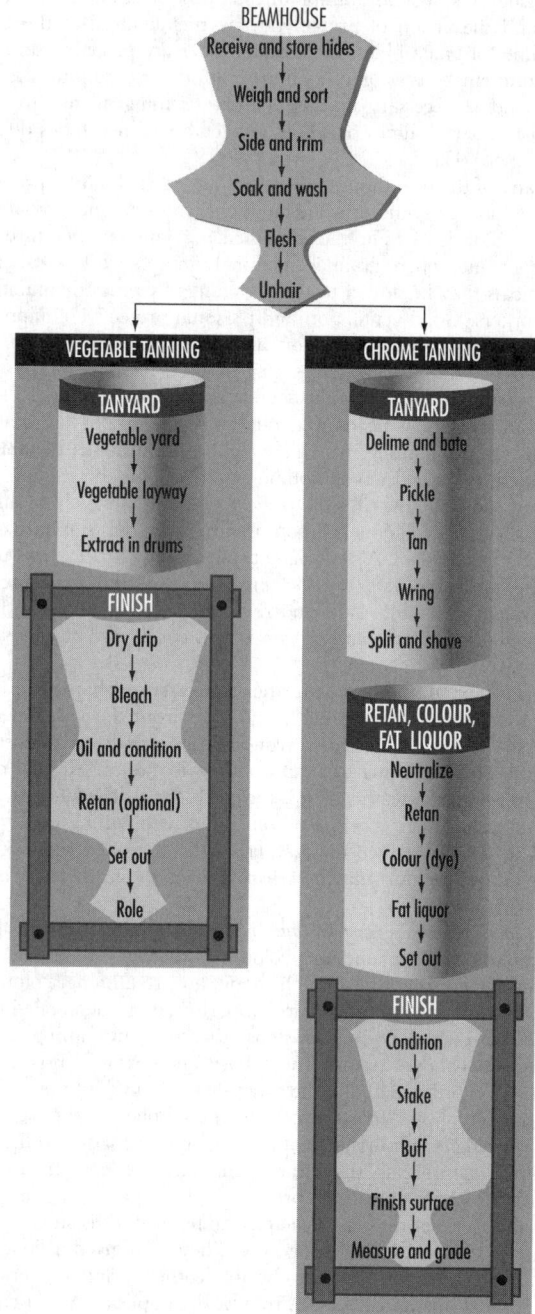

have an even surface and be well drained. Good maintenance and housekeeping are essential. Mechanized transfer of hides and skins from one operation to another and proper drainage of liquors from vats and drums will help to reduce spillage and manual-handling ergonomic problems. Open pits and vats should be fenced to prevent injuries due to drowning and scalds.

There are many hazards connected with the operating parts of the machines—for example, injuries caused by revolving drums, in-running rollers and knives. Efficient guarding should be provided. All transmission machinery, belts, pulleys and gear wheels should be guarded.

Several operations involve manual lifting of the hides and leather, which represents an ergonomic hazard. Noise associated with the machinery is another potential hazard.

Dust. Dust is produced in a variety of tanning operations. Chemical dust can be produced during the loading of hide-processing drums. Leather dust is produced during mechanical operations. Buffing is the major source of dust. The dust in tanneries may be impregnated with chemicals, as well as fragments of hair, mould and excrement. Effective ventilation is needed for dust removal.

Chemical hazards. The large variety of acids, alkalis, tannins, solvents, disinfectants and other chemicals can be respiratory and skin irritants. Dusts of vegetable tanning materials, lime and leather and chemical mists and vapours arising in the various processes may be responsible for causing chronic bronchitis. Several chemicals may cause contact dermatitis. Chrome ulceration may occur in chrome tanning, especially on the hands. Exposures in the beamhouse operations are mainly to sulphur compounds such as sulphides and sulphates. Since these are alkaline substances, there is a potential to generate hydrogen sulphide gas if these substances contact acids.

Potential cancer-causing agents used in leather tanning and finishing include hexavalent chromium salts (in the past), aniline and azo dyes, vegetable tannins, organic solvents, formaldehyde and chlorophenols. The International Agency for Research on Cancer (IARC) evaluated the leather tanning industry in the early 1980s and concluded that there was no evidence to suggest an association between leather tanning and nasal cancer (IARC 1981). Case reports and epidemiological studies since the IARC evaluation have indicated increased risk for cancers among leather tanning and finishing workers—including lung cancer, sinonasal cancer and pancreatic cancer associated with leather dust and tanning (Mikoczy et al. 1996) and bladder cancer and testicular cancer associated with dyes or solvents in the finishing process (Stern et al. 1987). None of these associations is clearly established at this time.

FUR INDUSTRY

*P.E. Braid**

Rudimentary means of preserving furs have been used since very early times and are still practised in many parts of the world. Typically, after the pelt is scraped and cleaned by washing, the skin is impregnated with animal oil, which serves to preserve it and make it more pliable. The pelt may be beaten or chewed after the oil treatment in order to effect better impregnation by the oil.

In the modern fur industry, pelts are obtained from fur farmers, trappers or hunters. At this stage they have been stripped from the

* Adapted from the article by the author that appeared in the 3rd edition of this *Encyclopaedia*. Acknowledgements to Gary Meisel and to Tom Cunningham of the United Food and Commercial Workers Union for reviewing and adapting this article.

Hazards and Their Prevention

Infectious hazards. In the early stages of the beamhouse operations, there may be some risk of infection due to zoonoses from the raw hides. Anthrax was a recognized hazard among workers engaged in handling hides and skins, particularly dry and dry-salted hides. This hazard has been virtually eliminated in tanneries due to disinfection of hides prior to shipment to the facilities. Colonies of fungi may develop on leathers and on the surface of the liquors.

Injuries. Slippery, wet and greasy floors form a serious hazard in all parts of a tannery. All floors should be of impervious material,

Figure 88.3 • Flow chart of fur dressing.

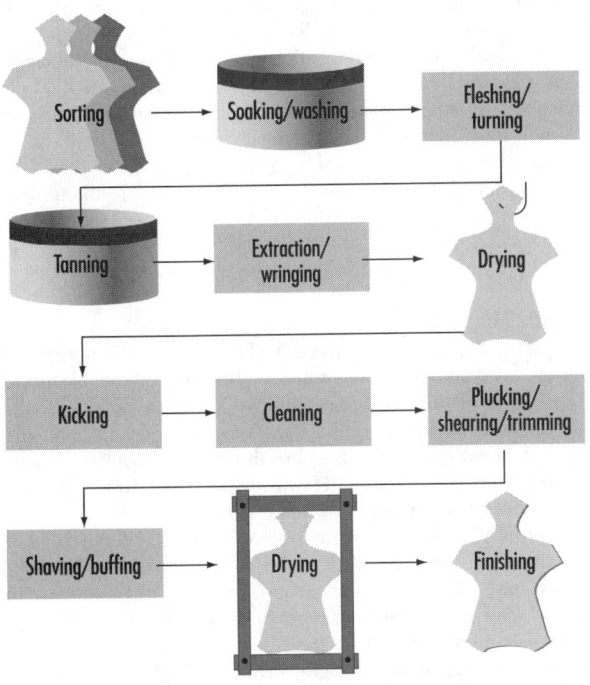

Figure 88.5 • Machine fleshing of lamb skins.

carcass, flesh and fatty deposits have been removed by scraping and the pelts have been stretched and air dried. The fur industry grades the pelts according to factors such as the general condition of the pelt, fur length, curl and patterning The pelts go through a series of treatment steps, called fur dressing, to preserve them (see figure 88.3). The furs may also be dyed. Fur dressing and dyeing are done in batches, with the pelts usually being transferred from one step to another using hand carts.

Fur Dressing

First, the pelts are sorted, stamped with an identifying mark, and cut open using knives and snippers. They are then soaked in salt water in tubs or barrels for several hours to re-soften them (see

figure 88.4). Rotating paddles are often used to help this soaking. Sometimes formic acid, lactic acid or sulphuric acid is used in the soaking step. The excess water is then removed in revolving drums.

Next, the underside of the pelt is drawn across razor-sharp round-knife fleshing machines by workers known as fleshers (figure 88.5). Hand turning (turning the pelt inside out) and trimming with knives is also done. This operation removes the loose connective tissue from the underside of the skin. The object is to remove, as far as possible, any tissue which is not involved in the attachment of the fur, thus producing the maximum degree of lightness and flexibility of the pelt.

The pelts are now ready for tanning and are soaked in alum solution in pits or tubs. As with soaking, paddles are used. The alum solution is usually acidified somewhat with hydrochloric or sulphuric acid. The alum treatment may be carried out in either an aqueous or an oil solution. Excess liquid is extracted and the pelts are dried in special drying rooms to set the skin collagen.

The tanned pelts are then treated with an oil solution in a kicking machine or similar type of machine to force the oil into

Figure 88.4 • Soaking department in a fur-processing works.

Office du film du Québec

Figure 88.6 • Shearing operation on Canadian beaver pelts.

Office du film du Québec

88. LEATHER, FUR AND FOOTWEAR

the skin. They are then cleaned in rotating drums containing sawdust, which absorbs moisture and excess oil.

Pelts contain guard hairs as well as the softer fur fibres. The guard hairs are stiffer and longer than the fur fibres and, depending on the type of fur and the final product desired, these hairs may be either partially or totally removed by machine or by hand plucking. Some pelts also require shearing or trimming with knives (see figure 88.6).

Other steps can include shaving or "paring out" with round-knife fleshers, buffing with buffing machines, drying and finishing. The latter can include degreasing, stretching, cleaning, buffing, brushing and lusterizing with lacquers and resins.

Dyeing

Although dyeing of furs was at one time not looked upon favourably, it is now an accepted part of fur preparation and is practised extensively. This can be done at the same time as tanning or in a subsequent step. The usual procedure involves treatment of the pelts with a weak alkaline solution (e.g., sodium carbonate) to remove dirt and oil residues. The pelts are then soaked in a mordant solution (e.g., ferric sulphate), after which they are steeped in dye solution until the desired colour is obtained. They are then repeatedly rinsed and drum-dried with the aid of sawdust.

Many other chemicals may be used in dyeing, including ammonia, ammonium chloride, formaldehyde, hydrogen peroxide, lead acetate or nitrate, oxalic acid, sodium perborate, *p*-phenylenediamine dyes, benzidine dyes and so forth.

Fur Garment Manufacture

Before being made into garments, pelts may be cut and "let out". This involves making a series of closely spaced diagonal or V-shaped slits in the skin, after which the pelt is pulled in order either to lengthen or to broaden it as needed. The pelt is then re-sewn (see figure 88.7). This type of operation requires great skill and experience. The pelts are next thoroughly moistened and then laid out and tacked on a board according to a chalked-on pattern, left to dry and sewn together. Finally, lining and other finishing steps complete the garment.

Hazards and Their Prevention

Accidents

Some of the machines used in fur processing present serious hazards unless sufficient guarding is maintained: in particular, all

Figure 88.7 • Operators engaged in the machine sewing of skins.

drums should be protected with an interlocking gate and the centrifuges used for extraction of moisture should be fitted with interlocking lids; fur clipping and fur cutting machines should be totally enclosed except for the feed and discharge openings.

Vats should be covered or effectively railed to prevent accidental immersion. Falls on wet and slippery floors can be largely prevented by maintenance of sound, impervious surfaces, well-drained and frequently cleaned. Dyeing vats should be surrounded by drainage channels. Accidents caused by hand tools can be reduced if the handles are well designed and the tools well maintained. In the fur manufacturing sector, sewing machines require similar protection to those used in the garment trade (e.g., guarding of driving mechanisms and of needles).

Health Hazards

The use by the fur industry of such a large proportion of pelts from animals bred in captivity has considerably reduced the likelihood of transmission of animal diseases to fur workers. Nevertheless, anthrax may occur in workers handling carcasses, skins, hides or hairs from infected animals; a vaccine may be administered to all likely to have contact. All concerned should be aware of the risk and trained to report any suspicious symptoms immediately.

Various chemicals used in the fur industry are potential skin irritants. These include alkalis, acids, alum, chromates, bleaching agents, oils, salt and the compounds involved in the dyeing process, which comprise various types of dyes as well as mordants.

Unpacking of bales which have been treated with dusting powder in their countries of origin, drumming, plucking, unhairing and shearing can all produce irritant dust. In dye houses and dye kitchens, where salts of lead, copper and chromium (and possibly carcinogenic dyes) are weighed and cooked, there is also a risk of ingestion of toxic dusts. Injurious vapours may arise from degreasing solvents and fumigating chemicals. There is also the possibility of development of contact sensitization (allergy) to some of these chemicals or to the dust from one or more of the types of fur being handled.

The main protection against the hazards of dust and vapours is the provision of local exhaust ventilation; good general ventilation is also necessary throughout the process. Good housekeeping is important to remove dust. Personal respiratory protective equipment may be necessary for short-term jobs or in addition to local exhaust at particularly dusty operations. Particular attention should be paid to potential confined space hazards in pits and vats used for soaking/washing, tanning and dyeing.

Protective clothing appropriate to the process is necessary at most stages of fur processing. Rubber hand protection, foot and leg protection and aprons are required for wet processes (e.g., at the dye and mordant vats) and as a protection against acids, alkalis and corrosive chemicals. Good sanitary and washing facilities, including showers, should be provided. Bleaches and strong alkali soaps should not be used for hand cleansing.

Ergonomic problems can result from manual lifting and moving of materials, especially pushing hand carts, and manual loading and unloading of pelts (particularly when wet). Automation of these processes can help solve these problems. Repetitive motions in fur garment manufacture are also a source of ergonomic problems.

Heat stress diseases can occur while working in the drying room. Preventive measures include adequate exhaust of hot air and supply of cool air, limiting exposure time, readily accessible drinking water and training in the recognition of heat stress symptoms and in first aid measures.

Noise can be a problem with many of the machines used, especially in drums and combing, shearing and lusterizing machines.

Pre-placement medical examination can assist in the prevention of dermatitis by proper placement of employees with a history of sensitivity. Medical supervision is desirable; well maintained first-aid provisions in the charge of trained personnel are essential. Strict attention to hygiene, ventilation and temperature are necessary in the many small workrooms in which much of the making of fur garments is done.

FOOTWEAR INDUSTRY

*F.L. Conradi and Paulo Portich**

The term *footwear* covers a vast range of products made from many different materials. Boots, shoes, sandals, slippers, clogs and so forth are made wholly or partly of leather, rubber, synthetic and plastics materials, canvas, rope and wood. This article deals with the footwear industry as generally understood (i.e., based on traditional manufacturing methods). The manufacture of rubber boots (or their synthetic equivalents) is essentially a section of the rubber industry, which is covered in the chapter *Rubber industry*.

Shoes, boots and sandals made from leather, felts and other materials have been made by hand over the centuries. Fine shoes are still made wholly or partly by hand, but in all the industrialized countries there are now large mass-production plants. Even so, some work may still be given out to be done as home work. Child labour continues as one of the more serious problems in the footwear industry, although several countries have taken action against child labour with the help of various international programmes in this area.

Boot and shoe plants usually locate close to leather-producing areas (i.e., near cattle-raising country); some slipper and light-shoe making developed where there was a plentiful supply of felts from the textile trade, and in most countries the industry tends to be localized in its original centres. Leathers of different type and quality, and some reptile skins, formed the original materials, with a tougher quality skin for the soles. In recent years leather has been increasingly displaced by other materials, in particular rubber and plastics. Linings may be made of wool or polyamide (nylon) fabric or sheepskin; laces are made of horsehair or synthetic fibres; paper, cardboard and thermoplastics are used for stiffening. Natural and coloured wax, aniline dyes and colouring agents are used in finishing.

Economic and other factors have transformed the footwear industry in recent years. Tennis shoe manufacturing is one of the major growth sectors of the industry and has moved from production in predominantly one country to worldwide production, especially in developing countries in Asia and South America, in order to increase production and reduce costs. This migration of production to developing countries has also occurred in other sectors of the footwear industry.

Processes

There may be over a hundred operations in the making of a shoe, and only a brief summary is possible here. Mechanization has been applied at all stages, but the pattern of the hand process has been closely followed. Introduction of new materials has modified the process without changing its broad outline.

In the making of the uppers (tops of shoes), the leather or other material is sorted and prepared, and the uppers are then cut out on stitching (or dinting) presses by shaped, loose-knife tools. The parts, including the linings, are then "closed" (i.e., sewn or stuck together). Perforating, eyeletting and button-holing may also be carried out.

For making the bottom stock, soles, insoles, heels and welts, pieces are cut out in revolving presses using loose-knife cutters, or in sole-moulding presses; heels are made by compression of leather or wood strips. The stock is trimmed, shaped, scoured and stamped.

The uppers and bottom stock are assembled and then stitched, glued, nailed or screwed together. These operations are followed by shaping and levelling between rollers. The final finishing of the shoe includes waxing, colouring, spraying, polishing and packaging.

Among the raw materials used in the manufacturing process, the most important from the point of view of occupational hazards are the adhesives. These include natural solid and liquid adhesives and adhesive solutions based on organic solvents.

Hazards and Their Prevention

The intensive use of flammable liquids constitutes a considerable fire hazard, and the widespread use of presses and assembling machines has introduced an increased risk of mechanical accidents into this industry. The main health hazards are toxic solvents, high atmospheric dust concentrations, ergonomic risks and noise from the machines.

Fire

The solvents and sprays used in adhesives and finishing materials may be highly flammable. Precautions include:

- using the lowest flash point solvents possible
- using good general ventilation and local exhaust ventilation in spray booths and drying racks to reduce the concentration of flammable vapours
- removing combustible residues from cabinets and workbenches and provide closed containers for solvent-containing and oily wastes
- maintaining unobstructed exits and gangways
- minimizing the amount of stored flammable liquids; keep them in approved containers, cabinets and storage rooms
- ensuring that all electrical equipment and wiring near flammable solvents meets appropriate electrical codes
- grounding adequately polishing machines and other sources of static electricity.

Accidents

Many of the operating parts of the machines present serious hazards, in particular presses, stampers, rollers and knives. The loose-knife cutters at stitching and revolving presses can cause serious injury. The appropriate precautions minimally include two-hand controls (a photo-electric cell device for automatically cutting power may be preferable), the reduction of stroke rate to a safe level in relation to the size of the cutter, and the use of well-designed, stable cutters of adequate height, with flanges fitted perhaps with handles. Sole-moulding and heel presses should be guarded to prevent hand access. Stamping machines can cause burns as well as crushing injuries unless hand access is prevented by guarding. Nips of rollers and knives of milling and shaping machines should be fitted with suitable machinery guarding. The shading and polishing wheels of finishing machines and the spindles on which they are mounted should also be guarded. There should be an effective lockout/tagout programme for repair and maintenance work.

Health hazards

Organic solvents can cause acute and chronic effects on the central nervous system. Benzene, which was formerly used in adhesives and solvents, has been replaced by toluene, xylene, hexane, methyl ethyl ketone (MEK) and methyl butyl ketone

* Adapted by P. Portich from the article in the 3rd edition of this *Encyclopaedia* by F.L. Conradi.

88. LEATHER, FUR AND FOOTWEAR

(MBK). Both *n*-hexane and MBK can cause peripheral neuropathy and should be replaced by heptane or other solvents.

Outbreaks of a disease known popularly as "shoemakers' paralysis" have appeared in a number of factories, presenting a clinical picture of a more or less severe form of paralysis. This paralysis is of the flaccid type, it is localized in the limbs (pelvic or thoracic) and gives rise to osteo-tendinous atrophy with areflexia and no alteration in superficial or deep sensitivity. Clinically, it is a syndrome resulting from functional inhibition or injury of the lower motor neurons of the voluntary motor system (pyramidal tract). The common outcome is neurological regression with extensive proximo-distal functional recuperation.

Good general ventilation and exhaust ventilation at the point of origin of the vapours should be provided to maintain concentrations well below maximum permissible levels. If these levels are observed, the fire risk will also be diminished. Minimizing the amount of solvent used, enclosure of solvent-using equipment and closing solvent containers are also important precautions.

Finishing machines produce dust, which should be removed from the atmosphere by exhaust ventilation. Some of the polishes, stains, colours and polychloroprene glues may carry a dermatitis risk. Good washing and sanitary facilities should be maintained and personal hygiene encouraged.

The increased intensive use of machines and equipment creates a significant noise hazard, necessitating source control of the noise or other preventive measures to prevent hearing loss. There should also be a hearing conservation programme.

Prolonged work on nailing machines which produce high levels of vibration may produce "dead hand" (Raynaud's phenomenon). It is advisable to restrict the time spent at these machines.

Low-back pain and repetitive strain injuries are two musculoskeletal diseases that are major problems in the footwear industry. Ergonomic solutions are essential for prevention of these problems. Pre-placement and periodic medical examinations linked to workplace hazards are an effective factor for protection of employees' health.

Environmental and Public Health Hazards

Earth Summit 1992, held in Rio de Janeiro, dealt with environmental concerns, and its proposals for future action, known as Agenda 21, could transform the footwear industry with its emphasis on recycling. In general, however, most waste materials are disposed of in landfills. Without proper precautions, this can result in contamination of the ground and groundwater.

Although home work has social advantages in decreasing unemployment and in the formation of cooperatives, the problems of ensuring proper precautions and working conditions in the home are enormous. In addition, other family members can be at risk if they are not already involved in the work. As discussed previously, child labour remains a serious problem.

● HEALTH EFFECTS AND DISEASE PATTERNS

Frank B. Stern

Leather Tanning

The major International Standard Industrial Classification (ISIC) group for the leather and fur processing is 323. In the United States, the Standard Industrial Classification (SIC) group for leather and leather manufacturing products industry is SIC 311 (OMB 1987). This group includes establishments engaged in tan-

ning, currying and finishing hides and skins, as well as establishments manufacturing finished leather and artificial leather products and some similar products made of other materials. Leather converter, belting and chamois leather are also included in SIC 311. In addition, parts of SIC 23 (i.e., SIC 2371 and 2386) include establishments involved in the manufacturing of coats, garments, accessories and trimmings made of fur and establishments involved in sheep-lined clothing.

There are many varieties of leather with different characteristics depending upon the animal species and the specific part of the body of the animal from which the hide is obtained. Hides are made from cattle or horse skins; fancy leather from the skin of the calf, pig, goat, sheep and so on; and reptile leather from crocodile, lizard, chameleon and so on.

Employment in the leather and leather manufacturing products industry has been associated with various diseases caused by biological, toxicological and carcinogenic agents. The specific disease associated with exposure in the leather industry depends upon the extent to which the worker is exposed to the agent(s), which is dependent upon the occupation and work area within the industry.

For the tanning process, the epidermis of the hide is first removed and only the dermis transformed into leather. During this process, infection is a constant hazard, since the hide serves as a medium for numerous micro-organisms. Colonies of fungi may develop, specifically *Aspergillus niger* and *Penicillus glaucum* (Martignone 1964). To avoid the development of fungi, chlorinated phenols, specifically pentachlorophenol, have been widely used; unfortunately, such chemicals have been found to be toxic to the worker. Yeasts of three genera (*Rhodotorula*, *Cladosporium* and *Torulopsis*) have also been found (Kallenberger 1978). Tetanus, anthrax, leptospirosis, epizootic aphtha, Q fever and brucellosis are examples of diseases that workers could contract during the tanning process due to infected hides (Valsecchi and Fiorio 1978).

Skin disorders such as eczema and contact (allergic) dermatitis have also been diagnosed among leather tanners exposed to preservatives applied to the hides (Abrams and Warr 1951). The leather tanning and finishing process has been shown to have the highest incidence of dermatoses of any working group in the United States (Stevens 1979). Irritations of the mucous membranes of the throat and nose and perforations of the nasal septum may also occur after inhaling chromic acid fumes liberated during the chrome-tanning process.

Tannery workers have the potential for exposure to numerous known or suspected occupational carcinogens, including hexavalent chromium salts, benzidine-based azo dyes, organic solvents (e.g., benzene and formaldehyde), pentachlorophenol, N-nitroso compounds, arsenic, dimethylformamide and airborne leather dusts. These exposures may result in the development of various site-specific cancers. An excess of lung cancer has been observed in studies carried out in Italy (Seniori, Merler and Saracci 1990; Bonassi et al. 1990) and in a case-control study carried out in the United States (Garabrant and Wegman 1984), but this result is not always supported by other studies (Mikoczy, Schutz and Hagmar 1994; Stern et al. 1987; Pippard and Acheson 1985). Chromium and arsenicals were mentioned as possible contributors to the lung cancer excess. A significantly increased risk of soft tissue sarcoma has been observed in at least two separate tannery studies, one in Italy and one in the United Kingdom; the investigators of both studies suggest that the chlorophenols used at the tanneries may have produced these malignancies (Seniori et al. 1989; Mikoczy, Schutz and Hagmar 1994). A threefold statistically significant excess in pancreatic cancer mortality was noted in a Swedish case control study (Erdling et al. 1986); a 50% increase in pancreatic cancer was also noted in another study examining three Swedish tanneries (Mikoczy, Schutz and Hagmar 1994) and in a study of an Italian tannery (Seniori et al. 1989). Despite the excess risk of pancreatic cancer, no specific environmental agent was identified, and dietary factors were considered a possibility. An excess risk of testicular cancer was observed among leather tanners from the finishing department of one tannery; all three workers with testicular cancer had worked during the same time period and were exposed to dimethylformamide (Levin et al. 1987; Calvert et al. 1990). An excess risk of sinonasal cancer among leather tannery workers was observed in a case-control study in Italy; chromium, leather dust and tannins were indicated as possible aetiological agents (Comba et al. 1992; Battista et al. 1995). However, IARC research in the early 1980s found no evidence of an association between leather tanning and nasal cancer (IARC 1981). The results of a study of the Chinese leather tanning industry showed a statistically significant excess morbidity from bladder cancer among those tanners ever exposed to benzidine-based dyes, which increased with duration of exposure (Chen 1990).

Accidents are also a leading cause of disability in leather tannery workers. Slips and falls on wet and greasy floors are common, as are knife cuts from the trimming of hides. In addition, the machines used to process the hides are capable of crushing and inflicting bruises, abrasions and amputations. For example, United States Bureau of Labor Statistics (BLS) data for 1994 have shown an incidence rate in SIC 311 for injuries and illnesses combined of 19.1 per 100 full-time workers and an incidence rate for injuries alone of 16.4. These results are over 50% higher than the all-manufacturing incidence for illnesses and injuries combined, 12.2 per 100 full-time workers, and the incidence of 10.4 for injuries alone (BLS 1995).

Footwear

The handling and processing of leather in the manufacturing of shoes and boots may entail exposures to some of the same chemicals used in the tanning and finishing processes as cited above, giving rise to similar diseases. Furthermore, different chemicals used may also produce other diseases. Exposures to the toxic solvents used in adhesives and cleaners and to airborne leather dusts are of particular concern. One solvent of specific concern is benzene, which can produce thrombocytopenia; depression of the red blood cell, platelet and white cell counts; and pancytopenia. Benzene has largely been eliminated from the footwear industry. Peripheral neuropathy has also been found among workers in shoemaking factories due to n-hexane in the adhesives. This, too, has largely been substituted for by less toxic solvents. Electroencephalographic changes, liver damage and behavioural alterations have also been reported in connection with exposure to solvents in shoeworkers.

Benzene has been judged to be a human carcinogen (IARC 1982), and various investigators have observed excess leukaemias among workers exposed to benzene in the shoe industry. One study included the largest shoe manufacturing facility in Florence, Italy, consisting of over 2,000 employees. The study results revealed a fourfold excess risk of leukaemia, and benzene was cited as the most likely exposure (Paci et al. 1989). A follow-up to this study showed an over fivefold risk for those shoe workers employed in jobs where benzene exposure was substantial (Fu et al. 1996). A study in the United Kingdom examining mortality among males employed in shoe manufacturing found an elevated risk for leukaemia among workers handling glues and solvents which contained benzene (Pippard and Acheson 1985). Various studies of shoe industry workers in Istanbul, Turkey, have reported an excess risk of leukaemia from exposure to benzene. When benzene was later replaced by petrol, the absolute number of cases and risk of leukaemia dropped considerably (Aksoy, Erdem and DinCol 1974; 1976; Aksoy and Erdem 1978).

Various types of nasal cancer (adenocarcinoma, squamous-cell carcinoma and transitional-cell carcinoma) have been associated with employment in shoe manufacture and repair. Relative risks in excess of tenfold have been reported from studies in Italy and the United Kingdom (Fu et al. 1996; Comba et al. 1992; Merler et al. 1986; Pippard and Acheson 1985; Acheson 1972, 1976; Cecchi et al. 1980) but not in the United States (DeCoufle and Walrath 1987; Walker et al. 1993). The elevated nasal cancer risks were almost entirely accounted for by employees "heavily" exposed to leather dust in the preparation and finishing rooms. The mechanism by which exposure to leather dust may increase the risk of nasal cancer is not known.

Excesses of digestive and urinary tract cancers, such as bladder (Malker et al. 1984; Morrison et al. 1985), kidney (Walker et al. 1993; Malker et al. 1984), stomach (Walrath, DeCoufle and Thomas 1987) and rectal (DeCoufle and Walrath 1983; Walrath, DeCoufle and Thomas 1987) cancers, have been found in other studies of shoe workers but have not been consistently reported and have not been linked with particular exposures in the industry.

Ergonomic hazards causing work-related musculoskeletal disorders (WRMDs) are major problems in the shoe manufacturing industry. These hazards are due to the specialized equipment used and hands-on work requiring repetitive movements, forceful exertions and awkward body postures. BLS data show men's footwear to be one of the "industries with the highest rates of nonfatal illness disorders associated with repeated trauma" (BLS 1995). The incidence rate for the total footwear industry for illnesses and injuries combined was found to be 11.9 per 100 workers, with 8.6 being the incidence rate for injuries alone. These rates are slightly less than the incidence rates for all manufacturing. WRMDs in the shoe manufacturing industry include conditions such as tendinitis, synovitis, tenosynovitis, bursitis, ganglionic cysts, strains, carpal tunnel syndrome, low-back pain and cervical spine injuries.

Fur Workers

Fur processing involves the activities of three categories of workers. Fur dressers flesh and tan skins; fur dyers then colour or tint the skins with natural or synthetic dyes; and finally fur service workers grade, match and bale dressed furs. Dressers and dyers are exposed to potential carcinogens including tannins, oxidative dyes, chromium and formaldehyde, whereas fur service workers are potentially exposed to residual tanning materials while handling previous dressed furs. Very few epidemiological studies have been conducted on fur workers. The only comprehensive study among these workers revealed statistically elevated risks of colorectal and liver cancer among the dyers, lung cancer among the dressers and cardiovascular diseases among the service workers as compared to overall rates in the United States (Sweeney, Walrath and Waxweiler 1985).

ENVIRONMENTAL PROTECTION AND PUBLIC HEALTH ISSUES

Jerry Spiegel

The treatment and processing of animal skins and hides can be a source of considerable environmental impact. Discharged wastewater contains pollutants from the hides, products from their decomposition and chemicals and various spent solutions used for hide preparation and during the tanning process. Solid wastes and some atmospheric emissions also may arise.

88. LEATHER, FUR AND FOOTWEAR

Figure 88.8 • Schematic diagram of environmental impacts associated with tannery operations.

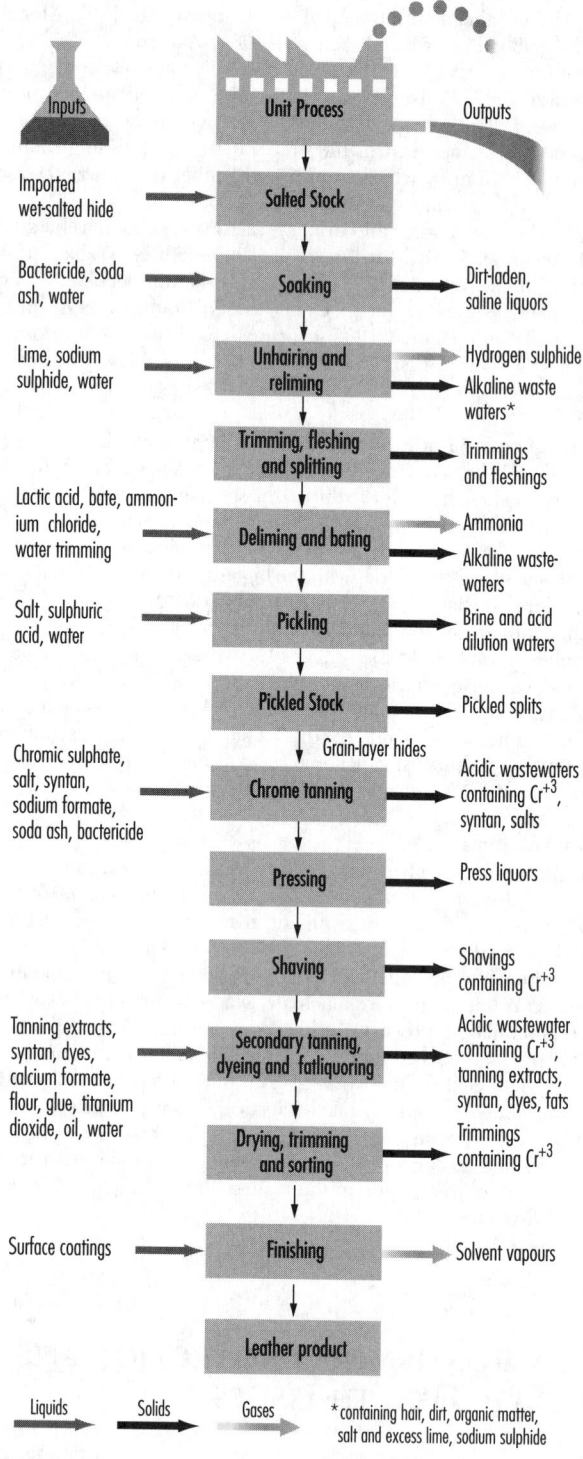

Liquids ➝ Solids ➝ Gases ➝ *containing hair, dirt, organic matter, salt and excess lime, sodium sulphide

agents and new processing chemicals which introduce problems of toxicity and persistence.

Simple measures intended to control pollution can themselves create secondary cross-media environmental impacts such as groundwater pollution, soil contamination, sludge dumping and chemical poisoning.

Tanning technology that is now available, based on a lower chemical and water consumption, has less impact on the environment than traditional processes. However, many obstacles remain to its widespread application.

Figure 88.8 presents the different wastes and environmental impacts associated with the various processes used in the tanning industry.

Pollution Control

Water pollution control

Untreated tannery wastes in surface waters can bring about a rapid deterioration of their physical, chemical and biological properties. Simple end-of-pipe effluent treatment processes can remove over 50% of suspended solids and biochemical oxygen demand (BOD) of effluent. More sophisticated measures are capable of higher levels of treatment.

As tannery effluents contain several chemical constituents that need to be treated, a sequence of treatment processes in turn must be used. Flow segregation is useful to allow separate treatment of concentrated waste streams.

Table 88.1 summarizes technological choices available for treatment of tannery effluents.

Air pollution control

Air emissions fall into three broad groups: odours, solvent vapours from finishing operations and gas emissions from the incineration of wastes.

Biological decomposition of organic matter as well as sulphide and ammonia emissions from wastewaters are responsible for the characteristic objectionable odours arising from tanneries. The siting of installations has been an issue because of the odours that have historically been associated with tanneries. Reduction of these odours is more a question of operational maintenance than of technology.

Solvent and other vapours from the finishing operations vary with the type of chemicals used and the technical methods em-

Table 88.1 • Technological choices for treatment of tannery effluents.

Pre-treatment	Mechanical screening to remove coarse material settling Flow equalization (balancing)
Primary treatment	Sulphide removal from beamhouse effluents Chromium removal from tanning effluents Physical-chemical treatment for BOD removal and neutralization
Secondary treatment	Biological treatment Activated sludge (oxidation ditch) Activated sludge (conventional) Lagooning (aerated, facultative or anaerobic)
Tertiary treatment	Nitrification and denitrification
Sedimentation and sludge handling	Different shapes and dimensions of tanks and basins

The major public concern over tanneries has traditionally been about odours and water pollution from untreated discharges. Other issues have arisen more recently from the increasing use of synthetic chemicals such as pesticides, solvents, dyes, finishing

Figure 88.9 • Flow chart for a communal plant for chrome recovery.

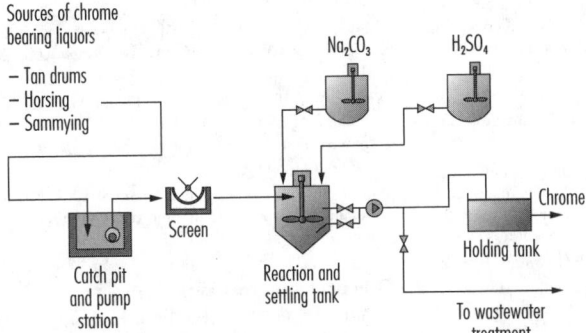

The incoming effluent, after analysis, is treated to produce chrome hydroxide. This is redissolved, polished and subjected to further analysis before being passed back for use in the tanning process.

Source: UNEP 1991.

ployed to reduce their generation and release. Up to 30% of the solvent used may be wasted through emissions, while modern processes are available to reduce this to around 3% in many cases.

The practice by many tanneries of incinerating solid wastes and offcuts raises the importance of adopting good incinerator design and following careful operating practices.

Waste management

Treatment of sludge constitutes the largest disposal problem, apart from effluent. Sludges of organic composition, if free from chrome or sulphides, have value as a soil conditioner as well as a small fertilizer effect from nitrogenous compounds contained therein. These benefits are best realized by ploughing immediately after application. Agricultural use of chrome-containing soils has been a matter of controversy in various jurisdictions, where guidelines have determined acceptable applications.

Various markets exist for the conversion of trimmings and fleshings into by-products used for a variety of purposes, including the production of gelatin, glue, leatherboard, tallow grease and proteins for animal feed. Process effluents, subject to suitable treatment and quality control, are sometimes used for irrigation where water is in short supply and/or effluent disposal is severely restricted.

To avoid problems of leachate generation and odour, only solids and dewatered sludges should be disposed of at landfill sites. Care must be taken to ensure that tannery wastes do not react with other industrial residues, such as acidic wastes, which can react to create toxic hydrogen sulphide gas. Incineration under uncontrolled conditions may lead to unacceptable emissions and is not recommended.

Pollution Prevention

Improving production technologies to increase environmental performance can achieve a number of objectives, such as:

- increasing the efficiency of chemical utilization
- reducing water or energy consumption
- recovering or recycling rejected materials.

Water consumption can vary considerably, ranging from less than 25 l/kg of raw hide to greater than 80 l/kg. Water use efficiency can be improved through the application of techniques such as increased volume control of processing waters, "batch" versus "running water" washes, low float modification of existing equipment; low float techniques using updated equipment, re-use of wastewater in less critical processes and recycling of individual process liquors.

Traditional soaking and unhairing account for over 50% of the BOD and chemical oxygen demand (COD) loads in typical tanning effluents. Various methods can be employed to substitute for sulphide, to recycle lime/sulphide liquors and to incorporate hairsaving techniques.

Reduction in chromium pollution can be achieved through measures to increase the levels of chrome that are fixed in the tanning bath and reduce the amounts that are "bled out" in subsequent processes. Other methods to reduce release of chromium are through direct recycling of used chrome liquors (which also reduces salinity of waste effluent) and the treatment of collected chrome-bearing liquors with alkali to precipitate the chromium as hydroxide, which can then be recycled. An illustration of a communal chrome recovery operation is shown in figure 88.9.

Where vegetable tanning is employed, preconditioning of hides can enhance the penetration and fixation of hides and contribute to decreased tannin concentrations in effluents. Other tanning agents such as titanium have been used as substitutes for chromium to produce salts of generally lower toxicity and to generate sludges that are inert and safer to handle.

References

Abrams, H and P Warr. 1951. Occupational diseases transmitted via contact with animals and animal products. *Ind Med Surgery* 20:341-351.

Acheson, E. 1972. Adenocarcinoma of the nasal cavity and sinuses in England and Wales. *Br J Ind Med* 29:21-30.

—. 1976. Nasal cancer in the furniture and boot and shoe manufacturing industries. *Prevent Med* 5:295-315.

Askoy, M and S Erdem. 1978. Followup study on the mortality and the development of leukemia in 44 pancytopenic patients with chronic exposure to benzene. *Blood* 52:285-292.

Askoy, M, S Erdem, and G DinCol. 1974. Leukemia in shoeworkers exposed chronically to benzene. *Blood* 44:837-841.

—. 1976. Types of leukemia in chronic benzene poisoning. A study in thirty-four patients. *Acta Haematol* 55:65-72.

Battista, G, P Comba, D Orsi, K Norpoth, and A Maier. 1995. Nasal cancer in leather workers: An occupational disease. *J Cancer Res Clin Oncol* 121:1-6.

Bonassi, S, F Merlo, R Puntoni, F Ferraris, and G Bottura. 1990. Epidemics of lung tumors in a Biella tannery. *Epidemiol Rev* 12:25-30.

Bureau of Labor Statistics (BLS). 1995. *Survey of Occupational Injuries and Illnesses, 1994.* Washington, DC: BLS.

Calvert, G, J Fajen, B Hills, and W Halperin. 1990. Testicular cancer, dimethylformamide, and leather tanneries. *Lancet* 336:1253-1254.

Cecchi, F, E Buiatti, D Kriebel, L Nastasi, and M Santucci. 1980. Adenocarcinoma of the nose and paranasal sinuses in shoemakers and woodmakers in the province of Florence, Italy. *Br J Ind Med* 37:222-226.

Chen, J. 1990. A cohort study of the cancer experience among workers exposed to benzidine-derived dyes in Shanghai (China) leather-tanning industry. *Chin J Prev Med* 24:328-331.

Comba, P, G Battista, S Bell, B de Capus, E Merler, D Orsi, S Rodella, C Vindieni, and O Axelson. 1992. A case-control study of cancer of the nose and paranasal sinuses and occupational exposures. *Am J Ind Med* 22:511-520.

DeCoufle, P and J Walrath. 1983. Proportionate mortality among US shoeworkers, 1966-1972. *Am J Ind Med* 4:523-532.

—. 1987. Nasal cancer in the US shoe industry: Does it exist? *Am J Ind Med* 12:605-613.

Erdling, C, H Kling, U Flodin, and O Axelson. 1986. Cancer mortality among leather tanners. *Br J Ind Med* 43:484-496.

Fu, H, P Demers, A Costantini, P Winter, D Colin, M Kogevinas, and P Boffetta. 1996. Cancer mortality

88. LEATHER, FUR AND FOOTWEAR

among shoe manufacturing workers: An analysis of two cohorts. *Occup Environ Med* 53:394-398.

Garabrant, D and D Wegman. 1984. Cancer mortality among shoe and leather workers in Massachusetts. *Am J Ind Med* 5:303-314.

International Agency for Research on Cancer (IARC). 1981. Wood, leather and some associated industries. Vol. 28. Lyon: IARC.

—. 1982. Some industrial chemicals and dyestuffs. Vol. 29. Lyon: IARC.

International Labour Organization (ILO). 1992. *Employment and Working Conditions and Competitiveness in the Leather and Footwear Industry*, Report II, Fourth Tripartite Technical Meeting for the Leather and Footwear Industry, Sectoral Activities Programme. Geneva: ILO.

Kallenberger, W. 1978. A study of yeasts in chrome tanning and processing. *J Am Leather Chem Assoc* 73:6-21.

Levin, S, D Baker, P Landrigan, S Monaghan, E Frumin, M Braithwaite, and W Towne. 1987. Testicular cancer in leather tanners exposed to dimethylformamide. *Lancet* 2:1153.

Malker, H, B Malker, J McLaughin, and W Blot. 1984. Kidney cancer among leather workers. *Lancet* I:50.

Martignone, G. 1964. *Treatise on Practical Tanning*. Turin: Levrotto and Bella.

Merler, E, A Baldesseroni, R Laria, P Faravelli, R Agostini, R Pisa, and F Berrino. 1986. On the causal association between exposure to leather dust and nasal cancer: Further evidence from a case-control study. *Br J Ind Med* 43:91-95.

Mikoczy, Z, A Schutz, and L Hagmar. 1994. Cancer incidence and mortality among Swedish leather tanners. *Occup Environ Med* 51:530-535.

Mikoczy, Z, A Schutz, U Stromberg, and L Hagmar. 1996. Cancer incidence and specific occupational

exposures in the Swedish leather tanning industry: A cohort based case-control study. *Occup Environ Med* 53:463-467.

Morrison, A, A Ahibom, W Verhock, K Aoli, I Leck, Y Ohno, and K Obata. 1985. Occupational and bladder cancer in Boston, USA, Manchester, UK, and Nagoya, Japan. *Japan Journal of Epidemiology and Community Health* 39:294-300.

Office of Management and Budget (OMB). 1987. *Standard Industrial Classification Manual*. Washington, DC: US GPO.

Paci, E, E Buiatti, A Costantini, L Miligi, N Puci, A Scarpelli, G Petrioli, L Simonato, R Winkelmann, and J Kaldor. 1989. Aplastic anemia, leukemia and other cancer mortality in a cohort of shoe workers exposed to benzene. *Scand J Work Environ Health* 15:313-318.

Pippard, E and E Acheson. 1985. The mortality of boot and shoe makers, with special reference to cancer. *Scand J Work Environ Health* 11:249-255.

Seniori, C, E Merler, and R Saracci. 1990. Epidemiological studies on occupational cancer risk in the tanning, leather and shoe industries. *Medicina del Lavaro* 81:184-211.

Seniori, C, E Paci, I Miligi, E Buiatti, C Martelli, and S Lenzi. 1989. Cancer mortality among workers in the Tuscan tannery industry. *Br J Ind Med* 46:384-388.

Stern, FB, JJ Beaumont, WE Halperin, LI Murphy, BW Hills, and JM Fajen. 1987. Mortality of chrome leather tannery workers and chemical exposures in tanneries. *Scand J Work Environ Health* 13:108-117.

Stevens, C. 1979. Assessing skin problems of occupational origin. *Occup Health Safety* 48(18):39-43.

Sweeney, M, J Walrath, and R Waxweiler. 1985. Mortality among retired fur workers: Dyers, dressers (tanners) and service workers. *Scand J Work Environ Health* 11:257-264.

United Nations Environment Program (UNEP). 1991. *Tanneries and the Environment. A Technical Guide to Reducing the Environmental Impact of Tannery Operations*. Industry and Environment Office. Technical Report Series No. 4. Paris: UNEP.

Valsecchi, M and A Fiorio. 1978. Operating cycle in the tanning industry and related risks. *Securities* 63:132-144.

Walker, J, T Bloom, F Stern, A Okun, M Fingerhut, and W Halperin. 1993. Mortality of workers employed in shoe manufacturing. *Scand J Work Environ Health* 19:89-95.

Walrath, J, P DeCoufle, and T Thomas. 1987. Mortality among workers in a shoe manufacturing company. *Am J Ind Med* 12:615-623.

Other relevant readings

Bequele, A and WE Myers. 1995. *First Things First in Child Labour: Eliminating Work Detrimental to Children*. Geneva: ILO/UNICEF.

Fyfe, A and M Jankanish. 1997. *Trade Unions and Child Labour: A Guide to Action*. Geneva: ILO.

Industrial Accident Prevention Association (IAPA). 1983. *Tanning Industry Safety and Health Guide for Hide Tanners and Fur Dressers*. Toronto: IAPA.

International Labour Organization. 1996. *Globalization of the Footwear, Textiles and Clothing Industries. Report for Discussion at the Tripartite Meeting on the Globalization of the Footwear, Textiles and Clothing Industries: Effects on Employment and Working Conditions*. Geneva: ILO.

—. 1996. *Child Labour: Targeting the Intolerable*, Report VI(1), International Labour Conference, 86th Session, 1998. Geneva: ILO.

Thorstensen, TC. 1985. *Practical leather technology*. Malabar, FL, US: Robert E. Krieger Publishing Company.

TEXTILE GOODS INDUSTRY

Chapter Editor
A. Lee Ivester and John D. Neefus

Contents

THE TEXTILE INDUSTRY: HISTORY AND HEALTH AND SAFETY

Leon J. Warshaw

The Textile Industry

The term *textile industry* (from the Latin *texere*, to weave) was originally applied to the weaving of fabrics from fibres, but now it includes a broad range of other processes such as knitting, tufting, felting and so on. It has also been extended to include the making of yarn from natural or synthetic fibres as well as the finishing and dyeing of fabrics.

Yarn making

In prehistoric eras, animal hair, plants and seeds were used to make fibres. Silk was introduced in China around 2600 BC, and in the middle of the 18th century AD, the first synthetic fibres were created. While synthetic fibres made from cellulose or petro-chemicals, either alone or in varied combinations with other synthetic and/or natural fibres, have seen increasingly widening use, they have not been able to totally eclipse fabrics made of natural fibres such as wool, cotton, flax and silk.

Silk is the only natural fibre formed in filaments which can be twisted together to make yarn. The other natural fibres must first be straightened, made parallel by combing and then drawn into a continuous yarn by spinning. The *spindle* is the earliest spinning tool; it was first mechanized in Europe around 1400 AD by the invention of the spinning wheel. The late 17th century saw the invention of the *spinning jenny,* which could operate a number of spindles simultaneously. Then, thanks to Richard Arkwright's invention of the *spinning frame* in 1769 and Samuel Crompton's introduction of the *mule,* which allowed one worker to operate 1,000 spindles at one time, yarn-making moved from being a cottage industry into the mills.

Making of fabric

The making of fabric had a similar history. Ever since its origins in antiquity, the hand loom has been the basic weaving machine. Mechanical improvements began in ancient times with the development of the *heddle,* to which alternate warp threads are tied; in the 13th century AD, the *foot treadle,* which could operate several sets of heddles, was introduced. With the addition of the *frame-mounted batten,* which beats the weft or filling yarns into place, the "mechanized" loom became the predominant weaving instrument in Europe and, except for traditional cultures where the original hand looms persisted, around the world.

John Kay's invention of the *flying shuttle* in 1733, which allowed the weaver to send the shuttle across the width of the loom automatically, was the first step in mechanization of weaving. Edmund Cartwright developed the *steam-powered loom* and in 1788, with James Watt, built the first steam-driven textile mill in England. This freed the mills from their dependence on water-driven machinery and allowed them to be constructed anywhere. Another significant development was the *punch-card* system, developed in France in 1801 by Joseph Marie Jacquard; this allowed automated weaving of patterns. The earlier power looms made of wood were gradually replaced by looms made of steel and other metals. Since then, technological changes have focused on making them larger, faster and more highly automated.

Dyeing and printing

Natural dyes were originally used to impart colour to yarns and fabrics, but with the 19th-century discovery of coal-tar dyes and the 20th-century development of synthetic fibres, dyeing processes have become more complicated. Block printing was originally used to colour fabrics (silk-screen printing of fabrics was developed in the mid-1800s), but it soon was replaced by roller printing. Engraved copper rollers were first used in England in 1785, followed by rapid improvements that allowed roller printing in six colours all in perfect register. Modern roller printing can produce over 180 m of fabric printed in 16 or more colours in 1 minute.

Finishing

Early on, fabrics were finished by brushing or shearing the nap of the fabric, filling or sizing the cloth, or passing it through calender rolls to produce a glazed effect. Today, fabrics are pre-shrunk, *mercerized* (cotton yarns and fabrics are treated with caustic solutions to improve their strength and lustre) and treated by a variety of finishing processes that, for example, increase crease resistance, crease holding and resistance to water, flame and mildew.

Special treatments produce *high-performance fibres,* so called because of their extraordinary strength and extremely high temperature resistance. Thus, Aramid, a fibre similar to nylon, is stronger than steel, and Kevlar, a fibre made from Aramid, is used to make bullet-proof fabrics and clothing that is resistant both to heat and chemicals. Other synthetic fibres combined with carbon, boron, silicon, aluminium and other materials are used to produce the lightweight, superstrong structural materials used in airplanes, spacecraft, chemical resistant filters and membranes, and protective sports gear.

From hand craft to industry

Textile manufacture was originally a hand craft practised by cottage spinners and weavers and small groups of skilled artisans. With the technological developments, large and economically important textile enterprises emerged, primarily in the United Kingdom and the Western European countries. Early settlers in North America brought cloth mills to New England (Samuel Slater, who had been a mill supervisor in England, constructed from memory a spinning frame in Providence, Rhode Island, in 1790), and the invention of Eli Whitney's *cotton gin,* which could clean harvested cotton with great speed, created a new demand for cotton fabrics.

This was accelerated by the commercialization of the *sewing machine.* In the early 18th century, a number of inventors produced machines that would stitch cloth. In France in 1830, Barthelemy Thimonnier received a patent for his sewing machine; in 1841, when 80 of his machines were busy sewing uniforms for the French army, his factory was destroyed by tailors who saw his machines as a threat to their livelihood. At about that time in England, Walter Hunt devised an improved machine but abandoned the project because he felt that it would throw poor seamstresses out of work. In 1848, Elias Howe received a US patent for a machine much like Hunt's, but became embroiled in legal battles, which he ultimately won, charging many manufacturers with infringement of his patent. The invention of the modern sewing machine is credited to Isaac Merritt Singer, who devised the overhanging arm, the presser foot to hold down the cloth, a wheel to feed the fabric to the needle and a foot treadle instead of a hand crank, leaving both hands free to manoeuvre the fabric. In addition to designing and manufacturing the machine, he created the first large-scale consumer-appliance enterprise, which featured such innovations as an advertising campaign, selling the machines on the installment plan, and providing a service contract.

Thus, the technological advances during the 18th century were not only the impetus for the modern textile industry but they can be credited with the creation of the factory system and the profound changes in family and community life that have been labelled the Industrial Revolution. The changes continue today as large textile establishments move from the old industrialized areas to new regions that promise cheaper labour and sources of energy, while competition fosters continuing technological developments such as computer-controlled automation to reduce labour needs and improve quality. Meanwhile, politicians debate quotas, tariffs and other economic barriers to provide and/or retain competitive advantages for their countries. Thus, the textile industry not only provides products essential for the world's growing population; it also has a profound influence on international trade and the economies of nations.

Safety and Health Concerns

As machines became larger, speedier and more complicated, they also introduced new potential hazards. As materials and processes became more complex, they infused the workplace with potential health hazards. And as workers had to cope with mechanization and the demand for increasing productivity, work stress, largely unrecognized or ignored, exerted an increasing influence on their well-being. Perhaps the greatest effect of the Industrial Revolution was on community life, as workers moved from the country to cities, where they had to contend with all of the ills of urbanization. These effects are being seen today as the textile and other industries move to developing countries and regions, except that the changes are more rapid.

The hazards encountered in different segments of the industry are summarized in the other articles in this chapter. They emphasize the importance of good housekeeping and proper maintenance of machines and equipment, the installation of effective guards and fences to prevent contact with moving parts, the use of local exhaust ventilation (LEV) as a supplement to good general ventilation and temperature control, and the provision of appropriate personal protective equipment (PPE) and clothing whenever a hazard cannot be completely controlled or prevented by design engineering and/or substitution of less hazardous materials. Repeated education and training of workers on all levels and effective supervision are recurrent themes.

Environmental Concerns

Environmental concerns raised by the textile industry stem from two sources: the processes involved in textile manufacture and hazards associated with the way the products are used.

Textile manufacture

The chief environmental problems created by textile manufacturing plants are toxic substances released into the atmosphere and into wastewater. In addition to potentially toxic agents, unpleasant odours are often a problem, especially where dyeing and printing plants are located near residential areas. Ventilation exhausts may contain vapours of solvents, formaldehyde, hydrocarbons, hydrogen sulphide and metallic compounds. Solvents may sometimes be captured and distilled for reuse. Particulates may be removed by filtration. Scrubbing is effective for water-soluble volatile compounds such as methanol, but it does not work in pigment printing, where hydrocarbons make up most of the emissions. Flammables may be burned off, although this is relatively expensive. The ultimate solution, however, is the use of materials that are as close to being emission-free as possible. This refers not only to the dyes, binders and cross-linking agents used in the printing, but also to the formaldehyde and residual monomer content of fabrics.

Contamination of wastewater by unfixed dyes is a serious environmental problem not only because of the potential health hazards to human and animal life, but also because of the discolouration that makes it highly visible. In ordinary dyeing, fixation of over 90% of the dyestuff can be achieved, but fixation

levels of only 60% or less are common in printing with reactive dyes. This means that more than one-third of the reactive dye enters the wastewater during the washing-off of the printed fabric. Additional amounts of dyes are introduced into the wastewater during the washing of screens, printing blankets and drums.

Limits on wastewater discolouration have been set in a number of countries, but it is often very difficult to heed them without an expensive wastewater purification system. A solution is found in the use of dyestuffs with a lesser contaminating effect and the development of dyes and synthetic thickening agents that increase the degree of dye fixation, thereby reducing the amounts of the excess to be washed away (Grund 1995).

Environmental concerns in textile use

Residues of formaldehyde and some heavy-metal complexes (most of these are inert) may be sufficient to cause skin irritation and sensitization in persons wearing the dyed fabrics.

Formaldehyde and residual solvents in carpets and fabrics used for upholstery and curtains will continue to vaporize gradually for some time. In buildings that are sealed, where the air-conditioning system recirculates most of the air rather than exhausting it to the outside environment, these substances may reach levels high enough to produce symptoms in the occupants of the building, as discussed elsewhere in this *Encyclopaedia*.

To ensure the safety of fabrics, Marks and Spencer, the British/Canadian clothing retailer, led the way by setting limits for formaldehyde in garments they would purchase. Since then, other garment manufacturers, notably Levi Strauss in the United States, have followed suit. In a number of countries, these limits have been formalized in laws (e.g., Denmark, Finland, Germany and Japan), and, in response to consumer education, fabric manufacturers have been voluntarily adhering to such limits in order to be able to use eco labels (see figure 89.1).

Conclusion

Technological developments are continuing to enhance the range of fabrics produced by the textile industry and to increase its

---

Figure 89.1 • Ecological labels used for textiles.

GuT ®

Eco-Tex ®

Oko-Tex Standard 100

Tox Proof ®

EU enviromental symbol

productivity. It is most important, however, that these develop-ments be guided also by the imperative of enhancing the health, safety and well-being of the workers. But even then, there is the problem of implementing these developments in older enterprises that are marginally financially viable and unable to make the necessary investments, as well as in developing areas eager to have new industries even at the expense of the health and safety of the workers. Even under these circumstances, however, much can be achieved by education and training of the workers to minimize the risks to which they may be exposed.

GLOBAL TRENDS IN THE TEXTILE INDUSTRY

Jung-Der Wang

Human beings have relied on clothing and food to survive ever since they appeared on earth. The clothing or textile industry thus began very early in human history. While early people used their hands to weave and knit cotton or wool into fabric or cloth, it was not until the late 18th and early 19th centuries that the Industrial Revolution changed the way of making clothes. People started to

Figure 89.3 • Combing.

Wilawan Juengprasert, Ministry of Public Health, Thailand

use various kinds of energy to supply power. Nevertheless, cotton, wool and cellulose fibres remained the major raw materials. Since the Second World War, the production of synthetic fibres devel-oped by the petrochemical industry has increased tremendously. The consumption volume of synthetic fibres of world textile prod-ucts in 1994 was 17.7 million tons, 48.2% of all fibres, and it is expected to exceed 50% after 2000 (see figure 89.2).

According to the world apparel fibre consumption survey by the Food and Agricultural Organization (FAO), the average an-nual rates of growth for textile consumption during 1969–89, 1979–89 and 1984–89 were 2.9%, 2.3% and 3.7% respectively. Based on the previous consumption trend, population growth, per capita GDP (gross domestic product) growth, and the increase of

Figure 89.2 • Change in fibre supply in the textile industry before 1994 and projected through 2004.

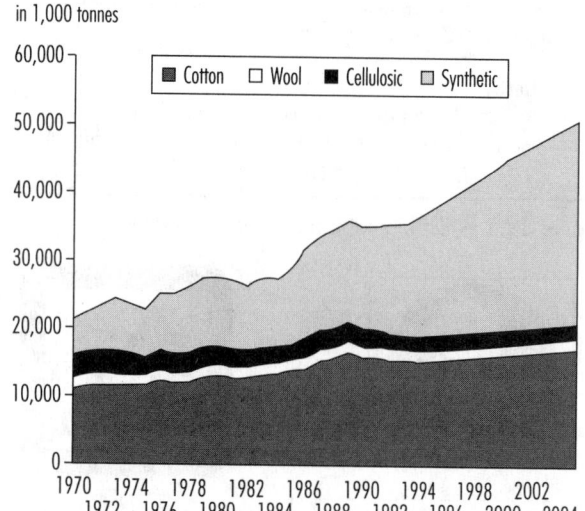

in 1,000 tonnes

Increase of supply in synthetic fibres is overwhelming.

	Total	Synthetic	Cotton
1994→2000	3.5%	5.8%	1.2%
2000→2005	2.5%	3.6%	1.2%

Supply of synthetic fibres will comprise more than half of all fibre supply by the year 2000.

	Synthetic	Cotton
1994	48.2%	41.3%
2000	55.2%	36.2%
2005	58.3%	34.0%

Source: Ministry of International Trade and Industry (Japan) 1996.

Figure 89.4 • Carding.

Wilawan Juengprasert, Ministry of Public Health, Thailand

Table 89.1 • Numbers of enterprises and employees in textile and apparel industries of selected countries and territories in the Asia-Pacific area in 1985 and 1995.

Number of	Year	Australia	China	Hong Kong	India	Indonesia	Korea, Republic of	Malaysia	New Zealand	Pakistan
Enterprises	1985	2,535	45,500	13,114	13,435	1,929	12,310	376	2,803	1,357
	1995	4,503	47,412	6,808	13,508	2,182	14,262	238	2,547	1,452
Employees ($\times 10^3$)	1985	96	4,396	375	1,753	432	684	58	31	N.A.
	1995	88	9,170	139	1,675	912	510	76	21	N.A.

consumption of each textile product with rising income, the demand for textile products in 2000 and 2005 will be 42.2 million tons and 46.9 million tons, respectively, as shown in figure 89.2. The trend indicates that there is a consistent growing demand for textile products, and that the industry will still employ a large workforce.

Another major change is the progressive automation of weaving and knitting, which, combined with rising labour costs, has shifted the industry from the developed to the developing countries. Although the production of yarn and fabric products, as well as some upstream synthetic fibres, has remained in more developed countries, a large proportion of the labour-intensive downstream apparel industry has already moved to the developing countries. The Asia-Pacific region's textile and clothing industry now accounts for approximately 70% of the world production; table 89.1 indicates a shifting trend of employment in this region. Thus, the occupational safety and health of textile workers has become a major issue in developing countries; figures 89.3 to 89.6 illustrate some textile industry processes as they are carried out in the developing world.

Figure 89.5 • A modern picker.

Wilawan Juengprasert, Ministry of Public Health, Thailand

Figure 89.6 • Warping.

Wilawan Juengprasert, Ministry of Public Health, Thailand

PRODUCTION AND GINNING OF COTTON

W. Stanley Anthony

Cotton Production

Cotton production practices begin after the previous crop is harvested. The first operations usually include shredding stalks, ripping out roots and disking the soil. Fertilizer and herbicides generally are applied and incorporated into the soil before the land is bedded in preparation for needed irrigation or planting. Since soil characteristics and past fertilization and cropping practices can cause a wide range of fertility levels in cotton soils, fertility programmes should be based on soil test analyses. Control of weeds is essential to obtain high lint yield and quality. Cotton yields and harvesting efficiency can be reduced by as much as 30% by weeds. Herbicides have been widely used in many countries for weed control since the early 1960s. Application methods include pre-planting treatment to foliage of existing weeds, incor-

89. TEXTILE GOODS INDUSTRY

poration into pre-plant soil and treatment at pre-emergence and post-emergence stages.

Several factors that play an important role in achieving a good stand of cotton plants include seed-bed preparation, soil moisture, soil temperature, seed quality, seedling disease infestation, fungicides and soil salinity. Planting high-quality seed in a well-prepared seed-bed is a key factor in achieving early, uniform stands of vigorous seedlings. High-quality planting seed should have a germination rate of 50% or higher in a cool test. In a cool/warm test, the seed vigour index should be 140 or higher. Seeding rates of 12 to 18 seeds/metre of row are recommended to obtain a plant population of 14,000 to 20,000 plants/hectare. A suitable planter metering system should be used to ensure uniform spacing of seed regardless of seed size. Seed germination and seedling emergence rates are closely associated with a temperature range of 15 to 38 °C.

Early-season seedling diseases can hamper uniform stands and result in the need to replant. Important seedling disease pathogens such as *Pythium*, *Rhizoctonia*, *Fusarium* and *Thielaviopsis* can reduce plant stands and cause long skips between seedlings. Only seed that has been properly treated with one or more fungicides should be planted.

Cotton is similar to other crops with respect to water use during different plant developmental stages. Water use is generally less than 0.25 cm/day from emergence to the first square. During this period, loss of soil moisture by evaporation may exceed the amount of water transpired by the plant. Water use increases sharply as the first blooms appear and reaches a maximum level of 1 cm/day during the peak bloom stage. Water requirement refers to the total amount of water (rainfall and irrigation) needed to produce a crop of cotton.

Insect populations can have an important impact on cotton quality and yield. Early-season population management is important in promoting balanced fruiting/vegetative development of the crop. Protecting early fruit positions is essential to achieving a profitable crop. Over 80% of the yield is set in the first 3 to 4 weeks of fruiting. During the fruiting period, producers should scout their cotton at least twice a week to monitor insect activity and damage.

A well-managed defoliation programme reduces leaf trash that can adversely affect the grade of the harvested cotton. Growth regulators such as PIX are useful defoliators because they control vegetative growth and contribute to earlier fruiting.

Harvesting

Two types of mechanical harvesting equipment are used to harvest cotton: the spindle picker and the cotton stripper. The *spindle picker* is a selective-type harvester that uses tapered, barbed spindles to remove seed cotton from bolls. This harvester can be used on a field more than once to provide stratified harvests. On the other hand, the *cotton stripper* is a nonselective or once-over harvester that removes not only the well-opened bolls but also the cracked and unopened bolls along with the burs and other foreign matter.

Agronomic practices that produce a high-quality uniform crop will generally contribute to good harvesting efficiency. The field should be well drained and rows laid out for effective use of machinery. Row ends should be free of weeds and grass, and should have a field border of 7.6 to 9 m for turning and aligning the harvesters with the rows. The border also should be free of weeds and grass. Disking creates adverse conditions in rainy weather, so chemical weed control or mowing should be used instead. Plant height should not exceed about 1.2 m for cotton that is to be picked, and about 0.9 m for cotton that is to be stripped. Plant height can be controlled to some extent by using chemical growth regulators at the proper growth stage. Produc-

tion practices that set the bottom boll at least 10 cm above the ground should be used. Culturing practices such as fertilization, cultivation and irrigation during the growing season should be carefully managed to produce a uniform crop of well-developed cotton.

Chemical defoliation is a culturing practice that induces abscission (shedding) of foliage. Defoliants may be applied to help minimize green-leaf-trash contamination and promote faster drying of early morning dew on the lint. Defoliants should not be applied until at least 60% of the bolls are open. After a defoliant is applied, the crop should not be harvested for at least 7 to 14 days (the period will vary depending on chemicals used and weather conditions). Chemical desiccants may also be used to prepare plants for harvest. Desiccation is the rapid loss of water from the plant tissue and subsequent death of the tissue. The dead foliage remains attached to the plant.

The current trend in cotton production is toward a shorter season and one-time harvest. Chemicals that accelerate the boll opening process are applied with the defoliant or soon after the leaves drop. These chemicals allow earlier harvests and increase the percentage of bolls that are ready to be harvested during the first harvest. Because these chemicals have the ability to open or partially open immature bolls, the quality of the crop may be severely impacted (i.e., the micronaire may be low) if the chemicals are applied too early.

Storage

The moisture content of cotton before and during storage is critical; excess moisture causes stored cotton to overheat, resulting in lint discolouration, lower seed germination and possibly spontaneous combustion. Seed cotton with a moisture content above 12% should not be stored. Also, the internal temperature of newly built modules should be monitored for the first 5 to 7 days of cotton storage; modules that experience a 11 °C rise or are above 49 °C should be ginned immediately to avoid the possibility of major loss.

Several variables affect seed and fibre quality during seed cotton storage. Moisture content is the most important. Other variables include length of storage, amount of high-moisture foreign matter, variation in moisture content throughout the stored mass, initial temperature of the seed cotton, temperature of the seed cotton during storage, weather factors during storage (temperature, relative humidity, rainfall) and protection of the cotton from rain and wet ground. Yellowing is accelerated at high temperatures. Both temperature rise and maximum temperature are important. Temperature rise is directly related to the heat generated by biological activity.

Ginning process

About 80 million bales of cotton are produced annually worldwide, of which about 20 million are produced by about 1,300 gins in the United States. The principal function of the cotton gin is to separate lint from seed, but the gin must also be equipped to remove a large percentage of the foreign matter from the cotton that would significantly reduce the value of the ginned lint. A ginner must have two objectives: (1) to produce lint of satisfactory quality for the grower's market and (2) to gin the cotton with minimum reduction in fibre spinning quality, so that the cotton will meet the demands of its ultimate users, the spinner and the consumer. Accordingly, quality preservation during ginning requires the proper selection and operation of each machine in a ginning system. Mechanical handling and drying may modify the natural quality characteristics of cotton. At best, a ginner can only preserve the quality characteristics inherent in the cotton when it enters the gin. The following paragraphs briefly discuss the function of the major mechanical equipment and processes in the gin.

Seed-cotton machinery

Cotton is transported from a trailer or module into a green-boll trap in the gin, where green bolls, rocks and other heavy foreign matter are removed. The automatic feed control provides an even, well-dispersed flow of cotton so that the gin's cleaning and drying system will operate more efficiently. Cotton that is not well dispersed can travel through the drying system in clumps, and only the surface of that cotton will be dried.

In the first stage of drying, heated air conveys the cotton through the shelves for 10 to 15 seconds. The temperature of the conveying air is regulated to control the amount of drying. To prevent fibre damage, the temperature to which the cotton is exposed during normal operation should never exceed 177° C. Temperatures above 150 °C can cause permanent physical changes in cotton fibres. Dryer-temperature sensors should be located as near as possible to the point where cotton and heated air come together. If the temperature sensor is located near the exit of the tower dryer, the mixpoint temperature could actually be 55 to 110 °C higher than the temperature at the downstream sensor. The temperature drop downstream results from the cooling effect of evaporation and from heat loss through the walls of machinery and piping. The drying continues as the warm air moves the seed cotton to the cylinder cleaner, which consists of 6 or 7 revolving spiked cylinders that rotate at 400 to 500 rpm. These cylinders scrub the cotton over a series of grid rods or screens, agitate the cotton and allow fine foreign materials, such as leaves, trash and dirt, to pass through the openings for disposal. Cylinder cleaners break up large wads and generally condition the cotton for additional cleaning and drying. Processing rates of about 6 bales per hour per metre of cylinder length are common.

The stick machine removes larger foreign matter, such as burs and sticks, from the cotton. Stick machines use the centrifugal force created by saw cylinders rotating at 300 to 400 rpm to "sling off" foreign material while the fibre is held by the saw. The foreign matter that is slung off the reclaimer feeds into the trash-handling system. Processing rates of 4.9 to 6.6 bales/hr/m of cylinder length are common.

Ginning (lint-seed separation)

After going through another stage of drying and cylinder cleaning, cotton is distributed to each gin stand by the conveyor-distributor. Located above the gin stand, the extractor-feeder meters seed cotton uniformly to the gin stand at controllable rates, and cleans seed cotton as a secondary function. The moisture content of cotton fibre at the extractor-feeder apron is critical. The moisture must be low enough that foreign matter can be easily removed in the gin stand. However, the moisture must not be so low (below 5%) as to result in the breakage of individual fibres as they are separated from the seed. This breakage causes an appreciable reduction both in fibre length and lint turnout. From a quality standpoint, cotton with a higher content of short fibres produces excessive waste at the textile mill and is less desirable. Excessive breakage of fibres can be avoided by maintaining a fibre moisture content of 6 to 7% at the extractor-feeder apron.

Two types of gins are in common use—the saw gin and the roller gin. In 1794, Eli Whitney invented a gin that removed fibre from the seed by means of spikes or saws on a cylinder. In 1796, Henry Ogden Holmes invented a gin having saws and ribs; this gin replaced Whitney's gin and made ginning a continuous-flow process rather than a batch process. Cotton (usually *Gossypium hirsutum*) enters the saw gin stand through a huller front. The saws grasp the cotton and draw it through widely spaced ribs known as huller ribs. The locks of cotton are drawn from the huller ribs into the bottom of the roll box. The actual ginning process—separation of lint and seed—takes place in the roll box of the gin stand. The ginning action is caused by a set of saws rotating between ginning ribs. The saw teeth pass between the ribs at the ginning point. Here the leading edge of the teeth is approximately parallel to the rib, and the teeth pull the fibres from the seed, which are too large to pass between the ribs. Ginning at rates above those recommended by the manufacturer can cause fibre quality reduction, seed damage and choke-ups. Gin stand saw speeds are also important. High speeds tend to increase the fibre damage done during ginning.

Roller-type gins provided the first mechanically aided means of separating extra-long staple cotton (*Gossypium barbadense*) lint from seed. The Churka gin, which has an unknown origin, consisted of two hard rollers that ran together at the same surface speed, pinching the fibre from the seed and producing about 1 kg of lint/day. In 1840, Fones McCarthy invented a more efficient roller gin that consisted of a leather ginning roller, a stationary knife held tightly against the roller and a reciprocating knife that pulled the seed from the lint as the lint was held by the roller and stationary knife. In the late 1950s, a rotary-knife roller gin was developed by the US Department of Agriculture (USDA) Agricultural Research Service's Southwestern Cotton Ginning Research Laboratory, US gin manufacturers and private ginneries. This gin is currently the only roller-type gin used in the United States.

Lint cleaning

Cotton is conveyed from the gin stand through lint ducts to condensers and formed again into a batt. The batt is removed from the condenser drum and fed into the saw-type lint cleaner. Inside the lint cleaner, cotton passes through the feed rollers and over the feed plate, which applies the fibres to the lint cleaner saw. The saw carries cotton under grid bars, which are aided by centrifugal force and remove immature seeds and foreign matter. It is important that the clearance between the saw tips and grid bars be properly set. The grid bars must be straight with a sharp leading edge to avoid reducing cleaning efficiency and increasing lint loss. Increasing the lint cleaner's feed rate above the manufacturer's recommended rate will decrease cleaning efficiency and increase loss of good fibre. Roller-ginned cotton is usually cleaned with non-aggressive, non-saw-type cleaners to minimize fibre damage.

Lint cleaners can improve the grade of cotton by removing foreign matter. In some cases, lint cleaners may improve the colour of a lightly spotted cotton by blending to produce a white grade. They may also improve the colour grade of a spotted cotton to light spotted or perhaps white colour grade.

Packaging

The cleaned cotton is compressed into bales, which must then be covered to protect them from contamination during transportation and storage. Three types of bales are produced: modified flat, compress universal density and gin universal density. These bales are packaged at densities of 224 and 449 kg/m^3 for the modified flat and universal density bales, respectively. In most gins cotton is packaged in a "double-box" press wherein the lint is initially compacted in one press box by a mechanical or hydraulic tramper; then the press box is rotated, and the lint is further compressed to about 320 or 641 kg/m^3 by modified flat or gin universal density presses, respectively. Modified flat bales are recompressed to become compress universal density bales in a later operation to achieve optimum freight rates. In 1995, about 98% of the bales in the United States were gin universal density bales.

Fibre quality

Cotton quality is affected by every production step, including selecting the variety, harvesting and ginning. Certain quality characteristics are highly influenced by genetics, while others are determined mainly by environmental conditions or by harvesting

89. TEXTILE GOODS INDUSTRY

Figure 89.7 • Moisture-ginning cleaning compromise for cotton.

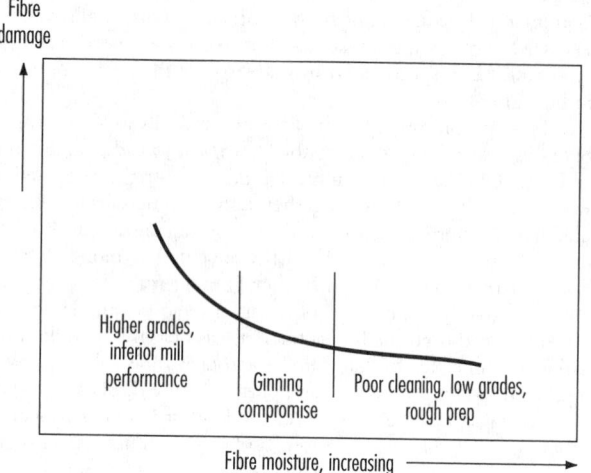

and ginning practices. Problems during any step of production or processing can cause irreversible damage to fibre quality and reduce profits for the producer as well as the textile manufacturer.

Fibre quality is highest the day a cotton boll opens. Weathering, mechanical harvesting, handling, ginning and manufacturing can diminish the natural quality. There are many factors that indicate the overall quality of cotton fibre. The most important ones include strength, fibre length, short fibre content (fibres shorter than 1.27 cm), length uniformity, maturity, fineness, trash content, colour, seedcoat fragment and nep content, and stickiness. The market generally recognizes these factors even though not all are measured on each bale.

The ginning process can significantly affect fibre length, uniformity and the content of seedcoat fragments, trash, short fibres and neps. The two ginning practices that have the most impact on quality are the regulation of fibre moisture during ginning and cleaning and the degree of saw-type lint cleaning used.

The recommended lint moisture range for ginning is 6 to 7%. Gin cleaners remove more trash at low moisture but not without more fibre damage. Higher fibre moisture preserves fibre length but results in ginning problems and poor cleaning, as illustrated in figure 89.7. If drying is increased to improve trash removal, yarn quality is reduced. Although yarn appearance improves with drying up to a point, because of increased foreign-matter removal, the effect of increased short-fibre content outweighs the benefits of foreign-matter removal.

Cleaning does little to change the true colour of the fibre, but combing the fibres and removing trash changes the perceived colour. Lint cleaning can sometimes blend fibre so that fewer bales are classified as spotted or light spotted. Ginning does not affect fineness and maturity. Each mechanical or pneumatic device used during cleaning and ginning increases the nep content, but lint cleaners have the most pronounced influence. The number of seedcoat fragments in ginned lint is affected by the seed condition and ginning action. Lint cleaners decrease the size but not the number of fragments. Yarn strength, yarn appearance and spinning-end breakage are three important spinning quality elements. All are affected by length uniformity and, therefore, by the proportion of short or broken fibres. These three elements are usually preserved best when cotton is ginned with minimum drying and cleaning machinery.

Recommendations for the sequence and amount of gin machinery to dry and clean spindle-harvested cotton were designed to achieve satisfactory bale value and to preserve the inherent quality of cotton. They have generally been followed and thus confirmed in the US cotton industry for several decades. The recommendations consider marketing-system premiums and discounts as well as the cleaning efficiency and fibre damage resulting from various gin machines. Some variation from these recommendations is necessary for special harvesting conditions.

When gin machinery is used in the recommended sequence, 75 to 85% of the foreign matter is usually removed from cotton. Unfortunately, this machinery also removes small quantities of good-quality cotton in the process of removing foreign matter, so the quantity of marketable cotton is reduced during cleaning. Cleaning cotton is therefore a compromise between foreign matter level and fibre loss and damage.

Safety and Health Concerns

The cotton ginning industry, like other processing industries, has many hazards. Information from workers' compensation claims indicates that the number of injuries is highest for the hand/fingers, followed by back/spine, eye, foot/toes, arm/shoulder, leg, trunk and head injuries. While the industry has been active in hazard reduction and safety education, gin safety remains a major concern. The reasons for the concern include the high frequency of accidents and workers' compensation claims, the large number of lost work days and the severity of the accidents. Total economic costs for gin injuries and health disorders include direct costs (medical and other compensation) and indirect costs (time lost from work, downtime, loss in earning power, higher insurance costs for workers' compensation, loss of productivity and many other loss factors). Direct costs are easier to determine and much less expensive than indirect costs.

Many international safety and health regulations affecting cotton ginning are derived from US legislation administered by the Occupational Safety and Health Administration (OSHA) and the Environmental Protection Agency (EPA), which promulgates pesticides regulations.

Other agricultural regulations may also apply to a gin, including requirements for slow-moving vehicle emblems on trailers/tractors operating on public roadways, provisions for rollover protective structures on tractors operated by employees and provisions for proper living facilities for temporary labour. While gins are considered agricultural enterprises and are not specifically covered by many regulations, ginners will likely want to conform to other regulations, such as OSHA's "Standards for General Industry, Part 1910". There are three specific OSHA standards that ginners should consider: those for fire and other emergency plans (29 CFR 1910.38a), exits (29 CFR 1910.35-40) and occupational noise exposure (29 CFR 1910.95). Major exit requirements are given in 29 CFR 1910.36 and 29 CFR 1910.37. In other countries, where agricultural workers are included in mandatory coverage, such compliance will be compulsory. Compliance with noise and other safety and health standards is discussed elsewhere in this *Encyclopaedia*.

Employee participation in safety programmes

The most effective loss control programmes are those in which management motivates employees to be safety conscious. This motivation can be accomplished by establishing a safety policy that gets the employees involved in each element of the programme, by participating in safety training, by setting a good example and by providing employees with appropriate incentives.

Occupational health disorders are lessened by requiring that PPE be used in designated areas and that employees observe acceptable work practices. Hearing (plugs or muffs) and respiratory (dust mask) PPE should be used whenever working in areas having high noise or dust levels. Some people are more susceptible to noise and respiratory problems than others, and even with PPE should be reassigned to work areas with lower noise or dust levels. Health hazards associated with heavy lifting and excessive heat can be handled by training, use of materials-handling equipment, proper dress, ventilation and breaks from the heat.

All persons throughout the gin operation must be involved in gin safety. A safe work atmosphere can be established when everyone is motivated to participate fully in the loss control programme.

COTTON YARN MANUFACTURING

Phillip J. Wakelyn

Cotton accounts for almost 50% of the worldwide consumption of textile fibre. China, the United States, the Russian Federation, India and Japan are the major cotton-consuming countries. Consumption is measured by the amount of raw cotton fibre purchased and used to manufacture textile materials. Worldwide cotton production is annually about 80 to 90 million bales (17.4 to 19.6 billion kg). China, the United States, India, Pakistan and Uzbekistan are the major cotton-producing countries, accounting for over 70% of world cotton production. The rest is produced by about 75 other countries. Raw cotton is exported from about 57 countries and cotton textiles from about 65 countries. Many countries emphasize domestic production to reduce their reliance on imports.

Yarn manufacturing is a sequence of processes that convert raw cotton fibres into yarn suitable for use in various end-products. A number of processes are required to obtain the clean, strong, uniform yarns required in modern textile markets. Beginning with a dense package of tangled fibres (cotton bale) containing varying amounts of non-lint materials and unusable fibre (foreign matter, plant trash, motes and so on), continuous operations of opening, blending, mixing, cleaning, carding, drawing, roving and spinning are performed to transform the cotton fibres into yarn.

Even though the current manufacturing processes are highly developed, competitive pressure continues to spur industry groups and individuals to seek new, more efficient methods and machines for processing cotton which, one day, may supplant today's systems. However, for the foreseeable future, the current conventional systems of blending, carding, drawing, roving and spinning will continue to be used. Only the cotton picking process seems clearly destined for elimination in the near future.

Yarn manufacturing produces yarns for various woven or knitted end-products (e.g., apparel or industrial fabrics) and for sewing thread and cordage. Yarns are produced with different diameters and different weights per unit length. While the basic yarn manufacturing process has remained unchanged for a number of years, processing speeds, control technology and package sizes have increased. Yarn properties and processing efficiency are related to the properties of the cotton fibres processed. End-use properties of the yarn are also a function of processing conditions.

Yarn Manufacturing Processes

Opening, blending, mixing and cleaning
Typically, mills select bale mixes with the properties needed to produce yarn for a specific end-use. The number of bales used by different mills in each mix ranges from 6 or 12 to over 50.

Processing begins when the bales to be mixed are brought to the opening room, where bagging and ties are removed. Layers of cotton are removed from the bales by hand and placed in feeders equipped with conveyors studded with spiked teeth, or entire bales are placed on platforms which move them back and forth under or over a plucking mechanism. The aim is to begin the sequential production process by converting the compacted layers of baled cotton into small, light, fluffy tufts that will facilitate the removal of foreign matter. This initial process is referred to as "opening". Since bales arrive at the mill in various degrees of density, it is common for bale ties to be cut approximately 24 hours before the bales are to be processed, in order to allow them to "bloom". This enhances opening and helps regulate the feeding rate. The cleaning machines in mills perform the functions of opening and first-level cleaning.

Carding and combing
The card is the most important machine in the yarn manufacturing process. It performs second- and final-level cleaning functions in an overwhelming majority of cotton textile mills. The card is composed of a system of three wire-covered cylinders and a series of flat, wire-covered bars that successively work small clumps and tufts of fibres into a high degree of separation or openness, remove a very high percentage of trash and other foreign matter, collect the fibres into a rope-like form called a "sliver" and deliver this sliver in a container for use in the subsequent process (see figure 89.4).

Historically, cotton has been fed to the card in the form of a "picker lap", which is formed on a "picker", a combination of feed rolls and beaters with a mechanism made up of cylindrical screens on which opened tufts of cotton are collected and rolled into a batt (see figure 89.5). The batt is removed from the screens in an even, flat sheet and then is rolled into a lap. However, labour requirements and the availability of automated handling systems with the potential for improved quality are contributing to the obsolescence of the picker.

The elimination of the picking process has been made possible by the installation of more efficient opening and cleaning equipment and chute-feed systems on the cards. The latter distribute opened and cleaned tufts of fibres to cards pneumatically through ducts. This action contributes to processing consistency and improved quality and reduces the number of workers required.

A small number of mills produce combed yarn, the cleanest and most uniform cotton yarn. Combing provides more extensive cleaning than is provided by the card. The purpose of combing is to remove short fibres, neps and trash so that the resulting sliver is very clean and lustrous. The comber is a complicated machine composed of grooved feed rolls and a cylinder that is partially covered with needles to comb out short fibres (see figure 89.3).

Drawing and roving
Drawing is the first process in yarn manufacturing that employs roller drafting. In drawing, practically all draft results from the action of rollers. Containers of sliver from the carding process are staked in the creel of the drawing frame. Drafting occurs when a sliver is fed into a system of paired rollers moving at different speeds. Drawing straightens the fibres in the sliver by drafting to make more of the fibres parallel to the axis of the sliver. Parallelization is necessary to obtain the properties desired when the fibres are subsequently twisted into yarn. Drawing also produces a sliver that is more uniform in weight per unit of length and helps to achieve greater blending capabilities. The fibres that are produced by the final drawing process, called finisher drawing, are nearly straight and parallel to the axis of the sliver. Weight per unit length of a finisher-drawing sliver is too high to permit drafting into yarn on conventional ring-spinning systems.

The roving process reduces the weight of the sliver to a suitable size for spinning into yarn and inserting twist, which maintains the integrity of the draft strands. Cans of slivers from finisher drawing or combing are placed in the creel, and individual slivers are fed through two sets of rollers, the second of which rotates faster, thus reducing the size of the sliver from about 2.5 cm in diameter to that of the diameter of a standard pencil. Twist is imparted to the fibres by passing the bundle of fibres through a roving "flyer". The product is now called "roving", which is packaged on a bobbin about 37.5 cm long with a diameter of about 14 cm.

Spinning

Spinning is the single most costly step in converting cotton fibres to yarn. Currently, over 85% of the world's yarn is produced on ring-spinning frames, which are designed to draft the roving into the desired yarn size, or count, and to impart the desired amount of twist. The amount of twist is proportional to the strength of the yarn. The ratio of the length to the length fed can vary on the order of 10 to 50. Bobbins of roving are placed onto holders that allow the roving to feed freely into the drafting roller of the ring-spinning frame. Following the drafting zone, the yarn passes through a "traveller" onto a spinning bobbin. The spindle holding this bobbin rotates at high speed, causing the yarn to balloon as twist is imparted. The lengths of yarn on the bobbins are too short for use in subsequent processes and are doffed into "spinning boxes" and delivered to the next process, which may be spooling or winding.

In the modern production of heavier or coarse yarns, open-end spinning is replacing ring spinning. A sliver of fibres is fed into a high-speed rotor. Here the centrifugal force converts the fibres into yarns. There is no need for the bobbin, and the yarn is taken up on the package required by the next step in the process.

Considerable research and development efforts are being devoted to radical new methods of yarn production. A number of new spinning systems currently under development may revolutionize yarn manufacturing and could cause changes in the relative importance of fibre properties as they are now perceived. In general, four of the different approaches used in the new systems appear practical for use on cotton. Core-spun systems are currently in use to produce a variety of specialty yarns and sewing threads. Twistless yarns have been produced commercially on a limited basis by a system that bonds the fibres together with a polyvinyl alcohol or some other bonding agent. The twistless yarn system offers potentially high production rates and very uniform yarns. Knit and other apparel fabrics from twistless yarn have excellent appearance. In air-vortex spinning, currently under study by several machinery manufacturers, drawing sliver is presented to an opening roller, similar to rotor spinning. Air-vortex spinning is capable of very high production speeds, but prototype models are particularly sensitive to fibre length variations and foreign matter content such as trash particles.

Winding and spooling

Once the yarn is spun, the manufacturers must prepare a correct package. The type of package depends on whether the yarn will be used for weaving or knitting. Winding, spooling, twisting and quilling are considered preparatory steps for weaving and knitting yarn. In general, the product of spooling will be used as *warp yarns* (the yarns that run lengthwise in woven fabric) and the product of winding will be used as *filling yarns*, or *weft yarns* (the yarns that run across the fabric). The products from open-end spinning by-pass these steps and are packaged for either the filling or warp. Twisting produces ply yarns, where two or more yarns are twisted together before further processing. In the quilling process yarn is wound onto small bobbins, small enough to fit

inside the shuttle of a box loom. Sometimes the quilling process takes place at the loom. (See also the article "Weaving and knitting" in this chapter.)

Waste handling

In modern textile mills where control of dust is important, the handling of waste is given greater emphasis. In classical textile operations, waste was collected manually and delivered to a "wastehouse" if it could not be recycled into the system. Here it was accumulated until there was enough of one type to make a bale. In the present state of the art, central vacuum systems automatically return waste from opening, picking, carding, drawing and roving. The central vacuum system is used for cleaning of machinery, automatically collecting waste from under machinery such as fly and motes from carding, and for returning unusable floor sweeps and wastes from filter condensers. The classical baler is a vertical upstroke press which still forms a typical 227-kg bale. In modern wastehouse technology, wastes are accumulated from the central vacuum system in a receiving tank which feeds a horizontal bale press. The various waste products of the yarn manufacturing industry can be recycled or reused by other industries. For example, spinning can be used in the waste spinning industry to make mop yarns, garnetting can be used in the cotton batting industry to make batting for mattresses or upholstered furniture.

Safety and Health Concerns

Machinery

Accidents may occur on all types of cotton textile machinery, though the frequency rate is not high. Effective guarding of the multiplicity of moving parts presents many problems and needs constant attention. Training of operators in safe practices is also essential, in particular to avoid attempting repairs while the machinery is in motion, the cause of many of the accidents. Each piece of machinery may have sources of energy (electrical, mechanical, pneumatic, hydraulic, inertial and so on) that need to be controlled before any repair or maintenance work is attempted. The facility should identify energy sources, provide necessary equipment and train personnel to ensure that all hazardous energy sources are turned off while working on equipment. An inspection should be performed on a regular basis to ensure that all lockout/tagout procedures are being followed and correctly applied.

Cotton dust inhalation (byssinosis)

Inhalation of the dust generated where cotton fibre is converted into yarn and fabric has been shown to cause an occupational lung disease, byssinosis, in a small number of textile workers. It usually takes 15 to 20 years of exposure to higher levels of dust (above 0.5 to 1.0 mg/m^3) for workers to become reactors. OSHA and the American Conference of Governmental Industrial Hygienists (ACGIH) standards set 0.2 mg/m^3 respirable cotton dust as measured by the vertical elutriator as the limit for occupational exposure to cotton dust in textile yarn manufacturing. The dust, an airborne particulate released into the atmosphere as cotton is handled or processed, is a heterogeneous, complex mixture of botanical trash, soil and microbiological material (i.e., bacteria and fungi), which varies in composition and biological activity. The aetiological agent and pathogenesis of byssinosis are not known. Cotton plant trash associated with the fibre and the endotoxin from gram-negative bacteria on the fibre and plant trash are thought to be the cause or to contain the causative agent. The cotton fibre itself, which is mainly cellulose, is not the cause, since cellulose is an inert dust that does not cause respiratory disease. Appropriate engineering controls in cotton textile processing

Figure 89.8 • Dust extraction system for a carding machine.

areas (see figure 89.8) along with work practices, medical surveillance and PPE can, for the most part, eliminate the byssinosis. A mild water washing of cotton by batch kier washing systems and continuous batt systems reduces the residual level of endotoxin in both lint and airborne dust to levels below those associated with the acute reduction in pulmonary function as measured by the 1-second forced expiratory volume.

Noise

Noise can be a problem in some processes in yarn manufacturing, but in a few modern textile mills the levels are below 90 dBA, which is the US standard but which exceeds noise exposure standards in many countries. Thanks to the abatement efforts of machinery manufacturers and industrial noise engineers, noise levels are continuing to decrease as machinery speeds increase. The solution for high noise levels is the introduction of more modern, quieter equipment. In the United States, a hearing conservation programme is required when noise levels exceed 85 dBA; this would include noise-level monitoring, audiometric testing and making hearing protection available to all employees when noise levels cannot be engineered below 90 dBA.

Heat stress

Since spinning sometimes requires high temperatures and artificial humidificaton of the air, careful monitoring attention is always necessary to ensure that permissible limits are not exceeded. Well designed and maintained air-conditioning plants are increasingly used in place of more primitive methods of temperature and humidity regulation.

Occupational safety and health management systems

Many of the more modern textile yarn manufacturing mills find it useful to have some type of occupational safety and health management system in place to control the workplace hazards that workers may encounter. This can be a voluntary programme like the "Quest for the Best in Health and Safety" developed by the American Textile Manufacturers Institute, or one that is mandated by regulations such as the US State of California Occupational Injury and Illness Prevention Program (Title 8, California Code of Regulations, Section 3203). When a safety and health management system is used, it should be flexible and adaptable enough to allow the mill to tailor it to its own needs.

WOOL INDUSTRY

D.A. Hargrave*

The origins of the wool industry are lost in antiquity. Sheep were easily domesticated by our remote ancestors and were important in satisfying their basic needs for food and clothing. Early human societies rubbed together the fibres collected from the sheep to form a yarn, and from this basic principle the processes of manipulating the fibre have increased in complexity. The wool textile industry has been in the forefront in developing and adapting mechanical methods and was therefore one of the early industries in the development of the factory system of production.

Raw Materials

The length of fibre when taken from the animal is the dominant, but not the only, factor determining how it is processed. The type of wool available may be broadly classified into (a) merino or botany, (b) crossbreds—fine, medium or coarse and (c) carpet wools. Within each group, however, there are various grades. Merino usually has the finest diameter and a short length, while the carpet wools are long-fibred, with a coarser diameter. Today, increasing quantities of synthetic fibres simulating wool are blended with the natural fibre and are processed in the same manner. Hair from other animals—for example, mohair (goat), alpaca (llama), cashmere (goat, camel), angora (goat) and vicuña (wild llama)—also plays an important, although subsidiary, role in the industry; it is relatively expensive and is usually processed by specialized firms.

Production

The industry has two distinctive processing systems—woollen and the worsted. The machinery is in many ways similar, but the purposes are distinct. In essence, the *worsted* system uses the longer stapled wools and in the carding, preparing, gilling and combing processes the fibres are kept parallel and the shorter fibres are rejected. Spinning produces a strong yarn of fine diameter, which then is woven to yield a light fabric with the familiar smooth and firm appearance of men's suits. In the *woollen* system, the aim is to intermingle and intertwine the fibres to form a soft and fluffy yarn, which is woven to give a cloth of full and bulky character with a "woolly" surface—for example, tweeds, blankets and heavy overcoatings. Since uniformity of fibre is not necessary in the woollen system, the manufacturer can blend together new wool, shorter fibres rejected by the worsted process, wools recovered from tearing up old wool garments and so on; "shoddy" is obtained from soft, and "mungo" from hard waste material.

It should be borne in mind, however, that the industry is particularly complex and that the condition and type of the raw material used and the specification for the finished cloth will influence the method of processing at each stage and the sequence of those stages. For example, wool may be dyed before processing, at the yarn stage or towards the end of the process when in the woven piece. Moreover, some of the processes may be carried on in separate establishments.

Hazards and Their Prevention

As in every section of the textile industry, large machines with rapidly moving parts pose both noise and mechanical injury hazards. Dust can also be a problem. The highest practicable form of guarding or enclosure should be provided for such generic parts of the equipment as spur gear wheels, chains and sprockets, revolving

* Adapted from 3rd edition, *Encyclopaedia of Occupational Health and Safety*.

shafting, belts and pulleys, and for the following parts of machinery used specifically in the wool textile trade:

- feed rollers and swifts of various types of preparatory opening machines (e.g., teasers, willeys, garnetts, rag-grinding machines and so on)
- licker-in or taker-in and adjacent rollers of scribbling and carding machines
- intake between swift and doffer cylinders of scribbling, carding and garnetting machines
- rollers and fallers of gill-boxes
- back shafts of drawing and roving frames
- traps between the carriage and headstock of mules
- projecting pins, bolts and other securing devices used on the beaming-off motion of warping machines
- squeeze rollers of scouring, milling and cloth-wringing machines
- intake between cloth and wrapper and roller of blowing machines
- revolving-knife cylinder of cropping machines
- blades of fans in pneumatic conveying systems (any inspection panel in the ducting of such a system should be at a safe distance from the fan, and the worker should have indelibly impressed on his or her memory the length of time it takes for the machine to slow and come to a stop after the power has been cut off; this is particularly important since the worker clearing a blockage in the system usually cannot see the moving blades)
- the flying shuttle, which presents a special problem (looms should be provided with well-designed guards to prevent the shuttle from flying out of the shed and to limit the distance it might travel should it fly).

The guarding of such dangerous parts presents practical problems. The design of the guard should take into account the working practices connected with the particular process and particularly should preclude possible removal of the guard when the operator is at the greatest risk (e.g., lockout arrangements). Special training and close supervision are required to prevent waste removal and cleaning while machinery is in motion. Much of the responsibility devolves on machinery manufacturers, who should ensure that such safety features are incorporated into new machines at the design stage, and on supervisory personnel, who should ensure that workers are adequately trained in safe handling of equipment.

Spacing of machinery

The risk of accidents is increased if insufficient space is allowed between the machines. Many older premises squeezed the maximum number of machines into the available floor area, thereby reducing the space available for aisles and passageways and for the temporary storage of raw and finished materials within the workroom. In some old mills, the gangways between the carding machines are so narrow that enclosure of the driving belts within a guard is impracticable and recourse has to be made to "wedge" guarding between the belt and the pulley at the in-running point; a well-made and smooth belt fastener is particularly important in these circumstances. Minimum spacing standards, as recommended by a British Government committee for certain wool textile machinery, are required.

Materials handling

When modern mechanical load-handling methods are not employed, there remains the risk of injury from the lifting of heavy loads. Materials handling should be mechanized to the fullest extent possible. Where this is not available, the precautions discussed elsewhere in this *Encyclopaedia* should be employed. Proper lifting technique is particularly important for workers who manipulate heavy beams into and out of looms or who handle heavy and cumbersome bales of wool in the early preparatory processes.

Wherever possible, hand-trucks and movable carts or skids should be used to move such bulky and heavy loads.

Fire

Fire is a serious hazard, especially in old multistorey mills. The mill structure and layout should conform to local regulations governing unobstructed gangways and exits, fire-alarm systems, fire extinguishers and hoses, emergency lights and so on. Cleanliness and good housekeeping will prevent accumulations of dust and fluff, which encourage the spread of fire. No repairs involving the use of flame cutting or flame-burning equipment should be carried on during working hours. Training of all staff in procedures in case of fire are necessary; fire drills, conducted if possible in concert with local fire, police and emergency medical services, should be practised at appropriate intervals.

General safety

Emphasis has been placed on those accident situations which are especially to be found in the wool textile industry. However, it should be noted that the majority of accidents in mills occur in circumstances that are common to all factories—for example, falls of persons and objects, handling of goods, use of hand tools and so on—and that the relevant fundamental safety principles to be followed apply no less in the wool industry than in most other industries.

Health Problems

Anthrax

The industrial disease usually associated with wool textiles is anthrax. It was at one time a great danger, particularly to wool sorters, but has been almost completely controlled in the wool textile industry as a result of:

- improvements in production methods in exporting countries where anthrax is endemic
- disinfection of materials liable to be carrying anthrax spores
- improvements in handling the possibly infected material under exhaust ventilation in the preparatory processes
- microwaving the wool bale sufficiently long to a temperature that will kill any fungi. This treatment also assists in the recovery of lanolin associated with the wool.
- significant advances in medical treatment, including immunization of workers in high-risk situations
- education and training of workers and the provision of washing facilities and, when necessary, personal protective equipment.

Besides anthrax fungal spores, it is known that spores of the fungus *Coccidiodes immitis* can be found in wool, especially from the southwestern United States. This fungus can cause the disease known as coccidioidomycosis, which, along with the respiratory disease from anthrax, usually has a poor prognosis. Anthrax has the added hazard of causing a malignant ulcer or carbuncle with a black centre when entering the body through a break in the skin barrier.

Chemical substances

Various chemicals are used—for example, for degreasing (diethylene dioxide, synthetic detergents, trichloroethylene and, in the past, carbon tetrachloride), disinfection (formaldehyde), bleaching (sulphur dioxide, chlorine) and dyeing (potassium chlorate, anilines). The risks include gassing, poisoning, irritation of the eyes, mucous membranes and lungs, and skin conditions. In general, prevention relies on:

- substitution of a less dangerous chemical
- local exhaust ventilation

- care in labelling, storage and transport of corrosive or noxious liquids
- personal protective equipment
- good washing facilities (including shower baths where practicable)
- strict personal hygiene.

Other hazards

Noise, inadequate lighting, and the high temperatures and humidity levels required for wool processing may have a deleterious effect on general health unless they are strictly controlled. In many countries, standards are prescribed. Steam and condensation may be difficult to control effectively in dyeing sheds, and expert engineering advice is often needed. In weaving sheds, noise control presents a serious problem on which much work remains to be done. A high standard of lighting is necessary everywhere, particularly where dark fabrics are being manufactured.

Dust

As well as the specific risk of anthrax spores in the dust produced in the earlier processes, dust in high quantities sufficient to induce irritation of the respiratory tract mucosae is produced at many machines, especially those with a tearing or carding action, and should be removed by effective LEV.

Noise

With all the moving parts in the machinery, particularly the looms, woollen mills are often very noisy places. While attenuation can be achieved by proper lubrication, the introduction of sound baffles and other engineering approaches should be considered as well. By and large, prevention of occupational hearing loss depends on the workers' use of ear plugs or muffs. It is essential that workers be trained in the proper use of such protective equipment and supervised to verify that they are using it. A hearing conservation programme with periodic audiograms is required in many countries. As equipment is replaced or repaired, appropriate noise-reduction steps should be taken.

Work stress

Work stress, with its attendant effects on workers' health and well-being, is a common problem in this industry. Since many of the mills operate around the clock, shift work is frequently required. To meet the production quotas, the machines operate continuously, with each worker being "tied" to one or more pieces of equipment and unable to leave it for bathroom or rest breaks until a "floater" has taken his or her place. Coupled with the ambient noise and use of noise protectors, their heavily routinized, repetitive activity makes for *de facto* isolation of the workers and a lack of social interaction that many find stressful. The quality of supervision and the availability of workplace amenities have a great influence on workers' job stress levels.

Conclusion

While larger enterprises are able to invest in new technological developments, many smaller and older mills continue to operate in old plants with out-dated but still functioning equipment. Economic imperatives dictate less rather than greater attention to workers' safety and health. Indeed, in many developed areas, mills are being abandoned in favour of new plants in developing countries and areas where cheaper labour is readily available and where health and safety regulations are either non-existent or are generally ignored. Worldwide, this is an important labour-intensive industry in which reasonable investments to workers' health and well-being can bring significant dividends to both the enterprise and its workforce.

SILK INDUSTRY

J. Kubota*

Silk is a lustrous, tough, elastic fibre produced by the larvae of silkworms; the term also covers the thread or cloth made from this fibre. The silk industry originated in China, as early as 2640 BC according to tradition. Towards the 3rd century AD, knowledge of the silkworm and its product reached Japan through Korea; it probably spread to India a little later. From there silk production was slowly carried westward through Europe to the New World.

The production process involves a sequence of steps not necessarily carried out in a single enterprise or plant. They include:

- *Sericulture.* The production of cocoons for their raw silk filament is known as *sericulture*, a term which covers feeding, cocoon formation and so on. The first essential is a stock of mulberry trees adequate to feed the worms in their larval state. The trays on which the worms are reared have to be kept in a room with a constant temperature of 25 °C; this involves artificial heating in colder countries and seasons. The cocoons are spun after about 42 days of feeding.
- *Spinning or filature.* The distinctive process in silk spinning is called *reeling*, in which the filaments from the cocoon are formed into a continuous, uniform and regular strand. First, the natural gum (sericin) is softened in scalding water. Then, in a bath or basin of hot water, the ends of the filaments from several cocoons are caught together, drawn up, attached to a reeling wheel and wound to form raw silk.
- *Throwing.* In this process, the threads are twisted and doubled into more substantial yarns.
- *Degumming.* In this phase, the raw silk is boiled in a solution of soap and water at approximately 95 °C.
- *Bleaching.* The raw or boiled silk is then bleached in hydrogen peroxide or sodium peroxide.
- *Weaving.* The silk thread is next woven into fabric; this usually takes place in separate factories.
- *Dyeing.* Silk may be dyed while in the filament or thread form, or it may be dyed as a fabric.

Health and Safety Hazards

Carbon monoxide

Symptoms of carbon monoxide toxicity consisting of headache, vertigo and sometimes nausea and vomiting, usually not severe, have been reported in Japan, where sericulture is a common home industry, as a result of the use of charcoal fires in poorly ventilated rearing rooms.

Dermatitis

Mal des bassines, a dermatitis of the hands of female workers reeling raw silk, was quite common, particularly in Japan, where, in the 1920s, a morbidity rate of 30 to 50% among reeling workers was reported. Fourteen per cent of the affected workers lost an average of three working days each year. The skin lesions, localized mainly on fingers, wrists and forearms, were characterized by erythema covered with small vesicles which became chronic, pustular or eczematous and extremely painful. The cause of this condition was usually attributed to the decomposition products of the dead chrysalis and to a parasite in the cocoon. More recently, however, Japanese observations have showed that it is probably

* Adapted from 3rd edition, *Encyclopaedia of Occupational Health and Safety.*

related to the temperature of the reeling bath: until 1960 almost all reeling baths were kept at 65 °C, but, since the introduction of new installations with a bath temperature of 30 to 45 °C, there have been no reports of the typical skin lesions among reel workers.

The handling of raw silk may produce allergic skin reactions in some reel workers. Facial swelling and ocular inflammation have been observed where there was no direct local contact with the reeling bath. Similarly, dermatitis has been found among silk throwers.

Respiratory tract problems

In the former Soviet Union, an unusual outbreak of tonsillitis among silk spinners was traced to bacteria in the water of reeling basins and in the ambient air of the cocoon department. Disinfection and frequent replacement of reel bath water, combined with exhaust ventilation at the cocoon reels, brought about a swift improvement.

Extensive long-term epidemiological observations also carried out in the former USSR have shown that workers in the natural silk industry may develop respiratory allergy featuring bronchial asthma, asthmatiform bronchitis and/or allergic rhinitis. It appears that natural silk can cause sensitization during all stages of production.

A situation causing respiratory distress among spinning-frame workers when packaging or repackaging silk on a spinning or winding frame has also been reported. Depending upon the speed of the machinery, it is possible to aerosolize the proteinaceous substance surrounding the silk filament. This aerosol, when respirable in size, will cause a lung reaction very similar to that of the byssinotic reaction to cotton dust.

Noise

Noise exposure can reach harmful levels for workers at machines spinning and winding the silk threads, and at looms where fabric is woven. Adequate lubrication of the equipment and the interposition of sound baffles may reduce the noise level somewhat, but the continuing exposure throughout the working day can have a cumulative effect. If effective abatement is not obtained, resort will have to be made to personal protective devices. As with all workers exposed to noise, a hearing protection programme featuring periodic audiograms is desirable.

Safety and Health Measures

Control of temperature, humidity and ventilation are important at all stages of the silk industry. Home workers should not escape supervision. Adequate ventilation of rearing rooms should be ensured, and charcoal or kerosene stoves should be replaced by electric heaters or other warming devices.

Lowering the temperature of reeling baths may be effective in preventing dermatitis. The water should be replaced frequently, and exhaust ventilation is desirable. Direct skin contact with raw silk immersed in reeling baths should be avoided as far as possible.

The provision of good sanitary facilities and attention to personal hygiene are essential. Hand washing with a 3% acetic acid solution has been found effective in Japan.

The medical examination of new entrants and medical supervision thereafter are desirable.

The hazards from machinery in silk manufacture are similar to those in the textile industry in general. Accident prevention is best achieved by good housekeeping, adequate guarding of moving parts, continuing worker training and effective supervision. Power looms should be provided with guards to prevent accidents from flying shuttles. Very good lighting is required for the yarn preparation and weaving processes.

VISCOSE (RAYON)

M.M. El Attal*

Rayon is a synthetic fibre produced from cellulose (wood pulp) that has been chemically treated. It is used alone or in blends with other synthetic or natural fibres to make fabrics that are strong, highly absorbent and soft, and which can be dyed in brilliant, long-lasting colours.

The manufacture of rayon had its origins in the quest for an artificial silk. In 1664, Robert Hooke, a British scientist noted for his observations of plant cells, predicted the possibility of duplicating silk by artificial means; almost two centuries later, in 1855, fibres were made from a mixture of mulberry twigs and nitric acid. The first successful commercial process was developed in 1884 by the French inventor Hilaire de Chardonnet, and in 1891, the British scientists Cross and Bevan perfected the viscose process. By 1895, rayon was being produced commercially on a rather small scale, and its use grew rapidly.

Production Methods

Rayon is made by a number of processes, depending on its intended use.

In the *viscose process*, cellulose derived from wood pulp is steeped in a sodium hydroxide solution, and the excess liquid is squeezed out by compression to form alkali cellulose. Impurities are removed and, after being torn into shreds similar to white crumbs that are allowed to age for several days at a controlled temperature, the shredded alkali cellulose is transferred to another tank where it is treated with carbon disulphide to form golden-orange crumbs of cellulose xanthate. These are dissolved in dilute sodium hydroxide to form a viscous orange liquid called *viscose*. Different batches of viscose are blended to obtain uniform quality. The mixture is filtered and ripened by several days of storage at rigidly controlled temperature and humidity. It is then extruded through metal nozzles with fine holes (spinnerets) into a bath of about 10% sulphuric acid. It can be wound as a continuous filament (cakes) or cut into the required lengths and spun like cotton or wool. Viscose rayon is used to make wearing apparel and heavy fabrics.

In the *cuprammonium process*, used to make silk-like fabrics and sheer hosiery, the cellulose pulp dissolved in the sodium hydroxide solution is treated with copper oxide and ammonia. The filaments come out of the spinnerets into a spinning funnel and are then stretched to the required fineness by the action of a jet stream of water.

In the viscose and cuprammonium processes, the cellulose is reconstituted, but acetate and triacetate are esters of the cellulose and are considered by some to be a separate class of fibre. Acetate fabrics are known for their ability to take brilliant colours and to drape well, features that make them particularly desirable for apparel. Short fibres of acetate are used as fillers in pillows, mattress pads and quilts. Triacetate yarns have many of the same properties as acetate but are particularly favoured for their ability to retain creases and pleats in garments.

Hazards and Their Prevention

The principal hazards in the viscose process are the exposures to carbon disulphide and hydrogen sulphide. Both have a variety of toxic effects depending on the intensity and duration of the exposure and the organ(s) affected; they range from fatigue and giddiness, respiratory irritation and gastrointestinal symptoms to profound neuropsychiatric disturbances, auditory and visual disorders, deep unconsciousness and death.

* Adapted from 3rd edition, *Encyclopaedia of Occupational Health and Safety*.

Moreover, with a flashpoint below −30 °C and explosive limits between 1.0 and 50%, carbon disulphide has a high risk of fire and explosion.

The acids and alkalis used in the process are fairly dilute, but there is always danger from the preparing of the proper dilutions and splashes into the eyes. The alkaline crumbs produced during the shredding process may irritate workers' hands and eyes, while the acid fumes and hydrogen sulphide gas emanating from the spinning bath may cause a kerato-conjunctivitis characterized by excessive lachrimation, photophobia and severe ocular pain.

Keeping the concentrations of carbon disulphide and hydrogen sulphide below the safe exposure limits requires diligent monitoring such as may be provided by an automatic continuous recording apparatus. Complete enclosure of the machinery with efficient LEV (with intakes at floor levels since these gases are heavier than air) is advisable. Workers must be trained in emergency responses in the event of leaks, and, in addition to being provided with proper personal protective equipment, maintenance and repair workers must be carefully schooled and supervised to avoid unnecessary levels of exposure.

Rest rooms and washing up facilities are necessities rather than mere amenities. Medical surveillance through preplacement and periodic medical examinations is desirable.

● SYNTHETIC FIBRES

A.E. Quinn and R. Mattiusi*

Synthetic fibres are made from polymers that have been synthetically produced from chemical elements or compounds developed by the petrochemical industry. Unlike natural fibres (wool, cotton and silk), which date back to antiquity, synthetic fibres have a relatively short history dating back to the perfection of the viscose process in 1891 by Cross and Bevan, two British scientists. A few years later, rayon production started on a limited basis, and by the early 1900s, it was being produced commercially. Since then, a large variety of synthetic fibres has been developed, each designed with special characteristics that make it suitable for a particular kind of fabric, either alone or in combination with other fibres. Keeping track of them is made difficult by the fact that the same fibre may have different trade names in different countries.

The fibres are made by forcing liquid polymers through the holes of a spinneret to produce a continuous filament. The filament can be directly woven into cloth or, to give it the characteristics of natural fibres, it can, for example, be textured to add bulkiness, or it can be chopped into staple and spun.

Classes of Synthetic Fibres

The main classes of synthetic fibres used commercially include:

- *Polyamides (nylons).* The names of the long-chain polymeric amides are distinguished by a number which indicates the number of carbon atoms in their chemical constituents, the diamine being considered first. Thus, the original nylon produced from hexamethylene diamine and adipic acid is known in the United States and the United Kingdom as nylon 66 or 6.6, since both the diamine and the dibasic acid contain 6 carbon atoms. In Germany, it is marketed as Perlon T, in Italy as Nailon, in Switzerland as Mylsuisse, in Spain as Anid and in the Argentine as Ducilo.

* Adapted from 3rd edition, *Encyclopaedia of Occupational Health and Safety.*

- *Polyesters.* First introduced in 1941, polyesters are made by reacting ethylene glycol with terephthalic acid to form a plastic material made of long chains of molecules, which is pumped in molten form from spinnerets, allowing the filament to harden in cold air. A drawing or stretching process follows. Polyesters are known, for example, as Terylene in the UK, Dacron in the United States, Tergal in France, Terital and Wistel in Italy, Lavsan in the Russian Federation, and Tetoran in Japan.
- *Polyvinyls.* Polyacrylonitrile or acrylic fibre, first produced in 1948, is the most important member of this group. It is known under a variety of trade names: Acrilan and Orlon in the United States, Crylor in France, Leacril and Velicren in Italy, Amanian in Poland, Courtelle in the UK and so on.
- *Polyolefins.* The most common fibre in this group, known as Courlene in the UK, is made by a process similar to that for nylon. The molten polymer at 300 °C is forced through spinnerets and cooled in either air or water to form the filament. It is then drawn or stretched.
- *Polypropylenes.* This polymer, known as Hostalen in Germany, Meraklon in Italy and Ulstron in the UK, is melt spun, stretched or drawn, and then annealed.
- *Polyurethanes.* First produced in 1943 as Perlon D by the reaction of 1,4 butanediol with hexamethylene diisocyanate, the polyurethanes have become the basis of a new type of highly elastic fibre called spandex. These fibres are sometimes called snap-back or elastomeric on account of their rubber-like elasticity. They are manufactured from a linear polyurethane gum, which is cured by heating at very high temperatures and pressures to produce a "vulcanized" cross-linked polyurethane which is extruded as a monofil. The thread, which is widely used in garments requiring elasticity, can be covered by rayon or nylon to improve its appearance while the inner thread provides the "stretch". Spandex yarns are known, for example, as Lycra, Vyrene and Glospan in the United States and Spandrell in the UK.

Special Processes

Stapling

Silk is the only natural fibre that comes in a continuous filament; other natural fibres come in short lengths or "staples". Cotton has a staple of about 2.6 cm, wool of 6 to 10 cm and flax from 30 to 50 cm. The continuous synthetic filaments are sometimes passed through a cutting or stapling machine to produce short staples like the natural fibres. They can then be re-spun on cotton or wool spinning machines in order to produce a finish free of the glassy appearance of some synthetic fibres. During the spinning, combinations of synthetic and natural fibres or mixtures of synthetic fibres may be made.

Crimping

To give synthetic fibres the look and feel of wool, the twisted and tangled cut or stapled fibres are crimped by one of a number of methods. They may be passed through a crimping machine, in which hot, fluted rollers impart a permanent crimp. Crimping can also be done chemically, by controlling the coagulation of the filament so as to produce a fibre with an asymmetrical cross section (i.e., one side being thick-skinned and the other thin). When this fibre is wet, the thick side tends to curl, producing a crimp. To make crinkled yarn, known in the United States as non-torque yarn, the synthetic yarn is knitted into a fabric, set and then wound from the fabric by back-winding. The newest method passes two nylon threads through a heater, which raises their temperature to 180 °C and then passes them through a high-speed revolving spindle to impart the crimp. The spindles in the first machine ran at 60,000 revolutions per minute (rpm), but newer models have speeds of the order of 1.5 million rpm.

Synthetic Fibres for Work Clothes

The chemical resistance of polyester cloth makes the fabric particularly suitable for protective clothing for acid-handling operations. Polyolefin fabrics are suitable for protection against long exposures to both acids and alkalis. High-temperature-resistant nylon is well adapted for clothing to protect against fire and heat; it has good resistance at room temperature to solvents such as benzene, acetone, trichlorethylene and carbon tetrachloride. The resistance of certain propylene fabrics to a wide range of corrosive substances makes them suitable for work and laboratory clothing.

The light weight of these synthetic fabrics makes them preferable to the heavy rubberized or plastic-coated fabrics that would otherwise be required for comparable protection. They are also much more comfortable to wear in hot and humid atmospheres. In selecting protective clothing made from synthetic fibres, care should be taken to determine the generic name of the fibre and to verify such properties as shrinkage; sensitivity to light, dry-cleaning agents and detergents; resistance to oil, corrosive chemicals and common solvents; resistance to heat; and susceptibility to electrostatic charging.

Hazards and Their Prevention

Accidents

In addition to good housekeeping, which means keeping floors and passageways clean and dry to minimize slips and falls (vats must be leak proof and, where possible, have baffles to contain splashes), machines, drive belts, pulleys and shaftings must be properly guarded. Machines for spinning, carding, winding and warping operations should be fenced to keep materials and parts from flying out and to prevent workers' hands from entering the dangerous zones. Lockout devices must be in place to prevent restart of machines while they are being cleaned or serviced.

Fire and explosion

The synthetic-fibres industry uses large amounts of toxic and flammable materials. Storage facilities for flammable substances should be out in the open or in a special fire-resistant structure, and they should be enclosed in bunds or dykes to localize spills. Automation of the delivery of toxic, flammable substances by a well-maintained system of pumps and pipes will reduce the hazard of moving and emptying containers. Appropriate fire-fighting equipment and clothing should be readily available and workers trained in their use through periodic drills, preferably conducted in concert with or under the observation of local fire-fighting authorities.

As the filaments emerge from the spinnerets to be dried in air or by means of spinning, large amounts of solvent vapours are released. These constitute a considerable toxic and explosion hazard and must be removed by LEV. Their concentration must be monitored to be sure that it remains below the solvent's explosive limits. The exhausted vapours may be distilled and recovered for further use or they may be burned off; on no account should they be released into the general environmental atmosphere.

Where flammable solvents are used, smoking should be prohibited and open lights, flames and sparks eliminated. Electrical equipment should be of certified flameproof construction, and machines should be earthed (grounded) to prevent the build-up of static electricity, which might lead to catastrophic sparks.

Toxic hazards

Exposures to potentially toxic solvents and chemicals should be maintained below the relevant maximum allowable concentrations by adequate LEV. Respiratory protective equipment should be available for use by maintenance and repair crews and by workers charged with responding to emergencies caused by leaks, spillage and/or fire.

NATURAL FELT PRODUCTS

Jerzy A. Sokal

Felt is a fibrous material made by interlocking fibres of fur, hair or wool through the application of heat, moisture, friction and other processes into an unwoven, densely matted fabric. There are also needleloom felts, in which the felt is attached to a loosely woven backing fabric, usually made of wool or jute.

Fur Felt Processing

Fur felt, used most frequently in hats, is usually made from the fur of rodents (e.g., rabbits, hares, muskrats, coypus and beavers), with other animals used less frequently. After sorting, the skins are carroted using hydrogen peroxide and sulphuric acid, and then the following processes are performed: cutting of hair, hardening and dyeing. For dyeing, synthetic dyestuffs are usually used (e.g., acid dyes or dyes containing complex metal compounds). The dyed felt is weighted using a shellac or vinyl polyacetate.

Wool Felt Processing

Wool used for felt manufacture may be unused or reclaimed. Jute, generally obtained from old sacks, is used for certain needlefelts, and other fibres such as cotton, silk and synthetic fibres may be added.

The wool is sorted and selected. To separate the fibres, it is ragged in a rag-grinding machine, a spiked cylinder that rotates and tears up the fabric, and then garnetted in a machine that has rollers and cylinders covered with fine saw-toothed wires. The fibres are carbonized in an 18% sulphuric acid solution and, after drying at a temperature of 100° C, they are blended and, when necessary, oiled with mineral oil with emulsifier. After teasing and carding, which further blends the fibres and arranges them more or less parallel to one another, the material is deposited on a moving belt as layers of a fine web that are wound up on poles to form batts. The loose batts are taken to the hardening room, where they are sprinkled with water and pressed between two heavy plates, the top one of which vibrates, causing the fibres to curl and cling together.

To complete the felting, the material is placed in bowls of dilute sulphuric acid and pounded by heavy wooden hammers. It is washed (with the addition of tetrachloroethylene), dewatered and dyed, usually with synthetic dyestuffs. Chemicals may be added to make the felt rot-resistant. The final steps include drying (at 65 °C for soft felts, 112 °C for hard felts), shearing, sanding, brushing, pressing and trimming.

Safety and Health Hazards

Accidents

The machines used in felt manufacturing have driving belts, chain and sprocket drives, rotating shafts, spiked drums and rollers used in garnetting and teasing, heavy presses, rollers and hammers, and so on, all of which must be properly guarded and have lockout/tagout systems to prevent injuries when they are being serviced or cleaned. Good housekeeping is also necessary to avoid slips and falls.

Noise

Many of the operations are noisy; when safe noise levels cannot be maintained by enclosures, baffles and proper lubrication, personal hearing protection must be made available. A hearing conservation programme featuring periodic audiograms is required in many countries.

Dust

Felt workplaces are dusty and are not recommended for persons with chronic respiratory diseases. While, fortunately, the dust is not associated with any specific disease, adequate exhaust ventilation is necessary. Animal hair can evoke allergic reactions in sensitive individuals, but bronchial asthma appears to be infrequent. Dust also can be a fire hazard.

Chemicals

The sulphuric acid solution used in felt making is usually dilute, but care is needed when diluting the supply of concentrated acid to the desired level. The danger of splashes and spills requires that eyewash facilities be nearby and that workers be fitted with protective clothing (e.g., goggles, aprons, gloves and shoes).

Tanning of certain papermakers' felts may involve the use of quinone, which can cause severe damage to skin and mucous membranes. The dust or vapour of this compound can cause staining of the conjunctivae and cornea of the eye and, with prolonged or repeated exposures, may affect vision. Quinone powder should be dampened to prevent dusting, and it should be handled in enclosed hoods or chambers fitted with LEV, by workers fitted with hand, arm, face and eye protection.

Heat and fire

The high temperature of the material (60 °C) involved in the manual hat-shaping process dictates the use of hand skin protection by the workers.

Fire is a common hazard during the early, dusty stages of felt manufacture. It may be caused by matches or sparks from metallic objects left in the waste wool, hot-running bearings or faulty electrical connections. It may also occur in finishing operations, when vapours of flammable solvents may collect in the drying ovens. Because it damages the material and corrodes the equipment, water is less popular for fire extinguishing than dry-powder extinguishers. Modern equipment is fitted with vents through which the extinguishing material can be sprayed, or with an automatic carbon dioxide releasing device.

Anthrax

Although rare, cases of anthrax have occurred as a result of exposure to contaminated wool imported from areas where this bacillus is endemic.

● DYEING, PRINTING AND FINISHING

*J.M. Strother and A.K. Niyogi**

Dyeing

Dyeing involves a chemical combination or a powerful physical affinity between the dye and the fibre of the fabric. An extensive variety of dyes and processes is used, depending on the type of fabric and the end-product desired.

Classes of dyes

Acid or basic dyes are used in a weak acid bath for wool, silk or cotton. Some acid dyes are used after mordanting the fibres with

---

* The section on dyeing is adapted from A.K. Niyogi's contribution to the 3rd edition of the *Encyclopaedia of Occupational Health and Safety*.

metallic oxide, tannic acid or dichromates. *Direct dyes*, which are not fast, are used for the dyeing of wool, rayon and cotton; they are dyed at the boil. For dyeing cotton fabrics with *sulphur dyes*, the dyebath is prepared by pasting the dye with soda ash and sodium sulphide and hot water. This dyeing is also carried out at the boil. For dyeing cotton with *azo dyes*, naphthol is dissolved in aqueous caustic soda. The cotton is impregnated with the solution of the sodium naphthoxide that is formed, and it is then treated with a solution of a diazo compound to develop the dye in the material. *Vat dyes* are made into leuco-compounds with sodium hydroxide and sodium hydrosulphite; this dyeing is done at 30 to 60 °C. *Disperse dyes* are used for the dyeing of all synthetic fibres which are hydrophobic. Swelling agents or carriers which are phenolic in nature must be used to enable the disperse dyes to act. *Mineral dyes* are inorganic pigments which are salts of iron and chromium. After impregnation, they are precipitated by addition of hot alkaline solution. *Reactive dyes* for cotton are used in a hot or a cold bath of soda ash and common salt.

Preparing fabrics for dyeing

The preparatory processes before dyeing cotton fabrics consist of the following sequence of steps: The cloth is passed through a shearing machine to cut the loosely adhering fibres and then, to complete the trimming process, it is passed rapidly over a row of gas flames and the sparks are extinguished by passing the material through a water box. Desizing is carried out by passing the cloth through a diastase solution which removes the size completely. To remove other impurities, it is scoured in a kier with dilute sodium hydroxide, sodium carbonate or turkey red oil for 8 to 12 hours at high temperature and pressure.

For coloured woven material, an open kier is used and sodium hydroxide is avoided. The natural colouring in the cloth is removed by hypochlorite solution in the bleaching pits, after which the cloth is aired, washed, dechlorinated by means of a sodium bisulphite solution, washed again and scoured with dilute hydrochloric or sulphuric acid. After a final, thorough washing, the cloth is ready for the dyeing or printing process.

Dyeing process

Dyeing is carried out in a jig or padding machine, in which the cloth is moved through a stationary dye solution prepared by dissolving the dyestuff powder in a suitable chemical and then diluting with water. After dyeing, the cloth is subjected to a finishing process.

Nylon dyeing

The preparation of polyamide (nylon) fibres for dyeing involves scouring, some form of setting treatment and, in some cases, bleaching. The treatment adopted for the scouring of woven polyamide fabrics depends mainly on the composition of the size used. Water-soluble sizes based on polyvinyl alcohol or polyacrylic acid can be removed by scouring in a liquor containing soap and ammonia or Lissapol N or similar detergent and soda ash. After scouring, the material is rinsed thoroughly and is then ready for dyeing or printing, usually in a jigger or winch dyeing machine.

Wool dyeing

The raw wool is first scoured by the emulsification process, in which soap and a soda ash solution are used. The operation is carried out in a washing machine which consists of a long trough provided with rakes, a false bottom and, at the exit, wringers. After thorough washing, the wool is bleached with hydrogen peroxide or with sulphur dioxide. If the latter is used, the damp goods are left exposed to the sulphur dioxide gas overnight. The acid gas is neutralized by passing the fabric through a sodium carbonate bath, and then it is thoroughly washed. After dyeing, the goods are rinsed, hydroextracted and dried.

Hazards in Dyeing and Their Prevention

Fire and explosion

The fire hazards found in a dye works are the flammable solvents used in the processes and certain flammable dyestuffs. Safe storage facilities should be provided for both: properly designed storerooms constructed of fire-resisting materials with a raised and ramped sill at the doorway so that escaping liquid is contained within the room and prevented from flowing to a place where it may be ignited. It is preferable that stores of this nature be located outside the main factory building. If large quantities of flammable liquids are kept in tanks outside the building, the tank area should be mounded to contain escaping liquid.

Similar arrangements should be made when the gaseous fuel used on the singeing machines is obtained from a light petroleum fraction. The gas-making plant and the storage facilities for the volatile petroleum spirit should preferably be outside the building.

Chemical hazards

Many factories use hypochlorite solution for bleaching; in others, the bleaching agent is gaseous chlorine or bleaching powder which releases chlorine when it is charged into the tank. In either case, workers may be exposed to dangerous levels of chlorine, a skin and eye irritant and a dangerous pulmonary tissue irritant causing delayed lung oedema. To limit the escape of chlorine into the workers' atmosphere, bleaching vats should be designed as closed vessels provided with vents that limit the escape of chlorine so that the relevant recommended maximum exposure levels are not exceeded. Atmospheric chlorine levels should be checked periodically to ensure that the exposure limit is not being exceeded.

The valves and other controls of the tank from which the liquid chlorine is supplied to the dyeworks should be controlled by a competent operator, since the possibilities of an uncontrolled leak could well be disastrous. When a vessel that has contained chlorine or any other dangerous gas or vapour has to be entered, all of the precautions advised for work in confined places should be taken.

The use of corrosive alkalis and acids and the treatment of cloth with boiling liquor expose the workers to the risk of burns and scalds. Both hydrochloric acid and sulphuric acid are used extensively in dyeing processes. Caustic soda is used in bleaching, mercerizing and dyeing. Chips from the solid material fly and create hazards for the workers. Sulphur dioxide, which is used in bleaching, and carbon disulphide, which is used as a solvent in the viscose process, can also pollute the workroom. Aromatic hydrocarbons such as benzol, toluol and xylol, solvent naphthas and aromatic amines such as aniline dyes are dangerous chemicals to which workers are likely to be exposed. Dichlorobenzene is emulsified with water with the help of an emulsifying agent, and is used for dyeing of polyester fibres. LEV is essential.

Many dyestuffs are skin irritants that cause dermatitis; in addition, workers are tempted to use harmful mixtures of abrasive, alkali and bleaching agents to remove dye stains from their hands.

Organic solvents used in the processes and for the cleaning of machines may themselves cause dermatitis or render the skin vulnerable to the irritant action of the other harmful substances that are used. Furthermore, they may be the cause of peripheral neuropathy—for example, methyl butyl ketone (MBK). Certain dyes, such as rhodamine B, magenta, β-naphthylamine and certain bases such as dianisidine, have been found to be carcinogenic. The use of β-naphthylamine has generally been abandoned

in dyestuffs, which are discussed more fully elsewhere in this *Encyclopaedia*.

In addition to the fibre materials and their contaminants, allergy may be caused by the sizing and even by the enzymes used to remove the sizing.

Suitable PPE, including eye-protective equipment, should be provided to prevent contact with these hazards. In certain circumstances when barrier creams have to be used, care should be taken to ensure that they are effective for the purpose and that they can be removed by washing. At best, however, the protection they provide is rarely as reliable as that afforded by properly designed gloves. Protective clothing should be cleaned at regular intervals, and when splashed or contaminated by dyestuffs, it should be replaced by clean clothing at the earliest opportunity. Sanitary facilities for washing, bathing and changing should be provided, and the workers should be encouraged to use them; personal hygiene is particularly important for dye workers. Unfortunately, even when all protective measures have been taken, some workers are found to be so sensitive to the effects of these substances that transfer to other work is the only alternative.

Accidents

Serious scalding accidents have occurred when hot liquor has been accidentally admitted to a kier in which a worker has been arranging the cloth to be treated. This can occur when a valve is accidentally opened or when hot liquor is discharged into a common discharge duct from another kier on the range and enters the occupied kier through an open outlet. When a worker is inside a kier for any purpose, the inlet and outlet should be closed, isolating that kier from the other kiers on the range. If the locking device is operated by a key, it should be retained by the worker who might be injured by an accidental admission of hot liquid until he or she leaves the vessel.

Printing

Printing is carried out on a roller printing machine. The dye or pigment is thickened with starch or made into emulsion which, in the case of pigment colours, is prepared with an organic solvent. This paste or emulsion is taken up by the engraved rollers which print the material, and the colour is subsequently fixed in the ager or curing machine. The printed cloth then receives the appropriate finishing treatment.

Wet printing

Wet printing is performed with dyeing systems similar to those used in dyeing, such as vat printing and fibre-reactive printing. These printing methods are used only for 100% cotton fabric and for rayon. The health hazards associated with this type of printing are the same as those discussed above.

Solvent-based pigment printing

Solvent-based printing systems use large amounts of solvents such as mineral spirits in the thickening system. The major hazards are:

- *Flammability*. The thickening systems contain up to 40% solvents and are highly flammable. They should be stored with extreme caution in properly ventilated and electrically grounded areas. Care should also be taken in transferring these products to avoid creating a spark from static electricity.
- *Air emissions*. Solvents in this print system will be flashed off from the oven during drying and curing. Local environmental regulations will dictate the permissible levels of volatile organic compound (VOC) emissions that can be tolerated.
- *Sludge*. Since this print system is solvent based, the print paste cannot be allowed to enter the wastewater treatment system. It

must be disposed of as a solid waste. Sites where sludge piles are used can have environmental problems with ground and groundwater contamination. These sludge storage areas should be equipped with waterproof linings to prevent this from occurring.

Aqueous-based pigment printing

None of the health hazards for solvent-based pigment printing apply to the aqueous-based printing systems. Although some solvents are used, the amounts are so small that they are not significant. The primary health hazard is the presence of formaldehyde.

Pigment printing requires the use of a cross-linker to assist in the bonding of the pigments to the fabric. These cross-linkers exist as stand-alone products (e.g., melamine) or as part of other chemicals such as binders, antiwicks, and even in the pigments themselves. Formaldehyde plays a necessary role in the function of the cross-linkers.

Formaldehyde is a sensitizer and an irritant that may produce reactions, sometimes violent, in workers who are exposed to it either by inhaling the air around the printing machine as it is operating or by coming into contact with the printed fabric. These reactions may range from simple eye irritation to welts on the skin and severe difficulty with breathing. Formaldehyde has been found to be carcinogenic in mice but it has not yet been conclusively associated with cancer in humans. It is classified as a Group 2A Carcinogen, "Probably Carcinogenic to Humans", by the International Agency for Research on Cancer (IARC).

To protect the local environment, emissions from the plant have to be monitored to ensure that levels of formaldehyde do not exceed those stipulated by applicable regulations.

Another potential hazard is ammonia. Since the print paste is pH (acidity) sensitive, ammonia is often used as a print-paste thickener. Care should be taken to handle ammonia in a well-ventilated area and to wear respiratory protection if necessary.

Since all dyes and pigments used in printing are usually in a liquid form, dust exposure is not a hazard in printing as it is in dyeing.

Finishing

Finishing is a term applied to a very broad range of treatments that are usually performed during the last manufacturing process before fabrication. Some finishing can also be performed after fabrication.

Mechanical finishing

This type of finishing involves processes that change the texture or appearance of a fabric without the use of chemicals. They include:

- *Sanforizing*. This is a process where a fabric is overfed between a rubber belt and a heated cylinder and then fed between a heated cylinder and an endless blanket to control shrinkage and create a soft hand.
- *Calendering*. This is a process where fabric is fed between large steel rollers under pressures that range up to 100 tonnes. These rolls can be heated with either steam or gas to temperatures up to 232 °C. This process is used to change the hand and appearance of the fabric.
- *Sanding*. In this process, fabric is fed over rolls which are covered with sand to change the surface of the fabric and give a softer hand.
- *Embossing*. This is a process where fabric is fed between heated steel rollers which have been engraved with a pattern which is permanently transferred to the fabric.
- *Heat-setting*. This is a process where synthetic fabric, usually polyester, is run through either a tenter frame or a semi-contact heat-set machine at temperatures that are high enough to begin the molecular melting of the fabric. This is done to stabilize the fabric for shrinkage.
- *Brushing*. This is a process where fabric is run across brushes revolving at high speeds to change the surface appearance and the hand of the fabric.
- *Sueding*. In this process, fabric is run between a small steel roller and a larger roller that is covered with sandpaper to change the appearance and the hand of the fabric.

The principal hazards are the presence of heat, the very high temperatures being applied and nip points in the moving machine parts. Care should be taken to properly guard the machinery to prevent accidents and physical injury.

Chemical finishing

Chemical finishing is performed on a variety of types of equipment (e.g., pads, jigs, jet dye machines, becks, spray bars, kiers, paddle machines, kiss roll applicators and foamers).

One type of chemical finishing does not involve a chemical reaction: the application of a softener or a hand builder to modify the feel and texture of the fabric, or to improve its sewability. This presents no significant hazards except for the possibility of irritation from skin and eye contact, which can be prevented by the use of proper gloves and eye protection.

The other type of chemical finishing involves a chemical reaction: resin finishing of cotton fabric to produce desired physical properties in the fabric such as low shrinkage and a good smoothness appearance. For cotton fabric, for example, a dimethyldihydroxyethylene urea (DMDHEU) resin is catalysed and bonds with the cotton molecules of the fabric to create a permanent change in the fabric. The primary hazard associated with this type of finishing is that most resins release formaldehyde as part of their reaction.

Conclusion

As in the rest of the textile industry, dyeing, printing and finishing operations present a mixture of old, generally small establishments in which worker safety, health and welfare are given little if any attention, and newer, larger establishments with ever-improving technology in which, to the extent possible, hazard control is built into the design of the machinery. In addition to the specific hazards outlined above, such problems as substandard lighting, noise, incompletely guarded machinery, lifting and carrying of heavy and/or bulky objects, poor housekeeping and so on remain ubiquitous. Therefore, a well-formulated and implemented safety and health programme that includes the training and effective supervision of workers is a necessity.

NONWOVEN TEXTILE FABRICS

William A. Blackburn and
Subhash K. Batra

The nonwoven textile fabric industry had an exploratory beginning in the late 1940s which entered into a development phase in the 1950s followed by commercial expansion in the 1960s. During the next 35 years, the nonwoven industry matured and established markets for nonwoven fabrics by either providing cost-effective performance as alternatives to conventional textiles or providing products specifically developed for targeted end-uses. The industry has survived recessions better than conventional textiles and has grown at a faster rate. Its health and safety problems are similar to those of the rest of the textile industry (i.e., noise, airborne fibres, chemicals used in bonding fibres, safe working surfaces, pinch points, burns from thermal exposures, back injuries and so on).

The industry generally has a good safety record, and the number of injuries per standard work unit is low. The industry has responded to challenges associated with clean water and clean air acts. In the United States, the Occupational Safety and Health Administration (OSHA) has promulgated a number of worker protection rules which require safety training and manufacturing practices that have improved worker protection significantly. Responsible companies throughout the world are adopting similar practices.

The raw materials used by the industry are generally similar to those used in conventional textiles. The industry has been estimated to use almost 1 billion kg of a mix of raw materials annually. The natural fibres used are predominately cotton and wood pulp. The manufactured fibres include rayon, polyolefins (both polyethylene and polypropylene), polyesters and, to a smaller degree, nylons, acrylics, aramids and others.

There was an early growth in the number of nonwoven processes to approximately ten. These include; spunbond, melt blown, air-laid pulp and blends, wet laid, dry laid (bonded by either needlepunching, thermal bonding or chemical bonding) and stitch bonding processes. In the United States, the industry has saturated many of its end-use markets and is currently searching for new ones. A major growth area for nonwovens is developing in the area of composites. Laminates of nonwovens with films and other coatings are broadening markets for nonwoven materials. The storage of nonwoven roll goods has recently come under scrutiny because of the flammability of some products that have very low densities and high surface areas. Rolls whose volume-to-weight ratio is greater than a certain roll loft factor are considered to pose storage problems.

Raw Materials

Cellulosic fibres

The volume of bleached cotton used in nonwoven fabrics has been steadily increasing, and cotton-polyester and rayon-polyester blends in nonwoven fabrics, bonded by hydroentangling, have become attractive combinations for medical and feminine hygiene applications. There has been an interest in using unbleached cotton in nonwoven processes, and some attractive experimental fabrics have been produced through the use of the hydroentangling process.

Rayon has encountered some pressure from environmentalists who are concerned about the impact that by-products of the process have on the environment. Some rayon-producing companies in the United States abandoned the industry rather than face the cost of complying with regulatory requirements imposed by the clean water and air acts. Those companies that chose to meet the requirements now appear to be comfortable with their modified processes.

Wood pulp fibres are a major component of disposable diapers, incontinence products and other absorbent products. Fibres from hardwood and kraft fibres are employed. In the United States alone, use of pulp fibres totals more than 1 billion kg annually. A small percentage is used in air-laid nonwoven processes. The products are popular as towels in applications which range from the kitchen to sports.

Synthetic fibres

The two most popular polyolefin fibres are polyethylene and polypropylene. These polymers are either converted into staple-length fibres which are subsequently converted into nonwoven fabrics, or else converted into spunbonded nonwoven fabrics by extruding the polymers to form filaments which are formed into webs and bonded by thermal processes. Some of the fabrics produced are converted into protective apparel, and by 1995, more than 400,000,000 coveralls had been made using a popular spunbonded polyethylene fabric.

The largest single use for a nonwoven fabric in the United States (approximately 10 billion square metres) is as the cover sheet in disposable diapers. This is the fabric which contacts the baby's skin and separates the baby from the other diaper components. Fabrics from these fibres are also used in durable products and in some geotextile applications where they are expected to last indefinitely. The fabrics will degrade in ultraviolet light or some other types of radiation.

Thermoplastic fibres from polyester polymers and copolymers are widely used in nonwovens in both staple fibre and spunbonded processes. The combined volume of polyester and polyolefin polymers used in the United States in nonwoven fabrics has been estimated to be more than 250 million kg annually. Blends of polyester fibres with wood pulp which are wet laid and then bonded by hydroentangling and subsequently treated with a repellent coating are widely used in disposable surgical gowns and drapes. By 1995, the use of disposable medical nonwovens in the United States alone exceeded 2 billion square metres annually.

Nylon fibres are used only sparingly in the form of staple fibres and in a limited volume in spunbonded nonwovens. One of the largest uses for spundbonded nylon nonwovens is in the reinforcement of carpet pads and in fibreglass filters. The fabrics provide a low friction surface to carpet pads that facilitates the installation of carpets. In fibreglass filters, the fabric helps retain the fibreglass in the filter and prevents glass fibres from entering the filtered air stream. Other specialty nonwovens, such as aramids, are used in niche markets where their properties, such as low flammability, recommend their use. Some of these nonwovens are used in the furniture industry as flame blockers, to reduce the flammability of sofas and chairs.

Processes

Spunbonded and meltblown

In the spunbonded and meltblown processes, suitable synthetic polymers are melted, filtered, extruded, drawn, charged electrostatically, laid down in web form, bonded and taken up as rolls. The process requires good safety practices common to working with hot extruders, filters, spinnerets and heated rolls used for bonding.

Workers should wear proper eye protection and avoid wearing loose clothing, neckties, rings or other jewellery that may be caught in moving equipment. Also, these processes almost always involve the use of large volumes of air, and special precautions must be taken to avoid designs that might lead to fires, such as placing light ballasts in an air duct. Extinguishing a fire in an air duct is difficult. It is important to maintain safe working-floor surfaces, and the floors around any nonwoven equipment should be free of contamination that can lead to unsafe footing.

Spunbonded and meltblown processes call for cleaning some of the process equipment by burning away any accumulated polymer residue. This usually involves the use of very hot ovens for both cleaning and storing the cleaned parts. Obviously, these operations require proper gloves and other thermal protection, as well as appropriate ventilation to reduce heat and exhaust fumes.

Spunbonded processes owe their economic advantages in part to the fact that they are relatively fast and the take-up rolls can be changed while the process continues to run. The design of the roll-changing equipment and the training of the operators should provide for an adequate margin of safety to handle these changeovers.

Dry laid

Processes that involve opening of bales of fibres, blending the fibres to provide a uniform feed to a carding machine, carding to form webs, cross-lapping the webs to provide optimum strength in all directions and then forwarding the web to some bonding process are similar in their safety requirements to conventional textile processes. All exposed points that could trap a worker's hands in roll interfaces need protection. Some dry-laid processes involve the generation of small amounts of airborne fibres. The worker should be provided with adequate respiratory PPE in order to avoid inhalation of any respirable part of these fibres.

If the webs formed are to be bonded thermally, there will normally be a small amount (on the order of 10% by weight) of a lower-melting fibre or powder that has been blended into the web. This material is melted by exposure to a hot air oven or to heated rollers and then cooled to form the fabric's bonds. Protection against exposure to the heated environments should be provided. In the United States, approximately 100 million kg of thermally bonded nonwovens are produced annually.

If the webs are bonded by needle punching, a needle loom is used. An array of needles is mounted in needle boards, and the needles are driven through the web. Needles capture surface fibres, carry them from the top to the bottom of the fabric and then release the fibres on the return stroke. The number of penetrations per unit area can range from a small number (in the case of high-loft fabrics) to a large number (in the case of needled felts). A loom may be used for needling from both the top and bottom sides of the web and for use with multiple boards. Broken needles must be replaced. Safety-locking the looms is required in order to prevent accidents during such maintenance. As in the case of carding, some small fibres may be generated by these processes, and ventilation and respirators are recommended. In addition, eye protection is advised to protect against flying debris from broken needles. In the United States, approximately 100 million kg of needlepunched nonwovens are manufactured annually.

If the webs are bonded by chemical adhesive, the process normally calls for spraying the adhesive on one side of the web and passing it through a curing area, normally a through-air oven. The web direction is then reversed, another application of the adhesive is made and the web is sent back through the oven. A third pass through the oven is sometimes used if needed to complete the curing process. Obviously, the area must exhaust the oven gases and it is necessary to capture and remove any toxic effluents (in the United States, this is required by various state and federal clean air acts). In the case of adhesive bonding, there has been worldwide pressure to reduce the release of formaldehyde into the environment. In the United States, the EPA has recently tightened limits on the release of formaldehyde to one tenth of the previously acceptable limits. There are concerns that the new limits challenge the precision of currently available laboratory methods. The adhesive industry has responded by offering new binders which are formaldehyde free.

Air laid

There is some nomenclature confusion in regard to air-laid nonwovens. One of the variations of carding processes includes a card that includes a section that randomizes the fibres being processed in an air stream. This process is often referred to as an "air-laid nonwoven process". Another, very different, process, also called air laid, involves the dispersion of fibres in an air stream, usually using a hammer mill, and directing the airborne fibre dispersion to a device that deposits the fibres on a moving belt. The web formed is then spray bonded and cured. The laydown process may be repeated in line with different types of fibres to produce nonwoven fabrics from layers with different fibre compositions.

The fibres used in this case can be very short, and protection to prevent exposure to such airborne fibres must be taken.

Wet laid

The wet laid nonwoven process borrows technology developed for making paper and calls for the formation of webs from dispersions of fibres in water. This process is assisted by the use of dispersion aids that help avoid non-uniform clumps of fibres. The fibre dispersion is filtered through moving belts and dewatered by pressing between felts. At some point in the process a binder is often added which bonds the web during the heat of drying. Alternatively, in a newer method, the web is bonded by hydroentangling using high-pressure jets of water. The final step involves drying and may include steps to soften the fabric by microcreping or some other similar technique. There are no known major hazards associated with this process, and the safety programmes normally are based on common good manufacturing practices.

Stitchbonding

This process is often excluded from some definitions of nonwovens because it can involve the use of yarns to stitch webs into fabrics. Some definitions of nonwovens exclude any fabrics which contain "yarn". In this process a web is presented to conventional stitchbonding machines to produce knit-like structures that offer a wide variety of combinations including the use of elastic yarns to produce fabrics with attractive stretch and recovery properties. Again, no exceptional hazards are associated with this process.

Finishing

Finishes for nonwoven fabrics include flame retardant, fluid repellent, antistatic, softeners, anti-bacterial, fusible, lubricants and other surface treatments. Finishes for nonwovens are applied either on-line or as off-line, post-manufacturing treatments, depending on the process and the type of finish. Frequently, antistatic finishes are added on-line, and surface treatment such as corona etching is normally an on-line process. Flame-retardant and -repellent finishes are often applied off-line. Some specialized fabric treatments include exposing the web to a high-energy plasma treatment to influence the polarity of fabrics and improve their performance in filtration applications. The safety of these chemical and physical processes varies with each application and must be considered separately.

WEAVING AND KNITTING

Charles Crocker

Weaving and knitting are the two primary textile processes for manufacturing fabrics. In the modern textile industry, these processes take place on electrically powered automated machines, and the resulting fabrics find their way into a wide range of end-uses, including wearing apparel, home furnishings and industrial applications.

Weaving

The weaving process consists of interlacing straight yarns at right angles to one another. It is the oldest technology of manufacturing fabric: hand-powered looms were used in pre-Biblical times. The basic concept of interlacing the yarns is still followed today.

Warp yarns are supplied from a large reel, called a *warp beam*, mounted at the back of the weaving machine. Each warp yarn

89. TEXTILE GOODS INDUSTRY

Figure 89.9 • Air-jet weaving machines.

Tsudakoma Corp

end is threaded through a *heddles harness*. The harness is used to lift or depress the warp yarns to allow the weaving to be done. The simplest weaving requires two harnesses, and more intricate woven fabrics require as many as six harnesses. Jacquard weaving equipment is used to manufacture the most decorative fabrics and has features to enable each individual warp yarn to be lifted or depressed. Each yarn end then is threaded through a *reed* of closely spaced thin parallel metal pieces mounted on the machine's *lay*, or *sley*. The lay is designed to move in a reciprocating arc around a pivotal anchor point. The yarn ends are attached to the take-up roll. The woven fabric is wound on this roll.

The oldest technology for feeding the filling yarn across the width of the warp yarns is the *shuttle*, which is propelled in a free-flight fashion from one side of the warp yarn to the other side and pays out the filling yarn from a small bobbin mounted in it. New and faster technology, shown in figure 89.9, called *shuttleless weaving*, uses air jets, water jets, small projectiles that ride in a guidetrack, or small, sword-like devices called *rapiers* to carry the filling yarn.

Employees in weaving are typically grouped into one of four job functions:

1. machine operators, commonly called *weavers*, who patrol their assigned production area to check on fabric production, correct some basic machine malfunctions such as yarn breaks and restart stopped machines
2. machine technicians, sometimes called *fixers*, who adjust and repair the weaving machines
3. direct production service workers, who transport and load raw materials (warp and filling yarn) onto the weaving machines and who unload and transport finished products (fabric rolls)
4. indirect production service workers, who perform cleaning, machine lubrication and so on.

Safety risks

Weaving presents only a moderate worker safety risk. However, there are a number of typical safety hazards and minimization measures.

Falls

Objects on the floor that cause worker falls include machine parts and oil, grease and water spots. Good housekeeping is particularly important in weaving, since many of the process workers spend most of their workday patrolling the area with eyes directed to the production process rather than toward objects on the floor.

Machinery

Power transmission devices and most other pinch points are typically guarded. The machine lay, harnesses and other parts that must be frequently accessed by weavers, however, are only partially enclosed. Ample walking and working space must be provided around the machines, and good work procedures help workers avoid these exposures. In shuttle weaving, guards mounted on the lay are needed to prevent the shuttle from being thrown out, or to deflect it in a downward direction. Lockouts, mechanical blocks and so on are also required in order to prevent the introduction of hazardous energy into areas when technicians or others are performing job duties on stopped machines.

Materials handling

These can include lifting and moving heavy cloth rolls, warp beams and so on. Hand-trucks to help unload, or doff, and transport small cloth rolls from take-ups on the weaving machine reduce the risk of worker strain injuries by alleviating the need to lift the full weight of the roll. Powered industrial trucks can be used to doff and transport large cloth rolls from bulk take-ups placed at the front of the weaving machine. Wheeled trucks with powered or manual hydraulic assists can be used to handle warp beams, which usually weigh several hundred kg. Warp-handling workers should wear safety shoes.

Fires and ignition

Weaving creates a fair amount of lint, dust and fibre flyings which can represent fire hazards if the fibres are combustible. Controls include dust-collection systems (located under the machines in modern facilities), regular machine cleanings by service workers and use of electrical equipment designed to prevent sparking (e.g., Class III, Division 1, Hazardous Locations).

Health risks

Health risks in modern weaving are generally limited to noise-induced hearing loss and to pulmonary disorders associated with some types of fibres used in the yarn.

Noise

Most weaving machines, operating in the numbers found in a typical production facility, produce noise levels that generally exceed 90 dBA. In some shuttle and high-speed shuttleless weaving, levels may even exceed 100 dBA. Appropriate hearing protectors and a hearing conservation programme are nearly always necessary for weaving workers.

Fibre dust

Pulmonary disorders (byssinosis) have long been linked with dusts associated with the processing of raw cotton and flax fibres, and are discussed elsewhere in this chapter and this *Encyclopaedia*. Generally, ventilation and room air filtration cleaning systems with dust collection points under the weaving machines and at other points in the weaving area maintain dusts at or below required maximum levels (e.g., 750 $\mu g/m^3$ of air in the OSHA cotton dust standard) in modern facilities. Additionally, dust respirators are needed for temporary protection during cleaning activities. A worker medical surveillance programme should be in place to identify workers who might be especially sensitive to the effects of these dusts.

Figure 89.10 • Circular-knitting machine.

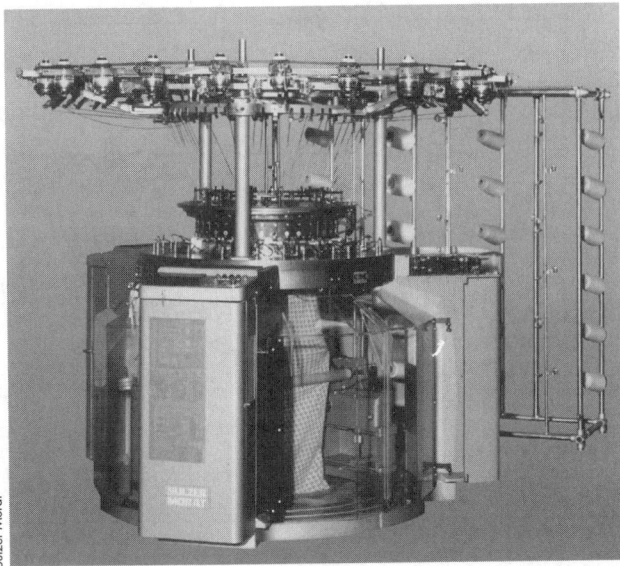

Sulzer Morat

Machine Knitting*

The mechanical knitting process consists of interconnecting loops of yarn on powered automated machines (see figure 89.10). The machines are equipped with rows of small, hooked needles to draw formed yarn loops through previously formed loops. The hooked needles have a unique latch feature that closes the hook to easily allow the loop drawing and then opens to allow the yarn loop to slide off the needle. Circular-knitting machines have needles arranged in a circle, and the fabric produced on them comes off the machine in the shape of a large tube that is wound onto a take-up roll. Flat-knitting machines and warp-knitting machines, on the other hand, have needles arranged in a straight row, and fabric comes off the machine in a flat sheet for roll take-up. Circular- and flat-knitting machines are generally fed from yarn cones, and warp-knitting machines are generally fed from warp beams that are smaller but similar to those used in weaving.

Employees in knitting are grouped into job functions with duties similar to those in weaving. Job titles appropriately parallel the process name.

Safety risks

Safety risks in knitting are similar to those in weaving though generally of a lesser degree. Oil on the floor often is a little more prevalent in knitting due to the high lubrication needs of the knitting needles. Machine entrapment risks are less in knitting since there are fewer pinch points on the machines than those found in weaving, and much of the machinery lends itself well to enclosure guarding. Energy-control lockout procedures remain a must.

Cloth roll handling still presents a worker strain injury risk, but the heavy warp-beam handling risks are not present except in warp knitting. Risk control measures are similar to those in weaving. Knitting does not produce the levels of lint, flyings and dust that are found in weaving, but the oil from the process helps keep

---

* There is a major cottage industry for the production of hand-knitted items. There are inadequate data on numbers of workers, generally women, thus engaged. The reader is referred to the chapter *Entertainment and the arts* for an overview of likely hazards. Editor.

the fire fuel load at a level that needs attention. Controls are similar to those in weaving.

Health risks

Health risks in knitting are also generally lower than those in weaving. Noise levels range in the mid-80-dBA to low-90-dBA levels. Respiratory disorders for knitting workers processing raw cotton and flax do not appear to be especially prevalent, and regulatory standards for these materials are often not applicable in knitting.

CARPETS AND RUGS

The Carpet and Rug Institute

Hand-woven or hand-knotted carpets originated several centuries BC in Persia. The first US woven carpet mill was built in 1791 in Philadelphia. In 1839, the industry was reshaped with Erastus Bigelow's invention of the power loom. The majority of carpet is machine-made in modern mills by one of two processes: *tufted* or *woven*.

Tufted carpet is now the predominant method of carpet production. In the United States, for example, approximately 96% of all carpet is machine tufted, a process that developed from tufted bedspread manufacturing centred in northwest Georgia. Tufted carpet is made by inserting a pile yarn into a primary backing fabric (usually polypropylene) and then attaching a secondary backing fabric with a synthetic latex to hold the yarns in place and attach the backings to each other, adding stability to the carpet.

Carpet Construction

Machine tufting

The tufting machine is comprised of hundreds of needles (up to 2,400) in a horizontal bar across the width of the machine (see figure 89.11). The creel, or yarn on cones arranged in racks, are passed overhead through small-diameter guide tubes to the machine needles on a *jerker* bar. Generally, two yarn spools are provided for each needle. The yarn end of the first spool is spliced together with the leading end of the second one, so that when yarn from the first spool has been used, yarn is supplied from the second without stopping the machine. A guide tube is provided for each yarn end, in order to prevent the yarns from becoming

Figure 89.11 • Tufting machine.

Carpet and Rug Institute

Figure 89.12 • Residential carpet profile.

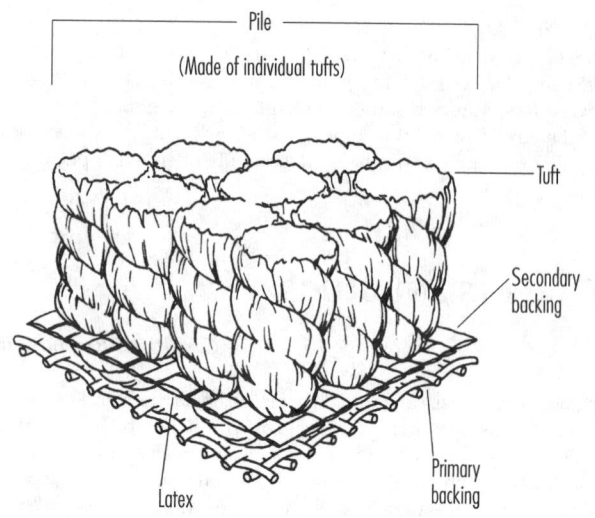

Figure 89.13 • Commercial carpet profile.

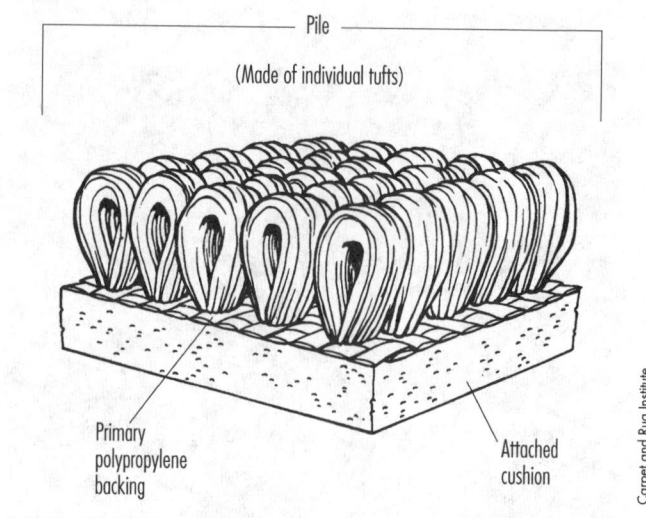

entangled. The yarns pass through a series of vertically aligned, fixed guides attached to the machine body and a guide located on the end of an arm extending from the moving needle bar of the machine. When the needle bar moves up and down, the relationship between the two guides is changed. Tufted product used for residential carpet is shown in figure 89.12.

The jerker bar takes up the slack yarn delivered during the upward stroke of the needles. The yarns are threaded through their respective needles in the needle bar. The needles are operated simultaneously at 500 or more strokes per minute in a vertical, reciprocating motion. A tufting machine can produce 1,000 to 2,000 square metres of carpet in 8 hours of operation.

The primary backing into which the yarns are inserted is supplied from a roll located in front of the machine. The speed of the roll of carpet backing controls the stitch length and the number of stitches per inch. The number of needles in the width per inch or cm of the machine determines the gauge of the fabric, such as 3/16 gauge or 5/32 gauge.

Located below the needle plate of the tufting machine are loopers or looper-and-knife combinations, which pick up and hold momentarily the yarns carried by the needles. When forming loop pile, loopers shaped like inverted hockey sticks are positioned in the machine so that the formed pile loops move away from the loopers as the backing is advanced through the machine.

Loopers for cut pile are a reversed "C" shape, with a cutting surface on the top inside edge of the crescent shape. They are used in combination with knives having a ground cutting edge on one end. As the backing advances through the machine toward the cut pile loopers, the yarns picked up from the needles are cut with a scissor-like action between the looper and knife cutting edge. Figures 89.13 and 89.14 show the tufts on a backing and the kinds of loops available.

Weaving

Woven carpet has a pile surface yarn woven simultaneously with warp and weft threads that form the integrated backing. Backing yarns are usually jute, cotton or polypropylene. Pile yarns can be wool, cotton or any of the synthetic fibres, such as nylon, polyester, polypropylene, acrylic and so on. A back coating is applied to add stability; however, a secondary back is unnecessary and is rarely applied. Variations of woven carpet include velvet, Wilton and Axminster.

Figure 89.14 • Level loop; cut and loop; velvet plush; saxony.

Level loop

Cut and loop

Velvet plush

Saxony

There are other methods of making carpet—knitted, needle-punched, fusion bonded—but those methods are used less often and for more specialized markets.

Fibre and Yarn Production

Carpet is manufactured primarily from synthetic yarns—nylon, polypropylene (olefin) and polyester—with lesser quantities of acrylic, wool, cotton and blends of any of these yarns. In the 1960s, synthetic fibres became predominant because they provide a durable, quality product in an affordable price range.

Synthetic yarns are formed by the extrusion of a molten polymer forced through the tiny holes of a metal plate, or spinneret. Additives to the molten polymer may provide solution-dyed colour or less transparent, whiter, more durable fibres and various other performance attributes. After the filaments emerge from the spinneret, they are cooled, drawn and texturized.

Synthetic fibres can be extruded in different shapes or cross-sections, such as round, trilobal, pentalobal, octalobal or square, depending upon the design and shape of the spinneret holes. These cross-sectional shapes can affect many properties of carpet, including lustre, bulkiness, texture retention, and soil-hiding abilities.

After fibre extrusion, post-treatments, such as drawing and annealing (heating/cooling), increase tensile strength and generally enhance the fibre's physical properties. The filament bundle then goes through a crimping or texturing process, which converts straight filaments to fibres with a repeating kinked, curled or sawtooth configuration.

Yarn can be produced as either bulked continuous filament (BCF) or staple. The BCF is continuous strands of synthetic fibre formed into yarn bundles. Extruded yarn is made by winding the proper number of filaments for the desired yarn denier directly onto "take-up" packages.

Staple fibres are converted into spun yarns by textile yarn spinning processes. When staple fibre is produced, large bundles of fibre called "tow" are extruded. After the crimping process, the tow is cut into fibre lengths of 10 to 20 cm. There are three critical preparation steps—blending, carding and drafting—before the staple fibres are spun. Blending carefully mixes bales of staple fibre to ensure that the fibres intermingle in a way so that yarn streaking will not occur in subsequent dyeing operations. Carding straightens the fibres and puts them in a continuous sliver (rope-like) configuration. Drafting has three main functions: it blends fibres, places them in a parallel form and continues to decrease the weight per unit length of the total fibre bundle to make it easy to spin into the final yarn.

After spinning, which draws the sliver down to the desired yarn size, the yarn is plied and twisted to provide various effects. The yarn is then wound onto yarn cones to prepare it for the heat-setting and yarn-twisting processes.

Colouration Techniques

Because the synthetic fibres have various shapes, they take dyestuffs differently and may have varying colouration performance characteristics. Fibres of the same generic type can be treated or modified so that their affinity for certain dyes is changed, producing a multicolour or two-toned effect.

Colouration for carpet can be achieved at two possible times in the manufacturing process—either by dyeing the fibre or yarn before the fabric is tufted (pre-dyeing) or by dyeing the tufted fabric (post-dyeing of greige goods) before the application of the secondary backing and the finishing process. Methods of pre-dyeing include solution dyeing, stock dyeing and yarn dyeing. Post-dyeing methods include piece dyeing, the application of colour

from an aqueous dye bath onto unfinished carpet; beck dyeing, which handles batches of greige goods of approximately 150 running metres; and continuous dyeing, a continuous process of dyeing almost unlimited quantities by distributing dye with an injection applicator across the full width of the carpet as it moves in open-width form under the applicator. Carpet printing uses machinery that is essentially enlarged, modified textile printing equipment. Both flat-bed and rotary-screen printers are used.

Carpet Finishing

Carpet finishing has three separate purposes: to anchor the individual tufts into the primary backing, to adhere the tufted primary backing to a secondary backing and to shear and clean the surface pile to give an attractive surface appearance. Adding a secondary backing material, such as woven polypropylene, jute or attached cushion material, adds dimensional stability to the carpet.

First, the back of the carpet is coated, usually by means of a roller rotating in a synthetic latex mix, and the latex is spread by a doctor blade. The latex is a viscous solution, usually from 8,000 to 15,000 centipose viscosity. Normally, between 22 and 28 ounces (625–795 g) of latex per square yard is applied.

A separate roll of secondary backing is positioned carefully onto the latex coating. The two materials are then carefully pressed together by a marriage roller. This laminate, remaining flat and unflexed, then passes through a long oven, usually 24 to 49 m long, where it is dried and cured at temperatures from 115 to 150 °C for 2 to 5 minutes through three zones of heating. A high rate of evaporation is important for carpet drying, with forced hot air moving along precisely controlled heating zones.

In order to clean the surface yarns that may have developed fuzzing on the tips of the fibre during the dyeing and finishing stages, the carpet is lightly sheared. The shear is a unit that heavily brushes the carpet pile to make it both erect and uniform; it passes the carpet through a series of rotary knives or blades that shear or cut off the fibre tips at a precise, adjustable height. Two or four shear blades operate in tandem. The "double shear" has a double set of hard bristle or nylon brushes and two shear blade heads per unit, used in tandem.

The carpet goes through an intense inspection process and is packaged and stored, or cut, packaged and shipped.

Safe Practices in Carpet Mills

Modern carpet and yarn mills provide safety policies, monitoring of safety performance and, when necessary, prompt and thorough accident investigation. Carpet manufacturing machinery is well guarded to protect employees. Keeping the equipment serviced and safe is of primary importance for enhancing quality and productivity and for protection of the workers.

Workers should be trained in the safe use of electrical equipment and work practices to avoid injuries resulting from the unexpected start-up of machines. They need training to recognize hazardous energy sources, the type and magnitude of the energy available and the methods necessary for energy isolation and control. They also should be trained to distinguish exposed live parts from other parts of electrical equipment; to determine the nominal voltage of exposed, energized parts; and to know the required clearance distances and corresponding voltages. In areas where lockout/tagout will be in effect, employees are instructed in the prohibition against restarting or re-energizing equipment.

Where older equipment is in use, careful inspections should be frequent and upgrades made when advisable. Rotating shafts, v-belts and pulley drives, chain and sprocket drives, and overhead hoists and rigging should be periodically inspected, and guards installed whenever possible.

89. TEXTILE GOODS INDUSTRY

Because hand-pushed yarn buggies are used to move material in a yarn mill, and because yarn fly waste or lint (the scrap from yarn production) accumulates on the floor, the wheels of the yarn buggies must be kept clean and free to roll.

Employees should be trained in the safe use of compressed air, which is frequently used in clean-up procedures.

Fork-lift trucks, either electric- or propane-powered, are used throughout the carpet manufacturing and warehouse facilities. Proper maintenance and attention to safe refuelling, battery changing and so on are essential. Because fork-lift trucks are used where other personnel are working, various ways may be employed to avoid accidents (e.g., walkways reserved exclusively for workers, in which the trucks are prohibited); portable stop signs where employees are required to work in aisles with heavy fork-lift truck traffic; limiting the warehouse/shipping-dock areas to fork-lift truck operators and shipping personnel; and/or instituting a one-way traffic system.

Redesign of machines to minimize repetitive motions should help to reduce the incidence of repetitive-motion injuries. Encouraging workers to regularly practise simple hand and wrist exercises along with adequate work breaks and frequent changes in work tasks may also be helpful.

Musculoskeletal injuries from lifting and carrying may be reduced by the use of mechanical lifting devices, hand-trucks and rolling carts, and by stacking materials on platforms or tables and, where possible, keeping their bulk and weight to more easily manageable dimensions. Training in proper lifting techniques and muscle strengthening exercises can also be helpful, especially for workers returning after an episode of back pain.

A hearing conservation programme is advisable to avoid injury from the noise levels created in some mill operations. Sound-level surveys of the manufacturing equipment will identify those areas in which engineering controls are not sufficiently effective and in which workers may be required to wear hearing-protection equipment and have annual audiometric testing.

Contemporary standards of ventilation and exhaust of heat, lint and dust should be met by the mills.

● HAND-WOVEN AND HAND-TUFTED CARPETS

M.E. Radjabi*

All "oriental" carpets are hand woven. Many are made in family workplaces, with all the members of the household, often including very small children, working long days and often into the night on the loom. In some cases it is only a part-time occupation of the family, and in some areas the carpet weaving has been moved from the home into factories that are usually small.

Processes

The processes involved in the manufacture of a carpet are: yarn preparation, consisting of wool sorting, washing, spinning and dyeing; designing; and the actual weaving.

Yarn preparation

In some cases the yarn is received at the weaving place already spun and dyed. In others, the raw fibre, usually wool, is prepared, spun and dyed at the weaving place. After the sorting of the wool fibre into grades, usually done by women sitting on the floor, it is

* Adapted from 3rd edition, *Encyclopaedia of Occupational Health and Safety*.

washed and spun by hand. The dyeing is carried out in open vessels using mostly aniline-based or alizarine dyestuffs; natural dyestuffs are no longer being used.

Designing and weaving

In handicraft weaving (or tribal weaving, as it is sometimes called), the designs are traditional, and no new designs need to be made. In industrial establishments employing a number of workers, however, there may be a designer who first sketches the design of a new carpet on a sheet of paper and then transfers it in colours onto squared paper from which the weaver can ascertain the number and arrangement of the various knots to be woven into the carpet.

In most cases the loom consists of two horizontal wooden rollers supported on uprights, one about 10 to 30 cm above floor level and the other about 3 m above it. The warp yarn passes from the top roller to the bottom roller in a vertical plane. There is usually one weaver working at the loom, but for wide carpets there may be as many as six weavers working side by side. In about 50% of the cases, the weavers squat on the floor in front of the bottom roller. In other cases, they may have a narrow horizontal plank on which to sit, which is raised up to 4 m above the floor as weaving proceeds. The weaver has to tie short pieces of woollen or silk yarn into knots around pairs of warp threads and then move the thread by hand across the whole length of the carpet. Picks of weft are beaten up into the fibre of the carpet by means of a beater or hand comb. The tufts of yarn protruding from the fibre are trimmed or cut down by scissors.

As the carpet is woven, it is usually wound onto the lower roller, which increases its diameter. When the workers squat on the floor, the position of the lower roller prevents them from stretching their legs, and as the diameter of the rolled-up carpet increases, they have to sit further back but must still lean forward to reach the position in which they tie in the knots of yarn (see figure 89.15). This is avoided when the weavers sit or squat on the plank, which may be raised as high as 4 m above the floor, but there may still not be enough room for their legs, and they are often forced into uncomfortable positions. In some instances, however, the weaver is provided with a back rest and a pillow (in effect, a legless chair), which may be moved horizontally along the plank as the work progresses. Recently, improved types of elevated looms have been developed that allow the weaver to sit on a chair, with ample room for his or her legs.

Figure 89.15 • Squat loom.

In some parts of the Islamic Republic of Iran, the warp in the carpet loom is horizontal instead of being vertical, and the worker sits on the carpet itself whilst working; this makes the task even more difficult.

Hazards of Carpet Weaving

As a largely cottage industry, carpet weaving is fraught with the hazards imposed by impoverished homes with small, crowded rooms that have poor lighting and inadequate ventilation. The equipment and processes are passed along from generation to generation with little or no opportunity for the education and training that might spark a break with the traditional methods. Carpet weavers are subject to skeletal deformations, eyesight disorders and mechanical and toxic hazards.

Skeletal deformation

The squatting position that the weavers must occupy on the old type of loom, and the need for them to lean forward to reach the place into which they knot the yarn, may, over time, lead to some very serious skeletal problems. These are often compounded by the nutritional deficiencies associated with poverty. Especially among those who start as young children, the legs may become deformed (*genu valgum*), or a crippling arthritis of the knee may develop. The constriction of the pelvis that sometimes occurs in females may make it necessary for them to have a Cesarean delivery when giving birth. Lateral curvature of the spinal column (scoliosis) and lordosis are also common maladies.

Vision disorders

The constant close focus on the point of weaving or knotting may cause considerable eyestrain, particularly when the lighting is inadequate. It should be noted that electric lighting is not available in many home workplaces, and the work, which is often continued into the night, must be performed by the light of oil lamps. There have been cases of almost total blindness occurring after only about 12 years of employment at this work.

Hand and finger disorders

The constant tying of small knots and the threading of the weft yarn through the warp threads may result in swollen finger joints, arthritis and neuralgia causing permanent disabilities of the fingers.

Stress

The high degree of skill and constant attention to detail over long hours are potent psychosocial stressors, which may be compounded by exploitation and harsh discipline. Children are often "robbed of their childhood", while adults, who often lack the social contacts essential for emotional balance, may develop nervous illness manifested by trembling of the hands (which may hamper their work performance) and sometimes mental troubles.

Mechanical hazards

As no power machinery is used, there are practically no mechanical hazards. If the looms are not properly maintained, the wooden lever tensioning the warp may break and strike the weaver as it falls. This hazard may be avoided by using special thread tensioning gears.

Chemical hazards

The dyestuffs used, particularly if they contain potassium or sodium bichromate, may cause skin infections or dermatitis. There is also the risk from the use of ammonia, strong acids and alkalis. Lead pigments are sometimes used by designers, and there have been cases of lead poisoning due to their practice of smoothing the tip of the paintbrush by placing it between the lips; lead pigments should be replaced by non-toxic colours.

Biological hazards

There is a danger of anthrax infection from contaminated raw wool from areas where the bacillus is endemic. The appropriate governmental authority should ensure that such wool is properly sterilized before it is delivered to any workshops or factories.

Preventive Measures

The sorting of the raw material—wool, camel hair, goat hair and so on—should be done over a metal grid fitted with exhaust ventilation to draw any dust into a dust collector located outside the workplace.

The rooms in which the wool-washing and dyeing processes take place should be adequately ventilated, and the workers provided with rubber gloves and waterproof aprons. All waste liquors should be neutralized before being discharged into waterways or sewers.

Good lighting is required for the designing room and for weaving work. As noted above, inadequate light is a serious problem where there is no electricity and when the work is continued after sundown.

Perhaps the most important mechanical improvement would be mechanisms that raise the lower roller of the loom. This would obviate the necessity of weavers having to squat on the floor in an unhealthy and uncomfortable fashion and allow them to sit in a comfortable chair. Such an ergonomic improvement will not only improve the health of the workers but, once adopted, will increase their efficiency and productivity.

The workrooms should be kept clean and well ventilated, and properly boarded or covered floors substituted for earth floors. Adequate heating is required during cold weather. Manual manipulation of the warp places great strain on the fingers and may cause arthritis; wherever possible, hooked knives should be used for holding and weaving operations. Pre-employment and annual medical examinations of all workers are highly desirable.

Hand-tufted Carpets

The manufacture of carpets by the tying of knots of yarn by hand is a very slow process. The number of knots varies from 2 to 360 per square centimetre according to the quality of the carpet. A very large carpet with an intricate design may take over a year to make and involve the tying of hundreds of thousands of knots.

Hand tufting is an alternative method of rug manufacture. It uses a special kind of hand tool fitted with a needle through which the yarn is threaded. A sheet of coarse cotton cloth on which the design of the carpet has been traced is suspended vertically, and when the weaver places the tool against the cloth and presses a button, the needle is forced through the cloth and retracts, leaving a loop of yarn about 10 mm deep on the reverse side. The tool is moved horizontally about 2 or 3 mm, leaving a loop on the face of the cloth, and the trigger button is pressed again to form another loop on the reverse side. With acquired dexterity, as many as 30 loops on each side can be made in 1 minute. Depending on the design, the weaver has to stop from time to time to change the colour of yarn as called for in different parts of the pattern. When the looping operation has been finished, the carpet is taken down and placed reverse side up on the floor. A rubber solution is applied to the back and a covering or backing of stout jute canvas placed over it. The carpet is then placed face upwards and the protruding loops of yarn are trimmed by portable electric clippers. In some cases the design of the carpet is made by cutting or trimming the loops to varying depths.

Hazards in this type of carpet making are considerably less than in the manufacture of hand-knotted carpets. The operator usually sits on a plank in front of the canvas and has plenty of leg room. The plank is raised as the work proceeds. The weaver would be made more comfortable by provision of a backrest and a cushioned seat which could be moved horizontally along the plank as work proceeds. There is less visual strain, and no hand or finger movements that are likely to cause trouble.

The rubber solution used for this carpet usually contains a solvent which is both toxic and highly flammable. The backing process should be carried out in a separate workroom with good exhaust ventilation, at least two fire exits, and with no open flames or lights. Any electrical connections and equipment in this room should be certified as meeting sparkproof/flameproof standards. No more than a minimum amount of the flammable solution should be kept in this room, and appropriate fire extinguishers should be provided. A fire-resistant storage facility for the flammable solutions should not be situated inside any occupied building, but preferably in an open yard.

Legislation

In most countries, the general provisions of factory legislation cover the necessary standards required for the safety and health of workers in this industry. They may not be applicable, however, to family undertakings and/or home work, and they are difficult to enforce in the scattered small enterprises which, in the aggregate, employ many workers. The industry is notorious for the exploitation of its workers and for its use of child labour, often in defiance of existing regulations. A nascent worldwide trend (mid-1990s) among purchasers of hand-woven and tufted carpets to refrain from buying products produced by illegal or overly exploited workers will, it is hoped by many, eliminate such servitude.

● RESPIRATORY EFFECTS AND OTHER DISEASE PATTERNS IN THE TEXTILE INDUSTRY

E. Neil Schachter

For nearly 300 years, work in the textile industry has been recognized as hazardous. Ramazzini (1964), in the early 18th century, described a peculiar form of asthma among those who card flax and hemp. The "foul and poisonous dust" which he observed "makes the workmen cough incessantly and by degrees brings on asthmatic troubles". That such symptoms did in fact occur in the early textile industry was illustrated by Bouhuys and colleagues (1973) in physiological studies at Philipsburg Manor (a restoration project of life in the early Dutch colonies in North Tarrytown, New York, in the United States). While numerous authors throughout the 19th and early 20th centuries in Europe described the respiratory manifestations of work-related illness in textile mills with increasing frequency, the disease remained essentially unrecognized in the United States until preliminary studies in the middle of the 20th century under the direction of Richard Schilling (1981) indicated that, despite pronouncements to the contrary by both industry and government, characteristic byssinosis did occur (*American Textile Reporter* 1969; Britten, Bloomfield and Goddard 1933; DOL 1945). Many subsequent investigations have shown that textile workers around the world are affected by their work environment.

Historical Overview of Clinical Syndromes in the Textile Industry

Work in the textile industry has been associated with many symptoms involving the respiratory tract, but by far the most prevalent and the most characteristic are those of *byssinosis*. Many but not all vegetable fibres when processed to make textiles may cause byssinosis, as discussed in the chapter *Respiratory system*. The distin-

guishing feature of the clinical history in byssinosis is its relationship to the work week. The worker, typically after having worked a number of years in the industry, describes chest tightness beginning on Monday (or the first day of the work week) afternoons. The tightness subsides that evening and the worker is well for the remainder of the week, only to re-experience the symptoms on the following Monday. Such Monday dyspnoea may continue unchanged for years or may progress, with symptoms occurring on subsequent workdays, until chest tightness is present throughout the work week, and ultimately also while away from work on weekends and during vacation. When the symptoms become permanent, dyspnoea is described as effort dependent. At this stage a non-productive cough may be present. Monday symptoms are accompanied by across-shift decreases in lung function, which may be present on other workdays even in the absence of symptoms, but the physiological changes are not so marked (Bouhuys 1974; Schilling 1956). Baseline (Monday pre-shift) lung function deteriorates as the disease progresses. The characteristic respiratory and physiological changes seen in byssinotic workers have been standardized into a series of grades (see table 89.2) which currently form the basis of most clinical and epidemiological investigations. Symptoms other than chest tightness, particularly cough and bronchitis, are frequent among textile workers. These symptoms probably represent variants of the airway irritation brought on by dust inhalation.

There is unfortunately no simple test capable of establishing the diagnosis of byssinosis. The diagnosis must be made on the basis of worker symptoms and signs as well as on the physician's awareness of and familiarity with the clinical and industrial settings in which the disease is likely to occur. Lung function data, although not always specific, may be very helpful in establishing the diagnosis and in characterizing the degree of impairment.

In addition to classic byssinosis, textile workers are subject to several other symptom complexes; in general, these are associated with fever and not related to the initial day of the work week.

Mill fever (cotton fever, hemp fever) is associated with fever, cough, chills and rhinitis which occurs with the worker's first contact with the mill or with return after a prolonged absence. Chest tightness does not appear to be associated with this syndrome. The frequency of these findings among workers is quite variable, from as low as 5% of the workers (Schilling 1956) to a majority of those employed (Uragoda 1977; Doig 1949; Harris et al. 1972). Characteristically, symptoms subside after a few days despite continued exposure in the mill. Endotoxin in vegetable dust is thought to be a causative agent. Mill fever has been associated with an entity now commonly described in industries using organic materials, the organic dust toxic syndrome (ODTS), which is discussed in the chapter *Respiratory system*.

Table 89.2 • Grades of byssinosis.

Grade 0	Normal—no symptoms of chest tightness or cough
Grade 1/2	Occasional chest tightness or cough or both on first day of the working week
Grade 1	Chest tightness on every first day of the working week
Grade 2	Chest tightness on every first day and other days of the working week
Grade 3	Grade 2 symptoms, accompanied by evidence of permanent incapacity from reduced ventilatory capacity

Source: Bouhuys 1974.

"Weaver's cough" is primarily an asthmatic condition characteristically associated with fever; it occurs in both new and senior workers. The symptoms (unlike mill fever) can persist for months. The syndrome has been associated with materials used to treat the yarn—for example, tamarind seed powder (Murray, Dingwall-Fordyce and Lane 1957) and locust bean gum (Vigliani, Parmeggiani and Sassi 1954).

The third non-byssinotic syndrome associated with textile processing is "mattress maker's fever" (Neal, Schneiter and Caminita 1942). The name refers to the context in which the disease was described when it was characterized by an acute outbreak of fever and other constitutional symptoms, including gastrointestinal symptoms and retrosternal discomfort in workers who were using low-grade cotton. The outbreak was attributed to contamination of the cotton with Aerobacter cloacae.

In general, these febrile syndromes are thought to be clinically distinct from byssinosis. For example, in studies of 528 cotton workers by Schilling (1956), 38 had a history of mill fever. The prevalence of mill fever among workers with "classic" byssinosis was 10% (14/134), compared to 6% (24/394) among workers who did not have byssinosis. The differences were not statistically significant.

Chronic bronchitis, as defined by medical history, is very prevalent among textile workers, and in particular among non-smoking textile workers. This finding is not surprising since the most characteristic histological feature of chronic bronchitis is mucous gland hyperplasia (Edwards et al. 1975; Moran 1983). Chronic bronchitis symptomatology should be carefully distinguished from classic byssinosis symptoms, although byssinotic and bronchitic complaints frequently overlap and in textile workers are probably different pathophysiological manifestations of the same airway inflammation.

Pathology studies of textile workers are limited, but reports have shown a consistent pattern of disease involving the larger airways (Edwards et al. 1975; Rooke 1981a; Moran 1983) but no evidence suggestive of destruction of lung parenchyma (e.g., emphysema) (Moran 1983).

Clinical Course of Byssinosis

Acute versus chronic disease

Implicit in the grading system given in table 89.2 is a progression from acute "Monday symptoms" to chronic and essentially irreversible respiratory disease in workers with byssinosis. That such a progression occurs has been suggested in cross-sectional data beginning with the early study of Lancashire, United Kingdom, cotton workers, which found a shift toward higher byssinosis grades with increasing exposure (Schilling 1956). Similar findings have since been reported by others (Molyneux and Tombleson 1970). Moreover, this progression may begin relatively soon after employment (e.g., within the first few years) (Mustafa, Bos and Lakha 1979).

Cross-sectional data have also shown that other chronic respiratory symptoms and symptom complexes, such as wheeze or chronic bronchitis, are much more prevalent in older cotton textile workers than in similar control populations (Bouhuys et al. 1977; Bouhuys, Beck and Schoenberg 1979). In all cases the cotton textile workers have displayed more chronic bronchitis than the controls, even when adjusting for sex and smoking status. Grade 3 byssinosis indicates that, in addition to symptoms, textile workers demonstrate changes in respiratory function. The progression from early byssinosis (grade 1) to late byssinosis (grade 3) is suggested by the association of lung function loss with the higher grades of byssinosis in cross-sectional studies of textile workers. Several of these cross-sectional studies have given support to the concept that across-shift changes in lung function (which correlate with the acute findings of chest tightness) are related to chronic irreversible changes.

Underlying the association between acute and chronic disease in textile workers is a dose-response relationship in acute symptoms, which was first documented by Roach and Schilling in a study reported in 1960. These authors found a strong linear relation between biological response and total dust concentrations in the workplace. Based on their findings they recommended 1 mg/m^3 gross dust as a reasonably safe level of exposure. This finding was later adopted by the ACGIH and was, until the late 1970s, the value used as the threshold limit value (TLV) for cotton dust in the United States. Subsequent observations demonstrated that the fine dust fraction ($<7 \text{ μm}$) accounted for practically all of the prevalence of byssinosis (Molyneux and Tombleson 1970; Mckerrow and Schilling 1961; McKerrow et al. 1962; Wood and Roach 1964). A 1973 study by Merchant and colleagues of respiratory symptoms and lung function in 1,260 cotton, 803 blend (cotton-synthetic) and 904 synthetic-wool workers was undertaken in 22 textile manufacturing plants in North Carolina (United States). The study confirmed the linear association between byssinosis prevalence (as well as decrements in lung function) and concentrations of lint-free dust.

The validation of changes in respiratory function suggested by cross-sectional studies has come from a number of longitudinal investigations which complement and extend the results of the earlier studies. These studies have highlighted the accelerated loss of lung function in cotton textile workers as well as the high incidence of new symptoms.

In a series of investigations involving several thousand mill workers examined in the late 1960s over a 5-year span of time, Fox and colleagues (1973a; 1973b) found an increase in byssinosis rates which correlated with years of exposure, as well as a sevenfold greater annual decrease in forced expired volume in 1 second (FEV_1) (as a per cent of predicted) when compared to controls.

A unique study of chronic lung disease in textile workers was initiated in the early 1970s by the late Arend Bouhuys (Bouhuys et al. 1977). The study was novel because it included both active and retired workers. These textile workers from Columbia, South Carolina, in the United States, worked in one of four local mills. The selection of the cohort was described in the original cross-sectional analysis. The original group of workers consisted of 692 individuals, but the analysis was restricted to 646 whites aged 45 years or older as of 1973. These individuals had worked an average of 35 years in the mills. The control group for the cross-sectional results consisted of whites aged 45 years and older from three communities studied cross-sectionally: Ansonia and Lebanon, Connecticut, and Winnsboro, South Carolina. In spite of geographic, socio-economic and other differences, the community residents did not differ in lung function from textile workers who held the least dusty jobs. Since no differences in lung function or respiratory symptoms were noted between the three communities, only Lebanon, Connecticut, which was studied in 1972 and 1978, was used as the control for the longitudinal study of textile workers studied in 1973 and in 1979 (Beck, Doyle and Schachter 1981; Beck, Doyle and Schachter 1982).

Both symptoms and lung function have been extensively reviewed. In the prospective study it was determined that the incidence rates for seven respiratory symptoms or symptom complexes (including byssinosis) were higher in textile workers than in controls, even when controlling for smoking (Beck, Maunder and Schachter 1984). When textile workers were separated into active and retired workers, it was noted that those workers retiring during the course of the study had the highest incidence rates of symptoms. These findings suggested that not only were active workers at risk for impairing respiratory symptoms but retired workers, presumably because of their irreversible lung damage, were at continuing risk.

In this cohort, loss of lung function was measured over a 6-year period. The mean decline for male and female textile workers (42 ml/yr and 30 ml/yr, respectively) was significantly greater than the decline in male and female controls (27 ml/yr and 15 ml/yr). When classified by smoking status, the cotton textile workers in general still had greater losses in FEV_1 than did the controls.

Many authors have previously raised the potential confounding issue of cigarette smoking. Because many textile workers are cigarette smokers, it has been claimed that the chronic lung disease associated with exposure to textile dust can in large part be attributed to cigarette smoking. Using the Columbia textile-worker population, this question was answered in two ways. One study by Beck, Maunder and Schachter (1984) used a two-way analysis of variance for all lung function measurements and demonstrated that the effects of cotton dust and smoking on lung function were additive—that is, the amount of lung function loss due to one factor (smoking or cotton dust exposure) was not changed by the presence or absence of the other factor. For FVC and FEV_1 the effects were similar in magnitude (average smoking history 56 pack-years, average mill exposure 35 years). In a related study, Schachter et al. (1989) demonstrated that using a parameter which described the shape of the maximum expiratory flow volume curve, angle beta, distinct patterns of lung function abnormalities could be shown for a smoking effect and for a cotton effect, similar to conclusions reached by Merchant earlier.

Mortality

Studies of cotton-dust exposure on mortality have not consistently demonstrated an effect. Review of experience in the late 19th and early 20th centuries in the United Kingdom suggested an excess of cardiovascular mortality in older textile workers (Schilling and Goodman 1951). By contrast, review of the experience in New England mill towns from late in the 19th century failed to demonstrate excess mortality (Arlidge 1892). Similar negative findings were observed by Henderson and Enterline (1973) in a study of workers who had been employed in Georgia mills from 1938 to 1951. By contrast, a study by Dubrow and Gute (1988) of male textile workers in Rhode Island who died during the period 1968 to 1978, showed a significant increase in proportionate mortality rate (PMR) for non-malignant respiratory disease. The elevations in PMR were consistent with increased dust exposure: carding, lapping and combing operatives had higher PMRs than did other workers in the textile industry. An interesting finding of this and other studies (Dubrow and Gute 1988; Merchant and Ortmeyer 1981) is the low mortality from lung cancer among these workers, a finding that has been used to argue that smoking is not a major cause of mortality in these groups.

Observations from a cohort in South Carolina suggest that chronic lung disease is indeed a major cause (or predisposing factor) for mortality, since among those workers aged 45 to 64 who died during a 6-year follow-up, lung function measured as residual FEV_1 (observed-to-predicted) showed marked impairment at the initial study (mean $RFEV_1 = -0.9l$) in male non-smokers who died during the 6-year follow-up (Beck et al. 1981). It may well be that the effect of mill exposure on mortality has been obscured by a selection effect (healthy worker effect). Finally, in terms of mortality, Rooke (1981b) estimated that of the average 121 deaths he observed annually among disabled workers, 39 had died as a result of byssinosis.

Increased Control, Decreased Disease

Recent surveys from the United Kingdom and the United States suggest that the prevalence as well as the pattern of lung disease seen in textile workers has been affected by the implementation of stricter air-quality standards in the mills of these countries. In 1996, Fishwick and his colleagues, for example, describe a cross-sectional study of 1,057 textile spinning operatives in 11 spinning mills in Lancashire. Ninety-seven per cent of the workforce was tested; the majority (713) worked with cotton and the remainder with synthetic fibre). Byssinosis was documented in only 3.5% of the operatives and chronic bronchitis in 5.3%. FEV_1, however, was reduced in workers exposed to high dust concentrations. These prevalences are much reduced from those reported in earlier surveys of these mills. This low prevalence of byssinosis and related bronchitis appears to follow the trend of decreasing dust levels in the United Kingdom. Both smoking habits and cotton dust exposures contributed to the lung function loss in this cohort.

In the United States, results of a 5-year prospective study of workers in 9 mills (6 cotton and 3 synthetic) was conducted between 1982 and 1987 by Glindmeyer and colleagues (1991; 1994), where 1,817 mill workers who were employed exclusively in cotton yarn manufacturing, slashing and weaving or in synthetics were studied. Overall, fewer than 2% of these workers were found to have byssinotic complaints. Nevertheless, workers in yarn manufacturing exhibited a greater annual loss of lung function than workers in slashing and weaving. The yarn workers exhibited dose-related lung function loss which was also associated with the grade of cotton used. These mills were in compliance with then current OSHA standards, and the mean airborne lint-free respirable cotton dust concentrations averaged over 8 hours were 196 $\mu g/m^3$ in yarn manufacture and 455 $\mu g/m^3$ in slashing and weaving. The authors (1994) related across-shift changes (the objective lung function equivalent of byssinotic symptoms) with longitudinal declines in lung function. Across-shift changes were found to be significant predictors of longitudinal changes.

While textile manufacture in the developed world appears now to be associated with less prevalent and less severe disease, this is not the case for developing countries. High prevalences of byssinosis can still be found worldwide, particularly where governmental standards are lax or non-existent. In his recent literature survey, Parikh (1992) noted byssinosis prevalences well above 20% in such countries as India, Cameroon, Ethiopia, Sudan and Egypt. In a study by Zuskin et al. (1991), 66 cotton textile workers were followed in a mill in Croatia where mean respirable dust concentrations remained at 1.0 mg/m^3. Byssinosis prevalences doubled, and annual declines in lung function were nearly twice those estimated from prediction equations for healthy non-smokers.

Non-Respiratory Disorders Associated with Work in the Textile Industry

In addition to the well-characterized respiratory syndromes which can affect textile workers, there are a number of risks that have been associated with working conditions and hazardous products in this industry.

Oncongenesis has been associated with work in the textile industry. A number of early studies indicate a high incidence of colorectal cancer among workers in synthetic textile mills (Vobecky et al. 1979; Vobecky, Devroede and Caro 1984). A retrospective study of synthetic textile mills by Goldberg and Theriault (1994a) suggested an association with length of employment in the polypropylene and cellulose triacetate extrusion units. Other associations with neoplastic diseases were noted by these authors but were felt to be "not persuasive" (1994b).

Exposure to azo dyes have been associated with bladder cancer in numerous industries. Siemiatycki and colleagues (1994) found a weak association between bladder cancer and work with acrylic fibres and polyethylene. In particular, workers who dye these textiles were found to be at an increased risk. Long-term workers in this industry presented a 10-fold excess risk (marginal statistical significance) for bladder cancer. Similar findings have been reported by other authors, although negative studies are also noted (Anthony and Thomas 1970; Steenland, Burnett and Osorio 1987; Silverman et al. 1989).

Repetitive-motion trauma is a recognized hazard in the textile industry related to high-speed manufacturing equipment (Thomas 1991). A description of carpal tunnel syndrome (Forst and Hryhorczuk 1988) in a seamstress working with an electrical sewing machine illustrates the pathogenesis of such disorders. A review of hand injuries referred to the Regional Plastic Surgery Unit treating Yorkshire wool workers between 1965 and 1984 revealed that while there was a fivefold decrease in employment in this industry, the yearly incidence of hand injuries remained constant, indicating increased risk in this population (Myles and Roberts 1985).

Hepatic toxicity in textile workers has been reported by Redlich and colleagues (1988) as a result of exposure to the solvent dimethylformanide in a fabric-coating factory. This toxicity was recognized in the context of an "outbreak" of liver disease in a New Haven, Connecticut, factory that produces polyurethane-coated fabrics.

Carbon disulphide (CS_2) is an organic compound used in the preparation of synthetic textiles which has been associated with increased mortality from ischemic heart disease (Hernberg, Partanen and Nordman 1970; Sweetnam, Taylor and Elwood 1986). This may relate to its effects on blood lipids and diastolic blood pressure (Eyeland et al. 1992). Additionally, this agent has been associated with peripheral neurotoxicity, injury to sensory organs and disturbances in hormonal and reproductive function. It is generally believed that such toxicity results from long-term exposure to concentrations in excess of 10 to 20 ppm (Riihimaki et al. 1992).

Allergic responses to reactive dyes including eczema, uticaria and asthma have been reported in textile-dyeing workers (Estlander 1988; Sadhro, Duhra and Foulds 1989; Seidenari, Mauzini and Danese 1991).

Infertility in men and women has been described as a result of exposures in the textile industry (Rachootin and Olsen 1983; Buiatti et al. 1984).

References

American Textile Reporter. 1969. (10 July).

Anthony, HM and GM Thomas. 1970. Tumors of the urinary bladder. *J Natl Cancer Inst* 45:879–95.

Arlidge, JT. 1892. *The Hygiene, Diseases and Mortality of Occupations.* London: Percival and Co.

Beck, GJ, CA Doyle, and EN Schachter. 1981. Smoking and lung function. *Am Rev Resp Dis* 123:149–155.

—. 1982. A longitudinal study of respiratory health in a rural community. *Am Rev Resp Dis* 125:375–381.

Beck, GJ, LR Maunder, and EN Schachter. 1984. Cotton dust and smoking effects on lung function in cotton textile workers. *Am J Epidemiol* 119:33–43.

Beck, GJ, EN Schachter, L Maunder, and A Bouhuys. 1981. The relation of lung function to subsequent employment and mortality in cotton textile workers. *Chest* suppl 79:26S–29S.

Bouhuys, A. 1974. *Breathing.* New York: Grune & Stratton.

Bouhuys, A, GJ Beck, and J Schoenberg. 1979. Epidemiology of environmental lung disease. *Yale J Biol Med* 52:191–210.

Bouhuys, A, CA Mitchell, RSF Schilling, and E Zuskin. 1973. A physiological study of byssinosis in colonial America. *Trans New York Acad Sciences* 35:537–546.

Bouhuys, A, JB Schoenberg, GJ Beck, and RSF Schilling. 1977. Epidemiology of chronic lung disease in a cotton mill community. *Lung* 154:167–186.

Britten, RH, JJ Bloomfield, and JC Goddard. 1933. *Health of Workers in Textile Plants.* Bulletin No. 207. Washington, DC: US Public Health Service.

Buiatti, E, A Barchielli, M Geddes, L Natasi, D Kriebel, M Franchini, and G Scarselli. 1984. Risk factors in male infertility. *Arch Environ Health* 39:266–270.

Doig, AT. 1949. Other lung diseases due to dust. *Postgrad Med J* 25:639–649.

Department of Labor (DOL). 1945. *Special Bulletin* No. 18. Washington, DC: DOL, Labor Standards Division.

Dubrow, R and DM Gute. 1988. Cause-specific mortality among male textile workers in Rhode Island. *Am J Ind Med* 13: 439–454.

Edwards, C, J Macartney, G Rooke, and F Ward. 1975. The pathology of the lung in byssinotics. *Thorax* 30:612–623.

Estlander, T. 1988. Allergic dermatoses and respiratory diseases from reactive dyes. *Contact Dermat* 18:290–297.

Eyeland, GM, GA Burkhart, TM Schnorr, FW Hornung, JM Fajen, and ST Lee. 1992. Effects of exposure to carbon disulphide on low density lipoprotein cholesterol concentration and diastolic blood pressure. *Brit J Ind Med* 49:287–293.

Fishwick, D, AM Fletcher, AC Pickering, R McNiven, and EB Faragher. 1996. Lung function in Lancashire cotton and man-made fibre spinning mill operatives. *Occup Environ Med* 53:46–50.

Forst, L and D Hryhorczuk. 1988. Occupational tarsal tunnel syndrome. *Brit J Ind Med* 45:277–278.

Fox, AJ, JBL Tombleson, A Watt, and AG Wilkie. 1973a. A survey of respiratory disease in cotton operatives: Part I. Symptoms and ventilation test results. *Brit J Ind Med* 30:42-47.

—. 1973b. A survey of respiratory disease in cotton operatives: Part II. Symptoms, dust estimation, and the effect of smoking habit. *Brit J Ind Med* 30:48-53.

Glindmeyer, HW, JJ Lefante, RN Jones, RJ Rando, HMA Kader, and H Weill. 1991. Exposure-related declines in the lung function of cotton textile workers. *Am Rev Respir Dis* 144:675–683.

Glindmeyer, HW, JJ Lefante, RN Jones, RJ Rando, and H Weill. 1994. Cotton dust and across-shift change in FEV$_1$ *Am J Respir Crit Care Med* 149:584–590.

Goldberg, MS and G Theriault. 1994a. Retrospective cohort study of workers of a synthetic textiles plant in Quebec II. *Am J Ind Med* 25:909–922.

—. 1994b. Retrospective cohort study of workers of a synthetic textiles plant in Quebec I. *Am J Ind Med* 25:889–907.

Grund, N. 1995. Environmental considerations for textile printing products. *Journal of the Society of Dyers and Colourists* 111 (1/2):7–10.

Harris, TR, JA Merchant, KH Kilburn, and JD Hamilton. 1972. Byssinosis and respiratory diseases in cotton mill workers. *J Occup Med* 14: 199–206.

Henderson, V and PE Enterline. 1973. An unusual mortality experience in cotton textile workers. *J Occup Med* 15: 717–719.

Hernberg, S, T Partanen, and CH Nordman. 1970. Coronary heart disease among workers exposed to carbon disulphide. *Brit J Ind Med* 27:313–325.

McKerrow, CB and RSF Schilling. 1961. A pilot enquiry into byssinosis in two cotton mills in the United States. *JAMA* 177:850–853.

McKerrow, CB, SA Roach, JC Gilson, and RSF Schilling. 1962. The size of cotton dust particles causing byssinosis: An environmental and physiological study. *Brit J Ind Med* 19:1–8.

Merchant, JA and C Ortmeyer. 1981. Mortality of employees of two cotton mills in North Carolina. *Chest* suppl 79: 6S–11S.

Merchant, JA, JC Lumsdun, KH Kilburn, WM O'Fallon, JR Ujda, VH Germino, and JD Hamilton. 1973. Dose-response studies in cotton textile workers. *J Occup Med* 15:222–230.

Ministry of International Trade and Industry (Japan). 1996. *Asia-Pacific Textile and Clothing Industry Form, June 3-4, 1996.* Tokyo: Ministry of International Trade and Industry.

Molyneux, MKB and JBL Tombleson. 1970. An epidemiological study of respiratory symptoms in Lancashire mills, 1963–1966. *Brit J Ind Med* 27:225–234.

Moran, TJ. 1983. Emphysema and other chronic lung disease in textile workers: An 18-year autopsy study. *Arch Environ Health* 38:267–276.

Murray, R, J Dingwall-Fordyce, and RE Lane. 1957. An outbreak of weaver's cough associated with tamarind seed powder. *Brit J Ind Med* 14:105–110.

Mustafa, KY, W Bos, and AS Lakha. 1979. Byssinosis in Tanzanian textile workers. *Lung* 157:39–44.

Myles, SM and AH Roberts. 1985. Hand injuries in the textile industry. *J Hand Surg* 10:293–296.

Neal, PA, R Schneiter, and BH Caminita. 1942. Report on acute illness among rural mattress makers using low grade, stained cotton. *JAMA* 119:1074–1082.

Occupational Safety and Health Administration (OSHA). 1985. Final Rule for Occupational Exposure to Cotton Dust. *Federal Register* 50, 51120–51179 (13 Dec. 1985). 29 CFR 1910.1043. Washington, DC: OSHA.

Parikh, JR. 1992. Byssinosis in developing countries. *Brit J Ind Med* 49:217–219.

Rachootin, P and J Olsen. 1983. The risk of infertility and delayed conception associated with exposures in the Danish workplace. *J Occup Med* 25:394–402.

Ramazzini, B. 1964. *Diseases of Workers* [*De morbis artificum*, 1713], translated by WC Wright. New York: Hafner Publishing Co.

Redlich, CA, WS Beckett, J Sparer, KW Barwick, CA Riely, H Miller, SL Sigal, SL Shalat, and MR Cullen. 1988. Liver disease associated with occupational exposure to the solvent dimethylformamide. *Ann Int Med* 108:680–686.

Riihimaki, V, H Kivisto, K Peltonen, E Helpio, and A Aitio. 1992. Assessment of exposures to carbon disulfide in viscose production workers from urinary 2-thiothiazolidine-4-carboxylic acid determinations. *Am J Ind Med* 22:85–97.

Roach, SA and RSF Schilling. 1960. A clinical and environmental study of byssinosis in the Lancashire cotton industry. *Brit J Ind Med* 17:1–9.

Rooke, GB. 1981a. The pathology of byssinosis. *Chest* suppl 79:67S–71S.

—. 1981b. Compensation for byssinosis in Great Britain. *Chest* suppl 79:124S–127S.

Sadhro, S, P Duhra, and IS Foulds. 1989. Occupational dermatitis from Synocril Red 3b liquid (CI Basic Red 22). *Contact Dermat* 21:316–320.

Schachter, EN, MC Kapp, GJ Beck, LR Maunder, and TJ Witek. 1989. Smoking and cotton dust effects in cotton textile workers. *Chest* 95: 997–1003.

Schilling, RSF. 1956. Byssinosis in cotton and other textile workers. *Lancet* 1:261–267, 319–324.

—. 1981. Worldwide problems of byssinosis. *Chest* suppl 79:3S–5S.

Schilling, RSF and N Goodman. 1951. Cardiovascular disease in cotton workers. *Brit J Ind Med* 8:77–87.

Seidenari, S, BM Mauzini, and P Danese. 1991. Contact sensitization to textile dyes: Description of 100 subjects. *Contact Dermat* 24:253–258.

Siemiatycki, J, R Dewar, L Nadon, and M Gerin. 1994. Occupational risk factors for bladder cancer. *Am J Epidemiol* 140:1061–1080.

Silverman, DJ, LI Levin, RN Hoover, and P Hartge. 1989. Occupational risks of bladder cancer in the United States. I. White men. *J Natl Cancer Inst* 81:1472–1480.

Steenland, K, C Burnett, and AM Osorio. 1987. A case control study of bladder cancer using city directories as a source of occupational data. *Am J Epidemiol* 126:247–257.

Sweetnam, PM, SWS Taylor, and PC Elwood. 1986. Exposure to carbon disulphide and ischemic heart disease in a viscose rayon factory. *Brit J Ind Med* 44:220–227.

Thomas, RE. 1991. Report on a multidisciplinary conference on control and prevention of cumulative trauma disorders (CDT) or repetitive motion trauma (RMT) in the textile, apparel and fiber industries. *Am Ind Hyg Assoc J* 52:A562.

Uragoda, CG. 1977. An investigation into the health of kapok workers. *Brit J Ind Med* 34:181–185.

Vigliani, EC, L Parmeggiani, and C Sassi. 1954. Studio de un epidemio di bronchite asmatica fra gli operi di una tessiture di cotone. *Med Lau* 45:349–378.

Vobecky, J, G Devroede, and J Caro. 1984. Risk of large-bowel cancer in synthetic fiber manufacture. *Cancer* 54:2537–2542.

Vobecky, J, G Devroede, J La Caille, and A Waiter. 1979. An occupational group with a high risk of large bowel cancer. *Gastroenterology* 76:657.

Wood, CH and SA Roach. 1964. Dust in cardrooms: A continuing problem in the cotton spinning industry. *Brit J Ind Med* 21:180–186.

Zuskin, E, D Ivankovic, EN Schachter, and TJ Witek. 1991. A ten year follow-up study of cotton textile workers. *Am Rev Respir Dis* 143:301–305.

Other relevant readings

Bouhuys, A, A Barbero, SE Lindell, SA Roach, and RSF Schilling. 1967. Byssinosis in hemp workers. *Arch Environ Health* 14:533–544.

Bouhuys, A, JV Duyn, and HJV Lennep. 1961. Byssinosis in flax workers. *Arch Environ Health* 3:499–509.

Bouhuys, A, LJ Heaply, RSF Schilling, and JW Welborn. 1967. Byssinosis in the United States. *N Engl J Med* 277:170–175.

Bouhuys, A, SE Lindell, SA Roach, and RSF Schilling. 1967. Byssinosis in hemp workers. *Arch Environ Health* 14:533–544.

Castellan, RM, SA Olenchock, KB Kingsley, and JL Hankinson. 1987. Inhaled endotoxin and decreased spirometric values: An exposure-response relationship for cotton dust. *N Engl J Med* 317:605.

Chwat, M and R Mordish. 1963. Byssinosis investigations into cotton plants in Israel. *14th International Conference in Occupational Health*. International Congress Series No 62. Amsterdam: Excerpta Medica.

Collis, EL. 1909. *Report of the Inspector of Factory Workshops*. London: Her Majesty's Stationery Office.

Corn, JK. 1981. Byssinosis—An historical perspective. *Am J Ind Med* 2:331–351.

Department of Employment. 1974. *Safety Recommendations—Joint Standing Committee on Safety in the Cotton and Allied Fibres Weaving Industry*. London: Her Majesty's Stationery Office.

Gandevia, B and J Milne. 1965. Ventilatory capacity changes on exposure to cotton dust and their relevance to byssinosis in Australia. *Brit J Ind Med* 22:295–304.

Gilson, JC, H Stott, BEC Hopwood, SA Roach, CB McKerrow, and RSF Schilling. 1962. Byssinosis: The acute effect on ventilatory capacity of dusts in cotton ginneries, cotton, sisal and jute mills. *Brit J Ind Med* 18:9–18.

Glindmeyer, HW, JJ Lefante, RN Jones, RJ Rando, HNA Kader, and H Weill. 1991. Exposure-related declines in lung function of cotton textile workers: Relationship to current workplace standards. *Am Rev Respir Dis* 144:675.

Grandjean, E. 1978. Management of the workplace SO_2. *Prevent Med* 23:372–378.

Greenhow, EH. 1860. *Third Report of the Medical Officer of the Privy Council, Sir John Simon*, Appendix 6. London: Her Majesty's Stationery Office.

Grund, N. 1995. Environmental considerations for textile printing products. *Journal of the Society of Dyers and Colourists* III(1/2):7-10.

Health and Safety Executive. 1975. *Safety in the Cotton and Allied Fibres Industry: Spinning, Winding, and Sizing*.

Health and Safety at Work Series No. 49C. London: Her Majesty's Stationery Office.

—. 1980. *Opening Processes: Cotton and Allied Fibres*. Health and Safety Series Booklet HS(G). London: Her Majesty's Stationery Office.

Heyden, S and P Pratt. 1980. Exposure to cotton dust and respiratory disease. Textile workers, brown lung and lung cancer. *JAMA* 244(16):1797–1798.

Hill, AB. 1930. *Sickness among Operatives in Lancashire Cotton Spinning Mills*. Industrial Health Research Board Report No. 59. London: Her Majesty's Stationery Office.

Hussman, T. 1996. Health effects of indoor-air microorganisms. *Scand J Work Environ Health* 22:5–13.

Kavaressi, N. 1976. Ergonomics in traditional Iranian industries. *J Hum Ergol* (Tokyo) 5:145–147.

Kay, JP. 1831. Observations and experiments concerning molecular irritation of the lungs as one source of tubercular consumption; and on spinner's phthisis. *North Engl Med Surg J* 1:348–363.

Leach, J. 1863. Surat cotton, as it bodily affects operatives in cotton mills. *Lancet* 2:648–649.

Lu, P, DC Christiani, T Ye, N Shi, Z Gong, H Pai, W Zhang, J Huang, and M Liu. 1987. The study of byssinosis in China. *Am J Ind Med* 12:743–753.

Manuaba, A. 1976. Problems of ergonomics in Bali, Indonesia. *J Hum Ergol* (Tokyo) 5:117–131.

Marks, R and ATC Robinson. 1976. *Principles of Weaving*. Manchester: Textile Institute.

Morgan, PGM and SG Ong. 1981. First report of byssinosis in Hong Kong. *Brit J Ind Med* 38:290–292.

Mustafa, KY, AS Lakha, MH Milla, and U Dalioma. 1978. Byssinosis, respiratory symptoms and spirometric lung function tests in Tanzanian sisal workers. *Brit J Ind Med* 35:123–128.

Perkins, HH Jr. and SA Olenchock. 1995. Washing cotton by batch processes to control dust and endotoxin. *Ann Agric Environ Med* 2:45.

Proust, AA. 1877. *Traité d'hygiène publique et privée*. Paris: Masson.

Rylander, R, HR Imbus, and MW Suh. 1979. Bacterial contamination of cotton as an indicator of respiratory effects among card room workers. *Brit J Ind Med* 36(4):299–304.

Schrag, PE and AD Gullett. 1970. Byssinosis in cotton textile mills. *Am Rev Repir Dis* 101:497–503.

Spencer, DJ. 1983. *Knitting Technology*. Oxford: Pergamon Press Ltd.

Takam, J and B Nemery. 1988. Byssinosis in a textile factory in Cameroon: A preliminary study. *Brit J Ind Med* 45: 803–809.

Wakelyn, PJ, GA Greenblatt, DF Brown, and VW Tripp. 1976. Chemical properties of cotton dust. *Am Ind Hyg Assoc J* 37(1):22–31.

Wakelyn, PJ, RR Jacobs, and IW Kirk (eds.). 1986. *Washed Cotton: Washing Techniques, Processing Characteristics, and Health Effects*. New Orleans, LA: USDA.

AEROSPACE MANUFACTURE AND MAINTENANCE

90

Chapter Editor
Buck Cameron

Contents

THE AEROSPACE INDUSTRY

Buck Cameron

General Profile

History and future trends

When Wilbur and Orville Wright made their first successful flight in 1903, aircraft manufacturing was a craft practised in the small shops of experimenters and adventurers. The small but dramatic contributions made by military aircraft during the First World War helped to take manufacturing out of the workshop and into mass production. Second-generation aircraft helped post-war operators to make inroads into the commercial sphere, particularly as carriers of mail and express cargo. Airliners, however, remained unpressurized, poorly heated and unable to fly above the weather. Despite these drawbacks, passenger travel increased by 600% from 1936 to 1941, but was still a luxury that relatively few experienced. The dramatic advances in aeronautical technology and the concomitant use of air power during the Second World War fostered the explosive growth of aircraft manufacturing capacity that survived the war in the United States, the United Kingdom and the Soviet Union. Since the Second World War, tactical and strategic missiles, reconnaissance and navigational satellites and piloted aircraft have taken on ever greater military significance. Satellite communication, geo-monitoring and weather-tracking technology have become of increasing commercial importance. The introduction of turbojet-powered civilian aircraft in the late 1950s made air travel faster and more comfortable and began a dramatic growth in commercial air travel. By 1993 over 1.25 trillion passenger miles were flown worldwide annually. This figure is projected to nearly triple by 2013.

Employment patterns

Employment in aerospace industries is highly cyclical. Direct aerospace employment in the European Union, North America and Japan peaked at 1,770,000 in 1989 before decreasing to 1,300,000 in 1995, with much of the employment loss occurring in the United States and the United Kingdom. The large aerospace industry in the Confederation of Independent States has been significantly disrupted subsequent to the break-up of the Soviet Union. Small but rapidly growing manufacturing capability exists in India and China. Manufacture of intercontinental and space missiles and long-range bombers has been largely restricted to the United States and the former Soviet Union, with France having developed commercial space launch capabilities. Shorter-range strategic missiles, tactical missiles and bombers, commercial rockets and fighter aircraft are more widely manufactured. Large commercial aircraft (those with 100 or greater seat capacity) are built by, or in cooperation with, manufacturers based in the United States and Europe. The manufacture of regional aircraft (less than 100 seat capacity) and business jets is more dispersed. The manufacture of aircraft for private pilots, based primarily in the United States, decreased from nearly 18,000 aircraft in 1978 to fewer than 1,000 in 1992 before rebounding.

Employment is divided in roughly equal measures among the manufacture of military aircraft, commercial aircraft, missiles and space vehicles and related equipment. Within individual enterprises, engineering, manufacturing and administrative positions each account for approximately one-third of the employed population. Males account for about 80% of the aerospace engineering and production workforce, with the overwhelming majority of highly skilled craftspeople, engineers and production managers being male.

Industry divisions

The markedly different needs and practices of governmental and civilian customers typically result in the segmentation of aerospace manufacturers into defense and commercial companies, or divisions of larger corporations. Airframes, engines (also called powerplants) and avionics (electronic navigational, communication and flight control equipment) are generally supplied by separate manufacturers. Engines and avionics each may account for one-quarter of the final cost of an airliner. Aerospace manufacturing requires the design, fabrication and assembly, inspection and testing of a vast array of components. Manufacturers have formed interconnected arrays of subcontractors and external and internal suppliers of components to meet their needs. Economic, technological, marketing and political demands have led to an increasing globalization of the manufacture of aircraft components and subassemblies.

Manufacturing Materials, Facilities and Processes

Materials

Airframes were originally made from wood and fabric, and then evolved to metal structural components. Aluminium alloys have been widely used due to their strength and light weight. Alloys of beryllium, titanium and magnesium are also used, particularly in high-performance aircraft. Advanced composite materials (arrays of fibre embedded in plastic matrices) are a family of strong and durable replacements for metallic components. Composite materials offer equal or greater strength, lower weight and greater heat resistance than currently used metals and have the additional advantage in military aircraft of significantly reducing the radar profile of the airframe. Epoxy resin systems are the most commonly used composites in aerospace, representing about 65% of materials used. Polyimide resin systems are used where high temperature resistance is required. Other resin systems used include phenolics, polyesters and silicones. Aliphatic amines are often used as curing agents. Supporting fibres include graphite, Kevlar and fibreglass. Stabilizers, catalysts, accelerators, antioxidants and plasticizers act as accessories to produce a desired consistency. Additional resin systems include saturated and unsaturated polyesters, polyurethanes and vinyl, acrylic, urea and fluorine-containing polymers.

Primer, lacquer and enamel paints protect vulnerable surfaces from extreme temperatures and corrosive conditions. The most common primer paint is composed of synthetic resins pigmented with zinc chromate and extended pigment. It dries very rapidly, improves adhesion of top coats and prevents corrosion of aluminium, steel and their alloys. Enamels and lacquers are applied to primed surfaces as exterior protective coatings and finishes and for colour purposes. Aircraft enamels are made of drying oils, natural and synthetic resins, pigments and appropriate solvents. Depending on their application, lacquers may contain resins, plasticizers, cellulose esters, zinc chromate, pigments, extenders and appropriate solvents. Rubber mixtures find common use in paints, fuel cell lining materials, lubricants and preservatives, engine mountings, protective clothing, hoses, gaskets and seals. Natural and synthetic oils are used to cool, lubricate and reduce friction in engines, hydraulic systems and machine tools. Aviation gasoline and jet fuel are derived from petroleum-based hydrocarbons. High-energy liquid and solid fuels have space flight applications and contain materials with inherently hazardous physical and chemical properties; such materials include liquid oxygen, hydrazine, peroxides and fluorine.

Many materials are used in the manufacturing process which do not become part of the final airframe. Manufacturers may have tens of thousands of individual products approved for use, although far fewer are in use at any time. A large quantity and variety of solvents are used, with environmentally damaging variants such as methyl ethyl ketone and freon being replaced with more environmentally friendly solvents. Chromium- and nickel-containing steel alloys are used in tooling, and cobalt- and tungsten carbide-containing hard-metal bits are used in cutting tools. Lead, formerly used in metal-forming processes, is now rarely used, having been replaced with kirksite.

In total, the aerospace industry uses more than 5,000 chemicals and mixtures of chemical compounds, most with multiple suppliers, and with many compounds containing between five and ten ingredients. The exact composition of some products is proprietary, or a trade secret, adding to the complexity of this heterogeneous group.

Facilities and manufacturing processes

Airframe manufacturing typically is done in large, integrated plants. Newer plants often have high-volume exhaust ventilation systems with controlled make-up air. Local exhaust systems may be added for specific functions. Chemical milling and large component painting are now routinely performed in closed, automated ranks or booths that contain fugitive vapour or mist. Older manufacturing facilities may provide much poorer control of environmental hazards.

A large cadre of highly trained engineers develop and refine the structural characteristics of the aircraft or space vehicle. Additional engineers characterize the strength and durability of component materials and develop effective manufacturing processes. Computers have taken on much of the calculating and drafting work that was previously performed by engineers, drafters and technicians. Integrated computer systems can now be used to design aircraft without the aid of paper drawings or structural mock-ups.

Manufacturing begins with fabrication: the making of parts from stock materials. Fabrication includes tool and jig making, sheet-metal working, machining, plastic and composite working and support activities. Tools are built as templates and work surfaces on which to construct metal or composite parts. Jigs guide cutting, drilling and assembly. Fuselage sub-sections, door panels and wing and tail skins (outer surfaces) are typically formed from aluminium sheets that are precisely shaped, cut and chemically treated. Machine operations are often computer controlled. Huge rail-mounted mills machine wing spars from single aluminium forgings. Smaller parts are precisely cut and shaped on mills, lathes and grinders. Ducting is formed from sheet metal or composites. Interior components, including flooring, are typically formed from composites or laminates of thin but rigid outer layers over a honeycomb interior. Composite materials are laid up (put into carefully arranged and shaped overlapping layers) by hand or machine and then cured in an oven or autoclave.

Assembly begins with the build-up of component parts into sub-assemblies. Major sub-assemblies include wings, stabilizers, fuselage sections, landing gear, doors and interior components. Wing assembly is particularly intensive, requiring a large number of holes to be precisely drilled and counter-sunk in the skins, through which rivets are later driven. The finished wing is cleaned and sealed from the inside to ensure a leak-proof fuel compartment. Final assembly takes place in huge assembly halls, some of which are among the world's largest manufacturing buildings. The assembly line comprises several sequential positions where the airframe remains for several days to more than a week while predetermined functions are performed. Numerous assembly operations take place simultaneously at each position, creating the potential for cross exposures to chemicals. Parts and sub-assemblies are moved on dollies, custom-built carriers and by overhead crane to the appropriate position. The airframe is moved between

positions by overhead crane until the landing and nose gear are installed. Subsequent movements are made by towing.

During final assembly, the fuselage sections are riveted together around a supporting structure. Floor beams and stringers are installed and the interior coated with a corrosion-inhibiting compound. Fore and aft fuselage sections are joined to the wings and wing stub (a box-like structure that serves as a main fuel tank and the structural center of the aircraft). The fuselage interior is covered with blankets of fibreglass insulation, electrical wiring and air ducts are installed and interior surfaces are covered with decorative panelling. Storage bins, typically with integrated passenger lights and emergency oxygen supplies, are then installed. Preassembled seating, galleys and lavatories are moved by hand and secured to floor tracks, permitting the rapid reconfiguration of the passenger cabin to conform to air carrier needs. Powerplants and landing and nose gear are mounted, and avionic components are installed. The functioning of all components is thoroughly tested prior to towing the completed aircraft to a separate, well-ventilated paint hanger, where a protective primer coat (normally zinc-chromate based) is applied, followed by a decorative top-coat of urethane or epoxy paint. Prior to delivery the aircraft is put through a rigorous series of ground and flight tests.

In addition to workers engaged in the actual engineering and manufacturing processes, many employees are engaged in planning, tracking and inspecting work and expediting the movement of parts and tools. Craftspeople maintain power tools and reface cutting bits. Large staffs are needed for building maintenance, janitorial services and ground vehicle operation.

SAFETY AND ERGONOMICS IN AIRFRAME MANUFACTURING

Douglas F. Briggs

Safety Management

The airframe manufacturing industry's safety management systems have reflected the evolutionary process of safety management within the traditional manufacturing setting. The health and safety programmes tended to be highly structured, with the company executives directing health and safety programmes and a hierarchical structure reflective of the traditional command and control management system. The large aircraft and aerospace companies have staffs of safety and health professionals (industrial hygienists, health physicists, safety engineers, nurses, physicians and technicians) that work with line management to address the various safety risks that are found within their manufacturing processes. This approach to line control safety programmes, with the operational supervisor responsible for the daily management of risks, supported by a core group of safety and health professionals, was the primary model since the establishment of the industry. The introduction of detailed regulations in the early 1970s in the United States caused a shift to a greater reliance on the safety and health professionals, not only for programme development, but also implementation and evaluation. This shift was a result of the technical nature of standards that were not readily understood and translated into the manufacturing processes. As a result, many of the safety management systems changed to compliance-based systems rather than injury/illness prevention. The previously integrated line control safety management programmes lost some of their effectiveness when the complexity of regulations forced a greater reliance on the core safety and health professionals for all aspects of the safety programmes and took some of the responsibility and accountability away from line management.

Table 90.1 • Aircraft and aerospace industry safety hazards.

Type of hazard	Common examples	Possible effects
Physical		
Falling objects	Rivet guns, bucking bars, fasteners, hand tools	Contusions, head injuries
Moving equipment	Trucks, tractors, bicycles, fork-lift vehicles, cranes	Contusions, fractures, lacerations
Hazardous heights	Ladders, scaffolding, aerostands, assembly jigs	Multiple serious injuries, death
Sharp objects	Knives, drill bits, router and saw blades	Lacerations, puncture wounds
Moving machinery	Lathes, punch presses, milling machines, metal shears	Amputations, avulsions, crush injuries
Airborne fragments	Drilling, sanding, sawing, reaming, grinding	Ocular foreign bodies, corneal abrasions
Heated materials	Heat-treated metals, welded surfaces, boiling rinses	Burns, keloid formation, pigmentation changes
Hot metal, dross, slag	Welding, flame cutting, foundry operations	Serious skin, eye and ear burns
Electrical equipment	Hand tools, cords, portable lights, junction boxes	Contusions, strains, burns, death
Pressurized fluids	Hydraulic systems, airless grease and spray guns	Eye injuries, serious subcutaneous wounds
Altered air pressure	Aircraft pressure testing, autoclaves, test chambers	Ear, sinus and lung injuries, bends
Temperature extremes	Hot metal working, foundries, cold metal fabrication work	Heat exhaustion, frostbite
Loud noises	Riveting, engine testing, high-speed drilling, drop hammers	Temporary or permanent loss of hearing
Ionizing radiation	Industrial radiography, accelerators, radiation research	Sterility, cancer, radiation sickness, death
Non-ionizing radiation	Welding, lasers, radar, microwave ovens, research work	Corneal burns, cataracts, retinal burns, cancer
Walking/working surfaces	Spilled lubricants, disarranged tools, hoses and cords	Contusions, lacerations, strains, fractures
Ergonomic		
Work in confined spaces	Aircraft fuel cells, wings	Oxygen deprivation, entrapment, narcosis, anxiety
Forceful exertions	Lifting, carrying, tub skids, hand tools, wire shop	Excess fatigue, musculoskeletal injuries, carpal tunnel syndrome
Vibration	Riveting, sanding	Musculoskeletal injuries, carpal tunnel syndrome
Human/machine interface	Tooling, awkward posture assembly	Musculoskeletal injuries
Repetitive motion	Data entry, engineering design work, plastic lay up	Carpal tunnel syndrome, musculoskeletal injuries

Adapted from Dunphy and George 1983.

With the increasing emphasis on total quality management throughout the world, the emphasis is again being placed back on the manufacturing shop floor. Airframe manufacturers are moving to programmes that incorporate safety as an integral component of a reliable manufacturing process. Compliance takes on a secondary role, in that it is believed that while focusing on a reliable process, injury/illness prevention will be a primary objective and the regulations or their intent will be satisfied in establishing a reliable process. The industry as a whole currently has some traditional programmes, procedural/engineered-based programmes and emerging applications of behaviour-based programmes. Regardless of the specific model, those demonstrating the greatest success in injury/illness prevention require three critical components: (1) visible commitment by both management and the employees, (2) a clearly stated expectation of outstanding performance in injury/illness prevention and (3) accountability and reward systems, based on both endpoint measures (such as injury/illness data) and process indicators (such as per cent safety behaviour) or other proactive prevention activities that have equal weighting with other critical organization goals. All of the above systems are leading to a positive safety culture, which is leadership driven, with extensive employee involvement in both the process design and process improvement efforts.

Physical Safety

A substantial number of potentially serious hazards can be encountered in the airframe manufacturing industry largely because of the sheer physical size and complexity of the products produced and the diverse and changing array of manufacturing and assembly processes utilized. Inadvertent or inadequately controlled exposure to these hazards can produce immediate, serious injuries. Table 90.1 provides an overview of the industry's recognized physical safety hazards.

Immediate, direct trauma can result from dropped rivet bucking bars or other falling objects; tripping on irregular, slippery or littered work surfaces; falling from overhead crane catwalks, ladders, aerostands and major assembly jigs; touching ungrounded electrical equipment, heated metal objects and concentrated chemical solutions; contact with knives, drill bits and router blades; hair, hand or clothes entanglement or entrapment in milling machines, lathes and punch presses; flying chips, particles and slag from drilling, grinding and welding; and contusions and cuts from bumping against parts and components of the airframe during the manufacturing process.

The frequency and severity of injuries related to the physical safety hazards have been reduced as the industry's safety processes have matured. The injuries and illnesses related to ergonomically related risks have mirrored the growing concern shared by all manufacturing and service-based industries.

Ergonomics

The airframe manufacturers have a long history in the use of human factors in developing critical systems on their product. The pilots' flight deck has been one of the most extensively studied areas in product design history, as human factors engineers worked to optimize flight safety. Today, the fast-growing area of ergonomics as it pertains to injury/illness prevention is an extension of the original work done in human factors. The industry has processes that involve forceful exertions, awkward postures, repetitiveness, mechanical contact stress and vibration. These exposures can be exacerbated by work in confined areas such as wing interiors and fuel cells. To address these concerns, the industry is using ergonomists in product and process design, as well as "participatory ergonomics", where cross-functional teams of manufacturing employees, supervision and tooling and facility designers are working together to reduce ergonomic risks in their processes.

In the airframe industry some of the key ergonomic concerns are the wire shops, which require many hand tools to strip or crimp and require strong grip forces. Most are being replaced by pneumatic tools that are suspended by balancers if they are heavy. Height-adjustable workstations to accommodate males and females provide options to sit or stand. Work has been organized into cells in which each worker performs a variety of tasks to reduce fatigue of any particular muscle group. In the winglines, another key area, padding of tooling, parts or workers is necessary to reduce mechanical contact stress in confined areas. Also in the wingline, height-adjustable work platforms are utilized instead of stepladders to minimize falls and place workers in neutral posture to drill or rivet. Riveters are still a major area of challenge, as they represent both a vibration and forceful exertion risk. To address this, low-recoil riveters and electromagnetic riveting are being introduced, but due both to some of the performance criteria of the products and also the practical limitations of these techniques in some aspects of the manufacturing process, they are not universal solutions.

With the introduction of composite materials both for weight and performance considerations, hand lay-up of composite material has also introduced potential ergonomic risks due to the extensive use of hands for forming, cutting and working the material. Additional tools with varying grip size, and some automated processes, are being introduced to reduce the risks. Also, adjustable tooling is being used to place the work in neutral posture positions. The assembly processes bring about an extensive number of awkward postures and manual handling challenges that are often addressed by the participatory ergonomics processes. Risk reductions are achieved by increased use of mechanical lifting devices where feasible, re-sequencing of work, as well as establishing other process improvements that typically not only address the ergonomic risks, but also improve productivity and product quality.

• FALL PROTECTION FOR TRANSPORT CATEGORY AIRCRAFT MANUFACTURE AND MAINTENANCE

Robert W. Hites

Transport category aircraft are used for transporting passengers and freight in the commercial airline/airfreight industry. Both the manufacturing and maintenance process involve operations that remove, fabricate, alter and/or install components all over the aircraft itself. These aircraft vary in size but some (e.g., Boeing 747, Airbus A340) are among the largest aircraft in the world. Due to the size of the aircraft, certain operations require personnel to work while elevated above the floor or ground surface.

There are many potential fall situations within both aircraft manufacturing and maintenance operations throughout the air transport industry. While each situation is unique and may require a different solution for protection, the preferred method of fall protection is by *preventing* falls through an aggressive plan for hazard identification and control.

Effective fall protection involves an institutional commitment addressing every aspect of hazard identification and control. Each operator must continually evaluate its operation for specific fall exposures and develop a protection plan comprehensive enough to address each exposure throughout their operation.

Fall Hazards

Any time an individual is elevated they have the potential to fall to a lower level. Falls from elevations often result in serious injuries or fatalities. For this reason, regulations, standards and policies have been developed to assist companies in addressing the fall hazards throughout their operations.

A fall hazard exposure consists of any situation in which an individual is working from an elevated surface where that surface is several feet above the next level down. Assessing the operation for these exposures involves identifying all areas or tasks where it is possible that individuals are exposed to elevated work surfaces. A good source of information is injury and illness records (labour statistics, insurance logs, safety records, medical records and so on); however, it is important to look further than historical events. Each work area or process must be evaluated to determine whether there are any instances where the process or task requires the individual to work from a surface or area that is elevated several feet above the next lower surface.

Fall Situation Categorization

Virtually any manufacturing or maintenance task performed on one of these aircraft has the potential to expose personnel to fall hazards because of the size of the aircraft. These aircraft are so large that virtually every area of the entire aircraft is several feet above ground level. Although this provides many specific situations where personnel could be exposed to fall hazards, all the situations may be categorized as either *work from platforms* or *work from aircraft surfaces*. The division between these two categories originates with the factors involved in addressing the exposures themselves.

The work-from-platforms category involves personnel using a platform or stand to access the aircraft. It includes any work performed from a non-aircraft surface that is specifically used to access the aircraft. Tasks performed from aircraft docking systems, wing platforms, engine stands, lift trucks and so on would all be in this category. Potential fall exposures from surfaces in this category may be addressed with traditional fall-protection systems or a variety of guidelines that are currently in existence.

The work from aircraft surfaces category involves personnel using the aircraft surface itself as the platform for access. It includes any work performed from an actual aircraft surface such as wings, horizontal stabilizers, fuselages, engines and engine pylons. Potential fall exposures from surfaces in this category are very diverse depending on the specific maintenance task and sometimes require non-conventional approaches for protection.

The reason for the distinction between these two categories becomes clear when attempting to implement protective measures. Protective measures are those steps that are taken to eliminate or control each fall exposure. The methods for controlling fall hazards may be engineering controls, personal protective equipment (PPE) or procedural controls.

Figure 90.1 • Boeing 747 portable rail system; a two-sided guardrail system attaches to side of aircraft body, providing fall protection during work on over-wing door and wing roof area.

Courtesy of The Boeing Company

Engineering Controls

Engineering controls are those measures which consist of *altering the facility* in such a way that the individual's exposure is minimized. Some examples of engineering controls are railings, walls or similar area reconstruction. Engineering controls are the preferred method for protecting personnel from fall exposures.

Engineering controls are the most common measure employed for platforms in both manufacturing and maintenance. They usually consist of standard railings; however, any barrier on all open sides of a platform effectively protects personnel from the fall exposure. If the platform were positioned right next to the aircraft, as is common, the side next to the aircraft would not need rails, as protection is provided by the aircraft itself. The exposures to be managed are then limited to gaps between the platform and the aircraft.

Engineering controls are usually not found in maintenance from aircraft surfaces, because any engineering controls designed into the aircraft add weight and decrease the aircraft's efficiency during flight. The controls themselves prove inefficient when designed to protect the perimeter of an aircraft surface, as they have to be specific to the aircraft type, area and location and must be positioned without causing damage to the aircraft. Figure 90.1 shows a portable rail system for an aircraft wing. Engineering controls are used extensively during manufacturing processes from aircraft surfaces. They are effective during manufacturing because the processes occur in the same location with the aircraft surface in the same position every time, so the controls may be customized to that location and position.

An alternative to railings for engineering controls involves netting positioned around the platform or aircraft surface to catch individuals when they fall. These are effective in stopping someone's fall but are not preferred, as individuals may be injured during the impact with the net itself. These systems also require a formal procedure for rescue/retrieval of personnel once they have fallen into the nets.

Personal Protective Equipment

PPE for falls consists of a full body harness with a lanyard attached to either a lifeline or other suitable anchorage. These systems are typically used for fall arrest; however, they may also be used in a fall restraint system.

Used in a personal fall arrest system (PFAS), PPE may be an effective means for preventing an individual from impacting the next lower level during a fall. To be effective, the anticipated fall distance must not exceed the distance to the lower level. It is important to note that with such a system the individual may still experience injuries as a result of the fall arrest itself. These systems also require a formal procedure for rescue/retrieval of personnel once they have fallen and been arrested.

PFASs are used with work from platforms most often when engineering controls are not functional—usually due to restriction of the work process. They are also used with work from aircraft surfaces because of the logistical difficulties associated with engineering controls. The most challenging aspects of PFASs and aircraft surface work are the fall distance with respect to personnel mobility and the added weight to the aircraft structure to support the system. The weight issue may be eliminated by designing the system to attach to the facility around the aircraft surface, rather than the aircraft structure; however, this also limits fall protection capability to that one facility location. Figure 90.2 shows a portable gantry used for providing a PFAS. PFASs are used more extensively in maintenance operations than manufacturing, but are used during certain manufacturing situations.

A fall restraint system (FRS) is a system designed so that the individual is prevented from falling over the edge. FRSs are very

Figure 90.2 • Engine gantry providing fall protection for aircraft engine worker.

Courtesy of The Boeing Company

Figure 90.3 • Boeing 747 wing lanyard system.

Courtesy of The Boeing Company

Figure 90.4 • Boeing 747 wing lanyard system fall protection zones.

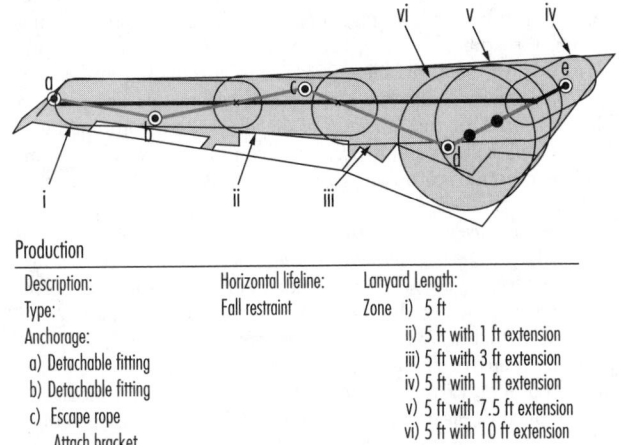

Production

Description:	Horizontal lifeline:	Lanyard Length:
Type:	Fall restraint	Zone i) 5 ft
Anchorage:		ii) 5 ft with 1 ft extension
a) Detachable fitting		iii) 5 ft with 3 ft extension
b) Detachable fitting		iv) 5 ft with 1 ft extension
c) Escape rope		v) 5 ft with 7.5 ft extension
Attach bracket		vi) 5 ft with 10 ft extension
d) Detachable fitting		Deceleration device: None
e) Bolt-on bracket		

Source: Courtesy of The Boeing Company.

similar to PFASs in that all the components are the same; however, the FRSs restrict the individual's range of movement such that the individual cannot reach close enough to the edge of the surface to fall over. FRSs are the preferred evolution of PPE systems for both manufacturing and maintenance operations, because they prevent any fall-related injury *and* they eliminate the need for a rescue process. They are not extensively used in either work from platforms or aircraft surfaces, because of the challenges of designing the system so that personnel have the mobility needed to perform the work process, but are restricted from reaching the edge of the surface. These systems decrease the weight/efficiency issue with work from aircraft surfaces, because FRSs do not require the strength that a PFAS requires. At the time of printing, only one aircraft type (the Boeing 747) had an airframe-based FRS available. See figures 90.3 and 90.4.

A horizontal lifeline attaches to permanent fittings on the wing surface, creating six fall protection zones. Employees connect a 1.5 m lanyard to D-rings or strap extensions that slide along the horizontal lifeline in zones i through iv, and are fixed in zones v and vi. The system allows access only to the edge of the wing, preventing the possibility of falling from the wing surface.

Procedural Controls

Procedural controls are used when both engineering controls and PPE are either ineffective or impractical. This is the least preferred method of protection, but is effective if managed properly. Procedural controls consist of designating the work surface as a restricted area for only those individuals that are required to enter during that specific maintenance process. Fall protection is achieved through very aggressive written procedures covering hazard exposure identification, communication and individual ac-

tions. These procedures mitigate the exposure as best as possible under the circumstances of the situation. They must be site specific and must address the specific hazards of that situation. These are very seldom used for work from platforms in either manufacturing or maintenance, but they are used for maintenance work from aircraft surfaces.

AIRCRAFT ENGINE MANUFACTURING ●

John B. Feldman

The manufacture of aircraft engines, whether piston or jet, involves the conversion of raw materials into extremely reliable precision machines. The highly stressed operating environments associated with air transport require the use of a broad range of high-strength materials. Both conventional and unique manufacturing methods are utilized.

Construction Materials

Aircraft engines are primarily constructed of metallic components, although recent years have seen the introduction of plastic composites for certain parts. Various aluminium and titanium alloys are used where strength and light weight are of primary importance (structural components, compressor sections, engine frames). Chromium, nickel and cobalt alloys are used where resistance to high temperature and corrosion are required (combustor and turbine sections). Numerous steel alloys are used in intermediate locations.

Since weight minimization on aircraft is a critical factor in reducing life-cycle costs (maximizing payload, minimizing fuel consumption), advanced composite materials have recently been introduced as light-weight replacements for aluminium, titanium and some steel alloys in structural parts and ductwork where high temperatures are not experienced. These composites consist primarily of polyimide, epoxy and other resin systems, reinforced with woven fibreglass or graphite fibres.

90. AEROSPACE MANUFACTURE AND MAINTENANCE

Manufacturing Operations

Virtually every common metalworking and machining operation is used in aircraft engine manufacture. This includes hot forging (airfoils, compressor disks), casting (structural components, engine frames), grinding, broaching, turning, drilling, milling, shearing, sawing, threading, welding, brazing and others. Associated processes involve metal finishing (anodizing, chromating and so on), electroplating, heat treating and thermal (plasma, flame) spraying. The high strength and hardness of the alloys used, combined with their complex shapes and precision tolerances, necessitate more challenging and rigorous machining requirements than other industries.

Some of the more unique metalworking processes include chemical and electrochemical milling, electro-discharge machining, laser drilling and electron-beam welding. *Chemical and electrochemical milling* involve the removal of metal from large surfaces in a manner which retains or creates a contour. The parts, depending upon their specific alloy, are placed in a highly concentrated controlled acid, caustic or electrolyte bath. Metal is removed by the chemical or electrochemical action. Chemical milling is often used after forging of airfoils to bring wall thicknesses into specification while maintaining the contour.

Electro-discharge machining and laser drilling are typically used for making small-diameter holes and intricate contours in hard metals. Many such holes are required in combustor and turbine components for cooling purposes. Metal removal is accomplished by high-frequency thermo-mechanical action of electro-spark discharges. The process is carried out in a dielectric mineral oil bath. The electrode serves as the reverse image of the desired cut.

Electron-beam welding is used to join parts where deep weld penetration is required in hard-to-reach geometries. The weld is generated by a focused, accelerated beam of electrons within a vacuum chamber. The kinetic energy of the electrons striking the workpiece is transformed into heat for welding.

Composite plastic fabrication involves either "wet" lay-up techniques or the use of pre-impregnated cloths. With wet lay-up, the viscous uncured resin mixture is spread over a tooling form or mould by either spraying or brushing. The fibre reinforcement material is manually laid into the resin. Additional resin is applied to obtain uniformity and contour with the tooling form. The completed lay-up is then cured in an autoclave under heat and pressure. Pre-impregnated materials consist of semi-rigid, ready-to-use, partially-cured sheets of resin-fibre composites. The material is cut to size, manually moulded to the contours of the tooling form and cured in an autoclave. Cured parts are conventionally machined and assembled into the engine.

Inspection and Testing

In order to assure the reliability of aircraft engines, a number of inspection, testing and quality-control procedures are performed during the fabrication and on the final product. Common non-destructive inspection methods include radiographic, ultrasonic, magnetic particle and fluorescent penetrant. They are used to detect any cracks or internal flaws within the parts. Assembled engines are usually tested in instrumented test cells prior to customer delivery.

Health and Safety Hazards and Their Control Methods

Health hazards associated with aircraft engine manufacture are primarily related to the toxicity of the materials used and their potential for exposure. Aluminium, titanium and iron are not considered significantly toxic, while chromium, nickel and cobalt are more problematic. Certain compounds and valence states of the latter three metals have indicated carcinogenic properties in humans and animals. Their metallic forms are generally not considered as toxic as their ionic forms, typically found in metal finishing baths and paint pigments.

In conventional machining, most operations are performed using coolants or cutting fluids which minimize the generation of airborne dust and fumes. With the exception of dry grinding, the metals usually do not present inhalation hazards, although there is concern about the inhalation of coolant mists. A fair amount of grinding is performed, particularly on jet engine parts, to blend contours and bring airfoils into their final dimensions. Small, hand-held grinders are typically used. Where such grinding is performed on chromium-, nickel- or cobalt-based alloys, local ventilation is required. This includes down-draft tables and self-ventilating grinders. Dermatitis and noise are additional health hazards associated with conventional machining. Employees will have varying degrees of skin contact with coolants and cutting fluids in the course of fixing, inspecting and removing parts. Repeated skin contact may manifest itself in various forms of dermatitis in some employees. Generally, protective gloves, barrier creams and proper hygiene will minimize such cases. High noise levels are often present when machining thin-walled, high-strength alloys, due to tool chatter and part vibration. This can be controlled to an extent through more rigid tooling, dampening materials, modifying machining parameters and maintaining sharp tools. Otherwise, PPE (e.g., ear muffs, plugs) is required.

Safety hazards associated with conventional machining operations mainly involve potential for physical injuries due to the point-of-operation, fixing and power transmission drive movements. Control is accomplished through such methods as fixed guards, interlocked access doors, light curtains, pressure-sensitive mats and employee training and awareness. Eye protection should always be used around machining operations for protection from flying chips, particles and splashes of coolants and cleaning solvents.

Metal-finishing operations, chemical milling, electrochemical milling and electroplating involve open surface tank exposures to concentrated acids, bases and electrolytes. Most of the baths contain high concentrations of dissolved metals. Depending upon bath operating conditions and composition (concentration, temperature, agitation, size), most will require some form of local ventilation to control airborne levels of gases, vapours and mists. Various lateral, slot-type hood designs are commonly used for control. Ventilation designs and operating guidelines for different types of baths are available through technical organizations such as the American Conference of Governmental Industrial Hygienists (ACGIH) and the American National Standards Institute (ANSI). The corrosive nature of these baths dictates the use of eye and skin protection (splash goggles, face shields, gloves, aprons and so on) when working around these tanks. Emergency eye-washes and showers must also be available for immediate use.

Electron-beam welding and laser drilling present radiation hazards to workers. Electron-beam welding generates secondary x-ray radiation (*bremsstrahlung* effect). In a sense, the welding chamber constitutes an inefficient x-ray tube. It is critical that the chamber be constructed of material or contain shielding which will attenuate the radiation to the lowest practical levels. Lead shielding is often used. Radiation surveys should be periodically performed. Lasers present ocular and skin (thermal) hazards. Also, there is potential for exposure to the metal fumes produced by the evaporation of the base metal. Beam hazards associated with laser operations should be isolated and contained, where possible, within interlocked chambers. A comprehensive programme should be rigorously followed. Local ventilation should be provided where metal fumes are generated.

The major hazards related to the fabrication of composite plastic parts involve chemical exposure to unreacted resin components and solvents during wet lay-up operations. Of particular concern are aromatic amines used as reactants in polyimide resins and hardeners in epoxy resin systems. A number of these compounds are confirmed or suspected human carcinogens. They also exhibit other toxic effects. The highly reactive nature of these resin systems, particularly epoxies, gives rise to skin and respiratory sensitization. Control of hazards during wet lay-up operations should include local ventilation and extensive use of personal protective equipment to prevent skin contact. Lay-up operations using pre-impregnated sheets usually do not present airborne exposures, but skin protection should be used. Upon curing, these parts are relatively inert. They no longer present the hazards of their constituent reactants. Conventional machining of the parts, though, can produce nuisance dusts of an irritant nature, associated with the composite reinforcement materials (fibreglass, graphite). Local ventilation of the machining operation is often required.

Health hazards associated with test operations usually involve radiation (x or gamma rays) from radiographic inspection and noise from final product tests. Radiographic operations should include a comprehensive radiation safety programme, complete with training, badge monitoring and periodic surveys. Radiographic inspection chambers should be designed with interlocked doors, operating lights, emergency shut-offs and proper shielding. Test areas or cells where assembled products are tested should be acoustically treated, particularly for jet engines. Noise levels at the control consoles should be controlled to below 85 dBA. Provisions should also be made to prevent any build-up of exhaust gases, fuel vapours or solvents in the test area.

In addition to the aforementioned hazards related to specific operations, there are several others worthy of note. They include exposure to cleaning solvents, paints, lead and welding operations. Cleaning solvents are used throughout manufacturing operations. There has been a recent trend away from the use of chlorinated and fluorinated solvents to aqueous, terpine, alcohol and mineral spirit types due to toxicity and ozone depletion effects. Although the latter group may tend to be more environmentally acceptable, they often present fire hazards. Quantities of any flammable or combustible solvents should be limited in the workplace, used only from approved containers and with adequate fire protection in place. Lead is sometimes used in airfoil forging operations as a die lubricant. If so, a comprehensive lead control and monitoring programme should be in effect due to lead's toxicity. Many types of conventional welding are used in manufacturing operations. Metal fumes, ultraviolet radiation and ozone exposures need to be evaluated for such operations. The need for controls will depend upon the specific operating parameters and metals involved.

CONTROLS AND HEALTH EFFECTS

Denis Bourcier

There is a growing market demand for the aerospace industry to decrease product development flow time while at the same time utilizing materials that meet increasingly stringent, and sometimes contradictory, performance criteria. Accelerated product testing and production may cause material and process development to outpace the parallel development of environmental health technologies. The result may be products which have been perform-

ance tested and approved but for which there exist insufficient data on health and environmental impact. Regulations such as the Toxic Substance Control Act (TSCA) in the United States require (1) testing of new materials; (2) the development of prudent lab practices for research and development testing; (3) restrictions on the import and export of certain chemicals; and (4) monitoring of health, safety and environmental studies as well as company records for significant health effects from chemical exposures.

The increased use of material safety data sheets (MSDSs) has helped provide health professionals with the information required to control chemical exposures. However, complete toxicological data exist for only a few hundred of the thousands of materials in use, providing a challenge to industrial hygienists and toxicologists. To the extent feasible, local exhaust ventilation and other engineering controls should be used to control exposure, particularly when poorly understood chemicals or inadequately characterized contaminant generation rates are involved. Respirators can play a secondary role when supported by a well-planned and rigorously enforced respiratory protection management programme. Respirators and other personal protective equipment must be selected to offer fully adequate protection without producing undue discomfort to workers.

Hazard and control information must be effectively communicated to employees prior to a product's introduction into the work area. Oral presentation, bulletins, videos or other means of communication may be used. The method of communication is important to the success of any workplace chemical introduction. In aerospace manufacturing areas, employees, materials and work processes change frequently. Hazard communication must therefore be a continuous process. Written communications are not likely to be effective in this environment without the support of more active methods such as crew meetings or video presentations. Provisions should always be made for responding to worker questions.

Extremely complex chemical environments are characteristic of airframe manufacturing facilities, particularly assembly areas. Intensive, responsive and well-planned industrial hygiene efforts are required to recognize and characterize hazards associated with the simultaneous or sequential presence of large numbers of chemicals, many of which may not have been adequately tested for health effects. The hygienist must be wary of contaminants released in physical forms not anticipated by the suppliers, and therefore not listed on MSDSs. For example, the repeated application and removal of strips of partially cured composite materials may release solvent-resin mixtures as an aerosol that will not be effectively measured using vapour-monitoring methods.

The concentration and combinations of chemicals may also be complex and highly variable. Delayed work performed out of normal sequence may result in hazardous materials being used without proper engineering controls or adequate personal protective measures. The variations in work practices between individuals and the size and configuration of different airframes may have a significant impact on exposures. Variations in solvent exposures among individuals performing wing tank cleaning have exceeded two orders of magnitude, due in part to the effects of body size on the flow of dilution air in extremely confined areas.

Potential hazards should be identified and characterized, and necessary controls implemented, before materials or processes enter the workplace. Safe usage standards must also be developed, established and documented with mandatory compliance before work begins. Where information is incomplete, it is appropriate to assume the highest reasonably expected risk and to provide appropriate protective measures. Industrial hygiene surveys should be performed at regular and frequent intervals to ensure that controls are adequate and working reliably.

90. AEROSPACE MANUFACTURE AND MAINTENANCE

Table 90.2 • Technological development requirements for health, safety and environmental control for new processes and materials.

Parameter	Technological requirement
Airborne levels of contaminants	Analytical methods for chemical quantification Air monitoring techniques
Potential health impact	Acute and chronic toxicology studies
Environmental fate	Bioaccumulation and biodegradation studies
Waste characterization	Chemical compatibility test Bioassays

The difficulty of characterizing aerospace workplace exposures necessitates close cooperation between hygienists, clinicians, toxicologists and epidemiologists (see table 90.2). The presence of a very well informed workforce and management cadre is also essential. Worker reporting of symptoms should be encouraged, and supervisors should be trained to be alert to signs and symptoms of exposure. Biological exposure monitoring may serve as an important supplement to air monitoring where exposures are highly variable or where dermal exposure may be significant. Biological monitoring can also be used to determine whether controls are effective in reducing employee uptake of contaminants. Analysis of medical data for patterns of signs, symptoms and complaints should be performed routinely.

Paint hangars, aircraft fuselages and fuel tanks may be served by very high volume exhaust systems during intensive painting, sealing and cleaning operations. Residual exposures and the inability of these systems to direct air flow away from workers usually require the supplemental use of respirators. Local exhaust ventilation is required for smaller painting, metal treating and solvent cleaning operations, for laboratory chemical work and for some plastics lay-up work. Dilution ventilation is usually adequate only in areas with minimal chemical usage or as a supplement to local exhaust ventilation. Significant air exchanges during winter can result in excessively dry interior air. Poorly designed exhaust systems which direct excessive cool air flow over workers' hands or backs in small parts assembly areas may worsen hand, arm and neck problems. In large, complex manufacturing areas, attention must be paid to properly locating ventilation exhaust and intake points to avoid re-entraining contaminants.

Precision manufacturing of aerospace products requires clear, organized and well controlled work environments. Containers, barrels and tanks containing chemicals must be labelled as to the potential hazards of the materials. First aid information must be readily available. Emergency response and spill control information also must be available on the MSDS or similar data sheet. Hazardous work areas must be placarded and access controlled and verified.

Health Effects of Composite Materials

Airframe manufacturers, in both the civilian and defence sectors, have come to rely increasingly on composite materials in the construction of both interior and structural components. Generations of composite materials have been increasingly integrated into production throughout the industry, particularly in the defence sector, where they are valued for their low radar reflectivity. This rapidly developing manufacturing medium typifies the problem of design technology outpacing public health efforts. Specific hazards of the resin or fabric component of the composite prior to combination and resin cure differs from the hazards of cured materials. Additionally, partially cured materials (pre-pregs) may

continue to preserve the hazard characteristics of the resin components during the various steps leading to producing a composite part (AIA 1995). Toxicological considerations of major resin categories are provided in table 90.3.

The degree and type of hazard posed by composite materials depends primarily on the specific work activity and degree of resin cure as the material moves from a wet resin/fabric to the cured part. Release of volatile resin components may be significant prior to and during initial reaction of resin and curing agent, but may also occur during the processing of materials which go through more than one level of cure. The release of these components tends to be greater in elevated temperature conditions or in poorly ventilated work areas and may range from trace to moderate levels. Dermal exposure to the resin components in the pre-cure state is often an important part of total exposure and therefore should not be neglected.

Off-gassing of resin degradation products may occur during various machining operations which create heat at the surface of the cured material. These degradation products have yet to be fully characterized, but tend to vary in chemical structure as a function of both temperature and resin type. Particles may be generated by machining of cured materials or by cutting pre-pregs which contain residues of resin materials which are released when the material is disturbed. Exposure to gases produced by oven cure has been noted where, through improper design or faulty operation, autoclave exhaust ventilation fails to remove these gases from the work environment.

It should be noted that dusts created by new fabric materials containing fibreglass, kevlar, graphite or boron/metal oxide coatings are generally considered to be capable of producing mild to moderate fibrogenic reaction; so far we have been unable to characterize their relative potency. Additionally, information on the relative contribution of fibrogenic dusts from various machining operations is still under investigation. The various composite operations and hazards have been characterized (AIA 1995) and are listed in table 90.4.

Table 90.3 • Toxicological considerations of major components of resins utilized in aerospace composite materials.[1]

Resin type	Components[2]	Toxicological consideration
Epoxy	Amine curing agents, epichlorohydrin	Sensitizer, suspect carcinogen
Polyimide	Aldehyde monomer, phenol	Sensitizer, suspect carcinogen, systemic[3]
Phenolic	Aldehyde monomer, phenol	Sensitizer, suspect carcinogen, systemic[3]
Polyester	Styrene, dimethylaniline	Narcosis, central nervous system depression, cyanosis
Silicone	Organic siloxane, peroxides	Sensitizer, irritant
Thermoplastics[4]	Polystyrene, polyphenylene sulphide	Systemic,[3] irritant

[1] Examples of typical components of the uncured resins are provided. Other chemicals of diverse toxicological nature may be present as curing agents, diluents and additives.

[2] Applies primarily to components of wet resin prior to reaction. Varying amounts of these materials are present in the partially cured resin, and trace quantities in the cured materials.

[3] Systemic toxicity, indicating effects produced in several tissues.

[4] Thermoplastics included as separate category, in that breakdown products listed are created during moulding operations when the polymerized starting material is heated.

Table 90.4 • Hazards of chemicals in the aerospace industry.

Chemical agent	Sources	Potential disease
Metals		
Beryllium dust	Machining beryllium alloys	Skin lesions, acute or chronic lung disease
Cadmium dust, mist	Welding, burning, spray painting	Delayed acute pulmonary oedema, kidney damage
Chromium dust/mist/fumes	Spraying/sanding primer, welding	Cancer of the respiratory tract
Nickel	Welding, grinding	Cancer of the respiratory tract
Mercury	Laboratories, engineering tests	Central nervous system damage
Gases		
Hydrogen cyanide	Electroplating	Chemical asphyxiation, chronic effects
Carbon monoxide	Heat treating, engine work	Chemical asphyxiation, chronic effects
Oxides of nitrogen	Welding, electroplating, pickling	Delayed acute pulmonary oedema, permanent lung damage (possible)
Phosgene	Welding decomposition of solvent vapour	Delayed acute pulmonary oedema, permanent lung damage (possible)
Ozone	Welding, high-altitude flight	Acute and chronic lung damage, cancer of the respiratory tract
Organic compounds		
Aliphatic	Machine lubricants, fuels, cutting fluids	Follicular dermatitis
Aromatic, nitro and amino	Rubber, plastics, paints, dyes	Anaemia, cancer, skin sensitization
Aromatic, other	Solvents	Narcosis, liver damage, dermatitis
Halogenated	Depainting, degreasing	Narcosis, anaemia, liver damage
Plastics		
Phenolics	Interior components, ducting	Allergic sensitization, cancer (possible)
Epoxy (amine hardeners)	Lay-up operations	Dermatitis, allergic sensitization, cancer
Polyurethane	Paints, internal components	Allergic sensitization, cancer (possible)
Polyimide	Structural components	Allergic sensitization, cancer (possible)
Fibrogenic dusts		
Asbestos	Military and older aircraft	Cancer, asbestosis
Silica	Abrasive blasting, fillers	Silicosis
Tungsten carbide	Precision tool grinding	Pneumoconiosis
Graphite, kevlar	Composite machining	Pneumoconiosis
Benign dusts (possible)		
Fibreglass	Insulating blankets, interior components	Skin and respiratory irritation, chronic disease (possible)
Wood	Mock-up and model making	Allergic sensitization, respiratory cancer

ENVIRONMENTAL AND PUBLIC HEALTH ISSUES

Steve Mason

Aerospace industries have been significantly affected by the enormous growth in environmental and community noise regulations passed primarily in the United States and Europe since the 1970s. Legislation such as the Clean Water Act, the Clean Air Act and the Resource Conservation and Recovery Act in the United States and companion Directives in the European Union have resulted in voluminous local regulations to meet environmental quality objectives. These regulations typically enforce the use of best available technology, whether new materials or processes or end of stack control equipment. Additionally, universal issues such as ozone depletion and global warming are forcing changes to traditional operations by banning chemicals such as chlorofluorocarbons entirely unless exceptional conditions exist.

Early legislation had little impact on aerospace operations until the 1980s. The continued growth of the industry and the concentration of operations around airports and industrialized areas made regulation attractive. The industry underwent a revolution in terms of programmes required to track and manage toxic emissions to the environment with the intent to ensure safety. Wastewater treatment from metal finishing and aircraft maintenance became standard at all large facilities. Hazardous waste segregation, classification, manifesting and, later, treatment prior to disposal were instituted where rudimentary programmes had previously existed. Clean-up programmes at disposal sites became major economic issues for many companies as costs rose to many millions at each site. In the later 1980s and early 1990s, air emissions, which constitute as much as 80% or more of the total emissions from aircraft manufacturing and operation, became the focus of regulation. The International Civil Aviation Organization (ICAO) adopted engine emission standards as early as 1981 (ICAO 1981).

Chemical emissions regulations affect essentially all chemical processing, engine and auxiliary power unit, fuelling and ground service vehicle operations. In Los Angeles, for example, ground-level ozone and carbon monoxide reductions to achieve Clean Air Act standards could require a reduction of 50% of flight operations at Los Angeles International Airport by the year 2005 (Donoghue 1994). Emissions there will be tracked daily to ensure limits on total emissions of volatile organic compounds and carbon monoxide are below the overall total permitted. In Sweden, a tax has been levied on aircraft carbon dioxide emissions due to their global warming potential. Similar regulations in some regions have resulted in a near total elimination of vapour degreasing using chlorinated solvents such as trichloroethane due to the historically high levels of emissions from open-topped degreasers and the ozone depleting potential and toxicity of 1,1,1 trichloroethane.

Perhaps the most broad-based regulation yet imposed is the Aerospace National Emission Standard for Hazardous Air Pollutants (NESHAP) of 1995, promulgated by the United States Environmental Protection Agency under the Clean Air Act Amendments of 1990. This regulation requires all aerospace operations to comply with the average of the best 12% of the current United States control practices to reduce the emission of pollutants from the processes of greatest emissions. The standard requires compliance by September 1998. The processes and materials most affected are manual wipe and flush cleaning, primers and topcoats, paint removal and chemical milling maskants. The regulation allows process change or control and charges local authorities with enforcement of material, equipment, work prac-

Table 90.5 • Summary of the United States NESHAP in manufacturing and reworking facilities.

Process	Requirements [1]
Manual wipe cleaning of aerospace components	Maximum composite pressure of 45 mmHg at 20 °C or use of specific preferred cleaners Exemptions for confined spaces, work near energized systems, etc. Immediate enclosure of wipers to contain further evaporation
Flush cleaning with VOCs[2] or HAPs[3] containing materials	Collection and containment of fluids
Application of primers and topcoats	Use of high transfer efficiency equipment[4]
Primer HAP content less water	350 g/l of primer as applied on average[5]
Top coat HAP content water	420 g/l of topcoat as applied on average[5]
Exterior surface paint removal	Zero HAP chemicals, mechanical blast, high-intensity light[6] Allowance for 6 assembled aircraft to be depainted per site/year with HAP-containing chemicals
Coatings containing inorganic HAPs	High efficiency control of particulate emissions
Chemical milling mask HAP content less water	160 g/l of material as applied or a high-efficiency vapour collection and control system
Overspray from coating operations with HAP	Multistage particulate filter
Air pollution control equipment	Minimum acceptable efficiencies plus monitoring
Spray gun cleaning	No atomization of cleaning solvent, provisions to capture waste

[1] Considerable record keeping, inspection and other requirements apply, not listed here.

[2] Volatile organic compounds. These have been shown to be photochemical reactive and precursors to ground-level ozone formation.

[3] Hazardous air pollutants. These are 189 compounds listed by the US Environmental Protection Agency as toxic.

[4] Listed equipment includes electrostatic or high-volume, low-pressure (HVLP) spray guns.

[5] Specialty coatings and other low-emission processes excluded.

[6] Touch-up allowed using 26 gallons per aircraft per year of HAP-containing remover (commercial), or 50 gallons per year (military).

Table 90.6 • Typical chemical hazards of manufacturing processes.

Common processes	Type of emission	Chemicals or hazards
Coatings, including temporary protective coatings, mask and paints	Overspray of solids and evaporation of solvents	Volatile organic compouds (VOCs) including methyl ethyl ketone, toluene, xylenes
		Ozone-depleting compounds (ODCs) (chlorofluorocarbons, trichloroethane and others)
		Organic toxins including tricholorethane, xylene, toluene
		Inorganic toxins including cadmium, chromates, lead
	Solid waste, (e.g., wipers)	VOCs or toxins as above
Solvent cleaning	Evaporation of solvents	VOCs, ozone depleters or toxins
	Solid waste (wipers)	VOCs or toxins
	Liquid waste	Waste solvent (VOCs) and/or contaminated water
Paint removal	Evaporation or entrainment of solvents	VOCs such as xylene, toluene, methyl ethyl ketone
		Organic toxins (methylene chloride, phenolics)
		Heavy metals (chromates)
	Corrosive liquid waste	Caustics and acids including formic acid
	Dust, heat, light	Toxic dust (blasting), heat (thermal stripping) and light
Anodizing aluminium	Ventilation exhaust	Acid mist
	Liquid waste	Concentrated acid usually chromic, nitric and hydrofluoric
Plating hard metals	Ventilation exhaust	Heavy metals, acids, complexed cyanides
	Rinsewaters	Heavy metals, acids, complexed cyanides
Chemical milling	Liquid waste	Caustics and heavy metals, other metals
Sealing	Evaporated solvent	VOCs
	Solid waste	Heavy metals, trace amounts of toxic organics
Alodining (conversion coating)	Liquid waste	Chromates, possibly complexed cyanide
	Solid waste	Chromates, oxidizers
Corrosion-inhibiting compounds	Particulates, solid waste	Waxes, heavy metals and toxic organics
Composite fabrication	Solid waste	Uncured volatiles
Vapour degreasing	Escaped vapour	Tricholorethane, trichoroethylene, perchloroethylene
Aqueous degreasing	Liquid waste	VOCs, silicates, trace metals

tice and record-keeping requirements. The significance of these rules is the imposition of the best practices with little regard to cost on every aerospace manufacturer. They force a comprehensive change to low vapour pressure solvent cleaning materials and to coatings low in solvent content, as well as application equipment technology as shown in table 90.5. Some exceptions were made where product safety or personnel safety (due to fire hazard and so on) would be compromised.

Summaries of typical chemical hazards and emission-control practices due to the impact of environmental regulations on manufacturing and maintenance operations in the United States are provided in tables 90.6 and 90.7 respectively. European regulations have for the most part not kept pace in the area of toxic air emissions, but have placed greater emphasis on the elimination of emission-control practices.

	Air emissions	Water emissions	Land emissions
Coating: overspray	Emission control equipment[1] for overspray (VOCs and solid particulate)	Onsite pretreatment and monitoring	Treat and landfill[3] paint-booth waste. Incinerate flammables and landfill ash. Recycle solvents where possible.
Solvent cleaning with VOCs	Emission controls[2] and/or material substitution	Onsite pretreatment and monitoring	Incinerate and landfill used wipers
Solvent cleaning with ODCs	Substitution due to ban on ODCs production	None	None
Solvent cleaning with toxins	Substitution	Onsite pretreatment and monitoring	Treat to reduce toxicity[4] and landfill
Paint removal	Emission controls or substitution with non-HAP or mechanical methods	Onsite pretreatment and monitoring	Treatment sludge stabilized and landfilled
Anodizing aluminium, plating hard metals, chemical milling and immersion conversion coating (Alodine)	Emission control (scrubbers) and/or substitution in some cases	Onsite pretreatment of rinsewaters. Acid and caustic concentrates treated on or off site	Treatment sludge stabilized and landfilled. Other solid waste treated and landfilled
Sealing	Usually none required	Usually none required	Incinerate and landfill used wipers
Corrosion-inhibiting compounds	Ventilation filtered	Usually none required	Wipers, residual compound and paint-booth filters[5] treated and landfilled
Vapour degreasing	Chillers to recondense vapours Enclosed systems, or Activated carbon collection	Degreasing solvent separation from wastewater	Toxic degreasing solvent recycled, residual treated and landfilled
Aqueous degreasing	Usually none required	Onsite pretreatment and monitoring	Pretreatment sludge managed as hazardous waste

[1] Most aerospace facilities are required to own an industrial wastewater pretreatment facility. Some may have full treatment.

[2] Control efficiency usually must be greater than 95% removal/destruction of incoming concentrations. Commonly 98% or greater is achieved by activated carbon or thermal oxidation units.

[3] Strict regulations on landfilling specify treatment and landfill construction and monitoring.

[4] Toxicity is measured by bioassay and/or leaching tests designed to predict results in solid waste landfills.

[5] Usually filtered paint booths. Work done out of sequence or touch up, etc. is usually exempt due to practical considerations.

toxins, such as cadmium, from the products and the accelerated phase-out of ozone depleter compounds. The Netherlands require operators to justify the use of cadmium as essential for flight safety, for example.

Noise regulations have followed a similar course. The United States Federal Aviation Administration and the International Civil Aviation Organization have set aggressive targets for the improvement of jet engine noise reduction (e.g., the United States Airport Noise and Capacity Act of 1990). Airlines are faced with the option of replacing older aircraft such as the Boeing 727 or McDonnell Douglas DC-9 (Stage 2 aircraft as defined by the ICAO) with new generation airplanes, re-engining or retrofitting these aircraft with "hush" kits. Elimination of noisy Stage 2 aircraft is mandated by 31 December 1999 in the United States, when Stage 3 rules take effect.

Another hazard posed by aerospace operation is the threat of falling debris. Items such as waste, aircraft parts and satellites descend with varying degrees of frequency. The most common in terms of frequency is the so-called blue ice which results when leaking toilet system drains allow waste to freeze outside the aircraft and then separate and fall. Aviation authorities are considering rules to require additional inspection and correction of leaking drains. Other hazards such as satellite debris may occasionally be hazardous (e.g., radioactive instruments or power sources), but present extremely low risk to the public.

Most companies have formed organizations to address emission reduction. Goals for environmental performance are established and policies are in place. Management of the permits, safe material handling and transportation, disposal and treatment require engineers, technicians and administrators.

Environmental engineers, chemical engineers and others are employed as researchers and administrators. In addition, programmes exist to help remove the source of chemical and noise emissions within the design or the process.

References

Aerospace Industries Association (AIA). 1995. *Advanced Composite Material Manufacturing Operations, Safety and Health Practice Observations and Recommendations*, edited by G. Rountree. Richmond, BC:AIA.

Donoghue, JA. 1994. Smog Alert. *Air Transport World* 31(9):18.

Dunphy, BE and WS George. 1983. Aircraft and aerospace industry. In *Encyclopaedia of Occupational Health and Safety*, 3rd edition. Geneva: ILO.

International Civil Aviation Organization (ICAO). 1981. *International Standards and Recommended Practices: Environmental Protection*. Annex 16 to the Convention on International Civil Aviation, Volume II. Montreal: ICAO.

Other relevant readings

Bourcier, DR, 1989. Exposure evaluation of composite materials with emphasis on cured composite dust. *Applied Industrial Hygiene* (December):40-46.

Suppliers of Advanced Composite Materials Association (SACMA). 1991. Safe Handling of Advanced Composite Materials, 2nd edition. Arlington, VA: SACMA.

90. AEROSPACE MANUFACTURE AND MAINTENANCE

MOTOR VEHICLES AND HEAVY EQUIPMENT

91

Chapter Editor
Franklin E. Mirer

Contents

AUTOMOBILE AND TRANSPORTATION EQUIPMENT INDUSTRY

Franklin E. Mirer

General Profile

Distinct segments of the automobile and transportation equipment industry produce:

- cars and light trucks
- medium and heavy trucks
- buses
- farm and construction equipment
- industrial trucks
- motorcycles.

The characteristic assembly line for the finished vehicle is supported by separate manufacturing facilities for various parts and components. Vehicle components may be manufactured within the parent enterprise or purchased from separate corporate entities. The industry is a century old. Production in the North American, European and (since the Second World War) Japanese sectors of the industry became concentrated in a few corporations which maintained branch assembly operations in South America, Africa and Asia for sales to those markets. International trade in finished vehicles has increased since the 1970s, and trade in original equipment and replacement auto parts from facilities in the developing world is increasingly important.

Table 91.1 • Production processes for automobile production.

Facility type	Product and process
Ferrous foundry	Castings for machining into engine blocks and heads, other components
Aluminium foundry and die cast	Engine blocks and heads, transmission casings, other cast components
Forging and heat treatment	Pre-machined parts for engines, suspensions and transmissions
Stamping	Body panels and subassemblies
Engine	Machining of castings, assembly into finished product
Transmission	Machining of castings and forgings, assembly into product
Glass	Windshields, side windows and backlights
Automotive parts	Machining, stamping and assembly, including brakes, suspension parts, heating and air conditioning, pollution-control equipment, vehicle lighting
Electrical and electronic	Ignition systems, radios, motors, controllers
Hardware and hard trim	Polymer moulded exterior body panels, trim components
Soft trim	Seat cushions, built up seats, dashboard assemblies, interior body panels
Vehicle assembly	Body shop, painting, chassis assembly, final assembly
Parts depots	Warehousing, parts painting and assembly, packaging and shipping

Manufacture of heavy trucks, buses and farm and construction equipment are distinct businesses from car production, although some auto producers manufacture for both markets, and farm and construction equipment are also made by the same corporations. This line of products uses large diesel engines rather than gasoline engines. Production rates are typically slower, volumes smaller and processes less mechanized.

The types of facilities, the production processes and the typical components in car production are shown in table 91.1. Figure 91.1 provides a flow chart for the steps in automobile production. The standard industrial classifications that are found in this industry include: motor vehicles and car body assembly, truck and bus body assembly, motor vehicle parts and accessories, iron and steel foundries, non-ferrous foundries, automotive stampings, iron and steel forgings, engine electrical equipment, auto and apparel trimmings and others. The number of people employed in the manufacture of parts exceeds that employed in assembly. These processes are supported by facilities for design of the vehicle, construction and maintenance of plant and equipment, clerical and managerial functions and a dealer and repair function. In the United States, car dealers, service stations and wholesale auto parts facilities employ about twice as many workers as the manufacturing functions.

The workforce is predominantly male. In the United States, for example, it is about 80% male. Female employment is higher in trim and other lighter manufacturing processes. There is limited opportunity for job transfer from hourly work to clerical work or to technical and professional employment. Assembly line supervisors do, however, often come from the production and maintenance units. About 20% of hourly employees are employed in the skilled trades, although the fraction of employees in any particular facility who are in skilled trades varies greatly, from less than 10% in assembly operations to almost 50% in stamping operations. Because of contractions in employment levels over the decade of the 1980s, the average age of the workforce in the late 1990s exceeds 45 years, with hiring of new workers appearing only since 1994.

Major Sectors and Processes

Ferrous casting

Founding or metal casting involves the pouring of molten metal into a hollow inside a heat-resistant mould, which is the outside or negative shape of the pattern of the desired metal object. The mould may contain a core to determine the dimensions of any internal cavity in the final metal object. Foundry work consists of the following basic steps:

- making a pattern of the desired article from wood, metal, plastic or some other material
- making the mould by pouring sand and a binder around the pattern and compacting or setting it
- removing the pattern, inserting any core and assembling the mould
- melting and refining the metal in a furnace
- pouring the molten metal into the mould
- cooling the metal casting
- removing the mould and core from the metal casting by the "punch-out" process (for small castings) and by vibrating screens (shakeout) or hydro-blasting
- removing extra metal (e.g., the metal in the sprue—the pathway for molten metal to enter the mould) and burnt-on sand from the finished casting (fettling) by blasting with steel shot, hand chipping and grinding.

Ferrous foundries of the production type are a characteristic auto industry process. They are used in the automobile industry to produce engine blocks, heads and other parts. There are two basic types of ferrous foundries: gray iron foundries and ductile

Figure 91.1 • Flow chart for automobile production.

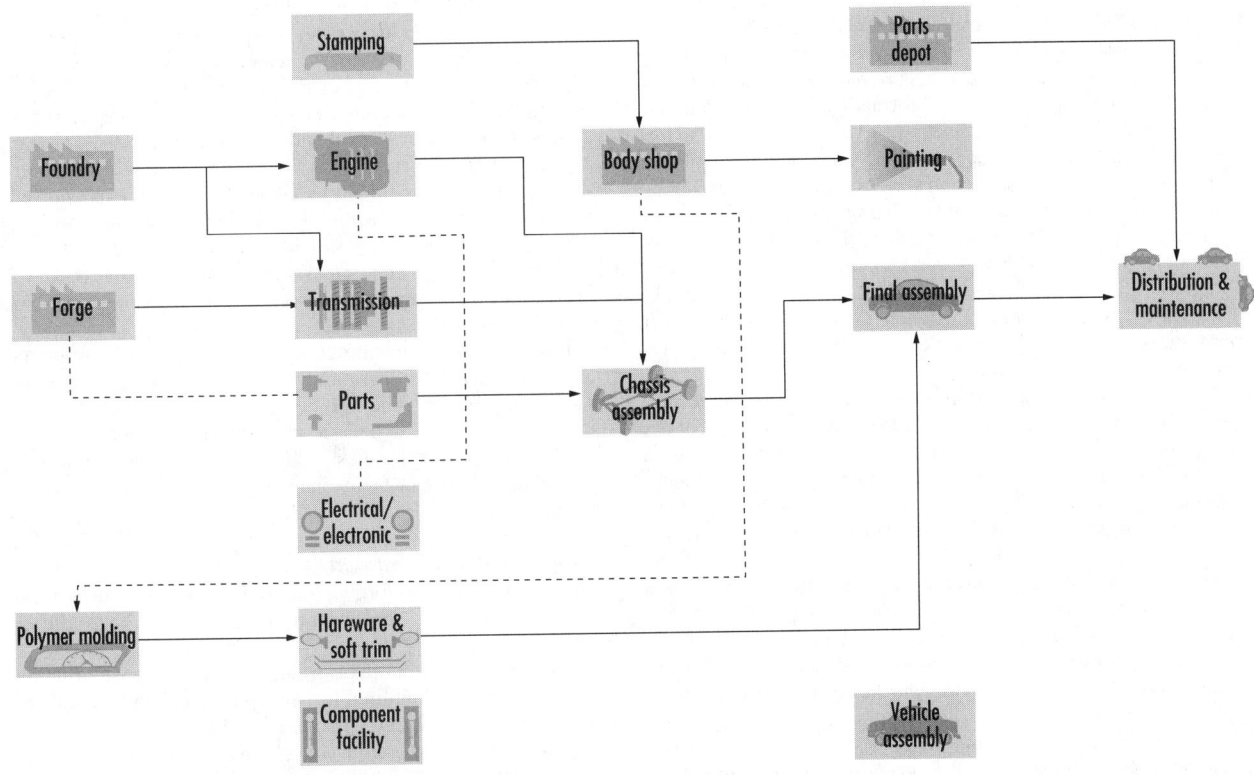

iron foundries. Gray iron foundries use scrap iron or pig iron (new ingots) to make standard iron castings. Ductile iron foundries add magnesium, cerium or other additives (often called *ladle additives*) to the ladles of molten metal before pouring to make nodular or malleable iron castings. The different additives have little impact on workplace exposures.

Typical automobile foundries use cupola or induction furnaces to melt the iron. A cupola furnace is a tall vertical furnace, open at the top, with hinged doors at the bottom. It is charged from the top with alternate layers of coke, limestone and metal; the molten metal is removed at the bottom. An induction furnace melts the metal by passing a high electric current through copper coils on the outside of the furnace. This induces an electric current in the outer edge of the metal charge, which heats the metal due to the high electrical resistance of the metal charge. Melting progresses from the outside of the charge to the inside.

In ferrous foundries, moulds are traditionally made from green sand (silica sand, coal dust, clay and organic binders), which is poured around the pattern, which is usually in two parts, and then compacted. This can be done manually or mechanically on a conveyor belt in production foundries. The pattern is then removed and the mould assembled mechanically or manually. The mould must have a sprue.

If the metal casting is to have a hollow interior, a core must be inserted into the mould. Cores can be made from thermosetting phenol-formaldehyde resins (or similar resins) mixed with sand which is then heated (*hot box* method) or from amine-cured urethane/sand mixtures which cure at room temperature (*cold box* method). The resin/sand mixture is poured into a core box which has a cavity in the desired shape of the core.

The products produced in gray iron castings are typically of a large size, such as engine blocks. The physical size increases the

physical hazards on the job and also presents more difficult dust control problems.

Atmospheric contaminants in foundry processes

Silica-containing dusts. Silica-containing dusts are found in finishing, in shakeout-knockout, in moulding, in core making and in sand system and melt department maintenance activities. Air sampling studies during the 1970s typically found severalfold overexposures to silica, with the highest levels in finishing. Exposures were higher in mechanized production foundries than job shops. Improved control measures including enclosure and exhaust of sand systems and shakeout, mechanization and periodic industrial hygiene measurements have reduced levels. Standard ventilation designs are available for most foundry operations. Exposures above current limits persist in finishing operations due to inadequate sand removal after shakeout and silica burn-in on casting surfaces.

Carbon monoxide. Acutely dangerous carbon monoxide levels are encountered during cupola furnace maintenance and during upsets in process ventilation in the melt department. Excessive levels can also be encountered in cooling tunnels. Carbon monoxide exposures have also been associated with cupola melting and with the combustion of carbon material in green sand moulds. Exposure to sulphur dioxide of unknown origin can also occur, perhaps from sulphur contaminants in the mould.

Metal fumes. Metal fumes are found in melting and pouring operations. It is necessary to use compensating hoods over pouring stations in order to exhaust both metal fumes and combustion gases. Excessive exposures to lead fumes are occasionally encountered in iron foundries and are pervasive in brass foundries; lead fumes in gray iron arise from lead contamination of the scrap iron starting materials.

Other chemical and physical hazards. Formaldehyde, amine vapours and isocyanate pyrolysis products can be found in coremaking and core burn-off products. High-production coremaking is characteristic of the auto industry. Hot box phenol-formaldehyde coremaking replaced oil-sand cores in the mid-1960s and brought substantial formaldehyde exposures, which, in turn, increased the risks of respiratory irritation, lung function abnormalities and lung cancer. Protection requires local exhaust ventilation (LEV) at the core machine, core check stations and conveyor and low emission resins. When the phenol-formaldehyde coremaking has been replaced by cold box amine-cured polyurethane systems, effective maintenance of seals at the core box, and LEV where the cores are stored prior to insertion in the mould, are needed to protect employees against ocular effects of amine vapours.

Workers who are employed in these areas should undergo preplacement and periodic medical examinations, including a chest x ray reviewed by an expert reader, a lung function test and a symptoms questionnaire, which are essential to detect early signs of pneumoconiosis, chronic bronchitis and emphysema. Periodic audiograms are needed, as hearing protection is often ineffective.

High levels of noise and vibration are encountered in processes such as furnace loading, mechanical de-coring, stripping and knockout of castings and fettling with pneumatic tools.

Foundry processes are heat intensive. The radiant heat load in melting, pouring, shakeout, core knockout and sprue removal requires special protective measures. Some of these measures include increased relief time (time away from the job), which is a common practice. Still extra relief during hot, summer months is also commonly provided. Workers should be outfitted with heat-protective clothing and eye and face protection in order to prevent the formation of cataracts. Climatized break areas near the work area improve the protective value of heat relief.

Aluminium casting

Aluminium casting (foundry and die-casting) is used to produce cylinder heads, transmission cases, engine blocks and other automotive parts. These facilities typically cast the products in permanent moulds, with and without sand cores, although the lost foam process has been introduced. In the lost foam process, the polystyrene foam pattern is not removed from the mould but is vaporized by the molten metal. Die casting involves the forcing of molten metal under pressure into metal moulds or dies. It is used to make large numbers of small, precise parts. Die-casting is followed by trim removal on a forge press and some finishing activities. Aluminium may be melted onsite or it can be delivered in molten form.

Hazards can arise because of significant pyrolysis of the core. Silica exposures may be found in permanent mould foundries where large cores are present. Local exhaust on shakeout is needed to prevent hazardous levels of exposure.

Other non-ferrous casting

Other non-ferrous die casting and electroplating processes are used to produce the trim on automotive products, the hardware and the bumpers. Electroplating is a process in which a metal is deposited onto another metal by an electrochemical process.

Bright metal trim traditionally was die-cast zinc, successively plated with copper, nickel and chrome, and then finished by polishing. Carburettor and fuel-injector parts are also die cast. Manual extraction of parts from die-casting machines is increasingly being replaced by mechanical extraction, and bright metal parts are being replaced by painted metal parts and plastic.

Bumpers had been produced by pressing steel, followed by plating, but these methods are increasingly being replaced by the use of polymer parts in passenger vehicles.

Electroplating with chrome, nickel, cadmium, copper and so on is normally carried out in separate workshops and involves exposure to, inhalation of or contact with vapours from the acid plating baths. An increased incidence of cancer has been associated with both chromic acid and sulphuric acid mists. These mists are also extremely corrosive to the skin and respiratory tract. Electroplating baths should be labelled as to contents and should be fitted with special push-pull local exhaust systems. Anti-foaming surface tension agents should be added to the liquid in order to minimize mist formation. Workers should wear eye and face protection, hand and arm protection and aprons. Workers need periodic health checks as well.

Inserting and removing components from open-surface tanks are very hazardous operations which are increasingly becoming more mechanized. The buffing and polishing of plated components on felt belts or discs is strenuous and entails exposure to cotton, hemp and flax dust. This hazard can be minimized by providing a fixture or by mechanizing with transfer-type polishing machines.

Forging and heat treatment

Hot forging and cold forging followed by heat treatment are used to produce engine, transmission and suspension parts and other components.

Historically, automotive forging involved heating iron billets (bars) in individual oil-fired furnaces set close to individually operated steam hammer forges. In these drop hammer forges, the heated iron is placed in the bottom half of a metal die; the top half of the die is attached to the drop hammer. The iron is formed into the desired size and shape by multiple impacts of the dropping hammer. Today, such processes are replaced by induction heating of billets, which are worked in forging presses, which use pressure instead of impact to form the metal part, and drop hammer forges (upsetters) or by cold forging followed by heat treatment.

The forging process is extremely noisy. Noise exposure can be abated by replacing oil furnaces with induction heating devices, and the steam hammers with forging presses and upsetters. The process is also smoky. Oil smoke can be reduced by modernizing the furnace.

Forging and heat treatment are heat-intensive operations. Spot cooling using make-up air that circulates over workers in process areas is needed to reduce heat stress.

Machining

High production machining of engine blocks, crankshafts, transmissions and other components is characteristic of the auto industry. Machining processes are found within various parts manufacturing facilities and are the dominant process in engine, transmission and bearing production. Components such as camshafts, gears, differential pinions and brake drums are produced in machining operations. One-person machining stations are increasingly replaced by multiple station machines, machining cells and transfer lines which may be up to 200 metres in length. Soluble oils and synthetic and semi-synthetic coolants increasingly predominate over straight oils.

Foreign body injuries are common in machining operations; increased mechanical material handling and personal protective equipment are key preventive measures. Increased automation, particularly long transfer lines, increases the risk of severe acute trauma; improved machine guarding and energy lockout are preventive programmes.

The highest level of control measures for coolant mist include full enclosure of machining stations and fluid circulation systems, local exhaust directed outside or recirculated only through a high-efficiency filter, coolant system controls to reduce mist generation and coolant maintenance to control micro-organisms. Addition of nitrite to amine-containing fluids must be prohibited due to risk of nitrosamine production. Oils with substantial polynuclear aromatic hydrocarbon (PAH) content must not be used.

In case-hardening, tempering, nitrate salt baths and other metal heat-treatment processes using furnaces and controlled atmospheres, the microclimate may be oppressive and various airborne toxic substances encountered (e.g., carbon monoxide, carbon dioxide, cyanides).

Machine attendants and workers handling swarf and centrifuging cutting oil prior to filtration and regeneration are exposed to the risk of dermatitis. Exposed workers should be provided with oil-resistant aprons and encouraged to wash thoroughly at the end of each shift.

Grinding and tool sharpening may present a danger of hard metal disease (interstitial lung disease) unless cobalt exposure is measured and controlled. Grinding wheels should be fitted with screens, and eye and face protection and respiratory protective equipment should be worn by grinders.

Machined parts are typically assembled into a finished component, with attendant ergonomic risks. In engine facilities engine testing and running-in must be carried out at test stations fitted with equipment for removing exhaust gases (carbon monoxide, carbon dioxide, unburned hydrocarbons, aldehydes, nitrogen oxides) and with noise-control facilities (booths with sound-absorbent walls, insulated bedplates). Noise levels may be as high as 100 to 105 dB with peaks at 600 to 800 Hz.

Stamping

Pressing of sheet metal (steel) into body panels and other components, often combined with subassembly by welding, is done in large facilities with large and small mechanical power presses. Individual load and unload presses were successively replaced by mechanical extraction devices and now shuttle transfer mechanisms which can load as well, yielding fully automated press lines. Fabrication of subassemblies such as hoods and doors is accomplished with resistance welding presses and is increasingly performed in cells with robot transfer of parts.

The main process is the pressing of steel sheet, strip and light sections on mechanical power presses ranging in capacity from roughly 20 to 2,000 tonnes.

Modern press safety requires effective machinery guarding, prohibition of hands in dies, safety controls including anti-tie down two-hand controls, part revolution clutches and brake monitors, automatic feed and ejection systems, collection of press scrap and the use of personal protective equipment such as aprons, foot and leg protection and hand and arm protection. Outmoded and hazardous full-revolution clutch machines and pull-back devices must be eliminated. Handling rolled steel with cranes and loading of decoilers prior to blanking at the head of a press lines poses a severe safety hazard.

Press operators are exposed to substantial mist levels from drawing compounds which are similar in composition to machining fluids such as soluble oils. Welding fumes are present in fabrication. Noise exposures are high in stamping. Control measures for noise include mufflers on air valves, lining metal chutes with vibration-damping equipment, quieting parts carts, and isolation of presses; the point of operation of the press is not the main site of noise generation.

Following pressing, the pieces are assembled into sub-groups such as hoods and doors using resistance welding presses. Chemical hazards include welding fumes from primarily resistance welding and pyrolysis products of surface coatings, including drawing compound and sealers.

Plastic body panels and trim components

Metal trim parts such as chrome strips are being increasingly replaced by polymer materials. Hard body parts may be made from fibrous glass-reinforced polyester polystyrene systems, acrylonitrile-butadiene-styrene (ABS) thermosetting systems or polyethylene. Polyurethane systems may be high density for body parts, such as nose cones, or low-density foam for seats and interior padding.

Polyurethane foam moulding presents severe respiratory sensitization problems from inhalation of di-isocyanate monomer and possibly catalysts. Complaints persist in operations which are in compliance with limits for toluene di-isocyanate (TDI). Methylene chloride exposures from gun flushing can be substantial. Pouring stations need enclosure and LEV; spills of isocyanate should be minimized by safety devices and cleaned promptly by trained crews. Fires in curing ovens are also a problem in these facilities. Seat manufacture has severe ergonomic stresses, which can be reduced by fixtures, especially for stretching upholstery over cushions.

Styrene exposure from fibrous glass lay-up should be controlled by enclosing storage of mats and local exhaust. Dusts from grinding cured parts contain fibrous glass and should also be controlled by ventilation.

Vehicle assembly

Assembly of components into the finished vehicle typically takes place on a mechanized conveyor involving upwards of a thousand employees per shift, with additional support personnel. The largest segment of employees in the industry are in this process type.

A vehicle assembly plant is divided into distinct units: the body shop, which can include subassembly activities also found in a stamping; paint; chassis assembly; cushion room (which can be outsourced); and final assembly. Paint processes have evolved toward lower-solvent, more reactive formulations in recent years, with increasing use of robot and mechanical application. The body shop has become increasingly automated with reduced arc welding and replacement of hand-operated spot-welding guns with robots.

Light truck assembly (vans, pickups, sport utility vehicles) is similar in process to car assembly. Heavy truck, farm and construction equipment manufacture involves less mechanization and automation, longer cycle jobs, heavier physical labour, more arc welding and different paint systems.

The body shop of an assembly plant assembles the shell of the vehicle. Resistance welding machines may be transfer type, robotic or individually operated. Suspended spot welding machines are heavy and cumbersome to manipulate even when fitted with a counterbalance system. Transfer machines and robots have eliminated many manual jobs and removed workers from close, direct exposure to hot metal, sparks and combustion products of the mineral oil which contaminates the sheet metal. However, increased automation carries increased risk of severe injury to maintenance workers; energy lockout programmes and more elaborate and automatic machine guarding systems, including presence-sensing devices, are needed in automated body shops. Arc welding is employed to a limited degree. During this work, employees are exposed to intense visible and ultraviolet radiation and risk inhalation of combustion gases. LEV, protective screens and partitions, welding visors or goggles, gloves and aprons are needed for arc welders.

The body shop has the greatest laceration and foreign body injury hazards.

In past years assembly techniques and body panel defect retouching processes entailed soldering with lead and tin alloys (also containing traces of antimony). Soldering and especially the grinding away of excess solder produced a severe risk of lead poisoning, including fatal cases when the process was introduced in the 1930s. Protective measures included an isolated solder grind booth, respirators supplying positive-pressure air for solder grinders, hygiene facilities and lead-in-blood monitoring. Nevertheless, increased body burdens of lead and occasional cases of lead poisoning among workers and families persisted into the 1970s. Lead body solder has been eliminated in US passenger vehicles. In addition, noise levels in these processes may range up to 95 to 98 dB, with peaks at 600 to 800 Hz.

Automobile bodies from the body shop enter the paint shop on a conveyor where they are degreased, often by the manual application of solvents, cleaned in a closed tunnel (bonderite) and undercoated. The undercoat is then rubbed down by hand with an oscillating tool using wet abrasive paper, and the final layers of paint are applied and then cured in an oven. In paint shops, workers may inhale toluene, xylene, methylene chloride, mineral spirits, naphtha, butyl and amyl acetate and methyl alcohol vapours from body, booth and paint gun cleaning. Spray painting is carried on in downdraft booths with a continuously filtered air supply. Solvent vapour at painting stations is typically well controlled by down-draft ventilation, which is needed for product quality. Inhalation of paint particulate was formerly less well controlled, and some paints in the past contained salts of chromium and lead. In a well controlled booth, the workers should not have to wear respiratory protective equipment to achieve compliance with exposure limits. Many voluntarily wear respirators for overspray. Recently introduced two-component polyurethane paints should be sprayed only when air-supplied helmets are used with suitable booth re-entry times. Environmental regulations have spurred the development of high-solids paints with lower solvent content. Newer resin systems may generate substantial formaldehyde exposure, and powdered paints now being introduced are epoxy formulations which may be sensitizers. Recirculation of paint booth and oven exhaust from roof ventilating units into work areas outside the booth is a common complaint; this problem can be prevented by exhaust stacks of sufficient height.

In the production of commercial vehicles (lorries (trucks), trams, trolley buses) and farm and construction equipment, manual spray painting is still widely employed due to the large surfaces to be covered and the need for frequent retouching. Lead and chromate paints may still be employed in these operations.

The painted body work is dried in hot air and infra-red ovens fitted with exhaust ventilation and then moves on to join the mechanical components in the final assembly shop, where the body, engine and transmission are joined together and the upholstery and internal trim are fitted. It is here that conveyor belt work is to be seen in its most highly developed version. Each worker carries out a series of tasks on each vehicle with cycle times of about 1 minute. The conveyor system transports the bodies gradually along the assembly line. These processes demand constant vigilance and may be highly monotonous and act as stressors on certain subjects. Although normally not imposing excessive metabolic lead, these processes virtually all involve moderate to severe risk factors for musculoskeletal disorders. The postures or movements the worker is obliged to adopt, such as when installing components inside the vehicle or working under the body (with hands and forearms above head level) are the most readily abated hazards, although force and repetition must also be reduced to abate risk factors. After final assembly the vehicle is tested, finished and dispatched. Inspection can be limited to roller tests on a roller bed (where ventilation of exhaust fumes is important) or can include track trials on different types of surface, water and dust tightness trials and road trials outside the factory.

Parts depots

Parts depots are integral to distributing the finished product and supplying repair parts. Workers in these high-production warehouses use order pickers to retrieve parts from elevated locations, with automated parts-delivery systems in three-shift operations. Manual handling of packaged parts is common. Painting and other production processes may be found in parts depots.

Testing of prototypes

Testing of automobile prototypes is specialized to the industry. Test drivers are exposed to a variety of physiological stresses, such as violent acceleration and deceleration, jolting and vibration, carbon monoxide and exhaust fumes, noise, work spells of prolonged duration and different ambient and climatic conditions. Endurance drivers endure special stresses. Fatal vehicle accidents occur in this occupation.

Assembly of heavy trucks and farm and construction equipment

The processes in these industry sectors are essentially the same as in the assembly of cars and light trucks. Contrasts include: slower pace of production, including non-assembly-line operations; more arc welding; riveting of truck cabs; movement of components by crane; use of chromate-containing pigments; and diesel on drive-off at the end of the assembly line. These sectors include more producers relative to volume and are less vertically integrated.

Manufacture of locomotives and rail cars

Distinct segments of railroad equipment manufacture include locomotives, passenger cars, freight cars and electric self-propelled passenger cars. Compared to car and truck manufacture, assembly processes involve longer cycles; there is more reliance on cranes for material handling; and arc welding is more heavily used. The large size of the products makes engineering control of spray paint operations difficult and creates situations where workers are completely enclosed in the product while welding and spray painting.

Health Problems and Disease Patterns

Production processes are not unique to the auto industry, but often the scale of production and the high degree of integration and automation combine to present special hazards to employees. Hazards to employees in this complex industry must be arrayed in three dimensions: process type, job classification group and adverse outcome.

Adverse outcomes with distinct cause and prevention methods can be distinguished as: fatal and severe acute injuries; injuries generally; repeated trauma disorders; short-onset chemical effects; occupational disease from long-term chemical exposure; service sector hazards (including infectious disease and client- or customer-initiated violence); and work environment hazards such as psychosocial stress.

Job classification groups in the automobile industry can usefully be divided by divergent hazard spectra: skilled trades (maintenance, service, fabrication and installation of production equipment); mechanical material handling (powered industrial truck and crane operators); production service (including non-skilled maintenance and cleaners); fixed production (the largest grouping, including assemblers and machine operators); clerical and technical; and executive and managerial.

Health and safety outcomes common to all processes

According to the US Bureau of Labor Statistics, the auto industry has one of the highest injury rates overall, with 1 in 3 employees hurt each year, 1 in 10 seriously enough to lose time from work. Lifetime risk of occupational fatality from acute traumatic injury is 1 in 2,000. Certain hazards are generally characteristic of occupational groupings throughout the industry. Other hazards, particularly chemicals, are characteristic of specific production processes.

Skilled trades and mechanical material-handling occupations are at high risk for fatal and severe acute traumatic injuries. The skilled trades are less than 20% of the workforce, yet suffer 46% of fatal occupational injuries. Mechanical material-handling occupations suffer 18% of fatalities. The skilled-trades fatalities largely occur during maintenance and service activities, with uncontrolled energy as the leading cause. Preventive measures include energy lockout programmes, machine guarding, fall prevention and industrial truck and crane safety, all based on directed job safety analysis.

By contrast, fixed production occupations suffer higher rates of injuries generally and repeated trauma disorders, but are at reduced risk to fatal injury. Musculoskeletal injuries, including repeated trauma disorders and closely related strains and sprains caused by overexertion or repetitive motion are 63% of disabling injuries in assembly facilities and about half the injuries in other process types. The chief preventive measures are ergonomics programmes based on risk factor analysis and structured reduction in force, frequency and postural stresses of high-risk jobs.

Production service occupations and skilled trades face the majority of acute and high-level chemical hazards. Typically these exposures occur during routine cleaning, response to spills and process upsets and in confined space entry during maintenance and service activities. Solvent exposures are prominent among these hazardous situations. The long-term health consequences of these intermittent high exposures are not known. High exposures to carcinogenic coal tar pitch volatiles are experienced by employees tarring wood block floors in many facilities or torching floor bolts in stamping plants. Excess mortality from lung cancer has been observed in such groups. Preventive measures focus on confined space entry and hazardous waste and emergency response programmes, although long-term prevention depends on process change to eliminate exposure.

Effects of chronic exposure to chemicals and some physical agents are most evident among fixed production workers, principally because these groups can more feasibly be studied. Virtually all the process-specific adverse effects described above arise from exposures in compliance with existing occupational exposure limits, so protection will depend on reduction of allowable limits. In the near term, best practices including well designed and maintained exhaust systems serve to reduce exposures and risks.

Noise-induced hearing loss is pervasive in all segments of the industry.

All sectors of the workforce are subject to psychosocial stress, although these are more apparent in the clerical, technical, administrative support, managerial and professional occupations because of their generally less intense exposure to other hazards. Nevertheless, job stress is likely more intense among production and maintenance employees, and stress effects are likely greater. No effective means of reducing stresses from night work and rotating shift work have been implemented, although shift preference agreements allow for some self selection, and shift premiums compensate those employees assigned to off shifts. Acceptance of rotating shifts by the workforce is historical and cultural. Skilled trades and maintenance employees work substantially more overtime and during holidays, vacations and shutdowns, compared to production employees. Typical work schedules include two production shifts and a shorter maintenance shift; this provides flexibility for overtime in periods of increased production.

The discussion which follows groups chemical and some specific physical hazards by production type and addresses injury and ergonomic hazards by job classification.

Foundries

Foundries stand out among auto industry processes with a higher fatality rate, arising from molten metal spills and explosions, cupola maintenance, including bottom drop, and carbon monoxide hazards during relining. Foundries report a higher fraction of foreign body, contusion and burn injuries and a lower fraction of musculoskeletal disorders than other facilities. Foundries also have the highest noise exposure levels (Andjelkovich et al. 1990; Andjelkovich et al. 1995; Koskela 1994; Koskela et al. 1976; Silverstein et al. 1986; Virtamo and Tossavainen 1976).

A recent review of mortality studies including the American auto industry showed that foundry workers experienced increased rates of deaths from lung cancer in 14 of 15 studies (Egan-Baum, Miller and Waxweiller 1981; Mirer et al. 1985). Because high lung cancer rates are found among cleaning room workers where the primary exposure is silica, it is likely that mixed silica-containing dust exposure is a major cause (IARC 1987, 1996), although polynuclear aromatic hydrocarbon exposures are also found. Increased mortality from non-malignant respiratory disease was found in 8 of 11 studies. Silicosis deaths were recorded as well. Clinical studies find x-ray changes characteristic of pneumoconiosis, lung function deficits characteristic of obstruction and increased respiratory symptoms in modern production foundries with the highest levels of controls. These effects arose from exposure conditions which prevailed from the 1960s onward and strongly indicate that health risks persist under current conditions as well.

Asbestos effects are found on x ray among foundry workers; victims include production as well as maintenance workers with identifiable asbestos exposures.

Machining operations

A recent review of mortality studies among workers in machining operations found apparent exposure-related increased stomach, oesophageal, rectal, pancreatic and laryngeal cancer in multiple studies (Silverstein et al. 1988; Eisen et al. 1992). Known carcinogenic agents historically present in coolants include polynuclear aromatic compounds, nitrosamines, chlorinated paraffins and formaldehyde. Present formulations contain reduced amounts of these agents, and exposures to coolant particulate are reduced, but cancer risk may still occur with present exposures. Clinical studies have documented occupational asthma, increased respiratory symptoms, cross-shift lung function drop and, in one case, legionnaire's disease associated with coolant mist exposure (DeCoufle 1978; Vena et al. 1985; Mallin, Berkeley and Young 1986; Park et al. 1988; Delzell et al. 1993). Respiratory effects are more prominent with synthetics and soluble oils, which contain chemical irritants such as petroleum sulphonates, tall oils, ethanolamines, formaldehyde and formaldehyde donor biocides, as well as bacterial products such as endotoxin. Skin disorders are still common among machining workers, with greater problems reported for those exposed to synthetic fluids.

Pressed metal operations

The characteristic injury hazards in mechanical power presswork are crushing and amputation injuries, especially of the hands, due to trapping in the press, and hand, foot and leg injuries, caused by scrap metal from the press.

Pressed metal facilities have twice the proportion of laceration injuries of auto industry facilities generally. Such operations have a higher proportion of skilled workers than typical for the industry, especially if die construction is pursued onsite. Die change is an especially hazardous activity.

Mortality studies in the metal-stamping industry are limited. One such study found increased mortality from stomach cancer; another found increased mortality from lung cancer among maintenance welders and millwrights exposed to coal tar pitch volatiles.

Hardware and electroplating

A mortality study of employees at an automotive hardware plant found excess mortality from lung cancer among workers in departments which integrated zinc die-cast and electroplating. Chromic and sulphuric acid mist or die-cast smoke were likely causes.

Vehicle assembly

Injury rates, including cumulative trauma disorders (CTDs), are now the highest in assembly of all processes in the auto sector, due largely to the high rate of musculoskeletal disorders from repetitive work or overexertion. Musculoskeletal disorders account for more than 60% of disabling injuries in this sector.

Several mortality studies in assembly plants observed increased deaths from lung cancer. No specific process within the assembly sector has been shown responsible, so this issue remains under investigation.

Testing of prototypes

Fatal vehicle accidents occur in this occupation.

Design work

The design staffs of auto companies have been the subject of health and safety concern. Prototype dies are made by first con-structing the pattern of wood, using extremely hard wood, laminates and particleboard. Plastic models are made by fibrous glass lay-up with polyester-polystyrene resins. Metal models are essentially dies constructed by precision machining. Wood, plastic and metal model and pattern makers have been shown to suffer excess incidence and mortality from colon and rectal cancer in repeated studies. A specific agent has not been identified.

Environmental and Public Health Issues

Environmental regulation aimed at stationary sources in the auto industry principally addresses volatile organic compounds from spray painting and other surface coatings. Pressure to reduce solvent content of paints has actually changed the nature of the coatings used. These rules affect supplier and parts plants as well as vehicle assembly. Foundries are regulated for air emissions of particulates and sulphur dioxide, while spent sand is treated as hazardous waste.

Vehicle emissions and vehicle safety are critical public health and safety issues regulated outside the occupational arena.

References

Andjelkovich, DA, RM Matthew, RB Richardson, and RJ Levine. 1990. Mortality of iron foundry workers. I. Overall findings. *J Occup Med* 32:529-540.

Andjelkovich, DA, DB Janszen, MH Brown, RB Richardson, and FJ Miller. 1995. Mortality of iron foundry workers. IV. Analysis of a subcohort exposed to formaldehyde. *J Occup Med* 37:826-837.

DeCoufle, P. 1978. Further analysis of cancer mortality patterns among workers exposed to cutting oil mists. *J Natl Cancer Inst* 61:1025-1030.

Delzell, E, M Macaluso, Y Honda, and H Austin. 1993. Mortality patterns among men in the motor vehicle manufacturing industry. *Am J Ind Med* 24:471-484.

Egan-Baum, E, BA Miller, and RJ Waxweiller. 1981. Lung cancer and other mortality patterns among foundrymen. *Scand J Work Environ Health* 7 suppl 4:73-89.

Eisen, EA, PE Tolbert, RR Monson, and TJ Smith. 1992. Mortality studies of machining fluid exposure in the automobile industry. I. A standardized mortality ratio analysis. *Am J Ind Med* 22:809-824.

International Agency for Research on Cancer (IARC). 1987. *Silica and Some Silicates*. Vol. 42. Lyon: IARC.

—. 1996. *Silica, Some Silicates, Coal Dust and Para-aramid Fibrils*. Vol. 68. Lyon: IARC.

Koskela, R-S. 1994. Cardiovascular diseases among foundry workers exposed to carbon monoxide. *Scand J Work Environ Health* 20:286-293.

Koskela, R-S, S Hernberg, R Karava, E Jarvinen, and M Murminen. 1976. A mortality study of foundry workers. *Scand J Work Environ Health* 2 suppl 1:73-89.

Mallin, K, L Berkeley, and Q Young. 1986. A proportional mortality ratio study of workers in a construction and diesel engine manufacturing plant. *Am J Ind Med* 10:127-141.

Mirer, F, M Silverstein, N Maizlish, R Park, B Silverstein, and L Brodsky. 1985. Dust measurements and cancer mortality at a ferrous foundry. In *Silica, Silicosis, and Cancer: Controversy in Occupational Medicine*, edited by DF Goldsmith. New York: Praeger.

Park, RM, DH Wegman, MA Silverstein, N Maizlish, and F Mirer. 1988. Causes of death among workers in a bearing plant. *Am J Ind Med* 13:569-580.

Silverstein, M, N Maizlish, RM Park, B Silverstein, L Brodsky, and F Mirer. 1986. Mortality among ferrous foundry workers. *Am J Ind Med* 10:27-43.

Silverstein, M, RM Park, M Marmor, N Maizlish, and F Mirer. 1988. Mortality among bearing plant workers exposed to metalworking fluids and abrasives. *J Occup Med* 30: 706-714.

Vena, JE, HA Sulty, RC Fielder, and RE Barnes. 1985. Mortality of workers in an automotive engine and parts manufacturing complex. *Br J Ind Med* 42:85-93.

Virtamo, M and A Tossaveinen. 1976. Carbon monoxide in foundry air. *Scand J Work Environ Health* 2:37-41.

Other relevant readings

Acquavella, J, T Leet, and G Johnson. 1993. Occupational experience and mortality among a cohort of metal components manufacturing workers. *Epidemiology* 4:428-434.

Park, RM. 1996. The healthy worker survivor effect and mortality at two automotive engine manufacturing plants. *Am J Ind Med* 30:655-663.

Rotimi, C, E Austin, E Delzell, K Day, M Macaluso, and Y Honda. 1993. Retrospective follow-up study of foundry and engine plant workers. *Am J Ind Med* 24:485-498.

SHIP AND BOAT BUILDING AND REPAIR

92

Chapter Editor
James R. Thornton

Contents

● GENERAL PROFILE

Chester Matthews

The complex merchant vessels, passenger ships and ships of war of the 1990s comprise tons of steel and aluminium as well as a variety of materials that range from the most common to the very exotic. Each vessel may contain hundreds or even thousands of kilometres of pipe and wire equipped with the most sophisticated power plants and electronic equipment available. They must be constructed and maintained to survive the most hostile of environments, while providing comfort and safety for the crews and passengers aboard and reliably completing their missions.

Ship construction and repair rank among the most hazardous industries in the world. According to the US Bureau of Labor Statistics (BLS), for example, shipbuilding and repair is one of the three most hazardous industries. While materials, construction methods, tools and equipment have changed, improved radically over time and continue to evolve, and while training and emphasis on safety and health have significantly improved the lot of the shipyard worker, the fact remains that throughout the world each year workers die or are seriously injured while employed in the construction, maintenance or repair of ships.

Despite advances in technology, many of the tasks and conditions associated with constructing, launching, maintaining and repairing today's vessels are essentially the same as they were when the very first keel was laid thousands of years ago. The size and shape of the components of a vessel and the complexity of the work involved in assembling and outfitting them largely preclude any kind of automated processes, although some automation has been made possible by recent technological advances. Repair work remains largely resistant to automation. Work in the industry is very labour intensive, requiring highly specialized skills, which often must be utilized under less than ideal circumstances and in a physically challenging situation.

The natural environment in itself poses a significant challenge for shipyard work. While there are a few shipyards that have the capability to construct or repair vessels under cover, in most cases shipbuilding and repairing is done largely out of doors. There are shipyards located in every climatic region of the world, and while the more extreme northern yards are dealing with winter (i.e., slippery conditions wrought by ice and snow, short daylight hours and the physical effects on workers of long hours on cold steel surfaces, often in uncomfortable postures), the yards in more southerly climes are faced with the potential for heat stress, sunburn, working surfaces hot enough to cook on, insects and even snake bites. Much of this work is done over, in, under or around the water. Often, swift tidal currents may be whipped by the wind, causing a pitching and rolling working surface on which workers must perform very exacting tasks in a variety of positions, with tools and equipment that have the potential for inflicting serious physical injury. That same often unpredictable wind is a force to be reckoned with when moving, suspending or placing units often weighing in excess of 1,000 tons with a single or multiple crane lift. The challenges presented by the natural environment are manifold and provide for a seemingly endless combination of situations for which safety and health practitioners must design preventive measures. A well-informed and trained workforce is critical.

As the ship grows from the first steel plates which comprise the keel, it becomes an ever-changing, ever-more-complex environment with a constantly changing subset of potential hazards and hazardous situations requiring not only well-founded procedures for accomplishing the work, but mechanisms for recognizing and dealing with the thousands of unplanned situations which invariably arise during the construction process. As the vessel grows, scaffolding or staging is added continuously to provide access to the hull. While the very construction of this staging is highly specialized and at times inherently hazardous work, its completion means that workers are subjected to greater and greater risk as the height of the staging over the ground or water increases. As the hull begins to take form, the interior of the ship is also taking shape as modern construction methods permit large subassemblies to be stacked on one another, and enclosed and confined spaces are formed.

It is at this point in the process that the labour-intensive nature of the work is most apparent. Safety and health measures must be well coordinated. Worker awareness (for the safety of both the individual worker and those nearby) is fundamental to accident-free work.

Each space within the confines of the hull is designed for a very specialized purpose. The hull may be a void which will contain ballast, or it may house tanks, cargo holds, sleeping compartments or a highly sophisticated combat control centre. In every case building it will require a number of specialized workers to perform a variety of tasks within close proximity of one another. A typical scenario may find pipefitters brazing valves into position, electricians pulling wire cable and installing circuit boards, brush painters doing touch-up, shipfitters positioning and welding deckplates, crews of insulators or carpenters and a test crew verifying that a system is activated in the same area at the same time. Such situations, and others even more complex, take place all day, every day, in an ever-changing pattern dictated by schedule or engineering changes, personnel availability and even the weather.

The application of coatings presents a number of hazards. Spray-painting operations must be accomplished, often in confined spaces and with volatile paints and solvents and/or a variety of epoxy-type coatings, notorious for their sensitizing characteristics.

Enormous progress in the area of safety and health for the shipyard worker has been made over the years through the development of improved equipment and construction methods, safer facilities and a highly-trained workforce. However, the greatest gains have been made and continue to be made as we turn our attention toward the individual worker and focus on eliminating behaviour which contributes so significantly to accidents. While this could be said of almost any industry, the labour-intensive character of shipyard work makes it especially important. As we move toward safety and health programmes which more actively involve the worker and incorporate his or her ideas, not only does the worker's awareness of the hazards inherent in the job and how to avoid them increase, he or she begins to feel ownership for the programme. It is with this ownership that true success in safety and health can be realized.

SHIP AND BOAT CONSTRUCTION AND REPAIR ●

James R. Thornton

Shipbuilding

The construction of a ship is a highly technical and complicated process. It involves the blending of many skilled trades and contract employees working under the control of a primary contractor. Shipbuilding is performed for both military and commercial purposes. It is an international business, with major shipyards around the globe competing for a fairly limited amount of work.

Figure 92.1 • Shipbuilding flow chart.

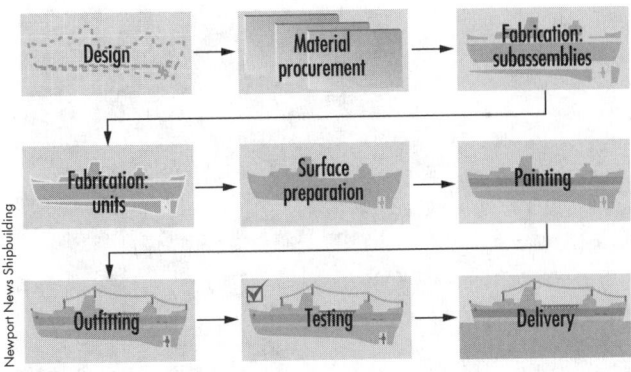

Figure 92.3 • Bending of steel sheet.

Shipbuilding has changed radically since the 1980s. Formerly, most construction took place in a building or graving dock, with the ship constructed almost piece by piece from the ground up. However, advances in technology and more detailed planning have made it possible to construct the vessel in subunits or modules that have utilities and systems integrated within. Thus, the modules may be relatively easily connected. This process is faster, less expensive and provides better quality control. Further, this type of construction lends itself towards automation and robotics, not only saving money, but reducing exposures to chemical and physical hazards.

Overview of the Ship Construction Process

Figure 92.1 gives an overview of shipbuilding. The initial step is design. The design considerations for various types of ships vary widely. Ships may transport materials or people, may be surface ships or subsurface, may be military or commercial and may be nuclear or non-nuclear powered. In the design phase, not only

should normal construction parameters be considered, but the safety and health hazards associated with the construction or repair process must be considered. In addition, environmental issues must be addressed.

The basic component of ship building is steel plate. The plates are cut, shaped, bent or otherwise manufactured to the desired configuration specified by the design (see figures 92.2 and 92.3). Typically the plates are cut by an automatic flame cutting process to various shapes. These shapes may be then welded together to form I and T beams and other structural members (see figure 92.4).

The plates are then sent to fabrication shops, where they are joined into various units and subassemblies (see figure 92.5). At this juncture, piping, electrical and other utility systems are assembled and integrated into the units. The units are assembled using automatic or manual welding or a combination of the two. Several types of welding processes are employed. The most common is stick welding, in which a consumable electrode is used to join

Figure 92.2 • Automatic flame cutting of steel plate in fabrication shop.

Figure 92.4 • Welded steel plate forming part of a ship's hull.

Figure 92.5 • Working on a ship subassembly.

the steel. Other welding processes use inert gas shielded arcs and even non-consumable electrodes.

The units or subassemblies are usually then transferred to an open-air platen or lay down area where erection, or joining of assemblies, occurs to form even larger units or blocks (see figure 92.6). Here, additional welding and fitting occurs. Further, the units and welds must undergo quality-control inspections and testing such as radiography, ultrasonic and other destructive or non-destructive tests. Those welds found defective must be removed by grinding, arc-air grouping or chiseling and then replaced. At this stage the units are abrasive blasted to ensure proper profiling, and painted (see figure 92.7). Paint may be applied by brush, roller or spray gun. Spraying is most commonly utilized. The paints may be flammable or toxic or pose an environmental threat. Control of abrasive blasting and painting operations must be performed at this time.

The completed larger units are then moved to the graving dock, shipway or final assembly area. Here, the larger units are joined together to form the vessel (see figure 92.8). Again, much welding and fitting occur. Once the hull is structurally complete and watertight, the vessel is launched. This may involve sliding it into the water from the shipway on which it was constructed, flooding of the dock in which it was constructed or lowering the vessel into the water. Launchings are almost always accompanied by great celebration and fanfare.

After the ship is launched, it enters the outfitting phase. A large amount of time and equipment are required. The work includes the fitting of cabling and piping, the furnishing of galleys and accommodations, insulation work, installation of electronic equipment and navigation aids and installation of propulsion and ancillary machinery. This work is performed by a wide variety of skilled trades.

After completion of the outfitting phase, the ship undergoes both dock and sea trials, during which all the ship's systems are proved to be fully functional and operational. Finally, after all testing and associated repair work is performed, the ship is delivered to the customer.

Steel fabrication

A detailed discussion of the steel fabrication process follows. It is discussed in the context of cutting, welding and painting.

Cutting

The "assembly line" of the shipyard starts in the steel storage area. Here, large steel plates of various strengths, sizes, and thicknesses are stored and readied for fabrication. The steel is then blasted with abrasive and primed with a construction primer that preserves the steel during the various phases of construction. The steel plate then is transported to a fabrication facility. Here the steel plate is cut by automatic burners to the desired size (see

Figure 92.6 • Combining of ship subassemblies into larger blocks.

Newport News Shipbuilding

Figure 92.7 • Abrasive blasting of ship units prior to painting.

Judi Baldwin

figure 92.2). The resulting strips are then welded together to form the structural components of the vessel (figure 92.4).

Welding

The structural framework of most ships is constructed of various grades of mild and high-strength steel. Steel provides the formability, machinability and weldability required, combined with the strength needed for ocean-going vessels. Various grades of steel predominate in the construction of most ships, although aluminium and other nonferrous materials are used for some superstructures (e.g., deck-houses) and other specific areas within the ship. Other materials found on ships, like stainless steel, galvanized steel and copper-nickel alloy, are used for a variety of corrosion-resistance purposes and to improve structural integrity. However, nonferrous materials are used in far less quantity than steel. Shipboard systems (e.g., ventilation, combat, navigational and piping) are usually where the more "exotic" materials are used. These materials are required to perform a wide variety of functions, including the ship propulsion systems, back-up power, kitchens, pump stations for fuel transfer and combat systems.

Steel used for construction can be subdivided into three types: mild, high-strength and high-alloy steel. Mild steels have valuable properties and are easy to produce, purchase, form and weld. On the other hand, high-strength steels are mildly alloyed to provide mechanical properties that are superior to the mild steels. Extremely high-strength steels have been developed specifically for use in naval construction. In general, the high-strength and high-yield steels are called HY-80, HY-100 and HY-130. They have strength properties in excess of the commercial-grade high-strength steels. More complicated welding processes are necessary for high-strength steels in order to prevent deterioration of their properties. Specific weld rods are needed for high-strength steel, and weld joint heating (preheating) is usually required. A third general class of steels, the high-alloy steels, are made by including relatively large amounts of alloying elements such as nickel, chromium and manganese. These steels, which include stainless steels,

Figure 92.8 • Adding ship's bow to the rest of a vessel.

Newport News Shipbuilding

have valuable corrosion-resistance properties and also require special welding processes.

Steel is an excellent material for shipbuilding purposes, and the choice of welding electrode is critical in all welding applications during construction. The standard goal is to obtain a weld with equivalent strength characteristics to that of the base metal. Since minor flaws are likely to occur in production welding, welds are often designed and welding electrodes chosen to produce welds with properties in excess of those of the base metal.

Aluminium has found increased application as a shipbuilding metal due to its high strength-to-weight ratio compared to steel. Although the use of aluminium for hulls has been limited, aluminium superstructures are becoming more common for both military and merchant ship construction. Vessels made solely from aluminium are primarily smaller-sized boats, such as fishing boats, pleasure boats, small passenger boats, gunboats and hydrofoils. The aluminium used for shipbuilding and repair is generally alloyed with manganese, magnesium, silicon and/or zinc. These alloys offer good strength, corrosion resistance and weldability.

Shipyard welding processes, or more specifically fusion welding, is performed at nearly every location in the shipyard environment. The process involves joining metals by bringing adjoining surfaces to extremely high temperatures to be fused together with a molten filler material. A heat source is used to heat the edges of the joint, permitting them to fuse with molten weld fill metal (electrode, wire or rod). The required heat is usually generated by an electric arc or a gas flame. Shipyards choose the type of welding process based on customer specifications, production rates and a variety of operating constraints including government regulations. Standards for military vessels are usually more stringent than commercial vessels.

An important factor with respect to the fusion-welding processes is arc shielding to protect the weld pool. The temperature of the weld pool is substantially higher than the adjoining metal's melting point. At extremely high temperatures, a reaction with oxygen and nitrogen in the atmosphere is rapid and has negative effects on the weld strength. Should oxygen and nitrogen from the atmosphere become trapped within the weld metal and molten rod, embrittlement of the weld area will occur. To protect against this weld impurity and ensure weld quality, shielding from the atmosphere is required. In most welding processes, shielding is accomplished by addition of a flux, a gas or a combination of the two. Where a flux material is used, gases generated by vaporization and chemical reaction at the electrode tip result in a combination of flux and gas shielding that protect the weld from nitrogen and oxygen entrapment. Shielding is discussed in the following sections, where specific welding processes are described.

In electric arc welding, a circuit is created between the work-piece and an electrode or wire. When the electrode or wire is held a short distance away from the work-piece, a high-temperature arc is created. This arc generates sufficient heat to melt the edges of the work-piece and the tip of the electrode or wire to produce a fusion-welding system. There are a number of electric arc welding processes suitable for use in shipbuilding. All processes require shielding of the weld area from the atmosphere. They may be subdivided into flux-shielded and gas-shielded processes.

Manufacturers of welding equipment and associated consumable and non-consumable products report that arc welding with consumable electrodes is the most universal welding process.

Shielded metal arc welding (SMAW). Flux-shielded electric arc welding processes are distinguished primarily by their manual or semi-automatic nature and the type of consumable electrode used. The SMAW process utilizes a consumable electrode (30.5 to 46 cm in length) with a dry flux coating, held in a holder and fed to the work-piece by the welder. The electrode consists of the solid metal filler rod core, made from either drawn or cast ma-

terial covered with a sheath of metal powders. SMAW is also frequently referred to as "stick welding" and "arc welding". The electrode metal is surrounded by flux that melts as welding progresses, covering the deposited molten metal with slag and enveloping the immediate area in an atmosphere of protective gas. Manual SMAW may be used for down hand (flat), horizontal, vertical and overhead welding. SMAW processes may also be used semi-automatically through the use of a gravity welding machine. Gravity machines use the weight of the electrode and holder to produce travel along the work-piece.

Submerged arc welding (SAW) is another flux-shielded electric arc welding process used in many shipyards. In this process, a blanket of granulated flux is deposited on the work-piece, followed by a consumable bare metal wire electrode. Generally, the electrode serves as the filler material, although in some cases metal granules are added to the flux. The arc, submerged in the blanket of flux, melts the flux to produce a protective insulated molten shield in the weld zone. High heat concentration permits heavy weld deposits at relatively high speeds. After welding, the molten metal is protected by a layer of fused flux, which is subsequently removed and may be recovered. Submerged arc welding must be performed down hand and is ideally suited to butt welding plates together on panel lines, platen areas and erection areas. The SAW process is generally fully automatic, with equipment mounted on a moving carriage or self-propelled platform on top of the work-piece. Since the SAW process is primarily automatic, a good portion of time is spent aligning the weld joint with the machine. Similarly, since the SAW arc operates under a covering of granulated flux, the fume generation rate (FGR) or fume formation rate (FFR) is low and will remain constant under various operating conditions provided that there is adequate flux cover.

Gas metal arc welding (GMAW). Another major category of electric arc welding comprises the gas-shielded processes. These processes generally use bare wire electrodes with an externally supplied shielding gas which may be inert, active or a combination of the two. GMAW, also commonly referred to as *metal inert gas* (MIG) welding, uses a consumable, automatically fed, small-diameter wire electrode and gas shielding. GMAW is the answer to a long-sought method of being able to weld continuously without the interruption of changing electrodes. An automatic wire feeder is required. A wire spooling system provides an electrode/wire filler rate that is at a constant speed, or the speed fluctuates with a voltage sensor. At the point where the electrode meets the weld arc, argon or helium being used as the shielding gas is supplied by the welding gun. It was found that for welding steel, a combination of CO_2 and/or an inert gas could be used. Often, a combination of the gases is used to optimize cost and weld quality.

Gas tungsten arc welding (GTAW). Another type of gas-shielded welding process is gas tungsten arc welding, sometimes referred to as *tungsten inert gas* (TIG) welding or the trade name Heliarc, because helium was initially used as the shielding gas. This was the first of the "new" welding processes, following stick welding by about 25 years. The arc is generated between the work-piece and a tungsten electrode, which is not consumed. An inert gas, usually argon or helium, provides the shielding and provides for a clean, low-fume process. Also, the GTAW process arc does not transfer the filler metal, but simply melts the material and the wire, resulting in a cleaner weld. GTAW is most often employed in shipyards for welding aluminium, sheet metal and small-diameter pipes and tubes, or to deposit the first pass on a multi-pass weld in larger pipe and fittings.

Flux core arc welding (FCAW) uses equipment similar to GMAW in that the wire is fed continuously to the arc. The main difference is that the FCAW electrode is a tubular electrode wire with a flux core centre that helps with localized shielding in the welding

Figure 92.9 • Underwater plasma-arc cutting of steel plate.

Caroline Kiehner

environment. Some flux cored wire provides adequate shielding with the flux core alone. However, many FCAW processes used in the shipbuilding environment require the addition of gas shielding for the quality requirements of the shipbuilding industry.

The FCAW process provides a high-quality weld with higher production rates and welder efficiency than the traditional SMAW process. The FCAW process allows for a full range of production requirements, such as overhead and vertical welding. FCAW electrodes tend to be a little more expensive than SMAW materials, although in many cases increased quality and productivity are worth the investment.

Plasma-arc welding (PAW). The last of the shielded gas welding processes is plasma-metal inert-gas welding. PAW is very similar to the GTAW process except that the arc is forced to pass through a restriction before reaching the work-piece. The result is a jet stream of intensely hot and fast-moving plasma. The plasma is an ionizing stream of gas that carries the arc, which is generated by constricting the arc to pass through a small orifice in the torch. PAW results in a more concentrated, high-temperature arc, and this permits faster welding. Aside from the use of the orifice to accelerate the gas, PAW is identical to GTAW, using a non-consumable tungsten electrode and an inert gas shield. PAW is generally manual and has minimal use in shipbuilding, although it is sometimes used for flame spraying applications. It is used primarily for steel cutting in the shipbuilding environment (see figure 92.9).

Gas welding, brazing and soldering. Gas welding employs heat generated by the burning of a gas fuel and generally uses a filler rod for the metal deposited. The most common fuel is acetylene, used in combination with oxygen (oxyacetylene gas welding). A hand-held torch directs the flame to the work-piece while simultaneously melting filler metal which is deposited on the joint. The surface of the work-piece melts to form a molten puddle, with filler material used to fill gaps or grooves. The molten metal, mainly filler metal, solidifies as the torch progresses along the work-piece. Gas welding is comparatively slow and not suitable for use with automatic or semiautomatic equipment. Consequently, it is rarely used for normal production welding in shipyards. The equipment is small and portable, and it can be useful for welding thin plate (up to about 7 mm), as well as for small-diameter pipe, heating, ventilating and air conditioning (HVAC) trunks (sheet metal), electrical cable ways and for brazing or soldering. Identical or similar equipment is used for cutting.

Soldering and brazing are techniques for bonding two metal surfaces without melting the parent metal. A liquid is made to flow into and fill the space between the two surfaces and then solidify. If the temperature of the filler metal is below 450 °C, the process is called soldering; if it is above 450 °C, the process is called brazing. Soldering is commonly done using heat from a soldering iron, flame, electrical resistance or induction. Brazing uses the heat from a flame, resistance or induction. Brazing may also be done by dipping parts in a bath. Soldered and brazed joints do not have the strength properties of welded joints. Consequently, brazing and soldering find limited application in shipbuilding and repair, except for primarily small-diameter pipe joints, sheet metal fabrication, small and infrequent joiner work and maintenance functions.

Other welding processes. There are additional types of welding that may be used in the shipyard environment in small quantities for a variety of reasons. *Electroslag welding* transfers heat through molten slag, which melts the work-piece and the filler metal. Although the equipment used is similar to that used for electric arc welding, the slag is maintained in a molten state by its resistance to the current passing between the electrode and the work-piece. Therefore, it is a form of electric resistance welding. Often a cooled backing plate is used behind the work-piece to contain the molten pool. *Electro-gas welding* employs a similar setup but uses a flux-coated electrode and CO_2 gas shielding. Both of these processes are very efficient for automatically making vertical butt welds and are highly advantageous for thicker plate. These techniques are expected to receive considerably wider application in shipbuilding.

Thermite welding is a process that uses superheated liquid metal to melt the work-piece and provided filler metal. The liquid metal results from a chemical reaction between a melt oxide and aluminium. The liquid metal is poured into the cavity to be welded, and the cavity is surrounded by a sand mould. Thermite welding is somewhat similar to casting and is primarily used to repair castings and forgings or to weld large structural sections such as a stern frame.

Laser welding is a new technology which uses a laser beam to melt and join the work-piece. Although the feasibility of laser welding has been proven, cost has prevented its commercial application to date. The potential for efficient, high-quality welding may make laser welding an important technique for shipbuilding in the future.

Another relatively new welding technique is called *electron beam welding*. The weld is made by firing a stream of electrons through an orifice to the work-piece, which is surrounded by an inert gas. Electron beam welding does not depend on thermal conductivity of the material to melt the metal. Consequently, both lower energy requirements and reduced metallurgical effects on the steel are significant benefits of this technique. As with laser welding, high cost is a major problem.

Stud welding is a form of electric arc welding in which the stud itself is the electrode. A stud welding gun holds the stud while the arc is formed and the plate and stud end become molten. The gun then forces the stud against the plate and the stud is welded to the plate. Shielding is obtained by the use of a ceramic ferrule surrounding the stud. Stud welding is a semi-automatic process commonly used in shipbuilding to facilitate installation of non-metallic materials, such as insulation, to steel surfaces.

Painting and finish coating

Painting is performed at almost every location in the shipyard. The nature of shipbuilding and repair requires several types of paints to be used for various applications. Paint types range from water-based coatings to high-performance epoxy coatings. The type of paint needed for a certain application depends on the environment to which the coating will be exposed. Paint application equipment ranges from simple brushes and rollers to airless sprayers and automatic machines. In general, shipboard paint requirements exist in the following areas:

- underwater (hull bottom)
- waterline
- topside superstructures
- internal spaces and tanks
- weather decks
- loose equipment.

Many different painting systems exist for each of these locations, but navy ships may require a specific type of paint for every application through a military specification (Mil-spec). There are many considerations when choosing paints, including environmental conditions, severity of environmental exposure, drying and curing times, applications equipment and procedures. Many shipyards have specific facilities and yard locations where painting occurs. Enclosed facilities are expensive, but yield higher quality

and efficiency. Open-air painting generally has a lower transfer efficiency and is limited to good weather conditions.

Shipyard paint coating systems. Paints are used for a variety of purposes on a variety of locations on the ships. No one paint can perform all of the desired functions (e.g., rust prevention, anti-fouling and alkaline resistance). Paints are made up of three main ingredients: pigment, a vehicle and a solvent. Pigments are small particles that generally determine the colour as well as the many properties associated with the coating. Examples of pigments are zinc oxide, talc, carbon, coal tar, lead, mica, aluminium and zinc dust. The vehicle can be thought of as the glue that holds the paint pigments together. Many paints are referred to by their binder type (e.g., epoxy, alkyd, urethane, vinyl, phenolic). The binder is also very important for determining the coating's performance characteristics (e.g., flexibility, chemical resistance, durability, finish). The solvent is added to thin the paint and allow for flowing application to surfaces. The solvent portion of the paint evaporates when the paint dries. Some typical solvents include acetone, mineral spirits, xylene, methyl ethyl ketone and water. Anticorrosive and anti-fouling paints are typically used on ships' hulls and are the main two types of paint used in the shipbuilding industry. The *anticorrosive paints* are either vinyl-, lacquer-, urethane- or newer epoxy-based coating systems. The epoxy systems are now very popular and exhibit all of the qualities which the marine environment requires. *Anti-fouling paints* are used to prevent the growth and attachment of marine organisms on the hulls of vessels. Copper-based paints are widely used as anti-fouling paints. These paints release minute quantities of toxic substances in the immediate vicinity of the vessel's hull. To achieve different colours, lampblack, red iron oxide or titanium dioxide may be added to the paint.

Shipyard primer coatings. The first coating system applied to raw steel sheets and parts is generally preconstruction primer, which is sometimes referred to as "shop primer". This coat is important for maintaining the condition of the part throughout the construction process. Preconstruction priming is performed on steel plates, shapes, sections of piping and ventilation ducting. Shop primer has two important functions: (1) preserving the steel material for the final product and (2) aiding in the productivity of construction. Most preconstruction primers are zinc rich, with organic or inorganic binders. Zinc silicates are predominant among the inorganic zinc primers. Zinc coating systems protect coatings in much the same manner as galvanizing. If zinc is coated on steel, oxygen will react with the zinc to form zinc oxide, which forms a tight layer that does not allow water and air to come into contact with the steel.

Paint-applying equipment. There are many types of paint application equipment used in the shipbuilding industry. Two common methods used are compressed-air and airless sprayers. Compressed-air systems spray both air and paint, which causes some paint to atomize (dry) quickly prior to reaching the intended surface. The transfer efficiency of air-assisted spray systems can vary from 65 to 80%. This low transfer efficiency is due mainly to overspray, drift and the air sprayer's inefficiencies; these sprayers are becoming obsolete because of their low transfer ability.

The most widely used form of paint application in the shipbuilding industry is the airless sprayer. The airless sprayer is a system which simply compresses paint in a hydraulic line and has a spray nozzle at the end; hydrostatic pressure, instead of air pressure, conveys the paint. To reduce the amount of overspray and spillage, shipyards are maximizing the use of airless paint sprayers. Airless sprayers are much cleaner to operate and have fewer leaking problems than compressed-air sprayers because the system requires less pressure. Airless sprayers have close to 90% transfer efficiency, depending on the conditions. A new technology which can be added to the airless sprayer is called high volume, low pressure (HVLP). HVLP offers an even higher transfer efficiency, in certain conditions. Measurements of transfer efficiency are estimates and include allowances for drips and spills which can occur when painting.

Thermal spray, also known as metal or flame spray, is the application of aluminium or zinc coatings to steel for long-term corrosion protection. This coating process is used on a wide variety of commercial and military applications. It is significantly different from conventional coating practices due to its specialized equipment and relatively slow production rates. There are two basic types of thermal coating machines: combustion wire and arc spray. The combustion wire type consists of combustible gases and a flame system with a wire feed controller. The combustible gases melt the material to be sprayed onto the parts. The *electric arc spray machine* instead uses a power supply arc to melt the flame sprayed material. This system includes an air-compression and filtration system, a power arc supply and controller and an arc flame spray gun. The surface must be properly prepared for proper adhesion of flame sprayed materials. The most common surface preparation technique is air blasting with fine grit (e.g., aluminium oxide).

The initial cost of thermal spray is usually high compared to painting, although when the lifecycle is taken into account, thermal spray becomes more economically attractive. Many shipyards have their own thermal spray machines, and other shipyards will subcontract their thermal coating work. Thermal spray can be done in a shop or on board the ship.

Painting practices and methods. Painting is performed in nearly every area in the shipyard, from the initial priming of the steel to the final paint detailing of the ship. Methods for painting vary greatly from process to process. Mixing of paint is performed both manually and mechanically and is usually done in an area surrounded by berms or secondary containment pallets; some of these are covered areas. Outdoor as well as indoor painting occurs in the shipyard. Shrouding fences, made of steel, plastic or fabric, are frequently used to help contain paint overspray or to block the wind and catch paint particles. New technology will aid in reducing the amount of airborne particles. Reducing the amount of overspray also reduces the amount of paint used and thus saves the shipyard money.

Surface preparation and painting areas in the shipyard

To illustrate painting and surface preparation practices in the shipbuilding and repair industry, practices can be generically described in five main areas. The following five areas help to illustrate how painting occurs in the shipyard.

Hull painting. Hull painting occurs on both repair ships and new construction ships. Hull surface preparation and painting on repair ships is normally performed when the ship is fully drydocked (i.e., on the graving dock of a floating drydock). For new construction, the hull is prepared and painted at a building position using one of the techniques discussed above. Air and/or water blasting with mineral grit are the most common types of surface preparation for hulls. Surface preparation involves blasting the surface from platforms or lifts. Similarly, paint is applied using sprayers and high-reach equipment such as man-lifts, scissor lifts or portable scaffolding. Hull painting systems vary in the number of coats required.

Superstructure painting. The superstructure of the ship consists of the exposed decks, deck houses and other structures above the main deck. In many cases, scaffolding will be used on board the ship to reach antennas, houses and other superstructures. If it is likely that paint or blast material will fall into adjacent waters, shrouding is put into place. On ships being repaired, the ship's superstructure is painted mostly while berthed. The surface is prepared using either hand tools or air-nozzle blasting. Once the

surface is prepared and the associated surface materials and grit are cleaned up and disposed of, then painting can commence. Paint systems usually are applied with airless paint sprayers. The painters access the superstructures with existing scaffolding, ladders and various lifting equipment that was used during surface preparation. The shrouding system (if applicable) that was used for blast containment will stay in place to help contain any paint overspray.

Interior tank and compartment painting. Tanks and compartments on board ships must be coated and re-coated to maintain the longevity of the ship. Re-coating of repair ship tanks requires a large amount of surface preparation prior to painting. The majority of the tanks are at the bottom of the ship (e.g., ballast tanks, bilges, fuel tanks). The tanks are prepared for paint by using solvents and detergents to remove grease and oil build-up. The wastewater developed during tank cleaning must be properly treated and disposed of. After the tanks are dried, they are abrasive blasted. During the blasting operation, the tank must have recirculating air and the grit must be vacuumed out. The vacuum systems used are either of a liquid ring or rotary screw type. These vacuums must be very powerful to remove the grit from the tank. The vacuum systems and ventilation systems are generally located on the dock's surface, and access to the tanks is through holes in the hull. Once the surface is blasted and the grit is removed, painting can begin. Adequate ventilation and respirators are required for all tank and compartment surface preparation and painting (i.e., in enclosed or confined spaces).

Paint surface preparation as stages of construction. Once the blocks, or multiple units, leave the assembly area, they are frequently transported to a blast area where the entire block is prepared for paint. At this point, the block is usually blasted back down to bare metal (i.e., the construction primer is removed) (see figure 92.7). The most frequent method for block surface preparation is air-nozzle blasting. The next stage is the paint application stage. Painters generally use airless spray equipment on access platforms. Once the block's coating system has been applied, the block is transported to the on-block stage, where outfitting materials are installed.

Small parts painting areas. Many parts comprising a ship need to have a coating system applied to them prior to installation. For example, piping spools, vent ducting, foundations and doors are painted before they are installed on block. Small parts are generally prepared for paint in a designated area of the shipyard. Small parts painting can occur in another designated location in the shipyard that best matches production needs. Some small parts are painted in the various shops, while others are painted in a standard location operated by the paint department.

Surface preparation and painting on block and on board

Final painting of the ship occurs on board, and touch-up painting will frequently occur on block (see figure 92.10). On-block touch-up painting occurs for several reasons. In some cases, paint systems are damaged on block and need to be resurfaced, or perhaps the wrong paint system was applied and needs to be replaced. On-block painting involves using portable blasting and painting equipment throughout the on-block outfitting areas. On-board painting involves preparing and painting the interface sections between the construction blocks and repainting areas damaged by welding, rework, on-board outfitting and other processes. The surfaces can be prepared by hand tools, sanding, brushing, solvent cleaning or any of the other surface preparation techniques. Paint is applied with portable airless sprayers, rollers and brushes.

Outfitting

Pre-erection outfitting of construction blocks is the current shipbuilding method used by all competitive shipbuilders worldwide.

Figure 92.10 • Touch-up painting on a ship's hull.

Newport News Shipbuilding

Outfitting is the process of installing parts and various subassemblies (e.g., piping systems, ventilation equipment, electrical components) on the block prior to joining the blocks together at erections. The outfitting of blocks throughout the shipyard lends itself to forming an assembly line approach to shipbuilding.

Outfitting at each stage of construction is planned to make the process flow smoothly throughout the shipyard. For simplicity, outfitting can be divided into three main stages of construction once the steel structure of the block has been assembled:

1. unit outfitting
2. on-block outfitting
3. on-board outfitting.

Unit outfitting is the stage where fittings, parts, foundations, machinery and other outfitting materials are assembled independent of the hull block (i.e., units are assembled separate from steel structural blocks). Unit outfitting allows workers to assemble shipboard components and systems on the ground, where they have easy access to the machinery and workshops. Units are installed at either the on-board or the on-block stage of construction. Units come in varying sizes, shapes and complexities. In some cases, units are as simple as a fan motor connected to a plenum and coil. Large, complex units are mainly composed of components in machinery spaces, boilers, pump rooms and other complex areas of the ship. Unit outfitting involves assembling piping spools and other components together, then connecting the components into units. Machinery spaces are areas on the ship where machinery is located (e.g., engine rooms, pump stations and generators) and outfitting there is intensive. Outfitting units on the ground increases safety and efficiency by reducing the work hours that would otherwise be allocated to on-block or on-board work in more confined spaces where conditions are more difficult.

On-block outfitting is the stage of construction where most of the outfitting material is installed onto the blocks. Outfitting materials installed on block consist of ventilation systems, piping systems, doors, lights, ladders, railings, electrical assemblies and so on. Many units are also installed at the on-block stage. Throughout the on-block outfitting stage, the block can be lifted, rotated and moved to efficiently facilitate installing outfitting materials on the ceilings, walls and floors. All of the shops and services in the shipyard must be in communication at the on-block stage to ensure that materials are installed at the right time and place.

On-board outfitting is performed after the blocks are lifted onto the ship under construction (i.e., after erection). At this time, the ship is either at a building position (building ways or building dock), or the ship could be berthed at pierside. The blocks are already outfitted to a large extent, although much more work is still needed before the ship is ready to operate. On-board outfitting involves the process of installing large units and blocks on board the ship. Installation includes lifting the large blocks and units on board the new ship and welding or bolting them into place. On-board outfitting also involves connecting the shipboard systems together (i.e., piping system, ventilation system and electrical system). All of the wiring systems are pulled throughout the ship at the on-board stage.

Testing

The operation and test stage of construction assesses the functionality of installed components and systems. At this stage, systems are operated, inspected and tested. If the systems fail the tests for any reason, the system must be repaired and retested until it is fully operational. All piping systems on board the ship are pressurized to locate leaks that may exist in the system. Tanks also need structural testing, which is accomplished by filling the tanks with fluids (i.e., salt water or fresh water) and inspecting for structural stability. Ventilation, electrical and many other systems are tested. Most system testing and operations occur while the ship is docked at pierside. However, there is an increasing trend to perform testing at earlier stages of construction (e.g., preliminary testing in the production shops). Performing tests at earlier stages of construction makes it easier to fix failures because of the increased accessibility to the systems, although complete systems tests will always need be done on board. Once all preliminary pierside testing is performed, the ship is sent to sea for a series of fully operational tests and sea trials before the ship is delivered to its owner.

Ship Repair

Steel ship repair practices and processes

Ship repair generally includes all ship conversions, overhauls, maintenance programmes, major damage repairs and minor equipment repairs. Ship repair is a very important part of the shipping and shipbuilding industry. Approximately 25% of the labour force in most private shipbuilding shipyards does repair and conversion work. Currently there are many ships that need updating and/or conversions to meet safety and environmental requirements. With fleets worldwide becoming old and inefficient, and with the high cost of new ships, the situation is putting a strain on shipping companies. In general, conversion and repair work in US shipyards is more profitable than new construction. In new-construction shipyards, repair contracts, overhauls and conversions also help to stabilize the workforce during times of limited new construction, and new construction augments the repair labour workload. The ship repair process is much like the new construction process, except that it is generally on a smaller scale and is performed at a faster pace. The repair process requires a more timely coordination and an aggressive bidding process for ship repair contracts. Repair work customers are generally the navy, commercial ship owners and other marine structure owners.

The customer usually provides contract specifications, drawings and standard items. Contracts can be *firm fixed price* (FFP), *firm fixed price award fee* (FFPAF), *cost plus fixed fee* (CPFF), *cost plus award fee*

(CPAF) or *urgent repair* contracts. The process starts in the marketing area when the shipyard is asked for a *request for proposal* (RFP) or an *invitation for bid* (IFB). The lowest price usually wins an IFB contract, while a RFP award can be based on factors other than price. The repair estimating group prepares the cost estimate and the proposal for the repair contract. Bid estimates generally include worker-hours and wage rates, materials, overhead, special service costs, subcontractor dollars, overtime and shift premiums, other fees, facilities cost of money and, based on these, the estimated price of the contract. Once the contract is awarded, a production plan must be developed.

Repair planning, engineering and production

Although some preliminary planning is performed at the proposal stage of the contract, much work is still needed to plan and execute the contract in a timely manner. The following steps should be accomplished: read and understand all contract specifications, categorize the work, integrate the work into a logical production plan and determine the critical path. Planning, engineering, materials, subcontracts and repair production departments must work closely together to perform the repair in the most timely and cost-effective manner. Prefabrication of piping, ventilation, electrical and other machinery is performed, in many cases, prior to the ship's arrival. Pre-outfitting and prepackaging of repair units takes cooperation with the production shops to perform work in a timely manner.

Common types of repair work

Ships are similar to other types of machinery in that they require frequent maintenance and, sometimes, complete overhauls to remain operational. Many shipyards have maintenance contracts with shipping companies, ships and/or ship classes that identify frequent maintenance work. Examples of maintenance and repair duties include:

- blasting and repainting the ship's hull, freeboard, superstructure, interior tanks and work areas
- major machinery rebuilding and installation (e.g., diesel engines, turbines, generators and pump stations)
- systems overhauls, maintenance and installation (e.g., flushing, testing and installation of a piping system)
- new system installation, either adding new equipment or replacing systems that are outdated (e.g., navigational systems, combat systems, communication systems or updated piping systems)
- propeller and rudder repairs, modification and alignment
- creation of new machinery spaces on the ship (e.g., cut-out of existing steel structure and adding new walls, stiffeners, vertical supports and webbing).

In many cases, repair contracts are an emergency situation with very little warning, which makes ship repair a fast moving and unpredictable environment. Normal repair ships will stay in the shipyard from 3 days to 2 months, while major repairs and conversions can last more than a year

Large repairs and conversion projects

Large repair contracts and major conversions are common in the ship repair industry. Most of these large repair contracts are performed by shipyards that have the ability to construct ships, although some primarily repair yards will perform extensive repairs and conversions.

Examples of major repair contracts are as follows:

- conversion of supply ships to hospital ships
- cutting a ship in half and installing a new section to lengthen the ship (see figure 92.11)

- replacing segments of a ship that has run aground (see figure 92.12)
- complete rip-out, structural reconfiguration and outfitting of combat systems
- major remodelling of ship's interior or exterior (e.g., complete overhauls of passenger cruise ships).

Most major repairs and conversions require a large planning, engineering and production effort. In many cases, a large quantity of steel work will need to be accomplished (e.g., major cut-out of existing ship structure and installation of new configurations). These projects can be divided into four major stages: removal, building new structure, equipment installation and testing. Subcontractors are required for most major and minor repairs and conversions. The subcontractors provide expertise in certain areas and help to even the workload in the shipyard. Some of the work that subcontractors perform are as follows:

- support of ship repair
- major combat systems installations (technical)
- boiler re-tubing and rebuilding
- air compressor overhauls
- asbestos removal and disposal
- tank cleaning
- blasting and painting
- pump system overhauls
- small structural fabrication
- winch overhauls
- main steam system modifications
- system fabrications (i.e., piping, ventilation, foundations and so on).

Figure 92.11 • Cutting a ship in half in order to install a new section.

Newport News Shipbuilding

Figure 92.12 • Replacing the prow of a ship that ran aground.

Newport News Shipbuilding

As with new construction, all installed systems must be tested and operational before the ship is returned to its owner. Testing requirements generally originate from the contract, although other sources of testing requirements do exist. The tests must be scheduled, tracked for proper completion and monitored by the proper groups (shipyard internal quality, vessel operation, government agencies, shipowners and so on). Once systems are in place and properly tested, the area, compartment and/or system can be considered sold to the ship (i.e., completed).

There are many similarities between new construction and repair processes. The primary similarities are that they both use the application of essentially the same manufacturing practices, processes, facilities and support shops. Ship repair and new construction work require highly skilled labour because many of the operations have limited potential for automation (especially ship repair). Both require excellent planning, engineering and interdepartmental communications. The repair process flow is generally as follows: estimate, plan and engineer the job; rip-out work; refitting of steel structures; repair production; test and trials; and deliver the ship. In many ways the ship repair process is similar to shipbuilding, although new construction requires a greater amount of organization because of the size of the workforce, size of the workload, number of parts and the complexity of the communications (i.e., production plans and schedules) surrounding the shipbuilding work flow.

Hazards and Precautions

Shipbuilding and repair is one of the most hazardous industries. Work must be done in a variety of highly hazardous situations, such as confined spaces and considerable heights. Much manual work is performed involving heavy equipment and material. Since the work is so interrelated, the results of one process may endanger personnel involved in another process. In addition, a great

portion of work is performed out-of-doors, and the effects of weather extremes can cause or aggravate hazardous conditions. Additionally, a number of chemicals, paints, solvents and coatings must be used, which may pose significant risks to employees.

Health hazards

Chemical hazards which pose health risks to employees in shipyards include:

- dusts from abrasive blasting operations
- exposure to asbestos and mineral fibres in insulation work
- vapours and spray mists from paints, coatings, solvents and thinners
- fumes from various welding, burning, soldering and brazing operations
- exposure to gases used in various welding, burning and heating processes
- exposure to specific toxic chemicals in epoxy resins, organo-tin and copper anti-fouling paints, lead paint, oils, greases, pigments and the like.

Physical hazards due to the manual nature of the work include:

- temperature and weather extremes associated with work performed out-of-doors
- electrical hazards
- ergonomic-related problems caused by repetitive handling of large and bulky materials
- ionizing and non-ionizing radiation
- noise and vibration
- oxygen deficiency potential and other confined space hazards associated with tanks, double bottoms and so on
- falls and trips from work on the same level as well as work from great heights.

Preventive measures

Although shipbuilding and repair is a very hazardous industry, the risks to personnel by these hazards can and should be minimized. The basis for hazard reduction is a well-founded health and safety programme that is rooted in a good partnership between management and the trade unions or employees.

There are a number of approaches that can be utilized to prevent or minimize hazards in shipyards once they are identified. These approaches may be broadly divided into several strategies.

Engineering controls are employed to eliminate or control hazards at their point of generation. These controls are the most desirable of the various types since they are most dependable:

- *Substitution or elimination.* Where possible, processes that produce hazards or toxic materials should be eliminated or replaced with less hazardous processes or materials. This is the most effective form of control. An example is the use of non-carcinogenic materials instead of asbestos insulation. Another example is the use of hydraulic lifting tables for handling heavy materials, instead of manual lifting. Replacement of solvent-based paints with water-based coatings is frequently possible. Automation or robotics can be used to eliminate process hazards.
- *Isolation.* Processes that are not amenable to substitution or elimination can sometimes be isolated from employees to minimize exposures. Frequently, sources of high noise can be relocated to place more distance between workers and the noise source, thus reducing exposure.
- *Enclosure.* Processes or personnel can sometimes be enclosed to eliminate or reduce exposures. Operators of equipment can be provided enclosed booths to minimize exposure to noise, heat, cold or even chemical hazards. Processes may also be enclosed. Paint-spray booths and welding booths are examples of process enclosure that reduce exposures to potentially toxic materials.

- *Ventilation*. Processes that produce toxic materials can be ventilated to capture the materials at their point of generation. This technique is used extensively in shipyards and boatyards, particularly to control welding fumes and gases, paint vapours and the like. Many fans and blowers are located on the decks of vessels and air is either exhausted from or blown into spaces to reduce exposure to hazards. Frequently fans are used in the blowing mode to direct fresh air into compartments to maintain acceptable oxygen levels.

Administrative controls are used to minimize exposures by administratively limiting the time spent by personnel in potentially hazardous situations. This is generally accomplished by rotating personnel from a relatively low hazard job to a higher hazard one. Although the aggregate amount of person-exposure time is not changed, exposure of each individual worker is reduced.

Administrative controls are not without their negative aspects. This technique requires additional training since workers must know both jobs and more workers are potentially exposed to a hazard. Also, since the number of personnel exposed to hazards has doubled from a legal standpoint, potential liabilities may be increased. However, administrative control can be an effective method if properly applied.

Personal protective controls. Shipyards must rely heavily on the various forms of personal protection. The nature of ship construction and repair does not lend itself to traditional engineering approaches. Ships are very confined spaces with limited access. A submarine under repair has 1 to 3 hatches that are .76 m in diameter, through which people and equipment must pass. The amount of ventilation tubing that can pass through is severely limited. Similarly, on large ships work is performed deep within the vessel, and although some ventilation may be smoked through the various levels to reach the desired operation, the amount is limited. Further, the fans pushing or pulling air through the vent tubing are generally located in fresh air, usually on a main deck, and they, too, have somewhat limited capacity.

In addition, ship construction and repair is not performed in an assembly line, but in separate work sites such that stationary engineering controls are impractical. Further, a ship may be under repair for a few days, and the extent to which engineering control may be utilized is again limited. Personal protective equipment is used extensively in these situations.

In shops, more extensive use may be made of traditional engineering control approaches. Most equipment and machinery in shops and assembly platens is very amenable to traditional guarding, ventilation and other engineering approaches. However, some personal protective equipment must be utilized in these situations as well.

A discussion of the various applications of personal protective equipment utilized in shipyards follows:

Welding, cutting and grinding. The basic process of constructing and repairing ships involves cutting, shaping and joining steel and other metals. In the process, metallic fumes, dusts and particulates are generated. Although ventilation can sometimes be utilized, more frequently welders must utilize respirators for protection from welding particulates and fumes. In addition, they must employ appropriate eye protection for ultraviolet and infrared illumination and other physical eye and face hazards. In order to provide protection from sparks and other forms of molten metal, the welder must be protected by welding gloves, long-sleeved clothing and other physical protection.

Abrasive blasting and painting. Much painting is performed in ship construction and repair. In many cases, the paints and coatings are specified by the ship's owner. Prior to painting, the equipment must be blasted with an abrasive to a certain profile that ensures good adhesion and protection.

Abrasive blasting of small parts may be performed in a closed system such as a glove box. However, most large components are abrasive blasted manually. Some blasting is performed in the open air, some in large bays of a building or shop designated for this purpose and some inside the vessels or vessel sections themselves. In any case, personnel performing abrasive blasting must use full-body protection, hearing protection and air-fed respiratory protection. They must be provided with an adequate supply of breathable air (i.e., at least Grade D breathing air).

In some countries the use of crystalline silica has been banned. Its use is generally not recommended. If silica-containing materials are used in blasting, preventive protective measures must be taken.

After abrasive blasting, materials must be quickly painted in order to prevent "flash rusting" of the surface. Although mercury, arsenic and other very toxic metals are no longer used in paints, paints used in shipyards generally contain solvents as well as pigments such as zinc. Other paints are of the epoxy type. Painters who apply these coatings must be protected. Most painters must use a negative or positive pressure respirator for their protection, as well as full-body coveralls, gloves, shoe covers and eye protection. Sometimes painting must be performed in confined or enclosed spaces. In these cases, air-supplied respiratory protection and full-body protection must be used, and there must be an adequate, permit-requiring confined-spaces programme.

Overhead hazards. Shipyards have many cranes, and a large amount of overhead work is performed. Hard-hat protection is generally required in all production areas of shipyards.

Insulation work. Piping systems and other components must be insulated to maintain component temperature and reduce heat in the ship's interior; in some cases, insulation is needed for noise reduction. In ship repair, existing insulation must be removed from piping to do repair work; in these cases, asbestos material is frequently encountered. In new work, fibreglass and mineral fibres are frequently used. In either case, appropriate respiratory protection and full-body protection must be worn.

Noise sources. Work in shipyards is notoriously noisy. Most processes involve working with metal; this typically produces noise levels above acceptable safe limits. Not all noise sources can be controlled to safe levels by utilizing engineering controls. Thus, personal protection must be used.

Foot hazards. Shipyards have a number of operations and processes that present hazards to the feet. It is often difficult and impractical to segregate the facility into foot hazard and non-foot hazard areas; safety shoes/boots are typically required for the entire production area of shipyards.

Eye hazards. There are many potential sources of hazards to the eyes in shipyards. Examples are various ultraviolet and infrared light hazards from welding arcs, physical hazards from various metal working dusts and particles, abrasive blasting grit, work with various pickling and metal baths, caustics and paint sprays. Due to the ubiquitous nature of these hazards, safety glasses are frequently required throughout the production areas of shipyards for practical and administrative simplicity. Special eye protection is required for specific individual processes.

Lead. Over the years, lead-based primers and coatings have been utilized extensively in ship construction. Although lead-containing paints and coatings are rarely used today, a significant amount of elemental lead is used in nuclear shipyards as a radiation shielding material. In addition, ship repair work often involves the removal of older coatings that frequently contain lead. In fact, repair work requires a great deal of sensitivity and concern for materials that have been applied or used previously. Work with lead requires full-body protection including coveralls, gloves, hat, shoe covers and respiratory protection.

Boat Building

In some ways boats can be thought of as relatively small ships in that many of the processes used to construct and repair boats are very similar to those used to construct and repair ships, only on a smaller scale. Generally, steel, wood and composites are chosen for construction of boat hulls. *Composites* include, in general, such materials as fibre-reinforced metals, fibre-reinforced cement, reinforced concrete, fibre-reinforced plastics and glass-reinforced plastics (GRPs). Development during the early 1950s of hand lay-up methods employing cold-cure polyester resin with glass reinforcement led to a rapid expansion of GRP boat construction, from 4% in the 1950s to over 80% in the 1980s and even higher currently.

In vessels over 40 m or so in length, steel rather than wood is the main alternative to GRP. As hull size is reduced, the relative cost of steel construction increases, becoming generally uncompetitive for hulls under 20 m in length. The need for corrosion margin tends also to lead to excessive weight in small steel boats. For vessels over 40 m, however, the low cost of heavy welded steel construction is normally a decisive advantage. Unless imaginative design, improved materials and automated fabrication can bring about a substantial reduction in costs, however, glass- or fibre-reinforced plastics seem unlikely to become competitive with steel for construction of ships over about 40 m in length except where special requirements exist (e.g., for transportation of corrosive or cryogenic bulk cargo, where a nonmagnetic hull is required or where substantial weight saving is necessary for performance reasons).

GRPs are now employed in a very wide range of boat hull applications including speedboats, coastal and ocean-going yachts, work boats, pilot and passenger launches and fishing boats. Its success in fishing boats, where wood has been the traditional material, is attributable to:

- competitive first cost, particularly where many hulls are built to the same design, enhanced by the increasing cost of wood and scarcity of skilled woodworkers
- trouble-free performance and low maintenance costs resulting from leak-proof, rot-proof qualities of GRP hulls, their resistance to marine boring organisms and low cost of repair
- the ease with which complex shapes, which may be required for hydrodynamic and structural purposes or for aesthetic reasons, can be fabricated.

Fabrication methods

The most common form of construction for shells, decks and bulkheads in large and small GRP hulls is single-skin laminate reinforced as necessary by stiffeners. Various methods of fabrication are employed in the construction of single-skin and sandwich hulls.

Contact moulding. By far the most common method of fabrication for single-skin GRP hulls of all sizes is contact moulding in an open or negative mould using cold-curing polyester resin and E-glass reinforcement.

The first step in the fabrication process is mould preparation. For hulls of small and moderate size, moulds are usually fabricated in GRP, in which case a positive plug, commonly of wooden construction finished in GRP, is first assembled, whose external surface accurately defines the required hull shape. Mould preparation is generally completed by wax polishing and application of a film of polyvinyl alcohol (PVA) or equivalent release agent. Laminating is usually started by application of pigmented gel coat of good-quality resin. Laminating is then continued, before the gel coat has fully cured, using one of the following processes:

- *Spray up.* Glass fibre rovings or reinforcements are sprayed simultaneously with polyester resin, the latter being mixed with catalyst and accelerator at the spray gun.
- *Hand lay-up.* Resin mixed with catalyst and accelerator is deposited liberally on the gel coat or on a previous ply of impregnated reinforcement by brush, roller-dispenser or spray gun.

The process outlined above can achieve efficient application of very heavy reinforcement (fabric of up to 4,000 g/m^2 has been used successfully, although for large-scale production a fabric weight of 1,500 to 2,000 g/m^2 has been preferred), giving a rapid laminating rate with low labour costs. A similar process can be applied for rapid lay-up of flat or nearly flat deck and bulkhead panels. Batch production of certain 49 m hulls, including installation of decks and bulkheads, has been achieved with a completion time of 10 weeks per hull.

Compression moulding. Compression moulding involves application of pressure, possibly accompanied by heat, to the surface of an uncured laminate, to increase fibre content and reduce voids by squeezing out excess resin and air.

Vacuum bag moulding. This process, which may be regarded as an elaboration of contact moulding, involves placing over the mould a flexible membrane, separated from the uncured laminate by a film of PVA, polythene or equivalent material, sealing the edges and evacuating the space under the membrane so that the laminate is subjected to a pressure of up to 1 bar. Curing may be speeded by placing the bagged component in an oven or employing a heated mould.

Autoclave moulding. Higher pressures (e.g., 5 to 15 bar) combined with elevated temperature, yielding increased fibre content and hence superior mechanical properties, may be achieved by carrying out the bag moulding process in an autoclave (pressurized oven).

Matched die moulding. The uncured moulding material, which in a large component such as a boat hull is likely to be a sprayed premix of resin and chopped-strand glass or a tailored preform of pre-impregnated glass fabric, is compressed between matched positive and negative moulds, usually of metallic construction, with application of heat if required. Because of the high first cost of moulds, this process is likely to be economical only for large production runs and is rarely used for boat hull fabrication.

Filament winding. Fabrication in this process is carried out by winding reinforcing fibres, in the form of a continuous roving which may be impregnated with resin just prior to winding (wet-winding) or may be pre-impregnated with partially cured resin (dry-winding), onto a mandrel which defines the internal geometry.

Sandwich construction. Sandwich hulls, decks and bulkheads may be fabricated by contact moulding, using room-temperature curing polyester resin, in much the same way as single-skin structures. The outer GRP skin is first laid up on the negative mould. Strips of core material are embedded on a layer of polyester or epoxy resin. Fabrication is then completed by laying up the internal GRP skin.

Polyester and epoxy resins. Unsaturated polyester resins are by far the most commonly used matrix materials for marine structural laminates. Their effectiveness follows from their moderate cost, ease of use within hand lay-up or spray-up fabrication processes and generally good performance in a marine environment. Three main types are available:

1. *Orthophthalic polyester,* made by a combination of maleic and phthalic anhydrides with a glycol (commonly propylene glycol), is the least expensive and most widely used matrix material for small boat construction.
2. *Isophthalic polyester,* containing isophthalic acid in place of phthalic anhydride, is more expensive, has somewhat superior

mechanical properties and water resistance and is commonly specified for higher-performance boat construction and marine gel coats.

3. *Bisphenol epoxy systems,* in which phthalic acid or anhydride is partly or completely replaced by bisphenol A, offers (at substantially higher cost) much improved water and chemical resistance.

Safety and health hazards

Although many of the chemical, physical and biological hazards in shipbuilding are common to boat building, a primary concern is exposure to various solvent vapours and epoxy dusts from the boat manufacturing process. Uncontrolled exposure to these hazards may produce central nervous system disorders, liver and kidney damage, and sensitization reactions, respectively. The controls for these potential hazards are essentially the same as those described previously in the shipbuilding section—namely, engineering controls, administrative controls and personal protective controls.

ENVIRONMENTAL AND PUBLIC HEALTH ISSUES

Frank H. Thorn, Page Ayres and Logan C. Shelman

The overriding principal behind regulating air emissions, water discharge and waste is protection of the public health and providing for the general welfare of the populace. Usually, the "populace" are considered to be those people living or working within the general area of the facility. However, wind currents may transport air pollutants from one area to another and even across national borders; discharges to water bodies may similarly travel nationally and internationally; and waste may be shipped across the country or the world.

Shipyards conduct a large variety of operations in the process of constructing or repairing ships and boats. Many of these operations emit water and air pollutants which are known or suspected to have detrimental effects on humans through direct physiological and or metabolic damage, such as cancer and lead poisoning. Pollutants may also act indirectly as mutagens (which damage future generations by affecting the biochemistry of reproduction) or teratogens (which damage the foetus after conception).

Both air and water pollutants have the potential to have secondary effects on humans. Air pollutants can fall into the water, affecting quality of the receiving stream or affecting crops and therefore the consuming public. Pollutants discharged directly to receiving streams may degrade the water quality to the point that drinking or even swimming in the water is a health risk. Water, ground and air pollution may also affect the marine life in the receiving stream, which may ultimately affect humans.

Air Quality

Air emissions can result from practically any operation involved in the construction, maintenance or repair of ships and boats. Air pollutants that are regulated in many countries include sulphur oxides, nitrogen oxides, carbon monoxide, particulates (smoke, soot, dust and so on), lead and volatile organic compounds (VOCs). Shipbuilding and ship repair activities which produce "oxide" criteria pollutants include combustion sources such as boilers and heat for metal treatment, generators and furnaces. Particulates are seen as the smoke from combustion, as well as

dust from woodworking, sand- or grit-blasting operations, sanding, grinding and buffing.

Lead ingots may in some instances have to be partially melted and reformed to mould into shapes for radiation protection on nuclear-powered vessels. Lead dust may be present in paint removed from vessels being overhauled or repaired.

Hazardous air pollutants (HAPs) are chemical compounds which are known or suspected to be harmful to humans. HAPs are produced in many shipyard operations, such as foundry and electroplating operations, which may emit chromium and other metallic compounds.

Some VOCs, such as naphtha and alcohol, used as solvents for paints, thinners and cleaners, as well as many glues and adhesives, are not HAPs. Other solvents used primarily in painting operations, such as xylene and toluene, as well as several chlorinated compounds most often used as solvents and cleaners, especially trichloroethylene, methylene chloride and 1,1,1-trichloroethane, are HAPs.

Water Quality

Since ships and boats are constructed on waterways, shipyards must meet the water quality criteria of their government-issued permits before they discharge any industrial waste waters to the adjacent waters. Most US shipyards, for example, have implemented a programme called "Best Management Practices" (BMPs), considered to be a major compilation of control technologies to help shipyards meet the discharge requirements of their permits.

Another control technology used in shipyards that have graving docks is a *dam and baffle* system. The dam stops the solids from getting to the sump and being pumped out to the adjacent waters. The baffle system keeps oil and floating debris out of the sump.

Storm water monitoring has recently been added to many shipyard permits. Facilities must have a storm water pollution prevention plan which implements different control technologies to eliminate pollutants from going into the adjacent water whenever there is rain.

Many ship and boat building facilities will also discharge some of their industrial wastewater to the sewage system. These facilities must meet the water-quality criteria of their local sewage regulations whenever they discharge to the sewer. Some shipyards are constructing their own pretreatment plants which are designed to meet local water-quality criteria. There are usually two different types of pretreatment facilities. One pretreatment facility is designed primarily to remove toxic metals from industrial wastewater, and the second type of pretreatment facility is designed primarily to remove petroleum products from the wastewater.

Waste Management

Different segments of the shipbuilding process produce their own types of waste that must be disposed of in accordance with regulations. Steel cutting and shaping generates wastes such as scrap metal from steel plate cutting and shaping, paint and solvent from coating the steel and spent abrasive from the removal of oxidation and unwanted coatings. Scrap metal poses no inherent environmental hazard and can be recycled. However, paint and solvent waste is flammable, and spent abrasive may be toxic depending on the characteristics of the unwanted coating.

As the steel is fabricated into modules, piping is added. Preparing the piping for the modules generates wastes such as acidic and caustic wastewater from pipe cleaning. This wastewater requires special treatment to remove its corrosive characteristics and contaminants such as oil and dirt.

Concurrent to the steel fabrication, electrical, machinery, piping and ventilation components are prepared for the outfitting phase of the ship's construction. These operations generate wastes such as metal-cutting lubricants and coolants, degreasers and electroplating wastewaters. Metal-cutting lubricants and coolants, as well as degreasers, must be treated to remove the dirt and oils prior to discharge of the water. Electroplating wastewaters are toxic and may contain compounds of cyanide that require special treatment.

Ships in need of repair usually need to unload wastes that were generated during the ship's cruise. Bilge wastewater must be treated to remove oil contamination. Sanitary wastewater must be discharged to a sewage system where it undergoes biological treatment. Even garbage and trash may be subject to special treatment in order to comply with regulations preventing the introduction of foreign plants and animals.

Other relevant readings

National Shipbuilding Research Program (NSRP). 1993. *Introduction to Production Processes and Facilities in the Steel Shipbuilding and Repair Industry.* NSRP 0382. Arlington, VA: NSRP, Office of Naval Research.

—. 1995. *Characterizing Shipyard Welding Emissions and Associated Control Options.* NSRP 0457. Arlington, VA: NSRP, Office of Naval Research.

Smith, CS. 1990. *Design of Marine Structures in Composite Materials.* London and New York: Elsevier Applied Science.

Todd, WF and SA Shulman. 1984. Control of styrene vapor in a large fiberglass boat manufacturing operation. *Am Ind Hyg Assoc J* 45:817–825.

CONSTRUCTION

93

Chapter Editor
*Knut Ringen, Jane L. Seegal and
James L. Weeks*

Contents

HEALTH AND SAFETY HAZARDS IN THE CONSTRUCTION INDUSTRY

James L. Weeks

Construction workers build, repair, maintain, renovate, modify and demolish houses, office buildings, temples, factories, hospitals, roads, bridges, tunnels, stadiums, docks, airports and more. The International Labour Organization (ILO) classifies the construction industry as government and private-sector firms erecting buildings for habitation or for commercial purposes and public works such as roads, bridges, tunnels, dams or airports. In the United States and some other countries, construction workers also clean hazardous waste sites.

Construction as a proportion of gross domestic product varies widely in industrialized countries. It is about 4% of GDP in the United States, 6.5% in Germany and 17% in Japan. In most countries, employers have relatively few full-time employees. Many companies specialize in skilled trades—electricity, plumbing or tile setting, for instance—and work as subcontractors.

The Construction Labour Force

A large portion of construction workers are unskilled labourers; others are classified in any of several skilled trades (see table 93.1). Construction workers include about 5 to 10% of the workforce in industrialized countries. Throughout the world, over 90% of construction workers are male. In some developing countries, the

Table 93.1 • Selected construction occupations.

Boilermakers
Bricklayers, concrete finishers and masons
Carpenters
Electricians
Elevator constructors
Glaziers
Hazardous materials (e.g., asbestos, lead, toxic dumps) removal workers
Installers of floors (including terrazzo), carpeting
Installers of drywall and ceilings (including ceiling tile)
Insulation workers (mechanical and floor, ceiling and wall)
Iron and steel workers (reinforcement and structural)
Labourers
Maintenance workers
Millwrights
Operating engineers (drivers of cranes and other heavy equipment maintenance workers)
Painters, plasterers and paperhangers
Plumbers and pipefitters
Roofers and shinglers
Sheet metal workers
Tunnel workers

proportion of women is higher and they tend to be concentrated in unskilled occupations. In some countries, the work is left to migrant workers, and in others, the industry provides relatively well-paid employment and an avenue to financial security. For many, unskilled construction work is the entry into the paid labour force in construction or other industries.

Work Organization and Labour Instability

Construction projects, especially large ones, are complex and dynamic. Several employers may work on one site simultaneously, with the mix of contractors changing with the phases of the project; for example, the general contractor is present at all times, excavating contractors early, then carpenters, electricians and plumbers, followed by floor finishers, painters and landscapers. And as the work develops—for instance, as a building's walls are erected, as the weather changes or as a tunnel advances—the ambient conditions such as ventilation and temperature change too.

Construction workers typically are hired from project to project and may spend only a few weeks or months at any one project. There are consequences for both workers and work projects. Workers must make and remake productive and safe working relationships with other workers whom they may not know, and this may affect safety at the work site. And in the course of the year, construction workers may have several employers and less than full employment. They might work an average of only 1,500 hours in a year while workers in manufacturing, for example, are more likely to work regular 40 hour weeks and 2,000 hours per year. In order to make up for slack time, many construction workers have other jobs—and exposure to other health or safety hazards—outside of construction.

For a particular project, there is frequent change in the number of workers and the composition of the labour force at any one site. This change results both from the need for different skilled trades at different phases of a work project and from the high turnover of construction workers, particularly unskilled workers. At any one time, a project may include a large proportion of inexperienced, temporary and transient workers who may not be fluent in the common language. Although construction work often must be done in teams, it is difficult to develop effective, safe teamwork under such conditions.

Like the workforce, the universe of construction contractors is marked by high turnover and consists mainly of small operations. Of the 1.9 million construction contractors in the United States identified by the 1990 Census, only 28% had *any* full-time employees. Just 136,000 (7%) had 10 or more employees. The degree of contractor participation in trade organizations varies by country. In the United States, only about 10 to 15% of contractors participate; in some European countries, this proportion is higher but still involves less than half of contractors. This makes it difficult to identify contractors and inform them of their rights and responsibilities under pertinent health and safety or any other legislation or regulations.

As in some other industries, an increasing proportion of contractors in the United States and Europe consists of individual workers hired as independent contractors by prime- or sub-contractors who employ workers. Ordinarily, an employing contractor does not provide subcontractors with health benefits, workers' compensation coverage, unemployment insurance, pension benefits or other benefits. Nor do prime contractors have any obligation to subcontractors under health and safety regulations; these regulations govern rights and responsibilities as they apply to their own employees. This arrangement gives some independence to individuals who contract for their services, but at the cost of removing a wide range of benefits. It also relieves employing contractors of the obligation to provide mandated benefits to individuals who are contractors. This private arrangement subverts public policy and has been successfully challenged in court, yet it persists and may become more of a problem for the health and safety of workers on the job, regardless of their employment relationship. The US Bureau of Labor Statistics (BLS) estimates that 9% of the US workforce is self-employed, but in construction as many as 25% of workers are self-employed independent contractors.

Health Hazards on Construction Sites

Construction workers are exposed to a wide variety of health hazards on the job. Exposure differs from trade to trade, from job to job, by the day, even by the hour. Exposure to any one hazard is typically intermittent and of short duration, but is likely to reoccur. A worker may not only encounter the *primary hazards* of his or her own job, but may also be exposed as a *bystander* to hazards produced by those who work nearby or upwind. This pattern of exposure is a consequence of having many employers with jobs of relatively short duration and working alongside workers in other trades that generate other hazards. The severity of each hazard depends on the concentration and duration of exposure for that particular job. Bystander exposures can be approximated if one knows the trade of workers nearby. Hazards present for workers in particular trades are listed in table 93.2.

Construction Hazards

As in other jobs, hazards for construction workers are typically of four classes: chemical, physical, biological and social.

Chemical hazards

Chemical hazards are often airborne and can appear as dusts, fumes, mists, vapours or gases; thus, exposure usually occurs by inhalation, although some airborne hazards may settle on and be absorbed through the intact skin (e.g., pesticides and some organic solvents). Chemical hazards also occur in liquid or semi-liquid state (e.g., glues or adhesives, tar) or as powders (e.g., dry cement). Skin contact with chemicals in this state can occur in addition to possible inhalation of the vapour resulting in systemic poisoning or contact dermatitis. Chemicals might also be ingested with food or water, or might be inhaled by smoking.

Several illnesses have been linked to the construction trades, among them:

- silicosis among sand blasters, tunnel builders and rock drill operators
- asbestosis (and other diseases caused by asbestos) among asbestos insulation workers, steam pipe fitters, building demolition workers and others
- bronchitis among welders
- skin allergies among masons and others who work with cement
- neurologic disorders among painters and others exposed to organic solvents and lead.

Elevated death rates from cancer of the lung and respiratory tree have been found among asbestos insulation workers, roofers, welders and some woodworkers. Lead poisoning occurs among bridge rehabilitation workers and painters, and heat stress (from wearing full-body protective suits) among hazardous-waste clean-up workers and roofers. White finger (Raynaud's syndrome) appears among some jackhammer operators and other workers who use vibrating drills (e.g., stoper drills among tunnellers).

Alcoholism and other alcohol-related disease is more frequent than expected among construction workers. Specific occupational causes have not been identified, but it is possible that it is related to stress resulting from lack of control over employment prospects, heavy work demands or social isolation due to unstable working relationships.

Physical hazards

Physical hazards are present in every construction project. These hazards include noise, heat and cold, radiation, vibration and barometric pressure. Construction work often must be done in extreme heat or cold, in windy, rainy, snowy, or foggy weather or at night. Ionizing and non-ionizing radiation is encountered, as are extremes of barometric pressure.

The machines that have transformed construction into an increasingly mechanized activity have also made it increasingly noisy. The sources of noise are engines of all kinds (e.g., on vehicles, air compressors and cranes), winches, rivet guns, nail guns, paint guns, pneumatic hammers, power saws, sanders, routers, planers, explosives and many more. Noise is present on demolition projects by the very activity of demolition. It affects not only the person operating a noise-making machine, but all those close-by and not only causes noise-induced hearing loss, but also masks other sounds that are important for communication and for safety.

Pneumatic hammers, many hand tools and earth-moving and other large mobile machines also subject workers to segmental and whole-body vibration.

Heat and cold hazards arise primarily because a large portion of construction work is conducted while exposed to the weather, the principal source of heat and cold hazards. Roofers are exposed to the sun, often with no protection, and often must heat pots of tar, thus receiving both heavy radiant and convective heat loads in addition to metabolic heat from physical labour. Heavy equipment operators may sit beside a hot engine and work in an enclosed cab with windows and without ventilation. Those that work in an open cab with no roof have no protection from the sun. Workers in protective gear, such as that needed for removal of hazardous waste, may generate metabolic heat from hard physical labour and get little relief since they may be in an air-tight suit. A shortage of potable water or shade contributes to heat stress as well. Construction workers also work in especially cold conditions during the winter, with danger of frostbite and hypothermia and risk of slipping on ice.

The principal sources of non-ionizing ultraviolet (UV) radiation are the sun and electric arc welding. Exposure to ionizing radiation is less common, but can occur with x-ray inspection of welds, for example, or it may occur with instruments such as flow meters that use radioactive isotopes. Lasers are becoming more common and may cause injury, especially to the eyes, if the beam is intercepted.

Those who work under water or in pressurized tunnels, in caissons or as divers are exposed to high barometric pressure. Such workers are at risk of developing a variety of conditions associated with high pressure: decompression sickness, inert gas narcosis, aseptic bone necrosis and other disorders.

Strains and sprains are among the most common injuries among construction workers. These, and many chronically disabling musculoskeletal disorders (such as tendinitis, carpal tunnel syndrome and low-back pain) occur as a result of either traumatic injury, repetitive forceful movements, awkward postures or overexertion (see figure 93.1). Falls due to unstable footing, unguarded holes and slips off scaffolding (see figure 93.2) and ladders are very common.

Biological hazards

Biological hazards are presented by exposure to infectious micro-organisms, to toxic substances of biological origin or animal attacks. Excavation workers, for example, can develop

Table 93.2 • Primary hazards encountered in skilled construction trades.

Each trade is listed below with an indication of the primary hazards to which a worker in that trade might be exposed. Exposure may occur to either supervisors or to wage earners. Hazards that are common to nearly all construction—heat, risk factors for musculoskeletal disorders and stress—are not listed.

The classifications of construction trades used here are those used in the United States. It includes the construction trades as classified in the Standard Occupational Classification system developed by the US Department of Commerce. This system classifies the trades by the principal skills inherent in the trade.

Occupations	Hazards
Brickmasons	Cement dermatitis, awkward postures, heavy loads
Stonemasons	Cement dermatitis, awkward postures, heavy loads
Hard tile setters	Vapour from bonding agents, dermatitis, awkward postures
Carpenters	Wood dust, heavy loads, repetitive motion
Drywall installers	Plaster dust, walking on stilts, heavy loads, awkward postures
Electricians	Heavy metals in solder fumes, awkward posture, heavy loads, asbestos dust
Electrical power installers and repairers	Heavy metals in solder fumes, heavy loads, asbestos dust
Painters	Solvent vapours, toxic metals in pigments, paint additives
Paperhangers	Vapours from glue, awkward postures
Plasterers	Dermatitis, awkward postures
Plumbers	Lead fumes and particles, welding fumes
Pipefitters	Lead fumes and particles, welding fumes, asbestos dust
Steamfitters	Welding fumes, asbestos dust
Carpet layers	Knee trauma, awkward postures, glue and glue vapour
Soft tile installers	Bonding agents
Concrete and terrazzo finishers	Awkward postures
Glaziers	Awkward postures
Insulation workers	Asbestos, synthetic fibres, awkward postures
Paving, surfacing and tamping equipment operators	Asphalt emissions, gasoline and diesel engine exhaust, heat
Rail- and track-laying equipment operators	Silica dust, heat
Roofers	Roofing tar, heat, working at heights
Sheetmetal duct installers	Awkward postures, heavy loads, noise
Structural metal installers	Awkward postures, heavy loads, working at heights
Welders	Welding emissions
Solderers	Metal fumes, lead, cadmium
Drillers, earth, rock	Silica dust, whole-body vibration, noise
Air hammer operators	Noise, whole-body vibration, silica dust
Pile driving operators	Noise, whole-body vibration
Hoist and winch operators	Noise, lubricating oil
Crane and tower operators	Stress, isolation
Excavating and loading machine operators	Silica dust, histoplasmosis, whole-body vibration, heat stress, noise
Grader, dozer and scraper operators	Silica dust, whole-body vibration, heat noise
Highway and street construction workers	Asphalt emissions, heat, diesel engine exhaust
Truck and tractor equipment operators	Whole-body vibration, diesel engine exhaust
Demolition workers	Asbestos, lead, dust, noise
Hazardous waste workers	Heat, stress

Figure 93.1 • Carrying without appropriate work clothing and protective equipment.

heavy workload, limited control and limited social support are the very factors associated with increased stress in other industries. These hazards are not unique to any trade, but are common to all construction workers in one way or another.

Evaluating Exposure

Evaluating either primary or bystander exposure requires knowing the tasks being done and the composition of ingredients and by-products associated with each job or task. This knowledge usually exists somewhere (e.g., material safety data sheets, MSDSs) but may not be available at the job site. With continually evolving computer and communications technology, it is relatively easy to obtain such information and make it available.

Controlling Occupational Hazards

Measuring and evaluating exposure to occupational hazards requires consideration of the novel manner in which construction workers are exposed. Conventional industrial hygiene measurements and exposure limits are based on 8-hour time-weighted averages. But since exposures in construction are usually brief, intermittent, varied but likely to be repeated, such measures and exposure limits are not as useful as in other jobs. Exposure measurement can be based on tasks rather than shifts. With this approach, separate tasks can be identified and hazards characterized for each. A task is a limited activity such as welding, soldering, sanding drywall, painting, installing plumbing and so on. As exposures are characterized for tasks, it should be possible to develop an exposure profile for an individual worker with knowledge of the tasks he or she performed or was near enough to

Figure 93.2 • Unsafe scaffolding in Kathmandu, Nepal, 1974.

histoplasmosis, an infection of the lung caused by a common soil fungus. Since there is constant change in the composition of the labour force on any one project, individual workers come in contact with other workers and, as a consequence, may become infected with contagious diseases—influenza or tuberculosis, for example. Workers may also be at risk of malaria, yellow fever or Lyme disease if work is conducted in areas where these organisms and their insect vectors are prevalent.

Toxic substances of plant origin come from poison ivy, poison oak, poison sumac and nettles, all of which can cause skin eruptions. Some wood dusts are carcinogenic, and some (e.g., western red cedar) are allergenic.

Attacks by animals are rare but may occur whenever a construction project disturbs them or encroaches on their habitat. This could include wasps, hornets, fire ants, snakes and many others. Underwater workers may be at risk from attack by sharks or other fish.

Social hazards

Social hazards stem from the social organization of the industry. Employment is intermittent and constantly changing, and control over many aspects of employment is limited because construction activity is dependent on many factors over which construction workers have no control, such as the state of an economy or the weather. Because of the same factors, there can be intense pressure to become more productive. Since the workforce is constantly changing, and with it the hours and location of work, and many projects require living in work camps away from home and family, construction workers may lack stable and dependable networks of social support. Features of construction work such as be exposed to. As knowledge of task-based exposure increases, one may develop task-based controls.

Exposure varies with the concentration of the hazard and the frequency and duration of the task. As a general approach to hazard control, it is possible to reduce exposure by reducing the concentration or the duration or frequency of the task. Since exposure in construction is already intermittent, administrative controls that rely on reducing the frequency or duration of exposure are less practical than in other industries. Consequently, the most effective way to reduce exposure is to reduce the concentration of hazards. Other important aspects of controlling exposure include provisions for eating and sanitary facilities and education and training.

Decreasing exposure concentration

For reducing exposure concentration, it is useful to consider the source, the environment in which a hazard occurs and the workers who are exposed. As a general rule, the closer controls are to a source, the more efficient and effective they are. Three general types of controls can be used to reduce the concentration of occupational hazards. These are, from most to least effective:

- engineering controls at the source
- environmental controls that remove the hazard from the environment
- personal protection provided to the worker.

Engineering controls

Hazards originate at a source. The most efficient way to protect workers from hazards is to change the primary source with some sort of engineering change. For example, a less hazardous substance can be substituted for one that is more hazardous. Non-respirable synthetic vitreous fibres can be substituted for asbestos, and water can be substituted for organic solvents in paints. Similarly, non-silica abrasives can replace sand in abrasive blasting (also known as sand blasting). Or a process can be fundamentally changed, such as by replacing pneumatic hammers with impact hammers that generate less noise and vibration. If sawing or drilling generates harmful dusts, particulate matter or noise, these processes could be done by shear cutting or punching. Technological improvements are reducing the risks of some musculoskeletal and other health problems. Many of the changes are straightforward—for example, a two-handed screwdriver with a longer handle increases torque on the object and reduces stress on the wrists.

Environmental controls

Environmental controls are used to remove a hazardous substance from the environment, if the substance is airborne, or to shield the source, if it is a physical hazard. Local exhaust ventilation (LEV) can be used at a particular job with a ventilation duct and a hood to capture the fumes, vapours or dust. However, since the location of tasks that emit toxic materials changes, and because the structure itself changes, any LEV would have to be mobile and flexible in order to accommodate these changes. Mobile truck-mounted dust collectors with fans and filters, independent power sources, flexible ducts and mobile water supplies have been used on many job sites to provide LEV for a variety of hazard-producing processes.

The simple and effective method for controlling exposure to radiant physical hazards (noise, ultraviolet (UV) radiation from arc welding, infrared radiant (IR) heat from hot objects) is to shield them with some appropriate material. Plywood sheets shield IR and UV radiation, and material that absorbs and reflects sound will provide some protection from noise sources.

Major sources of heat stress are weather and hard physical labour. Adverse effects from heat stress can be avoided through reductions in the workload, provision of water and adequate breaks in the shade and, possibly, night work.

Personal protection

When engineering controls or changes in work practices do not adequately protect workers, workers may need to use personal protective equipment (PPE) (see figure 93.3). In order for such equipment to be effective, workers must be trained in its use, and the equipment must fit properly and be inspected and maintained. Furthermore, if others who are in the vicinity may be exposed to the hazard, they should either be protected or prevented from entering the area.

The use of some personal controls can create problems. For instance, construction workers often perform as teams and thus have to communicate with each other, but respirators interfere with communication. And full-body protective gear can contribute to heat stress because it is heavy and because body heat is not allowed to dissipate.

Having protective gear without knowing its limitations can also give workers or employers the illusion that the workers are protected when, with certain exposure conditions, they are not protected. For instance, there are no gloves currently available that protect for more than 2 hours against methylene chloride, a common ingredient in paint strippers. And there are few data on whether gloves protect against solvent mixtures such as those containing both acetone and toluene or both methanol and xylene. The level of protection depends on how a glove is used. In addition, gloves are generally tested on one chemical at a time and rarely for more than 8 hours.

Eating and sanitary facilities

A lack of eating and sanitary facilities may also lead to increased exposures. Often, workers cannot wash before meals and must eat

Figure 93.3 • Construction worker in Nairobi, Kenya, without foot protection or hard hat.

in the work zone, which means they may inadvertently swallow toxic substances transferred from their hands to food or cigarettes. A lack of changing facilities at a worksite may result in transport of contaminants from the workplace to a worker's home.

Injuries and Illnesses in Construction

Fatal injuries

Because construction involves a large proportion of the workforce, construction fatalities also affect a large population. For instance, in the United States, construction represents 5 to 6% of the workforce but accounts for 15% of work-related fatalities—more than any other sector. The construction sector in Japan is 10% of the workforce but has 42% of the work-related deaths; in Sweden, the numbers are 6% and 13%, respectively.

The most common fatal injuries among construction workers in the United States are falls (30%), transportation accidents (26%), contact with objects or equipment (e.g., struck by an object or caught in machinery or materials) (19%) and exposure to harmful substances (18%), most of which (75%) are electrocutions from contact with electrical wiring, overhead power lines or electrically powered machinery or hand tools. These four types of events account for nearly all (93%) fatal injuries among construction workers in the United States (Pollack et al. 1996).

Among trades in the US, the rate of fatal injuries is highest among structural steel workers (118 fatalities per 100,000 full-time equivalent workers for 1992–1993 compared to a rate of 17 per 100,000 for other trades combined) and 70% of structural steel worker fatalities were from falls. Labourers experienced the greatest number of fatalities, with an annual average number of about 200. Overall, the rate of fatalities was highest for workers 55 years and older. The proportion of fatalities by event differed for each trade. For supervisors, falls and transportation accidents accounted for about 60% of all fatalities. For carpenters, painters, roofers and structural steel workers, falls were most common, accounting for 50, 55, 70 and 69% of all fatalities for those trades, respectively. For operating engineers and excavating machine operators, transportation accidents were the most common causes, accounting for 48 and 65% of fatalities for those trades, respectively. Most of these were associated with dump trucks. Fatalities from improperly sloped or shored trenches continue to be a major cause of fatalities (McVittie 1995). The primary hazards in the skilled trades are listed in table 93.2.

A study of Swedish construction workers did not find a high overall work-related mortality rate, but did find high death rates for particular conditions (see table 93.3).

Disabling or lost time injuries

In the United States and Canada, the most common causes of lost time injuries are overexertion; being struck by an object; falls to a lower level; and slips, trips and falls on the same level. The most common category of injury is strains and sprains, some of which become sources of chronic pain and impairment. The activities most often associated with lost time injuries are manual materials handling and installation (e.g., installing dry-wall, piping or ventilation duct-work). Injuries occurring in transit (e.g., walking, climbing, descending) are also common. Underlying many of these injuries is the problem of housekeeping. Many slips, trips and falls are caused by walking through construction debris.

Costs of Injuries and Illness

Occupational injuries and illnesses in construction are very costly. Estimates for the cost of injuries in construction in the US range from $10 billion to $40 billion annually (Meridian Research 1994); at $20 billion, the cost per construction worker would be

US$3,500 yearly. Workers' compensation premiums for three trades—carpenters, masons and structural iron workers— averaged 28.6% of payroll nationally in mid-1994 (Powers 1994). Premium rates vary enormously, depending on trade and jurisdiction. The average premium cost is several times higher than in most industrialized countries, where workers' compensation insurance premiums range from 3 to 6% of payroll. In addition to workers' compensation, there are liability insurance premiums and other indirect costs, including reduced work crew efficiency, clean-up (from a cave-in or collapse, for instance) or overtime necessitated by an injury. Such indirect costs can be several times the workers' compensation award.

Management for Safe Construction Work

Effective safety programmes have several features in common. They are manifest throughout organizations, from the highest offices of a general contractor to project managers, supervisors, union officials and workers on the job. Codes of practice are conscientiously implemented and evaluated. Costs of injury and illness are calculated and performance is measured; those that do well are rewarded, those that do not are penalized. Safety is an integral part of contracts and subcontracts. Everybody—managers, supervisors and workers—receives general, site-specific and site-relevant training and re-training. Inexperienced workers receive on-the-job training from experienced workers. In projects where such measures are implemented, injury rates are significantly lower than on otherwise comparable sites.

Table 93.3 • Construction occupations with excess standardized mortality rates (SMRs) and standardized incidence rates (SIRs) for selected causes.

Occupation	Significantly higher SMRs	Significantly higher SIRs
Bricklayers	—	Peritoneal tumour
Concrete workers	All causes,* all cancers,* stomach cancer, violent death,*accidental falls	Lip cancer, stomach and larynx cancer,*a lung cancerb
Crane drivers	Violent death*	—
Drivers	All causes,* cardiovascular*	Lip cancer
Insulators	All causes,*lung cancer, pneumoconiosis, violent death*	Peritoneal tumour, lung cancer
Machine operators	Cardiovascular,*other accidents	—
Plumbers	All cancers,*lung cancer, pneumoconiosis	All cancers, pleural tumour, lung cancer
Rock workers	All causes,* cardiovascular,*	—
Sheet metal workers	All cancers,* lung cancer, accidental falls	All cancers, lung cancer
Woodworkers/carpenters	—	Nose and nasal sinus cancer

* Cancers or causes of death are significantly higher in comparison to all other occupational groups combined. "Other accidents" includes typical work-related injuries.

a. The relative risk for larynx cancer among concrete workers, compared to carpenters, is 3 times higher.

b. The relative risk for lung cancer among concrete workers, compared to carpenters, is almost double.

Source: Engholm and Englund 1995.

Preventing Accidents and Injuries

Entities in the industry with lower injury rates share several common characteristics: they have a clearly defined *policy statement* that applies throughout the organization, from top management to the project site. This policy statement refers to a specific code of practice that describes, in detail, the hazards and their control for the pertinent occupations and tasks at a site. *Responsibilities are clearly assigned* and standards of performance are stated. Failures to meet these standards are investigated and penalties imposed as appropriate. Meeting or exceeding standards is rewarded. An *accounting system* is used that shows the costs of each injury or accident and the benefits of injury prevention. *Employees or their representatives are involved* in establishing and administering a programme of injury prevention. Involvement often occurs in the formation of a *joint labour or worker management committee. Physical examinations are performed to determine workers' fitness for duty and job assignment.* These exams are provided when first employed and when returning from a disability or other layoff.

Hazards are identified, analysed and controlled following the classes of hazards discussed in other articles in this chapter. The entire work site is inspected on a regular basis and results are recorded. Equipment is inspected to ensure its safe operation (e.g., brakes on vehicles, alarms, guards and so on). Injury hazards include those associated with the most common types of lost-time injuries: falls from heights or at the same level, lifting or other forms of manual materials handling, risk of electrocution, risk of injury associated with either highway or off-road vehicles, trench cave-ins and others. Health hazards would include airborne particles (such as silica, asbestos, synthetic vitreous fibres, diesel particulates), gases and vapours (such as carbon monoxide, solvent vapour, engine exhaust), physical hazards (such as noise, heat, hyperbaric pressure) and others, such as stress.

Preparations are made for emergency situations and emergency drills are conducted as needed. Preparations would include assignment of responsibilities, provision of first aid and immediate medical attention at the site, communication at the site and with others off the site (such as ambulances, family members, home offices and labour unions), transportation, designation of health care facilities, securing and stabilizing the environment where the emergency occurred, identifying witnesses and documenting events. As needed, emergency preparedness would also cover means of escape from an uncontrolled hazard such as fire or flood.

Accidents and injuries are investigated and recorded. The purpose of reports is to identify causes that could have been controlled so that, in the future, similar occurrences can be prevented. Reports should be organized with a standardized record-keeping system to better facilitate analysis and prevention. To facilitate comparison of injury rates from one situation to another, it is useful to identify the pertinent population of workers within which an injury occurred, and their hours worked, in order to calculate an injury rate (i.e., the number of injuries per hour worked or the number of hours worked between injuries).

Workers and supervisors receive training and education in safety. This education consists of teaching general principles of safety and health, is integrated into task training, is specific for each work site and covers procedures to follow in the event of an accident or injury. Education and training for workers and supervisors is an essential part of any effort to prevent injuries and disease. Training about safe work practices and procedures have been provided in many countries by some companies and trade unions. These procedures, include lockout and tagout of electrical power sources during maintenance procedures, use of lanyards while working at heights, shoring trenches, providing safe walking surfaces and so on. It is also important to provide site-specific training, covering unique features about the job site such as means of entry and exit. Training should include instruction about dangerous substances.

Performance or hands-on training, demonstrating that one knows safe practices, is much better for instilling safe behaviour than classroom instruction and written examination.

In the United States, training about certain hazardous substances is mandated by federal law. The same concern in Germany led to development of the Gefahrstoff-Informationssystem der Berufsgenossenschaften der Bauwirtschaft, or GISBAU, programme. GISBAU works with manufacturers to determine the content of all substances used on construction sites. Equally important, the programme provides the information in a form to suit the differing needs of health staff, managers and workers. The information is available through training programmes, in print and on computer terminals at work sites. GISBAU gives advice about how to substitute for some hazardous substances and tells how to safely handle others. (See the chapter *Using, storing and transporting chemicals.*)

Information about chemical, physical and other health hazards is available at the work site in the languages that workers use. If workers are to work intelligently on the job, they should have the information necessary to decide what to do in specific situations.

And finally, *contracts between contractors and subcontractors should include safety features.* Provisions could include establishing a unified safety organization at multi-employer work sites, performance requirements and rewards and penalties.

HEALTH RISKS OF UNDERGROUND CONSTRUCTION WORK

Bohuslav Málek

Hazards

Underground construction work includes tunnelling for roads, highways and railroads and laying pipelines for sewers, hot water, steam, electrical conduits, telephone lines. Hazards in this work include hard physical labour, crystalline silica dust, cement dust, noise, vibration, diesel engine exhaust, chemical vapours, radon and oxygen-deficient atmospheres. Occasionally this work must be done in a pressurized environment. Underground workers are at risk for serious and often fatal injuries. Some hazards are the same as those of construction on the surface, but they are amplified by working in a confined environment. Other hazards are unique to underground work. These include being struck by specialized machinery or being electrocuted, being buried by roof falls or cave-ins and being asphyxiated or injured by fires or explosions. Tunnelling operations may encounter unexpected impoundments of water, resulting in floods and drowning.

The construction of tunnels requires a great deal of physical effort. Energy expenditure during manual work is usually from 200 to 350 W, with a great part of static load of the muscles. Heart rate during work with compressed-air drills and pneumatic hammers reaches 150 to 160 per minute. Work is often done in unfavourable cold and humid microclimatic conditions, sometimes in cumbersome work postures. It is usually combined with exposure to other risk factors which depend on the local geological conditions and on the type of technology used. This heavy workload can be an important contribution to heat stress.

The need for heavy manual labour can be reduced by mechanization. But mechanization brings its own hazards. Large and powerful mobile machines in a confined environment introduce risks of serious injury to persons working nearby, who may be struck or crushed. Underground machinery also may generate dust, noise, vibration and diesel exhaust. Mechanization also results in fewer jobs, which reduces the number of persons exposed but at the expense of unemployment and all of its attendant problems.

Crystalline silica (also known as free silica and quartz) occurs naturally in many different types of rock. Sandstone is practically pure silica; granite may contain 75%; shale, 30%; and slate, 10%. Limestone, marble and salt are, for practical purposes, completely free of silica. Considering that silica is ubiquitous in the earth's crust, dust samples should be taken and analysed at least at the start of an underground job and whenever the type of rock changes as work progresses through it.

Respirable silica dust is generated whenever silica-bearing rock is crushed, drilled, ground or otherwise pulverized. The main sources of airborne silica dust are compressed-air drills and pneumatic hammers. Work with these tools most often occurs in the fore part of the tunnel and, therefore, workers in these areas are the most heavily exposed. Dust suppression technology should be applied in all instances.

Blasting generates not only flying debris, but also dust and nitrogen oxides. To prevent excessive exposure, the customary procedure is to prevent re-entry to the affected area until the dust and gases have cleared. A common procedure is to blast at the end of the last work shift of the day and to clear out debris during the next shift.

Cement dust is generated when cement is mixed. This dust is a respiratory and mucous membrane irritant in high concentrations, but chronic effects have not been observed. When it settles on skin and mixes with sweat, however, cement dust can cause dermatoses. When wet concrete is sprayed in place, it too can cause dermatoses.

Noise can be significant in underground construction work. Principal sources include pneumatic drills and hammers, diesel engines and fans. Since the underground work environment is confined, there is also considerable reverberant noise. Peak noise levels can exceed 115 dBA, with time-weighted average noise exposure equivalent to 105 dBA. Noise-reducing technology is available for most equipment and should be applied.

Underground construction workers can also be exposed to whole-body vibration from mobile machinery and to hand-arm vibration from pneumatic drills and hammers. The levels of acceleration transmitted to the hands from pneumatic tools can reach about 150 dB (comparable to 10 m/s^2). Harmful effects of hand-arm vibration can be aggravated by a cold and damp working environment.

If soil is highly saturated with water or if construction is conducted under water, the work environment may have to be pressurized to keep water out. For underwater work, caissons are used. When workers in such a hyperbaric environment make too rapid a transition to normal air pressure, they risk decompression sickness and related disorders. Since the absorption of most toxic gases and vapours depends on their partial pressure, more may be absorbed at higher pressure. Ten ppm of carbon monoxide (CO) at 2 atmospheres of pressure, for example, will have the effect of 20 ppm CO at 1 atmosphere.

Chemicals are used in underground construction in a variety of ways. For example, insufficiently coherent layers of rock may be stabilized with an infusion of urea formaldehyde resin, polyurethane foam or mixtures of sodium water glass with formamide or with ethyl and butyl acetate. Consequently, vapours of formaldehyde, ammonia, ethyl or butyl alcohol or di-isocyanates may be found in the tunnel atmosphere during application. Following application, these contaminants may escape into the tunnel from the surrounding walls, and it may therefore be difficult to fully control their concentrations, even with intensive mechanical ventilation.

Radon occurs naturally in some rock and may leak into the work environment, where it will decay into other radioactive isotopes. Some of these are alpha emitters that may be inhaled and increase the risk of lung cancer.

Tunnels constructed in inhabited areas can also be contaminated with substances from surrounding pipes. Water, heating and cooking gas, fuel oil, petrol and so on may leak into a tunnel or, if pipes carrying these substances are broken during excavation, they may escape into the work environment.

The construction of vertical shafts using mining technology poses similar health problems to those of tunnelling. In terrain where organic substances are present, products of microbiological decomposition may be expected.

Maintenance work in tunnels used for traffic differs from similar work on the surface mainly in the difficulty of installing safety and control equipment, for example, ventilation for electric arc welding; this may influence the quality of safety measures. Work in tunnels in which pipelines for hot water or steam are present is associated with great heat load, demanding a special regime of work and breaks.

Oxygen deficiency may occur in tunnels either because oxygen is displaced by other gases or because it is consumed by microbes or by the oxidation of pyrites. Microbes may also release methane or ethane, which not only displace oxygen but, in sufficient concentration, may create the risk of explosion. Carbon dioxide (commonly called blackdamp in Europe) is also generated by microbial contamination. The atmospheres in spaces which have been closed for a long time may contain mostly nitrogen, practically no oxygen and 5 to 15% carbon dioxide.

Blackdamp penetrates into the shaft from the surrounding terrain due to changes in the atmospheric pressure. The composition of the air in the shaft may change very quickly—it may be normal in the morning, but be deficient in oxygen by the afternoon.

Prevention

Prevention of exposure to dust should in the first place be implemented by technical means, such as wet drilling (and/or drilling with LEV), wetting of the material before it is pulled down and loaded to the transport, LEV of mining machines and mechanical ventilation of tunnels. Technical control measures may not be sufficient to lower the concentration of respirable dust to an acceptable level in some technological operations (e.g., during drilling and sometimes also in the case of wet drilling), and therefore it may be necessary to supplement the protection of the workers engaged in such operations by the use of respirators. The efficiency of technical control measures must be checked by monitoring the concentration of airborne dust. In the case of fibrogenic dust, it is necessary to arrange the programme of monitoring in such a way that it allows the registration of the exposure of individual workers. The individual exposure data, in connection with data about each worker's health, are necessary for the assessment of the risk of pneumoconiosis in particular work conditions, as well as for the assessment of the efficiency of control measures in the long-run. Last but not least, the individual registration of exposure is necessary for evaluating the ability of individual workers to continue in their jobs.

Due to the nature of underground work, protection against noise depends mostly on the personal protection of hearing. Effective protection against vibrations, on the other hand, can be achieved only by eliminating or decreasing the vibration by mechanization of risky operations. PPE is not effective. Similarly, the risk of diseases due to physical overload of the upper extremities can be lowered only by mechanization.

Exposure to chemical substances can be influenced by the selection of appropriate technology (e.g., the use of formaldehyde resins and formamide should be eliminated), by good maintenance (e.g., of diesel engines) and by adequate ventilation. Organization and work regime precautions are sometimes very effective, especially in the case of the prevention of dermatoses.

Work in underground spaces in which the composition of the air is not known demands strict adherence to safety rules. Entering such spaces without isolating breathing apparatuses must not be allowed. The work should be done only by a group of at least three people—one worker in the underground space, with breathing apparatus and safety harness, the others outside with a rope to secure the inside worker. In case of accident it is necessary to act quickly. Many lives have been lost in efforts to save the victim of an accident when the safety of the rescuer was disregarded.

Pre-placement, periodic and post-employment preventive medical examinations are a necessary part of the health and safety precautions for workers in tunnels. The frequency of periodic examinations and the type and scope of special examinations (x ray, lung functions, audiometry and so on) should be individually determined for each workplace and for each job according to the working conditions.

Prior to groundbreaking for underground work, the site should be inspected and soil samples should be taken in order to plan the excavation. Once work is underway, the work site should be inspected daily to prevent roof falls or cave-ins. The workplace of solitary workers should be inspected at least twice each shift. Fire suppression equipment should be strategically placed throughout the underground work site.

PREVENTIVE HEALTH SERVICES IN CONSTRUCTION

Pekka Roto

The construction industry forms 5 to 15% of the national economy of most countries and is usually one of the three industries having the highest rate of work-related injury risks. The following chronic occupational health risks are pervasive (Commission of the European Communities 1993):

- Musculoskeletal disorders, occupational hearing loss, dermatitis and lung disorders are the most common occupational diseases.
- An increased risk of respiratory tract carcinomas and mesothelioma caused by asbestos exposure has been observed in all countries where occupational mortality and morbidity statistics are available.
- Disorders resulting from improper nutrition, smoking or use of alcohol and drugs are associated especially with migrant workers, a substantial portion of construction employment in many countries.

Preventive health services for construction workers should be planned with these risks as priorities.

Types of Occupational Health Services

Occupational health services for construction workers consist of three main models:

1. specialized services for construction workers
2. occupational health care for construction workers rendered by providers of broad-based occupational health services
3. health services provided voluntarily by the employer.

Specialized services are the most effective but also the most expensive in terms of direct costs. Experiences from Sweden indicate that the lowest injury rates on construction sites worldwide and a very low risk for occupational diseases among construction workers are associated with extensive preventive work through specialized service systems. In the Swedish model, called Bygghälsan, technical and medical prevention have been combined. Bygghälsan operates through regional centres and mobile units. During the severe economic recession of the late 1980s, however, Bygghälsan severely cut back its health service activities.

In countries that have occupational health legislation, construction companies usually buy the needed health services from companies serving general industries. In such cases, the training of occupational health personnel is important. Without special knowledge of the circumstances surrounding construction, medical personnel cannot provide effective preventive occupational health programmes for construction companies.

Some large multinational companies have well-developed occupational safety and health programmes that are part of the culture of the enterprise. The cost-benefit calculations have proved these activities economically profitable. Nowadays, occupational safety programmes are included in quality management of most international companies.

Mobile health clinics

Because construction sites are often situated far from any established providers of health services, mobile health service units may be necessary. Practically all countries that have specialized occupational health services for construction workers use mobile units for delivering the services. The mobile unit's advantage is the saving of work time by bringing the services to worksites. Mobile health centres are contained in a specially equipped bus or trailer and are especially suitable for all types of screening procedures, such as periodic health examinations. Mobile services should be careful to arrange in advance for collaboration with local providers of health services in order to secure follow-up evaluation and treatment for workers whose test results suggest a health problem.

Standard equipment for a mobile unit includes a basic laboratory with a spirometer and an audiometer, an interview room and x-ray equipment, when needed. It is best to design module units as multipurpose spaces so they can be used for different types of projects. The Finnish experience indicates that mobile units are also suitable for epidemiological studies, which can be incorporated into occupational health programmes, if properly planned in advance.

Contents of preventive occupational health services

Identification of risk at construction sites should guide medical activity, although this is secondary to prevention through proper design, engineering and work organization. Risk identification requires a multidisciplinary approach; this requires close collaboration between the occupational health personnel and the enterprise. A systematic workplace survey of risks using standardized checklists is one option.

Preplacement and periodic health examinations are usually conducted according to requirements set by legislation or guidance provided by authorities. The examination's content depends on the exposure history of each worker. Short work contracts and frequent turnover of the construction workforce can result in "missed" or "inappropriate" health examinations, a failure to follow up on findings or unwarranted duplication of health examinations. Therefore, regular standard periodic examinations are recommended for all workers. A standard health examination should contain: an exposure history; symptom and illness histories with special emphasis on musculoskeletal and allergic diseases; a basic physical examination; and audiometry, vision, spirometry and blood pressure tests. The examinations should also provide health education and information on how to avoid occupational risks known to be common.

Surveillance and Prevention of Key Construction-related Problems

Musculoskeletal disorders and their prevention

Musculoskeletal disorders have multiple origins. Lifestyle, hereditary susceptibility and ageing, combined with improper physical strain and minor injuries, are commonly accepted risk factors for musculoskeletal disorders. The types of musculoskeletal problems have different exposure patterns in different construction professions.

There is no reliable test to predict an individual's risk for acquiring a musculoskeletal disorder. Medical prevention of musculoskeletal disorders is based on guidance in ergonomic matters and lifestyles. Preplacement and periodic examinations can be used for this purpose. Non-specific strength testing and routine x rays of the skeletal system have no specific value for prevention. Instead, early detection of symptoms and a detailed work history of musculoskeletal symptoms can be used as a basis for medical counselling. A programme that performs periodic symptom surveys to identify work factors that can be changed has been shown to be effective. Often, workers who have been exposed to heavy physical loads or strain think the work keeps them fit. Several studies have proved that this is not the case. Therefore, it is important that, in the context of health examinations, the examinees be informed about proper ways to maintain their physical fitness. Smoking has also been associated with lumbar disk degeneration and low-back pain. Therefore, anti-smoking information and therapy should be included in the periodic health examinations, too (Workplace Hazard and Tobacco Education Project 1993).

Occupational noise-induced hearing loss

The prevalence of noise-induced hearing loss varies among construction occupations, depending on levels and duration of exposure. In 1974, less than 20% of Swedish construction workers at age 41 had normal hearing in both ears. Implementation of a comprehensive hearing conservation programme increased the proportion in that age group having normal hearing to almost 40% by the late 1980s. Statistics from British Columbia, Canada, show that construction workers generally suffer significant loss of hearing after working more than 15 years in the trades (Schneider et al. 1995). Some factors are thought to increase susceptibility to occupational hearing loss (e.g., diabetic neuropathy, hypercholesterolemia and exposure to certain ototoxic solvents). Whole-body vibration and smoking may have an additive effect.

A large-scale programme for hearing conservation is advisable for the construction industry. This type of programme requires not only collaboration at the worksite level, but also supportive legislation. Hearing conservation programmes should be specific in work contracts.

Occupational hearing loss is reversible in the first 3 or 4 years after initial exposure. Early detection of hearing loss will provide opportunities for prevention. Regular testing is recommended to detect the earliest possible changes and to motivate workers to protect themselves. At the time of testing, the exposed workers should be educated in the principles of personal protection, as well as the maintenance and proper use of protection devices.

Occupational dermatitis

Occupational dermatitis is prevented mainly by hygienic measures. The proper handling of wet cement and skin protection are effective in promoting hygiene. During health examinations, it is important to stress the importance of avoiding skin contact with wet cement.

Occupational lung diseases

Asbestosis, silicosis, occupational asthma and occupational bronchitis can be found among construction workers, depending on their past work exposures (Finnish Institute of Occupational Health 1987).

There is no medical method to prevent the development of carcinomas after someone has been sufficiently exposed to asbestos. Regular chest x rays, every third year, are the most common recommendation for medical surveillance; there is some evidence that x-ray screening improves the outcome in lung cancer (Strauss, Gleanson and Sugarbaker 1995). Spirometry and anti-smoking information are usually included in the periodic health examination. Diagnostic tests for the early diagnosis of asbestos-related malignant tumours are not available.

Malignant tumours and other lung diseases related to asbestos exposure are widely underdiagnosed. Therefore, many construction workers eligible for compensation remain without benefits. In the late 1980s and early 1990s, Finland conducted a nationwide screening of workers exposed to asbestos. The screening revealed that only one-third of the workers with asbestos-related diseases and who had access to occupational health services had been diagnosed earlier (Finnish Institute of Occupational Health 1994).

Special needs of migrant workers

Depending on the construction site, the social context, sanitary conditions and climate may present important risks to construction workers. Migrant workers often suffer from psychosocial problems. They have a higher risk of work-related injuries than native workers. Their risk of carrying infectious diseases, such as HIV/AIDS, tuberculosis, and parasitic diseases must be taken into account. Malaria and other tropical diseases are problems for workers in areas where they are endemic.

In many large construction projects, a foreign workforce is used. A preplacement medical examination should be conducted in the home country. Also, the spreading of contagious diseases must be prevented through proper vaccination programmes. In the host countries, proper vocational training, health and safety education, and housing should be organized. Migrant workers should be provided the same access to health care and social security as native workers (El Batawi 1992).

In addition to preventing construction-related ailments, the health practitioner should work to promote positive changes in lifestyle, which can improve a worker's health overall. Avoiding alcohol and smoking are the most important and fruitful themes for health promotion for construction workers. It has been estimated that a smoker costs the employer 20 to 30% more than a non-smoking worker. Investments in anti-smoking campaigns pay not only in the short term, with lower accident risks and shorter sick leaves, but also in the long term, with lower risks of cardiovascular pulmonary diseases and cancer. In addition, tobacco smoke has harmful multiplier effects with most dusts, especially with asbestos.

Economic benefits

It is difficult to prove any direct economic benefit of occupational health services to an individual construction company, especially if the company is small. Indirect cost-benefit calculations show, however, that accident prevention and health promotion are economically beneficial. Cost-benefit calculations of investments in preventive programmes are available for companies to use internally. (For a model used extensively in Scandinavia, see Oxenburg 1991.)

HEALTH AND SAFETY REGULATIONS: THE NETHERLANDS EXPERIENCE

Leen Akkers

Implementation of the EC directive *Minimum Regulations for Health and Safety on Temporary and Mobile Building Sites* typifies the legal regulations emanating from the Netherlands and from the European Union. Their aim is to improve working conditions, to combat disability and to reduce sickness absenteeism. In the Netherlands, these regulations for the construction industry are expressed in the Arbouw Resolution, Chapter 2, Section 5.

As is often the case, the legislation seems to be following the social changes that began in 1986, when organizations of employers and employees joined to establish the Arbouw Foundation to provide services for construction companies in civil engineering and utility construction, earth works, roadbuilding and water construction and the completion sectors of the industry. Thus, the new regulations are scarcely a problem for the responsible companies already committed to implement health and safety considerations. The fact that these principles are often very difficult to put into practice, however, has led to non-observance and unfair competition and, consequently, the need for legal regulations.

Legal Regulations

The legal regulations focus on preventive measures before the construction project is started and while it is in progress. This will yield the greatest long-term benefit.

The Health and Safety Act stipulates that evaluations of risks must address not only those arising from materials, preparations, tools, equipment and so on, but also those involving special groups of workers (e.g., pregnant women, young and elderly workers and those with disabilities).

Employers are obliged to have written risk evaluations and inventories produced by certified experts, who may be employees or external contractors. The document must include recommendations for eliminating or limiting the risks and must also stipulate phases of the work when qualified specialists will be required. Some construction companies have developed their own approach to the evaluation, the General Business Investigation and Risk Inventory and Evaluation (ABRIE), which has become the prototype for the industry.

The Health and Safety Act obliges employers to offer a periodic health examination to their employees. The purpose is to identify health problems that may make certain jobs especially hazardous for some workers unless certain precautions are taken. This requirement echoes the various collective labour agreements in the construction industry which for years have required employers to provide employees with comprehensive occupational health care, including periodic medical examinations. The Arbouw Foundation has contracted with the Federation of Occupational Health and Safety Care Centres for the provision of these services. Over the years, a wealth of valuable information has been accumulated which has contributed to enhancement of the quality of the risk inventories and evaluations.

Absenteeism Policy

The Health and Safety Act also requires employers to have an absenteeism policy which includes a stipulation that experts in this field be retained to monitor and counsel disabled employees.

Joint Responsibility

Many health and safety risks can be traced to inadequacies in the building and organization choices or to poor planning of the work when setting up a project. To obviate this, the employers, employees and the government agreed in 1989 on a working conditions covenant. Among other things, it specified cooperation between clients and contractors and between contractors and subcontractors. This has resulted in a code of conduct which serves as a model for the implementation of the European directive on temporary and mobile building sites.

As part of the covenant, Arbouw formulated limits for exposure to hazardous substances and materials, along with guidelines for the application in various construction operations.

Under the leadership of Arbouw, the FNV Building Workers and Wood Workers Union, the FNV Industry Union and the Mineral Wool Association, Benelux, agreed to a contract that called for the development of glass wool and mineral wool products with less dust emission, development of the safest possible production methods for glass wool and mineral wool, formulation and promotion of working methods for the safest use of these products and performance of the research necessary to establish safe exposure limits to them. The exposure limit for respirable fibres was set at $2/cm^3$ although a limit of $1/cm^3$ was regarded as feasible. They also agreed to eliminate the use of raw and secondary materials that are health risks, using as criteria the exposure limits formulated by Arbouw. Performance under this agreement will be monitored until it expires on 1 January 1999.

Construction Process Quality

The implementation of the EC directive does not stand in isolation but is an integral part of company health and safety policies, along with quality and environmental policies. Health and safety policy is critical part of the quality policy of the companies. The laws and regulations will be enforceable only if the employers and employees of the construction industry have played a role in their development. The government has dictated the development of a model health and safety plan that is practicable and can be enforced to prevent unfair competition from companies that ignore or subvert it.

ORGANIZATIONAL FACTORS AFFECTING HEALTH AND SAFETY

Doug J. McVittie

Diversity of Projects and Work Activities

Many people outside the construction industry are unaware of the diversity and degree of specialization of work undertaken by the industry, though they see portions of it every day. In addition to traffic delays caused by encroachments on roads and street excavations, the public is frequently exposed to buildings being erected, subdivisions being constructed and, occasionally, to the demolition of structures. What is hidden away from view, in most cases, is the large amount of specialized work done either as part of a "new" construction project or as part of the ongoing repairs maintenance associated with almost anything constructed in the past.

The list of activities is very diverse, ranging from electrical, plumbing, heating and ventilating, painting, roofing and flooring work to very specialized work such as installing or repairing overhead doors, setting heavy machinery, applying fireproofing, refrigeration work and installing or testing communications systems.

The value of construction can be partially measured by the value of building permits. Table 93.4 shows the value of construction in Canada in 1993.

The health and safety aspects of the work depend in large measure on the nature of the project. Each type of project and each work activity presents different hazards and solutions. Often, the severity, scope or size of the problem is related to the size of the project as well.

Client-Contractor Relationships

Clients are the individuals, partnerships, corporations or public authorities for whom construction is carried out. The vast majority of construction is done under contractual arrangements between clients and contractors. A client may select a contractor based on past performance or through an agent such as an architect or engineer. In other cases, it may decide to offer the project through advertising and tendering. The methods used and the client's own attitude to health and safety can have a profound effect on the project's health and safety performance.

For example, if a client chooses to "pre-qualify" contractors to ensure that they meet certain criteria, then this process excludes inexperienced contractors, those who may not have had satisfactory performance and those without qualified personnel required for the project. While health and safety performance has not previously been one of the common qualifications sought or considered by clients, it is gaining in usage, primarily with large industrial clients and with government agencies that purchase construction services.

Some clients promote safety much more than others. In some cases, this is due to the risk of damage to their existing facilities when contractors are brought in to perform maintenance or to expand the client's facilities. Petrochemical companies in particular make it clear that contractor safety performance is a key condition of the contract.

Conversely, those firms who choose to offer their project through an unqualified open bidding process to obtain the lowest price often end up with contractors that may be unqualified to perform the work or who take short cuts to save on time and materials. This can have an adverse effect on health and safety performance.

Contractor-Contractor Relationships

Many people who are not familiar with the nature of the contractual arrangements common in construction presume that one contractor performs all or at least the major part of most building construction. For example, if a new office tower, sports complex or other high-visibility project is being constructed, the general contractor usually erects signs and often company flags to indicate its presence and to create the impression that this is "its project". Years ago, this impression may have been relatively accurate, since some general contractors actually undertook to perform substantial parts of the project with their own direct-hire forces. However, since the mid-1970s, many, if not most, general contractors have assumed more of a project management role on large projects, with the vast majority of the work contracted out to a network of subcontractors, each of which has special skills in a particular aspect of the project. (See table 93.5.)

As a result, the general contractor could actually have fewer staff onsite than any of several subcontractors on the project. In some cases the main contractor has no workforce directly involved in construction activities, but manages the work of subcontractors. On most major projects in the industrial, commercial and institutional (ICI) sector, there are several layers of subcontractors. Typically, the primary level of subcontractors have contracts with the general contractor. However, these subcontractors may contract part of their work out to other smaller or more specialized subcontractors.

The influence that this network of contractors may have on health and safety becomes fairly obvious when it is compared with a fixed worksite such as a factory or a mill. At a typical fixed-industry workplace, there is only one management entity, the employer. The employer has sole responsibility for the workplace, the lines of command and communication are simple and direct, and only one corporate philosophy applies. At a construction project, there may be ten or more employer entities (representing the general contractor and the usual subcontractors), and the lines of communication and authority tend to be more complex, indirect and often confused.

The attention given to health and safety by the person or company in charge can influence the health and safety performance of others. If the general contractor has attached a high degree of importance to health and safety, this can have a positive influence on the health and safety performance of the subcontractors on the project. The converse is also true.

Additionally, the overall health and safety performance of the site can be adversely affected by the performance of one subcontractor (e.g., if one subcontractor has poor housekeeping, leaving a mess behind as his or her forces move through the project, it can create problems for all of the other subcontractors onsite).

Regulatory efforts regarding health and safety are generally more difficult to introduce and administer in these multi-employer workplaces. It may be difficult to determine which employer has responsibility for which hazards or solutions, and any administrative controls which appear to be eminently workable in a single-employer workplace may need significant modification to be workable on a multi-employer construction project. For example, information regarding hazardous materials used on a construction project must be communicated to those who work with or near the materials, and workers must be

Table 93.4 • Value of construction projects in Canada, 1993 (based on value of building permits issued in 1993).

Type of project	Value ($ Cdn)	% of total
Residential buildings (houses, apartments)	38,432,467,000	40.7
Industrial buildings (factories, mining plants)	2,594,152,000	2.8
Commercial buildings (offices, stores, shops etc.)	11,146,469,000	11.8
Institutional buildings (schools, hospitals)	6,205,352,000	6.6
Other buildings (airports, bus stations, farm buildings, etc.)	2,936,757,000	3.1
Marine facilities (wharves, dredging)	575,865,000	0.6
Roads and highways	6,799,688,000	7.2
Water and sewage systems	3,025,810,000	3.2
Dams and irrigation	333,736,000	0.3
Electric power (thermal/nuclear/hydro)	7,644,985,000	8.1
Railway, telephone and telegraph	3,069,782,000	3.2
Gas and oil (refineries, pipelines)	8,080,664,000	8.6
Other engineering construction (bridges, tunnels, etc.)	3,565,534,000	3.8
Total	94,411,261,000	100

Source: Statistics Canada 1993.

Table 93.5 • Contractors/subcontractors on typical indus-
trial/commercial/institutional projects.

Project manager/general contractor	Glazing contractor
Excavating contractor	Masonry contractor
Formwork contractor	Finish carpentry/cabinet work contractor
Reinforcing steel contractor	
Structural steel contractor	Flooring contractor
Electrical contractor	Heating/ventilation/air conditioning contractor
Plumbing contractor	
Drywall contractor	Roofing contractor
Painting contractor	Landscaping contractor

adequately trained. At a fixed workplace with only one employer, all of the material and the information accompanying it is much more readily obtained, controlled and communicated, whereas on a construction project, any of the various subcontractors may be bringing in hazardous materials of which the general contractor has no knowledge. Additionally, workers employed by one subcontractor using a certain material may have been trained, but the crew working for another subcontractor in the same area but doing something entirely different may know nothing about the material and yet could be as much at risk as those using the material directly.

Another factor which emerges regarding contractor-contractor relationships relates to the bidding process. A subcontractor who bids too low may take short-cuts that compromise health and safety. In these cases, the general contractor must ensure that subcontractors adhere to the standards, specifications and statutes pertaining to health and safety. It is not uncommon on projects where everyone has bid very low to observe continuing health and safety problems coupled with excessive passing of responsibility, until regulatory authorities step in to impose a solution.

A further problem relates to the scheduling of work and the impact this can have on health and safety. With several different subcontractors on the site at one time, competing interests may create problems. Each contractor wants to get his or her work done as quickly as possible. When two or more contractors want to occupy the same space, or when one has to perform work overhead of another, problems can occur. This is typically a much more common problem in construction than in fixed industry, where the main competing interests tend to involve only operations versus maintenance.

Employer-Employee Relationships

The several employers on a particular project may have somewhat different relationships with their employees than those common at most fixed industrial workplaces. For example, unionized workers at a manufacturing facility tend to belong to one union. When the employer needs additional workers, it interviews and hires them and the new employees join the union. Where there are former unionized workers on layoff, they are re-hired generally on a seniority basis.

In the unionized part of the construction industry, a completely different system is used. Employers form collective associations which then enter into agreements with building and construction trade unions. The majority of the non-salaried direct-hire employees in the industry work through their union. When, for example, a contractor needs five additional carpenters at a project, he or she would call the local Carpenters' Union and

place a request for five carpenters to show up for work at the project on a certain day. The union would notify the five members at the top of the employment list that they are to report to the project to work for the particular firm. Depending on the provisions of the collective agreement between the employers and the union, the contractor may be able to "name hire" or select some of these workers. If there are no union members available to fill the employment call, the employer may be able to hire temporary workers who would join the union, or the union may bring in skilled workers from other locals to help fill the demand.

In non-unionized situations, employers use different processes to obtain additional staff. Prior employment lists, local employment centres, word of mouth and advertising in local newspapers are the principal methods used.

It is not uncommon for workers to be employed by several different employers in the course of a year. The employment duration varies with the nature of the project and the amount of work to be done. This places a large administrative load on the construction contractors compared with their fixed-industry counterparts (e.g., recordkeeping for income taxes, workers' compensation, unemployment insurance, union dues, pensions, licensing and other regulatory or contractual issues).

This situation presents some unique challenges compared to the typical fixed-industry workplace. Training and qualifications must not only be standardized but portable from one job or sector to another. These important issues affect the construction industry much more profoundly than fixed industries. Construction employers expect workers to come to the project with certain skills and capabilities. In most trades, this is accomplished by a comprehensive apprenticeship programme. If a contractor places a call for five carpenters, he or she expects to see five qualified carpenters at the project on the day they are needed. If health and safety regulations require special training, the employer needs to be able to access a pool of workers with this training, since the training may not be readily available at the time the work is scheduled to start. An example of this is the Certified Worker Programme required at larger construction projects in Ontario, Canada, which involves having joint health and safety committees. Since this training is not currently part of the apprenticeship programme, alternative training systems had to be put in place to create a pool of trained workers.

With growing emphasis on specialized training or at least confirmation of skill level, training programmes conducted in conjunction with the building and construction trades unions will likely grow in importance, number and variety.

Inter-union Relationships

The structure of organized labour mirrors the way in which contractors have specialized within the industry. On a typical construction project, five or more trades may be represented onsite at any one time. This involves many of the same problems posed by multiple employers. Not only are there competing interests to deal with, but lines of authority and communication are more complex and sometimes blurred when compared with a single-employer, single-union workplace. This influences many aspects of health and safety. For example, which worker from which union will represent all workers on the project if there is a regulatory requirement for a health and safety representative? Who gets trained in what and by whom?

In the case of rehabilitation and reinstatement of injured workers, the options for skilled construction workers are much more limited than those of their fixed-industry counterparts. For example, an injured worker at a factory may be able to return to some other job at that workplace without crossing important jurisdictional boundaries between one union and another, because there is typically only one union in the factory. In construction, each trade has fairly clearly defined jurisdiction over the types of work its members can perform. This greatly limits the options for injured workers who may not be able to perform their normal pre-injury job functions but could none the less perform some other related work at that workplace.

Occasionally, jurisdictional disputes arise over which union should perform certain types of work which have health and safety implications. Examples include scaffold erection, boom truck operation, asbestos removal and rigging. Regulations in these areas need to consider jurisdictional concerns, especially with respect to licensing and training.

The Dynamic Nature of Construction

Construction workplaces are in many respects quite different from fixed industry. Not only are they different, they tend to be constantly changing. Unlike a factory which operates at a given location day after day, with the same equipment, the same workers, the same processes and generally the same conditions, construction projects evolve and change from day to day. Walls are erected, new workers from different trades arrive, materials change, employers change as they complete their portions of the work, and most projects are affected to some degree just by the changes in the weather.

When one project is completed, workers and employers move on to other projects to start all over again. This indicates the dynamic nature of the industry. Some employers work in several different cities, provinces, states or even countries. Similarly, many skilled construction workers move with the work. These factors influence many aspects of health and safety, including workers' compensation, health and safety regulations, performance measurement and training.

Summary

The construction industry is presented with some very different conditions from those in fixed industry. These conditions must be considered when control strategies are being contemplated and may help to explain why things are done differently in the construction industry. Solutions developed with the input from both construction labour and construction management, who know these conditions and how to deal effectively with them, offer the best chance for improving health and safety performance.

● INTEGRATING PREVENTION AND QUALITY MANAGEMENT

Rudolf Scholbeck

Improving Occupational Health and Safety

Construction companies are increasingly adopting the *quality management systems* spelled out by the International Organization for Standardization (ISO), such as the ISO 9000 series and the subsequent regulations that have been based on it. Although no recommendations on occupational health and safety are specified in this set of standards, there are cogent reasons for including preventive measures when implementing a management system such as that required by the ISO 9000.

Occupational health and safety regulations are written and implemented and are continuously being adapted to technological progress as well as to new safety techniques and to advances in occupational medicine. All too often, however, they are not followed, either deliberately or out of ignorance. When this occurs, models for safety management, such as the ISO 9000 series, assist in integrating the structure and content of preventive measures into management. The advantages of such a comprehensive approach are obvious.

Integrated management means that occupational health and safety regulations are no longer looked at in isolation, but gain relevance from the corresponding sections of a quality management handbook, as well as in process and work instructions, thus creating a fully integrated system. This integral approach can improve the chances of greater attention to accident prevention measures in daily construction practice and, thereby, reduce the number of workplace accidents and injuries. Dissemination of a handbook that integrates occupational health and safety procedures into the processes it describes is crucial for this process.

New management methods are aimed at putting people closer to the centre of the processes. Co-workers are being more actively involved. Information, communication and cooperation are promoted across hierarchical barriers. The reduction of absences due to illness or workplace accidents enhances the implementation of the principles of quality management in construction.

With the development of new building methods and equipment, safety requirements increase steadily in number. The increasing concern with environmental protection makes the problem even more complex. Coping with the demands of modern prevention is difficult without appropriate regulations and a centrally directed articulation of the process and work instructions. Clear divisions of responsibility and effective coordination for the prevention plan should, therefore, be written into the quality management system.

Improving Competitiveness

Documentation of the existence of an occupational safety management system is increasingly required when contractors submit bids for work, and its effectiveness has become one of the criteria for awarding a contract.

The pressure of international competition could become even greater in the future. It seems prudent, therefore, to integrate preventive measures into the quality management system now, rather than waiting and being forced by increasing competitive pressure to do so later, when the pressure of time and the costs of personnel and financing will be much greater. Furthermore, a not inconsiderable benefit of an integrated prevention/quality management system is that having such a well-documented programme in place is likely to reduce the costs of coverage, not only for workers' compensation, but also for product liability.

Company Management

Company management must be committed to the integration of occupational health and safety into the management system. Goals specifying the content and time-frame of this effort should be defined and included in the basic statement of company policy. The necessary resources should be made available and appropriate personnel assigned to accomplish the project goals. Specialized safety personnel are generally required in large and mid-sized construction companies. In smaller companies, the employer must take the responsibility for the preventive aspects of the quality management system.

A periodic company management review closes the circle. The collective experiences in utilizing the integrated prevention/ quality management system should be examined and assessed, and plans for revision and for subsequent review should be formulated by company management.

Assessing Results

Assessment of results of the occupational safety management system that has been instituted is the second step in the integration of preventive measures and quality management.

The dates, kinds, frequency, causes and costs of accidents should be compiled, analysed and shared with all those in the company with relevant responsibilities. Such an analysis enables the company to set priorities in formulating or modifying process and work instructions. It also makes clear the extent to which occupational health and safety experience affects all divisions and all processes in the construction company. For this reason, defining the interface between company processes and preventive aspects takes on great importance. During bid preparation, the resources in time and money needed for comprehensive preventive measures, such as those incurred in clearing debris, can be precisely calculated.

When purchasing construction materials, attention should be paid to the availability of substitutes for potentially dangerous materials. From the beginning of a project responsibility for occupational health and safety should be assigned for particular aspects and each phase of the construction project. The need and availability for special training in occupational health and safety as well as the relative risks of injury and disease should be compelling considerations in the adoption of particular construction processes. These conditions must be recognized early on so that appropriately qualified workers can be selected and the courses of instruction can be arranged in a timely manner.

The responsibilities and authorities of the personnel assigned to safety and how they fit into the daily work should be documented in writing and collated with the onsite task descriptions. The construction company's occupational safety staff should appear shown in its organizational chart, which, along with a clear responsibility matrix and schematic flow-charts of processes, should appear in the quality management handbook.

An Example from Germany

In practice, there are four formal procedures and their combinations for integrating occupational health and safety into a quality management system that have been implemented in Germany:

1. *A quality management handbook and a separate occupational safety management handbook are developed. Each has its own procedures and work instructions.* In extreme cases, this creates ineffective, insular organizational solutions, which require twice the amount of work and in practice do not accomplish the desired results.

2. *An additional section is inserted into the quality management handbook with the heading "Occupational health and safety".* All statements on occupational health and safety are organized in this section. This path is chosen by some construction companies. Positioning a health and safety problem in a separate section may well highlight the importance of prevention, but it entails the risk being ignored as a "fifth wheel" and serves more as an evidence of intent rather than a command for appropriate action.

3. *All aspects of occupational health and safety are worked directly into the quality management system.* This is the most systematic implementation of the basic idea of integration. The

integrated and flexible structuring of the presentation models of the German DIN EN ISO 9001-9003 permits such an inclusion.

4. *The Underground Construction Trade Organization (Berufs-genossenschaft) favours a modular integration.* This concept is explained below.

Integration in Quality Management

Once the assessment is completed, at the latest, those responsible for the construction project should contact the quality management officers and decide on the steps for actually integrating occupational safety into the management system. Comprehensive preparatory work should facilitate setting common priorities during the work that promise the greatest preventive results.

The demands of prevention that come out of the assessment are first divided into those that can be categorized according to the processes specific to the company and those that should be considered separately since they are more widespread, more comprehensive or of such a special character that they demand separate consideration. The following question can be of assistance in this categorization: Where would the interested reader of the handbook (e.g., the "customer" or the worker) most likely look for the relevant preventive policy, the section of a chapter devoted to a process specific to the company, or in a special section on occupational health and safety? Thus, it appears, a specialized procedural instruction on transporting hazardous materials would make the most sense in almost all construction companies if it were included in section on handling, storing, packing, conserving and shipping.

Coordination and Implementation

After this formal categorization should come linguistic coordination to ensure easy readability (this means presentation in the appropriate language(s) and in terms easily understood by individuals with educational levels characteristic of the particular workforce). Finally, the final documents must be formally endorsed by the top management of the company. At this juncture, it would be useful to publicize the significance of the changed or newly-implemented procedures and work instructions in company bulletins, safety circles, memos and any other available media, and to promote their application.

General Audits

To assess the effectiveness of the instructions, appropriate questions may be prepared for inclusion into general audits. In this manner, the coherence of work processes and occupational health and safety considerations is made unmistakably clear to the worker. Experience has shown that workers may at first be surprised when an audit team on the construction site in their particular division routinely asks questions on accident prevention as a matter of course. The consequent increase in the attention paid to safety and health by the workforce confirms the value of the integration of prevention into the quality management programme.

MAJOR SECTORS

Jeffrey Hinksman

The term *construction industry* is used worldwide to cover what is a collection of industries with very different practices, brought together temporarily on the site of a building or civil engineering job. The scale of operations ranges from a single worker carrying out a job lasting minutes only (e.g., replacing a roof tile with equipment consisting of a hammer and nails and possibly a ladder) to vast building and civil engineering projects lasting many years that involve hundreds of different contractors, each with their own expertise, plant and equipment. However, despite the enormous variation in scale and complexity of operations, the major sectors of the construction industry have a great deal in common. There is always a client (known sometimes as the owner) and a contractor; except for the very smallest jobs, there will be a designer, either an architect or engineer, and if the project involves a range of skills, it will inevitably require additional contractors working as subcontractors to the main contractor (see also the article "Organizational factors affecting health and safety" in this chapter). While small-scale domestic or agricultural buildings may be built on the basis of an informal agreement between the client and builder, the vast majority of building and civil engineering work will be carried out under the terms of a formal contract between the client and contractor. This contract will set out details of the structure or other work that the contractor is to provide, the date by which it is to be built and the price. Contracts may contain a great deal besides the job, the time and the price, but those are the essentials.

The two broad categories of construction projects are *building* and *civil engineering*. Building applies to projects involving houses, offices, shops, factories, schools, hospitals, power and railway stations, churches and so on—all those kinds of structures that in everyday speech we describe as "buildings". *Civil engineering* applies to all the other built structures in our environment, including roads, tunnels, bridges, railways, dams, canals and docks. There are structures that appear to fall into both categories; an airport involves extensive buildings as well as civil engineering in the creation of the airfield proper; a dock may involve warehouse buildings as well excavation of the dock and raising of the dock walls.

Whatever the type of structure, building and civil engineering both involve certain processes such as building or erection of the structure, its commissioning, maintenance, repair, alteration and ultimately its demolition. This cycle of processes occurs regardless of the type of structure.

Small Contractors and the Self-employed

While there are variations from country to country, construction is typically an industry of small employers. As many as 70 to 80% of contractors employ less than 20 workers. This is because many contractors start out as a single tradesperson working alone on small-scale jobs, probably domestic ones. As their business expands, such tradespeople start to employ a few workers themselves. The workload in construction is rarely consistent or predictable, as some jobs finish and others start up at different times. There is a need in the industry to be able to move groups of workers with particular skills from job to job as the work requires. Small contractors fulfil this role.

Alongside the small contractors there is a population of self-employed workers. Like agriculture, construction has a very high proportion of self-employed workers. These again are usually tradespeople, such as carpenters, painters, electricians, plumbers and bricklayers. They are able to find a place in either small-scale domestic work or as part of the workforce on bigger jobs. In the boom construction period of the late 1980s, there was an increase in workers claiming to be self-employed. This was partly because of tax incentives for the individuals concerned and use by contractors of so-called self-employed who were cheaper than employees. Contractors were not faced with the same level of social security costs, were not required to train self-employed persons and could get rid of them more easily at the end of jobs.

The presence in construction of so many small contractors and self-employed individuals tends to militate against effective management of health and safety for the job as a whole and, with such a transitory workforce, certainly makes it more difficult to provide proper safety training. Analysis of fatal accidents in the United Kingdom over a 3-year period showed that about half the fatal accidents happened to workers who had been onsite for a week or less. The first few days on any site are especially hazardous to construction workers because, however experienced they may be as tradespeople, each site is a unique experience.

Public and Private Sectors

Contractors may be part of the public sector (e.g., the works department of a city or district council) or they are part of the private sector. A considerable amount of maintenance used to be done by such public works departments, especially on housing, schools and roads. Recently there has been a move to encourage greater competition in such work, partly as a result of pressures for better value for money. This has led firstly to a reduction in the size of public works departments, even their total disappearance in some places, and to the introduction of mandatory competitive tendering. Jobs previously done by public works departments are now done by private-sector contractors under severe "lowest tender wins" conditions. In their need to cut costs, contractors may be tempted to reduce what are seen as overheads such as safety and training.

The distinction between public and private sectors may also apply to clients. Central and local government (along with transportation and public utilities if under the control of central or local government) may all be clients for construction. As such they would generally be thought to be in the public sector. Transportation and utilities run by corporations would usually be considered to be in the private sector. Whether a client is in the public sector sometimes influences attitudes towards inclusion of some items of safety or training in the cost of construction work. Recently public- and private-sector clients have been under similar constraints as regards competitive tendering.

Work across National Boundaries

An aspect of public-sector contracts of increasing importance is the need for tenders to be invited from beyond national boundaries. In the European Union, for example, large-scale contracts beyond a value set out in Directives, must be advertised within the Union so that contractors from all member countries may tender. The effect of this is to encourage contractors to work across national boundaries. They are then required to work in accordance with the local national health and safety laws. One of the aims of the European Union is to harmonize standards between member states in health and safety laws and their application. Major contractors working in parts of the world subject to similar regimes must therefore be familiar with health and safety standards in those countries where they carry out work.

Designers

In buildings, the designer is usually an architect, although on small-scale domestic housing, contractors sometime provide such design expertise as is necessary. If the building is large or complex, there may be architects dealing with design of the overall scheme as well as structural engineers concerned with design of, for example, the frame, and specialist engineers involved with design of the services. The architect for the building will ensure that sufficient space is provided in the right places in the structure to permit installation of plant and services. Specialist designers will be concerned to ensure that the plant and services are designed to operate to the required standard when installed in the structure in the places provided by the architect.

In civil engineering, the lead in design is more likely to be taken by a civil or structural engineer, although in high-profile jobs where visual impact may be an important factor, an architect may have an important role in the design team. In tunnelling, railways and highways, the lead in design is likely to be taken by structural or civil engineers.

The role of the developer is to seek to improve the utilization of land or buildings and profit from that improvement. Some developers simply sell the improved land or buildings and have no further interest; others may retain ownership of land or even buildings and reap a continuing interest in the form of rents that are greater than before the improvements.

The skill of the developer is to identify sites either as empty land or under-utilized and out-of-date buildings where application of construction skills will improve their value. The developer may use his or her own finances, but perhaps more often exercises further skills in identifying and bringing together other sources of finance. Developers are not a modern phenomenon; the expansion of cities over the last 200 years owes a great deal to developers. Developers may themselves be clients for the construction work, or they may simply act as agents for other parties who provide finance.

Types of Contract

In the traditional contract, the client arranges for a designer to prepare a full design and specifications. Contractors are then invited by the client to tender or bid for doing the job in accordance with the design. The role of the contractor is largely confined to construction proper. The contractor's involvement in questions of design or specification is then mainly a matter of seeking such changes as will make it easier or more efficient to build—to improve "buildability".

The other common arrangement in construction is the *design and build contract*. The client requires a building (perhaps an office block or shopping development) but has no firm ideas on detailed aspects of its design other than the size of site, number of persons to be accommodated or scale of activities to be carried out in it. The client then invites tenders from either designers or contractors to submit both design and construction proposals. Contractors working in design and build either have their own design organization or have close links with an external designer who will work for them on the job. Design and build may involve two stages in design: an initial stage where a designer prepares an outline scheme which is then put out to tender; and a second stage where the successful design and build contractor will then carry out further design on detailed aspects of the job.

Maintenance and emergency contracts cover a wide variety of arrangements between clients and contractors and represent a significant proportion of the work of the construction industry. They generally run for a fixed period, require the contractor to do certain types of work or to work on a "call-off" basis (i.e., work that the client calls the contractor in to do). Emergency contracts are widely used by public authorities who are responsible for providing a public service that ought not to be interrupted; government agencies, public utilities and transportation systems make wide use of them. Operators of factories, particularly those with continuous processes such as petrochemicals, also make wide use of emergency contracts to deal with problems in their facilities. Having entered such a contract, the contractor undertakes to make available suitable workers and plant to carry out the work, often at very short notice (e.g., in the case of emergency contracts). The advantage to the client is that he or she does not need to retain workers on payroll or have plant and equipment that may only occasionally be used to deal with maintenance and emergencies.

Pricing of maintenance and emergency contracts may be on the basis of a fixed sum per annum, or on the basis of time spent carrying out work, or some combination.

Perhaps the most common publicly known example of such contractors is maintenance of roads and emergency repairs to gas main or power supplies that have either failed or been accidentally damaged.

Whatever the form of contract, the same possibilities arise for clients and designers to influence the health and safety of contractors by decisions made in the early stage of the job. Design and build perhaps permits closer liaison between the designer and contractor on health and safety.

Price

Price is always an element in a contract. It may simply be a single sum for the cost of doing the job, such as building a house. Even with a single lump sum, the client may have to pay part of the price in advance of the job starting, to enable the contractor to buy materials. The price may, however, be on a cost-plus basis, where the contractor is to recover his or her costs plus an agreed amount or percentage for profit. This arrangement tends to work to the disadvantage of the client, since there is no incentive for the contractor to keep costs down. The price may also have bonuses and penalties attached to it, so that the contractor will receive more money if, for example, the job is completed earlier than the agreed time. Whatever form the price takes for the job, it is usual for payments to be made in stages as the work progresses, either on completion of certain parts of the job by agreed dates or on the basis of some agreed method of measuring the work. At the end of construction proper, it is common for an agreed proportion of the price to be kept back by the clients until "snags" have been put right or the structure has been commissioned.

During the course of the job, the contractor may encounter problems that were not foreseen when the contract was made with the client. These might require changes to the design, the construction method or the materials. Usually such changes will create extra costs for the contractor, who then seeks to recover from the client on the basis that these items become agreed "variations" from the original contract. Sometimes recovery of the cost of variations can make the difference for the contractor between doing the job at a profit or loss.

The pricing of contracts can affect health and safety if inadequate provision is made in the contractor's tender to cover the costs of providing safe access, lifting equipment and so on. This becomes even more difficult where, in an attempt to ensure that they obtain value for money from contractors, clients pursue a vigorous policy of competitive tendering. Governments and local authorities apply policies of competitive tendering to their own contracts, and indeed there may be laws requiring that contracts can be awarded only on the basis of competitive tendering. In such a climate, there is always a risk that the health and safety of construction workers will suffer. In cutting costs, clients may resist a reduction in the standard of construction materials and methods, but at the same time be totally unaware that in accepting the lowest tender, they have accepted working methods that are more likely to endanger construction workers. Even in a situation of competitive tendering, contractors submitting tenders should have to make clear to the client that their bid adequately covers the cost of health and safety involved in their proposals.

Developers can influence health and safety in construction in ways similar to clients, firstly by using contractors who are competent in health and safety and architects who take health and safety into account in their designs, and secondly in not automatically accepting the lowest tenders. Developers generally want to be associated only with successful developments, and one measure of success ought to be projects where there are no major health and safety problems during the construction process.

Building Standards and Planning

In the case of buildings, whether housing, commercial or industrial, projects are subject to planning laws that dictate where certain types of development may take place (e.g., that a factory may not be built among houses). Planning laws may be very specific about the appearance, materials and size of buildings. Typically areas identified as industrial zones are the only places where factory buildings may be erected.

Often there are also building regulations or similar standards that specify in precise detail many aspects of the design and specification of buildings—for example, the thickness of walls and timbers, depth of foundations, insulation characteristics, size of windows and rooms, layout of electrical wiring and earthing, layout of plumbing and pipework and many other issues. These standards have to be followed by clients, designers, specifiers and contractors. They limit their choices but at the same time ensure that buildings are built to an acceptable standard. Planning laws and building regulations thus affect the design of buildings and their cost.

Housing

Projects to build housing may consist of a single house or vast estates of individual houses or flats. The client may be each individual householder, who will then normally be responsible for maintenance of his or her own house. The contractor will usually remain responsible for correcting defects in construction for a period of months after building is finished. However, if the project is for many houses, the client may be a public body, either in local or national government, with responsibility for providing housing. There are also large private bodies like housing associations for whom numbers of houses may be built. Public or private bodies with responsibilities for providing housing generally rent the finished houses to occupants, retaining a greater or lesser degree of responsibility for maintenance also. Building projects involving blocks of flats usually have a client for the block as a whole, who then lets out individual flats under a leasing arrangement. In this situation the owner of the block has responsibility for carrying out maintenance but passes on the cost to the tenants. In some countries ownership of individual flats in a block can rest with the occupants of each flat. There has to be some arrangement, sometimes through an estate management contractor, whereby maintenance can be carried out and the necessary costs raised among the occupants.

Often houses are built on a speculative basis, by a developer. Specific clients or occupants of those houses may not have been identified at the outset but come on the scene after construction has begun and purchase or rent the property like any other article. Houses are usually fitted out with electrical, plumbing and drainage services and heating systems; a gas supply may also be laid on. Sometimes in an attempt to cut costs, houses are only partially finished, leaving it to the purchaser to install some of the fittings and to paint or decorate the building.

Commercial Buildings

Commercial buildings include offices, factories, schools, hospitals, shops—an almost endless list of different types of buildings. In most cases these buildings are constructed for a particular client. However, offices and shops are often built on a speculative basis like housing, with the hope of attracting buyers or tenants. Some clients require an office or shop to be totally fitted out to their requirements, but very often the contract is for the structure and main services, with the client making arrangements to fit out the premises using specialist contractors in office and shop fitting.

Hospitals and schools are built for clients who have a clear idea of precisely what they want, and the clients often provide design input into the project. Plant and equipment in hospitals may cost more than the structure and involve a great deal of design that has to satisfy stringent medical standards. National or local government may also play a part in the design of schools by laying down very detailed requirements on space standards and equipment as part of its wider role in education. National governments usually have very detailed standards as to what is acceptable in hospital buildings and plant. Fitting out of hospitals and similarly complex buildings is a form of construction work usually carried out by specialist subcontractors. Such contractors not only require knowledge of health and safety in construction in general, but also need expertise in ensuring that their operations do not adversely affect the hospital's own activities.

Industrial Construction

Industrial building or construction involves use of the mass-production techniques of manufacturing industry to produce parts of buildings. The ultimate example is the house brick, but normally the expression is applied to building using concrete parts or units that are assembled onsite. Industrial construction expanded rapidly after the Second World War to meet the demand for cheap housing, and it is more commonly found in mass housing developments. Under factory conditions it is possible to mass produce cast units that are consistently accurate in a way that would be virtually impossible under normal site conditions.

Sometimes units for industrial construction are manufactured away from the construction site in factories that may supply a wide area; sometimes, where the individual development is itself very large, a factory is set up onsite to serve that sole site.

Units designed for industrial construction must be structurally strong enough to stand up to being moved, lifted and lowered; they must incorporate anchorage points, or slots to permit safe attachment of lifting tackle, and must also include appropriate lugs or recesses to permit the units to fit together both easily and strongly. Industrial construction demands plant for transporting and lifting units into position and space and arrangements to store units safely when delivered to site, so that units are not damaged and workers are not injured. This technique of building tends to produce visually unattractive buildings, but on a large scale it is cheap; a whole room can be assembled from six cast units with window and door openings in place.

Similar techniques are used to produce concrete units for civil engineering structures like elevated motorways and tunnel linings.

Turn-key Projects

Some clients for industrial or commercial buildings containing extensive complex plant wish simply to walk into a facility that will be up and running from their first day in the premises. Laboratories are sometimes constructed and fitted out on this basis. Such an arrangement is a "turn-key" project, and here the contractor will ensure that all aspects of plant and services are fully operational before handing the project over. The job may be done under a design and build contract so that, in effect, the turn-key contractor deals with everything from design to commissioning.

Civil Engineering and Heavy Construction

The civil engineering of which the public is most aware is work on highways. Some highway work is the creation of new roads on virgin land, but much of it is the extension and repair of existing highways. Contracts for highway work are usually for state or local government agencies, but sometimes roads remain under the control of contractors for some years after completion, during which time they are permitted to charge tolls. If civil engineering structures are being financed by government, then both the design and actual construction will be subject to a high degree of supervision by officials on behalf of government. Contracts for construction of highways are usually let to contractors on the basis of a contractor being responsible for a section of so many kilometres of the highway. There will be a main contractor for each section; but highway construction involves a number of skills, and aspects of the job such as steel work, concrete, shuttering and surfacing may be subcontracted by the main contractor to specialist firms. Highway construction is also sometimes carried out under management contract arrangements, where a civil engineering consultancy will provide management for the job, with all the work being done by subcontractors. Such a management contractor may also have been involved in design of the highway.

Construction of highways requires the creation of a surface whose gradients are suitable for the sort of traffic that will use it. In a generally level terrain, creation of the foundation of the highway may involve earthmoving—that is, shifting soil from cuttings to create embankments, building bridges across rivers and driving tunnels through mountainsides where it is not possible to go round the obstruction. Where labour costs are higher, such operations are carried out using mechanically powered plant such as excavators, scrapers, loaders and lorries. Where labour costs are lower, these processes may be carried out manually by large numbers of workers using hand tools. Whatever the actual methods adopted, highway construction requires high standards of route surveying and planning of the job.

Highway maintenance frequently requires roads to remain in use whilst repairs or improvements are carried out in part of the road. There is thus a hazardous interface between traffic movement and construction operations which makes good planning and management of the job even more important. There are often national standards for signage and coning off of roadworks and requirements as to the amount of separation there should be between construction and traffic, which may be difficult to achieve in a confined area. Control of traffic approaching roadworks is usually the responsibility of the local police, but requires careful liaison between them and the contractors. Highway maintenance creates traffic hold-ups, and accordingly contractors are put under pressure to finish jobs quickly; sometimes there are bonuses for finishing early and penalties for finishing late. Financial pressures must not undermine safety on what is very dangerous work.

Surfacing of highways may involve concrete, stone or tarmacadam. This requires a substantial logistical train to ensure that the required quantities of surfacing materials are in place in the right condition to ensure that surfacing proceeds without interruption. Tarmacadam requires special purpose spreading plant that keeps the surfacing material plastic while spreading it. Where the job is re-surfacing, plant will be required including picks and breakers so that the existing surface is broken up and

removed. A final finish is usually applied to the surfaces of highways involving use of heavy powered rollers.

Creation of cuttings and tunnels may require use of explosives and then arrangements to shift the muck displaced by the blasting. The sides of cuttings may require permanent supports to prevent landslides or falls of ground onto the finished road.

Elevated highways often require structures similar to bridges, especially if the elevated section passes through an urban area when space is limited. Elevated highways are often constructed from cast reinforced concrete sections that are either cast *in situ* or cast in a fabrication area and then shifted to the required position onsite. The work will require large-capacity lifting machinery to lift cast sections, shuttering and reinforcing.

Temporary support arrangements or "falsework" to support sections of either elevated highways or bridges while they are being cast in position need to be designed to take into account the uneven loads imposed by concrete as it is poured. Design of falsework is as important as design of the structure proper.

Bridges

Bridges in remote areas may be simple constructions from timber. More commonly today bridges are from reinforced concrete or steel. They may also be clad in brickwork or stone. If the bridge is to span a considerable gap, whether above water or not, its design will require specialist designers. Using today's materials, the strength of the bridge span or arch is not achieved by mass material, which would be simply too heavy, but by skilful design. The main contractor for a bridge building job is usually a major general civil-engineering contractor with management expertise and plant. However, specialist subcontractors may deal with major aspects of the job like erection of steel work to form the span or casting or placing cast sections of the span in place. If the bridge is over water, one or both abutments that support the ends of the bridge may themselves have to be constructed in water, involving piling, coffer dams, mass concrete or stone work. A new bridge may be part of a new highway system, and approach roads may have to be built, themselves possibly elevated. Good design is especially important in bridge building, so that the structure is strong enough to withstand the loads imposed on it in use and to ensure that it will not require maintenance or repair too frequently. The appearance of a bridge is often a very important factor, and again good design can balance the conflicting demands of sound engineering and aesthetics. Provision of safe means of access for maintenance of bridges needs to be taken into account during design.

Tunnels

Tunnels are a specialized form of civil engineering. They vary in size from the Channel Tunnel, with over 100 km of bores from 6 to 8 m in diameter, to mini-tunnels whose bores are too small for workers to enter and which are created by machines launched from access shafts and controlled from the surface. In urban areas, tunnels may be the only way to provide or improve transport routes or to provide water and drainage facilities. The proposed route of the tunnel requires as detailed a survey as possible to confirm the kind of ground that the tunnel workings will be in and whether there will be groundwater. The nature of the ground, the presence of groundwater and the end use of the tunnel all influence the choice of tunnelling method.

If the ground is consistent, like the chalk-clay beneath the English Channel, then machine digging may be possible. If high groundwater pressures are not encountered during pre-construction survey, then it is usually unnecessary for the workings to be pressurized to keep out the water. If working in compressed air cannot be avoided, this adds considerably to costs because airlocks have to be provided, workers need to be allowed time to decompress, and access to workings for plant and materials may be made more difficult. A large tunnel for a road or railway in consistent non-hard-rock ground might be dug using a full-face tunnel-boring machine (TBM). This is really a train of different machines linked together and moving forward on rails under its own power. The front face is a circular cutting head that rotates and feeds spoil back through the TBM. Behind the cutting head are various sections of the TBM that place the segments of tunnel lining rings in position around the surface of the tunnel, grout behind the lining rings and, in a very confined space, provide all the machinery to handle and place ring segments (each weighing some tonnes), remove spoil, bring grout and extra segments forward and house electric motors and hydraulic pumps to power the cutting head and segment-placing mechanisms.

A tunnel in non-hard-rock ground which is not consistent enough to use a TBM, may be dug using equipment such as *roadheaders* that bite into the face of the heading. Spoil falling from the roadheader onto the tunnel floor are to be collected by diggers and removed by lorry. This technique permits digging of tunnels that are not circular in section. The ground in which such a tunnel is dug will not usually have sufficient strength for it to remain unlined; without some form of lining there might be falls from roof and walls. The tunnel may be lined by liquid concrete sprayed onto a steel mesh held in position by rock bolts (the "New Austrian tunnelling method") or by cast concrete.

If the tunnel is in hard rock, the heading will be dug by means of blasting, using explosives placed into shot holes drilled into the rock face. The trick here is to use the minimum of blast to achieve a fall of rock in the position and sizes required, thereby making it easier to remove the spoil. On bigger jobs, multiple drills mounted on tracked bases will be used along with diggers and loaders to remove spoil. Hard rock tunnels are often simply trimmed to provide an even surface, but are not then further lined. If the rock surface remains friable with a risk of pieces falling, then a lining will be applied, usually some form of sprayed or cast concrete.

Whatever the method of construction adopted for the tunnel, the effective supply of tunnelling materials and removal of spoil are vital to the successful progress of the job. Large tunnelling jobs may require extensive narrow-gauge construction rail systems to provide logistical support.

Dams

Dams invariably contain large quantities of earth or rock to provide mass to resist the pressure from water behind them; some dams are also covered in masonry or reinforced concrete. Depending on the length of the dam, its construction often requires earthmoving on the very largest scale. Dams tend to be built in remote locations dictated by the need to ensure that water is available at a position where it is technically possible to restrict the flow of the river. Thus temporary roads may have to be built before dam building may start in order to get plant, materials and personnel to the site. Workers on dam projects may be so far from home that full-scale living accommodations have to be provided along with the usual construction site facilities. It is necessary to divert the river away from the site of the workings, and a coffer dam and temporary riverbed may have be created.

A dam constructed simply from earth or rock that has been shifted will require large scale excavation, digging and scraping plant as well as lorries. If the dam wall is covered by masonry or cast concrete, it will be necessary to employ high or long-reach cranes capable of depositing masonry, shuttering, reinforcing and concrete in the right places. A continuous supply of good-quality concrete will be necessary, and a concrete-mixing plant will be necessary alongside the dam workings, with the concrete either handled in batches by crane or pumped to the job.

Canals and docks

Construction and repair of canals and docks contain some aspects of other jobs that have been described, such as roadworks, tunnels and bridges. It is particularly important in canal building for surveying to be to the highest standard before work begins, especially regarding levels and to ensure that material that has had to be dug out can economically be used elsewhere in the job. Indeed the early railway engineers owed a great deal to the experience of canal builders a century before. The canal will require a source for its water and will either tap into a natural source such as a river or lake or create an artificial one in the form of a reservoir. Digging of docks may start on dry land, but sooner or later has to link up to either a river, a canal, the sea or another dock.

Canal and dock building requires excavators and loaders to open up the ground. Spoil may be removed by lorry or water transport may be used. Docks are sometimes developed on ground that has a long history of industrial use. Industrial wastes may have escaped into such ground over many years, and spoil removed in digging or extending the docks will be heavily contaminated. Work in repairing a canal or dock is likely to have to be carried out while adjacent parts of the system are kept in use. The workings may have to rely on coffer dams for protection. Failure of a coffer dam during extension of Newport Docks in Wales in the early years of this century resulted in nearly 100 deaths.

Clients for canals and docks are likely to be public authorities. However, sometimes docks are constructed for corporations alongside their major production plants or for corporate clients to handle a particular type of incoming or outgoing goods (e.g., motor cars). Repair and renovation of canals is nowadays often for the leisure industry. Like dams, both canal and dock construction may be in very remote situations, requiring provision of facilities for workers beyond those of a normal construction site.

Railroads

Construction of railroads or railways historically came after canals and before major highways. Clients in railway construction contracts may be rail operators themselves or governmental agencies, if the railways are financed by government. As with highways, design of a railroad that is economical and safe to build and operate depends on good surveying beforehand. In general, locomotives do not operate effectively on steep gradients, and therefore those designing layout of the track are concerned with avoiding changes in levels, going round or through obstacles rather than over them. Designers of railroads are subject to two constraints unique to the industry: first, curves in the track layout must generally conform to very large radii (otherwise trains cannot negotiate them); second, all the structures connected with the railway—its bridge arches, tunnels and stations—must be capable of accommodating the *envelope* of the largest locomotives and rolling stock that will use the track. The envelope is the silhouette of the rolling stock plus clearance to allow safe passage through bridges, tunnels and so on.

Contractors involved in building and repair of railroads require the usual construction plant and effective logistical arrangements to ensure that rail track and ballast as well as construction materials are always available in what may be remote locations. Contractors may use the track they have just laid to run trains supplying the works. Contractors involved in maintenance of existing operational railways have to ensure that their work does not interfere with the operations of the railway and endanger workers or the public.

Airports

The rapid expansion of air transportation since the middle of the 20th century has resulted in one of the biggest and most complex forms of construction: the building and extension of airports.

Clients for airport construction are usually governments at the national or local level or agencies representing the government. Some airports are built for major cities. Airports are rarely for private clients such as business corporations.

Planning the work is sometimes made more difficult because of environmental constraints that have been placed on the project in relation to noise and pollution. Airports require a lot of space, and if they are located in more heavily populated areas, creation of the runways and space for terminal buildings and car parks may require reinstatement of derelict or otherwise difficult land. Building an airport involves levelling a large area, which may require earth moving and even land reclamation, and then construction of a wide variety of often very large buildings, including hangars, maintenance workshops, control towers and fuel storage facilities, as well as terminal buildings and parking.

If the airport is being built on soft ground, buildings may require piled foundations. Actual runways require good foundations; hardcore supporting the surface layers of concrete or tarmac needs to be heavily compacted. Plant used on airport construction is similar in scale and type to that used in major highway projects, except that it is concentrated within a limited area rather than over the many miles of a highway.

Airport maintenance is a particularly difficult type of work where resurfacing the runways has to be integrated with continuing operation of the airport. Usually the contractor is allowed an agreed number of hours during the night when he or she can work on a runway that is temporarily taken out of use. All the contractor's plant, materials and workforce have to be marshalled off the runways, prepared to move immediately to the work site at the agreed start time. The contractor must finish his or her work and get off the runways again at the agreed time when flights may resume. Whilst working on the runway, the contractor must not impede or otherwise endanger aircraft movement on other runways.

TYPES OF PROJECTS AND THEIR ASSOCIATED HAZARDS

Jeffrey Hinksman

All new buildings and civil engineering structures go through the same cycle of conception or design, groundworks, building or erection (including the roof of a building), finishing and provision of utilities and final commissioning before being brought into use. In the course of years, those once new buildings or structures require maintenance including re-painting and cleaning; they are likely to be renovated by being updated or changed or repaired to correct damage by weather or accident; and finally they will need to be demolished to make way for a more modern facility or because their use is no longer required. This is true of houses; it is also true of large, complex structures like power stations and bridges. Each stage in the life of a building or civil engineering structure presents hazards, some of which are common to all work in construction (like the risk from falls) or unique to the particular type of project (such as the risk from collapse of excavations during preparation of foundations in either building or civil engineering).

For each type of project (and, indeed, each stage within a project) it is possible to forecast what will be the principal hazards to the safety of construction workers. The risk from falls is common to all construction projects, even those at ground level. This is supported by the evidence of accident data which show that up to half of fatal accidents to construction workers involve falls.

New Facilities

Conception (design)

Physical hazards to those engaged in design of new facilities normally arise from visits by professional staff to carry out surveys. Visits by unaccompanied staff to unknown or abandoned sites may expose them to risks from dangerous access, unguarded openings and excavations and, in a building, to electrical wiring and equipment in a dangerous condition. If the survey requires entry into rooms or excavations that have been closed for some time, there is the risk of being overcome by carbon dioxide or reduced oxygen levels. All hazards are increased if visits are made to an unlit site after dark or if the lone visitor has no means of communicating with others and summoning aid. As a general rule, professional staff should not be required to visit sites where they will be on their own. They should not visit after dark unless the site is well lit. They should not enter enclosed spaces unless these have been tested and shown to be safe. Lastly, they should be in communication with their base or have an effective means of getting help.

Conception or design proper should play an important part in influencing safety when contractors are actually working onsite. Designers, be they architects or civil engineers, should be expected to be more than mere producers of drawings. In creating their design, they should, by reason of their training and experience, have some idea how contractors are likely to have to work in putting the design into effect. Their competence should be such that they are able to identify to contractors the hazards that will arise from those methods of working. Designers should try to "design out" hazards arising from their design, making the structure more "buildable" as regards health and safety and, where possible, substituting safer materials in the specifications. They should improve access for maintenance at the design stage and reduce the need for maintenance workers to be put at risk by incorporating features or materials that will require less frequent attention during the life of the building.

In general, designers are able to design out hazards only to a limited extent; there will usually be significant residual risks that the contractors will have to take into account when devising their own safe systems of work. Designers should provide contractors with information on these hazards so that the latter are able to take both the hazards and necessary safety procedures into account, firstly when tendering for the job, and secondly when developing their systems of work to do the job safely.

The importance of specifying materials with better health and safety properties tends to be underestimated when considering safety by design. Designers and specifiers should consider whether materials are available with better toxic or structural properties or that can be used or maintained more safely. This requires designers to think about the materials that will be used and to decide whether following previous practice will adequately protect construction workers. Often cost is the determining factor in choice of materials. However, clients and designers should realize that while materials with better toxic or structural properties may have a higher initial cost, they often yield much bigger savings over the life of the building because construction and maintenance workers require less expensive access or protective equipment.

Excavation

Usually the first job to be done on the site after site surveys and laying out of the site once the contract has been awarded (assuming there is no need for demolition or site clearance) is groundworks for the foundations. In the case of domestic housing, the footings are unlikely to require excavations greater than half a metre and may be dug by hand. For blocks of flats, commercial and industrial buildings and some civil engineering, the foundations may need to be several metres below ground level. This will require the digging of trenches in which work will have to carried out to lay or erect the foundations. Trenches deeper than 1 m are likely to be dug using machines such as excavators. Excavations are also dug to permit laying of cables and pipes. Contractors often use special-purpose excavators capable of digging deep but narrow excavations. If workers have to enter these excavations, the hazards are essentially the same as those encountered in excavations for foundations. However, there is usually more scope in cable and pipe excavations or trenches to adopt methods of working that do not require workers to enter the excavation.

Work in excavations deeper then 1 m needs especially careful planning and supervision. The hazard is the risk of being struck by earth and debris as the ground collapses along the side of the excavation. Ground is notoriously unpredictable; what looks firm can be caused to slip by rain, frost or vibration from other construction activities nearby. What looks like firm, stiff clay dries out and cracks when exposed to the air or will soften and slip after rain. A cubic metre of earth weighs more than 1 tonne; a worker struck by only a small fall of ground risks broken limbs, crushed internal organs and suffocation. Because of the vital importance to safety of selecting a suitable method of support for the sides of the excavation, before work starts, the ground should be surveyed by a person experienced in safe excavation work to establish the type and condition of the ground, especially the presence of water.

Support for trench sides

Double-sided support. It is not safe to rely on cutting or "battering" back the sides of the excavation to a safe angle. If the ground is wet sand or silt, the safe angle of batter would be as low as 5 to 10° above horizontal, and there is generally not enough room onsite for such a wide excavation. The most common method of providing safety for work in excavations is to support both sides of the trench through *shoring*. With double-sided support, the loads from the ground on one side are resisted by similar loads acting through struts between the opposing sides. Timber of good quality must be used to provide vertical elements of the support system, known as *poling boards*. Poling boards are driven into the ground as soon as excavation begins; the boards are edge to edge, and thus provide a timber wall. This is done on each side of the excavation. As the excavation is dug deeper, the poling boards are driven into the ground ahead of the excavation. When the excavation is a metre deep, a row of horizontal boards (known as *walings* or *wales*) is placed against the poling boards and then held in position by timber or metal struts wedged between the opposing walings at regular intervals. As digging proceeds, the poling boards are driven further into the ground with their walings and struts, and it will be necessary to create a second row of walings and struts if the excavation is deeper than 1.2 m. Indeed, an excavation of 6 m could require up to four rows of walings.

The standard timber methods of support are unsuitable if the excavation is deeper than 6 m or the ground is water bearing. In these situations, other types of support for the sides of excavations are required, such as vertical steel trench sheets, closely spaced with horizontal timber walings and metal adjustable struts, or full-scale steel sheet piling. Both methods have the advantage that the trench sheets or sheet piles can be driven by machine before excavation proper starts. Also, trench sheets and sheet piles can be withdrawn at the end of the job and re-used. Support systems for excavations deeper than 6 m or in water-bearing ground should be custom designed; standard solutions will not be adequate.

Single-sided support. An excavation that is rectangular in shape and too large for the support methods described above to be practicable may have one or more of its sides supported by a row of poling boards or trench sheets. These are themselves supported first by one or more rows of horizontal walings which are themselves then held in place by angled rakes back to a strong anchorage or support point.

Other systems. It is possible to use manufactured steel boxes of adjustable width that may be lowered into excavations and within which work can be carried out safely. It is also possible to use proprietary waling frame systems, whereby a horizontal frame is lowered into the excavation between the poling boards or trench sheets; the waling frame is forced apart and applies pressure to keep the poling boards upright by the action of hydraulic struts across the frame which can be pumped from a position of safety outside the excavation.

Training and supervision. Whatever method of support is adopted, the work should be carried out by trained workers under supervision of an experienced person. The excavation and its supports should be inspected each day and after each occasion that they have been damaged or displaced (e.g., after a heavy rain). The only assumption one is entitled to make regarding safety and work in excavations is that all ground is liable to fail and therefore no work should ever be carried out with workers in an unsupported excavation deeper than 1 m. See also the article "Trenching" in this chapter.

Superstructure

Erection of the main part of the building or civil engineering structure (the *superstructure*) takes place after completion of the foundation. This part of the project usually requires work at heights above ground. The biggest single cause of fatal and major injury accidents is falls from heights or on the same level.

Ladder work

Even if the job is simply building a house, the number of workers involved, the amount of building materials to be handled and, in later stages, the heights at which work will have to be carried out all require more than simple ladders for access and safe places of work.

There are limitations on the sort of work that can be done safely from ladders. Work more than 10 m above ground is usually beyond the safe reach of ladders; lengthy ladders themselves become dangerous to handle. There are limitations on the reach of workers on ladders as well as on the amount of equipment and materials they can safely carry; the physical strain of standing on ladder rungs limits the time they can spend on such work. Ladders are useful for carrying out short-duration, light-weight work within safe reach of the ladder; typically, inspection and repair and painting of small areas of the building's surface. Ladders also provide access in scaffolds, in excavations and in structures where more permanent access has not yet been provided.

It will be necessary to use temporary working platforms, the most common of which is scaffolding. If the job is a multi-storey block of flats, office building or structure like a bridge, then scaffolding of varying degrees of complexity will be required, depending on the scale of the job.

Scaffolds

Scaffolds consist of easily assembled frameworks of steel or timber on which working platforms may be placed. Scaffolds may be fixed or mobile. Fixed scaffolds—that is, those erected alongside a building or structure—are either independent or *putlog*. The independent scaffold has uprights or standards along both sides of its platforms and is capable of remaining upright without support from the building. The putlog scaffold has standards along the outer edges of its working platforms, but the inner side is supported by the building itself, with parts of the scaffold frame, the putlogs, having flattened ends that are placed between courses of brickwork to gain support. Even the independent scaffold needs to be rigidly "tied" or secured to the structure at regular intervals if there are working platforms above 6 m or if the scaffold is sheeted for weather protection, thus increasing wind-loadings.

Working platforms on scaffolds consist of good-quality timber boards laid so that they are level and both ends are properly supported; intervening supports will be necessary if the timber is liable to sag due to loading by people or materials. Platforms should never be less than 600 mm in width if used for access and working or 800 mm if used also for materials. Where there is a risk of falling more than 2 m, the outer edge and ends of a working platform should be protected by a rigid guard rail, secured to the standards at a height of between 0.91 and 1.15 m above the platform. To prevent materials falling off the platform, a toe board rising at least 150 mm above the platform should be provided along its outer edge, again secured to the standards. If guard rails and toe-boards have to be removed to permit passage of materials, they should be replaced as soon as possible.

Scaffold standards should be upright and properly supported at their bases on base plates, and if necessary on timber. Access within fixed scaffolds from one working platform level to another is usually by means of ladders. These should be properly maintained, secured at top and bottom and extend at least 1.05 m above the platform.

The principal hazards in the use of scaffolds—falls of person or materials—usually arise from shortcomings either in the way the scaffold is first erected (e.g., a piece such as a guard rail is missing) or in the way it is misused (e.g., by being overloaded) or adapted during the course of the job for some purpose that is unsuitable (e.g., sheeting for weather protection is added without adequate ties to the building). Timber boards for scaffold platforms become displaced or break; ladders are not secured at top and bottom. The list of things that can go wrong if scaffolds are not erected by experienced persons under proper supervision is almost limitless. Scaffolders are themselves particularly at risk from falls during erection and dismantling of scaffolds, because they are often obliged to work at heights, in exposed positions without proper working platforms (see figure 93.4).

Tower scaffolds. Tower scaffolds are either fixed or mobile, with a working platform on top and an access ladder inside the tower frame. The mobile tower scaffold is on wheels. Such towers easily become unstable and should be subject to height limitations; for the fixed tower scaffold the height should not be more than 3.5 times the shortest base dimension; for mobile, the ratio is reduced to 3 times. The stability of tower scaffolds should be increased by use of outriggers. Workers should not be permitted on the top of mobile tower scaffolds while the scaffold is being moved or without the wheels being locked.

The principal hazard with tower scaffolds is overturning, throwing people off the platform; this may be due to the tower being too tall for its base, failure to use outriggers or lock wheels or unsuitable use of the scaffold, perhaps by overloading it.

Slung and suspended scaffolds. The other main category of scaffold is those that are slung or suspended. The slung scaffold is essentially a working platform hung by wire ropes or scaffold tubes from an overhead structure like a bridge. The suspended scaffold is again a working platform or cradle, suspended by wire ropes, but in this case it is capable of being raised and lowered. It is often provided for maintenance and painting contractors, sometimes as part of the equipment of the finished building. In either case, the building or structure must be capable of supporting the slung or suspended platform, the suspension arrangements must be strong enough and the platform itself should be sufficiently robust to

carry the intended load of people and materials with guard sides or rails to prevent them from falling out. For the suspended platform, there should be at least three turns of rope on the winch drums at the lowest position of the platform. Where there are no arrangements to prevent the suspended platform from falling in the event of failure of a rope, workers using the platform should wear a safety harness and rope attached to a secure anchorage point on the building. Persons using such platforms should be trained and experienced in their use.

The principal hazard with slung or suspended scaffolds is failure of the supporting arrangements, either of the structure itself or the ropes or tubes from which the platform is hung. This can arise from incorrect erection or installation of the slung or suspended scaffold or from overloading or other misuse. Failure of suspended scaffolds has resulted in multiple fatalities and can endanger the public.

All scaffolds and ladders should be inspected by a competent person at least weekly and before being used again after weather conditions that may have damaged them. Ladders which have cracked styles or broken rungs should not be used. Scaffolders who erect and dismantle scaffolds should be given specific training and experience to ensure their own safety and the safety of others who may use the scaffolds. Scaffolds are often provided by one, perhaps the main, contractor for use by all contractors. In this situation, tradespeople may modify or displace parts of scaffolds to make their own job easier, without restoring the scaffold afterwards or realizing the hazard they have created. It is important that the arrangements for coordination of health and safety across the site deal effectively with the action of one trade on the safety of another.

Figure 93.4 • Assembling scaffolding at a Geneva, Switzerland, construction site without adequate protection.

Powered access equipment

On some jobs, during both construction and maintenance, it may be more practicable to use powered access equipment than scaffolding in its various forms. Providing access to the underside of a factory roof undergoing recladding or access to the outside of a few windows in a building may be safer and cheaper than scaffolding out the whole structure. Powered access equipment comes in a variety of forms from manufacturers, for example, platforms that may be raised and lowered vertically by hydraulic action or the opening and closing of scissor jacks and hydraulically-powered articulated arms with a working platform or cage on the end of the arm, commonly called *cherry pickers*. Such equipment is generally mobile and can be moved to the place it is required and brought into use in a matter of moments. Safe use of powered access equipment requires that the job be within the specification for the machine as described by the manufacturer (i.e., the equipment must not overreach or be overloaded).

Powered access equipment requires a firm, level floor on which to operate; it may be necessary to put out outriggers to ensure that the machine does not tip over. Workers on the working platform should have access to operating controls. Workers should be trained in safe use of such equipment. Properly operated and maintained, powered access equipment can provide safe access where it may be virtually impossible to provide scaffolding, for example, during the early stages of erection of a steel frame or to provide access for steel erectors to the connecting points between columns and beams.

Steel erection

The superstructure of both buildings and civil engineering structures often involves erection of substantial steel frames, sometimes of great height. While responsibility for ensuring safe access for steel erectors who assemble these frames rests principally with the management of steel erection contractors, their difficult job can be made easier by the designers of the steel work. Designers should ensure that patterns of bolt holes are simple and facilitate easy insertion of bolts; the pattern of joints and bolt holes should be as uniform as possible throughout the frame; rests or perches should be provided on columns at joints with beams, so that the ends of beams may rest still while steel erectors are inserting bolts. As far as possible, the design should ensure that access stairs form part of the early frame so that steel erectors have to rely less on ladders and beams for access. Also, the design should provide for holes to be drilled in suitable places in the columns during fabrication and before the steel is delivered to site, which will permit securing of taut wire ropes, to which steel erectors wearing safety harnesses may secure their running lines. The aim should be to get floor plates in place in steel frames as soon as possible, to reduce the amount of time that steel erectors have to rely on safety lines and harnesses or ladders. If the steel frame has to remain open and without floors while erection continues to higher levels, then safety nets should be slung below the various working levels. As far as possible, the design of the steel frame and the working practices of the steel erectors should minimize the extent to which workers have to "walk steel".

Roof-work

While raising the walls is an important and hazardous stage in erecting a building, putting the roof in place is equally important and presents special hazards. Roofs are either flat or pitched. With flat roofs the principal hazard is of persons or materials falling either over the edge or down openings in the roof. Flat roofs are usually constructed either from wood or cast concrete, or slabs. Flat roofs must be sealed against entry of water, and various materials are used, including bitumen and felt. All materials required for the roof have to be raised to the required level, which may require goods hoists or cranes if the building is tall or the quantities of covering and sealant are substantial. Bitumen may have to be heated to assist spreading and sealing; this may involve taking on to the roof a gas cylinder and melting pot. Roof-workers and persons beneath can be burned by the heated bitumen and fires can be started involving the roof structure.

The hazard from falls can be prevented on flat roofs by erecting temporary edge protection in the form of guard rails of dimensions similar to the guard rails in scaffolds. If the building is still surrounded by external scaffolding, this can be extended up to roof level, to provide edge protection for roof-workers. Falls down openings in flat roofs can be prevented by covering them or, if they have to remain open, by erecting guard rails round them.

Pitched roofs are most commonly found on houses and smaller buildings. The pitch of the roof is achieved by erecting a wooden frame to which the outer covering of the roof, usually clay or concrete tiles, is attached. The pitch of the roof may exceed 45° above horizontal, but even a shallower pitch presents hazards when wet. To prevent roof-workers from falling while fixing battens, felt and tiles, roof ladders should be used. If the roof ladder cannot be secured or supported at its bottom end, it should have a properly designed ridge-iron that will hook over the ridge tiles. Where there is doubt about the strength of ridge tiles, the ladder should be secured by means of a rope from its top rung, over the ridge tiles and down to a strong anchorage point.

Fragile roofing materials are used on both pitched and curved or barrel roofs. Some roof lights are made of fragile materials. Typical materials include sheets of asbestos cement, plastic, treated chipboard and wood-wool. Because roof-workers frequently step through sheets they have just laid, safe access to where the sheets are to be laid, and a safe position from which to do it, are required. This is usually in the form of a series of roof ladders. Fragile roofing materials present an even greater hazard to maintenance workers, who may be unaware of their fragile nature. Designers and architects can improve the safety of roof-workers by not specifying fragile materials in the first place.

Laying of roofs, even flat roofs, can be dangerous in high winds or heavy rain. Materials such as sheets, normally safe to handle, become dangerous in such weather. Unsafe roof-work not only endangers roof-workers, but also presents hazards to the public beneath. Erection of new roofs is hazardous, but, if anything, maintenance of roofs is even more dangerous.

Renovation

Renovation includes both maintenance of the structure and changes to it during its life. Maintenance (including cleaning and repainting of woodwork or other exterior surfaces, repointing of cement and repairs to walls and the roof) presents hazards from falling similar to those of erection of the structure because of the need to gain access to high parts of the structure. Indeed, the hazards may be greater because during smaller, short-duration maintenance jobs, there is a temptation to cut costs on provision of safe access equipment, for example, by trying to do from a ladder what can be safely done only from a scaffold. This is especially true of roof work, where replacement of a tile may take only minutes but there is still the possibility of a worker falling to his or her death.

Maintenance and cleaning

Designers, especially architects, can improve safety for maintenance and cleaning workers by taking into account in their designs and specifications the need for safe access to roofs, to plant rooms, to windows and to other exposed positions on the outside of the structure. Avoiding the need for access at all is the best solution, followed next by permanent safe access as part of the structure, perhaps stairs or a walkway with guard rails or a powered access platform permanently slung from the roof. The least satisfactory situation for maintenance personnel is where a scaffold similar to that used to erect the building is the only way to provide safe access. This will be less of a problem for major, longer duration renovation work, but on short-duration jobs, the cost of full scaffolding is such that there is a temptation to cut corners and use mobile powered access equipment or tower scaffolds where they are unsuitable or inadequate.

If renovation involves major re-cladding of the building or wholesale cleaning using high-pressure water jetting or chemicals, total scaffolding may be the only answer that will not only protect the workers but also allow the hanging of sheeting to protect the public nearby. Protection of workers involved in cleaning using high-pressure water jets includes impervious clothing, boots and gloves, and a face screen or goggles to protect the eyes. Cleaning involving chemicals such as acids will require similar but acid-resistant protective clothing. If abrasives are used to clean the structure a silica-free substance should be used. Since use of abrasives will give rise to dust that may be injurious, approved respiratory equipment should be worn by the workers. Repainting of windows in a tall office building or block of flats cannot be done safely from ladders, although this is usually possible on domestic housing. It will be necessary to provide either scaffolding or to hang suspended scaffolds such as cradles from the roof, ensuring that suspension points are adequate.

Maintenance and cleaning of civil engineering structures, like bridges, tall chimneys or masts may involve working at such heights or in such positions (e.g., above water) that prohibit the erection of a normal scaffold. As far as possible, work should be done from a fixed scaffold slung or cantilevered from the structure. Where this is not possible, work should be done from a properly suspended cradle. Modern bridges often have their own cradles as parts of the permanent structure; these should be checked fully before being used for a maintenance job. Civil engineering structures are often exposed to the weather, and work should not be permitted in high winds or heavy rain.

Window cleaning

Window cleaning presents its own hazards, especially where it is done from the ground on ladders, or with improvised arrangements for access on taller buildings. Window cleaning is not usually regarded as part of the construction process, and yet is a widespread operation that can endanger both the window cleaners and the public. Safety in window cleaning is, however, influenced by one part of the construction process-design. If architects fail to take into account the need for safe access, or alternatively to specify windows of a design that can be cleaned from inside, then the job of the window cleaning contractor will be much more hazardous. Whilst designing out the need for external window cleaning or installing proper access equipment as part of the original design may initially cost more, there should be considerable savings over the life of the building in maintenance costs and a reduction in hazards.

Refurbishment

Refurbishment is an important and hazardous aspect of renovation. It takes place when for example, the essential structure of the building or bridge is left in place but other parts are repaired or replaced. Typically in domestic housing, refurbishment involves stripping out windows, possibly floors and stairs, along with wiring and plumbing, and replacing them with new and usually upgraded items. In a commercial office building, refurbishment involves windows and possibly floors, but also is likely to involve stripping out and replacing cladding to a framed building, installing new heating and ventilation equipment and lifts or total rewiring.

In civil engineering structures such as bridges, refurbishment may involve stripping the structure back to its basic frame, strengthening it, renewing parts and replacing the roadway and any cladding.

Refurbishment presents the usual hazards to construction workers: falling and falling materials. The hazard is made more difficult to control where the premises remain occupied during refurbishment, as is often the case in domestic premises such as blocks of flats, when alternative accommodations to house occupants are simply not available. In that situation the occupants, especially children, face the same hazards as construction workers. There may be hazards from power cables to portable tools such as saws and drills required during refurbishment. It is important that the work be carefully planned to minimize hazards to both workers and the public; the latter need to know what will be going on and when. Access to rooms, stairs or balconies where work is to be carried out should be prevented. Entrances to blocks of flats may have to be protected by fans to protect persons from falling materials. At the close of the working shift, ladders and scaffolds should be removed or closed off in a manner that does not allow children to get onto them and endanger themselves. Similarly, paints, gas cylinders and power tools should be removed or stored safely.

In occupied commercial buildings where services are being refurbished, it should not be possible for liftway doors to be opened. If refurbishment interferes with fire and emergency equipment, special arrangements need to be made to warn both occupants and workers if fire breaks out. Refurbishment of both domestic and commercial premises may require removal of asbestos-containing materials. This presents major health risks to the workers and the occupants when they return. Such asbestos removal should be carried out only by specially trained and equipped contractors. The area where asbestos is being removed will need to be sealed off from other parts of the building. Before the occupants return to areas from which asbestos has been stripped, the atmosphere in those rooms should be monitored and the results evaluated to ensure that asbestos fibre levels in air are below permissible levels.

Usually the safest way to carry out refurbishment is to totally exclude occupants and members of the public; however, this is sometimes simply not practicable.

Utilities

Provision of utilities in buildings, such as electricity, gas, water and telecommunications, is usually carried out by specialist subcontractors. Principal hazards are falls due to poor access, dust and fumes from drilling and cutting and electric shock or fire from electrical and gas services. The hazards are the same in houses, only on a smaller scale. The job is easier for contractors if proper allowance has been made by the architect in designing the structure to accommodate the utilities. They require space for ducts and channels in walls and floors plus sufficient additional space for installers to operate effectively and safely. Similar considerations apply to maintenance of utilities after the building has been taken into use. Proper attention to the detailing of ducts, channels and openings in the initial design of the structure should mean that these are either cast or built into the structure. It will then not be necessary for construction workers to chase out channels and ducts or to open up holes using power tools, which create large quantities of harmful dust. If adequate space is provided for heating and air conditioning ducts and equipment, the job of the installers is both easier and safer because it is then possible to work from safe positions rather than, for example, standing on boards wedged across the inside of vertical ducts. If lighting and wiring have to be installed overhead in rooms with high ceilings, contractors may need scaffolding or tower scaffolds in addition to ladders.

Installation of utility services should be conform to recognized local standards. These should, for example, cover all safety aspects of electrical and gas installations so that contractors are in no doubt as to standards required for wiring, insulation, earthing (grounding), fusing, isolation and, for gas, protection for pipework, isolation, adequate ventilation and fitting of safety devices for flame failure and loss of pressure. Failure by contractors to deal adequately with these matters of detail in the installation or maintenance of utilities will create hazards for both their own workers and the occupants of the building.

Interior finishing

If the structure is of brick or concrete, the interior finish may require initial plastering to provide a surface which can be painted. Plastering is a traditional craft trade. The principal hazards are severe strain to the back and arms from handling bagged material and plaster boards and then the actual plastering process, especially when the plasterer is working overhead. After plastering, surfaces may be painted. The hazard here is from vapours given off by thinners or solvents and sometimes from the paint itself. If possible, water-based paints should be used. If solvent-based paints have to be used, the rooms should be well ventilated, if necessary by the use of fans. If materials used are toxic and adequate ventilation cannot be achieved, then respiratory and other personal protection should be worn.

Sometimes interior finishing may require the fixing of cladding or linings to the walls. If this involves use of cartridge guns to secure the panels to timber studding the hazard will principally arise from the way the gun is operated. Cartridge-driven nails can easily be fired through walls and partitions or can ricochet on striking something hard. Contractors need to plan this work carefully, if necessary excluding other persons from the vicinity.

Finishing may require tiles or slabs of various materials to be fixed to walls and floors. Cutting large quantities of ceramic tiles or stone slabs using powered cutters gives rise to great quantities of dust and should either be done wet or in an enclosed area. The principal hazard with tiles, including carpet tiles, arises from the need to stick them in position. Adhesives used are solvent based and give off vapours that are harmful, and in an enclosed space they can be flammable. Unfortunately, those laying tiles are kneeling down low over the point where vapours are given off. Water-based adhesives should be used. Where solvent-based adhesives have to be used, rooms should be well ventilated (fan assisted), the quantity of adhesives brought into the workroom should be kept to a minimum and drums should be decanted into smaller tins used by tilers outside the workroom.

If finishing requires installations of sound- or heat-insulation materials, as is often the case in blocks of flats and commercial buildings, these may be in the form of sheets or slabs that are cut, blocks that are laid and fixed together or to a surface by a cement or in a wet form that is sprayed. Hazards include exposure to dust that may both irritate and be harmful. Asbestos-containing materials should not be used. If artificial mineral fibres are used, respiratory protection and protective clothing should be worn to prevent skin irritation.

Fire hazards in interior finishing

Many of the finishing operations in a building involve use of materials that greatly increase the fire hazard. The basic structure may be relatively non-flammable steel, concrete and brick. However, the finishing trades introduce wood, possibly paper, paints and solvents.

At the same time that interior finishing is being performed work may be going on nearby using electric powered tools, or the electrical services may be being installed. Nearly always there is a source of ignition for flammable vapour and materials used in finishing. Many very costly fires have been ignited during finishing, putting workers at risk and usually damaging not only the finishing of the building but also its main structure. A building undergoing finishing is an enclosure in which possibly hundreds of workers are using flammable materials. The main contractor should ensure that proper arrangements are made to provide and protect means of escape, keep access routes clear from obstructions, reduce the quantity of flammable materials stored and in use inside the building, warn contractors of fire and, when necessary, evacuate the building.

Exterior finishing

Some of the materials used in internal finishing may also be used on the exterior, but exterior finishing is generally concerned with cladding, sealing and painting. The cement courses in brick and block work are generally "pointed" or finished as the bricks or blocks are laid and require no further attention. The exterior of walls may be cement that is to be painted or have an application of a layer of small stones, as in stucco or roughcast. Exterior finishing, like general construction work, is done outdoors and is subject to the effects of the weather. By far the greatest hazard is the risk of falling, often heightened by difficulties in handling components and materials. Use of paints, sealants and adhesives containing solvents is less of a problem than in internal finishing because natural ventilation prevents a build-up of harmful or flammable concentrations of vapour.

Again, designers can influence the safety of exterior finishing by specifying cladding panels that can be safely handled (i.e., not too heavy or large) and making arrangements so that cladding can be done from safe positions. The frames or floors of the building should be designed to incorporate features like lugs or recesses that permit easy landing of cladding panels, especially when placed in position by crane or hoist. Specification of materials such as plastics for window frames and fascias eliminates the need for painting and repainting and reduces subsequent maintenance. This benefits the safety of both construction workers and the occupants of house or flat.

Landscaping

Landscaping on a large scale may involve earth-moving similar to that involved in highway and canal works. It may require deep excavations to install drains; extensive areas may have to be slabbed or concreted; rocks may have to be moved. Finally, the client may wish to create the impression of a mature, well-established development, so that fully grown trees will be planted. All of this requires excavation, digging and loading. It often also requires considerable lifting capacity.

Landscape contractors are usually specialists who do not spend much of their time working as part of construction contracts. The main contractor should ensure that landscape contractors are brought to the site at an appropriate time (not necessarily towards the end of the contract). Major excavation and pipe laying may best be carried out early in the life of the project, when similar work is being done for the foundations of the building. Landscaping must not undermine or endanger the building or overload the structure by heaping earth on or against it and its outbuildings in a dangerous manner. If topsoil is to be removed and later placed back in position, sufficient space to heap it in a safe manner will have to be provided.

Landscaping may also be required at industrial premises and public utilities for safety and environmental reasons. Around a petrochemical plant it may be necessary to level off the ground or provide a particular direction of slope, possibly covering the ground with stone chips or concrete to prevent the growth of vegetation. On the other hand, if landscaping around industrial premises is intended to improve appearance or environmental reasons (e.g., to reduce noise or hide an unsightly plant), it may require embankments and erection of screens or planting of trees. Highways and railroad tracks today have to include features that will reduce noise if they are near urban areas or hide the operations if they are in environmentally sensitive areas. Landscaping is not just an afterthought, because as well as improving the appearance of the building or plant, it may, depending on the nature of the development, preserve the environment and improve safety generally. Therefore, it needs to be designed and planned as an integral part of the project.

Demolition

Demolition is perhaps the most dangerous construction operation. It has all the hazards of working at heights and being struck by falling materials, but it is carried out in a structure that has been weakened either as part of the demolition, or as the result of storms, damage produced by flood, fire, explosions or simple wear and tear. The hazards during demolition are falls, being struck or buried in falling material or by the unintentional collapse of the structure, noise and dust. One of the practical problems with ensuring health and safety during demolition is that it can proceed very rapidly; with modern equipment a great deal can be demolished in a couple of days.

There are three principal ways of demolishing a structure: take it down piecemeal; knock it or push it down; or blast it down using explosives. Choice of method is dictated by the condition of the structure, its surroundings, the reasons for the demolition and cost. Use of explosives will usually not be possible when other buildings are close by. Demolition needs to be planned as carefully as any other construction process. The structure to be demolished should be thoroughly surveyed and any drawings obtained, so that as much information as possible on the nature of the structure, its method of construction and materials is available to the demolition contractor. Asbestos is commonly found in buildings and other structures that are to be demolished and requires contractors who are specialists in handling it.

Planning of the demolition process should ensure that the structure is not overloaded or unevenly loaded with debris and that there are suitable openings for chuting of debris for safe removal. If the structure is to be weakened by cutting parts of the frame (especially reinforced concrete or other highly stressed types of structure) or by removing parts of a building such as floors or internal walls, this must not so weaken the structure that it may collapse unexpectedly. Debris and scrap materials should be planned to fall in such a way that they can be removed or saved safely and appropriately; sometimes the cost of a demolition job depends on salvaging valuable scrap or components.

If the structure is to be demolished piecemeal (i.e., taken down bit by bit), without using remotely operated powered picks and cutters, workers will inevitably have to do the job using hand tools or hand-held powered tools. This means they may have to work at heights on exposed faces or above openings created to allow debris to fall. Accordingly, temporary scaffold working platforms will be necessary. The stability of such scaffolds should not be endangered by removal of parts of the structure or fall of debris. If stairs are no longer available for use by workers because the stairwell opening is being used to chute debris external ladders or scaffolds will be necessary.

Removal of points, spires or other tall features on the top of buildings is sometimes done most safely by workers operating from properly-designed buckets slung from the safety hook of a crane.

In piecemeal demolition, the safest method is to take the building down in a sequence opposite to the way it was put up. Debris should be removed regularly so that working places and access do not become obstructed.

If the structure is to be pushed or pulled over or knocked down, it is usually pre-weakened, with the attendant hazards. Pulling down is sometimes done by removing floors and internal walls, attaching wire ropes to strong points on the upper parts of the building and using an excavator or other heavy machine to pull on the wire rope. There is a real hazard from flying wire ropes if they break due to overload or failure of the anchorage point on the building. This technique is not suitable for very tall buildings. Pushing over, again after pre-weakening, involves use of heavy plant such as crawler-mounted grabs or pushers. The cabs of such equipment should be shielded to prevent drivers from being injured by falling debris. The site should not be allowed to become so obstructed by fallen debris as to create instability for machine used to pull or push the building down.

Balling

The most common form of demolition (and if done properly, in many ways the safest) is "balling" down, using a steel or concrete ball suspended from a hook on a crane with a jib strong enough to withstand the special strains imposed by balling. The jib is moved sideways and the ball swung against the wall to be demolished. The principal hazard is trapping the ball in the structure or debris, then trying to extricate it by raising the crane hook. This grossly overloads the crane, and either the crane cable or the jib may fail. It may be necessary for a worker to climb up to where the ball is wedged and free it. However, this should not be done if there is a risk of that part of the building collapsing on the worker. Another hazard associated with less skilled crane operators is balling too hard, so that unintended parts of the building are accidentally brought down.

Explosives

Demolition using explosives can be done safely, but it must be carefully planned and carried out only by experienced workers under competent supervision. Unlike military explosives, the purpose of blasting to demolish a building is not to totally reduce the building to a heap of rubble. The safe way to do it is, after pre-weakening, to use no more explosive than will safely bring down the structure so that debris can be safely removed and scrap salvaged. Contractors carrying out blasting should survey the structure, obtain drawings and as much information as possible on its method of construction and materials. Only with this information is it possible to determine whether blasting is appropriate in the first place, where charges should be placed, how much explosive should be used, what steps may be necessary to prevent ejection of debris and what sort of separation zones will be required around the site to protect workers and the public. If there are a number of explosive charges, electrical shotfiring with detonators will usually be more practical, but electrical systems can develop faults, and on simpler jobs the use of detonator cord may be more practical and safer. Aspects of blasting that require careful preliminary planning are what is to be done if there is either a misfire or if the structure does not fall as planned and is left hanging in a dangerous state of instability. If the job is close to housing, highways or industrial developments, the people in the area should be warned; local police are usually involved in clearing the area and halting pedestrian and vehicular traffic.

Tall structures like television towers or cooling towers may be felled using explosives, providing they have been pre-weakened so that they fall safely.

Demolition workers are exposed to high noise levels because of noisy machinery and tools, falling debris or blasts from explosives.

Hearing protection will usually be required. Dust is produced in large quantities as buildings are demolished. A preliminary survey should ascertain whether and where lead or asbestos are present; if possible, these should be removed before the start of the demolition. Even in the absence of such notable hazards, dust from demolition is often irritating if not actually injurious, and an approved dust mask should be worn if the work area cannot be kept wet to control the dust.

Demolition is both dirty and arduous, and a high level of welfare facilities should be provided, including toilets, washplaces, cloakrooms for both normal clothing and work clothes and a place to shelter and take meals.

Dismantling

Dismantling differs from demolition in that part of the structure or, more commonly, a large piece of machinery or equipment is disassembled and removed from site. For example, removal of part or the whole of a boiler from a power house in order to replace it, or replacement of a steel girder bridge span is dismantling rather than demolition. Workers involved in dismantling tend to do a great deal of oxyacetylene or gas cutting of steel work, either to remove parts of the structure or to weaken it. They may use explosives to knock over an item of equipment. They use heavy lifting machinery to remove large girders or pieces of machinery. Generally, workers engaged in such activities face all the same hazards of falling, things falling on them, noise, dust and harmful substances that are met in demolition proper. Contractors who carry out dismantling require a sound knowledge of structures to ensure that they are taken apart in a sequence that does not cause a sudden and unexpected collapse of the main structure.

Overwater Work

Work over and alongside water as in bridge building and maintenance, in docks and sea and river defence work presents special hazards. The hazard may be increased if the water is flowing or tidal, as opposed to still; rapid water movement makes it more difficult to rescue those who fall in. Falling in water presents the hazard of drowning (in even quite shallow water if the person is injured in the fall as well as hypothermia if the water is cold and infection if it is polluted).

The first precaution is to prevent workers from falling by ensuring that there are proper walkways and workplaces with guard rails. These should not be allowed to become wet and slippery. If walkways are not possible, as perhaps in the earlier stages of steel erection, the workers should wear harnesses and ropes attached to secure anchorage points. These should be supplemented with safety nets slung beneath the work position. Ladders and grablines should be provided to assist fallen workers to climb out of the water, as, for example, at the edges of docks and sea defences. While workers are not on a properly boarded out platform with guard rails or are travelling to and from their worksite, they should wear buoyancy aids. Lifebuoys and rescue lines should be placed at regular intervals along the edge of the water.

Work in docks, river maintenance and sea defences often involves use of barges to carry piling rigs and excavators to remove dredged out spoil. Such barges are equivalent to working platforms and should have suitable guard rails, lifebuoys and rescue and grab lines. Safe access from the shore, dock or river side should be provided in the form of walkways or gangways with guard rails. This should be so arranged as to adjust safely with the changing levels of tidal water.

Rescue boats should be available, fitted with grablines and with lifebuoys and rescue lines on board. If the water is cold or flowing, the boats should be continuously staffed, and should be powered and ready to carry out a rescue mission immediately. If water is polluted with industrial effluent or sewage, arrangements should be made to transport those who fall into such water to a medical centre or hospital for immediate treatment. Water in urban areas may be contaminated with the urine of rats, which may infect open skin abrasions, causing Weil's disease.

Work over water is often carried out in locations that are subject to strong winds, driving rain or icing conditions. These increase the risk of falls and heat loss. Severe weather may make it necessary to stop work, even in the middle of a shift; to avoid excessive heat loss it may be necessary to supplement normal wet or cold weather protective clothing with thermal underclothing.

Underwater Work

Diving

Diving is a specialized form of working underwater. The hazards faced by divers are drowning, decompression sickness (or the "bends"), hypothermia from the cold and becoming trapped below water. Diving may be required during construction or maintenance of docks, sea and river defences and at piers and abutments of bridges. It is often required in waters where visibility is poor or in locations where there is a risk of entanglement for the diver and his or her equipment. Diving may be carried out from dry land or from a boat. If the work requires only a single diver, then as a minimum a team of three will be required for safety. The team consists of the diver in the water, a fully equipped standby diver ready to enter the water immediately in the event of an emergency and a diving supervisor in charge. The diving supervisor should be at the safe position on land or in the boat from which the diving is to take place. Diving at depths less than 50 m is usually carried out by divers wearing wet suits (i.e., suits that do not exclude water) and wearing self-contained underwater breathing apparatus with an open face mask (i.e., SCUBA diving gear). At depths greater than 50 m or in very cold water, it will be necessary for divers to wear suits that are heated by a supply of pumped warm water and closed diving masks, and equipment for breathing not compressed air but air plus a mixture of gases (i.e., mixed-gas diving). Divers must wear a suitable safety line and be able to communicate with the surface and in particular with their diving supervisor. The local emergency services should be advised by the diving contractor that diving is to take place.

Both divers and equipment require examination and testing. Divers should be trained to a recognized national or international standard, firstly and always for air diving and secondly for mixed-gas diving if this is to take place. They should be required to provide written evidence of successful completion of a diver training course. Divers should have an annual medical examination with a doctor experienced in hyperbaric medicine. Each diver should have a personal logbook in which a record of physicals and of his or her dives is kept. If a diver has been suspended from diving as a result of the physical, this also should be recorded in the logbook. A diver under suspension should not be allowed to dive or act as a standby diver. Divers should be asked by their diving supervisor if they are well, especially whether they have any respiratory illness, before being allowed to dive. Diving equipment, suits, belts, ropes, masks and cylinders and valves should be checked every day before use.

Satisfactory operation of cylinder and demand valves should be demonstrated by divers for their diving supervisor.

In the event of an accident or other reasons for the sudden ascent of a diver to the surface, he or she may experience the bends or be at risk of them and require to be recompressed. For this reason it is desirable that the whereabouts of a medical or other decompression chamber suitable for divers is located before diving starts. Those in charge of the chamber should be alerted to the fact that diving is taking place. Arrangements should be available for the rapid transport of divers requiring decompression.

Because of their training and equipment, plus all the backup required for safety, use of divers is very expensive, and yet the amount of time they are actually working on the riverbed may be limited. For these reasons there are temptations for diving contractors to use untrained or amateur divers or a diving team that is deficient in numbers and equipment. Only reputable diving contractors should be used for diving in construction, and particular care needs to be taken over the selection of divers who claim to have been trained in other countries where standards may be lower.

Caissons

Caissons are rather like a large inverted saucepans whose rims sit on the bed of the harbour or river. Sometimes open caissons are used, which, as their name implies, have an open top. They are used on land to sink a shaft into soft ground. The bottom edge of the caisson is sharpened, workers excavate inside the caisson, and it sinks into the ground as soil is removed, thus creating the shaft. Similar open caissons are used in shallow water, but their depth may be extended by adding sections on top as the caisson sinks into the river or harbour bed. Open caissons rely on pumping to control the entry of water and soil into the base of the caisson. For deeper work still, a closed caisson will have to be used. Compressed air is pumped into it to displace the water, and workers are able to enter through an airlock, usually on top, and go down to work in air on that bed. Workers are able to work under water but are freed from the constraints of wearing diving equipment, and visibility is much better. The hazards in "pneumatic" caisson work are the bends and, as in all types of caisson including the simplest open caisson, drowning if water gets into the caisson through any structural failure or loss of air pressure. Because of the risk of entry of water, means of escape such as ladders up to the entry point should be available at all times in both open and pneumatic caissons.

Caissons should be inspected daily before they are used by someone competent and experienced in caisson work. Caissons may be raised and lowered as single units by heavy lifting equipment, or they may be constructed from components in the water. Construction of caissons should be under the supervision of a similarly competent person.

Tunnelling underwater

Tunnelling, when carried out in porous ground beneath water, may need to be done under compressed air. Driving tunnels for public transportation systems in city centres beneath rivers is a widespread practice, owing to lack of space above ground and environmental considerations. Compressed air working will be as limited as possible because of its danger and inefficiency.

Tunnels beneath water in porous ground will be lined with concrete or cast iron rings and grouted. But at the actual heading where the tunnel is being dug and in the short length where tunnel rings are being placed in position, there will not be a sufficiently water-tight surface for the work to proceed without some means of keeping out the water. Working under compressed air may still be used for the tunnel head and ring or segment placing part of the tunnel driving and lining process. Workers involved in driving the heading (i.e., on a TBM operating the rotating cutting head) or using hand tools, and those operating ring and segment placing equipment, will have to pass through an airlock. The rest of the now lined tunnel will not require to be compressed, and thus there will be easier transit of personnel and materials.

Tunnellers who have to work in compressed air face the same hazard of the bends as divers and caisson workers. The airlock giving access to the compressed-air workings should be supplemented by a second airlock through which workers pass at the end of the shift to be decompressed. If there is only a single airlock, this may create bottlenecks and also be dangerous. Hazards arise if workers are not decompressed sufficiently slowly at the end of their shift or if lack of airlock capacity holds up entry of vital equipment to the workings under pressure. Airlocks and decompression chambers should be under the supervision of a competent person experienced in compressed-air tunnelling and proper decompression.

TRENCHING

Jack L. Mickle

Trenches are confined spaces usually dug to bury utilities or to place footings. Trenches are normally deeper than they are wide, as measured at the bottom, and are usually less than 6 m deep; they are also known as shallow excavations. A confined space is defined as a space that is large enough for a worker to enter and perform work, has limited means of entry and exit, and is not designed for continuous occupancy. Several ladders should be provided to enable workers to escape the trench.

Typically trenches are open only for minutes or hours. The walls of any trench will eventually collapse; it is merely a matter of time. Short-term apparent stability is a temptation for a contractor to send workers into a dangerous trench in hopes of rapid progress and financial gain. Death or serious injuries and mutilations can result.

In addition to being exposed to the possibility of collapsing trench walls, workers in trenches, can be harmed or killed by engulfment in water or sewage, exposure to hazardous gases or reduced oxygen, falls, falling equipment or materials, contact with severed electrical cables and improper rescue.

Cave-ins account for at least 2.5% of annual work-related deaths in the United States, for example. The average age of workers killed in trenches in the US is 33. Often a young person is trapped by a cave-in and other workers attempt a rescue. With failed rescue attempts, most of the dead are would-be rescuers. Emergency teams trained in trench rescue should be contacted immediately in the event of a cave-in.

Routine inspections of the trench walls and worker protection systems are essential. Inspections should occur daily before the start of work and after any occurrence—such as rainstorms, vibration or broken pipes—that may increase hazards. Following are descriptions of the hazards and how to prevent them.

Trench Wall Collapse

The main cause of deaths related to trenching is collapsed trench walls, which can crush or suffocate workers.

Trench walls may be weakened by activities outside but near a trench. Heavy loads must not be placed on the edge of the wall. Trenches should not be dug close to structures, such as buildings or railroads, because the trenching may undermine the structures and weaken the foundations, thus causing the structures and trench walls to collapse. Competent engineering assistance should be sought in the planning stages. Vehicles must not be permitted to approach too close to the sides of a trench; stop logs or soil berms should be in place to prevent vehicles from doing so.

Types of soil and environment

Proper selection of a worker protection system depends on soil and environmental conditions. Soil strength, the presence of water and vibration from equipment or nearby sources affect the stability of trench walls. Previously excavated soils never regain their strength. Accumulation of water in a trench, regardless of depth, signals the most dangerous situation.

The soil must be classified and the construction scene evaluated before an appropriate worker protection system is selected. A project safety and health plan should address unique conditions and hazards related to the project.

Soils can be divided into two main groups: cohesive and granular. Cohesive soils contain a minimum of 35% clay and will not break when rolled into threads 50 mm long and 3 mm in diameter and held by one end. With cohesive soils, trench walls will stand vertically for short periods of time. These soils are responsible for as many cave-in deaths as any other soil, because the soil appears stable and precautions often are not taken.

Granular soils consist of silt, sand, gravel or larger material. These soils exhibit apparent cohesion when wet (the sand-castle effect); the finer the particle, the greater the apparent cohesion. When submerged or dry, however, the coarser granular soils will immediately collapse to a stable angle, 30 to 45°, depending on their particle angularity or roundness.

Worker protection

Sloping prevents trench failure by removing the weight (of the soil) that can lead to trench instability. Sloping, including benching (sloping done in a series of steps), requires a wide opening at the top of a trench. The angle of a slope depends on the soil and environment, but slopes range from 0.75 horizontal: 1 vertical to 1.5 horizontal: 1 vertical. The slope of 1.5 horizontal: 1 vertical is set back 1.5 m on each side at the top for each meter of depth. Even the slightest slope is beneficial. However, the width requirements of slopes often make this approach impracticable on construction sites.

Shoring can be used for all conditions. A shore consists of an upright on each side of a trench, with braces in between (see figure 93.5). Shores help prevent trench wall collapse by exerting outward forces on a trench wall. *Skip shores* consist of vertical

Figure 93.5 • Shores consist of uprights on each side of a trench with cross braces in between.

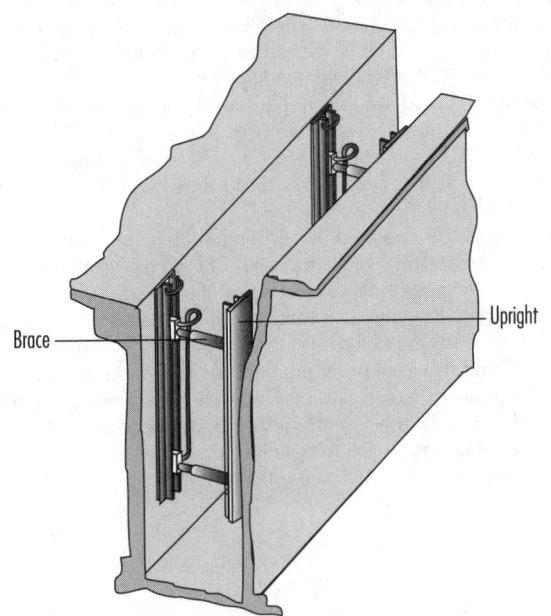

Figure 93.6 • Wales hold uprights in place, allowing greater distance between cross braces.

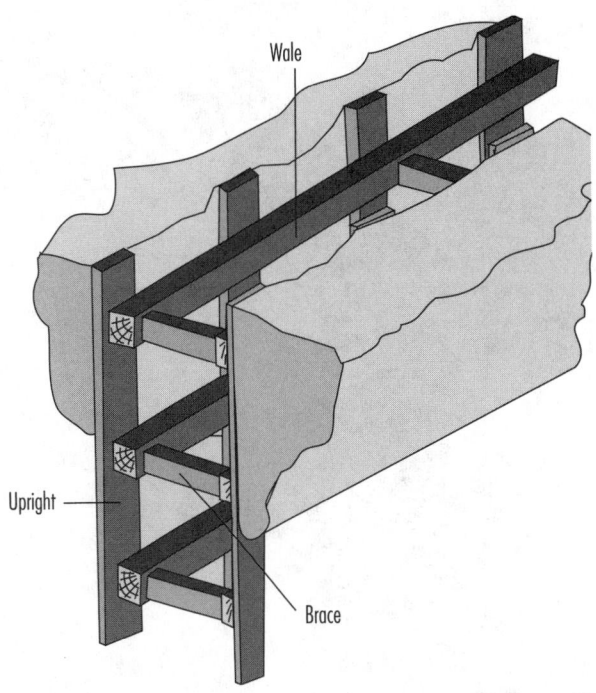

uprights and cross braces with soil arching between; they are used in clays, the most cohesive soils. Shores must be no more than 2 m apart from each other. Greater distances between cross braces can be achieved by using wales (or walings) to hold the uprights in place (see figure 93.6). *Close sheeting* is used in granular and weaker cohesive soils; the trench walls are covered entirely with sheeting (see figure 93.7). Sheeting can be made of wood, metal or fibreglass; steel trench sheets are common. *Tight sheeting* is used when flowing or seeping water is encountered. Tight sheeting prevents water from eroding and bringing soil particles into a trench. A shoring system must always be kept tight against the soil to prevent collapse. Braces can be of wood or of screw, hydraulic or pneumatic jacks. Wales can be of wood or metal.

Shields, or trench boxes, are large personal protective devices; they do not prevent trench wall collapse but protect workers who are inside. Shields are generally made of steel or aluminium and their size commonly ranges from approximately 1 m to 3 m high and 2 to 7 m long; many other sizes are available. Shields may be stacked on top of each other (figure 93.8). Guard systems must be in place against hazardous movements of shields in the event of a trench wall collapse. One way is to backfill on both sides of a shield.

New products are available that combine the qualities of a shore and a shield; some devices are useable in particularly hazardous ground. Shield-shore units can be used as static shields or can act as a shore by hydraulically or mechanically exerting forces on the trench wall. The smaller units are particularly useful when repairing breaks in utility pipes in city streets. Massive units with shield panels can be forced into the ground by mechanical or hydraulic means. Soil is then excavated from inside the shield.

Drowning

Several steps are recommended to prevent engulfment by water or sewage in a trench. First, known utilities should be contacted

Figure 93.7 • Close sheeting is used in granular soils.

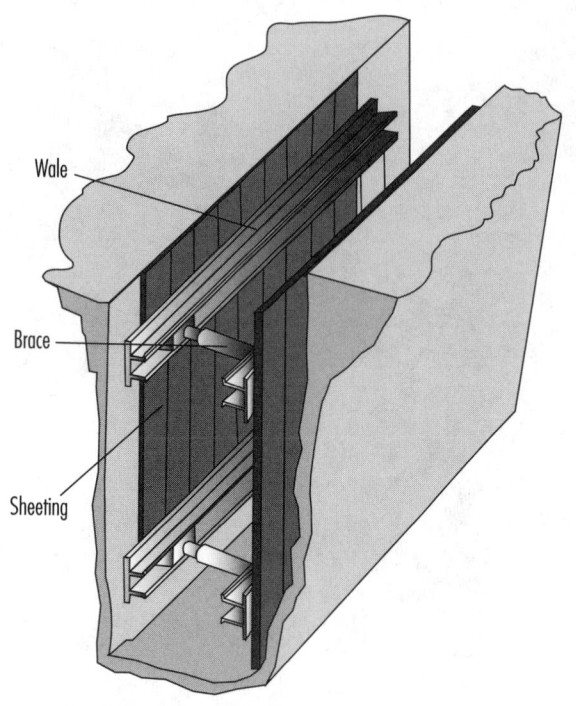

Figure 93.8 • Shields protect workers from trench wall collapse.

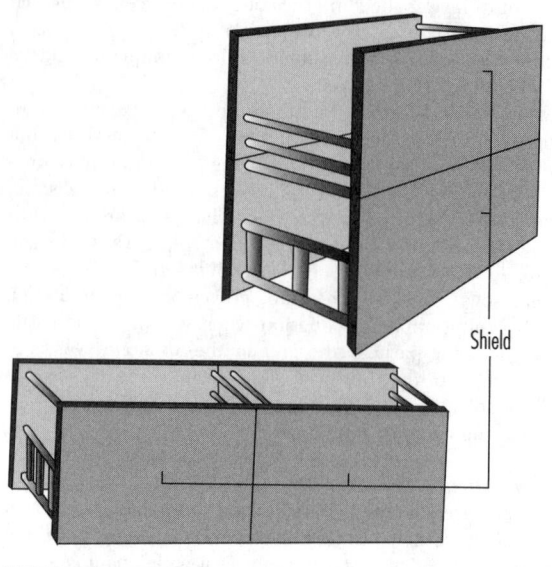

before digging to learn where water (and other) pipes are located. Second, water valves that feed pipes into the trench should be closed. Cave-ins that break water mains or cause accumulations of water or sewage must be avoided. All utility pipes and other utility equipment need to be supported.

Deadly Gases and Fumes and Insufficient Oxygen

Harmful atmospheres can lead to worker death or injury resulting from a lack of oxygen, fire or explosion or toxic exposures. All trench atmospheres where abnormal conditions are present or suspected should be tested. This is especially true around buried garbage, vaults, fuel tanks, manholes, swamps, chemical processors and other facilities that can release deadly gases or fumes or deplete oxygen in the air. Construction equipment exhausts must be dispersed.

Air quality should be determined with instruments from outside the trench. This can be done by lowering a meter or its probe into the trench. The air in trenches should be tested in the following order. First, oxygen must be 19.5 to 23.5%. Second, flammability or explosibility must be no higher than 10% of the lower flammable or explosive limits (LFLs or LELs). Third, levels of potentially toxic substances—such as hydrogen sulphide —should be compared with published information. (In the US, one source is the National Institute for Occupational Safety and Health *Pocket Guide to Chemical Hazards*, which gives, permissible exposure limits (PELs)). If the atmosphere is normal, workers may enter. Ventilation may correct an abnormal atmosphere, but monitoring must continue. Sewers and similar spaces where the air is constantly changing usually require (or should require) a permit-entry procedure. Permit-entry procedures require full equipment and a three-person team: a supervisor, an attendant and an entrant.

Falls and Other Hazards

Falls into and within trenches can be prevented by providing safe and frequent means for entering and exiting a trench, safe walkways or bridges where workers or equipment are permitted or required to cross over trenches and barriers adequate to stop other workers or bystanders or equipment from approaching a trench.

Falling equipment or materials can cause death or injury through blows to the head and body, crushing and suffocation. The spoil pile should be kept at least 0.6 m from the edge of a trench, a barrier should be provided that will prevent soil and rock material from rolling into the trench. All other materials, such as pipes, must also be prevented from falling or rolling into a trench. Workers must not be permitted to work under suspended loads or loads handled by digging equipment.

All utilities should be marked prior to digging in order to prevent electrocution or severe burns caused by contact with live power lines. Equipment booms must not be operated near overhead power lines; if necessary, overhead lines must be grounded out or removed.

Often, one death or severe injury in a trench is compounded by a poorly thought-out rescue attempt. The victim and rescuers may become trapped and overcome by deadly gases, fumes or lack of oxygen; drowned; or mutilated by machines or rescue ropes. These compounded tragedies can be prevented by following a safety and health plan. Equipment such as air testing meters, water pumps and ventilators should be well-maintained, properly assembled and available on the job. Management should train and require workers to follow safe work practices and wear all necessary personal protective equipment.

● TOOLS

Scott P. Schneider

Tools are particularly important in construction work. They are primarily used to put things together (e.g., hammers and nail guns) or to take them apart (e.g., jackhammers and saws). Tools are often classified as *hand tools* and *power tools*. Hand tools include all non-powered tools, such as hammers and pliers. Power tools are divided into classes, depending on the power source: electrical tools (powered by electricity), pneumatic tools (powered by compressed air), liquid-fuel tools (usually powered by gasoline), powder-actuated tools (usually powered by an explosive and operated like a gun) and hydraulic tools (powered by pressure from a liquid). Each type presents some unique safety problems.

Hand tools include a wide range of tools, from axes to wrenches. The primary hazard from hand tools is being struck by the tool or by a piece of the material being worked on. Eye injuries are very common from the use of hand tools, as a piece of wood or metal can fly off and lodge in the eye. Some of the major problems are using the wrong tool for the job or a tool that has not been properly maintained. The size of the tool is important: some women and men with relatively small hands have difficulty with large tools. Dull tools can make the work much harder, require more force and result in more injuries. A chisel with a mushroomed head might shatter on impact and send fragments flying. It is also important to have the proper work surface. Cutting material at an awkward angle can result in a loss of balance and an injury. In addition, hand tools can produce sparks that can ignite explosions if the work is being done around flammable liquids or vapours. In such cases, spark-resistant tools, such as those made from brass or aluminium, are needed.

Power tools, in general, are more dangerous than hand tools, because the power of the tool is increased. The biggest dangers from power tools are from accidental start-up and slipping or losing one's balance during use. The power source itself can cause injuries or death, for example, through electrocution with electrical tools or gasoline explosions from liquid-fuel tools. Most power tools have a guard to protect the moving parts while the tool is not in operation. These guards need to be in working order and not overridden. A portable circular saw, for example, should have an upper guard covering the top half of the blade and a retractable lower guard which covers the teeth while the saw is not operating. The retractable guard should automatically return to cover the lower half of the blade when the tool is finished working. Power tools often also have safety switches that shut off the tool as soon as a switch is released. Other tools have catches that must be engaged before the tool can operate. One example is a fastening tool that must be pressed against the surface with a certain amount of pressure before it will fire.

One of the main hazards of *electrical tools* is the risk of electrocution. A frayed wire or a tool that does not have a ground (that directs the electrical circuit to the ground in an emergency) can result in electricity running through the body and death by electrocution. This can be prevented by using double-insulated tools (insulated wires in an insulated housing), grounded tools and ground-fault circuit interrupters (which will detect a leak of electricity from a wire and automatically shut off the tool); by never using electrical tools in damp or wet locations; and by wearing insulated gloves and safety footwear. Power cords have to be protected from abuse and damage.

Other types of power tools include powered abrasive-wheel tools, like grinding, cutting or buffing wheels, which present the risk of flying fragments coming off the wheel. The wheel should be tested to make sure it is not cracked and will not fly apart during use. It should spin freely on its spindle. The user should never stand directly in front of the wheel during start-up, in case it breaks. Eye protection is essential when using these tools.

Pneumatic tools include chippers, drills, hammers and sanders. Some pneumatic tools shoot fasteners at high speed and pressure into surfaces and, as a result, present the risk of shooting fasteners into the user or others. If the object being fastened is thin, the fastener may go through it and strike someone at a distance. These tools can also be noisy and cause hearing loss. Air hoses should be well connected before use to prevent them from disconnecting and whipping around. Air hoses should be protected from abuse and damage as well. Compressed-air guns should never be pointed at anyone or against oneself. Eye, face and hearing protection should be required. Jackhammer users should also wear foot protection in case these heavy tools are dropped.

Gas-powered tools present fuel explosion hazards, particularly during filling. They should be filled only after they have been shut down and allowed to cool off. Proper ventilation must be provided if they are being filled in a closed space. Using these tools in a closed space can also cause problems from carbon monoxide exposure.

Powder-actuated tools are like loaded guns and should be operated only by specially trained personnel. They should never be loaded until immediately before use and should never left loaded and unattended. Firing requires two motions: bringing the tool into position and pulling the trigger. Powder-actuated tools should require at least 5 pounds (2.3 kg) of pressure against the surface before they can be fired. These tools should not be used in explosive atmospheres. They should never be pointed at anyone and should be inspected before each use. These tools should have a safety shield at the end of the muzzle to prevent the release of flying fragments during firing. Defective tools should be taken out of service immediately and tagged or locked out to make sure no one else uses them until they are fixed. Powder-actuated fastening tools should not be fired into material where the fastener could pass through and hit somebody, nor should these tools be used near an edge where material might splinter and break off.

Hydraulic power tools should use a fire-resistant fluid and be operated under safe pressures. A jack should have a safety mechanism to prevent it from being jacked up too high and should display its load limit prominently. Jacks have to be set up on a level surface, centred, bear against a level surface and apply force evenly to be used safely.

In general, tools should be inspected before use, be well-maintained, be operated according to the manufacturer's instructions and be operated with safety systems (e.g., guards). Users should have proper PPE, such as safety glasses.

Tools can present two other hazards that are often overlooked: vibration and sprains and strains. Power tools present a considerable vibration hazard to workers. The most well-known example is chain-saw vibration, which can result in "white-finger" disease, where the nerves and blood vessels in the hands are damaged. Other power tools can present hazardous exposures to vibration for construction workers. As much as possible, workers and contractors should purchase tools where vibration has been dampened or reduced; anti-vibration gloves have not been shown to solve this problem.

93. CONSTRUCTION

Poorly designed tools can also contribute to fatigue from awkward postures or grips, which, in turn, can also lead to accidents. Many tools are not designed for use by left-handed workers or individuals with small hands. Use of gloves can make it harder to grip a tool properly and requires tighter gripping of power tools, which can result in excessive fatigue. Use of tools by construction workers for repetitive jobs can also lead to cumulative trauma disorders, like carpal tunnel syndrome or tendinitis. Using the right tool for the job and choosing tools with the best design features that feel most comfortable in the hand while working can assist in avoiding these problems.

● EQUIPMENT, MACHINERY AND MATERIALS

Hans Göran Linder

Construction work has undergone major changes. Once dependent upon craftsmanship with simple mechanical aids, the industry now relies largely on machines and equipment.

New equipment, machinery, materials and methods have contributed to the industry's development. Around the middle of the 20th century, building cranes appeared, as did new materials like light-weight concrete. As time went on, the industry began using prefabricated construction units along with new techniques in the construction of buildings. Designers began to use computers. Thanks to such equipment as lifting devices, some of the work has become easier physically, but it has also become more complicated.

Instead of small, basic materials, such as bricks, tiles, board and light concrete, prefabricated construction units are commonly used today. Equipment has expanded from simple hand tools and transport facilities to complex machinery. Similarly, methods have changed, for instance, from wheelbarrowing to the pumping of concrete and from manual lifting of materials to the lifting of integrated elements with the assistance of cranes.

Innovations in equipment, machinery and materials can be expected to continue to appear.

European Community Directives Relating to Workers' Health and Safety

In 1985, the European Community (EC) decided on a "New Approach to Technical Harmonization and Standards" in order to facilitate the free movement of goods. The New Approach directives are Community laws which set out essential requirements for health and safety that must be met before products may be supplied among member countries or imported to the Community. One example of a directive with a fixed level of demands is the Machine Directive (Council of the European Communities 1989). Products meeting the requirements of such a directive are marked and can be supplied anywhere in the EC. Similar systems exist for products covered by the Construction Products Directive (Council of the European Communities 1988).

Besides the directives with such a fixed level of demands, there are directives setting minimum criteria for workplace conditions. Community member states must meet these criteria or, if they exist, satisfy a more stringent safety level stipulated in their national regulations. Of specific relevance to construction work are the Directive on the Minimum Safety and Health Requirements for the Use of Work Equipment by Workers at Work (89/655/EEC) and the Directive on the Minimum Safety and Health Requirements at Temporary or Mobile Construction sites (92/57/EEC).

Scaffolding

One of the types of construction equipment that frequently affects worker safety is scaffolding, the primary means of providing a work surface at elevations. Scaffolds are used in connection with construction, rebuilding, restoration, maintenance and servicing of buildings and other structures. Scaffold components may be used for other constructions such as support towers (which are not considered scaffolds) or for the erection of temporary structures such as grandstands (i.e., seating for spectators) and stages for concerts and other public presentations. Their use is associated with many occupational injuries, particularly those caused by falls from heights (see also the article "Lifts, escalators and hoists" in this chapter).

Types of scaffolds

Support scaffolds may be erected using vertical and horizontal tubing connected by loose couplers. Prefabricated scaffolds are assembled from parts manufactured in accord with standardized procedures that are permanently attached to fixation devices. There are several types: the traditional frame or modular type for building facades, mobile access towers (MATs), craftsmen scaffolds and suspended scaffolds.

Vertical adjustment of the scaffold

The working planes of a scaffold are normally stationary. Some scaffolds, however, have working planes that may be adjusted to different vertical positions; they may be suspended from wires that raise and lower them, or they may stand on the ground and be adjusted by hydraulic lifts or winches.

Erection of prefabricated facade scaffolds

The erection of prefabricated facade scaffolds should follow the following guidelines:

- Detailed erection instructions should be provided by the manufacturer and kept at the building site, and the work should be supervised by trained personnel. Precautions should be taken to protect anyone walking under the scaffold by blocking off the area, erecting additional scaffolding for the pedestrians to walk under or creating a protective overhang.
- The base of the scaffold should be placed on a firm, level surface. An adjustable steel base plate should be placed on planking or boards to create a sufficient surface area for weight distribution.
- A scaffold that is more than 2 to 3.5 m off the ground should be equipped with fall protection comprising a guard rail at a height of at least 1 m above the platform, an intermediate guard rail and a toe board. To move tools and supplies on or off the platform, the smallest possible opening in the guard rail may be created with a foot stop and guard rail on either side of it.
- Access to the scaffold should normally be provided by stairs and not ladders.
- The scaffold should be firmly secured to the wall of the building as directed by the manufacturer's instructions.
- The stability of the scaffold should be reinforced using diagonal elements (braces) according to the manufacturer's instructions.
- The scaffold should be as close as possible to the facade of the building; if more than 350 mm, a second guard rail on the inside of the platform may be needed.
- If planks are used for the platform, they must be secured to the scaffold structure. A forthcoming European standard stipulates that the deflection (bending) should be not more than 25 mm.

Earth-moving machinery

Earth-moving machinery is designed primarily to loosen, pick up, move, transport and distribute or grade rock or earth and is of great importance in construction, road-building and agricultural and industrial work (see figure 93.9). Properly used, these machines are versatile and can eliminate many of the risks associated with the manual handling of materials. This type of equipment is highly efficient and is used worldwide.

Earth-moving machines that are used in construction work and in road-building include tractor-dozers (bulldozers), loaders, backhoe loaders (figure 93.10), hydraulic excavators, dumpers, tractor-scrapers, graders, pipelayers, trenchers, landfill compactors and rope excavators.

Earth-moving machinery can endanger the operator and people working nearby. The following summary of the hazards associated with earth-moving machines is based on the European Community's Standard EN 474-1 (European Committee for Standardization 1994). It points out the safety related factors to be considered when acquiring and using these machines.

Access

The machine should provide safe access to the operator's station and maintenance areas.

Operator's station

The minimum space available to the operator should allow for all manoeuvres necessary for the safe operation of the machinery without excessive fatigue. It should not be possible for the operator to have accidental contact with the wheels or tracks or the working equipment. The engine exhaust system should direct the exhaust gas away from the operator's station.

A machine with an engine performance above 30 kW should be equipped with an operator's cab, unless the machine is being operated where the year-round climate permits comfortable operation without a cab. Machines having an engine performance less than 30 kW should be fitted with a cab when intended for use where the air quality is poor. The airborne sound power level of excavators, dozers, loaders and backhoe loaders should be measured according to the international standard for measure-

Figure 93.10 • Example of an articulated steer backhoe loader.

The machine is versatile. It can be used for excavating, loading and lifting. The angling of the machine (articulation) enables it to be used in confined spaces.

ment of airborne exterior noise emitted by earth-moving machinery (ISO 1985b).

The cab should protect the operator against foreseeable weather conditions. The interior of the cab should not present any sharp edges or acute angles that may injure the operator if he or she falls or is thrown against them. Pipes and hoses located inside the cab containing fluids that are dangerous because of their pressure or temperature should be reinforced and guarded. The cab should have an emergency exit separate from the usual doorway. The minimum height of the ceiling above the seat (i.e., seat-index point) depends on the size of the machine's engine; for engines between 30 and 150 kW it should be 1,000 mm. All glass should be shatter-proof. The sound pressure level at the operator's station should not exceed 85 dBA (ISO 1985c).

The design of the operator's station should enable the operator to see the travelling and work areas of the machine, preferably without having to lean forward. Where the operator's view is obscured, mirrors or remote cameras with a monitor visible to the operator should enable him or her to see the work area.

The front window and, if required, the rear window, should be fitted with motorized windscreen wipers and washers. Equipment for defogging and defrosting at least the front window of the cab should be provided.

Roll-over and falling object protection

Loaders, dozers, scrapers, graders, articulated steer dumpers and backhoe loaders with an engine performance of more than 15 kW should have a structure that will protect against roll-over. Machines intended for use where there is a risk of falling objects should be designed for and fitted with a structure that will protect the operator against falling material.

Operator's seat

Machinery with provision for a seated operator should be fitted with an adjustable seat that keeps the operator in a stable position and allows him or her to control the machine under all expected operating conditions. Adjustments to accommodate to the operator's size and weight should be easily made without the use of any tool.

The vibrations transmitted by the operator's seat shall comply with the relevant international vibration standard (ISO 1982) for tractor-dozers, loaders and tractor-scrapers.

Figure 93.9 • Mechanical excavation at a construction site in France.

Controls and indicators

The main controls, indicators, hand levers, pedals, switches and so on should be selected, designed and arranged so that they are clearly defined, legibly labelled and within easy reach of the operator. Controls for machine components should be designed so that they cannot accidentally start or be moved, even if exposed to interference from radio or telecommunications equipment.

Pedals should have an appropriate size and shape, be surfaced with a non-skid tread to prevent slipping and be adequately spaced. To avoid confusion the machine should be designed to be operated like a motor vehicle, with pedals located in the same way (i.e., with the clutch on the left, the brake in the centre and the accelerator on the right).

Remote-controlled earth-moving machinery should be so designed that it stops automatically and remains immobile when controls are deactivated or the power supply to them is interrupted.

Earth-moving machinery should be equipped with:

- stop lights and direction indicators for machines designed with a permissible travelling speed over 30 km/h
- an audible warning device controlled from the operator's station and of which the sound level should be at least 93 dBA at a 7 m distance from the front-end of the machine and
- a device which allows a flashing light to be fitted.

Uncontrolled movement

Creep (drift away) from the stopping position, for whatever reason (e.g., internal leakage) other than action of the controls, should be such that it does not create a hazard to bystanders.

Steering and braking systems

The steering system should be such that the movement of the steering control shall correspond to the intended direction of steering. The steering system of rubber-tyred machinery with a travelling speed of more than 20 km/h should comply with the international steering system standard (ISO 1992).

Machinery should be fitted with service, secondary and parking brake systems that are efficient under all foreseeable conditions of service, load, speed, ground conditions and slope. The operator should be able to slow down and stop the machine by means of the service brake. In case it fails, a secondary brake should be provided. A mechanical parking device should be provided to keep the stopped machine from moving, and it should be capable of remaining in the applied position. The braking system should comply with the international braking system standard (ISO 1985a).

Lighting

To permit night work or work in dusty conditions, earth-moving machines should be fitted with large enough and bright enough lights to adequately illuminate both the travelling and the work areas.

Stability

Earth-moving machinery, including components and attachments, should be designed and constructed to remain stable under anticipated operating conditions.

Devices intended to increase the stability of earth-moving machinery in working mode, such as outriggers and oscillating axle locking, should be fitted with interlocking devices which keep them in position, even in case of hydraulic hose failure.

Guards and covers

Guards and covers should be designed to be securely held in place. When access is rarely required, the guards should be fixed and fitted so that they are detachable only with tools or keys. Whenever possible, guards should remain hinged to the machine when open. Covers and guards should be fitted with a support system (springs or gas cylinders) to secure them in the opened position up to a wind speed of 8 m/s.

Electrical components

Electrical components and conductors should be installed in such a way as to avoid abrasion of wires and other wear and tear as well as exposure to dust and environmental conditions which can cause them to deteriorate.

Storage batteries should be provided with handles and be firmly attached in proper position while being easily disconnected and removed. Or, an easily accessible switch placed between the battery and the earth should allow the isolation of the battery from the rest of the electrical installation.

Tanks for fuel and hydraulic fluid

Tanks for fuel and hydraulic and other fluids should have means for relieving any internal pressure in case of opening and repair. They should have easy access for filling and be provided with lockable filler caps.

Fire protection

The floor and interior of the operator's station should be made of fire-resistant materials. Machines with an engine performance exceeding 30 kW should have a built-in fire extinguisher system or a location for installing a fire extinguisher that is easily reached by the operator.

Maintenance

Machines should be designed and built so that lubrication and maintenance operations can be conducted safely, whenever possible with the engine stopped. When maintenance can be performed only with equipment in a raised position, the equipment should be mechanically secured. Special precautions such as erecting a shield or, at least, warning signs, must be taken if maintenance must be performed when the engine is running.

Marking

Each machine should bear, legibly and indelibly, the following information: the name and address of the manufacturer, mandatory marks, designation of series and type, the serial number (if any), the engine power (in kW), the mass of the most usual configuration (in kg) and, if appropriate, the maximum drawbar pull and maximum vertical load.

Other markings that may be appropriate include: conditions for use, mark of conformity (CE) and reference to instructions for installation, use and maintenance. The CE mark means that the machine meets the requirements of European Community directives relevant to the machine.

Warning signs

When the movement of a machine creates hazards not obvious to a casual spectator, warning signs should be affixed to the machine to warn against approaching it while it is in operation.

Verification of safety requirements

It is necessary to verify that safety requirements have been incorporated in the design and manufacture of an earth-moving machine. This should be achieved through a combination of measurement, visual examination, tests (where a method is prescribed) and assessment of the contents of the documentation that is required to be maintained by the manufacturer. The manufacturer's documentation would include evidence that bought-in components, such as windscreens, have been manufactured as required.

Operating manual

A handbook giving instructions for operation and maintenance should be supplied and kept with the machine. It should be written in at least one of the official languages of the country in which the machine is to be used. It should describe in simple, readily understood terms the health and safety hazards that may be encountered (e.g., noise and hand-arm or whole-body vibration) and specify when personal protective equipment (PPE) is needed. A space intended for the safekeeping of the handbook should be provided in the operator's station.

A service manual giving adequate information to enable trained service personnel to erect, repair and dismantle machinery with minimum risk should also be provided.

Operating conditions

In addition to the above requirements for design, the instruction handbook should specify conditions that limit use of the machine (e.g., the machine should not travel at a greater angle of inclination than is recommended by the manufacturer). If the operator discovers faults, damage or excessive wear that may present a safety hazard, the operator should immediately inform the employer and shut down the machine until the necessary repairs are completed.

The machine must not attempt to lift a load heavier than specified in the capacity chart in the operating manual. The operator should check how the slings are attached to the load and to the lifting hook and if he or she finds that the load is not attached safely or has any concerns about its safe handling, the lift should not be attempted.

When a machine is moved with a suspended load, the load should be kept as near to the ground as possible to minimize potential instability, and the travel speed should be adjusted to prevailing ground conditions. A rapid change of speed should be avoided and care should be taken so the load does not begin to swing.

When the machine is in operation, no one should enter the work area without warning the operator. When the work requires individuals to remain within a machine's work area, they should observe great care and avoid unnecessarily moving or remaining under a raised or suspended load. When someone is within the work area of the machine, the operator should be particularly careful and operate the machine only when that person is in the operator's view or his or her location has been signalled to the operator. Similarly, for rotating machines, such as cranes and backhoes, the swing radius behind the machine should be kept clear. If a truck must be positioned for loading in a way such that falling debris might hit the driver's cab, no one should remain in it, unless it is strong enough to withstand impact of the falling materials.

At the beginning of the shift, the operator should check brakes, locking devices, clutches, steering and the hydraulic system in addition to making a functional test without a load. When checking the brakes, the operator should make certain that the machine can be slowed down rapidly, then stopped and safely held in position.

Before leaving the machine at the end of the shift, the operator should place all operating controls in the neutral position, turn off the power supply and take all necessary precautions to prevent unauthorized operation of the machine. The operator should consider potential weather conditions that might affect the supporting surface, perhaps causing the machine to be frozen fast, tipped over or sunk, and take appropriate measures to prevent such occurrences.

Replacement parts and components, such as hydraulic hoses, should be in compliance with the specifications in the operating manual. Before attempting any replacement or repair work in the hydraulic or compressed air systems, the pressure should be relieved. The instructions and precautions issued by the manufacturer should be observed when, for instance, a working attachment is installed. PPE, such as a helmet and safety glasses, should be worn when repair and maintenance work are done.

Positioning a machine for work

When positioning a machine, the hazards of overturning, sliding and subsidence of the ground beneath it should be considered. When these appear to be present appropriate blocking of adequate strength and surface area should be provided to assure stability.

Overhead power lines

When operating a machine near overhead power lines, precautions against contact with the energized lines should be taken. In this connection, cooperation with the power distributor is advisable.

Underground pipes, cables and power lines

Prior to starting a project, the employer has the responsibility to determine if any underground power lines, cables or gas, water or sewer pipes are located within the work site and, if so, to determine and mark their precise location. Specific instructions for avoiding them must be given to the machine operator, for instance, through a "call before you dig" program.

Operation on roads with traffic

When a machine is operated on a road or other place open to public traffic, road signs, barriers and other safety arrangements appropriate for the traffic volume, vehicle speed and local road regulations should be used.

It is recommended that transport of a machine on a public highway should be executed by truck or trailer. The hazard of overturning should be considered when the machine is being loaded or unloaded, and it should be secured so that it will not shift while in transit.

Materials

Materials used in construction include asbestos, asphalt, brick and stone, cement, concrete, flooring, foil sealing agents, glass, glue, mineral wool and synthetic mineral fibres for insulation, paints and primers, plastic and rubber, steel and other metals, wallboard, gypsum and wood. Many of these are covered in other articles in this chapter or elsewhere in this *Encyclopaedia*.

Asbestos

The use of asbestos for new construction is prohibited in some countries but, almost inevitably, it will be encountered during the renovation or demolition of older buildings. Accordingly, stringent precautions are required to protect both the workers and the public against exposures to asbestos that was previously installed.

Bricks, concrete and stone

Bricks are made of fired clay and grouped into facing bricks and brick stones. They can be solid or designed with holes. Their physical properties depend on the clay used, any added materials, the method of manufacture and the incineration temperature. The higher the incineration temperature, the less absorbency the brick will exhibit.

Bricks, concrete and stone containing quartz can produce silica dust when cut, drilled or blasted. Unprotected exposures to crystalline silica can increase susceptibility to tuberculosis and cause silicosis, a disabling, chronic and potentially fatal lung disease.

Flooring

Materials commonly used for interior flooring include stone, brick, floorboard, textile carpeting, linoleum and plastic. The installation of terrazzo, tile or wood flooring can expose a worker to dusts that can cause skin allergies or damage the nasal passages or lungs. In addition, the glues or adhesives used for installing tiles or carpeting often contain potentially toxic solvents.

Carpetlayers can damage their knees from kneeling and striking a "kicker" with the knee in stretching the carpeting to fit the space.

Glue

Glue is used to join materials through adhesion. Water-based glue contains a binding agent in water and hardens when water evaporates. Solvent glues harden when the solvent evaporates. Since the vapours can be harmful to health, they should not be used in very close or poorly ventilated areas. Glues consisting of components that harden when mixed can produce allergies.

Mineral wool and other insulation

The function of insulation in a building is to achieve thermal comfort and to reduce energy consumption. To achieve acceptable insulation, porous materials, such as mineral wool and synthetic mineral fibres, are used. Great care must be taken to avoid inhaling the fibres. Sharp fibres can even penetrate the skin and cause an annoying dermatitis.

Paints and primers

Paints are used to decorate the exterior and interior of the building, protect materials like steel and wood against corrosion or decay, make objects easier to clean and provide signals or road-markings.

Lead-based paints are now being avoided, but they may be encountered during the renovation or demolition of older structures, particularly those made of metal, such as bridges and viaducts. Inhaled or swallowed fumes or dusts can cause lead poisoning with kidney damage or permanent nervous system damage; they are particularly dangerous for children who may be exposed to lead dusts carried home on work clothes or shoes. Precautionary measures must be taken whenever lead-based paints are used or encountered.

Use of cadmium- and mercury-based paints is prohibited for use in most countries. Cadmium can cause kidney problems and some forms of cancer. Mercury can damage the nervous system.

Oil-based paints and primers contain solvents which may be potentially hazardous. To minimize solvent exposures, the use of water-based paints is recommended.

Plastic and rubber

Plastic and rubber, known as polymers, can be grouped into thermoplastic or thermosetting plastic and rubber. These materials are used in construction for tightening, insulation, coating, and for products like piping and fittings. Foil made of plastic or rubber is used for tightening and moisture-proof lining and may cause reactions in workers sensitized to these materials.

Steel, aluminium and copper

Steel is used in construction work as a supporting structure, in reinforcement rods, mechanical components and facing material. Steel may be carbon or alloy; stainless steel is a type of alloy. Important steel properties are its strength and toughness. Fracture toughness is important in order to avoid brittle fractures.

The properties of steel depends on its chemical composition and structure. Steel is heat-treated in order to release internal strain and to improve weldability, strength and fracture toughness.

Concrete can withstand considerable pressure, but reinforcement bars and nets are required for acceptable tensile strength. These bars typically have a considerable carbon content (0.40%).

Carbon steel or "mild" steel contains manganese, which, when released in fumes during welding, can cause a Parkinson's disease-like syndrome, which can be a crippling nervous disorder. Aluminium and copper can also, under certain conditions, be harmful to health.

Stainless steels contain chromium, which increases corrosion resistance, and other alloy elements, such as nickel and molybdenum. But welding of stainless steel can expose workers to chromium and nickel fumes. Some forms of nickel can cause asthma or cancer; some forms of chromium can cause cancer and sinus problems and "nose holes" (erosion of the nasal septum).

Next to steel, aluminium is the most commonly used metal in construction, because the metal and its alloys are light, strong and corrosion-resistant.

Copper is one of the most important metals in engineering, because of its corrosion-resistance and high conductivity for electricity and heat. It is used in energized lines, as roof and wall coating and for piping. When used as a roof coating, copper salts in the rain runoff can be harmful to the immediate environment.

Wallboard and gypsum

Wallboard, often coated with asphalt or plastic, is used as a protective layer against water and wind and to prevent seepage of moisture through the building elements. Gypsum is crystallized calcium sulphate. Gypsum board consists of a sandwich of gypsum between two layers of cardboard; it is widely used as wall covering, and is fire-resistant.

Dust produced when cutting wallboard can lead to skin allergies or lung damage; carrying oversize or heavy board in awkward postures can cause musculoskeletal problems.

Wood

Wood is widely used for construction. It is important to use seasoned timber for construction work. For beams and roof trusses of considerable span, glue-laminated wood units are used. Measures are advisable to control wood dust, which, depending on the species, can cause a variety of ailments including cancer. Under certain conditions, wood dust can also be explosive.

CRANES

Francis Hardy

A crane is a machine with a boom, primarily designed to raise and lower heavy loads. There are two basic crane types: mobile and stationary. Mobile cranes can be mounted on motor vehicles, boats or railroad cars. Stationary cranes can be of a tower type or mounted on overhead rails. Most cranes today are power driven, though some still operate manually. Their capacity, depending on the type and size, ranges from a few kilograms to hundreds of tonnes. Cranes are also used for pile driving, dredging, digging, demolition and personnel work platforms. Generally, a crane's capacity is greater when the load is closer to its mast (centre of rotation) and less when the load is further away from its mast.

...volving cranes are usually costly and spectacular. ...s and fatalities involve not only workers, but sometimes innocent bystanders. Hazards exist in all facets of crane operation, including assembly, dismantling, travel and servicing. Some of the most common hazards involving cranes are:

- *Electrical hazards.* Overhead powerline contact and arcing of electrical current through the air can occur if the machine or hoist line is close enough to the powerline. When powerline contact occurs, the danger is not just limited to the operator of the hoist, but extends to all personnel in the immediate vicinity. Twenty three percent of crane fatalities in the United States, for example, in 1988–1989 involved powerline contact. Aside from injury to humans, electrical current can cause structural damage to the crane.

- *Structural failure and overloading.* Structural failure occurs when a crane or its rigging components are overloaded. When a crane is overloaded, the crane and its rigging components are subject to structural stresses that may cause irreversible damage. Swinging or sudden dropping of the load, using defective components, hoisting a load beyond capacity, dragging a load and side-loading a boom can cause overloading.

- *Instability failure.* Instability failure is more common with mobile cranes than stationary ones. When a crane moves a load, swings its boom and moves beyond its stability range, the crane has a tendency to topple. Ground conditions can also cause instability failure. When a crane is not levelled, its stability is reduced when the boom is oriented in certain directions. When a crane is positioned on ground that cannot bear its weight, the ground can give way, causing the crane to topple. Cranes have also been known to tip when travelling on poorly compacted ramps on construction sites.

- *Material falling or slipping.* Material can fall or slip if not properly secured. Falling material can injure workers in the vicinity or cause property damage. Undesired movement of material can pinch or crush workers involved in the rigging process.

- *Improper servicing, assembling and dismantling procedures.* Poor access, lack of fall protection and poor practices have injured and killed workers when servicing, assembling and dismantling cranes. This problem is most common with mobile cranes where service is performed in the field and there is lack of access equipment. Many cranes, particularly older models, do not provide handrails or steps to facilitate getting to some sections of the crane. Servicing around the boom and top of the cab is dangerous when workers walk on the boom without fall-arrest equipment. On lattice-boom cranes, incorrect loading and unloading as well as assembly and disassembly of the boom has caused sections to fall onto the workers. The boom sections were either not properly supported during these operations, or the rigging of the lines to support the boom was improper.

- *Hazard to the helper or oiler.* A very hazardous pitch point is created as the upper portion of a crane rotates past the stationary lower section during normal operations. All helpers working around the crane should stay clear of the deck of the crane during operation.

- *Physical, chemical and stress hazards to the crane operator.* When the cab is not insulated, the operator can be subjected to excessive noise, causing loss of hearing. Seats that are not properly designed can cause back pain. Lack of adjustment to the seat height and tilt can result in poor visibility from operating positions. Poor cab design also contributes to poor visibility. Exhaust from gasoline or diesel engines on cranes contains fumes that are hazardous in confined areas. There is also concern over the effect of whole-body vibration from the engine, par-

ticularly in older cranes. Time constraints or fatigue can also play a part in crane accidents.

Control Measures

Safe operation of a crane is the responsibility of all parties involved. Crane manufacturers are responsible for designing and manufacturing cranes that are stable and structurally sound. Cranes must be rated properly so that there are enough safeguards to prevent accidents caused by overloading and instability. Instruments such as load-limiting devices and angle and boom length indicators aid operators in the safe operation of a crane. (Powerline sensory devices have proved to be unreliable.) Every crane should have a reliable, efficient, automatic safe-load indicator. In addition, crane manufacturers must make accommodations in the design that facilitate safe access for servicing and safe operation. Hazards can be reduced by clear design of control panels, providing a chart at the operator's fingertips that specifies load configurations, handrails, non-glare windows, windows that extend to the cab floor, comfortable seats and both noise and thermal insulation. In some climates, heated and air-conditioned cabs contribute to the worker's comfort and reduce fatigue.

Crane owners are responsible for keeping their machines in good condition by ensuring regular inspection and proper maintenance and employing competent operators. Crane owners must be knowledgeable so that they can recommend the best machine for a particular job. A crane assigned to a project should have the capacity to handle the heaviest load it must carry. The crane should be fully inspected by a competent person before being assigned to a project, and then daily and periodically (as suggested by the manufacturer), with a maintenance record kept. Ventilation should be provided to remove or dilute engine exhaust from cranes working in enclosed areas. Hearing protection, when necessary, should be provided. Site supervisors must plan ahead. With proper planning operating near overhead powerlines can be avoided. When work must be done near high-voltage power lines, clearance requirements should be followed (see table 93.6). When working near powerlines cannot be avoided, the line should either be de-energized or insulated.

Signallers should be used to aid the operator near the limit of approach around powerlines. The ground, including access in and around the site, must have the ability to bear the weight of the crane and the load it is lifting. If possible, the crane operating area should be roped off to prevent injuries from overhead lifting. A signaller must be used when the operator cannot see the load clearly. The crane operator and the signaller must be trained and competent in hand signals and other aspects of the job. Proper

Table 93.6 • Required clearance for normal voltage in operation near high-voltage power lines.

Normal voltage in kilovolts (phase to phase)	Minimum required clearance in metres (and feet)*
Up to 50	3.1 (10)
From 50 to 200	4.6 (15)
From 200 to 350	6.1 (20)
From 350 to 500	7.6 (25)
From 500 to 750	10.7 (35)
From 750 to 1,000	13.7 (45)

* Meters have been converted from recommendations in feet.
Source: ASME 1994.

rigging attachments must be supplied so that riggers can secure the load from falling or slipping. The rigging crew must be trained in the attachment and dismantling of loads. Good communication is vital in safe crane operations. The operator must carefully follow the manufacturer's recommended procedures when assembling and disassembling the boom before operating the crane. All safety features and warning devices should be in working order and should not be disconnected. The crane must be levelled and be operated according to the crane load chart. Outriggers must be fully extended or set according to manufacturers' recommendations. Overloading can be prevented by the operator's knowing the weight to be lifted in advance and by using load-limiting devices as well as other indicators. The operator should always use sound craning practices. All loads must be fully secured before they are lifted. Movement with a load must be slow; the boom should never be extended or lowered so that it compromises the stability of the crane. Cranes should not be operated when visibility is poor or when the wind can cause the operator to lose control of the load.

Standards and Legislation

There are numerous written standards or guidelines for recommended manufacturing and operating practices. Some are based on design principles, some on performance. Subjects covered in these standards include methods of testing various safety devices; design, construction and characteristics of the cranes; inspection, testing, maintenance and operation procedures; recommended equipment and control lay-out. These standards form the basis of government and company health and safety regulations and operator training.

● ELEVATORS, ESCALATORS AND HOISTS

J. Staal and John Quackenbush*

Elevators

An elevator (lift) is a permanent lifting installation serving two or more defined landing levels, comprising an enclosed space, or car, whose dimensions and means of construction clearly permit the access of people, and which runs between rigid vertical guides. A lift, therefore, is a vehicle for raising and lowering people and/or goods from one floor to another floor within a building directly (single push-button control) or with intermediate stops (collective control).

A second category is the service lift (dumb waiter), a permanent lifting installation serving defined levels, but with a car that is too small to transport people. Service lifts transport foods and supplies in hotels and hospitals, books in libraries, mail in office buildings and so on. Generally, the floor area of such a car does not exceed 1 m², its depth 1 m, and its height 1.20 m.

Elevators are driven directly by an electric motor (electric lifts; see figure 93.11) or indirectly, through the movement of a liquid under pressure generated by a pump driven by an electric motor (hydraulic lifts).

Electric lifts are almost exclusively driven by traction machines, geared or gearless, depending on car speed. The designation "traction" means that the power from an electric motor is transmitted to the multiple rope suspension of the car and a

counterweight by fricti[...] the driving or traction shea[...]

Hydraulic lifts have become [...] transport of goods and passenge[...] ceeding six floors. Hydraulic oil is [...] direct-acting system with a ram supportin[...] the simplest one.

Standardization

Technical Committee 178 of the ISO has drafted stan[...] loads and speeds up to 2.50 m/s; car and hoistway dimensi[...] accommodate passengers and goods; bed and service lifts for residential buildings, offices, hotels, hospitals and nursing homes; control devices, signals and additional accessories; and selection and planning of lifts in residential buildings. Each building should be provided with at least one lift accessible to handicapped people

Figure 93.11 • A cut-away view of an elevator installation showing the essential components.

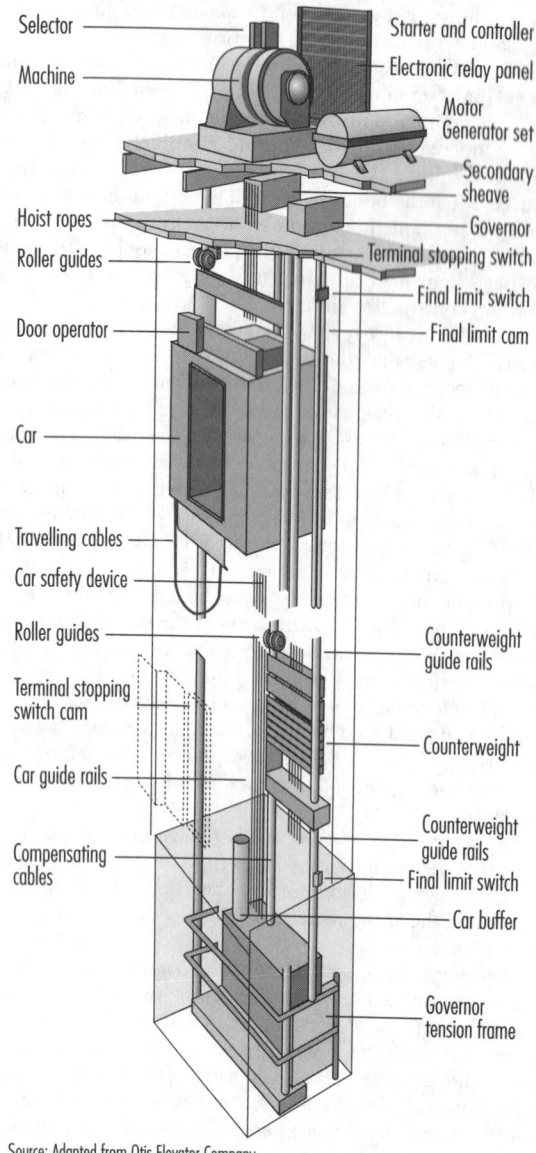

Source: Adapted from Otis Elevator Company.

---

* Adapted from the 3rd edition *Encyclopaedia of Occupational Health and Safety* article authored by J. Staal.

in wheelchairs. The Association française de normalisation (AFNOR) is in charge of the Secretariat of this Technical Committee.

General safety requirements

Every industrialized country has a safety code drawn up and kept up to date by a national standards committee. Since this work was started in the 1920s, the various codes have gradually been made more similar, and differences now are generally not fundamental. Large manufacturing firms produce units that comply with the codes.

In the 1970s the ILO, in close cooperation with the International Committee for the Reglementation of Lifts (CIRA), published a code of practice for the construction and installation of lifts and service lifts and, a few years later, for escalators. These directives are intended as a guide for countries engaged in the drafting or modification of safety rules. A standardized set of safety rules for electric and hydraulic lifts, service lifts, escalators and passenger conveyors, the object being the elimination of technical barriers to trade among the member countries of the European Community, is also under the purview of the European Committee for Standardization (CEN). The American National Standards Institute (ANSI) has devised a safety code for lifts and escalators.

Safety rules are aimed at several types of possible accidents with lifts: shearing, crushing, falling, impact, trapping, fire, electric shock, damage to material, accidents due to wear, and accidents due to corrosion. People to be safeguarded are: users, maintenance and inspection personnel and people outside the hoistway and the machine room. Objects to be safeguarded are: loads in the car, components of the lift installation and the building.

Committees drawing up safety rules have to assume that all components are correctly designed, are of sound mechanical and electrical construction, are made of material of adequate strength and suitable quality and are free from defects. Potential imprudent acts of users have to be taken into account.

Shearing is prevented by providing adequate clearances between moving components and between moving and fixed parts. Crushing is prevented by providing sufficient headroom at the top of the hoistway between the roof of the car in its highest position and the top of the shaft and a clear space in the pit where someone can remain safely when the car is in its lowest position. These spaces are assured by buffers or stops.

Protection against falling down the hoistway is obtained by solid landing doors and an automatic cut off that prevents movement of the cab until the doors are fully closed and locked. Landing doors of the power-operated sliding type are preferred for passenger lifts.

Impact is limited by restraining the kinetic energy of closing power-operated doors; trapping of passengers in a stalled car is prevented by providing an emergency unlocking device on the doors and a means for specially trained personnel to open them and extricate the passengers.

Overloading of a car is prevented by a strict ratio between the rated load and the net floor area of the car. Doors are required on all the cars passenger lifts to keep passengers from being trapped in the space between the car sill and the hoistway or the landing doors. Car sills must be fitted with a toe guard of a height of not less than 0.75 m to prevent accidents, as shown in figure 93.12. Cars have to be provided with safety gear capable of stopping and holding a fully loaded car in the event of overspeed or failure of the suspension. The gear is operated by an overspeed governor driven by the car by means of a rope (see figure 93.11). As passengers stand upright and move in a vertical direction, the retardation during the operation of the safety device should lie between 0.2 and 1.0 g (m/s^2) to guard against injuries (g = standard acceleration of free fall).

Depending on national legislation, lifts intended mainly for the transport of goods, vehicles and motor cars accompanied by authorized and instructed users may have one or two opposite car entrances not provided with car doors, under the condition that the rated speed does not exceed 0.63 m/s, the car depth is not less than 1.50 m and the wall of the hoistway facing the entrance, including the landing doors, is flush and smooth. On heavy-duty freight elevators (goods lifts), the landing doors are usually vertical bi-parting power-operated doors, which usually do not meet these conditions. In such a case, the required car door is a vertically sliding mesh gate. The clear width of the lift car and the landing doors must be the same to avoid damage to panels on the lift car by fork trucks or other vehicles entering or leaving the lift. The whole design of such a lift has to take account of the load, the weight of the handling equipment and the heavy forces involved in running, stopping and reversing these vehicles. The lift car guides require special reinforcement. When the transport of people is permitted, the number allowed should correspond to the maximum available area of the car floor. For example, the car floor area of a lift for a rated load of 2,500 kg should be 5 m^2, corresponding to 33 persons. Loading and accompanying a load must be done with great care. Figure 93.13 shows a faulty situation.

Controls

All modern lifts are push-button and computer controlled, the car switch system operated by an attendant having been abandoned.

Single lifts and those grouped in two- to eight-car arrangements are usually equipped with collective controls which are interconnected in the case of multiple installations. The main feature of collective controls is that calls can be given at any moment, whether the car is moving or standstill and whether the landing doors are open or closed. Landing and car calls are collected and stored until answered. Regardless of the sequence in which they are received, calls are answered in the order that most efficiently operates the system.

Examinations and tests

Before a lift is put into service, it should be examined and tested by an organization approved by the public authorities to establish

Figure 93.12 • Layout of the toe guard on the car sill to prevent trapping.

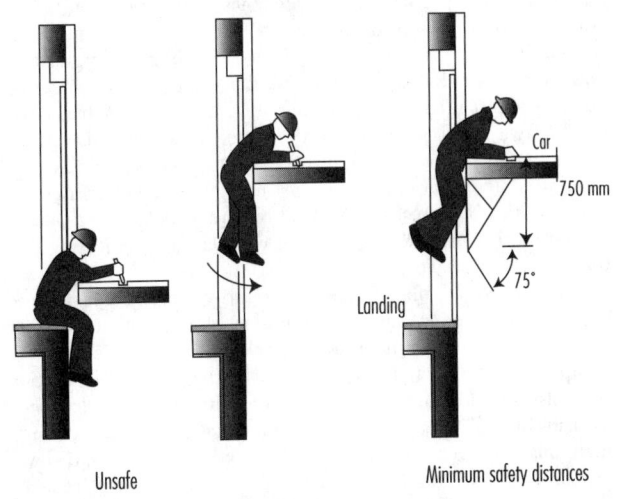

Unsafe   Minimum safety distances

Figure 93.13 • Example of dangerous loading of a freight elevator (goods-lift).

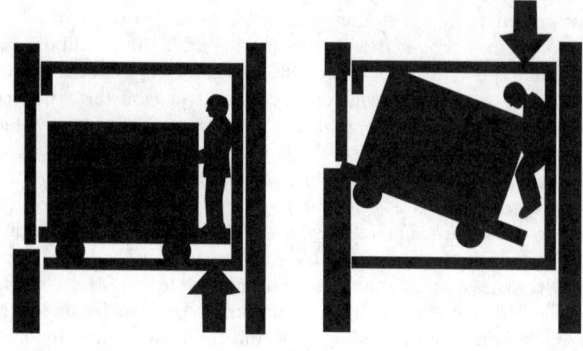

the lift's conformity with the safety rules in the country where it has been installed. A technical dossier should be submitted to the inspector by the manufacturers. The elements to be examined and tested and the way the tests should be run are listed in the safety code. Specific tests by an approved laboratory are required for: locking devices, landing doors (possibly including fire tests), safety gear, overspeed governors and oil buffers. Certificates of the corresponding components used in the installation should be included in the register. After a lift is put into service, periodic safety examinations should be conducted, with the intervals depending on traffic volume. These tests are intended to ensure compliance with the code and the proper operation of all safety devices. Components that do not function in normal service, such as the safety gear and buffers, should be tested with a car empty and at reduced speed to prevent excessive wear and stresses that can impair the safety of a lift.

Maintenance and inspection

A lift and its components should be inspected and maintained in good and safe working order at regular intervals by competent technicians who have obtained skill and a thorough knowledge of the mechanical and electrical details of the lift and the safety rules under the guidance of a qualified instructor. Preferably the technician is employed by the supplier or erector of the lift. Normally a technician is responsible for a specific number of lifts. Maintenance involves routine servicing such as adjustment and cleaning, lubrication of moving parts, preventive servicing to anticipate possible problems, emergency visits in the case of breakdowns and major repairs, which are usually done after consultation with a supervisor. The overriding safety hazard, however, is fire. Because of the risk that a lit cigarette or other burning object might fall into the crack between the car sill and the hoistway and ignite lubricating grease in the hoistway or debris at the bottom, the hoistway should regularly be cleaned out. All systems should be at zero energy level before maintenance work is begun. In single-unit buildings, before any work is started, notices should be posted at each landing indicating that the lift is out of service.

For preventive maintenance, careful visual inspection and checks of free movement, the condition of contacts and proper operation of the equipment are generally sufficient. The hoistway equipment is inspected from the top of the car. An inspection control is provided on the car roof comprising: a bi-stable switch to bring it into operation and to neutralize the normal control, including the operation of power-operated doors. Up and down constant pressure buttons allow movement of the car at reduced speed (not exceeding 0.63 m/s). The inspection operation must

remain dependent on the safety devices (closed and locked doors and so on) and it should not be possible to overrun the limits of normal travel.

A stop switch on the inspection control station prevents unexpected movement of the car. The safest direction of travel is down. The technician must be in a safe position to observe the work environment when moving the car and possess the appropriate inspection devices. The technician must have a firm hold when the car is in motion. Before leaving, the technician must report to the person in charge of the lift.

Escalators

An escalator is a continuous moving, inclined stairway which conveys passengers upward and downward. Escalators are used in commercial buildings, department stores and railway and underground stations, to guide a stream of people in a confined route from one level to another.

General safety requirements

Escalators consist of a continuous chain of steps moved by a motor-driven machine by means of two roller chains, one at each side. The steps are guided by rollers on tracks which keep the step treads horizontal in the usable area. At the entrance and exit, guides ensure that over a distance of 0.80 to 1.10 m, depending on the speed and rise of the escalator, some steps form a horizontal flat surface. Step dimensions and construction are shown in figure 93.14. On the top of each balustrade, a handrail should be provided at a height of 0.85 to 1.10 m above the nose of the steps running parallel to the steps at substantially the same speed. The handrail at each extremity of the escalator, where the steps move horizontally, should extend at least 0.30 m beyond the landing plate and the newel including the handrail at least 0.60 m beyond (see figure 93.15). The handrail should enter the newel at a low point above the floor, and a guard should be installed with a safety switch to stop the escalator if fingers or hands are trapped at this point. Other risks of injury to users are formed by the clearances necessary between the side of the steps and the balustrades, between steps and combs and between treads and step risers, the latter more particularly in the upward direction at the curvature where a relative movement between consecutive steps occurs. The cleating and smoothness of the risers should prevent this risk.

People may ride with their shoes sliding against the balustrade, which can cause trapping at the points where the steps straighten

Figure 93.14 • Escalator step unit 1.

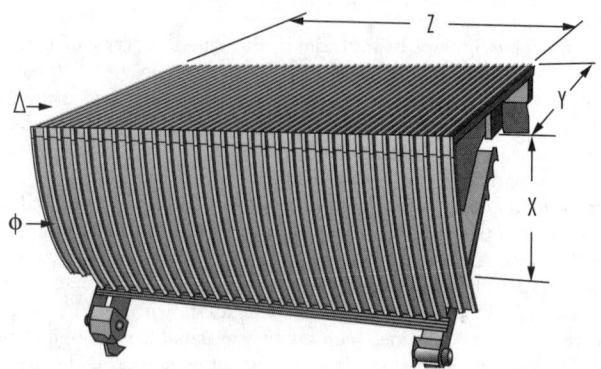

X: Height to next step (not greater than 0.24 m); Y: Depth (at least 0.38 m); Z: Width (between 0.58 and 1.10 m). Δ: Grooved step tread. Φ: Cleated step riser.

out. Clearly legible signs and notices, preferably pictographs, should warn and instruct users. A sign should instruct adults to hold the hands of children, who may not be able to reach the handrail, and that children should stand at all times. Both ends of an escalator should be barricaded when it is out of service.

The incline of an escalator should not exceed 30°, though it may be increased to 35° if the vertical rise is 6 m or less and the speed along the incline is limited to 0.50 m/s. Machine rooms and driving and return stations should be easily accessible to specially-trained maintenance and inspection personnel only. These spaces can lie inside the truss or be separate. The clear height should be 1.80 m with covers, if any, opened and the space should be sufficient to ensure safe working conditions. The clear height above the steps at all points should be not less than 2.30 m.

The starting, stopping or reversal of movement of an escalator should be effected by authorized people only. If the country code permits operating a system that starts automatically when a passenger moves past an electric sensor, the escalator should be in operation before the user reaches the comb. Escalators should be equipped with an inspection control system for operation during maintenance and inspection.

Maintenance and inspection

Maintenance and inspection along the lines described above for lifts are usually required by authorities. A technical dossier should be available listing the main calculation data of the supporting structure, steps, step driving components, general data, layout drawings, schematic wiring diagrams and instructions. Before an escalator is put into service, it should be examined by a person or organization approved by the public authorities; subsequently periodic inspections at given intervals are needed.

Moving Walkways (Passenger Conveyors)

A passenger conveyor, or power-driven continuous moving walkway, may be used for the conveyance of passengers between two points at the same or at different levels. Passenger conveyors are used to transport a great number of people in airports from the main station to the gates and back and in department stores and supermarkets. When the conveyors are horizontal, baby carriages, pushcarts and wheelchairs, luggage and food trolleys can be carried without risk, but on inclined conveyors these vehicles, if rather heavy, should be used only if they lock into place automatically. The ramp consists of metal pallets, similar to the step treads of escalators but longer, or rubber belt. The pallets must be grooved in the direction of travel, and combs should be placed at each end. The angle of inclination should not exceed 12° or more than 6° at the landings. The pallets and belt should move horizontally over a distance of not less than 0.40 m before entering the landing. The walkway runs between balustrades that are topped with a moving handrail that travels at substantially the same speed. The speed should not exceed 0.75 m/s unless the movement is horizontal, in which case 0.90 m/s is permitted provided the width does not exceed 1.10 m.

The safety requirements for passenger conveyors are generally similar to those for escalators and should be included in the same code.

Figure 93.15 • Escalator step unit 2.

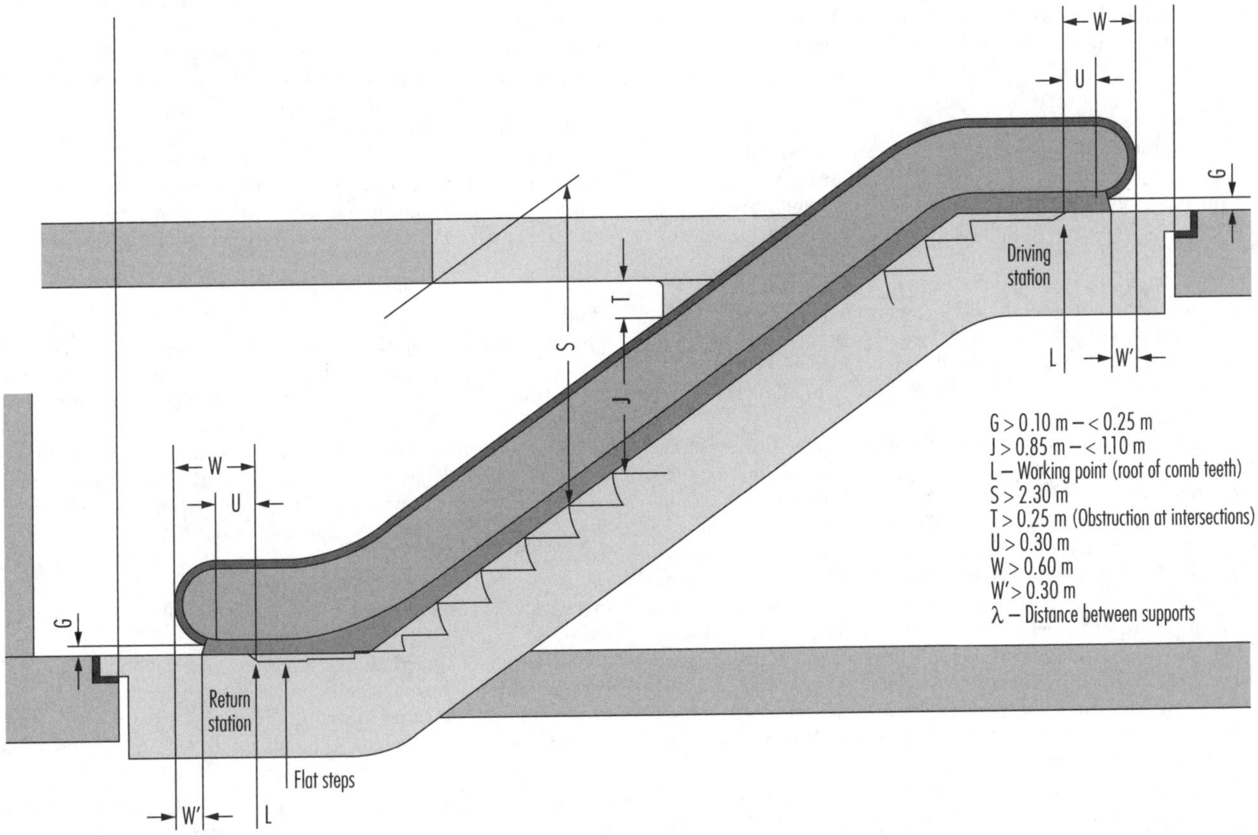

G > 0.10 m − < 0.25 m
J > 0.85 m − < 1.10 m
L − Working point (root of comb teeth)
S > 2.30 m
T > 0.25 m (Obstruction at intersections)
U > 0.30 m
W > 0.60 m
W' > 0.30 m
λ − Distance between supports

Building Hoists

Building hoists are temporary installations used on construction sites for the transport of persons and materials. Each hoist is a guided car and should be operated by an attendant inside the car. In recent years, rack and pinion design has enabled the use of building hoists for efficient movement along radio towers or very tall smoke stacks for servicing. No one should ride a material hoist, except for inspection or maintenance.

The standards of safety vary considerably. In a few cases, these hoists are installed with the same standard of safety as permanent goods and passenger lifts in buildings, except that the hoistway is enclosed by strong wire mesh instead of solid materials to reduce the wind load. Strict regulations are needed although they need not be as strict as for passenger lifts; many countries have special regulations for these building hoists. However, in many cases the standard of safety is low, the construction poor, the hoists driven by a diesel engine winch and the car suspended by only a single steel wire rope. A building hoist should be driven by electric motors to ensure that the speed is kept within safe limits. The car should be enclosed and be provided with car entrance protections. Hoistway openings at the landings should be fitted with doors that are solid up to a height of 1 m from the floor, the upper part in wire mesh of maximum 10 × 10 mm aperture. Sills of landing doors and cars should have suitable toe guards. Cars should be provided with safety gear. One common type of accident results when workers travel on a platform hoist designed only for carrying goods, which do not have side walls or gates to keep the workers from striking a part of the scaffolding or from falling off the platform during the journey. A belt lift consists of steps on a moving vertical belt. A rider is at risk of being carried over the top, being unable to make an emergency stop, striking his or her head or shoulders on the edge of a floor opening, jumping on or off after the step has passed the floor level or being unable to reach the landing because of power failure or the belt's stopping. Accordingly, such a lift should be used only by specially trained personnel employed by the building owner or a designee.

Fire Hazards

Generally, the hoistway for any lift extends over the full height of a building and interconnects the floors. A fire or the smoke from a fire breaking out in the lower part of a building may spread up the hoistway to other floors and, under certain circumstances, the well or hoistway may intensify a fire because of a chimney effect. Therefore, a hoistway should not form part of a building's ventilation system. The hoistway should be totally enclosed by solid walls of non-combustible material that would not give off harmful fumes in case of a fire. A vent should be provided at the top of the lift hoistway or in the machine room above it to allow smoke to escape to open air.

Like the hoistway, the entrance doors should be fire resistant. Requirements are usually laid down in national building regulations and vary according to countries and conditions. Landing doors cannot be made smokeproof if they are to operate reliably.

No matter how tall the building, passengers should not use lifts in case of fire, because of the risks of the lift stopping at a floor in the fire zone and of passengers being trapped in the car in the event of failure of the electrical supply. In general, one lift that serves all floors is designated as a lift for firefighters that can be put at their disposal by means of a switch or special key on the main floor. The capacity, speed and car dimensions of the firefighters' lift have to meet certain specifications. When firefighters use lifts, the normal operational controls are overridden.

The construction, maintenance and refinishing of elevator interiors, installation of carpeting and cleaning of the elevator (inside or out) may involve the use of volatile organic solvents, mastics or glues, which can present a risk to the central nervous system, as well as a fire hazard. Although these materials are used on other metal surfaces, including staircases and doors, the hazard is severe with elevators because of their small space, in which vapour concentrations can become excessive. The use of solvents on the outside of an elevator car can also be risky, again because of limited air flow, particularly in a blind hoistway, where venting may be impeded. (A blind hoistway is one without an exit door, usually extending for several floors between two destinations; where a group of elevators serves floors 20 and above, a blind hoistway would extend between floors 1 and 20.)

Lifts and Health

While lifts and hoists involve hazards, their use can also help reduce fatigue or serious muscle injury due to manual handling, and they can reduce labour costs, especially in building construction work in some developing countries. On some such sites where no lifts are used, workers have to carry heavy loads of bricks and other building materials up inclined runways numerous floors high in hot, humid weather.

CEMENT AND CONCRETE

L. Prodan and G. Bachofen*

Cement

Cement is a hydraulic bonding agent used in building construction and civil engineering. It is a fine powder obtained by grinding the clinker of a clay and limestone mixture calcined at high temperatures. When water is added to cement it becomes a slurry that gradually hardens to a stone-like consistency. It can be mixed with sand and gravel (coarse aggregates) to form mortar and concrete.

There are two types of cement: natural and artificial. The natural cements are obtained from natural materials having a cement-like structure and require only calcining and grinding to yield hydraulic cement powder. Artificial cements are available in large and increasing numbers. Each type has a different composition and mechanical structure and has specific merits and uses. Artificial cements may be classified as portland cement (named after the town of Portland in the United Kingdom) and aluminous cement.

Production

The portland process, which accounts for by far the largest part of world cement production, is illustrated in figure 93.16. It comprises two stages: clinker manufacture and clinker grinding. The raw materials used for clinker manufacture are calcareous materials such as limestone and argillaceous materials such as clay. The raw materials are blended and ground either dry (dry process) or in water (wet process). The pulverised mixture is calcined either in vertical or rotary-inclined kilns at a temperature ranging from 1,400 to 1,450 °C. On leaving the kiln, the clinker is cooled rapidly to prevent the conversion of tricalcium silicate, the main ingredient of portland cement, into bicalcium silicate and calcium oxide.

The lumps of cooled clinker are often mixed with gypsum and various other additives which control the setting time and other properties of the mixture in use. In this way it is possible to obtain a wide range of different cements such as normal portland

* Adapted from the 3rd edition *Encyclopaedia of Occupational Health and Safety* articles "Cement" by L. Prodan and "Concrete and reinforced concrete work" by G. Bachofen.

cement, rapid-setting cement, hydraulic cement, metallurgical cement, trass cement, hydrophobic cement, maritime cement, cements for oil and gas wells, cements for highways or dams, expansive cement, magnesium cement and so on. Finally, the clinker is ground in a mill, screened and stored in silos ready for packaging and shipping. The chemical composition of normal portland cement is:

- calcium oxide (CaO): 60 to 70%
- silicon dioxide (SiO_2) (including about 5% free SiO_2): 19 to 24%
- aluminium trioxide (Al_3O_3): 4 to 7%
- ferric oxide (Fe_2O_3): 2 to 6%
- magnesium oxide (MgO): less than 5%

Aluminous cement produces mortar or concrete with high initial strength. It is made from a mixture of limestone and clay with a high aluminium oxide content (without extenders) which is calcined at about 1,400 °C. The chemical composition of aluminous cement is approximately:

- aluminium oxide (Al_2O_3): 50%
- calcium oxide (CaO): 40%
- ferric oxide (Fe_2O_3): 6%
- silicon dioxide (SiO_2): 4%

Fuel shortages lead to the increased production of natural cements, especially those using tuff (volcanic ash). If necessary, this is calcined at 1,200 °C, instead of 1,400 to 1,450 °C as required for portland. The tuff may contain 70 to 80% amorphous free silica and 5 to 10% quartz. With calcination the amorphous silica is partially transformed to tridimite and crystobalite.

Uses

Cement is used as a binding agent in mortar and concrete —a mixture of cement, gravel and sand. By varying the processing method or by including additives, different types of concrete may be obtained using a single type of cement (e.g., normal, clay, bituminous, asphalt tar, rapid-setting, foamed, waterproof, microporous, reinforced, stressed, centrifuged concrete and so on).

Hazards

In the quarries from which the clay, limestone and gypsum for cement are extracted, workers are exposed to the hazards of climatic conditions, dusts produced during drilling and crushing, explosions and falls of rock and earth. Road transport accidents occur during haulage to the cement works.

During cement processing, the main hazard is dust. In the past, dust levels ranging from 26 to 114 mg/m³ have been recorded in quarries and cement works. In individual processes the following dust levels were reported: clay extraction—41.4 mg/m³; raw materials crushing and milling—79.8 mg/m³; sieving— 384 mg/m³; clinker grinding—140 mg/m³; cement packing— 256.6 mg/m³; and loading, etc.—179 mg/m³. In modern factories using the wet process, 15 to 20 mg dust/m³ air are occasionally the upper short-time values. The air pollution in the neighbourhood of cement factories is around 5 to 10% of the old values, thanks in particular to the widespread use of electrostatic filters. The free silica content of the dust usually varies between the level in raw material (clay may contain fine particulate quartz, and sand may be added) and that of the clinker or the cement, from which all the free silica will normally have been eliminated.

Other hazards encountered in cement works include high ambient temperatures, especially near furnace doors and on furnace platforms, radiant heat and high noise levels (120 dB) in the vicinity of the ball mills. Carbon monoxide concentrations ranging from trace quantities up to 50 ppm have been found near limestone kilns.

Other hazardous conditions encountered in cement industry workers include diseases of the respiratory system, digestive disorders, skin diseases, rheumatic and nervous conditions and hearing and visual disorders.

Respiratory tract diseases

Respiratory tract disorders are the most important group of occupational diseases in the cement industry and are the result of inhalation of airborne dust and the effects of macroclimatic and microclimatic conditions in the workplace environment. Chronic bronchitis, often associated with emphysema, has been reported as the most frequent respiratory disease.

Figure 93.16 • The manufacture of cement.

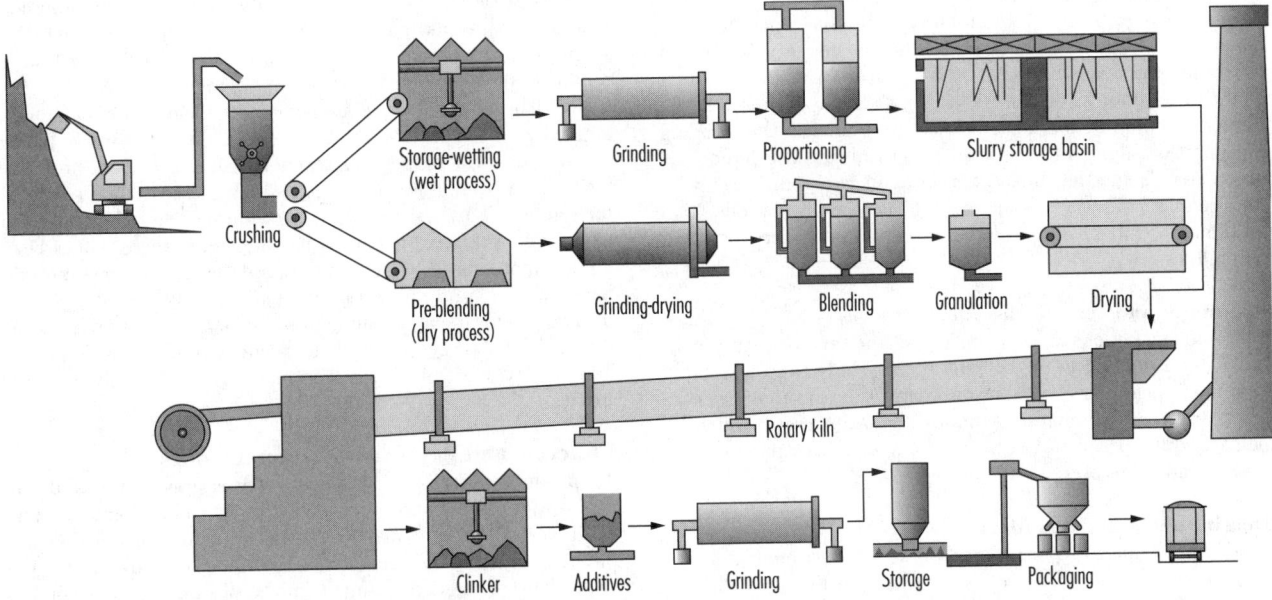

Normal portland cement does not cause silicosis because of the absence of free silica. However, workers engaged in cement production may be exposed to raw materials which present great variations in free silica content. Acid-resistant cements used for refractory plates, bricks and dust contain high amounts of free silica, and exposure to them involves a definite risk of silicosis.

Cement pneumoconiosis has been described as a benign pinhead or reticular pneumoconiosis, which may appear after prolonged exposure, and presents a very slow progression. However, a few cases of severe pneumoconiosis have also been observed, most likely following exposure to materials other than clay and portland cement.

Some cements also contain varying amounts of diatomaceous earth and tuff. It is reported that when heated, diatomaceous earth becomes more toxic due to the transformation of the amorphous silica into cristobalite, a crystalline substance even more pathogenic than quartz. Concomitant tuberculosis may complicate the course of the cement pneumoconiosis.

Digestive disorders

Attention has been drawn to the apparently high incidence of gastroduodenal ulcers in the cement industry. Examination of 269 cement plant workers revealed 13 cases of gastroduodenal ulcer (4.8%). Subsequently, gastric ulcers were induced in both guinea pigs and a dog fed on cement dust. However, a study at a cement works showed a sickness absence rate of 1.48 to 2.69% due to gastroduodenal ulcers. Since ulcers may pass through an acute phase several times a year, these figures are not excessive when compared with those for other occupations.

Skin diseases

Skin diseases are widely reported in the literature and have been said to account for about 25% and more of all the occupational skin diseases. Various forms have been observed, including inclusions in the skin, periungual erosions, diffuse eczematous lesions and cutaneous infections (furuncles, abscesses and panaritiums). However, these are more frequent among cement users (e.g., bricklayers and masons) than among cement manufacturing plant workers.

As early as 1947 it was suggested that cement eczema might be due to the presence in the cement of hexavalent chromium (detected by the chromium solution test). The chromium salts probably enter the dermal papillae, combine with proteins and produce a sensitization of an allergic nature. Since the raw materials used for cement manufacture do not usually contain chromium, the following have been listed as the possible sources of the chromium in cement: volcanic rock, the abrasion of the refractory lining of the kiln, the steel balls used in the grinding mills and the different tools used for crushing and grinding the raw materials and the clinker. Sensitization to chromium may be the leading cause of nickel and cobalt sensitivity. The high alkalinity of cement is considered an important factor in cement dermatoses.

Rheumatic and nervous disorders

The wide variations in macroclimatic and microclimatic conditions encountered in the cement industry have been associated with the appearance of various disorders of the locomotor system (e.g., arthritis, rheumatism, spondylitis and various muscular pains) and the peripheral nervous system (e.g., back pain, neuralgia and radiculitis of the sciatic nerves).

Hearing and vision disorders

Moderate cochlear hypoacusia in workers in a cement mill has been reported. The main eye disease is conjunctivitis, which normally requires only ambulatory medical care.

Accidents

Accidents in quarries are due in most cases to falls of earth or rock, or they occur during transportation. In cement works the main types of accidental injuries are bruises, cuts and abrasions which occur during manual handling work.

Safety and health measures

A basic requirement in the prevention of dust hazards in the cement industry is a precise knowledge of the composition and, especially, of the free silica content of all the materials used. Knowledge of the exact composition of newly-developed types of cement is particularly important.

In quarries, excavators should be equipped with closed cabins and ventilation to ensure a pure air supply, and dust suppression measures should be implemented during drilling and crushing. The possibility of poisoning due to carbon monoxide and nitrous gases released during blasting may be countered by ensuring that workers are at a suitable distance during shotfiring and do not return to the blasting point until all fumes have cleared. Suitable protective clothing may be necessary to protect workers against inclement weather.

All dusty processes in cement works (grinding, sieving, transfer by conveyor belts) should be equipped with adequate ventilation systems, and conveyor belts carrying cement or raw materials should be enclosed, with special precautions being taken at conveyor transfer points. Good ventilation is also required on the clinker cooling platform, for clinker grinding and in cement packing plants.

The most difficult dust control problem is that of the clinker kiln stacks, which are usually fitted with electrostatic filters, preceded by bag or other filters. Electrostatic filters may be used also for the sieving and packing processes, where they must be combined with other methods for air pollution control. Ground clinker should be conveyed in enclosed screw conveyors.

Hot work points should be equipped with cold air showers, and adequate thermal screening should be provided. Repairs on clinker kilns should not be undertaken until the kiln has cooled adequately, and then only by young, healthy workers. These workers should be kept under medical supervision to check their cardiac, respiratory and sweat function and prevent the occurrence of thermal shock. Persons working in hot environments should be supplied with salted drinks when appropriate.

Skin disease prevention measures should include the provision of shower baths and barrier creams for use after showering. Desensitization treatment may be applied in cases of eczema: after removal from cement exposure for 3 to 6 months to allow healing, 2 drops of 1:10,000 aqueous potassium dichromate solution is applied to the skin for 5 minutes, 2 to 3 times per week. In the absence of local or general reaction, contact time is normally increased to 15 minutes, followed by an increase in the strength of the solution. This desensitization procedure can also be applied in cases of sensitivity to cobalt, nickel and manganese. It has been found that chrome dermatitis—and even chrome poisoning—may be prevented and treated with ascorbic acid. The mechanism for the inactivation of hexavalent chromium by ascorbic acid involves reduction to trivalent chromium, which has a low toxicity, and subsequent complex formation of the trivalent species.

Concrete and Reinforced Concrete Work

To produce concrete, aggregates, such as gravel and sand, are mixed with cement and water in motor-driven horizontal or vertical mixers of various capacities installed at the construction site, but sometimes it is more economical to have ready-mixed concrete delivered and discharged into a silo on the site. For this purpose concrete mixing stations are installed in the periphery of towns or near gravel pits. Special rotary-drum lorries are used to avoid separation of the mixed constituents of the concrete, which would lower the strength of concrete structures.

Tower cranes or hoists are used to transport the ready-mixed concrete from the mixer or silo to the framework. The size and height of certain structures may also require the use of concrete pumps for conveying and placing the ready-mixed concrete. There are pumps which lift the concrete to heights of up to 100 m. As their capacity is by far greater than that of cranes or hoists, they are used in particular for the construction of high piers, towers and silos with the aid of climbing formwork. Concrete pumps are generally mounted on lorries, and the rotary-drum lorries used for transporting ready-mixed concrete are now frequently equipped to deliver the concrete directly to the concrete pump without passing through a silo.

Formwork

Formwork has followed the technical development rendered possible by the availability of larger tower cranes with longer arms and increased capacities, and it is no longer necessary to prepare shuttering *in situ*.

Prefabricated formwork up to 25 m² in size is used in particular for making the vertical structures of large residential and industrial buildings, such as facades and dividing walls. These structural-steel formwork elements, which are prefabricated in the site shop or by the industry, are lined with sheet-metal or wooden panels. They are handled by crane and removed after the concrete has set. Depending on the type of building method,

prefabricated formwork panels are either lowered to the ground for cleaning or taken to the next wall section ready for pouring.

So-called formwork tables are used to make horizontal structures (i.e., floor slabs for large buildings). These tables are composed of several structural-steel elements and can be assembled to form floors of different surfaces. The upper part of the table (i.e., the actual floor-slab form) is lowered by means of screw jacks or hydraulic jacks after the concrete has set. Special beak-like load-carrying devices have been devised to withdraw the tables, to lift them to the next floor and to insert them there.

Sliding or climbing formwork is used to build towers, silos, bridge piers and similar high structures. A single formwork element is prepared *in situ* for this purpose; its cross-section corresponds to that of the structure to be erected, and its height may vary between 2 and 4 m. The formwork surfaces in contact with the concrete are lined with steel sheets, and the entire element is linked to jacking devices. Vertical steel bars anchored in the concrete which is poured serve as jacking guides. The sliding form is jacked upwards as the concrete sets, and the reinforcement work and concrete placing continue without interruption. This means that work has to go on around the clock.

Climbing forms differ from sliding ones in that they are anchored in the concrete by means of screw sleeves. As soon as the poured concrete has set to the required strength, the anchor screws are undone, the form is lifted to the height of the next section to be poured, anchored and prepared for receiving the concrete.

Case studies: Prevention of occupational dermatosis among workers exposed to cement dust

The most common form of occupational dermatosis to be found among construction workers is caused by exposure to cement. Depending on the country, 5 to 15% of construction workers—most of them masons—acquire dermatosis during their work lives. Two types of dermatosis are caused by exposure to cement: (1) toxic contact dermatitis, which is local irritation of skin exposed to wet cement and is caused mainly by the alkalinity of the cement; and (2) allergic contact dermatitis, which is a generalized allergic skin reaction to exposure to the water-soluble chromium compound found in most cement. One kilogramme of normal cement dust contains 5 to 10 mg of water-soluble chromium. The chromium originates both in the raw material and the production process (mainly from steel structures used in production).

Allergic contact dermatitis is chronic and debilitating. If not properly treated, it can lead to decreased worker productivity and, in some cases, early retirement. In the 1960s and 1970s, cement dermatitis was the most common reported cause of early retirement among construction workers in Scandinavia. Therefore, technical and hygienic procedures were undertaken to prevent cement dermatitis. In 1979, Danish scientists suggested that reducing hexavalent water-soluble chromium to trivalent insoluble chromium by adding ferrous sulphate during production would prevent chromium-induced dermatitis (Fregert, Gruvberger and Sandahl 1979).

Denmark passed legislation requiring the use of cement with lower levels of hexavalent chromium in 1983. Finland followed with a legislative decision at the beginning of 1987, and Sweden and Germany adopted administrative decisions in 1989 and 1993, respectively. For the four countries, the accepted level of water-soluble chromium in cement was determined to be less than 2 mg/kg.

Before Finland's action in 1987, the Board of Labour Protection wanted to evaluate the occurrence of chromium dermatitis in Finland. The Board asked the Finnish Institute of Occupational Health to

monitor the incidence of occupational dermatosis among construction workers to assess the effectiveness of adding ferrous sulphate to cement in order to prevent chromium-induced dermatitis. The Institute monitored the incidence of occupational dermatitis through the Finnish Register of Occupational Diseases from 1978 through 1992. The results indicated that chromium-induced hand dermatitis practically disappeared among construction workers, whereas the incidence of toxic contact dermatitis remained unchanged during the study period (Roto et al. 1996).

In Denmark, chromate sensitization from cement was detected in only one case among 4,511 patch tests conducted between 1989 and 1994 among patients of a large dermatological clinic, 34 of whom were construction workers. The expected number of chromate-positive construction workers was 10 of 34 subjects (Zachariae, Agner and Menn J1996).

There seems to be increasing evidence that the addition of ferrous sulphate to cement prevents chromate sensitization among construction workers. In addition, there has been no indication that, when added to cement, ferrous sulphate has negative effects on the health of exposed workers. The process is economically feasible, and the properties of the cement do not change. It has been calculated that adding ferrous sulphate to cement increases the production costs by US$1.00 per tonne. The reductive effect of ferrous sulphate lasts 6 months; the product must be kept dry before mixing because humidity neutralizes the effect of the ferrous sulphate.

The addition of ferrous sulphate to cement does not change its alkalinity. Therefore workers should use proper skin protection. In all circumstances, construction workers should avoid touching wet cement with unprotected skin. This precaution is especially important in initial cement production, where minor adjustments to moulded elements are made manually.

Pekka Roto

So-called form cars are frequently used in civil engineering, in particular for making bridge deck slabs. Especially when long bridges or viaducts are built, a form car replaces the rather complex falsework. The deck forms corresponding to one length of bay are fitted to a structural-steel frame so that the various form elements can be jacked into position and be removed laterally or lowered after the concrete has set. When the bay is finished, the supporting frame is advanced by one bay length, the form elements are again jacked into position, and the next bay is poured.

When a bridge is built using the so-called cantilever technique the form-supporting frame is much shorter than the one described above. It does not rest on the next pier but must be anchored to form a cantilever. This technique, which is generally used for very high bridges, often relies on two such frames which are advanced by stages from piers on both sides of the span.

Prestressed concrete is used particularly for bridges, but also in building especially designed structures. Strands of steel wire wrapped in steel-sheet or plastic sheathing are embedded in the concrete at the same time as the reinforcement. The ends of the strands or tendons are provided with head plates so that the prestressed concrete elements may be pretensioned with the aid of hydraulic jacks before the elements are loaded.

Prefabricated elements

Construction techniques for large residential buildings, bridges and tunnels have been rationalized even further by prefabricating elements such as floor slabs, walls, bridge beams and so on, in a special concrete factory or near the construction site. The prefabricated elements, which are assembled on the site, do away with the erection, displacement and dismantling of complex formwork and falsework, and a great deal of dangerous work at height can be avoided.

Reinforcement

Reinforcement is generally delivered to the site cut and bent according to bar and bending schedules. Only when prefabricating concrete elements on the site or in the factory are the reinforcement bars tied or welded to each other to form cages or mats which are inserted into the forms before the concrete is poured.

Prevention of accidents

Mechanization and rationalization have eliminated many traditional hazards on building sites, but have also created new dangers. For instance, fatalities due to falls from height have considerably diminished thanks to the use of form cars, form-supporting frames in bridge building and other techniques. This is due to the fact that the work platforms and walkways with their guard rails are assembled only once and displaced at the same time as the form car, whereas with traditional formwork the guard rails were often neglected. On the other hand, mechanical hazards are increasing and electrical hazards are particularly serious in wet environments. Health hazards arise from cement itself, from substances added for curing or waterproofing and from lubricants for formwork.

Some important accident prevention measures to be taken for various operations are given below.

Concrete mixing

As concrete is nearly always mixed by machine, special attention should be paid to the design and layout of switchgear and feed-hopper skips. In particular, when concrete mixers are being cleaned, a switch may be unintentionally actuated, starting the drum or the skip and causing injury to the worker. Therefore, switches should be protected and also arranged in such a manner that no confusion is possible. If necessary, they should be interlocked or provided with a lock. The skips should be free from

danger zones for the mixer attendant and workers moving on passageways near it. It must also be ensured that workers cleaning the pits beneath feed-hopper skips are not injured by the accidental lowering of the hopper.

Silos for aggregates, especially sand, present a hazard of fatal accidents. For example, workers entering a silo without a standby person and without a safety harness and lifeline may fall and be buried in the loose material. Silos should therefore be equipped with vibrators and platforms from which sticking sand can be poked down, and corresponding warning notices should be displayed. No person should be allowed to enter the silo without another standing by.

Concrete handling and placing

The proper layout of concrete transfer points and their equipment with mirrors and bucket receiving cages obviates the danger of injuring a standby worker who otherwise has to reach out for the crane bucket and guide it to a proper position.

Transfer silos which are jacked up hydraulically must be secured so that they are not suddenly lowered if a pipeline breaks.

Work platforms fitted with guard rails must be provided when placing the concrete in the forms with the aid of buckets suspended from the crane hook or with a concrete pump. The crane operators must be trained for this type of work and must have normal vision. If large distances are covered, two-way telephone communication or walkie-talkies have to be used.

When concrete pumps with pipelines and placer masts are used, special attention should be paid to the stability of the installation. Agitating lorries (cement mixers) with built-in concrete pumps must be equipped with interlocked switches which make it impossible to start the two operations simultaneously. The agitators must be guarded so that the operating personnel cannot come into contact with moving parts. The baskets for collecting the rubber ball which is pressed through the pipeline to clean it after the concrete has been poured, are now replaced by two elbows arranged in opposite directions. These elbows absorb almost all the pressure needed to push the ball through the placing line; they not only eliminate the whip effect at the line end, but also prevent the ball from being shot out of the line end.

When agitating lorries are used in combination with placing plant and lifting equipment, special attention has to be paid to overhead electric lines. Unless the overhead line can be displaced they must be insulated or guarded by protective scaffolds within the work range to exclude any accidental contact. It is important to contact the power supply station.

Formwork

Falls are common during the assembly of traditional formwork composed of square timber and boards because the necessary guard rails and toe boards are often neglected for work platforms which are only required for short periods. Nowadays, steel supporting structures are widely used to speed up formwork assembly, but here again the available guard rails and toe boards are frequently not installed on the pretext that they are needed for so short a time.

Plywood form panels, which are increasingly used, offer the advantage of being easy and quick to assemble. However, often after being used several times, they are frequently misappropriated as platforms for rapidly required scaffolds, and it is generally forgotten that the distances between the supporting transoms must be considerably reduced in comparison with normal scaffold planks. Accidents resulting from breakage of form panels misused as scaffold platforms are still rather frequent.

Two outstanding hazards must be borne in mind when using prefabricated form elements. These elements must be stored in such a manner that they cannot turn over. Since it is not always feasible to store form elements horizontally, they must be secured by stays. Form elements permanently equipped with platforms, guard rails and toeboards may be attached by slings to the crane hook as well as being assembled and dismantled on the structure under construction. They constitute a safe workplace for the personnel and do away with the provision of work platforms for placing the concrete. Fixed ladders may be added for safer access to platforms. Scaffold and work platforms with guard rails and toe boards permanently attached to the form element should be used in particular with sliding and climbing formwork.

Experience has shown that accidents due to falls are rare when work platforms do not have to be improvised and rapidly assembled. Unfortunately, form elements fitted with guard rails cannot be used everywhere, especially where small residential buildings are being erected.

When the form elements are raised by crane from storage to the structure, lifting tackle of appropriate size and strength, such as slings and spreaders, must be used. If the angle between the sling legs is too large, the form elements must be handled with the aid of spreaders.

The workers cleaning the forms are exposed to a health hazard which is generally overlooked: the use of portable grinders to remove concrete residues adhering to the form surfaces. Dust measurements have shown that the grinding dust contains a high percentage of respirable fractions and silica. Therefore, dust control measures must be taken (e.g., portable grinders with exhaust devices linked to a filter unit or an enclosed form-board cleaning plant with exhaust ventilation.

Assembly of prefabricated elements

Special lifting equipment should be used in the manufacturing plant so that the elements can be moved and handled safely and without injury to the workers. Anchor bolts embedded in the concrete facilitate their handling not only in the factory but also on the assembly site. To avoid bending of the anchor bolts by oblique loads, large elements must be lifted with the aid of spreaders with short rope slings. If a load is applied to the bolts at an oblique angle, concrete may spill off and the bolts may be torn out. The use of inappropriate lifting tackle has caused serious accidents resulting from falling concrete elements.

Appropriate vehicles must be used for the road transport of prefabricated elements. They must be approximately secured against overturning or sliding—for example, when the driver has to brake the vehicle suddenly. Visibly displayed weight indications on the elements facilitate the task of the crane operator during loading, unloading and assembly on the site.

Lifting equipment on the site should be adequately chosen and operated. Tracks and roads must be kept in good condition in order to avoid overturning of loaded equipment during operation.

Work platforms protecting personnel against falls from height must be provided for the assembly of the elements. All possible means of collective protection, such as scaffolds, safety nets and overhead travelling cranes erected before completion of the building, should be taken into consideration before recourse is taken to reliance on PPE. It is, of course, possible to equip the workers with safety harnesses and lifelines, but experience has shown that there are workers who use this equipment only when they are under constant close supervision. Lifelines are indeed a hindrance when certain tasks are performed, and certain workers are proud of being capable of working at great heights without using any protection.

Before starting to design a prefabricated building, the architect, the manufacturer of the prefabricated elements and the building contractor should meet to discuss and study the course and safety of all operations. When it is known beforehand what types of handling and lifting equipment are available on the site, the concrete elements may be provided in the factory with fastening devices for guard rails and toe boards. The façade ends of floor elements, for instance, are then easily fitted with prefabricated guard rails and toe boards before the elements are lifted into place. The wall elements corresponding to the floor slab may thereafter be safely assembled because the workers are protected by guard rails.

For the erection of certain high industrial structures, mobile work platforms are lifted into position by crane and hung from suspension bolts embedded in the structure itself. In such cases it may be safer to transport the workers to the platform by crane (which should have high safety characteristics and be run by a qualified operator) than to use improvised scaffolds or ladders.

When post-tensioning concrete elements, attention should be paid to the design of the post-tensioning recesses, which should enable the tensioning jacks to be applied, operated and removed without any hazard for the personnel. Suspension hooks for tensioning jacks or openings for passing the crane rope must be provided for post-tensioning work beneath bridge decks or in box-type elements. This type of work, too, requires the provision of work platforms with guard rails and toe boards. The platform floor should be sufficiently low to allow for ample work space and safe handling of the jack. No person should be permitted at the rear of the tensioning jack because serious accidents may result from the high energy released in the breakage of an anchoring element or a steel tendon. The workers should also avoid being in front of the anchor plates as long as the mortar pressed into the tendon sheaths has not set. As the mortar pump is connected with hydraulic pipes to the jack, no person should be permitted in the area between pump and jack during tensioning. Continuous communication among the operators and with supervisors is also very important.

Training

Thorough training of plant operators in particular and all construction site personnel in general is becoming more and more important in view of increasing mechanization and the use of many types of machinery, plant and substances. Unskilled labourers or helpers should be employed in exceptional cases only, if the number of construction site accidents is to be reduced.

ASPHALT

John Finklea

Asphalts can generally be defined as complex mixtures of chemical compounds of high molecular weight, predominantly asphaltenes, cyclic hydrocarbons (aromatic or naphthenic) and a lesser quantity of saturated components of low chemical reactivity. The chemical composition of asphalts depends both on the original crude oil and on the process used during refining. Asphalts are predominantly derived from crude oils, especially heavier residue crude oil. Asphalt also occurs as a natural deposit, where it is usually the residue resulting from the evaporation and oxidation of liquid petroleum. Such deposits have been found in California, China, the Russian Federation, Switzerland, Trinidad and Tobago and Venezuela. Asphalts are non-volatile at ambient temperatures and soften gradually when heated. Asphalt should not be confused with tar, which is physically and chemically dissimilar.

A wide variety of applications include paving streets, highways and airfields; making roofing, waterproofing and insulating materials; lining irrigation canals and reservoirs; and the facing of dams and levees. Asphalt is also a valuable ingredient of some paints and varnishes. It is estimated that the current annual world

Classes of bitumens/asphalts

Class 1: *Penetration bitumens* are classified by their penetration value. They are usually produced from the residue from atmospheric distillation of petroleum crude oil by applying further distillation under vacuum, partial oxidation (air rectification), solvent precipitation or a combination of these processes. In Australia and the United States, bitumens that are approximately equivalent to those described here are called *asphalt cements* or *viscosity-graded asphalts*, and are specified on the basis of viscosity measurements at 60 °C.

Class 2: *Oxidized bitumens* are classified by their softening points and penetration values. They are produced by passing air through hot, soft bitumen under controlled temperature conditions. This process alters the characteristics of the bitumen to give reduced temperature susceptibility and greater resistance to different types of imposed stress. In the United States, bitumens produced using air blowing are known as *air-blown asphalts* or *roofing asphalts* and are similar to oxidized bitumens.

Class 3: *Cutback bitumens* are produced by mixing penetration bitumens or oxidized bitumens with suitable volatile diluents from petroleum crudes such as white spirit, kerosene or gas oil, to reduce their viscosity and render them more fluid for ease of handling. When the diluent evaporates, the initial properties of bitumen are recovered. In the United States, cutback bitumens are sometimes referred to as *road oils*.

Class 4: *Hard bitumens* are normally classified by their softening point. They are manufactured similarly to penetration bitumens, but have lower penetration values and higher softening points (i.e., they are more brittle).

Class 5: *Bitumen emulsions* are fine dispersions of droplets of bitumen (from classes 1, 3 or 6) in water. They are manufactured using high-speed shearing devices, such as colloid mills. The bitumen content can range from 30 to 70% by weight. They can be anionic, cationic or non-ionic. In the United States, they are referred to as *emulsified asphalts*.

Class 6: *Blended or fluxed bitumens* may be produced by blending bitumens (primarily penetration bitumens) with solvent extracts (aromatic by-products from the refining of base oils), thermally cracked residues or certain heavy petroleum distillates with final boiling points above 350 °C.

Class 7: *Modified bitumens* contain appreciable quantities (typically 3 to 15% by weight) of special addidtives, such as polymers, elastomers, sulphur and other products used to modify their properties; they are used for specialized applications.

Class 8: *Thermal bitumens* were produced by extended distillation, at high temperature, of a petroleum residue. Currently, they are not manufactured in Europe or in the United States.

Source: IARC1985.

production of asphalts is over 60 million tonnes, with more than 80% being used in need construction and maintenance and more than 15% used in roofing materials.

Asphalt mixes for road construction are produced by first heating and drying mixtures of graded crushed stone (such as granite or limestone), sand and filler and then mixing with penetration bitumen, referred to in the US as straight-run asphalt. This is a hot process. The asphalt is also heated using propane flames during application to a road bed.

Exposures and Hazards

Exposures to particulate polynuclear aromatic hydrocarbons (PAHs) in asphalt fumes have been measured in a variety of settings. Most of the PAHs found was composed of naphthalene derivatives, not the four- to six-ring compounds which are more likely to pose a significant carcinogenic risk. In refinery asphalt processing units, respirable PAH levels range from non-detectable to 40 mg/m^3. During drum-filling operations, 4 hour breathing zone samples ranged from 1.0 mg/m^{3}upwind to 5.3 mg/m^3 downwind. At asphalt mixing plants, exposures to benzene-soluble organic compounds ranged from 0.2 to 5.4 mg/m^3. During paving operations, exposures to respirable PAH ranged from less than 0.1 mg/m^3 to 2.7 mg/m^3. Potentially noteworthy worker exposures may also occur during the manufacture and application of asphalt roofing materials. Little information is available regarding exposures to asphalt fumes in other industrial situations and during the application or use of asphalt products.

Handling of hot asphalt can cause severe burns because it is sticky and is not readily removed from the skin. The principal concern from the industrial toxicological aspect is irritation of the skin and eyes by fumes of hot asphalt. These fumes may cause dermatitis and acne-like lesions as well as mild keratoses on prolonged and repeated exposure. The greenish-yellow fumes given off by boiling asphalt can also cause photosensitization and melanosis.

Although all asphaltic materials will combust if heated sufficiently, asphalt cements and oxidized asphalts will not normally burn unless their temperature is raised about 260 °C. The flammability of the liquid asphalts is influenced by the volatility and amount of petroleum solvent added to the base material. Thus, the rapid-curing liquid asphalts present the greatest fire hazard, which becomes progressively lower with the medium- and slow-curing types.

Because of its insolubility in aqueous media and the high molecular weight of its components, asphalt has a low order of toxicity.

The effects on the tracheobronchial tree and lungs of mice inhaling an aerosol of petroleum asphalt and another group inhaling smoke from heated petroleum asphalt included congestion, acute bronchitis, pneumonitis, bronchial dilation, some peribronchiolar round cell infiltration, abscess formation, loss of cilia, epithelial atrophy and necrosis. The pathological changes were patchy, and in some animals were relatively refractory to treatment. It was concluded that these changes were a non-specific reaction to breathing air polluted with aromatic hydrocarbons, and that their extent was dose dependent. Guinea pigs and rats inhaling fumes from heated asphalt showed effects such as chronic fibrosing pneumonitis with peribronchial adenomatosis, and the rats developed squamous cell metaplasia, but none of the animals had malignant lesions.

Steam-refined petroleum asphalts were tested by application to the skin of mice. Skin tumours were produced by undiluted asphalts, dilutions in benzene and a fraction of steam-refined asphalt. When air-refined (oxidized) asphalts were applied to the skin of mice, no tumour was found with undiluted material, but, in one experiment, an air-refined asphalt in solvent (toluene) produced topical skin tumours. Two cracking-residue asphalts produced skin tumours when applied to the skin of mice. A pooled mixture of steam- and air-blown petroleum asphalts in benzene produced tumours at the site of application on the skin of mice. One sample of heated, air-refined asphalt injected subcutaneously into mice produced a few sarcomas at the injection sites. A pooled mixture of steam- and air-blown petroleum asphalts produced sarcomas at the site of subcutaneous injection in mice. Steam-distilled asphalts injected intramuscularly produced local sarcomas in one experiment in rats. Both an extract of road-surfacing asphalt and its emissions were mutagenic to *Salmonella typhimurium*.

Evidence for carcinogenicity to humans is not conclusive. A cohort of roofers exposed to both asphalts and coal tar pitches showed an excess risk for respiratory cancer. Likewise, two Danish studies of asphalt workers found an excess risk for lung cancer, but some of these workers may also have been exposed to coal tar, and they were more likely to be smokers than the comparison group. Among Minnesota (but not California) highway workers, increases were noted for leukaemia and urological cancers. Even though the epidemiological data to date are inadequate to demonstrate with a reasonable degree of scientific certainty that asphalt presents a cancer risk to humans, general agreement exists, on the basis of experimental studies, that asphalt may pose such a risk.

Safety and Health Measures

Since heated asphalt will cause severe skin burns, those working with it should wear loose clothing in good condition, with the neck closed and the sleeves rolled down. Hand and arm protection should be worn. Safety shoes should be about 15 cm high and laced so that no openings are left through which hot asphalt may reach the skin. Face and eye protection is also recommended when heated asphalt is handled. Changing rooms and proper washing and bathing facilities are desirable. At crushing plants where dust is produced and at boiling pans from which fumes escape, adequate exhaust ventilation should be provided.

Asphalt kettles should be set securely and be levelled to preclude the possibility of their tipping. Workers should stand upwind of a kettle. The temperature of heated asphalt should be checked frequently in order to prevent overheating and possible ignition. If the flash point is approached, the fire under a kettle must be put out at once and no open flame or other source of ignition should be permitted nearby. Where asphalt is being heated, fire-extinguishing equipment should be within easy reach. For asphalt fires, dry chemical or carbon dioxide types of extinguishers are considered most appropriate. The asphalt spreader and the driver of an asphalt paving machine should be offered half-face respirators with organic vapour cartridges. In addition, to prevent the inadvertent swallowing of toxic materials, workers should not eat, drink or smoke near a kettle.

If molten asphalt strikes the exposed skin, it should be cooled immediately by quenching with cold water or by some other method recommended by medical advisers. An extensive burn should be covered with a sterile dressing and the patient should be taken to a hospital; minor burns should be seen by a physician. Solvents should not be used to remove asphalt from burned flesh. No attempt should be made to remove particles of asphalt from the eyes; instead the victim should be taken to a physician at once.

GRAVEL

James L. Weeks

Gravel is a loose conglomerate of stones that have been mined from a surface deposit, dredged from a river bottom or obtained from a quarry and crushed into desired sizes. Gravel has a variety of uses, including: for rail beds; in roadways, walkways and roofs; as filler in concrete (often for foundations); in landscaping and gardening; and as a filter medium.

The principal safety and health hazards to those who work with gravel are airborne silica dust, musculoskeletal problems and noise. Free crystalline silicon dioxide occurs naturally in many rocks that are used to make gravel. The silica content of bulk species of stone varies and is not a reliable indicator of the percentage of airborne silica dust in a dust sample. Granite contains about 30% silica by weight. Limestone and marble have less free silica.

Silica can become airborne during quarrying, sawing, crushing, sizing and, to a lesser extent, spreading of gravel. Generation of airborne silica can usually be prevented with water sprays and jets, and sometimes with local exhaust ventilation (LEV). In addition to construction workers, workers exposed to silica dust from gravel include quarry workers, railroad workers and landscape workers. Silicosis is more common among quarry or stone-crushing workers than among construction workers who work with gravel as a finished product. An elevated risk of mortality from pneumoconiosis and other non-malignant respiratory disease has been observed in one cohort of workers in the crushed-stone industry in the United States.

Musculoskeletal problems can occur as a result of manual loading or unloading of gravel or during manual spreading. The larger the individual pieces of stone and the larger the shovel or other tool used, the more difficult it is to manage the material with hand tools. The risk of sprains and strains can be reduced if two or more workers work together on strenuous tasks, and more so if draught animals or powered machines are used. Smaller shovels or rakes carry or push less weight than larger ones and can reduce the risk of musculoskeletal problems.

Noise accompanies mechanical processing or handling of stone or gravel. Stone crushing using a ball mill generates considerable low-frequency noise and vibration. Transporting gravel through metal chutes and mixing it in drums are both noisy processes. Noise can be controlled by using sound-absorbing or -reflecting materials around the ball mill, by using chutes lined with wood or other sound-absorbing (and durable) material or by using noise-insulated mixing drums.

References

American Society of Mechanical Engineers (ASME). 1994. *Mobile and Locomotive Cranes: An American National Standard.* ASME B30.5-1994. New York: ASME.

Arbetarskyddsstyrelsen (National Board of Occupational Safety and Health of Sweden). 1996. Personal communication.

Burkhart, G, PA Schulte, C Robinson, WK Sieber, P Vossenas, and K Ringen. 1993. Job tasks, potential exposures, and health risks of laborers employed in the construction industry. *Am J Ind Med* 24:413-425.

California Department of Health Services. 1987. *California Occupational Mortality, 1979-81.* Sacramento, CA: California Department of Health Services.

Commission of the European Communities. 1993. *Safety and Health in the Construction Sector.* Luxembourg: Office for Official Publications of the European Union.

Commission on the Future of Worker-Management Relations. 1994. *Fact Finding Report.* Washington, DC: US Department of Labor.

Construction Safety Asociation of Ontario. 1992. *Construction Safety and Health Manual.* Toronto: Construction Safety Association of Canada.

Council of the European Communities. 1988. *Council Directive of 21 December 1988 on the Approximation of Laws, Regulations and Administrative Provisions of the Member States Relating to Construction Products (89/106/EEC).* Luxembourg: Office for Official Publications of the European Communities.

Council of the European Communities. 1989. *Council Directive of 14 June 1989 on the Approximation of the Laws of the Member States Relating to Machinery (89/392/EEC).* Luxembourg: Office for Official Publications of the European Communities.

El Batawi, MA. 1992. Migrant workers. In *Occupational Health in Developing Countries,* edited by J Jeyaratnam. Oxford: Oxford University Press.

Engholm, G and A Englund. 1995. Morbidity and mortality patterns in Sweden. *Occup Med: State Art Rev* 10:261-268.

European Committee for Standardization (CEN). 1994. EN 474-1. *Earth-moving Machinery—Safety—Part 1: General Requirements.* Brussels: CEN.

Finnish Institute of Occupational Health. 1987. *Systematic Workplace Survey: Health and Safety in the Construction*

Industry. Helsinki: Finnish Institute of Occupational Health.

—. 1994. *Asbestos Program, 1987-1992*. Helsinki: Finnish Institute of Occupational Health.

Fregert, S, B Gruvberger, and E Sandahl. 1979. Reduction of chromate in cement by iron sulphate. *Contact Dermat* 5:39-42.

Hinze, J. 1991. *Indirect Costs of Construction Accidents*. Austin, TX: Construction Industry Institute.

Hoffman, B, M Butz, W Coenen, and D Waldeck. 1996. *Health and Safety at Work: System and Statistics*. Saint Augustin, Germany: Hauptverband der gewerblichen berufsgenossenschaften.

International Agency for Research on Cancer (IARC). 1985. Polynuclear aromatic compounds, Part 4: Bitumens, coal tars and derived products, shale oils and soots. In *IARC Monographs on the Evaluation of the Carcinogenic Risk of Chemicals to Humans*. Vol. 35. Lyon: IARC.

International Labour Organization (ILO). 1995. *Safety, Health and Welfare on Construction Sites: A Training Manual*. Geneva: ILO.

International Organization for Standardization (ISO). 1982. ISO 7096. *Earth-moving Machinery—Operator Seat—Transmitted Vibration*. Geneva: ISO.

—. 1985a. ISO 3450. *Earth-moving Machinery—Wheeled Machines—Performance Requirements and Test Procedures for Braking Systems*. Geneva: ISO.

—. 1985b. ISO 6393. *Acoustics—Measurement of Airborne Noise Emitted by Earth-moving Machinery—Operator's Position—Stationary Test Condition*. Geneva: ISO.

—. 1985c. ISO 6394. *Acoustics—Measurement of Airborne Noise Emitted by Earth-moving Machinery—Method for Determining Compliance with Limits for Exterior Noise—Stationary Test Condition*. Geneva: ISO.

—. 1992. ISO 5010. *Earth-moving Machinery—Rubber-tyred Machinery—Steering Capability*. Geneva: ISO.

Jack, TA and MJ Zak. 1993. *Results from the First National Census of Fatal Occupational Injuries, 1992*. Washington, DC: Bureau of Labor Statistics.

Japan Construction Safety and Health Association. 1996. Personal communication.

Kisner, SM and DE Fosbroke. 1994. Injury hazards in the construction industry. *J Occup Med* 36:137-143.

Levitt, RE and NM Samelson. 1993. *Construction Safety Management*. New York: Wiley & Sons.

Markowitz, S, S Fisher, M Fahs, J Shapiro, and PJ Landrigan. 1989. Occupational disease in New York State: A comprehensive reexamination. *Am J Ind Med* 16:417-436.

Marsh, B. 1994. Chance of getting hurt is generally far higher at smaller companies. *Wall Street J*.

McVittie, DJ. 1995. Fatalities and serious injuries. *Occup Med: State Art Rev* 10:285-293.

Meridian Research. 1994. *Worker Protection Programs in Construction*. Silver Spring, MD: Meridian Research.

Oxenburg, M. 1991. *Increasing Productivity and Profit through Health and Safety*. Sydney: CCH International.

Pollack, ES, M Griffin, K Ringen, and JL Weeks. 1996. Fatalities in the construction industry in the United States, 1992 and 1993. *Am J Ind Med* 30:325-330.

Powers, MB. 1994. Cost fever breaks. *Engineering News-Record* 233:40-41.

Ringen, K, A Englund, and J Seegal. 1995. Construction workers. In *Occupational Health: Recognizing and Preventing Work-related Disease*, edited by BS Levy and DH Wegman. Boston, MA: Little, Brown and Co.

Ringen, K, A Englund, L Welch, JL Weeks, and JL Seegal. 1995. Construction safety and health. *Occup Med: State Art Rev* 10:363-384.

Roto, P, H Sainio, T Reunala, and P Laippala. 1996. Addition of ferrous sulfate to cement and risk of chomium dermatitis among construction workers. *Contact Dermat* 34:43-50.

Saari, J and M Nasanen. 1989. The effect of positive feedback on industrial housekeeping and accidents. *Int J Ind Erg* 4:201-211.

Schneider, S and P Susi. 1994. Ergonomics and construction: A review of potential in new construction. *Am Ind Hyg Assoc J* 55:635-649.

Schneider, S, E Johanning, J-L Bjlard, and G Enghjolm. 1995. Noise, vibration, and heat and cold. *Occup Med: State Art Rev* 10:363-383.

Statistics Canada. 1993. *Construction in Canada, 1991-1993*. Report #64-201. Ottawa: Statistics Canada.

Strauss, M, R Gleanson, and J Sugarbaker. 1995. Chest X-ray screening improves outcome in lung cancer: A reappraisal of randomized trials on lung cancer screening. *Chest* 107:270-279.

Toscano, G and J Windau. 1994. The changing character of fatal work injuries. *Monthly Labor Review* 117:17-28.

Workplace Hazard and Tobacco Education Project. 1993. *Construction Workers' Guide to Toxics on the Job*. Berkeley, CA: California Health Foundation.

Zachariae, C, T Agner, and JT Menn. 1996. Chromium allergy in consecutive patients in a country where ferrous sulfate has been added to cement since 1991. *Contact Dermat* 35:83-85.

Other relevant readings

American National Standards Institute (ANSI). 1993a. *American Standard Safety Code for Elevators and Escalators*. New York: ANSI.

—. 1993b. *Inspectors Manual for Electric Elevators*. New York: ANSI.

—. 1994a. *Inspectors Manual for Elevators and Moving Walks*. New York: ANSI.

—. 1994b. *Inspectors Manual for Hydraulic Elevators*. New York: ANSI.

Arbouw Foundation. 1994. *Atlas of Health and Work Perception in the Construction Industry*. Amsterdam: Arbouw Foundation.

Bureau of Labor Statistics (BLS) 1993. *Fatal Workplace Injuries in 1991: A Collection of Data and Analysis*. Washington, DC: BLS.

Canadian Standards Association (CSA). 1974. *CSA Standard Z150-1974: Safety Code for Mobile Cranes*. Ontario: CSA.

Chiazze, L, DK Watkins, and J Amsel. 1991. Asphalt and risk of cancer in man. *Br J Ind Med* 48:538-542.

Construction Safety Association of Canada. 1985. *Hearing Protection for the Construction Industry*. Toronto: Construction Safety Association of Ontario.

Construction Safety Association of Ontario. 1989. *Workplace Hazardous Materials Information System (WHMIS) in Construction*. Toronto: Construction Safety Association of Ontario.

—. 1992. *Construction Safety and Health Manual*. Toronto: Construction Safety Association of Ontario.

Dickie, DE and P Eng. 1975a. *Crane Handbook*. Toronto: Construction Safety Association of Ontario.

—. 1975b. *Rigging Manual*. Toronto: Construction Safety Association of Ontario.

—. 1982. *Mobile Crane Manual*. Toronto: Construction Safety Association of Ontario.

International Labour Organization (ILO). 1972. *Code of Practice for the Safe Construction and Installation of Electric Passenger, Goods and Service Lifts*. Geneva: ILO.

Klein Tools. 1987. *Proper Use and Care of Hand Tools, Pliers, Screwdrivers, Wrenches, Striking and Struck Tools*. Chicago, IL: Klein Tools.

MacCollum, DV. 1993. *Crane Hazards and Their Prevention*. Des Plaines, IL: American Society of Safety Engineers.

National Institute for Occupational Safety and Health (NIOSH). 1977. *Criteria for a Recommended Standard—Occupational Exposure to Asphalt Fumes*. Cincinnati, OH: NIOSH.

Occupational Safety and Health Administration (OSHA). 1988. *Hand and Power Tools*. Washington, DC: OSHA.

Ontario Ministry of Labour. Undated. *Investigation Reports on Fatal Accidents in Ontario's Construction Industry*. Ottawa: Ontario Ministry of Labour. Unpublished.

Society of Automotive Engineers (SAE). 1995. *SAE Handbook: On-highway Vehicles and Off-highway Machinery*. Vol. 3. Warrendale, PA: SAE.

Syracuse Research Corporation. 1985. *Monograph on Human Exposure to Chemicals in the Workplace: Asphalt*. Techinical Report 85-188. Syracuse, NY: Syracuse Research Corporation.

World Health Organization (WHO). 1995. *Guidelines on Medical Surveillance of Workers Exposed to Mineral Dusts*. Geneva: WHO.

Chapter Editor
Michael McCann

Contents

GENERAL PROFILE

E. Gelpi*

The scope of the teaching profession extends from the nursery school to the postgraduate institution. Teaching involves not only academic instruction but also scientific, artistic and technical training, in laboratories, art studios and workshops, and physical training on sports grounds and in gymnasia and swimming pools. In most countries almost everyone comes at some time under the influence of the profession, and the teachers themselves have backgrounds as diverse as the subjects taught. Many senior members of the profession also have administrative and managerial duties.

In addition, the development of policies and activities to promote life-long education necessitates a reassessment of the conventional concept of teachers within traditional establishments (schools, universities). Members of the teaching profession carry out their tasks using formal and informal educational methods, in basic and continuous training, in educational establishments and institutions as well as outside them.

Apart from pupils of school age and university students, new kinds of students and trainees are coming forward in ever-increasing numbers in a great many countries: young jobseekers, women wishing to return to the employment market, retired persons, migrant workers, the handicapped, community groups and so on. In particular, we find categories of persons who were formerly excluded from normal educational establishments: illiterates and the handicapped.

There is nothing new in the variety of apprenticeship facilities available, and private self-education has always existed; life-long education has always existed in one form or another. There is, however, one new factor: the growing development of formal life-long educational facilities in places not originally intended as places of education and through new means—for example, in factories, offices and leisure facilities and through associations, mass communication media and assisted self-education. This growth and spread of educational activities has resulted in an increasing number of persons engaged in teaching on a professional or voluntary basis.

Many types of activity falling within the field of education may overlap: teachers, instructors, lecturers, promoters and organizers of educational projects, educational and vocational guidance workers, career advisers, adult education specialists and administrators.

Regarding the membership of the teaching profession as represented in employment markets, one finds that in most countries they make up one of the most significant categories of the salaried workforce.

Recently, the importance of teachers' trade unions has increased continuously, keeping pace with the ever-increasing number of teachers. The flexibility of their working hours has enabled teachers to play a significant role in the political life of many countries.

A new type of educator—those who are not exactly teachers in the previously held conception of the term—can now be found in many systems, where the school has become a centre for permanent or life-long educational facilities. These are professionals from various sectors, including handicrafts experts, artists and so on, who contribute permanently or occasionally to these educational activities.

Educational establishments are opening their doors to diverse groups and categories, turning more and more towards external and extramural activities. Two major tendencies can be observed in this connection: on the one hand, relations have been established with the industrial workforce, with industrial plants and processes; and on the other, a growing relation has been established with community development, and there is increasing interaction between institutional education and community education projects.

Universities and colleges endeavour to renew teachers' initial training through refresher training. Apart from specifically pedagogical aspects and disciplines, they provide for educational sociology, economy and anthropology. A trend still facing many obstacles is to have future teachers acquire experience by doing training periods in community settings, in workplaces or in various educational and cultural establishments. The national service, which has become general in certain countries, is a useful experience in the field for future teachers.

The immense investments in communication and information are auspicious for different types of individual or collective self-teaching. The relation between self-teaching and teaching is an emerging problem. The change-over from the autodidactic training of those who had not attended school to the permanent self-teaching of young people and adults has not always been correctly appreciated by educational institutions.

These new educational policies and activities give rise to various problems such as hazards and their prevention. Permanent education, which is not limited to school experience, turns various places, such as the community, the workplace, the laboratory and the environment, into training premises. The teachers should be assisted in these activities, and insurance coverage should be provided. In order to prevent hazards, efforts should be made to adapt the various premises for educational activities. There are several instances where schools have been adapted to become open centres for the entire population and have been equipped so as to be not only educational institutions but also places for creative and productive activities and for meetings.

The relationship of teachers and instructors with these various periods in the lives of trainees and students, such as leisure time, working time, family life and the duration of apprenticeships, also requires a considerable effort as regards information, research and adaptation.

Relations between teachers and students' families are also on the increase; sometimes members of families occasionally attend lectures or classes at the school. Dissimilarities between family models and educational models necessitate a great effort from teachers to reach mutual understanding from the psychological, sociological and anthropological standpoint. Family models influence the behaviour pattern of some students, who can experience sharp contradictions between family training and behavioural models and norms prevailing in the school.

However great the variety, all teaching has certain common characteristics: the teacher not only instructs in specific knowledge or skills but also seeks to convey a way of thought; he or she has to prepare the pupil for the next stage of development and stimulate the pupil's interest and participation in the process of learning.

ELEMENTARY AND SECONDARY SCHOOLS

Michael McCann

Elementary and secondary schools employ many different types of personnel, including teachers, teachers' aides, administrators, clerical personnel, maintenance personnel, cafeteria personnel, nurses and many others required to keep a school functioning. In

* Adapted from 3rd edition, *Encyclopaedia of Occupational Health and Safety*.

Preschool Programmes

Child-care, which involves the physical care and often education of young children, takes many forms in different parts of the world. In many countries where extended families are common, grandparents and other female relatives care for young children when the mother has to work. In countries where the nuclear family and/or single parents predominate and the mother is working, the care of healthy children below school age often occurs in private or public day-care centres or nursery schools outside the home. In many countries—for example, Sweden—these child-care facilities are operated by municipalities. In the United States, most child-care facilities are private, although they are usually regulated by local health departments. An exception is the Head Start Program for preschool children, which is funded by the government.

Staffing of child-care facilities usually depends on the number of children involved and the nature of the facility. For small numbers of children (usually less than 12), the child-care facility might be a home where the children include the preschool children of the caregiver. The staff can include one or more qualified adult assistants to meet staff-to-child ratio requirements. Larger, more formal child-care facilities include day-care centres and nursery schools. The staff members for these are usually required to have more education and can include a qualified director, trained teachers, nursing staff under the supervision of a physician, kitchen staff (nutrition specialists, food service managers and cooks) and other personnel, such as transportation staff and maintenance staff. The premises of the day-care centre should have such amenities as an outdoor play area, cloakroom, reception area, indoor classroom and play area, kitchen, sanitary facilities, administrative rooms, laundry room and so on.

Staff duties include supervision of children in all their activities, changing diapers of infants, emotional nurturing of the children, teaching, food preparation and service, recognition of signs of illness and/or safety hazards and many other functions.

Day-care workers face many of the same hazards found in normal indoor environments, including indoor air pollution, poor lighting, inadequate temperature control, slips and falls and fire hazards. (See the article "Elementary and Secondary Schools".) Stress (often resulting in burnout) and infections, however, are the major hazards for day-care workers. The lifting and carrying of children and exposure to possibly hazardous art supplies are other hazards.

Stress

Causes of stress in day-care workers include: high responsibility for the welfare of children without adequate pay and recognition; a perception of being unskilled even though many day-care workers have above-average education; image problems due to highly publicized incidents of day-care workers mistreating and abusing children, which have resulted in innocent day-care workers being fingerprinted and treated as potential criminals; and poor working conditions. The latter include low staff-to-child ratios, continual noise, lack of adequate time and facilities for meals and breaks separate from the children and inadequate mechanisms for parent-worker interaction, which can result in unnecessary and possibly unfair pressure and criticism from parents.

Preventive measures to reduce stress in day-care workers include: higher wages and better benefits; higher staff-to-child ratios to allow job rotation, rest breaks, sick leave and better performance, with resulting increase in job satisfaction; establishing formal mechanisms for parent-worker communications and cooperation (possibly including a parent-workers health and safety committee); and improved working conditions, such as adult-size chairs, regular "quiet" times, a separate workers' break area and so on.

Infections

Infectious diseases, such as diarrhoeal diseases, streptococcal and meningococcal infections, rubella, cytomegalovirus and respiratory infections, are major occupational hazards of day-care workers (see table 94.1). A study of day-care workers in Belgium found an increased risk of hepatitis A (Abdo and Chriske 1990). Up to 30% of the 25,000 cases of hepatitis A reported annually in the United States have been linked to day-care centres. Some organisms causing diarrhoeal diseases, such as *Giardia lamblia*, which causes giardiasis, are extremely infectious. Outbreaks can occur in day-care centres serving affluent populations as well as those serving poor areas (Polis et al. 1986). Some infections—for example, German measles and cytomegalovirus—can be especially hazardous for pregnant women, or women planning to have children, because of the risk of birth defects caused by the virus.

Sick children can spread diseases, as can children who have no overt symptoms but are carrying an illness. The most common routes of exposure are faecal-oral and respiratory. Young children usually have poor personal hygiene habits. Hand-to-mouth and toy-to-mouth contact are common. Handling contaminated toys and food is one type of entry route. Some organisms can live on inanimate objects for extended periods ranging from hours to weeks. Food can also be a vector if the food handler has contaminated hands or is ill. Inhalation of airborne respiratory droplets due to sneezing and coughing without protection such as tissues can result in transmission of infections. Such air-borne aerosols can remain suspended in the air for hours.

Day care employees working with children under the age of three years, especially if the children are not toilet-trained, are at greatest risk, particularly when changing and handling soiled diapers which are contaminated by disease-bearing organisms.

Precautions include: convenient facilities for handwashing; regular handwashing by children and staff members; changing diapers in designated areas which are regularly disinfected; disposal of soiled diapers in closed, plastic-lined receptacles which are emptied frequently; separating food preparation areas from other areas; frequent washing of toys, play areas, blankets and other items that could become contaminated; good ventilation; adequate staff-to-child ratios to allow proper implementation of a hygiene programme; a policy of excluding, isolating or restricting sick children, depending on the illness; and adequate sick-leave policies to allow sick day-care workers to stay home.

Adapted from Women's Occupational Health Resource Center 1987

general, school personnel face all the potential hazards found in normal indoor and office environments, including indoor air pollution, poor lighting, inadequate heating or cooling, use of office machines, slips and falls, ergonomics problems from poorly designed office furniture and fire hazards. Precautions are the standard ones developed for this type of indoor environment, although building and fire codes usually have specific requirements for schools because of the large number of children present. Other general concerns found in schools include asbestos (especially among custodial and maintenance workers), chipping lead paint, pesticides and herbicides, radon and electromagnetic fields (especially for schools built near high-voltage transmission power lines). Eye and respiratory complaints related to the painting of rooms and the tarring of school roofs while the building is occupied are

Table 94.1 • Infectious diseases affecting day-care workers and teachers.

Disease	Where found	Mode of transmission	Comments
Amoebiasis	Especially tropics and subtropics	Water and food contaminated with infected faeces	Use good food and water sanitation.
Chicken pox	Worldwide	Generally person-to-person direct contact, but also possible by airborne respiratory droplets	Chicken pox is more serious in adults than children; risk of birth defects; reportable disease in most countries.
Cytomegalovirus (CMV)	Worldwide	Airborne respiratory droplets; contact with urine, saliva or blood	Highly contagious; risk of birth defects.
Erythema infectiosum (Parvovirus-B-19)	Worldwide	Direct person-to-person contact or airborne respiratory droplets	Mildly contagious; risk to foetus during pregnancy.
Gastroenteritis, bacterial (Salmonella, Shigella, Campylobacter)	Worldwide	Person-to-person transmission, food or water via faecal-oral route	Use good food and water sanitation; require strict handwashing procedures; reportable disease in most countries.
Gastroenteritis, viral (Rotaviruses)	Worldwide	Person-to-person transmission, food or water via faecal-oral route; also by inhalation of dust containing virus	Use good food and water sanitation.
German measles (rubella)	Worldwide	Airborne respiratory droplets; direct contact with infected people	Risk of birth defects; all children and employees should be vaccinated; reportable disease in most countries.
Giardiasis (intestinal parasite)	Worldwide, but especially tropics and subtropics	Contaminated food and water; also possible by person-to-person transmission	Use good food and water sanitation; reportable disease in most countries.
Hepatitis A virus	Worldwide, but especially Mediterranean areas and developing countries	Faecal-oral transmission, especially contaminated food and water; also possible by direct person-to-person contact	Risk of spontaneous abortions and stillbirths; use good food and water sanitation; reportable disease in most countries.
Hepatitis B virus	Worldwide, especially Asia and Africa	Sexual contact, contact of broken skin or mucous membranes with blood or other body fluids	Higher incidence in institutionalized children (e.g., developmentally disabled); vaccination recommended in high-risk situations; use universal precautions for all exposures to blood and other body fluids; reportable disease in most countries.
Herpes Simplex Type I and II	Worldwide	Contact with mucous membranes	Extremely contagious; common in adults and age group 10 to 20 years.
Human Immune Deficiency Virus (HIV) infection	Worldwide	Sexual contact, contact of broken skin or mucous membranes with blood or other body fluids	Leads to Acquired Immune Deficiency Syndrome (AIDS); use universal precautions for all exposures to blood and body fluids (e.g., nosebleeds); anonymous reporting of disease required in most countries.
Infectious mononucleosis (Epstein-Barr virus)	Worldwide	Airborne respiratory droplets; direct contact with saliva	Especially common in age group 10 to 20 years.
Influenza	Worldwide	Airborne respiratory droplets	Highly contagious; high-risk individuals should get immunization shots.
Measles	Worldwide	Airborne respiratory droplets	Highly contagious, but for adults mostly a risk to non-immunized individuals working with unvaccinated children; reportable disease in most countries.
Meningococcus meningitis (bacterial)	Mostly tropical Africa and Brazil	Airborne respiratory droplets, especially close contact	Reportable disease in most countries.
Mumps	Worldwide	Airborne respiratory droplets and contact with saliva	Highly contagious; exclude infected children; may cause infertility in adults; outbreaks reportable in some countries.
Mycoplasma infections	Worldwide	Airborne transmission after close contact	A major cause of primary atypical pneumonia; mainly affects children aged 5 to 15 years.
Pertussis (whooping cough)	Worldwide	Airborne respiratory droplets	Not as severe in adults; all children under 7 years should be immunized.
Scabies	Worldwide	Direct skin-to-skin contact	Infectious skin disease caused by mites.
Streptococcus infections	Worldwide	Direct person-to-person contact	Strep throat, scarlet fever and community-acquired pneumonia are examples of infections.
Tuberculosis (respiratory)	Worldwide	Airborne respiratory droplets	Highly infectious; tuberculosis screening should be conducted for all day care workers; a reportable disease in most countries.

Table 94.2 • Hazards and precautions for particular classes.

Class	Activity/subject	Hazards	Precautions
Elementary classes			
Science	Animal handling	Bites and scratches, zoonoses, parasites	Allow only live, healthy animals. Handle animals with heavy gloves. Avoid animals which can carry disease-transmitting insects and parasites.
	Plants	Allergies, poisonous plants	Avoid plants which are known to be poisonous or cause allergic reaction.
	Chemicals	Skin and eye problems, toxic reactions, allergies	Avoid using toxic chemicals with children. Wear proper personal protective equipment when doing teacher demonstrations with toxic chemicals.
	Equipment	Electrical hazards, safety hazards	Follow standard electrical safety procedures. Ensure all equipment is properly guarded. Store all equipment, tools, etc., properly.
Art			Use only non-toxic art materials. Avoid solvents, acids, alkalis, spray cans, chemical dyes, etc.
	Painting and drawing	Pigments, solvents	Use only children's paints. Do not use pastels, dry pigments.
	Photography	Photochemicals	Do not do photoprocessing. Send out film for developing or use Polaroid cameras or blueprint paper and sunlight.
	Textile and fibre arts	Dyes	Avoid synthetic dyes; use natural dyes such as onion skins, tea, spinach, etc.
	Printmaking	Acids, solvents	Use water-based block printing inks.
		Cutting tools	Use linoleum cuts instead of woodcuts.
	Woodworking	Tools	Use soft woods and hand tools only.
		Glues	Use water-based glues.
	Ceramics	Silica, toxic metals, heat, kiln fumes	Use wet clay only, and wet mop. Paint pottery rather than using ceramic glazes. Do not fire kiln inside classroom.
Secondary classes			
Chemistry	General		All school laboratories should have the following: laboratory hood if toxic, volatile chemicals are used; eyewash fountains; emergency showers (if concentrated acids, bases or other corrosive chemicals are present); first aid kits; proper fire extinguishers; protective goggles, gloves and lab coats; proper disposal receptacles and procedures; spill control kit. Avoid carcinogens, mutagens and highly toxic chemicals like mercury, lead, cadmium, chlorine gas, etc.
	Organic chemistry	Solvents	Use only in laboratory hood. Use least toxic solvents. Do semi-micro- or microscale experiments.
		Peroxides and explosives	Do not use explosives or chemicals such as ether, which can form explosive peroxides.
	Inorganic chemistry	Acids and bases	Avoid concentrated acids and bases when possible.
	Analytical chemistry	Hydrogen sulphide	Do not use hydrogen sulphide. Use substitutes.
	Storage	Incompatibilities	Avoid alphabetical storage, which can place incompatible chemicals in close proximity. Store chemicals by compatible groups.
		Flammability	Store flammable and combustible liquids in approved flammable-storage cabinets.
Biology	Dissection	Formaldehyde	Do not dissect specimens preserved in formaldehyde. Use smaller, freeze-dried animals, training films and videotapes, etc.
	Anaesthetizing insects	Ether, cyanide	Use ethyl alcohol for anaesthetization of insects. Refrigerate insects for counting.
	Drawing of blood	HIV, Hepatitis B	Avoid if possible. Use sterile lancets for blood typing under close supervision.
	Microscopy	Stains	Avoid skin contact with iodine and gentian violet.
	Culturing bacteria	Pathogens	Use sterile technique with all bacteria, assuming there could be contamination by pathogenic bacteria.
Physical sciences	Radioisotopes	Ionizing radiation	Use radioisotopes only in "exempt" quantities not requiring a licence. Only trained teachers should use these. Develop a radiation safety programme.
	Electricity and magnetism	Electrical hazards	Follow standard electrical safety procedures.

Continues on next page.

94. EDUCATION AND TRAINING SERVICES

Table 94.2 • Hazards and precautions for particular classes.
Continued.

Class	Activity/subject	Hazards	Precautions
	Lasers	Eye and skin damage, electrical hazards	Use only low-power (Class I) lasers. Never look directly into a laser beam or pass the beam across face or body. Lasers should have a key lock.
Earth sciences	Geology	Flying chips	Crush rocks in canvas bag to prevent flying chips. Wear protective goggles.
	Water pollution	Infection, toxic chemicals	Do not take sewage samples because of infection risk. Avoid hazardous chemicals in field testing of water pollution.
	Atmosphere	Mercury manometers	Use oil or water manometers. If mercury manometers are used for demonstration, have mercury spill control kit.
	Volcanoes	Ammonium dichromate	Do not use ammonium dichromate and magnesium to simulate volcanoes.
	Solar observation	Infrared radiation	Never view sun directly with eyes or through lenses.
Art and Industrial Arts	All	General	Avoid most dangerous chemicals and processes. Have proper ventilation. See also precautions under Chemistry
	Painting and drawing	Pigments, solvents	Avoid lead and cadmium pigments. Avoid oil paints unless cleanup is done with vegetable oil. Use spray fixatives outside.
	Photography	Photochemicals, acids, sulphur dioxide	Avoid colour processing and toning. Have dilution ventilation for darkroom. Have eyewash fountain. Use water instead of acetic acid for stop bath.
	Textile and fibre arts	Dyes, dyeing assistants, wax fumes	Use aqueous liquid dyes or mix dyes in glove box. Avoid dichromate mordants. Do not use solvents to remove wax in batik. Have ventilation if ironing out wax.
	Papermaking	Alkali, beaters	Do not boil lye. Use rotten or mulched plant materials, or recycle paper and cardboard. Use large blender instead of more dangerous industrial beaters to prepare paper pulp.
	Printmaking	Solvents	Use water-based instead of solvent-based silk screen inks. Clean intaglio press beds and inking slabs with vegetable oil and dishwashing liquid instead of solvents. Use cut paper stencils instead of lacquer stencils for silk screen printing.
		Acids, potassium chlorate	Use ferric chloride to etch copper plates instead of Dutch mordant or nitric acid on zinc plates. If using nitric acid etching, have emergency shower and eyewash fountain and local exhaust ventilation.
		Dichromates	Use diazo instead of dichromate photoemulsions. Use citric acid fountain solutions in lithography to replace dichromates.
	Woodworking	Woods and wood dust	Have dust collection system for woodworking machines. Avoid irritating and allergenic hardwoods, preserved woods (e.g., chromated copper arsenate treated). Clean up wood dust to remove fire hazards.
		Machinery and tools	Have machine guards. Have key locks and panic button.
		Noise	Reduce noise levels or wear hearing protectors.
		Glues	Use water-based glues when possible. Avoid formaldehyde/resorcinol glues, solvent-based glues.
		Paints and finishes	Use water-based paints and finishes. Use shellac based on ethyl alcohol rather than methyl alcohol.
	Ceramics	Lead, silica, toxic metals, kiln fumes	Purchase wet clay. Do not use lead glazes. Buy prepared glazes rather than mixing dry glazes. Spray glazes only in spray booth. Fire kiln outside or have local exhaust ventilation. Wear infrared goggles when looking into hot kiln.
	Sculpture	Silica, plastics resins, dust	Use only hand tools for stone sculpture to reduce dust levels. Do not use sandstone, granite or soapstone, which might contain silica or asbestos. Do not use highly toxic polyester, epoxy or polyurethane resins. Have ventilation if heating plastics to remove decomposition products. Wet mop or vacuum dusts.
	Jewellery	Soldering fumes, acids	Avoid cadmium silver solders and fluoride fluxes. Use sodium hydrogen sulphate rather than sulphuric acid for pickling. Have local exhaust ventilation.
	Enamelling	Lead, burns, infrared radiation	Use only lead-free enamels. Ventilate enamelling kiln. Have heat-protective gloves and clothing, and infrared goggles.

Continues on next page.

Table 94.2 • Hazards and precautions for particular classes.
Continued.

Class	Activity/subject	Hazards	Precautions
	Lost wax casting	Metal fumes, silica, infrared radiation, heat	Use 50/50 30-mesh sand/plaster instead of cristobalite investments. Have local exhaust ventilation for wax burnout kiln and casting operation. Wear heat-protective clothing and gloves.
	Stained glass	Lead, acid fluxes	Use copper foil technique rather than lead. Use lead- and antimony-free solders. Avoid lead glass paints. Use acid- and rosin-free soldering fluxes.
	Welding	Metal fumes, ozone, nitrogen dioxide, electrical and fire hazards	Do not weld metals coated with zinc, lead paints, or alloys with hazardous metals (nickel, chromium, etc.). Weld only metals of known composition.
	Commercial art	Solvents, photochemicals, video display terminals	Use double-sided tape instead of rubber cement. Use heptane-based, not hexane rubber cements. Have spray booths for air brushing. Use water-based or alcohol-based permanent markers instead of xylene types. See Photography section for photoprocesses. Have proper ergonomic chairs, lighting, etc., for computers.
Performing Arts	Theatre	Solvents, paints, welding fumes, isocyanates, fire	Use water-based paints and dyes. Do not use polyurethane spray foams. Separate welding from other areas. Have safe rigging procedures. Avoid pyrotechnics, firearms, fog and smoke, and other hazardous special effects. Fireproof all stage scenery. Mark all trap doors, pits and elevations.
	Dance	Acute injuries, repetitive strain injuries	Have a proper dance floor. Avoid full schedules after period of inactivity. Assure proper warm-up before and cool-down after dance activity. Allow sufficient recovery time after injuries.
	Music	Musculoskeletal injuries (e.g., carpal tunnel syndrome)	Use proper sized instruments. Have adequate instrument supports. Allow sufficient recovery time after injuries.
		Noise	Keep sound levels at acceptable levels. Wear musician's ear plugs if needed. Position speakers to minimize noise levels. Use sound-absorbing materials on walls.
		Vocal strain	Assure adequate warm-up. Provide proper vocal training and conditioning.
Automotive Mechanics	Brake drums	Asbestos	Do not clean brake drums unless approved equipment is used.
	Degreasing	Solvents	Use water-based detergents. Use parts cleaner.
	Car motors	Carbon monoxide	Have tailpipe exhaust.
	Welding		See above.
	Painting	Solvents, pigments	Spray paint only in spray booth, or outdoors with respiratory protection.
Home Economics	Food and nutrition	Electrical hazards	Follow standard electrical safety rules.
		Knives and other sharp utensils	Always cut away from body. Keep knives sharpened.
		Fire and burns	Have stove hoods with grease filters that exhaust to outside. Wear protective gloves with hot objects.
		Cleaning products	Wear goggles, gloves and apron with acidic or basic cleaning products.

also a common problem. Painting and tarring should be done when the building is not occupied.

Basic academic duties required of all teachers include: lesson preparation, which can include the development of learning strategies, copying of lecture notes and the making of visual aids such as illustrations, graphs and the like; lecturing, which requires presenting information in an organized fashion that arouses the attention and concentration of students, and can involve the use of blackboards, film projectors, overhead projectors and computers; writing, giving and grading examinations; and individual counselling of students. Most of this instruction takes place in classrooms. In addition, teachers with specialities in science, arts, vocational education, physical education and other areas will conduct much of their teaching in facilities such as laboratories, art studios, theatres, gymnasiums and the like. Teachers may also take students on class trips outside the school to locations such as museums and zoos.

Teachers also have special duties, which can include supervision of students in hallways and the cafeteria; attending meetings with administrators, parents and others; organization and supervision of after-school leisure and other activities; and other administrative duties. In addition, teachers attend conferences and other educational events in order to keep current with their field and advance their career.

There are specific hazards facing all teachers. Infectious diseases such as tuberculosis, measles and chicken pox can easily spread throughout a school. Vaccinations (both of students and teachers), tuberculosis testing and other standard public health measures are essential (see table 94.2). Overcrowded classrooms, classroom noise, overloaded schedules, inadequate facilities,

Figure 94.1 • Industrial arts metal shop in a high school.

Michael McCann

career advancement questions, job security and general lack of control over working conditions contribute to major stress problems, absenteeism and burnout in teachers. Solutions include both institutional changes to improve working conditions and stress reduction programmes where possible. A growing problem, especially in urban environments, is violence against teachers by students and, sometimes, intruders. In the United States, many secondary-level students, especially in urban schools, carry weapons, including guns. In schools where violence is a problem, organized violence-prevention programmes are essential. Teachers' aides face many of the same hazards.

Teachers in specialized classes can have additional occupational hazards, including chemical exposures, machinery hazards, accidents, electrical hazards, excessive noise levels, radiation and fire, depending on the particular classroom. Figure 94.1

Figure 94.2 • High school science laboratory with fume hoods and an emergency shower.

Michael McCann

shows an industrial arts metal shop in a high school, and figure 94.2 shows a high school science lab with fume hoods and an emergency shower. Table 94.2 summarizes special precautions, particularly substitution of safer materials, for use in schools. Information on standard precautions can be found in the chapters relevant to the process (e.g., *Entertainment and the arts* and *Using, storing and transporting chemicals*).

Teachers in special education programmes can sometimes be at greater risk. Examples of hazards include violence from emotionally disturbed students and transmission of infections such as hepatitis A, B and C from institutionalized, developmentally disabled students (Clemens et al. 1992).

VOCATIONAL TRAINING AND APPRENTICESHIPS

Gary Gibson

The teaching of trades through the apprenticeship system dates at least as far back as the Roman Empire, and continues to this day in classic trades such as shoemaking, carpentry, stone masonry and so forth. Apprenticeships can be informal, where a person desiring to learn a trade finds a skilled employer willing to teach him or her in exchange for work. However, most apprenticeships are more formal and involve a written contract between the employer and the apprentice, who is bound to serve the employer for a given time in return for training. These formal apprenticeship programmes usually have standard rules regarding qualifications for completing the apprenticeship that are set by an institution such as a trade union, guild or employer organization. In some countries, trade unions and employer organizations run the apprenticeship programme directly; these programmes usually involve a combination of structured on-the-job training and classroom instruction.

In today's technological world, however, there is a growing need for skilled labour in many areas, such as laboratory technicians, mechanics, machinists, cosmetologists, cooks, service trades and many more. The learning of these skilled trades usually takes place in vocational programmes in schools, vocational institutes, polytechnics, colleges with two-year programmes and similar institutions. These sometimes include internships in actual work settings.

Both the teachers and the students in these vocational programmes face occupational hazards from the chemicals, machinery, physical agents and other hazards associated with the particular trade or industry. In many vocational programmes, students are learning their skills using old machinery donated by industry. These machines often are not equipped with modern safety features such as proper machine guards, fast-acting brakes, noise-control measures and so forth. The teachers themselves often have not had adequate training in the hazards of the trade and appropriate precautions. Often, the schools do not have adequate ventilation and other precautions.

Apprentices often face high-risk situations because they are assigned the dirtiest and most hazardous tasks. Often they are used as a source of cheap labour. In these situations, it is even more likely that the apprentice's employers have not had adequate training in the hazards and precautions of their trade. Informal apprenticeships are usually not regulated, and there is often no recourse for apprentices facing such exploitation or hazards.

Another common problem with both apprenticeship programmes and vocational training is age. Apprenticeship entry age is generally between 16 and 18 year of age. Vocational training can begin at elementary school. Studies have shown that young workers (aged 15 to 19 years) account for a disproportionate percentage of lost-time injury claims. In Ontario, Canada, for the year 1994, the largest proportion of injured young workers were employed in the service industry.

These statistics indicate that students entering these programmes may not understand the importance of health and safety training. Students also can have different attention spans and comprehension levels than adults, and this should be reflected in their training. Finally, extra attention is needed in sectors such as service industries, where health and safety has generally not received the attention found in other industries.

In any apprenticeship or vocational programme, there should be built-in safety and health training programmes, including hazard communication. The teachers or employers should be properly trained in the hazards and precautions, both to protect themselves and to teach the students properly. The work or training setting should have adequate precautions.

• COLLEGES AND UNIVERSITIES

Susan Magor

The large number and wide variety of operations and hazardous materials involved in teaching, research and support service activities present a challenge to health and safety management in colleges and universities. The very nature of research implies risk: challenging the limits of current knowledge and technology. Many research activities in science, engineering and medicine require sophisticated and expensive facilities, technology and equipment which may not be readily available or have yet to be developed. Research activities within existing facilities may also evolve and change without the facilities being modified to contain them safely. Many of the most hazardous activities are performed infrequently, periodically or on an experimental basis. Hazardous materials used in teaching and research often include some of the most dangerous substances and hazards with unavailable or poorly documented safety and toxicity data. These are commonly used in relatively small quantities under less than ideal conditions by poorly trained personnel. Health and safety hazards are not always easily recognized or readily acknowledged by highly educated academics with specialized fields of expertise who may have a poor regard for legislative or administrative controls when these are perceived to limit academic freedom.

Academic freedom is a sacred principle, fiercely guarded by academics, some of whom may be experts in their disciplines. Any legislative or institutional constraints which are perceived as encroaching on this principle will be fought and may even be disregarded. Methods for the identification and control of health and safety hazards associated with teaching and research activities cannot be readily imposed. Academics need to be persuaded that health and safety policies support and enhance the primary mission rather than confine it. Policies, where they exist, tend to protect the academic mission and the rights of individuals, rather than to conform with external regulations and standards. Liability and accountability issues affecting teachers and researchers directly may have more effect than rules.

Most health and safety legislation, standards and guidance criteria are developed for industry with large quantities of relatively few chemicals, well documented hazards, established procedures and a stable workforce within a well defined management system. The academic environment differs from industry in almost every aspect. In some jurisdictions academic institutions may even be exempt from health and safety legislation.

Academic institutions are generally hierarchical in their management systems, with academics at the top followed by non-academic professionals, technicians and support staff. Graduate students are often employed on a part-time basis to perform a variety of teaching and research functions. Academics are appointed to senior management positions for specific terms with little management experience or training. Frequent turn-over may result in a lack of continuity. Within this system, senior researchers, even within large institutions, are granted relative autonomy to manage their affairs. They are usually in control of their own budgets, facility design, purchasing, organization of work and hiring of personnel. Hazards may be overlooked or go unrecognized.

It is common practice for researchers in academic institutions to employ graduate students as research assistants in a master/apprentice relationship. These individuals are not always protected under health and safety laws. Even if covered by legislation, they are frequently reluctant to exercise their rights or to voice safety concerns to their supervisors who may also be responsible for evaluating their academic performance. Long hours under great pressure, overnight and weekend work with minimal supervision and skeleton support services are routine. Cost saving and energy conservation efforts may even reduce essential services such as security and ventilation during nights and weekends. Though students are not usually protected by health and safety legislation, due diligence requires that they are treated with the same level of care as is provided for employees.

Potential Hazards

The range of hazards can be extremely broad depending upon the size and nature of the institution, the type of academic programmes offered and the nature of research activities (see table 94.3). Small colleges offering only liberal arts programmes may have relatively few hazards while comprehensive universities with schools of medicine, engineering and fine arts and extensive research programmes may have a complete range, including some very serious hazards, such as toxic chemicals, biohazards, reproductive hazards, ionizing and non-ionizing radiations and various other physical agents.

Maintenance and groundskeeping, hazardous materials handling, machine and motor vehicle operations and office work are common to most institutions and comprise hazards which are covered elsewhere in this *Encyclopaedia*.

Workplace violence is an emerging issue of particular concern for teaching staff, front-line personnel, money handlers and security personnel.

Large institutions may be compared to small towns where a population lives and works. Issues of personal and community safety interface with occupational health and safety concerns.

Control of Hazards

Hazard identification through the usual processes of inspection and incident and injury investigation need to be preceded by careful review of proposed programmes and facilities prior to the start up of activities. The occupational and environmental risk aspects of new research projects and academic programmes should be taken into consideration in the earliest stages of the planning process. Researchers may not be aware of legislative requirements or safety standards applicable to their operations.

Table 94.3 • Summary of hazards in colleges and universities.

Type of hazard	Sources	Locations/activities
Toxic chemicals (carcinogens, teratogens, caustics, heavy metals, asbestos, silica)	Lab chemicals, solvents, degreasers, glues, art supplies, manometers, thermometers, photochemicals, dyes, hazardous waste	Laboratories, art studios, workshops, health care facilities, maintenance operations, machine shops, theatres, darkrooms, engineering, hockey arenas
Flammables and explosives	Lab chemicals, cleaning agents, solvents, fuels	Laboratories, maintenance operations, workshops, art studios, construction sites
Pesticides	Fumigation, rodent and pest control, disinfectants	Housekeeping, groundskeeping, greenhouse, agriculture
Biological agents	Animal handling, cell and tissue cultures, blood and body fluids, diagnostic specimens, contaminated sharps, solid waste	Animal care facilities, health care, housekeeping, laboratories
Non-ionizing radiation	Lasers, microwaves, magnets, electronics, ultraviolet light	Laboratories, electrical operations, health care facilities, workshops, technical operations
Ionizing radiation	Radioisotopes, gas chromatography, x rays, calibration, reactors, neutron generators, waste management	Laboratories, medical facilities, engineering
Ergonomics	Materials handling, office work, computers	Libraries, offices, maintenance operations, movers, truck drivers, food services
Heat/cold	Outdoor work, overexertion	Groundskeeping, public safety, maintenance, field work, agriculture and forestry
Noise	Machinery, boilers and pressure vessels, computers, construction and maintenance, ventilation systems	Boiler rooms, print shops, maintenance and grounds, construction operations, computer rooms, labs, machine shops, art studios
Violence	Internal community, external community, domestic disputes, civil disobedience	Classrooms, places of assembly, accounts, stores, food service, personnel department, security operations
Electrical	Electrical equipment, construction and maintenance operations, amateur wiring jobs, special events	Laboratories, workshops, maintenance shops, construction sites, electronic shops, residences, theatre, special events
Compressed gases	Laboratory equipment and operations, welding operations, coolants, ice-making equipment, construction	Laboratories, metal shops, construction sites, machine shops, hockey arenas
Machine hazards	Materials handling, robots, maintenance and construction work	Printing shops, maintenance and grounds operations, engineering, science and technical laboratories, machine shops
Sharp objects	Broken glass, cutting instruments, needles, lab vessels, test tubes	Housekeeping, laboratories, health care, art studios, workshops

For many projects, researchers and safety professionals need to work together to develop the safety procedures as the research proceeds and new hazards emerge.

Ideally the safety culture is incorporated into the academic mission—for example, through inclusion of relevant health and safety information into course curricula and laboratory and procedure manuals for students as well as specific health and safety information and training for employees. Hazard communication, training and supervision are critical.

In laboratories, art studios and workshops, general ventilation control needs to be augmented by local exhaust ventilation. Containment of biohazards and isolation or shielding of radioisotopes are necessary in certain cases. Personal protective equipment, while not a primary prevention method in most situation, may be the option of choice for temporary set-ups and some experimental conditions.

Hazardous materials and waste management programmes are usually required. Centralized purchasing and distribution of commonly used chemicals and micro-scale experiments in teaching prevent the storage of large volumes in individual laboratories, studios and workshops.

The maintenance of an emergency response and disaster recovery plan in anticipation of major events which overwhelm the normal response capabilities will mitigate the health and safety effects of a serious incident.

ART TEACHING

Ted Rickard

Health and safety problems in art programmes can be similar in educational institutions ranging from junior high schools to universities. Arts programmes are a special problem because their hazards are not often recognized and, especially at the college level, can be semi-industrial in scale. Hazards can include inhalation of airborne contaminants; ingestion or dermal absorption of toxins; injury from machinery and tools; slips, trips and falls; and repetitive strain and other musculoskeletal injuries. Precautions include the provision of adequate ventilation (both dilution and local exhaust), the safe handling and storage of chemicals, machine-guarding and competent maintenance of machinery, efficient clean-up, good housekeeping and adjustable work stations. A key precaution in avoiding occupational safety and health problems of all kinds is adequate and mandatory training.

Elementary and Secondary School Teachers

Hazards at the elementary and secondary school levels include practices such as spraying and unsafe use of solvents and other chemicals and poor ventilation of processes. There is frequently a lack of proper equipment and sufficient knowledge of materials to ensure a safe workplace. Precautions include efficient engineering controls, better knowledge of materials, the elimination of hazardous art supplies from schools and substitution with safer ones (see table 94.2). This will help protect not only teachers, technicians, maintenance workers and administrators, but also students.

College and University Teachers

Hazards at the college and university levels include, in addition to those mentioned above, the fact that students, teachers and technicians tend to be more experimental and tend to use more potentially dangerous materials and machinery. They also often work on a larger scale and for longer periods of time. Precautions must include education and training, the provision of engineering controls and personal protective equipment, written safety policies and procedures and insistence on compliance with these.

Artistic Freedom

Many art teachers and technicians are artists in their own right, resulting in multiple exposures to the hazards of art materials and processes which can significantly increase their health risks. When confronted with hazards in their field about which they have not known or which they have ignored, many teachers become defensive. Artists are experimental and frequently belong to an anti-establishment culture which encourages defiance of institutional rules. It is important, however, for the school administration to realize that the quest for artistic freedom is not a valid argument against working safely.

Liability and Training

In many jurisdictions teachers will be subject to both a personal and a school liability for the safety of their students, particularly the younger ones. "Because of the age, maturity, and experience limitations of most students, and because teachers stand *in loco parentis* (in the place of a parent), schools are expected to provide a safe environment and establish reasonable behaviour for the protection of students" (Qualley 1986).

Health and Safety Programmes

It is important that schools take the responsibility for training both art teachers and school administrators in the potential hazards of art materials and processes and in how to protect their students and themselves. A prudent school administration will ensure that there are in place written health and safety policies, procedures and programmes, compliance with these, regular safety training and a real interest in teaching how to create art safely.

● HEALTH PROBLEMS AND DISEASE PATTERNS

Steven D. Stellman and Joshua E. Muscat

Teachers comprise a large and growing segment of the workforce in many countries. For example, over 4.2 million workers were classified as preschool through high school teachers in the United States in 1992. In addition to classroom teachers, other professional and technical workers are employed by schools, including custodial and maintenance workers, nurses, food service workers and mechanics.

Teaching has not traditionally been regarded as an occupation that entails exposure to hazardous substances. Consequently, few studies of occupationally related health problems have been carried out. Nevertheless, school teachers and other school personnel may be exposed to a wide variety of recognized physical, chemical, biological and other occupational hazards.

Indoor air pollution is an important cause of acute illnesses in teachers. A major source of indoor air pollution is inadequate maintenance of heating, ventilation and air conditioning systems (HVAC). Contamination of HVAC systems can cause acute respiratory and dermatological illnesses. Newly constructed or renovated school buildings release chemicals, dusts and vapours into the air. Other sources of indoor air pollution are roofing, insulation, carpets, drapes and furniture, paint, caulk and other chemicals. Unrepaired water damage, as from roof leakage, can lead to the growth of micro-organisms in building materials and ventilation systems and the release of bioaerosols that affect the respiratory systems of teachers and students alike. Contamination of school buildings by micro-organisms can cause severe health conditions such as pneumonia, upper respiratory infections, asthma and allergic rhinitis.

Teachers who specialize in certain technical fields may be exposed to specific occupational hazards. For example, arts and craft teachers frequently encounter a variety of chemicals, including organic solvents, pigments and dyes, metals and metal compounds, minerals and plastics (Rossol 1990). Other art materials cause allergic reactions. Exposure to many of these materials is strictly regulated in the industrial workplace but not in the classroom. Chemistry and biology teachers work with toxic chemicals such as formaldehyde and other biohazards in school laboratories. Shop teachers work in dusty environments and may be exposed to high levels of wood dust and cleaning materials, as well as high noise levels.

Teaching is an occupation that is often characterized by a high degree of stress, absenteeism and burnout. There are many sources of teacher stress, which may vary with grade level. They include administrative and curriculum concerns, career advancement, student motivation, class size, role conflict and job security. Stress may also arise from dealing with children's misbehaviours and possibly violence and weapons in schools, in addition to physical or environmental hazards such as noise. For example, desirable classroom sound levels are 40 to 50 decibels (dB) (Silverstone 1981), whereas in one survey of several schools, classroom sound levels averaged between 59 and 65 dB (Orloske and Leddo 1981). Teachers who are employed in second jobs after work or during the summer may be exposed to additional workplace hazards that can affect performance and health. The fact that the majority of teachers are women (three-fourths of all teachers in the United States are women) raises the question of how the dual role of worker and mother may affect women's health. However, despite perceived high levels of stress, the rate of cardiovascular disease mortality in teachers was lower than in other occupations in several studies (Herloff and Jarvholm 1989), which could be due to lower prevalence of smoking and less consumption of alcohol.

There is a growing concern that some school environments may include cancer-causing materials such as asbestos, electromagnetic fields (EMF), lead, pesticides, radon and indoor air pollution (Regents Advisory Committee on Environmental Quality in Schools 1994). Asbestos exposure is a special concern among custodial and maintenance workers. A high prevalence of abnormalities associated with asbestos-related diseases has been documented in school custodians and maintenance employees (Anderson et al. 1992). The airborne concentration of asbestos has been reported higher in certain schools than in other buildings (Lee et al. 1992).

Some school buildings were built near high-voltage transmission power lines, which are sources of EMF. Exposure to EMF also comes from video display units or exposed wiring. Excess exposure to EMF has been linked to the incidence of leukaemia as well as breast and brain cancers in some studies (Savitz 1993). Another source of concern is exposure to pesticides that are applied to control the spread of insect and vermin populations in schools. It has been hypothesized that pesticide residues measured in adipose tissue and serum of breast cancer patients may be related to the development of this disease (Wolff et al. 1993).

The large proportion of teachers who are women has led to concerns about possible breast cancer risks. Unexplained increased breast cancer rates have been found in several studies. Using death certificates collected in 23 states in the United States between 1979 and 1987, the proportionate mortality ratios (PMRs) for breast cancer were 162 for White teachers and 214 for Black teachers (Rubin et al. 1993). Increased PMRs for breast cancer were also reported among teachers in New Jersey and in the Portland-Vancouver area (Rosenman 1994; Morton 1995). While these increases in observed rates have so far not been linked either to specific environmental factors or to other known risk factors for breast cancer, they have given rise to heightened breast cancer awareness among some teachers' organizations, resulting in screening and early detection campaigns.

Environmental and Public Health Issues

Susan Magor

Educational institutions are responsible for ensuring that their facilities and practices are in conformity with environmental and public health legislation and comply with accepted standards of care towards their employees, students and the surrounding community. Students are not generally covered under occupational health and safety legislation, but educational institutions must exercise diligence towards their students to at least the same degree as is required by legislation designed to protect workers. In addition, teaching institutions have a moral responsibility to educate their students on matters of personal, public, occupational and environmental safety which relate to them and to their activities.

Colleges and Universities

Large institutions such as college and university campuses may be compared to large towns or small cities in terms of the size of the population, geographic area, type of basic services required and complexity of activities being carried out. In addition to the occupational health and safety hazards found within such institutions (covered in the chapter *Public and government services*), there is a vast range of other concerns, relating to large populations living, working and studying in a defined area, that need to be addressed.

Waste management on campus is often a complex challenge. Environmental legislation in many jurisdictions requires stringent control of water and gas emissions from teaching, research and service activities. In certain situations external community concerns may require public relations attention.

Chemical and solid waste disposal programmes must take into consideration occupational, environmental and community health concerns. Most large institutions have comprehensive programmes for the management of the wide variety of wastes produced: toxic chemicals, radioisotopes, lead, asbestos, biomedical waste as well as trash, wet garbage and construction materials. One problem is the coordination of waste management programmes on campuses due to the large number of different departments, which often have poor communication with each other.

Colleges and universities differ from industry in the amounts and types of hazardous waste produced. Campus laboratories, for example, usually produce small amounts of many different hazardous chemicals. Methods of hazardous waste control can include neutralization of acids and alkalis, small-scale solvent recovery by distillation and "lab" packing, where small containers of compatible hazardous chemicals are placed in drums and separated by sawdust or other packing materials to prevent breakage. Since campuses can generate large quantities of paper, glass, metal and plastic waste, recycling programmes can usually be implemented as a demonstration of community responsibility and as part of the educational mission.

A few institutions located within urban areas may rely heavily upon external community resources for essential services such as police, fire protection and emergency response. The vast majority of medium-size and larger institutions establish their own public safety services to service their campus communities, often working in close cooperation with external resources. In many college towns, the institution is the largest employer and consequently may be expected to provide protection to the population which supports it.

Colleges and universities are no longer entirely remote or separate from the communities in which they are located. Education has become more accessible to a larger sector of society: women, mature students and the disabled. The very nature of educational institutions puts them at particular risk: a vulnerable population where the exchange of ideas and differing opinions is valued, but where the concept of academic freedom may not always be balanced with professional responsibility. In recent years educational institutions have reported more acts of violence toward educational community members, coming from the external community or erupting from within. Acts of violence perpetrated against individual members of the educational community are no longer extremely rare events. Campuses are frequent sites for demonstrations, large public assemblies, political and sports events where public safety and crowd control need to be considered. The adequacy of security and public safety services and emergency response and disaster recovery plans and capabilities needs to be constantly evaluated and periodically updated to meet community needs. Hazard identification and controls must be taken into consideration for sports programmes, field trips and a variety of sponsored recreational activities. Emergency medical service needs to be available even for off-campus activities. Personal safety is best managed through hazard reporting and education programmes.

Public health issues associated with campus life, such as control of communicable diseases, sanitation of food services and residence facilities, provision of fresh water, clean air and uncontaminated soil, must be addressed. Programmes for inspection, evaluation and control are required. Education of students in this regard is usually the responsibility of student service personnel, but occupational health and safety professionals are often involved. Education regarding sexually transmitted diseases, drug and alcohol abuse, blood-borne pathogens, stress and mental illness is particularly important in a campus community, where risky behaviour may increase the probability of exposure to associated hazards. Medical and psychological services must be available.

Elementary and Secondary Schools

Grade schools have many of the same environmental and public health issues as colleges and universities, only on a smaller scale. Often, however, schools and school districts do not have effective waste management programmes. A serious problem faced by many schools is the disposal of explosive ether and picric acid that have been stored in school laboratories for many years (National

Research Council 1993). Attempts to dispose of these materials by unqualified personnel have caused explosions in several instances. One problem is that school districts can have many schools separated by several miles. This can create difficulties in centralizing hazardous waste programmes by having to transport hazardous waste on public roads.

References

Abdo, R and H Chriske. 1990. HAV-Infektionsrisiken im Krankenhaus, Altenheim und Kindertagesstätten. In *Arbeitsmedizin im Gesundheitsdienst, Bd. V*, edited by F Hofmann and U Stößel. Stuttgart: Gentner Verlag.

Anderson, HA, LP Hanrahan, DN Higgins, and PG Sarow. 1992. A radiographic survey of public school building maintenance and custodial employees. *Environ Res* 59:159–66.

Clemens, R, F Hofmann, H Berthold, G Steinert et al. 1992. Prävalenz von Hepatitis A, B und C bei ewohern einer Einrichtung für geistig Behinderte. *Sozialpädiatrie* 14:357–364.

Herloff, B and B Jarvholm. 1989. Teachers, stress, and mortality. *Lancet* 1:159–160.

Lee, RJ, DR Van Orden, M Corn, and KS Crump. 1992. Exposure to airborne asbestos in buildings. *Regul Toxicol Pharmacol* 16: 93-107.

Morton, WE. 1995. Major differences in breast cancer risks among occupations. *J Occup Med* 37:328–335.

National Research Council. 1993. *Prudent Practices in the Laboratory: Handling and Disposal of Chemicals*. Washington, DC: National Academy Press.

Orloske, AJ and JS Leddo. 1981. Environmental effects on children's hearing: How can school systems cope. *J Sch Health* 51:12–14.

Polis, M et al. 1986. Transmission of Giardia lamblia from a day care center to a community. *Am J Public Hlth* 76:1,142–1,144.

Qualley, CA. 1986. *Safety in the Artroom*. Worcester, MA: Davis Publications.

Regents Advisory Committee on Environmental Quality in Schools. 1994. Report to the New York State Board of Regents on the Environmental Quality of Schools. Albany: University of the State of New York, State Education Department.

Rosenman, KD. 1994. Causes of mortality in primary and secondary school teachers. *Am J Indust Med* 25:749–58.

Rossol, M. 1990. *The Artist's Complete Health and Safety Guide*. New York: Allworth Press.

Rubin, CH, CA Burnett, WE Halperin, and PJ Seligman. 1993. Occupation as a risk identifier for breast cancer. *Am J Public Health* 83:1,311–1,315.

Savitz, DA. 1993. Overview of epidemiologic research on electric and magnetic fields and cancer. *Am Ind Hyg Assoc J* 54:197–204.

Silverstone, D. 1981. Considerations for listening and noise distractions. In *Designing Learning Environments*, edited by PJ Sleeman and DM Rockwell. New York: Longman, Inc.

Wolff, MS, PG Toniolo, EW Lee, M Rivera, and N Dubin. 1993. Blood levels of organochlorine residues and risk of breast cancer. *J Natl Cancer Inst* 85:648–652.

Women's Occupational Health Resource Center. 1987. *Women's Occupational Health Resource Center News* 8(2): 3-4.

Other relevant readings

Council of State Science Supervisors. 1984. *School Science Laboratories: A Guide to Some Hazardous Substances*. Washington, DC: US Consumer Product Safety Commission.

McCann, M. 1992. *Art Safety Procedures: A Health and Safety Manual for Art Schools and Art Departments*. New York: Center for Safety in the Arts.

National Institute for Occupational Safety and Health (NIOSH). 1979. *Occupational Safety and Health in Vocational Education*. Cincinnati, OH: NIOSH.

New York State United Teachers (NYSUT). 1992. *Health and Safety Manual for School Employees*. Albany: NYSUT.

94. EDUCATION AND TRAINING SERVICES

EMERGENCY AND SECURITY SERVICES

95

Chapter Editor
Tee L. Guidotti

Contents

EMERGENCY AND SECURITY SERVICES

Tee L. Guidotti

Emergency and security services exist to deal with extraordinary and threatening situations. The people who work in such services are therefore confronted with events and circumstances that lie outside the usual experience of human beings in their daily lives. Although each of the occupations has its own set of hazards, risks and traditions, they share several features in common. These include the following:

- long periods of relative quiet or routine interrupted abruptly by periods of intense psychological stress
- long periods of relative inactivity interrupted abruptly by periods of intense physical activity
- rigid codes of behaviour and high expectations for performance, often accompanied by detailed orders for how to do the job and high penalties for failure
- personal danger; the worker allows himself or herself to be exposed to hazards that are unusual for anyone else in the community
- a primary objective of rescuing or protecting others who are not able to save themselves
- a secondary objective of protecting property from destruction or damage
- teamwork under demanding conditions
- a rigid hierarchy or "chain of command" to reduce uncertainty and to make sure that procedures are followed correctly.

The form of organization and the means by which the mission of these services is carried out varies. The circumstances of the mission of a service affect the attitude and approach to the job; these differences are perhaps best understood by considering the object of control for each emergency service.

Firefighting is perhaps the most representative emergency and security service. This occupation arose historically as a way to limit property damage from fires, and started as a private service in which fire-fighters might save the businesses and houses of persons who paid insurance premiums but would let the property of others burn, even if they were right next door. Soon, society determined that private fire services were inefficient and that it would be much more practical and useful to make them public. Thus, firefighting became a municipal or local government function in most parts of the world. Private firefighting services still exist in industry, at airports and in other settings where they are coordinated with municipal services. In general, fire-fighters enjoy a great deal of trust and respect in their communities. In firefighting, the object of control, or the "enemy", is the fire; it is an external threat. When a fire-fighter is injured on the job, it is perceived as the result of an external agent, although it might be an indirect assault if the fire were set by an arsonist.

Police services and the military are given the responsibility by society to maintain order, generally in response to an internal threat (such as crime) or to an external threat (such as war). Armed force is the essential means of accomplishing the mission, and the use of appropriate tactics and investigative techniques (whether criminal investigation or military intelligence) is standard procedure. Because of the high potential for abuse and misuse of force, society in general has imposed strict limitations on how force is used, especially toward civilians. Police especially are watched more closely than other emergency and security personnel to ensure that they use their monopoly on force correctly. This sometimes leads to the perception by police officers that they are not trusted. For the police and for soldiers, the object of control, or the "enemy", is another human being. This creates many situations of

uncertainty, feelings of guilt and questions about rights and proper behaviour that fire-fighters do not have to face. When police or soldiers are injured in the line of duty, it is usually the direct result of intentional human action taken against them.

Paramedical and rescue personnel are responsible for recovering, stabilizing and rendering initial treatment to people who are injured, ill or trapped in circumstances from which they cannot escape by themselves. Often they work side by side with fire-fighters and police. For them, the object of control is the patient or victim whom they are trying to help; the victim is not an "enemy". Moral and ethical issues in these occupations are most prominent when the victim is partially responsible for his or her condition, as when a driver is intoxicated by alcohol or a patient refuses to take medication. Sometimes, victims who are not rational or who are angry or under stress may act in an abusive or threatening way. This is confusing and frustrating for paramedical and rescue personnel, who feel that they are doing their best under difficult circumstances. When one of these workers is injured on the job, it is perceived as almost a betrayal, because they were trying to help the victim.

Hazardous materials response teams are often part of fire services and have a similar organization on a small scale. They evaluate and take initial steps to control chemical or physical hazards that may present a threat to the public. Hazardous waste remediation workers are less tightly organized that these other occupations and exist to clean up a problem that has been around for a while. In both cases, the workers are dealing with a potential hazard in which the fundamental problem is uncertainty. Unlike the other occupations, in which it was clear who or what was the object of control, these workers are controlling a risk that may be difficult to identify. Even when the chemical or hazard is known, the future risk of cancer or disease is usually uncertain. Workers often cannot know whether they have been injured on the job because the effects of exposure to chemicals may not be known for many years.

Potential Occupational Hazards

The common hazard to all of these workers is psychogenic stress. In particular, they are all subject to so-called critical events, which are situations perceived to be of grave or uncertain but probably serious danger that a person cannot escape. Unlike a member of the general public, a worker in one of these occupations cannot simply walk away or leave the scene. Much of their own sense of self-esteem comes from how they handle just such situations. For workers who survive critical events, there is often a period of denial followed by a period of depression and distracted behaviour. Thoughts of what the worker has seen and a sense of guilt or inadequacy intrude on his or her thinking. It is difficult to concentrate, and the worker may have nightmares. The worst critical events are generally considered to be those in which victims have died because of a mistake or because it was not possible for the rescuer to save them, in spite of his or her best efforts.

Many of these occupations also involve the rescue and stabilization of people who may be ill with communicable diseases. The infections that most commonly present a problem are AIDS and HIV infection generally, hepatitis B and C and tuberculosis. HIV and hepatitis B and C viruses are both transmitted by human body fluids and may therefore pose a hazard to emergency response personnel when there is bleeding or if the worker is deliberately bitten. Emergency response personnel are now usually trained to consider all subjects (victims or criminals) as potentially infected and infective. HIV precautions are described elsewhere. Tuberculosis is transmitted by sputum and by coughing. The risk is particularly great during the resuscitation of persons with active cavitary tuberculosis, an increasingly frequent problem in economically disadvantaged inner city areas.

Injury is a risk common to all of these occupations. Fires are always unsafe, and the hazards of the fire itself may be combined with the risk of structures breaking apart, unstable floors, falling objects and falls from a height. Violence is a more common hazard of police and military combat services, obviously, because that is what they were created to control. However, aside from intentional violence there is a potential for hazards from traumatic incidents involving automotive traffic, mishandling of weapons and, especially in the military, occupational injuries in support areas. Hazardous materials workers may deal with a variety of unknown chemicals which may have a hazard of explosion or fire in addition to their toxic properties.

These occupations vary greatly in their potential for health problems. Aside from stress-related outcomes and the potential for communicable diseases mentioned, each occupation is different in its health concerns.

Preventive Guidelines

Each occupation differs in its approach to prevention. However, there are a few measures that are common to all or most of them.

Many services now require their workers to go through a process called critical event debriefing following such incidents. During these debriefings, the workers discuss the event in the presence of a trained mental health worker—how they feel about it, and their feelings about their own actions. Critical event debriefing has been shown to be very effective in preventing later problems, such as post-traumatic stress syndrome, following critical events.

Rigorous fitness screening at the time of hire is usually part of the selection process for police and fire personnel, and many services require these members to stay fit through regular exercise and training. This is intended to ensure satisfactory and consistent performance, but it has the additional effect of reducing the likelihood of injuries.

Infectious hazards are difficult to anticipate because victims may not show outward signs of infection. Emergency response personnel are now taught to use "universal precautions" in handling body fluids and to use protective equipment such as gloves and safety eyeglasses if there is a risk of coming into contact with body fluids. Often, however, such events are unpredictable or difficult to control if the victim is violent or irrational. Routine immunization with hepatitis B vaccine is advised where the risk is high. Disposable resuscitation equipment is recommended to reduce the risk of transmitting communicable diseases. Special care should be taken with needles and other sharp objects. Human bites should be cleaned thoroughly and treatment given with penicillin or a penicillin-like drug. When HIV infection has been confirmed in the person who was the source, or contamination and transmission may have taken place by needlestick or invasive contact with blood or body fluids, a physician's advice should be sought about the advisability of prescribing antiviral drugs that reduce the chance of infection in the worker. Tuberculosis infection in an exposed worker can be confirmed by skin test and then treated prophylactically before it becomes a serious disease.

Other preventive measures are specific to the particular occupations.

FIREFIGHTING PROCEDURES

Alan D. Jones

Firefighting is one of the world's most honoured but hazardous operations. By becoming fire-fighters, people join an organization rich in heritage of dedication, unselfish sacrifice and inspired

human action. The job of a fire-fighter is not comfortable or easy. It is one that requires a high sense of personal dedication, a genuine desire to help people and a devotion to a profession that requires a high level of skill. It is also a profession that exposes an individual to a high level of personal danger.

Whenever there is a disaster, the fire department is one of the first called to the scene. Because it is a disaster, the conditions will not always be favourable. There will be hard, fast work that will drain energy and test endurance. The situation will not always involve fire. There will be cave-ins, building collapses, auto accidents, aircraft crashes, tornadoes, dangerous-goods incidents, civil disturbances, rescue operations, explosions, water incidents and medical emergencies. The emergency list is unlimited.

All fire-fighters use the same tactics and strategies to combat a fire. The strategies are simple—fight this fire offensively or defensively. Regardless, the goal is the same—extinguishment of the fire. Urban firefighting deals with structural firefighting. (The management of forest fires is dealt with in the chapter *Forestry*.) It includes dealing with hazardous goods, water and ice, as well as high-angle rescue and emergency medicine. Fire service personnel must respond day and night to emergencies.

The tactical priorities that fire-fighters engage in during the course of the fire are shown in figure 95.1. It is during these operations that hose lays using attack lines, back up lines and supply lines can be employed. Other commonly used equipment are ladders and pushing/pulling and striking tools like axes and pike poles. Specialty equipment includes tarps that are used for salvage or hydraulic tools used for a rescue. The fire-fighter must use and be familiar with all of them. See figure 95.1.

Figure 95.2 shows a fire-fighter with appropriate personal protection laying water on a structural fire with a fire hose.

These operations expose the fire-fighter to the greatest risks and injuries regardless of the tool used or the operation engaged in. Back injuries, sprains, fall-related injuries and heat stress commonly occur. Heart and lung diseases are quite common among fire-fighters, which is thought to be due, in part, to the toxic gases and the level of physical activity required on the fire ground. Therefore, many departments are aggressively pursuing the addition of fitness programmes within their departments' overall safety programme. Many jurisdictions have programmes in place to deal with critical incident stress, because the fire-fighter faces incidents that can create severe emotional reactions. Such reactions are normal reactions in the face of very abnormal situations.

The mission of every fire department is the preservation of life and property; therefore, safety on the fire ground is of paramount importance. Many of the operations discussed here have an underlying goal of providing greater safety on the fire ground. Many of the dangers that exist on the fire ground are due to the nature of fire. Backdraft and flashover kill fire-fighters. *Backdraft* is caused by the introduction of air into a superheated oxygen-starved area. *Flashover* is the build-up of heat within an area until it suddenly ignites everything within that area. These two conditions reduce the level of safety and increase property damage. Ventilation is one method of control that fire-fighters use. Increasing ventilation can lead to much damage to property. The fire-fighter is often observed breaking windows or cutting holes in the roof and intensity of the fire appears to grow. This is because smoke and toxic gases are released from the fire area. But this is a necessary part of firefighting. Special attention must be paid to roof collapse, to establishing a quick means of egress and to back-up hose lines for protection of the personnel and property.

The fire-fighter must put safety first and must work with a safety-conscious attitude and within organizational environments that promote safety. In addition, proper protective clothing must be provided and maintained. Clothing should be designed for freedom of movement and protection from heat. The structural

Figure 95.1 • The tactical priorities of structural firefighting operations.

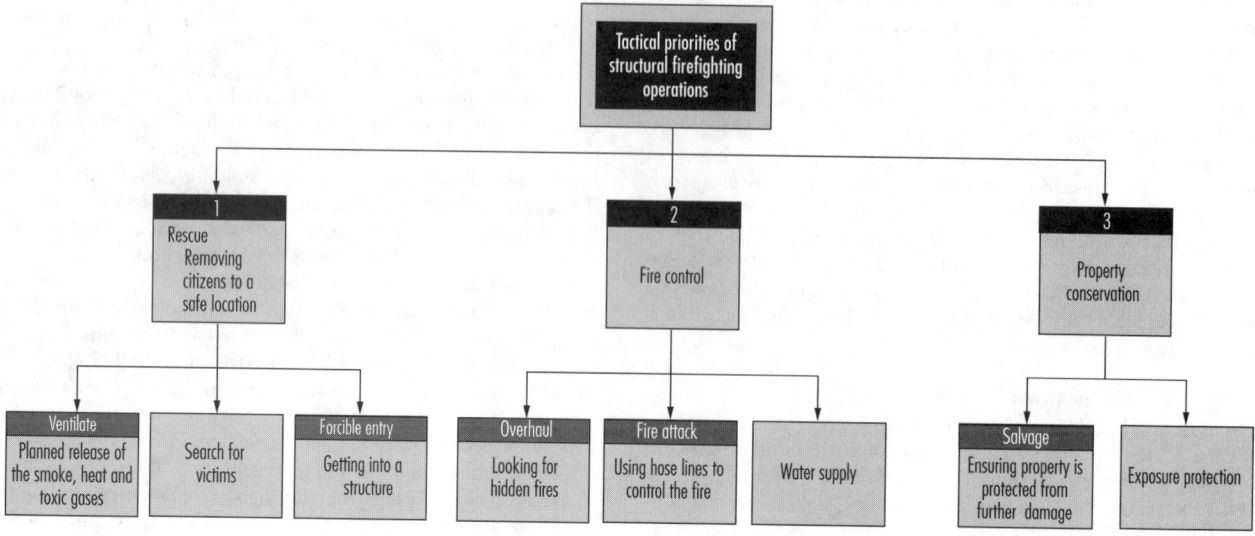

fire-fighter must be outfitted with heavy fire-resistant fibre suits and a self-contained breathing apparatus.

The type of clothing worn is generally specific to the types of hazards faced by the fire-fighter outside the fire area on the fire line; the urban fire-fighter is generally inside a structure where intense heat and toxic gases are present. Helmets, boots and gloves designed specifically for the hazard that is faced by the fire-fighter provide head, foot and hand protection. Fire crews need training to ensure that fire-fighters have the knowledge and skills necessary to perform safely and efficiently. Training is usually provided through an in-house training programme, which can consist of a combination of on-the-job training and a formalized theory programme. Most provincial and state governments have agencies that promote various types of training programmes.

North America leads the world in property loss and many North American departments engage in preventive programmes to reduce the life and property losses within their jurisdictions. Public education and enforcement programmes are aggressively pursued by the most pro-active departments because, according to available statistics, the cost of prevention is cheaper than the cost of rebuilding. Furthermore, only 10% of businesses that suffer a total fire loss successfully rebuild. Thus the costs of a fire loss to a community can be staggering, since in addition to the cost to rebuild, sources of tax revenue, jobs and lives may also be lost forever. It is important, therefore, that both the community and the fire service work together to ensure that lives and property are preserved.

Figure 95.2 • Firefighter laying water on a structural fire.

FIREFIGHTING HAZARDS

*Tee L. Guidotti**

Fire-brigade personnel may be engaged on a full-time, part-time, paid-on-call or unpaid, volunteer basis—or on a combination of these systems. The type of organization employed will, in most cases, depend on the size of the community, the value of the property to be protected, the types of fire risk and the number of

* We thank the Edmonton Fire-fighters' Union for their interest and generous support of the development of this chapter. The *Edmonton Sun* and the *Edmonton Journal* graciously allowed their news photographs to be used in the articles on firefighting. Ms. Beverly Cann of the Manitoba Federation of Labour Occupational Health Centre contributed invaluable advice on the article on paramedical personnel and ambulance attendants.

calls typically answered. Cities of any appreciable size require regular fire brigades with full crews on duty equipped with the appropriate apparatus.

Smaller communities, residential districts and rural areas having few fire calls usually depend upon volunteer or paid-on-call fire-fighters for either full staffing of their firefighting apparatus or to assist a skeleton force of full-time regulars.

Although there are a great many efficient, well equipped volunteer fire departments, full-time, paid fire departments are essential in larger communities. A call or volunteer organization does not lend itself as readily to the continuous fire-prevention inspection work that is an essential activity of modern fire departments. Using volunteer and call systems, frequent alarms may call out workers who hold other jobs, causing a loss of time with seldom any direct benefit to employers. Where full-time fire-fighters are not employed, the volunteers must come to a central fire hall before response can be made to a call, causing a delay. Where there are only a few regulars, a supplementary group of well-trained call or volunteer fire-fighters should be provided. There should be a reserve arrangement that make assistance available for the response of neighbouring departments on a mutual-aid basis.

Firefighting is a highly unusual occupation, in that it is perceived of as dirty and dangerous but is indispensable and even prestigious. Fire-fighters enjoy public admiration for the essential work that they do. They are well aware of the hazards. Their work involves intermittent periods of exposure to extreme physical and psychological stress on the job. Fire-fighters are also exposed to serious chemical and physical hazards, to a degree unusual in the modern workforce.

Hazards

Occupational hazards experienced by fire-fighters may be categorized as physical (mostly unsafe conditions, thermal stress and ergonomic stress), chemical and psychological. The level of exposure to hazards that may be experienced by a fire-fighter in a given fire depends on what is burning, the combustion characteristics of the fire, the structure that is on fire, the presence of non-fuel chemicals, the measures taken to control the fire, the presence of victims that require rescue and the position or line of duty held by the fire-fighter while fighting the fire. The hazards and levels of exposure experienced by the first fire-fighter to enter a burning building are also different from those of the fire-fighters who enter later or who clean up after the flames are extinguished. There is usually rotation among the active firefighting jobs in each team or platoon, and a regular transfer of personnel between fire halls. Fire-fighters may also have special rank and duties. Captains accompany and direct the crews but are still actively involved in fighting the fire on site. Fire chiefs are the heads of the fire service and are called out only in the worst fires. Individual fire-fighters may still experience unusual exposures in particular incidents, of course.

Physical hazards

There are many physical dangers in firefighting that can lead to serious physical injury. Walls, ceilings and floors can collapse abruptly, trapping fire-fighters. *Flashovers* are explosive eruptions of flame in a confined space that occur as a result of the sudden ignition of flammable gas products driven out of burning or hot materials and combined with superheated air. Fire situations that lead to flashovers may engulf the fire-fighter or cut off escape routes. The extent and number of injuries can be minimized by intensive training, job experience, competency and good physical fitness. However, the nature of the job is such that fire-fighters may be placed in dangerous situations by miscalculation, circumstance or during rescues.

Some fire departments have compiled computerized databases on structures, materials and potential hazards likely to be encountered in the district. Quick access to these databases assists the crew in responding to known hazards and anticipating possibly dangerous situations.

Thermal hazards

Heat stress during firefighting may come from hot air, radiant heat, contact with hot surfaces or endogenous heat that is produced by the body during exercise but which cannot be cooled during the fire. Heat stress is compounded in firefighting by the insulating properties of the protective clothing and by physical exertion, which result in heat production within the body. Heat may result in local injury in the form of burns or generalized heat stress, with the risk of dehydration, heat stroke and cardiovascular collapse.

Hot air by itself is not usually a great hazard to the fire-fighter. Dry air does not have much capacity to retain heat. Steam or hot, wet air can cause serious burns because much more heat energy can be stored in water vapour than in dry air. Fortunately, steam burns are not common.

Radiant heat is often intense in a fire situation. Burns may occur from radiant heat alone. Fire-fighters may also show skin changes characteristic of prolonged exposure to heat.

Chemical hazards

Over 50% of fire-related fatalities are the result of exposure to smoke rather than burns. One of the major contributing factors to mortality and morbidity in fires is hypoxia because of oxygen depletion in the affected atmosphere, leading to loss of physical performance, confusion and inability to escape. The constituents

Figure 95.3 • Fire-fighter rescuing another fire-fighter who was trapped in the toxic smoke from a fire in a tire warehouse.

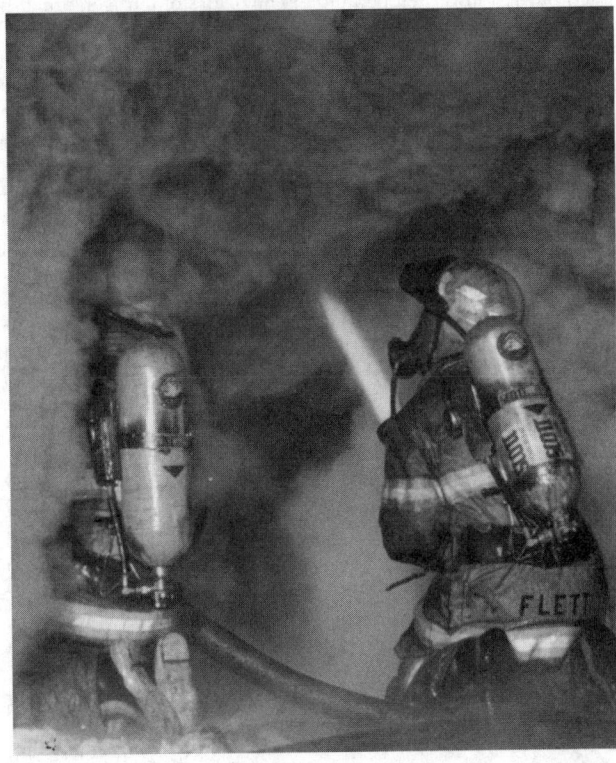

of smoke, singly and in combination, are also toxic. Figure 95.3 shows a fire-fighter using self-contained breathing apparatus (SCBA) rescuing an unprotected fire-fighter who was trapped in a very smoky fire in a tire warehouse. (The fire-fighter being rescued ran out of air, took off his SCBA to breathe as best he could, and was fortunate enough to be rescued before it was too late.)

All smoke, including that from simple wood fires, is hazardous and potentially lethal with concentrated inhalation. Smoke is a variable combination of compounds. The toxicity of smoke depends primarily on the fuel, the heat of the fire and whether or how much oxygen is available for combustion. Fire-fighters on the scene of a fire are frequently exposed to carbon monoxide, hydrogen cyanide, nitrogen dioxide, sulphur dioxide, hydrogen chloride, aldehydes and organic compounds such as benzene. Different gas combinations present different degrees of hazard. Only carbon monoxide and hydrogen cyanide are commonly produced in lethal concentrations in building fires.

Carbon monoxide is the most common, characteristic and serious acute hazard of firefighting. Carboxyhaemoglobin accumulates rapidly in the blood with duration of exposure, as a result of the affinity of carbon monoxide for haemoglobin. High levels of carboxyhaemoglobin may result, particularly when heavy exertion increases minute ventilation and therefore delivery to the lung during unprotected firefighting. There is no apparent correlation between the intensity of smoke and the amount of carbon monoxide in the air. Fire-fighters should particularly avoid cigarette smoking during the clean-up phase, when burning material is smouldering and therefore burning incompletely, as this adds to the already elevated levels of carbon monoxide in the blood. Hydrogen cyanide is formed from the lower temperature combustion of nitrogen-rich materials, including natural fibres such as wool and silk, as well as common synthetics such as polyurethane and polyacrylonitrile.

Light-molecular-weight hydrocarbons, aldehydes (such as formaldehyde) and organic acids may be formed when hydrocarbon fuels burn at lower temperatures. The oxides of nitrogen are also formed in quantity when temperatures are high, as a consequence of the oxidation of atmospheric nitrogen, and in lower temperature fires where the fuel contains significant nitrogen. When the fuel contains chlorine, hydrogen chloride is formed. Polymeric plastic materials pose particular hazards. These synthetic materials were introduced into building construction and furnishings in the 1950s and thereafter. They combust into particularly hazardous products. Acrolein, formaldehyde and volatile fatty acids are common in smouldering fires of several polymers, including polyethylene and natural cellulose. Cyanide levels increase with temperature when polyurethane or polyacrylonitriles are burned; acrylonitrile, acetonitrile pyridine and benzonitrile occur in quantity above 800 but below 1,000 °C. Polyvinyl chloride has been proposed as a desirable polymer for furnishings because of its self-extinguishing characteristics due to the high chlorine content. Unfortunately, the material produces large quantities of hydrochloric acid and, sometimes, dioxins when fires are prolonged.

Synthetic materials are most dangerous during smouldering conditions, not in conditions of high heat. Concrete retains heat very efficiently and may act as a "sponge" for trapped gases that are then released from the porous material, releasing hydrogen chloride or other toxic fumes long after a fire has been extinguished.

Psychological hazards

A fire-fighter enters a situation that others are fleeing, walking into immediate personal danger greater than in almost any other civilian occupation. There is much that can go wrong in any fire, and the course of a serious fire is often unpredictable. Besides personal security, the fire-fighter must be concerned with the safety of others threatened by the fire. Rescuing victims is an especially stressful activity.

The professional life of a fire-fighter is more than an endless round of anxious waiting punctuated by stressful crises, however. Fire-fighters enjoy the many positive aspects of their work. Few occupations are so respected by the community. Job security is largely assured in urban fire departments once a fire-fighter is hired, and the pay usually compares well with other jobs. Fire-fighters also enjoy a strong sense of team membership and group bonding. These positive aspects of the job offset the stressful aspects and tend to protect the fire-fighter against the emotional consequences of repeated stress.

At the sound of an alarm, a fire-fighter experiences a degree of immediate anxiety because of the inherent unpredictability of the situation he or she is about to encounter. The psychological stress experienced at this moment is as great and perhaps greater than any of the stresses that follow during the course of responding to an alarm. Physiological and biochemical indicators of stress have shown that fire-fighters on duty have sustained psychological stress that reflects subjectively perceived patterns of psychological stress and activity levels at the station.

Health Risks

The acute hazards of firefighting include trauma, thermal injury and smoke inhalation. The chronic health effects that follow recurrent exposure have not been so clear until recently. This uncertainty has led to a patchwork of employment and workers' compensation board policies. The occupational risks of fire-fighters have received a great deal of attention because of their known exposure to toxic agents. A large body of literature has developed on the mortality experience of fire-fighters. This literature has grown with the addition of several substantial studies in recent years, and a sufficient database is now available to describe certain patterns in the literature.

The critical compensation issue is whether a general presumption of risk can be made for all fire-fighters. This means that one must decide whether all fire-fighters can be assumed to have an elevated risk of a particular disease or injury because of their occupation. To satisfy the usual compensation standard of proof that the occupational cause must be more likely than not responsible for the outcome (giving the benefit of the doubt to the claimant), a general presumption of risk requires a demonstration that the risk associated with occupation must be at least as great as the risk in the general population. This can be demonstrated if the usual measure of risk in epidemiological studies is at least double the expected risk, making allowances for uncertainty in the estimate. Arguments against presumption in the specific, individual case under consideration are called "rebuttal criteria", because they can be used to question, or rebut, the application of the presumption in an individual case.

There are a number of unusual epidemiological characteristics that influence the interpretation of studies of fire-fighters and their occupational mortality and morbidity. Fire-fighters do not show a strong "healthy worker effect" in most cohort mortality studies. This may suggest an excess mortality from some causes compared to the rest of the healthy, fit workforce. There are two types of healthy worker effect that may conceal excess mortality. One healthy worker effect operates at the time of hire, when new workers are screened for firefighting duty. Because of the strenuous fitness requirements for duty, this effect is very strong and might be expected to have an effect of reducing mortality from cardiovascular disease, especially in the early years following hire, when few deaths would be expected anyway. The second healthy worker effect occurs when workers become unfit following employment due to obvious or subclinical illness and are reassigned to other duties or are lost to follow-up. Their relative high contribution to total risk is lost by undercount. The magnitude of this effect is not known but there is a strong evidence that this effect occurs among fire-fighters. This effect would not be apparent for cancer because, unlike cardiovascular disease, the risk of cancer has little to do with fitness at the time of hire.

Lung Cancer

Lung cancer has been the most difficult cancer site to evaluate in epidemiological studies of fire-fighters. A major issue is whether the large-scale introduction of synthetic polymers into building materials and furnishings after about 1950 increased the risk of cancer among fire-fighters because of exposure to the combustion products. Despite the obvious exposure to carcinogens inhaled in smoke, it has been difficult to document an excess in mortality from lung cancer big enough and consistent enough to be compatible with occupational exposure.

There is evidence that work as a fire-fighter contributes to risk of lung cancer. This is seen mostly among fire-fighters who had the highest exposure and who worked the longest time. The added risk may be superimposed on a greater risk from smoking.

Evidence for an association between firefighting and lung cancer suggests that the association is weak and does not attain the attributable risk required to conclude that a given association is "more likely than not" due to occupation. Certain cases with unusual characteristics may warrant this conclusion, such as cancer in a relatively young non-smoking fire-fighter.

Cancer at Other Sites

Other cancer sites have been shown recently to be more consistently associated with firefighting than lung cancer.

The evidence is strong for an association with genito-urinary cancers, including kidney, ureter and bladder. Except for bladder, these are rather uncommon cancers, and the risk among fire-fighters appears to be high, close to or in excess of a doubled relative risk. One could therefore consider any such cancer to be work-related in a fire-fighter unless there is a convincing reason to suspect otherwise. Among the reasons one might doubt (or rebut) the conclusion in an individual case would be heavy cigarette smoking, prior exposure to occupational carcinogens, schistosomiasis (a parasitic infection—this applies to bladder only), analgesic abuse, cancer chemotherapy and urologic conditions that result in stasis and prolonged residence time of urine in the urinary tract. These are all logical rebuttal criteria.

Cancer of the brain and central nervous system has shown highly variable findings in the extant literature, but this is not surprising since the numbers of cases in all reports are relatively small. It is unlikely that this association will be clarified any time soon. It is therefore reasonable to accept a presumption of risk for fire-fighters on the basis of current evidence.

The increased relative risks for lymphatic and haematopoietic cancers appear to be unusually high. However, the small numbers of these relatively rare cancers make it difficult to evaluate the significance of the association in these studies. Because they are individually rare, epidemiologists group them together in order to make statistical generalizations. The interpretation is even more difficult because grouping these very different cancers together makes little sense medically.

Heart Disease

There is no conclusive evidence for an increased risk of death overall from heart disease. Although a single large study has shown an excess of 11%, and a smaller study confined to ischemic heart disease suggested a significant excess of 52%, most studies cannot conclude that there is a consistently increased population risk. Even if the higher estimates are correct, the relative risk estimates still fall far short of what would be required to make a presumption of risk in the individual case.

There is some evidence, primarily from clinical studies, to suggest a risk of sudden cardiac decompensation and risk of a heart attack with sudden maximal exertion and following exposure to carbon monoxide. This does not seem to translate into an excess risk of fatal heart attacks later in life, but if a fire-fighter did have a heart attack during or within a day after a fire it would be reasonable to call it work-related. Each case must therefore be interpreted with a knowledge of individual characteristics, but the evidence does not suggest a generally elevated risk for all fire-fighters.

Aortic Aneurysm

Few studies have accumulated sufficient deaths among fire-fighters from this cause to achieve statistical significance. Although one study conducted in Toronto in 1993 suggests an association with work as a fire-fighter, it should be considered an unproven hypothesis at present. Should it be ultimately confirmed, the magnitude of risk suggests that it would merit acceptance on a schedule of occupational diseases. Rebuttal criteria would logically include severe atherosclerosis, connective tissue disease and associated vasculitis and a history of thoracic trauma.

Lung Disease

Unusual exposures, such as intense exposure to the fumes of burning plastics, can certainly cause severe lung toxicity and even permanent disability. Ordinary firefighting may be associated with short-term changes similar to asthma, resolving over days. This does not appear to result in an increased lifetime risk of dying from chronic lung disease unless there has been an unusually intense exposure (the risk of dying from the consequences of smoke inhalation) or smoke with unusual characteristics (particularly involving burning polyvinyl chloride (PVC)).

Chronic obstructive pulmonary disease has been extensively studied among fire-fighters. The evidence does not support an association with firefighting, and therefore there can be no presumption. An exception may be in rare cases when a chronic lung disease follows an unusual or severe acute exposure and there is a compatible history of medical complications.

A general presumption of risk is not easily or defensibly justified in situations of weak associations or when diseases are common in the general population. A more productive approach may be to take the claims on a case-by-case basis, examining individual risk factors and overall risk profile. A general presumption of risk is more easily applied to unusual disorders with high relative risks, particularly when they are unique to or characteristic of certain occupations. Table 95.1 presents a summary of specific recommendations, with criteria that could be used to rebut, or question, presumption in the individual case.

Injuries

Injuries associated with firefighting are predictable: burns, falls and being struck by falling objects. Mortality from these causes is markedly increased among fire-fighters compared to other workers. Jobs in firefighting have a high risk of burns, especially, include those involving early entry and close-in firefighting, such as holding the nozzle. Burns are also more commonly associated with basement fires, recent injury before the incident and training outside the fire department of present employment. Falls tend to be associated with SCBA use and assignment to truck companies.

Table 95.1 • Summary of recommendations, with rebuttal criteria and special considerations, for compensation decisions.

	Risk estimate (approximate)	Recommendations	Rebuttal criteria
Lung cancer	150	A NP	− Smoking, previous occupational carcinogens
Cardiovascular disease	<150	NA NP	+ Acute event at or soon following exposure
Aortic aneurysm	200	A P	− Atherosclerosis (advanced), connective tissue disorders, history of thoracic trauma
Cancers of genitourinary tract	>200	A P	+ Occupational carcinogens − Heavy cigarette smoking, previous occupational carcinogens, schistosomiasis (bladder only), analgesic abuse, cancer chemotherapy (chlornaphazine), conditions resulting in urinary stasis / Coffee consumption, artificial sweeteners
Brain cancer	200	A P	− Heritable neoplasms (rare), previous vinyl chloride exposure, radiation to head / Trauma, family history, smoking
Cancers of lymphatic and haematopoietic system	200	A P	− Ionizing radiation, previous occupational carcinogens (benzene), immunosuppressed state, cancer chemotherapy + Hodgkin's disease
Cancer of colon and rectum	A NP NA NP	A NP	+ Low risk profile − Familial syndromes, ulcerative colitis / Other occupational exposures
Acute lung disease	NE NE	A P	Circumstances of case
Chronic lung disease (COPD)	NE NE	NA NP	+ Sequela of severe acute exposure, followed by recovery − Smoking, protease deficiency

Key:

A = epidemiological association but not sufficient for presumption of association with firefighting.
P = presumption of association with firefighting; risk exceeds doubling over general population.
+ = suggests increased risk due to firefighting.
− = suggests increased risk due to exposures unrelated to firefighting.
/ = no likely contribution to risk.

NA = no consistent epidemiological evidence for association.   NE = Not established.
NP = no presumption; risk does not exceed doubling over general population.

Ergonomics

Firefighting is a very strenuous occupation and is often performed under extreme environmental conditions. The demands of firefighting are sporadic and unpredictable, characterized by long periods of waiting between bouts of intense activity.

Fire-fighters maintain their level of exertion at a relatively constant, intense level once active firefighting begins. Any additional burden in the form of an encumbrance by protective equipment or victim rescue, however necessary for protection, reduces performance because fire-fighters are already exerting themselves to the maximum. The use of personal protection equipment has imposed new physiological demands on fire-fighters but has removed others by reducing exposure levels.

A great deal is known about the exertion characteristics of fire-fighters as a result of many careful studies on the ergonomics of firefighting. Fire-fighters adjust their levels of exertion in a characteristic pattern during simulated fire conditions, as reflected by heart rate. Initially, their heart rate increases rapidly to 70 to 80% of maximal within the first minute. As firefighting progresses, they maintain their heart rates at 85 to 100% maximal.

The energy requirements for firefighting are complicated by the severe conditions encountered in many inside fires. The metabolic demands of coping with retained body heat, heat from the fire and fluid loss through sweating add to the demands of physical exertion.

The most demanding activity known is building search and victim rescue by the "lead hand" (first fire-fighter to enter building), resulting in the highest average heart rate of 153 beats/minute and highest rise in rectal temperature of 1.3 °C. Serving as "secondary help" (entering a building at a later time to fight the fire or to conduct additional searches and rescues) is next most demanding, followed by exterior firefighting and serving as crew captain (directing the firefighting, usually at some distance from the fire). Other demanding tasks, in decreasing order of energy costs, are climbing ladders, dragging the fire hose, carrying a travelling ladder and raising a ladder.

During firefighting, core body temperature and heart rate follow a cycle over a period of minutes: they both increase slightly in response to work in preparation for entry, then both increase more as a result of environmental heat exposure and subsequently increase more steeply as a result of high work loads under conditions of heat stress. After 20 to 25 minutes, the usual length of time allowed for interior work by the SCBA used by fire-fighters, the physiological stress remains within limits tolerable by a healthy individual. However, in extended firefighting involving multiple re-entries, there is insufficient time between SCBA air bottle changes to cool off, leading to a cumulative rise in core temperature and an increasing risk of heat stress.

Personal Protection

Fire-fighters exert themselves to maximal levels while fighting fires. Under fire conditions, physical demands are complicated by the metabolic demands of coping with heat and loss of fluids. The combined effect of internally generated heat during work and of external heat from the fire may result in markedly increased body temperatures that climb to unusually high levels in an intense firefighting situation. Half-hour interval breaks to change SCBAs are not enough to arrest this climb in temperature, which can reach dangerous levels in prolonged firefighting. Although essential, personal protection, particularly SCBAs, imposes a considerable additional energy burden on the fire-fighter. The protective clothing also becomes much heavier when it gets wet.

The SCBA is an effective personal protection device that prevents exposure to the products of combustion when used properly. Unfortunately, it is often used only during the "knockdown" phase, when the fire is being actively fought, and not during the "overhaul" phase, when the fire is over but the debris is being examined and embers and smouldering flames are being extinguished.

Fire-fighters tend to judge the level of hazard they face by the intensity of smoke and decide whether to use an SCBA solely on the basis of what they see. This may be very misleading, after the flames are extinguished. While the fire scene may appear to be safe at this stage, it can still be dangerous.

The additional burden or energy cost of using personal protective equipment has been a major area of emphasis in occupational health research on firefighting. This undoubtedly reflects the degree to which firefighting is an extreme case of a matter of general interest, the implications for performance of using personal protection.

Although fire-fighters are obliged to use several forms of personal protection in their work, it is respiratory protection that is most problematic and which has received the most attention. A 20% decrement has been found in work performance imposed by carrying an SCBA, which is a substantial restraint under extreme and dangerous conditions. Investigations have identified several factors of importance in evaluating the physiological demands imposed by respirators in particular, among them the characteristics of the respirator, physiological characteristics of the user and the interactive effects with other personal protection and with environmental conditions.

The fire-fighter's typical "turnout" gear may weigh 23 kg and imposes a high energy cost. Chemical protective clothing (17 kg), as used for clean-up of spills, is the next most demanding gear to wear, followed by the use of SCBA gear while wearing light clothing, which is only slightly more demanding than wearing light, flame-resistant clothing with a low-resistance mask. The firefighting apparatus has been associated with significantly greater retention of internally generated heat and rise in body temperature.

Fitness

Numerous studies have evaluated the physiological characteristics of fire-fighters, usually in the context of other studies to determine the response to firefighting-related demands.

Studies of the fitness of fire-fighters have shown fairly consistently that most fire-fighters are as or somewhat more fit than the general adult male population. They are not, however, necessarily fit to an athletically trained level. Fitness and health maintenance programmes have been developed for fire-fighters but have not been convincingly evaluated for their effectiveness.

The entrance of female applicants into firefighting has caused a re-evaluation of performance tests and studies comparing the sexes. In studies of trained individuals capable of achieving their potential maximum performance, rather than typical applicants, women demonstrated lower scores on average than men in all performance items, but a subgroup of women performed nearly as well in some tasks. The overall difference in performance was attributed primarily to lower absolute lean body weight, which correlated most strongly and consistently with performance differences. The most difficult tests for women were the stair-climbing exercises.

LAW ENFORCEMENT

Jeremy Brown

Law enforcement is difficult, stressful, demanding work. There is evidence that much of the work is sedentary, but the small part of the work which is not sedentary is physically demanding. This is also the part of the work which is often the most critical. In this respect, police work has been likened to the work of a lifeguard at a swimming pool. Most of the time, the lifeguard is watching from the water's edge, but when it is necessary to intervene the emotional and physical demands are extreme and there is usually no warning. Unlike the lifeguard, the police officer may be exposed to attack with a knife or a gun, and may be exposed to intentional violence from some members of the public. Routine activities include patrolling streets, subways, country roads, parks and many other areas. Patrols may be carried out on foot, in vehicles (such as automobiles, helicopters or snowmobiles) and sometimes on horseback. There is a need for constant vigilance and, in many parts of the world, there is the constant threat of violence. Police officers may be called upon to provide assistance to the public in cases of robbery, riot, assault or domestic disputes. They may be involved in crowd control, search and rescue, or assistance to the public in the event of natural disaster. There is an episodic need to chase criminals on foot or in a vehicle, to grapple with, tackle and control criminals and, occasionally, to resort to the use of a lethal weapon. Routine activities can escalate to life-threatening violence with little or no warning. Some police officers work undercover, sometimes for prolonged periods. Others, particularly forensic specialists, are exposed to toxic chemicals. Almost all are exposed to biohazard risk from blood and body fluids. Police officers usually work shifts. Often their shifts are extended by administrative work or court appearances. The actual physical demands of police work and the physical tasks of policing have been extensively studied and are remarkably similar in different police forces and different geographical locations. The question of whether any specific medical condition may be attributable to the occupation of policing is controversial.

Violence

Violence is, unfortunately, a reality of police work. In the United States the homicide rate for police is more than double that for the general population. Work-related violent assault is common among police officers. The particular activities that are likely to result in violent conflict have been the subject of much recent research. The notion that domestic dispute calls were particularly dangerous has been seriously questioned (Violanti, Vena and Marshall 1986). More recently, the activities most likely to result in the assault of a police officer were ranked as follows: First, arresting/controlling suspects; second, robbery in progress; and third, domestic dispute.

The type of violence to which police officers are exposed varies from one country to another. Firearms are more common in the United States than Britain or Western Europe. Countries where political unrest is recent may see police officers exposed to attack from large-calibre or automatic-fire weaponry of a military type. Knife wounds are encountered everywhere, but large-blade knives, particularly machetes, seem more common in tropical countries.

Police officers must maintain a high level of physical fitness. Police training must include training in the physical control of suspects where necessary, as well as training in the use of firearms and other types of tools such as CS gas, pepper spray or hand-held batons. Personal protective equipment such as the "bullet proof" vest is necessary in some communities. Similarly, a communication system that allows the police officer to summon assistance is often important. The most important training, however, must be in the prevention of violence. Current police theory underscores the idea of community policing, with the police officer an integral part of the community. It is to be hoped that as this approach replaces the philosophy of armed military incursion into the community, the need for weaponry and for armour will be reduced.

The sequelae of violence need not be physical. Violent encounters are exceedingly stressful. This stress is particularly likely if the incident has resulted in serious injury, bloodshed or death. Particularly important is the assessment for post-traumatic stress disorder (PTSD) after such incidents.

Emotional and Psychological Stress

It is apparent that police work is stressful. For many police officers the excess of paperwork, as opposed to active law enforcement, is seen as a major stressor. The combination of shiftwork and the uncertainty about what may happen during the shift provides a powerfully stressful situation. In times of fiscal restraint, these stressors are often dramatically amplified by inadequate staffing and inadequate equipment. Situations where there is a potential for violence are stressful in themselves; the stress is dramatically increased where staffing is such that there is inadequate back-up, or when the police officer is seriously overworked.

In addition, the high stress levels which may result from police work have been blamed for marital difficulties, alcohol abuse and suicides among police officers. Much of the data supporting such associations are variable from one geographic region to another. Nevertheless, these problems may well result from the occupation of police work in some cases.

The need for constant vigilance for evidence of stress-related problems or post-traumatic stress disorder cannot be overemphasized. Stress-related disease may manifest as behavioural problems, marital or family problems or, sometimes, as alcohol or substance abuse.

Atherosclerotic Heart Disease

There have been numerous studies suggesting that atherosclerotic disease is more common among police officers (Vena et al. 1986; Sparrow, Thomas and Weiss 1983); there are also studies suggesting that this is not the case. It has been suggested that the increase in the prevalence of heart disease among police officers was almost entirely due to the increased risk of acute myocardial infarction.

This is intuitively satisfying since it is well known that sudden exertion, in the face of underlying heart disease, is an important risk factor for sudden death. The functional job analysis for a general-duty constable clearly indicates that a police officer may be expected, in the course of duty, to go from the sedentary state to maximal exertion with little or no warning and with no preparation. Indeed, much police work is sedentary, but, when re-quired, the police officer is expected to run and chase, to grapple and tackle, and to forcibly subdue a suspect. It is therefore not unexpected that even if the rate of underlying coronary disease is not much different among police officers than the rest of the population, the risk of suffering an acute myocardial infarction, because of the nature of the work, may well be higher (Franke and Anderson 1994).

The demographics of the police population must be considered when assessing the risks for heart disease. Heart disease is most commonly found among middle-aged men, and this group makes up a very large proportion of police officers. Women, who have a significantly lower rate of heart disease during their pre-menopausal years, are significantly under-represented in the demographics of most police forces.

If one is to effectively reduce the risk of cardiac disease in police officers, the regular assessment of the police officer, by a physician knowledgeable about police work and the potential cardiac risks that are associated with police work, is essential (Brown and Trottier 1995). The periodic health assessment must include health education and counselling about cardiac risk factors. There is good evidence that work-based health promotion programmes have a salutary effect on employee health and that the modification of cardiac risk factors reduces the risks of cardiac death. Smoking cessation programmes, nutritional advice, hypertension awareness and cholesterol monitoring and modification are all appropriate activities that will help modify risk factors for cardiac disease among police officers. Regular exercise may be particularly important in police work. The generation of a work environment that educates the worker about positive nutritional and lifestyle choices and that encourages such choices is likely to be beneficial.

Lung Disease in Police Work

The evidence suggests that the prevalence of lung disease in police work is lower than in the general population. There is, however, evidence of an increased rate of cancer of the respiratory system. The majority of police officers are not routinely exposed to inhaled toxins at a rate any greater than other residents of the communities they police. There are exceptions to this general rule, however, the most notable exception being police officers working in forensic identification. There is good evidence that these individuals may suffer from an increased prevalence of respiratory symptoms and, possibly, occupational asthma (Souter, van Netten and Brands 1992; Trottier, Brown and Wells 1994). Cyanoacrylate, used in uncovering latent fingerprints, is a known respiratory sensitizer. In addition to this, there are a large number of chemical carcinogens routinely used in this type of work. For these reasons it is recommended that police officers who work in forensic identification, particularly those who do fingerprint work, should undergo annual chest x ray and spirometry. Similarly, periodic health assessment of these officers must include a careful assessment of the respiratory system.

Even though the practice of smoking cigarettes is becoming less common, a significant number of police officers continue to smoke. This may be the reason why some studies have shown an increased risk of lung and laryngeal cancers among police officers. Smoking is, of course, a major risk factor for cardiac disease. It is also the leading cause of lung cancer. When a police officer gets lung cancer the question frequently asked is whether the cancer is due to occupational exposure, in particular to the carcinogens known to be present in fingerprint powders. If the police officer smokes, it will be impossible to confidently assign blame to any occupational exposure. In summary, respiratory disease is not normally an occupational hazard of police work except for forensic identification workers.

Cancer

There is some evidence that police officers suffer a somewhat higher risk of cancer than expected in the general population. In particular, the risk of digestive tract cancers such as cancer of the oesophagus, cancer of the stomach and cancer of the large bowel is reported to be elevated among police officers. There may be an increased risk of cancer of the lung and larynx. The risk of cancer among police officers working in forensic identification and forensic laboratory work has been briefly discussed above. The controversial issue of testicular cancer associated with the use of police "radar" to detect speeders must also be addressed.

The data suggesting an increase in the risk of cancer of the digestive tract among police officers is scant, but it is a question that must be seriously examined. In the case of lung and oesophageal cancer, it is difficult to see how the activities of police work would be expected to increase the risk. Smoking, of course, is known to increase the risk of both lung and oesophageal cancer, and significant numbers of police officers are known to continue to smoke cigarettes. Another substance known to increase the risk of oesophageal cancer is alcohol, particularly whisky. Police work is known to be exceedingly stressful, and there have been some studies that suggest police officers may sometimes use alcohol to relieve the tension and stress of their work.

The same research that demonstrated an increased risk of cancers of the digestive tract also demonstrated a peculiar increase in the incidence of cancers of the lymphatic and haemopoietic systems in some police officers. The increased risk was restricted to one group and the overall risk was not elevated. Given this very peculiar distribution, and the small numbers, this finding may well turn out to be a statistical aberration.

The risk of cancer among police officers involved in forensic identification work and forensic laboratory work has been discussed. The expected toxicities of chronic low-level exposure to various chemicals are determined by the level of exposure and the use of personal protective equipment. Based on these exposures a periodic health examination has been developed, performed annually and tailored to risks specific for these exposures.

Recent work has suggested a possible increase in the risk of skin cancer, including melanoma, among police officers. Whether this is due to the amount of sun exposure experienced by some police officers who work out of doors is purely speculative.

The question of cancer resulting from exposure to microwaves from "police radar" units has created much controversy. There is certainly some evidence that there may be clustering of certain kinds of cancers among police officers exposed (Davis and Mostofi 1993). The particular concern is about exposure from hand-held units. Alternatively, recent work with large populations refutes any risk of carcinogenicity from exposure to these units. Testicular cancer, in particular, has been reported to be associated with such exposure. The circumstance said to pose the greatest risk is that where the hand-held unit is turned on and resting on the lap of the police officer. This could result in considerable cumulative exposure of the testes over the long term. Whether such exposure causes cancer remains unproven. In the meantime it is recommended that police radar units be mounted outside the police car, be directed away from the police officer, not be used inside the car, be turned off when not in use and be tested regularly for microwave leakage. In addition the periodic examination of police officers should include careful palpation of the testes.

Back Pain

Low-back pain is a major cause of absenteeism throughout the Western world. It is a condition most common among middle-aged males. The factors which predispose to chronic low-back pain are multiple and some, such as the correlation to smoking, seem intuitively difficult to comprehend.

With respect to the occupation of driving, there is ample evidence that individuals who drive for a living are at a dramatically increased risk of low-back pain. This observation includes police officers for whom driving plays a significant part in their daily work. The majority of police cars continue to be equipped with the seats that were installed at the time of their manufacture. Various back supports and prosthetic devices are available which may improve the support of the lumbar spine, but the problem remains.

There is evidence that physical confrontation may play a role in the development of back pain. Motor vehicle accidents, particularly in police vehicles, may play a part. Some police equipment, such as thick leather belts festooned with heavy equipment, may also play a role.

It is important to remember that stress may precipitate or exacerbate back pain and that back pain, as a reason for sick-leave, may be perceived by some police officers as more acceptable than the need to recover from emotional trauma.

There is no doubt that specific exercises designed to maintain flexibility and strengthen the muscles of the back can significantly improve function and symptoms. Numerous classification systems of back pain have been promulgated. These different patterns of pain have distinct approaches of active intervention through specific muscle strengthening programmes. It is important that specific symptom patterns be sought out among police officers and that appropriate intervention and treatment be initiated. This requires periodic assessment by physicians knowledgeable in this clinical syndrome and capable of early effective intervention. It is equally important that a good level of overall fitness be maintained in order to avoid disability from this common chronic, costly syndrome.

Biohazard Risks

There are reports of police officers said to have contracted AIDS from their work. In May 1993 the US Federal Bureau of Investigations reported that there had been seven cases of police officers contacting AIDS through their work over 10 years (Bigbee 1993). Let us begin by noting that this is a surprisingly small number of cases over a 10-year period in the entire United States. Let us next observe that there was some controversy about whether these cases were all to be considered job-related. Nevertheless, it is clearly possible to become infected with HIV as a result of police work.

Since there is no cure for AIDS, and no vaccine that prevents the disease, the best defence a police officer has against this infection is prevention. Latex gloves should be worn, whenever possible, any time that contact with blood or blood-contaminated evidence is foreseen. This is especially important if there are any skin breaks on the hands.

Any open sores or cuts that a police officer has sustained must be kept covered with an occlusive dressing while on duty. Needles should be handled with extreme care, and needles or syringes must be transported in a sharps container that can effectively prevent the needle from penetrating through the container. Sharp edges must be avoided and sharp exhibits handled with extreme care, particularly when contaminated with fresh blood. Where possible, such exhibits should be picked up with instruments rather than by hand.

Latex gloves and a barrier mask should be used if resuscitation attempts are undertaken, and latex gloves must always be worn when rendering first aid. It is important to bear in mind, however, that the risk of becoming infected with HIV from resuscitation procedures is very remote.

There are also some traditional techniques in policing that must be avoided. "Pat down" searches are dangerous to the police officer. There are numerous cases of police officers suffering needle stick injuries from this type of procedure. Also dangerous is searching containers, bags or even pockets by rummaging through them. All containers must be emptied into a flat surface and their contents examined in plain view. Similarly sweep searches under car seats and between seats and backs of couches and chairs must not be performed. It is preferable to dismantle furniture rather than have police officers putting their hands blindly in places where needles and syringes may be hidden. Latex gloves do not protect from needlestick injury.

Eye protection and face masks may be appropriate in circumstances where spatter of body fluid such as saliva or blood can reasonably be foreseen. There must be a system in place for the safe disposal of personal protective equipment. There must be a facility for police officers to wash their hands. Given the fact that few patrol cars have running water and sinks, prepackaged washing solutions for cleaning skin should be provided. Lastly, the question of what should be done for a police officer who, in spite of all the best precautions, suffers a percutaneous exposure to HIV should be asked. After appropriate wound care the first step is to try to determine whether the source of the exposure is truly HIV positive. This is not always possible. Secondly, it is imperative that the police officer be educated about the true risks of infection. Many non-medical personnel assume that the risk is much higher than it really is. Thirdly, the police officer must be informed of the need to retest for at least six months and possibly nine months in order to ensure that the officer has not been infected. Steps must be taken to prevent potential infection of the officer's sexual partner(s) for at least six months. Lastly, the question of post-exposure prophylaxis must be discussed. There is increasing evidence that prophylaxis with antiviral drugs may be helpful in reducing the risk of seroconversion after percutaneous exposure. These are discussed elsewhere in the *Encyclopaedia*. In addition, the area of prophylaxis is under intense research scrutiny so that current references must be consulted to assure the most appropriate approach.

There are numerous case reports of occupationally acquired hepatitis among law enforcement personnel. The quantitative risk is not dramatically high when compared to other occupations. Nevertheless it is a real risk and must be seen as a possible occupational disease. The preventive approach to HIV infection that was outlined above applies equally well to the blood-borne disease hepatitis B. Given the fact that hepatitis B is so much more contagious than AIDS, and more likely to cause disease or death in the short term, this disease ought to be an even more compelling reason for following universal precautions.

There is an effective vaccine against hepatitis B. All police officers regardless of whether they are involved in forensics or general-duty policing, should be vaccinated against hepatitis B. Other conditions, including hepatitis C, tuberculosis and airborne pathogens, may also be encountered by police officers.

● SECURITY GUARDS: THE DEVELOPMENT AND STATE OF OCCUPATIONAL SAFETY IN GERMANY

Manfred Fischer

Growing security needs as a result of generally rising criminal activity, the opening of the borders to the East and within the European Union, as well as the accession of the former German Democratic Republic, have led to a disproportionate growth in the number of commercial guard and security companies as well as the number of employees of these companies in Germany.

At the start of 1995 the number of employees in the more than 1,200 guard and security companies stood at over 155,000. The mid-sized companies have mostly 20 to 200 employees. There are also companies, however, with fewer than 10 employees and others with several thousand. Company mergers are increasingly common.

The Administration Trade Organization is responsible for legal accident insurance for these companies and their employees.

Accident Prevention Regulations

Background of the accident prevention regulations and their scope of application

With the rising occurrence of accidents, the "Guard and Security Services" (VBG 68) Accident Prevention Regulation that had been in force since May 1964 in guard and security work became outdated. It has therefore been reworked and completely redrafted, with the participation of representatives of the affected employers, employees, accident insurance companies, manufacturers' and trade organizations as well as representatives of the Federal Minister of Labour and Social Questions, the state industrial oversight authorities, the Federal Minister of Defence, the Federal Crime Office, the state police authorities, other institutions and a specialized committee. This committee is an organ of the central office of the Safety and Health Trade Organization of the industrial trade organizations, under the responsibility of the Administration Trade Organization.

The newly drafted accident regulation went into effect 1 October 1990, after several years of consultations. The regulation is the legal standard for all employers and employees in guard and security companies. It lays out duties and lines of authority upon which newly drafted governmental ordinances specific to each specialty are based.

Guard and security work to protect persons and valuables includes:

- private guard duty, such as gate-keepers and park watchmen
- security at construction sites and rail yards
- guarding private property, including factory guards
- guarding military installations and atomic power plants
- ranger and patrol duty on various properties
- security service for performances, trade fairs and expositions
- crowd control
- courier service
- investigative services
- money and valuables transport
- personal protection
- staffing alarm centres
- responding to alarms.

General responsibilities of the employer

The employer or his or her agent may employ only persons who are currently qualified and adequately instructed for the desired guard and security activity. These qualifications are set out in writing.

The conduct of the personnel, including notification of deficiencies and particular dangers, must be regulated with detailed service instructions.

If particular dangers result from guard and security work, adequate supervision of the personnel must be ensured.

Guard and security tasks should be taken on only when avoidable dangers in the working area have been eliminated or secured.

To this end, the scope and course of the security, including known side activities, must be set out in writing.

The employer or his or her agent, independent of the client's duties, must ensure that the property to be secured has been inspected for dangers. Records of these inspections must be kept. These inspections must take place on a regular basis and also immediately when the occasion warrants.

The employer or his or her agent must require of the client that avoidable dangers be eliminated or dangerous locations be secured. Until these security measures are implemented, regulations should be formulated that guarantee the safety of the guard and security personnel in another manner. Inadequately secured danger zones should be excluded from surveillance.

The guard and security personnel must be instructed on the property to be secured and its specific dangers during the time period when the guard and safety activity will take place.

The guard and security personnel must be supplied with all necessary facilities, equipment and resources, especially appropriate footwear, effective flashlights in darkness, as well as personal protective gear in good condition, as needed. The personnel must be adequately instructed in the use of such resources. Equipment and other resources that are worn must not unduly restrict freedom of movement, especially of the hands.

General duties of the employee

Employees must abide by all occupational safety measures and follow the service instructions. They should not accede to any directives from the client that contravene the safety instructions.

Deficiencies and dangers that are discovered, as well as corrective measures taken, must be reported to the employer or his or her agent.

The employees must use the equipment and resources provided appropriately. They may not use or enter installations if not authorized.

Employees must not use alcoholic beverages or other intoxicants while on duty. This also applies for an appropriate time period before work: the employee must start work sober.

Employees who must wear glasses to correct their vision during guard or security work must secure these against loss or bring a replacement pair. This also applies to contact lenses.

Use of dogs

In general, only dogs tested and approved by appropriately certified and competent dog handlers are to be used for guard and security work. Untested dogs should be used only for warning tasks when they are clearly under the control of their handler, but not for additional security tasks. Dogs that have vicious tendencies or that are no longer sufficiently competent must not be used.

Excessive demands should not be put on the dogs. Adequate education and training based on the results of research on animal behaviour must be provided. Proper limits for period of service, minimum rest times and total daily service times need to be set.

The competence of the dog handler must be regularly certified. If the handler is no longer adequately qualified, authorization to handle dogs should be withdrawn.

Regulations must be formulated to guarantee smooth and safe handling of dogs, contact with the dog, the taking over and turning over of the dog, leashing and unleashing, a uniform set of commands used by different handlers, the handling of the leash and conduct when third persons are encountered.

Minimal requirements are prescribed for dog kennels concerning condition and equipping as well as setting access authorization.

When transporting dogs, a separation between transport area and passenger area must be maintained. Car trunks are not suit-able under any circumstances. Separate facilities for each dog must be provided.

Use of firearms

Employees must use firearms only on express instructions of the employer or his or her agent, in accordance with all legal requirements and only when the employee is appropriately reliable, suited and trained.

Those carrying firearms must regularly participate in target practice at authorized firing ranges and prove their skill and knowledge. Corresponding records must be kept. If an employee no longer fulfils the requirements, firearms must be withdrawn.

Only officially tested and approved firearms are to be used. The firearms should be tested by experts periodically, and also whenever an inadequacy is suspected; they must be repaired by trained and officially approved persons.

Guards and security personnel must not have or use blank- or gas-firing weapons. In confrontations with armed perpetrators, these weapons provide a false sense of security that leads to extreme danger without adequate possibility of self-defence.

Strict regulations guarantee the flawless and safe use, carrying, transfer, loading and unloading, and storage of firearms and ammunition.

Transporting money and valuables

Due to the high risk of robbery, at least two couriers must be employed for transporting money in publicly accessible areas. One of these must be exclusively occupied with security. This applies also to the couriers' movements between money transport vehicles and the locations where the money is picked up or delivered.

Exceptions are permitted only if: (1) the money transport is not recognizable by outsiders as a transport of money either from the clothing or equipment of the personnel, or from the vehicle used, the route taken or the course of the transport; (2) the incentive for robbery is significantly reduced by technical equipment that must be clearly recognizable by outsiders; or (3) only coin is being transported, and this is clearly recognizable by outsiders from the conduct and course of the transport.

Technical equipment that considerably reduces the incentive for robbery includes, for example, devices that either constantly or during the entire transport are firmly attached to the money transport container and that, in the case of a forced conveyance or snatching during delivery, automatically either immediately or after a timed delay set off an optical alarm by means of a release of coloured smoke. Additional devices such as simultaneous acoustic alarms are advisable.

The design, form, size and weight of money transport containers must be adequately manageable for carrying. They must not be attached to the courier, as this poses an increased risk.

Money transport with vehicles should in general be carried out only in vehicles specially secured for this purpose. These vehicles are adequately secured when their construction and equipment meet the requirements of Accident Prevention Regulation "Vehicles" (VBG 12) and especially the "Safety Rules for Money Transport Vehicles" (ZH1/209).

Money transport in unsecured vehicles is permissible only when exclusively coin, clearly recognizable as such, is being transported, or it is completely unrecognizable as a transport of money. In this case neither the clothing nor equipment of the personnel, nor the construction, equipping or markings of the vehicle used should indicate that money is being transported.

Transport times and routes as well as loading and unloading locations needs to be varied. Money transport vehicles must also be constantly occupied by at least one person behind barred doors during loading and unloading in public areas.

Alarm centres and vaults

Alarm centres and vaults must be adequately secured against assault. The minimal requirements are the Accident Prevention Regulation "Tellers' windows" (VBG 120), which governs securing and equipping credit and money-changing institutions that deal with cash.

Final Considerations

There are practical limits in all attempts to improve occupational safety. This is especially clear in guard and security work. Whereas in other areas, structural measures and improvements lead to success, these play only a secondary role in guard and security work. Significant improvements in this area ultimately can be achieved only by changing the company organizational structure and human conduct. The newly drafted Accident Prevention Regulation "Guard and Security Services" (VBG 68), which may seem exaggerated and too detailed on superficial viewing, nevertheless takes this basic knowledge into very particular consideration.

Thus it is not surprising that since regulations have taken effect, the reportable accidents and occupational diseases in commercial guard and security companies have declined by about 20%, despite the generally increasing crime rate. Some companies which have especially conscientiously implemented the Accident Prevention Regulation, and additionally have voluntarily applied supplementary security measures based on a criteria catalogue that is available, were able to register decreases in occurrences of accidents and occupational diseases of up to 50%. This was especially true in the use of dogs.

Furthermore, the totality of the measures taken led to a reduction in the mandatory premiums for legal accident insurance for commercial guard and security companies, despite rising costs.

Overall it is clear that secure conduct can be achieved in the long run only with precise norms and organizational regulations, as well as through constant training and checking.

● ARMED FORCES

Joel C. Gaydos, Richard J. Thomas, David M. Sack and Relford Patterson

Nations maintain military forces to deter aggression, discourage conflict and, should the need arise, to be prepared to fight and win their wars. Military forces are also used in non-combat roles that are referred to as "peacetime engagements" or "operations other than war". These include: humanitarian missions such as emergency disaster assistance; peacemaking and peacekeeping operations; counter-drug and counter-terrorism work; and security assistance.

Men and women of the armed forces work under the sea, on surface ships, above the earth, on all kinds of terrain, in extremes of temperature and at high elevations. Many military jobs relate to maintaining the skills needed to operate equipment unique to the military (like submarines, fighter aircraft and tanks) in action against an armed enemy. The military also has a large number of uniformed people who perform maintenance, repair, administrative, medical and other functions to support those who fight battles.

All military people maintain proficiency in basic military skills, such as marksmanship, and a high level of physical fitness so that they may react appropriately if they become involved in warfare. Exercise programmes are used extensively to develop and main-

tain strength and aerobic fitness. If used in excess or poorly managed, these programmes may cause excessive injuries.

In addition to their job exposures, uniformed people are often at enhanced risk of acquiring infectious diseases. Basic training camp environments and close living spaces, as found on ships, may contribute to outbreaks of acute respiratory and other infectious diseases. Noise is a universal problem. Also, service in many parts of the world brings with it exposure to contaminated food and water, and to disease vectors carrying protozoan, viral and bacterial agents.

The armed forces rely on many civilian employees to do research and development and provide maintenance, administrative and other support services. Some civilians are paid by the military; others work for companies under contract to the military. In the past, civilian workers did not routinely accompany members of the armed forces into hostile areas. Recently, civilians have been performing many support functions in close proximity to deployed military forces, and may face similar occupational and environmental exposures.

The Fixed Workplace

In many fixed military facilities (such as repair depots, administrative offices and hospitals) uniformed members and civilians perform operations that are similar to those found in non-military workplaces. These include painting; degreasing; welding; grinding; chipping; electroplating; handling hydraulic fluids, fuels and cleaning agents; using microcomputers; and managing patients with infectious diseases. However, performing industrial operations in confined spaces in ships and submarines, or inside armoured vehicles, increases the risk of overexposure to toxicants. Additionally, some work must be done by divers at various depths.

In some fixed facilities, militarily unique items are developed, manufactured, serviced or stored. These items may include: nerve and mustard agent munitions; military explosives, propellants and special fuels, such as hydroxylammonium nitrate; laser range finders and target designators; microwave radiation sources in radar and communications equipment; and ionizing radiation from munitions, armour and nuclear power plants. Composite materials are not militarily unique but are common in military equipment. Where older military equipment is used, workers may be exposed to polychlorinated biphenyls in electrical systems, asbestos in the lagging around steam pipes and lead-based paints.

The Militarily Unique Workplace

People in the armed forces are always on duty, but commanders try to maintain acceptable work-rest cycles. However, battles are not fought on prearranged schedules, and military forces train as they expect to fight. During intense training, fatigue and sleep deprivation are common. The situation is worsened by quickly transporting military forces across time zones and having them perform their jobs immediately upon arrival. In all military operations, and particularly large operations that cover wide areas and involve air, land and sea forces from different countries, there is considerable pressure to maintain effective coordination and communication among the various elements to reduce the risk of accidents, such as placing weapons fire upon a friendly target. Stress is increased if operations result in long family separations, or if the possibility of hostile action exists.

Naval Vessels

On naval vessels, the tight spaces, multiple doors and ladders and narrow passageways close to operating equipment are hazardous. The confined spaces also restrict movement during work and contribute to ergonomic injuries (see figure 95.4). In submarines, air quality is a major concern that requires constant monitoring

Figure 95.4 • On aircraft carriers, naval flight deck personnel must work in extremely close proximity to operating fixed-wing jets and helicopters, and their associated safety hazards, exhaust combustion products and noise.

US Army

and the restriction of unnecessary contaminants. In all military environments where exposure to nuclear power plants, nuclear weapons or other radioactive material may occur, exposures are assessed, controls are implemented and monitoring is conducted as appropriate.

Aircraft

Flight operations in the aerospace environment involve a variety of fixed-wing and rotary-wing (helicopter) aircraft. Military air crews experience exposures that are different from those in the civilian environment. Many military aircraft are unique in their design, flight characteristics and mission performance. Air crew members are frequently at risk of exposure to excessive accelerative forces (centrifugal and gravitational), decompression sickness, circadian desynchrony resulting from long missions or night operations and spatial disorientation. Vibration originating from the aircraft and/or atmospheric turbulence may affect vision, result in motion sickness, produce fatigue and contribute to the development of disorders of the lumbar spine, particularly in helicopter pilots. Exposure to products of combustion from engine exhaust, overheating or burning of aircraft components may pose a toxic hazard if the aircraft is damaged during combat operations. Fatigue is a major concern when flight operations occur over extended periods of time, or involve long distances. Spatial disorientation and illusionary sensations of aircraft attitude and motion can be causes of mishaps, particularly when flights occur at high speeds in close proximity to the ground. Ground crews may be under considerable time pressure to perform maintenance

and resupply (often with aircraft engines running) under difficult working conditions.

Helicopters are used extensively in the military as low-altitude weapons systems and observation platforms, and as medical evacuation and utility vehicles. These rotary-wing aircraft are associated with unique physical hazards, mission profiles and physiological implications for air crews. Helicopters have the ability to fly forward, sideward and rearward, but are inherently unstable flight platforms. Consequently, helicopter air crews must maintain constant concentration and have exceptional vision and muscle coordination to operate flight control systems and avoid collisions with terrain and other obstructions during low-level flight. Fatigue is a serious concern for crew members involved in extended flights, large numbers of short missions and/or low-level, nap-of-the-earth (NOE) flights in which pilots fly as close to terrain contours as the speed and performance contours will allow. Low-level flights at night are particularly challenging. Night vision goggles are commonly used by helicopter pilots in military aviation and law enforcement; however, their use may restrict depth perception, field of view and colour differentiation. Engines, transmissions and rotors of helicopters produce unique vibration spectra which can adversely affect visual acuity and contribute to muscle strain and fatigue. These aircraft components also produce intense noise levels which can disrupt cockpit communications and contribute to hearing loss. Shrouds enclosing noisy components, acoustic blankets as insulation in cockpit/cabin areas and hearing protective devices are used to reduce the risk of hearing loss. Heat stress may be a special problem for helicopter air crews given the lower altitudes at which helicopters

Figure 95.5 • This mechanized smoke generator produces a curtain of fog oil smoke through heat evaporation; fog oil may cause a slipping hazard.

US Army

operate. Helicopter crashes tend to involve vertical impacts with the ground, often at relatively low forward speeds (in contrast to the longitudinal pattern of fixed-wing aircraft). Compression fractures of the spine and basilar skull fractures are common injuries in crash victims. Design features employed to prevent and control injuries include protective helmets, crash-worthy fuel systems, strengthened cockpit areas to prevent intrusion of the rotor system or transmission, and special seats and restraint systems utilizing shock-absorbing devices.

Ground Forces

Ground troops fire rifles, large guns and rockets, and ride in vehicles over rough terrain. At times they work under the cover of smokes produced from fog oil, diesel fuel or other chemicals (see figure 95.5). Exposures to noise, blast overpressure from large guns, vibration and propellant combustion products are common. Ballistic eye injuries occur but can be prevented by protective eyewear. The possibility of adverse health effects is increased when rockets and large guns are fired in enclosed areas, as in buildings. Armoured vehicle crew compartments are closed spaces where carbon monoxide concentrations may reach thousands of parts per million after weapons firing, and require effective ventilation systems. Heat stress in some vehicles may necessitate the use of cooling vests. Troops may also experience heat stress from wearing special clothing, hoods and masks to protect against chemical and biological agent attacks. These personal protective measures may contribute to accidents because of interference with vision and mobility. In field medical facilities, infection control practices and containment of waste anaesthetic gases may present unique challenges.

Military personnel face injury and illness from a variety of weapons. The more conventional weapons produce casualties using projectiles and fragments, blast effects (which may result in lung contusion trauma) and flame and incendiary devices, such as those containing napalm and phosphorus. Eye injuries from lasers may occur accidentally or when lasers are used as offensive weapons. Other weapons systems employ biological material, such as anthrax spores, or chemicals like anticholinesterase agents.

Extensive use of mines has caused concern because of the casualties that have occurred in civilian non-combatants. Narrowly defined, a mine is an explosive ordinance designed to be buried in the ground. In reality, a mine is any hidden explosive that lies in wait and may be detonated by enemy forces, friendly forces, non-combatants or animals. Mines may be employed against *matériel* or people. Anti-*matériel* mines are directed at military vehicles and may contain about 5 to 10 kg of explosive, but require 135 kg or more of compressive force to be activated. Antipersonnel mines are designed to maim rather than to kill. Less than 0.2 kg of explosive buried in the ground can blow off a foot. The dirt particles surrounding a mine become missiles that grossly contaminate wounds. The radius in which a mine can produce casualties was expanded with the development of the "pop-up mine". In these mines a small explosive charge sends a canister about a metre into the air. The canister immediately detonates, spraying fragments to a distance of 35 m. Modern mine designs, like the "Claymore", can be detonated electrically, by timed fuse or by a trip wire, and can send hundreds of steel spheres, each weighing 0.75 g, over a 60° arc for distances up to 250 m. Within 50 m, gross mutilation and lethal injuries are common.

A range of chemical agents have been employed in warfare. Herbicides (e.g., 2,4-D *n*-butyl ester mixed with 2,4,5-T *n*-butyl ester, also known as Agent Orange) were used in Vietnam to control terrain. Some chemicals (e.g., tear gas) have been used as incapacitating agents to produce transient physical or mental effects, or both. Other chemicals are extremely toxic and capable of producing serious injury or death. This category includes the anticholinesterase agents (e.g., Tabun and Sarin), the vesicants or blister agents (e.g., mustard and arsenicals), the lung-damaging or "choking" agents (e.g., phosgene and chlorine) and the blood agents that block the oxidative processes (e.g., hydrogen cyanide and cyanogen chloride).

In addition to armed conflict, other potential sources of exposure to chemical agents include: terrorist activities; storage sites for old military chemical stocks, where leaking containers may occur; sites where military chemical stocks are being destroyed through incineration or other means; and the accidental unearthing of old, forgotten chemical disposal sites.

The Medical Care System

Medical care for the armed forces and civilian workers is focused on prevention. Often, medical personnel study military vehicles and equipment during development to identify potential health hazards to users and maintainers so that these can be controlled. Training and user manuals and educational programmes address protection against hazards. Medical care includes initial medical screening, periodic medical assessment, health education and promotion, and disability evaluations, in addition to primary care and emergency services. Medical personnel also participate in accident investigations. When people deploy to areas presenting new health risks, medical risk assessments are used to identify threats and interventions like vaccines, prophylactic drugs, personnel protective measures and educational programmes.

Medical personnel who provide preventive and primary care to members of the armed forces must be knowledgeable about the characteristics of weapons used in training and on the battlefield to: predict and prepare for the casualties that may occur; take preventive actions that may reduce morbidity and/or mortality; and provide appropriate treatment when casualties do occur. Personal protective equipment is important in defending against chemical and biological agents and eye injuries from missiles and lasers. Other measures to be considered are vaccines and chemoprophylactic drugs for biological agents, and drug pre-treatment and antidotes for chemical agents. Training medical personnel in the early detection and management of illnesses and injuries caused by weapons is critical. Early recognition can result in rapid initiation of appropriate therapy and possibly a reduction in future morbidity and mortality. Also, military surgical staffs are better prepared to take care of their patients and themselves if they are knowledgeable about the wounds they are treating. For example: wounds made by high-velocity rifles often do not require extensive debridement for soft-tissue destruction; wounds made by fragmentation bullets may require extensive exploration; and wounds may contain unexploded munitions.

● HEALTH AND SAFETY HAZARDS OF MARITIME RESCUES

Timothy J. Ungs

Oceans, lakes, rivers and other large bodies of water present extremes of environmental conditions demanding the maximum in human performance. The defining attribute that characterizes health and safety hazards of maritime rescues is the pervasive presence of the water itself.

Maritime rescues share many of the health and safety hazards experienced in land-based rescues. The risk of communicable disease transmission, exposure to toxic substances, threat of inter-

personal violence and exposure to various physical agents (e.g., noise, vibration, radiation) are examples of commonly shared hazards of water and land rescues. The maritime environment, however, presents several unique or exaggerated hazards compared to the land-based environment. This article will focus on those health and safety hazards most identified with at-sea rescues.

Modes of Response

Before discussing specific health and safety hazards it is important to understand that maritime rescues can take place by either surface vessel or aircraft, or a combination of both. The importance of understanding the mode of response is that characteristics of hazard exposure are determined, in part, by the mode.

Surface vessels typically used in maritime rescues travel at speeds under 40 knots (74.1 km/h), have a relatively limited operational range (under 200 miles (320 km)), are heavily influenced by water surface and weather conditions, are subject to damage by floating debris and generally are not sensitive to weight consideration. Helicopters, the most commonly used aircraft in maritime rescue, can travel in excess of 150 knots (278 km/h), may have an effective operational range of 300 miles (480 km) (more with in-flight refuelling), are more influenced by weather than water conditions and are very sensitive to weight concerns.

Factors that determine the mode of response include distance, urgency, geographic location, resource availability, environmental conditions and character of the responding rescue organization. Factors that tend to favour surface vessel response are closer proximity, lower urgency, proximity to metropolitan or developed regions, milder water surface conditions and a less well developed aviation system and infrastructure. Rescue by air tends to be favoured by longer distances, higher urgency, remoteness from metropolitan or developed regions, harsher water surface conditions, and regions with better-developed aviation systems and infrastructure. Figures 95.6 and 95.7 show both types of rescue.

Maritime Hazards

The dominant hazards of maritime rescues are those intrinsic to the watery environment. Rescue personnel are directly exposed to maritime elements and must be prepared for survival themselves.

Drowning is the most common cause of occupation-related death in the maritime environment. People require specialized flotation equipment to survive in water for any length of time. Even the best swimmers require flotation assistance to survive in rough weather. Prolonged (more that several hours) survival in

Figure 95.6 • Maritime rescue by ship.

US Army

95. EMERGENCY AND SECURITY SERVICES

Figure 95.7 • Maritime rescue by helicopter.

US Army

stormy weather is usually impossible without specialized survival suits or rafts. Injuries, reduced level of consciousness, confusion and panic or uncontrolled fear will reduce the likelihood of water survival.

Water is more efficient than air at conducting away body heat. The risk of death due to hypothermia or hypothermia-induced drowning increases rapidly as water temperature decreases below 24 °C. As water temperatures approach freezing, effective survival time is measured in minutes. Prolonged survival in cold water, even when the surface is calm, is possible only with the assistance of specialized survival suits or rafts.

The maritime environment exhibits the extremes of weather conditions. Wind, rain, fog, snow and icing can be severe. Visibility and the ability to communicate can be seriously restricted. Rescuers are constantly at risk for getting wet through wave and splash action, wind-driven rain or spray, and vessel- or aircraft-generated spray. Water, especially salt water, can damage mechanical and electrical equipment essential for vessel or flight operations.

Exposure to salt water can result in skin, mucosal and eye irritation. Ingestion of water-borne infectious micro-organisms (e.g., *Vibrio spp.*) increases the likelihood of gastro-intestinal disease. The water around rescue sites can be contaminated with pollutants (e.g., sewage) or substances hazardous to human health (e.g., petroleum products). Potential envenomation by water snakes and by various coelenterates (e.g., jellyfish) can occur in areas supporting these organisms. Water and thermal protective

clothing is often cumbersome, restrictive and prone to promote heat stress. During sunny conditions, rescuers can experience skin and eye damage due to reflected ultraviolet light.

The surface of large bodies of water, such as the oceans, typically has undulant wave motion with coexistent surface chop. Rescue personnel, therefore, conduct work on a moving platform, which complicates any movement or procedures. Motion sickness is a constant threat. Surface vessels travelling through rough conditions can experience severe pounding and instability which promotes fatigue, an increased likelihood of falls or being struck by falling objects and equipment failure. Aircraft operating in stormy weather experience turbulence that can induce motion sickness, accelerate fatigue and compound the risks of surface-to-air evacuation.

Planning and Prevention

The maritime environment can be extremely hostile. However, the health and safety hazards associated with maritime rescues can be controlled or minimized through careful planning and prevention efforts. Safe and effective rescues can take place.

Rescue organizations must be acutely aware of the nature of the maritime environment, understand the operational characteristics and limitations of response equipment and personnel, practice system safety and provide suitable equipment, training and leadership. Rescue personnel must be in good physical and mental condition, know their equipment and procedures, stay alert, be prepared, remain proficient and understand the specifics of the situation they are dealing with.

Rescue personnel can be involved in vessel or aviation mishaps. The difference between being a rescuer and needing to be rescued can be only a matter of moments. Ultimate mishap survival is dependent on:

- survival of the impact itself
- successful egress
- enduring post-mishap until rescued.

Each stage of mishap survival has its own set of necessary training, equipment, ergonomics and procedures to maximize survival. Maritime rescue personnel usually act in isolation, without immediate backup, and often at long distances from shore. A rule of thumb is for rescuers to have the necessary resources to survive the time it takes to be rescued themselves in the event of their own mishap. Rescuers need to be trained, equipped and prepared to survive in the worst of conditions.

PARAMEDICAL PERSONNEL AND AMBULANCE ATTENDANTS

John D. Meyer

Paramedical personnel, including emergency medical technicians (EMTs) and ambulance attendants, provide the initial medical response at the scene of an accident, disaster or acute illness, and transport patients to the point where more definitive treatment can be rendered. Advances in medical equipment and communications have increased the capabilities of these workers to resuscitate and stabilize victims en route to an emergency centre. The increased capabilities of EMTs is matched by the increase in hazards which they now face in performance of their duties. The emergency medical responder works as a member of a small unit, usually two to three persons. Job tasks must often be performed rapidly in poorly equipped locations with limited access. The work environment may present unanticipated or uncontrolled biological, physical and chemical hazards. Dynamic, rapidly changing situations and hostile patients and surroundings magnify the dangers of the work. A consideration of the health risks to paramedical personnel is important in the design of strategies to reduce and prevent injury at work.

Risks to paramedical personnel fall broadly into four main categories: physical hazards, inhalation risks, infectious exposures and stress. Physical hazards involve both musculoskeletal injuries related to job tasks, and effects of the environment in which the work takes place. Heavy and awkward lifting is the predominant physical hazard for these workers, accounting for over one-third of injuries. Back strains constitute the most common type of injury; one retrospective survey found 36% of all reported injuries were due to lower-back strain (Hogya and Ellis 1990). Patient and equipment lifting appear to be the main factors in lower-back injury; nearly two-thirds of back injuries occur at the scene of response. Recurrent back injuries are common and may lead to prolonged or permanent disability and early retirement of experienced workers. Other frequent injuries include contusions of the head, neck, trunk, legs and arms, ankle sprains, wrist and hand sprains and finger wounds. Falls, assaults (both by patients and by bystanders) and motor vehicle accidents are additional major sources of injury. Collisions account for the majority of motor vehicle accidents; associated factors may be heavy work schedules, time pressures, poor weather conditions and inadequate training.

Thermal injury from both cold and hot environments has been reported. Local climate and weather conditions, along with improper clothing and equipment, may contribute to heat stress and cold injury. Accelerated hearing loss from exposure to sirens, which produce ambient noise levels exceeding mandated thresholds, has also been observed in ambulance personnel.

Smoke inhalation and poisoning by gases, including carbon monoxide, represent significant respiratory hazards for paramedics. Though occurring infrequently, these exposures can have dire consequences. Responders arriving on the scene may initially be inadequately prepared for rescue work, and can be overcome by smoke or toxic gases before additional help and equipment are available.

In common with other health-care workers, paramedical personnel are at increased risk of infection with blood-borne pathogenic viruses, especially hepatitis B virus (HBV) and presumably hepatitis C. Serologic markers for HBV infection were found in 13 to 22% of emergency medical technicians, a prevalence level three to four times that of the general population (Pepe et al. 1986). In one survey, evidence of infection was found to correlate with years worked as an EMT. Measures for protection against HBV and HIV transmission established for health-care workers apply to paramedical technicians, and are outlined elsewhere in this *Encyclopaedia*. As a sidelight, use of latex gloves for protection against blood-borne pathogens may lead to an increased risk for contact urticaria and other manifestations of allergy to rubber products similar to those noted in health-care workers in hospital settings.

Paramedical and ambulance work, which involves work in uncontrolled and hazardous environments as well as responsibility for important decisions with limited equipment and time pressures, leads to high levels of occupational stress. Impaired professional performance, work dissatisfaction and loss of concern for patients, all of which may arise from the effects of stress, endanger both providers and the public. Intervention by mental health workers after major disasters and other traumatic incidents, along with other strategies to reduce burnout among emergency workers, have been proposed to mitigate the destructive effects of stress in this field (Neale 1991).

Few specific recommendations exist for screening and preventive measures in paramedical workers. Blood-borne pathogen training and immunization to HBV should be undertaken in all employees with exposure to infectious fluids and materials. In the United States, health-care facilities are required to inform an emergency response employee who sustains an unprotected exposure to a blood-borne disease or to an airborne, uncommon or rare infectious disease, including tuberculosis (NIOSH 1989). Similar guidelines and statutes exist for other countries (Laboratory Center for Disease Control 1995). Compliance with standard immunization practices for infectious agents (e.g., measles-mumps-rubella vaccine) and tetanus is essential. Periodic screening for tuberculosis is recommended if the potential for high-risk exposure is present. Properly designed equipment, instruction in body mechanics and scene hazard education have been proposed to reduce lifting injuries, although the setting in which much ambulance work is performed may render the most well-designed controls ineffective. The environment in which paramedical work occurs should be considered carefully, and appropriate clothing and protective equipment provided when necessary. Respirator training is appropriate for personnel who may be exposed to toxic gases and smoke. Finally, the erosive effects of stress on paramedical workers and emergency technicians must be borne in mind, and strategies for counselling and intervention should be developed to lessen its impact.

HAZARDOUS-RESPONSE PERSONNEL

M. Joseph Fedoruk

Employees in occupations that respond to hazardous-substance emergencies or incidents can be broadly classified as hazardous-response personnel. A hazardous-substance emergency or incident can be defined as an uncontrolled or illegal release or threatened release of a hazardous material or its hazardous by-products. A hazardous-substance emergency can arise from a transportation-related incident or at a fixed-site facility. Transportation-related incidents can occur as a result of accidents on land, water or in the air. Fixed-site facilities include industrial facilities, commercial office buildings, schools, farms or any other fixed site that contains hazardous materials.

Employees whose primary responsibility is response to hazardous-materials incidents are generally considered members of hazardous materials (HAZMAT) response teams. HAZMAT team professionals include public-sector employees such as fire-fighters, police and transportation officials who have received specialized training in managing hazardous-substance emergencies. Fixed-site facilities such as manufacturing plants, oil refineries or research laboratories often have internal HAZMAT teams who are trained to manage hazardous-materials incidents inside their facilities. Environmental regulations may necessitate that such facilities report incidents to public agencies when the surrounding community is at risk, or if a threshold quantity of a regulated hazardous material has been released. Public health professionals with training in exposure assessment and hazardous materials management, such as industrial (occupational) hygienists, are often members of public- or private-sector HAZMAT teams.

Police and fire personnel are frequently the first professionals to respond to hazardous-substance emergencies, since they may encounter a leak or release of a hazardous substance associated with a transportation accident or structural fire. These employees are typically considered to be first responders, and their primary responsibility is to isolate the public from the release by denying public access to the site of the incident. This is generally achieved through physical control measures such as physical barriers and crowd- and traffic-control measures. First responders typically do not take actions to contain or control the release. First responders may be at greater risk of exposure to hazardous materials than other HAZMAT teams since they may encounter a hazardous-material release without the benefit of full personal protective equipment, or encounter an unexpected exposure. First responders typically notify HAZMAT team members to manage the incident. The specific health concerns of police and fire personnel are described elsewhere in this chapter.

The primary responsibility of the HAZMAT team is to contain and control the release. This activity can be very hazardous when the incident involves explosive or highly toxic materials such as chlorine gas. The incident commander is responsible for deciding what actions should be taken to resolve the emergency. It may take a considerable amount of time to develop a plan of control for complex accidents such as a multiple railroad car derailment or a chemical plant explosion and fire. In some circumstances where mitigation measures involve a significant risk of major injury to HAZMAT personnel, a decision may be reached not to take specific containment measures, and the hazardous material may be released into the environment.

The final phase of a hazardous-substance emergency often involves the clean-up of residual hazardous substances. This is frequently done by labourers. In some jurisdictions, health and safety regulations mandate that such workers receive specialized training in hazardous-material response and participate in a programme of medical surveillance. These employees may be at a greater risk of exposure since clean-up operations can involve close contact with the hazardous materials. Other occupations at risk of chemical exposure from hazardous-substance emergencies are emergency heath-care providers including emergency medical technicians, paramedics, emergency room medical staff and other hospital personnel.

Potential Hazards

The potential hazards associated with a hazardous-substance emergency are incident specific and can include chemical, radiological and biological hazards. These agents can be gases or vapours, aerosols including mists, fumes, dusts or particulates, solids and/or liquids. The potential hazards faced by hazardous-substance response personnel depend on the exposure potential of the agent, reactivity (flammability, explosivity and so on) and toxicity potential.

Information regarding the type of agents involved in hazardous-substance emergencies is available in the United States from the Agency for Toxic Substances and Disease Registry (ATSDR) Hazardous Substances Emergency Events Surveillance (HSEES)

system. The HSEES system is an active surveillance system which tracks incidents that have a public-health impact (Hall et al. 1994). The HSEES system was developed because of reported deficiencies in other national US systems that track releases of hazardous substances (Binder 1989). HSEES does not identify all releases since limited spills at fixed-site facilities are not recorded. The registry was established in 1990 and initially involved five states, but has grown to include eleven states. In 1993 HSEES recorded 3,945 hazardous-substances emergencies. Other countries and states also have systems that record hazardous-material events (Winder et al. 1992).

HSEES data summarizing the types of chemical substances released during hazardous substance emergencies including those associated with personnel injuries, during the two-year period 1990–1992 showed that the most common chemical classes of substances released were volatile organic compounds, herbicides, acids and ammonia. The greatest risk of developing an injury occurred during incidents involving cyanides, insecticides, chlorine, acids and bases. During 1990–1992, 93% of the incidents involved the release of only one chemical, and 84% of the releases occurred at fixed-site facilities.

Health Outcomes

Hazardous-substance personnel face several distinct types of acute health threats. The first category of health threat relates to the toxicity potential of the agent as well as potential contact with blood and other body fluids of incident victims. The second threat is the risk of sustaining major physical trauma including burns associated with an explosion and/or fire from an unexpected chemical reaction, or with structural collapse of a building or container. The third type of acute health effect is risk of heat stress or exhaustion associated with performing heavy work, often in chemical protective clothing, which impairs the body's efficiency of evaporative cooling. Employees with pre-existing health problems such as cardiovascular disease, respiratory disease, diabetes, disorders of consciousness, or those who take medications that may impair heat exchange or cardiorespiratory response to exercise, are at additional risk when performing such arduous work.

There is limited information concerning the health outcomes of hazardous-substance personnel responding to hazardous-substance emergencies. The HSEES registry indicated that for 1990 to 1992, 467, or 15%, of 4,034 emergency response events resulted in 446 injuries. Two hundred of the injured persons were classified as first responders, including fire-fighters, law-enforcement personnel, emergency medical response personnel and

---

Figure 95.8 • Preventive guidelines.

PREVENTION	INCIDENT MANAGEMENT	HEALTH MEASURES
• Regulatory—adoption of regulations concerning hazardous materials storage, chemical process safety, treatment, discharge and transportation	• Emergency response plan—pre-emergency planning—roles and lines of authority and communication	• First aid
• Regulatory—right to know	• Safe work practices and safe equipment	• Decontamination procedures of personnel and clothing
• Training of workers, personnel, transportation officials on safe work practices, emergency recognition and prevention	• Safe distances and places of refuge	• Emergency medical treatment
• Safe work practices	• Personal protective equipment: selection, use and limitations of personal protective equipment specific to hazard	• Medical surveillance
	• Decontamination procedures of clothing, equipment and personnel	
	• Emergency recognition and prevention	

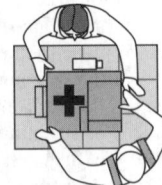
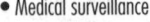
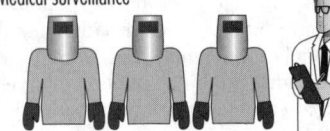

HAZMAT team members. Nearly one-quarter of first responders (22%) did not utilize any type of personal protective equipment.

The principle reported health effects among all persons sustaining injuries included respiratory irritation (37.3%), eye irritation (22.8%) and nausea (8.9%). Chemical burns were reported in 6.1% of those injured. Heat stress was reported in 2%. Eleven deaths were recorded, including one in a first responder. The causes of death among the entire group were reported as trauma, chemical burns, asphyxiation, thermal burns, heat stress and cardiac arrest. Other reports have suggested that first responders are at risk of being injured in acute responses.

The health risks associated with chronic exposures to a wide array of hazardous-materials incidents have not been characterized. Epidemiological studies have not been completed of HAZMAT team members. Epidemiological studies of fire-fighters who perform first response activities at fire scenes have revealed that they may be at greater risk of developing several types of malignancies (see the article "Firefighting hazards" in this chapter).

Preventive Measures

Several measures can reduce the incident of hazardous-substance emergencies. These are described in figure 95.8. First, prevention through the adoption and enforcement of regulations involving production, storage, transportation and use of hazardous substances can lessen the potential for unsafe work practices. Training of employees in proper workplace practices and hazard management is critical in preventing accidents.

Second, proper management and supervision of the incident can lessen the impact of an incident. The management of the activities of the first responders and clean-up workers by the incident commander is critical. There must be supervision and evaluation of the progress of the emergency response to ensure that the response objectives are being met safely, effectively and efficiently.

The third measure includes health-related actions that are taken during and after an incident. These actions include the provision of appropriate first aid at the scene and proper decontamination procedures. Failure to properly decontaminate a victim may result in ongoing absorption of the hazardous agent and place the HAZMAT or medical staff at risk of exposure from direct patient contact (Cox 1994). Medical personnel should also be trained regarding specific treatment and personal protective measures for unusual chemical events.

Participation in a medical surveillance programme by workers is a measure that can be utilized to prevent health problems among hazardous-response personnel. Medical surveillance can potentially detect conditions at an early stage before significant adverse health effects have occurred in workers. In addition, medical conditions which may place employees at significantly greater risk from performing the work, such as cardiovascular disease, can be identified and monitored. Sensory impairments that can interfere with field communications, including hearing and vision defects, can also be identified to determine whether they would pose a significant threat during hazardous emergency response.

Most of the identified preventive measures are based upon community awareness of local hazards. Implementation of hazardous-substance emergency plans by adequately trained staff and the wise allocation of resources are imperative. Community awareness of hazards includes informing communities of hazardous materials which are at fixed facilities or materials that are being transported through a community (e.g., by road, rail, airport or water). This information should enable fire departments and other agencies to plan for emergency incidents. Fixed facilities and transporters of hazardous materials should also have individual response plans developed that include specific provisions for notification of public agencies in a timely manner. Emergency medical personnel should have the necessary knowledge of the potential hazards in their local community. Trained medical staff should be available to provide appropriate treatment and diagnosis for the symptoms, signs and specific treatment recommendations for hazardous substances in their communities. Fixed site facilities should establish liaisons with local emergency departments and inform them of potential hazards in the workplace and the need for special supplies or mediations needed to manage potential incidents at these facilities. Planning and training should help enhance the provision of appropriate medical care and decrease the number of injuries and deaths from incidents.

The potential also exists for hazardous-substance emergencies to occur as a result of a natural disaster such as floods, earthquakes, lightning, hurricanes, winds or severe storms. Although the number of such events appears to be increasing, planning and preparation for these potential emergencies is very limited (Showalter and Myers 1994). Planning efforts need to include natural causes of emergency incidents.

References

Bigbee, D. 1993. Pathogenic microorganisms—Law enforcement's silent enemies. *FBI Law Enforcement Bull* May 1993:1–5.

Binder, S. 1989. Deaths, injuries, and evacuation from acute hazardous materials releases. *Am J Public Health* 79:1042–1044.

Brown, J and A Trottier. 1995. Assessing cardiac risks in police officers. *J Clinical Forensic Med* 2:199–204.

Cox, RD. 1994. Decontamination and management of hazardous materials exposure victims in the emergency department. *Ann Emerg Med* 23(4):761–770.

Davis, RL and FK Mostofi. 1993. Cluster of testicular cancer in police officers exposed to hand held radar. *Am J Ind Med* 24:231–233.

Franke, WD and DF Anderson. 1994. Relationship between physical activity and risk factors for cardiovascular disease among law enforcement officers. *J Occup Med* 36(10):1127–1132.

Hall, HI, VD Dhara, PA Price-Green, and WE Kaye. 1994. Surveillance for emergency events involving hazardous substances—United States, 1990–1992. *MMWR CDC Surveil Summ* 43(2):1–6.

Hogya, PT and L Ellis. 1990. Evaluation of the injury profile of personnel in a busy urban EMS system. *Am J Emerg Med* 8:308–311.

Laboratory Center for Disease Control. 1995. A national consensus on guidelines for establishment of a post-exposure notification protocol for emergency responders. *Canada Communicable Disease Report* 21–19:169–175.

National Institute for Occupational Safety and Health (NIOSH). 1989. *A Curriculum Guide for Public-safety and Emergency Response Workers. Prevention of Transmission of Human Immunodeficiency Virus and Hepatitis B Virus.* Cincinnati: NIOSH.

Neale, AV. 1991. Work stress in emergency medical technicians. *J Occup Med* 33:991–997.

Pepe, PE, FB Hollinger, CL Troisi, and D Heiberg. 1986. Viral hepatitis risk in urban emergency medical services personnel. *Ann Emerg Med* 15:454–457.

Showalter, PS and MF Myers. 1994. Natural disasters in the United States as release agents of oil, chemicals, or radiological materials between 1980–1989. *Risk Anal* 14(2):169–182.

Souter, FCG, C van Netten and R Brands. 1992. Morbidity in policemen occupationally exposed to fingerprint powders. *Int J Envir Health Res* 2:114–119.

Sparrow, D, HE Thomas, and ST Weiss. 1983. Coronary heart disease in police officers participating in the normative aging study. *Am J Epidemiol* 118(No. 4):508–512.

Trottier, A, J Brown, and GA Wells. 1994. Respiratory symptoms among forensic ident workers. *J Clin Forensic Med* 1:129–132.

Vena, JE, JM Violanti, J Marshall and RC Fiedler. 1986. Mortality of a municipal worker cohort: III: Police officers. *Am J Ind Med* 10:383–397.

Violanti, JM, JE Vena and JR Marshall. 1986. Disease risk and mortality among police officers: New evidence and contributing factors. *J Police Sci Admin* 14(1):17–23.

95. EMERGENCY AND SECURITY SERVICES

Winder, C, A Tottszer, J Navratil and R Tandon. 1992. Hazardous materials incidents reporting—Result of a nationwide trial. *J Haz Mat* 31(2):119–134.

Other relevant readings

Bellamy, RF and R Zajtchuk. 1990. *Conventional Warfare, Ballistic, Blast, and Burn Injuries. Textbook of Military Medicine Series*. Washington, DC: Walter Reed Army Medical Center.

Blau, TH. 1994. *Psychological Services for Law Enforcement*. New York: John Wiley & Sons.

Bonneau, J and J Brown. 1955. Physical ability, fitness and police work. *J Clin Forensic Med* 2:157–164.

Deeter, DP and JC Gaydos. 1993. *Occupational Health, the Soldier and the Industrial Base. Textbook of Military Medicine Series*. Washington, DC: Borden Institute, Walter Reed Army Medical Center.

DeHart, R. 1985. *Fundamentals of Aerospace Medicine*. Philadelphia: Lea and Febiger.

Ernsting, J and P King. 1988. *Aviation Medicine*. London: Butterworths.

Gaydos, JC. 1992. A historical review of the need for military toxicology and the U.S. Army's response. In *Chemical Risk Assessment in the Department of Defense(DoD): Science, Policy and Practice*. Cincinnati: American Conference of Governmental Industrial Hygienists.

Gaydos, JC and GA Luz. 1994. Military participation in emergency humanitarian assistance. *J Disaster Studies and Management* March 1994:48–57.

Guidotti, TL. 1992. Human factors in firefighting: Ergonomic, cardiovascular, and psychogenic stress-related issues. *Int Arch Occup Environ Health* 64:1–12.

—. 1992. Occupational health concerns of firefighting. *Annu Rev Publ Health* 13:151–171.

—. 1995. Occupational mortality among firefighters: Assessing the asociation. *J Occup and Envir Med* 37:1348–1356.

Landrock, AH. 1983. *Handbook of Plastics Flammability and Combustion Technology*. Park Ridge, NJ: Noyes Publications.

Legters, LJ and CH Llewellyn. 1992. Military medicine. In *Public Health and Preventive Medicine*, edited by KF Maxey, MJ Rosenau and JM Last. East Norwalk, CT: Appleton and Lange.

Marrs, TC, RL Maynard, and FR Sidell. 1996. *Chemical Warfare Agents, Toxicology and Treatment*. New York: John Wiley & Sons.

Orris, P, J Melius, and RM Duffy. 1995. Firefighters' safety and health. *Occup Med: State Art Rev* 10(4):691–883.

Rayman, RB. 1990. *Clinical Aviation Medicine*. Malvern, PA, US: Lea and Febiger.

Trottier, A and J Brown. 1993. *Police Health 1994: A Physicians's Guide for the Assessment of Police Officers*. Ottawa: Canada Communication Group.

—. 1995. Occupational medicine for policing. *J Clin Forensic Med* 2:105–110.

—. 1995. Risks to police officers from biohazards encountered in police work. *J Clin Forensic Med* 2:11–116.

Tuve, RL. 1976. *Principles of Fire Protection Chemistry*. Boston: National Fire Protection Association.

Chapter Editor
Michael McCann

Contents

● ENTERTAINMENT AND THE ARTS

Michael McCann

Entertainment and the arts have been a part of human history ever since prehistoric people drew cave paintings of animals they hunted or acted out in song and dance the success of the hunt. Every culture from earliest times has had its own style of visual and performing arts, and decorated everyday objects like clothing, pottery and furniture. Modern technology and more leisure time has led to a major part of the world's economy being devoted to satisfying the need for people to see or own beautiful objects and to be entertained.

The entertainment industry is a miscellaneous grouping of non-commercial institutions and commercial companies that provide these cultural, amusement and recreational activities for people. By contrast, artists and craftspeople are workers who create artwork or handicrafts for their own pleasure or for sale. They usually work alone or in groups of fewer than ten people, often organized around families.

The people who make this entertainment and art possible—artists and craftspeople, actors, musicians, circus performers, park attendants, museum conservators, professional sports players, technicians and others—often face occupational hazards that can result in injuries and illnesses. This chapter will discuss the nature of those occupational hazards. It will not discuss the hazards to people doing arts and crafts as hobbies or attending these entertainment events, although in many instances the hazards will be similar.

Entertainment and the arts can be thought of as a microcosm of all industry. The occupational hazards encountered are, in most instances, similar to those found in more conventional industries, and the same types of precautions can be used, although costs may be prohibitive factors for some engineering controls in the arts and crafts. In these instances, emphasis should be on substitution of safer materials and processes. Table 96.1 lists standard types of precautions associated with the various hazards found in the arts and entertainment industries.

Arts and Crafts

Artists and craftspeople are usually self-employed, and the work is done in homes, studios or backyards, using small amounts of capital and equipment. Skills are often handed down from generation to generation in an informal apprenticeship system, particularly in developing countries (McCann 1996). In industrialized countries, artists and craftspeople often learn their trade in schools.

Today, arts and crafts involve millions of people across the world. In many countries, craftwork is a major part of the economy. However, few statistics are available on the number of artists and craftspeople. In the United States, estimates gathered from a variety of sources indicate there are at least 500,000 professional artists, craftspeople and art teachers. In Mexico, it has been estimated that there are 5,000 families involved in the home-based pottery industry alone. The Pan American Health Organization found that 24% of the workforce in Latin America from 1980 to 1990 were self-employed (PAHO 1994). Other studies of the informal sector have found similar or higher percentages (WHO 1976; Henao 1994). What percentage of these are artists and craftspeople is unknown.

Arts and crafts evolve with the technology available and many artists and craftspeople adopt modern chemicals and processes for their work, including plastics, resins, lasers, photography and so on (McCann 1992a; Rossol 1994). Table 96.2 shows the range of physical and chemical hazards found in art processes.

The arts and crafts industry, like much of the informal sector, is almost completely unregulated and is often exempted from workers' compensation laws and other occupational safety and health regulations. In many countries, government agencies responsible for occupational safety and health are unaware of the risks facing artists and craftspeople, and occupational health services do not reach out to this group of workers. Special attention is needed to find ways to educate artists and craftspeople about the hazards and precautions needed with their materials and processes, and to make occupational health services available to them.

Health problems and disease patterns

Few epidemiological studies have been done on workers in the visual arts. This is mostly due to the decentralized and often unregistered nature of most of these industries. Much of the data that are available come from individual case reports in the literature.

The traditional arts and crafts can result in the same occupational diseases and injuries found in larger-scale industry, as evidenced by such old terms as potter's rot, weaver's back and painter's colic. The hazards of such crafts as pottery, metalworking and weaving were first described by Bernardino Ramazzini almost three centuries ago (Ramazzini 1713). Modern materials and processes also are causing occupational illnesses and injuries.

Lead poisoning is still one of the most common occupational illnesses among artists and craftspeople, with examples of lead poisoning being found in:

- a stained-glass artist in the United States (Feldman and Sedman 1975)
- potters and their families in Mexico (Ballestros, Zuniga and Cardenas 1983; Cornell 1988) and Barbados (Koplan et al. 1977)
- families in Sri Lanka recovering gold and silver from jeweller's waste using a molten lead procedure (Ramakrishna et al. 1982).

Other examples of occupational illnesses in the arts and crafts include:

- chromium sensitization in a fibre artist (MMWR 1982)
- neuropathy in a silk-screen artist (Prockup 1978)
- heart attacks from methylene chloride in a furniture refinisher (Stewart and Hake 1976)
- respiratory problems in photographers (Kipen and Lerman 1986)
- mesothelioma in jewellers (Driscoll et al. 1988)
- silicosis and other respiratory diseases in agate workers in India (Rastogi et al. 1991)
- asthma from carving ivory from elephant tusks in Africa (Armstrong, Neill and Mossop 1988)
- respiratory problems and ergonomic problems among carpet weavers in India (Das, Shukla and Ory 1992)
- as many as 93 cases of peripheral neuropathy from the use of hexane-based adhesives in sandal-making in Japan in the late 1960s (Sofue et al. 1968)
- paralysis in 44 apprentice shoemakers in Morocco due to glues containing tri-orthocresyl phosphate (Balafrej et al. 1984)
- leg, arm and back pain and other occupational health problems in home-based workers making ready-made garments in India (Chaterjee 1990).

A major problem in the arts and crafts is the prevalent lack of knowledge of hazards, materials and processes and how to work safely. Individuals who do develop occupational diseases often do not realize the connection between their illness and their exposures to hazardous materials, and are less likely to obtain

Table 96.1 • Precautions associated with hazards in the arts and entertainment industries.

Hazard	Precautions
Chemical hazards	
General	Training in hazards and precautions
	Substitution of safer materials
	Engineering controls
	Adequate storage and handling
	No eating, drinking or smoking in work areas
	Personal protective equipment
	Spill and leak control procedures
	Safe disposal of hazardous materials
Airborne contaminants (vapours, gases, spray mists, fogs, dusts, fumes, smoke)	Enclosure
	Dilution or local exhaust ventilation
	Respiratory protection
Liquids	Cover containers
	Gloves and other personal protective clothing
	Splash goggles and face shields as needed
	Eyewash fountain and emergency showers when needed
Powders	Purchasing in liquid or paste form
	Glove boxes
	Local exhaust ventilation
	Wet mopping or vacuuming
	Respiratory protection
Solids	Gloves
Physical hazards	
Noise	Quieter machinery
	Proper maintenance
	Sound dampening
	Isolation and enclosure
	Hearing protectors
Ultraviolet radiation	Enclosure
	Skin protection and UV goggles
Infrared radiation	Skin protection and infrared goggles
Lasers	Using lowest-power laser possible
	Enclosure
	Beam restrictions and proper emergency cutoffs
	Laser goggles
Heat	Acclimatization
	Light, loose clothing
	Rest breaks in cool areas
	Adequate liquid intake

Hazard	Precautions
Cold	Warm clothing
	Rest breaks in heated areas
Electrical hazards	Adequate wiring
	Properly grounded equipment
	Ground fault circuit interrupters where needed
	Insulated tools, gloves, etc.
Ergonomic hazards	Ergonomic tools, instruments, etc., of proper size
	Properly designed work stations
	Proper posture
	Rest breaks
Safety hazards	
Machinery	Machine guards
	Accessible stop switch
	Good maintenance
Flying particles (e.g., grinders)	Enclosure
	Eye and face protection as needed
Slips and falls	Clean and dry walking and working surfaces
	Fall protection for elevated work
	Guardrails and toeboards on scaffolds, catwalks, etc.
Falling objects	Safety hats
	Safety shoes
Fire hazards	Proper exit routes
	Proper fire extinguishers, sprinklers, etc.
	Fire drills
	Removal of combustible debris
	Fireproofing of exposed materials
	Proper storage of flammable liquids and compressed gases
	Grounding and bonding when dispensing flammable liquids
	Removal of sources of ignition around flammables
	Proper disposal of solvent- and oil-soaked rags
Biological hazards	
Moulds	Humidity control
	Removal of standing water
	Cleanup after flooding
Bacteria, viruses	Vaccination where appropriate
	Universal precautions
	Disinfection of contaminated materials, surfaces

proper medical assistance. In addition, whole families can be at risk—not only those adults and children actively working with the materials, but also younger children and infants who are present, since these arts and crafts are commonly done in the home (McCann et al. 1986; Knishkowy and Baker 1986).

A proportionate mortality ratio (PMR) study of 1,746 White professional artists by the United States National Cancer Institute found significant elevations in deaths of painters, and to a lesser degree for other artists, from arteriosclerotic heart disease and from cancers of all sites combined. For male painters, rates of leukaemia and cancers of the bladder, kidney and colorectum were significantly elevated. Proportionate cancer mortality rates were also elevated, but to a lesser degree. A case control study of

bladder cancer patients found an overall relative risk estimate of 2.5 for artistic painters, confirming the results found in the PMR study (Miller, Silverman and Blair 1986). For other male artists, PMRs for colorectal and kidney cancer were significantly elevated.

Performing and Media Arts

Traditionally, the performing arts include theatre, dance, opera, music, storytelling and other cultural events that people would come to see. With music, the type of performance and their venue can vary widely: individuals performing music on the street, in taverns and bars, or in formalized concert halls; small musical groups playing in small bars and clubs; and large orchestras

Table 96.2 • Hazards of art techniques.

Technique	Material/process	Hazard
Airbrush	Pigments	Lead, cadmium, manganese, cobalt, mercury, etc.
	Solvents	Mineral spirits, turpentine
Batik	Wax	Fire, wax, decomposition fumes
	Dyes	*See* Dyeing
Ceramics	Clay dust	Silica
	Glazes	Silica, lead, cadmium and other toxic metals
	Slip casting	Talc, asbestiform materials
	Kiln firing	Sulphur dioxide, carbon monoxide, fluorides, infrared radiation, burns
Commercial art	Rubber cement	N-hexane, heptane, fire
	Permanent markers	Xylene, propyl alcohol
	Spray adhesives	N-hexane, heptane, 1,1,1-trichloroethane, fire
	Airbrushing	*See* Airbrush
	Typography	*See* Photography
	Photostats, proofs	Alkali, propyl alcohol
Computer art	Ergonomics	Carpal tunnel syndrome, tendinitis, poorly designed work stations
	Video display	Glare, Elf radiation
Drawing	Spray fixatives	N-hexane, other solvents
Dyeing	Dyes	Fibre-reactive dyes, benzidine dyes, naphthol dyes, basic dyes, disperse dyes, vat dyes
	Mordants	Ammonium dichromate, copper sulphate, ferrous sulphate, oxalic acid, etc.
	Dyeing assistants	Acids, alkalis, sodium hydrosulphite
Electroplating	Gold, silver	Cyanide salts, hydrogen cyanide, electrical hazards
	Other metals	Cyanide salts, acids, electrical hazards
Enamelling	Enamels	Lead, cadmium, arsenic, cobalt, etc.
	Kiln firing	Infrared radiation, burns
Fibre arts	*See also* Batik, Weaving	
	Animal fibres	Anthrax and other infectious agents
	Synthetic fibres	Formaldehyde
	Vegetable fibres	Moulds, allergens, dust
Forging	Hammering	Noise
	Hot forge	Carbon monoxide, polycyclic aromatic hydrocarbons, infrared radiation, burns
Glassblowing	Batch process	Lead, silica, arsenic, etc.
	Furnaces	Heat, infrared radiation, burns
	Colouring	Metal fumes
	Etching	Hydrofluoric acid, ammonium hydrogen fluoride
	Sandblasting	Silica
Holography (*see also* Photography)	Lasers	Non-ionizing radiation, electrical hazards
	Developing	Bromine, pyrogallol
Intaglio	Acid etching	Hydrochloric and nitric acids, nitrogen dioxide, chlorine gas, potassium chlorate
	Solvents	Alcohol, mineral spirits, kerosene
	Aquatint	Rosin dust, dust explosion
	Photoetching	Glycol ethers, xylene
Jewellery	Silver soldering	Cadmium fumes, fluoride fluxes
	Pickling baths	Acids, sulphur oxides
	Gold reclaiming	Mercury, lead, cyanide
Lapidary	Quartz gemstones	Silica
	Cutting, grinding	Noise, silica
Lithography	Solvents	Mineral spirits, isophorone, cyclohexanone, kerosene, gasoline, methylene chloride, etc.
	Acids	Nitric, phosphoric, hydrofluoric, hydrochloric, etc.
	Talc	Asbestiform materials
	Photolithography	Dichromates, solvents

Table continues.

Table 96.2. • Hazards of art techniques.
Continued.

Technique	Material/process	Hazard
Lost wax casting	Investment	Cristobalite
	Wax burnout	Wax decomposition fumes, carbon monoxide
	Crucible furnace	Carbon monoxide, metal fumes
	Metal pouring	Metal fumes, infrared radiation, molten metal, burns
	Sandblasting	Silica
Painting	Pigments	Lead, cadmium, mercury, cobalt, manganese compounds, etc.
	Oil, alkyd	Mineral spirits, turpentine
	Acrylic	Trace amounts ammonia, formaldehyde
Papermaking	Fibre separation	Boiling alkali
	Beaters	Noise, injuries, electrical
	Bleaching	Chlorine bleach
	Additives	Pigments, dyes, etc.
Pastels	Pigment dusts	*See* Painting Pigments
Photography	Developing bath	Hydroquinone, monomethyl-*p*-aminophenol sulphate, alkalis
	Stop bath	Acetic acid
	Fixing bath	Sulphur dioxide, ammonia
	Intensifier	Dichromates, hydrochloric acid
	Toning	Selenium compounds, hydrogen sulphide, uranium nitrate, sulphur dioxide, gold salts
	Colour processes	Formaldehyde, solvents, colour developers, sulphur dioxide
	Platinum printing	Platinum salts, lead, acids, oxalates
Relief printing	Solvents	Mineral spirits
	Pigments	*See* Painting Pigments
Screen printing	Pigments	Lead, cadmium, manganese and other pigments
	Solvents	Mineral spirits, toluene, xylene
	Photoemulsions	Ammonium dichromate
Sculpture, clay	*See* Ceramics	
Sculpture, lasers	Lasers	Non-ionizing radiation, electrical hazards
Sculpture, neon	Neon tubes	Mercury, cadmium phosphors, electrical hazards, ultraviolet radiation
Sculpture, plastics	Epoxy resin	Amines, diglycidyl ethers
	Polyester resin	Styrene, methyl methacrylate, methyl ethyl ketone peroxide
	Polyurethane resins	Isocyanates, organotin compounds, amines, mineral spirits
	Acrylic resins	Methyl methacrylate, benzoyl peroxide
	Plastic fabrication	Heat decomposition products (e.g., carbon monoxide, hydrogen chloride, hydrogen cyanide, etc.)
Sculpture, stone	Marble	Nuisance dust
	Soapstone	Silica, talc, asbestiform materials
	Granite, sandstone	Silica
	Pneumatic tools	Vibration, noise
Stained glass	Lead came	Lead
	Colourants	Lead-based compounds
	Soldering	Lead, zinc chloride fumes
	Etching	Hydrofluoric acid, ammonium hydrogen fluoride
Weaving	Looms	Ergonomic problems
	Dyes	*See* Dyeing
Welding	General	Metal fumes, burns, sparks
	Oxyacetylene	Carbon monoxide, nitrogen oxides, compressed gases
	Arc	Ozone, nitrogen dioxide, fluoride and other flux fumes, ultraviolet and infrared radiation, electrical hazards
	Metal fumes	Oxides of copper, zinc, lead, nickel, etc.
Woodworking	Machining	Injuries, wood dust, noise, fire
	Glues	Formaldehyde, epoxy, solvents
	Paint strippers	Methylene chloride, toluene, methyl alcohol, etc.
	Paints and finishes	Mineral spirits, toluene, turpentine, ethyl alcohol, etc.
	Preservatives	Chromated copper arsenate, pentachlorophenol, creosote

Source: Adapted from McCann 1992a.

performing in large concert halls. Theatre and dance companies can be of several types, including: small informal groups associated with schools or universities; non-commercial theatres, which are usually subsidized by governments or private sponsors; and commercial theatres. Performing arts groups may also tour from one location to another.

Modern technology has seen the growth of the media arts, such as the print media, radio, television, motion pictures, videotapes and so on, which enable the performing arts, stories and other events to be recorded or broadcast. Today the media arts are a multi-billion-dollar industry.

Workers in the performing and media arts include the performers themselves—actors, musicians, dancers, reporters and others visible to the public. In addition, there are the technical crews and front office people—stage carpenters, scenic artists, electricians, special effects experts, motion picture or television camera crews, ticket sellers and others—who work backstage, behind the cameras and on other non-performing jobs.

Health effects and disease patterns

Actors, musicians, dancers, singers and other performers are also subject to occupational injuries and illnesses, which can include accidents, fire hazards, repetitive strain injuries, skin irritation and allergies, respiratory irritation, performance anxiety (stage fright) and stress. Many of these types of injuries are specific to particular groups of performers, and are discussed in separate articles. Even minor physical problems can often affect a performer's peak performance capability, and subsequently end in lost time and even lost jobs. In recent years, the prevention, diagnosis and treatment of injuries to performers has led to the new field of arts medicine, originally an offshoot of sports medicine. (See the box "History of performing arts medicine" in this chapter.)

A PMR study of screen and stage actors found significant elevations for lung, oesophagus and bladder cancers in women, with the rate for stage actresses 3.8 times that of screen actresses (Depue and Kagey 1985). Male actors had significant PMR (but not proportionate cancer mortality ratio) increases for pancreatic and colon cancer; testicular cancer was twice the expected rate by both methods. PMRs for suicide and non–motor vehicle accidents were significantly elevated for both men and women, and the PMR for cirrhosis of the liver was elevated in men.

A recent survey of injuries among 313 performers in 23 Broadway shows in New York City found that 55.5% reported at least one injury, with a mean of 1.08 injuries per performer (Evans et al. 1996). For Broadway dancers, the most frequent sites of injury were the lower extremities (52%), back (22%) and neck (12%), with raked or slanted stages being a significant contributing factor. For actors, the most frequent sites of injuries were lower extremities (38%), the lower back (15%) and vocal cords (17%). The use of fogs and smoke on stage was listed as a major cause for the last.

In 1991, the United States National Institute for Occupational Safety and Health investigated the health effects of the use of smoke and fogs in four Broadway shows (Burr et al. 1994). All the shows used glycol-type fogs, although one also used mineral oil. A questionnaire survey of 134 actors in these shows with a control group of 90 actors in five shows not using fogs found significantly higher levels of symptoms in actors exposed to fogs, including upper-respiratory symptoms such as nasal symptoms and irritation of mucous membranes, and lower-respiratory symptoms such as coughing, wheezing, breathlessness and chest tightness. A follow-up study could not demonstrate a correlation between fog exposure and asthma, possibly due to the low number of responses.

The motion picture production industry has a high accident rate, and in California is classified as high risk, mostly as a result of stunts. During the 1980s, there were over 40 fatalities in American-produced motion pictures (McCann 1991). California statistics for 1980–1988 show an incidence of 1.5 fatalities per 1,000 injuries, compared to the California average of 0.5 for the same period.

A large number of studies have shown that dancers have high overuse and acute injury rates. Ballet dancers, for example, have high incidences of overuse syndrome (63%), stress fractures (26%) and major (51%) or minor (48%) problems during their professional careers (Hamilton and Hamilton 1991). One questionnaire study of 141 dancers (80 females), 18 to 37 years old, from seven professional ballet and modern dance companies in the United Kingdom, found that 118 (84%) of the dancers reported at least one dance-related injury that affected their dancing, 59 (42%) in the last six months (Bowling 1989). Seventy-four (53%) reported that they were suffering from at least one chronic injury that was giving them pain. The back, neck and ankles were the most common sites of injury.

As with dancers, musicians have a high incidence of overuse syndrome. A 1986 questionnaire survey by the International Conference of Symphony and Opera Musicians of 4,025 members from 48 American orchestras showed medical problems affecting performance in 76% of the 2,212 respondents, with severe medical problems in 36% (Fishbein 1988). The most common problem was overuse syndrome, reported by 78% of string players. A 1986 study of eight orchestras in Australia, the United States and England found a 64% occurrence of overuse syndrome, 42% of which involved a significant level of symptoms (Frye 1986).

Hearing loss among rock musicians has had significant press coverage. Hearing loss is also found, however, among classical musicians. In one study, sound level measurements at the Lyric Theatre and Concert Hall in Gothenberg, Sweden, averaged 83 to 89 dBA. Hearing tests of 139 male and female musicians from both theatres indicated that 59 musicians (43%) showed worse pure tone thresholds than would be expected for their age, with brass wind instrumentalists showing the greatest loss (Axelsson and Lindgren 1981).

A 1994-1996 study of sound level measurements in the orchestra pits of 9 Broadway shows in New York City showed average sound levels from 84 to 101 dBA, with a normal showtime of 2½ hours (Babin 1996).

The carpenters, scenic artists, electricians, camera crews and other technical support workers face, in addition to many safety hazards, a wide variety of chemical hazards from materials used in scene shops, prop shops and costume shops. Many of the same materials are used in the visual arts. However, there are no available injury or illness statistics on these workers.

Entertainment

The "Entertainment" section of the chapter covers a variety of entertainment industries that are not covered under "Arts and Crafts" and "Performing and Media Arts", including: museums and art galleries; zoos and aquariums; parks and botanical gardens; circuses, amusement and theme parks; bullfighting and rodeos; professional sports; the sex industry; and nightlife entertainment.

Health effects and disease patterns

There are a wide variety of types of workers involved in the entertainment industry, including performers, technicians, museum conservators, animal handlers, park rangers, restaurant workers, cleaning and maintenance personnel and many more. Many of the hazards found in the arts and crafts and performing and media arts are also found among particular groups of entertainment workers. Additional hazards such as cleaning products, toxic plants, dangerous animals, AIDS, zoonoses, hazardous drugs, violence and so forth are also occupational hazards to particular groups of entertainment workers. Because of the disparateness of the various industries, there are no overall injury and illness statistics. The individual articles include relevant injury and illness statistics, where available.

DRAWING, PAINTING AND PRINTMAKING

Jack W. Snyder

Drawing involves making marks on a surface to express a feeling, experience or vision. The most commonly used surface is paper; drawing media include dry implements such as charcoal, coloured pencils, crayons, graphite, metalpoint and pastels, and liquids such as inks, markers and paints. Painting refers to processes that apply an aqueous or non-aqueous liquid medium ("paint") to sized, primed or sealed surfaces such as canvas, paper or panel. Aqueous media include water-colours, tempera, acrylic polymers, latex and fresco; non-aqueous media include linseed or stand oils, dryers, varnish, alkyds, encaustic or molten wax, organic solvent-based acrylics, epoxy, enamels, stains and lacquers. Paints and inks typically consists of colouring agents (pigments and dyes), a liquid vehicle (organic solvent, oil or water), binders, bulking agents, antioxidants, preservatives and stabilizers.

Prints are works of art made by transferring a layer of ink from an image on a printing surface (such as woodblock, screen, metal plate or stone) onto paper, fabric or plastic. The printmaking process involves several steps: (1) preparation of the image; (2) printing; and (3) cleanup. Multiple copies of the image can be made by repeating the printing step. In monoprints, only one print is made.

Intaglio printing involves incising lines by mechanical means (e.g., engraving, drypoint) or etching the metal plate with acid to create depressed areas in the plate, which form the image. Various solvent-containing resists and other materials such as rosin or spray paint (aquatinting) can be used to protect the part of the plate not being etched. In printing, the ink (which is linseed oil based) is rolled onto the plate, and the excess wiped off, leaving ink in the depressed areas and lines. The print is made by placing the paper on the plate and applying pressure by a printing press to transfer the ink image to the paper.

Relief printing involves the cutting away of the parts of woodblocks or linoleum that are not to be printed, leaving a raised image. Water- or linseed oil–based inks are applied to the raised image and the ink image transferred to paper.

Stone lithography involves making an image with a greasy drawing crayon or other drawing materials that will make the image receptive to the linseed oil–based ink, and treating the plate with acids to make non-image areas water receptive and ink repellent. The image is washed out with mineral spirits or other solvents, inked with a roller and then printed. Metal plate lithography can involve a preliminary counteretch that often contains dichromate salts. Metal plates may be treated with vinyl lacquers containing ketone solvents for long print runs.

Screen printing is a stencil process where a negative image is made on the fabric screen by blocking out portions of the screen. For water-based inks, the blockout materials must be water insoluble; for solvent-based inks, the reverse. Cut plastic stencils are frequently used and adhered to the screen with solvents. The prints are made by scraping ink across the screen, forcing the ink through the unblocked parts of the screen onto paper located underneath the screen, thus creating the positive image. Large print runs using solvent-based inks involve the release of large amounts of solvent vapours into the air.

Collographs are made using either intaglio or relief printing techniques on a textured surface or collage, which can be made of many materials glued onto the plate.

Photoprintmaking processes can use either presensitized plates (often diazo) for lithography or intaglio, or the photoemulsion can be applied directly to the plate or stone. A mixture of gum arabic and dichromates have often been used on stones (gum printing). The photographic image is transferred to the plate, and then the plate exposed to ultraviolet light (e.g., carbon arcs, xenon lights, sunlight). When developed, the non-exposed portions of the photoemulsion are washed away, and the plate then printed. The coating and developing agents can often contain hazardous solvents and alkalis. In photo screen processes, the screen can be coated with dichromate or diazo photoemulsion directly, or an indirect process can be used, which involves adhering sensitized transfer films to the screen after exposure.

In printmaking techniques using oil-based inks, the ink is cleaned up with solvents or with vegetable oil and dishwashing liquid. Solvents also have to be used for cleaning lithography rollers. For water-based inks, water is used for cleanup. For solvent-based inks, large amounts of solvents are used for cleanup, making this one of the most hazardous processes in printmaking. Photoemulsions can be removed from screens using chlorine bleach or enzyme detergents.

Artists who draw, paint or make prints face significant health and safety hazards. The major sources of hazards for these artists include acids (in lithography and intaglio), alcohols (in paint, shellac, resin and varnish thinners and removers), alkalis (in paints, dye baths, photodevelopers and film cleaners), dusts (in chalks, charcoal and pastels), gases (in aerosols, etching, lithography and photoprocesses), metals (in pigments, photochemicals and emulsions), mists and sprays (in aerosols, air-brushing and aquatinting), pigments (in inks and paints), powders (in dry pigments and photochemicals, rosin, talc and whiting), preservatives (in paints, glues, hardeners and stabilizers) and solvents (such as aliphatic, aromatic and chlorinated hydrocarbons, glycol ethers and ketones). Common routes of exposure associated with these hazards include inhalation, ingestion and skin contact.

Among the well-documented health problems of painters, drawers and printmakers are: *n*-hexane-induced peripheral nerve damage in art students using rubber cement and spray adhesives; solvent-induced peripheral and central nervous system damage in silk-screen artists; bone marrow suppression related to solvents and glycol ethers in lithographers; onset or aggravation of asthma following exposure to sprays, mists, dusts, moulds and gases; abnormal heart rhythms following exposure to hydrocarbon solvents such as methylene chloride, freon, toluene and 1,1,1-trichloroethane found in glues or correction fluids; acid, alkali or phenol burns or irritation of the skin, eyes and mucous membranes; liver damage induced by organic solvents; and irritation, immune reaction, rashes and ulceration of the skin following exposure to nickel, dichromates and chromates, epoxy hardeners, turpentine or formaldehyde.

Although not well-documented, painting, drawing and printmaking may be associated with an increased risk of leukaemia, kidney tumours and bladder tumours. Suspected carcinogens to which painters, drawers and printmakers may be exposed include chromates and dichromates, polychlorinated biphenyls, trichloroethylene, tannic acid, methylene chloride, glycidol, formaldehyde, and cadmium and arsenic compounds.

The most important precautions in painting, drawing and printmaking include: substitution of water-based materials for materials based on organic solvents; proper use of general dilution

Figure 96.1 • Silk screen printing with slot exhaust hood.

Michael McCann

ventilation and local exhaust ventilation (see figure 96.1); proper handling, labelling, storage and disposal of paints, flammable liquids and waste solvents; appropriate use of personal protective equipment such as aprons, gloves, goggles and respirators; and avoidance of products that contain toxic metals, especially lead, cadmium, mercury, arsenic, chromates and manganese. Solvents to be avoided include benzene, carbon tetrachloride, methyl *n*-butyl ketone, *n*-hexane and trichloroethylene.

Additional efforts designed to reduce the risk of adverse health effects associated with painting, drawing and printmaking include early and continuous education of young artists concerning the hazards of art materials, and laws mandating labels on art materials that warn of both short-term and long-term health and safety hazards.

● SCULPTURE

Giuseppe Battista

In ancient times, the art of sculpture included engraving and carving of stone, wood, bone and other materials. Later, sculpture developed and refined modelling techniques in clay and plaster, and moulding and welding techniques in metals and glass. During the last century various additional materials and techniques have been used for the art of sculpture, including plastic foams, paper, found materials and several sources of energy such as light, kinetic energy and so on. The aim of many modern sculptors is to involve the viewer actively.

Sculpture often utilizes the natural colour of the material or treats its surface to achieve a certain colour or to emphasize the natural characteristics or to modify the light reflections. Such techniques belong to the finishing touches of the art piece. Health and safety risks for artists and their assistants arise from the characteristics of the materials; from the use of tools and equipment; from the various forms of energy (mainly electricity) used for the functioning of tools; and from heat for welding and fusing techniques.

Artists' lack of information and their focusing on the work lead to underestimating the importance of safety; this can result in serious accidents and the development of occupational diseases.

The risks are sometimes linked to the design of the workplace or to the organization of the work (e.g., carrying out many working operations at the same time). Such risks are common to all workplaces, but in the arts and crafts environment they can have more serious outcomes.

General Precautions

These include: appropriate design of the studio, considering the type of power sources employed and the placement and movement of the artistic material; segregation of hazardous operations controlled with adequate warning displays; installation of exhaust systems for control and removal of powders, gases, fumes, vapours and aerosols; use of well-fitted and convenient personal protective equipment; efficient clean-up facilities, such as showers, sinks, eye-wash fountains and so on; knowledge of the risks associated with the use of chemical substances and of the regulations that govern their use, in order to avoid or at least reduce their potential harm; keeping informed on the possible risks of accidents and on hygiene regulations and being trained in first aid and. Local ventilation to remove airborne dust is necessary at its source, when it is produced in abundance. Daily vacuum cleaning, either wet or dry, or wet mopping of the floor and of work surfaces is highly recommended.

Main Sculpturing Techniques

Stone sculpture involves carving hard and soft stones, precious stones, plaster, cement and so on. Sculpture shaping involves work on more pliable materials—plaster and clay modelling and casting, wood sculpture, metalworking, glassblowing, plastic sculpture, sculpture in other materials and mixed techniques. See also the articles "Metalworking" and "Woodworking". Glassblowing is discussed in the chapter *Glass, ceramics and related materials*.

Stone sculptures

Stones used for sculpture can be divided into soft stones and hard stones. The soft stones can be worked manually with tools such as saws, chisels, hammers and rasps, as well as with electric tools.

Hard stones such as granite, and other materials, such as cement blocks, can be used to create works of art and ornaments. This involves working with electric or pneumatic tools. The final stages of the work can be partially executed by hand.

Risks

Prolonged inhalation of high quantities of certain stone dusts containing free crystalline silica, which comes out of freshly cut

Table 96.3 • Hazards of common stones.

Hazardous ingredient	Stones
Free crystalline silica	Hard stones: Granites, basalt, jasper, porphyry, onyx, pietra serena
	Soft stones: steatite (soapstone), sandstone, slate, clays, some limestone
Possible asbestos contamination	Soft stones: soapstone, serpentine
Free silica and asbestos	Hard stones: marble, travertine
	Soft stones: alabaster, tufa, marble, plaster

surfaces, can lead to silicosis. Electric and pneumatic tools can cause a higher concentration in the air of dust which is finer than that produced by manual tools. Marble, travertine and limestone are inert materials and not pathogenic to the lungs; plaster (calcium sulphate) is irritating to the skin and to the mucous membranes.

Asbestos fibre inhalation, even in small quantities, can lead to a risk of lung cancer (laryngeal, tracheal, bronchial, lung and pleural malignancies) and probably also cancer of the digestive tract and of other organ systems. Such fibres can be found as impurities in serpentine and in talc. Asbestosis (fibrosis of the lung) can be contracted only through the inhalation of high doses of asbestos fibres, which is unlikely at this type of work. See table 96.3 for a list of the hazards of common stones.

High noise levels can be produced by the use of pneumatic hammers, electric saws and sanders, as well as manual tools. This can result in hearing loss and other effects on the autonomic nervous system (increase of heart rate, gastric disturbances and so on), psychological problems (irritability, attention deficits and so on), as well as general health problems, including headaches.

The use of electric and pneumatic tools can provoke damage to finger micro-circulation with the possibility of Raynaud's phenomenon, and facilitate degenerative phenomena to the upper arm.

Work in difficult positions and lifting heavy objects can produce low-back pain, muscle strains, arthritis and joint bursitis (knee, elbow).

The risk of accidents is frequently connected with the use of sharp tools moved by powerful forces (manual, electric or pneumatic). Often stone splinters are violently shot into the working environment during the breaking of stones; falling or rolling of improperly fixed blocks or surfaces also occurs. The use of water can lead to slipping on wet floors, and to electric shocks.

Pigment and colourant substances (especially of spray type) used to cover the final layer (paints, lakes) expose the worker to the risk of inhalation of toxic compounds (lead, chromium, nickel) or of irritating or allergenic compounds (acrylic or resins). This can affect the mucous membranes as well as the respiratory tract.

Inhalation of evaporating paints solvents in high quantities over the course of the working day or in lower concentrations for longer periods, can provoke acute or chronic toxic effects on the central nervous system.

Precautions

Alabaster is a safer substitute for soapstone and other hazardous soft stones.

Pneumatic or electric tools with portable dust collectors should be used. The working environment should be cleaned frequently using vacuum cleaners or wet mopping; adequate general ventilation must be provided.

The respiratory system can be protected from the inhalation of dusts, solvents and aerosol vapours through use of proper respirators. Hearing can be protected with ear plugs and eyes can be protected with proper goggles. To reduce the risk of hand accidents leather gloves (when necessary) or lighter rubber gloves, lined with cotton, should be used to prevent contact with chemical substances. Anti-slipping and safety shoes should be used to prevent damage to the feet caused by the possible fall of heavy objects. During complicated and long operations, proper clothes should be worn; ties, jewellery and clothes which could easily get stuck in the machines should not be worn. Long hair should be put up or under a cap. A shower should be taken at the end of every work period; work clothes and shoes should never be taken home.

Pneumatic tool compressors should be placed out of the work area; noisy areas should be insulated; numerous breaks should be taken in warm areas during the working day. Pneumatic and electric tools equipped with comfortable handles (better

if equipped with mechanical shock absorbers) which are able to direct the air away from the hands of the operator should be used; stretching and massage are suggested during the work period.

Sharp tools should be operated as far as possible from hands and body; broken tools should not be used.

Flammable substances (paints, solvents) must be kept far from flames, lit cigarettes and heat sources.

Sculpture shaping

The most common material used for sculpture shaping is clay (mixed with water or naturally soft clay); wax, plaster, concrete

---

Table 96.4 • Main risks associated with material used for sculpture shaping.

Materials	Hazards and precautions
Clays	Hazards: Free crystalline silica; talc can be contaminated by asbestos; during heating operations, toxic gases can be released.
	Precautions: See "Ceramics".
Plasticine	Hazards: Solvents and preservatives can cause irritation to skin and mucous and allergic reactions in certain individuals.
	Precautions: Susceptible individuals should find other materials.
Hard clays	Hazards: Some hardening or polymer clay plasticizers (phthalates) are possible reproductive or carcinogen toxins. During heating operations, hydrogen chloride can be released, especially if overheated.
	Precautions: Avoid overheating or using in an oven also used for cooking.
Waxes	Hazards: Overheated vapours are flammable and explosive. Acrolein fumes, produced by decomposition from overheating wax, are strong respiratory irritants and sensitizers. Wax solvents can be toxic by contact and inhalation; carbon tetrachloride is carcinogenic and highly toxic to the liver and kidneys.
	Precautions: Avoid open flames. Do not use electric hot plates with exposed heating elements. Heat to minimum temperature necessary. Do not use carbon tetrachloride.
Finished plastics	Hazards: Heating, machining, cutting plastics can result in decomposition to hazardous materials such as hydrogen chloride (from polyvinyl chloride), hydrogen cyanide (from polyurethanes and amino plastics), styrene (from polystyrene) and carbon monoxide from the combustion of plastics. Solvents used for glueing plastics are also fire and health hazards.
	Precautions: Have good ventilation when working with plastics and solvents.
Plastics resins	Hazards: Most resin monomers (e.g., styrene, methyl methacrylate, formaldehyde) are hazardous by skin contact and inhalation. Methyl ethyl ketone peroxide hardener for polyester resins can cause blindness if splashed in the eyes. Epoxy hardeners are skin and respiratory irritants and sensitizers. Isocyanates used in polyurethane resins can cause severe asthma.
	Precautions: Use all resins with proper ventilation, personal protective equipment (gloves, respirators, goggles), fire precautions and so forth. Do not spray polyurethane resins.
Glassblowing	See Glass, ceramics and related materials.

96. ENTERTAINMENT AND THE ARTS

and plastic (sometimes reinforced with glass fibres) are also commonly used.

The facility with which a sculpture is shaped is directly proportional to the malleability of the material used. A tool (wood, metal, plastic) is often used.

Some materials, such as clays, can become hard after being heated in a furnace or kiln. Also, talc can be used as semi-liquid clay (slip), which can be poured into moulds and then fired in a kiln after drying.

These types of clays are similar to those used in the ceramic industry and may contain considerable amounts of free crystalline silica. See the article "Ceramics".

Non-hardening clays, such as plasticine, contain fine particles of clays mixed with vegetable oils, preservatives and sometimes solvents. The hardening clays, also called polymer clays, are actually formed with polyvinyl chloride, with plasticizing materials such as various phthalates.

Wax is usually shaped by pouring it into a mould after it is heated, but it can also be formed with heated tools. Wax can be of natural or synthetic compounds (coloured waxes). Many types of waxes can be dissolved with solvents such as alcohol, acetone, mineral or white spirits, ligroin and carbon tetrachloride.

Plaster, concrete and papier mâché have different characteristics: it is not necessary to heat or to melt them; they are usually worked on a metal or fibreglass frame, or cast in moulds.

Plastic sculpture techniques can be divided into two main areas:

- work with already polymerized materials (casting, plate or sheet). They can be heated, softened, glued, cut, refined, refurbished and so on.
- work with non-polymerized plastic. The material is worked with monomers, obtaining a chemical reaction leading to polymerization.

Plastics can be formed by polyester, polyurethane, amino, phenolic, acrylic, epoxy and silicon resins. During polymerization, they can be poured into moulds, applied by hand layup, printed, laminated and skimmed by using catalyzers, accelerators, hardeners, loads and pigments.

See table 96.4 for a list of the hazards and precautions for common sculpture shaping materials.

PHOTOGRAPHY

David Richardson

Black-and-White Processing

In black-and-white photographic processing, exposed film or paper is removed from a light-tight container in a darkroom and sequentially immersed in trays containing aqueous solutions of developer, stop bath and fixer. After a water washing and drying, the film or paper is ready for use. The developer reduces the light-exposed silver halide to metallic silver. The stop bath is a weakly acidic solution that neutralizes the alkaline developer solution and stops further reduction of the silver halide. The fixer forms a soluble complex with the unexposed silver halide, which, together with various water-soluble salts, buffers and halide ions, is subsequently removed from the emulsion in the washing process. Rolls of film are usually processed in closed canisters to which the various solutions are added.

Potential health hazards

Because of the wide variety of formulae used by various suppliers, and different methods of packaging and mixing photoprocessing chemicals, only a few generalizations can be made regarding the types of chemical hazards in black-and-white photoprocessing. The most frequent health issue is the potential for contact dermatitis, which most frequently arises from skin contact with developer solutions. Developer solutions are alkaline and usually contain hydroquinone; in some cases they may contain *p*-methylaminophenolsulphate (also known as Metol or KODAK ELON) as well. Developers are skin and eye irritants and may cause an allergic skin reaction in sensitive individuals. Acetic acid is the principal hazardous component in most stop baths. Although concentrated stop baths are strongly acidic and may cause skin and eye burns following direct contact, the working-strength solutions are usually slight to moderate skin and eye irritants. Fixers contain photographic hypo (sodium thiosulphate) and various sulphite salts (e.g., sodium metabisulphite), and present a low health hazard.

In addition to potential skin and eye hazards, gases or vapours emitted from some photoprocessing solutions may present an inhalation hazard, as well as contribute to unpleasant odours, especially in poorly ventilated areas. Some photochemicals (e.g., fixers) may emit gases such as ammonia or sulphur dioxide resulting from the degradation of ammonium or sulphite salts, respectively. These gases may be irritating to the upper respiratory tract and eyes. In addition, acetic acid emitted from stop baths may also be irritating to the upper respiratory tract and eyes. The irritant effect of these gases or vapours is concentration dependent and is usually observed only at concentrations that exceed occupational exposure limits. However, because of a wide variation in individual susceptibility, some individuals (e.g., persons with pre-existing medical conditions such as asthma) may experience effects at concentrations below occupational exposure limits. Some of these chemicals may be detectable by odour because of the chemical's low odour threshold. Although the odour of a chemical is not necessarily indicative of a health hazard, strong odours or odours that are increasing in intensity may indicate that the ventilation system is inadequate and should be reviewed.

Risk management

The key to working safely with photoprocessing chemicals is to understand the potential health hazards of exposure and to manage the risk to an acceptable level. Recognition and control of potential hazards begins with reading and understanding product labels and safety data sheets.

Avoiding skin contact is an important goal in darkroom safety. Neoprene gloves are particularly useful in reducing skin contact, especially in mixing areas where more concentrated solutions are encountered. Gloves should be of sufficient thickness to prevent tears and leaks, and should be inspected and cleaned frequently—preferably thorough washing of the outer and inner surfaces with a non-alkaline hand cleaner. In addition to gloves, tongs may also be used to prevent skin contact; barrier creams are not appropriate for use with photochemicals because they are not impervious to all photochemicals and may contaminate processing solutions. A protective apron, smock or lab coat should be worn in the darkroom, and frequent laundering of work clothing is desirable. Protective goggles also should be used, especially in areas where concentrated photochemicals are handled.

If photoprocessing chemicals contact the skin, the affected area should be flushed as rapidly as possible with copious amounts of water. Because materials such as developers are alkaline, washing with a non-alkaline hand cleaner (pH of 5.0 to 5.5) may aid in reducing the potential to develop dermatitis. Clothing should be changed immediately if there is any contamination with chemicals, and spills or splashes should be immediately cleaned up. Hand-washing facilities and provisions for rinsing the eyes are particularly important in the mixing and processing areas. If concentrated or glacial acetic acid is used, emergency shower facilities should be available.

Adequate ventilation is also a key factor to safety in the darkroom. The amount of ventilation required varies according to room conditions and processing chemicals. General room ventilation (e.g., 4.25 m³/min supply and 4.8 m³/min exhaust, equivalent to ten air changes per hour in a 3×3×3 m room), with a minimum outside air replenishment rate of 0.15 m³/min/m² floor area, is usually adequate for photographers who undertake basic black-and-white photoprocessing. The exhaust air should be discharged outside the building to avoid redistributing potential air contaminants. Special procedures such as toning (which involves the replacement of silver by silver sulphide, selenium or other metals), intensifying (which involves making parts of the image darker by the use of chemicals such as potassium dichromate or potassium chlorochromate) and mixing operations (where concentrated solutions or powders are handled) may require supplementary local exhaust ventilation or respiratory protection.

Colour Processing

There are a number of colour processes that are more complex and also involve the use of potentially hazardous chemicals. Colour processing is described in the chapter *Printing, photography, and reproduction industries*. As with black-and-white photoprocessing, avoiding skin and eye contact and providing adequate ventilation are key factors to safety in colour processing.

● METALWORKING

Angela Babin

Metalworking involves casting, welding, brazing, forging, soldering, fabrication and surface treatment of metal. Metalworking is becoming even more common as artists in developing countries are also starting to use metal as a basic sculptural material. While many art foundries are commercially run, art foundries are also often part of college art programmes.

Hazards and Precautions

Casting and foundry

Artists either send work out to commercial foundries, or can cast metal in their own studios. The lost wax process is often used for casting small pieces. Common metals and alloys used are bronze, aluminium, brass, pewter, iron and stainless steel. Gold, silver and sometimes platinum are used for casting small pieces, particularly for jewellery.

The lost wax process involves several steps:

1. making the positive form
2. making the investment mould
3. burning out of the wax
4. melting the metal
5. slagging
6. pouring the molten metal into the mould
7. removing the mould

The positive form can be made directly in wax; it can also be made in plaster or other materials, a negative mould made in rubber and then the final positive form cast in wax. Heating the wax can result in fire hazards and in decomposition of the wax from overheating.

The mould is commonly made by applying an investment containing the cristobalite form of silica, creating the risk of silico-

Figure 96.2 • Pouring molten metal in art foundry.

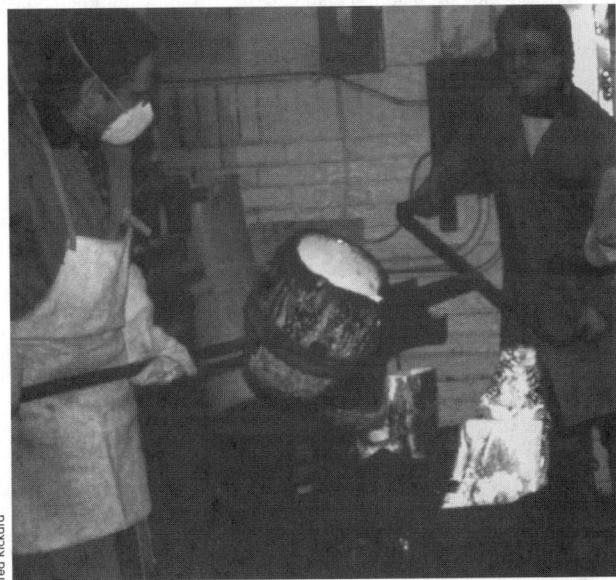

Ted Rickard

sis. A 50/50 mixture of plaster and 30-mesh sand is a safer substitute. Moulds can also be made using sand and oil, formaldehyde resins and other resins as binders. Many of these resins are toxic by skin contact and inhalation, requiring skin protection and ventilation.

The wax form is burnt out in a kiln. This requires local exhaust ventilation to remove the acrolein and other irritating wax decomposition products.

Melting the metal is usually done in a gas-fired crucible furnace. A canopy hood exhausted to the outside is needed to remove carbon monoxide and metal fumes, including zinc, copper, lead, aluminium and so on.

The crucible containing the molten metal is then removed from the furnace, the slag on the surface removed and the molten metal poured into the moulds (figure 96.2). For weights under 80 pounds of metal, manual lifting is normal; for greater weights, lifting equipment is needed. Ventilation is needed for the slagging and pouring operations to remove metal fumes. Resin sand moulds can also produce hazardous decomposition products from the heat. Face shields protecting against infrared radiation and heat, and personal protective clothing resistant to heat and molten metal splashes are essential. Cement floors must be protected against molten metal splashes by a layer of sand.

Breaking away the mould can result in exposure to silica. Local exhaust ventilation or respiratory protection is needed. A variation of the lost wax process called the foam vaporization process involves using polystyrene or polyurethane foam instead of wax, and vaporizing the foam during pouring of the molten metal. This can release hazardous decomposition products, including hydrogen cyanide from polyurethane foam. Artists often use scrap metal from a variety of sources. This practice can be dangerous due to possible presence of lead- and mercury-containing paints, and to the possible presence of metals like cadmium, chromium, nickel and so on in the metals.

Fabrication

Metal can be cut, drilled and filed using saws, drills, snips and metal files. The metal filings can irritate the skin and eyes. Electric tools can cause electric shock. Improper handling of these tools can result in accidents. Goggles are needed to protect the eyes from flying chips and filings. All electrical equipment should be properly grounded. All tools should be carefully handled and stored. Metal to be fabricated should be securely clamped to prevent accidents.

Forging

Cold forging utilizes hammers, mallets, anvils and similar tools to change the shape of metal. Hot forging involves additionally heating the metal. Forging can create great amounts of noise, which can cause hearing loss. Small metal splinters may damage the skin or eyes if precautions are not taken. Burns are also a hazard with hot forging. Precautions include good tools, eye protection, routine clean-up, proper work clothing, isolation of the forging area and wearing ear plugs or ear muffs.

Hot forging involves the burning of gas, coke or other fuels. A canopy hood for ventilation is needed to exhaust carbon monoxide and possible polycyclic aromatic hydrocarbon emissions, and to reduce heat build-up. Infrared goggles should be worn for protection against infrared radiation.

Surface treatment

Mechanical treatment (chasing, repousse) is done with hammers, engraving with sharp tools, etching with acids, photoetching with acids and photochemicals, electroplating (plating a metallic film onto another metal) and electroforming (plating a metallic film onto a non-metallic object) with acids and cyanide solutions and metal colouring with many chemicals.

Electroplating and electroforming often use cyanide salts, ingestion of which can be fatal. Accidental mixing of acids and the cyanide solution will produce hydrogen cyanide gas. This is hazardous through both skin absorption and inhalation—death can occur within minutes. Disposal and waste management of spent cyanide solutions is strictly regulated in many countries. Electroplating with cyanide solutions should be done in a commercial plant; otherwise use substitutes that do not contain cyanide salts or other cyanide-containing materials.

Acids are corrosive, and skin and eye protection is needed. Local exhaust ventilation with acid-resistant ductwork is recommended.

Anodizing metals such as titanium and tantalum involves oxidizing these at the anode of an electrolytic bath to colour them. Hydrofluoric acid can be used for precleaning. Avoid using hydrofluoric acid or use gloves, goggles and a protective apron.

Patinas used to colour metals can be applied cold or hot. Lead and arsenic compounds are very toxic in any form, and others can give off toxic gases when heated. Potassium ferricyanide solutions will give off hydrogen cyanide gas when heated, arsenic acid solutions give off arsine gas and sulphide solutions give off hydrogen sulphide gas. Very good ventilation is needed for metal colouring (figure 96.3). Arsenic compounds and heating of potassium ferrocyanide solutions should be avoided.

Finishing processes

Cleaning, grinding, filing, sandblasting and polishing are some final treatments for metal. Cleaning involves the use of acids (pickling). This involves the hazards of handling acids and of the gases produced during the pickling process (such as nitrogen dioxide from nitric acid). Grinding can result in the production of fine metal dusts (which can be inhaled) and heavy flying particles (which are eye hazards).

Sandblasting (abrasive blasting) is very hazardous, particularly with actual sand. Inhalation of fine silica dust from sandblasting can cause silicosis in a short time. Sand should be replaced with glass beads, aluminium oxide or silicon carbide. Foundry slags should be used only if chemical analysis shows no silica or danger-

Figure 96.3 • Applying a patina to metal with slot exhaust hood.

Ken Jones

ous metals such as arsenic or nickel. Good ventilation or respiratory protection is needed.

Polishing with abrasives such as rouge (iron oxide) or tripoli can be hazardous since rouge can be contaminated with large amounts of free silica, and tripoli contains silica. Good ventilation of the polishing wheel is needed.

Welding

Physical hazards in welding include the danger of fire, electric shock from arc-welding equipment, burns caused by molten metal sparks, and injuries caused by excessive exposure to infrared and ultraviolet radiation. Welding sparks can travel 40 feet.

Infrared radiation can cause burns and eye damage. Ultraviolet radiation can cause sunburn; repeated exposure may lead to skin cancer. Electric arc welders in particular are subject to pink eye (conjunctivitis), and some have cornea damage from UV exposure. Skin protection and welding goggles with UV- and IR-protective lenses are needed.

Oxyacetylene torches produce carbon monoxide, nitrogen oxides and unburned acetylene, which is a mild intoxicant. Commercial acetylene contains small amounts of other toxic gases and impurities.

Compressed gas cylinders can be both explosive and fire hazards. All cylinders, connections and hoses must be carefully maintained and inspected. All gas cylinders must be stored in a location which is dry, well ventilated and secure from unauthorized persons. Fuel cylinders must be stored separately from oxygen cylinders.

Arc welding produces enough energy to convert the air's nitrogen and oxygen to nitrogen oxides and ozone, which are lung irritants. When arc welding is done within 20 feet of chlorinated degreasing solvents, phosgene gas can be produced by the UV radiation.

Metal fumes are generated by the vaporization of metals, metal alloys and the electrodes used in arc welding. Fluoride fluxes produce fluoride fumes.

Ventilation is needed for all welding processes. While dilution ventilation may be adequate for mild steel welding, local exhaust ventilation is necessary for most welding operations. Moveable flanged hoods, or lateral slot hoods should be used. Respiratory protection is needed if ventilation is not available.

Many metal dusts and fumes can cause skin irritation and sensitization. These include brass dust (copper, zinc, lead and tin), cadmium, nickel, titanium and chromium.

In addition, there are problems with welding materials that may be coated with various substances (e.g., lead or mercury paint).

• NEW TECHNOLOGY IN ART

William E. Irwin

This article describes the basic health and safety concerns associated with the use of lasers, neon sculpture and computers in the arts. Creative artists often work very intimately with the technology, and in experimental ways. This scenario too often increases the risk of injury. The primary concerns are for eye and skin protection, for reducing the possibilities of electrical shock and for preventing exposure to toxic chemicals.

Lasers

Laser radiation may be hazardous to the eyes and skin of artists and audiences by both direct viewing and reflection. The degree of laser injury is a function of power. Higher-power lasers are more likely to cause serious injury and more hazardous reflections. Lasers are classified and labelled by their manufacturer in classes I to IV. Class I lasers exhibit no laser radiation hazard and Class IV are very dangerous.

Artists have used all laser classes in their work, and most use visible wavelengths. Besides the safety controls required of any laser system, artistic applications require special considerations.

In laser exhibits, it is important to isolate the audience from direct beam contact and scattered radiation, using plastic or glass enclosures and opaque beam stops. For planetariums and other indoor light shows, it is critical to maintain direct beam or reflected laser radiation at Class I levels where the audience is exposed. Class III or IV laser radiation levels must be kept at safe distances from performers and the audience. Typical distances are 3 m away when an operator controls the laser and 6 m away without continuous operator control. Written procedures are needed for set-up, alignment and testing of Class III and IV lasers. Required safety controls include warning in advance of energizing these lasers, key controls, fail-safe safety interlocks and manual reset buttons for Class IV lasers. For Class IV lasers, appropriate laser goggles should be worn.

Scanning laser art displays often used in the performing arts use rapidly moving beams that are generally safer since the duration of inadvertent eye or skin contact with the beam is short. Still, operators must employ safeguards to ensure exposure limits will not be exceeded if the scanning equipment fails. Outdoor displays cannot allow aircraft to fly through hazardous beam levels, or the illumination with greater than Class I levels of radiation of tall buildings or personnel in high-reach equipment.

Holography is the process of producing a three-dimensional photograph of an object using lasers. Most images are displayed off-axis from the laser beam, and intrabeam viewing is typically not a hazard. A transparent display case around the hologram can help reduce the possibilities of injury. Some artists create permanent images from their holograms, and many chemicals used in the development process are toxic and must be managed

for accident prevention. These include pyrogallic acid, alkalis, sulphuric and hydrobromic acids, bromine, parabenzoquinone and dichromate salts. Safer substitutes are available for most of these chemicals.

Lasers also have serious non-radiological hazards. Most performance-level lasers use high voltages and amperage, creating significant risks of electrocution, particularly during design stages and maintenance. Dye lasers use toxic chemicals for the active lasing medium, and high-powered lasers may generate toxic aerosols, especially when the beam strikes a target.

Neon Art

Neon art uses neon tubes to produce lighted sculptures. Neon signage for advertising is one application. Producing a neon sculpture involves bending leaded glass to the desired shape, bombarding the evacuated glass tube at a high voltage to remove impurities from the glass tube, and adding small amounts of neon gas or mercury. A high voltage is applied across electrodes sealed into each end of the tube to give the luminous effect by exciting the gases trapped in the tube. To obtain a wider range of colours, the glass tube can be coated with fluorescent phosphors, which convert the ultraviolet radiation from the mercury or neon into visible light. The high voltages are achieved by using step-up transformers.

Electrical shock is a threat mostly when the sculpture is connected to its bombarding transformer to remove impurities from the glass tube, or to its electrical power source for testing or display (figure 96.4). The electrical current passing through the glass tube also causes the emission of ultraviolet light that in turn interacts with the phosphor-covered glass to form colours. Some near-ultraviolet radiation (UVA) may pass through the glass and present an eye hazard to those nearby; therefore, eyewear that blocks UVA should be worn.

Some phosphors that coat the neon tube are potentially toxic (e.g., cadmium compounds). Sometimes mercury is added to the neon gas to create a particularly vivid blue colour. Mercury is highly toxic by inhalation and is volatile at room temperature.

Figure 96.4 • Neon sculpture manufacture showing an artist behind a protective barrier.

Fred Tschida

Mercury should be added to the neon tube with great care and stored in unbreakable sealed containers. The artist should use trays to contain spillage, and mercury spill kits should be available. Mercury should not be vacuumed up, as this may disperse a mist of mercury through the vacuum cleaner's exhaust.

Computer Art

Computers are used in art for a variety of purposes, including painting, displaying scanned photographic images, producing graphics for printing and television (e.g., on-screen credits), and for a variety of animated and other special effects for motion pictures and television. The latter is a rapidly expanding use of computer art. This can bring about ergonomic problems, typically due to repetitive tasks and uncomfortably arranged components. The predominant complaints are discomfort in the wrists, arms, shoulders and neck, and vision problems. Most complaints are of a minor nature, but disabling injuries such as chronic tendinitis or carpal tunnel syndrome are possible.

Creating with computers often involves long periods manipulating the keyboard or mouse, designing or fine tuning the product. It is important that computer users take a break away from the screen periodically. Short, frequent breaks are more effective than long breaks every couple of hours.

Regarding the proper arrangement of components and the user, design solutions for correct posture and visual comfort are the key. Computer work station components should be easy to adjust for the variety of tasks and people involved.

Eye strain may be prevented by taking periodic visual breaks, preventing glare and reflection and by placing the top of the monitor so that it is at eye level. Vision problems may also be avoided if the monitor has a refresh rate of 70 Hz, so that image flicker is reduced.

Many kinds of radiation effects are possible. Ultraviolet, visible, infrared, radio frequency and microwave radiation emissions from computer hardware are generally at or below normal background levels. The possible health effects of lower-frequency waves from the electrical circuitry and electronic components are not well understood. To date, however, no solid evidence identifies a health risk from exposure to the electromagnetic fields associated with computer monitors. Computer monitors do not emit hazardous levels of x rays.

• FIBRE AND TEXTILE CRAFTS

Gail Coningsby Barazani

Contemporary fibre or textile artists use a wide range of processes, such as weaving, needlework, papermaking, leatherworking and so forth. These can be done by hand or aided by machines (see table 96.5). They may also use many processes for preparing fibres or finished textile, such as carding, spinning, dyeing, finishing and bleaching (see table 96.6). Finally the fibreworks or textiles may be painted, silk-screened, treated with photographic chemicals, scorched or otherwise modified. See separate articles in this chapter describing these techniques.

No material is off limits for artists, who may use any of thousands of animal, vegetable or synthetic materials in their work. They gather materials such as weeds, vines or animal hair from the outdoors, or purchase products from suppliers who may have altered them by treating them with oils, fragrances, dyes, paints or pesticides (e.g., rat poison in twine or rope intended for agricultural use). Imported animal or vegetable materials that have been processed to eliminate disease carrying insects, spores or fungi are also used. Old rags, bones, feathers, wood, plastics or glass are among many other materials incorporated in fibre crafts.

Potential Sources of Health Hazards in the Fibre Arts

Chemicals

Health hazards in fibre or textile arts, as in any workplace, include air pollutants such as dusts, gases, fumes and vapours that are inherent in the materials or are produced in the work process, and can be inhaled or affect the skin. In addition to chemical hazards of dyes, paints, acids, alkalis, mothproofing agents and so on, fibre or textile materials may be contaminated with biological materials that can cause disease.

Vegetable dusts

Workers heavily exposed to dusts of raw cotton, sisal, jute and other vegetable fibres in industrial workplaces have developed various chronic lung problems such as "brown lung" (byssinosis), which begins with chest tightness and shortness of breath, and can be disabling after many years. Exposure to vegetable dusts in general may cause lung irritation or other effects such as asthma, hay fever, bronchitis and emphysema. Other materials associated with vegetable fibres, such as moulds, mildew, sizing materials and dyes, may also cause allergic or other reactions.

Animal dusts

Animal products used by fibre artists such as wool, hair, hides and feathers may be contaminated with bacteria, moulds, lice or mites that are capable of causing "Q" fever, mange, respiratory symptoms, skin rashes, anthrax, allergies and so on, if they are not treated or fumigated before use. Fatal cases of inhalation anthrax have occurred in craft weavers, including the 1976 death of a California weaver.

Synthetic materials

The effects of dusts of polyesters, nylon, acrylic, rayon and acetates are not well known. Some plastic fibres may release gas or components or residues which are left in the fabric after processing, as in the case of formaldehyde released by polyesters or permanent-press fabrics. Sensitive individuals have reported allergic responses in rooms or stores where these materials were present, and some have developed skin rashes after wearing clothing of these fabrics, even after repeated washings.

Heating, scorching or otherwise altering synthetic materials chemically may release potentially hazardous gases or fumes.

Physical Effects of Working with Fibres and Textiles

The physical characteristics of materials may affect the user. Rough, thorny or abrasive materials can cut or abrade skin. Glass fibres or stiff grasses or rattan can penetrate the skin and cause infections or rashes.

Much of fibre or fabric work is done while the worker is seated for prolonged periods, and involves repetitive motion of arms, wrists, hands and fingers, and often the entire body. This may produce pain and eventual repetitive strain injuries. Weavers, for example, can develop back problems, carpal tunnel syndrome, skeletal deformation from weaving in a squatting position on older types of looms (particularly in young children), hand and finger disorders (e.g., swollen joints, arthritis, neuralgia) from threading and tying knots, and eyestrain from poor lighting (figure 96.5). Many of the same problems can occur in other fibre crafts involving sewing, tying knots, knitting and so forth. Needlework crafts can also involve hazards of needle pricks.

Lifting of large papermaking screens containing water-saturated pulp can cause possible back injuries due to the weight of the water and pulp.

Table 96.5 • Description of fibre and textile crafts.

Process	Description
Basketry	Basketry is the making of baskets, bags, mats, etc., by hand weaving, plaiting and coiling techniques using materials such as reeds, cane and sisal fibre. Knives and scissors are often used, and coiled baskets are often sewed together.
Batik	Batik involves the creating of dye patterns on fabric by applying molten wax to the fabric with a djanting to form a resist, dyeing the fabric and removing the wax with solvents or by ironing between newsprint.
Crocheting	Crocheting is similar to knitting except that a hook is used to loop threads into the fabric.
Embroidery	The embellishment of a fabric, leather, paper or other materials by sewing of designs worked in thread with a needle. Quilting comes under this category.
Knitting	Knitting is the craft of forming a fabric by interlocking of yarn in a series of connected loops using long hand or mechanized needles.
Lacemaking	Lacemaking involves the production of ornamental openwork of threads that have been twisted, looped and intertwined to form patterns. This can involve very fine and intricate hand stitching.
Leatherworking	Leather crafts involve two basic steps: cutting, carving, sewing and other physical processes; and cementing, dyeing and finishing the leather. The first can involve a variety of tools. The latter can involve the use of solvents, dyes, lacquers and such. For tanning, see the chapter *Leather, fur and footwear*.
Macramé	Macramé is the ornamental knotting of yarn into bags, wall hangings or similar materials.
Papermaking	Papermaking involves preparing the pulp and then making the paper. A variety of plants, wood, vegetables, used paper rags and so forth can be used. The fibres must be separated out, often by boiling in alkali. The fibres are washed and placed in a beater to complete preparation of the pulp. Then paper is made by trapping the pulp on a wire or fabric screen, and allowed to dry in the air or by being pressed between layers of felt. The paper can be treated with sizings, dyes, pigments and other materials.
Silk screen printing	See "Printmaking".
Weaving	Weaving uses a machine called a loom to combine two sets of yarn, the warp and the weft, to produce fabric. The warp is wound on large reels, called beams, which run the length of the loom. The warp yarns are threaded through the loom to form vertical parallel threads. The weft is fed from the side of the loom by bobbins. The loom shuttle carries the weft yarns across the loom horizontally under and above alternate warp threads. A starch sizing is used to protect warp threads from breaking during weaving. There are many types of looms, both hand-operated and mechanical.

Table 96.6 • Description of fibre and textile processes.

Process	Description
Carding	Process of cleaning and straightening fibres into parallel lines by combing it (by hand or by special machinery) and twisting the fibres into a rope-like form. This process can create large amounts of dust.
Spinning	A foot-pedal-operated spinning wheel is used to turn the spindle, which combines several fibres into twisted, elongated yarn.
Finishing	The woven fabric can be singed to remove projecting hairs, desized with enzymes, and scoured by boiling in alkali to remove fats and waxes.
Dyeing	Yarn or fabric can be dyed using a variety of types of dyes (natural, direct, acid, basic, disperse, fibre-reactive and more) depending upon the type of fabric. Many dyeing processes involve heating the dyebath to near boiling. Many dyeing assistants can be used, including acids, alkalis, salt, sodium hydrosulphite and, in the case of natural dyes, mordants such as urea, ammonium dichromate, ammonia, copper sulphate, and ferrous sulphate. Dyes are usually purchased in powder form. Some dyes may contain solvents.
Bleaching	Fabrics can be bleached with chlorine bleaches to remove colour.

ventilation and lighting also affect the health of the artist or craftsperson. One or two hours a week spent at a loom in a dusty environment may not affect a person seriously, unless that person is highly allergic to dusts, but a prolonged period of work in the same environment over months or years may result in some health effects. However, even one episode of untrained lifting of a heavy object can cause injury to the spine.

Figure 96.5 • Weaving with a hand loom.

Precautions

As with all work, the adverse effects depend upon the amount of time spent working on a project each day, the number of work-days, weeks or years, the quantity of work and the nature of the workplace, and the type of work itself. Other factors such as

96. ENTERTAINMENT AND THE ARTS

Generally, for prolonged or regular work in fibre art or textiles:

- Obtain and use only treated or fumigated animal or vegetable materials. Other materials should be cleaned or washed, and stored in closed containers to minimize dusts.
- Damp mop or wipe work area surfaces frequently.
- In many countries, manufacturers are required to provide information that describes the hazardous aspects of chemicals such as dyes, adhesives, paints or solvents in any product purchased, such as a manufacturer's Material Safety Data Sheet (MSDS). Request such information.
- Avoid eating, drinking or smoking in the work area.
- Take frequent rest and exercise periods when work involves repetitive motion.
- Modify work processes to reduce the need for excessive lifting or straining. For example, in papermaking use smaller screens or have another person assist in lifting the screen with the pulp.
- Use exhaust ventilation for regular or prolonged use of dusty materials, spray painting, heating of wax or work with solvent-containing materials such as oil-based paints or permanent ink markers.
- Avoid boiling acids and alkalis if possible. Wear gloves, goggles, face shield and protective apron.
- Remember that dusts, gases and vapours travel throughout buildings and may affect others present, particularly infants, children, the aged and the chronically ill.
- Consult an industrial hygienist or safety and health professional when planning a production workshop.

CERAMICS

Monona Rossol

Foodware, sculpture, decorative tiles, dolls and other ceramic or clay items are made in both large and small professional studios and shops, classrooms in public schools, universities and trade schools, and in homes as a hobby or cottage industry. The methods can be divided into ceramics and pottery, although terminology can vary in different countries. In ceramics, objects are made by slip casting—pouring a slurry of water, clay and other ingredients into a mould. The clay objects are removed from the mould, trimmed and fired in a kiln. Some ware (bisque ware) is sold after this stage. Other types are decorated with glazes that are mixtures of silica and other substances which form a glass surface. In pottery, objects are formed from plastic clay, usually by hand-forming or wheel-throwing, after which they are dried and fired in a kiln. Objects may then be glazed. Slip cast ceramics usually are glazed with china paints, which are commercially produced in dry or liquid pre-packaged form (figure 96.6). Potters may glaze their ware with these commercial glazes or with glazes they compound themselves. All types of ware are produced, from terra cotta and earthenware, which are fired at low temperatures, to stoneware and porcelain, which are fired at high temperatures.

Clay and Glaze Materials

All clays and glazes are mixtures of silica, aluminium and metallic minerals. These ingredients usually contain significant amounts of respirable-sized particles such as those in silica flour and ball clays. Clay bodies and glazes are composed of essentially the same types of minerals (see table 96.7), but glazes are formulated to melt at lower temperatures (have more flux) than the bodies on which they are applied. Lead is a common flux. Raw lead minerals such as galena and lead oxides derived from burning car battery plates and other scrap are used as fluxes, and have poisoned potters and their families in some developing countries. Commercially sold glazes for industrial and hobby use are more likely to contain lead and other chemicals which have been mixed and pre-fired into powdered frits. Glazes are formulated to mature in either oxidation or reduction firing (see below) and may contain metal compounds as colourants. Lead, cadmium, barium and other metals may leach into food when glazed ceramic wares are used.

Other special surface treatments include metallic lustre glazes containing tack oils and solvents such as chloroform, iridescent effects obtained by fuming metallic salts (usually chlorides of tin, iron, titanium or vanadium) onto surfaces during firing, and new paints containing plastic resins and solvents, which look like fired ceramic glazes when dry. Specially textured clay bodies may include fillers such as vermiculite, perlite and grog (ground fire brick).

Exposure to clay and glaze ingredients occurs during mixing, sanding and spray-applying glazes, and when grinding or chipping fired glaze imperfections from the bottoms of pottery or from kiln shelves (figure 96.7). Cleaning kiln shelves exposes workers to flint, kaolin and other kiln wash ingredients. Silica dust from fired kiln wash or bisque is more hazardous because it is in the cristobalite form. Hazards include: silicosis and other pneumoconioses from inhalation of minerals such as silica, kaolin, talc and fibrous amphibole asbestos in some talcs; toxicity from exposure to metals such as lead, barium and lithium; dermatitis from sensitizing metals such as chrome, nickel and cobalt; cumulative trauma disorders such as carpal tunnel syndrome ("potter's thumb") from wheel throwing; back injuries from digging clay, lifting 100-pound sacks of bulk minerals or from wedging (hand working clay to remove air bubbles); slips and falls on wet floors; shocks from electric pottery wheels and other equipment used in wet areas; allergies to moulds in clay; fungal and bacterial infections of nail beds and skin; and accidents with clay mixers, pug mills, blungers, slab rollers and the like.

Precautions: outlaw open lead burning; use substitutes for raw lead, lead frits, cadmium and asbestos-containing materials; isolate work from family areas and children; practise housekeeping

Figure 96.6 • Decorating a pot with China paints.

Table 96.7 • Ingredients of ceramic bodies and glazes.

Basic constituents		
Clays (hydroaluminium silicates)	**Alumina**	**Silica**
Kaolins and other white clays Red iron-rich clays Fire clays Ball clays Bentonite	Aluminium oxide, corundum, usual source in glazes is from clays and feldspars	Quartz from flint, sand, diatomaceous earth; cristobalite from calcined silica or fired silica minerals

Other ingredients and some mineral sources		
Fluxes	**Opacifiers**	**Colourants**
Sodium, potassium, lead, magnesium, lithium, barium, boron, calcium, strontium, bismuth	Tin, zinc, antimony, zirconium, titanium, fluorine, cerium, arsenic	Cobalt, copper, chrome, iron, manganese, cadmium, vanadium, nickel, uranium
Sources include oxides and carbonates of metals above, feldspars, talc, nepheline syenite, borax, colemanite, whiting, lead frits, lead silicates	Sources include oxides and carbonates of metals above, cryolite fluorspar, rutile, zirconium silicate	Sources include oxides, carbonates and sulphates of metals above, chromates, spinels and other metal complexes

and hygiene; control dust; use local exhaust ventilation for glaze spraying and dusty processes (figure 96.8); use respiratory protection; work with adequate rest periods; lift safely; guard machines; and use ground fault interrupters on wheels and all other electrical equipment.

Kiln Firing

Kilns vary from railroad-car size to a few cubic inches for firing test tiles and miniatures. They are heated with electricity or fuels such as gas, oil or wood. Electric kilns produce ware fired in primarily oxidizing atmospheres. Reduction firing is achieved by adjusting fuel/air ratios in fuel-fired kilns to create chemically reducing atmospheres. Firing methods include salt firing, raku (putting red-hot pots into organic matter such as damp hay to produce a smoky reduced clay body), climbing kilns (many-chambered wood or coal fired kilns built on hillsides), sawdust firing (kilns packed tight with pots and sawdust) and open-pit firing with many fuels including grass, wood and dung.

Primitive fuel-fired kilns are poorly insulated because they are usually made of fired clay, brick or mud. Such kilns can burn large amounts of wood and can contribute to fuel shortages in developing countries. Commercial kilns are insulated with refractory brick, castable refractory or ceramic fibre. Asbestos insulation is still found in older kilns. Refractory ceramic fibre is in very wide use in industry and hobby kilns. There are even small fibre kilns which are heated by putting them in home kitchen microwave ovens.

Kiln emissions include combustion products from fuels and from organic matter that contaminates clay and glaze minerals, sulphur oxides, fluorine and chlorine from minerals such as cryolite and sodalite, and metal fumes. Salt firing emits hydrochloric

Figure 96.7 • Exposure to clay and glaze dusts while hand sanding a pot.

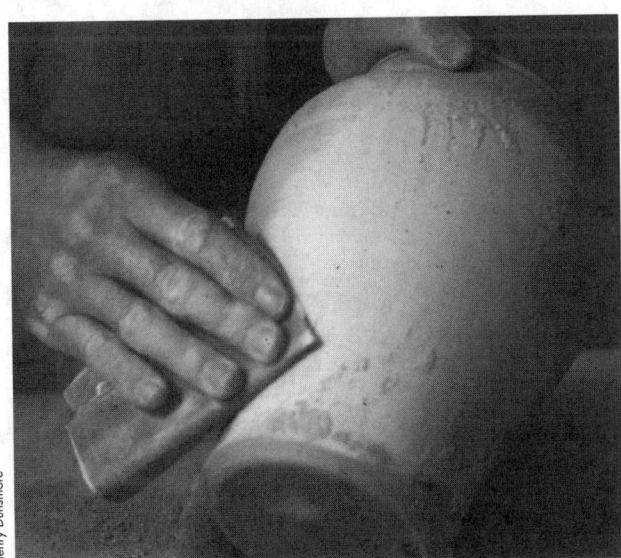

Henry Dunsmore

Figure 96.8 • Local exhaust ventilation for clay mixing.

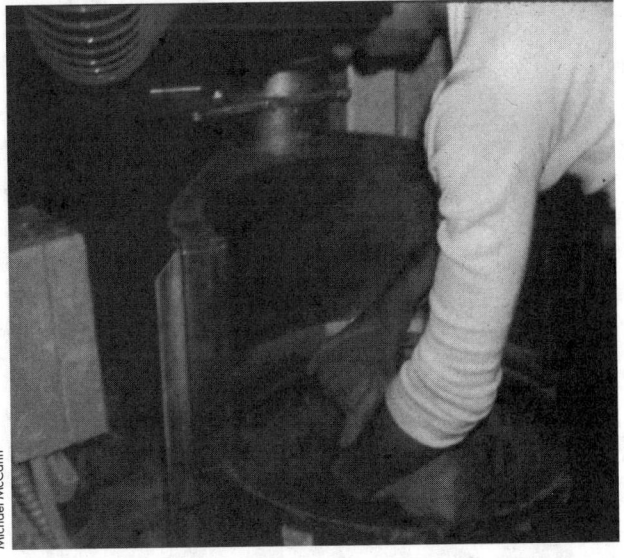

Michael McCann

acid. Emissions are especially hazardous when fuels such as painted or treated wood and waste oils are burned. Hazards include: respiratory irritation or sensitization from aldehydes, sulphur oxides, halogens and other emissions; asphyxiation from carbon monoxide; cancer from inhalation of asbestos or ceramic fibre; eye damage from infrared radiation from glowing hot kilns; and thermal injury and burns.

Precautions: use clean-burning fuels; design fuel-efficient, well-insulated kilns; substitute refractory brick for asbestos or ceramic fibre; encapsulate or remove existing fibre insulation; locally vent indoor kilns; locate kilns in areas free of combustible materials; equip electric kilns with two automatic shut-offs; wear infrared-blocking goggles and gloves when handling hot objects.

• WOODWORKING

Michael McCann

Woodworking is practised as an art form and utilitarian craft all over the world. It includes wood sculpture, furniture and cabinet making (figure 96.9), musical instrument making and so on. Techniques include carving (figure 96.10), laminating, joining, sawing, sanding, paint removing, painting and finishing. Woodworking uses a large number of different types of hard and soft woods, including many exotic tropical woods, plywood and composition boards, and sometimes woods treated with pesticides and wood preservatives.

Figure 96.9 • Furniture making.

Figure 96.10 • Carving wood with hand tools.

Hazards and Precautions

Woods

Many woods are hazardous, especially tropical hardwoods. Types of reactions can include skin allergies and irritation from the sap, wood dust or sometimes the wood, as well as conjunctivitis, respiratory allergies, hypersensitivity pneumonia and toxic reactions. Inhalation of hardwood dust is associated with a particular type of nasal and nasal sinus cancer (adenocarcinoma). See the chapter *Woodworking industry*.

Precautions include avoiding use of sensitizing woods for people who have a history of allergies, or for objects where people would be in frequent contact with the wood, and controlling dust levels by using local exhaust ventilation or wearing a toxic-dust respirator. When handling woods that can cause skin irritation or allergies, the artist should wear gloves or apply a barrier cream. Hands should be washed carefully after work.

Plywoods and composition board

Plywood and composition board (e.g., particle board) are made by gluing thin sheets of wood, or wood dust and chips, together with either urea-formaldehyde glues or phenol-formaldehyde glues. These materials can emit unreacted formaldehyde for some years after manufacture, with composition board emitting more formaldehyde. Heating these materials or machining them can cause decomposition of the glue to release formaldehyde. Formaldehyde is a skin, eye and respiratory irritant and strong sensitizer, and a probable human carcinogen.

Precautions include using low-formaldehyde products whenever possible, not storing large amounts of plywood or composition board in the shop, and using dust collectors connected to woodworking machines that are exhausted to the outside.

Wood preservatives and other treatments

Pesticides and preservatives are often applied to wood when it is being timbered, processed or shipped. Pentachlorophenol and its salts, creosote and chromated copper arsenate (CCA) have been banned for sale in the United States as wood preservatives because of possible carcinogenicity and reproductive hazards. They can, however, still be found in older woods, and chromated copper arsenate is still allowed as a commercial treatment (e.g., "green" lumber, playground equipment and other outdoor uses). A variety of other chemicals can be used in treating wood, including fire retardants and bleaches.

Precautions include not handling woods that have been treated with pentachlorophenol or creosote, using local exhaust ventilation when machining CCA-treated wood or wearing a respirator with high-efficiency filters. Wood that has been treated with creosote, pentachlorophenol or chromated copper arsenate should not be burned.

Carving and machining wood

Woods can be hand carved with chisels, rasps, hand saws, sandpaper and the like, or they can be machined with electric saws, sanders and other woodworking machines. Hazards include exposure to wood dusts, excessive noise levels from woodworking machines, accidents from using tools and machines, electrical shock or fire from faulty wiring, and wood fires. Vibrating tools—for example, chain saws—can cause "white fingers" (Raynaud's phenomenon), involving numbness of the fingers and hands.

Precautions include equipping woodworking machines with dust collectors (figure 96.11) and machine guards, cleaning up sawdust to avoid fire hazards, wearing goggles (and sometimes face shields) and reducing noise. Using the appropriate machine for the desired operation, and repairing defective machines immediately; keeping hand tools sharpened, and using them safely; keeping all electrical equipment and wiring in good repair, and avoiding extension cords which can be tripped over; not wearing ties, long loose hair, loose sleeves or other items that could catch in machinery are some other precautions.

Gluing wood

A variety of glues are used for laminating and joining wood, including contact adhesives, casein glue, epoxy glues, formaldehyde-resin glues, hide glues, white glue (polyvinyl acetate emulsion) and the cyanoacrylate "instant" glues. Many of these contain toxic solvents or other chemicals, and can be skin, eye and respiratory hazards.

Precautions include avoiding formaldehyde resin glues; using water-based glues rather then solvent-type glues; wearing gloves or barrier creams when using epoxy glues, solvent-based adhesives or formaldehyde-resin glues; and having good ventilation when using epoxy glues, cyanoacrylate glues and solvent-based glues. Sources of ignition should be avoided when using flammable solvents.

Painting and finishing

Wood can be painted with most types of paint; can be stained, lacquered or varnished; and can be treated with linseed or other types of oil. Other materials that are used in finishing wood include shellacs, polyurethane coatings and waxes. Many materials are sprayed. Some woodworkers mix their own paints from dry pigments. Hazards include inhalation of toxic pigment powder (especially lead chromate pigments), skin and inhalation hazards from solvents, fire hazards from flammable solvents, and spontaneous combustion from rags soaked with oil or turpentine.

Precautions include using ready-made paints rather than mixing your own; avoiding eating, drinking or smoking in the work area; using water-based paints rather than solvent-based ones; and placing oil- and solvent-soaked rags in self-closing oily-waste cans, or even a pail of water.

Figure 96.11 • Woodworking machines with dust collector.

Michael McCann

Precautions with solvents include wearing gloves and goggles, as well as having adequate ventilation; doing the operation outside; or wearing a respirator with organic vapour cartridges. Materials should be brushed on whenever possible, to avoid the hazards of spraying. Spraying finishes inside an explosion-proof spray booth, or wearing a respirator with organic vapour cartridges and spray filters; avoiding open flames, lit cigarettes and other sources of ignition (e.g., lit pilot lights) in the area when applying flammable finishes, or when spraying, are other precautions to be taken.

Paint stripping

Stripping old paint and varnish from wood and furniture is done with paint and varnish removers containing a wide variety of toxic and often flammable solvents. "Non-flammable" paint strippers contain methylene chloride. Caustic soda (sodium hydroxide), acids, blowtorches and heat guns are also used to remove old paint. Old stains on wood are often removed with bleaches, which can contain corrosive alkalis and oxalic acid, hydrogen peroxide or hypochlorite. Heat guns and torches can vaporize the paint, possibly causing lead poisoning with lead-based paint, and are a fire hazard.

See the previous section for precautions with solvent-based paint strippers. Gloves and goggles should be worn when handling caustic soda, oxalic acid bleaches or chlorine-type bleaches. An eyewash fountain and emergency shower should be available. Avoid using torches or heat guns to remove lead-containing paint.

JEWELLERY

Tsun-Jen Cheng and Jung-Der Wang

Jewellery manufacturing can include working with a variety of materials, such as precious and semi-precious stones, synthetic stones, shells, coral, pearls, precious metals, metal enamels and newer materials such as epoxy resins and vinyl polymers. These can be used to make rings, earrings, necklaces, pendants and a variety of other personal decorative items. Jewellery manufacturing shops vary in size, and different manufacturing processes may be adopted. Thus, health hazards may vary from one workshop to another.

Processes, Hazards and Precautions

Precious stones and settings

Much jewellery manufacturing involves the setting of precious stones into bases of precious metals or alloys of precious metals. Stones are initially cut into desired sizes, then polished. Base metals are cast, then ground and polished. Traditionally, the metal settings were made using "injection" mouldings. Alloys of low melting point, including alloys of cadmium and mercury, have also been used for metal casting. Recently, "lost wax" methods have been used to achieve a better quality of casting. Stones are held on metal bases using adhesives, soldering or mechanical clamping by parts of the metal frame. Metal bases are usually plated with precious metals.

Health hazards may result from exposure to metal fumes, wax fumes or dust of stones and metals, and visual impairment from poor lighting. Working with fine parts of jewellery items generally requires proper ventilation, adequate illumination and the use of magnifying lenses. In addition, proper ergonomic design in the workplace is recommended.

Stone cutting and polishing

Precious, semi-precious and synthetic stones (including diamond, jade, ruby, garnet, jasper, agate, travertine, opal, turquoise and amethyst) are usually cut to the desired size with small saws before setting. Injury hazards include abrasions and lacerations of the skin or eyes; other health hazards include dust inhalation (e.g., silicosis from quartz stones).

Precautions include proper ventilation, dust collectors, using magnifying lenses, local illumination, eye protection and ergonomic design of tools and working environments.

Lost wax metal casting

Rubber or silicon moulds are made from original moulds that are custom-made or designed by artists. Wax is subsequently injected into these moulds. Moulds (called investments) of plaster of Paris and/or silica are made to enclose these wax moulds. The whole investment is then heated in the kiln or oven to drain the wax out of the block, then filled with molten metal with the aid of centrifugation. The mould is shattered to recover the metal piece. This is polished, and also may be electroplated with a thin layer of precious metal.

Precious metals and their alloys, including gold, silver, platinum and copper as well as zinc and tin, are commonly used in constructing metal pieces. Injury hazards include fire or explosion from flammable gas used for melting metals, and burns from heated plaster casts or blocks, molten metal spillage, oxyacetylene torches or ovens; other health hazards include inhalation of metal fumes or dusts of silver, gold, zinc, lead, tin and so on.

Precautions include using alternative casting methods to lower the level of exposures and toxicity, proper local exhaust ventilation for metal dust and fumes, dust collectors, personal protective equipment including goggles, insulating gloves and working gowns, and proper storage of flammable gas.

Enamelling

Enamelling involves the fusion of pre-ground, powdered lead or borosilicate glass particles mixed with various coloured oxides onto a base metal to form an enamelled surface. Base metals can include silver, gold or copper. Common colourants include antimony, cadmium, cobalt, chromium, manganese, nickel and uranium.

Cleaning

The metal surface must first be cleaned with a torch or in a kiln to burn off oils and grease; it is then pickled with dilute nitric or sulphuric acid, or the safer sodium bisulphate, to remove firescale. Hazards include thermal and acid burns. Precautions include protective gloves, goggles and apron.

Application

Some enamellists grind and sift their enamels to obtain desired particle sizes. Application techniques include brushing, spraying, stencilling and sifting or wet packing of the enamel onto the metal surface. Inhalation of enamel powder or spray mist is the greatest hazard, particularly with lead-based enamels. Precautions include use of lead-free enamels and respiratory protection. In cloisonné, different enamel colours are separated by metal wires that have been soldered onto the metal. (See the discussion on silver soldering below). In champleve, designs are etched with ferric chloride or nitric acid, and depressed areas filled with enamels. Another technique involves applying enamels mixed with resin in turpentine. Ventilation and precautions to prevent skin contact are required.

Firing

The enamelled metal is then fired in a small kiln. Ventilation is required to remove toxic metal fumes, fluorides and decomposition products (from gums and other organic materials in the enamel). Other hazards include thermal burns and infrared radiation. Infrared goggles and heat-protective gloves are recommended.

The enamel piece can then be finished by such methods as filing the edges and grinding and sanding the enamelled surface. Standard precautions against dust inhalation and eye contact are needed.

Metal jewellery

Metal jewellery can be made by cutting, bending and otherwise fabricating metals, electroplating, anodizing, soldering, gluing, finishing and so on. Many of these processes are discussed in "Metalworking". Some specific applications are discussed below.

Electroplating

Gold, silver, copper and strong acid as well as cyanide are used in the electroplating process. Injury hazards include electrical shock and burns from acid or alkali spillage; other health hazards include the inhalation of metal, acid and cyanide mist, organic solvents, as well as hydrogen cyanide gas.

Precautions include substitution of non-cyanide plating solutions, avoidance of mixing cyanide solution with acids, local exhaust ventilation, using a tank cover to reduce mist production, proper storage of chemicals, electrical precautions and adequate personal protective equipment.

Soldering or gluing

Soldering involves metals such as tin, lead, antimony, silver, cadmium, zinc and bismuth. Safety hazards include burns; other health hazards include the inhalation of metal fumes, including lead and cadmium (Baker et al. 1979), and fluoride and acid fluxes.

Using epoxy resin and quick-drying agents with solvents to bind stones and metal pieces is a common practice. Injury hazards from gluing include fire and explosion; other health hazards include the inhalation of solvents and skin contact with epoxy resin, other adhesives and solvents.

Precautions include avoidance of lead and cadmium solders, adequate local exhaust ventilation, proper storage of chemicals, adequate illumination and personal protective equipment.

Metal grinding and polishing

Rotating wheels and linear actuators of varied sizes are used for grinding, polishing and cutting. Injury hazards include skin abrasions; other health hazards include the inhalation of metal dusts, as well as repetitive motion, vibration, awkward position and forces.

Precautions include adequate local exhaust ventilation, dust collectors, goggles for eye protection and ergonomic designs for workplaces and tools.

Shells

Mother-of-pearl (from oyster shells) and coral, as well as abalone and other shells, can be made into jewellery by cutting, drilling, sawing, shaving, grinding, polishing, finishing and so on. Hazards include hand and eye injuries from flying particles and sharp edges, respiratory irritation and allergic reactions from inhalation of fine shell dust, and, in the case of mother-of-pearl, possible hypersensitivity pneumonia and ossification with inflammation of tissues covering the bones, especially in young people.

Precautions include cleaning shells thoroughly to remove organic matter, wet grinding and polishing techniques, and local exhaust ventilation or respiratory protection. Goggles should be worn to prevent eye injury.

Beads

Beads can be made from a variety of materials, including glass, plastic, seed, bone, shells, pearls, gemstones and so on. A newer material used for beads and other jewellery is heat-cured polyvinyl chloride (polymer clays). Hazards include inhalation of dust from drilling the holes for the string or wire used to hold the beads, and possible eye injuries. Precautions include wet drilling, ventilation or respiratory protection and goggles. The polymer clays can release hydrogen chloride, a respiratory irritant, if heated above recommended temperatures. Using cooking ovens for heat curing is not recommended. There has also been concern about plasticizers such as diethylhexyl phthalate, a possible carcinogen and reproductive toxin, present in these polymer clays.

GRAPHIC ARTS

Stephanie Knopp

The term *graphic arts* (also called *graphic design, commercial art, visual design* or *visual communication*) refers to the organization of ideas and concepts in a visual form that conveys a particular message to a target audience. Graphic designers work in a wide array of venues, including magazines, books, posters, packaging, film, video, exhibition design and, most recently, in digital forms such as computer screen design, multimedia presentations and pages on the World Wide Web. There are two types of visual communicators: graphic designers, who work with typography and page layout as well as photography and illustration; and illustrators, who work exclusively with visual images. Frequently the two roles overlap, but most commonly graphic designers hire illustrators to create visualizations of the ideas that will be used within a typographic context.

Graphic Design

The hazards of graphic design were very different in the late 1990s compared to only a few years earlier when some designers were still producing traditional mechanicals for offset printing (figure 96.12). Now, virtually all page layout and graphic design is produced in a digital format before it is printed on paper. Much graphic design is even created exclusively for a final digital form: a floppy disk, CD-ROM or a page on the Internet. Graphic design-

Figure 96.12 • Hand lettering for graphic arts.

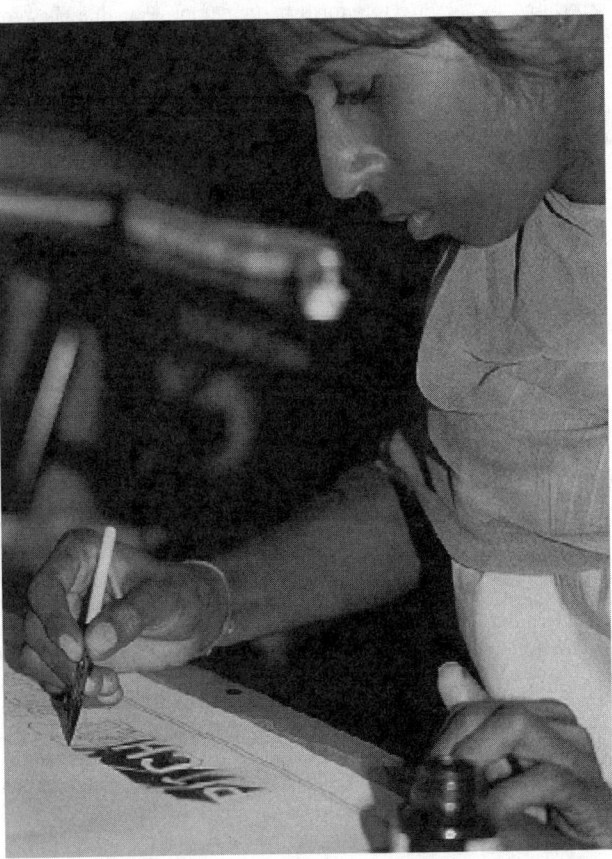

ers use computers to create and store both text and images. These digitally created artworks are stored on floppy disks, removable storage cartridges or CD-ROMs, and then given to the client for the final presentation (package design, magazine, film titles, poster, business stationery or many other applications).

Graphic designers must now be concerned with the potential hazards of prolonged work at a computer. Unfortunately, this technology is too new to know all the associated hazards. At present the hazards identified from working for extended periods at a visual display unit (VDU) (also called a video display terminal, or VDT) include eyestrain, headaches, backaches, stiff necks, sore hands and wrists, dizziness, nausea, irritability and stress. There have also been reports of skin rashes and dermatitis associated with VDU use. While the health effects of VDU use have been studied for a couple of decades, there are no proven links between long-term use of VDUs and long-term health problems. VDUs do emit comparatively low-level radiation, but there are no hard data to support any permanent adverse health effects from VDU use.

Ergonomic computer workstations, elimination of glare and frequent work breaks enable graphic designers to work more safely than most other artistic professions. Generally the digital revolution has greatly reduced the health hazards previously associated with the graphic design profession.

Illustration

Illustrators create images in a wide variety of media and techniques for use in various commercial venues. For example, an illustrator may create work for magazines, book jackets, packaging, movie posters, advertising and many other forms of promotion and publicity. Generally illustrators are freelancers who are hired by art directors for a particular project, though some illustrators work for publishing houses and greeting card companies. Since illustrators generally create their own workspaces, the burden for creating a safe working environment usually falls upon the individual.

The materials used by professional illustrators are as varied as the techniques and styles exhibited in contemporary illustration. Therefore, it is imperative that each individual artist be aware of any hazards associated with his or her particular medium. Among the materials commonly used by illustrators are drawing and painting materials such as markers, water colours, oil paints, coloured inks, coloured pencils, dry pastels, oil pastels, dyes, acrylic paints and gouache.

Many commonly used colours contain hazardous ingredients such as xylene and petroleum distillates; pigments may contain such dangerous ingredients as mercury, cadmium, cobalt and lead. Precautions include working in a well-ventilated studio, wearing gloves and a respirator when using oil-based materials (particularly from aerosols) and substituting safer materials (water- and alcohol-based colours) when possible. Materials such as pastels can be hazardous when they become airborne dust; good ventilation is particularly important when using any material that can be breathed into the lungs. A final general precaution is to avoid eating, drinking or smoking while working with any toxic artists' materials.

The wide assortment of materials used by illustrators requires an individual approach to safe working conditions, since each artist has a personal technique and selection of materials. Manufacturers in some countries are required by law to provide information about product ingredients and hazards. Each individual artist should carefully scrutinize every material used, working in the safest possible manner with the available media.

Adhesives

Adhesives used include rubber cement, spray mount, contact cement, electric waxers, dry-mount tissues, glue sticks, hot-melt glue guns, adhesive transfer materials, double-coated tape and water-soluble glues. Associated hazards include: dangerous chemicals such as *n*-hexane (a neurotoxin) in some rubber cements and contact cement; cyanoacrylate instant-action glues; airborne toxic chemicals and fire hazards associated with spray adhesives; and possible burns from hot-melt glue gun use. Many of the commonly used adhesives (rubber cement in particular) can also cause skin irritation.

Proper ventilation and use of gloves can prevent many of the hazards associated with common adhesives. Substitution of non-toxic adhesives whenever possible, such as electric waxers, adhesive transfer materials, dry-mount tissues, double-coated tapes, and water-soluble glues is recommended. Heptane-containing rubber cements and spray adhesives are less toxic than hexane types, although they are still flammable.

Solvents

Solvents include rubber cement thinner, turpentine, acetone, correction fluid and mineral spirits.

Hazards include skin irritation, headaches, damage to respiratory and nervous systems, kidney and liver damage, and flammability. Primary precautions include substituting safer solvents whenever possible (for example, mineral spirits are less toxic than turpentine) or switching to water-based pigments that do not require solvents for cleanup. Excellent ventilation or respiratory protection, careful storage, use of gloves and chemical splash goggles are also important when using any solvents.

Aerosol sprays

Aerosol sprays include fixative spray, spray markers, varnish, texture sprays and airbrush colours.

Hazards include respiratory problems, skin irritation, headaches, dizziness and nausea from toxic chemicals such as toluene and xylene; long-term adverse effects include damage to kidneys, liver and central nervous system. Sprays are also frequently flammable; care must be exercised to use them away from heat or flames. Precautions include using a respirator or adequate studio ventilation (such as a spray booth), and working with non-toxic pigments when using an airbrush.

Cutting tools

The various types of cutting tools can include paper cutters, razor knives and mat cutters. The hazards can range from cuts and, in the case of large paper cutters, the severing of fingers. Precautions include careful use of knives and cutters, keeping hands away from blades, and maintaining blades in sharp condition.

PERFORMING AND MEDIA ARTS

● DANCERS

Itzhak Siev-Ner

Dance involves patterned and rhythmic body movements, usually performed to music, that serve as a form of expression or communication. There are many different types of dances, including ceremonial, folk, ballroom, classical ballet, modern dance, jazz, flamenco, tap and so forth. Each of these has its unique movements and physical demands. Audiences associate dance with grace and enjoyment, yet very few people regard dance as one of the most demanding and strenuous athletic activities. Sixty-five to 80% of dance-related injuries are in the lower limbs, out of which about 50% are in the foot and ankle (Arheim 1986). Most of the injuries are due to over-use (about 70%) and the rest are of the acute type (ankle sprain, fractures and so on).

Dance medicine is a multidisciplinary profession because causes of injuries are multifactorial and hence treatment should be comprehensive and take into consideration the specific needs of dancers as artists. The goal of the treatment should be to prevent potentially dangerous specific stresses, allowing the dancer to keep active, acquiring and perfecting physical creativity and psychological well-being.

Training should preferably start at an early age in order to develop strength and flexibility. However, incorrect training results in injury to young dancers. Proper technique is the main concern, as incorrect posture and other bad dancing habits and methods will cause permanent deformities and over-use injuries (Hardaker 1987). One of the most basic movements is the turn-out—opening of the lower limbs outwards. This should take place in the hip joints; if it is forced more than the anatomic external rotation these joints will allow, compensations occur. The most common compensations are rolling-in of the feet, internal flexing of the knees and hyperlordosis of the lower back. These positions contribute to deformities such as hallux valgus (displacement of the great toe towards the other toes). Inflammations of tendons such as the flexor hallucis longus (the

History of performing arts medicine

While interest in the physiology of music making dates back to antiquity, the first real summary of the occupational diseases of performing artists is Bernardino Ramazzini's 1713 treatise *Diseases of Workers*. Sporadic interest in arts medicine continued through the eighteenth and nineteenth centuries. In 1932 the English translation of Kurt Singer's *Diseases of the Music Profession: A Systematic Presentation of Their Causes, Symptoms and Methods of Treatment* appeared. This was the first textbook to bring together all the current knowledge on performing arts medicine. After World War II, the medical literature began to feature case reports of injured artists. The musical literature also began to carry short items and letters. There was a parallel growth of awareness among dancers.

One of the catalysts for the development of performing arts medicine as a cross-disciplinary field was the Danube Symposium on Neurology, held in Vienna in 1972. The conference focused on music and led to the publication of *Music and the Brain: Studies in the Neurology of Music,* by MacDonald Critchley and R.A. Henson. Also in 1972 the first Care of the Professional Voice Symposium was organized by the Voice Foundation. This has become an annual conference, with proceedings appearing in the *Journal of Voice.*

While injured performers and the health professionals serving them began to cooperate more closely, the general public was unaware of these developments. In 1981 a *New York Times* article described the hand problems suffered by pianists Gary Graffman and Leon Fleisher, and their treatment at Massachusetts General Hospital. These were virtually the first well-known musicians to admit to physical problems, so the publicity generated by their cases brought forth a large, previously unknown group of injured artists.

Since then, the field of performing arts medicine has advanced rapidly, with conferences, publications, clinics and associations. In 1983 the first Medical Problems of Musicians and Dancers symposium was held, in conjunction with the Aspen Music Festival, in Aspen, Colorado. This has become an annual conference and is perhaps the most important in the field. Meetings such as these usually include lectures by health professionals as well as demonstrations and master classes by artists.

In 1986 the journal *Medical Problems of Performing Artists* was launched. This is the only journal completely dedicated to arts medicine, and it publishes many of the Aspen symposium presentations. Related journals include the *Journal of Voice, Kinesiology and Medicine for Dance,* and the *International Journal of Arts-Medicine.* In 1991 the *Textbook of Performing Arts Medicine,* edited by Robert Sataloff, Alice Brandfonbrener and Richard Lederman, became the first modern, comprehensive text on the subject.

As publishing grew and conferences continued, clinics serving the performing arts community were organized. Generally these clinics are in large cities that support an orchestra or dance company, such as New York, San Francisco and Chicago. There are now more than twenty such centres in the United States and several in various other countries.

Those active in the field of performing arts medicine have also founded associations to further research and education. The Performing Arts Medicine Association, set up in 1989, now co-sponsors the Aspen symposiums. Other organizations include the International Association for Dance Medicine and Science, the International Arts-Medicine Association and the Association of Medical Advisors to British Orchestras.

Research in performing arts medicine has grown from case reports and prevalence studies to sophisticated projects using advanced technology. New treatments, more responsive to the artists' specific needs, are being developed and the emphasis is beginning to shift to prevention and education.

Susan Harman

---

tendon for the great toe) and others may also result (Hamilton 1988; Sammarco 1982).

Being cognizant of individual anatomic differences in addition to the unusual biomechanical loads, such as in point position (standing on the tip of the toes), allows one to take actions to prevent some of these undesired outcomes (Teitz, Harrington and Wiley 1985).

The environment of dancers has great influence on their well-being. A proper floor should be resilient and absorb shock to prevent cumulative trauma to the feet, legs and spine (Seals 1987). Temperature and humidity also influence performance. Diet is a major issue as dancers are always under pressure to keep slim and look light and pleasing (Calabrese, Kirkendal and Floyd 1983). Psychological maladjustment may lead to anorexia or bulimia.

Psychological stress may contribute to some hormonal disturbances, which may present as amenorrhoea. The incidence of stress fractures and osteoporosis may increase in hormonally imbalanced dancers (Warren, Brooks-Gunn and Hamilton 1986). Emotional stress due to competition between peers, and direct pressure from choreographers, teachers and directors may enhance psychological problems (Schnitt and Schnitt 1987).

A good screening method for both students and professional dancers should detect psychological and physical risk factors and avoid problems.

Any change in activity levels (whether return from a holiday, sickness or pregnancy), intensity of work (rehearsals before a premiere tour), choreographer, style or technique, or environment (such as floors, stages or even type of dance shoes) makes the dancer more vulnerable.

MUSICIANS

John P. Chong

The musician relies on the skilled use of the muscles, nerves and bones (neuromusculoskeletal system). Playing an instrument requires finely controlled repetitive motions and often entails working in unnatural postures for extended periods of practice and performance (figure 96.13). These demands on the body can result in specific types of health problems. In addition, adverse working conditions, such as excessive sound exposure levels, prolonged periods of performance without rest, and inadequate preparation for new and difficult repertoire or instruments may affect the health of musicians in all age groups and at all levels of performing ability. Recognition of these hazards, accurate diagnosis and early treatment will prevent occupational disabilities that may interfere with, interrupt or end careers.

Neuromusculoskeletal Problems

Studies from the United States, Australia and Canada suggest that around 60% of musicians will face career-threatening injuries during their working lifetime. Clinical cross-sectional studies have examined the prevalence of muscle-tendon disorders,

Figure 96.13 • Orchestra.

of peripheral nerve entrapment syndromes and motor control problems. These studies have revealed several common diagnoses, which include various overuse syndromes, including strain of the muscles and connective tissue which control the bending and extending motions in the wrist and fingers. These syndromes result from the repetitive forceful movement of the muscle-tendon units. Other common diagnoses relate to pain in body parts which are involved in prolonged strain from awkward and imbalanced postures while playing musical instruments. Playing the instruments in the groups described below involves putting pressure on the branches of the nerves in the wrist and forearm, the shoulders, arm and neck. Occupational cramp or muscle spasms (focal dystonia) are also common problems which often can affect performers at the pinnacle of their careers.

String instruments: Violin, viola, cello, bass, harp, classical guitar and electric guitar

Health problems in musicians who play string instruments often are caused by the manner in which the musician supports the instrument and the posture assumed while sitting or standing and playing. For example, most violinists and violists support their instruments between the left shoulder and chin. Often the musician's left shoulder will be elevated and the left chin and jaw will bear down in order to allow the left hand to move over the fingerboard. Elevating a joint and bearing down at the same time leads to a state of static contraction which promotes neck and shoulder pain, temporomandibular joint disorders involving the nerves and muscles of the jaw, and thoracic outlet syndrome, which can include pain or numbness in the neck, shoulder and upper chest area. Prolonged static sitting postures, particularly while assuming a bent posture, promote pain in the large muscle groups which support posture. Static twisting rotation of the spine is often required to play the string bass, harp and classical guitar. Heavy electric guitars are usually supported by a strap over the

left neck and shoulder, contributing to pressure on the nerves of the shoulder and upper arm (the brachial plexus) and thus to pain. These problems of posture and support contribute to the development of strain and pressure of the nerves and muscles of the wrist and fingers by promoting their faulty alignment. For example, the left wrist may be used for excessive repetitive bending motions which result in strain of the extensor muscles of the wrist and fingers and the development of carpal tunnel syndrome. Pressure on the nerves of the shoulder and arm (lower trunks of the brachial plexus) may contribute to problems with the elbow, such as a double crush syndrome and ulnar neuropathy.

Keyboard instruments: Piano, harpsichord, organ, synthesizers and electronic keyboards

Playing a keyboard instrument requires assuming a similar posture to that of typing. Often the forward and downward orientation of the head to look at the keys and hands and repetitive upward movement to look at the music causes pain in the nerves and muscles of the neck and back. The shoulders will often be rounded, combined with a forward head poking posture and a shallow breathing pattern. A condition known as thoracic outlet syndrome can develop from chronic compression of the nerves and blood vessels that pass between the muscles in the neck, shoulder and rib cage. In addition, a musician's tendency to bend the wrists and curl the fingers while keeping the hand/finger joints flat places excessive strain on the wrist and finger muscles in the forearm. Additionally, the repeated use of the thumb kept in a position under the hand strains the thumb muscles which extend and binds the finger extensor muscles across the back of the hand. The high repetitive force needed to play large chords or octaves may strain the capsule of the wrist joint and result in ganglion formation. Prolonged co-contraction of the muscles that turn and move the arms up and down can lead to nerve entrapment syndromes. Muscle spasms and cramps (focal dystonia) are common among this group of instrumentalists, sometimes requiring long periods of neuromuscular retraining to correct movement patterns which can lead to these difficulties.

Wind and brass instruments: Flute, clarinet, oboe, saxophone, bassoon, trumpet, french horn, trombone, tuba and bagpipes

A musician who plays one of these instruments will vary his or her posture according to the need to control airflow since posture will control the area from which diaphragmatic and intercostal breath is drawn. Playing these instruments depends on the way the mouthpiece is held (the embouchure) which is controlled by the facial and pharyngeal muscles. The embouchure controls sound production of vibrating reeds or the mouthpiece. Posture also affects how the musician supports the instrument while sitting or standing and in operating the keys or valves of the instrument that govern the pitch of the note played by the fingers. For example, the traditional French open-holed flute requires sustained adduction and flexion (bending forward) of the left shoulder, sustained abduction (drawing away) of the right shoulder and rotation of the head and neck to the left in slight movement. The left wrist is often held in an extremely bent position while the hand is also extended in order to support the instrument by the curled left index finger and both thumbs, counter balanced by the right little finger. This promotes strain of the forearm muscles and the muscles which permit extension of the fingers and thumbs. The tendency to project the head and neck forward and use shallow breathing increases the chances of developing thoracic outlet syndrome.

Percussion instruments: Drums, timpani, cymbals, xylophone, marimba, tabla and taiko

The use of sticks, mallets and bare hands to strike various percussion instruments results in rapid pulling back of the wrists and fingers at impact. The impulse vibration caused by striking the instrument is transmitted up the hand and arm and contributes to repetitive strain injuries of the muscle-tendon units and the peripheral nerves. Biomechanical factors, such as the amount of force used, the repetitive nature of the playing and static load placed on the muscles can add to the injuries. Carpal tunnel syndrome and nodule formation in tendon sheaths are common in this group of musicians.

Hearing Loss

The risk of hearing loss from music exposure depends on the intensity and duration of exposure. It is not uncommon to have exposure levels of 100 dB during a quiet passage of orchestral music, with peak values of 126 dB measured at the shoulder of an instrumentalist in the middle of the orchestra. At the position of the conductor or teacher, levels of 110 dB in an orchestra or band are common. Exposure levels for pop/rock and jazz musicians may be significantly higher, depending on the physical acoustics of the stage or pit, amplification system and placement of speakers or other instruments. The average duration of exposure may be approximately 40 hours per week, but many professional musicians will perform 60 to 80 hours per week on occasion. Hearing loss among musicians is far more common than expected, with approximately 89% of professional musicians who were found to have suffered musculoskeletal injuries also showing an abnormal hearing test result, with a hearing loss in the 3 to 6 KHz region.

Personal ear protection can be used but it must be adapted for each instrument type (Chasin and Chong 1992). By inserting an acoustic attenuator or filter into custom-moulded earplugs, the intensity of higher frequency sounds transmitted by ordinary earplugs is reduced to a flat attenuation as measured at the eardrum, which should be less damaging to the ear. The use of a tuned or adjustable vent in a custom earplug will allow the lower frequencies and some harmonic energy to pass through the earplug unattenuated. Earplugs can be designed to provide a slight amplification to alter perception of the singer's voice, thus allowing the artist to reduce the risk of vocal strain. Depending on the psychoacoustical nature of the instrument and surrounding music exposures, substantial reduction in risk for the development of hearing loss can be obtained. Improvement in the perception of the relative intensity of the musician's own performance may reduce the risk of repetitive strain injuries by a relative reduction of the force of repetitive movements.

There are practical strategies for reducing the exposure of musicians that do not interfere with music production (Chasin and Chong 1995). Loudspeaker enclosures can be elevated above floor level, which results in minimal loss of low-frequency sound energy, while preserving sufficient loudness for the musician to perform at a lower intensity level. Musicians who play high-intensity, highly directional instruments such as trumpets and trombones should be on risers so that the sound passes above the other musicians, thereby lowering its impact. There should be 2 m of unobstructed floor space in front of the orchestra. Small stringed instruments should always have at least 2 m of unobstructed space above them.

● SINGERS

Anat Keidar

The term *singer* applies to any person whose career, avocation or livelihood relies heavily on the use of his or her voice in a musical context rather than ordinary speech. Unlike percussionists, pianists or violinists, the singer is the instrument. Hence, the well-being of a singer depends not only on the health of his or her larynx (where the sound originates) or vocal tract (where the sound is modified), but also on proper functioning and maximal coordination of most mind and body systems.

Of the many styles of singing documented throughout the world, some reflect a unique liturgical, cultural, linguistic, ethnic or geo-political heritage, while others are more universal in nature. Among the common styles of singing in the United States and Western world are: traditional classical (including oratorio, opera, art songs and so on), barbershop, jazz, musical theatre (Broadway), choral, gospel, folk, country (and western), popular, rhythm and blues, rock 'n' roll (including heavy metal, alternative rock and so on) and others. Each style of delivery has its typical settings, patterns, habits and associated risk factors.

Vocal Problems

Unlike non-singers, who may not be significantly hindered by vocal problems, for the classical singer, the effect of subtle vocal impairment can be devastating. Even within that category of trained singers, vocal impairment is much more debilitating for the higher voice classifications (sopranos and tenors) than for lower classifications (mezzo sopranos, altos, baritones and basses). On the other hand, some vocal performers (pop, gospel or rock, for example) go to great lengths to achieve a unique trademark and enhance their marketability by inducing vocal pathologies which often yield a breathy, husky, muffled diplophonic (simultaneous multiple pitches) quality. Owing, in part, to their impairment, they tend to sing with great effort, struggling particularly to produce the high notes. To many listeners, this struggle adds a dramatic effect, as if the singer is sacrificing his or her self while engaging in the artistic process.

The prevalence of occupation-related injuries in general, and voice disorders in particular, among singers is not well documented in the literature. This author estimates that on the average, between 10 and 20% of singers in the United States sustain some form of chronic voice disorder. However, the incidence of vocal injury varies significantly with many factors. Because many singers must adhere to specific artistic/aesthetic criteria, performance practices, popular (consumer) demands, financial constraints and social pressures, they often stretch their vocal capabilities and endurance to the limits. Furthermore, singers generally tend to deny, trivialize or ignore warning signs and even diagnoses of vocal injury (Bastian, Keidar and Verdolini-Marston 1990).

The most common problems among singers are benign mucosal disorders. The mucosa is the outer layer, or cover, of the vocal folds (commonly called vocal cords) (Zeitels 1995). Acute problems can include laryngitis and transient vocal fold swelling (oedema). Chronic mucosal lesions include vocal fold swellings, nodules ("calluses"), polyps, cysts, sub-mucosal haemorrhage (bleeding), capillary ectasia (widening), chronic laryngitis, leukoplakia (white spots or patches), mucosal tears and glottic sulci (deep furrows in the tissue). Although these disorders can be exacerbated by smoking and excessive alcohol consumption, it is important to note that these benign mucosal lesions are typically related to the amount and manner of voice use, and are the product of vibratory trauma (Bastian 1993).

Causes of Vocal Problems

In looking at the causes of vocal problems in singers, one should distinguish between intrinsic and extrinsic factors. Intrinsic factors are those related to personality, vocal behaviour (including speaking) on and off stage, vocal technique, and intake habits (primarily if substance abuse, improper medication, malnutrition and/or dehydration is involved). Extrinsic factors are related to environmental pollutants, allergies and so on. Based on clinical experience, intrinsic factors tend to be most important.

Performance anxiety

Performance anxiety is, like fear, joy or grief, an emotion which includes physical and psychological components. Motor responses, autonomic reactions, memories, ideas and thoughts continuously interact. Performance anxiety is no longer thought of as an isolated symptom but rather as a syndrome comprising attitudes, traits and unconscious conflicts that become activated in particular circumstances.

Nearly every person must deal with performance anxiety in one form or another at one time or another. By the nature of their profession, however, performing artists, or those for whom public performance is an important part of their profession, have to deal with performance anxiety more frequently and often more intensely than do others. Even those with years of experience may still have a performance anxiety problem.

Performance anxiety is mainly characterized by an irrational situational anxiety accompanied by unwanted physical symptoms which can lead to dysfunction and/or uncontrolled behaviour. It occurs especially in those situations in which a task has to be done that could subject the performer to possible criticism from others. Examples of such situations include public speaking, giving a concert, writing exams, sexual performance, etc. Performance anxiety can cause a broad range of possible physical symptoms of distress, such as trembling hands, trembling lips, diarrhoea, sweating hands and palpitations of the heart. These symptoms can not only affect the quality of a performance but may also negatively influence the sufferer's future and career.

Some experts believe that the causes of performance anxiety include improper practice and preparation habits, insufficient performance experience, having an inappropriate repertoire and so on. Other theories view performance anxiety as mainly caused by negative thoughts and poor self-esteem. Still others are of the opinion that the stress and fear of performance anxiety is closely related to so-called career stress, which includes feelings of inadequacy, anticipation of punishment or criticism and loss of status. Although there is no agreement as to the cause of performance anxiety, and the explanation cannot be simple, it is clear that the problem is widespread and that even world-famous artists such as Yehudi Menuhin or Pablo Casals are known to have suffered from performance anxiety and fear all their lives.

Personal traits are undoubtedly related to performance anxiety. A challenge for one person can be a catastrophe for another. The experience of performance anxiety depends to a great extent on the personal perception of a fearful situation. Some introverted individuals may, for example, be more prone to stressful events and thus more likely to suffer performance anxiety than others. For some people, success can also cause fear and performance anxiety. This in turn reduces and undermines the communicative and creative aspects of the performer.

To achieve an optimum performance a bit of fear and stress and a certain amount of nervousness may be unavoidable. The margin between the degree of (still) acceptable performance anxiety and the necessity of therapeutic intervention, however, can be set only by the performer.

Performance anxiety is a complex phenomenon; its various components lead to variable and changing reactions depending on the situation. Individual aspects, work situations, social factors, personal development and so on play a considerable role, making it difficult to give general rules.

Methods for diminishing performance anxiety include developing personal coping strategies or learning relaxation techniques such as biofeedback. Such approaches are directed towards transforming task-irrelevant negative thoughts and worrisome anticipations into task-relevant demands and the positive task-orientated self. Medical interventions, such as beta-blockers and tranquillizers are also commonly used (Nubé 1995). The taking of drugs however, remains controversial and should be done only under medical supervision due to possible side effects and contra-indications.

Jacqueline Nubé

Vocal injury is usually a cumulative process of misuse and/or overuse during the singer's productive (performance-related) and/or non-productive (domestic, social) activities. It is difficult to ascertain how much of the damage is attributable directly to the former versus the latter. Performance risk factors can include unreasonably long dress rehearsals requiring full-voice singing, performing with an upper-respiratory infection in the absence of a replacement and excessive singing. Most vocalists are advised not to sing for more than about 1.5 hours (net) per day. Unfortunately, many singers do not respect the limitations of their apparatus. Some tend to get caught up in the exploratory excitement of new technical skills, new means of artistic expression, new repertoire and so on, and practice 4, 5 or 6 hours daily. Even worse is the beating of the voice into shape when distress signals of injury (such as loss of high notes, inability to sing softly, breathy delay in sound initiation, unstable vibrato and increased phonatory effort) are manifested. The culpability of vocal overtaxing is shared with other taskmasters such as the booking agent who squeezes multiple performances into an impossible time frame, and the recording agent who leases the studio for 12 consecutive hours during which the singer is expected to record a complete CD sound track from start to finish.

Although every singer may encounter acute episodes of voice problems at some point in his or her career, it is generally believed that those singers who are musically literate and can adjust the musical score to their voice limitations, and those who have had proper voice training, are less likely to encounter severe problems of a chronic nature than their untrained peers, who often learn their repertoire by rote, repeatedly imitating or singing along with demo tapes or recordings of other performers. In doing so, they frequently sing in a key, range or style unsuitable for their voices. Singers who lend themselves to periodic tutelage and maintenance by proficient voice experts are less likely to resort to faulty compensatory vocal manoeuvres if confronted by physical impairment, and are more inclined to establish a reasonable balance between artistic demands and vocal longevity. A good teacher is aware of the normal (expected) capabilities of each instrument, can usually distinguish between technical and physical limitations, and often is the first to detect warning signs of vocal impairment.

Sound amplification can also create problems for singers. Many rock groups, for example, amplify not only the singer, but the entire band. When the noise level interferes with auditory feedback, the singer is often unaware that he or she is singing too loudly and using faulty technique. This may contribute significantly to the development and exacerbation of vocal pathology.

Non-performance factors can also be important. Singers must realize that they do not have separate laryngeal mechanisms for singing and speaking. Although most professional singers spend much more time talking than singing, speaking technique is commonly discarded or rejected, which can adversely affect their singing.

Many of today's singers must travel regularly from one performance venue to another, on trains, tour buses or airplanes. Ongoing touring requires not only psychological adaptation, but also physical adjustments on many levels. In order for singers to function optimally, they must receive adequate quality and quantity of sleep. Radical rapid changes in time zones causes jet lag, which forces singers to remain awake and alert when their internal clock is cueing various body systems to shut down for sleep, and conversely, to sleep when their brain systems are aroused to plan and execute normal daytime activities. Such interruption may result in a host of debilitating symptoms, including chronic insomnia, headaches, sluggishness, dizziness, irritability and forgetfulness (Monk 1994). Aberrant sleep patterns are also a common problem among those singers who perform late at night. These abnormal sleep patterns are all too often mismanaged with alcohol or recreational, prescription or over-the-counter (OTC) drugs (most of which adversely affect the voice). Frequent and/or prolonged confinement to a closed cabin of a motor vehicle, train or aircraft may create additional problems. Inhalation of poorly filtered (often recycled), contaminated, dehumidified (dry) air (Feder 1984), according to many singers, can cause respiratory discomfort, tracheitis, bronchitis or laryngitis that may linger on for hours or even days following a trip.

Owing to environmental instability and hectic scheduling, many singers develop erratic, unhealthful eating habits. In addition to reliance on restaurant food and unpredictable changes in meal times, many singers eat the main meal of the day after their performance, usually late at night. Particularly for the overweight singer, and especially if spicy, greasy or acidic foods, alcohol or coffee were consumed, lying down soon after having filled the stomach is likely to result in gastroesophageal reflux. Reflux is the retrograde flow of acids from the stomach up the oesophagus and into the throat and larynx. The resulting symptoms can be devastating to the singer. Eating disorders are quite common among singers. In the operatic and classical realm, overeating and obesity are quite common. In the musical theatre and pop domain, particularly among young females, reportedly one-fifth of all singers have encountered some form of eating disorder, such as anorexia or bulimia. The latter involves various purging methods, of which vomiting is thought to be particularly hazardous to the voice.

A detrimental factor to voice production is exposure to pollutants, such as formaldehyde, solvents, paints and dusts, and allergens, such as tree, grass or weed pollens, dust, mould spores, animal danders and perfumes (Sataloff 1996). Such exposure may occur on and off stage. In their work milieu, singers can be exposed to these and other pollutants associated with vocal symptoms, including cigarette smoke and theatrical smoke and fog effects. Singers use a greater percentage of their vital capacity than ordinary speakers. Furthermore, during intense aerobic activity (such as dancing), the number of breathing cycles per minute increases, and mouth breathing prevails. This results in the inhalation of larger amounts of cigarette smoke and fogs during performances.

Treatment of Vocal Problems

Two major issues in the treatment of vocal problems of singers are self-medication and improper treatment by physicians who are not knowledgeable about the voice and its problems. Sataloff (1991, 1995) surveyed the potential side effects associated with medications commonly used by singers. Whether recreational, prescription, over the counter or food supplements, most drugs are likely to have some effect on phonatory function. In an attempt to control "allergies", "phlegm" or "sinus congestion", the self-medicating singer will ultimately ingest something that will damage the vocal system. Likewise, the physician who keeps prescribing steroids to reduce chronic inflammation caused by abus-

ive vocal habits and ignores the underlying causes will eventually hurt the singer. Vocal dysfunction resulting from poorly indicated or ill-performed phonosurgery has been documented (Bastian 1996). To avoid injuries secondary to treatment, singers are advised to know their instruments, and consult only with health care professionals who understand and have experience and expertise managing the vocal problems of singers, and who possess the patience to educate and empower singers.

ACTORS

Sandra Karen Richman

Acting involves placing your mind in the world of fantasy and bringing forth a character for a performance. Actors are involved in many arts and entertainment areas, including theatre, film, television, amusement and theme parks and so on. Hazards faced by actors include stress, physical hazards and chemical hazards. Stage fright (performance anxiety) is considered in a separate box.

Stress

Causes of stress include the fierce competition for scarce jobs, the pressure of performing shows daily or even more frequently (e.g., theme parks and matinee days), working at night, touring shows, filming deadlines, frequent retakes (especially while filming television commercials) and so on. There are also psychological pressures involved in adopting and maintaining a character role, including the pressure to express certain emotions upon demand, and the tactics often used by directors to obtain a given reaction from an actor. As a result, actors have higher rates of alcoholism and suicide. The solution to many of these causes of stress involves improved working and living conditions, especially when touring and on location. In addition, personal measures such as therapy and relaxation techniques can also help.

Costumes

Many costumes are a fire hazard near open flames or other ignition sources. Special effects costumes and masks can create problems of heat stress and excess weight.

The costumes of all actors working near open flames must be treated with an approved fire retardant. Actors wearing heavy costumes or costumes not suitable to the climate should be given adequate work breaks. With heavy metal or wood framework costumes, supplying cool air inside the costume might be necessary. Provision should also be made for easy escape from such costumes in case of emergency.

Theatrical Makeup

Theatrical makeup can cause allergic skin and eye reactions and irritation in some people. The widespread practice of sharing makeup or applying it to many people from the same container can create risks of transmitting bacterial infections. According to medical experts, transmission of the HIV and other viruses is not likely through shared makeup. The use of hair sprays and other spray products in unventilated dressing rooms is also a problem. Special effects makeup can involve the use of more hazardous materials such as polyurethane and silicone rubber resins and a variety of solvents.

Basic precautions when applying makeup include washing hands before and after; not using old makeup; no smoking, eating or drinking during application; using potable water and not saliva for moistening brushes; avoiding creation of airborne dust; and using pump sprays instead of aerosol sprays. Each performer should have his or her own makeup kit when practi-

96. ENTERTAINMENT AND THE ARTS

cal. When applying makeup to several individuals, disposable sponges, brushes and individual applicators, individual lipsticks (or sliced and labelled lipsticks) and so on should be used. The least toxic materials possible should be used for special effects makeup. The dressing room should have a mirror, good lighting and comfortable chairs.

Stunts

A stunt can be defined as any action sequence that involves a greater than normal risk of injury to performers or others on the set. In many such situations, actors are doubled by stunt performers who have extensive experience and training in carrying out such action sequences. Examples of potentially hazardous stunts include falls, fights, helicopter scenes, car chases, fires and explosions. Careful preplanning and written safety procedures are necessary. See the article "Motion picture and television production" for detailed information on stunts.

Other Hazards

Other hazards to actors, especially on location, include environmental conditions (heat, cold, polluted water, etc.), water scenes with possible risk of hypothermia and special effects (fogs and smoke, pyrotechnics, etc.). Special consideration must be given to these factors before filming starts. In theatres, scenes with dirt, gravel, artificial snow and so on can create eye and respiratory irritation problems when hazardous materials are used, or when materials are swept up and reused, resulting in possible biological contamination. An additional hazard is the growing phenomenon of stalking of well-known actors, actresses and other celebrities, with resultant threats or actuality of violence.

Child Actors

The use of children in theatre and motion picture production can lead to exploitation unless careful procedures are enforced to ensure that children do not work long hours, are not placed in hazardous situations and receive adequate education. Concern has also been expressed about the psychological effects on children participating in theatre or motion picture scenes involving simulated violence. Child labour laws in many countries do not adequately protect child actors.

● THEATRE AND OPERA

Claës-W. Englund

Occupational safety and health in the theatre and opera comprises diverse aspects, including all the problems of industry in general plus specific artistic and cultural aspects. More than 125 different professions are involved in the process of making theatre or opera performances; these performances can take place in classrooms and small theatres, as well as large opera houses or convention halls. Very often theatre and opera companies tour around the country and abroad, performing in diverse buildings.

There are the artistic professions—artists, actors, singers (soloists and choirs), musicians, dancers, coaches, choreographers, conductors and directors; the technical and production professions—technical directors and managers, lighting manager, chief electrician, sound engineer, chief machinist, armourer, wigmaster, dyeing and wardrobe director, property maker, costume maker and others; and the administrative professions—chief accountant, personnel managers, house managers, catering managers, contracts managers, marketing personnel, box office personnel, advertising managers and so on.

The theatre and opera involve general industrial safety hazards such as lifting of heavy objects and accident risks as a result of irregular working hours, combined with factors specific to the theatre, such as the layout of the premises, complex technical arrangements, bad lighting, extreme temperatures and the need to work to tight schedules and meet deadlines. These risks are the same for artists and technical personnel.

A serious attitude towards occupational safety and health demands taking care of the hand of a violinist or the wrist of a ballet dancer, as well as a broader view of the situation of theatre employees as a whole, including both physical and psychological risks. Theatre buildings are also open to the public, and this aspect of safety and health must be taken care of.

Fire Safety

There are many types of potential fire hazards in theatres and opera houses. These include: general hazards such as blocked or locked exits, inadequate number and size of exits, lack of training in procedures in the event of fire; backstage hazards such as improper storage of paints and solvents, unsafe storage of scenery and other combustibles, welding in close proximity to combustible materials and lack of proper exits for dressing rooms; on-stage hazards such as pyrotechnics and open flames, lack of fireproofing of drapes, decorations, props and scenery, and lack of stage exits and sprinkler systems; and audience hazards such as permitting smoking, blocked aisles and exceeding the legal number of occupants. In case of a fire in the theatre building all aisles, passages and staircases must be kept entirely free from chairs or any other obstructions, to help evacuation. Fire escapes and emergency exits must be marked. The alarm bells, fire alarms, fire extinguishers, sprinkler systems, heat and smoke detectors and emergency lights must function. The fire curtain must be lowered and raised in the presence of each audience, unless a deluge sprinkler system is installed. When the audience must leave, whether in an emergency or at the end of a performance, all exit doors must be open.

Fire safety procedures must be established and fire drills held. One or more trained fire guards must be present at all performances unless the fire department assigns firefighters. All scenery, props, drapes and other combustible materials present on the stage must be fireproofed. If pyrotechnics or open flames are present, fire permits must be obtained when required and safe procedures established for their use. Stage and backstage lighting equipment and electrical systems must meet standards and be properly maintained. Combustible materials and other fire hazards should be removed. Smoking should not be allowed in any theatre except in properly designated areas.

Grids and Rigging

Theatre and opera stages have overhead grids from which lights are hung, and rigging systems to fly (raise and lower) scenery and sometimes performers. There are ladders and overhead catwalks for lighting technicians and others to work overhead. On the stage, discipline is required from both the artists and the technical staff because of all the hanging equipment above. Theatre scenery can be moved vertically and horizontally. Horizontal movement of scenery at the side of the stage can be done manually or mechanically through the ropes from the grids in the rope house. Safety routines are very important in rope and counterweight flying. There are different kinds of rigging systems, using hydraulic and electric power. Rigging should be done by trained and qualified personnel. Safety procedures for rigging include: inspection of all rigging equipment before use and after alterations; ensuring load capacities are not exceeded; following safe procedures when loading, unloading or operating rigging systems; maintaining visual contact with a moving piece at all times; warning everyone before moving any rigged object; and ensuring no one is

Figure 96.14 • Arranging lights in a lowered lighting grid.

William Avery

underneath when moving scenery. The lighting crew must take appropriate safety measures while mounting, connecting and directing spotlights (figure 96.14). Lights should be fastened to the grid with safety chains. Safety shoes and helmets should be worn by personnel working on stage when any work is proceeding overhead.

Costumes and Makeup

Costumes

Costumes can be made in the theatres' own ateliers by the wardrobe attendants. It is a heavy job, especially the handling and transportation of old classical costumes. Body aches, headaches, musculoskeletal strains and sprains and other injuries can result from operating sewing machines, dryers, irons, ironing boards and electrical equipment; dust from textiles is a health hazard. Cleaning and dying of costumes, wigs and shoes can use a variety of hazardous liquid solvents and aerosol sprays.

Wearing heavy costumes can be hot under stage lights. Frequent costume changes between scenes can be a source of stress. If flames are present, fireproofing of costumes is essential.

Precautions for wardrobe attendants include proper electrical safety; adequate lighting and ventilation for solvents and spraying; adequate adjustable chairs, work tables and ironing boards; and knowledge of textiles health hazards.

Makeup

Performers usually have to wear heavy layers of makeup for several hours for every performance. Application of makeup and hair styling is usually done by makeup and hair artists in commercial theatre and opera. Often the makeup artist has to work on several performers in a short period of time. Makeup can contain a wide variety of solvents, dyes and pigments, oils, waxes and other ingredients, many of which can cause skin or eye irritation or allergies. Special effects makeup

can involve the use of hazardous adhesives and solvents. Eye injuries can result from abrasions during application of eye makeup. Shared makeup is a concern for transmission of bacterial contamination (but not hepatitis or HIV). The use of aerosol hair sprays in enclosed dressing rooms is an inhalation hazard. For makeup removal, large quantities of cold creams are used; solvents are also used for removing special effects makeup.

Precautions include washing off the makeup with soap after every performance, cleaning of brushes and sponges or using disposable ones, using individual applicators for makeup and keeping all makeup cold. The makeup room must have mirrors, flexible lighting and adequate chairs.

Setting Up and Striking Sets

Scenery at a theatre may require one standing set, which can be constructed of heavy materials; more frequently there can be several changes of scenery during a performance, requiring movability. Similarly, for a repertory theatre, changeable scenery can be constructed which is easily transportable. Scenery can be built on wheels, for mobility.

Stage crews risk injury when building, disassembling and moving scenery, and when moving counterbalances. Hazards include back, leg and arm injuries. Accidents often occur when breaking down (striking) the set when a show's run is over, due to fatigue. Precautions include wearing hard hats and safety shoes, safe lifting procedures and equipment, banning of unnecessary personnel and not working when fatigued.

For scene decorators or painters painting, nailing and laying out backdrops, paint and other chemicals are also health hazards. For carpenters, unsafe worksites, noise and vibration as well as air contamination are all problems. Wig and mask makers generally have problems with working postures as well as health risks associated with the use of resins—for example, when working on bald

96. ENTERTAINMENT AND THE ARTS

Scenery shops

Theatres, motion pictures, television, theme and amusement parks and similar entertainment enterprises all build and paint scenery and make props for their presentations. In many cases, these are made in-house. There are also commercial scenic shops that specialize in making large scenery which is then transported to the site. The major difference between making scenery backstage in a small theatre and building huge sets or even houses for a motion picture, for example, is the scale of the work and who does the work. In small theatres, there is little division of tasks, whereas in larger facilities, there would be a division of labour among carpenters, scenic painters, welders, prop makers and so on.

The scenery for a theatre play, motion picture set or television studio might look realistic, but is often an illusion. The walls of a room are usually not solid but are composed of lightweight flats (panels of painted canvas stretched on wooden frames). Background scenery often consists of backdrops (huge curtains painted to represent the background) which can be lowered and raised for different scenes. Other solid-looking props, such as trees, rocks, vases, mouldings, sculptures and so forth, might be made out of *papier mâché*, plaster, polyurethane foam or other materials. Today, a wide variety of materials are used to make scenery, including wood, metal, plastics, synthetic fabrics, paper and other modern industrial products. For scenery which performers will walk or climb on, the structures must be solid and meet proper safety standards.

The basic processes and chemicals used for making sets and props tend to be similar for the various types of entertainment facilities. Outdoor sets, however, can often use heavy construction materials such as cement on a large scale, which would be impractical inside due to smaller load-bearing capacities. The degree of hazard depends on the types and amounts of chemicals used, and the precautions taken. A theatre might use quarts of polyurethane foam resin for making small props, while the inside of a tunnel in a theme park set might use hundreds of gallons of the resin. Small in-house shops tend to have less awareness of the hazards, and overcrowding often creates additional hazards due to the proximity of incompatible processes such as welding and use of flammable solvents.

Woodworking

Wood, plywood, particle board and Plexiglas are commonly used in constructing sets. Hazards include: accidents with woodworking machinery, power tools and hand tools; electrical shock; fire from combustible wood dust; and toxic effects from inhalation of wood dust, formaldehyde and methyl methacrylate decomposition products from machining plywood, particle board and Plexiglas, and solvents used with contact adhesives.

Precautions include machine guards, proper electrical safety, housekeeping and adequate storage to reduce fire hazards, dust collectors, adequate ventilation and eye protection.

Welding, cutting and brazing

Steel and aluminium frameworks are commonly used for the construction of sets. These are often welded using oxyacetylene torches and arc welders of various types. Injury hazards include fire from flying sparks, fire and explosion from compressed gases, and electrical shock from arc welders; health hazards include metal fumes, fluxes, welding gases (ozone, nitrogen oxides, carbon monoxide) and ultraviolet radiation.

Precautions include removal or protection of combustible materials, proper storage and handling of compressed gas cylinders, electrical safety, adequate ventilation and personal protective equipment.

Scenic painting

Paints, lacquers, varnishes, dye solutions and other coatings are used for painting scenery flats and fabric drops. The paints and dye solutions can be either solvent based or water based. Powdered pigments and dyes are usually mixed in the shop, with the use of lead chromate pigments still being common. Large flats and drops are often sprayed. Solvents are used for dissolving dyes and resins, thinning, removing paint and other coatings and for cleaning tools, brushes and even hands. Hazards include skin contact with solvents and inhalation of solvent vapours, spray mists and powdered dyes and pigments. Solvents are also fire hazards, particularly when sprayed.

Precautions include elimination of lead pigments, using water-based paints and dyes, adequate ventilation for use of solvents, respiratory protection for spraying, proper storage and handling of flammable liquids and proper disposal of waste solvents and paints.

Plastic resins

Polyurethane foam resins, epoxy resins, polyester resins and other resins are commonly used to make large sets and props. Spraying of polyurethane foam resins containing diphenylmethane diisocyanate (MDI) is particularly dangerous, with hazards of chemical pneumonia and asthma. Epoxy resins, polyester resins and solvents have skin, eye and inhalation hazards, and are fire hazards.

Precautions include substitution of safer materials (such as cement or *celastic* instead of spray polyurethane foams, or water-based materials to replace solvent-based types), local exhaust ventilation, proper storage and handling, proper disposal of waste materials and adequate personal protective equipment.

Props and models

Plastic resins are also used to make body armour, face masks, breakaway glass and other props and models, as are wood, plaster, metal, plastics and so on. A variety of water-based and solvent-based adhesives are also used. Solvents are used in cleanup. Precautions are similar to those already discussed.

Michael McCann

heads and false noses. Health risks include toxic chemicals and possible allergies, skin irritation and asthmatic complaints.

Regulations

There are often national laws, for example, building codes, and local regulations for fire safety. For grids and rigging, directives from the European Economic Commission—for instance, on machinery (89/392 EEC) and on lifting appliances for persons—may influence national legislation. Other countries also have safety and health legislation that can affect theatres and opera houses.

MOTION PICTURE AND TELEVISION PRODUCTION

Michael McCann

The motion picture and television industry is found throughout the world. Motion picture production can take place in fixed studios, on large commercial studio lots or on location anywhere. Film production companies range in size from large corporations' own studios to small companies that rent space in commercial studios. The production of television shows, soap operas, videos and commercials has much in common with motion picture production.

Motion picture production involves many stages and a crew of interacting specialists. The planning stages include obtaining a finished script, determining the budget and schedule, choosing types of location and studios, designing the scene-by-scene appearance of the film, selecting costumes, planning sequence of action and camera locations and lighting schemes.

Once the planning is completed, the detailed process of choosing the location, building sets, gathering the props, arranging the lighting and hiring the actors, stunt performers, special effects operators and other needed support personnel begins. Filming follows the preproduction stage. The final step is film processing and editing, which is not discussed in this article.

Motion picture and television production can involve a wide variety of chemical, electrical and other hazards, many of which are unique to the film industry.

Hazards and Precautions

Filming location
Filming in a studio or on a studio lot has the advantage of permanent facilities and equipment, including ventilation systems, power, lighting, scene shops, costume shops and more control over environmental conditions. Studios can be very large in order to accommodate a variety of filming situations.

Filming on location, especially outdoors in remote locations, is more difficult and hazardous than in a studio because transportation, communications, power, food, water, medical services, living quarters and so on must be provided. Filming on location can expose the film crew and actors to a wide variety of hazardous conditions, including wild animals, poisonous reptiles and plants, civil unrest, climate extremes and adverse local weather conditions, communicable diseases, contaminated food and water, structurally unsafe buildings, and buildings contaminated with asbestos, lead, biological hazards and so on. Filming on water, in the mountains, in deserts and other dangerous locales poses obvious hazards.

The initial survey of possible filming locations should involve evaluating these and other potential hazards to determine the need for special precautions or alternative locations.

Fabricating scenery for motion pictures can involve constructing or modifying a building or buildings, building of indoor and outdoor sets and so on. These can be full size or scaled down. Stages and scenery should be strong enough to bear the loads under consideration (see the box "Scenery shops" in this chapter).

Life safety
Basic life safety includes ensuring adequate exits, keeping access routes and exits marked and clear of equipment and electrical cables and removal or proper storage and handling of combustible materials, flammable liquids and compressed gases. Dry vegetation around outdoor locations and combustible materials used in filming such as sawdust and tents must be removed or flameproofed.

Automobiles, boats, helicopters and other means of transportation are common on film locations and a cause of many accidents and fatalities, both when used for transportation and while filming. It is essential that all drivers of vehicles and aircraft be fully qualified and obey all relevant laws and regulations.

Scaffolding and rigging
On location and in studios, lights are rigged to sets, scaffolding or permanent overhead grids, or are free standing. Rigging is also used to fly scenery or people for special effects. Hazards include collapsing scaffolds, falling lights and other equipment and failures of rigging systems.

Precautions for scaffolds include safe construction, guardrails and toeboards, proper supporting of rolling scaffolds and securing of all equipment. Construction, operation, maintenance, inspection and repair of rigging systems should be done only by properly trained and qualified persons. Only assigned personnel should have access to work areas such as scaffolds and catwalks.

Electrical and lighting equipment
Large amounts of power are usually needed for camera lights and everyday electrical needs on a set. In the past direct current (DC) power was used, but alternating current (AC) power is common today. Often, and especially on location, independent sources of power are used. Examples of electrical hazards include shorting of electrical wiring or equipment, inadequate wiring, deteriorated wiring or equipment, inadequate grounding of equipment and working in wet locations. Tie-ins to the power sources and un-ties at the end of filming are two of the most dangerous activities.

All electrical work should be done by licensed electricians and should follow standard electrical safety practices and codes. Safer direct current should be used around water when possible, or ground fault circuit interrupters installed.

Lighting can pose both electrical and health hazards. High-voltage gas discharge lamps such as neons, metal halide lamps and carbon arc lamps are especially hazardous and can pose electrical, ultraviolet radiation and toxic fume hazards.

Lighting equipment should be kept in good condition, regularly inspected and adequately secured to prevent lights from tipping or falling. It is particularly important to check high-voltage discharge lamps for lens cracks that could leak ultraviolet radiation.

Cameras
Camera crews can film in many hazardous situations, including shooting from a helicopter, moving vehicle, camera crane or side of a mountain. Basic types of camera mountings include fixed tripods, dollies for mobile cameras, camera cranes for high shots and insert camera cars for shots of moving vehicles. There have been several fatalities among camera operators while filming under unsafe conditions or near stunts and special effects.

Basic precautions for camera cranes include testing of lift controls, ensuring a stable surface for the crane base and pedestal; properly laid tracking surfaces, ensuring safe distances from high-tension electrical wires; and body harnesses where required.

Insert camera cars that have been engineered for mounting of cameras and towing of the vehicle to be filmed are recommended instead of mounting cameras on the outside of the vehicle being filmed. Special precautions include having a safety checklist, limiting the number of personnel on the car, rigging done by experts, abort procedures and having a dedicated radio communications procedure.

Actors, extras and stand-ins
See the article "Actors" in this chapter.

Costumes
Costumes are made and cared for by wardrobe attendants, who may be exposed to a wide variety of dyes and paints, hazardous solvents, aerosol sprays and so on, often without ventilation.

Hazardous chlorinated cleaning solvents should be replaced with safer solvents such as mineral spirits. Adequate local exhaust ventilation should be used when spraying dyes or using solvent-containing materials. Mixing of powders should be done in a enclosed glove box.

96. ENTERTAINMENT AND THE ARTS

Special effects

A wide variety of special effects are used in motion picture production to simulate real events that would otherwise be too dangerous, impractical or expensive to execute. These include fogs, smoke, fire, pyrotechnics, firearms, snow, rain, wind, computer-generated effects and miniature or scaled-down sets. Many of these have significant hazards. Other hazardous special effects can involve the use of lasers, toxic chemicals such as mercury to give silvery effects, flying objects or people with rigging and electric hazards associated with rain and other water effects. Appropriate precautions would need to be taken with such special effects.

General precautions for hazardous special effects include adequate preplanning, having written safety procedures, using adequately trained and experienced operators and the least hazardous special effects possible, coordinating with the fire department and other emergency services, making everyone aware of the intended use of special effects (and being able to refuse to participate), not allowing children in the vicinity, running detailed rehearsals with testing of the effects, clearing the set of all but essential personnel, having a dedicated emergency communications system, minimizing the number of retakes and having procedures ready to abort production.

Pyrotechnics are used to create effects involving explosions, fires, light, smoke and sound concussions. Pyrotechnics materials are usually low explosives (mostly Class B), including flash powder, flash paper, gun cotton, black powder and smokeless powder. They are used in bullet hits (squibs), blank cartridges, flash pots, fuses, mortars, smoke pots and many more. Class A high explosives, such as dynamite, should not be used, although detonating cord is sometimes used. The major problems associated with pyrotechnics include premature triggering of the pyrotechnic effect; causing a fire by using larger quantities than needed; lack of adequate fire extinguishing capabilities; and having inadequately trained and experienced pyrotechnics operators.

In addition to the general precautions, special precautions for explosives used in pyrotechnics include proper storage, the use of appropriate type and in smallest amounts necessary to achieve the effect, and testing them in the absence of spectators. When pyrotechnics are used smoking should be banned and firefighting equipment and trained personnel should be on hand. The materials should be set off by electronic firing controls and adequate ventilation is needed.

The uses of *fire effects* range from ordinary gas stoves and fireplaces to the destructive fires involved in burning cars, houses, forests and even people (figure 96.15). In some cases, fires can be simulated by flickering lights and other electronic effects. Materials used to create fire effects include propane gas burners, rubber cement, gasoline and kerosene. They are often used in conjunction with pyrotechnic special effects. Hazards are directly related to the fire getting out of control and the heat they generate. Poor maintenance of fire generating equipment and the excessive use of flammable materials or the presence of other unintended combustible materials, and improper storage of combustible and flammable liquids and gases are all risks. Inexperienced special effects operators can also be a cause of accidents as well.

Special precautions are similar to those needed for pyrotechnics, such as replacing gasoline, rubber cement and other flammable substances with the safer combustible gels and liquid fuels which have been developed in recent years. All materials in the fire area should be non-combustible or flame-proofed. This precaution includes flame-proofed costumes for actors in the vicinity.

Fogs and smoke effects are common in filming. Dry ice (carbon dioxide), liquid nitrogen, petroleum distillates, zinc chloride smoke generators (which might also contain chlorinated hydro-

Figure 96.15 • Fire special effect.

William Avery

carbons), ammonium chloride, mineral oil, glycol fogs and water mists are common fog-generating substances. Some materials used, such as petroleum distillates and zinc chloride, are severe respiratory irritants and can cause chemical pneumonia. Dry ice, liquid nitrogen and water mists represent the least chemical hazards, although they can displace oxygen in enclosed areas, possibly making the air unfit for supporting life, especially in enclosed areas. Microbiological contamination can be a problem associated with water-mist generating systems. Some evidence is forthcoming that respiratory irritation is possible from those fogs and smokes that were thought to be safest, such as mineral oil and glycols.

Special precautions include eliminating the most hazardous fogs and smoke; using a fog with the machine designed for it; limiting duration of use, including limiting the number of retakes; and avoiding use in enclosed spaces. Fogs should be exhausted as soon as possible. Respiratory protection for the camera crew should be provided.

Firearms are common in films. All types of firearms are used, ranging from antique firearms to shotguns and machine guns. In many countries (not including the United States) live ammunition is banned. However, blank ammunition, which is commonly used in conjunction with live bullet hits in order to simulate actual bullet impacts, has caused many injuries and fatalities. Blank ammunition used to consist of a metal casing with a percussion primer and smokeless powder topped with a paper wad, which could be ejected at high velocity when fired. Some modern safety blanks use special plastic inserts with a primer and flash powder, giving only a flash and noise. Blank ammunition is commonly used in conjunction with bullet hits (squibs), consisting of a plastic-cased detonator imbedded in the object to be struck by the bullet to simulate actual bullet impacts. Hazards, besides the use of live ammunition, include the effects of use of blanks at close range, mixing up live and blank ammunition or using the wrong ammunition in a firearm. Improperly modified firearms can be dangerous, as can the lack of adequate training in the use of blank-firing firearms.

Live ammunition and unmodified firearms should be banned from a set and non-firing facsimile weapons used whenever possible. Firearms that can actually fire a bullet should not be used, only proper safety blanks. Firearms should be checked regularly by the property master or other firearms expert. Firearms should be locked away, as should all ammunition. Guns should never be pointed at actors in a scene, and the camera crew and others in close proximity to the set should be protected with shields from blanks fired from weapons.

Stunts

A *stunt* can be defined as any action sequence that involves a greater than normal risk of injury to performers or others on the set. With increasing demands for realism in films, stunts have become very common. Examples of potentially hazardous stunts include high falls, fights, helicopter scenes, car chases, fires and explosions. About half the fatalities occurring during filming are stunt-related, often also involving special effects.

Stunts can endanger not only the stunt performer but often the camera crew and other performers may be injured as well. Most of the general precautions described for special effects also apply to stunts. In addition, the stunt performer should be experienced in the type of stunt being filmed. A stunt coordinator should be in charge of all stunts since a person cannot perform a stunt and be in adequate control of safety, especially when there are several stunt performers.

Aircraft, especially helicopters, have been involved in the most serious multiple fatality accidents in motion picture production. Pilots are often not adequately qualified for stunt flying. Acrobatic manoeuvres, hovering close to the ground, flying too close to sets using pyrotechnics and filming from helicopters with open doors or from the pontoons without adequate fall protection are some of the most dangerous situations. See the article "Heliocopters" elsewhere in the *Encyclopaedia*.

One precaution is to employ an independent aviation consultant, in addition to the pilot, to recommend and oversee safety procedures. Restriction of personnel within 50 feet of grounded aircraft and clear written procedures for filming on ground near aircraft with their engines running or during aircraft landings or takeoffs are other safety measures. Coordination with any pyrotechnics or other hazardous special effects operators is essential, as are procedures to ensure the safety of camera operators filming from aircraft. Procedures for aborting an operation are needed.

Vehicle action sequences have also been a source of many accidents and fatalities. Special effects, such as explosions, crashes, driving into rivers and car chase scenes with multiple cars, are the most common cause of accidents. Motorcycle scenes can be even more

hazardous than automobiles because the operator of the motorcycle suffers from the lack of personal protection.

Special precautions include using camera cars. Using stunt drivers for all cars in a stunt scene can lower the accident rate, as can special training for non-stunt passengers. Other safety rules include proper safety equipment, inspection of all ramps and other equipment to be used during a stunt, using dummies in cars during crashes, explosions and other extremely high risk sequences and not driving cars directly towards cameras if there is a camera operator behind the camera. See figure 96.16 for an example of using dummies in a roller coaster stunt. Adequate ventilation is needed for automobiles that are being filmed indoors with engines running. Stunt motorcycles should be equipped with a deadman switch so that the motor shuts off when the rider separates from the motorcycle.

Stunts using *fire and explosion* place performers at higher risk and require special precautions beyond those used just for the special effects. Protection for stunt performers directly exposed to flames includes wearing a protective barrier gel (e.g., Zel Jel) on the hair, the skin, clothing and so on. Proper protective clothing, including fireproof suits under costumes; flame-resistant gloves and boots; and sometimes hidden oxygen tanks, should be supplied. Specially trained personnel equipped with carbon dioxide fire extinguishers should be on hand in case of an emergency.

Fight scenes can involve performers in fistfights or other unarmed combat or the use of knives, swords, firearms and other combat equipment. Many film and stage fights do not involve the use of stunt performers, thus increasing the risk of injury because of the lack of training.

Simulated weapons, such as knives and swords with retractable blades, are one safeguard. Weapons should be stored carefully. Training is key. The performer should know how to fall and how to use specific weapons. Adequate choreography and rehearsals of the fights is needed, as is proper protective clothing and equipment. A blow should never be aimed directly at an actor. If a fight involves a high degree of hazard, such as falling down a flight of stairs or crashing through a window, a professional stunt double should be used.

Falls in stunts can range from falling down a flight of stairs to falling off a horse, being thrown through the air by a trampoline or ratchet catapult system, or a high fall off a cliff or building (figure 96.17). There have been many injuries and fatalities from poorly prepared falls.

Only experienced stunt performers should attempt fall stunts. When possible, the fall should be simulated. For example, falling down a flight of stairs can be filmed a few stairs at a time so the stunt performer is never out of control, or a fall off a tall building simulated by a fall of a few feet onto a net and using a dummy for the rest of the fall. Precautions for high falls involve a high fall coordinator and a specialized fall/arrest system for safe deceleration. Falls of more than 15 feet require two safety spotters. Other precautions for falls include airbags, crash pads of canvas filled with sponge rubber, sand pits and so on, depending on the type of fall. Testing of all equipment is crucial.

Animal scenes are potentially very hazardous because of the unpredictability of animals. Some animals, such as large cats, can attack if startled. Large animals like horses can be a hazard just because of their size. Dangerous, untrained or unhealthy animals should not be used on sets. Venomous reptiles such as rattlesnakes are particularly hazardous. In addition to the hazards to personnel, the health and safety of the animals should be considered.

Only trained animal handlers should be allowed to work with animals. Adequate conditions for the animals are needed, as is basic animal safety equipment, such as fire extinguishers, fire hoses, nets and tranquilizing equipment. Animals should be allowed adequate time

Figure 96.16 • Using dummies for a roller coaster stunt.

William Avery

96. ENTERTAINMENT AND THE ARTS

Figure 96.17 • High fall stunt.

William Avery

to become familiar with the set, and only required personnel should be permitted on the set. Conditions that could upset animals should be eliminated and animals kept from exposure to loud noises or light flashes whenever possible, thus ensuring the animals will not be injured and will not become unmanageable. Certain situations—for example, those using venomous reptiles or large numbers of horses—will require special precautions.

Water stunts can include diving, filming in fast-moving water, speedboat stunts and sea battles. Hazards include drowning, hypothermia in cold water, underwater obstructions and contaminated water. Emergency teams, including certified safety divers, should be on hand for all water stunts. Diver certification for all performers or camera operators using self-contained underwater breathing apparatus (SCUBA) and provision of standby breathing equipment are other precautions. Emergency decompression procedures for dives over 10 m should be in place. Safety pickup boats for rescue and proper safety equipment, such as use of nets and ropes in fast-moving water, are needed.

Health and Safety Programmes

Most major film studios have a full-time *health and safety officer* to oversee the health and safety programme. Problems of responsibility and authority can occur, however, when a studio rents facilities to a production company, as is increasingly common. Most production companies do not have a health and safety programme. A health and safety officer, with authority to establish safety procedures and to ensure they are carried out, is essential. There is a need to coordinate the activities of others charged with production planning, such as stunt coordinators, special effects operators, firearms experts and the key grip (who is usually the individual most responsible for the safety of sets, cameras, scaffolding, etc.), each of whom has specialized safety knowledge

and experience. A health and safety committee that meets regularly with representatives from all departments and unions can provide a conduit between the management and employees. Many unions have an independent health and safety committee which can be a source of health and safety expertise.

Medical services

Both non-emergency and emergency medical services are essential during film production. Many film studios have a permanent medical department, but most production companies do not. The first step in determining the degree of on-location medical services to be provided is a needs assessment, to identify potential medical risks, including the need for vaccination in certain countries, possible local endemic diseases, evaluation of local environmental and climate conditions, and an evaluation of the quality of local medical resources. The second, pre-planning stage involves a detailed analysis of major risks and availability of adequate emergency and other medical care in order to determine what type of emergency planning is essential. In situations where there are high risks and/or remote locations, trained emergency physicians would be needed on location. Where there is quick access to adequate emergency facilities, paramedics or emergency medical technicians with advanced training would suffice. In addition, adequate emergency transportation should be arranged beforehand. There have been several fatalities due to the lack of adequate emergency transportation (Carlson 1989; McCann 1989).

Standards

There are few occupational safety and health regulations aimed specifically at the film production industry. However, many general regulations, such as those affecting fire safety, electrical hazards, scaffolding, lifts, welding and so on, are applicable. Local fire departments generally require special fire permits for filming and may require that standby fire personnel be present on filming sites.

Many productions have special requirements for the licensing of certain special effects operators, such as pyrotechnicians, laser operators and firearms users. There can be regulations and permits required for specific situations, such as the sale, storage and use of pyrotechnics, and the use of firearms.

RADIO AND TELEVISION BROADCASTING

Nancy Clark

The production of television and radio broadcasts involves camera shoots and recordings on location and in the studio, video- and audiotape editing, transmitting and receiving broadcasts, managing electronic information and graphics, and maintenance of equipment and tape. Broadcast engineers and technicians produce pre-taped and live broadcasts for major network and cable companies, local stations and production companies. Major occupations include: camera operator, sound person, tape editor, computer operator, maintenance engineer, news broadcaster and other television and radio artists.

Broadcasting and its support activities can take place in remote locations, in the studio or in various maintenance and specialty shops. Employees can be exposed to many hazards typical of the technological workplace, including poor indoor air quality, poor workplace design and low-frequency electromagnetic radiation (since microwave technology is used to transmit and receive broadcasts, and the density of electronic equipment produces relatively high levels of low-frequency energy fields). Proper shielding and placement of equipment are prudent measures to protect operators from these fields.

Hazards and Precautions

Remote locations

Roving camera and audio crews cover news and special events for networks and local stations. Crews carry to the site everything needed for the broadcast, including camera, sound recorder, lights, tripod and electrical cords. Since the advent of lightweight cameras equipped with sound recorders, a single person may be assigned to operate the equipment. The hazards can include trips, slips and falls and musculoskeletal stress. Violence in riots and wars can lead to injuries and fatalities. Bad weather, crowds, environmental disasters and rough terrain increase the potential for serious injuries and illnesses among the crew.

The danger can be reduced through assessing the location for the potential for violence and the securing of safe operating locations. Personal protective equipment, such as bullet-proof vests and helmets, may also be needed. Adequate staffing and material-handling equipment and safe lifting practices can reduce musculoskeletal stresses.

News and traffic reports are frequently recorded or aired from helicopters. Broadcast personnel have been killed and injured in crashes and unplanned landings. Strict adherence to proper training and certification of pilots, preventive maintenance of equipment and prohibition of unsafe flying practices (such as flying too close to other helicopters or to structures) are crucial for protecting these employees. See the article "Heliocopters" elsewhere in this volume.

Sporting events, such as golf tournaments and car races, and other special events are often shot from elevated platforms and scaffolds. Motorized lifts and cranes are also used to position equipment and personnel. These structures and machines are typical of those used in general building construction and motion picture production, and one may encounter the same hazards, such as falling off the structure, being struck by falling objects, being struck by lightning in open areas and being electrocuted from contact with overhead power lines and live electrical equipment.

Proper inspection and erection of platforms, full guardrails with toe boards to prevent objects from falling, access ladders, grounding and guarding of electrical equipment and observance of weather alerts, as in construction work, are some appropriate precautions to be taken.

Studio productions

Studio productions have the advantages of familiar surroundings where employees operate cameras, sound equipment and special effects equipment. The hazards are similar to those described in motion picture production and include: musculoskeletal stresses, electrical hazards, noise (especially in rock radio studios) and exposure to theatrical smokes and fogs. Appropriate ergonomic design of work spaces and equipment, electrical safeguards, control of sound levels, careful selection of smokes and fogs and adequate ventilation are all possible preventive measures.

Film editing, handling and storage

Before being broadcast, video- and audiotapes must be edited. The conditions will depend on the size of the facility, but it is not uncommon for several editing operations to be going on at the same time. Editing work requires close attention to the material, and editing rooms can be noisy, overcrowded and poorly lit, with poor indoor air quality and electrical hazards. The space and the equipment can have poor ergonomic design; tasks may be repeti-

tive. There may be noise and fire hazards. Proper workspace design including space, lighting and ventilation, soundproofing and electrical safeguards are all necessary. Special inspection and handling procedures are required for old film storage. Some production companies have libraries that contain old cellulose nitrate (nitrocellulose) films. These films are no longer made, but those that are in storage are severe fire and life hazards. Nitrocellulose can combust and explode readily.

Computer graphics are common in taped programmes and require long hours at visual display units. Working conditions vary based on the size and layout of the facility. Workspace design requirements are similar to other computer workstations.

Maintenance Shops

Technicians and engineers maintain cameras, recorders, editing machines and other broadcasting equipment, and their working conditions resemble those of their industrial counterparts. Low-residue organic solvents, such as freons, acetone, methanol, methyl ethyl ketone and methylene chloride are used to clean electronic parts and electrical contacts. Metal components are repaired using welding, soldering and power tools. The hazards can include inhalation of solvent vapours and metal fumes, skin contact with solvents, fire and machine hazards. The substitution of safer materials, local exhaust ventilation for solvent vapours and fumes from welding and soldering, as well as machine guards, are all possible safeguards.

JOURNALISM

Aidan White

Journalism is one of the romantic professions, but it is also one of the most dangerous. Between 1990 and 1997 more than 500 journalists and media workers were killed, many the victims of gangsters, paramilitary groups and terrorists. Each year, hundreds of reporters and writers are injured, both physically and psychologically, by the horrors of war and social conflict. See figure 96.18

The tendency to try to manipulate or control information is becoming more evident as the speed and range of communication increases. Today information speeds around the world in seconds thanks to satellite technology. News and information can be beamed into people's homes as it happens.

Consequently, journalists and their visible helpers—camera and technical staff, for instance—pose a threat to any group, official or otherwise, that wants to avoid public scrutiny. This leads to specific and targeted attacks on journalists and media organizations.

The problem of "censorship by violence" is exacerbated by the nature of commercial competition in the media industry and by unregulated patterns of employment. Media networks compete vigorously for market share, and this is leading to greater pressure on journalists to provide ever more dramatic and sensationalist images and reportage. Many media people are taking greater risks than before.

The situation is made worse because few media organizations provide training for their staff in how to deal with situations of violence and conflict. Such training is essential. Media staff need to be able to make coherent and sensible "risk assessment" judgements about fast-moving reporting situations. They need a basic knowledge of first aid and advice from media veterans on how to report from dangerous scenes.

The most vulnerable group of media workers—freelance journalists and casual staff—are the ones least likely to receive training

96. ENTERTAINMENT AND THE ARTS

Figure 96.18 • Algiers, Algeria, 11 February 1996: The devastated offices of *Le Soir*, one of three newspapers hit by a terrorist car bomb.

Le Soir

even where it is available. More freelance staff are employed than ever before and many of them are hired from the regions where the reported action is taking place. Sometimes they are hired without any life or health insurance. If they get hurt, they are not entitled to compensation.

Because they often work in very unpredictable circumstances, some journalists will always be at risk. Often it will be impossible to avoid injury, even death. But much more can be done to minimize the levels of risk. For instance, in Algeria, where some 60 journalists were assassinated between June 1994 and March 1996, journalists' unions, employers and the authorities have combined their efforts to minimize risks.

Much more needs to be done by media organizations and representatives of media workers and journalists to provide protections for media personnel. In particular there is a need for:

- Adequate preparation by journalists and media before going on assignment. Media organizations should provide technical assistance and establish training programmes specifically designed to improve levels of personal safety and to carry out risk assessment related to specific assignments.
- Health and life insurance for everyone reporting in the field, with established procedures to ensure that anyone who is likely to be at risk, including freelance staff or stringers, is covered.

In addition, media organizations must reverse recent trends that undermine the social and professional conditions in which journalists work. There should be increased investment in professional training and journalistic ethics to emphasize the importance of investigative journalism to the good health of democratic society.

Journalists themselves have a key role to play. All journalists must take responsibility to exercise the highest standards of personal safety and minimize risks to themselves and their colleagues. Journalists need to maintain the highest professional standards and conduct and should not compromise the ethics of journalism in any aspect of the gathering, production or dissemination of news and information.

But it is not only the professionals that need to take practical steps to address the issue. Governments, which have a responsibility to protect the lives and security of citizens, must ensure that journalists and media organizations are provided with the maximum security and protection from violence.

Government and public authorities must not regard journalists as part of the state security apparatus and must not demand information or materials from media organizations in order to assist inquiries which are the responsibility of official agencies.

One of the worrying features of journalism has always been that governments are prepared to use the cover of journalistic activity in order to carry out surveillance and espionage. It is a practice which exposes all travelling journalists to suspicion and intimidation.

The key is to reduce the risk. There are no absolute guarantees of safety, but governments, journalists and media organizations need to avoid creating the conditions which make it easier to commit violence against media. A starting point would be recognition that no single story, no matter how dramatic, is worth a life.

ENTERTAINMENT

● MUSEUMS AND ART GALLERIES

Kathryn A. Makos

Museums and art galleries are a popular source of entertainment and education for the general public. There are many different types of museums, such as art, history, science, natural history and children's museums. The exhibits, lectures and publications offered to the public by museums, however, are only one part of the function of museums. The broad mission of museums and art galleries is to collect, conserve, study and display items of artistic, historical, scientific or cultural importance. Supportive research (fieldwork, literary and laboratory) and behind-the-scenes collection care typically represent the largest proportion of work activi-

ties. Collections on display generally represent a small fraction of the total acquisitions of the museum or gallery, with the remainder in on-site storage or on loan to other exhibits or research projects. Museums and galleries may be stand-alone entities or affiliated with larger institutions such as universities, government agencies, armed services installations, park service historic sites or even specific industries.

A museum's operations can be divided into several main functions: general building operations, exhibit and display production, educational activities, collection management (including field studies) and conservation. Occupations, which may overlap depending on size of staff, include building maintenance trades and custodians, carpenters, curators, illustrators and artists, librarians and educators, scientific researchers, specialized shipping and receiving and security.

General Building Operations

The operation of museums and galleries poses potential safety and health hazards both common to other occupations and unique to museums. As buildings, museums are subject to poor indoor air quality and to risks associated with maintenance, repair, custodial and security activities of large public buildings. Fire prevention systems are critical to protect the lives of staff and a multitude of visitors, as well as the priceless collections.

General tasks involve custodians; heating, ventilation and air-conditioning (HVAC) specialists and boiler engineers; painters; electricians; plumbers; welders; and machinists. Safety hazards include slips, trips and falls; back and limb strains; electrical shock; and fires and explosions from compressed gas cylinders or hot work. Health hazards include exposures to hazardous materials, noise, metal fumes, flux fumes and gases, and ultraviolet radiation; and dermatitis from cutting oils, solvents, epoxies and plasticizers. Custodial staff are exposed to splash hazards from diluting cleaning chemicals, chemical reactions from improperly mixed chemicals, dermatitis, inhalation hazards from dry sweeping of lead paint chips or residual preservative chemicals in collection storage areas, injury from broken laboratory glassware or working around sensitive laboratory chemicals and equipment, and biological hazards from cleaning building exteriors of bird debris.

Older buildings are prone to mould and mildew growth and poor indoor air quality. They often lack exterior wall vapour barriers and have air handling systems which are old and difficult to maintain. Renovation may lead to uncovering material hazards in both centuries-old buildings and modern ones. Lead paints, mercury linings on old mirrored surfaces and asbestos in decorative finishes and insulation are some examples. With historic buildings, the need to preserve historic integrity must be balanced against design requirements of life safety codes and accommodations for persons with disabilities. Exhaust ventilation system installations should not destroy historic facades. Rooflines or skyline restrictions in historic districts may pose serious challenges to construction of exhaust stacks with sufficient height. Barriers used to separate construction areas often must be free-standing units that cannot be attached to walls that have historic features. Renovation should not mar underlying supports which may consist of valuable wood or finishes. These restrictions may lead to increased dangers. Fire detection and suppression systems and fire-rated construction are essential.

Precautions include the use of personal protective equipment (PPE) for eyes, face, head, hearing and respiration; electrical safety; machine guards and lock-out/tag-out programmes; good housekeeping; compatible hazardous material storage and secure compressed gas cylinders; fire detection and suppression systems; dust collectors, local exhaust and use of high efficiency particulate air (HEPA) filtered vacuum cleaners; safe lifting and material handling training; fork-lift safety; use of hoists, slings and hydraulic lifts; chemical spill control; safety showers and eye washes; first aid kits; and hazard communication and employee training programmes in hazards of materials and jobs (particularly for custodians in laboratories) and means for protection.

Exhibit and Display Production

The production and installation of museum exhibits and displays can involve a wide range of activities. For example, an animal exhibit in a natural history museum could involve the production of display cases; the construction of a reproduction of the animal's natural habitat; the fabrication of the animal model itself; written, oral and illustrated materials to accompany the exhibit; appropriate lighting; and more. Processes involved in the exhibit production can include: carpentry; metalworking; working with plastics, plastics resins and many other materials; graphic arts; and photography.

Exhibit fabrication and graphics shops share similar risks with general woodworkers, sculptors, graphic artists, metalworkers and photographers. Specific health or safety risks may arise from installation of exhibits in halls without adequate ventilation, cleaning of display cases containing residues of hazardous treatment materials, formaldehyde exposure during photography set-up of fluid collection specimens and high-speed cutting of wood treated with fire retardant, which may liberate irritating acid gases (oxides of sulphur, phosphorus).

Precautions include appropriate personal protective equipment, acoustic treatment and local exhaust controls on woodworking machinery; adequate ventilation for graphics tables, silkscreen wash booths, paint-mixing areas, plastics resin areas, and photo development; and use of water-based ink systems.

Educational Activities

Museum educational activities can include lectures, distribution of publications, hands-on arts and science activities and more. These can be directed either towards adults or children. Arts and science activities can often involve use of toxic chemicals in rooms not equipped with proper ventilation and other precautions, handling arsenic-preserved stuffed birds and animals, electrical equipment and more. Safety risks may exist for both museum education staff and participants, particularly children. Such programmes should be evaluated to determine what types of precautions are needed and whether they can be done safely in the museum setting.

Art and Artefact Collections Management

Collections management involves field collection or acquisition, inventory control, proper storage techniques, preservation and pest management. Fieldwork can involve digging on archaeological expeditions, preserving botanical, insect and other specimens, making casts of specimens, drilling fossil rocks and more. The duties of curatorial staff in the museum include handling the specimens, examining them with a variety of techniques (e.g., microscopy, x ray), pest management, preparing them for exhibits and handling travelling exhibitions.

Hazards can occur at all stages of collections management, including those associated with field work, hazards inherent in the handling of the object or specimen itself, residues of old preservation or fumigation methods (which may not have been well documented by the original collector) and hazards associated with pesticide and fumigant application. Table 96.8 gives the hazards and precautions associated with some of these operations.

There are also hazards associated with the collection objects themselves. Wet collections in general have the following risks: exposure to formaldehyde used for field-fixing and permanent storage; sorting specimens from formaldehyde to alcohol storage (usually ethanol or isopropanol); and "mystery liquids" on incoming loans. Dry collections in general have the following risks: residual particulate preservatives, such as arsenic trioxide, mercuric chloride, strychnine and DDT; and vaporizing compounds leaving residues or recrystallization, such as dichlorvos/vapona pest strips, paradichlorobenzene (PDB) and naphthalene. See table 96.9 for a list of many of the particular hazards found in collection management. This table also includes hazards associated with conservation of these specimens.

Occupational health and safety considerations are similar to those of general industry. Precautions include occupational maintenance of a good inventory of collection treatment methods, personal protective equipment, including vinyl (not latex) gloves for dry specimen handling, and impervious gloves and splash protection for liquids. Medical surveillance with regard to general and reproductive hazards; good hygiene practices—lab coats and

Table 96.8 • Hazards and precautions of collection management processes.

Process	Hazards and precautions
Field work and handling of specimens	Ergonomic injuries from repetitive drilling on fossil rock and heavy lifting; biohazards from surface cleaning of bird debris, allergic response (pulmonary and dermal) from insect frass, handling both living and dead specimens, particularly birds and mammals (plaque, Hanta virus) and other diseased tissues; and chemical hazards from preserving media.
	Precautions include ergonomic controls; HEPA vacuums for control of detritus allergens, insect eggs, larvae; universal precautions for avoiding staff exposure to animal disease agents;.and adequate ventilation or respiratory protection when handling hazardous preserving agents.
Taxidermy and osteological preparation	Health hazards in the preparation of skins, whole mounts and skeletal specimens, and in the cleaning and restoration of older mounts, arise from exposure to solvents and degreasers used to clean skins and skeletal remains (after maceration); residual preservatives, especially arsenic (internal and external applications); osteological preparation (ammonium hydroxide, solvents, degreasers); formaldehyde for preserving organ parts after autopsy (or necropsy); frass allergens; contact with diseased specimens; asbestos-plaster in old mounts. Safety and fire risks include heavy lifting strains; injury from use of power tools, knives or sharps on specimens; and use of flammable or combustible mixtures.
	Precautions include local exhaust ventilation; respirators, gloves, aprons; use of brushes and HEPA vacuums to clean fur and rearrange nap instead of low-pressure compressed air or vigorous brushing alone; and use of disinfectants in necropsy and other handling areas. Check with local environmental authority on current approval status for taxidermy and preservation chemical applications.
Illustrators and microscopic examinations by curators and their technicians	Exposure to hazardous storage media at close range and xylene, alcohols, formaldehyde/glutaraldehyde and osmium tetroxide used in histology (sectioning, staining, slide mounting) for scanning and transmission electron microscopy.
	See laboratory research for appropriate precautions.
Fumigant and pesticide use	Insect damage to collections cannot be tolerated, but indiscriminate use of chemicals can have adverse side effects on staff health and collections. Integrated pest management (IPM) programmes are now utilized as practical means for pest control while reducing health and collection risks. Commonly used chemical pesticides and fumigants (many now banned or restricted) include(d): DDT, naphthalene, PDB, dichlorvos, ethylene oxide, carbon tetrachloride, ethylene dichloride, methyl bromide and sulphuryl fluoride. Many have poor warning properties, are extremely toxic or lethal to humans at low concentrations and should be applied by professional, licensed exterminators or fumigators offsite or outside occupied areas. All require complete airing in a well-ventilated area to remove all off-gassing products from porous collection materials.
	Precautions include PPE, respirator, ventilation, splash protection, medical surveillance, HEPA vacuums, regulatory licensing for applicators and air sampling before reentry into fumigated spaces.
Laboratory research	Hazardous tasks involve molecular systematics; DNA research and general storage of living cells and tissue cultures (growth media); DMSO, radioactive isotopes, a wide variety of solvents, acids, ethyl ether; cryogenic liquids for freeze-drying (nitrogen, etc.); and use of benzidine-based dyes.
	Precautions include cryogenic protection (gloves, face shields, aprons, well-ventilated areas, safety relief valves, systems for high-pressure transport and storage), biosafety cabinets, radiation laboratory hoods and respirators, local exhaust enclosures for weighing and microscope stations; clean benches with HEPA-grade filters, gloves and lab coats, eye protection, HEPA vacuums for control of detritus allergens, insect eggs, larvae; and universal precautions for avoiding laboratory and custodial staff exposure to animal disease agents.
Shipping, receiving and preparing of loaned collections for exhibitions	Exposure to unknown storage media and potentially hazardous shipping material (e.g., crates lined with asbestos paper) from countries without stringent environmental reporting requirements.
	Precautions include appropriate hazard warnings on outgoing loaned exhibitions, and ensuring that incoming exhibition documents stipulate contents.

work clothes laundered separately from family clothes (or best at work in a dedicated washer); avoidance of dry sweeping (use HEPA vacuum cleaners); avoiding water-trap vacuum cleaners on suspect collections; proper hazardous waste disposal methods; and chemical hazard information training for staff are some examples.

Conservation Laboratories

Conservation work, often in full-scale laboratories, involves the cleaning and restoration (by chemical or physical means) of items such as paintings, paper, photographs, books, manuscripts, stamps, furniture, textiles, ceramics and glass, metals, stone, musical instruments, uniforms and costumes, leather, baskets, masks and other ethnographic objects. Hazards unique to conservation range from highly intermittent exposures to dropper-size amounts of restoration chemicals, to potentially heavy exposures when using large quantities of chemicals to treat statuary or large vertebrate specimens. Ergonomic injuries are possible from awkward hand-and-brush positions over painting or statuary restoration work, and heavy lifting. A wide variety of solvents and other chemicals are used in cleaning and restoration of collection objects. Many of the techniques used for the restoration of damaged artwork, for example, are the same, and involve the same hazards and precautions as those of the original art process. Hazards also arise from the composition and finish of the object itself, as described in table 96.9. For precautions see the previous section.

Table 96.9 • Hazards of collection objects.

Source of hazard	Hazard
Botanicals, vertebrates and invertebrates	Storage media containing formaldehyde, acetic acid, alcohol, formaldehyde used in field fixing, sorting to alcohol storage, mercuric chloride on dry-mounted plant specimens, arsenic- and mercury-preserved birds and mammals, dry-mount adhesives; insect frass allergens.
Decorative arts, ceramics, stone and metal	Pigments or preservatives may contain mercury. Silver- or gold-plated objects may have cyanide bound into finish (which can be liberated by water-washing). Celluloid objects (French ivory) are fire hazards. Fiesta-ware and enamel jewellery may contain radioactive uranium pigments.
Entomology	Naphthalene, paradichlorobenzene (PDB) exposures while replenishing storage drawers or observing specimens; field collection bottle preparations using cyanide salts.
Furniture	The furniture may have been treated with pentachlorophenol-containing wood preservatives, lead and other toxic pigments. Cleaning and restoration may involve treatment with mineral spirits, methylene chloride paint strippers, varnishes and lacquers.
Minerals	Radioactive specimens, natural ores of high-toxicity metals and minerals (lead/asbestiform), noise from section preparations, epoxies for slide/section preparation.
Miscellaneous hazards	Old pharmaceuticals in medical, dental and veterinary collections (which may have degraded, are illegal substances or have converted into reactive or explosive compounds); gunpowder, firearms; carbon tetrachloride in nineteenth- and twentieth-century fire-extinguishing devices; vehicle battery acid; PCBs in transformers, capacitors and other electrical collections; mercury felts in static generators, lighthouses and science collections; asbestos from plasters in trophy mounts, casts and a variety of household appliances, ceramic glazes, wiring and textiles.
Paintings, print and paper	These may contain high-toxicity pigments of lead (white flake, white lead, chrome yellow), cadmium, chromium (carcinogenic in chromate form), cobalt (particularly cobalt violet or cobalt arsenate), manganese and mercury. Cyanide may be present in some printers' inks and in old (nineteenth century) wallpapers; mercury was added to some paintings and fabrics as mildew prevention; lampblack and coal tar dyes are carcinogenic. Cleaning and restoration of these materials can involve the use of solvents, varnishes, lacquers, chlorine dioxide bleaches and more.
Paleobiological specimens	Ergonomic and health risks from fossil preparation involving drilling or chipping rock matrix containing free crystalline silica, asbestos or radioactive ore; epoxies and liquid plastics for fossil casts; noise; solvents and acids for rock digestion (hydrofluoric most hazardous).
Photographs	Nitrocellulose film has the risk of spontaneous combustion, and nitric acid burns from decomposing film. It should be copied to modern film. Selenium toning restoration can involve hazards of selenium and sulphur dioxide exposure, and requires adequate ventilation.
Storage cases	Lead and cadmium surface paint, arsenic-treated felt gaskets and asbestos insulation render cases difficult to dispose of. Residues and chips containing these substances pose hazards during interior and exterior case cleaning; vacuum debris may be considered hazardous waste.
Textiles, clothing	Hazards include dyes (particularly benzidine based), fibre levels, arsenic for lace and other component preservation, mercury for felt treatment; poisonous plant materials used for clothing decorations; mould, mildew, allergens from insect parts and excrement (frass).

ZOOS AND AQUARIUMS

Ken Sims

Zoological gardens, wildlife parks, safari parks, bird parks and collections of aquatic wildlife share similar methods for the maintenance and handling of exotic species. Animals are held for exhibition, as an educational resource, for conservation and for scientific study. Traditional methods of caging animals and preparing aviaries for birds and tanks for water creatures remain common, but more modern, progressive collections have adopted different enclosures designed to meet more of the needs of particular species. The quality of space accorded to an animal is more important than the quantity, however, which has consequential beneficial effects on keeper safety. The danger to keepers is often related to the size and natural ferocity of the species attended, but many other factors can affect the danger.

The main animal groupings are mammals, birds, reptiles, amphibians, fish and invertebrates. Problem areas that are common to all the animal groups are toxins, diseases that are contractible from animals (zoonoses) and changing animal moods.

Mammals

Mammals' varied forms and habits require a wide range of husbandry techniques. The largest land forms are herbivorous, such as elephants, and are limited in their ability to climb, jump, burrow or gnaw, so their control is similar to domestic forms. Remote control of gates can offer high degrees of safety. Large predators such as big cats and bears require enclosures with wide margins of safety, double entry doors and in-built catch-ups and crushes. Agile climbing and jumping species pose special problems to keepers, who lack comparable mobility. The use of electric shock fence wiring is now widespread. Capture and handling methods include corralling, nets, crushing, roping, sedation and immobilization with drugs injected by dart.

Birds

Few birds are too large to be restrained by gloved hands and nets. The largest flightless birds—ostriches and cassowar-

96. ENTERTAINMENT AND THE ARTS

ies—are strong and have a very dangerous kick; they require crating for restraint.

Reptiles

Large carnivorous reptile species have violent strike attack capability; many snakes do too. Captive specimens may seem docile and induce keeper complacency. An attacking large constricting snake can overwhelm and suffocate a panicking keeper of much greater weight. A few venomous snakes can "spit"; thus eye protection against them should be mandatory. Restraint and handling methods include nets, bags, hooks, grabs, nooses and drugs.

Amphibians

Only a large giant salamander or big toad can give an unpleasant bite; otherwise risks from amphibians are from toxin excretion.

Fish

Few fish specimens are hazardous except for venomous species, electric eels and bigger predatory forms. Careful netting minimizes risk. Electric and chemical stunning may be occasionally appropriate.

Invertebrates

Some lethal invertebrate species are kept which require indirect handling. Mis-identification and specimens hidden by camouflage and small size can endanger the unwary.

Toxins

Many animal species have evolved complex poisons for feeding or defence, and deliver them by biting, stinging, spitting and secretion. Delivered quantities may vary from the inconsequential to lethal doses. Worst case scenarios should be the model for accident anticipation procedures. Single keeper exposure to lethal species should not be practised. Husbandry must include risk evaluation, unambiguous warning signs, restriction of handling to those trained, maintenance of stocks of antidotes (if any) in close liaison with local trained medical practitioners, predetermination of handler reaction to antidotes and an efficient alarm system.

Zoonoses

A good animal health programme and personal hygiene will keep the risk from zoonoses very low. However, there are many which are potentially lethal, such as rabies, which is untreatable in later stages. Almost all are avoidable, and treatable if diagnosed correctly early enough. As with work elsewhere, the incidence of allergy-related illness is rising and it is best treated by non-exposure to the irritant when identified.

"Non-venomous" bites and scratches require careful attention, as even a bite which appears not to break skin can lead to rapid blood poisoning (septicaemia). Carnivore and monkey bites should be especially suspect. An extreme example is the bite of a komodo dragon; the microflora in its saliva are so virulent that bitten large prey that escapes an initial attack will rapidly die from shock and septicaemia.

Routine prophylaxis against tetanus and hepatitis may be appropriate for many staff.

Moods

Animals can give an infinite variety of responses, some very dangerous, to close human presence. Observable mood changes can alert keepers to danger, but few animals show signs readable by humans. Moods can be influenced by a combination of seen and unseen stimuli such as season, day length, time of day, sexual rhythms, upbringing, hierarchy, barometric pressure and high-frequency noise from electrical equipment. Animals are not pro-

Figure 96.19 • Handling animals with voice and body language.

Ken Sims

duction line machines; they may have predictable patterns of behaviour but all have the capacity to do the unexpected, against which even the most skilled attendant must guard.

Personal safety

Risk appreciation should be taught by the skilled to the inexperienced. An undiminishing high level of caution will enhance personal safety, particularly, for example, when food is offered to larger carnivores. Animal responses will vary to different keepers, especially to those of different sex. An animal submissive to one person may attack another. The understanding and use of body language can enhance safety; animals naturally understand it better than humans. Voice tone and volume can calm or cause chaos (figure 96.19).

Clothing should be chosen with special care, avoiding bright, flapping material. Gloves may protect and reduce handling stress but are inappropriate for handling snakes because tactile sensitivity is reduced.

If keepers and other staff are expected to manage trespassing, violent or other problem visitors, they should be schooled in people management and have back-up on call to minimize risks to themselves.

Regulations

Despite the variety of potential risks from exotic species, the greater workplace hazards are conventional ones arising from plant and machinery, chemicals, surfaces, electricity and so on, so standard health and safety regulations must be applied with common sense and regard for the unusual nature of the work.

PARKS AND BOTANICAL GARDENS

Paul V. Lynch

The occupational safety and health hazards for those who work in parks and botanical gardens fall in the following general categories: environmental, mechanical, biological or chemical, vegetation, wildlife and caused by human beings. The risks differ depending on where the site is located. Urban, suburban, developed or undeveloped wildland will differ.

Environmental Hazards

As parks and garden personnel are found in all geographical areas and generally spend a great deal, if not all, of their working time outdoors, they are exposed to the widest variety and extremes of temperature and climatic conditions, with the resultant risks ranging from heat stroke and exhaustion to hypothermia and frostbite.

Those who work in urban areas may be in facilities where vehicular traffic is significant and may be exposed to toxic exhaust emissions such as carbon monoxide, unburned carbon particles, nitrous oxide, sulphuric acid, carbon dioxide and palladium (from the breakdown of catalytic converters).

Because some facilities are located in the higher elevations of mountainous regions, altitude sickness may be a risk if an employee is new to the area or is prone to high or low blood pressure.

Park area workers are usually called upon to perform search and rescue and disaster control activities during and following natural disasters such as earthquakes, hurricanes, flooding, volcanic eruptions and the like affecting their area, with all of the risks inherent in such events.

It is essential that all personnel be thoroughly trained in the potential environmental risks inherent in their areas and be provided with the proper clothing and equipment, such as adequate cold- or hot-weather gear, water and rations.

Mechanical Hazards

Personnel in parks and gardens are called upon to be thoroughly familiar with and operate an extremely wide variety of mechanical equipment, ranging from small hand tools and power tools and powered lawn and garden equipment (mowers, thatchers, rototillers, chainsaws, etc.) to heavy equipment such as small tractors, snow ploughs, trucks and heavy construction equipment. Additionally, most facilities have their own shops equipped with heavy power tools such as table saws, lathes, drill presses, air pressure pumps and so on.

Employees must be thoroughly trained in the operation, hazards and safety devices for all types of equipment they could potentially operate, and be provided and trained in the use of the appropriate personal protection equipment. Since some personnel may also be required to operate or ride the full range of motor vehicles, and fixed- or rotary-wing aircraft, they must be thoroughly trained and licensed, and regularly tested. Those that ride as passengers must have knowledge of the risks and training in safe operation of such equipment.

Biological and Chemical Hazards

Continuous, close contact with the general public is inherent in almost every occupation in park and garden work. The risk of contracting viral or bacterial diseases is always present. Additionally, the risk of contact with infected wildlife that carry rabies, psitticosis, Lyme disease and so on is present.

Park and botanical garden workers are exposed to various amounts and concentrations of pesticides, herbicides, fungicides, fertilizers and other agricultural chemicals, as well as toxic paints, thinners, varnishes, lubricants and so on used in maintenance and transport work and equipment.

With the proliferation of illegal drugs, it is becoming common for personnel in national parks and forests to come across illegal drug-manufacturing laboratories. The chemicals found in these can cause death or permanent neurological damage. Personnel in urban and rural areas may also encounter discarded drug paraphernalia such as used hypodermic syringes, needles, spoons and pipes. If any of these punctures the skin or enters the body, illness ranging from hepatitis to HIV could result.

Thorough training in the risks and preventive measures is essential; regular physical examinations should be provided and immediate medical attention sought if a person is so exposed. It is essential that the type and duration of exposure be recorded, if possible, to be given to the treating physician. Whenever illegal drug paraphernalia is encountered personnel should not touch it but rather should secure the area and refer the matter to trained law enforcement personnel.

Vegetation Hazards

Most types of vegetation pose no health risk. However, in wildland areas (and some urban and suburban park areas) poisonous plants such as poison ivy, poison oak and poison sumac can be found. Health problems ranging from a minor rash to a severe allergic reaction can result, depending on the susceptibility of the individual and the nature of the exposure.

It should be noted that roughly 22% of the total population suffers from allergic reactions of one form or another, ranging from mild to severe; an allergic individual may respond to only a few substances, or to many hundreds of different types of vegetation and animal life. Such reactions can result in death, in extreme cases, if immediate treatment is not found.

Prior to working in any environment with plant life, it should be determined whether an employee has any allergies to potential allergens and should take or carry appropriate medication.

Personnel should also be cognizant of plant life that is not safe to ingest, and should know the signs of ingestion illness and the antidotes.

Wildlife Hazards

Parks workers will encounter the full spectrum of wildlife that exists around the world. They must be familiar with the types of animals, their habits, the risks and, where necessary, the safe handling of the wildlife expected to be encountered. Wildlife ranges from urban domestic animals, such as dogs and cats, to rodents, insects and snakes, to wildland animals and bird species including bears, mountain lions, poisonous snakes and spiders, and so on.

Proper training in the recognition and handling of wildlife, including the diseases affecting such wildlife, should be provided. Appropriate medical response kits for poisonous snakes and insects should be available, along with training in how to use them. In remote wildland areas, it may be necessary to have personnel trained in the use of, and be equipped with, firearms for personal protection.

Human-caused Hazards

In addition to the aforementioned risk of contact with a visitor having a contagious illness, a major share of the risks faced by personnel who work in the parks, and to a lesser degree botanical gardens, are the result of either accidental or deliberate action of facilities visitors. Those risks range from the need of park employees to perform search and rescue activities for lost or injured visitors (some in the most remote and dangerous environments) to responding to acts of vandalism, drunkenness, fighting and other disruptive activities, including assault on park or garden employees. Additionally, the park or garden employee is at risk of vehicular accidents caused by visitors or others who are driving by or in the vicinity of the employee.

Approximately 50% of all wildland fires have a human cause, attributable to either arson or negligence, to which the park employee may be required to respond.

Wilful damage or destruction of public property is also, unfortunately, a risk the park or garden employee may well be required to respond to and repair, and, depending on the type of property and degree of damage, a significant safety risk may be present (i.e., damage to wilderness trails, foot bridges, interior doors, plumbing equipment and so on).

Personnel who work with the environment are, generally, sensitive and attuned to the outdoors and to preservation. As a result, many such personnel suffer from varying degrees of stress and related illnesses because of the unfortunate actions of some of those who visit their facilities. It is important, therefore, to be aware of the onset of stress and take remedial action. Classes in stress management are helpful for all such personnel.

Violence

Violence in the workplace is, unfortunately, becoming an increasing common risk and cause of injury. There are two general classes of violence: physical and psychological. The types of violence range from simple verbal threats to mass murder, as evidenced by the 1995 bombing of the US federal office building, Oklahoma City, Oklahoma. In 1997 a tribal police officer was killed while trying to serve a warrant on a Southwest Indian reservation. There is also a less discussed, but common, psychological violence that has been classed euphemistically as "office politics" that can have equally debilitating effects.

Physical. In the United States, attacks on federal, state and local governmental personnel who work in remote and semi-remote parks and recreation areas are not uncommon. The majority of these result in injury only, but some involve assaults with dangerous weapons. There have been instances where disgruntled members of the public have entered federal land-managing agencies' offices brandishing firearms, threatened the employees and had to be restrained.

Such violence can result in injury ranging from minor to fatal. It can be inflicted by unarmed assault or the use of the widest variety of weapons, ranging from simple club and stick to handguns, rifles, knives, explosives and chemicals. It is not uncommon for such violence to be inflicted upon the vehicles and structures owned or used by the governmental agency that operates the park or recreational facility.

It is also not uncommon for disgruntled or dismissed employees to seek retaliation against current or former supervisors. It is also becoming common for outdoor recreation, forest and park employees to encounter persons growing and/or manufacturing illegal drugs in remote areas. Such persons do not hesitate to resort to violence to protect their perceived territory. Park and recreation personnel, particularly those involved in law enforcement, are required to deal with persons under the influence of drugs or alcohol who break the law and become violent when apprehended.

Psychological. Not as well publicized, but in some instances equally damaging, is psychological violence. Commonly called "office politics", it has been in use probably since the beginning of civilization to gain status over co-workers, gain an advantage in the workplace and/or weaken a perceived opponent. It consists of destroying the credibility of another person or group, usually without that other person or group being aware that it is being done.

In some instances, it is done openly, through the media, legislative bodies and so on, in an attempt to gain political advantage (for example, destroying the credibility of a governmental agency in order to cut its funding).

This usually has a significant negative result on the morale of the individual or group involved and, in rare, extreme instances, can cause a recipient of the violence to take his or her own life.

It is not uncommon for victims of violence to suffer from post-traumatic stress disorder, which may affect them for years. It has the same effect as "shell shock" among military personnel

who have experienced prolonged and intense combat. It may require extensive psychological counselling.

Protective measures. Because of the constantly increased risk of encountering violence in the workplace, it is essential that employees receive extensive training in the recognition and avoidance of potentially dangerous situations, including training in how to deal with persons who are violent or out of control.

- Where possible, additional security needs to be added to high-density occupancy areas.
- Employees who work away from a standard office or shop location should be provided with two-way radio communication to be able to summon help when needed.
- In some instances, it may be necessary to train employees in the use of firearms and arm them for self-protection.
- Each agency responsible for managing park or outdoor recreation areas should conduct an annual security survey of all its facilities to determine current risk and what measures are necessary to protect employees.
- Management at all levels needs to exercise extra vigilance to counter the psychological risk whenever it occurs, seek out and correct unfounded rumours and assure that all employees have accurate facts concerning the operation and future plans of their agency and workplace.

Post-incidence assistance. It is equally essential, not only for the affected employees or employers, but all agency employees as well, that any employee subjected to on-the-job violence be given not only prompt medical attention, but equally prompt psychological assistance and stress counselling. The effects of such violence can remain with the employee long after the physical wounds heal and can have a significant negative effect on his or her ability to function in the workplace.

As the population increases, the incidence of violence will increase. Preparation and prompt and effective response are, at present, the only remedies open to those at risk.

Conclusion

Because personnel are required to work in all types of environments, good health and physical fitness is essential. A consistent regimen of moderate physical training should be adhered to. Regular physical examinations, geared to the type of work to be performed, should be obtained. All personnel should be completely trained in types of work to be performed, the hazards involved and hazard avoidance.

Equipment should be maintained in sound operating condition.

All personnel expected to work in remote areas should carry two-way radio communication equipment and be in regular contact with a base station.

All personnel should have basic—and if possible, advanced—first aid training, including cardio-pulmonary resuscitation, in the event a visitor or co-worker is injured and medical help is not immediately available.

CIRCUSES AND AMUSEMENT AND THEME PARKS

William Avery

The common product shared between circuses and amusement and theme parks is creating and providing entertainment for the public's enjoyment. Circuses can take place in a large temporary tent equipped with bleachers or in permanent buildings. Attending a circus is a passive activity in which the customer views the various animal, clown and acrobatic acts from a seated position. Amusement and theme parks, on the other hand, are locations where customers actively walk around the park and can participate in a wide variety of activities. Amusement parks can have many different types of rides, exhibits, games of skill, sales booths and stores, grandstand shows and other types of entertainment. Theme parks have exhibits, buildings and even small villages that illustrate the particular theme. Costume characters, who are actors dressed in costumes illustrating the theme—for example, historical costumes in historic villages or cartoon costumes for parks with a cartoon theme—will participate in shows or walk around among the visiting crowds. Local country fairs are another type of event where activities can include rides, animal and other side shows, such as fire-eating, and agricultural and farm animal exhibitions and competitions. The size of the operation can be as small as one person running a pony cart ride in a parking lot, or as large as a major theme park employing thousands. The larger the operation, the more background services that can be present, including parking lots, sanitation facilities, security and other emergency services and even hotels.

Occupations vary widely as do the levels of skills required for individual tasks. People employed in these activities include ticket sellers, acrobatic performers, animal handlers, food service workers, engineers, costume characters and ride operators, among a long list of other workers. The occupational safety and health risks include many of those found in general industry and others that are unique to circuses and amusement and theme park operations. The following information provides a review of entertainment-related hazards and precautions found within this segment of the industry.

Acrobatics and Stunts

Circuses, in particular, have many acrobatic and stunt acts, including high-wire tightrope walking and other aerial acts, gymnastic acts, fire-juggling acts and displays of horsemanship. Amusement and theme parks can also have similar activities. Hazards include falls, misjudged clearances, improperly inspected equipment and physical fatigue due to multiple daily shows. Typical accidents involve muscular, tendon and skeletal injuries.

Precautions include the following: Performers should receive comprehensive physical conditioning, proper rest and a good diet, and show schedules should be rotated. All equipment, props, rigging, safety devices and blocking should be carefully reviewed before each performance. Show personnel should not perform when they are ill, injured or taking medication which may affect required abilities to safely meet the needs of the show.

Animal Handling

Animals are most commonly found in circuses and county fairs, although they can also be found in activities such as pony rides in amusement parks. Animals are found in circuses in wild-animal training acts, for example, with lions and tigers, horse riding acts and other trained animal acts. Elephants are used as show performers, rides, exhibits and work animals. In country fairs, farm animals such as pigs, cattle and horses are exhibited in competitions. In some places, exotic animals are displayed in cages and in such acts as snake handling. Hazards include the unpredictable characteristics of animals combined with the potential for animal handlers to become overly confident and let their guard down. Serious injury and death are possible in this occupation. Elephant handling is considered one of the most dangerous professions. Some estimates indicate there are approximately 600 keepers in the United States and Canada. During the course of an average year there will be one elephant handler killed. Venomous snakes,

Figure 96.20 • Worker wearing a heavy costume.

William Avery

if used in snake-handling acts, can also be very dangerous, with possible fatalities from snake bites.

Precautions include intense and ongoing animal-handling training. It must be instilled in employees to remain on their guard at all times. The use of protected contact systems is recommended where keepers work alongside animals capable of causing serious injury or death. Protected contact systems always separate the animal handler and the animal by means of bars or closed-off areas. When animals perform on stage to live audiences, noise and other stimuli conditioning must be a part of the required safety training. With venomous reptiles, proper anti-venom antidotes and protective equipment such as gloves, leg guards, snake pincers and carbon dioxide bottles should be available. Care and feeding of animals when they are not being exhibited also requires careful attention on the part of the animal caretakers to prevent injury.

Costume Characters

Costume characters acting the role of cartoon figures or historical period characters often wear heavy and bulky costumes. They can act on stages or mingle with the crowds. Hazards are back and neck injuries associated with wearing such costumes with uneven weight distribution (figure 96.20). Other exposures are fatigue, heat-related problems, crowd pushing and hitting. See also "Actors".

Precautions include the following: Costumes should be correctly fitted to the individual. The weight load, especially above the shoulders, should be kept at a minimum. Costume characters should drink plenty of water during periods of warm weather. Interaction with the public should be of short duration because of the stress of such work. Character duties should be rotated, and non-costumed escorts should be with characters at all times to manage crowds.

Fireworks

Fireworks displays and pyrotechnics special effects can be a common activity (figure 96.21). Hazards can involve accidental discharge, non-planned explosions and fire.

Precautions include the following: Only appropriately trained and licensed pyrotechnicians should detonate explosives. Storage, transportation and detonation procedures must be followed (figure 96.22). Applicable codes, laws and ordinances in the jurisdiction where operating must be adhered to. Pre-approved

Figure 96.21 • Loading pyrotechnics for fireworks show.

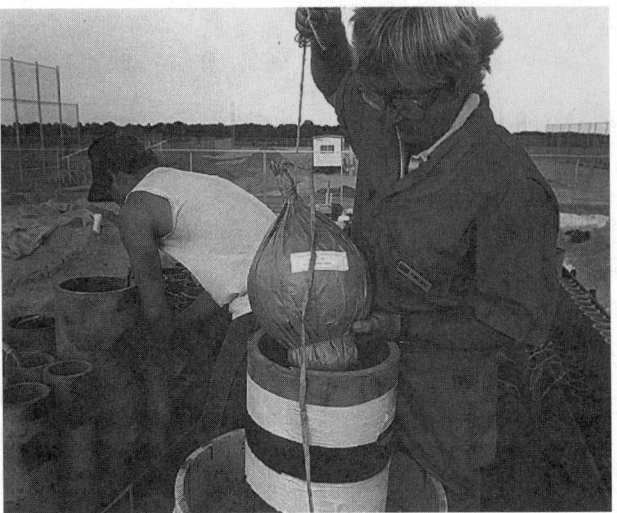

William Avery

Figure 96.22 • Bunker storage for fireworks.

William Avery

personal safety equipment and fire extinguishing equipment must be at the detonation site where there is immediate access.

Food Service

Food can be bought at circuses and amusement and theme parks from individuals with trays of food, at vendor carts, booths, or even restaurants. Hazards common to food service operations at these events involve serving large captive audiences during high periods of demand in a very short period of time. Falls, burns, cuts and repetitive motion trauma are not uncommon in this occupational classification. Carrying food around on trays can involve back injuries. The risks are increased during periods of high volume. A common example of injury occurring in high-volume food service areas is repetitive motion trauma that can result in tendinitis and carpal tunnel syndrome. One example of a job description where such injuries occur is an ice-cream scooper.

Precautions include the following: Increased staffing during high-volume periods is essential to the safety of the operation. Specific duties such as mopping, sweeping and cleaning should be addressed. Precautions for repetitive motion trauma: regarding the example given above, using softer ice cream can make scooping less strenuous, employees can be regularly rotated, scoops can be warmed to promote easier penetration of the ice cream and the use of ergonomically designed handles should be considered.

Scenery, Props and Exhibits

Stage shows, exhibits, booths, artificial scenery and buildings must be built. Hazards include many of the same hazards as found in construction, including electrocution, severe lacerations, and eye and other injuries associated with the use of power tools and equipment. The outdoor building and use of props, scenery and exhibits increases the potential hazards such as collapse if construction is inadequate. Handling of these components can result in falls and back and neck injuries (see also the box "Scenery shops" in this chapter).

Precautions include the following: The manufacturer's warnings, safety equipment recommendations and safe operating instructions for power tools and machinery must be followed. The weight of props and their sections should be minimized to reduce the possibility of lifting-associated injuries. Props, scenery and

exhibits designed for outdoor use must be reviewed for wind load ratings and other outdoor exposures. Props designed for use with live loads should be appropriately rated and the built-in safety factor verified. Fire rating of the material should be considered based on the intended use, and any fire regulations that may be applicable must be followed.

Ride Operators and Maintenance Personnel

There are a wide variety of amusement park rides, including Ferris wheels, roller coasters, water flume rides, looping boats and aerial tramways. Ride operators and maintenance personnel work in areas and under conditions where there are increased risks of serious injury. The exposures include electrocution, being struck by equipment and caught in or between equipment and machinery. Besides the rides, ride and maintenance personnel must also operate and maintain the associated electrical power plants and transformers.

Precautions include an effective programme that can reduce the potential for serious injury in a lock out, tag out and block out

Figure 96.23 • Erecting an amusement park ride with a crane.

William Avery

procedure. This programme should include: personally assigned padlocks with single keys; written procedures for working on electrical circuitry, machinery, hydraulics, compressed air, water and other sources of possible energy release; and tests to ensure that the energy supply has been shut off. When more than one person is working on the same piece of equipment, each person should have and use his or her own lock.

Travelling Shows

Circuses and many amusement rides can travel from one location to another. This can be by truck for small operations, or by train for large circuses. Hazards include falls, severed body parts and possible death during erection, dismantling or transportation of equipment (figure 96.23). A particular problem is expedited work procedures, resulting in skipping time-consuming safety procedures, in an effort to meet play date deadlines.

Precautions include the following: Employees must be well trained, exercise caution and follow manufacturer's safety instructions for assembly, dismantling, loading, unloading and transportation of the equipment. When animals are used, such as an elephant to pull or push heavy equipment, additional safety precautions are required. Equipment such as cables, ropes, hoists, cranes and fork-lifts should be inspected before each use. Over-the-road drivers must follow highway transportation safety guidelines. Employees will require additional training in safety and emergency procedures for train operations where animals, personnel and equipment travel together.

• BULLFIGHTING AND RODEOS

Michael McCann

Bullfighting, or the *corrida* as it is commonly called, is popular in Spain, Spanish-speaking countries in Latin America (especially Mexico), southern France and Portugal. It is highly ritualized, with pageants, well-defined ceremonies and colourful traditional costumes. Matadors are highly respected and often begin their training at an early age in an informal apprenticeship system.

Rodeos, on the other hand, are a more recent sports event. They are an outgrowth of skills contests between cowboys illustrating their everyday activities. Today, rodeos are formalized sports events popular in the western United States, western Canada and Mexico. Professional rodeo cowboys (and some cowgirls) travel the rodeo circuit from one rodeo to another. The most common rodeo events are bronco riding, bull riding, steer wrestling (bulldogging) and calf roping.

Bullfights. Participants in a bullfight include the matadors, their assistants (the banderilleros and picadors) and the bulls. When the bull first enters the arena from the bull pen gate, the matador attracts its attention with a series of passes with his large cape. The bull is attracted by the movement of the cape, not the colour, since bulls are colour-blind. The matador's reputation is based on how close he gets to the horns of the bull. These fighting bulls have been bred and trained for centuries for their aggressiveness. The next part of the bullfight involves the weakening of the bull by mounted picadors placing lances in the bull, and then banderilleros, working on foot, placing barbed sticks called banderillas in the bull's shoulder in order to lower the bull's head for the kill.

The final stage of the fight involves the matador trying to kill the bull by inserting his sword blade between the shoulder blades of the bull into the aorta. This stage involves many formalized

Figure 96.24 • Bullfighting.

El País

passes with the cape before the final kill. The greater the risks taken by the matador, the greater the acclaim, and of course the greater the risk of being gored (see figure 96.24). Bullfighters generally receive at least one goring per season, which could involve as many as 100 bullfights per year per matador.

The primary hazard facing the matadors and their assistants is being gored or even killed by the bull. Another potential hazard is tetanus from being gored. One epidemiological study in Madrid, Spain, indicated that only 14.9% of bullfighting professionals had complete anti-tetanus vaccination, while 52.5% had suffered occupational injuries (Dominguez et al. 1987). Few precautions are taken. The mounted picadors wear steel leg armour. Otherwise, the bullfighting professionals depend on the training and skills of themselves and their horses. One essential precaution is adequate planning for onsite emergency medical care (see "Motion picture and television production" in this chapter).

Rodeos. The most hazardous common rodeo events are bronco or bull riding and steer wrestling. In bronco or bull riding, the

Figure 96.25 • Rodeo clown distracting a bull from a fallen rider.

Don Hubbell

96. ENTERTAINMENT AND THE ARTS

purpose is to stay on the bucking animal for a predetermined time. Bronco riding can be either bareback or with a saddle. In steer wrestling, a rider on horseback attempts to throw the steer to the ground by diving off the horse, grabbing the bull by its horns and wrenching it to the ground. Calf roping involves roping a calf from horseback, jumping off the horse and then hog-tying the front and back legs of the calf together in the shortest possible time.

Besides the rodeo contestants, those at risk include the pickup riders or outriders, whose role is to rescue the thrown rider and capture the animal, and the rodeo clowns, whose job is to distract the animal, especially bulls, to give the thrown rider a chance to escape (figure 96.25). They do this while on foot and dressed in a colourful costume to attract the animal's attention. Hazards include being trampled, being gored by the bull's horns, injuries from being bucked off, knee injuries from jumping off the horse, elbow injuries in bronco and bull riders from holding on to the animal with one hand and facial injuries from bulls tossing their heads back. Injuries also occur from bronco or bull riders being smashed against the sides of the chute while waiting for the gate to open and the animal to be released. Severe injuries and fatalities are not infrequent. Bull riders sustain 37% of all rodeo-related injuries (Griffin et al. 1989). In particular, brain and spinal cord injuries are of concern (MMWR 1996). One study of 39 professional rodeo cowboys showed a total of 76 elbow abnormalities in 29 bronco and bull riders (Griffin et al. 1989). They concluded that the injuries were a result of constant hyperextension of the arm gripping the animal, as well as injuries in falls.

The main way of preventing injuries lies in the skills of the rodeo cowboys, pickup riders and rodeo clowns. Well-trained horses are also essential. Taping elbows and wearing elbow pads has also been recommended for bronco and bull riding. Safety vests, mouth guards and safety helmets are rare, but becoming more accepted. Face masks have occasionally been used for bull riding. As in bullfighting, an essential precaution is adequate planning for on-site emergency medical care.

In both rodeos and bullfighting, of course, the animal keepers, feeders and so on are also at risk. For more information on this aspect, see "Zoos and aquariums" in this chapter.

● PROFESSIONAL SPORTS

Gordon Huie, Peter J. Bruno and
W. Norman Scott

Sports activities involve a great number of injuries. Precautions, conditioning and safety equipment, when used properly, will minimize sports injuries.

In all sports, conditioning year round is encouraged. Bone, ligaments and muscles respond in a physiological fashion by gaining both size and strength (Clare 1990). This increases the athlete's agility to avoid any injurious physical contact. All sports requiring weightlifting and strengthening should be under the supervision of a strength coach.

Contact Sports

Contact sports such as American football and hockey are particularly dangerous. The aggressive nature of football requires the player to strike or tackle the opposing player. The focus of the game is to possess the ball with the intent of physically striking anyone in one's path. The equipment should be well-fitting and offer adequate protection. (figure 96.26). The helmet with

Figure 96.26 • Snug fitting football pads.

Source: American Academy of Orthopedic Surgeons 1991

Figure 96.27 • American football helmet.

Source: Clare 1990

appropriate face mask is standard and is critical in this sport (figure 96.27). It should not slide or twist and the straps should be applied snugly (American Academy of Orthopedic Surgeons 1991).

Unfortunately, the helmet is sometimes used in an unsafe manner whereby the player "spears" an opponent. This can lead to cervical spine injuries and possible paralysis. It can also lead to careless play in sports like hockey, when players feel they can be more free with the use of their stick and risk slashing the face and body of the opponent.

Knee injuries are quite common in football and basketball. In minor injuries, an elastic "sleeve" (figure 96.28) which provides compressive support may be useful. The ligaments and cartilage of the knee are prone to stress as well as impact trauma. The classic combination of cartilage and ligamentous insult was first described by O'Donoghue (1950). An audible "pop" may be heard and felt, followed by swelling, if there are ligament injuries.

Figure 96.28 • Patella cut-out sleeve.

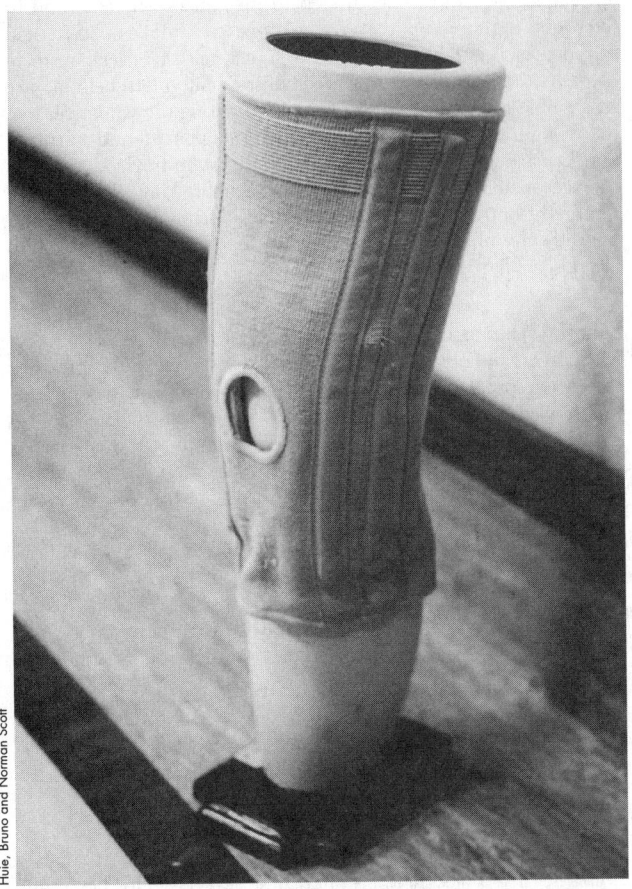

Huie, Bruno and Norman Scott

Figure 96.29 • Padded hockey gloves.

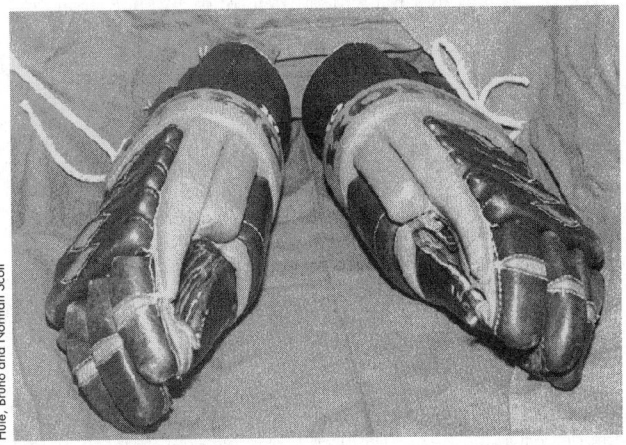

Huie, Bruno and Norman Scott

The most common injury to the basketball player are ankle sprains. Evidence of ankle sprains has been noted in about 45% of players (Garrick 1977; Huie and Scott 1995). The ligaments involved are the deltoid ligament medially and the anterior talofibular, posterior talofibular, and calcaneofibular ligaments laterally. X rays should be obtained to rule out any fractures which may occur. These radiographs should include the entire lower leg to rule out a Maisonneuve fracture (VanderGriend, Savoie and Hughes 1991). In the chronically sprained ankle, use of a semi-rigid ankle stirrup will minimize further insult to the ligaments (figure 96.30).

Figure 96.30 • Rigid ankle stirrup.

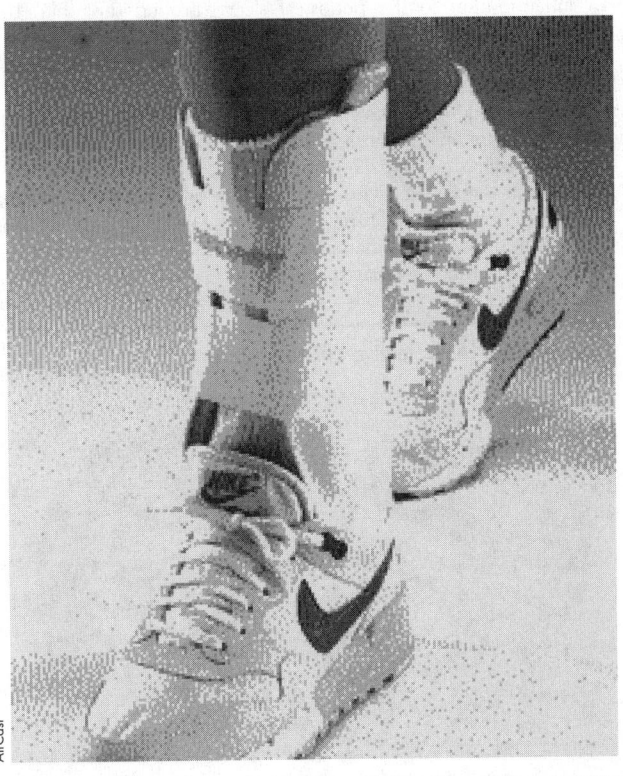

AirCast

Surgical intervention may be needed before the player may resume activities. A derotational brace may be worn post-operatively and by players with partial tear of the anterior cruciate ligament but with enough intact fibres able to sustain their activities. These braces must be well padded to protect the injured extremity and other players (Sachare 1994a).

In hockey, the velocity of both the players and the hard hockey puck warrants the use of protective padding and helmet (figure 96.29). The helmet should have a face shield to prevent facial and dental injuries. Even with helmets and protective padding to vital areas, severe injuries such as fractures of extremities and spine do occur in football and hockey.

In both American football and hockey, a complete medical kit (which includes diagnostic instruments, resuscitation equipment, immobilization devices, medication, wound care supplies, spine board and stretcher) and emergency personnel should be available (Huie and Hershman 1994). If possible, all contact sports should have this available. Radiographs should be obtained of all injuries to rule out any fractures. Magnetic resonance imaging has been found to be very helpful in determining soft tissue injuries.

Basketball

Basketball is also a contact sport, but protective equipment is not worn. The focus of the player is to have possession of the ball and their intent is not to strike the opposing players. Injuries are minimized due to the player's conditioning and speed in averting any hard contact.

Finger injuries may result in ruptures of the supporting ligamentous structures. This can result in a Mallet finger, Swann Neck deformity and Boutonierre deformity (Bruno, Scott and Huie 1995). These injuries are quite common and are due to direct trauma with the ball, other players and the backboard or rim. Prophylactic taping of ankles and fingers helps minimize any accidental twisting and hyperextension of the joints.

Facial injuries (lacerations) and fractures of the nose due to contact with opponents' flailing arms or bony prominences, and contact with the floor or other stationary structures have been encountered. A clear light-weight protective mask may help in minimizing this type of injury.

Baseball

Baseballs are extremely hard projectiles. The player must always be cognizant of the ball not only for safety reasons but for the strategy of the game itself. Batting helmets for the offensive player, and chest protector and catcher's mask/helmet (figure 96.31) for the defensive player are required protective equipment. The ball is hurled at times in excess of 95 mph, sometimes resulting in bone fractures. Any head injuries should have a full neurological work-up, and, if loss of consciousness is present, radiographs of the head should be taken.

Soccer

Soccer can be a contact sport resulting in trauma to the lower extremity. Ankle injuries are very common. The protection that would minimize this would be taping and the use of a semi-rigid ankle stirrup. It has been found that the effectiveness of the taped ankle diminishes after about 30 minutes of vigorous activities. Tears of the anterior cruciate ligament of the knee are often encountered and most likely will require a reconstructive procedure if the player wishes to continue participating in this sport. Anterior medial tibial stress syndrome (shin splints) is extremely common. The hypothesis is that there may be an inflammation to the periosteal sleeve around the tibia. In extreme situations, a stress fracture may occur. The treatment requires rest for 3 to 6 weeks and the use of non-steroidal anti-inflammatory drugs (NSAID), but high-level and professional-level players tend to compromise the treatment once the symptoms diminish as early as 1 week and thus go back to the impact activity. Hamstring pulls and groin pulls are common in the athletes who do not permit enough time to warm and stretch the musculature of the legs. Direct trauma to the lower extremities, particularly the tibia, may be minimized with the use of anterior shin guards.

Figure 96.31 • Protective catcher's mask

Huie, Bruno and Norman Scott

Skiing

Skiing as a sport does not require any protective equipment, although goggles are encouraged to prevent eye injuries and to filter out the sun's glare off the snow. Ski boots offer a rigid support for the ankles and have a "quick-release" mechanism in the event of a fall. These mechanisms, although helpful, are susceptible to circumstances of the fall. During the winter season, many injuries to the knee resulting in ligament and cartilage damage are encountered. This is found in the novice as well as the seasoned skier. In professional downhill skiing, helmets are required to protect the head due to the velocity of the athlete and the difficulty of stopping in the event the trajectory and direction are miscalculated.

Martial Arts and Boxing

Martial arts and boxing are hard contact sports, with little or no protective equipment. The gloves used on the professional boxing level are, however, weighted, which increases their effectiveness. Head guards at the amateur level help soften the impact of the blow. As with skiing, conditioning is extremely important. Agility, speed and strength minimize the combatant's injuries. The blocking forces are deflected more than absorbed. Fractures and soft tissue insults are very common in this sport. Similar to volleyball, the repetitive trauma to the fingers and carpal bones of the hand results in fractures, subluxation, dislocation and ligamentous disruptions. Taping and padding of the hand and wrist may provide some support and protection, but this is minimal. Studies have shown that long-term brain damage is a serious concern for boxers (Council on Scientific Affairs of the American Medical Association 1983). Half of a group of professional boxers with more than 200 fights each had neurological signs consistent with traumatic encephalopathy.

Horse Racing

Horse racing at the professional and amateur levels requires a riding helmet. These helmets offer some protection for head injuries from falls, but they offer no attachment for the neck or spine. Experience and common sense help minimize falls, but even seasoned riders can sustain serious injuries and possibly paralysis if they land on their head. Many jockeys today also wear protective vests since being trampled under horses' hooves is a major risk in falls and has resulted in fatalities. In harness racing, where horses pull two-wheeled carts called sulkies, collisions between sulkies has resulted in multiple pile-ups and serious injuries. For hazards to stable hands and others involved in handling the horses, see the chapter *Livestock rearing*.

First Aid

As a general rule, immediate icing (figure 96.32), compression, elevation and NSAIDs following most injuries will suffice. Pressure dressings should be applied to any open wounds, followed by an evaluation and suturing. The player should be removed from the game immediately to prevent any blood-borne contamination to other players (Sachare 1994b). Any head trauma with loss of consciousness should have a mental status and neurological work-up.

Physical Fitness

Professional athletes with asymptomatic or symptomatic cardiac conditions may be hesitant in disclosing their pathology. In recent years, several professional athletes have been found to have cardiac problems that resulted in their deaths. The economic incentives of playing professional-level sports may inhibit athletes from disclosing their conditions for fear of disqualifying themselves from strenuous activities. Carefully obtained past medical and family histories followed by EKG and treadmill stress tests prove

Figure 96.32 • Cold compressive therapy.

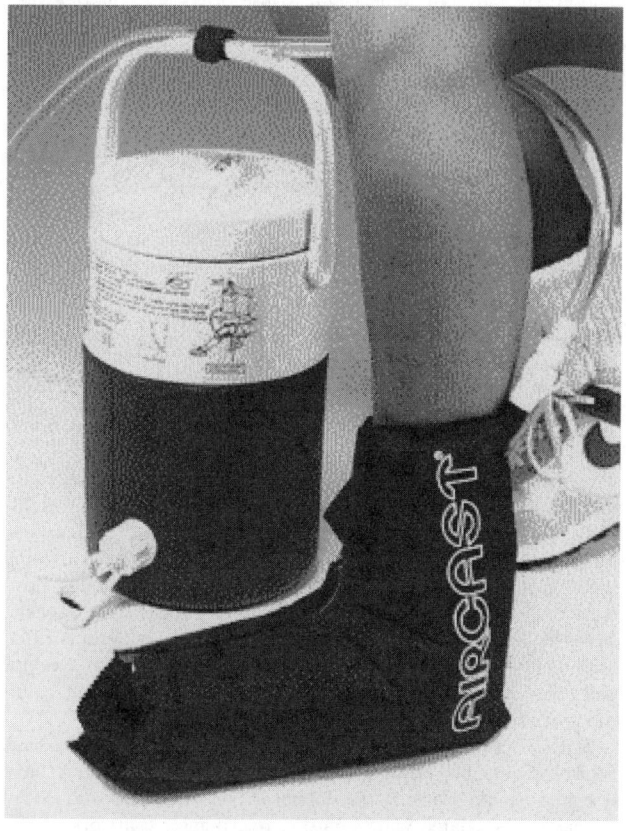

AirCast

to be valuable in detecting those who are at risk. If a player is identified as a risk and still wishes to continue competing regardless of the medical-legal issues, emergency resuscitative equipment and trained personnel must be present at all practices and games.

Referees are present not only to keep the flow of the game going but to protect the players from hurting themselves and others. Referees, for the most part, are objective and have the authority to suspend any activity should an emergency condition arise. As with all competitive sports, emotion and adrenaline are flowing high; the referees are present to help the players harness these energies in a positive fashion.

Proper conditioning, warm-up and stretching prior to engaging in any competitive activity is vital to the prevention of strains and sprains. This procedure enables the muscles to perform at peak efficiency and minimizes the possibilities of strains and sprains (micro-tears). Warm-ups may very well be a simple jog or callisthenics for about 3 to 5 minutes followed by gentle stretching out of the extremities for an additional 5 to 10 minutes. With the muscle at its peak efficiency, the athlete may be able to quickly manoeuvre away from a threatening position.

• SEX INDUSTRY

Priscilla Alexander

The sex industry is a major industry both in developing countries, where it is a major source of foreign currency, and in industrial-

ized countries. The two main divisions of the sex industry are (1) prostitution, which involves the direct exchange of a sexual service for money or other means of economic compensation and (2) pornography, which involves the performance of sex-related tasks, sometimes involving two or more people, for still photographs, in motion pictures and videotapes, or in a theatre or nightclub, but does not include direct sexual activity with the paying client. The line between prostitution and pornography is not very clear, however, as some prostitutes restrict their work to erotic acting and dance for private clients, and some workers in the pornography industry go beyond display to engaging in direct sexual contact with members of the audience, for example, in strip- and lap-dancing clubs.

The legal status of prostitution and pornography varies from one country to another, ranging from complete prohibition of the sex-money exchange and the businesses in which it takes place, as in the United States; to decriminalization of the exchange itself but prohibition of the businesses, as in many European countries; to toleration of both independent and organized prostitution, for example, in the Netherlands; to regulation of the prostitute under public health law, but prohibition for those who fail to comply, as in a number of Latin American and Asian countries. Even where the industry is legal, governments have remained ambivalent and few, if any, have attempted to use occupational safety and health regulations to protect the health of sex workers. However, since the early 1970s, both prostitutes and erotic performers have been organizing in many countries (Delacoste and Alexander 1987; Pheterson 1989), and have increasingly addressed the issue of occupational safety as they attempt to reform the legal context of their work.

A particularly controversial aspect of sex work is the involvement of young adolescents in the industry. There is not enough space to discuss this at any length here, but it is important that solutions to the problems of adolescent prostitution be developed in the context of responses to child labour and poverty, in general, and not as an isolated phenomenon. A second controversy has to do with the extent to which adult sex work is coerced or the result of individual decision. For the vast majority of sex workers, it is a temporary occupation, and the average worklife, worldwide, is from 4 to 6 years, including some who work only for a few days or intermittently (e.g., between other jobs), and others who work for 35 years or more. The primary factor in the decision to do sex work is economics, and in all countries, work in the sex industry pays much better than other work for which extensive training is not required. Indeed, in some countries, the higher-paid prostitutes earn more than some physicians and attorneys. It is the conclusion of the sex workers' rights movement that it is difficult to establish issues like consent and coercion when the work itself is illegal and heavily stigmatized. The important thing is to support sex workers' ability to organize on their own behalf, for example, in trade unions, professional associations, self-help projects and political advocacy organizations.

Hazards and Precautions

Sexually transmitted diseases (STDs). The most obvious occupational hazard for sex workers, and the one which has received the most attention historically, is STDs, including syphilis and gonorrhoea, chlamydia, genital ulcer disease, trichomonas and herpes, and, more recently, the human immunodeficiency virus (HIV) and AIDS.

In all countries, the risk of infection with HIV and other STDs is greatest among the lowest-income sex workers, whether on the street in the industrial countries, in low-income brothels in Asia and Latin America or in residential compounds in impoverished communities in Africa. In industrialized countries, studies have found HIV infection among female prostitutes to be associated with injecting drug use by either the prostitute or her ongoing personal partner, or with the prostitute's use of "crack", a smokeable form of cocaine—not with the number of clients or with prostitution *per se*. There have been few if any studies of pornography workers, but it is likely to be similar. In developing countries, the primary factors are less clear, but may include a higher prevalence of untreated conventional STDs, which some researchers think facilitate transmission of HIV, and a reliance on informal street vendors or poorly equipped clinics for treatment of STDs, if treatment involves injections with unsterile needles. Injection of recreational drugs is also associated with HIV infection in some developing countries (Estébanez, Fitch and Nájera 1993). Among male prostitutes, HIV infection is more often associated with homosexual activity, but is also associated with injecting drug use and sex in the context of drug dealing.

Precautions involve the consistent use of latex or polyurethane condoms for fellatio and vaginal or anal intercourse, where possible with lubricants (water-based for latex condoms, water or oil-based for polyurethane condoms), latex or polyurethane barriers for cunnilingus and oral-anal contact and gloves for hand-genital contact. While condom use has been increasing among prostitutes in most countries, it is still the exception in the pornography industry. Women performers sometimes use spermicides to protect themselves. However, while the spermicide nonoxynol-9 has been shown to kill HIV in the laboratory, and reduces the incidence of conventional STD in some populations, its efficacy for HIV prevention in actual use is far less clear. Moreover, the use of nonoxynol-9 more than once a day has been associated with significant rates of vaginal epithelial disruption (which could increase the female sex worker's vulnerability to HIV infection) and sometimes an increase in vaginal yeast infections. No one has studied its use for anal sex.

Access to sex worker–sensitive health care is also important, including care for other health problems, not just STDs. Traditional public health approaches that involve mandatory licensing or registration, and regular health examinations, have not been effective in reducing the risk of infection for the workers, and are contrary to World Health Organization policies that oppose mandatory testing.

Injuries. Although there have not been any formal studies of other occupational hazards, anecdotal evidence suggests that repetitive stress injuries involving the wrist and shoulder are common among prostitutes who do "hand jobs", and jaw pain is sometimes associated with performing fellatio. In addition, street prostitutes and erotic dancers may develop foot, knee and back problems related to working in high heels. Some prostitutes have reported chronic bladder and kidney infections, due to working with a full bladder or not knowing how to position oneself to prevent deep penetration during vaginal intercourse. Finally, some groups of prostitutes are very vulnerable to violence, especially in countries where the laws against prostitution are heavily enforced. The violence includes rape and other sexual assault, physical assault and murder, and is committed by police, clients, sex work business managers and domestic partners. The risk of injury is greatest among younger, less experienced prostitutes, especially those who begin working during adolescence.

Precautions include ensuring that sex workers are trained in the least stressful way to perform different sexual acts to prevent repetitive stress injuries and bladder infections, and self-defence training to reduce vulnerability to violence. This is particularly important for young sex workers. In the case of violence, another important remedy is to increase the willingness of police and prosecuting attorneys to enforce the laws against rape and other violence when the victims are sex workers.

Alcohol and drug use. When prostitutes work in bars and nightclubs, they are often required by management to encourage clients to drink, as well as to drink with clients, which can be a serious hazard for individuals who are vulnerable to alcohol addiction. In addition, some begin to use drugs (e.g., heroin, amphetamines and cocaine) to help deal with the stress of their work, while others used drugs prior to beginning sex work, and turned to sex work in order to pay for their drugs. With injecting drug use, vulnerability to HIV infection, hepatitis and a range of bacterial infections increases if drug users share needles.

Precautions include workplace regulations to ensure that prostitutes can drink non-alcoholic beverages when with clients, the provision of sterile injection equipment and, where possible, legal drugs to sex workers who inject drugs, and increasing access to drug and alcohol addiction treatment programmes.

NIGHTLIFE ENTERTAINMENT

Angela Babin

This grouping of extremely varied and miscellaneous entertainment occupations includes work locations such as bars, nightclubs, discotheques, dancehalls, topless bars, go-go clubs, casinos, bingo and gambling parlours, and pool halls, as well as cinema theatres. Occupations include bartenders, waiters, hostess/host, card dealers, bouncers (security personnel), musicians, dancers, strippers and movie projectionists. Hotels and restaurants often have night entertainment venues within them. There are several categories of hazards common to almost all nightlife entertainment workers.

Shiftwork. Entertainment workers such as bartenders may have routine nightshifts, while musicians working in a club may have irregular shifts. Various physiological, psychological and social effects are associated with nightshift or irregular shiftwork. Often bartenders and cocktail waitresses work shifts that are 10 to 14 hours long.

Violence. Workplace violence is a major problem in establishments that serve alcohol, as well as in gambling enterprises. The United States National Institute for Occupational Safety and Health studied homicide rates among workers in the United States during 1980–1989. They found bartenders to be ranked the eighth highest occupational group, with a homicide rate of 2.1 per 100,000, compared to the average homicide rate of 0.7 homicides per 100,000 for all workers. The exchange of money with the public, often working alone or in small numbers and working late at night or early in the morning, as well as working in high-crime areas, were all found to be factors related to the high rate. Preventive measures for lowering the violence rate include increasing the visibility of the workplace, such as by installing better lighting. The amounts of cash on hand should be minimized and signs posted which clearly indicate that little or no cash in on hand. Silent alarms and hidden cameras can be installed and workers can be trained in non-violent response techniques for emergencies, such as robberies. Arrangements can be made for having routine police checks on workers' safety, and workers may even be provided bullet-proof barriers and vests if needed.

Fire Safety. Many smaller nightclubs, dancehalls, movie theatres and bars may not meet with local assembly, building or fire code requirements. There have been several high-profile fatal fires in urban clubs, which are often more crowded than permissible by law. Adherence to fire and assembly codes, a fire safety and emergency programme and availability of fire extinguishers and training in their use, as well as other emergency procedures, can reduce risks (Malhotra 1984).

Second-hand smoke. In many locations where there is nightlife entertainment, second-hand cigarette smoke is a significant hazard. The risk of lung cancer and heart disease is increased with exposure to cigarette smoke in the workplace (NIOSH 1991). The risk of laryngeal cancer, also associated with tobacco use, is elevated in bartenders and food servers. Often, smaller bars and night entertainment clubs do not have adequate ventilation for cigarette smoke. In many countries, efforts are being made to regulate exposure to second-hand smoke; but such governmental restriction are not universal. Ventilation and air cleaning devices, such as electrostatic precipitators, as well as the restriction of smoking will decrease exposure.

Alcohol and drug abuse. Working in certain occupations has been found to be correlated to increased alcohol consumption, and one suggestive study has found that death from liver cirrhosis, a disease associated with alcohol consumption, is elevated among waiters, bartenders and musicians (Olkinuora 1984). In nightlife entertainment work there is easy access to alcohol and a social pressure to drink. Often there is isolation from a usual homelife because of working during the night shift or because of touring through different locations. Poor management and lack of supervision can contribute to the problem. Performance anxiety (in the case of musicians), or the need to stay awake during night shift, as well as the fact that patrons may be apt to abuse drugs, can also increase the risks for drug abuse among workers in the nightlife environment. The risks for alcohol and drug abuse intervention programmes can be decreased by well-designed training programmes which assist workers dealing with these problems.

Noise. Excessive noise exposure can be a problem in bars and restaurants. While the problem of noise is obvious in discotheques and music clubs which feature excessively high sound levels, noise overexposure can also be a problem in bars and other locations in which there is only pre-recorded or jukebox music, which can also be played very loudly. Sound levels of over 100 decibels (dB) are common in discos (Tan, Tsang and Wong 1990). One survey of 55 nightclubs in New Jersey in the United States revealed noise levels from 90 to 107 dB. Placement of speakers and jukeboxes away from work stations can reduce worker exposure, and acoustic baffling and barriers can also help. In some cases a general reduction in volume may be possible. If possible, wearing ear plugs can reduce worker exposure.

Dermatitis. Nightlife workers share many skin problems with food handlers. Skin infections, such as candidiasis of the hands, can arise from extensive contact with soiled glassware, washing and cleaning fluids and water. Automatic dish- and glass-washing equipment can address this problem. Food sensitivities are also known, such as contact dermatitis in a bartender with a sensitivity to lemon and lime peels (Cardullo, Ruszkowski and Deleo 1989). Bartenders have developed eczema from handling mint. Other specific sensitivities leading to dermatitis have been reported, such as dermatitis in a professional blackjack dealer who developed a sensitivity to chromate salts used in the green dye for the felt on gaming tables (Fisher 1976).

Musculoskeletal problems. Repetitive motion injuries and other problems associated with workplace design can be found among nightlife workers. For example, musicians and dancers are prone to specific musculoskeletal problems, as discussed elsewhere in this chapter. Bartenders who continually wash glassware and card dealers who must shuffle and deal cards for games in casinos have been found to suffer from carpal tunnel syndrome. More frequent breaks during shifts, in addition to job and task redesign, may reduce these hazards. Bartenders, cocktail waitresses, casino dealers and food servers often must stand for their entire workshift, which may be 10 to 12 hours long. Excessive standing can result in back strain and other circulatory and musculoskeletal problems. Corrugated rubber floor mats and comfortable, supportive shoes can lessen the strain.

Film projection booths. Projection booths are small and problems of excessive heat can arise. Older film projection booths use a carbon arc light source to project images, while more modern booths employ xenon lamps. In either case, ultraviolet (UV) radiation and ozone gas exposure can occur. Levels of ozone that ranged from 0.01 to 0.7 parts per million have been reported. The ozone is generated by the UV radiation, which ionizes oxygen found in the air. (Maloy 1978). In addition, use of carbon arc light sources is associated with rare earth metal fumes, carbon dioxide, carbon monoxide, ozone, electromagnetic radiation (EMF) and heat exposures. Local exhaust ventilation is required.

Special effects. Many different special effects can be used in clubs and discotheques, including, various smokes and fogs, laser light shows and even pyrotechnics. Adequate training in laser operation and safety and other special effects is necessary. UV light emitted from "black" lights may pose additional hazards, especially to strippers and go-go dancers (Schall et al. 1969). It has been suggested that a glass barrier between the black light and the performers would help decrease the hazards. These effects are described in more detail in other articles in this chapter.

ENVIRONMENTAL PROTECTION AND PUBLIC HEALTH ISSUES

Michael McCann

Visual Arts

The visual arts produce a wide range of potential environmental problems and raise a number of public health issues. The visual arts use a broad range of chemicals and techniques which can create air and water pollution problems similar to that of the comparable industrial processes, only on a much smaller scale.

Hazardous waste produced by artists can include: (1) toxic and extremely toxic wastes, including solvents, lead compounds, chromates and cyanide solutions; (2) flammable waste, including flammable and combustible liquids (e.g., rags soaked with oil and turpentine), oxidizing substances such as potassium chlorate and dichromates, and ignitable compressed gases; (3) corrosive waste, including acids with a pH less than 2 and alkalis with a pH greater than 12; and (4) reactive wastes, such as organic peroxides, cyanide solutions and sulphide solutions. Artists and artisans are less likely, however, to know how to dispose of this waste or even to know what is hazardous. The most common method of waste disposal for artists is pouring down the sink or onto the ground, tossing in the garbage or evaporation. Although the individual amounts of pollutants are small, cumulatively they can result in significant pollution.

In the United States and Canada and many other countries, artists working in their homes are usually exempted from industrial hazardous waste regulations under a household hazardous waste exemption. Many localities, however, do provide special household hazardous waste days when households can bring their hazardous waste to a central site for collection. However, even in countries which do regulate artists as small businesses, there is little enforcement of hazardous waste regulations for these cottage industries.

Types of waste management methods available include many of the same ones used by industry, including source reduction, waste separation and concentration, recycling, energy and material recovery, incineration or treatment, and secure land disposal. Some of these methods are more available to artists than others.

The best way of managing hazardous waste is to actually eliminate or minimize its production by substituting materials which

96. ENTERTAINMENT AND THE ARTS

are less toxic—for example, using lead-free glazes instead of leaded glazes in pottery and enamelling, and using water-based screen printing inks and other coating materials instead of solvent-based ones.

Separating hazardous materials from non-hazardous materials—for example, separating solvent-based paints and water-based paints—can be a simple method to reduce the amount of hazardous waste and prevent it from contaminating regular garbage.

Traditional industrial methods of concentration, such as evaporation of large volumes of photographic wastes, are usually not feasible for artists.

Recycling can involve the reusing of materials (such as solvents used for oil painting cleanup) by the individual, or the passing of unwanted materials to someone else who can use them. Large printmaking facilities, which generate many solvent- or oil-soaked rags, can contract for laundering and reuse them.

Treatment can involve several processes. The most common one used by artists is neutralization of acids or alkaline solutions. Incineration is usually restricted to burning wood dust. Evaporation of solvents is also commonly done. This reduces the amount of hazardous waste potentially contaminating water supplies, although it does contaminate the atmosphere to some degree.

The least favourable option is secure land disposal in a proper hazardous waste disposal site. This is usually not a viable option for artists, especially in developing countries.

A public health issue that is common to many of the visual arts is the problem of the exposure of children to toxic chemicals found in many art materials, including those intended for use by children. Examples include solvents in permanent felt-tip markers and lead in ceramic glazes. Children and other family members can be exposed to hazardous substances and conditions in the home.

A widespread problem in many countries is lead poisoning, including fatalities from cooking and storing food in containers that have been made with lead-containing pottery glazes. In the commercial industry, the problem of lead leaching from glazed pottery has been mostly eliminated through government regulations and good quality control. The World Health Organization has standards for lead and cadmium leaching from pottery intended for food and drink use. The cost of the testing required, however, is not feasible for craft potters, and therefore craft potters should use only lead-free glazes for food and drink containers.

Performing and Media Arts

Theatres, scenery shops and motion picture and television production areas also can produce hazardous waste, since they use many of the same chemicals as are used in the visual arts. The same solutions apply. In particular, the widespread shift from solvent-based paints to water-based paints has greatly decreased the amount of solvent pollution.

One of the main public health issues for theatres (and other places of public assembly) is fire safety. Many theatres and other performance spaces, especially small, non-commercial ones, do not meet applicable fire codes and are dangerously overcrowded. There have been many disastrous fires with numerous fatalities in the performing arts. The use of fogs and smokes for special effects in theatre and opera can also pose the risk of asthma attacks in asthmatic audience members in the front of the theatre if the building does not have adequate exhaust ventilation to prevent the fog or smoke from affecting the audience.

Entertainment Industry

Entertainment industries such as amusement and theme parks can face all the solid waste and other pollution problems of a small town. Zoos, circuses and other types of entertainment involving animals can have many of the same pollution problems as livestock raising, but on a smaller scale.

A public health concern at all entertainment events where food is sold is the possibility of developing salmonella poisoning, hepatitis or other diseases if there are not adequate public health controls.

Crowd control is another major public health concern in many large entertainment events, such as certain types of popular concerts and sports events. Widespread use of drugs and alcohol, overcrowding, allowing extensive standing room (festival seating) and lack of adequate preplanning have led to many incidents involving riots and panic, with resulting multiple injuries and fatalities. In addition, lack of adequate construction standards has caused fires and collapses of seating areas in several countries. There is a need for better regulations and provision of proper crowd control measures in these situations.

Visitors to parks and zoos can also present hazards to themselves. There have been many incidents where zoo visitors have been maimed or killed after entering animal enclosures. Visitors who get too close to wild animals in the parks have also experienced attacks, many of which have been fatal. The problems of inexperienced parks visitors getting lost, caught in storms, or falling from mountains is also a constant public health risk which can use up extensive resources for rescue.

The sex industry, especially prostitution, is particularly infamous for the possibility of patrons being robbed and possibly contracting sexually transmitted diseases. This is particularly true in countries where prostitution is not legally controlled. Criminal activities are often associated with prostitution.

References

American Academy of Orthopedic Surgeons. 1991. Protective equipment. In *Athletic Training and Sports Medicine*. Park Ridge, IL: APOS.

Arheim, DD. 1986. *Dance Injuries: Their Prevention and Care*. St. Louis, MO: CV Mosby Co.

Armstrong, RA, P Neill, and R Mossop. 1988. Asthma induced by ivory dust: A new occupational cause. *Thorax* 43(9):737-738.

Axelsson, A and F Lindgren. 1981. Hearing in classical musicians. *Acta Oto-Laryngologica* 92 Suppl. 377:3-74.

Babin, A 1996. Orchestra pit sound level measurements in Broadway shows. Presented at the 26th Annual Meeting of the American Public Health Association. New York, 20 November.

Baker, EL, WA Peterson, JL Holtz, C Coleman, and PJ Landrigan. 1979. Subacute cadmium intoxication in jewellery workers: an evaluation of diagnostic procedures. *Arch Environ Health* 34:173-177.

Balafrej, A, J Bellakhdar, M El Haitem, and H Khadri. 1984. Paralysis due to glue in young apprentice shoemakers in the medina of Fez. *Rev Pediatrie* 20(1):43-47.

Ballesteros, M, CMA Zuniga, and OA Cardenas. 1983. Lead concentrations in the blood of children from pottery-making families exposed to lead salts in a Mexican village. *B Pan Am Health Organ* 17(1):35-41.

Bastian, RW. 1993. Benign mucosal and saccular disorders; benign laryngeal tumors. In *Otolaryngology-Head and Neck Surgery*, edited by CW Cumming. St. Louis, MO: CV Mosby Co.

—. 1996. Vocal fold microsurgery in singers. *Journal of Voice* 10(4):389-404

Bastian, R, A Keidar, and K Verdolini-Marston. 1990. Simple vocal tasks for detecting vocal fold swelling. *Journal of Voice* 4(2):172-183.

Bowling, A. 1989. Injuries to dancers: Prevalence, treatment and perception of causes. *British Medical Journal* 6675:731-734.

Bruno, PJ, WN Scott, and G Huie. 1995. Basketball. In *The Team Physicians's Handbook*, edited by MB Mellion, WM Walsh and GL Shelton. Philadelphia, PA: Mosby Yearbook.

Burr, GA, TJ Van Gilder, DB Trout, TG Wilcox, and R Friscoll. 1994. *Health Hazard Evaluation Report: Actors' Equity Association/The League of American Theaters and Producers, Inc.* Doc. HETA 90-355-2449. Cincinnati, OH: US National Institute for Occupational Safety and Health.

Calabrese, LH, DT Kirkendal, and M Floyd. 1983. Menstrual abnormalities, nutritional patterns and body composition in female classical ballet dancers. *Phys Sports Med* 11:86-98.

Cardullo, AC, AM Ruszkowski, and VA DeLeo. 1989. Allergic contact dermatitis resulting from sensitivity to citrus peel, geriniol, and citral. *J Am Acad Dermatol* 21(2):395-397.

Carlson, T. 1989. Lights! Camera! Tragedy. *TV Guide* (26 August):8-11.

Chasin, M and JP Chong. 1992. A clinically efficient hearing protection program for musicians. *Med Prob Perform Artists* 7(2):40-43.

—. 1995. Four environmental techniques to reduce the effect of music exposure on hearing. *Med Prob Perform Artists* 10(2):66-69.

Chaterjee, M. 1990. Ready-made garment workers in Ahmedabad. *B Occup Health Safety* 19:2-5.

Clare, PR. 1990. Football. In *The Team Physicians's Handbook*, edited by MB Mellion, WM Walsh, and GL Shelton. St. Louis, MO: CV Mosby Co.

Cornell, C. 1988. Potters, lead and health—Occupational safety in a Mexican village (meeting abstract). *Abstr Pap Am Chem S* 196:14.

Council on Scientific Affairs of the American Medical Association. 1983. Brain injury in boxing. *JAMA* 249:254-257.

Das, PK, KP Shukla, and FG Ory. 1992. An occupational health programme for adults and children in the carpet weaving industry, Mirzapur, India: A case study in the informal sector. *Soc Sci Med* 35(10):1293-1302.

Delacoste, F and P Alexander. 1987. *Sex Work: Writings by Women in the Sex Industry*. San Francisco, CA: Cleis Press.

Depue, RH and BT Kagey. 1985. A proportionate mortality study of the acting profession. *Am J Ind Med* 8:57-66.

Dominguez, R, JR DeJuanes Paardo, M Garcia Padros, and F Rodriguez Artalejo. 1987. Antitetanic vaccination in a high-risk population. *Med Segur Trab* 34:50-56.

Driscoll, RJ, WJ Mulligan, D Schultz, and A Candelaria. 1988. Malignant mesothelioma: a cluster in a Native American population. *New Engl J Med* 318:1437-1438.

Estébanez, P, K Fitch, and Nájera 1993. HIV and female sex workers. *Bull WHO* 71(3/4):397-412.

Evans, RW, RI Evans, S Carjaval, and S Perry. 1996. A survey of injuries among Broadway performers. *Am J Public Health* 86:77-80.

Feder, RJ. 1984. The professional voice and airline flight. *Otolaryngology-Head and Neck Surgery*, 92(3):251-254.

Feldman, R and T Sedman. 1975. Hobbyists working with lead. *New Engl J Med* 292:929.

Fishbein, M. 1988. Medical problems among ICSOM musicians. *Med Prob Perform Artists* 3:1-14.

Fisher, AA. 1976. "Blackjack disease" and other chromate puzzles. *Cutis* 18(1):21-22.

Frye, HJH. 1986. Incidence of overuse syndrome in the symphony orchestra. *Med Prob Perform Artists* 1:51-55.

Garrick, JM. 1977. The frequency of injury, mechanism of injury and epidemiology of ankle sprains. *Am J Sports Med* 5:241-242.

Griffin, R, KD Peterson, J Halseth, and B Reynolds. 1989. Radiographic study of elbow injuries in professional rodeo cowboys. *Phys Sports Med* 17:85-96.

Hamilton, LH and WG Hamilton. 1991. Classical ballet: Balancing the costs of artistry and athleticism. *Med Prob Perform Artists* 6:39-44.

Hamilton, WG. 1988. Foot and ankle injuries in dancers. In *Sports Clinics of North America*, edited by L Yokum. Philadelphia, PA: Williams and Wilkins.

Hardaker, WTJ. 1987. Medical considerations in dance training for children. *Am Fam Phys* 35(5):93-99.

Henao, S. 1994. *Health Conditions of Latin American Workers*. Washington, DC: American Public Health Association.

Huie, G and EB Hershman. 1994. The team clinician's bag. *Am Acad Phys Asst* 7:403-405.

Huie, G and WN Scott. 1995. Assessment of ankle sprains in athletes. *Phys Assist J* 19(10):23-24.

Kipen, HM and Y Lerman. 1986. Respiratory abnormalities among photographic developers: A report of 3 cases. *Am J Ind Med* 9:341-347.

Knishkowy, B and EL Baker. 1986. Transmission of occupational disease to family contacts. *Am J Ind Med* 9:543-550.

Koplan, JP, AV Wells, HJP Diggory, EL Baker, and J Liddle. 1977. Lead absorption in a community of potters in Barbados. *Int J Epidemiol* 6:225-229.

Malhotra, HL. 1984. Fire safety in assembly buildings. *Fire Safety J* 7(3):285-291.

Maloy, E. 1978. Projection booth safety: New findings and new dangers. *Int Assoc Electr Inspect News* 50(4):20-21.

McCann, M. 1989. 5 dead in movie heliocopter crash. *Art Hazards News* 12:1.

—. 1991. *Lights! Camera! Safety! A Health and Safety Manual for Motion Picture and Television Production*. New York: Center for Safety in the Arts.

—. 1992a. *Artist Beware*. New York: Lyons and Burford.

—. 1992b. *Art Safety Procedures: A Health and Safety Manual for Art Schools and Art Departments*. New York: Center for Safety in the Arts.

—. 1996. Hazards in cottage industries in developing countries. *Am J Ind Med* 30:125-129.

McCann, M, N Hall, R Klarnet, and PA Peltz. 1986. Reproductive hazards in the arts and crafts. Presented at the Annual Conference of the Society for Occupational and Environmental Health Conference on Reproductive Hazards in the Environment and Workplace, Bethesda, MD, 26 April.

Miller, AB, DT Silverman, and A Blair. 1986. Cancer risk among artistic painters. *Am J Ind Med* 9:281-287.

MMWR. 1982. Chromium sensitization in an artist's workshop. *Morb Mort Weekly Rep* 31:111.

—. 1996. Bull riding-related brain and spinal cord injuries—Louisiana, 1994-1995. *Morb and Mort Weekly Rep* 45:3-5.

Monk, TH. 1994. Circadian rhythms in subjective activation, mood, and performance efficiency. In *Principles and Practice of Sleep Medicine*, 2nd edition, edited by M. Kryger and WC. Roth. Philadelphia, PA: WB Saunders.

National Institute for Occupational Safety and Health (NIOSH). 1991. *Environmental Tobacco Smoke in the Workplace: NIOSH Current Intelligence Bulletin 54*. Cincinnati, OH: NIOSH.

Norris, RN. 1990. Physical disorders of visual artists. *Art Hazards News* 13(2):1.

Nubé, J. 1995. *Beta Blockers and Performing Musicians*. Doctoral thesis. Amsterdam: University of Amsterdam.

O'Donoghue, DH. 1950. Surgical treatment of fresh injuries to major ligaments of the knee. *J Bone Joint Surg* 32:721-738.

—. 1976. Injuries to the knee. In *Treatment of Injuries to Athletes*, edited by DH O'Donoghue. Philadelphia, PA: WB Saunders.

Pan American Health Organization, (PAHO). 1994. *Health Conditions in the Americas*. Vol. 1. Washington, DC: PAHO.

Pheterson, G. 1989. *The Vindication of the Rights of Whores*. Seattle, WA: Seal Press.

Prockup, L. 1978. Neuropathy in an artist. *Hosp Pract* (November):89.

Qualley, CA. 1986. *Safety in the Artroom*. Worcester, MA: Davis Publications.

Ramakrishna, RS, P Muthuthamby, RR Brooks, and DE Ryan. 1982. Blood lead levels in Sri Lankan families recovering gold and silver from jewellers' waste. *Arch Environ Health* 37(2):118-120.

Ramazzini, B. 1713. *De morbis artificum (Diseases of Workers)*. Chicago, IL: University of Chicago Press.

Rastogi, SK, BN Gupta, H Chandra, N Mathur, PN Mahendra, and T Husain. 1991. A study of the prevalence of respiratory morbidity among agate workers. *Int Arch Occup Environ Health* 63(1):21-26.

Rossol, M. 1994. *The Artist's Complete Health and Safety Guide*. New York: Allworth Press.

Sachare, A.(ed.). 1994a. Rule #2. Section IIC. In *The Official NBA Basketball Encyclopedia*. New York: Villard Books.

—. 1994b. Basic Principle P: Guidelines for infection control. In *The Official NBA Basketball Encyclopedia*. New York: Villard Books.

Sammarco, GJ. 1982. The foot and ankle in classical ballet and modern dance. In *Disorders of the Foot*, edited by MH Jahss. Philadelphia, PA: WB Saunders.

Sataloff, RT. 1991. *Professional Voice: The Science and Art of Clinical Care*. New York: Raven Press.

—. 1995. Medications and their effect on the voice. *Journal of Singing* 52(1):47-52.

—. 1996. Pollution: Consequences for singers. *Journal of Singing* 52(3):59-64.

Schall, EL, CH Powell, GA Gellin, and MM Key. 1969. Hazards to go-go dancers to exposures to "black" light from fluorescent bulbs. *Am Ind Hyg Assoc J* 30:413-416.

Schnitt, JM and D Schnitt. 1987. Psychological aspects of dance. In *The Science of Dance Training*, edited by P Clarkson and M Skrinar. Champaign, IL: Human Kinetics Press.

Seals, J. 1987. Dance surfaces. In *Dance Medicine: A Comprehensive Guide*, edited by A Ryan and RE Stephens. Chicago, IL: Pluribus Press.

Sofue, I, Y Yamamura, K Ando, M Iida, and T Takayanagi. 1968. N-hexane polyneuropathy. *Clin Neurol* 8:393-403.

Stewart, R and C Hake. 1976. Paint remover hazard. *JAMA* 235:398.

Tan, TC, HC Tsang, and LL Wong. 1990. Noise surveys in discotheques in Hong Kong. *Ind Health* 28(1):37-40.

Teitz, C, RM Harrington, and H Wiley. 1985. Pressure on the foot in point shoes. *Foot Ankle* 5:216-221.

VanderGriend, RA, FH Savoie, and JL Hughes. 1991. Fracture of the ankle. In *Rockwood and Green's Fractures in Adults*, edited by CA Rockwood, DP Green, and RW Bucholz. Philadelphia, PA: JB Lippincott Co.

Warren, M, J Brooks-Gunn, and L Hamilton. 1986. Scoliosis and fracture in young ballet dancers: Relationship to delayed menarcheal age and amenorrhea. *New Engl J Med* 314:1338-1353.

World Health Organization (WHO). 1976. *Meeting on Organization of Health Care in Small Industries*. Geneva: WHO.

Zeitels, S. 1995. Premalignant epithelium and microinvasive cancer of the vocal fold: the evolution of phonomicrosurgical management. *Laryngoscope* 105(3):1-51.

Other relevant readings

Alexander, P. 1995. Sex workers fight against AIDS: An international perspective. In *Women Resisting AIDS: Strategies of Empowerment*, edited by BE Schneider and N Stoller. Philadelphia, PA: Temple University Press.

—. 1997. Making a living: Women who go out. In *Women's Experiences with AIDS*, edited by M Ankrah and L Long. New York: Columbia University Press.

American National Standards Institute (ANSI). 1993. *American National Standard for Safe Use of Lasers.* New York: ANSI.

Association of Systematics Collections. 1994. *Guidelines for Institutional Policies and Planning in Natural History Collections.* Washington, DC: Association of Systematics Collections.

Avery, B. 1992. *Special Event & Show Safety Guide (Fireworks, Animal Handling, Power Tools).* Orlando, FL.

Babin, A and M McCann. 1992. *Waste Management and Disposal for Artists and Schools.* New York: Center for Safety in the Arts.

Barnard, MA. 1993. Violence and vulnerability: Conditions of work for streetwalking prostitutes. *Sociology of Health and Illness* 15(5):683-705.

Bastian, RW. 1987. Vocal fold surgery in singers. *Med Prob of Perform Artists* 66: 49-52.

—. 1988. Factors leading to successful evaluation and management of patients with voice disorders. *Ear, Nose and Throat Journal* 67:411-420.

—. 1990. Prevention of voice disorders. In *The Principles of Singing,* 2nd edition, edited by KE Miller. Englewood Cliffs, NJ: Prentice-Hall.

Bastian, R, K. Verdolini, and A. Keidar. 1989. The team approach to management of patients with voice disorders. *NATS Journal* 45(5):16-19.

Bouchayer, M and G Cornut. 1988. Microsurgery for benign mucosal disorders. *Ear, Nose and Throat Journal* 67:446-466.

California State Fire Marshall Film Advisory Committee. 1988. *Film Industry Fire/life Safety Handbook.* Sacramento, CA: California State Fire Marshall.

Canadian Centre for Occupational Health and Safety (CCOHS). 1988. *Infograms on Hand Tools.* Hamilton, ONT: CCOHS.

—. 1988. *Infograms on Powered Hand Tools.* Hamilton, ONT: CCOHS.

—. 1988. *Infograms on Woodworking Machines.* Hamilton, ONT: CCOHS.

Chong, JP. 1996. The human performance approach to prevention. In *Musicians and the Prevention of Hearing Loss,* edited by M Chasin. San Diego, CA: Singular Publishing, Inc.

—. 1997. Physical therapy for physical problems. In *Chronic Musculoskeletal Injuries in the Workplace,* edited by D Ranney. Philadelphia, PA: WB Saunders.

Chong, JP, M Lynden, D Harvey, and M Peebles. 1989. Occupational health problems of musicians. *Can Fam Phys* 35:2341-2348.

Clark, N. 1990. *Health and Safety Manual for Broadcast Employees.* New York: National Association of Broadcast Employees and Technicians Local 16.

Colton, R and J Casper. 1990. *Understanding Voice Problems: A Physiological Perspective for Diagnosis and Treatment.* Baltimore, MD: Williams and Wilkins.

Critchley, M and RA Henson. 1980. *Music and the Brain: Studies in the Neurology of Music.* London: Heinemann.

Ford, C and D Bless. 1990. *Phonosurgery: Assessment and Surgical Management of Voice Disorders.* Philadelphia, PA: Raven Press.

Health and Safety Commission. 1985. *Zoos—Safety, Health and Welfare Standards for Employers and Persons at Work.* London: Her Majesty's Stationery Office.

Industry Wide Labor-Management Safety Committee for the Motion Picture and Television Industry. 1986. *Safety Bulletins.* Hollywood, CA: Industry Wide Labor-Management Safety Committee for the Motion Picture and Television Industry.

Kleinsasser, O. 1979. *Microlaryngoscopy and Endolaryngeal Microsurgery: Technique and Typical Findings,* 2nd edition. Baltimore, MD: University Park Press.

Lockwood, AH. 1989. Medical problems of musicians. *New Engl J Med* 320:221-227.

Massachusetts Institute of Technology (MIT). 1994. *Health and Safety Guidelines for Computer Use at MIT.* Cambridge, MA: MIT.

Miller, PL. 1991. *Arsenic, Old Lace, and Stuffed Owls May Be Dangerous to Your Health: Hazards in Museum Collections.* Champaign, IL: Illinois Heritage Association.

Morrison, M and L Rammage. 1994. *The Management of Voice Disorders.* San Diego, CA: Singular Publishing Group, Inc.

National Institute for the Conservation of Cultural Property (reference library): Washington, DC.

National Fire Protection Association (NFPA). 1991. *Protection of Museums and Museum collections.* Quincy, MA: NFPA.

Ontario Film and Television Industry Section 11 Advisory Committee. 1990. *Safety Guidelines for the Film and Television Industry in Ontario.* Toronto: Ontario Ministry of Labor.

Pheterson G. *The Prostitution Prisim.* Amsterdam: University of Amsterdam Press.

Phongpaichit, P. 1982. *From Peasant Girls to Bangkok Masseuses.* Geneva: ILO.

Phoon, WO. 1988. Chemical hazards: Metals. In *Practical Occupational Health,* edited by WO Phoon. Singapore, Hong Kong and New Delhi: PG Publishing.

Reid, F. 1978. *The Staging Handbook.* London: AC Black.

Rose, CL. 1995. *Storage of Natural History Collections.* Pittsburgh, PA: Society for the Preservation of Natural History Collections.

Rossol, M. 1991. *Stage Fright: Health and Safety in the Theater.* New York: Allworth Press.

—. 1996. *Keeping Clay Work Safe and Legal,* 2nd edition. Brandon, OR: National Council on Education in the Ceramic Arts.

Sataloff, RT, AG Brandfonbrener, and RJ Lederman. 1990. *Textbook of Performing Arts Medicine.* Philadelphia, PA: Raven Press.

Shaver, FM. 1995. Prostitution: On the dark side of the service industry. In *Post-Critical Criminology.* Scarborough, ONT: Prentice Hall.

Singer, K. 1932. *Diseases of the Musical Profession: A Systematic Presentation of Their Causes, Symptoms and Methods of Treatment.* New York: Greenberg.

Sliney, D and M Wolbarsht. 1985. *Safety with Lasers and Other Optical Sources.* New York: Plenum Press.

Smith, S and HFT Holt. 1993. *The Artist's Manual.* New York: Mayflower Books.

Spandorfer, M, D Curtiss, and JW Snyder. 1993. *Making Art Safely.* New York: Van Nostrand Reinhold.

Sundberg, J. 1987. *The Science of the Singing Voice.* Dekalb, IL: Northern Illinois University Press.

Swedish Theatre Federation and Lund University. 1989. *A Study of the Theatre's Working Environment and Its Future Development.* Report of a research circle working in cooperation with the Swedish Theatre Federation and Lund University. Sweden: Swedish Theatre Federation and Lund University.

Titze, I. 1993. *Principles of Voice Production.* Englewood Cliffs, NJ: Prentice Hall.

Truong, T-D. 1990. *Sex, Money and Morality: Prostitution and Tourism in South-East Asia.* London: Zed Books.

Vanwesenbeeck, I. 1994 *Prostitutes' Well-being and Risk.* Amsterdam: VU University Press.

White, L. 1990. *The Comforts of Home: Prostitution in Colonial Nairobi.* Chicago, IL: University of Chicago Press.

Zycherman, LA and JR Schrock. 1988. *A Guide to Museum Pest Control.* Washington, DC: Association of Systematics Collections.

HEALTH CARE FACILITIES AND SERVICES

Chapter Editor
Annalee Yassi

Contents

HEALTH CARE: ITS NATURE AND ITS OCCUPATIONAL HEALTH PROBLEMS

Annalee Yassi and Leon J. Warshaw

Health care is a labour intensive industry and, in most countries, health care workers (HCWs) constitute a major sector of the workforce. They comprise a wide range of professional, technical and support personnel working in a large variety of settings. In addition to health professionals, laboratory technicians, pharmacists, social workers and others involved in clinical services, they include administrative and clerical personnel, housekeeping and dietary staff, laundry workers, engineers, electricians, painters and maintenance workers who repair and refurbish the building and the equipment it contains. In contrast with those providing direct care, these support workers usually have only casual, incidental contact with patients.

HCWs represent diverse educational, social and ethnic levels and are usually predominantly female. Many, particularly in home care, are employed in entry-level positions and require considerable basic training. Table 97.1 lists samples of health care functions and associated occupations.

A segment of the health sector (unfortunately, often too small and under-resourced in most communities) is devoted to direct and indirect preventive services. The major focus of the health care industry, however, is the diagnosis, treatment and care of the sick. This creates a special set of dynamics, for the sick exhibit varying levels of physical and emotional dependencies that set them apart from the customers in such personal services industries as, for example, retail trade, restaurants and hotels. They require, and traditionally receive, special services and considerations, often on an emergency basis, provided frequently at the expense of the HCWs' personal comfort and safety.

Reflecting their size and numbers of employees, acute and long-term care facilities constitute perhaps the most prominent elements in the health care industry. They are supplemented by outpatient clinics, "surgicenters" (facilities for outpatient surgery), clinical and pathological laboratories, pharmacies, x-ray and im-

---

Are they health care workers, too?

Often overlooked when considering the safety and well-being of health care workers are students attending medical, dental, nursing and other schools for health professionals and volunteers serving *pro bono* in healthcare facilities. Since they are not "employees" in the technical or legal sense of the term, they are ineligible for workers' compensation and employment-based health insurance in many jurisdictions. Health care administrators have only a moral obligation to be concerned about their health and safety.

The clinical segments of their training bring medical, nursing and dental students into direct contact with patients who may have infectious diseases. They perform or assist in a variety of invasive procedures, including taking blood samples, and often do laboratory work involving body fluids and specimens of urine and faeces. They are usually free to wander about the facility, entering areas containing potential hazards often, since such hazards are rarely posted, without an awareness of their presence. They are usually supervised very loosely, if at all, while their instructors are often not very knowledgeable, or even interested, in matters of safety and health protection.

Volunteers are rarely permitted to participate in clinical care but they do have social contacts with patients and they usually have few restrictions with respect to areas of the facility they may visit.

Under normal circumstances, students and volunteers share with health care workers the risks of exposure to potentially harmful hazards. These risks are exacerbated at times of crisis and in emergencies when they step into or are ordered into the breech. Clearly, even though it may not be spelled out in laws and regulations or in organizational procedure manuals, they are more than entitled to the concern and protection extended to "regular" health care workers.

Leon J. Warshaw

Table 97.1 • Examples of health care functions and associated occupations.*

Functions	Occupational category	Specific occupations
Direct patient care	Health-diagnosing occupations	Physicians Dentists
	Health-assessment-and-treating occupations	Registered nurses Pharmacists Physicians' assistants Therapists (e.g., inhalation and physical) Optometrists Dietitians and nutritionists
	Counselling	Social workers Clergy
Technical support	Health technicians	Clinical laboratory technicians Dental hygienists Health record technicians Radiology technicians Licensed practical nurses Emergency services technicians
Services	Health services	Dental assistants Health aides, other than nursing Nursing aides, orderlies and attendants
	Food services	Cooks Kitchen workers
	Personal services	Barbers and hairdressers
	Laundry services	Laundry workers
	Building services	Plumbers, electricians and other crafts Janitors and cleaners Boiler room operators Gardeners and groundskeepers
	Security services	Guards
	Transportation services	Ambulance drivers
Administrative support	Clerical services	Billing clerks Records processing occupations Computer equipment operators Physicians' office workers Telephone operators
Research	Scientific occupations	Scientists and research physicians
	Laboratory workers	Laboratory technicians Animal caretakers

* Occupational categories are, in part, adapted from those used by the US Department of Labor, Bureau of Labor Statistics.

Figure 97.1 • Handling contaminated biological material.

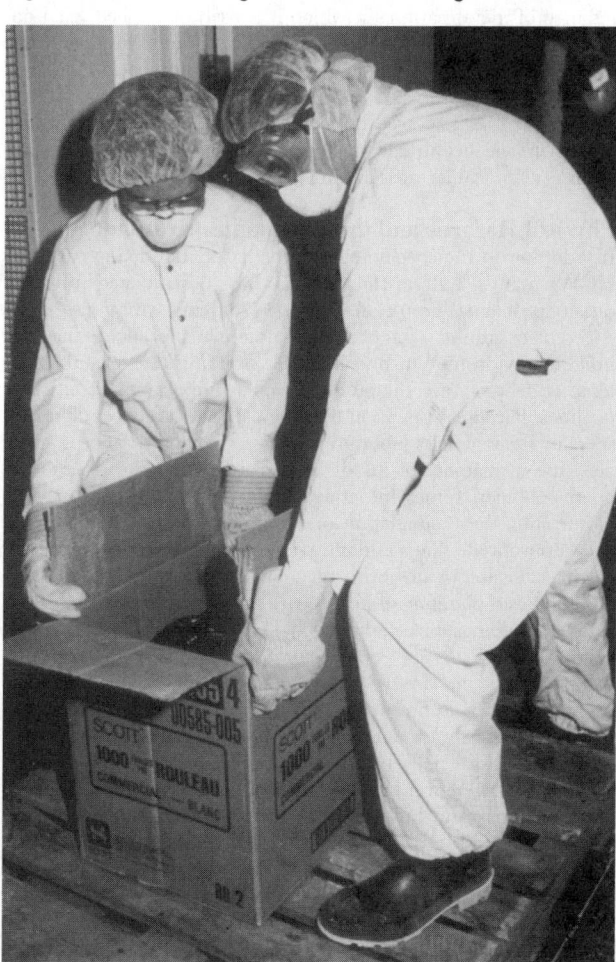

Health Sciences Centre, Winnipeg, Manitoba, Canada

aging centres, ambulance and emergency care services, individual and group offices, and home care services. These may be located within a hospital or operated elsewhere under its aegis, or they may be free-standing and operated independently. It should be noted that there are profound differences in the way health services are delivered, ranging from the well-organized, "high tech" care available in urban centres in developed countries to the underserved areas in rural communities, in developing countries and in inner-city enclaves in many large cities.

Superimposed on the health care system is a massive educational and research establishment in which students, faculty, researchers and support staffs often come in direct contact with patients and participate in their care. This comprises schools of medicine, dentistry, nursing, public health, social work and the variety of technical disciplines involved in health care.

The health care industry has been undergoing profound changes during the past few decades. Ageing of the population, especially in developed countries, has amplified the use of nursing homes, domiciliary facilities and home care services. Scientific and technological developments have not only led to the creation of new types of facilities staffed by new classes of specially-trained personnel, but they have also de-emphasized the role of the acute care hospital. Now, many services requiring inpatient care are being provided on an ambulatory basis. Finally, fiscal constraints dictated by the continuing escalation of health care costs have been reconfiguring the health care industry, at least in developing countries, resulting

in pressure for cost-containment to be achieved through changes in the organization of health care services.

HCWs who are in direct contact with the sick, wherever they work, are exposed to a number of unique hazards. They face the risk of acquiring infections from the patients they serve, as well as the risk of musculoskeletal injuries when lifting, transferring or restraining them. Support staff not directly involved in patient care (e.g., laundry and housekeeping and materials handling workers) are not only routinely exposed to chemicals, such as cleaning agents and disinfectants of industrial strength, but are also exposed to biological hazards from contaminated linens and wastes (see figure 97.1). There is also the ethos of health care which, especially in emergency situations, requires HCWs to put the safety and comfort of their patients above their own. Coping with the stress of therapeutic failures, death and dying often takes its toll in worker burnout. All this is compounded by shift work, deliberate or inadvertent understaffing and the necessity of catering to the sometimes unreasonable demands from patients and their families. Finally, there is the threat of abuse and violence from patients, particularly when the job requires them to work alone or takes them into unsafe areas. All these are described in greater detail in other articles in this chapter and elsewhere in this *Encyclopaedia*.

The US National Institute for Occupational Safety and Health (NIOSH) reported that needle punctures, musculoskeletal sprains and back injuries probably were the most common injuries in the health care industry (Wugofski 1995). The World Health Organization (WHO) Conference on Occupational Hazards in 1981 identified as its five main areas of concern:

- cuts, lacerations and fractures
- back injuries
- lack of personal safety equipment
- poor maintenance of mechanical and electrical systems
- assault by patients.

Biological Hazards

Biological hazards, which pose a risk for infectious disease, are common throughout the world, but they are particularly problematic in developing countries. While the hepatitis B virus (HBV) is a nearly universal threat to HCWs, it is particularly important in African and Asian countries where this virus is endemic. As discussed later in this chapter, the risk of HBV transmission after percutaneous exposure to hepatitis B surface antigen (HBsAg) positive blood is approximately 100-fold higher than the risk of transmitting the human immunodeficiency virus (HIV) through percutaneous exposure to HIV-infected blood (i.e., 30% versus 0.3%). Nonetheless, there has indeed been an evolution of concern regarding parenteral exposure to blood and body fluids from the pre-HIV to the AIDS era. McCormick et al. (1991) found that the annual reported incidents of injuries from sharp instruments increased more than threefold during a 14-year period and among medical house officers the reported incidents increased ninefold. Overall, nurses incur approximately two-thirds of the needlestick injuries reported. Yassi and McGill (1991) also noted that nursing staff, particularly nursing students, are at highest risk for needlestick injuries, but they also found that approximately 7.5% of medical personnel reported exposures to blood and body fluids, a figure that is probably low because of underreporting. These data were consistent with other reports which indicated that, while there is increased reporting of needlesticks reflecting concerns about HIV and AIDS, certain groups continue to underreport. Sterling (1994) concludes that underreporting of needlestick injuries ranges from 40 to 60%.

Certain risk factors clearly enhance the likelihood of transmission of bloodborne diseases; these are discussed in the article "Prevention of occupational transmission of bloodborne pathogens". Frequent exposure has indeed been associated with high

Figure 97.2 • Disposal container for sharp instruments and devices.

Health Sciences Centre, Winnipeg, Manitoba, Canada

seroprevalence rates of hepatitis B among laboratory workers, surgeons and pathologists. The risk of hepatitis C is also increased. The trend towards greater attention to prevention of needlestick injuries is, however, also noteworthy. The adoption of *universal precautions* is an important advance. Under universal precautions, it is assumed that *all* blood-containing fluid is potentially infectious and that appropriate safeguards should *always* be invoked. Safe disposal containers for needles and other sharp instruments are increasingly being placed in conveniently accessible locations in treatment areas, as illustrated in figure 97.2. The use of new devices, such as the needle-less access system for intravenous treatment and/or blood sampling has been shown to be a cost-effective method of reducing needlestick injuries (Yassi and McGill 1995).

Blood and body fluids are not the only source of infection for HCWs. Tuberculosis (TB) is also on the rise again in parts of the world where previously its spread had been curtailed and, as discussed later in this chapter, is a growing occupational health concern. In this, as in other nosocomial infections, such concern is heightened by the fact that so many of the organisms involved have become drug-resistant. There is also the problem of new outbreaks of deadly infectious agents, such as the Ebola virus. The article "Overview of infectious diseases" summarizes the major infectious disease risks for HCWs.

Chemical Hazards

HCWs are exposed to a wide variety of chemicals, including disinfectants, sterilants, laboratory reagents, drugs and anaesthetic agents, to name just a few of the categories. Figure 97.3 shows a storage cabinet in an area of a large hospital where prosthetics are fabricated and clearly illustrates the vast array of chemicals that are present in health care facilities. Some of these substances are highly irritating and may also be sensitizing. Some disinfectants and antiseptics also tend to be quite toxic, also with irritating and sensitizing propensities that may induce skin or respiratory tract disease. Some, like formaldehyde and ethylene oxide, are classi-

fied as mutagens, teratogens and human carcinogens as well. Prevention depends on the nature of the chemical, the maintenance of the apparatus in which it is used or applied, environmental controls, worker training and, in some instances, the availability of correct personal protective equipment. Often such control is straightforward and not very expensive. For example, Elias et al. (1993) showed how ethylene oxide exposure was controlled in one health care facility. Other articles in this chapter address chemical hazards and their management.

Physical Hazards and the Building Environment

In addition to the specific environmental contaminants faced by HCWs, many health care facilities also have documented indoor air quality problems. Tran et al. (1994), in studying symptoms experienced by operating room personnel, noted the presence of the "sick building syndrome" in one hospital. Building design and maintenance decisions are, therefore, extremely important in health care facilities. Particular attention must be paid to correct ventilation in specific areas such as laboratories, operating rooms and pharmacies, the availability of hoods and avoidance of the insertion of chemical-laden fumes into the general air-conditioning system. Controlling the recirculation of air and using special equipment (e.g., appropriate filters and ultraviolet lamps) is needed to prevent the transmission of air-borne infectious agents. Aspects of the construction and planning of health care facilities are discussed in the article "Buildings for health care facilities".

Physical hazards are also ubiquitous in hospitals (see "Exposure to physical agents" in this chapter). The wide variety of electrical equipment used in hospitals can present an electrocution hazard to patients and staff if not properly maintained and grounded (see figure 97.4). Especially in hot and humid environments, heat exposure may present a problem to workers in such areas as laundries, kitchens and boiler rooms. Ionizing radiation is a special concern for staff in diagnostic radiology (i.e., x ray, angiography, dental radiography and computerized axial tomography (CAT) scans) as well as for those in therapeutic radiology. Controlling such radiation exposures is a routine matter in designated departments where there is careful supervision, well-trained technicians and properly shielded and maintained equipment, but it can be a problem when portable equipment is used in emergency rooms, intensive care units and operating rooms. It can also be a problem to housekeeping and other support staff whose duties take them

Figure 97.3 • Storage cabinet for hazardous chemicals.

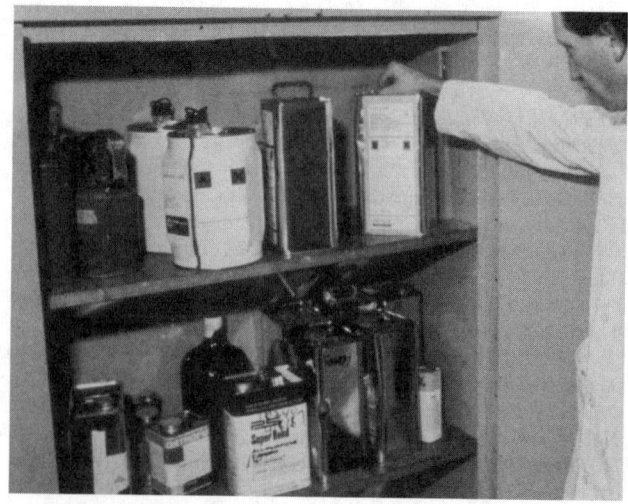

Health Sciences Centre, Winnipeg, Manitoba, Canada

Figure 97.4 • Electrical equipment in hospital.

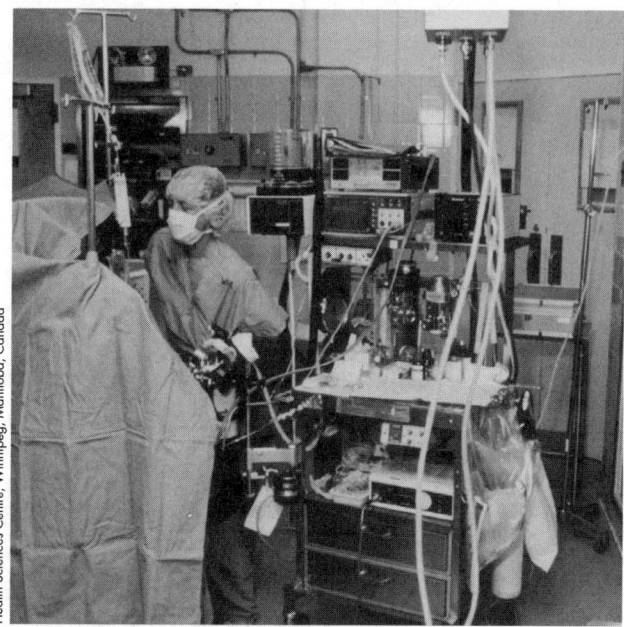

Health Sciences Centre, Winnipeg, Manitoba, Canada

Table 97.2 • 1995 integrated sound levels.

Area monitored	dBA (lex) Range
Cast room	76.32 to 81.9
Central energy	82.4 to 110.4
Nutrition and food services (main kitchen)	
Bakery	82.0
Cooking area	82.1
Pot wash	89.3
Stripper/dishwasher	81.6
Offices	<80
Cart drivers	85.3
Beltline	81.6
Tubefeed	88
Salad area	89.3
ICG	78.3
Garbage	87.4
Nutrition and food services (dishrooms)	
Oasis café	<80
Rehab kitchen	80
General	85.4 to 85.8
Courtyard café (runner)	89.6
Tunnel café — (runner)	82.2
— (dishroom)	80
Housekeeping	
Autoscrubbers	71.4 to 80.0
Burnishers	90.0 to 100.00
Laundry	
Dryer/washer	85.7 to 98.7
Flat ironers	83.3 to 89.7
Compressed air jets	79.4 to 86.5
Rough dry	83.5
Sewing room	81.8
Linen service	76.3 to 91.0
Mailroom	
Tubefeed	<80
Post meter	<80
Maintenance	
Carpentry	81.6 to 82.4
Mechanical	80.5 to 83.4
Grounds	84.4
Equipment and furnishings	80.4
Materials handling	
Carts	88 to 89
Print shop	
Copier	74.9 to 81.5
Press operator	80.7 to 90.0
Rehabilitation engineering	
Orthotics	80.0 to 94.3
Prosthetics	79.9
Machine shop	80.1 to 80.1

Note: "Lex" means the equivalent sound level or the steady sound level in dBA which, if present in a workplace for 8 hours, would contain the same acoustic energy.

into areas of potential exposure. In many jurisdictions these workers have not been properly trained to avoid this hazard. Exposure to ionizing radiation may also present a problem in diagnostic and therapeutic nuclear medicine units and in preparing and distributing doses of radioactive pharmaceuticals. In some cases, however, radiation exposure remains a serious problem (see the article "Occupational health and safety practice: The Russian experience" in this chapter).

Contradicting the prevailing impression of hospitals as quiet workplaces, Yassi et al. (1991) have documented the surprising extent of noise-induced hearing loss among hospital workers (see table 97.2. The articles "Control of physical hazards in health care facilities" and "Ergonomics of the physical work environment" in this chapter offer useful recommendations for controlling this hazard, as does table 97.3.

By far the most common and most costly type of injury faced by HCWs is back injury. Nurses and attendants are at greatest risk of musculoskeletal injuries due to the large amount of patient lifting and transferring that their jobs require. The epidemiology of back injury in nurses was summarized by Yassi et al. (1995a) with respect to one hospital. The pattern they observed mirrors those that have been universally reported. Hospitals are increasingly turning to preventive measures which may include staff training and the use of mechanical lifting devices. Many are also providing up-to-date diagnostic, therapeutic and rehabilitation health services that will minimize lost time and disability and are cost-effective (Yassi et al. 1995b). Hospital ergonomics has taken on increasing importance and, therefore, is the subject of a review article in this chapter. The specific problem of the prevention and management of back pain in nurses as one of the most important problems for this cohort of HCWs is also discussed in the article "Prevention and management of back pain in nurses" in this chapter. Table 97.4 lists the total number of injuries in a one-year period.

In discussing musculoskeletal and ergonomic problems, it is important to note that while those engaged in direct patient care may be at greatest risk (see figure 97.5) many of the support personnel in hospital must contend with similar ergonomic burdens (see figures 97.6 and 97.7). The ergonomic problems facing hospital laundry workers have been well-documented (Wands and Yassi 1993) (see figures 97.8, 97.9 and 97.10) and they also are common among dentists, otologists, surgeons and especially microsurgeons, obstetricians, gynaecologists and other health personnel who often must work in awkward postures.

Table 97.3 • Ergonomic noise reduction options.

Work area	Process	Control options
Central energy	General area	Enclose the source Personnel acoustic booth
Dietetics	Pot washer	Automate process Use sound barriers and deflectors Relocate
Housekeeping	Burnishing	Purchasing criteria
Laundry	Dryer/washer	Isolate and reduce vibration Use sound barriers and deflectors Relocate Damping materials Modify air jets Reposition machines
Mailroom	Tuberoom Stamp machine	Purchasing criteria Enclosure
Maintenance	Various equipment	Purchasing criteria Proper maintenance Relocation Damping materials
Materiel handling and transport/linen service	Carts	Maintenance Smoother floors Reduce vibration Damping materials
Print shop	Press operator	Maintenance Purchasing criteria Enclose source Relocate machines Sound barriers and deflectors
Rehabilitation engineering	Orthotics	Purchasing criteria Sound absorbing materials Sound barriers and deflectors

Organizational Problems

The article "Strain in health care work" contains a discussion of some of the organizational problems in hospitals and a summary of the principal findings of Leppanen and Olkinuora (1987), who reviewed Finnish and Swedish studies of stress among HCWs. With the rapid changes currently under way in this industry, the extent of alienation, frustration and burnout among HCWs is considerable. Added to that is the prevalence of staff abuse, an increasingly troublesome problem in many facilities (Yassi 1994). While it is often thought that the most difficult psychosocial problem faced by HCWs is dealing with death and dying, it is being recognized increasingly that the nature of the industry itself, with its hierarchical structure, its growing job insecurity and the high demands unsupported by adequate resources, is the cause of the variety of stress-related illness faced by HCWs.

The Nature of the Health Care Sector

In 1976, Stellman wrote, "If you ever wondered how people can manage to work with the sick and always stay healthy themselves, the answer is that they can't" (Stellman 1976). The answer has not changed, but the potential hazards have clearly expanded from infectious diseases, back and other injuries, stress and burnout to include a large variety of potentially toxic environmental, physical and psychosocial exposures. The world of the HCW continues to be largely unmonitored and largely unregulated. None the less, progress is being made in addressing occupational

Figure 97.5 • Patient lifting is an ergonomic hazard in most hospitals.

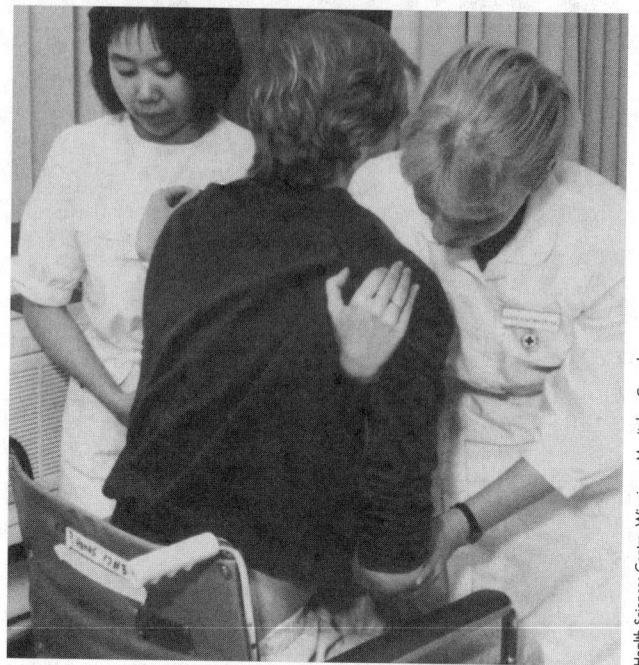

Health Sciences Centre, Winnipeg, Manitoba, Canada

health and safety hazards in hospitals. The International Commission on Occupational Health (ICOH) has a sub-committee addressing this problem, and several international conferences have been held with published proceedings that offer useful information (Hagberg et al. 1995). The US Centers for Disease Control and Prevention (CDC) and NIOSH have proposed guidelines to address many of the problems of the health care industry discussed in this article (e.g., see NIOSH 1988). The number of articles and books addressing health and safety issues for HCWs has been growing rapidly, and good overviews of health and

Figure 97.6 • Overhead painting: A typical ergonomic hazard for a tradesworker.

Health Sciences Centre, Winnipeg, Manitoba, Canada

Figure 97.7 • Cast-making involves many ergonomic stresses.

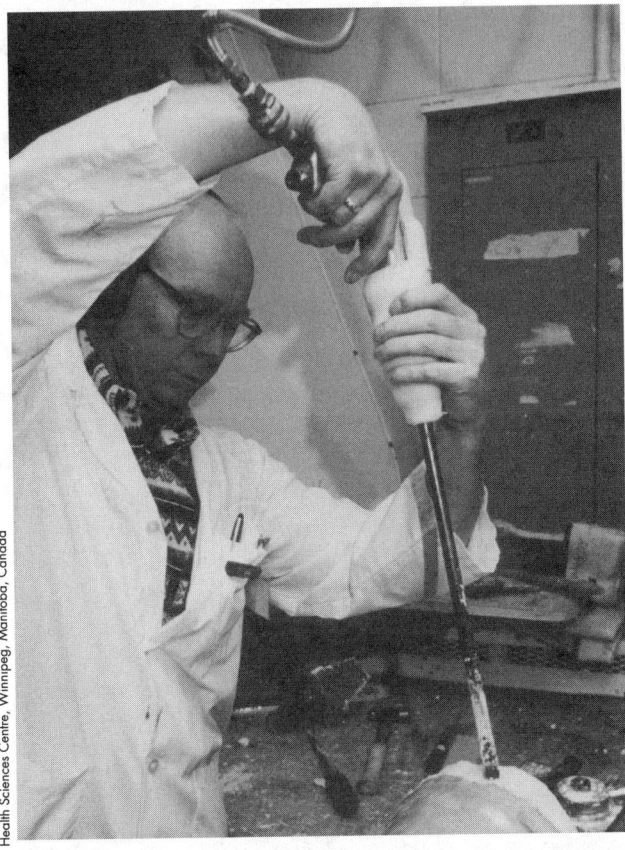

safety in the US health care industry have been published (e.g., Charney 1994; Lewy 1990; Sterling 1994). The need for systematic data collection, study and analysis regarding hazards in the health care industry and the desirability of assembling interdisci-

Figure 97.8 • Laundry work such as this can cause repetitive stress injury to the upper limbs.

Figure 97.9 • This laundry task requires working in an awkward position.

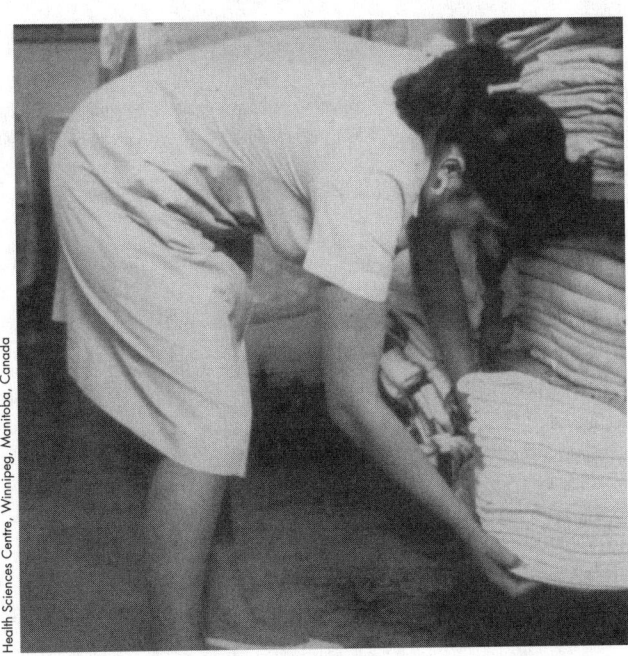

plinary occupational health teams to address them have become increasingly evident.

When considering occupational health and safety in the health care industry, it is crucial to appreciate the enormous changes currently taking place in it. Health care "reform", being instituted in most of the developed countries of the world, is creating extraor-

Figure 97.10 • A poorly designed laundry operation can cause back strain.

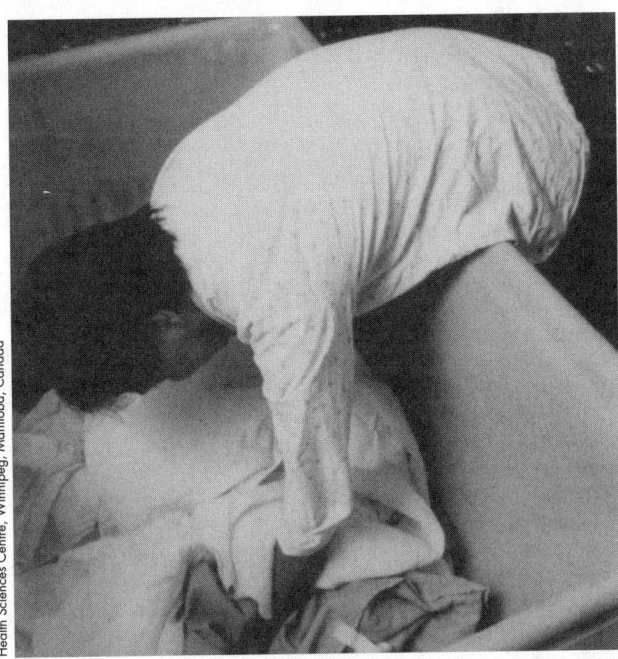

Table 97.4 • Total number of injuries, mechanism of injury and nature of injury (one hospital, all departments), 1 April 1994 to 31 March 1995.

Mechanism of injury	Nature of injury sustained												Total
	Blood/ body fluid	Cut/ laceration[1]	Bruise/ crush/ abrasion	Sprain/ strain	Fracture/ dislocation	Burn/ scald/ shock	Human bite	Broken glasses	Headaches/ breathing symptoms	Occupational conditions[2]	Other[3]	Unknown[4]	
Exertion													
Transferring patient				105									105
Lifting patient				83									83
Assisting patient				4									4
Turning patient				27									27
Breaking fall				28									28
Pushing equipment			1	25									26
Lifting equipment	1			52	1								54
Pulling equipment				14									14
Combination-equipment/ patient				38									38
Other				74									74
Fall		3	45	67	3			1					119
Struck/bumped/ poked		66	76	5				2		2	1		152
Caught in/ under/ between		13	68	8	1			1					91
Exp. hazardous substances		3	1			4			19	16	12		55
Staff abuse													
Patient	16	11	51	28			8	3		1	2		120
Visitor													0
Other													0
Spill/splashes (blood/body fluids)	80										1		81
Drug/immuniza- tion reaction											2		2
Exp. infectious diseases										5	5		10
Needlesticks	159	22											181
Scalpel cuts	34	14											48
Other[5]		3	1			29				1	6		40
Unknown (no accident reported)												8	8
Total	289	136	243	558	5	33	8	7	19	25	29	8	1,360

[1] No blood/body fluid.   [2] This includes rashes/dermatitis/work-related illness/burning eyes, irritated eyes.   [3] Exposure to chemical or physical agents but with no documented injuries affects.   [4] Accident not reported.   [5] Exposure to cold/heat, unknown.

dinary turbulence and uncertainty for HCWs, who are being asked to absorb rapid changes in their work tasks often with greater exposure to risks. The transformation of health care is spurred, in part, by advances in medical and scientific knowledge, the development of innovative technological procedures and the acquisition of new skills. It is also being driven, however, and perhaps to an even greater extent, by concepts of cost-effectiveness and organizational efficiency, in which "downsizing" and "cost control" have often seemed to become goals in themselves. New institutional incentives are being introduced at different organizational levels in different countries. The contracting out of jobs and services that had traditionally been carried out by a large stable workforce is now increasingly becoming the norm. Such contracting out of work is reported to have helped the health administrators and politicians achieve their long-term goal of making the process of health care more flexible and more accountable. These changes have also brought changes in roles that were previously rather well-defined, undermining the traditional hierarchical relationships among planners, administrators, physicians and other health professionals. The rise of investor-owned health care organizations in many countries has introduced a new dynamic in the financing and management of health services. In many situations, HCWs have been forced into new working relationships that involve such changes as downgrading services so that they can be performed by less-skilled workers at lower pay, reduced staffing levels, staff redeployments involving split shifts and part-time assignments. At the same time, there has been a slow but steady growth in the numbers of such physician surrogates as physician assistants, nurse practitioners, midwives and psychiatric social workers who command lower rates of pay than the physicians they are replacing. (The ultimate social and health costs both to HCWs and to the public, as patients and payers, is still to be determined.)

A growing trend in the US that is also emerging in the UK and northern European countries is "managed care". This generally involves the creation of organizations paid on a per capita basis by insurance companies or government agencies to provide or contract for the provision of a comprehensive range of health services to a voluntarily-enrolled population of subscribers. Their aim is to reduce the costs of health care by "managing" the process: using administrative procedures and primary care physicians as "gatekeepers" to control the utilization of expensive in-patient hospital days, reducing referrals to high-priced specialists and use of costly diagnostic procedures, and denying coverage for expensive new forms of "experimental" treatment. The growing popularity of these managed care systems, fuelled by aggressive marketing to employer- and government-sponsored groups and individuals, has made it difficult for physicians and other health care providers to resist becoming involved. Once engaged, there is a variety of financial incentives and disincentives to influence their judgement and condition their behaviour. The loss of their traditional autonomy has been particularly painful for many medical practitioners and has had a profound influence on their patterns of practice and their relationships with other HCWs.

These rapid changes in the organization of the health care industry are having profound direct and indirect effects on the health and safety of HCWs. They affect the ways health services are organized, managed, delivered and paid for. They affect the ways HCWs are trained, assigned and supervised and the extent to which considerations of their health and safety are addressed. This should be kept in mind as the various occupational health hazards faced by HCWs are discussed in this chapter. Finally, although it may not appear to be directly relevant to the content of this chapter, thought should be given to the implications of the well-being and performance of HCWs to the quality and effectiveness of the services they provide to their patients.

SOCIAL SERVICES

Susan Nobel

Overview of the Social Work Profession

Social workers function in a wide variety of settings and work with many different kinds of people. They work in community health centres, hospitals, residential treatment centres, substance-abuse programmes, schools, family service agencies, adoption and foster care agencies, day-care facilities and public and private child welfare organizations. Social workers often visit homes for interviews or inspections of home conditions. They are employed by businesses, labour unions, international aid organizations, human rights agencies, prisons and probation departments, agencies for the ageing, advocacy organizations, colleges and universities. They are increasingly entering politics. Many social workers have full- or part-time private practices as psychotherapists. It is a profession that seeks to "improve social functioning by the provision of practical and psychological help to people in need" (Payne and Firth-Cozens 1987).

Generally, social workers with doctorates work in community organization, planning, research, teaching or combined areas. Those with bachelor's degrees in social work tend to work in public assistance and with the elderly, mentally retarded and developmentally disabled; social workers with master's degrees are usually found in mental health, occupational social work and medical clinics (Hopps and Collins 1995).

Hazards and Precautions

Stress

Studies have shown that stress in the workplace is caused, or contributed to, by job insecurity, poor pay, work overload and lack of autonomy. All of these factors are features of the work life of social workers in the late 1990s. It is now accepted that stress is often a contributing factor to illness. One study has shown that 50 to 70% of all medical complaints among social workers are linked to stress (Graham, Hawkins and Blau 1983).

As the social work profession has attained vendorship privileges, managerial responsibilities and increased numbers in private practice, it has become more vulnerable to professional liability and malpractice suits in countries such as the United States which permit such legal actions, a fact which contributes to stress. Social workers are also increasingly dealing with bioethical issues—those of life and death, of research protocols, of organ transplantation and of resource allocation. Often there is inadequate support for the psychological toll confronting these issues can take on involved social workers. Increased pressures of high caseloads as well as increased reliance on technology makes for less human contact, a fact which is likely true for most professions, but particularly difficult for social workers whose choice of work is so related to having face to face contact.

In many countries, there has been a shift away from government-funded social programmes. This policy trend directly affects the social work profession. The values and goals generally held by social workers—full employment, a "safety net" for the poor, equal opportunity for advancement—are not supported by these current trends. The movement away from spending on programmes for the poor has produced what has been called an "upside-down welfare state" (Walz, Askerooth and Lynch 1983). One result of this, among others, has been increased stress for social workers. As resources decline, demand for services is on the rise; as the safety net frays, frustration and anger must rise, both for clients and for social workers themselves. Social workers may increasingly find themselves in conflict over respecting the values of the profession versus meeting statutory requirements. The code of ethics of the US National Association of Social Workers, for example, mandates confidentiality for clients which may be broken only when it is for "compelling professional reasons". Further, social workers are to promote access to resources in the interest of "securing or retaining social justice". The ambiguity of this could be quite problematic for the profession and a source of stress.

Violence

Work-related violence is a major concern for the profession. Social workers as problem-solvers on the most personal level are particularly vulnerable. They work with powerful emotions, and it is the relationship with their clients which becomes the focal point for expression of these emotions. Often, an underlying implication is that the client is unable to manage his or her own problems and needs the help of social workers to do so. The client may, in fact, be seeing social workers involuntarily, as, for example, in a child welfare setting where parental abilities are being evaluated. Cultural mores might also interfere with accepting offers of help from someone of another cultural background or sex (the preponderence of social workers are women) or outside of the immediate family. There may be language barriers, necessitating the use of translators. This can be distracting at least or even totally disruptive and may present a skewed picture of the situation at hand. These language barriers certainly affect the ease of communication, which is essential in this field. Further, social workers may work in locations which are in high-crime areas, or the work might take them into the "field" to visit clients who live in those areas.

Application of safety procedures is uneven in social agencies, and, in general, insufficient attention has been paid to this area. Prevention of violence in the workplace implies training, managerial procedures and modifications of the physical environment and/or communication systems (Breakwell 1989).

A curriculum for safety has been suggested (Griffin 1995) which would include:

- training in constructive use of authority
- crisis intervention
- field and office safety
- physical plant set-up
- general prevention techniques
- ways to predict potential violence.

Other Hazards

Because social workers are employed in such a variety of settings, they are exposed to many of the hazards of the workplace discussed elsewhere in this *Encyclopaedia*. Mention should be made, however, that these hazards include buildings with poor or unclean air flow ("sick buildings") and exposures to infection. When funding is scarce, maintenance of physical plants suffers and risk of exposure increases. The high percentage of social workers in hospital and out-patient medical settings suggests vulnerability to infection exposure. Social workers see patients with conditions like hepatitis, tuberculosis and other highly contagious diseases as well as human immunodeficiency virus (HIV) infection. In response to this risk for all health workers, training and measures for infection control are necessary and have been mandated in many countries. The risk, however, persists.

It is evident that some of the problems faced by social workers are inherent in a profession which is so centred on lessening human suffering as well as one which is so affected by changing social and political climates. At the end of the twentieth century, the profession of social work finds itself in a state of flux. The values, ideals and rewards of the profession are also at the heart of the hazards it presents to its practitioners.

HOME CARE WORKERS: THE NEW YORK CITY EXPERIENCE

Lenora Colbert

Massive use of home care workers in New York City began in 1975 as a response to the needs of the growing population of chronically ill and frail elderly and as an alternative to more expensive care in nursing homes, many of which had long lists of such people waiting for admission. Additionally, it allowed for more personal assistance at a time when nursing homes were perceived as impersonal and uncaring. It also provided entry-level employment to unskilled individuals, mostly women, many of whom were recipients of welfare.

Initially, these workers were employees of the City's Department of Human Resources but, in 1980, this service was "privatized" and they were recruited, trained and employed by non-profit, community-based social agencies and traditional health care organizations such as hospitals which had to be certified by the State of New York as providers of home care services. The workers are categorized as home makers, personal care workers, health aides, home care attendants and housekeepers, depending on their levels of skills and the kinds of services they provide. Which of these services a particular client uses depends on an evaluation of that person's health status and needs which is conducted by a licensed health professional, such as a physician, nurse or social worker.

The Home Care Workforce

Home care workers in New York City present a conglomerate of characteristics that provide a unique profile. A recent survey by Donovan, Kurzman and Rotman (1993) found that 94% are female with an average age of 45. About 56% were not born within the continental US and about 51% never completed high school. Only 32% were identified as married, 33% were separated or divorced and 26% were single, while 86% have children, 44% with children under 18 years of age. According to the survey, 63% live with their children and 26% live with a spouse.

The median family income for this group in 1991 was $12,000 per year. In 81% of these families, the home care worker was the primary breadwinner. In 1996, the annual salary of full-time home care workers' ranged between $16,000 and $28,000; part-time workers earned less.

Such low earnings represent significant economic hardship to the survey respondents: 56% said they could not afford adequate housing; 61% reported being unable to afford furniture or household equipment; 35% said they lacked funds to purchase enough food for their families; and 36% were ineligible for Medicare and unable to afford needed medical care for themselves and their families. As a group, their financial status will inevitably worsen as cuts in government funding force curtailment of the amount and intensity of home care services being provided.

Home Care Services

The services provided by home care workers depend on the needs of the clients being served. Those with greater disability require assistance with the "basic activities of daily living", which consist of bathing, dressing, toileting, transferring (moving in or out of bed and chairs) and feeding. Those with higher levels of functional capacity need help with the "instrumental activities of daily living", which comprise housekeeping (cleaning, bed making, dishwashing, and so forth), shopping, food preparation and serving, laundry, using public or private transportation and managing finances. Home care workers may give injections, dispense medications and provide such treatments as passive exercise and massage as prescribed by the client's physician. A most appreciated service is companionship and assisting the client to participate in recreational activities.

The difficulty of the home care worker's job is directly related to the home environment and, in addition to physical status, the behaviour of the client and any family members who may be on the scene. Many clients (and the workers as well) live in poor neighbourhoods where crime rates are high, public transportation often marginal and public services substandard. Many live in deteriorated housing with no or non-functioning elevators, dark and dirty stairwells and hallways, lack of heat and hot water, dilapidated plumbing and poorly functioning household appliances. Commuting to and from the client's home may be arduous and time-consuming.

Many of the clients may have very low levels of functional capacity and require assistance at every turn. Clients' muscle weakness and lack of coordination, loss of vision and hearing and incontinence of bladder and/or bowels add to the burden of care. Mental difficulties such as senile dementia, anxiety and depression and difficulties in communication because of memory loss and language barriers may also magnify the difficulty. Finally, abusive and demanding behaviour on the part of both clients and their family members may sometimes escalate into acts of violence.

Home Care Work Hazards

Work hazards commonly encountered by home care workers include:

- working alone without assistance
- lack of education and training and remote, if any, supervision
- working in substandard housing in high risk neighbourhoods
- back pain and musculoskeletal injuries incurred while lifting, transferring and supporting clients who may be heavy, weak and poorly coordinated
- violence in the home and in the neighbourhood
- infectious diseases (the health care worker may not have been fully informed of the client's medical status; recommended gloves, gowns and masks may not be available)
- household chemicals and cleaning supplies (often incorrectly labelled and stored)
- sexual harassment
- work stress.

Stress is probably the most ubiquitous hazard. It is compounded by the fact the worker is usually alone in the home with the client with no simple way to report trouble or summon assistance. Stress is being exacerbated as cost-containment efforts are reducing the hours of service allowed for individual clients.

Prevention Strategies

A number of strategies have been suggested to promote occupational health and safety for home care workers and to improve their lot. They include:

- development and promulgation of standards of practice for home care accompanied by improved education and training so that home care workers can meet them
- education and training in the recognition and avoidance of chemical and other hazards in the home
- training in lifting, carrying and giving physical support to clients as needed in the course of providing services
- preliminary needs assessment of clients supplemented by inspections of their homes so that potential hazards can be identified and eliminated or controlled and needed materials and equipment can be procured
- periodic meetings with supervisors and other home care workers to compare notes and receive instruction. Videotapes may be developed and used for skills demonstrations. The meetings

---

Case study: Violence in health care work

A psychotic patient in his thirties had been forcibly committed to a large psychiatric hospital in the suburbs of a city. He was not regarded as having violent tendencies. After a few days he escaped from his secure ward. The hospital authorities were informed by his relatives that he had returned to his own house. As was routine an escort of three male psychiatric nurses set out with an ambulance to bring the patient back. En route they stopped to pick up a police escort as was routine in such cases. When they arrived at the house, the police escort waited outside, in case a violent incident developed. The three nurses entered and were informed by the relatives that the patient was sitting in an upstairs bedroom. When approached and quietly invited to come back to hospital for treatment the patient produced a kitchen knife which he had hidden. One nurse was stabbed in the chest, another a number of times in the back and the third in the hand and the arm. All three nurses survived but had to spend time in hospital. When the police escort entered the bedroom the patient quietly surrendered the knife.

Daniel Murphy

---

may be supplemented by telephone networks through which workers may communicate with each other to exchange information and alleviate any feelings of isolation.

- establishment of a health and safety committee within each agency to review work-related accidents and problems and develop appropriate preventive interventions
- establishment of an Employee Assistance Programme (EAP) through which the workers may receive counselling for their own psychosocial problems both on- and off-the-job.

Educational and training sessions should be conducted during working hours at a place and time convenient for the workers. They should be supplemented by the distribution of instructional materials designed for the low educational levels of most of the workers and, when necessary, they should be multilingual.

OCCUPATIONAL HEALTH AND SAFETY PRACTICE: THE RUSSIAN EXPERIENCE

Valery P. Kaptsov and Lyudmila P. Korotich

The work of people in the medical profession has great social value, and in recent years the urgent problem of the labour conditions and the state of health of HCWs has been studied actively. However, the nature of this work is such that any preventive and ameliorating measures cannot eliminate or reduce the main source of the hazards in the work of physicians and other HCWs: contact with a sick patient. In this respect the problem of prevention of occupational illness in medical workers is rather complicated.

In many cases the diagnostic and medical equipment and the methods of treatment used in medical institutions can affect the health of HCWs. Therefore, it is necessary to follow hygienic standards and precautionary measures to control the levels of exposure to unfavourable factors. Studies carried out in a number of Russian medical institutions have revealed that the labour conditions at many workplaces were not optimum and could induce the deterioration of the health of medical and support personnel, and sometimes cause the development of occupational diseases.

Among the physical factors that can substantially affect the health of medical personnel in the Russian Federation, ionizing radiation should be ranked as one of the first. Tens of thousands of Russian medical workers encounter sources of ionizing radiation at work. In the past, special laws were adopted to limit the doses and levels of irradiation at which specialists could work for a long period without health risk. In recent years x-ray control procedures were extended to cover not only radiologists, but surgeons, anaesthetists, traumatologists, rehabilitation specialists and mid-level personnel. The levels of radiation at worksites and the x-ray doses received by these individuals sometimes are even higher than the doses received by the radiologists and radiology laboratory assistants.

Instruments and equipment generating non-ionizing radiation and ultrasound are also widespread in modern medicine. Since many physiotherapy procedures are used precisely because of the therapeutic benefits of such treatment, the same biological effects may be hazardous to those involved in administering them. Persons encountering instruments and machines generating non-ionizing radiation are often reported to have functional disturbances in the nervous and cardiovascular systems.

Studies of working conditions where ultrasound is used for diagnostic or therapeutic procedures revealed that the personnel were exposed during as much as 85 to 95% of their working day to levels of high frequency, low intensity ultrasound comparable to the exposures experienced by operators of industrial ultrasonic defectoscopy. They experienced such impairments of the peripheral neuro-vascular system as angiodistonic syndrome, vegetative polyneuritis, vegetative vascular malfunction and so on.

Noise is rarely reported as a substantial factor of occupational risk in the work of Russian medical personnel, except at dental institutions. When using high-speed drills (200,000 to 400,000 rev/min) the maximum energy of the sound falls at a frequency of 800 Hz. The noise levels at a distance of 30 cm from the drill placed in the mouth of the patient vary from 80 to 90 dBA. One-third of the whole sound spectrum falls within the range most harmful to the ear (i.e., between 1000 and 2000 Hz).

Many noise sources gathered in one place can generate levels exceeding permissible limits. To create optimum conditions it is recommended that anaesthetizing machines, respiratory equipment and artificial blood circulation pumps be taken out of operating rooms.

In surgery departments, especially in operating rooms and in rehabilitation and intensive care departments, as well as in some other special rooms, it is necessary to maintain the required parameters of temperature, humidity and air circulation. The optimal layout of modern medical institutions and the installation of ventilation and air-conditioning plants provide the favourable microclimate. However, in operating suites built without optimal planning, occlusive clothing (i.e., gowns, masks, caps and gloves) and exposure to heat from lighting and other equipment lead many surgeons and other members of the operating teams to complain of "overheating". Perspiration is mopped from surgeons' brows lest it interfere with their vision or contaminate the tissues in the surgical field.

As a result of the introduction into medical practice of treatment in hyperbaric chambers, physicians and nurses now are often exposed to heightened atmospheric pressure. In most cases this affects surgical teams performing operations in such chambers. Exposure to conditions of increased atmospheric pressure is believed to lead to unfavourable changes in a number of body functions, depending on the level of the pressure and the duration of the exposure.

Working posture is also of great importance for physicians. Although most tasks are performed in sitting or standing positions, some activities require long periods in awkward and uncomfortable positions. This is particularly the case with dentists, otologists, surgeons (especially microsurgeons), obstetricians, gynaecologists and physiotherapists. Work requiring long periods of standing in one position has been associated with the development of varicose veins in the legs and haemorrhoids.

Continual, intermittent or casual exposure to potentially hazardous chemicals used in medical institutions also can affect medical personnel. Among these chemicals, inhalation anaesthetics are considered to have the most unfavourable influence on humans. These gases can accumulate in large amounts not only in operating and delivery rooms but also in pre-op areas where anaesthesia is induced and in recovery rooms where they are exhaled by patients coming out of anaesthesia. Their concentration depends on the content of the gas mixtures being administered, the type of equipment being used and the duration of the procedure. Concentrations of anaesthetic gases in the breathing zones of surgeons and anaesthetists in the operating room have been found ranging from 2 to 14 times the maximum allowable concentration (MAC). Exposure to anaesthetic gases has been associated with impaired reproductive capacity of both male and female anaesthetists and abnormalities in the foetuses of pregnant female anaesthetists and the spouses of male anaesthetists (see chapter *Reproductive system* and the article "Waste anaesthetic gases" in this chapter).

In the treatment rooms where many injections are performed, the concentration of a medicine in the respiration zone of nurses can exceed permissible levels. Airborne drug exposure can happen when washing and sterilizing syringes, removing air bubbles from a syringe, and while dispensing aerosol therapy.

Among chemicals which could affect the health of medical personnel are hexachlorophene (possibly causing teratogenic effects), formalin (an irritant, sensitizer and carcinogen), ethylene oxide (which has toxic, mutagenic and carcinogenic characteristics), antibiotics that cause allergies and suppressed immune response, vitamins and hormones. There is also the possibility of exposure to industrial chemicals used in cleaning and maintenance work and as insecticides.

Many of the drugs used in the treatment of cancer are themselves mutagenic and carcinogenic. Special training programmes have been developed to prevent workers involved in preparing and administering them from exposure to such cytotoxic agents.

One of the features of job assignments of medical workers of many specialties is contact with infected patients. Any infectious disease incurred as a result of such contact is considered to be an occupational one. Viral serum hepatitis has proved to be the most dangerous for the staff of medical institutions. Viral hepatitis infections of laboratory assistants (from examining blood samples), staff members of haemodialysis departments, pathologists, surgeons, anaesthetists and other specialists who had occupational contact with the blood of infected patients have been reported (see the article "Prevention of occupational transmission of blood-borne pathogens" in this chapter).

There has apparently been no recent improvement in the health status of HCWs in the Russian Federation. The proportion of cases of work-related, temporary disability remained at the level of 80 to 96 per 100 working doctors and 65 to 75 per 100 mid-level medical workers. Although this measure of work loss is quite high, it should also be noted that self-treatment and informal, unreported treatment are widespread among HCWs, which means that many cases are not captured by the official statistics. This was confirmed by a survey among physicians which found that 40% of the respondents were ill four times a year or more but did not apply to a practising physician for medical care and did not submit a disability form. These data were corroborated by medical examinations which found evidence of disability in 127.35 cases per 100 workers examined.

Morbidity also increases with age. In these examinations, it was six times more frequent among HCWs with 25 years of service than among those with less than 5 years of service. The most common diseases included circulatory impairments (27.9%), diseases of the digestive organs (20.0%) and musculoskeletal disorders (20.72%). Except for the last, most of the cases were non-occupational in origin.

Sixty per cent of doctors and 46% of mid-level personnel were found to have chronic diseases. Many of these were directly associated with job assignments.

Many of the observed diseases were directly associated with job assignments of those examined. Thus, microsurgeons working in an awkward posture were found to have frequent osteochondroses; chemotherapists were found to suffer frequently from chromosome abnormalities and anaemia; nurses who were in contact with a large variety of medicines suffered various allergic diseases, ranging from dermatoses to bronchial asthma and immunodeficiency.

In Russia, health problems of medical workers were first addressed in the 1920s. In 1923 a special scientific-consultative bureau was founded in Moscow; the results of its studies were published in five collections entitled *Labour and Life of Medical Workers of Moscow and Moscow Province*. Since that time other studies have appeared devoted to this problem. But this work has been carried on in the most fruitful way only since 1975, when the Laboratory of Labour Hygiene of Medical Workers was established in the RAMS Institute of Occupational Health, which coordinated all the studies of this problem. After analysis of the then-current situation, research was directed at:

- studies of the features of labour processes in the main medical specialties
- assessment of the factors of the occupational environment
- analysis of the morbidity of medical workers
- elaboration of measures for optimization of labour conditions, reduction of fatigue and prevention of morbidity.

Based on the studies carried out by the Laboratory and other institutions, a number of recommendations and suggestions were prepared, aimed at reduction and prevention of the occupational diseases of medical workers.

Instructions were established for pre-employment and periodic medical examinations of health care workers. The aim of these examinations was to determine the fitness of the worker for the job and to prevent common and occupational diseases as well as occupational accidents. A list of hazardous and dangerous factors in the work of medical personnel was prepared which included recommendations for frequency of examinations, the range of specialists to take part in the examinations, the number of labora-

tory and functional studies as well as a list of medical contra-indications for work with a specific hazardous occupational factor. For every studied group there was a list of occupational diseases, enumerating the nosological forms, approximate list of job assignments and hazardous factors which can cause the respective occupational conditions.

In order to control the working conditions in treatment and prevention institutions, a Certificate of Sanitary and Technical Conditions of Labour in the health care institutions was developed. The certificate can be used as a guide for conducting sanitary measures and improvement of labour safety. For an institution to complete the certificate, it is necessary to carry out a study, with the help of specialists in sanitary service and other respective organizations, of the general situation in the departments, rooms and wards, to measure the levels of health and safety hazards.

Departments of hygiene of the preventive medicine institutions have been established in the modern centres of sanitary-epidemic inspections. The mission of these departments includes perfecting measures for the prevention of nosocomial infections and their complications in hospitals, creating optimal conditions for treatment and protecting the safety and health of HCWs. Public health doctors and their assistants conduct the preventive monitoring of design and construction of buildings for health care institutions. They see to the compliance of the new premises with the climate conditions, required arrangement of worksites, comfortable labour conditions and systems of rest and nutrition during the work shifts (see the article "Buildings for health care facilities" in this chapter). They also control technical documentation for the new equipment, technological procedures and chemicals. The routine sanitary inspection includes the monitoring of the occupational factors at the worksites and accumulation of the received data in the above-mentioned Certificate of Sanitary and Technical Conditions of Labour. Quantitative measurement of working conditions and prioritization of health improvement measures are established according to hygienic criteria for assessments of labour conditions which are based on indicators of the hazard and danger of labour environment factors and the heaviness and intensity of the working process. The frequency of laboratory studies is determined by the specific needs of each case. Each study usually includes measurement and analysis of microclimate parameters; measurement of indicators of air environment (e.g., content of bacteria and hazardous substances); assessment of the effectiveness of ventilation systems; assessment of the levels of natural and artificial illumination; and measurement of noise levels, ultrasound, ionizing radiation and so on. It is also recommended that time-keeping monitoring of the exposures of the unfavourable factors be conducted, based on the guideline documents.

According to instructions of the Russian government, and in keeping with current existing practice, the hygienic and medical standards should be revised following the accumulation of new data.

ERGONOMICS AND HEALTH CARE

● HOSPITAL ERGONOMICS: A REVIEW

Madeleine R. Estryn-Béhar

Ergonomics is an applied science that deals with the adaptation of work and the workplace to the characteristics and capabilities of the worker so that he or she may perform the duties of the job effectively and safely. It addresses the worker's physical capacities in relation

to the physical requirements of the job (e.g., strength, endurance, dexterity, flexibility, ability to tolerate positions and postures, visual and auditory acuity) as well as his or her mental and emotional status in relation to the way the work is organized (e.g., work schedules, workload and work-related stress). Ideally, adaptations are made to the furniture, equipment and tools used by the worker and to the work environment to enable the worker to perform adequately without risk to himself/herself, co-workers and the public. Occasionally, it is necessary to improve the worker's adaptation to the job through, for example, special training and the use of personal protective equipment.

Since the mid 1970s, the application of ergonomics to hospital workers has broadened. It is directed now at those involved in direct patient care (e.g., physicians and nurses), those involved in ancillary services (e.g., technicians, laboratory staff, pharmacists and social workers) and those providing support services (e.g., administrative and clerical personnel, food service staff, housekeeping staff, maintenance workers and security staff).

Extensive research has been conducted into the ergonomics of hospitalization, with most studies attempting to identify the extent to which hospital administrators should allow hospital personnel latitude in developing strategies to reconcile an acceptable workload with good quality of care. Participatory ergonomics has become increasingly widespread in hospitals in recent years. More specifically, wards have been reorganized on the basis of ergonomic analyses of activity undertaken in collaboration with medical and paramedical personnel, and participatory ergonomics has been used as the basis for the adaptation of equipment for use in health care.

In studies of hospital ergonomics, workstation analysis must extend at least to the departmental level—the distance between rooms and the amount and location of equipment are all crucial considerations.

Physical strain is one of the primary determinants of the health of HCWs and the quality of care that they dispense. This being said, the frequent interruptions that hinder care-giving and the effect of psychological factors associated with confrontations with serious illness, ageing and death must also be addressed. Accounting for all these factors is a difficult task, but approaches focusing only on single factors will fail to improve either working conditions or the quality of care. Similarly, patients' perception of the quality of their hospital stay is determined by the effectiveness of the care they receive, their relationship with physicians and other personnel, the food and the architectural environment.

Basic to hospital ergonomics is study of the sum and interaction of personal factors (e.g., fatigue, fitness, age and training) and circumstantial factors (e.g., work organization, schedule, floor layout, furniture, equipment, communication and psychological support within the work team), which combine to affect the performance of work. Precise identification of the actual work performed by health care workers depends on ergonomic observation of entire workdays and collection of valid and objective information on the movements, postures, cognitive performance and emotional control called upon to satisfy work requirements. This helps to detect factors that may interfere with effective, safe, comfortable and healthy work. This approach also sheds light on the potential for workers' suffering or taking pleasure in their work. Final recommendations must take the interdependence of the various professional and ancillary personnel attending the same patient into account.

These considerations lay the groundwork for further, specific research. Analysis of strain related to the use of basic equipment (e.g., beds, meal carts and mobile x-ray equipment) may help clarify the conditions of acceptable use. Measurements of lighting levels may be complemented by information on the size and contrast of medication labels, for example. Where alarms emitted by different intensive-care-unit equipment can be confused, analysis of their acoustic spectrum may prove useful. Computerization of patient charts should not be undertaken unless the formal and informal information-support structures have been analysed. The interdependence of the various elements of the work environment of any given caregiver should therefore always be borne in mind when analysing isolated factors.

Analysis of the interaction of different factors influencing care—physical strain, cognitive strain, affective strain, scheduling,

ambience, architecture and hygiene protocols—is essential. It is important to adapt schedules and common work areas to the needs of the work team when attempting to improve overall patient management. Participatory ergonomics is a way of using specific information to bring about wide-ranging and relevant improvements to the quality of care and to working life. Involving all categories of personnel in key stages of the search for solution helps ensure that the modifications finally adopted will have their full support.

Working Postures

Epidemiological studies of joint and musculoskeletal disorders. Several epidemiological studies have indicated that inappropriate postures and handling techniques are associated with a doubling of the number of back, joint and muscle problems requiring treatment and time off the job. This phenomenon, discussed in greater detail elsewhere in this chapter and *Encyclopaedia*, is related to physical and cognitive strain.

Working conditions differ from country to country. Siegel et al. (1993) compared conditions in Germany and Norway and found that 51% of German nurses, but only 24% of Norwegian nurses, suffered lower-back pain on any given day. Working conditions in the two countries differed; however, in German hospitals, the patient-nurse ratio was twice as high and the number of adjustable-height beds half that in Norwegian hospitals, and fewer nurses had patient handling equipment (78% versus 87% in Norwegian hospitals).

Epidemiological studies of pregnancy and its outcome. Because the hospital workforce is usually predominantly female, the influence of work on pregnancy often becomes an important issue (see articles on pregnancy and work elsewhere in this *Encyclopaedia*). Saurel-Cubizolles et al. (1985) in France, for example, studied 621 women who returned to hospital work after giving birth and found that a higher rate of premature births were associated with heavy housekeeping chores (e.g., cleaning windows and floors), carrying heavy loads and long periods of standing. When these tasks were combined, the rate of premature births was increased: 6% when only one of these factors was involved and up to 21% when two or three were involved. These differences remained significant after adjustment for seniority, social and demographic characteristics and professional level. These factors were also associated with a higher frequency of contractions, more hospital admissions during pregnancy and, on average, longer sick leave.

In Sri Lanka, Senevirane and Fernando (1994) compared 130 pregnancies borne by 100 nursing officers and 126 by clerical workers whose jobs presumably were more sedentary; socio-economic backgrounds and use of prenatal care were similar for both groups. Odds-ratios for complications of pregnancy (2.18) and preterm delivery (5.64) were high among nursing officers.

Ergonomic Observation of Workdays

The effect of physical strain on health care workers has been demonstrated through continuous observation of workdays. Research in Belgium (Malchaire 1992), France (Estryn-Béhar and Fouillot 1990a) and Czechoslovakia (Hubacova, Borsky and Strelka 1992) has shown that health care workers spend 60 to 80% of their workday standing (see table 97.5). Belgian nurses were observed to spend approximately 10% of their workday bent over; Czechoslovakian nurses spent 11% of their workday positioning patients; and French nurses spent 16 to 24% of their workday in uncomfortable positions, such as stooping or squatting, or with their arms raised or loaded.

In France, night-shift nurses spent somewhat more time sitting, but they end their shift by making beds and dispensing care, both

Table 97.5 • Distribution of nurses' time in three studies.

	Czechoslovakia	Belgium	France
Authors	Hubacova, Borsky and Strelka 1992[1]	Malchaire 1992[2]	Estryn-Béhar and Fouillot 1990a[3]
Departments	5 medical and surgical departments	Cardiovascular surgery	10 medical and surgical departments
Average time for the main postures and total distance walked by nurses:			
Per cent working hours standing and walking	76%	Morning 61% Afternoon 77% Night 58%	Morning 74% Afternoon 82% Night 66%
Including stooping, squatting, arms raised, loaded	11%		Morning 16% Afternoon 30% Night 24%
Standing flexed		Morning 11% Afternoon 9% Night 8%	
Distance walked		Morning 4 km Afternoon 4 km Night 7 km	Morning 7 km Afternoon 6 km Night 5 km
Per cent working hours with patients	Three shifts: 47%	Morning 38% Afternoon 31% Night 26%	Morning 24% Afternoon 30% Night 27%

Number of observations per shift: [1] 74 observations on 3 shifts. [2] Morning: 10 observations (8 h); afternoon: 10 observations (8 h); night: 10 observations (11 h). [3] Morning: 8 observations (8 h); afternoon: 10 observations (8 h); night: 9 observations (10–12 h).

of which involve work in uncomfortable positions. They are assisted in this by a nurses' aide, but this should be contrasted with the situation during the morning shift, where these tasks are usually performed by two nurses' aides. In general, nurses working day shifts spend less time in uncomfortable positions. Nurses' aides were on their feet constantly, and uncomfortable positions, due largely to inadequate equipment, accounted for 31% (afternoon shift) to 46% (morning shift) of their time. Patient facilities in these French and Belgian teaching hospitals were spread out over large areas and consisted of rooms containing one to three beds. Nurses in these wards walked an average of 4 to 7 km per day.

Detailed ergonomic observation of entire workdays (Estryn-Béhar and Hakim-Serfaty 1990) is useful in revealing the interaction of the factors that determine quality of care and the manner in which work is performed. Consider the very different situations in a paediatric intensive care unit and a rheumatology ward. In paediatric resuscitation units, the nurse spends 71% of her time in patients' rooms, and each patient's equipment is kept on individual carts stocked by nurses' aides. The nurses in this ward change location only 32 times per shift, walking a total of 2.5 km. They are able to communicate with physicians and other nurses in the adjoining lounge or nurses' station through intercoms which have been installed in all the patients' rooms.

By contrast, the nursing station in the rheumatology ward is very far from patients' rooms, and care preparation is lengthy (38% of shift time). As a result, the nurses spend only 21% of their time in patients' rooms and change location 128 times per shift, walking a total of 17 km. This clearly illustrates the interrelationship between physical strain, back problems and organizational and psychological factors. Because they need to move rapidly and get equipment and information, nurses only have time for hallway consultations—there is no time to sit while dispensing care, listen to patients and give patients personalized and integrated responses.

Continuous observation of 18 Dutch nurses in long-term-stay wards revealed that they spent 60% of their time performing physically demanding work with no direct contact with their patients (Engels, Senden and Hertog 1993). Housekeeping and preparation account for most of the 20% of the time described as spent in "slightly hazardous" activities. In all, 0.2% of shift time was spent in postures requiring immediate modification and 1.5% of shift time in postures requiring rapid modification. Contact with patients was the type of activity most frequently associated with these hazardous postures. The authors recommend modifying patient-handling practices and other less hazardous but more frequent tasks.

Given the physiological strain of the work of nurses' aides, continuous measurement of heart rate is a useful complement to observation. Raffray (1994) used this technique to identify arduous housekeeping tasks and recommended not restricting personnel to this type of task for the whole day.

Electro-myographical (EMG) fatigue analysis is also interesting when body posture must remain more or less static—for example, during operations using an endoscope (Luttman et al. 1996).

Influence of architecture, equipment and organization

The inadequacy of nursing equipment, particularly beds, in 40 Japanese hospitals was demonstrated by Shindo (1992). In addition, patients' rooms, both those lodging six to eight patients and single rooms reserved for the very ill, were poorly laid out and extremely small. Matsuda (1992) reported that these observations should lead to improvements in the comfort, safety and efficiency of nursing work.

In a French study (Saurel 1993), the size of patient rooms was problematic in 45 of 75 medium- and long-term-stay wards. The most common problems were:

- lack of space (30 wards)
- difficulty in manoeuvring patient-transfer gurneys (17)

- inadequate space for furniture (13)
- the need to take beds out of the room to transfer patients (12)
- difficult access and poor furniture layout (10)
- doors that were too small (8)
- difficulty moving between beds (8).

The mean available area per bed for patients and nurses is at the root of these problems and decreases as the number of beds per room increases: 12.98 m², 9.84 m², 9.60 m², 8.49 m² and 7.25 m² for rooms with one, two, three, four and more than four beds. A more accurate index of the useful area available to personnel is obtained by subtracting the area occupied by the beds themselves (1.8 to 2.0 m²) and by other equipment. The French Department of Health prescribes a useful surface area of 16 m² for single rooms and 22 m² for double rooms. The Quebec Department of Health recommends 17.8 m² and 36 m², respectively.

Turning to factors favouring the development of back problems, variable-height mechanisms were present on 55.1% of the 7,237 beds examined; of these, only 10.3% had electric controls. Patient-transfer systems, which reduce lifting, were rare. These systems were systematically used by 18.2% of the 55 responding wards, with over half the wards reporting using them "rarely" or "never". "Poor" or "rather poor" manoeuvrability of meal carts was reported by 58.5% of 65 responding wards. There was no periodic maintenance of mobile equipment in 73.3% of 72 responding wards.

In almost half the responding wards, there were no rooms with seats that nurses could use. In many cases, this appears to have been due to the small size of the patient rooms. Sitting was usually possible only in the lounges—in 10 units, the nursing station itself had no seats. However, 13 units reported having no lounge and 4 units used the pantry for this purpose. In 30 wards, there were no seats in this room.

According to statistics for 1992 provided by the Confederation of Employees of the Health Services Employees of the United Kingdom (COHSE), 68.2% of nurses felt that there were not enough mechanical patient lifts and handling aides and 74.5% felt that they were expected to accept back problems as a normal part of their work.

In Quebec, the Joint Sectoral Association, Social Affairs Sector (Association pour la santé et la sécurité du travail, secteur afffaires sociales, ASSTAS) initiated its "Prevention-Planning-Renovation-Construction" project in 1993 (Villeneuve 1994). Over 18 months, funding for almost 100 bipartite projects, some costing several million dollars, was requested. This programme's goal is to maximize investments in prevention by addressing health and safety concerns early in the design stage of planning, renovation and design projects.

The association completed the modification of the design specifications for patient rooms in long-term-care units in 1995. After noting that three-quarters of occupational accidents involving nurses occur in patient rooms, the association proposed new dimensions for patients' rooms, and new rooms must now provide a minimum amount of free space around beds and accommodate patient lifts. Measuring 4.05 by 4.95 m, the rooms are more square than the older, rectangular rooms. To improve performance, ceiling-mounted patient lifts were installed, in collaboration with the manufacturer.

The association is also working on the modification of construction standards for washrooms, where many occupational accidents also occur, although to a lesser extent than in the rooms themselves. Finally, the feasibility of applying anti-skid coatings (with a coefficient of friction above the minimum standard of 0.50) on floors is being studied, since patient autonomy is best promoted by providing a non-skid surface on which neither they nor nurses can slip.

Evaluation of equipment that reduces physical strain

Proposals for improving beds (Teyssier-Cotte, Rocher and Mereau 1987) and meal carts (Bouhnik et al. 1989) have been formulated, but their impact is too limited. Tintori et al. (1994) studied adjustable-height beds with electric trunk-lifts and mechanical mattress-lifts. The trunk-lifts were judged satisfactory by the staff and patients, but the mattress-lifts were very unsatisfactory, since adjusting the beds required more than eight pedal strokes, each of which exceeded standards for foot force. Pushing a button located close to the patient's head while talking to her or him is clearly preferable to pumping a pedal eight times from the foot of the bed (see figure 97.11). Because of time constraints, the mattress lift was often simply not used.

Van der Star and Voogd (1992) studied health care workers caring for 30 patients in a new prototype of bed over a period of six weeks. Observations of the workers' positions, the height of work surfaces, physical interaction between nurses and patients and the size of the work space were compared to data collected on the same ward over a seven-week period prior to the introduction of the prototype. Use of the prototypes reduced the total time spent in uncomfortable positions while washing patients from 40% to 20%; for bed-making the figures were 35% and 5%. Patients also enjoyed greater autonomy and often changed positions on their own, raising their trunks or legs by means of electric control buttons.

In Swedish hospitals, each double room is equipped with ceiling-mounted patient lifts (Ljungberg, Kilbom and Goran 1989). Rigorous programmes such as the April Project evaluate the interrelation of working conditions, work organization, the establishment of a back school and the improvement of physical fitness (Öhling and Estlund 1995).

In Quebec, ASSTAS developed a global approach to the analysis of working conditions causing back problems in hospitals (Villeneuve 1992). Between 1988 and 1991, this approach led to modifications of the work environment and equipment used in 120 wards and a 30% reduction in the frequency and severity of occu-

Figure 97.11 • Electronically-operated trunk-lifts on beds effectively reduce lifting accidents.

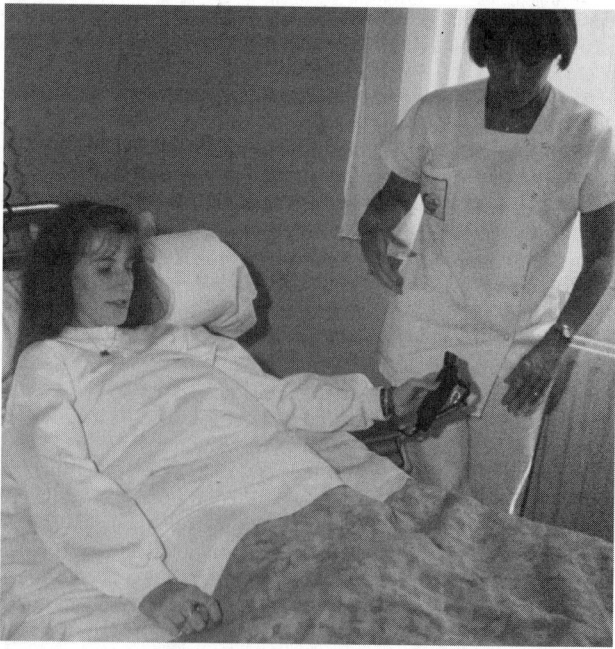

B. Floret

Figure 97.12 • Using ceiling-mounted patient lifts to reduce lifting accidents.

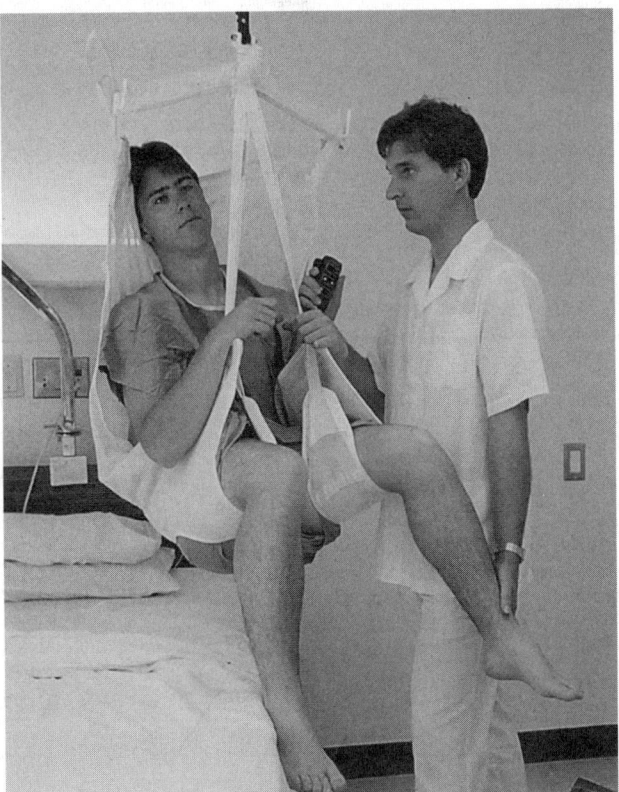

pational injuries. In 1994, a cost-benefit analysis performed by the association demonstrated that the systematic implementation of ceiling-mounted patient lifts would reduce occupational accidents and increase productivity, compared to the continued use of mobile, ground-based lifts (see figure 97.12).

Accounting for individual variation and facilitating activity

The female population in France is generally not very physically active. Of 1,505 nurses studied by Estryn-Béhar et al. (1992), 68% participated in no athletic activity, with inactivity more pronounced among mothers and unskilled personnel. In Sweden, fitness programmes for hospital personnel have been reported to be useful (Wigaeus Hjelm, Hagberg and Hellstrom 1993), but are feasible only if potential participants do not end their work day too tired to participate.

The adoption of better work postures is also conditioned by the possibility of wearing appropriate clothing (Lempereur 1992). The quality of shoes is particularly important. Hard soles are to be avoided. Anti-skid soles prevent occupational accidents caused by slips and falls, which in many countries are the second-leading cause of accidents leading to work absence. Ill-fitting overshoes or boots worn by operating room personnel to minimize the build-up of static electricity may be a hazard for falls.

Slips on level floors can be prevented by using low-slip floor surfaces that require no waxing. The risk of slips, particularly at doorways, can also be reduced by using techniques that do not leave the floor wet for long. The use of one mop per room, recommended by hygiene departments, is one such technique and has the additional advantage of reducing the handling of buckets of water.

In Vasteras County (Sweden), the implementation of several practical measures reduced painful syndromes and absenteeism by at least 25% (Modig 1992). In the archives (e.g., record or file rooms), ground- and ceiling-level shelves were eliminated, and an adjustable sliding board on which personnel can take notes while consulting the archives was installed. A reception office equipped with movable filing units, a computer and a telephone was also constructed. The height of the filing units is adjustable, allowing employees to adjust them to their own needs and facilitating the transition from sitting to standing during work.

Importance of "anti-lifting"

Manual patient-handling techniques designed to prevent back injuries have been proposed in many countries. Given the poor results of these techniques that have been reported to date (Dehlin et al. 1981; Stubbs, Buckle and Hudson 1983), more work in this area is needed.

The department of kinesiology of the University of Groningen (Netherlands) has developed an integrated patient-handling programme (Landewe and Schröer 1993) consisting of:

- recognition of the relationship between patient-handling and back strain
- demonstration of the value of the "anti-lifting" approach
- sensitization of nursing students throughout their studies to the importance of avoiding back strain
- the use of problem-resolution techniques
- attention to implementation and evaluation.

In the "anti-lifting" approach, the resolution of problems associated with patient transfers is based on the systematic analysis of all aspects of transfers, especially those related to patients, nurses, transfer equipment, teamwork, general working conditions and environmental and psychological barriers to the use of patient lifts (Friele and Knibbe 1993).

The application of European standard EN 90/269 of 29 May 1990 on back problems is an example of an excellent starting point for this approach. Besides requiring employers to implement appropriate work organization structures or other appropriate means, particularly mechanical equipment, to avoid manual handling of loads by workers, it also emphasizes the importance of "no-risk" handling policies that incorporate training. In practice, the adoption of appropriate postures and handling practices depends on the amount of functional space, presence of appropriate furniture and equipment, good collaboration on work organization and quality of care, good physical fitness and comfortable work clothing. The net effect of these factors is improved prevention of back problems.

STRAIN IN HEALTH CARE WORK

Madeleine R. Estryn-Béhar

Cognitive Strain

Continuous observation has revealed that nurses' workdays are characterized by continual reorganization of their work schedules and frequent interruptions.

Belgian (Malchaire 1992) and French (Gadbois et al. 1992; Estryn-Béhar and Fouillot 1990b) studies have revealed that nurses perform 120 to 323 separate tasks during their workday (see table 97.6). Work interruptions are very frequent throughout the day, ranging from 28 to 78 per workday. Many of the units studied were large, short-term-stay units in which the nurses' work consisted of a long series of spatially dispersed, short-duration

Table 97.6 • Number of separate tasks undertaken by nurses, and interruptions during each shift.

	Belgium	France	France
Authors	Malchaire 1992[1]	Gadbois et al. 1992[2]	Estryn-Béhar and Fouillot 1990b[3]
Departments	Cardiovascular surgery	Surgery (S) and medicine (M)	Ten medical and surgical departments
Number of separate tasks	Morning 120/8 h Afternoon 213/8 h Night 306/8 h	S (day) 276/12 h M (day) 300/12 h	Morning 323/8 h Afternoon 282/8 h Night 250/10–12 h
Number of interruptions		S (day) 36/12 h M (day) 60/12 h	Morning 78/8 h Afternoon 47/8 h Night 28/10–12 h

Number of hours of observation: [1] Morning: 80 h; afternoon: 80 h; night: 110 h. [2] Surgery: 238 h; medicine: 220 h. [3] Morning : 64 h; afternoon: 80 h; night: 90 h.

tasks. Planning of work schedules was complicated by the presence of incessant technical innovation, close interdependence of the work of the various staff members and a generally haphazard approach to work organization.

Gadbois et al. (1992) observed an average of 40 interruptions per workday, of which 5% were caused by patients, 40% by inadequate transmission of information, 15% by telephone calls and 25% by equipment. Ollagnier and Lamarche (1993) systematically observed nurses in a Swiss hospital and observed 8 to 32 interruptions per day, depending on the ward. On average, these interruptions represented 7.8% of the workday.

Work interruptions such as these, caused by inappropriate information supply and transmission structures, prevent workers from completing all their tasks and lead to worker dissatisfaction. The most serious consequence of this organizational deficiency is the reduction of time spent with patients (see table 97.5). In the first three studies cited above, nurses spent at most 30% of their time with patients on average. In Czechoslovakia, where multiple-bed rooms were common, nurses needed to change rooms less frequently, and spent 47% of their shift time with patients (Hubacova, Borsky and Strelka 1992). This clearly demonstrates how architecture, staffing levels and mental strain are all interrelated.

Estryn-Béhar et al. (1994) observed seven occupations and schedules in two specialized medical wards with similar spatial organization and located in the same high-rise building. While work in one ward was highly sectorized, with two teams of a nurse and a nurses' aide attending half of the patients, there were no sectors in the other ward, and basic care for all patients was dispensed by two nurses' aides. There were no differences in the frequency of patient-related interruptions in the two wards, but team-related interruptions were clearly more frequent in the ward without sectors (35 to 55 interruptions compared to 23 to 36 interruptions). Nurses' aides, morning-shift nurses and afternoon-shift nurses in the non-sectorized ward suffered 50, 70 and 30% more interruptions than did their colleagues in the sectorized one.

Sectorization thus appears to reduce the number of interruptions and the fracturing of work shifts. These results were used to plan the reorganization of the ward, in collaboration with the medical and paramedical staff, so as to facilitate sectorization of the office and the preparation area. The new office space is modular and easily divided into three offices (one for physicians and one for each of the two nursing teams), each separated by sliding glass partitions and furnished with at least six seats. Installation of two counters facing each other in the common preparation area means that nurses who are interrupted during preparation can return and find their materials in the same position and state, unaffected by their colleagues' activities.

Reorganization of work schedules and technical services
Professional activity in technical departments is much more than the mere sum of tasks associated with each test. A study conducted in several nuclear medicine departments (Favrot-Laurens 1992) revealed that nuclear medicine technicians spend very little of their time performing technical tasks. In fact, a significant part of technicians' time was spent coordinating activity and workload at the various workstations, transmitting information and making unavoidable adjustments. These responsibilities stem from technicians' obligation to be knowledgeable about each test and to possess essential technical and administrative information in addition to test-specific information such as time and injection site.

Information processing necessary for the delivery of care
Roquelaure, Pottier and Pottier (1992) were asked by a manufacturer of electroencephalography (EEG) equipment to simplify the use of the equipment. They responded by facilitating the reading of visual information on controls which were excessively complicated or simply unclear. As they point out, "third-generation" machines present unique difficulties, due in part to the use of visual display units packed with barely legible information. Deciphering these screens requires complex work strategies.

On the whole, however, little attention has been paid to the need to present information in a manner that facilitates rapid decision-making in health care departments. For example, the legibility of information on medicine labels still leaves much to be desired, according to one study of 240 dry oral and 364 injectable medications (Ott et al. 1991). Ideally, labels for dry oral medication administered by nurses, who are frequently interrupted and attend several patients, should have a matte surface, characters at least 2.5 mm high and comprehensive information on the medication in question. Only 36% of the 240 medications examined satisfied the first two criteria, and only 6% all three. Similarly, print smaller than 2.5 mm was used in 63% of labels on the 364 injectable medications.

In many countries where English is not spoken, machine control panels are still labelled in English. Patient-chart software is being developed in many countries. In France, this type of software development is often motivated by a desire to improve hospital management and undertaken without adequate study of the software's compatibility with actual working procedures (Estryn-Béhar 1991). As a result, the software may actually increase the complexity of nursing, rather than reduce cognitive strain. Requiring nurses to page through multiple screens of information to obtain the information they need to fill a prescription may increase the number of errors they make and memory lapses they suffer.

While Scandinavian and North American countries have computerized much of their patient records, it must be borne in mind that hospitals in these countries benefit from a high staff-to-patient ratio, and work interruptions and constant reshuffling of priorities are therefore less problematic there. In contrast, patient-chart software designed for use in countries with lower staff-to-patient ratios must be able to easily produce summaries and facilitate reorganization of priorities.

Human error in anaesthesia

Cooper, Newbower and Kitz (1984), in their study of the factors underlying errors during anaesthesia in the United States, found equipment design to be crucial. The 538 errors studied, largely drug administration and equipment problems, were related to the distribution of activities and the systems involved. According to Cooper, better design of equipment and monitoring apparatus would lead to a 22% reduction in errors, while complementary training of anaesthesiologists, using new technologies such as anaesthesia simulators, would lead to a 25% reduction. Other recommended strategies focus on work organization, supervision and communications.

Acoustic alarms in operating theatres and intensive-care units

Several studies have shown that too many types of alarms are used in operating theatres and intensive-care units. In one study, anaesthetists identified only 33% of alarms correctly, and only two monitors had recognition rates exceeding 50% (Finley and Cohen 1991). In another study, anaesthetists and anaesthesia nurses correctly identified alarms in only 34% of cases (Loeb et al. 1990). Retrospective analysis showed that 26% of nurses' errors were due to similarities in alarm sounds and 20% to similarities in alarm functions. Momtahan and Tansley (1989) reported that recovery-room nurses and anaesthetists correctly identified alarms in only 35% and 22% of cases respectively. In another study by Momtahan, Hétu and Tansley (1993), 18 physicians and technicians were able to identify only 10 to 15 of 26 operating-theatre alarms, while 15 intensive-care nurses were able to identify only 8 to 14 of 23 alarms used in their unit.

De Chambost (1994) studied the acoustic alarms of 22 types of machines used in an intensive-care unit in the Paris region. Only the cardiogram alarms and those of one of the two types of automated-plunger syringes were readily identified. The others were not immediately recognized and required personnel first to investigate the source of the alarm in the patient's room and then return with the appropriate equipment. Spectral analysis of the sound emitted by eight machines revealed significant similarities and suggests the existence of a masking effect between alarms.

The unacceptably high number of unjustifiable alarms has been the object of particular criticism. O'Carroll (1986) characterized the origin and frequency of alarms in a general intensive-care unit over three weeks. Only eight of 1,455 alarms were related to a potentially fatal situation. There were many false alarms from monitors and perfusion pumps. There was little difference between the frequency of alarms during the day and night.

Similar results have been reported for alarms used in anaesthesiology. Kestin, Miller and Lockhart (1988), in a study of 50 patients and five commonly used anaesthesia monitors, reported that only 3% indicated a real risk for the patient and that 75% of alarms were unfounded (caused by patient movement, interference and mechanical problems). On average, ten alarms were triggered per patient, equivalent to one alarm every 4.5 minutes.

A common response to false alarms is simply to disable them. McIntyre (1985) reported that 57% of Canadian anaesthetists admitted deliberately inactivating an alarm. Obviously, this could lead to serious accidents.

These studies underscore the poor design of hospital alarms and the need for alarm standardization based on cognitive ergonomics. Both Kestin, Miller and Lockhart (1988) and Kerr (1985) have proposed alarm modifications that take into account risk and the expected corrective responses of hospital personnel. As de Keyser and Nyssen (1993) have shown, the prevention of human error in anaesthesia integrates different measures—technological, ergonomic, social, organizational and training.

Technology, human error, patient safety and perceived psychological strain

Rigorous analysis of the error process is very useful. Sundström-Frisk and Hellström (1995) reported that equipment deficiencies and/or human error were responsible for 57 deaths and 284 injuries in Sweden between 1977 and 1986. The authors interviewed 63 intensive-care-unit teams involved in 155 incidents ("near-accidents") involving advanced medical equipment; most of these incidents had not been reported to authorities. Seventy typical "near-accident" scenarios were developed. Causal factors identified included inadequate technical equipment and documentation, the physical environment, procedures, staffing levels and stress. The introduction of new equipment may lead to accidents if the equipment is poorly adapted to users' needs and is introduced in the absence of basic changes in training and work organization.

In order to cope with forgetfulness, nurses develop several strategies for remembering, anticipating and avoiding incidents. They do still occur and even when patients are unaware of errors, near-accidents cause personnel to feel guilty. The accompanying box deals with some aspects of the problem.

Emotional or Affective Strain

Nursing work, especially if it forces nurses to confront serious illness and death, can be a significant source of affective strain, and may lead to burn-out, which is discussed more fully elsewhere in this *Encyclopaedia*. Nurses' ability to cope with this stress depends on the extent of their support network and their possibility to discuss and improve patients' quality of life. The following section summarizes the principal findings of Leppanen and Olkinuora's (1987) review of Finnish and Swedish studies on stress.

In Sweden, the main motivations reported by health professionals for entering their profession were the "moral calling" of the work, its usefulness and the opportunity to exercise competence. However, almost half of nurses' aides rated their knowledge as inadequate for their work, and one-quarter of nurses, one-fifth of registered nurses, one-seventh of physicians and one-tenth of head nurses considered themselves incompetent at managing some types of patients. Incompetence in managing psychological problems was the most commonly cited problem and was particularly prevalent among nurses' aides, although also cited by nurses and head nurses. Physicians, on the other hand, consider themselves competent in this area. The authors focus on the difficult situation of nurses' aides, who spend more time with patients than the others but are, paradoxically, unable to inform patients about their illness or treatment.

Several studies reveal the lack of clarity in delineating responsibilities. Pöyhönen and Jokinen (1980) reported that only 20% of Helsinki nurses were always informed of their tasks and the goals of their work. In a study conducted in a paediatric ward and an institute for disabled persons, Leppanen showed that the distribution of tasks did not allow nurses enough time to plan and prepare their work, perform office work and collaborate with team members.

Responsibility in the absence of decision-making power appears to be a stress factor. Thus, 57% of operating-room nurses

Human error and critical tasks in remote afterloading brachytherapy: Approaches for improved system performance

Remote afterloading brachytherapy (RAB) is a medical process used in the treatment of cancer. RAB uses a computer-controlled device to remotely insert and remove radioactive sources, close to a target (or tumour) in the body. Problems related to the dose delivered during RAB have been reported and attributed to human error (Swann-D'Emilia, Chu and Daywalt 1990). Callan et al. (1995) evaluated human error and critical tasks associated with RAB in 23 sites in the United States. Evaluation included six phases:

Phase 1: Functions and tasks. Preparation for treatment was considered to be the most difficult task, as it was responsible for the greatest cognitive strain. In addition, distractions had the greatest effect on preparation.

Phase 2: Human-system interferences. Personnel were often unfamiliar with interfaces they used infrequently. Operators were unable to see control signals or essential information from their workstations. In many cases, information on the state of the system was not given to the operator.

Phase 3: Procedures and practices. Because procedures used to move from one operation to the next, and those used to transmit information and equipment between tasks, were not well defined, essential information could be lost. Verification procedures were often absent, poorly structured or inconsistent.

Phase 4: Training policies. The study revealed the absence of formal training programmes at most sites.

Phase 5: Organizational support structures. Communication during RAB was particularly subject to error. Quality-control procedures were inadequate.

Phase 6: Identification and classification or circumstances favouring human error. In all, 76 factors favouring human error were identified and categorized. Alternative approaches were identified and evaluated.

Ten critical tasks were subject to error:

- patient scheduling, identification and tracking
- applicator placement stabilization
- target volume localization
- dwell position localization
- dosimetry
- treatment set-up
- treatment plan entry
- source exchange
- source calibration
- record-keeping and routine quality assurance

Treatment was the function associated with the greatest number of errors. Thirty treatment-related errors were analysed and errors were found to occur during four of five treatment sub-tasks. The majority of errors occurred during treatment delivery. The second-highest number of errors were associated with the planning of treatment and were related to the calculation of dose. Improvements of equipment and documentation are under way, in collaboration with manufacturers.

---

felt that ambiguities concerning their responsibilities aggravated their cognitive strain; 47% of surgical nurses reported being unfamiliar with some of their tasks and felt that patients' and nurses' conflicting expectations were a source of stress. Further, 47% reported increased stress when problems occurred and physicians were not present.

According to three European epidemiological studies, burn-out affects approximately 25% of nurses (Landau 1992; Saint-Arnaud et al. 1992; Estryn-Béhar et al. 1990) (see table 97.7). Estryn-Béhar et al. studied 1,505 female health care workers, using a cognitive strain index that integrates information on work interruptions and reorganization and an affective strain index that integrates information on work ambience, teamwork, congruity of qualification and work, time spent talking to patients and the frequency of hesitant or uncertain responses to patients. Burn-out was observed in 12% of nurses with low, 25% of those with moderate and 39% of those with high cognitive strain. The relationship between burn-out and affective strain increases was even stronger: burn-out was observed in 16% of nurses with low, 25% of those with moderate and 64% of those with high affective strain. After adjustment by logistic multivariate regression analysis for social and demographic factors, women with a high affective strain index had an odds ratio for burn-out of 6.88 compared to those with a low index.

Saint-Arnaud et al. reported a correlation between the frequency of burn-out and the score on their composite cognitive and affective strain index. Landau's results support these findings.

Finally, 25% of 520 nurses working in a cancer treatment centre and a general hospital in France were reported to exhibit high burn-out scores (Rodary and Gauvain-Piquard 1993). High scores were most closely associated with a lack of support. Feelings that their department did not regard them highly, take their knowledge of the patients into account or put the highest value on their patients' quality of life were reported more frequently by nurses with high scores. Reports of being physically afraid of their patients

---

Table 97.7 • Cognitive and affective strain and burn-out among health workers.

	Germany[1]	Canada[2]	France[3]
Number of subjects	24	868	1,505
Method	Maslach Burn-out Inventory	Ilfeld Psychiatric Symptoms Index	Goldberg General Health Questionnaire
High emotional exhaustion	33%	20%	26%
Degree of burn-out, by shift	Morning 2.0; afternoon 2.3; split shift 3.4; night 3.3		Morning 25%; afternoon 25%; night 29%
Percentage suffering high emotional exhaustion, by strain level		Cognitive and affective strain: low 16.5%; high 36.6%	Cognitive strain: low 12%, middle 25%, high 39% Affective strain: low 16%, middle 35%, high 64%

[1] Landau 1992. [2] Saint Arnand et. al. 1992. [3] Estryn-Béhar et al. 1990.

and unable to organize their work schedule as they wished were also more frequent among these nurses. In light of these results, it is interesting to note that Katz (1983) observed a high suicide rate among nurses.

Impact of workload, autonomy and support networks

A study of 900 Canadian nurses revealed an association between workload and five indices of cognitive strain measured by the Ilfeld questionnaire: the global score, aggression, anxiety, cognitive problems and depression (Boulard 1993). Four groups were identified. Nurses with a high workload, high autonomy and good social support (11.76%) exhibited several stress-related symptoms. Nurses with a low workload, high autonomy and good social support (35.75%) exhibited the lowest stress. Nurses with high workload, little autonomy and little social support (42.09%) had a high prevalence of stress-related symptoms, while nurses with a low workload, little autonomy and little social support (10.40%) had low stress, but the authors suggest that these nurses may experience some frustration.

These results also demonstrate that autonomy and support, rather than moderating the relationship between workload and mental health, act directly on workload.

Role of head nurses

Classically, employee satisfaction with supervision has been considered to depend on the clear definition of responsibilities and on good communication and feedback. Kivimäki and Lindström (1995) administered a questionnaire to nurses in 12 wards of four medical departments and interviewed the wards' head nurses. Wards were classified into two groups on the basis of the reported level of satisfaction with supervision (six satisfied wards and six dissatisfied wards). Scores for communication, feedback, participation in decision-making and the presence of a work climate that favours innovation were higher in "satisfied" wards. With one exception, head nurses of "satisfied" wards reported conducting at least one confidential conversation lasting one to two hours with each employee annually. In contrast, only one of the head nurses of the "dissatisfied" wards reported this behaviour.

Head nurses of the "satisfied" wards reported encouraging team members to express their opinions and ideas, discouraging team members from censuring or ridiculing nurses who made suggestions, and consistently attempting to give positive feedback to nurses expressing different or new opinions. Finally, all the head nurses in "satisfied" wards, but none of the ones in "dissatisfied" ones, emphasized their own role in creating a climate favourable to constructive criticism.

Psychological roles, relationships and organization

The structure of nurses' affective relationships varies from team to team. A study of 1,387 nurses working regular night shifts and 1,252 nurses working regular morning or afternoon shifts revealed that shifts were extended more frequently during night shifts (Estryn-Béhar et al. 1989a). Early shift starts and late shift ends were more prevalent among night-shift nurses. Reports of a "good" or "very good" work ambience were more prevalent at night, but a "good relationship with physicians" was less prevalent. Finally, night-shift nurses reported having more time to talk to patients, although that meant that worries and uncertainties about the appropriate response to give patients, also more frequent at night, were harder to bear.

Büssing (1993) revealed that depersonalization was greater for nurses working abnormal hours.

Stress in physicians

Denial and suppression of stress are common defence mechanisms. Physicians may attempt to repress their problems by work-

ing harder, distancing themselves from their emotions or adopting the role of a martyr (Rhoads 1977; Gardner and Hall 1981; Vaillant, Sorbowale and McArthur 1972). As these barriers become more fragile and adaptive strategies break down, bouts of anguish and frustration become more and more frequent.

Valko and Clayton (1975) found that one-third of interns suffered severe and frequent episodes of emotional distress or depression, and that one-quarter of them entertained suicidal thoughts. McCue (1982) believed that a better understanding of both stress and reactions to stress would facilitate physician training and personal development and modify societal expectations. The net effect of these changes would be an improvement in care.

Avoidance behaviours may develop, often accompanied by a deterioration of interpersonal and professional relationships. At some point, the physician finally crosses the line into a frank deterioration of mental health, with symptoms which may include substance abuse, mental illness or suicide. In yet other cases, patient care may be compromised, resulting in inappropriate examinations and treatment, sexual abuse or pathological behaviour (Shapiro, Pinsker and Shale 1975).

A study of 530 physician suicides identified by the American Medical Association over a five-year period found that 40% of suicides by female physicians and less than 20% of suicides by male physicians occurred in individuals younger than 40 years (Steppacher and Mausner 1974). A Swedish study of suicide rates from 1976 to 1979 found the highest rates among some of the health professions, compared to the overall active population (Toomingas 1993). The standardized mortality ratio (SMR) for female physicians was 3.41, the highest value observed, while that for nurses was 2.13.

Unfortunately, health professionals with impaired mental health are often ignored and may even be rejected by their colleagues, who attempt to deny these tendencies in themselves (Bissel and Jones 1975). In fact, slight or moderate stress is much more prevalent among health professionals than are frank psychiatric disorders (McCue 1982). A good prognosis in these cases depends on early diagnosis and peer support (Bitker 1976).

Discussion groups

Studies on the effect of discussion groups on burn-out have been undertaken in the United States. Although positive results have been demonstrated (Jacobson and MacGrath 1983), it should be noted that these have been in institutions where there was sufficient time for regular discussions in quiet and appropriate settings (i.e., hospitals with high staff-patient ratios).

A literature review of the success of discussion groups has shown these groups to be valuable tools in wards where a high proportion of patients are left with permanent sequelae and must learn to accept modifications in their lifestyle (Estryn-Béhar 1990).

Kempe, Sauter and Lindner (1992) evaluated the merits of two support techniques for nurses near burn-out in geriatrics wards: a six-month course of 13 professional counselling sessions and a 12-month course of 35 "Balint group" sessions. The clarification and reassurance provided by the Balint group sessions were effective only if there was also significant institutional change. In the absence of such change, conflicts may even intensify and dissatisfaction increase. Despite their impending burn-out, these nurses remained very professional and sought ways of carrying on with their work. These compensatory strategies had to take into account extremely high workloads: 30% of nurses worked more than 20 hours of overtime per month, 42% had to cope with understaffing during more than two-thirds of their working hours and 83% were often left alone with unqualified personnel.

The experience of these geriatrics nurses was compared to that of nurses in oncology wards. Burnout score was high in young oncology nurses, and decreased with seniority. In contrast, burnout score among geriatrics nurses increased with seniority, attaining levels much higher than those observed in oncology nurses. This lack of decrease with seniority is due to the characteristics of the workload in geriatrics wards.

The need to act on multiple determinants

Some authors have extended their study of effective stress management to organizational factors related to affective strain.

For example, analysis of psychological and sociological factors was part of Theorell's attempt to implement case-specific improvements in emergency, paediatric and juvenile psychiatry wards (Theorell 1993). Affective strain before and after the implementation of changes was measured through the use of questionnaires and the measurement of plasma prolactin levels, shown to mirror feelings of powerlessness in crisis situations.

Emergency-ward personnel experienced high levels of affective strain and frequently enjoyed little decisional latitude. This was attributed to their frequent confrontation with life-and-death situations, the intense concentration demanded by their work, the high number of patients they frequently attended and the impossibility of controlling the type and number of patients. On the other hand, because their contact with patients was usually short and superficial, they were exposed to less suffering.

The situation was more amenable to control in paediatric and juvenile psychiatry wards, where schedules for diagnostic procedures and therapeutic procedures were established in advance. This was reflected by a lower risk of overwork compared to emergency wards. However, personnel in these wards were confronted with children suffering from serious physical and mental disease.

Desirable organizational changes were identified through discussion groups in each ward. In emergency wards, personnel were very interested in organizational changes and recommendations concerning training and routine procedures—such as how to treat rape victims and elderly patients with no relations, how to evaluate work and what to do if a called physician doesn't arrive—were formulated. This was followed by the implementation of concrete changes, including the creation of the position of head physician and the ensuring of the constant availability of an internist.

The personnel in juvenile psychiatry were primarily interested in personal growth. Reorganization of resources by the head physician and the county allowed one-third of the personnel to undergo psychotherapy.

In paediatrics, meetings were organized for all the personnel every 15 days. After six months, social support networks, decisional latitude and work content all had improved.

The factors identified by these detailed ergonomic, psychological and epidemiological studies are valuable indices of work organization. Studies which focus on them are quite different from in-depth studies of multi-factor interactions and instead revolve around the pragmatic characterization of specific factors.

Tintori and Estryn-Béhar (1994) identified some of these factors in 57 wards of a large hospital in the Paris region in 1993. Shift overlap of more than 10 minutes was present in 46 wards, although there was no official overlap between the night and morning shifts in 41 wards. In half the cases, these information communication sessions included nurses' aides in all three shifts. In 12 wards, physicians participated in the morning-afternoon sessions. In the three months preceding the study, only 35 wards had held meetings to discuss patients' prognoses, discharges and patients' understanding of and reaction to their illnesses. In the year preceding the study, day-shift workers in 18 wards had received no training and only 16 wards had dispensed training to their night-shift workers.

Some new lounges were not used, since they were 50 to 85 metres from some of the patients' rooms. Instead, the personnel preferred holding their informal discussions around a cup of cof-

fee in a smaller but closer room. Physicians participated in coffee breaks in 45 day-shift wards. Nurses' complaints of frequent work interruptions and feelings of being overwhelmed by their work are no doubt attributable in part to the dearth of seats (less than four in 42 of the 57 wards) and cramped quarters of the nursing stations, where more than nine people must spend a good part of their day.

The interaction of stress, work organization and support networks is clear in studies of the home-care unit of the hospital in Motala, Sweden (Beck-Friis, Strang and Sjöden 1991; Hasselhorn and Seidler 1993). The risk of burn-out, generally considered high in palliative care units, was not significant in these studies, which in fact revealed more occupational satisfaction than occupational stress. Turnover and work stoppages in these units were low, and personnel had a positive self-image. This was attributed to selection criteria for personnel, good teamwork, positive feedback and continuing education. Personnel and equipment costs for terminal-stage cancer hospital care are typically 167 to 350% higher than for hospital-based home care. There were more than 20 units of this type in Sweden in 1993.

WORK SCHEDULES AND NIGHT WORK IN HEALTH CARE

Madeleine R. Estryn-Béhar

For a long time, nurses and nursing assistants were among the only women working at night in many countries (Gadbois 1981; Estryn-Béhar and Poinsignon 1989). In addition to the problems already documented among men, these women suffer additional problems related to their family responsibilities. Sleep deprivation has been convincingly demonstrated among these women, and there is concern about the quality of care they are able to dispense in the absence of appropriate rest.

Organization of Schedules and Family Obligations

It appears that personal feelings about social and family life are at least partially responsible for the decision to accept or refuse night work. These feelings, in turn, lead workers to minimize or exaggerate their health problems (Lert, Marne and Gueguen 1993; Ramaciotti et al. 1990). Among non-professional personnel, financial compensation is the main determinant of the acceptance or refusal of night work.

Other work schedules may also pose problems. Morning-shift workers sometimes must rise before 05:00 and so lose some of the sleep that is essential for their recovery. Afternoon shifts finish between 21:00 and 23:00, limiting social and family life. Thus, often only 20% of women working in large university hospitals have work schedules in synchrony with the rest of society (Cristofari et al. 1989).

Complaints related to work schedules are more frequent among health care workers than among other employees (62% versus 39%) and indeed are among the complaints most frequently voiced by nurses (Lahaye et al. 1993).

One study demonstrated the interaction of work satisfaction with social factors, even in the presence of sleep deprivation (Verhaegen et al. 1987). In this study, nurses working only night shifts were more satisfied with their work than nurses working rotating shifts. These differences were attributed to the fact that all the night-shift nurses chose to work at night and organized their family life accordingly, while rotating-shift nurses found even rare night-shift work a disturbance of their personal and family lives. However, Estryn-Béhar et al. (1989b) reported that mothers working only night shifts

Table 97.8 • Prevalence of work complaints according to shift.

	Rotating shifts (%)	Day shifts (%)
Arduous physical work	55.5	31.3
Arduous mental work	80.2	61.9
Work often too tiring	46.8	24.8
Under-staffing	74.8	43.8
Insufficient time for breaks	78.4	56.6
Interference of work with private life	52.8	31.0
Dissatisfaction with schedules	36.9	2.7
Frequent lack of sleep	34.9	19.5
Frequent fatigue on rising	31.3	17.3

Source: Van Deursen et al. 1993.

were more tired and went out less frequently compared with male night-shift nurses.

In the Netherlands, the prevalence of work complaints was higher among nurses working rotating shifts than among those working only day shifts (Van Deursen et al. 1993) (see table 97.8).

Sleep disturbances

On workdays, night-shift nurses sleep an average of two hours less than other nurses (Escribà Agüir et al. 1992; Estryn-Béhar et al. 1978; Estryn-Béhar et al. 1990; Nyman and Knutsson 1995). According to several studies, their quality of sleep is also poor (Schroër et al. 1993; Lee 1992; Gold et al. 1992; Estryn-Béhar and Fonchain 1986).

In their interview study of 635 Massachusetts nurses, Gold et al. (1992) found that 92.2% of nurses working alternating morning and afternoon shifts were able to maintain a nocturnal "anchor" sleep of four hours at the same schedule throughout the month, compared to only 6.3% of night-shift nurses and none of the nurses working alternating day and night shifts. The age- and seniority-adjusted odds ratio for "poor sleep" was 1.8 for night-shift nurses and 2.8 for rotating-shift nurses with night work, compared to morning- and afternoon-shift nurses. The odds ratio for taking sleep medication was 2.0 for night- and rotating-shift nurses, compared to morning- and afternoon-shift nurses.

Affective Problems and Fatigue

The prevalence of stress-related symptoms and reports of having stopped enjoying their work was higher among Finnish nurses working rotating shifts than among other nurses (Kandolin 1993). Estryn-Béhar et al. (1990) showed that night-shift nurses' scores on the General Health Questionnaire used to evaluate mental health, compared to day-shift nurses (odds ratio of 1.6) showed poorer general health.

In another study, Estryn-Béhar et al. (1989b), interviewed a representative sample of one-quarter of night-shift employees (1,496 individuals) in 39 Paris-area hospitals. Differences appear according to sex and qualification ("qualified" = head nurses and nurses; "unqualified" = nurses' aides and orderlies). Excessive fatigue was reported by 40% of qualified women, 37% of unqualified women, 29% of qualified men and 20% of unqualified men. Fatigue on rising was reported by 42% of qualified women, 35% of unqualified women, 28% of qualified men and 24% of unqualified men. Frequent irritability was reported by one-third of night-shift workers and by a significantly greater proportion of women.

Women with no children were twice as likely to report excessive fatigue, fatigue on rising and frequent irritability than were comparable men. The increase compared to single men with no children was even more marked for women with one or two children, and greater still (a four-fold increase) for women with at least three children.

Fatigue on rising was reported by 58% of night-shift hospital workers and 42% of day-shift workers in a Swedish study using a stratified sample of 310 hospital workers (Nyman and Knutsson 1995). Intense fatigue at work was reported by 15% of day-shift workers and 30% of night-shift workers. Almost one-quarter of night-shift workers reported falling asleep at work. Memory problems were reported by 20% of night-shift workers and 9% of day-shift workers.

In Japan, the health and safety association publishes the results of medical examinations of all the country's salaried employees. This report includes the results of 600,000 employees in the health and hygiene sector. Nurses generally work rotating shifts. Complaints concerning fatigue are highest in night-shift nurses, followed in order by evening- and morning-shift nurses (Makino 1995). Symptoms reported by night-shift nurses include sleepiness, sadness and difficulty concentrating, with numerous complaints about accumulated fatigue and disturbed social life (Akinori and Hiroshi 1985).

Sleep and Affective Disorders among Physicians

The effect of work content and duration on young physicians' private lives, and the attendant risk of depression, has been noted. Valko and Clayton (1975) found that 30% of young residents suffered a bout of depression lasting an average of five months during their first year of residency. Of the 53 residents studied, four had suicidal thoughts and three made concrete suicide plans. Similar rates of depression have been reported by Reuben (1985) and Clark et al. (1984).

In a questionnaire study, Friedman, Kornfeld and Bigger (1971) showed that interns suffering from sleep deprivation reported more sadness, selfishness and modification of their social life than did more-rested interns. During interviews following the tests, interns suffering from sleep deprivation reported symptoms such as difficulty reasoning, depression, irritability, depersonalization, inappropriate reactions and short-term memory deficits.

In a one-year longitudinal study, Ford and Wentz (1984) evaluated 27 interns four times during their internship. During this period, four interns suffered at least one major bout of depression meeting standard criteria and 11 others reported clinical depression. Anger, fatigue and mood swings increased throughout the year and were inversely correlated with the amount of sleep the preceding week.

A literature review has identified six studies in which interns having spent one sleepless night exhibited deteriorations of mood, motivation and reasoning ability and increased fatigue and anxiety (Samkoff and Jacques 1991).

Devienne et al. (1995) interviewed a stratified sample of 220 general practitioners in the Paris area. Of these, 70 were on call at night. Most of the on-call physicians reported having had their sleep disturbed while on call and finding it particularly difficult to get back to sleep after having been awakened (men: 65%; women: 88%). Waking up in the middle of the night for reasons unrelated to service calls was reported by 22% of men and 44% of women. Having or almost having a car accident due to sleepiness related to being on call was reported by 15% of men and 19% of women. This risk was greater among physicians who were on call more than four times per month (30%) than in those on call three or four times per month (22%) or one to three times per month (10%). The day after being on call, 69% of women and 46% of men reported having difficulty concentrating and feeling

97. HEALTH CARE FACILITIES AND SERVICES

less effective, while 37% of men and 31% of women reported experiencing mood swings. Accumulated sleep deficits were not recovered the day following on-call work.

Family and Social Life

A survey of 848 night-shift nurses found that over the previous month one-quarter had not gone out and had entertained no guests, and half had participated in such activities only once (Gadbois 1981). One-third reported refusing an invitation because of fatigue, and two-thirds reported going out only once, with this proportion rising to 80% among mothers.

Kurumatani et al. (1994) reviewed the time sheets of 239 Japanese nurses working rotating shifts over a total of 1,016 days and found that nurses with young children slept less and spent less time on leisure activities than did nurses without young children.

Estryn-Béhar et al. (1989b) observed that women were significantly less likely than men to spend at least one hour per week participating in team or individual sports (48% of qualified women, 29% of unqualified women, 65% of qualified men and 61% of unqualified men). Women were also less likely to frequently (at least four times per month) attend shows (13% of qualified women, 6% of unqualified women, 20% of qualified men and 13% of unqualified men). On the other hand, similar proportions of women and men practised home-based activities such as watching television and reading. Multivariate analysis showed that men with no children were twice as likely to spend at least one hour per week on athletic activities than were comparable women. This gap increases with the number of children. Child care, and not gender, influences reading habits. A significant proportion of the subjects in this study were single parents. This was very rare among qualified men (1%), less rare among unqualified men (4.5%), common in qualified women (9%) and extremely frequent in unqualified women (24.5%).

In Escribà Agüir's (1992) study of Spanish hospital workers, incompatibility of rotating shifts with social and family life was the leading source of dissatisfaction. In addition, night-shift work (either permanent or rotating) disturbed the synchronization of their schedules with those of their spouses.

Lack of free time interferes severely with the private life of interns and residents. Landau et al. (1986) found that 40% of residents reported major conjugal problems. Of these residents, 72% attributed the problems to their work. McCall (1988) noted that residents have little time to spend on their personal relationships; this problem is particularly serious for women nearing the end of their low-risk-pregnancy years.

Irregular Shift Work and Pregnancy

Axelsson, Rylander and Molin (1989) distributed a questionnaire to 807 women employed at the hospital in Mölna, Sweden. The birth weights of children born to non-smoking women working irregular shifts were significantly lower than that of children born to non-smoking women who only worked day shifts. The difference was greatest for infants of at least grade 2 (3,489 g versus 3,793 g). Similar differences were also found for infants of at least grade 2 born to women working afternoon shifts (3,073 g) and shifts alternating every 24 hours (3,481 g).

Vigilance and Quality of Work among Night-Shift Nurses

Englade, Badet and Becque (1994) performed Holter EEGs on two groups of nine nurses. It showed that the group not allowed to sleep had attention deficits characterized by sleepiness, and in some cases even sleep of which they were unaware. An experimental group practised polyphasic sleep in an attempt to recover a little sleep during work hours, while the control group was not allowed any sleep recovery.

These results are similar to those reported by a survey of 760 California nurses (Lee 1992), in which 4.0% of night-shift nurses and 4.3% of nurses working rotating shifts reported suffering frequent attention deficits; no nurses from the other shifts mentioned lack of vigilance as a problem. Occasional attention deficits were reported by 48.9% of night-shift nurses, 39.2% of rotating-shift nurses, 18.5% of day-shift nurses and 17.5% of evening-shift nurses. Struggling to stay awake while dispensing care during the month preceding the survey was reported by 19.3% of night-shift and rotating-shift nurses, compared to 3.8% of day- and evening-shift nurses. Similarly, 44% of nurses reported having had to struggle to stay awake while driving during the preceding month, compared to 19% of day-shift nurses and 25% of evening-shift nurses.

Smith et al. (1979) studied 1,228 nurses in 12 American hospitals. The incidence of occupational accidents was 23.3 for nurses working rotating shifts, 18.0 for night-shift nurses, 16.8 for day-shift nurses and 15.7 for afternoon-shift nurses.

In an attempt to better characterize problems related to attention deficits among night-shift nurses, Blanchard et al. (1992) observed activity and incidents throughout a series of night shifts. Six wards, ranging from intensive care to chronic care, were studied. In each ward, one continuous observation of a nurse was performed on the second night (of night work) and two observations on the third or fourth nights (depending on the wards' schedule). Incidents were not associated with serious outcomes. On the second night, the number of incidents rose from 8 in the first half of the night to 18 in the second half. On the third or fourth night, the increase was from 13 to 33 in one case and from 11 to 35 in another. The authors emphasized the role of sleep breaks in limiting risks.

Gold et al. (1992) collected information from 635 Massachusetts nurses on the frequency and consequences of attention deficits. Experiencing at least one episode of sleepiness at work per week was reported by 35.5% of rotating-shift nurses with night work, 32.4% of night-shift nurses and 20.7% of morning-shift and afternoon-shift nurses working exceptionally at night. Less than 3% of nurses working the morning and afternoon shifts reported such incidents.

The odds ratio for sleepiness while driving to and from work was 3.9 for rotating-shift nurses with night work and 3.6 for night-shift nurses, compared to morning- and afternoon-shift nurses. The odds ratio for total accidents and errors over the past year (car accidents driving to and from work, errors in medication or work procedures, occupational accidents related to sleepiness) was almost 2.00 for rotating-shift nurses with night work compared to morning- and afternoon-shift nurses.

Effect of Fatigue and Sleepiness on the Performance of Physicians

Several studies have shown that the fatigue and sleeplessness induced by night-shift and on-call work leads to deteriorations of physician performance.

Wilkinson, Tyler and Varey (1975) conducted a postal questionnaire survey of 6,500 British hospital physicians. Of the 2,452 who responded, 37% reported suffering a degradation of their effectiveness due to excessively long work hours. In response to open-ended questions, 141 residents reported committing errors due to overwork and lack of sleep. In a study performed in Ontario, Canada, 70% of 1,806 hospital physicians reported often worrying about the effect of the quantity of their work had on its quality (Lewittes and Marshall 1989). More specifically, 6% of the sample—and 10% of interns—reported often worrying about fatigue affecting the quality of care they dispensed.

Given the difficulty in performing real-time evaluations of clinical performance, several studies on the effects of sleep deprivation on physicians have relied upon neuropsychological tests.

In the majority of studies reviewed by Samkoff and Jacques (1991), residents deprived of sleep for one night exhibited little deterioration in their performance of rapid tests of manual dexterity, reaction time and memory. Fourteen of these studies used extensive test batteries. According to five tests, the effect on performance was ambiguous; according to six, a performance deficit was observed; but according to eight other tests, no deficit was observed.

Rubin et al. (1991) tested 63 medical-ward residents before and after an on-call period of 36 hours and a subsequent full day of work, using a battery of self-administered computerized behavioural tests. Physicians tested after being on call exhibited significant performance deficits in tests of visual attention, coding speed and accuracy and short-term memory. The duration of sleep enjoyed by the residents while on call was as follows: two hours at most in 27 subjects, four hours at most in 29 subjects, six hours at most in four subjects and seven hours in three subjects. Lurie et al. (1989) reported similarly brief sleep durations.

Virtually no difference has been observed in the performance of actual or simulated short-duration clinical tasks—including filling out a laboratory requisition (Poulton et al. 1978; Reznick and Folse 1987), simulated suturing (Reznick and Folse 1987), endotracheal intubation (Storer et al. 1989) and venous and arterial catheterization (Storer et al. 1989)—by sleep-deprived and control groups. The only difference observed was a slight lengthening of the time required by sleep-deprived residents to perform arterial catheterization.

On the other hand, several studies have demonstrated significant differences for tasks requiring continuous vigilance or intense concentration. For example, sleep-deprived interns committed twice as many errors when reading 20-minute ECGs as did rested interns (Friedman et al. 1971). Two studies, one relying on 50-minute VDU-based simulations (Beatty, Ahern and Katz 1977), the other on 30-minute video simulations (Denisco, Drummond and Gravenstein 1987), have reported poorer performance by anaesthesiologists deprived of sleep for one night. Another study has reported significantly poorer performance by sleep-deprived residents on a four-hour test exam (Jacques, Lynch and Samkoff 1990). Goldman, McDonough and Rosemond (1972) used closed-circuit filming to study 33 surgical procedures. Surgeons with less than two hours of sleep were reported to perform "worse" than more-rested surgeons. The duration of surgical inefficiency or indecision (i.e., of poorly planned manoeuvres) was over 30% of the total duration of the operation.

Bertram (1988) examined the charts of emergency admissions by second-year residents over a one-month period. For a given diagnosis, less information on medical histories and the results of clinical examinations was gathered as the number of hours worked and patients seen increased.

Smith-Coggins et al. (1994) analysed the EEG, mood, cognitive performance and motor performance of six emergency-ward physicians over two 24-hour periods, one with diurnal work and nocturnal sleep, the other with nocturnal work and diurnal sleep.

Physicians working at night slept significantly less (328.5 versus 496.6 minutes) and performed significantly less well. This poorer motor performance was reflected in the increased time required to perform a simulated intubation (42.2 versus 31.56 seconds) and an increased number of protocol errors.

Their cognitive performance was evaluated at five test periods throughout their shift. For each test, physicians were required to review four charts drawn from a pool of 40, rank them and list the initial procedures, the treatments and the appropriate laboratory tests. Performance deteriorated as the shift progressed for both night-shift and day-shift physicians. Night-shift physicians were less successful at providing correct responses than day-shift physicians.

Physicians working during the day rated themselves as less sleepy, more satisfied and more lucid than did night-shift physicians.

Recommendations in English-speaking countries concerning the work schedules of physicians-in-training have tended to take these results into account and now call for work-weeks of at most 70 hours and the provision of recovery periods following on-call work. In the US, following the death of a patient attributed to errors by an overworked, poorly supervised resident physician which received much media attention, New York State enacted legislation limiting work hours for hospital staff physicians and defining the role of attending physicians in supervising their activities.

Content of Night Work in Hospitals

Night work has long been undervalued. In France, nurses used to be seen as *guardians*, a term rooted in a vision of nurses' work as the mere monitoring of sleeping patients, with no delivery of care. The inaccuracy of this vision became increasingly obvious as the length of hospitalization decreased and patients' uncertainty about their hospitalization increased. Hospital stays require frequent technical interventions during the night, precisely when the nurse:patient ratio is lowest.

The importance of the amount of time spent by nurses in patients' rooms is demonstrated by the results of a study based on continuous observation of the ergonomics of nurses' work in each of three shifts in ten wards (Estryn-Béhar and Bonnet 1992). The time spent in rooms accounted for an average of 27% of the day and night shifts and 30% of the afternoon shift. In four of the ten wards, nurses spent more time in the rooms during the night than during the day. Blood samples were of course taken less frequently during the night, but other technical interventions such as monitoring vital signs and medication, and administering, adjusting and monitoring intravenous drips and transfusions were more frequent during the night in six of seven wards where detailed analysis was performed. The total number of technical and nontechnical direct-care interventions was higher during the night in six of seven wards.

Nurses' work postures varied from shift to shift. The percentage of time spent seated (preparation, writing, consultations, time spent with patients, breaks) was higher at night in seven of ten wards, and exceeded 40% of shift time in six wards. However, the time spent in painful postures (bent over, crouched, arms extended, carrying loads) exceeded 10% of shift time in all wards and 20% of shift time in six wards at night; in five wards the percentage of time spent in painful positions was higher at night. In fact, night-shift nurses also make beds and perform tasks related to hygiene, comfort and voiding, tasks which are all normally performed by nurses' aides during the day.

Night-shift nurses may be obliged to change location very frequently. Night-shift nurses in all the wards changed location over 100 times per shift; in six wards, the number of changes of location was higher at night. However, because rounds were scheduled at 00:00, 02:00, 04:00 and 06:00, nurses did not travel greater distances, except in juvenile intensive-care wards. Nonetheless, nurses walked over six kilometres in three of the seven wards where podometry was performed.

Conversations with patients were frequent at night, exceeding 30 per shift in all wards; in five wards these conversations were more frequent at night. Conversations with physicians were much rarer and almost always brief.

Leslie et al. (1990) conducted continuous observation of 12 of 16 interns in the medical ward of a 340-bed Edinburgh (Scotland) hospital over 15 consecutive winter days. Each ward cared for approximately 60 patients. In all, 22 day shifts (08:00 to 18:00) and 18 on-call shifts (18:00 to 08:00), equivalent to 472 hours of work, were observed. The nominal duration of the interns' work week was 83 to 101 hours, depending on whether or not they were on call during the weekends. However, in addition to the official work schedule, each intern also spent an average of 7.3 hours each week on miscellaneous hospital activities. Information on the time spent performing each of 17 activities, on a minute-by-minute basis, was collected by trained observers assigned to each intern.

The longest continuous work period observed was 58 hours (08:00 Saturday to 06:00 Monday) and the longest work period was 60.5 hours. Calculations showed that a one-week sickness leave of one intern would require the other two interns in the ward to increase their workload by 20 hours.

In practice, in wards admitting patients during on-call shifts, interns working consecutive day, on-call and night shifts worked all but 4.6 of the 34 elapsed hours. These 4.6 hours were devoted to meals and rest, but interns remained on call and available during this time. In wards that did not admit new patients during on-call shifts, interns' workload abated only after midnight.

Due to the on-call schedules in other wards, interns spent approximately 25 minutes outside their home ward each shift. On average, they walked 3 kilometres and spent 85 minutes (32 to 171 minutes) in other wards each night shift.

Time spent filling out requests for examinations and charts, in addition, is often performed outside of their normal work hours. Non-systematic observation of this additional work over several days revealed that it accounts for approximately 40 minutes of additional work at the end of each shift (18:00).

During the day, 51 to 71% of interns' time was spent on patient-oriented duties, compared to 20 to 50% at night. Another study, conducted in the United States, reported that 15 to 26% of work time was spent on patient-oriented duties (Lurie et al. 1989).

The study concluded that more interns were needed and that interns should no longer be required to attend other wards while on call. Three additional interns were hired. This reduced interns' work week to an average of 72 hours, with no work, excepting on-call shifts, after 18:00. Interns also obtained a free half-day following an on-call shift and preceding a weekend when they were to be on call. Two secretaries were hired on a trial basis by two wards. Working 10 hours per week, the secretaries were able to fill out 700 to 750 documents per ward. In the opinion of both senior physicians and nurses, this resulted in more efficient rounds, since all the information had been entered correctly.

THE PHYSICAL ENVIRONMENT AND HEALTH CARE

● EXPOSURE TO PHYSICAL AGENTS

Robert M. Lewy

Health care workers (HCWs) confront numerous physical hazards.

Electrical Hazards
Failure to meet standards for electrical equipment and its use is the most frequently cited violation in all industries. In hospitals, electrical malfunctions are the second leading cause of fires. Additionally, hospitals require that a wide variety of electrical equipment be used in hazardous environments (i.e., in wet or damp locations or adjacent to flammables or combustibles).

Recognition of these facts and the danger they may pose to patients has led most hospitals to put great effort into electrical safety promotion in patient-care areas. However, non-patient areas are sometimes neglected and employee- or hospital-owned appliances may be found with:

- three-wire (grounded) plugs attached to two-wire (ungrounded) cords
- ground prongs bent or cut off
- ungrounded appliances attached to ungrounded multiple-plug "spiders"
- extension cords with improper grounding
- cords moulded to plugs not properly wired (25% of the x-ray equipment in one hospital study was incorrectly wired).

Prevention and control
It is critical that all electrical installations be in accordance with prescribed safety standards and regulations. Measures that can be taken to prevent fires and avoid shocks to employees include the following:

- provision for regular inspection of all employee work areas by an electrical engineer to discover and correct hazardous conditions such as ungrounded or poorly maintained appliances or tools

- inclusion of electrical safety in both orientation and in-service training programmes.

Employees should be instructed:

- not to use electrical equipment with wet hands, on wet surfaces or when standing on wet floors
- not to use devices that blow a fuse or trip a circuit breaker until they have been inspected
- not to use any appliance, equipment or wall receptacle that appears to be damaged or in poor repair
- to use extension cords only temporarily and only in emergency situations
- to use extension cords designed to carry the voltage required
- to turn off equipment before unplugging it
- to report all shocks immediately (including small tingles) and not to use equipment again until it has been inspected.

Heat
Although heat-related health effects on hospital workers can include heat stroke, exhaustion, cramps and fainting, these are rare. More common are the milder effects of increased fatigue, discomfort and inability to concentrate. These are important because they may increase the risk of accidents.

Heat exposure can be measured with wet bulb and globe thermometers, expressed as the Wet Bulb Globe Temperature (WBGT) Index, which combines the effects of radiant heat and humidity with the dry bulb temperature. This testing should only be done by a skilled individual.

The boiler room, laundry and kitchen are the most common high-temperature environments in the hospital. However, in old buildings with inadequate ventilation and cooling systems heat may be a problem in many locations in summer months. Heat exposure may also be a problem where ambient temperatures are elevated and health care personnel are required to wear occlusive gowns, caps, masks and gloves.

Prevention and control
Although it may be impossible to keep some hospital settings at a comfortable temperature, there are measures to keep tempera-

tures at acceptable levels and to ameliorate the effects of heat upon workers, including:

- provision of adequate ventilation. Central air-conditioning systems may need to be supplemented by floor fans, for example.
- making cool drinking water easily accessible
- rotating employees so that periodic relief is scheduled
- scheduling frequent breaks in cool areas.

Noise

Exposure to high levels of noise in the workplace is a common job hazard. The "quiet" image of hospitals notwithstanding, they can be noisy places to work.

Exposure to loud noises can cause a loss in hearing acuity. Short-term exposure to loud noises can cause a decrease in hearing called a "temporary threshold shift" (TTS). While these TTSs can be reversed with sufficient rest from high noise levels, the nerve damage resulting from long-term exposure to loud noises cannot.

The US Occupational Safety and Health Administration (OSHA) has set 90 dBA as the permissible limit per 8 hours of work. For 8-hour average exposures in excess of 85 dBA, a hearing conservation programme is mandated. (Sound level meters, the basic noise measuring instrument, are provided with three weighting networks. OSHA standards use the A scale, expressed as dBA.)

The effects of noise at the 70-dB level are reported by the National Institute of Environmental Health Sciences to be:

- blood vessel constriction that can lead to higher blood pressure and decreased circulation in the hands and feet (perceived as coldness)
- headaches
- increased irritability
- difficulty in communicating with co-workers
- reduced ability to work
- more difficulty with tasks that require alertness, concentration and attention to detail.

Food service areas, laboratories, engineering areas (which usually includes the boiler room), business office and medical records and nursing units can be so noisy that productivity is reduced. Other departments where noise levels are sometimes quite high are laundries, print shops and construction areas.

Prevention and control

If a noise survey of the facility shows that employees' noise exposure is in excess of the OSHA standard, a noise abatement programme is required. Such a programme should include:

- periodic measurement
- engineering controls such as isolating noisy equipment, installing mufflers and acoustic ceilings and carpets
- administrative controls limiting workers' exposure time to excessive noise.

In addition to abatement measures, a hearing conservation programme should be established that provides for:

- hearing tests for new employees to provide baselines for future testing
- annual audiometric testing
- hearing protection for use while controls are being implemented and for situations where levels cannot be brought within approved limits.

Inadequate Ventilation

The specific ventilation requirements for various types of equipment are engineering matters and will not be discussed here.

However, both old and new facilities present general ventilation problems that warrant mentioning.

In older facilities built before central heating and cooling systems were common, ventilation problems must often be solved on a location-by-location basis. Frequently, the problem rests in achieving uniform temperatures and correct circulation.

In newer facilities that are hermetically sealed, a phenomenon called "tight-building syndrome" or "sick building syndrome" is sometimes experienced. When the circulation system does not exchange the air rapidly enough, concentrations of irritants may build up to the extent that employees may experience such reactions as sore throat, runny nose and watery eyes. This situation can provoke severe reaction in sensitized individuals. It can be exacerbated by various chemicals emitted from such sources as foam insulation, carpeting, adhesives and cleaning agents.

Prevention and control

While careful attention is paid to ventilation in sensitive areas such as surgical suites, less attention is given to general-purpose areas. It is important to alert employees to report irritant reactions that appear only in the workplace. If local air quality cannot be improved with venting, it may be necessary to transfer individuals who have become sensitized to some irritant in their workstation.

Laser Smoke

During surgical procedures using a laser or electrosurgical unit, the thermal destruction of tissue creates smoke as a by-product. NIOSH has confirmed studies showing that this smoke plume can contain toxic gases and vapours such as benzene, hydrogen cyanide and formaldehyde, bioaerosols, dead and live cellular material (including blood fragments) and viruses. At high concentrations, the smoke causes ocular and upper respiratory tract irritation in health care personnel and may create visual problems for the surgeon. The smoke has an unpleasant odour and has been shown to have mutagenic material.

Prevention and control

Exposure to airborne contaminants in such smoke can be effectively controlled by proper ventilation of the treatment room, supplemented by local exhaust ventilation (LEV) using a high-efficiency suction unit (i.e., a vacuum pump with an inlet nozzle held within 2 inches of the surgical site) that is activated throughout the procedure. Both the room ventilation system and the local exhaust ventilator should be equipped with filters and absorbers that capture particulates and absorb or inactivate airborne gases and vapours. These filters and absorbers require monitoring and replacement on a regular basis and are considered a possible biohazard requiring proper disposal.

Radiation

Ionizing radiation

When ionizing radiation strikes cells in living tissue, it may either kill the cell directly (i.e., cause burns or hair loss) or it may alter the genetic material of the cell (i.e., cause cancer or reproductive damage). Standards involving ionizing radiation may refer to exposure (the amount of radiation the body is exposed to) or dose (the amount of radiation the body absorbs) and may be expressed in terms of millirem (mrem), the usual measure of radiation, or rems (1,000 millirems).

Various jurisdictions have developed regulations governing the procurement, use, transportation and disposal of radioactive materials, as well as established limits for exposure (and in some places specific limits for dosage to various parts of the body), providing a strong measure of protection for radiation workers. In addition, institutions using radioactive materials in treatment and research generally develop their own internal controls in addition to those prescribed by law.

The greatest dangers to hospital workers are from scatter, the small amount of radiation that is deflected or reflected from the beam into the immediate vicinity, and from unexpected exposure, either because they are inadvertently exposed in an area not defined as a radiation area or because the equipment is not well maintained.

Radiation workers in diagnostic radiology (including x ray, fluoroscopy and angiography for diagnostic purposes, dental radiography and computerized axial tomography (CAT) scanners), in therapeutic radiology, in nuclear medicine for diagnostic and therapeutic procedures, and in radiopharmaceutical laboratories are carefully followed and checked for exposure, and radiation safety is usually well managed in their workstations, although there are many localities in which control is inadequate.

There are other areas not usually designated as "radiation areas", where careful monitoring is needed to ensure that appropriate precautions are being taken by staff and that correct safeguards are provided for patients who might be exposed. These include angiography, emergency rooms, intensive care units, locations where portable x rays are being taken and operating rooms.

Prevention and control

The following protective measures are strongly recommended for ionizing radiation (x rays and radioisotopes):

- Rooms that house radiation sources should be properly marked and entered only by authorized personnel.
- All films should be held in place by patients or members of the patient's family. If the patient must be held, a member of the family should do so. If staff must hold film or patients, the task should be rotated through the staff to minimize the overall dose per individual.
- Where portable x-ray units and radioisotopes are used, only the patient and trained personnel should be allowed in the room.
- Adequate warning should be given to nearby workers when x rays using portable units are about to be taken.
- X-ray controls should be located to prevent the unintentional energizing of the unit.
- X-ray room doors should be kept closed when equipment is in use.
- All x-ray machines should be checked before each use to ensure that the secondary radiation cones and filters are in place.
- Patients who have received radioactive implants or other therapeutic radiology procedures should be clearly identified. Bedding, dressings, wastes and so forth from such patients should be so labelled.

Lead aprons, gloves and goggles must be worn by employees working in the direct field or where scatter radiation levels are high. All such protective equipment should be checked annually for cracks in the lead.

Dosimeters must be worn by all personnel exposed to ionizing radiation sources. Dosimeter badges should be regularly analysed by a laboratory with good quality control, and the results should be recorded. Records must be kept not only of each employee's personal radiation exposure but also of the receipt and disposition of all radioisotopes.

In therapeutic radiology settings, periodic dose checks should be done using lithium fluoride (LiF) solid-state dosimeters to check on system calibration. Treatment rooms should be equipped with radiation monitor-door interlock and visual-alarm systems.

During internal or intravenous treatment with radioactive sources, the patient should be housed in a room located to minimize exposure to other patients and staff and signs posted warning others not to enter. Staff contact time should be limited, and staff should be careful in handling bedding, dressings and wastes from these patients.

During fluoroscopy and angiography, the following measures can minimize unnecessary exposure:

- full protective equipment
- minimal number of personnel in the room
- "dead-man" switches (must have active operator control)
- minimal beam size and energy
- careful shielding to reduce scatter.

Full protective equipment should also be used by operating-room personnel during radiation procedures, and, when possible, personnel should stand 2 m or more from the patient.

Non-ionizing radiation

Ultraviolet radiation, lasers and microwaves are non-ionizing radiation sources. They are generally far less hazardous than ionizing radiation but nevertheless require special care to prevent injury.

Ultraviolet radiation is used in germicidal lamps, in certain dermatology treatments and in air filters in some hospitals. It is also produced in welding operations. Exposure of the skin to ultraviolet light causes sunburn, ages the skin and increases the risk of skin cancer. Eye exposure can result in temporary but extremely painful conjunctivitis. Long-term exposure can lead to partial loss of vision.

Standards regarding exposure to ultraviolet radiation are not widely applicable. The best approach to prevention is education and wearing shaded protective eyeglasses.

The Bureau of Radiological Health of the US Food and Drug Administration regulates lasers and classifies them into four classes, I to IV. The laser used to position patients in radiology is considered Class I and represents minimal risk. Surgical lasers, however, can pose a significant hazard to the retina of the eye where the intense beam can cause total loss of vision. Because of the high voltage supply required, all lasers present the risk of electrical shock. The accidental reflection of the laser beam during surgical procedures can result in injury to the staff. Guidelines for laser use have been developed by the American National Standards Institute and the US Army; for example, laser users should wear protective goggles specifically designed for each type of laser and take care not to focus the beam on reflecting surfaces.

The primary concern regarding exposure to microwaves, which are used in hospitals chiefly for cooking and heating food and for diathermy treatments, is the heating effect they have on the body. The eye lens and gonads, having fewer vessels with which to remove heat, are most vulnerable to damage. The long-term effects of low-level exposure have not been established, but there is some evidence that nervous system effects, decreased sperm count, sperm malformations (at least partially reversible after exposure ceases) and cataracts may result.

Prevention and control

The OSHA standard for exposure to microwaves is 10 milliwatts per square centimetre (10 mW/cm). This is the level established to protect against the thermal effects of microwaves. In other countries where levels have been established to protect against reproductive and nervous system damage, the standards are as much as two orders of magnitude lower, that is, 0.01 mW/cm^2 at 1.2 m.

To ensure the safety of workers, microwave ovens should be kept clean to protect the integrity of the door seals and should be checked for leakage at least every three months. Leakage from diathermy equipment should be monitored in the vicinity of the therapist before each treatment.

Hospital workers should be aware of the radiation hazards of ultraviolet exposure and of infrared heat used for therapy. They should have appropriate eye protection when using or repairing ultraviolet equipment, such as germicidal lamps and air purifiers or infrared instruments and equipment.

Conclusion

Physical agents represent an important class of hazards to workers in hospitals, clinics and private offices where diagnostic and therapeutic procedures are performed. These agents are discussed in more detail elsewhere in this *Encyclopaedia*. Their control requires education and training of all health professionals and support staff who may be involved and constant vigilance and systemic monitoring of both the equipment and the way it is used.

● ERGONOMICS OF THE PHYSICAL WORK ENVIRONMENT

Madeleine Estryn-Béhar

Several countries have established recommended noise, temperature and lighting levels for hospitals. These recommendations are, however, rarely included in the specifications given to hospital designers. Further, the few studies examining these variables have reported disquieting levels.

Noise

In hospitals, it is important to distinguish between machine-generated noise capable of impairing hearing (above 85 dBA) and noise which is associated with a degradation of ambiance, administrative work and care (65 to 85 dBA).

Machine-generated noise capable of impairing hearing

Prior to the 1980s, a few publications had already drawn attention to this problem. Van Wagoner and Maguire (1977) evaluated the incidence of hearing loss among 100 employees in an urban hospital in Canada. They identified five zones in which noise levels were between 85 and 115 dBA: the electrical plant, laundry, dish-washing station and printing department and areas where maintenance workers used hand or power tools. Hearing loss was observed in 48% of the 50 workers active in these noisy areas, compared to 6% of workers active in quieter areas.

Yassi et al. (1992) conducted a preliminary survey to identify zones with dangerously high noise levels in a large Canadian hospital. Integrated dosimetry and mapping were subsequently used to study these high-risk areas in detail. Noise levels exceeding 80 dBA were common. The laundry, central processing, nutrition department, rehabilitation unit, stores and electrical plant were all studied in detail. Integrated dosimetry revealed levels of up to 110 dBA at some of these locations.

Noise levels in a Spanish hospital's laundry exceeded 85 dBA at all workstations and reached 97 dBA in some zones (Montoliu et al. 1992). Noise levels of 85 to 94 dBA were measured at some workstations in a French hospital's laundry (Cabal et al. 1986). Although machine re-engineering reduced the noise generated by pressing machines to 78 dBA, this process was not applicable to other machines, due to their inherent design.

A study in the United States reported that electrical surgical instruments generate noise levels of 90 to 100 dBA (Willet 1991). In the same study, 11 of 24 orthopaedic surgeons were reported to suffer from significant hearing loss. The need for better instrument design was emphasized. Vacuum and monitor alarms have been reported to generate noise levels of up to 108 dBA (Hodge and Thompson 1990).

Noise associated with a degradation of ambiance, administrative work and care

A systematic review of noise levels in six Egyptian hospitals revealed the presence of excessive levels in offices, waiting rooms and corridors (Noweir and al-Jiffry 1991). This was attributed to the characteristics of hospital construction and of some of the machines. The authors recommended the use of more appropriate building materials and equipment and the implementation of good maintenance practices.

Work in the first computerized facilities was hindered by the poor quality of printers and the inadequate acoustics of offices. In the Paris region, groups of cashiers talked to their clients and processed invoices and payments in a crowded room whose low plaster ceiling had no acoustic absorption capacity. Noise levels with only one printer active (in practice, all four usually were) were 78 dBA for payments and 82 dBA for invoices.

In a 1992 study of a rehabilitation gymnasium consisting of 8 cardiac rehabilitation bicycles surrounded by four private patient areas, noise levels of 75 to 80 dBA and 65 to 75 dBA were measured near cardiac rehabilitation bicycles and in the neighbouring kinesiology area, respectively. Levels such as these render personalized care difficult.

Shapiro and Berland (1972) viewed noise in operating theatres as the "third pollution", since it increases the fatigue of the surgeons, exerts physiological and psychological effects and influences the accuracy of movements. Noise levels were measured during a cholecystectomy and during tubal ligation. Irritating noises were associated with the opening of a package of gloves (86 dBA), the installation of a platform on the floor (85 dBA), platform adjustment (75 to 80 dBA), placing surgical instruments upon each other (80 dBA), suctioning of trachea of patient (78 dBA), continuous suction bottle (75 to 85 dBA) and the heels of nurses' shoes (68 dBA). The authors recommended the use of heat-resistant plastic, less noisy instruments and, to minimize reverberation, easily cleaned materials other than ceramic or glass for walls, tiles and ceilings.

Noise levels of 51 to 82 dBA and 54 to 73 dBA have been measured in the centrifuge room and automated analyser room of a medical analytical laboratory. The Leq (reflecting full-shift exposure) at the control station was 70.44 dBA, with 3 hours over 70 dBA. At the technical station, the Leq was 72.63 dBA, with 7 hours over 70 dBA. The following improvements were recommended: installing telephones with adjustable ring levels, grouping centrifuges in a closed room, moving photocopiers and printers and installing hutches around the printers.

Patient Care and Comfort

In several countries, recommended noise limits for care units are 35 dBA at night and 40 dBA during the day (Turner, King and Craddock 1975). Falk and Woods (1973) were the first to draw attention to this point, in their study of noise levels and sources in neonatology incubators, recovery rooms and two rooms in an intensive-care unit. The following mean levels were measured over a 24-hour period: 57.7 dBA (74.5 dB) in the incubators, 65.5 dBA (80 dB linear) at the head of patients in the recovery room, 60.1 dBA (73.3 dB) in the intensive care unit and 55.8 dBA (68.1 dB) in one patient room. Noise levels in the recovery room and intensive-care unit were correlated with the number of nurses. The authors emphasized the probable stimulation of patients' hypophyseal-corticoadrenal system by these noise levels, and the resultant increase in peripheral vasoconstriction. There was also some concern about the hearing of patients receiving aminoglycoside antibiotics. These noise levels were considered incompatible with sleep.

Several studies, most of which have been conducted by nurses, have shown that noise control improves patient recovery and quality of life. Reports of research conducted in neonatology wards caring for low-birth-weight babies emphasized the need to reduce the noise caused by personnel, equipment and radiology activities (Green 1992; Wahlen 1992; Williams and Murphy 1991; Oëler 1993; Lotas 1992; Halm and Alpen 1993). Halm and Alpen (1993) have studied the relationship between noise levels in intensive-care units and the psychological well-being of patients and their families (and in extreme cases, even of post-resuscitation psychosis). The effect of ambient noise on the quality of sleep has been rigorously evaluated under experimental conditions (Topf 1992). In intensive care units, the playing of pre-recorded sounds was associated with a deterioration of several sleep parameters.

A multi-ward study reported peak noise levels at the head of patients in excess of 80 dBA, especially in intensive- and respiratory-care units (Meyer et al. 1994). Lighting and noise levels were recorded continuously over seven consecutive days in a medical intensive-care unit, one-bed and multi-bed rooms in a respiratory-care unit and a private room. Noise levels were very high in all cases. The number of peaks exceeding 80 dBA was particularly high in the intensive- and respiratory-care units, with a maximum observed between 12:00 and 18:00 and a minimum between 00:00 and 06:00. Sleep deprivation and fragmentation were considered to have a negative impact on the respiratory system of patients and impair the weaning of patients from mechanical ventilation.

Blanpain and Estryn-Béhar (1990) found few noisy machines such as waxers, ice machines and hotplates in their study of ten Paris-area wards. However, the size and surfaces of the rooms could either reduce or amplify the noise generated by these machines, as well as that (albeit lower) generated by passing cars, ventilation systems and alarms. Noise levels in excess of 45 dBA (observed in 7 of 10 wards) did not promote patient rest. Furthermore, noise disturbed hospital personnel performing very precise tasks requiring close attention. In five of 10 wards, noise levels at the nursing station reached 65 dBA; in two wards, levels of 73 dBA were measured. Levels in excess of 65 dBA were measured in three pantries.

In some cases, architectural decorative effects were instituted with no thought to their effect on acoustics. For example, glass walls and ceilings have been in fashion since the 1970s and have been used in patient admission open-space offices. The resultant noise levels do not contribute to the creation of a calm environment in which patients about to enter the hospital can fill out forms. Fountains in this type of hall generated a background noise level of 73 dBA at the reception desk, requiring receptionists to ask one-third of people requesting information to repeat themselves.

Heat stress

Costa, Trinco and Schallenberg (1992) studied the effect of installing a laminar flow system, which maintained air sterility, on heat stress in an orthopaedic operating theatre. Temperature in the operating theatre increased by approximately 3 °C on average and could reach 30.2 °C. This was associated with a deterioration of the thermal comfort of operating-room personnel, who must wear very bulky clothes that favour heat retention.

Cabal et al. (1986) analysed heat stress in a hospital laundry in central France prior to its renovation. They noted that the relative humidity at the hottest workstation, the "gown-dummy", was 30%, and radiant temperature reached 41 °C. Following installation of double-pane glass and reflective outside walls, and implementation of 10 to 15 air changes per hour, thermal comfort parameters fell within standard levels at all workstations, regardless of the weather outside. A study of a Spanish hospital laundry has shown that high wet-bulb temperatures result in oppressive

work environments, especially in ironing areas, where temperatures may exceed 30 °C (Montoliu et al. 1992).

Blanpain and Estryn-Béhar (1990) characterized the physical work environment in ten wards whose work content they had already studied. Temperature was measured twice in each of ten wards. The nocturnal temperature in patient rooms may be below 22 °C, as patients use covers. During the day, as long as patients are relatively inactive, a temperature of 24 °C is acceptable but should not be exceeded, since some nursing interventions require significant exertion.

The following temperatures were observed between 07:00 and 07:30: 21.5 °C in geriatric wards, 26 °C in a non-sterile room in the haematology ward. At 14:30 on a sunny day, the temperatures were as follows: 23.5 °C in the emergency room and 29 °C in the haematology ward. Afternoon temperatures exceeded 24 °C in 9 of 19 cases. The relative humidity in four out of five wards with general air-conditioning was below 45% and was below 35% in two wards.

Afternoon temperature also exceeded 22 °C at all nine care preparation stations and 26 °C at three care stations. The relative humidity was below 45% in all five stations of wards with air-conditioning. In the pantries, temperatures ranged between 18 °C and 28.5 °C.

Temperatures of 22 °C to 25 °C were measured at the urine drains, where there were also odour problems and where dirty laundry was sometimes stored. Temperatures of 23 °C to 25 °C were measured in the two dirty-laundry closets; a temperature of 18 °C would be more appropriate.

Complaints concerning thermal comfort were frequent in a survey of 2,892 women working in Paris-area wards (Estryn-Béhar et al. 1989a). Complaints of being often or always hot were reported by 47% of morning- and afternoon-shift nurses and 37% of night-shift nurses. Although nurses were sometimes obliged to perform physically strenuous work, such as making several beds, the temperature in the various rooms was too high to perform these activities comfortably while wearing polyester-cotton clothes, which hinder evaporation, or gowns and masks necessary for the prevention of nosocomial infections.

On the other hand, 46% of night-shift nurses and 26% of morning- and afternoon-shift nurses reported being often or always cold. The proportions reporting never suffering from the cold were 11% and 26%.

To conserve energy, the heating in hospitals was often lowered during the night, when patients are under covers. However nurses, who must remain alert despite chronobiologically mediated drops in core body temperatures, were required to put on jackets (not always very hygienic ones) around 04:00. At the end of the study, some wards installed adjustable space-heating at nursing stations.

Studies of 1,505 women in 26 units conducted by occupational physicians revealed that rhinitis and eye irritation were more frequent among nurses working in air-conditioned rooms (Estryn-Béhar and Poinsignon 1989) and that work in air-conditioned environments was related to an almost twofold increase in dermatoses likely to be occupational in origin (adjusted odds ratio of 2) (Delaporte et al. 1990).

Lighting

Several studies have shown that the importance of good lighting is still underestimated in administrative and general departments of hospitals.

Cabal et al. (1986) observed that lighting levels at half of the workstations in a hospital laundry were no higher than 100 lux. Lighting levels following renovations were 300 lux at all workstations, 800 lux at the darning station and 150 lux between the washing tunnels.

Blanpain and Estryn-Béhar (1990) observed maximum night lighting levels below 500 lux in 9 out of 10 wards. Lighting levels were below 250 lux in five pharmacies with no natural lighting and were below 90 lux in three pharmacies. It should be recalled that the difficulty in reading small lettering on labels experienced by older persons may be mitigated by increasing the level of illumination.

Building orientation can result in high day-time lighting levels that disturb patients' rest. For example, in geriatric wards, beds furthest from the windows received 1,200 lux, while those nearest the windows received 5,000 lux. The only window shading available in these rooms were solid window blinds and nurses were unable to dispense care in four-bed rooms when these were drawn. In some cases, nurses stuck paper on the windows to provide patients with some relief.

The lighting in some intensive-care units is too intense to allow patients to rest (Meyer et al. 1994). The effect of lighting on patients' sleep has been studied in neonatology wards by North American and German nurses (Oëler 1993; Boehm and Bollinger 1990).

In one hospital, surgeons disturbed by reflections from white tiles requested the renovation of the operating theatre. Lighting levels outside the shadow-free zone (15,000 to 80,000 lux) were reduced. However, this resulted in levels of only 100 lux at the instrument nurses' work surface, 50 to 150 lux at the wall unit used for equipment storage, 70 lux at the patients' head and 150 lux at the anaesthetists' work surface. To avoid generating glare capable of affecting the accuracy of surgeons' movements, lamps were installed outside of surgeons' sight-lines. Rheostats were installed to control lighting levels at the nurses' work surface between 300 and 1,000 lux and general levels between 100 and 300 lux.

Construction of a hospital with extensive natural lighting

In 1981, planning for the construction of Saint Mary's Hospital on the Isle of Wight began with a goal of halving energy costs (Burton 1990). The final design called for extensive use of natural lighting and incorporated double-pane windows that could be opened in the summer. Even the operating theatre has an outside view and paediatric wards are located on the ground floor to allow access to play areas. The other wards, on the second and third (top) floors, are equipped with windows and ceiling lighting. This design is quite suitable for temperate climates but may be problematic where ice and snow inhibit overhead lighting or where high temperatures may lead to a significant greenhouse effect.

Architecture and Working Conditions

Flexible design is not multi-functionality

Prevailing concepts from 1945 to 1985, in particular the fear of instant obsolescence, were reflected in the construction of multi-purpose hospitals composed of identical modules (Games and Taton-Braen 1987). In the United Kingdom this trend led to the development of the "Harnes system", whose first product was the Dudley Hospital, built in 1974. Seventy other hospitals were later built on the same principles. In France, several hospitals were constructed on the "Fontenoy" model.

Building design should not prevent modifications necessitated by the rapid evolution of therapeutic practice and technology. For example, partitions, fluid circulation subsystems and technical duct-work should all be capable of being easily moved. However, this flexibility should not be construed as an endorsement of the goal of complete multi-functionality—a design goal which leads to the construction of facilities poorly suited to *any* speciality. For example, the surface area needed to store machines, bottles, dis-

posable equipment and medication is different in surgical, cardiology and geriatric wards. Failure to recognize this will lead to rooms being used for purposes they were not designed for (e.g., bathrooms being used for bottle storage).

The Loma Linda Hospital in California (United States) is an example of better hospital design and has been copied elsewhere. Here, nursing and technical medicine departments are located above and below technical floors; this "sandwich" structure permits easy maintenance and adjustment of fluid circulation.

Unfortunately, hospital architecture does not always reflect the needs of those who work there, and multi-functional design has been responsible for reported problems related to physical and cognitive strain. Consider a 30-bed ward composed of one- and two-bed rooms, in which there is only one functional area of each type (nursing station, pantry, storage of disposable materials, linen or medication), all based on the same all-purpose design. In this ward, the management and dispensation of care obliges nurses to change location extremely frequently, and work is greatly fragmented. A comparative study of ten wards has shown that the distance from the nurses' station to the farthest room is an important determinant of both nurses' fatigue (a function of the distance walked) and the quality of care (a function of the time spent in patients' rooms) (Estryn-Béhar and Hakim-Serfaty 1990).

This discrepancy between the architectural design of spaces, corridors and materials, on the one hand, and the realities of hospital work, on the other, has been characterized by Patkin (1992), in a review of Australian hospitals, as an ergonomic "debacle".

Preliminary analysis of the spatial organization in nursing areas

The first mathematical model of the nature, purposes and frequency of staff movements, based on the Yale Traffic Index, appeared in 1960 and was refined by Lippert in 1971. However, attention to one problem in isolation may in fact aggravate others. For example, locating a nurses' station in the centre of the building, in order to reduce the distances walked, may worsen working conditions if nurses must spend over 30% of their time in such windowless surroundings, known to be a source of problems related to lighting, ventilation and psychological factors (Estryn-Béhar and Milanini 1992).

The distance of the preparation and storage areas from patients is less problematic in settings with a high staff-patient ratio and where the existence of a centralized preparation area facilitates the delivery of supplies several times per day, even on holidays. In addition, long waits for elevators are less common in high-rise hospitals with over 600 beds, where the number of elevators is not limited by financial constraints.

Research on the design of specific but flexible hospital units

In the United Kingdom in the late 1970s, the Health Ministry created a team of ergonomists to compile a database on ergonomics training and on the ergonomic layout of hospital work areas (Haigh 1992). Noteworthy examples of the success of this programme include the modification of the dimensions of laboratory furniture to take into account the demands of microscopy work and the redesign of maternity rooms to take into account nurses' work and mothers' preferences.

Cammock (1981) emphasized the need to provide distinct nursing, public and common areas, with separate entrances for nursing and public areas, and separate connections between these areas and the common area. Furthermore, there should be no direct contact between the public and nursing areas.

The Krankenanstalt Rudolfsstiftung is the first pilot hospital of the "European Healthy Hospitals" project. The Viennese pilot project consists of eight sub-projects, one of which, the "Service

Reorganization" project, is an attempt, in collaboration with ergonomists, to promote functional reorganization of available space (Pelikan 1993). For example, all the rooms in an intensive care unit were renovated and rails for patient lifts installed in the ceilings of each room.

A comparative analysis of 90 Dutch hospitals suggests that small units (floors of less than 1,500 m²) are the most efficient, as they allow nurses to tailor their care to the specifics of patients' occupational therapy and family dynamics (Van Hogdalem 1990). This design also increases the time nurses can spend with patients, since they waste less time in changes of location and are less subject to uncertainty. Finally, the use of small units reduces the number of windowless work areas.

A study carried out in the health administration sector in Sweden reported better employee performance in buildings incorporating individual offices and conference rooms, as opposed to an open plan (Ahlin 1992). The existence in Sweden of an institute dedicated to the study of working conditions in hospitals, and of legislation requiring consultation with employee representatives both before and during all construction or renovation projects, has resulted in the regular recourse to participatory design based on ergonomic training and intervention (Tornquist and Ullmark 1992).

Architectural design based on participatory ergonomics

Workers must be involved in the planning of the behavioural and organizational changes associated with the occupation of a new work space. The adequate organization and equipping of a workplace requires taking into account the organizational elements that require modification or emphasis. Two detailed examples taken from two hospitals illustrate this.

Estryn-Béhar et al. (1994) report the results of the renovation of the common areas of a medical ward and a cardiology ward of the same hospital. The ergonomics of the work performed by each profession in each ward was observed over seven entire workdays and discussed over a two-day period with each group. The groups included representatives of all occupations (department heads, supervisors, interns, nurses, nurses' aides, orderlies) from all the shifts. One entire day was spent developing architectural and organizational proposals for each problem noted. Two more days were spent on the simulation of characteristic activities by the entire group, in collaboration with an architect and an ergonomist, using modular cardboard mock-ups and scale models of objects and people. Through this simulation, representatives of the various occupations were able to agree on distances and the distribution of space within each ward. Only after this process was concluded was the design specification drawn up.

The same participatory method was used in a cardiac intensive-care unit in another hospital (Estryn-Béhar et al. 1995a, 1995b). It was found that four types of virtually incompatible activities were conducted at the nursing station:

- care preparation, requiring the use of a drain-board and sink
- decontamination, which also used the sink
- meeting, writing and monitoring; the area used for these activities was also sometimes used for the preparation of care
- clean-equipment storage (three units) and waste storage (one unit).

These zones overlapped, and nurses had to cross the meeting-writing-monitoring area to reach the other areas. Because of the position of the furniture, nurses had to change direction three times to get to the drain-board. Patient rooms were laid out along a corridor, both for regular intensive care and highly intensive care. The storage units were located at the far end of the ward from the nursing station.

In the new layout, the station's longitudinal orientation of functions and traffic is replaced with a lateral one which allows direct and central circulation in a furniture-free area. The meeting-writing-monitoring area is now located at the end of the room, where it offers a calm space near windows, while remaining accessible. The clean and dirty preparation areas are located by the entrance to the room and are separated from each other by a large circulation area. The highly intensive care rooms are large enough to accommodate emergency equipment, a preparation counter and a deep washbasin. A glass wall installed between the preparation areas and the highly intensive care rooms ensures that patients in these rooms are always visible. The main storage area was rationalized and reorganized. Plans are available for each work and storage area.

Architecture, ergonomics and developing countries

These problems are also found in developing countries; in particular, renovations there frequently involve the elimination of common rooms. The performance of ergonomic analysis would identify existing problems and help avoid new ones. For example, the construction of wards comprised of only one- or two-bed rooms increases the distances that personnel must travel. Inadequate attention to staffing levels and the layout of nursing stations, satellite kitchens, satellite pharmacies and storage areas may lead to significant reductions in the amount of time nurses spend with patients and may render work organization more complex.

Furthermore, the application in developing countries of the multi-functional hospital model of developed countries does not take into account different cultures' attitudes toward space utilization. Manuaba (1992) has pointed out that the layout of developed countries' hospital rooms and the type of medical equipment used is poorly suited to developing countries, and that the rooms are too small to comfortably accommodate visitors, essential partners in the curative process.

Hygiene and Ergonomics

In hospital settings, many breaches of asepsis can be understood and corrected only by reference to work organization and work space. Effective implementation of the necessary modifications requires detailed ergonomic analysis. This analysis serves to characterize the interdependencies of team tasks, rather than their individual characteristics, and identify discrepancies between real and nominal work, especially nominal work described in official protocols.

Hand-mediated contamination was one of the first targets in the fight against nosocomial infections. In theory, hands should be systemtically washed on entering and leaving patients' rooms. Although initial and ongoing training of nurses emphasizes the results of descriptive epidemiological studies, research indicates persistent problems associated with hand-washing. In a study conducted in 1987 and involving continuous observation of entire 8-hour shifts in 10 wards, Delaporte et al. (1990) observed an average of 17 hand-washings by morning-shift nurses, 13 by afternoon-shift nurses and 21 by night-shift nurses.

Nurses washed their hands one-half to one-third as often as is recommended for their number of patient contacts (without even considering care-preparation activities); for nurses' aides, the ratio was one-third to one-fifth. Hand-washing before and after each activity is, however, clearly impossible, in terms of both time and skin damage, given the atomization of activity, number of technical interventions and frequency of interruptions and attendant repetition of care that personnel must cope with. Reduction of work interruptions is thus essential and should take precedence over simply reaffirming the importance of hand-washing, which, in any event, cannot be performed over 25 to 30 times per day.

Similar patterns of hand-washing were found in a study based on observations collected over 14 entire workdays in 1994 during the reorganization of the common areas of two university hospital wards (Estryn-Béhar et al. 1994). In every case, nurses would have been incapable of dispensing the required care if they had returned to the nursing station to wash their hands. In short-term-stay units, for example, almost all the patients have blood samples drawn and subsequently receive oral and intravenous medication at virtually the same time. The density of activities at certain times also renders appropriate hand-washing impossible: in one case, an afternoon-shift nurse responsible for 13 patients in a medical ward entered patients' rooms 21 times in one hour. Poorly organized information provision and transmission structures contributed to the number of visits he was obliged to perform. Given the impossibility of washing his hands 21 times in one hour, the nurse washed them only when dealing with the most fragile patients (i.e., those suffering from pulmonary failure).

Ergonomically based architectural design takes several factors affecting hand-washing into account, especially those concerning the location and access to wash-basins, but also the implementation of truly functional "dirty" and "clean" circuits. Reduction of interruptions through participatory analysis of organization helps to make hand-washing possible.

● PREVENTION AND MANAGEMENT OF BACK PAIN IN NURSES

Ulrich Stössel

Epidemiology

The significance of back pain among instances of disease in developed industrial societies is currently on the rise. According to data provided by the National Center for Health Statistics in the United States, chronic diseases of the back and of the vertebral column make up the dominant group among disorders affecting employable individuals under 45 in the US population. Countries such as Sweden, which have at their disposal traditionally good occupational accident statistics, show that musculoskeletal injuries occur twice as frequently in the health services as in all other fields (Lagerlöf and Broberg 1989).

In an analysis of accident frequency in a 450-bed hospital in the United States, Kaplan and Deyo (1988) were able to demonstrate an 8 to 9% yearly incidence of injury to lumbar vertebrae in nurses, leading on average to 4.7 days of absence from work. Thus of all employee groups in hospitals, nurses were the one most afflicted by this condition.

As is clear from a survey of studies done in the last 20 years (Hofmann and Stössel 1995), this disorder has become the object of intensive epidemiological research. All the same, such research—particularly when it aims at furnishing internationally comparable results—is subject to a variety of methodological difficulties. Sometimes all employee categories in the hospital are investigated, sometimes simply nurses. Some studies have suggested that it would make sense to differentiate, within the group "nurses", between registered nurses and nursing aides. Since nurses are predominantly women (about 80% in Germany), and since reported incidence and prevalence rates regarding this disorder do not differ significantly for male nurses, gender-related differentiation would seem to be of less importance to epidemiological analyses.

More important is the question of what investigative tools should be used to research back pain conditions and their gradations. Along with the interpretation of accident, compensation and treatment statistics, one frequently finds, in the international literature, a retrospectively applied standardized questionnaire, to be filled out by the person tested. Other investigative approaches operate with clinical investigative procedures such as orthopaedic function studies or radiological screening procedures. Finally, the more recent investigative approaches also use biomechanical modelling and direct or video-taped observation to study the pathophysiology of work performance, particularly as it involves the lumbo-sacral area (see Hagberg et al. 1993 and 1995).

An epidemiological determination of the extent of the problem based on self-reported incidence and prevalence rates, however, poses difficulties as well. Cultural-anthropological studies and comparisons of health systems have shown that perceptions of pain differ not only between members of different societies but also within societies (Payer 1988). Also, there is the difficulty of objectively grading the intensity of pain, a subjective experience. Finally, the prevailing perception among nurses that "back pain goes with the job" leads to under-reporting.

International comparisons based on analyses of governmental statistics on occupational disorders are unreliable for scientific evaluation of this disorder because of variations in the laws and regulations related to occupational disorders among different countries. Further, within a single country, there is the truism that such data are only as reliable as the reports upon which they are based.

In summary, many studies have determined that 60 to 80% of all nursing staff (averaging 30 to 40 years in age) have had at least one episode of back pain during their working lives. The reported incidence rates usually do not exceed 10%. When classifying back pain, it has been helpful to follow the suggestion of Nachemson and Anderson (1982) to distinguish between back pain and back pain with sciatica. In an as-yet unpublished study a subjective complaint of sciatica was found to be useful in classifying the results of subsequent CAT scans (computer assisted tomography) and magnetic resonance imaging (MRI).

Economic Costs

Estimates of the economic costs differ greatly, depending, in part, on the possibilities and conditions of diagnosis, treatment and compensation available at the particular time and/or place. Thus, in the US for 1976, Snook (1988b) estimated that the costs of back pain totalled US$14 billion, while a total cost of US$25 billion was calculated for 1983. The calculations of Holbrook et al. (1984), which estimated 1984 costs to total just under US$16 billion, appear to be most reliable. In the United Kingdom, costs were estimated to have risen by US$2 billion between 1987 and 1989 according to Ernst and Fialka (1994). Estimates of direct and indirect costs for 1990 reported by Cats-Baril and Frymoyer (1991) indicate that the costs of back pain have continued to increase. In 1988 the US Bureau of National Affairs reported that chronic back pain generated costs of US$80,000 per chronic case per year.

In Germany, the two largest workers' accident insurance funds (*Berufsgenossenschaften*) developed statistics showing that, in 1987, about 15 million work days were lost because of back pain. This corresponds to roughly one-third of all missed work days annually. These losses appear to be increasing at a current average cost of DM 800 per lost day.

It may therefore be said, independently of national differences and vocational groups, that back disorders and their treatment represent not simply a human and a medical problem, but also an enormous economic burden. Accordingly, it seems advisable to pay special attention to the prevention of these disorders in particularly burdened vocational groups such as nursing.

In principle one should differentiate, in research concerning the causes of work-related disorders of the lower back in nurses, between those attributed to a particular incident or accident and those whose genesis lacks such specificity. Both may give rise to chronic back pain if not properly treated. Reflecting their presumed medical knowledge, nurses are much more prone to use self-medication and self-treatment, without consulting a physician, than other groups in the working population. This is not always a disadvantage, since many physicians either do not know how to treat back problems or give them short shrift, simply prescribing sedatives and advising heat applications to the area. The latter reflects the oft-repeated truism that "backaches come with the job", or the tendency to regard workers with chronic back complaints as malingerers.

Detailed analyses of work accident occurrences in the area of spinal disorders have only just begun to be made (see Hagberg et al. 1995). This is also true of the analysis of so-called near-accidents, which can provide a particular sort of information concerning the precursor conditions of a given work accident.

The cause of low back disorders has been attributed by the majority of the studies to the physical demands of the work of nursing, i.e., lifting, supporting and moving of patients and handling heavy and/or bulky equipment and materials, often without ergonomic aids or the help of additional personnel. These activities are often conducted in awkward body positions, where footing is uncertain, and when, out of wilfulness or dementia, the nurse's efforts are resisted by the patient. Trying to keep a patient from falling often results in injury to the nurse or the attendant. Current research, however, is characterized by a strong tendency to speak in terms of multicausality, whereby both the biomechanical basis of demands made upon the body and the anatomical preconditions are discussed.

In addition to faulty biomechanics, injury in such situations can be pre-conditioned by fatigue, muscular weakness (especially of the abdominals, back extensors and quadriceps), diminished flexibility of joints and ligaments and various forms of arthritis. Excessive psychosocial stress can contribute in two ways: (1) prolonged unconscious muscular tension and spasm leading to muscular fatigue and proneness to injury, and (2) irritation and impatience which prompts injudicious attempts to work hurriedly and without waiting for assistance. Enhanced ability to cope with stress and the availability of social support in the workplace are helpful (Theorell 1989; Bongers et al. 1992) when work-related stressors cannot be eliminated or controlled.

Diagnosis

Certain risk situations and dispositions may be added to the risk factors deriving from the biomechanics of the forces acting on the spine and from the anatomy of the support and movement apparatus, ones which are attributable to the work environment. Even though current research is not clear on this point, there is still some indication that the increased and recurrent incidence of psychosocial stress factors in nursing work has the capacity to reduce the threshold of sensitivity to physically burdensome activities, thus contributing to an increased level of vulnerability. In any case, whether such stress factors exist appears to be less decisive in this connection than how nursing staff manages them in a demanding situation and whether they can count on social support in the workplace (Theorell 1989; Bongers et al. 1992).

The proper diagnosis of low back pain requires a complete medical and a detailed occupational history including accidents resulting in injury or near-misses and prior episodes of back pain. The physical examination should include evaluation of gait and posture, palpation for areas of tenderness and evaluation of mus-

cle strength, range of motion and joint flexibility. Complaints of weakness in the leg, areas of numbness and pain that radiate below the knee are indications for neurological examination to seek evidence of spinal cord and/or peripheral nerve involvement. Psychosocial problems may be disclosed through judicious probing of emotional status, attitudes and pain tolerance.

Radiological studies and scans are rarely helpful since, in the vast majority of cases, the problem lies in the muscles and ligaments rather than the bony structures. In fact, bony abnormalities are found in many individuals who have never had back pain; ascribing the back pain to such radiological findings as disc space narrowing or spondylosis may lead to needlessly heroic treatment. Myelography should not be undertaken unless spinal surgery is contemplated.

Clinical laboratory tests are useful in assessing general medical status and may be helpful in disclosing systemic diseases such as arthritis.

Treatment

Various modes of management are indicated depending on the nature of the disorder. Besides ergonomic interventions to enable the return of injured workers to the workplace, surgical, invasive-radiological, pharmacological, physical, physiotherapeutic and also psychotherapeutic management approaches may be necessary—sometimes in combination (Hofmann et al. 1994). Again, however, the vast majority of cases resolve regardless of the therapy offered. Treatment is discussed further in the accompanying box.

Prevention in the Work Environment

Primary prevention of back pain in the workplace involves the application of ergonomic principles and the use of technical aids, coupled with physical conditioning and training of the workers.

Despite the reservations frequently held by nursing staff regarding the use of technical aids for the lifting, positioning and moving of patients, the importance of ergonomic approaches to prevention is increasing (see Estryn-Béhar, Kaminski and Peigné 1990; Hofmann et al. 1994).

In addition to the major systems (permanently installed ceiling lifters, mobile floor lifters), a series of small and simple systems has been introduced noticeably into nursing practice (turntables, walking girdles, lifting cushions, slide boards, bed ladders, anti-slide mats and so on). When using these aids it is important that their actual use fits in well with the care concept of the particular area of nursing in which they are used. Wherever the use of such lifting aids stands in contradiction to the care concept practised, acceptance of such technical lifting aids by nursing staff tends to be low.

Even where technical aids are employed, training in techniques of lifting, carrying and supporting are essential. Lidström and Zachrisson (1973) describe a Swedish "Back School" in which physiotherapists trained in communication conduct classes explaining the structure of the spine and its muscles, how they work in different positions and movements and what can go wrong with them, and demonstrating appropriate lifting and handling techniques that will prevent injury. Klaber Moffet et al. (1986) describe the success of a similar programme in the UK. Such training in lifting and carrying is particularly important where, for one reason or another, use of technical aids is not possible. Numerous studies have shown that training in such techniques must constantly be reviewed; knowledge gained through instruction is frequently "unlearned" in practice.

Unfortunately, the physical demands presented by patients' size, weight, illness and positioning are not always amenable to nurses' control and they are not always able to modify the physical environment and the way their duties are structured. Accord-

Treatment of back pain

Most episodes of acute back pain respond promptly to several days of rest followed by the gradual resumption of activities within the limits of pain. Non-narcotic analgesics and non-steroidal anti-inflammatory drugs may be helpful in relieving pain but do not shorten the course. (Since some of these drugs affect alertness and reaction time, they should be used with caution by individuals who drive vehicles or have assignments where momentary lapses may result in harm to patients.) A variety of forms of physiotherapy (e.g., local applications of heat or cold, diathermy, massage, manipulation, etc.) often provide short periods of transient relief; they are particularly useful as a prelude to graded exercises that will promote the restoration of muscle strength and relaxation as well as flexibility. Prolonged bed rest, traction and the use of lumbar corsets tend to delay recovery and often lengthen the period of disability (Blow and Jayson 1988).

Chronic, recurrent back pain is best treated by a secondary prevention regimen. Getting enough rest, sleeping on a firm mattress, sitting in straight chairs, wearing comfortable, well-fitted shoes, maintaining good posture and avoiding long periods of standing in one position are important adjuncts. Excessive or prolonged use of medications increase the risk of side effects and should be avoided. Some cases are helped by the injection of "trigger points", localized tender nodules in muscles and ligaments, as originally advocated in the seminal report by Lange (1931).

Exercise of key postural muscles (upper and lower abdominal, back, gluteal and thigh muscles) is the mainstay of both chronic care and prevention of back pain. Kraus (1970) has formulated a regimen that features strengthening exercises to correct muscle weakness, relaxing exercises to relief tension, spasticity and rigidity, stretching exercises to minimize contractures and exercises to improve balance and coordination. These exercises, he cautions, should be individualized on the basis of examination of the patient and functional tests of muscle strength, holding power and elasticity (e.g., the Kraus-Weber tests (Kraus 1970)). To avoid adverse effects of exercise, each session should include warm-up and cool-down exercises as well as limbering and relaxing exercises, and the number, duration and intensity of the exercises should be increased gradually as conditioning improves. Simply giving the patient a printed exercise sheet or booklet is not enough; initially, he or she should be given individual instruction and observed to be sure that the exercises are being done correctly.

In 1974, the YMCA in New York introduced the "Y's Way to a Healthy Back Program", a low-cost course of exercise training based on the Kraus exercises; in 1976 it became a national programme in the US and, later, it was established in Australia and in several European countries (Melleby 1988). The twice-a-week, six week programme is given by specially-trained YMCA exercise instructors and volunteers, mainly in urban YMCAs (arrangements for courses at the worksite have been made by a number of employers), and it emphasizes the indefinite continuation of the exercises at home. Approximately 80% of the thousands of individuals with chronic or recurrent back pain who have participated in this program have reported elimination or improvement in their pain.

Leon J. Warshaw

ingly, it is important for institutional managers and nursing supervisors to be included in the educational programme so that, when making decisions about work environments, equipment and job assignments, factors making for "back friendly" working conditions can be considered. At the same time, deployment of staff, with particular reference to nurse-patient ratios and the availability of "helping hands", must be appropriate to the nurses' well-being as well as consistent with the care concept, as hospitals in the Scandinavian countries seem to have managed to do in exemplary fashion. This is becoming ever more important where fiscal constraints dictate staff reductions and cut-backs in equipment procurement and maintenance.

Recently developed holistic concepts, which see such training not simply as instruction in bedside lifting and carrying techniques but rather as movement programmes for both nurses and patients, could take the lead in future developments in this area. Approaches to "participatory ergonomics" and programmes of health advancement in hospitals (understood as organizational development) must also be more intensively discussed and researched as future strategies (see article "Hospital ergonomics: A review").

Since psychosocial stress factors also exercise a moderating function in the perception and mastering of the physical demands made by work, prevention programmes should also ensure that colleagues and superiors work to ensure satisfaction with work, avoid making excessive demands on the mental and physical capacities of workers and provide an appropriate level of social support.

Preventive measures should extend beyond professional life to include work in the home (housekeeping and caring for small children who have to be lifted and carried are particular hazards) as well as in sports and other recreational activities. Individuals with persistent or recurrent back pain, however it is acquired, should be no less diligent in following an appropriate preventive regimen.

Rehabilitation

The key to a rapid recovery is early mobilization and a prompt resumption of activities with the limits of tolerance and comfort. Most patients with acute back injuries recover fully and return to their usual work without incident. Resumption of an unrestricted range of activity should not be undertaken until exercises have fully restored muscle strength and flexibility and banished the fear and temerity that make for recurrent injury. Many individuals exhibit a tendency to recurrences and chronicity; for these, physiotherapy coupled with exercise and control of psychosocial factors will often be helpful. It is important that they return to some form of work as quickly as possible. Temporary elimination of more strenuous tasks and limitation of hours with a graduated return to unrestricted activity will promote a more complete recovery in these cases.

Fitness for work

The professional literature attributes only a very limited prognostic value to screening done before employees start work (US Preventive Services Task Force 1989). Ethical considerations and laws such as the Americans with Disabilities Act mitigate against pre-employment screening. It is generally agreed that pre-employment back x rays have no value, particularly when one considers their cost and the needless exposure to radiation. Newly-hired nurses and other health workers and those returning from an episode of disability due to back pain should be evaluated to detect any predisposition to this problem and provided with access to educational and physical conditioning programmes that will prevent it.

Conclusion

The social and economic impact of back pain, a problem particularly prevalent among nurses, can be minimized by the application of ergonomic principles and technology in the organization of their work and its environment, by physical conditioning that enhances the strength and flexibility of the postural muscles, by education and training in the performance of problematic activi-

ties and, when episodes of back pain do occur, by treatment that emphasizes a minimum of medical intervention and a prompt return to activity.

HEALTH CARE WORKERS AND INFECTIOUS DISEASES

● OVERVIEW OF INFECTIOUS DISEASES

Friedrich Hofmann

Infectious diseases play a significant part in worldwide occurrences of occupational disease in HCWs. Since reporting procedures vary from country to country, and since diseases considered job-related in one country may be classified as non-occupational elsewhere, accurate data concerning their frequency and their proportion of the overall number of occupational diseases among HCWs are difficult to obtain. The proportions range from about 10% in Sweden (Lagerlöf and Broberg 1989), to about 33% in Germany (BGW 1993) and nearly 40% in France (Estryn-Béhar 1991).

The prevalence of infectious diseases is directly related to the efficacy of preventive measures such as vaccines and post-exposure prophylaxis. For example, during the 1980s in France, the proportion of all viral hepatitides fell to 12.7% of its original level thanks to the introduction of vaccination against hepatitis B (Estryn-Béhar 1991). This was noted even before hepatitis A vaccine became available.

Similarly, it may be presumed that, with the declining immunization rates in many countries (e.g., in the Russian Federation and Ukraine in the former Soviet Union during 1994-1995), cases of diphtheria and poliomyelitis among HCWs will increase.

Finally, occasional infections with streptococci, staphylococci and *Salmonella typhi* are being reported among health care workers.

Epidemiological Studies

The following infectious diseases—listed in order of frequency—are the most important in worldwide occurrences of occupational infectious diseases in health care workers:

- hepatitis B
- tuberculosis
- hepatitis C
- hepatitis A
- hepatitis, non A-E.

Also important are the following (not in order of frequency):

- varicella
- measles
- mumps
- rubella
- *Ringelröteln* (parvovirus B 19 virus infections)
- HIV/AIDS
- hepatitis D
- EBV hepatitis
- CMV hepatitis.

It is very doubtful that the very many cases of enteric infection (e.g., salmonella, shigella, etc.) often included in the statistics are, in fact, job-related, since these infections are transmitted faecally/orally as a rule.

Much data is available concerning the epidemiological significance of these job-related infections mostly in relation to hepatitis B and its prevention but also in relation to tuberculosis, hepatitis A and hepatitis C. Epidemiological studies have also dealt with measles, mumps, rubella, varicella and *Ringenröteln*. In using them, however, care must be taken to distinguish between incidence studies (e.g., determination of annual hepatitis B infection rates), sero-epidemiological prevalence studies and other types of prevalence studies (e.g., tuberculin tests).

Hepatitis B

The risk of hepatitis B infections, which are primarily transmitted through contact with blood during needlestick injuries, among HCWs, depends on the frequency of this disease in the population they serve. In northern, central and western Europe, Australia and North America it is found in about 2% of the population. It is encountered in about 7% of the population in southern and south-eastern Europe and most parts of Asia. In Africa, the northern parts of South America and in eastern and south-eastern Asia, rates as high as 20% have been observed (Hollinger 1990).

A Belgian study found that 500 HCWs in northern Europe became infected with hepatitis B each year while the figure for southern Europe was 5,000 (Van Damme and Tormanns 1993). The authors calculated that the annual case rate for western Europe is about 18,200 health care workers. Of these, about 2,275 ultimately develop chronic hepatitis, of whom some 220 will develop cirrhosis of the liver and 44 will develop hepatic carcinoma.

A large study involving 4,218 HCWs in Germany, where about 1% of the population is positive for hepatitis B surface antigen (HBsAg), found that the risk of contracting hepatitis B is approximately 2.5 greater among HCWs than in the general population (Hofmann and Berthold 1989). The largest study to date, involving 85,985 HCWs worldwide, demonstrated that those in dialysis, anaesthesiology and dermatology departments were at greatest risk of hepatitis B (Maruna 1990).

A commonly overlooked source of concern is the HCW who has a chronic hepatitis B infection. More than 100 instances have been recorded worldwide in which the source of the infection was not the patient but the doctor. The most spectacular instance was the Swiss doctor who infected 41 patients (Grob et al. 1987).

While the most important mechanism for transmitting the hepatitis B virus is an injury by a blood-contaminated needle (Hofmann and Berthold 1989), the virus has been detected in a number of other body fluids (e.g., male semen, vaginal secretions, cerebrospinal fluid and pleural exudate) (CDC 1989).

Tuberculosis

In most countries around the world, tuberculosis continues to rank first or second in importance of work-related infections among HCWs (see the article "Tuberculosis prevention, control and surveillance"). Many studies have demonstrated that although the risk is present throughout the professional life, it is greatest during the period of training. For example, a Canadian study in the 1970s demonstrated the tuberculosis rate among female nurses to be double that of women in other professions (Burhill et al. 1985). And, in Germany, where the tuberculosis incidence ranges around 18 per 100,000 for the general population, it is about 26 per 100,000 among health care workers (BGW 1993).

A more accurate estimate of the risk of tuberculosis may be obtained from epidemiological studies based on the tuberculin test. A positive reaction is an indicator of infection by *Mycobacterium tuberculosis* or other mycobacteria or a prior inoculation with the BCG vaccine. If that inoculation was received 20 or more years earlier, it is presumed that the positive test indicates at least one contact with tubercle bacilli. Today, tuberculin testing is done by means of the patch test in which the response is read within five to seven days after the application of the "stamp". A large-scale German study based on such skin tests showed a rate of positives among health professionals that was only moderately higher than that among the general population (Hofmann et al. 1993), but long-range studies demonstrate that a greatly heightened risk of tuberculosis does exist in some areas of health care services.

More recently, anxiety has been generated by the increasing number of cases infected with drug-resistant organisms. This is a matter of particular concern in designing a prophylactic regimen for apparently healthy health care workers whose tuberculin tests "converted" to positive after exposure to patients with tuberculosis.

Hepatitis A

Since the hepatitis A virus is transmitted almost exclusively through faeces, the number of HCWs at risk is substantially smaller than for hepatitis B. An early study conducted in West Berlin showed that paediatric personnel were at greatest risk of this infection (Lange and Masihi 1986). These results were subsequently confirmed by a similar study in Belgium (Van Damme et al. 1989). Similarly, studies in Southwest Germany showed increase risk to nurses, paediatric nurses and cleaning women (Hofmann et al. 1992; Hofmann, Berthold and Wehrle 1992). A study undertaken in Cologne, Germany, revealed no risk to geriatric nurses in contrast to higher prevalence rates among the personnel of child care centres. Another study showed increased risk of hepatitis A among paediatric nurses in Ireland, Germany and France; in the last of these, greater risk was found in workers in psychiatric units treating children and youngsters. Finally, a study of infection rates among handicapped people disclosed higher levels of risk for the patients as well as the workers caring for them (Clemens et al. 1992).

Hepatitis C

Hepatitis C, discovered in 1989, like hepatitis B, is primarily transmitted through blood introduced via needle puncture wounds. Until recently, however, data relating to its threat to HCWs have been limited. A 1991 New York study of 456 dentists and 723 controls showed an infection rate of 1.75% among the dentists compared with 0.14% among the controls (Klein et al. 1991). A German research group demonstrated the prevalence of hepatitis C in prisons and attributed it to the large number of intravenous drug users among the inmates (Gaube et al. 1993). An Austrian study found 2.0% of 294 health care personnel to be seropositive for hepatitis C antibodies, a figure thought to be much higher than that among the general population (Hofmann and Kunz 1990). This was confirmed by another study of HCWs conducted in Cologne, Germany (Chriske and Rossa 1991).

A study in Freiburg, Germany, found that contact with handicapped residents of nursing homes, particularly those with infantile cerebral paresis and trisomia-21, patients with haemophilia and those dependent on drugs administered intravenously presented a particular risk of hepatitis C to workers involved in their care. A significantly increased prevalence rate was found in dialysis personnel and the relative risk to all health care workers was estimated to be 2.5% (admittedly calculated from a relatively small sample).

A possible alternative path of infection was demonstrated in 1993 when a case of hepatitis C was shown to have developed after a splash into the eye (Sartori et al. 1993).

Varicella

Studies of the prevalence of varicella, an illness particularly grave in adults, have consisted of tests for varicella antibodies (anti VZV) conducted in Anglo-Saxon countries. Thus, a seronegative rate of 2.9% was found among 241 hospital employees aged 24 to 62, but the rate was 7.5% for those under the age of 35 (McKinney, Horowitz and Baxtiola 1989). Another study in a paediatric clinic yielded a negative rate of 5% among 2,730 individuals tested in the clinic, but these data become less impressive when it is noted that the serological tests were performed only on persons without a history of having had varicella. A significantly increased risk of varicella infection for paediatric hospital personnel, however, was demonstrated by a study conducted in Freiburg, which found that, in a group of 533 individuals working in hospital care, paediatric hospital care and administration, evidence of varicella immunity was present in 85% of persons younger than 20 years.

Mumps

In considering risk levels of mumps infection, a distinction must be made between countries in which mumps immunization is mandatory and those in which these inoculations are voluntary. In the former, nearly all children and young people will have been immunized and, therefore, mumps poses little risk to health care workers. In the latter, which includes Germany, cases of mumps are becoming more frequent. As a result of lack of immunity, the complications of mumps have been increasing, particularly among adults. A report of an epidemic in a non-immune Inuit population on St. Laurance Island (located between Siberia and Alaska) demonstrated the frequency of such complications of mumps as orchitis in men, mastitis in women and pancreatitis in both sexes (Philip, Reinhard and Lackman 1959).

Unfortunately, epidemiological data on mumps among HCWs are very sparse. A 1986 study in Germany showed that the rate of mumps immunity among 15 to 10 year-olds was 84% but, with voluntary rather than mandatory inoculation, one may presume that this rate has been declining. A 1994 study involving 774 individuals in Freiburg indicated a significantly increased risk to employees in paediatric hospitals (Hofmann, Sydow and Michaelis 1994).

Measles

The situation with measles is similar to that with mumps. Reflecting its high degree of contagiousness, risks of infection among adults emerge as their immunization rates fall. A US study reported an immunity rate of over 99% (Chou, Weil and Arnmow 1986) and two years later 98% of a cohort of 163 nursing students were found to have immunity (Wigand and Grenner 1988). A study in Freiburg yielded rates of 96 to 98% among nurses and paediatric nurses while the rates of immunity among non-medical personnel were only 87 to 90% (Sydow and Hofman 1994). Such data would support a recommendation that immunization be made mandatory for the general population.

Rubella

Rubella falls between measles and mumps with respect to its contagiousness. Studies have shown that about 10% of HCWs are not immune (Ehrengut and Klett 1981; Sydow and Hofmann 1994) and, therefore, at high risk of infection when exposed. Although generally not a serious illness among adults, rubella may be responsible for devastating effects on the foetus during the first 18 weeks of pregnancy: abortion, stillbirth or congenital defects (see table 97.9) (South, Sever and Teratogen 1985; Miller, Vurdien and Farrington 1993). Since these may be produced even before the woman knows that she is pregnant and, since health care workers, particularly those in contact with paediatric

Table 97.9 • Congenital abnormalities following rubella infection in pregnancy.

Studies by South, Sever and Teratogen (1985)					
Week of pregnancy	<4	5–8	9–12	13–16	>17
Deformity rate (%)	70	40	25	40	8
Studies by Miller, Vurdien and Farrington (1993)					
Week of pregnancy	<10	11–12	13–14	15–16	>17
Deformity rate (%)	90	33	11	24	0

patients, are likely to be exposed, it is especially important that inoculation be urged (and perhaps even required) for all female health care workers of child-bearing age who are not immune.

HIV/AIDS

During the 1980s and 1990s, HIV seroconversions (i.e., a positive reaction in an individual previously found to have been negative) became a minor occupational risk among HCWs, although clearly not one to be ignored. By early 1994, reports of some 24 reliably documented cases and 35 possible cases were collected in Europe (Pérez et al. 1994) with an additional 43 documented cases and 43 possible cases were reported in the US (CDC 1994a). Unfortunately, except for avoiding needlesticks and other contacts with infected blood or body fluids, there are no effective preventive measures. Some prophylactic regimens for individuals who have been exposed are recommended and described in the article "Prevention of occupational transmission of bloodborne pathogens".

Other infectious diseases

The other infectious diseases listed earlier in this article have not yet emerged as significant hazards to HCWs either because they have not been recognized and reported or because their epidemiology has not yet been studied. Sporadic reports of single and small clusters of cases suggest that the identification and testing of serological markers should be explored. For example, a 33-month study of typhus conducted by the Centers for Disease Control (CDC) revealed that 11.2% of all sporadic cases not associated with outbreaks occurred in laboratory workers who had examined stool specimens (Blazer et al. 1980).

The future is clouded by two simultaneous problems: the emergence of new pathogens (e.g., new strains such as hepatitis G and new organisms such as the Ebola virus and the equine morbillivirus recently discovered to be fatal to both horses and humans in Australia) and the continuing development of drug resistance by well-recognized organisms such as the tuberculus bacillus. HCWs are likely to be the first to be systematically exposed. This makes their prompt and accurate identification and the epidemiological study of their patterns of susceptibility and transmission of the utmost importance.

Prevention of Infectious Diseases among Health Care Workers

The first essential in the prevention of infectious disease is the indoctrination of all HCWs, support staff as well as health professionals, in the fact that health care facilities are "hotbeds" of infection with every patient representing a potential risk. This is important not only for those directly involved in diagnostic or therapeutic procedures, but also those who collect and handle blood, faeces and other biological materials and those who come in contact with dressings, linens, dishes and other fomites. In some instances, even breathing the same air may be a possible

hazard. Each health care facility, therefore, must develop a detailed procedure manual identifying these potential risks and the steps needed to eliminate, avoid or control them. Then, all personnel must be drilled in following these procedures and monitored to ensure that they are being properly performed. Finally, all failures of these protective measures must be recorded and reported so that revision and/or retraining may be undertaken.

Important secondary measures are the labelling of areas and materials which may be especially infectious and the provision of gloves, gowns, masks, forceps and other protective equipment. Washing the hands with germicidal soap and running water (wherever possible) will not only protect the health care worker but also will minimize the risk of his or her transmitting the infection to co-workers and other patients.

All blood and body fluid specimens or splashes and materials stained with them must be handled as though they are infected. The use of rigid plastic containers for the disposal of needles and other sharp instruments and diligence in the proper disposal of potentially infectious wastes are important preventive measures.

Careful medical histories, serological testing and patch testing should be performed prior to or as soon as health care workers report for duty. Where advisable (and there are no contraindications), appropriate vaccines should be administered (hepatitis B, hepatitis A and rubella appear to be the most important) (see table 97.10). In any case, seroconversion may indicate an acquired infection and the advisability of prophylactic treatment.

Table 97.10 • Indications for vaccinations in health service employees.

Disease	Complications	Who should be vaccinated?
Diptheria		In the event of an epidemic, all employees without demonstrable immunization, beyond this vaccination recommended, combination vaccine td used, if threat of epidemic all employees
Hepatitis A		Employees in the paediatric field as well as in infection stations, in microbiological laboratories and in kitchens, cleaning women
Hepatitis B		All seronegative employees with possibility of contact with blood or bodily fluid
Influenza		Regularly offered to all employees
Measles	Encephalitis	Seronegative employees in the paediatric field
Mumps	Meningitis Otitis Pancreatitis	Seronegative employees in the paediatric field
Rubella	Embryopathy	Seronegative employees in paediatry/midwifery/ambulances, seronegative women capable of giving birth
Poliomyelitis		All employees, e.g., those involved in vaccination campaigns
Tetanus		Employees in gardening and technical fields obligatory, offered to all employees, TD combination vaccine used
Tuberculosis		In all events employees in pulmonology and lung surgery on a voluntary basis (BCG)
Varicellas	Foetal risks	Seronegative employees in paediatry or at least in the encephalomyelitis paediatric oncology (protection of patient) and oncological wards

Prophylactic therapy

In some exposures when it is known that the worker is not immune and has been exposed to a proven or highly suspected risk of infection, prophylactic therapy may be instituted. Especially if the worker presents any evidence of possible immunodeficiency, human immunoglobulin may be administered. Where specific "hyperimmune" serum is available, as in mumps and hepatitis B, it is preferable. In infections which, like hepatitis B, may be slow to develop, or "booster" doses are advisable, as in tetanus, a vaccine may be administered. When vaccines are not available, as in meningococcus infections and plague, prophylactic antibiotics may be used either alone or as a supplement to immune globulin. Prophylactic regimens of other drugs have been developed for tuberculosis and, more recently, for potential HIV infections, as discussed elsewhere in this chapter.

PREVENTION OF OCCUPATIONAL TRANSMISSION OF BLOODBORNE PATHOGENS

Linda S. Martin, Robert J. Mullan and David M. Bell

Prevention of occupational transmission of bloodborne pathogens (BBP) including the human immunodeficiency virus (HIV), hepatitis B virus (HBV) and more recently hepatitis C virus (HCV), has received significant attention. Although HCWs are the primary occupational group at risk of acquisition of infection, any worker who is exposed to blood or other potentially infectious body fluids during the performance of job duties is at risk. Populations at risk for occupational exposure to BBP include workers in health care delivery, public safety and emergency response workers and others such as laboratory researchers and morticians. The potential for occupational transmission of bloodborne pathogens including HIV will continue to increase as the number of persons who have HIV and other bloodborne infections and require medical care increases.

In the US, the Centers for Disease Control and Prevention (CDC) recommended in 1982 and 1983 that patients with the acquired immunodeficiency syndrome (AIDS) be treated according to the (now obsolete) category of "blood and body fluid precautions" (CDC 1982; CDC 1983). Documentation that HIV, the causative agent of AIDS, had been transmitted to HCWs by percutaneous and mucocutaneous exposures to HIV-infected blood, as well as the realization that the HIV infection status of most patients or blood specimens encountered by HCWs would be unknown at the time of the encounter, led CDC to recommend that blood and body fluid precautions be applied to *all* patients, a concept known as "universal precautions" (CDC 1987a, 1987b). The use of universal precautions eliminates the need to identify patients with bloodborne infections, but is not intended to replace general infection control practices. Universal precautions include the use of handwashing, protective barriers (e.g., goggles, gloves, gowns and face protection) when blood contact is anticipated and care in the use and disposal of needles and other sharp instruments in all health care settings. Also, instruments and other reusable equipment used in performing invasive procedures should be appropriately disinfected or sterilized (CDC 1988a, 1988b). Subsequent CDC recommendations have addressed prevention of transmission of HIV and HBV to public safety and emergency responders (CDC 1988b), management of occupational exposure to HIV, including the recommendations for the use of zidovudine (CDC 1990), immunization against HBV and management of HBV exposure (CDC

1991a), infection control in dentistry (CDC 1993) and the prevention of HIV transmission from HCWs to patients during invasive procedures (CDC 1991b).

In the US, CDC recommendations do not have the force of law, but have often served as the foundation for government regulations and voluntary actions by industry. The Occupational Health and Safety Administration (OSHA), a federal regulatory agency, promulgated a standard in 1991 on Occupational Exposure to Bloodborne Pathogens (OSHA 1991). OSHA concluded that a combination of engineering and work practice controls, personal protective clothing and equipment, training, medical surveillance, signs and labels and other provisions can help to minimize or eliminate exposure to bloodborne pathogens. The standard also mandated that employers make available hepatitis B vaccination to their employees.

The World Health Organization (WHO) has also published guidelines and recommendations pertaining to AIDS and the workplace (WHO 1990, 1991). In 1990, the European Economic Council (EEC) issued a council directive (90/679/EEC) on protection of workers from risks related to exposure to biological agents at work. The directive requires employers to conduct an assessment of the risks to the health and safety of the worker. A distinction is drawn between activities where there is a deliberate intention to work with or use biological agents (e.g., laboratories) and activities where exposure is incidental (e.g., patient care). Control of risk is based on a hierarchical system of procedures. Special containment measures, according to the classification of the agents, are set out for certain types of health facilities and laboratories (McCloy 1994). In the US, CDC and the National Institutes of Health also have specific recommendations for laboratories (CDC 1993b).

Since the identification of HIV as a BBP, knowledge about HBV transmission has been helpful as a model for understanding modes of transmission of HIV. Both viruses are transmitted via sexual, perinatal and bloodborne routes. HBV is present in the blood of individuals positive for hepatitis B e antigen (HBeAg, a marker for high infectivity) at a concentration of approximately 10^8 to 10^9 viral particles per millilitre (ml) of blood (CDC 1988b). HIV is present in blood at much lower concentrations: 10^3 to 10^4 viral particles/ml for a person with AIDS and 10 to 100/ml for a person with asymptomatic HIV infection (Ho, Moudgil and Alam 1989). The risk of HBV transmission to a HCW after percutaneous exposure to HBeAg-positive blood is approximately 100-fold higher than the risk of HIV transmission after percutaneous exposure to HIV-infected blood (i.e., 30% versus 0.3%) (CDC 1989).

Hepatitis

Hepatitis, or inflammation of the liver, can be caused by a variety of agents, including toxins, drugs, autoimmune disease and infectious agents. Viruses are the most common cause of hepatitis (Benenson 1990). Three types of bloodborne viral hepatitis have been recognized: hepatitis B, formerly called serum hepatitis, the major risk to HCWs; hepatitis C, the major cause of parenterally transmitted non-A, non-B hepatitis; and hepatitis D, or delta hepatitis.

Hepatitis B. The major infectious bloodborne occupational hazard to HCWs is HBV. Among US HCWs with frequent exposure to blood, the prevalence of serological evidence of HBV infection ranges between approximately 15 and 30%. In contrast, the prevalence in the general populations averages 5%. The cost-effectiveness of serological screening to detect susceptible individuals among HCWs depends on the prevalence of infection, the cost of testing and the vaccine costs. Vaccination of persons who already have antibodies to HBV has not been shown to cause adverse effects. Hepatitis B vaccine provides protection against hepatitis B for at least 12 years after vaccination; booster doses

Table 97.11 • Recommendation for post-exposure prophylaxis for percutaneous or permucosal exposure to hepatitis B virus, United States.

Exposed person	When source is		
	HBsAg[1] positive	HBsAg negative	Source not tested or unknown
Unvaccinated	HBIG[2]×1 and initiate HB vaccine[3]	Initiate HB vaccine	Initiate HB vaccine
Previously vaccinated			
Known responder	No treatment	No treatment	No treatment
Known non-responder	HBIG×2 or HBIG×1 and initiate revaccination	No treatment	If known high-risk source treat as if source were HBsAg positive
Response unknown	Test exposed for anti-HBs[4] 1. If adequate[5], no treatment 2. If inadequate, HBIGx1 and vaccine booster	No treatment	Test exposed for anti-HBs 1. If adequate, no treatment 2. If inadequate, vaccine booster

[1] HBsAg = Hepatitis B surface antigen. [2] HBIG = Hepatitis B immune globulin; dose 0.06 mL/kg IM.
[3] HB vaccine = hepatitis B vaccine. [4] Anti-HBs = antibody to hepatitis B surface antigen. [5] Adequate anti-HBs is ≥10 mIU/mL.

currently are not recommended. The CDC estimated that in 1991 there were approximately 5,100 occupationally acquired HBV infections in HCWs in the United States, causing 1,275 to 2,550 cases of clinical acute hepatitis, 250 hospitalizations and about 100 deaths (unpublished CDC data). In 1991, approximately 500 HCWs became HBV carriers. These individuals are at risk of long-term sequelae, including disabling chronic liver disease, cirrhosis and liver cancer.

The HBV vaccine is recommended for use in HCWs and public safety workers who may be exposed to blood in the workplace (CDC 1991b). Following a percutaneous exposure to blood, the decision to provide prophylaxis must include considerations of several factors: whether the source of the blood is available, the HBsAg status of the source and the hepatitis B vaccination and vaccine-response status of the exposed person. For any exposure of a person not previously vaccinated, hepatitis B vaccination is recommended. When indicated, hepatitis B immune globulin (HBIG) should be administered as soon as possible after exposure since its value beyond 7 days after exposure is unclear. Specific CDC recommendations are indicated in table 97.11 (CDC 1991b).

Article 14(3) of EEC Directive 89/391/EEC on vaccination required only that effective vaccines, where they exist, be made available for exposed workers who are not already immune. There was an amending Directive 93/88/EEC which contained a recommended code of practice requiring that workers at risk be offered vaccination free of charge, informed of the benefits and disadvantages of vaccination and non-vaccination, and be provided a certificate of vaccination (WHO 1990).

The use of hepatitis B vaccine and appropriate environmental controls will prevent almost all occupational HBV infections. Reducing blood exposure and minimizing puncture injuries in the health care setting will reduce also the risk of transmission of other bloodborne viruses.

Hepatitis C. Transmission of HCV is similar to that of HBV, but infection persists in most patients indefinitely and more frequently progresses to long-term sequelae (Alter et al. 1992). The prevalence of anti-HCV among US hospital-based health care workers averages 1 to 2% (Alter 1993). HCWs who sustain accidental injuries from needlesticks contaminated with anti-HCV-positive blood have a 5 to 10% risk of acquiring HCV infection (Lampher et al. 1994; Mitsui et al. 1992). There has been one report of HCV transmission after a blood splash to the conjunctiva (Sartori et al. 1993). Prevention measures again consist of adherence to universal precautions and percutaneous injury prevention, since no vaccine is available and immune globulin does not appear to be effective.

Hepatitis D. Hepatitis D virus requires the presence of hepatitis B virus for replication; thus, HDV can infect persons only as a coinfection with acute HBV or as a superinfection of chronic HBV infection. HDV infection can increase the severity of liver disease; one case of occupationally acquired HDV infection hepatitis has been reported (Lettau et al. 1986). Hepatitis B vaccination of HBV-susceptible persons will also prevent HDV infection; however, there is no vaccine to prevent HDV superinfection of an HBV carrier. Other prevention measures consist of adherence to universal precautions and percutaneous injury prevention.

HIV

The first cases of AIDS were recognized in June of 1981. Initially, over 92% of the cases reported in the United States were in homosexual or bisexual men. However, by the end of 1982, AIDS cases were identified among injection drug users, blood transfusion recipients, haemophilia patients treated with clotting factor concentrates, children and Haitians. AIDS is the result of infection with HIV, which was isolated in 1985. HIV has spread rapidly. In the United States, for example, the first 100,000 AIDS cases occurred between 1981 and 1989; the second 100,000 cases occurred between 1989 and 1991. As of June 1994, 401,749 cases of AIDS had been reported in the United States (CDC 1994b).

Globally, HIV has affected many countries including those in Africa, Asia and Europe. As of 31 December 1994, 1,025,073 cumulative cases of AIDS in adults and children had been reported to the WHO. This represented a 20% increase from the 851,628 cases reported through December 1993. It was estimated that 18 million adults and about 1.5 million children have been infected with HIV since the beginning of the pandemic (late 1970s to early 1980s) (WHO 1995).

Although HIV has been isolated from human blood, breast milk, vaginal secretions, semen, saliva, tears, urine, cerebrospinal fluid and amniotic fluid, epidemiological evidence has implicated only blood, semen, vaginal secretions and breast milk in the transmission of the virus. The CDC has also reported on the transmission of HIV as the result of contact with blood or other body secretions or excretions from an HIV-infected person in the household (CDC 1994c). Documented modes of occupational HIV transmission include having percutaneous or mucocutaneous contact with HIV-infected blood. Exposure by the percutaneous route is more likely to result in infection transmission than is mucocutaneous contact.

There are a number of factors which may influence the likelihood of occupational bloodborne pathogen transmission, including: the volume of fluid in the exposure, the virus titre, the length of time of the exposure and the immune status of the worker. Additional data are needed to determine precisely the importance of these factors. Preliminary data from a CDC case-control study indicate that for percutaneous exposures to HIV-infected blood, HIV transmission is more likely if the source patient has advanced HIV disease and if the exposure involves a larger inoculum of blood (e.g., injury due to a large-bore hollow needle) (Cardo et al.

1995). Virus titre can vary between individuals and over time within a single individual. Also, blood from persons with AIDS, particularly in the terminal stages, may be more infectious than blood from persons in earlier stages of HIV infection, except possibly during the illness associated with acute infection (Cardo et al. 1995).

Occupational exposure and HIV infection

As of December 1996, CDC reported 52 HCWs in the United States who have seroconverted to HIV following a documented occupational exposure to HIV, including 19 laboratory workers, 21 nurses, six physicians and six in other occupations. Forty-five of the 52 HCWs sustained percutaneous exposures, five had mucocutaneous exposures, one had both a percutaneous and a mucocutaneous exposure and one had an unknown route of exposure. In addition, 111 possible cases of occupationally acquired infection have been reported. These possible cases have been investigated and are without identifiable non-occupational or transfusion risks; each reported percutaneous or mucocutaneous occupational exposures to blood or body fluids, or laboratory solutions containing HIV, but HIV seroconversion specifically resulting from an occupational exposure was not documented (CDC 1996a).

In 1993, the AIDS Centre at the Communicable Disease Surveillance Centre (UK) summarized reports of cases of occupational HIV transmission including 37 in the United States, four in the UK and 23 from other countries (France, Italy, Spain, Australia, South Africa, Germany and Belgium) for a total of 64 documented seroconversions after a specific occupational exposure. In the possible or presumed category there were 78 in the United States, six in the UK and 35 from other countries (France, Italy, Spain, Australia, South Africa, Germany, Mexico, Denmark, Netherlands, Canada and Belgium) for a total of 118 (Heptonstall, Porter and Gill 1993). The number of reported occupationally acquired HIV infections is likely to represent only a portion of the actual number due to under-reporting and other factors.

HIV post-exposure management

Employers should make available to workers a system for promptly initiating evaluation, counselling and follow-up after a reported occupational exposure that may place a worker at risk of acquiring HIV infection. Workers should be educated and encouraged to report exposures immediately after they occur so that appropriate interventions can be implemented (CDC 1990).

If an exposure occurs, the circumstances should be recorded in the worker's confidential medical record. Relevant information includes the following: date and time of exposure; job duty or task being performed at the time of exposure; details of exposure; description of source of exposure, including, if known, whether the source material contained HIV or HBV; and details about counselling, post-exposure management and follow-up. The source individual should be informed of the incident and, if consent is obtained, tested for serological evidence of HIV infection. If consent cannot be obtained, policies should be developed for testing source individuals in compliance with applicable regulations. Confidentiality of the source individual should be maintained at all times.

If the source individual has AIDS, is known to be HIV seropositive, refuses testing or the HIV status is unknown, the worker should be evaluated clinically and serologically for evidence of HIV infection as soon as possible after the exposure (baseline) and, if seronegative, should be retested periodically for a minimum of 6 months after exposure (e.g., six weeks, 12 weeks and six months after exposure) to determine whether HIV infection has occurred. The worker should be advised to report and seek medical evaluation for any acute illness that occurs during the follow-up period. During the follow-up period, especially the first six to 12 weeks after the exposure, exposed workers should be advised to refrain from blood, semen or organ donation and to abstain from, or use measures to prevent HIV transmission, during sexual intercourse.

In 1990, CDC published a statement on the management of exposure to HIV including considerations regarding zidovudine (ZDV) post-exposure use. After a careful review of the available data, CDC stated that the efficacy of zidovudine could not be assessed due to insufficient data, including available animal and human data (CDC 1990).

In 1996, information suggesting that ZDV post-exposure prophylaxis (PEP) may reduce the risk for HIV transmission after occupational exposure to HIV-infected blood (CDC 1996a) prompted a US Public Health Service (PHS) to update a previous PHS statement on management of occupational exposure to HIV with the following findings and recommendations on PEP (CDC 1996b). Although failures of ZDV PEP have occurred (Tokars et al. 1993), ZDV PEP was associated with a decrease of approximately 79% in the risk for HIV seroconversion after percutaneous exposure to HIV-infected blood in a case-control study among HCWs (CDC 1995).

Although information about the potency and toxicity of antiretroviral drugs is available from studies of HIV-infected patients, it is uncertain to what extent this information can be applied to uninfected persons receiving PEP. In HIV-infected patients, combination therapy with the nucleosides ZDV and lamivudine (3TC) has greater antiretroviral activity than ZDV alone and is active against many ZDV-resistant HIV strains without significantly increased toxicity (Anon. 1996). Adding a protease inhibitor provides even greater increases in antiretroviral activity; among protease inhibitors, indinavir (IDV) is more potent than saquinavir at currently recommended doses and appears to have fewer drug interactions and short-term adverse effects than ritonavir (Niu, Stein and Schnittmann 1993). Few data exist to assess possible long-term (i.e., delayed) toxicity resulting from use of these drugs in persons not infected with HIV.

The following PHS recommendations are provisional because they are based on limited data regarding efficacy and toxicity of PEP and risk for HIV infection after different types of exposure. Because most occupational exposures to HIV do not result in infection transmission, potential toxicity must be carefully considered when prescribing PEP. Changes in drug regimens may be appropriate, based on factors such as the probable antiretroviral drug resistance profile of HIV from the source patient, local availability of drugs and medical conditions, concurrent drug therapy and drug toxicity in the exposed worker. If PEP is used, drug-toxicity monitoring should include a complete blood count and renal and hepatic chemical function tests at baseline and two weeks after starting PEP. If subjective or objective toxicity is noted, drug reduction or drug substitution should be considered, and further diagnostic studies may be indicated.

Chemoprophylaxis should be recommended to exposed workers after occupational exposures associated with the highest risk for HIV transmission. For exposures with a lower, but non-negligible risk, PEP should be offered, balancing the lower risk against the use of drugs having uncertain efficacy and toxicity. For exposures with negligible risk, PEP is not justified (see table 97.12). Exposed workers should be informed that knowledge about the efficacy and toxicity of PEP is limited, that for agents other than ZDV, data are limited regarding toxicity in persons without HIV infection or who are pregnant and that any or all drugs for PEP may be declined by the exposed worker.

PEP should be initiated promptly, preferably with 1 to 2 hours post-exposure. Although animal studies suggest that PEP probably is not effective when started later than 24 to 36 hours post-

Table 97.12 • Provisional US Public Health Service recommendations for chemoprophylaxis after occupational exposure to HIV, by type of exposure and source of material, 1996.

Type of exposure	Source material[1]	Antiretroviral prophylaxis[2]	Antiretroviral regimen[3]
Percutaneous	Blood		
	Highest risk[4]	Recommend	ZDV plus 3TC plus IDV
	Increased risk[4]	Recommend	ZDV plus 3TC, ± IDV[5]
	No increased risk[4]	Offer	ZDV plus 3TC
	Fluid containing visible blood, other potentially infectious fluid[6], or tissue	Offer	ZDV plus 3TC
	Other body fluid (e.g., urine)	Not offer	
Mucous membrane	Blood	Offer	ZDV plus 3TC, ± IDV[5]
	Fluid containing visible blood, other potentially infectious fluid[6], or tissue	Offer	ZDV, ± 3TC[5]
	Other body fluid (e.g., urine)	Not offer	
Skin, increased risk[7]	Blood	Offer	ZDV plus 3TC, ± IDV[5]
	Fluid containing visible blood, other potentially infectious fluid[6], or tissue	Offer	ZDV, ± 3TC[5]
	Other body fluid (e.g., urine)	Not offer	

[1] Any exposure to concentrated HIV (e.g., in a research laboratory or production facility) is treated as percutaneous exposure to blood with highest risk. [2] *Recommend*—Postexposure prophylaxis (PEP) should be recommended to the exposed worker with counselling. *Offer*—PEP should be offered to the exposed worker with counselling. *Not offer*—PEP should not be offered because these are not occupational exposures to HIV. [3] Regimens: zidovudine (ZDV), 200 mg three times a day; lamivudine (3TC), 150 mg two times a day; indinavir (IDV), 800 mg three times a day (if IDV is not available, saquinavir may be used, 600 mg three times a day). Prophylaxis is given for 4 weeks. For full prescribing information, see package inserts. [4] Risk definitions for percutaneous blood exposure: *Highest risk*—BOTH larger volume of blood (e.g., deep injury with large diameter hollow needle previously in source patient's vein or artery, especially involving an injection of source-patient's blood) AND blood containing a high titre of HIV (e.g., source with acute retroviral illness or end-stage AIDS; viral load measurement may be considered, but its use in relation to PEP has not been evaluated). *Increased risk*—EITHER exposure to larger volume of blood OR blood with a high titre of HIV. *No increased risk*—NEITHER exposure to larger volume of blood NOR blood with a high titre of HIV (e.g., solid suture needle injury from source patient with asymptomatic HIV infection). [5] Possible toxicity of additional drug may not be warranted. [6] Includes semen; vaginal secretions; cerebrospinal, synovial, pleural, peritoneal, pericardial and amniotic fluids. [7] For skin, risk is increased for exposures involving a high titre of HIV, prolonged contact, an extensive area, or an area in which skin integrity is visibly compromised. For skin exposures without increased risk, the risk for drug toxicity outweighs the benefit of PEP.

exposure (Niu, Stein and Schnittmann 1993; Gerberding 1995), the interval after which there is no benefit from PEP for humans is undefined. Initiating therapy after a longer interval (e.g., 1 to 2 weeks) may be considered for the highest risk exposures; even if infection is not prevented, early treatment of acute HIV infection may be beneficial (Kinloch-de-los et al. 1995).

If the source patient or the patient's HIV status is unknown, initiating PEP should be decided on a case-by-case basis, based on the exposure risk and likelihood of infection in known or possible source patients.

Other Bloodborne Pathogens

Syphilis, malaria, babesiosis, brucellosis, leptospirosis, arboviral infections, relapsing fever, Creutzfeldt-Jakob disease, human T-lymphotropic virus type 1 and viral haemorrhagic fever have also been transmitted by the bloodborne route (CDC 1988a; Benenson 1990). Occupational transmission of these agents has only rarely been recorded, if ever.

Prevention of Transmission of Bloodborne Pathogens

There are several basic strategies which relate to the prevention of occupational transmission of bloodborne pathogens. Exposure prevention, the mainstay of occupational health, can be accomplished by substitution (e.g., replacing an unsafe device with a safer one), engineering controls (i.e., controls that isolate or remove the hazard), administrative controls (e.g., prohibiting recapping of needles by a two-handed technique) and use of personal protective equipment. The first choice is to "engineer out the problem".

In order to reduce exposures to bloodborne pathogens, adherence to general infection control principles, as well as strict compliance with universal precaution guidelines, is required. Important components of universal precautions include the use of appropriate personal protective equipment, such as gloves, gowns and eye protection, when exposure to potentially infectious body fluids is anticipated. Gloves are one of the most important barriers between the worker and the infectious material. While they do not prevent needlesticks, protection for the skin is provided. Gloves should be worn when contact with blood or body fluids is anticipated. Washing of gloves in not recommended. Recommendations also advise workers to take precautions to prevent injuries by needles, scalpels and other sharp instruments or devices during procedures; when cleaning used instruments; during disposal of used needles; and when handling sharp instruments after procedures.

Percutaneous exposures to blood

Since the major risk of infection results from parenteral exposure from sharp instruments such as syringe needles, engineering controls such as resheathing needles, needleless IV systems, blunt suture needles and appropriate selection and use of sharps disposal containers to minimize exposures to percutaneous injuries are critical components of universal precautions.

The most common type of percutaneous inoculation occurs through inadvertent needlestick injury, many of which are associated with recapping of needles. The following reasons have been indicated by workers as reasons for recapping: inability to properly dispose of needles immediately, sharps disposal containers too far away, lack of time, dexterity problems and patient interaction.

Needles and other sharp devices can be redesigned to prevent a significant proportion of percutaneous exposures. A fixed barrier should be provided between hands and the needle after use. Worker's hands should remain behind the needle. Any safety feature should be an integral part of the device. The design should be simple and little or no training should be required (Jagger et al. 1988).

Implementing safer needle devices must be accompanied by evaluation. In 1992, the American Hospital Association (AHA) published a briefing to assist hospitals with the selection, evaluation and adoption of safer needle devices (AHA 1992). The briefing stated that "because safer needle devices, unlike drugs and other therapies, do not undergo clinical testing for safety and efficacy before they are marketed, hospitals are essentially 'on their own' when it comes to selecting appropriate products for their specific institutional needs". Included in the AHA document are guidance for the evaluation and adoption of safer needle devices, case studies of the use of safety devices, evaluation forms and listing of some, but not all, products on the US market.

Prior to implementation of a new device, health care institutions must ensure that there is an appropriate needlestick surveillance system in place. In order to accurately assess the efficacy of new devices, the number of reported exposures should be expressed as an incidence rate. Possible denominators for reporting the number of needlestick injuries include patient days, hours worked, number of devices purchased, number of devices used and number of procedures performed. The collection of specific information on device-related injuries is an important component of the evaluation of the effectiveness of a new device. Factors to be considered in collecting information on needlestick injuries include: new product distribution, stocking and tracking; identification of users; removal of other devices; compatibility with other devices (especially IV equipment); ease of use; and mechanical failure. Factors which may contribute to bias include compliance, subject selection, procedures, recall, contamination, reporting and follow-up. Possible outcome measures include rates of needlestick injuries, HCW compliance, patient care complications and cost.

Finally, training and feedback from workers are important components of any successful needlestick prevention programme. User acceptance is a critical factor, but one that seldom receives enough attention.

Elimination or reduction of percutaneous injuries should result if adequate engineering controls are available. If HCWs, product evaluation committees, administrators and purchasing departments all work together to identify where and what safer devices are needed, safety and cost effectiveness can be combined. Occupational transmission of bloodborne pathogens is costly, both in terms of money and the impact on the employee. Every needlestick injury causes undue stress on the employee and may affect job performance. Referral to mental health professionals for supportive counselling may be required.

In summary, a comprehensive approach to prevention is essential to maintaining a safe and healthy environment in which to provide health care services. Prevention strategies include the use of vaccines, post-exposure prophylaxis and prevention or reduction of needlestick injuries. Prevention of needlestick injuries can be accomplished by improvement in the safety of needle-bearing devices, development of procedures for safer use and disposal and adherence to infection control recommendations.

Acknowledgements: The authors thank Mariam Alter, Lawrence Reed and Barbara Gooch for their manuscript review.

● TUBERCULOSIS PREVENTION, CONTROL AND SURVEILLANCE

Robert J. Mullan

Transmission of *Mycobacterium tuberculosis* is a recognized risk in health care facilities. The magnitude of the risk to HCWs varies considerably by the type of health care facility, the prevalence of TB in the community, the patient population served, the HCW's occupational group, the area of the health care facility in which the HCW works and the effectiveness of TB infection-control interventions. The risk may be higher in areas where patients with TB are provided care before diagnosis and initiation of TB treatment and isolation precautions (e.g., in clinic waiting areas and emergency departments) or where diagnostic or treatment procedures that

stimulate coughing are performed. Nosocomial transmission of *M. tuberculosis* has been associated with close contact with persons who have infectious TB and with the performance of certain procedures (e.g., bronchoscopy, endotracheal intubation and suctioning, open abscess irrigation and autopsy). Sputum induction and aerosol treatments that induce coughing may also increase the potential for transmission of *M. tuberculosis*. Personnel in health care facilities should be particularly alert to the need for preventing transmission of *M. tuberculosis* in those facilities in which immunocompromised persons (e.g., HIV-infected persons) work or receive care—especially if cough-inducing procedures, such as sputum induction and aerosolized pentamidine treatments, are being performed.

Transmission and Pathogenesis

M. tuberculosis is carried in airborne particles, or droplet nuclei, that can be generated when persons who have pulmonary or laryngeal TB sneeze, cough, speak or sing. The particles are an estimated 1 to 5 μm in size and normal air currents can keep them airborne for prolonged time periods and spread them throughout a room or building. Infection occurs when a susceptible person inhales droplet nuclei containing *M. tuberculosis* and these droplet nuclei traverse the mouth or nasal passages, upper respiratory tract and bronchi to reach the alveoli of the lungs. Once in the alveoli, the organisms are taken up by alveolar macrophages and spread throughout the body. Usually within two to ten weeks after initial infection with *M. tuberculosis*, the immune response limits further multiplication and spread of the tubercle bacilli; however, some of the bacilli remain dormant and viable for many years. This condition is referred to as latent TB infection. Persons with latent TB infection usually have positive purified protein derivative (PPD)-tuberculin skin-test results, but they do not have symptoms of active TB, and they are not infectious.

In general, persons who become infected with *M. tuberculosis* have approximately a 10% risk for developing active TB during their lifetimes. This risk is greatest during the first two years after infection. Immunocompromised persons have a greater risk for the progression of latent TB infection to active TB disease; HIV infection is the strongest known risk factor for this progression. Persons with latent TB infection who become co-infected with HIV have approximately an 8 to 10% risk per year for developing active TB. HIV-infected persons who are already severely immunosuppressed and who become newly infected with *M. tuberculosis* have an even greater risk for developing active TB.

The probability that a person who is exposed to *M. tuberculosis* will become infected depends primarily on the concentration of infectious droplet nuclei in the air and the duration of exposure. Characteristics of the TB patient that enhance transmission include:

- disease in the lungs, airways or larynx
- presence of cough or other forceful expiratory measures
- presence of acid-fast bacilli (AFB) in the sputum
- failure of the patient to cover the mouth and nose when coughing or sneezing
- presence of cavitation on chest radiograph
- inappropriate or short duration of chemotherapy
- administration of procedures that can induce coughing or cause aerosolization of *M. tuberculosis* (e.g., sputum induction).

Environmental factors that enhance the likelihood of transmission include:

- exposure in relatively small, enclosed spaces
- inadequate local or general ventilation that results in insufficient dilution and/or removal of infectious droplet nuclei
- recirculation of air containing infectious droplet nuclei.

Characteristics of the persons exposed to *M. tuberculosis* that may affect the risk for becoming infected are not as well defined. In general, persons who have been infected previously with *M. tuberculosis* may be less susceptible to subsequent infection. However, reinfection can occur among previously infected persons, especially if they are severely immunocompromised. Vaccination with Bacille of Calmette and Guérin (BCG) probably does not affect the risk for infection; rather, it decreases the risk for progressing from latent TB infection to active TB. Finally, although it is well established that HIV infection increases the likelihood of progressing from latent TB infection to active TB, it is unknown whether HIV infection increases the risk for becoming infected if exposed to *M. tuberculosis*.

Epidemiology

Several TB outbreaks among persons in health care facilities have been reported recently in the United States. Many of these outbreaks involved transmission of multidrug-resistant strains of *M. tuberculosis* to both patients and HCWs. Most of the patients and some of the HCWs were HIV-infected persons in whom new infection progressed rapidly to active disease. Mortality associated with those outbreaks was high (with a range of 43 to 93%). Furthermore, the interval between diagnosis and death was brief (with a range of median intervals of 4 to 16 weeks). Factors contributing to these outbreaks included delayed diagnosis of TB, delayed recognition of drug resistance and delayed initiation of effective therapy, all of which resulted in prolonged infectiousness, delayed initiation and inadequate duration of TB isolation, inadequate ventilation in TB isolation rooms, lapses in TB isolation practices and inadequate precautions for cough-inducing procedures and lack of adequate respiratory protection.

Fundamentals of TB infection control

An effective TB infection-control programme requires early identification, isolation and effective treatment of persons who have active TB. The primary emphasis of the TB infection-control plan should be on achieving these three goals. In all health care facilities, particularly those in which persons who are at high risk for TB work or receive care, policies and procedures for TB control should be developed, reviewed periodically and evaluated for effectiveness to determine the actions necessary to minimize the risk for transmission of *M. tuberculosis*.

The TB infection-control programme should be based on a hierarchy of control measures. The first level of the hierarchy, and that which affects the largest number of persons, is using administrative measures intended primarily to reduce the risk for exposing uninfected persons to persons who have infectious TB. These measures include:

- developing and implementing effective written policies and protocols to ensure the rapid identification, isolation, diagnostic evaluation and treatment of persons likely to have TB
- implementing effective work practices among HCWs in the health care facility (e.g., correctly wearing respiratory protection and keeping doors to isolation rooms closed)
- educating, training and counselling HCWs about TB
- screening HCWs for TB infection and disease.

The second level of the hierarchy is the use of engineering controls to prevent the spread and reduce the concentration of infectious droplet nuclei. These controls include:

- direct source control using local exhaust ventilation
- controlling direction of airflow to prevent contamination of air in areas adjacent to the infectious source

- diluting and removing contaminated air via general ventilation
- air cleaning via air filtration or ultraviolet germicidal irradiation (UVGI).

The first two levels of the hierarchy minimize the number of areas in the health care facility where exposure to infectious TB may occur, and they reduce, but do not eliminate, the risk in those few areas where exposure to *M. tuberculosis* can still occur (e.g., rooms in which patients with known or suspected infectious TB are being isolated and treatment rooms in which cough-inducing or aerosol-generating procedures are performed on such patients). Because persons entering such rooms may be exposed to *M. tuberculosis*, the third level of the hierarchy is the use of personal respiratory protective equipment in these and certain other situations in which the risk for infection with *M. tuberculosis* may be relatively higher.

Specific measures to reduce the risk for transmission of *M. tuberculosis* include the following:

1. *Assigning to specific persons in the health care facility the supervisory responsibility for designing, implementing, evaluating and maintaining the TB infection-control programme.*
2. *Conducting a risk assessment to evaluate the risk for transmission of* M. tuberculosis *in all areas of the health care facility, developing a written TB infection-control programme based on the risk assessment and periodically repeating the risk assessment to evaluate the effectiveness of the TB infection-control programme.* TB infection-control measures for each health care facility should be based on a careful assessment of the risk for transmission of *M. tuberculosis* in that particular setting. The first step in developing the TB infection-control programme should be to conduct a baseline risk assessment to evaluate the risk for transmission of *M. tuberculosis* in each area and occupational group in the facility. Appropriate infection-control interventions can then be developed on the basis of actual risk. Risk assessments should be performed for all inpatient and outpatient settings (e.g., medical and dental offices).

   Classification of risk for a facility, for a specific area and for a specific occupational group should be based on the profile of TB in the community, the number of infectious TB patients admitted to the area or ward, or the estimated number of infectious TB patients to whom HCWs in an occupational group may be exposed and the results of analysis of HCW PPD test conversions (where applicable) and possible person-to-person transmission of *M. tuberculosis*. Regardless of risk level, the management of patients with known or suspected infectious TB should not vary. However, the index of suspicion for infectious TB among patients, the frequency of HCW PPD skin testing, the number of TB isolation rooms and other factors will depend on the level of risk for transmission of *M. tuberculosis* in the facility, area or occupational group.
3. *Developing, implementing and enforcing policies and protocols to ensure early identification, diagnostic evaluation and effective treatment of patients who may have infectious TB.* A diagnosis of TB may be considered for any patient who has a persistent cough (i.e., a cough lasting for longer than 3 weeks) or other signs or symptoms compatible with active TB (e.g., bloody sputum, night sweats, weight loss, anorexia or fever). However, the index of suspicion for TB will vary in different geographic areas and will depend on the prevalence of TB and other characteristics of the population served by the facility. The index of suspicion for TB should be very high in geographic areas or among groups of patients in which the prevalence of TB is high. Appropriate diagnostic measures should be conducted and TB precautions implemented for patients in whom active TB is suspected.

4. *Providing prompt triage for and appropriate management of patients in the outpatient setting who may have infectious TB.* Triage of patients in ambulatory-care settings and emergency departments should include vigorous efforts to identify promptly patients who have active TB. HCWs who are the first points of contact in facilities that serve populations at risk for TB should be trained to ask questions that will facilitate identification of patients with signs and symptoms suggestive of TB. Patients with signs or symptoms suggestive of TB should be evaluated promptly to minimize the amount of time they are in ambulatory-care areas. TB precautions should be followed while the diagnostic evaluation is being conducted for these patients.

TB precautions in the ambulatory-care setting should include placing these patients in a separate area apart from other patients and not in open waiting areas (ideally, in a room or enclosure meeting TB isolation requirements), giving these patients surgical masks to wear and instructing them to keep their masks on and giving these patients tissues and instructing them to cover their mouths and noses with the tissues when coughing or sneezing. Surgical masks are designed to prevent the respiratory secretions of the person wearing the mask from entering the air. When not in a TB isolation room, patients suspected of having TB should wear surgical masks to reduce the expulsion of droplet nuclei into the air. These patients do not need to wear particulate respirators, which are designed to filter the air before it is inhaled by the person wearing the mask. Patients suspected of having or known to have TB should never wear a respirator that has an exhalation valve, because the device would provide no barrier to the expulsion of droplet nuclei into the air.

5. *Promptly initiating and maintaining TB isolation for persons who may have infectious TB and who are admitted to the inpatient setting.* In hospitals and other inpatient facilities, any patient suspected of having or known to have infectious TB should be placed in a TB isolation room that has currently recommended ventilation characteristics (see below). Written policies for initiating isolation should specify the indications for isolation, the person(s) authorized to initiate and discontinue isolation, the isolation practices to follow, the monitoring of isolation, the management of patients who do not adhere to isolation practices and the criteria for discontinuing isolation.

6. *Effectively planning arrangements for discharge.* Before a TB patient is discharged from the health care facility, the facility's staff and public health authorities should collaborate to ensure continuation of therapy. Discharge planning in the health care facility should include, at a minimum, a confirmed outpatient appointment with the provider who will manage the patient until the patient is cured, sufficient medication to take until the outpatient appointment and placement into case management (e.g., directly observed therapy (DOT)) or outreach programmes of the public health department. These plans should be initiated and in place before the patient's discharge.

7. *Developing, installing, maintaining and evaluating ventilation and other engineering controls to reduce the potential for airborne exposure to* M. tuberculosis. Local exhaust ventilation is a preferred source control technique, and it is often the most efficient way to contain airborne contaminants because it captures these contaminants near their source before they can disperse. Therefore, the technique should be used, if feasible, wherever aerosol-generating procedures are performed. Two basic types of local exhaust devices use hoods: the enclosing type, in which the hood either partially or fully encloses the infectious source, and the exterior type, in which the infectious source is near but outside the hood. Fully enclosed hoods, booths or

tents are always preferable to exterior types because of their superior ability to prevent contaminants from escaping into the HCW's breathing zone. General ventilation can be used for several purposes, including diluting and removing contaminated air, controlling airflow patterns within rooms and controlling the direction of airflow throughout a facility. General ventilation maintains air quality by two processes: dilution and removal of airborne contaminants. Uncontaminated supply air mixes with the contaminated room air (i.e., dilution), which is subsequently removed from the room by the exhaust system. These processes reduce the concentration of droplet nuclei in the room air. Recommended general ventilation rates for health care facilities are usually expressed in number of air changes per hour (ACH). This number is the ratio of the volume of air entering the room per hour to the room volume and is equal to the exhaust airflow (Q, in cubic feet per minute) divided by the room volume (V, in cubic feet) multiplied by 60 (i.e., $ACH = Q / V \times 60$). For the purposes of reducing the concentration of droplet nuclei, TB isolation and treatment rooms in existing health care facilities should have an airflow of greater than 6 ACH. Where feasible, this airflow rate should be increased to at least 12 ACH by adjusting or modifying the ventilation system or by using auxiliary means (e.g., recirculation of air through fixed HEPA filtration systems or portable air cleaners). New construction or renovation of existing health care facilities should be designed so that TB isolation rooms achieve an airflow of at least 12 ACH. The general ventilation system should be designed and balanced so that air flows from less contaminated (i.e., more clean) to more contaminated (less clean) areas. For example, air should flow from corridors into TB isolation rooms to prevent spread of contaminants to other areas. In some special treatment rooms in which operative and invasive procedures are performed, the direction of airflow is from the room to the hallway to provide cleaner air during these procedures. Cough-inducing or aerosol-generating procedures (e.g., bronchoscopy and irrigation of tuberculous abscesses) should not be performed in rooms with this type of airflow on patients who may have infectious TB. HEPA filters may be used in a number of ways to reduce or eliminate infectious droplet nuclei from room air or exhaust. These methods include placement of HEPA filters in exhaust ducts discharging air from booths or enclosures into the surrounding room, in ducts or in ceiling- or wall-mounted units, for recirculation of air within an individual room (fixed recirculation systems), in portable air cleaners, in exhaust ducts to remove droplet nuclei from air being discharged to the outside, either directly or through ventilation equipment, and in ducts discharging air from the TB isolation room into the general ventilation system. In any application, HEPA filters should be installed carefully and maintained meticulously to ensure adequate functioning.

For general use areas in which the risk for transmission of *M. tuberculosis* is relatively high, ultraviolet lamps (UVGI) may be used as an adjunct to ventilation for reducing the concentration of infectious droplet nuclei, although the effectiveness of such units has not been evaluated adequately. Ultraviolet (UV) units can be installed in a room or corridor to irradiate the air in the upper portion of the room, or they can be installed in ducts to irradiate air passing through the ducts.

8. *Developing, implementing, maintaining and evaluating a respiratory protection programme.* Personal respiratory protection (i.e., respirators) should be used by persons entering rooms in which patients with known or suspected infectious TB are being isolated, persons present during cough-inducing or aerosol-

generating procedures performed on such patients and persons in other settings where administrative and engineering controls are not likely to protect them from inhaling infectious airborne droplet nuclei. These other settings include transporting patients who may have infectious TB in emergency transport vehicles and providing urgent surgical or dental care to patients who may have infectious TB before a determination has been made that the patient is non-infectious.

9. *Educating and training HCWs about TB, effective methods for preventing transmission of* M. tuberculosis *and the benefits of medical screening programmes.* All HCWs, including physicians, should receive education regarding TB that is relevant to persons in their particular occupational group. Ideally, training should be conducted before initial assignment and the need for additional training should be re-evaluated periodically (e.g., once a year). The level and detail of this education will vary according to the HCW's work responsibilities and the level of risk in the facility (or area of the facility) in which the HCW works. However, the programme may include the following elements:

- the basic concepts of *M. tuberculosis* transmission, pathogenesis and diagnosis, including information concerning the difference between latent TB infection and active TB disease, the signs and symptoms of TB and the possibility of reinfection

- the potential for occupational exposure to persons who have infectious TB in the health care facility, including information concerning the prevalence of TB in the community and facility, the ability of the facility to properly isolate patients who have active TB, and situations with increased risk for exposure to *M. tuberculosis*

- the principles and practices of infection control that reduce the risk for transmission of *M. tuberculosis*, including information concerning the hierarchy of TB infection-control measures and the written policies and procedures of the facility. Site-specific control measures should be provided to HCWs working in areas that require control measures in addition to those of the basic TB infection-control programme.

- the importance of proper maintenance for engineering controls (e.g., cleaning UVGI lamps and ensuring negative pressure in TB isolation rooms)

- the purpose of PPD skin testing, the significance of a positive PPD test result and the importance of participating in the skin-test programme

- the principles of preventive therapy for latent TB infection; these principles include the indications, use, effectiveness and the potential adverse effects of the drugs

- the HCW's responsibility to seek prompt medical evaluation if a PPD test conversion occurs or if symptoms develop that could be caused by TB. Medical evaluation will enable HCWs who have TB to receive appropriate therapy and will help to prevent transmission of *M. tuberculosis* to patients and other HCWs.

- the principles of drug therapy for active TB

- the importance of notifying the facility if the HCW is diagnosed with active TB so that contact investigation procedures can be initiated

- the responsibilities of the facility to maintain the confidentiality of the HCW while ensuring that the HCW who has TB receives appropriate therapy and is non-infectious before returning to duty

- the higher risks associated with TB infection in persons who have HIV infection or other causes of severely impaired cell-mediated immunity, including (a) the more fre-

quent and rapid development of clinical TB after infection with *M. tuberculosis*, (b) the differences in the clinical presentation of disease and (c) the high mortality rate associated with multiple drug resistant-TB in such persons

- the potential development of cutaneous anergy as immune function (as measured by CD4+ T-lymphocyte counts) declines

- information regarding the efficacy and safety of BCG vaccination and the principles of PPD screening among BCG recipients

- the facility's policy on voluntary work reassignment options for immunocompromised HCWs.

10. *Developing and implementing a programme for routine periodic counselling and screening of HCWs for active TB and latent TB infection.* A TB counselling, screening and prevention programme for HCWs should be established to protect both HCWs and patients. HCWs who have positive PPD test results, PPD test conversions or symptoms suggestive of TB should be identified, evaluated to rule out a diagnosis of active TB and started on therapy or preventive therapy if indicated. In addition, the results of the HCW PPD screening programme will contribute to evaluation of the effectiveness of current infection-control practices. Because of the increased risk for rapid progression from latent TB infection to active TB in human immunodeficiency virus, HIV-infected or otherwise severely immunocompromised persons, all HCWs should know if they have a medical condition or are receiving a medical treatment that may lead to severely impaired cell-mediated immunity. HCWs who may be at risk for HIV infection should know their HIV status (i.e., they should be encouraged to voluntarily seek counselling and testing for HIV antibody status). Existing guidelines for counselling and testing should be followed routinely. Knowledge of these conditions allows the HCW to seek the appropriate preventive measures and to consider voluntary work reassignments.

11. *All HCWs should be informed about the need to follow existing recommendations for infection control to minimize the risk for exposure to infectious agents; implementation of these recommendations will greatly reduce the risk for occupational infections among HCWs.* All HCWs should also be informed about the potential risks to severely immunocompromised persons associated with caring for patients who have some infectious diseases, including TB. It should be emphasized that limiting exposure to TB patients is the most protective measure that severely immunosuppressed HCWs can take to avoid becoming infected with *M. tuberculosis*. HCWs who have severely impaired cell-mediated immunity and who may be exposed to *M. tuberculosis* may consider a change in job-setting to avoid such exposure. HCWs should be advised of the legal option in many jurisdictions that severely immunocompromised HCWs can choose to transfer voluntarily to areas and work activities in which there is the lowest possible risk for exposure to *M. tuberculosis*. This choice should be a personal decision for HCWs after they have been informed of the risks to their health.

12. *Employers should make reasonable accommodations (e.g., alternative job assignments) for employees who have a health condition that compromises cell-mediated immunity and who work in settings where they may be exposed to* M. tuberculosis. HCWs who are known to be immunocompromised should be referred to employee health professionals who can individually counsel the employees regarding their risk for TB. Upon the request of the immunocompromised HCW, employers should offer, but not compel, a work setting in which the HCW would have the lowest possible risk for occupational exposure to *M. tuberculosis*.

13. *All HCWs should be informed that immunosuppressed HCWs should have appropriate follow-up and screening for infectious diseases, including*

TB, provided by their medical practitioner. HCWs who are known to be HIV-infected or otherwise severely immunosuppressed should be tested for cutaneous anergy at the time of PPD testing. Consideration should be given to retesting, at least every 6 months, those immunocompromised HCWs who are potentially exposed to *M. tuberculosis* because of the high risk for rapid progression to active TB if they become infected.

14. *Information provided by HCWs regarding their immune status should be treated confidentially.* If the HCW requests voluntary job reassignment, the privacy of the HCW should be maintained. Facilities should have written procedures on confidential handling of such information.

15. *Promptly evaluating possible episodes of* M. tuberculosis *transmission in health care facilities, including PPD skin-test conversions among HCWs, epidemiologically associated cases among HCWs or patients and contacts of patients or HCWs who have TB and who were not promptly identified and isolated.* Epidemiological investigations may be indicated for several situations. These include, but are not limited to, the occurrence of PPD test conversions or active TB in HCWs, the occurrence of possible person-to-person transmission of *M. tuberculosis* and situations in which patients or HCWs with active TB are not promptly identified and isolated, thus exposing other persons in the facility to *M. tuberculosis.* The general objectives of the epidemiological investigations in these situations are as follows:

- to determine the likelihood that transmission of and infection with *M. tuberculosis* has occurred in the facility
- to determine the extent to which *M. tuberculosis* has been transmitted
- to identify those persons who have been exposed and infected, enabling them to receive appropriate clinical management
- to identify factors that could have contributed to transmission and infection and to implement appropriate interventions
- to evaluate the effectiveness of any interventions that are implemented and to ensure that exposure to and transmission of *M. tuberculosis* have been terminated.

16. *Coordinating activities with the local public health department, emphasizing reporting and ensuring adequate discharge follow-up and the continuation and completion of therapy.* As soon as a patient or HCW is known or suspected to have active TB, the patient or HCW should be reported to the public health department so that appropriate follow-up can be arranged and a community contact investigation can be performed. The health department should be notified well before patient discharge to facilitate follow-up and continuation of therapy. A discharge plan coordinated with the patient or HCW, the health department and the inpatient facility should be implemented.

CHEMICALS IN THE HEALTH CARE ENVIRONMENT

• OVERVIEW OF CHEMICAL HAZARDS IN HEALTH CARE

Jeanne Mager Stellman

Exposure to potentially hazardous chemicals is a fact of life for health care workers. They are encountered in the course of diagnostic and therapeutic procedures, in laboratory work, in preparation and clean-up activities and even in emanations from patients, to say nothing of the "infrastructure" activities common to all worksites such as cleaning and housekeeping, laundry, painting, plumbing and maintenance work. Despite the constant threat of such exposures and the large numbers of workers involved—in most countries, health care invariably is one of the most labour-intensive industries—this problem has received scant attention from those involved in occupational health and safety research and regulation. The great majority of chemicals in common use in hospitals and other health care settings are not specifically covered under national and international occupational exposure standards. In fact, very little effort has been made to date to identify the chemicals most frequently used, much less to study the mechanisms and intensity of exposures to them and the epidemiology of the effects on the health care workers involved.

This may be changing in the many jurisdictions in which right-to-know laws, such as the Canadian Workplace Hazardous Materials Information Systems (WHMIS) are being legislated and enforced. These laws require that workers be informed of the name and nature of the chemicals to which they may be exposed on the job. They have introduced a daunting challenge to administrators in the health care industry who must now turn to occupational health and safety professionals to undertake a *de novo* inventory of the identity and location of the thousands of chemicals to which their workers may be exposed.

The wide range of professions and jobs and the complexity of their interplay in the health care workplace require unique diligence and astuteness on the part of those charged with such occupational safety and health responsibilities. A significant complication is the traditional altruistic focus on the care and well-being of the patients, even at the expense of the health and well-being of those providing the services. Another complication is the fact that these services are often required at times of great urgency when important preventive and protective measures may be forgotten or deliberately disregarded.

Categories of Chemical Exposures in the Health Care Setting

Table 97.13 lists the categories of chemicals encountered in the health care workplace. Laboratory workers are exposed to the

Table 97.13 • Categories of chemicals used in health care.

Types of chemicals	Locations most likely to be found
Disinfectants	Patient areas
Sterilants	Central supply Operating theatres Physician offices Rehabilitation centres
Medicines	Patient areas Pharmacy
Laboratory reagents	Laboratories
Housekeeping/maintenance chemicals	Hospital-wide
Food ingredients and products	Kitchen Cafeteria
Pesticides	Hospital-wide

broad range of chemical reagents they employ, histology technicians to dyes and stains, pathologists to fixative and preservative solutions (formaldeyde is a potent sensitizer), and asbestos is a hazard to workers making repairs or renovations in older health care facilities.

Even when liberally applied in combating and preventing the spread of infectious agents, detergents, disinfectants and sterilants offer relatively little danger to patients whose exposure is usually of brief duration. Even though individual doses at any one time may be relatively low, their cumulative effect over the course of a working lifetime may, however, constitute a significant risk to health care workers.

Occupational exposures to drugs can cause allergic reactions, such as have been reported over many years among workers administering penicillin and other antibiotics, or much more serious problems with such highly carcinogenic agents as the antineoplastic drugs. The contacts may occur during the preparation or administration of the dose for injection or in cleaning up after it has been administered. Although the danger of this mechanism of exposure had been known for many years, it was fully appreciated only after mutagenic activity was detected in the urine of nurses administering antineoplastic agents.

Another mechanism of exposure is the administration of drugs as aerosols for inhalation. The use of antineoplastic agents, pentamidine and ribavarin by this route has been studied in some detail, but there has been, as of this writing, no report of a systematic study of aerosols as a source of toxicity among health care workers.

Anaesthetic gases represent another class of drugs to which many health care workers are exposed. These chemicals are associated with a variety of biological effects, the most obvious of which are on the nervous system. Recently, there have been reports suggesting that repeated exposures to anaesthetic gases may, over time, have adverse reproductive effects among both male and female workers. It should be recognized that appreciable amounts of waste anaesthetic gases may accumulate in the air in recovery rooms as the gases retained in the blood and other tissues of patients are eliminated by exhalation.

Chemical disinfecting and sterilizing agents are another important category of potentially hazardous chemical exposures for health care workers. Used primarily in the sterilization of non-disposable equipment, such as surgical instruments and respiratory therapy apparatus, chemical sterilants such as ethylene oxide are effective because they interact with infectious agents and destroy them. Alkylation, whereby methyl or other alkyl groups bind chemically with protein-rich entities such as the amino groups in haemoglobiin and DNA, is a powerful biological effect. In intact organisms, this may not cause direct toxicity but should be considered potentially carcinogenic until proven otherwise. Ethylene oxide itself, however, is a known carcinogen and is associated with a variety of adverse health effects, as discussed elsewhere in the *Encyclopaedia*. The potent alkylation capability of ethylene oxide, probably the most widely-used sterilant for heat-sensitive materials, has led to its use as a classic probe in studying molecular structure.

For years, the methods used in the chemical sterilization of instruments and other surgical materials have carelessly and needlessly put many health care workers at risk. Not even rudimentary precautions were taken to prevent or limit exposures. For example, it was the common practice to leave the door of the sterilizer partially open to allow the escape of excess ethylene oxide, or to leave freshly-sterilized materials uncovered and open to the room air until enough had been assembled to make efficient use of the aerator unit.

The fixation of metallic or ceramic replacement parts so common in dentistry and orthopaedic surgery may be a source of potentially hazardous chemical exposure such as silica. These and the acrylic resins often used to glue them in place are usually biologically inert, but health care workers may be exposed to the monomers and other chemical reactants used during the preparation and application process. These chemicals are often sensitizing agents and have been associated with chronic effects in animals. The preparation of mercury amalgam fillings can lead to mercury exposure. Spills and the spread of mercury droplets is a particular concern since these may linger unnoticed in the work environment for many years. The acute exposure of patients to them appears to be entirely safe, but the long-term health implications of the repeated exposure of health care workers have not been adequately studied.

Finally, such medical techniques as laser surgery, electro-cauterization and use of other radiofrequency and high-energy devices can lead to the thermal degradation of tissues and other substances resulting in the formation of potentially toxic smoke and fumes. For example, the cutting of "plaster" casts made of polyester resin impregnated bandages has been shown to release potentially toxic fumes.

The hospital as a "mini-municipality"

A listing of the varied jobs and tasks performed by the personnel of hospitals and other large health care facilities might well serve as a table of contents for the commercial listings of a telephone directory for a sizeable municipality. All of these entail chemical exposures intrinsic to the particular work activity in addition to those that are peculiar to the health care environment. Thus, painters and maintenance workers are exposed to solvents and lubricants. Plumbers and others engaged in soldering are exposed to fumes of lead and flux. Housekeeping workers are exposed to soaps, detergents and other cleansing agents, pesticides and other household chemicals. Cooks may be exposed to potentially carcinogenic fumes in broiling or frying foods and to oxides of nitrogen from the use of natural gas as fuel. Even clerical workers may be exposed to the toners used in copiers and printers. The occurrence and effects of such chemical exposures are detailed elsewhere in this *Encyclopaedia*.

One chemical exposure that is diminishing in importance as more and more HCWs quit smoking and more health care facilities become "smoke-free" is "second hand" tobacco smoke.

Unusual chemical exposures in health care

Table 97.14 presents a partial listing of the chemicals most commonly encountered in health care workplaces. Whether or not they will be toxic will depend on the nature of the chemical and its biological proclivities, the manner, intensity and duration of the exposure, the susceptibilities of the exposed worker, and the speed and effectiveness of any countermeasures that may have been attempted. Unfortunately, a compendium of the nature, mechanisms, effects and treatment of chemical exposures of health care workers has not yet been published.

There are some unique exposures in the health care workplace that substantiate the dictum that a high level of vigilance is necessary to protect workers fully from such risks. For example, it was recently reported that health care workers had been overcome by toxic fumes emanating from a patient under treatment from a massive chemical exposure. Cases of cyanide poisoning arising from patient emissions have also been reported. In addition to the direct toxicity of waste anaesthetic gases to anaesthetists and other personnel in operating theatres, there is the often unrecognized problem created by the frequent use in such areas of high-energy sources which can transform the anaesthetic gases to free radicals, a form in which they are potentially carcinogenic.

Table 97.14 • Chemicals cited in Hazardous Substances Database (HSDB).

The following chemicals are listed in the HSDB as being used in some area of the health care environment. The HSDB is produced by the US National Library of Medicine and is a compilation of more than 4,200 chemicals with known toxic effects in commercial use. Absence of a chemical from the list does not imply that it is not toxic, but that it is not present in the HSDB.

Use list in the HSDB	Chemical name	CAS number*
Disinfectants; antiseptics	benzylalkonium chloride	0001-54-5
	borax	1303-96-4
	boric acid	10043-35-3
	cetyl pyridinium chloride	123-03-5
	m-cresol	95-57-8
	2-chlorophenol	106-48-9
	4-chlorophenol	70-30-4
	hexachlorophene	108-39-4
	methyl ethyl ketone	78-93-3
	phenol	108-95-2
	tri-m-cresyl phosphate (lysol)	563-04-2
Sterilants	beta-propiolactone	57-57-8
	crotonaldehyde	4170-30-3
	ethylene oxide	75-21-8
	formaldehyde	50-00-0
	glutaraldehyde	111-30-8
Laboratory reagents: Biological stains	2,4-xylidine (magenta-base)	3248-93-9
	acridine-red	2465-29-4
	basic parafuchsine	569-61-9
	basic-magenta	3248-93-9
	Cl-acid-blue-9	129-17-9
	Cl-acid-green-3	4680-78-8
	Cl-acid-red-14	3567-69-9
	Cl-direct-blue-1	2429-74-5
	Cl-direct-red-28	573-58-0
	Cl-direct-yellow-11	1325-37-7
	Cl-acid-green-3	4680-78-8
	curcumin	458-37-7
	Heamtoxylin	517-28-2
	hexamethyl-p-rosaniline chloride (violet)	548-62-9
	malachite green	569-64-2
	osmiun tetroxide	20816-12-0
	ponceau 3R	3564-09-8

* Chemical Abstracts Service identification number.

MANAGING CHEMICAL HAZARDS IN HOSPITALS

Annalee Yassi

The vast array of chemicals in hospitals, and the multitude of settings in which they occur, call for a systematic approach to their control. A chemical-by-chemical approach to prevention of exposures and their deleterious outcome is simply too inefficient to handle a problem of this scope. Moreover, as noted in the article "Overview of chemical hazards in health care", many chemicals in the hospital environment have been inadequately studied; new chemicals are constantly being introduced and for others, even some that have become quite familiar (e.g., gloves made of latex), new hazardous effects are only now becoming manifest. Thus, while it is useful to follow chemical-specific control guidelines, a more comprehensive approach is needed whereby individual chemical control policies and practices are superimposed on a strong foundation of general chemical hazard control.

The control of chemical hazards in hospitals must be based on classic principles of good occupational health practice. Because health care facilities are accustomed to approaching health through the medical model, which focuses on the individual patient and treatment rather than on prevention, special effort is required to ensure that the orientation for handling chemicals is indeed preventive and that measures are principally focused on the workplace rather than on the worker.

Environmental (or engineering) control measures are the key to prevention of deleterious exposures. However, it is necessary to train each worker correctly in appropriate exposure prevention techniques. In fact, right-to-know legislation, as described below, requires that workers be informed of the hazards with which they work, as well as of the appropriate safety precautions. Secondary prevention at the level of the worker is the domain of medical services, which may include medical monitoring to ascertain whether health effects of exposure can be medically detected; it also consists of prompt and appropriate medical intervention in the event of accidental exposure. Chemicals that are less toxic must replace more toxic ones, processes should be enclosed wherever possible and good ventilation is essential.

While all means to prevent or minimize exposures should be implemented, if exposure does occur (e.g., a chemical is spilled), procedures must be in place to ensure prompt and appropriate response to prevent further exposure.

Applying the General Principles of Chemical Hazard Control in the Hospital Environment

The first step in hazard control is *hazard identification*. This, in turn, requires a knowledge of the physical properties, chemical constituents and toxicological properties of the chemicals in question. Material safety data sheets (MSDSs), which are becoming increasingly available by legal requirement in many countries, list such properties. The vigilant occupational health practitioner, however, should recognize that the MSDS may be incomplete, particularly with respect to long-term effects or effects of low-dose chronic exposure. Hence, a literature search may be contemplated to supplement the MSDS material, when appropriate.

The second step in controlling a hazard is *characterizing the risk*. Does the chemical pose a carcinogenic risk? Is it an allergen? A teratogen? Is it mainly short-term irritancy effects that are of concern? The answer to these questions will influence the way in which exposure is assessed.

The third step in chemical hazard control is to *assess the actual exposure*. Discussion with the health care workers who use the product in question is the most important element in this endeavour. Monitoring methods are necessary in some situations to ascertain that exposure controls are functioning properly. These may be area sampling, either grab sample or integrated, depending on the nature of the exposure; it may be personal sampling; in some cases, as discussed below, medical monitoring may be contemplated, but usually as a last resort and only as back-up to other means of exposure assessment.

Once the properties of the chemical product in question are known, and the nature and extent of exposure are assessed, a determination could be made as to the degree of risk. This generally requires that at least some dose-response information be available.

After evaluating the risk, the next series of steps is, of course, to *control the exposure*, so as to eliminate or at least minimize the risk.

This, first and foremost, involves applying the general principles of exposure control.

Organizing a Chemical Control Programme in Hospitals

The traditional obstacles

The implementation of adequate occupational health programmes in health care facilities has lagged behind the recognition of the hazards. Labour relations are increasingly forcing hospital management to look at all aspects of their benefits and services to employees, as hospitals are no longer tacitly exempt by custom or privilege. Legislative changes are now compelling hospitals in many jurisdictions to implement control programmes.

However, obstacles remain. The preoccupation of the hospital with patient care, emphasizing treatment rather than prevention, and the staff's ready access to informal "corridor consultation", have hindered the rapid implementation of control programmes. The fact that laboratory chemists, pharmacists and a host of medical scientists with considerable toxicological expertise are heavily represented in management has, in general, not served to hasten the development of programmes. The question may be asked, "Why do we need an occupational hygienist when we have all these toxicology experts?" To the extent that changes in procedures threaten to have an impact on the tasks and services provided by these highly skilled personnel, the situation may be made worse: "We cannot eliminate the use of Substance X as it is the best bactericide around." Or, "If we follow the procedure that you are recommending, patient care will suffer." Moreover, the "we don't need training" attitude is commonplace among the health care professions and hinders the implementation of the essential components of chemical hazard control. Internationally, the climate of cost constraint in health care is clearly also an obstacle.

Another problem of particular concern in hospitals is preserving the confidentiality of personal information about health care workers. While occupational health professionals should need only to indicate that Ms. X cannot work with chemical Z and needs to be transferred, curious clinicians are often more prone to push for the clinical explanation than their non-health care counterparts. Ms. X may have liver disease and the substance is a liver toxin; she may be allergic to the chemical; or she may be pregnant and the substance has potential teratogenic properties. While the need to alter the work assignment of particular individuals should not be routine, the confidentiality of the medical details should be protected if it is necessary.

Right-to-know legislation

Many jurisdictions around the world have implemented right-to-know legislation. In Canada, for example, WHMIS has revolutionized the handling of chemicals in industry. This country-wide system has three components: (1) the labelling of all hazardous substances with standardized labels indicating the nature of the hazard; (2) the provision of MSDSs with the constituents, hazards and control measures for each substance; and (3) the training of workers to understand the labels and the MSDSs and to use the product safely.

Under WHMIS in Canada and OSHA's Hazard Communications requirements in the United States, hospitals have been required to construct inventories of all chemicals on the premises so that those that are "controlled substances" can be identified and addressed according to the legislation. In the process of complying with the training requirements of these regulations, hospitals have had to engage occupational health professionals with appropriate expertise and the spin-off benefits, particularly when bipartite train-the-trainer programmes were conducted, have included a new spirit to work cooperatively to address other health and safety concerns.

Corporate commitment and the role of joint health and safety committees

The most important element in the success of any occupational health and safety programme is corporate commitment to ensure its successful implementation. Policies and procedures regarding the safe handling of chemicals in hospitals must be written, discussed at all levels within the organization and adopted and enforced as corporate policy. Chemical hazard control in hospitals should be addressed by general as well as specific policies. For example, there should be a policy on responsibility for the implementation of right-to-know legislation that clearly outlines each party's obligations and the procedures to be followed by individuals at each level of the organization (e.g., who chooses the trainers, how much work time is allowed for preparation and provision of training, to whom should communication regarding non-attendance be communicated and so on). There should be a generic spill clean-up policy indicating the responsibility of the worker and the department where the spill occurred, the indications and protocol for notifying the emergency response team, including the appropriate in-hospital and external authorities and experts, follow-up provisions for exposed workers and so on. Specific policies should also exist regarding the handling, storage and disposal of specific classes of toxic chemicals.

Not only is it essential that management be strongly committed to these programmes; the workforce, through its representatives, must also be actively involved in the development and implementation of policies and procedures. Some jurisdictions have legislatively mandated joint (labour-management) health and safety committees that meet at a minimum prescribed interval (bimonthly in the case of Manitoba hospitals), have written operating procedures and keep detailed minutes. Indeed in recognizing the importance of these committees, the Manitoba Workers' Compensation Board (WCB) provides a rebate on WCB premiums paid by employers based on the successful functioning of these committees. To be effective, the members must be appropriately chosen—specifically, they must be elected by their peers, knowledgeable about the legislation, have appropriate education and training and be allotted sufficient time to conduct not only incident investigations but regular inspections. With respect to chemical control, the joint committee has both a pro-active and a re-active role: assisting in setting priorities and developing preventive policies, as well as serving as a sounding board for workers who are not satisfied that all appropriate controls are being implemented.

The multidisciplinary team

As noted above, the control of chemical hazards in hospitals requires a multidisciplinary endeavour. At a minimum, it requires occupational hygiene expertise. Generally hospitals have maintenance departments that have within them the engineering and physical plant expertise to assist a hygienist in determining whether workplace alterations are necessary. Occupational health nurses also play a prominent role in evaluating the nature of concerns and complaints, and in assisting an occupational physician in ascertaining whether clinical intervention is warranted. In hospitals, it is important to recognize that numerous health care professionals have expertise that is quite relevant to the control of chemical hazards. It would be unthinkable to develop policies and procedures for the control of laboratory chemicals without the involvement of lab chemists, for example, or procedures for handling anti-neoplastic drugs without the involvement of the oncology and pharmacology staff. While it is wise for occupational health professionals in all industries to consult with line staff prior to implementing control measures, it would be an unforgivable error to fail to do so in health care settings.

Data collection

As in all industries, and with all hazards, data need to be compiled both to help in priority setting and in evaluating the success of programmes. With respect to data collection on chemical hazards in hospitals, minimally, data need to be kept regarding accidental exposures and spills (so that these areas can receive special attention to prevent recurrences); the nature of concerns and complaints should be recorded (e.g., unusual odours); and clinical cases need to be tabulated, so that, for example, an increase in dermatitis from a given area or occupational group could be identified.

Cradle-to-grave approach

Increasingly, hospitals are becoming cognizant of their obligation to protect the environment. Not only the workplace hazardous properties, but the environmental properties of chemicals are being taken into consideration. Moreover, it is no longer acceptable to pour hazardous chemicals down the drain or release noxious fumes into the air. A chemical control programme in hospitals must, therefore, be capable of tracking chemicals from their purchase and acquisition (or, in some cases, synthesis on site), through the work handling, safe storage and finally to their ultimate disposal.

Conclusion

It is now recognized that there are thousands of potentially very toxic chemicals in the work environment of health care facilities; all occupational groups may be exposed; and the nature of the exposures are varied and complex. Nonetheless, with a systematic and comprehensive approach, with strong corporate commitment and a fully informed and involved workforce, chemical hazards can be managed and the risks associated with these chemicals controlled.

● WASTE ANAESTHETIC GASES

Xavier Guardino Solá

The use of inhaled anaesthetics was introduced in the decade of 1840 to 1850. The first compounds to be used were diethyl ether, nitrous oxide and chloroform. Cyclopropane and trichloroethylene were introduced many years later (circa 1930-1940), and the use of fluoroxene, halothane and methoxiflurane began in the decade of the 1950s. By the end of the 1960s enflurane was being used and, finally, isoflurane was introduced in the 1980s. Isoflurane is now considered the most widely used inhalation anaesthetic even though it is more expensive than the others. A summary of the physical and chemical characteristics of methoxiflurane, enflurane, halothane, isoflurane and nitrous oxide, the most commonly used anaesthetics, is shown in table 97.15 (Wade and Stevens 1981).

All of them, with the exception of nitrous oxide (N_2O), are hydrocarbons or chlorofluorinated liquid ethers that are applied by vapourization. Isoflurane is the most volatile of these compounds; it is the one that is metabolized at the lowest rate and the one that is least soluble in blood, in fats and in the liver.

Normally, N_2O, a gas, is mixed with a halogenated anaesthetic, although they are sometimes used separately, depending on the type of anaesthesia that is required, the characteristics of the patient and the work habits of the anaesthetist. The normally used concentrations are 50 to 66% N_2O and up to 2 or 3% of the halogenated anaesthetic (the rest is usually oxygen).

The anaesthesia of the patient is usually started by the injection of a sedative drug followed by an inhaled anaesthetic. The volumes given to the patient are in the order of 4 or 5 litres/minute. Parts of the oxygen and of the anaesthetic gases in the mixture are retained by the patient while the remainder is exhaled directly into the atmosphere or is recycled into the respirator, depending among other things on the type of mask used, on whether the patient is intubated and on whether or not a recycling system is available. If recycling is available, exhaled air can be recycled after it is cleaned or it can be vented to the atmosphere, expelled from the operating room or aspirated by a vacuum. Recycling (closed circuit) is not a common procedure and many respirators do not have exhaust systems; all the air exhaled by the patient, including the waste anaesthetic gases, therefore, ends up in the air of the operating room.

The number of workers occupationally exposed to waste anaesthetic gases is high, because it is not only the anaesthetists and their assistants who are exposed, but all the other people who spend time in operating rooms (surgeons, nurses and support staff), the dentists who perform odontological surgery, the personnel in delivery rooms and intensive care units where patients may be under inhaled anaesthesia and veterinary surgeons. Similarly, the presence of waste anaesthetic gases is detected in recovery rooms, where they are exhaled by patients who are recovering from surgery. They are also detected in other areas adjacent to operating rooms because, for reasons of asepsis, operating rooms are kept at positive pressure and this favours the contamination of surrounding areas.

Health Effects

Problems due to the toxicity of anaesthetic gases were not seriously studied until the 1960s, even though a few years after the use of inhaled anaesthetics became common, the relationship between the illnesses (asthma, nephritis) that affected some of the first professional anaesthetists and their work as such was already suspected (Ginesta 1989). In this regard the appearance of an epidemiological study of more than 300 anaesthetists in the Soviet Union, the Vaisman (1967) survey, was the starting point for several other epidemiological and toxicological studies. These studies—mostly during the 1970s and the first half of the 1980s—focused on the effects of anaesthetic gases, in most cases nitrous oxide and halothane, on people occupationally exposed to them.

The effects observed in most of these studies were an increase in spontaneous abortions among women exposed during or before pregnancy, and among women partners of exposed men; an increase in congenital malformations in children of exposed mothers; and the occurrence of hepatic, renal and neurological problems and of some types of cancer in both men and women (Bruce et al. 1968, 1974; Bruce and Bach 1976). Even though the toxic effects of nitrous oxide and of halothane (and probably its substitutes as well) on the body are not exactly the same, they are commonly studied together, given that exposure generally occurs simultaneously.

It appears likely that there is a correlation between these exposures and an increased risk, particularly for spontaneous abortions and congenital malformations in children of women exposed during pregnancy (Stoklov et al. 1983; Spence 1987; Johnson, Buchan and Reif 1987). As a result, many of the people exposed have expressed great concern. Rigorous statistical analysis of these data, however, casts doubt on the existence of such a relationship. More recent studies reinforce these doubts while chromosomal studies yield ambiguous results.

The works published by Cohen and colleagues (1971, 1974, 1975, 1980), who carried out extensive studies for the American Society of Anaesthetists (ASA), constitute a fairly extensive series

Table 97.15 • Properties of inhaled anaesthetics.

	Isoflurane, Forane	Enflurane, Ethrane	Halothane, Fluothane	Methoxyflurane, Penthrane	Dinitrogen oxide, Nitrous oxide
Molecular weight	184.0	184.5	197.4	165.0	44.0
Boiling point	48.5 °C	56.5 °C	50.2 °C	104.7 °C	—
Density	1.50	1.52 (25 °C)	1.86 (22 °C)	1.41 (25 °C)	—
Vapour pressure at 20 °C	250.0	175.0 (20 °C)	243.0 (20 °C)	25.0 (20 °C)	—
Smell	Pleasant, sharp	Pleasant, like ether	Pleasant, sweet	Pleasant, fruity	Pleasant, sweet
Separation coefficients:					
Blood/gas	1.40	1.9	2.3	13.0	0.47
Brain/gas	3.65	2.6	4.1	22.1	0.50
Fat/gas	94.50	105.0	185.0	890.0	1.22
Liver/gas	3.50	3.8	7.2	24.8	0.38
Muscle/gas	5.60	3.0	6.0	20.0	0.54
Oil/gas	97.80	98.5	224.0	930.0	1.4
Water/gas	0.61	0.8	0.7	4.5	0.47
Rubber/gas	0.62	74.0	120.0	630.0	1.2
Metabolic rate	0.20	2.4	15–20	50.0	—

of observations. Follow-up publications criticized some of the technical aspects of the earlier studies, particularly with respect to the sampling methodology and, especially, the proper selection of a control group. Other deficiencies included lack of reliable information on the concentrations to which the subjects had been exposed, the methodology for dealing with false positives and the lack of controls for factors such as tobacco and alcohol use, prior reproductive histories and voluntary infertility. Consequently, some of the studies are now even considered invalid (Edling 1980; Buring et al. 1985; Tannenbaum and Goldberg 1985).

Laboratory studies have shown that exposure of animals to ambient concentrations of anaesthetic gases equivalent to those found in operating rooms does cause deterioration in their development, growth and adaptive behaviour (Ferstandig 1978; ACGIH 1991). These are not conclusive, however, since some of these experimental exposures involved anaesthetic or subanaesthetic levels, concentrations significantly higher than the levels of waste gases usually found in operating room air (Saurel-Cubizolles et al. 1994; Tran et al. 1994).

Nevertheless, even acknowledging that a relationship between the deleterious effects and exposures to waste anaesthetic gases has not been definitively established, the fact is that the presence of these gases and their metabolites is readily detected in the air of operating rooms, in exhaled air and in biological fluids. Accordingly, since there is concern about their potential toxicity, and because it is technically feasible to do so without inordinate effort or expense, it would be prudent to take steps to eliminate or reduce to a minimum the concentrations of waste anaesthetic gases in operating rooms and nearby areas (Rosell, Luna and Guardino 1989; NIOSH 1994).

Maximum Allowable Exposure Levels

The American Conference of Governmental Industrial Hygienists (ACGIH) has adopted a threshold limit value-time weighted average (TLV-TWA) of 50 ppm for nitrous oxide and halothane (ACGIH 1994). The TLV-TWA is the guideline for the production of the compound, and the recommendations for operating rooms are that its concentration be kept lower, at a level below 1 ppm (ACGIH 1991). NIOSH sets a limit of 25 ppm for nitrous oxide and of 1 ppm for halogenated anaesthetics, with the additional recommendation that when they are used together, the concentration of halogenated compounds be reduced to a limit of 0.5 ppm (NIOSH 1977b).

With regard to values in biological fluids, the recommended limit for nitrous oxide in urine after 4 hours of exposure at average ambient concentrations of 25 ppm ranges from 13 to 19 µg/L, and for 4 hours of exposure at average ambient concentrations of 50 ppm, the range is 21 to 39 µg/L (Guardino and Rosell 1995). If exposure is to a mixture of a halogenated anaesthetic and nitrous oxide, the measurement of the values from nitrous oxide is used as the basis for controlling exposure, because as higher concentrations are used, quantification becomes easier.

Analytical Measurement

Most of the procedures described for measuring residual anaesthetics in air are based on the capture of these compounds by adsorption or in an inert bag or container, later to be analysed by gas chromatography or infrared spectroscopy (Guardino and Rosell 1985). Gas chromatography is also employed to measure nitrous oxide in urine (Rosell, Luna and Guardino 1989), while isoflurane is not readily metabolized and is therefore seldom measured.

Common Levels of Residual Concentrations in the Air of Operating Rooms

In the absence of preventive measures, such as the extraction of residual gases and/or introducing an adequate supply of new air into the operating suite, personal concentrations of more than 6,000 ppm of nitrous oxide and 85 ppm of halothane have been measured (NIOSH 1977). Concentrations of up to 3,500 ppm and 20 ppm, respectively, in the ambient air of operating rooms, have been measured. The implementation of corrective measures can reduce these concentrations to values below the environmental limits cited earlier (Rosell, Luna and Guardino 1989).

Factors that Affect the Concentration of Waste Anaesthetic Gases

The factors which most directly affect the presence of waste anaesthetic gases in the environment of the operating room are the following.

Method of anaesthesia. The first question to consider is the method of anaesthesia, for example, whether or not the patient is intubated and the type of face mask being used. In dental, laryngeal or other forms of surgery in which intubation is precluded, the patient's expired air would be an important source of emissions of waste gases, unless equipment specifically designed to trap these exhalations is properly placed near the patient's breathing zone. Accordingly, dental and oral surgeons are considered to be particularly at risk (Cohen, Belville and Brown 1975; NIOSH 1977a), as are veterinary surgeons (Cohen, Belville and Brown 1974; Moore, Davis and Kaczmarek 1993).

Proximity to the focus of emission. As is usual in industrial hygiene, when the known point of emission of a contaminant exists, proximity to the source is the first factor to consider when dealing with personal exposure. In this case, the anaesthetists and their assistants are the persons most directly affected by the emission of waste anaesthetic gases, and personal concentrations have been measured in the order of two times the average levels found in the air of operating rooms (Guardino and Rosell 1985).

Type of circuit. It goes without saying that in the few cases in which closed circuits are used, with reinspiration after the cleansing of the air and the resupply of oxygen and the necessary anaesthetics, there will be no emissions except in the case of equipment malfunction or if a leak exists. In other cases, it will depend on the characteristics of the system used, as well as on whether or not it is possible to add an extraction system to the circuit.

The concentration of anaesthetic gases. Another factor to take into account is the concentrations of the anaesthetics used since, obviously, those concentrations and the amounts found in the air of the operating room are directly related (Guardino and Rosell 1985). This factor is especially important when it comes to surgical procedures of long duration.

Type of surgical procedures. The duration of the operations, the time elapsed between procedures done in the same operating room and the specific characteristics of each procedure—which often determine which anaesthetics are used—are other factors to consider. The duration of the operation directly affects the residual concentration of anaesthetics in the air. In operating rooms where procedures are scheduled successively, the time elapsed between them also affects the presence of residual gases. Studies done in large hospitals with uninterrupted use of the operating rooms or with emergency operating rooms that are used beyond standard work schedules, or in operating rooms used for prolonged procedures (transplants, laryngotomies), show that substantial levels of waste gases are detected even before the first procedure of the day. This contributes to increased levels of waste gases in subsequent procedures. On the other hand, there are procedures that require temporary interruptions of inhalation anaesthesia (where extracorporeal circulation is needed, for example), and this also interrupts the emission of waste anaesthetic gases into the environment (Guardino and Rosell 1985).

Characteristics specific to the operating room. Studies done in operating rooms of different sizes, design and ventilation (Rosell, Luna and Guardino 1989) have demonstrated that these characteristics greatly influence the concentration of waste anaesthetic gases in the room. Large and non-partitioned operating rooms tend to have the lowest measured concentrations of waste anaesthetic gases, while in small operating rooms (e.g., paediatric operating rooms) the measured concentrations of waste gases are usually higher. The general ventilation system of the operating room and its proper operation is a fundamental factor for the reduction of the concentration of waste anaesthetics; the design of the ventilation system also affects the circulation of waste gases within the operating room and the concentrations in different locations and at various heights, something that can be easily verified by carefully taking samples.

Characteristics specific to the anaesthesia equipment. The emission of gases into the environment of the operating room depends directly on the characteristics of the anaesthesia equipment used. The design of the system, whether it includes a system for the return of excess gases, whether it can be attached to a vacuum or vented out of the operating room, whether it has leaks, disconnected lines and so on are always to be considered when determining the presence of waste anaesthetic gases in the operating room.

Factors specific to the anaesthetist and his or her team. The anaesthetist and his or her team are the last element to consider, but not necessarily the least important. Knowledge of the anaesthesia equipment, of its potential problems and the level of maintenance it receives—both by the team and by the maintenance staff in the hospital—are factors that affect very directly the emission of waste gases into the air of the operating room (Guardino and Rosell 1995). It has been clearly shown that, even when using adequate technology, the reduction of the ambient concentrations of anaesthetic gases cannot be achieved if a preventive philosophy is absent from the work routines of anaesthetists and their assistants (Guardino and Rosell 1992).

Preventive Measures

The basic preventive actions required to reduce occupational exposure to waste anaesthetic gases effectively can be summarized in the following six points:

1. *Anaesthetic gases should be thought of as occupational hazards.* Even if from a scientific standpoint it has not been conclusively shown that anaesthetic gases have a serious deleterious effect on the health of people who are occupationally exposed, there is a high probability that some of the effects mentioned here are directly related to the exposure to waste anaesthetic gases. For that reason it is a good idea to consider them toxic occupational hazards.

2. *Scavenger systems should be used for waste gases.* Scavenger systems are the most effective technical hardware for the reduction of waste gases in the air of the operating room (NIOSH 1975). These systems must fulfil two basic principles: they must store and/or adequately eliminate the whole volume of air expired by the patient, and they must be designed to guarantee that neither the respiration of the patient nor the proper functioning of the anaesthesia equipment will be affected—with separate safety devices for each function. The techniques most commonly employed are: a direct connection to a vacuum outlet with a flexible regulating chamber that allows for the discontinuous emission of gases of the respiratory cycle; directing the flow of the gases exhaled by the patient to the vacuum without a direct connection; and directing the flow of gases coming from the patient to the return of the ventilation system installed in the operating room and expelling these gases from the operating room and from the building. All these systems are technically easy to implement and very cost-efficient; the use of installed respirators as part of the design is recommended.

   In cases where systems that eliminate waste gases directly cannot be used because of the special characteristics of a procedure, localized extraction can be employed near the source of emission as long as it does not affect the general ventilation system or the positive pressure in the operating room.

3. *General ventilation with a minimum of 15 renewals/hour in the operating room should be guaranteed.* The general ventilation of the operating room should be perfectly regulated. It should not only maintain positive pressure and respond to the thermohygrometric characteristics of the ambient air, but should also provide a minimum of 15 to 18 renewals per hour. Also, a monitoring procedure should be in place to ensure its proper functioning.

4. *Preventive maintenance of the anaesthesia circuit should be planned and regular.* Preventive maintenance procedures should be set up that include regular inspections of the respirators. Verifying that no gases are being emitted to the ambient air should be part of the protocol followed when the equipment is first turned on, and its proper functioning with regard to the safety of the patient should be checked. The proper functioning of the anaesthesia circuit should be verified by checking for leaks, periodically replacing filters and checking the safety valves.

5. *Environmental and biological controls should be used.* The implementation of environmental and biological controls provides information not only about the correct functioning of the various technical elements (extraction of gases, general ventilation) but also about whether the working procedures are adequate for curtailing the emission of waste gases into the air. Today these controls do not present technical problems and they can be implemented economically, which is why they are recommended.

6. *Education and training of the exposed personnel is crucial.* Achieving an effective reduction of occupational exposure to waste anaesthetic gases requires educating all operating room personnel about the potential risks and training them in the required procedures. This is particularly applicable to anaesthetists and their assistants who are most directly involved and those responsible for the maintenance of the anaesthesia and air-conditioning equipment.

Conclusion

Although not definitively proven, there is enough evidence to suggest that exposures to waste anaesthetic gases may be harmful to HCWs. Stillbirths and congenital malformations in infants born to female workers and to the spouses of male workers represent the major forms of toxicity. Since it is technically feasible at a low cost, it is desirable to reduce the concentration of these gases in the ambient air in operating rooms and adjacent areas to a minimum. This requires not only the use and correct maintenance of anaesthesia equipment and ventilation/air conditioning systems but also the education and training of all personnel involved, especially anaesthetists and their assistants, who generally are exposed to higher concentrations. Given the work conditions peculiar to operating rooms, indoctrination in the correct work habits and procedures is very important in trying to reduce the amounts of anaesthetic waste gases in the air to a minimum.

● HEALTH CARE WORKERS AND LATEX ALLERGY

Leon J. Warshaw

With the advent of the universal precautions against bloodborne infections which dictate the use of gloves whenever HCWs are exposed to patients or materials that might be infected with hepatitis B or HIV, the frequency and severity of allergic reactions to

natural rubber latex (NRL) have zoomed upward. For example, the Department of Dermatology at the Erlangen-Nuremberg University in Germany reported a 12-fold increase in the number of patients with latex allergy between 1989 and 1995. More serious systemic manifestations increased from 10.7% in 1989 to 44% in 1994-1995 (Hesse et al. 1996).

It seems ironic that so much difficulty is attributable to rubber gloves when they were intended to protect the hands of nurses and other HCWs when they were originally introduced toward the end of the nineteenth century. This was the era of antiseptic surgery in which instruments and operative sites were bathed in caustic solutions of carbolic acid and bichloride of mercury. These not only killed germs but they also macerated the hands of the surgical team. According to what has become a romantic legend, William Stewart Halsted, one of the surgical "giants" of the time who is credited with a host of contributions to the techniques of surgery, is said to have "invented" rubber gloves around 1890 to make it more pleasant to hold hands with Caroline Hampton, his scrub nurse, whom he later married (Townsend 1994). Although Halsted may be credited with introducing and popularizing the use of rubber surgical gloves in the United States, many others had a hand in it, according to Miller (1982) who cited a report of their use in the United Kingdom published a half century earlier (Acton 1848).

Latex Allergy

Allergy to NRL is succinctly described by Taylor and Leow (see the article "Rubber contact dermatitis and latex allergy" in the chapter *Rubber industry*) as "an immunoglobulin E-mediated, immediate, Type I allergic reaction, most always due to NRL proteins present in medical and non-medical latex devices. The spectrum of clinical signs ranges from contact urticaria, generalized urticaria, allergic rhinitis, allergic conjunctivitis, angioedema (severe swelling) and asthma (wheezing) to anaphylaxis (severe, life-threatening allergic reaction)". Symptoms may result from direct contact of normal or inflamed skin with gloves or other latex-containing materials or indirectly by mucosal contact with or inhalation of aerosolized NRL proteins or talcum powder particles to which NRL proteins have adhered. Such indirect contact can cause a Type IV reaction to the rubber accelerators. (Approximately 80% of "latex glove allergy" is actually a Type IV reaction to the accelerators.) The diagnosis is confirmed by patch, prick, scratch or other skin sensitivity tests or by serological studies for the immune globulin. In some individuals, the latex allergy is associated with allergy to certain foods (e.g., banana, chestnuts, avocado, kiwi and papaya).

While most common among health care workers, latex allergy is also found among employees in rubber manufacturing plants, other workers who habitually use rubber gloves (e.g., greenhouse workers (Carillo et al. 1995)) and in patients with a history of multiple surgical procedures (e.g., spina bifida, congenital urogenital abnormalities, etc.) (Blaycock 1995). Cases of allergic reactions after the use of latex condoms have been reported (Jonasson, Holm and Leegard 1993), and in one case, a potential reaction was averted by eliciting a history of an allergic reaction to a rubber swimming cap (Burke, Wilson and McCord 1995). Reactions have occurred in sensitive patients when hypodermic needles used to prepare doses of parenteral medications picked up NRL protein as they were pushed through the rubber caps on the vials.

According to a recent study of 63 patients with NRL allergy, it took an average of 5 years of working with latex products for the first symptoms, usually a contact urticaria, to develop. Some also had rhinitis or dyspnoea. It took, on average, an additional 2 years for the appearance of lower respiratory tract symptoms (Allmeers et al. 1996).

Frequency of latex allergy

To determine the frequency of NRL allergy, allergy tests were performed on 224 employees at the University of Cincinnati College of Medicine, including nurses, laboratory technicians, physicians, respiratory therapists, housekeeping and clerical workers (Yassin et al. 1994). Of these, 38 (17%) tested positive to latex extracts; the incidence ranged from 0% among housekeeping workers to 38% among dental staff. Exposure of these sensitized individuals to latex caused itching in 84%, a skin rash in 68%, urticaria in 55%, lachrymation and ocular itching in 45%, nasal congestion in 39% and sneezing in 34%. Anaphylaxis occurred in 10.5%.

In a similar study at the University of Oulo in Finland, 56% of 534 hospital employees who used protective latex or vinyl gloves on a daily basis had skin disorders related to the usage of the gloves (Kujala and Reilula 1995). Rhinorrhoea or nasal congestion was present in 13% of workers who used powdered gloves. The prevalence of both skin and respiratory symptoms was significantly higher among those who used the gloves for more than 2 hours a day.

Valentino and colleagues (1994) reported latex induced asthma in four health care workers in an Italian regional hospital, and the Mayo Medical Center in Rochester Minnesota, where 342 employees who reported symptoms suggestive of latex allergy were evaluated, recorded 16 episodes of latex-related anaphylaxis in 12 subjects (six episodes occurred after skin testing) (Hunt et al. 1995). The Mayo researchers also reported respiratory symptoms in workers who did not wear gloves but worked in areas where large numbers of gloves were being used, presumably due to air-borne talcum powder/latex protein particles.

Control and Prevention

The most effective preventive measure is modification of standard procedures to replace the use of gloves and equipment made with NRL with similar items made of vinyl or other non-rubber materials. This requires involvement of the purchasing and supply departments, which should also mandate the labelling of all latex-containing items so that they may be avoided by individuals with latex sensitivity. This is important not only to the staff but also to patients who may have a history suggestive of latex allergy. Aerosolized latex, from latex powder, is also problematic. HCWs who are allergic to latex and who do not use latex gloves may still be affected by the powdered latex gloves used by co-workers. A significant problem is presented by the wide variation in content of latex allergen among gloves from different manufacturers and, indeed, among different lots of gloves from the same manufacturer.

Glove manufacturers are experimenting with gloves using formulations with smaller amounts of NRL as well as coatings that will obviate the need for talcum powder to make the gloves easy to put on and take off. The goal is to provide comfortable, easy to wear, non-allergenic gloves that still provide effective barriers to the transmission of the hepatitis B virus, HIV and other pathogens.

A careful medical history with a particular emphasis on prior latex exposures should be elicited from all health care workers who present symptoms suggestive of latex allergy. In suspect cases, evidence of latex sensitivity may be confirmed by skin or serological testing. Since there is evidently a risk of provoking an anaphylactic reaction, the skin testing should only be performed by experienced medical personnel.

At the present time, allergens for desensitization are not available so that the only remedy is avoidance of exposure to products containing NRL. In some instances, this may require a change of job. Weido and Sim (1995) at the University of Texas Medical Branch at Galveston suggest advising individuals in high-risk groups to carry self-injectable epinephrine to use in the event of a systemic reaction.

Following the appearance of several clusters of latex allergy cases in 1990, the Mayo Medical Center in Rochester, Minnesota, formed a multidisciplinary work group to address the problem (Hunt et al. 1996). Subsequently, this was formalized in a Latex Allergy Task Force with members from the departments of allergy, preventive medicine, dermatology and surgery as well as the Director of Purchasing, the Surgical Nursing Clinical Director and the Director of Employee Health. Articles on latex allergy were published in staff newsletters and information bulletins to educate the 20,000 member workforce to the problem and to encourage those with suggestive symptoms to seek medical consultation. A standardized approach to testing for latex sensitivity and techniques for quantifying the amount of latex allergen in manufactured products and the amount and particle size of air-borne latex allergen were developed. The latter proved to be sufficiently sensitive to measure the exposure of individual workers while performing particular high-risk tasks. Steps were initiated to monitor a gradual transition to low-allergen gloves (an incidental effect was a lowering of their cost by concentrating glove purchases among the fewer vendors who could meet the low allergen requirements) and to minimize exposures of staff and patients with known sensitivity to NLR.

To alert the public to the risks of NLR allergy, a consumer group, the Delaware Valley Latex Allergy Support Network has been formed. This group has created an Internet website (http://www.latex.org) and maintains a toll-free telephone line (1-800 LATEXNO) to provide up-to-date factual information about latex allergy to persons with this problem and those who care for them. This organization, which has a Medical Advisory Group, maintains a Literature Library and a Product Center and encourages the exchange of experiences among those who have had allergic reactions.

Conclusion

Latex allergies are becoming an increasingly important problem among health care workers. The solution lies in minimizing contact with latex allergen in their work environment, especially by substituting non-latex surgical gloves and appliances.

THE HOSPITAL ENVIRONMENT

● ## BUILDINGS FOR HEALTH CARE FACILITIES

*Cesare Catananti, Gianfranco Damiani
and Giovanni Capelli*

The health maintenance and enhancement, the safety and the comfort of people in health care facilities are seriously affected if specific building requirements are not met. Health care facilities are rather unique buildings, in which heterogeneous environments coexist. Different people, several activities in each environment and many risk factors are involved in the pathogenesis of a broad spectrum of diseases. Functional organization criteria classify health care facility *environments* as follows: nursing units, operating theatres, diagnostic facilities (radiology unit, laboratory units and so on), outpatients' departments, administration area (offices), dietary facilities, linen services, engineering services and equipment areas, corridors and passages. The group of *people* which attends a hospital is composed of health personnel, staff personnel, patients (long-stay inpatients, acute inpatients and outpatients) and visitors. The *processes* include health care specific activities—diagnostic activities, therapeutic activities, nursing activities—and activities common to many public buildings—office work, technological maintenance, food preparation and so on. The *risk factors* are physical agents (ionizing and non-ionizing radiation, noise, lighting and microclimatic factors), chemicals (e.g., organic solvents and disinfectants), biological agents (viruses, bacteria, fungi and so on), ergonomics (postures, lifting and so on) and psychological and organizational factors (e.g., environmental perceptions and work hours). The *illnesses* related to the above-mentioned factors range from environmental annoyance or discomfort (e.g., thermal discomfort or irritative symptoms) to severe diseases (e.g., hospital-acquired infections and traumatic accidents). In this perspective, the risk assessment and control require an interdisciplinary approach involving physicians, hygienists, engineers, architects, economists and so on and fulfilment of preventive measures in the building planning, design, construction and management tasks. Specific building requirements are extremely important among these preventive measures, and, according to the guidelines for healthy buildings introduced by Levin (1992), they should be classified as follows:

- site planning requirements
- architectural design requirements
- requirements for building materials and furnishings
- requirements for heating, ventilation and air-conditioning systems and for microclimatic conditions.

This article focuses on general hospital buildings. Obviously, adaptations would be required for specialty hospitals (e.g., orthopaedic centres, eye and ear hospitals, maternity centres, psychiatric institutions, long-term care facilities and rehabilitation institutes), for ambulatory care clinics, emergency/urgent care facilities and offices for individual and group practices. These will be determined by the numbers and types of patients (including their physical and mental status) and by the number of HCWs and the tasks they perform. Considerations promoting the safety and well-being of both patients and staff that are common to all health care facilities include:

- ambience, including not only decoration, lighting and noise control but also partitioning and placement of furniture and equipment that avoid entrapment of workers with potentially violent patients and visitors
- ventilation systems that minimize exposure to infectious agents and potentially toxic chemicals and gases
- storage facilities for clothing and effects of patients and their visitors that minimize potential contamination
- lockers, changing rooms, wash-up facilities and rest rooms for staff
- conveniently-located hand-washing facilities in each room and treatment area
- doorways, elevators and toilets that accommodate wheel chairs and stretchers
- storage and filing areas designed to minimize workers' stooping, bending, reaching and heavy lifting
- automatic and worker-controlled communication and alarm systems
- mechanisms for collection, storage and disposition of toxic wastes, contaminated linens and clothing and so on.

Site Planning Requirements

The health care facility site must be chosen following four main criteria (Catananti and Cambieri 1990; Klein and Platt 1989;

Decree of the President of Ministers Council 1986; Commission of the European Communities 1990; NHS 1991a, 1991b):

1. *Environmental factors.* The terrain should be as level as possible. Ramps, escalators and elevators can offset sides of hills, but they hinder the access of elderly and handicapped people, adding both a higher cost to the project and an extra burden to fire departments and evacuation teams. Heavy wind sites should be avoided, and the area should be far from sources which create pollution and noise (especially factories and landfills). Radon and radon daughters levels should be assessed, and measures to reduce exposure should be taken. In colder climates, consideration should be given to embedding snow-melting coils in sidewalks, entrance ways and parking areas to minimize falls and other accidents.

2. *Geological configuration.* Earthquake-prone areas should be avoided, or at least anti-seismic construction criteria must be followed. The site must be chosen following an hydrogeological assessment, to avoid water infiltrations into the foundations.

3. *Urbanistic factors.* The site should be easily accessible to potential users, ambulances and service vehicles for goods supply and waste disposal. Public transportation and utilities (water, gas, electricity and sewers) should be available. Fire departments should be nearby, and fire-fighters and their apparatus should find ready access to all parts of the facility.

4. *Space availability.* The site should allow some scope for expansion and provision of adequate car parking.

Architectural Design

Health care facilities architectural design usually follows several criteria:

- class of the health care facility: hospital (acute-care hospital, community hospital, rural hospital), large or small health care centre, nursing homes (extended care facilities, skilled nursing homes, residential care homes), general medical practice premise (NHS 1991a; NHS 1991b; Kleczkowski, Montoya-Aguilar and Nilsson 1985; ASHRAE 1987)
- catchment area dimensions
- management issues: costs, flexibility (susceptibility to adaptation)
- ventilation provided: an air-conditioned building is compact and deep with as small an amount of external walls as possible, to reduce the heat transfer between outside and inside; a naturally ventilated building is long and thin, to maximize exposure to breezes and to minimize internal distances from windows (Llewelyn-Davies and Wecks 1979)
- building/area ratio
- environmental quality: safety and comfort are extremely relevant targets.

The listed criteria lead health care facilities planners to choose the best building shape for each situation, ranging essentially from an extended horizontal hospital with scattered buildings to a monolithic vertical or horizontal building (Llewelyn-Davies and Wecks 1979). The first case (a preferable format for low-density buildings) is normally used for hospitals up to 300 beds, because of its low costs in construction and management. It is particularly considered for small rural hospitals and community hospitals (Llewelyn-Davies and Wecks 1979). The second case (usually preferred for high-density buildings) becomes cost-effective for hospitals with more than 300 beds, and it is advisable for acute-care hospitals (Llewelyn-Davies and Wecks 1979). The internal space dimensions and distribution have to cope with many variables, among which one can consider: functions, processes, circulation and connections to other areas, equipment, predicted workload, costs, and flexibility, convertibility and susceptibility of shared use.

Compartments, exits, fire alarms, automatic extinction systems and other fire prevention and protection measures should follow local regulations. Furthermore, several specific requirements have been defined for each area in health care facilities:

1. *Nursing units*. Internal layout of nursing units usually follows one of the following three basic models (Llewelyn-Davies and Wecks 1979): an open ward (or "Nightingale" ward)—a broad room with 20 to 30 beds, heads to the windows, ranged along both walls; the "Rigs" layout—in this model beds were placed parallel to the windows, and, at first, they were in open bays on either side of a central corridor (as at Rigs Hospital in Copenhagen), and in later hospitals the bays were often enclosed, so that they became rooms with 6 to 10 beds; small rooms, with 1 to 4 beds. Four variables should lead the planner to choose the best layout: bed need (if high, an open ward is advisable), budget (if low, an open ward is the cheapest one), privacy needs (if considered high, small rooms are unavoidable) and intensive care level (if high, the open ward or Rigs layout with 6 to 10 beds are advisable). The space requirements should be at least: 6 to 8 square metres (sqm) per bed for open wards, inclusive of circulation and ancillary rooms (Llewelyn-Davies and Wecks 1979); 5 to 7 sqm/bed for multiple bedrooms and 9 sqm for single bedrooms (Decree of the President of Ministers Council 1986; American Institute of Architects Committee on Architecture for Health 1987). In open wards, toilet facilities should be close to patients' beds (Llewelyn-Davies and Wecks 1979). For single and multiple bedrooms, handwashing facilities should be provided in each room; lavatories may be omitted where a toilet room is provided to serve one single-bed room or one two-bed room (American Institute of Architects Committee on Architecture for Health 1987). Nursing stations should be large enough to accommodate desks and chairs for record keeping, tables and cabinets for preparation of drugs, instruments and supplies, chairs for sit-down conferences with physicians and other staff members, a wash-up sink and access to a staff toilet.

2. *Operating theatres*. Two main classes of elements should be considered: operating rooms and service areas (American Institute of Architects Committee on Architecture for Health 1987). Operating rooms should be classified as follows:
   - general operating room, needing a minimum clear area of 33.5 sqm.
   - room for orthopaedic surgery (optional), needing enclosed storage space for splints and traction equipment
   - room for cardiovascular surgery (optional), needing a minimum clear area of 44 sqm. In the clear area of the surgical suite, nearby the operating room, an additional pump room should be designed, where extracorporeal pump supplies and accessories are stored and serviced.
   - room for endoscope procedures, needing a minimum clear area of 23 sqm
   - rooms for waiting patients, induction of anaesthesia and recovery from anaesthesia.
   Service areas should include: sterilizing facility with high-speed autoclave, scrub facilities, medical gas storage facilities and staff clothing change areas.

3. *Diagnostic facilities:* Each *radiology unit* should include (Llewelyn-Davies and Wecks 1979; American Institute of Architects Committee on Architecture for Health 1987):
   - appointment desk and waiting areas
   - diagnostic radiographic rooms, needing 23 sqm for fluoroscopic procedures and about 16 sqm for radiographic ones, plus a shielded control area, and rigid support structures for ceiling-mounted equipment (where necessary)

- dark room (where necessary), needing almost 5 sqm and appropriate ventilation for the developer
- contrast media preparation area, clean-up facilities, film quality control area, computer area and film storage area
- viewing area where films can be read and reports dictated.
The wall thickness in a radiology unit should be 8 to 12 cm (poured concrete) or 12 to 15 cm (cinder block or bricks).

The diagnostic activities in health care facilities may require tests in haematology, clinical chemistry, microbiology, pathology and cytology. Each *laboratory area* should be provided with work areas, sample and material storage facilities (refrigerated or not), specimen collection facilities, facilities and equipment for terminal sterilization and waste disposal, and a special facility for radioactive material storage (where necessary) (American Institute of Architects Committee on Architecture for Health 1987).

4. *Outpatient departments*. Clinical facilities should include (American Institute of Architects Committee on Architecture for Health 1987): general-purpose examination rooms (7.4 sqm), special-purpose examination rooms (varying with the specific equipment needed) and treatment rooms (11 sqm). In addition, administrative facilities are needed for the admittance of outpatients.

5. *Administration area (offices)*. Facilities such as common office building areas are needed. These include a loading dock and storage areas for receiving supplies and equipment and dispatching materials not disposed of by the separate waste removal system.

6. *Dietary facilities (optional)*. Where present, these should provide the following elements (American Institute of Architects Committee on Architecture for Health 1987): a control station for receiving and controlling food supplies, storage spaces (including cold storage), food preparation facilities, handwashing facilities, facility for assembling and distributing patients' meals, dining space, dishwashing space (located in a room or an alcove separated from the food preparation and serving area), waste storage facilities and toilets for dietary staff.

7. *Linen services (optional)*. Where present, these should provide the following elements: a room for receiving and holding soiled linen, a clean-linen storage area, a clean-linen inspection and mending area and handwashing facilities (American Institute of Architects Committee on Architecture for Health 1987).

8. *Engineering services and equipment areas*. Adequate areas, varying in size and characteristics for each health care facility, have to be provided for: boiler plant (and fuel storage, if necessary), electrical supply, emergency generator, maintenance workshops and stores, cold-water storage, plant rooms (for centralized or local ventilation) and medical gases (NHS 1991a).

9. *Corridors and passages*. These have to be organized to avoid confusion for visitors and disruptions in the work of hospital personnel; circulation of clean and dirty goods should be strictly separated. Minimum corridor width should be 2 m (Decree of the President of Ministers Council 1986). Doorways and elevators must be large enough to allow easy passage of stretchers and wheelchairs.

Requirements for Building Materials and Furnishings

The choice of materials in modern health care facilities is often aimed to reduce the risk in accidents and fire occurrence: materials must be non-inflammable and must not produce noxious gases or smokes when burnt (American Institute of Architects Committee on Architecture for Health 1987). Trends in hospital floor-covering materials have shown a shift from stone materials and linoleum to polyvinyl chloride (PVC). In operating rooms, in particular, PVC is considered the best choice to avoid electrostatic effects that may cause explosion of anaesthetic flammable gases.

Table 97.16 • Criteria and variables to be considered in the choice of materials.

Criteria	Variables
Functional performance	Static load, transit load, impact load, durability, construction requirements
Safety	Collapse risk, fire risk (reaction to fire, fire resistance, flammability), static electric charge (explosion risk), disperse electric power (electric shock risk), sharp surface (wound risk), poisoning risk (hazardous chemical emission), slip risk, radioactivity
Comfort and pleasantness	Acoustic comfort (features related to noise), optical and visual comfort (features related to light), tactile comfort (consistence, surface), hygrothermal comfort (features related to heat), aesthetics, odour emissions, indoor air quality perception
Hygienicity	Living beings habitat (insects, moulds, bacteria), susceptibility to stains, susceptibility to dust, easiness in cleaning, washing and disinfecting, maintenance procedures
Flexibility	Susceptibility to modifications, conformational factors (tile or panel dimensions and morphology)
Environmental impact	Raw material, industrial manufacturing, waste management
Cost	Material cost, installation cost, maintenance cost

Source: Catananti et al. 1994.

Up to some years ago, walls were painted; today, PVC coverings and fibreglass wallpaper are the most used wall finishes. False ceilings are today built mainly from mineral fibres instead of gypsum board; a new trend appears to be that of using stainless steel ceilings (Catanati et al. 1993). However, a more complete approach should consider that each material and furnishing may cause effects in the outdoor and indoor environmental systems. Accurately chosen building materials may reduce environmental pollution and high social costs and improve the safety and comfort of building occupants. At the same time, internal materials and finishes may influence the functional performance of the building and its management. Besides, the choice of materials in hospitals should also consider specific criteria, such as ease of cleaning, washing and disinfecting procedures and susceptibility to becoming a habitat for living beings. A more detailed classification of criteria to be considered in this task, derived from the European Community Council Directive No. 89/106 (Council of the European Communities 1988), is shown in table 97.16.

On the matter of odour emissions, it should be observed that a correct ventilation after floor or wall-coverings installation or renovation work reduces exposure of personnel and patients to indoor pollutants (especially volatile organic compounds (VOCs)) emitted by building materials and furnishings.

Requirements for Heating, Ventilation and Air-Conditioning Systems and for Microclimatic Conditions

The control of microclimatic conditions in health care facilities areas may be carried out by heating, ventilation and/or air-conditioning systems (Catananti and Cambieri 1990). Heating systems (e.g., radiators) permit only temperature regulation and may be sufficient for common nursing units. Ventilation, which induces changes of air speed, may be natural (e.g., by porous building materials), supplementary (by windows) or artificial (by mechanical systems). The artificial ventilation is especially recommended for kitchens, laundries and engineering services. Air-conditioning systems, particularly recommended for some health care facility areas such as operating rooms and intensive-care units, should guarantee:

- the control of all microclimatic factors (temperature, relative humidity and air speed)
- the control of air purity and concentration of micro-organisms and chemicals (e.g., anaesthetic gases, volatile solvents, odours and so on). This target may be achieved by adequate air filtration and air changes, right pressure relationships among adjacent areas and laminar airflow.

General requirements of air-conditioning systems include outdoor intake locations, air filter features and air supply outlets (ASHRAE 1987). Outdoor intake locations should be far enough, at least 9.1 m, from pollution sources such as exhaust outlets of combustion equipment stacks, medical-surgical vacuum systems, ventilation exhaust outlets from the hospital or adjoining buildings, areas that may collect vehicular exhaust and other noxious fumes, or plumbing vent stacks. Besides, their distance from ground level should be at least 1.8 m. Where these components are installed above the roof, their distance from roof level should be at least 0.9 m.

Number and efficiency of filters should be adequate for the specific areas supplied by air conditioning systems. For example, two filter beds of 25 and 90% efficiency should be used in operating rooms, intensive-care units and transplant organ rooms. Installation and maintenance of filters follow several criteria: lack of leakage between filter segments and between the filter bed and its supporting frame, installation of a manometer in the filter system in order to provide a reading of the pressure so that filters can be identified as expired and provision of adequate facilities for maintenance without introducing contamination into the air flow. Air supply outlets should be located on the ceiling with perimeter or several exhaust inlets near the floor (ASHRAE 1987).

Ventilation rates for health care facility areas permitting air purity and comfort of occupants are listed in table 97.17.

Specific requirements of air-conditioning systems and microclimatic conditions regarding several hospital areas are reported as follows (ASHRAE 1987):

Nursing units. In common patient rooms a temperature (T) of 24 °C and a 30% relative humidity (RH) for winter and a T of 24 °C with 50% RH for summer are recommended. In intensive-care units a variable range temperature capability of 24 to 27 °C and a RH of 30% minimum and 60% maximum with a positive air pressure are recommended. In immunosuppressed patient units a positive pressure should be maintained between patient room and adjacent area and HEPA filters should be used.

In full-term nursery a T of 24 °C with RH from 30% minimum to 60% maximum is recommended. The same microclimatic conditions of intensive-care units are required in special-care nursery.

Operating theatres. Variable temperature range capability of 20 to 24 °C with RH of 50% minimum and 60% maximum and positive air pressure are recommended in operating rooms. A separate air-exhaust system or special vacuum system should be provided in order to remove anaesthetic gas traces (see "Waste anaesthetic gases" in this chapter).

Diagnostic facilities. In the radiology unit, fluoroscopic and radiographic rooms require T of 24 to 27 °C and RH of 40 to 50%. Laboratory units should be supplied with adequate hood exhaust systems to remove dangerous fumes, vapours and bioaerosols. The exhaust air from the hoods of the units of clinical chemistry, bacteriology and pathology should be discharged to the outdoors with no recirculation. Also, the exhaust air from infectious disease

Table 97.17 • Ventilation requirements in health care facilities areas.

Areas	Pressure relationships to adjacent areas	Minimum air changes of outdoor air per hour supplied to room	Minimum total air changes per hour supplied to room	All air exhausted directly to outdoors	Recirculated within room units
Nursing units					
Patient room	+/−	2	2	Optional	Optional
Intensive care	P	2	6	Optional	No
Patient corridor	+/−	2	4	Optional	Optional
Operating theatres					
Operating room (all outdoor system)	P	15	15	Yes[1]	No
Operating room (recirculating system)	P	5	25	Optional	No[2]
Diagnostic facilities					
X ray	+/−	2	6	Optional	Optional
Laboratories					
Bacteriology	N	2	6	Yes	No
Clinical chemistry	P	2	6	Optional	No
Pathology	N	2	6	Yes	No
Serology	P	2	6	Optional	No
Sterilizing	N	Optional	10	Yes	No
Glasswashing	N	2	10	Yes	Optional
Dietary facilities					
Food preparation centres[3]	+/−	2	10	Yes	No
Dishwashing	N	Optional	10	Yes	No
Linen service					
Laundry (general)	+/−	2	10	Yes	No
Soiled linen sorting and storage	N	Optional	10	Yes	No
Clean linen storage	P	2 (Optional)	2	Optional	Optional

P = Positive. N = Negative. +/− = Continuous directional control not required.
[1] For operating rooms, use of 100% outside air should be limited to these cases where local codes require it, only if heat recovery devices are used; [2] recirculating room units meeting the filtering requirement for the space may be used; [3] food preparation centres shall have ventilation systems that have an excess of air supply for positive pressure when hoods are not in operation. The number of air changes may be varied to any extent required for odour control when the space is not in use.
Source: ASHRAE 1987.

and virology laboratories requires sterilization before being exhausted to the outdoors.

Dietary facilities. These should be provided with hoods over the cooking equipment for removal of heat, odours and vapours.

Linen services. The sorting room should be maintained at a negative pressure in relation to adjoining areas. In the laundry processing area, washers, flatwork ironers, tumblers, and so on should have direct overhead exhaust to reduce humidity.

Engineering services and equipment areas. At work stations, the ventilation system should limit temperature to 32 °C.

Conclusion

The essence of specific building requirements for health care facilities is the accommodation of external standard-based regulations to subjective index-based guidelines. In fact, subjective indices, such as Predicted Mean Vote (PMV) (Fanger 1973) and olf, a measure of odour (Fanger 1992), are able to make predictions of the comfort levels of patients and personnel without neglecting the differences related to their clothing, metabolism and physical status. Finally, the planners and architects of hospitals should follow the theory of

"building ecology" (Levin 1992) which describes dwellings as a complex series of interactions among buildings, their occupants and the environment. Health facilities, accordingly, should be planned and built focusing on the whole "system" rather than any particular partial frames of reference.

HOSPITALS: ENVIRONMENTAL AND PUBLIC HEALTH ISSUES

M.P. Arias

A hospital is not an isolated social environment; it has, given its mission, very serious intrinsic social responsibilities. A hospital needs to be integrated with its surroundings and should minimize its impact upon them, thus contributing to the welfare of the people who live near it.

From a regulatory perspective, the health industry has never been considered to be on the same level as other industries when they are ranked according to the health risks they pose. The result is that specific legislation in this sphere has been non-existent until recently, although in the last few years this deficiency has been addressed. While in many other kinds of industrial activities, health and safety is an integral part of the organization, most health centres still pay little or no attention to it.

One reason for this could be the attitudes of HCWs themselves, who may be preoccupied more with research and the acquisition of the latest technologies and diagnostic and treatment techniques than with looking into the effects that these advances could have on their own health and on the environment.

New developments in science and health care must be combined with environmental protection, because environmental policies in a hospital affect the quality of life of HCWs within the hospital and those who live outside it.

Integrated Health, Safety and Environmental Programmes

HCWs represent a major group, comparable in size to the large enterprises of the private sector. The number of people who pass through a hospital every day is very large: visitors, inpatients, outpatients, medical and commercial representatives, subcontractors and so on. All of them, to a greater or lesser degree, are exposed to the potential risks posed by the activities of the medical centre and, at the same time, contribute on a certain level to the improvement or the worsening of the safety and the care of the centre's surroundings.

Strict measures are needed in order to safeguard HCWs, the general public and the surrounding environment from the deleterious effects that may stem from hospital activities. These activities include the use of ever more sophisticated technology, the more frequent use of extremely powerful drugs (the effects of which can have a profound and irreparable impact on the people who prepare or administer them), the too-often uncontrolled use of chemical products and the incidence of infectious diseases, some of which are incurable.

The risks of working in a hospital are many. Some are easy to identify, while others are very hard to detect; the measures to be taken should therefore always be rigorous.

Different groups of health professionals are particularly exposed to risks common to the health care industry in general, as well as to specific risks related to their profession and/or to the activities they perform in the course of their work.

The concept of *prevention*, therefore, must of necessity be incorporated to the health care field and encompass:

- *safety* in the broadest sense, including psychosociology and ergonomics as part of the programmes to improve the quality of life in the workplace
- *hygiene*, minimizing as much as possible any physical, chemical or biological factor that may affect the health of people in the work environment
- *environment*, following policies to protect nature and people in the surrounding community and decreasing the impact on the environment.

We should be aware that the environment is directly and intimately related to the safety and hygiene in the workplace, because natural resources are consumed at work, and because these resources are later reincorporated into our surroundings. Our quality of life will be good or bad depending on whether we make correct use of these resources and use appropriate technologies.

Everyone's involvement is necessary in order to contribute to further:

- nature conservancy policies, designed to guarantee the survival of the natural heritage that surrounds us

- environmental improvement policies as well as policies to control indoor and environmental pollution in order to integrate human activity with the environment
- environmental research and training policies to improve working conditions as well as to reduce environmental impact
- planning organizational policies designed to set goals and develop norms and methodology for workers' health and the environment.

Goals

Such a programme should endeavour to:

- change the culture and habits of health professionals in order to stimulate behaviour more conducive to safeguarding their health
- set goals and develop internal safety, hygiene and environmental guidelines through adequate planning and organization
- improve the methods of work to avoid a negative impact on health and the environment through environmental research and education
- increase the involvement of all personnel and have them take responsibility for health in the workplace
- create an adequate programme to establish and publicize the guidelines as well as to monitor their continued implementation
- correctly classify and manage the waste generated
- optimize costs, avoiding added expenditures that cannot be justified by the increased levels of safety and health or environmental quality.

Plan

A hospital should be conceived as a system that, through a number of processes, generates services. These services are the main goal of the activities performed in a hospital.

For the *process* to begin, certain commitments of energy, investments and technology are needed, which in turn will generate their own emissions and wastes. Their only aim is to *provide service*.

In addition to these prerequisites, consideration should be given to the conditions of the areas of the building where these activities will take place, since they have been designed a certain way and built with basic construction materials.

Control, planning and coordination are all necessary for an integrated safety, health and environmental project to succeed.

Methodology

Because of the complexity and the variety of risks in the health care field, multidisciplinary groups are required if solutions to each particular problem are to be found.

It is important for health care workers to be able to collaborate with safety studies, participating in the decisions that will be made to improve their working conditions. This way changes will be seen with a better attitude and the guidelines will be more readily accepted.

The safety, hygiene and environmental service should advise, stimulate and coordinate the programmes developed at the health centre. Responsibility for their implementation should fall upon whoever heads up the service where this programme will be followed. This is the only way to involve the entire organization.

In each particular case, the following will be selected:

- the system involved
- the parameters of the study
- the time needed to carry it out.

The study will consist of:

- an initial diagnosis
- analysis of the risk
- deciding on the course of action.

In order to implement the plan successfully it will always be necessary to:

- educate and inform people of the risks
- improve the management of human resources
- improve the channels of communication.

This type of study may be a global one encompassing the centre as a whole (e.g., internal plan for the disposal of hospital wastes) or partial, encompassing only one concrete area (e.g., where cancer chemotherapeutic drugs are prepared).

The study of these factors will give an idea of the degree to which safety measures are disregarded, as much from the legal as from the scientific point of view. The concept of "legal" here encompasses advances in science and technology as they occur, which requires the constant revision and modification of established norms and guidelines.

It would be convenient indeed if the regulations and the laws by which safety, hygiene and the environment are regulated were the same in all countries, something that would make the installation, management and use of technology or products from other countries much easier.

Results

The following examples show some of the measures that can be taken while following the aforementioned methodology.

Laboratories

An *advisory service* can be developed involving professionals of the various laboratories and coordinated by the safety and hygiene service of the medical centre. The main goal would be to improve the safety and health of the occupants of all the labs, involving and giving responsibility to the entire professional staff of each and trying at the same time to make sure that these activities do not have a negative impact on public health and the environment.

The measures taken should include:

- instituting the sharing of materials, products and equipment among the different laboratories, in order to optimize resources
- reducing the stocks of chemical products in laboratories
- creating a manual of basic norms of safety and hygiene
- planning courses to educate all laboratory workers on these matters
- training for emergencies.

Mercury

Thermometers, when broken, release mercury into the environment. A pilot project has been started with "unbreakable" thermometers to consider eventually substituting them for the glass thermometers. In some countries, such as the United States, electronic thermometers have replaced mercury thermometers to a very great extent.

Training the workers

The training and the commitment of the workers is the most important part of an integrated safety, health and environment programme. Given enough resources and time, the technicalities of almost any problem can be solved, but a complete solution will not be achieved without informing the workers of the risks and training them to avoid or control them. The training and education must be continuous, integrating health and safety techniques into all the other training programmes in the hospital.

Conclusions

The results that have been achieved so far in applying this work model allow us so far to be optimistic. They have shown that when people are informed about the whys and wherefores, their attitude toward change is very positive.

The response of health care personnel has been very good. They feel more motivated in their work and more valued when they have participated directly in the study and in the decision-making process. This participation, in turn, helps to educate the individual health care worker and to increase the degree of responsibility he or she is willing to accept.

The attainment of the goals of this project is a long-term objective, but the positive effects it generates more than compensate for the effort and the energy invested in it.

HOSPITAL WASTE MANAGEMENT

M.P. Arias

An adaptation of current guidelines on the disposal of hospital wastes, as well as improvements in internal safety and hygiene, must be part of an overall plan of hospital waste management that establishes the procedures to follow. This should be done through properly coordinating internal and external services, as well as defining responsibilities in each of the management phases. The main goal of this plan is to protect the health of health care personnel, patients, visitors and the general public both in the hospital and beyond.

At the same time, the health of the people who come in contact with the waste once it leaves the medical centre should not be overlooked, and the risks to them should also be minimized.

Such a plan should be campaigned for and applied according to a global strategy that always keeps in mind the realities of the workplace, as well as the knowledge and the training of the personnel involved.

Stages followed in the implementation of a waste management plan are:

- informing the management of the medical centre
- designating those responsible at the executive level
- creating a committee on hospital wastes made up of personnel from the general services, nursing and medical departments that is chaired by the medical centre's waste manager.

The group should include personnel from the general services department, personnel from the nursing department and personnel from the medical department. The medical centre's waste manager should coordinate the committee by:

- putting together a report on the present performance of the centre's waste management
- putting together an internal plan for advanced management
- creating a training programme for the entire staff of the medical centre, with the collaboration of the human resources department
- launching the plan, with follow-up and control by the waste management committee.

Classification of hospital wastes

Until 1992, following the classical waste management system, the practice was to classify most hospital wastes as hazardous. Since then, applying an advanced management technique, only a very small proportion of the large volume of these wastes is considered hazardous.

The tendency has been to adopt an advanced management technique. This technique classifies wastes starting from the baseline assumption that only a very small percentage of the volume of wastes generated is hazardous.

Wastes should always be classified at the point where they are generated. According to the *nature* of the wastes and their *source*, they are classified as follows:

- Group I: those wastes that can be assimilated into urban refuse
- Group II: non-specific hospital wastes
- Group III: specific hospital wastes or hazardous wastes
- Group IV: cytostatic wastes (surplus antineoplastic drugs that are not fit for therapeutic use, as well as the single-use materials that have been in contact with them, e.g., needles, syringes, catheters, gloves and IV set-ups).

According to their *physical state,* wastes can be classified as follows:

- solids: wastes that contain less than 10% liquid
- liquids: wastes that contain more than 10% liquid

Gaseous wastes, such as CFCs from freezers and refrigerators, are not normally captured (see article "Waste anaesthetic gases").

By definition, the following wastes are not considered sanitary wastes:

- radioactive wastes that, because of their very nature, are already managed in a specific way by the radiological protection service
- human cadavers and large anatomical parts which are cremated or incinerated according to regulations
- waste water.

Group I Wastes

All wastes generated within the medical centre that are not directly related to sanitary activities are considered solid urban wastes (SUW). According to the local ordinances in Cataluna, Spain, as in most communities, the municipalities must remove these wastes selectively, and it is therefore convenient to facilitate this task for them. The following are considered wastes that can be assimilated to urban refuse according to their point of origin:

Kitchen wastes:

- food wastes
- wastes from leftovers or single-use items
- containers.

Wastes generated by people treated in the hospital and non-medical personnel:

- wastes from cleaning products
- wastes left behind in the rooms (e.g., newspapers, magazines and flowers)
- wastes from gardening and renovations.

Wastes from administrative activities:

- paper and cardboard
- plastics.

Other wastes:

- glass containers
- plastic containers
- packing cartons and other packaging materials
- dated single-use items.

So long as they are not included on other selective removal plans, SUW will be placed in white polyethylene bags that will be removed by janitorial personnel.

Group II Wastes

Group II wastes include all those wastes generated as a by-product of medical activities that do not pose a risk to health or the environment. For reasons of safety and industrial hygiene the type of internal management recommended for this group is different from that recommended for Group I wastes. Depending on where they originate, Group II wastes include:

Wastes derived from hospital activities, such as:

- blood-stained materials
- gauze and materials used in treating non-infectious patients
- used medical equipment
- mattresses
- dead animals or parts thereof, from rearing stables or experimental laboratories, so long as they have not been inoculated with infectious agents.

Group II wastes will be deposited in yellow polyethylene bags that will be removed by janitorial personnel.

Group III Wastes

Group III includes hospital wastes which, due to their nature or their point of origin, could pose risks to health or the environment if several special precautions are not observed during handling and removal.

Group III wastes can be classified in the following way:

Sharp and pointed instruments:

- needles
- scalpels.

Infectious wastes. Group III wastes (including single-use items) generated by the diagnosis and treatment of patients who suffer from one of the infectious diseases are listed in table 97.18.

Laboratory wastes:

- material contaminated with biological wastes
- waste from work with animals inoculated with biohazardous substances.

Wastes of the Group III type will be placed in single-use, rigid, colour-coded polyethylene containers and hermetically sealed (in Cataluna, black containers are required). The containers should be clearly labelled as "Hazardous hospital wastes" and kept in the room until collected by janitorial personnel. Group III wastes should never be compacted.

To facilitate their removal and reduce risks to a minimum, containers should not be filled to capacity so that they can be closed easily. Wastes should never be handled once they are placed in these rigid containers. It is forbidden to dispose of biohazardous wastes by dumping them into the drainage system.

Group IV Wastes

Group IV wastes are surplus antineoplastic drugs that are not fit for therapeutic use, as well as all single-use material that has been in contact with the same (needles, syringes, catheters, gloves, IV set-ups and so on).

Given the danger they pose to persons and the environment, Group IV hospital wastes must be collected in rigid, watertight, sealable single-use, colour-coded containers (in Cataluna, they are blue) which should be clearly labelled "Chemically contaminated material: Cytostatic agents".

Other Wastes

Guided by environmental concerns and the need to enhance waste management for the community, medical centres, with the cooperation of all personnel, staff and visitors, should encourage and facilitate the selective disposal (i.e., in special containers designated for specific materials) of recyclable materials such as:

Table 97.18 • Infectious diseases and Group III wastes.

Infections	Wastes contaminated with
Viral haemorrhagic fevers Congo-Crimean fever Lassa fever Marburg virus Ebola Junin fever Machupo fever Arbovirus Absettarow Hanzalova Hypr Kumlinge Kiasanur Forest Disease Omsk fever Russian spring-summer encephalitis	All wastes
Brucellosis	Pus
Diphtheria	Pharyngeal diphtheria: respiratory secretions Cutaneous diphtheria: secretions from skin lesions
Cholera	Stools
Creutzfelt-Jakob encephalitis	Stools
Borm	Secretions from skin lesions
Tularaemia	Pulmonary tularaemia: respiratory secretions Cutaneous tularaemia: pus
Anthrax	Cutaneous anthrax: pus Respiratory anthrax: respiratory secretions
Plague	Bubonic plague: pus Pneumonic plague: respiratory secretions
Rabies	Respiratory secretions
Q Fever	Respiratory secretions
Active tuberculosis	Respiratory secretions

- paper and cardboard
- glass
- used oils
- batteries and power cells
- toner cartridges for laser printers
- plastic containers.

The protocol established by the local sanitation department for the collection, transport and disposal of each of these types of materials should be followed.

Disposal of large pieces of equipment, furniture and other materials not covered in these guidelines should follow the directions recommended by the appropriate environmental authorities.

Internal transport and storage of wastes
Internal transport of all the wastes generated within the hospital building should be done by the janitorial personnel, according to established schedules. It is important that the following recommendations be observed when transporting wastes within the hospital:

- The containers and the bags will always be closed during transport.

- The carts used for this purpose will have smooth surfaces and be easy to clean.
- The carts will be used exclusively for transporting waste.
- The carts will be washed daily with water, soap and lye.
- The waste bags or containers should never be dragged on the floor.
- Waste should never be transferred from one receptacle to another.

The hospital must have an area specifically for the storage of wastes; it should conform to current guidelines and fulfil, in particular, the following conditions:

- It should be covered.
- It should be clearly marked by signs.
- It should be built with smooth surfaces that are easy to clean.
- It should have running water.
- It should have drains to remove the possible spillage of waste liquids and the water used for cleaning the storage area.
- It should be provided with a system to protect it against animal pests.
- It should be located far away from windows and from the intake ducts of the ventilation system.
- It should be provided with fire extinguishing systems.
- It should have restricted access.
- It should be used exclusively for the storage of wastes.

All the transport and storage operations that involve hospital wastes must be conducted under conditions of maximum safety and hygiene. In particular, one must remember:

- Direct contact with the wastes must be avoided.
- Bags should not be overfilled so that they may be closed easily.
- Bags should not be emptied into other bags.

Liquid Wastes: Biological and Chemical
Liquid wastes can be classified as biological or chemical.

Liquid biological wastes
Liquid biological wastes can usually be poured directly into the hospital's drainage system since they do not require any treatment before disposal. The exceptions are the liquid wastes of patients with infectious diseases and the liquid cultures of microbiology laboratories. These should be collected in specific containers and treated before being dumped.

It is important that the waste be dumped directly into the drainage system with no splashing or spraying. If this is not possible and wastes are gathered in disposable containers that are difficult to open, the containers should not be forced open. Instead, the entire container should be disposed of, as with Group III solid wastes. When liquid waste is eliminated like Group III solid waste, it should be taken into consideration that the conditions of work differ for the disinfection of solid and liquid wastes. This must be kept in mind in order to ensure the effectiveness of the treatment.

Liquid chemical wastes
Liquid wastes generated in the hospital (generally in the laboratories) can be classified in three groups:

- liquid wastes that should not be dumped into the drains
- liquid wastes that can be dumped into the drains after being treated
- liquid wastes that can be dumped into the drains without being previously treated.

This classification is based on considerations related to the health and quality of life of the entire community. These include:

- protection of the water supply

- protection of the sewer system
- protection of the waste water purification stations.

Liquid wastes that can pose a serious threat to people or to the environment because they are toxic, noxious, flammable, corrosive or carcinogenic should be separated and collected so that they can subsequently be recovered or destroyed. They should be collected as follows:

- Each type of liquid waste should go into a separate container.
- The container should be labelled with the name of the product or the major component of the waste, by volume.
- Each laboratory, except the pathological anatomy laboratory, should provide its own individual receptacles to collect liquid wastes that are correctly labelled with the material or family of materials it contains. Periodically (at the end of each work day would be most desirable), these should be emptied into specifically labelled containers which are held in the room until collected at appropriate intervals by the assigned waste removal subcontractor.
- Once each receptacle is correctly labelled with the product or the family of products it contains, it should be placed in specific containers in the labs.
- The person responsible for the laboratory, or someone directly delegated by that person, will sign and stamp a control ticket. The subcontractor will then be responsible for delivering the control ticket to the department that supervises safety, hygiene and the environment.

Mixtures of chemical and biological liquid wastes

Treatment of chemical wastes is more aggressive than treatment of biological wastes. Mixtures of these two wastes should be treated using the steps indicated for liquid chemical wastes. Labels on containers should note the presence of biological wastes.

Any liquid or solid materials that are carcinogenic, mutagenic or teratogenic should be disposed of in rigid colour-coded containers specifically designed and labelled for this type of waste.

Dead animals that have been inoculated with biohazardous substances will be disposed of in closed rigid containers, which will be sterilized before being reused.

Disposal of Sharp and Pointed Instruments

Sharp and pointed instruments (e.g., needles and lancets), once used, must be placed in specifically designed, rigid "sharps" containers that have been strategically placed throughout the hospital. These wastes will be disposed of as hazardous wastes even if used on uninfected patients. They must never be disposed of except in the rigid sharps container.

All HCWs must be repeatedly reminded of the danger of accidental cuts or punctures with this type of material, and instructed to report them when they occur, so that appropriate preventive measures may be instituted. They should be specifically instructed not to attempt to recap used hypodermic needles before dropping them into the sharps container.

Whenever possible, needles to be placed in the sharps container without recapping may be separated from the syringes which, without the needle, can generally be disposed of as Group II waste. Many sharps containers have a special fitting for separating the syringe without risk of a needlestick to the worker; this saves space in the sharps containers for more needles. The sharps containers, which should never be opened by hospital personnel, should be removed by designated janitorial personnel and forwarded for appropriate disposal of their contents.

If it is not possible to separate the needle in adequately safe conditions, the whole needle-syringe combination must be considered as biohazardous and must be placed in the rigid sharps containers.

These sharps containers will be removed by the janitorial personnel.

Staff Training

There must be an ongoing training programme in waste management for all hospital personnel aimed at indoctrinating the staff on all levels with the imperative of always following the established guidelines for collecting, storing and disposing wastes of all kinds. It is particularly important that the housekeeping and janitorial staffs be trained in the details of the protocols for recognizing and dealing with the various categories of hazardous waste. The janitorial, security and fire-fighting staff must also be drilled in the correct course of action in the event of an emergency.

It is also important for the janitorial personnel to be informed and trained on the correct course of action in case of an accident.

Particularly when the programme is first launched, the janitorial staff should be instructed to report any problems that may hinder their performance of these assigned duties. They may be given special cards or forms on which to record such findings.

Waste Management Committee

To monitor the performance of the waste management programme and resolve any problems that may arise as it is implemented, a permanent waste management committee should be created and meet regularly, quarterly at a minimum. The committee should be accessible to any member of the hospital staff with a waste disposal problem or concern and should have access as needed to top management.

Implementing the Plan

The way the waste management programme is implemented may well determine whether it succeeds or not.

Since the support and cooperation of the various hospital committees and departments is essential, details of the programme should be presented to such groups as the administrative teams of the hospital, the health and safety committee and the infection control committee. It is necessary also to obtain validation of the programme from such community agencies as the departments of health, environmental protection and sanitation. Each of these may have helpful modifications to suggest, particularly with respect to the way the programme impinges on their areas of responsibility.

Once the programme design has been finalized, a pilot test in a selected area or department should permit rough edges to be polished and any unforeseen problems resolved. When this has been completed and its results analysed, the programme may be implemented progressively throughout the entire medical centre. A presentation, with audio-visual supports and distribution of descriptive literature, can be delivered in each unit or department, followed by delivery of bags and/or containers as required. Following the start-up of the programme, the department or unit should be visited so that any needed revisions may be instituted. In this manner, the participation and support of the entire hospital staff, without which the programme would never succeed, can be earned.

MANAGING HAZARDOUS WASTE DISPOSAL UNDER ISO 14000

Jerry Spiegel and John Reimer

A formal Environmental Management System (EMS), using the International Organization for Standardization (ISO) standard

Table 97.20 • Role and responsibilities.

Organizational unit	Responsibility
S&DS Supply and Distribution Services	Operates the process and is the process owner/leader, and arranges responsible disposal of waste.
UD–User Departments the source of waste materials	Identifies waste, selects packaging, initiates disposal activities.
DOEM Department of Occupational and Environmental Medicine	Provides specialist technical support in identifying risks and protective measures associated with materials used by HSC and identifies improvement opportunities.
EPE Environmental Protection Engineer	Provides specialist support in process performance monitoring and reporting, identifies emerging regulatory trends and compliance requirements, and identifies improvement opportunities.
ALL–All participants	Shares responsibility for process development activities.

Process description

The initial step in preparing a process description is to identify the inputs (see table 97.21).

The next process component is the list of specific activities required for proper disposal of waste (see table 97.22).

Communication

To support the process description, the hospital produced a *Disposal Guide for Hazardous Waste* to assist staff in the proper disposal of hazardous waste materials. The guide contains information on the specific steps to follow in identifying hazardous waste and preparing it for disposal. Supplemental information is also provided on legislation, the Workplace Hazardous Materials Information System (WHMIS) and key contacts for assistance.

A database was developed to track all relevant information pertaining to each hazardous waste event from originating source to final disposal. In addition to waste data, information is also collected on the performance of the process (e.g., source and frequency of phone calls for assistance to identify areas which may require further training; source, type, quantity and frequency of

disposal requests from each user department; consumption of containers and packaging). Any deviations from the process are recorded on the corporate incident reporting form. Results from performance monitoring are reported to the executive and the board of directors. To support effective implementation of the process, a staff education programme was developed to elaborate on the information in the guide. Each of the core participants in the process carries specific responsibilities on staff education.

Continuous Improvement

To explore continuous improvement opportunities, the HSC established a multidisciplinary Waste Process Improvement Team. The Team's mandate is to address all issues pertaining to waste management. Further to encourage continuous improvement, the hazardous waste process includes specific triggers to initiate process revisions. Typical improvement ideas generated to date include:

• prepare list of high hazard materials to be tracked from time of procurement

Table 97.21 • Process inputs.

Organiza- tional unit	Examples of process inputs and supporting inputs
S&DS (S&DS)	Maintain stock of Hazardous Waste Disposal Requisition forms and labels — order requisition forms and labels.
S&DS (UD, DOEM, EPE) (S&DS)	Maintain supply of packaging containers in warehouse for UDs — determine appropriate packaging for each waste class — build adequate stock of containers for requisitioning by UD.
DOEM	Produce SYMBAS Classification Decision Chart.
EPE	Produce the list of materials for which HSC is registered as a waste generator with regulatory department.
S&DS	Produce a database of SYMBAS classifications, packaging requirements, TDG classifications, and tracking information for each material disposed by HSC.

Table 97.22 • List of activities.

Unit	Examples of activities required
UD	Order Hazardous Waste Disposal Requisition, label and packaging from S&DS as per standard stock ordering procedure.
S&DS	Deliver Requisition, label and packaging to UD.
UD	Determine whether a waste material is hazardous (check MSDS, DOEM, and such considerations as dilution, mixture with other chemicals, etc.).
UD	Assign the Classification to the waste material using SYMBAS Chemical Decision Chart and WHMIS information. Classification can be checked with the S&DS Data Base for materials previously disposed by HSC. Call first S&DS and second DOEM for assistance if required.
UD	Determine appropriate packaging requirements from WHMIS information using professional judgement or from S&DS Data Base of materials previously disposed by HSC. Call first S&DS and second DOEM for assistance if required.

- develop material "shelf life" information, where appropriate, for inclusion in the materials classification database
- review shelving for physical integrity
- purchase spill containing trays
- examine potential for spills entering sewer system
- determine whether present storage rooms are adequate for anticipated waste volume
- produce a procedure for disposing of old, incorrectly identified materials.

The ISO standards require regulatory issues to be addressed and state that business processes must be in place for this purpose. Under the ISO standards, the existence of corporate commitments, performance measuring and documentation provide a more visible and more convenient trail for regulators to check for compliance. It is conceivable that the opportunity for consistency provided by the ISO documents could automate reporting of key environmental performance factors to government authorities.

References

Abdo, R and H Chriske. 1990. HAV-Infektionsrisiken im Krankenhaus, Altenheim und Kindertagesstätten. In *Arbeitsmedizin im Gesundheitsdienst, Band 5*, edited by F Hofmann and U Stössel. Stuttgart: Gentner Verlag.

Acton, W. 1848. On the advantages of caouchoue and gutta-percha in protecting the skin against the contagion of animal poisons. *Lancet* 12:588.

Ahlin, J. 1992. Interdisciplinary case studies in offices in Sweden. In *Corporate Space and Architecture*. Vol. 2. Paris: Ministére de l'équipment et du logement.

Akinori, H and O Hiroshi. 1985. Analysis of fatigue and health conditions among hospital nurses. *J Science of Labour* 61:517-578.

Allmeers, H, B Kirchner, H Huber, Z Chen, JW Walter, and X Baur. 1996. The latency period between exposure and the symptoms in allergy to natural latex: Suggestions for prevention. *Dtsh Med Wochenschr* 121 (25/26):823-828.

Alter, MJ. 1986. Susceptibility to varicella zoster virus among adults at high risk for exposure. *Infec Contr Hosp Epid* 7:448-451.

—. 1993. The detection, transmission, and outcome of hepatitis C infection. *Infect Agents Dis* 2:155-166.

Alter, MJ, HS Margolis, K Krawczynski, FN Judson, A Mares, WJ Alexander, PY Hu, JK Miller, MA Gerber, and RE Sampliner. 1992. The natural history of community-acquired hepatitis C in the United States. *New Engl J Med* 327:1899-1905.

American Conference of Governmental Industrial Hygienists (ACGIH). 1991. *Documentation of the Threshold Limit Values and Biological Exposure Indices*, 6th edition. Cincinnati, OH: ACGIH.

—. 1994. *TLVs: Threshold Limit Values and Biological Exposure Indices for 1994-1995*. Cincinnati, OH: ACGIH.

American Hospital Association (AHA). 1992. *Implementing Safer Needle Practice*. Chicago, IL: AHA.

American Institute of Architects. 1984. *Determining Hospital Space Requirements*. Washington, DC: American Institute of Architects Press.

American Institute of Architects Committee on Architecture for Health. 1987. *Guidelines for Construction and Equipment of Hospital and Medical Facilities*. Washington, DC: American Institute of Acrchitects Press.

American Society of Heating, Refrigerating and Air-conditioning Engineers (ASHRAE). 1987. Health facilities. In *ASHRAE Handbook: Heating, Ventilating and Air-conditioning Systems and Applications*. Atlanta, GA: ASHRAE.

Anon. 1996. New drugs for HIV infection. *Medical Letter of Drugs and Therapeutics* 38:37.

Axelsson, G, R Rylander, and I Molin. 1989. Outcome of pregnancy in relation to irregular and inconvenient work schedules. *Brit J Ind Med* 46:393-398.

Beatty, J SK Ahern, and R Katz. 1977. Sleep deprivation and the vigilance of anesthesiologists during simulated surgery. In *Vigilance*, edited by RR Mackie. New York: Plenum Press.

Beck-Friis, B, P Strang, and PO Sjöden. 1991. Work stress and job satisfaction in hospital-based home care. *Journal of Palliative Care* 7(3):15-21.

Benenson, AS (ed.). 1990. *Control of Communicable Disease in Man*, 15th edition. Washington, DC: American Public Health Association.

Bertold, H, F Hofmann, M Michaelis, D Neumann-Haefelin, G Steinert, and J Wölfle. 1994. Hepatitis C—Risiko für Beschäftigte im Gesundheitsdienst? In *Arbeitsmedizin im Gesundheitsdienst, Band 7*, edited by F Hofmann, G Reschauer, and U Stössel. Stuttgart: Gentner Verlag.

Bertram, DA. 1988. Characteristics of shifts and second-year resident performance in an emergency department. *NY State J Med* 88:10-14.

Berufsgenossenschaft für Gesundheitsdienst und Wohlfahrtspflege (BGW). 1994. Geschäftsbericht.

Bissel, L and R Jones. 1975. Disabled doctors ignored by peers. Presented at the American Medical Association Conference on the Imparied Physician, 11 April, San Francisco, CA.

Bitker, TE. 1976. Reaching out to the depressed physician. *JAMA* 236(15):1713-1716.

Blanchard, M, MM Cantel, M Faivre, J Girot, JP Ramette, D Thely, and M Estryn-Béhar. 1992. Incidence des rythmes biologiques sur le travail de nuit. In *Ergonomie à l'hôpital*, edited by M Estryn-Béhar, C Gadbois, and M Pottier. Toulouse: Edition Octares.

Blanpain, C and M Estryn-Béhar. 1990. Measures d'ambiance physique dans dix services hospitaliers. *Performances* 45:18-33.

Blaycock, B. 1995. Latex allergies: Overview, prevention and implications for nursing care. *Ostomy Wound Manage* 41(5):10-12,14-15.

Blazer, MJ, FJ Hickman, JJ Farmer, and DJ Brenner. 1980. *Salmonella typhi*: The laboratory as a reservoir of infection. *Journal of Infectious Diseases* 142:934-938.

Blow, RJ and MIV Jayson. 1988. Back pain. In *Fitness for Work: The Medical Approach*, edited by FC Edwards, RL McCallum, and PJ Taylor. Oxford: Oxford University Press.

Boehm, G and E Bollinger. 1990. Significance of environmental factors on the tolerated enteral feeding volumes for patients in neonatal intensive care units. *Kinderarzliche Praxis* 58(6):275-279.

Bongers, P, RD Winter, MAJ Kompier, and VV Hildebrandt. 1992. *Psychosocial Factors at Work and Musculoskeletal Diseases. Review of the literature*. Leiden, Netherlands: TNO.

Bouhnik, C, M Estryn-Béhar, B Kapitaniak, M Rocher, and P Pereau. 1989. Le roulage dans les établissements de soins. Document pour le médecin du travail. *INRS* 39:243-252.

Boulard, R. 1993. Les indices de santé mentale du personnel infirmier: l'impact de la charge de travail, de l'autonomie et du soutien social. In *La psychologie du travail à l'aube du XXI° siècle. Actes du 7° Congrès de psychologie du travail de langue française*. Issy-les-Moulineaux: Editions EAP.

Breakwell, GM. 1989. *Facing Physical Violence*. London: British Psychological Society.

Bruce, DL and MJ Bach. 1976. *Effects of Trace Concentrations of Anesthetic Gases on Behavioral Performance of Operating Room Personnel*. DHEW (NIOSH) Publication No. 76-169. Cincinnati, OH: NIOSH.

Bruce, DL, KA Eide, HW Linde, and JE Eckenhoff. 1968. Causes of death among anesthesiologists: A 20 years survey. *Anesthesiology* 29:565-569.

Bruce, DL, KA Eide, NJ Smith, F Seltzer, and MH Dykes. 1974. A prospective survey of anesthesiologists' mortality, 1967-1974. *Anesthesiology* 41:71-74.

Burhill, D, DA Enarson, EA Allen, and S Grzybowski. 1985. Tuberculosis in female nurses in British Columbia. *Can Med Assoc J* 132:137.

Burke, FJ, MA Wilson, and JF McCord. 1995. Allergy to latex gloves in clinical practice: Case reports. *Quintessence Int* 26(12):859-863.

Buring, JE, CH Hennekens, SL Mayrent, B Rosner, ER Greenberg, and T Colton. 1985. Health experiences of operating room personnel. *Anesthesiology* 62: 325-330.

Burton, R. 1990. St. Mary's Hospital, Isle of Wight: A suitable background for caring. *Brit Med J* 301:1423-1425.

Büssing, A. 1993. Stress and burnout in nursing: Studies in different work structures and work schedules. In *Occupational Health for Health Care Workers*, edited by M Hagberg, F Hofmann, U Stössel, and G Westlander. Landsberg/Lech: Ecomed Verlag.

Cabal, C, D Faucon, H Delbart, F Cabal, and G Malot. 1986. Construction d'une blanchisserie industrielle aux CHU de Saint-Etienne. *Arch Mal Prof* 48(5):393-394.

Callan, JR, RT Kelly, ML Quinn, JW Gwynne, RA Moore, FA Muckler, J Kasumovic, WM Saunders, RP Lepage, E Chin, I Schoenfeld, and DI Serig. 1995. *Human Factors Evaluation of Remote Afterloading Brachytherapy*. NUREG/CR-6125. Vol. 1. Washington, DC: Nuclear Regulatory Commission

Cammock, R. 1981. *Primary Health Care Buildings: Briefing and Design Guide for Architects and Their Clients*. London: Architectural Press.

Cardo, D, P Srivastava, C Ciesielski, R Marcus, P McKibben, D Culver, and D Bell. 1995. Case-control study of HIV seroconversion in health care workers after percutaneous exposure to HIV-infected blood (abstract). *Infect Control Hosp Epidemiol* 16 suppl:20.

Carillo, T, C Blanco, J Quiralte, R Castillo, M Cuevas, and F Rodriguez de Castro. 1995. Prevalence of latex allergy among greenhouse workers. *J Allergy Clin Immunol* 96(5/1):699-701.

Catananti, C and A Cambieri. 1990. *Igiene e Tecnica Ospedaliera (Hospital Hygiene and Organization)*. Roma: II Pensiero Scientifico Editore.

Catananti, C, G Damiani, G Capelli, and G Manara. 1993. Building design and selection of materials and furnishings in the hospital: A review of international guidelines. *In Indoor Air '93, Proceedings of the 6th International Conference on Indoor Air Quality and Climate* 2:641-646.

Catananti, C, G Capelli, G Damiani, M Volpe, and GC Vanini. 1994. Multiple criteria evaluation in planning selection of materials for health care facilities. Preliminary identification of criteria and variables. In *Healthy Buildings '94, Proceedings of the 3rd International Conference* 1:103-108.

Cats-Baril, WL and JW Frymoyer. 1991. The economics of spinal disorders. In *The Adult Spine*, edited by JW Frymoyer. New York: Raven Press.

Centers for Disease Control (CDC). 1982. Acquired immunodeficiency syndrome (AIDS): Precautions for clinical laboratory staffs. *Morb Mortal Weekly Rep* 31:577-580.

—. 1983. Acquired immunodeficiency syndrome (AIDS): Precautions for health-care workers and allied professionals. *Morb Mortal Weekly Rep* 32:450-451.

—. 1987a. Human immunodeficiency virus infection in health-care workers exposed to blood of infected patients. *Morb Mortal Weekly Rep* 36:285-289.

—. 1987b. Recommendations for prevention of HIV transmission in health-care settings. *Morb Mortal Weekly Rep* 36 suppl 2:3S-18S.

—. 1988a. Universal precautions for prevention of transmission of human immunodeficiency virus, hepatitis B virus, and other bloodborne pathogens in health-care settings. *Morb Mortal Weekly Rep* 37:377-382,387-388.

—. 1988b. Guidelines for prevention of transmission of human immunodeficiency virus and hepatitis B virus to health-care and public-safety workers. *Morb Mortal Weekly Rep* 37 suppl 6:1-37.

—. 1989. Guidelines for prevention of transmission of human immunodeficiency virus and hepatitis B virus to health-care and public-safety workers. *Morb Mortal Weekly Rep* 38 suppl 6.

—. 1990. Public Health Service statement on management of occupational exposure to human immunodeficiency virus, including considerations regarding post-exposure use. *Morb Mortal Weekly Rep* 39 (No. RR-1).

—. 1991a. Hepatitis B virus: A comprehensive strategy for eliminating transmission in the United States through universal childhood vaccination: Recommendations of the Immunization Practices Advisory Committee (ACIP). *Morb Mortal Weekly Rep* 40 (No. RR-13).

—. 1991b. Recommendations for preventing transmission of human immunodeficiency virus and hepatitis B virus to patients during exposure-prone invasive procedures. *Morb Mortal Weekly Rep* 40 (No. RR-8).

—. 1993a. Recommended infection-control practices in dentistry. *Morb Mortal Weekly Rep* 42 (No. RR-8):1-12.

—. 1993b. *Biosafety in Microbial and Biomedical Laboratories*, 3rd edition. DHHS (CDC) Publication No. 93-8395. Atlanta, GA: CDC.

—. 1994a. *HIV/AIDS Surveillance Report*. Vol. 5(4). Atlanta, GA: CDC.

—. 1994b. *HIV/AIDS Prevention Newsletter*. Vol. 5(4). Atlanta, GA: CDC.

—. 1994c. Human immunodeficiency virus in household contacts—United States. *Morb Mortal Weekly Rep* 43:347-356.

—. 1994d. *HIV/AIDS Surveillance Report*. Vol. 6(1). Atlanta, GA: CDC.

—. 1994e. Guidelines for preventing the transmission of *Mycobacterium tuberculosis* in health-care facilities. *Morb Mortal Weekly Rep* 43 (No. RR-13):5-50.

—. 1995. Case-control study of HIV seroconversion in health-care workers after percutaneous exposure to HIV-infected blood—France, United Kingdom, and United States. *Morb Mortal Weekly Rep* 44:929-933.

—. 1996a. *HIV/AIDS Surveillance Report*. Vol 8(2). Atlanta, GA: CDC.

—. 1996b. Update: Provisional Public Health Service recommendations for chemoprophylaxis after occupational exposure to HIV. *Morb Mortal Weekly Rep* 45:468-472.

Charney, W (ed.). 1994. *Essentials of Modern Hospital Safety*. Boca Raton, FL: Lewis Publishers.

Chou, T, D Weil, and P Arnmow. 1986. Prevalence of measles antibodies in hospital personnel. *Infec Contr Hosp Epid* 7:309-311.

Chriske, H and A Rossa. 1991. Hepatitis-C-Infektionsgefährdung des medizinischen Personals. In *Arbeitsmedizin im Gesundheitsdienst, Band 5*, edited by F Hofmann and U Stössel. Stuttgart: Gentner Verlag.

Clark, DC, E Salazar-Gruesco, P Grabler, J Fawcett. 1984. Predictors of depression during the first 6 months of internship. *Am J Psychiatry* 141:1095-1098.

Clemens, R, F Hofmann, H Berthold, and G Steinert. 1992. Prävalenz von Hepatitis, A, B und C bei Bewohern einer Einrichtung für geistig Behinderte. *Sozialpädiatrie* 14:357-364.

Cohen, EN. 1980. *Anasthetic Exposure in the Workplace*. Littleton, MA: PSG Publishing Co.

Cohen, EN, JW Bellville, and BW Brown, Jr. 1971. Anesthesia, pregnancy and miscarriage: A study of operating room nurses and anesthetists. *Anesthesiology* 35:343-347.

—. 1974. Occupational disease among operating room personnel: A national study. *Anesthesiology* 41:321-340.

—. 1975. A survey of anethestic health hazards among dentists. *J Am Dent Assoc* 90:1291-1296.

Commission of the European Communities. 1990. Recommendation of the Commission February 21, 1990, about Protection of People against Exposure to Radon in Indoor Environments. 90/143/Euratom (Italian Translation).

Cooper, JB. 1984. Toward prevention of anesthesic mishaps. *International Anesthesiology Clinics* 22:167-183.

Cooper, JB, RS Newbower, and RJ Kitz. 1984. An analysis of major errors and equipment failures in anesthesia management: Considerations for prevention and detection. *Anesthesiology* 60(1):34-42.

Costa, G, R Trinco, and G Schallenberg. 1992. Problems of thermal comfort in an operating room equipped with laminar air flow system In *Ergonomie à l'hôpital (Hospital Ergonomics)*, edited by M Estryn-Béhar M, C Gadbois, and M Pottier. International Symposium Paris 1991. Toulouse: Editions Octares.

Cristofari, M-F, M Estryn-Béhar, M Kaminski, and E Peigné. 1989. Le travail des femmes à l'hôpital. *Informations Hospitalières* 22/23:48-62.

Council of the European Communities. 1988. Directive December 21, 1988, to Draw Near the Laws of Member Countries about Building Products. 89/106/EEC (Italian translation).

de Chambost, M. 1994. Alarmes sonnantes, soignantes trébuchantes. *Objectif soins* 26:63-68.

de Keyser, V and AS Nyssen. 1993. Les erreurs humaines en anesthésies. *Le Travail humain* 56(2/3):243-266.

Decree of the President of Ministers Council. 1986. Directive to the Regions about Private Health Care Facilities Requirements. 27 June.

Dehlin, O, S Berg, GBS Andersson, and G Grimby. 1981. Effect of physical training and ergonomic counselling on the psychosocial perception of work and on the subjective assesment of low-back insuffuciency. *Scand J Rehab* 13:1-9.

Delaporte, MF, M Estryn-Béhar, G Brucker, E Peigne, and A Pelletier. 1990. Pathologie dermatologique et exercice professionnel en milieu hospitalier. *Arch Mal Prof* 51(2):83-88.

Denisco, RA, JN Drummond, and JS Gravenstein. 1987. The effect of fatigue on the performance of a simulated anesthetic monitoring task. *J Clin Monit* 3:22-24.

Devienne, A, D Léger, M Paillard, A Dômont. 1995. Troubles du sommeil et de la vigilance chez des

généralistes de garde en région parisienne. Arch Mal Prof 56(5):407-409.

Donovan, R, PA Kurzman, and C Rotman. 1993. Improving the lives of home care workers: A partnership of social work and labor. *Soc Work* 38(5):579-585..

Edling, C. 1980. Anesthetic gases as an occupational hazard. A review. *Scand J Work Environ Health* 6:85-93.

Ehrengut, W and T Klett. 1981. Rötelnimmunstatus von Schwesternschülerinnen in Hamberger Krankenhäusern im Jahre 1979. *Monatsschrift Kinderheilkdunde* 129:464-466.

Elias, J, D Wylie, A Yassi, and N Tran. 1993. Eliminating worker exposure to ethylene oxide from hospital sterilizers: An evaluation of cost and effectiveness of an isolation system. *Appl Occup Environ Hyg* 8(8):687-692.

Engels, J, TH Senden, and K Hertog. 1993. Working postures of nurses in nursing homes. In *Occupational Health for Health Care Workers*, edited by M Hagberg, F Hofmann, U Stössel, and G Westlander. Landsberg/Lech: Ecomed Verlag.

Englade J, E Badet and G Becque. 1994. Vigilance et qualité de sommeil des soignants de nuit. *Revue de l'infirmière* 17:37-48.

Ernst, E and V Fialka. 1994. Idiopathic low back pain: Present impact, future directions. *European Journal of Physical Medicine and Rehabilitation* 4:69-72.

Escribà Agüir, V. 1992. Nurses' attitudes towards shiftwork and quality of life, *Scand J Soc Med* 20(2):115-118.

Escribà Agüir V, S Pérez, F Bolumar, and F Lert. 1992. Retentissement des horaires de travail sur le sommeil des infirmiers. In *Ergonomie à l'hôpital (Hospital Ergonomics)*, edited by M Estryn-Béhar, C Gadbois, and M Pottier. International Symposium Paris 1991. Toulouse: Editions Octares.

Estryn-Béhar, M. 1990. Les groupes de parole: Une stratégie d'amélioration des relations avec les malades. *Le concours médical* 112(8):713-717.

—. 1991. *Guide des risques professionnels du personnel des services de soins*. Paris: Editions Lamarre.

Estryn-Béhar, M and N Bonnet. 1992. Le travail de nuit à l'hôpital. Quelques constats à mieux prendre en compte. *Arch Mal Prof* 54(8):709-719.

Estryn-Béhar, M and F Fonchain. 1986. Les troubles du sommeil du personnel hospitalier effectuant un travail de nuit en continu. *Arch Mal Prof* 47(3):167-172;47(4):241.

Estryn-Béhar, M and JP Fouillot. 1990a. Etude de la charge physique du personnel soignant, Documents pour le médecin du travail. *INRS*: 27-33.

—. 1990b. Etude de la charge mentale et approche de la charge psychique du personnel soignant. Analyse du travail des infirmières et aides-soignantes dans 10 services de soins. Documents pour le médecin du travail *INRS* 42:131-144.

Estryn-Béhar, M and C Hakim-Serfaty. 1990. Organisation de l'espace hospitalier. *Techn hosp* 542:55-63.

Estryn-Béhar, M and G Milanini. 1992. Concevoir les espaces de travail en services de soins. *Technique Hospitalière* 557:23-27.

Estryn-Béhar, M and H Poinsignon. 1989. *Travailler à l'hopital*. Paris: Berger Levrault.

Estryn-Béhar, M, C Gadbois, and E Vaichere. 1978. Effets du travail de nuit en équipes fixes sur une population féminine. Résultats d'une enquête dans le secteur hospitalier. *Arch Mal Prof* 39(9):531-535.

Estryn-Béhar, M, C Gadbois, E Peigné, A Masson, and V Le Gall. 1989b. Impact of nightshifts on male and female hospital staff, in *Shiftwork: Health and Performance*, edited by G Costa, G Cesana, K Kogi, and A Wedderburn. Proceedings of the International Symposium on Night and Shift Work. Frankfurt: Peter Lang.

Estryn-Béhar, M, M Kaminski, and E Peigné. 1990. Strenuous working conditions and musculoskeletal disorders among female hospital workers. *Int Arch Occup Environ Health* 62:47-57.

Estryn-Béhar, M, M Kaminski, M Franc, S Fermand, and F Gerstle F. 1978. Grossesse er conditions de travail en milieu hospitalier. *Revue franç gynec* 73(10) 625-631.

Estryn-Béhar, M, M Kaminski, E Peigné, N Bonnet, E Vaichère, C Gozlan, S Azoulay, and M Giorgi. 1990. Stress at work and mental health status. *Br J Ind Med* 47:20-28.

Estryn-Béhar, M, B Kapitaniak, MC Paoli, E Peigné, and A Masson. 1992. Aptitude for physical exercise in a population of female hospital workers. *Int Arch Occup Environ Health* 64:131-139.

Estryn Béhar, M, G Milanini, T Bitot, M Baudet, and MC Rostaing. 1994. La sectorisation des soins: Une organisation, un espace. *Gestion hospitalière* 338:552-569.

Estryn-Béhar, M, G Milanini, MM Cantel, P Poirier, P Abriou, and the ICU's study group. 1995a. Interest of participative ergonomic methodology to improve an intensive care unit. In *Occupational Health for Health Care Workers*, 2nd edition, edited by M Hagberg, F Hofmann, U Stössel, and G Westlander. Landsberg/Lech: Ecomed Verlag.

—. 1995b. Participative ergonomic methodology for the new fitting out of a cardiologic intensive care unit. In *Occupational Health for Health Care Workers*, 2nd edition, edited by M Hagberg, F Hofmann, U Stössel, and G Westlander. Landsberg/Lech: Ecomed Verlag.

Estryn-Béhar, M, E Peigné, A Masson, C Girier-Desportes, JJ Guay, D Saurel, JC Pichenot, and J Cavaré. 1989a. Les femmes travaillant à l'hôpital aux différents horaires, qui sont-elles? Que décrivent-elles comme conditions de travail? Que souhaitent-elles? *Arch Mal Prof* 50(6):622-628.

Falk, SA and NF Woods. 1973. Hospital noise-levels and potential health hazards, *New England J Med* 289:774-781.

Fanger, PO. 1973. Assessment of man's thermal comfort in practice. *Br J Ind Med* 30:313-324.

—. 1992. Sensory characterization of air quality and pollution sources. In *Chemical, Microbiological, Health and Comfort Aspects of Indoor Air Quality—State of the Art in SBS*, edited by H Knoppel and P Wolkoff. Dordrecht, NL: Kluwer Academic Publishers.

Favrot-Laurens. 1992. Advanced technologies and work organization of hospital teams. In *Ergonomie à l'hôpital (Hospital Ergonomics)*, edited by M Estryn-Béhar, C Gadbois, and M Pottier. International Symposium Paris 1991. Toulouse: Editions Octares.

—. 1992. Sensory characterization of air quality and pollution sources. In *Chemical, Microbiological, Health and Comfort Aspects of Indoor Air Quality—State of the Art in Sick Building Syndrome*, edited by H Koppel and P Wolkoff. Brussels and Luxembourg: EEC.

Ferstandig, LL. 1978. Trace concentrations of anesthetic gases: A critical review of their disease potential. *Anesth Analg* 57:328-345.

Finley, GA and AJ Cohen. 1991. Percieved urgency and the anaesthetist: Responses to common operating room monitor alarms. *Can J Anaesth* 38(8):958-964

Ford, CV and DK Wentz. 1984. The internship year: A study of sleep, mood states, and psychophysiologic parameters. *South Med J* 77:1435-1442.

Friedman, RC, DS Kornfeld, and TJ Bigger. 1971. Psychological problems associated with sleep deprivation in interns. *Journal of Medical Education* 48:436-441.

Friele, RD and JJ Knibbe. 1993. Monitoring the barriers with the use of patient lifts in home care as perceived by nursing personnel. In *Occupational Health for Health Care Workers*, edited by M Hagberg, F Hofmann, U Stössel, and G Westlander. LandsbergLech: Ecomed Verlag.

Gadbois, CH. 1981. Aides-soignantes et infirmières de nuit. In *Conditions de travail et vie quotidienne*. Montrougs: Agence Nationale pour l'Amélioration des Conditions de Travail.

Gadbois, C, P Bourgeois, MM Goeh-Akue-Gad, J Guillaume, and MA Urbain. 1992. Contraintes temporelles et structure de l'espace dans le processus de travail des équipes de soins. In *Ergonomie à l'hôpital (Hospital Ergonomics)*, edited by M Estryn-Béhar, C Gadbois, and M Pottier. International Symposium Paris 1991. Toulouse: Editions Octares.

Games, WP, and W Tatton-Braen. 1987. *Hospitals Design and Development*. London: Architectural Press.

Gardner, ER and RC Hall. 1981. The professional stress syndrome. *Psychosomatics* 22:672-680.

Gaube, J, H Feucht, R Laufs, D Polywka, E Fingscheidt, and HE Müller. 1993. Hepatitis A, B und C als desmoterische Infecktionen. *Gessundheitwesen und Desinfextion* 55:246-249.

Gerberding, JL. N.d. *Open trial of Zidovudine Postexposure-chemoprophylaxis in Health Care Workers with Occupational Exposures to Human Immunodeficiency Virus*. Skript SFGH.

—. 1995. Management of occupational exposures to blood-borne viruses. *New Engl J Med* 332:444-451.

Ginesta, J. 1989. Gases anestésicos. In *Riesgos del Trabajo del Personal Sanitario*, edited by JJ Gestal. Madrid: Editorial Interamericana McGraw-Hill.

Gold, DR, S Rogacz, N Bock, TD Tosteson, TM Baum, FE Speizer, and CA Czeiler. 1992. Rotating shift work, sleep and accidents related to sleepiness in hospital nurses. *Am J Public Health* 82(7):1011-1014.

Goldman, LI, MT McDonough, and GP Rosemond. 1972. Stresses affecting surgical performance and learning: Correlation of heart rate, electrocardiogram, and operation simultaneously recorded on videotapes. *J Surg Res* 12:83-86.

Graham, C, C Hawkins, and W Blau. 1983. Innovative social work practice in health care: Stress management. In *Social Work in a Turbulent World*, edited by M Dinerman. Washington, DC: National Association of Social Workers.

Green, A. 1992. How nurses can ensure the sounds patients hear have a positive rather than negative effect upon recovery and quality of life. *Intensive & Critical Care Nursing Journal* 8(4):245-248.

Griffin, WV. 1995. Social worker and agency safety. In *Encyclopaedia of Social Work*, 19th edition. Washington, DC: National Association of Social Workers.

Grob, PJ. 1987. Cluster of hepatitis B transmission by a physician. *Lancet* 339:1218-1220.

Guardino, X and MG Rosell. 1985. Exposicion laboral a gases anestésicos. In *Notas Técnicas de Prevención*. No. 141. Barcelona: INSHT.

—. 1992. Exposure at work to anesthetic gases. A controlled risk? *Janus* 12:8-10.

—. 1995. Exposure monitoring to anesthetic gases. In *Occupational Health for Health Care Workers*, edited by M

Hagburg, F Hoffmann, U Stössel, and G Westlander. Solna: National Institute of Occupational Health.

Hagberg, M, F Hofmann, U Stössel, and G Westlander (eds.). 1993. *Occupational Health for Health Care Workers*. Landsberg/Lech: Ecomed Verlag.

Hagberg, M, F Hofmann, U Stössel, and G Westlander (eds.). 1995. *Occupational Health for Health Care Workers*. Singapore: International Commission on Occupational Health.

Haigh, R. 1992. The application of ergonomics to the design of workplace in health care buildings in the U.K. In *Ergonomie à l'hôpital (Hospital Ergonomics)*, edited by M Estryn-Béhar, C Gadbois, and M Pottier. International Symposium Paris 1991. Toulouse: Editions Octares.

Halm, MA and MA Alpen, 1993. The impact of technology on patient and families. *Nursing Clinics of North America* 28(2):443-457.

Harber, P, L Pena, and P Hsu. 1994. Personal history, training, and worksite as predictors of back pain of nurses. *Am J Ind Med* 25:519-526.

Hasselhorn, HM. 1994. Antiretrovirale prophylaxe nach kontakt mit HIV-jontaminierten. In *Flüssigkeiten in Infektiologie*, edited by F Hofmann. Landsberg/Lech: Ecomed Verlag.

Hasselhorn, HM and E Seidler.1993. Terminal care in Sweden—New aspects of the professional care of dying. In *Occupational Health for Health Care* Workers, edited by M Hagberg, F Hofmann, U Stössel U, and G Westlander. Landsberg/Lech: Ecomed Verlag.

Heptonstall, J, K Porter, and N Gill. 1993. *Occupational Transmission of HIV: Summary of Published Reports*. London: Communicable Disease Surveillance Centre AIDS Centre.

Hesse, A, Lacher A, HU Koch, J Kublosch, V Ghane, and KF Peters. 1996. Update on the latex allergy topic. *Hauzarzt* 47(11):817-824.

Ho, DD, T Moudgil, and M Alam. 1989. Quantitation of human immunodeficiency virus type 1 in the blood of infected persons. *New Engl J Med* 321:1621-1625.

Hodge, B and JF Thompson. 1990. Noise pollution in the operating theatre. *Lancet* 335:891-894.

Hofmann, F and H Berthold. 1989. Zur Hepatitis-B-Gefährdung des Krankenhauspersonals-Möglichkeiten der prae-und postexpositionellen Prophylaxe. *Medizinische Welt* 40:1294-1301.

Hofmann, F and U Stössel. 1995. Environmental health in the health care professions: Biological, physical, psychic, and social health hazards. *Reviews on Environmental Health* 11:41-55.

Hofmann, F, H Berthold, and G Wehrle. 1992. Immunity to hepatitis A in hospital personnel. *Eur J Clin Microbiol Infect Dis* 11(12):1195.

Hofmann, F, U Stössel, and J Klima. 1994. Low back pain in nurses (I). *European Journal of Physical and Medical Rehabilitation* 4:94-99.

Hofmann, F, B Sydow, and M Michaelis. 1994a. Mumps—berufliche Gefährdung und Aspekte der epidemiologischen Entwicklung. *Gessundheitwesen und Desinfextion* 56:453-455.

—. 1994b. Zur epidemiologischen Bedeutung der Varizellen. *Gessundheitwesen und Desinfextion* 56:599-601.

Hofmann, F, G Wehrle, K Berthold, and D Köster. 1992. Hepatitis A as an occupational hazard. *Vaccine* 10 suppl 1:82-84.

Hofmann, F, U Stössel, M Michaelis, and A Siegel. 1993. Tuberculosis—Occupational risk for health care workers? In *Occupational Health for Health Care Workers*, edited by M Hagberg. Landsberg/Lech: Ecomed Verlag.

Hofmann, F, M Michaelis, A Siegel, and U Stössel. 1994. *Wirbelsäulenerkrankungen im Pflegeberuf. Medizinische Grundlagen und Prävention.* Landsberg/Lech: Ecomed Verlag.

Hofmann, F, M Michaelis, M Nübling, and FW Tiller. 1995. *European Hepatitis—A Study.* Publikation in Vorereitung.

Hofmann, H and C Kunz. 1990. Low risk of health care workers for infection with hepatitis-C virus. *Infection* 18:286-288.

Holbrook, TL, K Grazier, JL Kelsey, and RN Stauffer. 1984. *The Frequency of Occurrence, Impact, and Cost of Selected Musculoskeletal Conditions in the United States.* Park Ridge, Il: American Academy of Orthopedic Surgeons.

Hollinger, FB. 1990. Hepatitis B virus. In *Virology*, edited by BN Fiedles and DM Knipe. New York: Raven Press.

Hopps, J and P Collins. 1995. Social work profession overview. In *Encyclopedia of Social Work*, 19th edition. Washington, DC: National Association of Social Workers.

Hubacova, L, I Borsky, and F Strelka. 1992. Work physiology problems of nurses working in inpatients departments. In *Ergonomie à l'hôpital (Hospital Ergonomics)*, edited by M Estryn-Béhar, C Gadbois, and M Pottier. International Symposium Paris 1991. Toulouse: Editions Octares.

Hunt, LW, AF Fransway, CE Reed, LK Miller, RT Jones, MC Swanson, and JW Yunginger. 1995. An epidemic of occupational allergy to latex involving health care workers. *J Occup Environ Med* 37(10):1204-1209.

Jacobson, SF and HK MacGrath. 1983. *Nurses under Stress.* New York: John Wiley & Sons.

Jacques, CHM, MS Lynch and JS Samkoff. 1990. The effects of sleep loss on cognitive performance of resident physicians. *J Fam Pract* 30:223-229.

Jagger, J, EH Hunt, J Brand-Elnagger, and RD Pearson. 1988. Rates of needle-stick injury caused by various devices in a university hospital. *New Engl J Med* 319:284-288.

Johnson, JA, RM Buchan, and J S Reif. 1987. Effect of waste anesthetic gas and vapor exposure on reproductive outcome in veterinary personnel. *Am Ind Hyg Assoc J* 48(1):62-66.

Jonasson, G, JO Holm, and J Leegard. Rubber allergy: An increasing health problem? *Tuidsskr Nor Laegeforen* 113(11):1366-1367.

Kandolin, I. 1993. Burnout of female and male nurses in shiftwork. *Ergonomics* 36(1/3):141-147.

Kaplan, RM and RA Deyo. 1988. Back pain in health care workers. In *Back Pain in Workers*, edited by RA Deyo. Philadelphia, PA: Hanley & Belfus.

Katz, R. 1983. Causes of death among nurses. *Occup Med* 45:760-762.

Kempe, P, M Sauter and I Lindner. 1992. Special characteristics of nurses for the aged who made use of a training program aimed to reduce burn-out symptoms and first results on treatment outcome. In *Ergonomie à l'hôpital (Hospital Ergonomics)*, edited by M Estryn-Béhar, C Gadbois, and M Pottier. International Symposium Paris 1991. Toulouse: Editions Octares.

Kerr, JH. 1985. Warning devices. *Br J Anaesth* 57:696-708.

Kestin, IG, RB Miller, and CJ Lockhart. 1988. Auditory alarms during anesthesia monitoring. *Anesthesiology* 69(1):106-109.

Kinloch-de-los, S, BJ Hirschel, B Hoen, DA Cooper, B Tindall, A Carr, H Sauret, N Clumeck, A Lazzarin, and E Mathiesen. 1995. A controlled trial of Zi-

dovudine in primary human immunodeficiency virus infection. New Engl J Med 333:408-413.

Kivimäki, M and K Lindström. 1995. The crucial role of the head nurse in a hospital ward. In *Occupational Health for Health Care Workers*, edited by M Hagberg, F Hofmann, U Stössel, and G Westlander. Landsberg/Lech: Ecomed Verlag.

Klaber Moffet, JA, SM Chase, I Portek, and JR Ennis. 1986. A controlled study to evaluate the efectiveness of the back pain school in the relief of chronic low back pain. *Spine* 11:120-122.

Kleczkowski, BM, C Montoya-Aguilar, and NO Nilsson. 1985. *Approaches to Planning and Design of Health Care Facilities in Developing Areas.* Vol. 5. Geneva: WHO.

Klein, BR and AJ Platt. 1989. *Health Care Facility Planning and Construction.* New York: Van Nostrand Reinhold.

Kelin, R, K Freemann, P Taylor, C Stevens. 1991. Occupational risk for hepatits C virus infection among New York City dentists. *Lancet* 338:1539-1542.

Kraus, H. 1970. *Clinical Treatment of Back and Neck Pain.* New York: McGraw-Hill.

Kujala, VM and KE Reilula. 1995. Glove-induced dermal and respiratory symptoms among health care workers in one Finnish hospital. *Am J Ind Med* 28(1):89-98.

Kurumatani, N, S Koda, S Nakagiri, K Sakai, Y Saito, H Aoyama, M Dejima, and T Moriyama. 1994. The effects of frequently rotating shiftwork on sleep and the family life of hospital nurses. *Ergonomics* 37:995-1007.

Lagerlöf, E and E Broberg. 1989. Occupational injuries and diseases. In *Occupational Hazards in the Health Professions*, edited by DK Brune and C Edling. Boca Raton, FL: CRC Press.

Lahaye, D, P Jacques, G Moens, and B Viaene. 1993. The registration of medical data obtained by preventive medical examinations on health care workers. In *Occupational Health for Health Care Workers*, edited by M Hagberg, F Hofmann, U Stössel and G Westlander. Landsberg/Lech: Ecomed Verlag.

Lampher, BP, CC Linneman, CG Cannon, MM DeRonde, L Pendy, and LM Kerley. 1994. Hepatitis C virus infection in health care workers: Risk of exposure and infection. *Infect Control Hosp Epidemiol* 15:745-750.

Landau, C, S Hall, SA Wartman, and MB Macko. 1986. Stress in social and family relationships during medical residency. *Journal of Medical Education* 61:654-660.

Landau, K. 1992. Psycho-physical strain and the burn-out phenomen amongst health care professionals. In *Ergonomie à l'hôpital (Hospital Ergonomics)*, edited by M Estryn-Béhar, C Gadbois, and M Pottier. International Symposium Paris 1991. Toulouse: Editions Octares.

Landewe, MBM and HT Schröer. 1993. Development of a new, integrated patient transfer training program—Primary prevention of low back pain. In *Occupational Health for Health Care Workers*, editeb by M Hagberg, F Hofmann, U Stössel, and G Westlander. Landsberg/Lech: Ecomed Verlag.

Lange, M. 1931. *Die Muskelhärten (Myogelosen).* Munich: JF Lehman Verlag.

Lange, W and KN Masihi. 1986. Durchseuchung mit Hepatitis-A- und B-Virus bei medizinischem Personal. *Bundesgesundheitsol* 29;183-87.

Lee, KA. 1992. Self-reported sleep disturbances in employed women. *Sleep* 15(6):493-498.

Lempereur, JJ. 1992. Prévention des dorso-lombalgies. Influence du vêtement de travail sur le comportement gestuel. Spécifications ergonomiques. *Cah Kinésither* 156;:4.

Leppanen, RA and MA Olkinuora. 1987. Psychological stress experienced by health care personnel. *Scand J Work Environ Health* 13:1-8.

Lert, F, MJ Marne, and A Gueguen. 1993. Evolution des conditions de travail des infirmières des hôpitaux publics de 1980 à 1990. *Revue de l'Epidémiologie et de santé publique* 41:16-29.

Leslie, PJ, JA Williams, C McKenna, G Smith and RC Heading. 1990. Hours, volume, and type of work of preregistration house officers. *Brit Med J* 300:1038-1041.

Lettau, LA, HJ Alfred, RH Glew, HA Fields, MJ Alter, R Meyer, SC Hadler, and JE Maynard. 1986. Nosocomial transmission of delta hepatitis. *Ann Intern Med* 104:631-635.

Levin, H. 1992. Healthy buildings—Where do we stand, where do we go? In *Chemical, Microbiological, Health and Comfort Aspects of Indoor Air Quality: State of the Art in Sick Building Syndrome*, edited by H Knoppel and P Wolkoff. Brussels and Luxembourg: EEC.

Lewittes, LR and VW Marshall. 1989. Fatigue and concerns about quality of care among Ontario interns and residents. *Can Med Assoc J* 140:21-24.

Lewy, R. 1990. *Employees at Risk: Protection and Health of Health Care Workers.* New York: Van Nostrand Reinhold.

Lindström, A and M Zachrisson. 1973. Ryggbesvär och arbetssoförmaga Ryyggskolan. Ett Försok till mer rationeli fysikalist terapi. *Socialmet T* 7:419-422.

Lippert. 1971. Travel in nursing units. *Human Factors* 13(3):269-282.

Ljungberg, AS, A Kilbom, and MH Goran. 1989. Occupational lifting by nursing aides and warehouse workers. *Ergonomics* 32:59-78.

Llewelyn-Davies, R and J Wecks. 1979. In-patient areas. In *Approaches to Planning and Design of Health Care Facilities in Developing Areas*, edited by BM Kleczkowski and R Piboleau. Geneva: WHO.

Loeb, RG, BR Jones, KH Behrman, and RJ Leonard. 1990. Anesthetists cannot identify audible alarms. *Anesthesiology* 73(3A):538.

Lotas, MJ. 1992. Effects of light and sound in the neonatal intensive care unit environment on the low-birth-weight infant. *NAACOGS Clinical Issues in Perinatal & Womens Health Nursing* 3(1):34-44.

Lurie, HE, B Rank, C Parenti, T Wooley, and W Snoke. 1989. How do house officers spend their nights? A time study of internal medicine house staff on call. *New Engl J Med* 320:1673-1677.

Luttman, A, M Jäger, J Sökeland, and W Laurig. 1996. Electromyographical study on surgeons in urology II. Determination of muscular fatigue. *Ergonomics* 39(2):298-313.

Makino, S. 1995. Health problems in health care workers in Japan. In *Occupational Health for Health Care Workers*, edited by M Hagberg, F Hofmann, U Stössel, and G Westlander. Landsbeg/Lech: Ecomed Verlag.

Malchaire, JB. 1992. Analysis of the work load of nurses. In *Ergonomie à l'hôpital (Hospital Ergonomics)*, edited by M Estryn-Béhar, C Gadbois, and M Pottier. International Symposium Paris 1991. Toulouse: Editions Octares.

Manuaba, A. 1992. Social-cultural approach is a must in designing hospital in developing countries, Indonesia as a case study. In *Ergonomie à l'hôpital (Hospital Ergonomics)*, edited by M Estryn-Béhar, C Gadbois, and M Pottier. International Symposium Paris 1991. Toulouse: Editions Octares.

Maruna, H. 1990. Zur Hepatitis-B-Durchseuchung in den Berufen des Gesundheits und Fürsorgewesens der Republik Österreichs, Arbeitsmed. Präventivmed. *Sozialmed* 25:71-75.

Matsuda, A. 1992. Ergonomics approach to nursing care in Japan. In *Ergonomie à l'hôpital (Hospital Ergonomics)*, edited by M Estryn-Béhar, C Gadbois, and M Pottier. International Symposium Paris 1991. Toulouse: Editions Octares.

McCall, T. 1988. The impact of long working hours on resident physicians. *New Engl J Med* 318(12):775-778.

McCloy, E. 1994. Hepatitis and the EEC Directive. Presented at the 2nd International Conference on Occupational Health for Health Care Workers, Stockholm.

McCormick, RD, MG Meuch, IG Irunk, and DG Maki. 1991. Epidemiology for hospital sharp injuries: A 14-year prospective study in the pre-AIDS and AIDS era. *Am J Med* 3B:3015-3075.

McCue, JD. 1982. The effects of stresses on physicians and their medical practice. *New Engl J Med* 306:458-463.

McIntyre, JWR. 1985. Ergonomics: Anaesthetists' use of auditory alarms in the operating room. *Int J Clin Monit Comput* 2:47-55

McKinney, PW, MM Horowitz, and RJ Baxtiola. 1989. Susceptibility of hospital-based health care personnel to varicella zoster virus infection. *Am J Infect Control* 18:26-30.

Melleby, A. 1988. Exercise program for a healthy back. In *Diagnosis and Treatment of Muscle Pain*. Chicago, IL: Quintessence Books.

Meyer,TJ, SE Eveloff, MS Bauer, WA Schwartz, NS Hill, and PR Millman. 1994. Adverse environmental conditions in the respiratory and medical intensive care unit settings. *Chest* 105:1211-1216.

Miller, E, J Vurdien, and P Farrington. 1993. Shift age in chickenpox. *Lancet* 1:341.

Miller, JM. 1982. William Stewart Halsted and the use of the surgical rubber glove. *Surgery* 92:541-543.

Mitsui, T, K Iwano, K Maskuko, C Yanazaki, H Okamoto, F Tsuda, T Tanaka, and S Mishiros. 1992. Hepatitis C virus infection in medical personnel after needlestick accidents. *Hepatology* 16:1109-1114.

Modig, B. 1992. Hospital ergonomics in a biopsychosocial perspective. In *Ergonomie à l'hôpital (Hospital Ergonomics)*, edited by M Estryn-Béhar, C Gadbois, and M Pottier. International Symposium Paris 1991. Toulouse: Editions Octares.

Momtahan, K, R Hétu, and B Tansley. 1993. Audibility and identification of auditory alarms in the operating room and intensive care unit. *Ergonomics* 36(10):1159-1176.

Momtahan, KL and BW Tansley. 1989. An ergonomic analysis of the auditory alarm signals in the operating room and recovery room. Presented at the Annual Meeting of the Canadian Acoustical Association, 18 October, Halifax, NS.

Montoliu, MA, V Gonzalez, B Rodriguez, JF Quintana, and L Palenciano.1992. Conditions de travail dans la blanchisserie centrale des grands hôpitaux de Madrid. In *Ergonomie à l'hôpital (Hospital Ergonomics)*, edited by M Estryn-Béhar, C Gadbois, and M Pottier. International Symposium Paris 1991. Toulouse: Editions Octares.

Moore, RM, YM Davis, and RG Kaczmarek. 1993. An overview of occupational hazards among veterinarians, with particular reference to pregnant women. *Am J Ind Hyg Assoc* 54(3):113-120.

Morel, O. 1994. Les agents des services hospitaliers. Vécu et santé au travail. *Arch mal prof* 54(7):499-508.

Nachemson, AL and GBJ Anderson. 1982. Classification of low back pain. *Scand J Work Environ Health* 8:134-136.

National Health Service (NHS). 1991a. *Design Guide. The Design of Community Hospitals*. London: Her Majesty's Stationery Office.

—. 1991b. *Health Building Note 46: General Medical Practice Premises for the Provision of Primary Health Care Service*. London: Her Majesty's Stationery Office.

National Institute for Occupational Safety and Health (NIOSH). 1975. *Development and Evaluation of Methods for the Elimination of Waste Anesthetic Gases and Vapors in Hospitals*. DHEW (NIOSH) Publication No. 75-137. Cincinnati, OH: NIOSH.

—. 1997a. *Control of Occupational Exposure to N2O in the Dental Operatory*. DHEW (NIOSH) Publication No. 77-171. Cincinnati, OH: NIOSH.

—. 1977b. *Criteria for a Recommended Standard: Occupational Exposure to Waste Anesthetic Gases and Vapors*. DHEW (NIOSH) Publication No. 77-1409. Cincinnati, OH: NIOSH.

—. 1988. *Guidelines for Protecting the Safety and Health of Health Care Workers*. DHHS (NIOSH) Publication No. 88-119. Cincinnati, OH: NIOSH.

—. 1994. *NIOSH Alert: Request for Assistance in Controlling Exposures to Nitrous Oxide during Anesthetic Administration*. DHHS (NIOSH) Publication No. 94-100. Cincinnati, OH: NIOSH.

Niu, MT, DS Stein, and SM Schnittmann. 1993. Primary human immunodeficiency virus type 1 infection: Review of pathogenesis and early treatment interventions in human and animal retrovirus infections. *J Infect Dis* 168:1490-1501.

Noweir, MH and MS al-Jiffry. 1991. Study of noise pollution in Jeddah hospitals. *Journal of the Egyptian Public Health Association* 66 (3/4):291-303.

Nyman, I and A Knutsson. 1995. Psychosocial wellbeing and sleep quality in hospital night and day workers. In *Occuptional Health for Health Care Workers*, edited by M Hagberg, F Hofmann, U Stössel, and G Westlander. Landsberg/Lech: Ecomed Verlag.

Objectif Prévention Nº spécial. 1994. Le lève personne sur rail au plafond: Outil de travail indispensable. *Objectif Prévention* 17(2):13-39.

O'Carroll, TM. 1986. Survey of alarms in an intensive therapy unit. *Anaesthesia* 41:742-744.

Occupational Safety and Health Administration (OSHA). 1991. *Occupational Exposure to Bloodborne Pathogens: Final Rule*. 29 CFR Part 1910.1030. Washington, DC: OSHA.

Oëler, JM. 1993. Developmental care of low birth weight infants. *Nursing Clinics of North America* 28(2):289-301.

Öhling, P and B Estlund. 1995. Working technique for health care workers. In *Occupational Health for Health Care Workers*, edited by M Hagberg, F Hofmann, U Stössel, and G Westlander G. Landsberg/Lech: Ecomed Verlag.

Ollagnier, E and Lamarche MJ. 1993. Une intervention ergonomique dans un hôpital suisse: Impact sur la santé de l'organisation du personnel et des patients. In *Ergonomie et santé*, edited by D Ramaciotti and A Bousquet. Actes du XXVIIIᵉ congrès de la SELF. Geneva: SELF.

Ott, C, M Estryn-Béhar, C Blanpain, A Astier, and G Hazebroucq. 1991. Conditionnement du médicament et erreurs de médication. *J Pharm Clin* 10:61-66.

Patkin, M. 1992. Hospital architecture: An ergonomic debacle. In *Ergonomie à l'hôpital (Hospital Ergonomics)*, edited by M Estryn-Béhar, C Gadbois, and M Pottier. International Symposium Paris 1991. Toulouse: Editions Octares.

Payer, L. 1988. *Medicine and Culture: The Variety of Treatment in the United States, England, West Germany and France*. New York: H. Holt.

Payne, R and J Firth-Cozens (eds.). 1987. *Stress in Health Professions*. New York: John Wiley & Sons.

—. 1995. Determination of dinitrogen oxide (N2O) in urine as control to anesthetic exposure. In *Occupational Health for Health Care Workers*, edited by M Hagberg, F Hoffmann, U Stössel, and G Westlander. Solna: National Institute of Occupational Health.

Pelikan, JM. 1993. Improving occupational health for health care workers within the health promoting hospital: Experiences from the Vienna WHO model project "health and hospital". In *Occupational Health for Health Care Workers*, edited by M Hagberg, F Hofmann, U Stössel, and G Westlander. Landsberg/Lech: Ecomed Verlag.

Pérez, L, R De Andrés, K. Fitch, and R Najera. 1994. Seroconversiones a VIH tras Sanitarios en Europa. Presented at the 2nd Reunión Nacional sobre el SIDA Cáceres.

Philip, RN, KRT Reinhard, and DB Lackman. 1959. Observations on a mumps epidemic in a "virgin" population. *Am J Hyg* 69:91-111.

Pottier, M. 1992. Ergonomie à l'hôpital-hospital ergonomics. In *Ergonomie à l'hôpital (Hospital Ergonomics)*, edited by M Estryn-Béhar, C Gadbois, and M Pottier. International Symposium Paris 1991. Toulouse: Editions Octares.

Poulton, EC, GM Hunt, A Carpenter, and RS Edwards. 1978. The performance of junior hospital doctors following reduced sleep and long hours of work. *Ergonomics* 21:279-295.

Pöyhönen, T and M Jokinen. 1980. *Stress and Other Occupational Health Problems Affecting Hospital Nurses*. Vantaa, Finland: Tutkimuksia.

Raffray, M. 1994. Etude de la charge physique des AS par mesure de la fréquence cardiaque. *Objectif soins* 26:55-58.

Ramaciotti, D, S Blaire, A Bousquet, E Conne, V Gonik, E Ollagnier, C Zummermann, and L Zoganas. 1990. Processus de régulation des contraintes économiques physiologiques et sociales pour différents groupes de travail en horaires irréguliers et de nuit. *Le travail humain* 53(3):193-212.

Reuben, DB. 1985. Depressive symptoms in medical house officers: Effects of level of training and work rotation. *Arch Intern Med* 145:286-288.

Reznick, RK and JR Folse. 1987. Effect of sleep deprivation on the performance of surgical residents. *Am J Surg* 154:520-52.

Rhoads, JM.1977. Overwork. *JAMA* 237:2615-2618.

Rodary, C and A Gauvain-Piquard 1993. Stress et épuisement professionnel. *Objectif soins* 16:26-34.

Roquelaure, Y, A Pottier, and M Pottier. 1992. Approche ergonomique comparative de deux enregistreurs electroencéphalographiques. In *Ergonomie à l'hôpital (Hospital Ergonomics)*, edited by M Estryn-Béhar, C Gadbois, and M Pottier. International Symposium Paris 1991. Toulouse: Editions Octares.

Rosell, MG, P Luna, and X Guardino. 1989. *Evaluacion y Control de Contaminantes QuPmicos en Hospitales*. Technical Document No. 57. Barcelona: INSHT.

Rubin, R, P Orris, SL Lau, DO Hryhorczuk, S Furner, and R Letz. 1991. Neurobehavioral effects of the on-call experience in housestaff physicians. *J Occup Med* 33:13-18.

Saint-Arnaud, L, S Gingras, R Boulard., M Vezina and H Lee-Gosselin. 1992. Les symptômes psychologiques en milieu hospitalier. In *Ergonomie à l'hôpital (Hospital Ergonomics)*, edited by M Estryn-Béhar, C Gadbois, and M Pottier. International Symposium Paris 1991. Toulouse: Editions Octares.

Samkoff, JS, CHM Jacques. 1991. A review of studies concerning effects of sleep deprivation and fatigue on residents' performance. *Acad Med* 66:687-693.

Sartori, M, G La Terra, M Aglietta, A Manzin, C Navino, and G Verzetti. 1993. Transmission of hepatitis C via blood splash into conjunctiva. *Scand J Infect Dis* 25:270-271.

Saurel, D. 1993. *CHSCT Central, Enquete "Rachialgies" Résultats*. Paris: Assistance Publique-Hôpitaux de Paris, Direction du personnel et des relations sociales.

Saurel-Cubizolles, MJ, M Hay, and M Estryn-Béhar. 1994. Work in operating rooms and pregnancy outcome among nurses. *Int Arch Occup Environ Health* 66:235-241.

Saurel-Cubizolles, MJ, MKaminski, J Llhado-Arkhipoff, C Du Mazaubrum, M Estryn-Behar, C Berthier, M Mouchet, and C Kelfa. 1985. Pregnancy and its outcome among hospital personnel according to occupation and working condition. *Journal of Epidemiology and Community Health* 39:129-134.

Schröer, CAP, L De Witte, and H Philipsen. 1993. Effects of shift work on quality of sleep, health complaints and medical consumption of female nurses. In *Occupational Health for Health Care Workers*, edited by M Hagberg, F Hofmann, U Stössel, and G Westlander. Landsberg/Lech: Ecomed Verlag.

Senevirane, SR, De A and DN Fernando. 1994. Influence of work on pregnancy outcome. *Int J Gynecol Obstet* VOL: 35-40.

Shapiro, ET, H Pinsker and JH Shale. 1975. The mentally ill physician as practitioner. *JAMA* 232(7):725-727.

Shapiro, RA and T Berland. 1972. Noise in the operating room. *New Engl J Med* 287(24):1236-1238.

Shindo, E. 1992. The present condition of nursing ergonomics in Japan. In *Ergonomie à l'hôpital (Hospital Ergonomics)*, edited by M Estryn-Béhar, C Gadbois, and M Pottier. International Symposium Paris 1991. Toulouse: Editions Octares.

Siegel, A, M Michaelis, F Hofmann, U Stössel, and W Peinecke. 1993. Use and acceptance of lifting aids in hospitals and geriatric homes. In *Occupational Health for Health Care Workers*, edited by M Hagberg, F Hofmann, U Stössel, and G Westlander. Landsberg/Lech: Ecomed Verlag.

Smith, MJ, MJ Colligan, IJ Frocki, and DL Tasto. 1979. Occupational injury rates among nurses as a function of shift schedule. *Journal of Safety Research* 11(4):181-187.

Smith-Coggins, R, MR Rosekind, S Hurd, and KR Buccino. 1994. Relationship of day versus night sleep to physician performance and mood. *Ann Emerg Med* 24:928-934.

Snook, SH. 1988a. Approaches to the control of back pain in industry. In *Back Pain in Workers*, edited by RA Deyo. Philadelphia: Hanley & Belfus.

—. 1988b. The costs of back pain in industry. In *Back Pain in Workers*, edited by RA Deyo. Philadelphia: Hanley & Belfus.

South, MA, JL Sever, and L Teratogen. 1985. Update: The congenital rubella syndrome. *Teratology* 31:297-392.

Spence, AA. 1987. Environmental pollution by inhalation anaesthetics. *Br J Anaesth* 59:96-103.

Stellman, JM. 1976. *Women's Work, Women's Health: Myths and Realities*. New York: Pantheon.

Steppacher, RC and JS Mausner. 1974. Suicide in male and female physicians. *JAMA* 228(3):323-328.

Sterling, DA. 1994. Overview of health and safety in the health care environment. In *Essentials of Modern Hospital Safety*, edited by W Charney. Boca Raton, FL: Lewis Publishers.

Stoklov, M, P Trouiller, P Stieglitz, Y Lamalle, F Vincent, A Perdrix, C Marka, R de Gaudemaris, JM Mallion, and J Faure. 1983. L'exposition aux gaz anethésiques: Risques et prévention. *Sem Hôs* 58(29/39):2081-2087.

Storer, JS, HH Floyd, WL Gill, CW Giusti, and H Ginsberg. 1989. Effects of sleep deprivation on cognitive ability and skills of pediatrics residents. *Acad Med* 64:29-32.

Stubbs, DA, PW Buckle, and PM Hudson. 1983. Back pain in the nursing profession; I Epidemiology and pilot methodology. *Ergonomics* 26:755-765.

Sundström-Frisk C and M Hellström.1995. The risk of making treatment errors, an occupational stressor. In *Occupational Health for Health Care Workers*, edited by M Hagberg, F Hofmann, U Stössel, and G Westlander. Landsberg/Lech: Ecomed Verlag.

Swann-D'Emilia, B, JCH Chu, and J Daywalt. 1990. Misadministration of prescribed radiation dose. *Medical Dosimetry* 15:185-191.

Sydow, B and F Hofmann. 1994. Unpublished results.

Tannenbaum, TN and RJ Goldberg. 1985. Exposure to anaesthetic gases and reproductive outcome: A review of epidemiologic literature. *J Occup Med* 27:659-671.

Teyssier-Cotte, C, M Rocher, and P Mereau. 1987. Les lits dans les établissements de soins. Documents pour le médecin du travail. *INRS* 29:27-34.

Theorell, T. 1989. The psychosocial working environment. In *Occupational Hazards in the Health Professions*, edited by DK Brune and C Edling. Boca Raton, FL: CRC Press.

Theorell T. 1993. On the psychosocial environment in care. In *Occupational Health for Health Care Workers*, edited by M Hagberg, F Hofmann, U Stössel, and G Westlander. Landsberg/Lech : Ecomed Verlag.

Tintori, R and M Estryn-Béhar. 1994. Communication: Où, quand, comment? Critères ergonomiques pour améliorer la communication dans les services de soins. *Gestions Hospitalières* 338:553-561.

Tintori, R, M Estryn-Behar, J De Fremont, T Besse, P Jacquenot, A Le Vot, and B Kapitaniak. 1994. Evaluation des lits à hauteur variable. Une démarche de recherche en soins infirmiers. *Gestions Hospitalières* 332:31-37.

Tokars, JI, R Marcus, DH Culver, CA Schable, PS McKibben, CL Bandea, and DM Bell. 1993. Surveillance of HIV infection and zidovudine use among health care workers after occupational exposure to HIV-infected blood. *Ann Intern Med* 118:913-919.

Toomingas, A. 1993. The health situation among Swedish health care workers. In *Occupational Health for Health Care Workers*, edited by M Hagberg, F Hofmann, U Stössel, and G Westlander. Landsberg/Lech: Ecomed Verlag.

Topf, M. 1992. Effects of personal control over hospital noise on sleep. *Research in Nursing & Health* 15(1):19-28.

Tornquist, A and P Ullmark. 1992. *Corporate Space and Architecture, Actors and Procedures*. Paris: Ministère de l'équipement du logement et des transports.

Townsend, M. 1994. Just a glove? *Br J Theatre Nurs* 4(5):7,9-10.

Tran, N, J Elias, T Rosenber, D Wylie, D Gaborieau, and A Yassi. 1994. Evaluation of waste anesthetic gases, monitoring strategies and corelations between nitrous oxide levels and health symptoms. *Am Ind Hyg Assoc J* 55(1):36-42.

Turner, AG, CH King, and G Craddock. 1975. Measuring and reducing noise. Noise profile of hospital shows that even "quiet" areas are too noisy. *Hospital JAHA* 49:85-89.

US Preventive Services Task Force. 1989. *Guide to Clinical Preventive Services: An Assessment of the Effectiveness of 169 interventions*. Baltimore: Williams & Wilkins.

Vaillant, GE, NC Sorbowale, and C McArthur. 1972. Some psychologic vulnerabilities of physicians. *New Engl J Med* 287:372-375.

Vaisman, AI. 1967. Working conditions in surgery and their effects on the health of anesthesiologists. *Eskp Khir Anesteziol* 12:44-49.

Valentino, M, MA Pizzichini, F Monaco, and M Governa. 1994. Latex-induced asthma in four health-care workers in a regional hospital. *Occup Med (Oxf)* 44(3):161-164.

Valko, RJ and PJ Clayton. 1975. Depression in the internships. *Dis Nerv Syst* 36:26-29.

Van Damme, P and GA Tormanns. 1993. European risk model. In *Proceedings of the European Conference on Hepatitis B as an Occupatiooal Hazard*. 10-12.

Van Damme, P, R Vranckx, A Safary, FE Andre, and A Mehevs. 1989. Protective efficacy of a recombinant deoxyribonucleic acid hepatitis B vaccine in institutionalized mentally handicapped clients. *Am J Med* 87(3A):265-295.

Van der Star, A and M Voogd. 1992. User participation in the design and evaluation of a new model hospital bed. In *Ergonomie à l'hôpital (Hospital Ergonomics)*, edited by M Estryn-Béhar, C Gadbois, and M Pottier. International Symposium Paris 1991. Toulouse: Editions Octares.

Van Deursen, CGL, CAM Mul, PGW Smulders and CR De Winter. 1993. Health and working situation of day nurses compared with a matched group of nurses on rotating shift work. In *Occupational Health for Health Care Workers*, edited by M Hagberg, F Hofmann, U Stössel, and G Westlander. Landsberg/Lech: Ecomed Verlag.

Van Hogdalem, H. 1990. Design guidelines for architects and users. In *Building for People in Hospitals, Workers and Consumers*. Luxembourg: European Foundation for the Improvement of Living and Working Conditions.

Van Wagoner, R and N Maguire. 1977. A study of hearing loss among employees in a large urban hospital. *Canadian Journal of Public Health* 68:511-512.

Verhaegen, P, R Cober, DE Smedt, J Dirkx, J Kerstens, D Ryvers, and P Van Daele. 1987. The adaptation of night nurses to different work schedules. *Ergonomics* 30(9):1301-1309.

Villeneuve, J. 1992. Une demarche d'ergonomie participative dans le secteur hôspitalier. In *Ergonomie à l'hôpital (Hospital ergonomics)*, edited by M Estryn-Béhar, C Gadbois, and M Pottier. International Symposium Paris 1991. Toulouse: Editions Octares.

—. 1994. PARC: Des fondations solides pour un projet de rénovation ou de construction *Objectif prévention* (Montreal) 17(5):14-16.

Wade, JG and WC Stevens. 1981. Isoflurane: An ansaesthetic for the eighties? *Anesth Analg* 60(9):666-682.

Wahlen, L. 1992. Noise in the intensive care setting. *Canadian Critical Care Nursing Journal*, 8/9(4/1):9-10.

Walz, T, G Askerooth, and M Lynch. 1983. The new upside-down welfare state. In *Social Work in a Turbulent World*, edited by M Dinerman. Washington, DC: National Association of Social Workers.

Wands, SE and A Yassi. 1993. Modernization of a laundry processing plant: Is it really an improvement? *Appl Ergon* 24(6):387-396.

Weido, AJ and TC Sim. 1995. The burgeoning problem of latex sensitivity. Surgical gloves are only the beginning. *Postgrad Med* 98(3):173-174,179-182,184.

Wiesel, SW, HL Feffer, and RH Rothmann. 1985. *Industrial Low Back Pain*. Charlottesville,VA: Michie.

Wigaeus Hjelm, E, M Hagberg, and S Hellstrom. 1993. Prevention of musculoskeletal disorders in nursing aides by physical training. In *Occupational Health for Health Care Workers*, edited by M Hagberg, F Hofmann, U Stössel, and G Westlander. Landsberg/Lech: Ecomed Verlag.

Wigand, R and Y Grenner. 1988. Personaluntersuchungen auf Immunität gegen Masern, Varizellen und Röteln, Saarländ. *Ärztebl* 41:479-480.

Wilkinson, RT, PD Tyler and CA Varey. 1975. Duty hours of young hospital doctors: Effects on the quality of work. *J Occup Psychol* 48:219-229.

Willet, KM. 1991. Noise-induced hearing loss in orthopaedic staff. *J Bone Joint Surg* 73:113-115.

Williams, M and JD Murphy. 1991. Noise in critical care units: A quality assurance approach. *Journal of Nursing Care Quality* 6(1):53-59.

World Health Organization (WHO). 1990. *Guidelines on AIDS and First Aid in the Workplace*. WHO AIDS Series No. 7. Geneva: WHO.

—. 1991. *Biosafety Guidelines for Diagnostic and Research Laboratories Working with HIV*. WHO AIDS Series No. 9. Geneva: WHO.

—. 1995. *Weekly Epidemiological Report* (13 January).

Wugofski, L. 1995. Occupational accident in health care workers—Epidemiology and prevention. In *Occupational Health for Health Care Workers*, edited by M Hagberg, F Hofmann, U Stössel, and G Westlander. Singapore: International Commission on Occupational Health.

Yassi, A. 1994. Assault and abuse of health care workers in a large teaching hospital. *Can Med Assoc J* 151(9):1273-1279.

Yassi, A and M McGill. 1991. Determinants of blood and body fluid exposure in a large teaching hospital: Hazards of the intermittent intravenous procedure. *American Journal of Infection Control* 19(3):129-135.

Table 97.19 • HSC EMS documentation hierarchy.

EMS level	Purpose
Governance document Mission/strategic plan	Includes the Board's expectations on each core performance category and its requirements for corporate competency in each category.
Level 1 Output requirements	Prescribes the outputs that will be delivered in response to customer and stakeholder (C/S) needs (including government regulatory requirements).
Level 2 Corporate policy	Prescribes the methodologies, systems, processes and resources to be used for achieving C/S requirements; the goals, objectives and performance standards essential for confirming that the C/S requirements have been met (e.g., a schedule of required systems and processes including responsibility centre for each).
Level 3 System descriptions	Prescribes the design of each business system or process that will be operated to achieve the C/S requirements (e.g., criteria and boundaries for system operation; each information collection and data reporting point; position responsible for the system and for each component of the process, etc.).
Level 4 Work instructions	Prescribes detailed task instructions (specific methods and techniques), for each work activity (e.g., describe the task to be done; identify the position responsible for completing the task; state skills required for the task; prescribe education or training methodology to achieve required skills; identify task completion and conformance data, etc.).
Level 5 Records of work and process compliance	Organizes and records measurable outcome data on the operation of systems, processes and tasks designed to verify completion according to specification. (e.g., measures for system or process compliance; resource allocation and budget compliance; effectiveness, efficiency, quality, risk, ethics, etc.).
Level 6 Performance reports	Analyses records and processes to establish corporate performance in relation to standards set for each output requirement (Level 1) related to C/S needs (e.g., compliance, quality, effectiveness, risk, utilization, etc.); and financial and staff resources.

14001 as the performance specification, has been developed and is being implemented in one of the largest teaching health care complexes in Canada. The Health Sciences Centre (HSC) consists of five hospitals and associated clinical and research laboratories, occupying a 32-acre site in central Winnipeg. Of the 32 segregated solid waste streams at the facility, hazardous wastes account for seven. This summary focuses on the hazardous waste disposal aspect of the hospital's operations.

ISO 14000

The ISO 14000 standards system is a typical continuous improvement model based on a controlled management system. The ISO 14001 standard addresses the environmental management system structure exclusively. To conform with the standard, an organization must have processes in place for:

- adopting an environmental policy that sets environmental protection as a high priority
- identifying environmental impacts and setting performance goals
- identifying and complying with legal requirements
- assigning environmental accountability and responsibility throughout the organization
- applying controls to achieve performance goals and legal requirements
- monitoring and reporting environmental performance; auditing the EMS system
- conducting management reviews/ identifying opportunities for improvement.

The hierarchy for carrying out these processes in the HSC is presented in table 97.19.

ISO standards encourage businesses to integrate all environmental considerations into mainstream business decisions and not restrict attention to concerns that are regulated. Since the ISO standards are not technical documents, the function of specifying numerical standards remains the responsibility of governments or independent expert bodies.

Management System Approach

Applying the generic ISO framework in a health care facility requires the adoption of management systems along the lines of those in table 97.19, which describes how this has been addressed by the HSC. Each level in the system is supported by appropriate documentation to confirm diligence in the process. While the volume of work is substantial, it is compensated by the resulting performance consistency and by the "expert" information that remains within the corporation when experienced persons leave.

The main objective of the EMS is to establish consistent, controlled and repeatable processes for addressing the environmental aspects of the corporation's operations. To facilitate management review of the hospital's performance, an EMS Score Card was conceived based on the ISO 14001 standard. The Score Card closely follows the requirements in the ISO 14001 standard and, with use, will be developed into the hospital's audit protocol.

Application of the EMS to the Hazardous Waste Process

Facility hazardous waste process

The HSC hazardous waste process currently consists of the following elements:

- procedure statement assigning responsibilities
- process description, in both text and flowchart formats
- *Disposal Guide for Hazardous Waste* for staff
- education programme for staff
- performance tracking system
- continuous improvement through multidisciplinary team process
- a process for seeking external partners.

The roles and responsibilities of the four main organizational units involved in the hazardous waste process are listed in table 97.20.

—. 1995. Efficacy and cost-effectiveness of a needleless intravenous access system. *American Journal of Infection Control* 22(2):57-64.

Yassi, A, J Gaborieau, J Elias, and D Willie. 1992. Identification and control of hazardous noise levels in a hospital complex. In *Ergonomie à l'hôpital (Hospital Ergonomics)*, edited by M Estryn-Béhar, C Gadbois, and M Pottier. International Symposium Paris 1991. Toulouse: Editions Octares.

Yassi, A, D Gaborieau, I Gillespie, J Elias, and G Seyoum. 1991. The noise hazard in a large health care facility. *J Occup Med* 33(10):1067-1070.

Yassi, A, J Khokhar, R Tate, J Cooper, C Snow, and S Vallentyne. 1995a. The epidemiology of back injuries in nurses at a large Canadian tertiary care hospital: Implications for prevention. *Occup Med* 45(4):215-220.

Yassi, A, R Tate, JE Cooper, C Snow, S Vallentyne, and J Khokhar. 1995b. Early intervention for back-injured nurses at a large Canadian tertiary care hospital: An evaluation of the effectiveness and cost benefits of a two-year pilot project. *Occup Med* 45(4):209-214.

Yassin, MS, MB Lierl, TJ Fisher, K O'Brien, J Cross, and C Steinmetz. 1994. Latex allergy in hospital employees. *Ann Allergy* 72(3):245-249.

Other relevant readings

Adegboye, AA, GB Moss, F Soyinka, and JK Krieiss. 1994. The epidemiology of needlestick and sharp instrument accidents in a Nigerian hospital. *Infec Contr Hosp Epid* 15:27-31.

Alter, MJ. 1994. Occupational exposure to heapatitis C virus: A dilemma. *Infec Contr Hosp Epid* 15:742-744.

American Hospital Association (AHA). 1983. *Chemical Hazardous Waste Assessment*. Chicago, IL: AHA.

Bell, DM and JW Curran. 1992. Human immunodefiency virus infection. In *Hospital Infections*, edited by JV Bennett and PS Brachman. Boston: Little, Brown & Co.

Browden, FJ, B Pollet, F Birrell, and EM Dax. 1993. Occupational exposure to the human immunodefiency virus and other blood-borne pathogens. A six-year prospective study. *Med J Austral* 158:810-812.

Centre Nationale de l'équipment hospitalier. 1982. *Guide technique pour la gestion de l'élimination des dèchets hospitaliers*. Paris: Centre Nationale de l'équipement hospitalier.

Cockcroft, A, K Oakley, C Gooch, and S Mastin. 1994. Anxiety and perception of risk of HIV and hepatitis B infection among health-care workers reporting accidental exposures to blood and other body fluids. *AIDS Care* 6:205-214.

Environmental Protection Agency. 1986. *Guide for Infectious Waste Management*. Washington, DC: EPA.

Estryn-Béhar, M. 1996. *Ergonomie hospitalière: Théorie et pratique*. Paris: Estem éditions.

—. 1997. *Stress et souffrance des soignants à l'hôpital—Reconnaissance, analyse et prévention*. Paris: Estem éditions.

Francioli, P and J Jost. 1994. Mise a jour sur les exposition au VIH en milieu medical: mesures generales, chimioprophylaxie, declaration. *Bulletin de l'Office Federale de la Sante Publique (Suisse)* 37:617-630.

Gaffney, K, M Murphy, and F Mulcahy. 1992. Phlebotomy practices, needlestick injuries, hepatitis B status, among interns in a Dublin hospital. *Irish Medical Journal* 85:102-104.

Garner, JS and MS Favero. 1985. *Guideline for Handwashing and Hospital Environmental Control*. Atlanta, GA: CDC.

Garner, JS and BP Simmons. 1983. Guideline for isolation precautions in hospitals. *Infec Contr Hosp Epid* 4:245-325.

Gerberding, JL. 1994. Incidence and prevalence of human immunodeficiency virus, hepatitis B virus, hepatitis C virus, and cytomegalovirus among health care personnel at risk for blood exposure: Final report from a longitudinal study. *Journal of Infectious Diseases* 170:1410-1417.

Gestall, JJ. 1993. *Risegos del trabajo del personal sanitario*. Madrid: Interamericana-McGraw Hill.

Guardino, X. 1992. *Seguridad y Condiciones de Trabajo en el Laboratorio*. Madrid: INSHT.

Hersey, JC and LS Martin. 1994. Use of infection control guidelines by workers in health care facilities to prevent occupational transmission of HBV and HIV: Results from a national survey. *Infec Contr Hosp Epid* 15:243-252.

Ippolito, G, G DeCarli, V Puro, N Petrosillo, and R Bertucci. 1994. Device-specific risk of needlestick injury in Italian health care workers. *JAMA* 272:607-610.

Klein, RS, K Freeman, PE Taylor, and CE Stevens. 1992. Occupational risk for hepatitis C virus infection among New York City dentists. *Lancet* 338:1539-1542.

Lot, F and D Abiteboul. 1994. Infections professionelles par le VIH en France; le point as 31 decembre 1993. *Bulletin Epidemiologique Hebdormadaire* 25:111-113.

Mallon, DF, W Shearwood, SA Mallal, MA French, and RL Dawkins. 1992. Exposure to blood borne infections in health care workers. *Med J Austral* 157:592-595.

Marcus, R, DH Culver, and DM Bell. 1993. Risk of human immunodeficiency virus infection among emergency department workers. *Am J Med* 94:363-370.

Marcus, R, P Srivastava, and DM Bell. 1995. Occupational blood contact among pre-hospital emergency medical service workers: a prospective study. *Annals of Emergency Medicine* in press.

Nelsing, S, TL Nielsen, and JO Nielsn. 1993. Exposure to blood and risk of infection among health personnel. *Ugeskrift for Laeger* 155:3359-3363.

Panlilio, AL, CN Shapiro, and CN Schable. 1995. Serosurvey of human immunodeficiency virus, hepatitis B virus, and hepatitis C virus infection among hospital-based surgeons. *Journal of the American College of Surgeons* 180:16-24.

Panlilio, AL, BA Welch, and DM Bell. 1992. Blood and amniotic fluid contact sustained by obstetrical personnel during deliveries. *Am J Obstet Gynecol* 67:703-708.

Puro, V, G Ippolito, and E Guzzanti. 1992. Zidovudine prophylaxis after accidental exposure to HIV: The Italian experience. *AIDS Care* 6:963-969.

Puro, V, E Lo Presti, I D'Ascanio, S Aaniratti, A Benedetto, and G Ippolito. 1993. The seroprevalance of HIV, HBV, and HCV infections in patients coming to the departments of general surgery of a public hospital (S. Camillo, Rome). *Mnerva Chirurgica* 48:349-354.

Rhodes, RS and DN Bell. 1995. Prevention of bloodborne pathogen transmission in surgery and obstetrics. *Surgical Clinics of North America* in press.

Stellman, JM, SD Stellman, J Berek, and A Ezraty. 1978. The role of the Union Health and Safety Committee in evaluating the health hazards of hospital workers: A case study. *Preventive Medicine* 7(3):332-337.

Thomé-Kozmiensky, KJ. 1982. *Recycling International*. Berlin: E. Freitag.

Tokars, JI, DM Bell, and DH Culver. 1992. Percutaneous injuries during surgical procedures. *JAMA* 267:2899-2904.

Tokars, JI, ME Chamberland, and CA Schable. 1992. A survey of occupational blood contact and human immunodeficiency virus infection among orthopedic surgeons. *JAMA* 268:489-494.

World Health Organization (WHO). 1985. *Management of Waste from Hospital and Other Health Care Establishments*. Copenhagen: WHO Regional Office for Europe.

Williams, WW. 1983. Guideline for infection control in hospital personnel. *Infec Contr Hosp Epid* 4 suppl:326-349.

HOTELS AND RESTAURANTS

98

Chapter Editor
Pam Tau Lee

Contents

GENERAL PROFILE

Pam Tau Lee

Hotels and restaurants are found in every country. The economy of hotels and restaurants is intimately tied to the tourism industry, to business travel and to conventions. In many countries, the tourism industry is a major part of the overall economy.

The primary function of a restaurant is to provide food and drink to people outside the home. Types of restaurants include restaurants (which are often costly) with dining rooms and extensive serving staffs; smaller, "family-style" restaurants and cafes which often service the local community; "diners", or restaurants where serving short-order meals at counters is the major feature; fast food restaurants, where people line up at counters to place their orders and where meals are available in a few minutes, often for taking out to eat elsewhere; and cafeterias, where people go through serving lines and make their selections from a variety of already prepared foods, which are usually displayed in cases. Many restaurants have separate bar or lounge areas, where alcoholic beverages are served, and many larger restaurants have special banquet rooms for groups of people. Street vendors serving food from carts and stalls are common in most countries, often as part of the informal sector of the economy.

The primary function of a hotel is to provide lodging for guests. Types of hotels range from basic overnight facilities, such as inns and motels that cater to business travellers and tourists, to elaborate luxury complexes, such as resorts, spas and convention hotels. Many hotels offer auxiliary services such as restaurants, bars, laundries, health and fitness clubs, beauty salons, barber shops, business centres and gift shops.

Restaurants and hotels can be individually or family-owned and operated, owned by partnerships or owned by large corporate entities. Many corporations do not actually own individual restaurants or hotels in the chain but rather grant a franchise of a name and style to local owners.

The restaurant workforce can include chefs and other kitchen staff, waiters and head waiters, table busing staff, bartenders, a cashier and coatroom personnel. Larger restaurants have staffs which can be highly specialized in their job functions.

The workforce in large a hotel typically will include reception clerks, door and bell persons, security personnel, parking and garage staff, housekeepers, laundry workers, maintenance personnel, kitchen and restaurant workers and office staff.

Most hotel jobs are "blue collar" and require minimal language and literacy skills. Women and immigrant workers comprise the bulk of the workforce in most hotels in developed countries today. In developing countries, hotels tend to be staffed by local residents. Because hotel occupancy levels tend to be seasonal, there is usually a small group of full-time employees with a sizeable number of part-time and seasonal workers. Salaries tend to be in the middle to low income range. As a result of these factors, employee turnover is relatively high.

In restaurants, workforce characteristics are similar, although men comprise a larger proportion of the workforce in restaurants than in hotels. In many countries salaries are low, and the staff waiting on and busing tables may depend on gratuities for a major portion of their income. In many places, a service charge is automatically added to the bill. In fast food restaurants, the workforce are often teenagers and the pay is at the minimum wage.

RESTAURANTS

Neil Dalhouse

Restaurants can range in size from a small local diner to a large hotel restaurant, and generally consist of three main areas: the kitchen, where the preparation and cooking of meals takes place; the food service, which provides the service of food to guests in the restaurant; and the bar, a lounge which provides live or recorded entertainment and sales of alcoholic beverages and food.

Kitchens

Kitchen personnel include chefs and cooks, who are responsible for preparing and cooking food; pantry persons, who prepare the food for cooking and also keep an inventory of stock; and stewards, who are responsible for the cleaning and maintenance of the kitchen area.

Several different types of accidents can occur in the kitchen area, such as burns from deep fryers, slipping on grease and cuts from knives. Lack of maintenance or improper maintenance in the kitchen area can lead to accidents. Floors that have been mopped should always have a "Wet Floor" placard posted, or kitchen personnel may slip and injure themselves. Trays of food or dishes must be stored securely or they will topple over. Non-slip mats and non-slip floor waxes should be used at entrances and exits. Passageways should always be kept free of boxes, trash cans and other obstacles. Conditions that could cause an accident, such as loose floor tiles, exposed wiring, spills and so on, should always be reported and dealt with as soon as possible and a reporting mechanism should be in place in the workplace.

Another cause of accidents is not using the proper equipment to reach items kept on upper shelves. Items on high shelves should only be retrieved by using a ladder or step stool and not by climbing on boxes or chairs. This means that ladders and step stools must be kept in a convenient location and be in good repair.

Machines, cutting equipment and knives

Accidents and injuries can be common in the kitchen unless safety procedures are properly exercised. The type of machinery used and the high level of activity and pressure in restaurant kitchens during serving hours increase the risk of accidents.

Some common types of machinery used in kitchens are meat grinders, mixers, ice machines and dishwashing machines. Misuse or improper use of this machinery can result in cuts, limbs caught in moving parts and electric shock. To prevent these types of accidents from occurring, kitchen personnel should receive thorough training prior to using the equipment, and should follow the manufacturer's instructions for safe operation. Other measures to prevent injury are: ensuring equipment is turned off and unplugged before cleaning; wearing snug-fitting clothing with no loose jewellery that can fall off or be caught in the equipment while operating the machinery (long-haired employees should wear hair nets for the same reason); and regular servicing by authorized personnel. One must always avoid pushing food through equipment with one's hands.

Meat slicers are commonly used in kitchens for slicing meats, fruits and vegetables, and are potentially the most dangerous of any kitchen equipment. Mechanical machine guards must always be in place when slicers are being used. Caution must always be used when cleaning the equipment, particularly when the blades are exposed. When workers finish using the slicer, it should be returned to the zero position and unplugged.

Knives can inflict severe wounds if they are improperly used or stored. Kitchen personnel frequently use knives to chop and dice vegetables and meat prior to cooking. Methods to prevent injuries include: using knives only for the purpose for which they were intended (e.g., not as can openers); ensuring that knives are sharp, since a dull knife requires more pressure and is more likely to slip; carrying knives by the handle, with the blade pointed down; and storing knives in their proper place immediately after cleaning.

Stoves and ovens

Skin burns are the main hazard experienced by kitchen personnel using stoves and ovens. Burns can range from a slight scald to a third-degree burn. Preventive measures include always using oven mitts when lifting pot lids, when transporting pots and when removing hot items from the oven. Oven areas must always be kept free of grease build-up to prevent slipping or accidental fires. If gas ovens are being used, the pilot light must be lit before lighting the oven.

Deep fat fryers are commonly used in kitchens for deep frying various meats and vegetables. The most common hazard associated with these units is skin burns from the splashing of hot grease. Measures that can be taken to ensure the safe use of deep fat fryers are: ensuring that the oil does not overheat and start a fire; cleaning away any grease on the floor around the fryer; preventing overflows by not overfilling the fryer with oil; and using extreme care when filtering or changing the fat in the fryer. Personal protective equipment such as gloves, aprons and long sleeved shirts should always be worn.

Microwave ovens are frequently used in kitchens in order to quickly heat or cook food. The hazards associated with improperly maintained microwave ovens are electrical shock or exposure to leaked microwave radiation. Depending on the amount of leaked radiation and the length of exposure, microwave radiation can damage sensitive human organs. The radiation can also damage medical equipment implanted in the human body, such as pacemakers. Microwave ovens must be kept free of food and grease spills around the doors and seals, since these residues may prevent the oven doors from closing properly and lead to leakage of microwaves. Notices should be posted near the ovens with full instructions on their safe use. All ovens should be checked regularly for proper performance and microwave leakage. They should be repaired or adjusted by trained service personnel.

Tableside cooking

Tableside cooking or serving of flaming foods can result in severe burn injuries to both the server and the customer if improper techniques are used. This type of service should be performed only by staff trained in tableside cooking and in the use of liquid or semi-solid fuel. A carbon dioxide fire extinguisher should be available in case of fire.

Walk-in refrigerators and freezers

Large walk-in refrigerators and freezers are commonly used in restaurant kitchens to store prepared food and ingredients. In addition to the temperature, the major hazard associated with walk-in refrigeration units is that kitchen personnel can be trapped in them if the door accidentally closes behind them. All walk-in cooling equipment must be equipped with interior door opening handles and with alarm switches, and all personnel who use these units should be familiar with the location of these devices.

Care should be taken when walking inside refrigeration units since condensation can cause the floors to become very slippery. To further prevent falling injuries, refrigerator floors should always be kept clear of food scraps and grease. At closing time, a check should always be made to ensure that no one has remained behind in the refrigerators.

Temperature extremes

In the restaurant kitchen almost all personnel are exposed to heat stress; however, the chef or cook is the most exposed since he or she works in close proximity to hot stoves and ovens. Dangerously high air temperatures near stoves and ovens, combined with the heavy uniforms many chefs are required to wear, can cause a number of heat-related health problems. For example, high blood pressure, skin disorders, headaches and fatigue have often been experienced by kitchen personnel. Heat exhaustion and heat stroke can also occur. In extreme cases, fainting and loss of consciousness have been known to happen.

Methods to prevent heat stress include improving ventilation with oven hoods that draw away hot air, implementing work/rest schedules and drinking plenty of water while working. Kitchen personnel should also be educated in recognizing the symptoms of heat disorders.

Kitchen personnel are often exposed to temperature extremes when walking back and forth between walk-in refrigerators and hot kitchens. These sudden changes in temperature can result in respiratory problems. Some kitchen workers are required to work inside refrigerators for extended periods of time, unpacking produce, while arranging boxes of meats and cleaning the interior. These individuals should be given appropriate protective garments to wear while working in these areas.

Ventilation

Good ventilation systems are necessary to remove odour, grease and smoke from kitchen areas. Airborne grease can settle on kitchen equipment and cause it to become slippery. Ventilation systems include fans, air ducts and hoods. These systems should have filters removed and cleaned regularly.

Clean-up

Dish washing

Dishwashing machines can cause skin burns from handling hot dishes and can scald a worker who reaches into the machines before the dishwashing cycle is finished. Dishwashing machines should never be overloaded, since this could cause the machine to jam or to stop operating. Gloves should be used when removing hot dishes directly from the dishwasher.

Cleaning products

In order to keep restaurant kitchens as clean and hygienic as possible, several types of cleaning products and agents are used. Ammonia solutions are often used to clean grease from oven ranges and can be particularly irritating to skin and eyes. Good ventilation should always be provided by fans or oven hoods when using ammonia products.

Other products used include drain cleaners, which are caustic and can cause skin burns and damage to eyes. To protect against splashing, rubber gloves or a face mask should be worn when using these cleaners. Soaps and detergents that are present in floor cleaning products may cause dermatitis or throat irritation, if soap dust is inhaled. Disposable respirators (face masks) may be needed by employees who are sensitive to this type of dust.

To further ensure that cleaning products do not pose a risk to employees, proper handling procedures should always be followed. Cleaning products should always be stored in clearly labelled containers, far away from where food containers are stored. Cleaning products should never be combined, particularly with chlorine bleach, which can cause a hazardous situation if mixed with other cleaning products. Material safety data sheets (MSDSs) are available in many countries for learning about the contents of cleaning products, their effects and how to handle them properly.

Trash compactors

Trash compactors are used for compacting the large amounts of food waste generated in the kitchen into a much smaller volume. These machines should be designed not to operate with the lids open, in order to prevent catching hands or hair in them. The water supply should also be sufficient for the unit to operate safely and efficiently. Care should always be taken to ensure that glass, metal or plastics do not get into the compactor unit, since these materials will cause the machine to jam and lock out.

Pesticides

Pesticides are often used in restaurants to combat insects that are attracted by a food environment. Most pesticides used in restaurants and kitchens are of low hazard to humans. However, some individuals may be sensitive to such products and may develop skin irritation and other allergic reactions.

To prevent misuse of pesticides, training in the use of pesticides should be provided to janitors and other cleaning staff, and serious insect infestations should be treated by a licensed exterminator. Instructions should be printed on all pesticide containers and must be read prior to use, particularly to determine whether the pesticide can be used safely in food areas.

Food Service

Food service personnel include dining room waiters, cocktail waiters, bartenders, hosts, banquet waiters and buspersons. These individuals are responsible for serving meals and beverages, showing guests to their tables and cleaning and maintaining the dining room

Slips and falls

Injuries can result from slips on wet floors or falling over boxes, carts or garbage containers left in the kitchen or dining room area. These injuries could include sprains, broken limbs, injured necks and backs and cuts from falling on sharp objects. To help prevent these accidents, employees should wear sturdy, low-heeled, rubber-soled shoes at all times. All water, grease or food spills should be wiped up immediately, and loose electrical cords and wiring should always be taped down to the floor.

All area rugs in the dining room should be of the non-slip type, with a rubber or other appropriate backing. Carpeting should be checked for frayed or raised edges that can cause food service personnel to trip and fall. Areas where the flooring changes from carpet to tile should always be clearly marked to alert food service personnel of the surface change.

The layout of the dining room is also important in preventing accidents. Tight corners, dim lighting and small exits to the kitchen can result in collisions between food service personnel. Wider corners and clearly marked, well lit exits will lead to safer traffic patterns.

Burns

Food service personnel can suffer skin burns through spilling of hot liquids such as coffee or soup, or from melted wax if tables are candle lit. To prevent spilling of hot liquids, waiters should never overreach when serving hot beverages at a table. When filling soup bowls, food service personnel should be careful to avoid splashes and try not to overfill the bowls.

When carrying hot coffee pots and urns to the dining room, servers should use a small towel to protect hands.

Musculoskeletal injuries

Repetitive strain injuries (RSIs) and other musculoskeletal problems can be experienced by food service personnel who must routinely carry heavy trays, bend and reach to clear, wipe and set tables or carry boxes of restaurant supplies. Well designed workstations and work schedules, such as rotating tasks among food service personnel so that repetitiveness of tasks can be reduced, can diminish the risks.

Training in ergonomics (as well as training in identifying RSI risk factors) can also be helpful to all food service personnel in order to prevent strain injuries.

Many back and neck injuries occur because of improper lifting techniques. For many food service personnel, improper carrying of overloaded trays of dishes and glasses can cause strain on the back and increase the risk of dropping the tray and injuring someone. Training in proper loading and lifting of trays can reduce the risk of injury. For example, distributing the glasses and dishes evenly on the tray and placing one palm under the center of the tray while holding the front edge with the other hand will help create a safer dining room environment.

Stress

The restaurant dining room can be a very high stress environment because of the pressure of performing efficiently while working within tight schedules. Other causes of stress among food service personnel include working shifts, uncertain income because of dependence on gratuities and dealing with irate, difficult customers. Physical stressors such as noise and poor air quality can also be experienced in the restaurant environment. Some symptoms of stress can include headaches, racing heart, ulcers, irritability, insomnia and depression.

Methods to prevent or cope with stress include having workplace meetings that allow employees to share their views about improving work procedures, seminars on stress management techniques, improving air quality and reducing noise. These issues are discussed more fully elsewhere in this *Encyclopaedia*.

Bars and lounges

Bars or lounges can range in size from a small club or piano lounge to a vast dance/entertainment complex. Most of the hazards presented here are discussed in more detail elsewhere in this *Encyclopaedia*.

Broken glass is often a hazard in a bar environment because of the large amount of glassware used. Shards from broken glasses can accidentally be ingested by staff and customers. Glass fragments can cause cuts to fingers. There are several methods which can be used to minimize broken glass in the bar areas. Glasses should be inspected regularly for chips and cracks. Any damaged glasses should be discarded immediately. Picking up several glasses in one hand by placing fingers inside the glasses and bringing them together is hazardous since glasses carried in this manner may break.

A glass should never be used to scoop up the ice. A metal ice scoop should always be used when filling glasses with ice. If a glass does break in the ice area, the ice should be melted and all pieces of glass carefully removed. Broken glass should never be handled with bare hands.

Second-hand smoke. Bar personnel are exposed to heavy amounts of second-hand smoke due to the crowded conditions in many bars and lounges. These conditions can pose a risk since second-hand smoke has been linked to lung cancer and other respiratory problems. Every effort possible should be made to improve ventilation in bars and/or to set up non-smoking rooms in the bar areas.

Slips and falls. The rushed environment of a busy bar can contribute to slips and falls. Spilled drinks and leaking beverage containers can result in the area behind the bar being particularly hazardous for bartenders. Buspersons should regularly dry mop behind the bar throughout the evening. Outside the bar area, all spilled drinks should be cleaned up immediately. If the area is carpeted, there should be checks to ensure that there are no ragged edges where people could trip. All bar personnel should wear non-slip rubber-soled shoes.

If the bar has a dance floor, the floor should be made of wood or a material that allows gliding, but the floor should also be clearly distinct in colour from other walking surfaces.

Lifting. Bartenders are often required to lift heavy boxes or kegs of beer. Where possible, dollies should be used to transport kegs and boxes of beer. If proper lifting techniques are not used, back, neck and knee injuries can occur. All heavy lifting should be done using safe lifting techniques.

Bar waiters often carry heavy trays of drinks, which can put considerable stress on the back and neck. Proper tray carrying techniques should be shown to all bar waiters. Physical fitness is important for avoiding back injuries.

Noise. Excessive noise from live entertainment in bars and lounges can result in hearing damage among bar staff. Noise levels of 90 decibels (dB), which is the legal limit in some countries, like the United States, is a level that will lead to hearing loss in some individuals. Annual hearing testing (audiometric testing) is a requirement for all bar personnel exposed to 85 to 90 dB noise levels for 8 hours daily.

To prevent hearing damage among bar personnel, exposure to high noise levels should be limited to short periods of time, and attempts should be made to reduce the sound volume. If these methods are not feasible, then personal protective equipment such as ear plugs should be issued.

Compressed gases. Compressed gases are found in the bar areas where carbonated beverages are served. The canisters of gas must be kept in an upright position at all times or an explosion may occur.

Fire safety

All restaurant employees should be trained in the use of fire extinguishers and should know the location of all the fire alarms. An effective fire prevention programme includes training employees in spotting fire hazards and in proper procedures if a fire does occur. The telephone numbers of emergency-response personnel and instructions on how to summon them should be posted in a prominent area, and all employees should be familiar with an evacuation plan and escape routes. Kitchen personnel in particular should be trained in how to extinguish small fires that may occur in the kitchen.

Good housekeeping is key to fire prevention in restaurants. All areas of the restaurant should be checked for build-up of trash, grease and oil. Combustible materials such as aerosols and greasy rags should be kept in suitable covered containers and garbage cans when not in use. Ducts, filters and fans in the kitchen must be kept free of grease. This will also result in the equipment running more efficiently.

Fire exits from the restaurant must be clearly marked, and passageways to the exits must be free of boxes, trash and other debris. The use of fire detection devices and sprinkler systems should also be part of a good fire prevention programme.

Cashiers

Restaurant cashiers are generally responsible for operating the cash register, handling incoming cash, processing guest receipts and answering the phone. Restaurants can often be targets for hold-ups and robberies, resulting in injuries and even death for cashiers. Management should provide training to cashiers in proper cash-handling procedures and behaviour during a robbery. Other preventive measures are ensuring that the cashiers'

area is well lit and open, and furnishing the cashier area with alarms that can summon security during a robbery. The entire restaurant should be securable after closing, with all exits alarmed and labelled for emergency use only.

Ergonomics

Cashiers in fast food restaurants and cafeterias in particular may develop repetitive motion injuries due to the design of the job and the high workload. Precautions include well-designed work stations with cash registers at comfortable heights. Flexible seats will allow cashiers to sit and relieve lower-back and leg pressures.

HOTELS

Pam Tau Lee

Departmental operations within a hotel usually consist of: *reception,* which oversees reservations and guest reception services; *housekeeping,* which cleans and stocks guest rooms and public areas; *maintenance,* which does heavy cleaning, setup, painting, repair and remodelling; *food and beverage; office and accounting;* and other *miscellaneous services* such as health centres, beauty salons, barber shops and gift shops.

Hazards by Department

Reception

Reception includes the following job classifications: managers, desk clerks, telephone operators, bell and door staff, security personnel, concierges, drivers and parking attendants. Key job safety and health hazards include:

Visual display units (VDUs). Desk clerks, telephone operators and other front desk personnel often use computer terminals. It has been shown that computer use under some conditions can cause various repetitive strain injuries (RSIs), such as carpal tunnel syndrome (in the wrist) as well as shoulder, neck and back problems. Employees are at special risk if workstations are poorly adjusted and require awkward body postures, or if VDU work is continuous without adequate breaks. VDU work can also produce eyestrain and other visual problems. Preventive measures include providing adjustable computer workstations, training staff on how to adjust their equipment properly and maintain correct postures, and ensuring that employees take rest and stretch breaks.

Shift work. Many guest service employees work shifts that can vary according to the level of daily hotel occupancy. Staff members may be required to work both day and evening shifts, or split shifts with random days off. Physiological and psychological health effects of shift work can include disturbed sleep patterns, stomach trouble and stress. Staff may also use drugs or medicines as sleeping aids to adjust to unusual work hours. Workers should receive training on health hazards related to shift work. Whenever possible workers should have adequate time off between rotating shifts to allow for sleep adjustments.

Special consideration should also be paid to other issues associated with swing and graveyard shifts, such as safety concerns, access to healthy meals while on duty and proper ventilation (as air conditioning is often turned off in the evening).

Poor indoor-air quality. Employees can be exposed to second-hand smoke in the lobby, bar, dining rooms and guest rooms. Where ventilation is inadequate, second-hand smoke can pose a risk of cancer and heart disease.

Lifting. Lifting hazards affect staff who load, unload and carry luggage and convention supplies. Back, neck, knee and ankle injuries can result when staff are not trained on proper lifting techniques. Luggage carts should be available. They should be well maintained and equipped with smooth-rolling wheels and safety locks.

Parking and garage hazards. Garage jobs in hotels range from valet parking, to collecting fees, to site maintenance. Employees may work part time, and turnover is often high.

Workers can be struck by vehicles, can inhale exhaust fumes (which contain carbon monoxide among other toxins), or can be exposed to chemicals in automotive products, cleaning products and paints. They can be exposed to asbestos from brake dusts. They can fall from ladders or other maintenance equipment, and can trip or fall due to fluid spills, broken pavement or snow. They can also be assaulted or robbed.

Measures to prevent auto accidents include having clearly marked traffic lanes and walkways, warnings indicating the direction of traffic flow, stop signs for crossing lanes and roped-off areas wherever maintenance work is being done.

Workers exposed to car exhaust, paint fumes and other chemicals should have access to fresh air. Training should be provided about chemical hazards and health effects.

Kerosene heaters sometimes used to warm workers in parking garages can release toxic fumes, and should be prohibited. If heaters are necessary, properly guarded and grounded electric heaters should be used.

Oil spills, water and debris should be cleaned up immediately to prevent falls. Snow should be removed and not allowed to accumulate.

Housekeeping

This group includes housekeepers, laundry workers and supervisors. The department is usually responsible for cleaning and maintaining guest rooms, public areas and meeting and recreational facilities. It may also supply laundry services for guests. Typical safety and health hazards can include:

Repetitive strain injuries (RSIs). Housekeepers are subject to strains from repeated lifting, pushing, bending, reaching and wiping when cleaning bathrooms, changing bed linen, vacuuming rugs, wiping furniture and walls and pushing supply carts from room to room. Laundry workers are also at risk for to RSI injuries due to reaching and to rapid motions from folding, sorting and loading laundry.

Housekeeping carts help transport supplies and equipment, but carts need to be well maintained, with smooth-rolling wheels, and designed to carry heavy loads without tipping over. Carts also need to be relatively light and easy to manoeuvre, with sufficient clearance above the cart so housekeepers can see where they are going.

Training in both ergonomics and proper lifting should be available for housekeepers and laundry workers. Training should include RSI risk factors and methods for reducing them.

Chemical products. Housekeepers and maids use chemical cleaning products for sinks, tubs, toilets, floors and mirrors. Some products can cause dermatitis, respiratory distress and other problems. Some general cleaning agents containing ammonia, detergents and solvents can irritate the skin, eyes, nose and throat. Certain solvent-based products can damage the kidneys and reproductive organs. Disinfectants often contain phenol compounds, which can cause irritation and are suspected to cause cancer.

Preventive measures include supplying protective gloves and substituting with less hazardous products. Proper ventilation should be provided through open windows, mechanical air vents or fans. Chemical storage areas should be well maintained and away from break and eating areas.

Training should be provided about chemical hazards and health effects. It should be conducted in a way staff can understand. To be effective, some training procedures may need translation into workers' first languages.

Trips and falls. Housekeepers are required to move quickly. Speed can result in slipping on wet floors, falling from tubs and other surfaces when cleaning, and tripping over cords, sheets and bed covers and debris. Laundry staff may slip on wet floors.

Training should be offered emphasizing safety measures to prevent falls and work methods that reduce the need to rush.

Cuts. Cuts from glass, discarded razor blades and debris can be reduced by using liners in wastebaskets and by installing razor blade disposal devices in bathrooms. Workers should be trained in proper waste-handling techniques.

Needlesticks. Used hypodermic needles left by guests in wastebaskets, linens or rooms put hotel staff at risk of getting infectious diseases from accidental punctures. Housekeeping and laundry personnel are the most likely to encounter a discarded needle. Staff should be instructed on how to report and dispose of needles. Staff should have access to approved types of needle receptacle boxes. Management should also have effective medical and counselling procedures to assist staff who have been stuck by a discarded needle.

Heat stress. Hotel laundry workers wash, iron, fold and deliver linen. Heat from machinery, combined with poor ventilation, can result in an oppressive work environment and cause heat stress. Symptoms may include headache, nausea, irritability, fatigue, fainting and accelerated pulse. Eventually these can lead to convulsions and more serious problems if early symptoms are not treated.

Heat stress can be prevented by installing air conditioning, insulating sources of heat, ventilating hot areas with hoods that draw hot air away, taking frequent short breaks in cool areas, drinking plenty of water and wearing loose-fitting clothes. If the work area is only moderately hot (below 35 °C), fans may be useful.

Maintenance

Maintenance staff do heavy cleaning, set-up, painting, repair, remodelling and grounds work. Hazards include:

Chemical products. Maintenance staff may use toxic cleaning products to strip and polish floors as well as to clean carpets, walls, furniture, brass fixtures and marble. Certain products can irritate the skin, eyes, nose and throat; can affect the nervous system; and can damage the kidneys, lungs, liver and reproductive system.

Solvents may be present in painting and remodelling materials. Fast-drying paints are used to enable rooms and public areas to be available quickly, but these paints contain high solvent concentrations. Glues used in laying carpet and flooring and in other remodelling jobs may also contain toxic solvents. Solvents can irritate the skin, eyes, nose and throat. Some may damage the nervous system, kidneys, lungs, liver and reproductive organs. Certain solvents are known to cause cancer.

Pesticides and herbicides may be applied in kitchens, dining rooms, public areas, locker rooms and outside the hotel in gardens and driveways. Some of these chemicals can cause respiratory problems; can irritate the skin, eyes, nose and throat; and can damage the nervous system, kidneys, liver and other organs.

Preventive measures include training about chemicals, proper ventilation and proper use of personal protective equipment. If respirators are required, staff should be trained on how to select the proper respirator and cartridge, and how to fit test, use and maintain the equipment. In addition, employees should be given a medical exam to ensure that they are physically fit to work wearing a respirator. Wherever possible, less toxic chemicals should be used.

Asbestos. Asbestos is present in many hotels. Used for years as an insulator and fire retardant, it is found around pipes and in ceiling materials and floor coverings. This highly toxic substance can cause asbestosis, lung cancer or mesothelioma (another form of cancer).

Asbestos is most hazardous when it ages or is damaged. It may begin to break up, creating dust. Hotels should regularly inspect areas where asbestos-containing materials are present to ensure that the asbestos is in good condition.

Extreme caution must be used to protect workers and guests when asbestos dust is present (through ageing or damage or during asbestos abatement jobs). Hotel workers and guests must be kept away from the area, warning signs must be posted and only skilled and licensed personnel should be hired to abate the hazard. The area should be inspected by qualified professionals when work in completed. In new construction or renovation, substitute products should be used in lieu of asbestos.

Trips and falls. Maintenance staff may fall when using ladders and hoists to reach high places such as ceilings, chandeliers, light fixtures, walls and balconies. Training should be provided.

Food and beverage

These staff members include kitchen workers, dishwashers, restaurant servers, room service personnel, hosts and bartenders. Among the hazards are:

Repetitive strain injuries (RSIs). RSIs can occur when room service personnel or restaurant servers deliver food. Trays can be heavy and the server may have to walk long distances. To reduce the risk of injury, room service carts can be used to deliver orders. Carts should be easy to manoeuvre and well maintained. If carts are equipped with heating boxes, the staff should be trained on their proper use.

Trips and falls. Floor surfaces in the kitchen, as well as in all areas to which serving personnel must go, should be kept clean and dry to prevent falls. Spills should be cleaned up immediately. See also the article "Restaurants" in this chapter.

Miscellaneous services

Swimming pools and fitness centres. Many hotels provide swimming facilities or fitness centres for guests. Often showers, saunas, whirlpools, weight rooms and locker rooms are available.

Chemicals used to clean and disinfect showers and locker rooms can cause skin and respiratory irritation. In addition, employees who maintain swimming pools may handle solid or gaseous chlorine. Chlorine leaks can cause burns and severe respiratory problems. If mishandled, it can explode. Employees should be trained on how to handle all these chemicals properly.

Workers who maintain pool and fitness facilities are exposed to injuries from slips and falls. Nonskid, well-maintained and well-drained walking surfaces are important. Water puddles should be wiped up immediately.

Gift shops. Hotels often provide gift and convenience shops for guests. Employees are subject to falls, strains and cuts associated with unpacking and stocking merchandise. They should be trained on proper lifting techniques and should have hand carts to aid in transporting merchandise. Aisles should be kept clear to avoid accidents.

Beauty salons and barber shops. Barbers and cosmetologists risk injuries including skin irritation from hair chemicals, burns from hot towels and curling irons, and cuts and punctures from scissors and razors.

Special hazards include a risk of respiratory problems and possibly even cancer from repeated exposure to certain chemicals such as some hair dye ingredients. There is also a risk of RSIs due to continual use of the hands in awkward postures. Employees should be trained to recognize chemical and ergonomic hazards, and to work in a way that minimizes the risk. They should be supplied with proper gloves and aprons when working with dyes, bleaches, permanent-wave solutions and other chemical products. Shop areas should be properly ventilated to provide fresh air and remove fumes, especially in areas where employees are mixing solutions. Scissors and razors should be properly maintained for ease in cutting, as discussed elsewhere in this *Encyclopaedia*.

All Occupations

Sexual harassment. Housekeepers and other hotel employees may be exposed to sexual advances from guests or others. Employees should be trained about sexual harassment issues.

Management should have a clear policy on how to report and respond to such incidents.

Fires and other emergencies. Emergencies and disasters can result in loss of life and injuries to both guests and staff. Hotels should have clear emergency response plans, including designated evacuation routes, emergency procedures, an emergency communication system and methods for clearing guests out of the hotel quickly. Certain managers as well as the switchboard operators should have clear instructions on how to coordinate emergency communication with guests and staff.

Staff training and joint labor-management safety meetings are vital components of an effective emergency prevention and response programme. Training sessions and meetings should include translation for staff who need it. Training should be frequent since there is high turnover among hotel workers. Periodic emergency drills should be scheduled, incorporating "walk-throughs" of evacuation routes, staff roles and other emergency procedures.

There should also be a fire prevention programme, including regular inspections. Management and staff members should ensure that exits are not blocked, flammable materials are properly stored, kitchen hoods are regularly cleaned and electrical equipment is well maintained (without frayed wires). Fire retardant materials should be used in interior decorating projects, and there should be screens around fireplaces. Ashtrays should be properly emptied, and candles should be used only in semi-enclosed containers.

Hotel accommodations as well as all facilities attached to the hotel, such as beauty shops, restaurants and gift shops, should be in compliance with all fire codes. Guest rooms and public areas should be equipped with smoke detectors and water sprinklers. Fire extinguishers should be available throughout the hotel. Exits should be well marked and illuminated. Back-up generators should be available to provide emergency lighting and other services.

Evacuation instructions should be posted in each guest room. Many hotels now provide in-room videos with information on fire safety. Guests who are hearing impaired should have rooms equipped with alarms using bright lights to alert them to an emergency. Visually impaired guests should receive emergency procedure information in Braille.

There should be a central alarm system which can display the exact location of a suspected fire. It should also automatically communicate to local emergency services, and broadcast messages over the public address system for guests and staff.

HEALTH EFFECTS AND DISEASE PATTERNS

Leon J. Warshaw

Hotels and restaurants constitute a large, diversified, labour-intensive service industry made up predominantly of small enterprises. While there are a number of giant corporations, some of which attempt to standardize procedures and working rules, their hotels and restaurants are usually operated individually, often on a franchise rather than a directly owned basis. Frequently, the eating and drinking establishments in hotels are leased to franchise operators.

There is a high degree of failure among the enterprises in this industry, with many being very close to the edge of financial insolvency for some time before closing their doors. This often dictates economies in staffing, in the purchase and maintenance of equipment and in the provision of necessary supplies. It also often forces neglect of employee training programmes and a reluctance to spend scarce resources on measures to promote and protect employee safety and health.

The majority of the jobs are unskilled and provide low or minimal wages (in some of the jobs, these may be supplemented by gratuities that depend on the largesse of the patrons). Consequently, they attract only workers with minimal education and experience, and because minimal language and literacy skills are required, many of the jobs are filled by immigrants and ethnic minorities. Many are entry-level positions with little or no opportunities for advancement. Shift work is required in hotels because they operate around the clock; in restaurants, the flurries of activity at meal times are often covered by part-time workers. Because their patronage is seasonal, many establishments curtail their operations or shut down entirely during the off-season, and, as a result, there may be little or no job security. The end result of all of this is a high rate of turnover in the workforce.

Job Stress

Because of the periods of intense activity and the necessity of pleasing the patrons on whose gratuities their livelihoods often depend, many of the workers in this industry are subject to high levels of job stress. They must often comply with seemingly unreasonable or even impossible requests and may be subjected to abusive behaviour on the part of supervisors as well as customers. Many of the jobs, particularly those in kitchens and laundries, must be carried out in stressful environments featuring high heat and humidity, poor ventilation, poor lighting and noise (Ulfvarson, Janbell and Rosen 1976).

Violence

Hotels and restaurants rank high on the lists of workplaces with the greatest incidence of occupational violent crime. According to one survey, over 50% of such incidents involving hotel and restaurant workers resulted in death (Hales et al. 1988). These workers are exposed to many of the risk factors for workplace homicide: exchange of money with the public, working alone or in small numbers, working late night or early morning hours and guarding valuable property or possessions (Warshaw and Messite 1996).

Types of Injuries and Diseases

According to the US Bureau of Labor Statistics, food and beverage preparation and housekeeping departments accounted for 76% of all work injuries and accidents in hotels (US Bureau of Labor Statistics 1967), while a Danish survey found that these were predominantly skin and musculoskeletal problems (Direk-

toratet for Arbejdstilsynet 1993). Most of the skin problems may be traced to exposure to soap and hot water, to the chemicals in detergents and other cleaning/polishing materials and, in some instances, to pesticides. Except for the special problems noted below, the majority of musculoskeletal injuries result from slips and falls and from lifting and handling heavy and/or bulky objects.

Sprains, strains and repetitive motion injuries

Back injuries and other sprains and strains commonly occur among doormen, porters and bellmen lifting and carrying luggage (a particular problem when large tour groups arrive and depart); kitchen workers and others receiving and storing bulk supplies; and housekeeping workers lifting mattresses, making beds and handling bundles of laundry. A unique type of injury is carpal tunnel syndrome among food service workers who use scoops to prepare servings of hard ice cream and other frozen desserts.

Cuts and lacerations

Cuts and lacerations are common among restaurant workers and dishwashers who deal with broken glass and crockery, and who handle or clean sharp knives and slicing machines. They are also common among chambermaids who encounter broken glasses and discarded razor blades in cleaning out waste baskets; they may be protected by lining the baskets with plastic bags which can be removed *en masse*.

Burns and scalds

Burns and scalds are common among chefs, dishwashers and other kitchen workers and laundry workers. Grease burns occur from splatters during cooking or as food is dropped into deep-fat fryers, when hot grease is added, filtered or removed, and when grills and fryers are cleaned while hot. Many result when workers slip on wet or slippery floors and fall on or against hot grills and open flames. A unique type of burn occurs in restaurants where flaming desserts, entrees and drinks are served (Achauer, Bartlett and Allyn 1982).

Industrial chemicals

Hotel and restaurant establishments share with other small enterprises a propensity for improper storage, handling and disposal of industrial chemicals. All too frequently cleaning supplies, disinfectants, pesticides and other "household" poisons are stored in unlabelled containers, are placed above open food containers or food preparation areas or, when used in spray form, are excessively inhaled.

The fast food industry

The fast food industry, one of the most rapidly growing in the United States and becoming increasingly popular in other countries, is one of the largest employers of young people. Lacerations and burns are common hazards in these establishments. It has also been noted that the home delivery of pizzas and other prepared food is often extremely hazardous because of policies which encourage reckless driving on bicycles as well as in motor vehicles (Landrigan et al. 1992).

Preventive Measures

Standardized work processes, adequate training and proper supervision are key elements in the prevention of work-related injuries and illnesses among workers in the hotel and restaurant industry. It is essential that, because of their generally low educational levels and language difficulties, the educational materials and training exercises be readily understood (they may have to be conducted in several languages). Also, because of the high turnover, training must be repeated at frequent intervals. The training exercises should be supplemented by frequent inspections to assure that the basic principles of good housekeeping and elimination of accident hazards are observed.

Emergency drills

In addition to regular inspections to verify that firefighting equipment (e.g., smoke alarms, sprinkler systems, fire extinguishers and hoses and emergency lighting equipment) is in good working order and that emergency exits are clearly marked and not blocked, frequent drills are necessary to train the workers in how to prevent themselves and the patrons from being trapped and overcome in the event of a fire or an explosion. It is desirable to hold at least some of these drills in concert with the community fire, rescue and police organizations.

Conclusion

Apropriately designed and diligently practised preventive measures will do much to lower the frequency of occupational injuries and illnesses among hotel and restaurant workers. Language barriers and relatively low educational levels often represent formidable challenges to the effectiveness of training and indoctrination programmes, while the high rate of turnover dictates the frequent repetition of these programmes. It is important to remember that the health and safety of the workers in this industry is an essential element in the enjoyment and satisfaction of the patrons, upon whose good will the success—and even the survival—of the enterprise depends.

References

Achauer, BM, RH Bartlett, and PA Allyn. 1982. Face flambe. *JAMA.* 247:2271.

Direktoratet for Arbejdstilsynet. 1993 *Hotel og restauration* Copenhagen: Direktoratet for Arbejdstilsynet.

Hales, T, PJ Seligman, SC Newman, and CL Timbrook. 1988 Occupational injuries due to violence. *J Occup Med.* 30:483-487.

Landrigan, PJ, SH Pollack, R Belleville, and JG Godbold. 1992. Child labor in the United States: His-

torical background and current crisis. *Mount Sinai Journal of Medicine* 59:498-503.

Ulfvarson, U, H Janbell, and G Rosen. 1976. Fyskaliska och kemiska faktorer i hotell—och restauranganställdas arbetsmiljö. *Arbete och hälsa—Vetenskaplig skriftserie.* Stockholm: Arbetarskyddsverket.

US Bureau of Labor Statistics. 1967. *Work Injuries and Accident Causes in Hotels,* BLS Report No. 329. Washington, DC: US Department of Labor.

Warshaw, LJ and J Messite. 1996. Workplace violence: Preventive and interventive strategies. *Journal of Occupational and Environmental Medicine* 38:993-1006.

Other relevant readings

Kohr, RL. 1991. *Accident Prevention for Hotels, Motels and Restaurants.* New York: Van Nostrand Reinhold.

Chapter Editor
Jonathan Rosen

Contents

THE NATURE OF OFFICE AND CLERICAL WORK

Charles Levenstein, Beth Rosenberg and
Ninica Howard

Work Organization and Stress

Office and sales work are traditionally thought of as clean, easy, safe work. While life-threatening, acute injuries are rare in these fields, occupational hazards exist that diminish the quality of life and in some cases, cause serious injury and death.

Stress can be defined as a physical or psychological stimulus that produces strain or disruption of the individual's normal physiological equilibrium. Stress reactions include headaches, gastro-intestinal and sleep disturbances, high blood pressure and other cardiovascular disease, anxiety, depression and increased use of alcohol and drugs. Work in offices and retail trades is stressful both because of the structure of the industries and because of the organization of work.

The Structure of Work

Employers are increasingly using part-time and temporary workers ("temps" or contract workers). Often, this arrangement provides the desired flexibility in working hours. But there are costs. Government labour statistics show that the average part-time worker in the United States, for example, earns only 60% as much as a full-time worker on an hourly basis. Not only are they paid less, but their benefits, like health insurance, pensions, paid sick leave and vacation, are substantially less than those received by full-time workers. Fewer than 25% of part-time workers have employer-paid health insurance, compared to nearly 80% of full-time workers. Sixty per cent of full-time workers have pensions, while only 25% of part-time workers have this coverage. In 1990 in the US, there were nearly 5 million part-time workers who would have preferred to be employed full time. Other countries are also undergoing similar transformations of work.   For example, in the European Union, 15% of the workforce and roughly 20% of clerical and sales worked had part-time jobs in 1991, and 8.4% of clerical workers were temps (De Grip, Hovenberg and Willems 1997).

In addition to lower pay and few benefits, there are other negative aspects of this restructuring of work. Temps often live with the stress of not knowing when they will be working. They also tend to work more overtime because they are often hired for "crunch" periods. Neither part-time workers nor temps receive equal protection under many government laws, including occupational safety and health regulations, unemployment insurance and pension regulations. Few are represented by labour unions. A case study commissioned by the US Occupational Safety and Health Administration of contract labour in the petrochemical industry shows that contract workers get less health and safety training and have higher injury rates than non-contract workers (Murphy and Hurrell 1995). The health consequences of an increasingly non-unionized, temporary workforce should not be underestimated.

Work organization

When the well-known long-term study of heart disease, the US Framingham Heart Study, examined the relationship between employment status and the incidence of coronary heart disease, it found that 21% of women clerical workers develop coronary heart disease, a rate almost twice that of non-clerical workers or housewives. According to Karasek's demand control model of job stress, work that is characterized by high demands and low control, or decision-making latitude, is the most stressful, because of

the imbalance between responsibility and ability to respond (Karasek 1979, 1990). Occupations such as clerical work, electronics manufacturing, garment work and poultry processing are characterized by tedium, ergonomic hazards and low job control. Clerical work ranked among the most stressful in this regard.

Recognizing the social, economic and physical determinants of health effects related to occupational stressors instead of focusing solely on personal pathology is a first step in the complete and long-term management of stress-related problems. While many people may benefit from programmes that provide individual coping and relaxation exercises, workplace stress management programmes should also acknowledge the broader social and economic constraints that provide the context for the daily lives of working people.

Air Quality

Many buildings have serious indoor air pollution problems. In offices, the combination of poor ventilation design, sealed buildings and the build-up of chemicals from building materials, office machines and cigarette smoke has resulted in an office smog in many buildings. Micro-organisms (e.g., moulds, bacteria) can flourish in the air-conditioning and humidifying systems, evaporative condensers and cooling towers in many office buildings. The result may be "tight building syndrome", which can involve a wide range of symptoms depending on the situation, including allergies and respiratory infections, such as legionnaires' disease, that sometimes can reach epidemic proportions. Perhaps the most common office air pollutant is cigarette smoke, which can increase the level of respirable particles in the air to 5 times that of a non-smoking office. Since research has linked the cigarette smoking of a spouse with the increased lung cancer risk of a non-smoking spouse, non-smoking office workers may also be at risk.

Ergonomic Hazards

Ergonomic hazards in the retail trade have risen in recent years as new technologies and organizational structures have been introduced. The trend in retail has been towards self-service operations and towards larger retail outlets. The introduction of the electronic scanner has created shorter cycle times and increased repetitiveness. In addition, the work space is often not adapted to the new technology, and many work practices can lead to musculoskeletal stress.

Many studies and investigations have found a higher rate of cumulative trauma disorders in cashiers than in non-cashiers, and a dose-response relationship between the work and these disorders. These jobs usually require high levels of upper extremity activity, and, as a result, carpal tunnel syndrome, tendinitis and tenosynovitis are experienced by a large proportion of cashiers. General merchandise clerks have been shown to have moderate levels of wrist activity and high levels of ankle activity. The check stand design can greatly influence the cashier's posture and movement patterns, causing awkward positions, long reaches and frequent lifts. As a result other common areas of discomfort are the neck, shoulder, elbow and back. Prolonged standing for cashiers and clerks can also lead to back pain from the compressive forces associated with the activity. Additionally, prolonged standing may cause discomfort in the legs, knees and feet, and varicose veins. Further risk to the back comes from moving stacks which can be too heavy and/or too large.

There are many other sectors within the retail trades that experience these disorders as well as many more. For example, retail floristry and hairdressing are frequently associated with skin problems such as rashes and chronic dermatitis. The most common injuries in eating and drinking establishments are lacerations and burns. Take these factors into account along with the high turnover rate of employees and the inadequate training that can occur as a consequence, and the result is a setting that is conducive to chronic pain, discomfort and eventual cumulative trauma disorders.

Office Trades

The image of white-collar work being safe and clean is often deceptive. The dramatic change in workforce characteristics where job specialization, the repetitiveness of tasks and physical demands have all increased and available work space has decreased has led to many ergonomic injuries and illnesses. The most obvious injuries are associated with safety, such as falls on slippery floors, trips over electrical cords, collisions with open file cabinet drawers and moving heavy objects such as boxes of paper and furniture. However, with the ubiquitous use of computers in offices today, a new pattern of health problems exists. The areas of the body most frequently affected by cumulative trauma disorders are the upper limbs and neck. However, prolonged visual disply unit (VDU) use can lead to inflammation in the muscles, joints and tendons of the back and legs as well. Serious wrist disorders such as carpal tunnel syndrome, tendinitis and tenosynovitis are often associated with VDU use. These conditions can result from continuous wrist extension during keyboard use or from direct mechanical pressure on the wrist from such things as the sharp edge of the desk. Disorders of the fingers may result from the numerous, rapid fine finger movements that occur during typing. Shoulders being held in a static elevated position, resulting from too high a work surface, can possibly lead to tendinitis. As is often the case, prolonged sitting, which is characteristic of VDU use, can reduce the blood circulation and increase blood pooling in the legs and feet as the soft tissue in the legs is compressed. Lower-back pain is often a disorder associated with prolonged sitting, as the compressive forces in the spine can be elevated, especially if the chair is poorly designed. Other common health effects of VDU use are eye strain and headaches from improper lighting or VDU flicker. The computer is rarely the only piece of equipment in large offices. The noise level generated by the combination of copiers, typewriters, printers, phones and the ventilation system is often higher than the 45 to 55 dBA recommended for easy office and phone conservation and can interfere with concentration and elevate annoyance and stress levels, which have been associated with heart disease.

Environmental Hazards

The leading environmental hazards related to office and retail trades are primarily concerned with the consumer society: mall development and groundwater problems related to "green fields" development. In many suburban communities in advanced industrial nations, retail trade and office development in malls threatens the viability of both downtown urban areas and open space in the suburbs. In Asia and Africa the problems are different: along with the vast, unplanned growth of urban areas has come even sharper geographic division of social classes. But in the North and in the South, some cities have become dumping grounds for the poor and disenfranchised, as shopping centres and office complexes—and the more privileged classes—have abandoned urban areas. Neither the work of the future nor the consumption possibilities associated with it are available, and the urban environment has deteriorated accordingly. The new efforts of environmental justice organizations have sharpened the discussion of urban development, living, shopping and work.

The development of offices also presents the problem of wasteful uses of paper. Paper presents a problem of resource depletion (the cutting of forests for paper pulp) and the problem of solid waste. An international campaign against chlorine has also pointed out the chemical hazards associated with paper production. The recycling of paper, however, has captured the imagination of the environmentally conscious, and the paper and pulp industry has been induced to increase production of recycled paper products, as well as to find alternatives to the use of chlorine compounds. Electronic communication and record keeping may very well pose a long-term solution to this problem.

The enormous problem of excess packaging materials is a critical environmental concern. For example, Fresh Kills landfill, New York City's dump for residential garbage, the largest landfill in the United States, covers about 3,000 acres and receives approximately 14,000 tons of trash a day. At present, in some places, the landfill reaches 150 feet (about 50 m) deep, but is projected to go to 450 feet (about 140 m) in 10 years. This does not include commercial or industrial non-toxic waste. Much of this waste is paper and plastic, which could be recycled. In Germany, producers of goods are required to take back packaging materials. Thus, companies are strongly encouraged to reduce their own wasteful retail marketing practices.

PROFESSIONALS AND MANAGERS

Nona McQuay

The workplace, especially in industrialized countries, has become increasingly a world of white-collar workers. For example, in the United States in 1994, white-collar work was done by 57.9% of the workforce, and service occupations accounted for 13.7% of the workforce. The professional occupations have moved from the fourth to the third largest occupational group (AFL-CIO 1995). Table 99.1 lists standard professional jobs according to the International Standard Classification of Occupations (ISCO-88). White-collar membership in national unions and organizations has grown from 24% in 1973 to 45% in 1993 (AFL-CIO 1995). Professional, managerial and technical occupational employment is expected to grow faster than average.

One characteristic of professional office staff and managers is that their work function may require decision-making and responsibility for the work of others. Some managers or professional staff (for example, engineers, nurse administrators or social workers) may be located in industry and experience industrial hazards shared with the line staff. Others with managerial and executive functions work in buildings and offices remote from the industry itself. Both groups of administrative workers have risk from the hazards of office work: occupational stress, poor indoor air quality, chemical and biological agents, repetitive strain injuries (RSIs), fire safety concerns, sexual harassment and violence or assault in the workplace. See also the article "Offices: A hazard summary" in this chapter.

Demographic Changes

In a study of executive "hardiness" in the 1970s, not enough women could be found in executive positions to be included in the study (Maddi and Kobasa 1984). In the 1990s, women and minorities have had increasing representation in positions of authority, professional jobs and non-traditional jobs. However, a "glass ceiling" clusters most women in the lower levels of the organizational hierarchy: only 2% of senior management positions are held by women in the United States, for example.

As women enter traditionally male occupations, the question arises as to whether their experience in the workplace will result in an increase in coronary heart disease similar to that of men. In the past, women have been less reactive than men in stress hormone secretions when faced with the pressure to achieve. However, in studies of women in non-traditional roles (female engineering

Table 99.1 • Standard professional jobs.

Professionals	

Physicists, chemists and related professionals
  Physicists and astronomers
  Meteorologists
  Chemists
  Geologists and geophysicists
Mathematicians, statisticians and related professionals
  Mathematicians and related professionals
  Statisticians
Computing professionals
  Computer systems designers and analysts
  Computer programmers
  Other computing professionals
Architects, engineers and related professionals
  Architects, town and traffic planners
  Civil engineers
  Electrical engineers
  Electronics and telecommunications engineers
  Mechanical engineers
  Chemical engineers
  Mining engineers, metallurgists and related professionals
  Cartographers and surveyors
  Other architects and engineers
Life science and health professionals
  Biologists, zoologists and related professionals
  Pharmacologists, pathologists and related professionals
  Agronomists and related professionals
Health professionals (except nursing)
  Medical doctors
  Dentists
  Veterinarians
  Pharmacists
  Other health professionals
	Nursing and midwifery professionals
	College, university and higher education teaching professionals
	Secondary education teaching professionals
	Primary and pre-primary education teaching professionals
	Special education teaching professionals
	Other teaching professionals
	  Education methods specialists
	  School inspectors
	Business professionals
	  Accountants
	  Personnel and career professionals
	  Other business professionals
	Legal professionals
	  Lawyers
	  Judges
	  Other legal professionals
	Archivists, librarians and related information professionals
	  Archivists and curators
	  Librarians and related professionals
	Social science and related professionals
	  Economists
	  Sociologists, anthropologists and related professionals
	  Philosophers, historians and political scientists
	  Philologists, translators and interpreters
	  Psychologists
	  Social work professionals
	Writers and creative or performing artists
	  Authors, journalists and other writers
	  Sculptors, painters and related artists
	  Composers, musicians and singers
	  Choreographers and dancers
	  Film, stage and related actors and directors
	Religious professionals

Source: ILO 1990a.

students, bus drivers and lawyers) a laboratory experiment showed that women had almost as sharp an increase in epinephrine secretion as men exposed to a difficult task, considerably higher than female clerical workers in traditional roles. A study of male and female managers in 1989 showed that both sexes had a heavy workload, time pressure, deadlines and responsibility for others. Women managers reported lack of communication at work and conflict between work and family as sources of stress, whereas male managers did not. Male managers reported the highest work satisfaction. The female managers were not found to have the support of a strong work network. Studies of professional women and their spouses showed child care responsibilities to be more heavily borne by women, with men shouldering chores with less time-specific demands, such as lawn care (Frankenhaeuser, Lundberg and Chesney 1991).

Although studies do not indicate that working leads to smoking, workplace stress is associated with increased smoking rates and difficulties in smoking cessation. In 1988, a higher rate of smoking was observed among female professionals as compared to male professional workers (Biener 1988). Smoking is a behavioural style of coping with stress. For example, nurses who smoked cigarettes reported higher levels of job stress than non-smoking nurses. In the Women and Health study, salaried workers were more likely to report job strain (45%) than hourly wage workers (31%), and more difficulty unwinding after work (57%) than hourly workers (35%) (Tagliacozzo and Vaughn 1982).

International changes have caused political and social restructuring that lead to large numbers of people emigrating from their country of birth. Workplace adaptation to minority groups results in more diverse workers represented in managerial positions. Implications of these changes include human factor analyses, personnel policies and diversity education. Ergonomic changes may be needed to accommodate diverse body types and sizes. Cultures may clash; for example, values regarding high productivity or time management may vary among nations. Sensitivity to such cultural differences is taught more often today as a global economy is envisioned (Marsella 1994).

New Structures of Work Organization

An increase in the use of participative techniques for input and governance of organizations, such as joint labour-management committees and quality improvement programmes, have changed the typical hierarchical structures of some organizations. As a result, role ambiguity and new skill requirements are frequently mentioned as stressors for those in managerial positions.

If the condition of managerial and supervisory work remains challenging, then the high stress/low illness individual can be described as a "hardy executive". Such executives have been characterized as being *committed* to various parts of their lives (e.g., family, work, interpersonal relationships), as feeling a greater sense of *control* over what occurs in their lives and as regarding *challenge* in a positive mode. If stressful life events (e.g., staff reductions) can debilitate a worker, the model of hardiness provides a buffering or protective effect. For example, during periods of organizational change, efforts to maintain a feeling of control among workers could include increased clarity in work activities and job descriptions, and perceptions of the change as having possibilities, rather than as a loss (Maddi and Kobasa 1984).

Change in Workplace Technology

Work has altered so that in addition to the mental skills required of the professional, technological expertise is expected. The use of the computer, fax, telephone and video-conferencing, electronic mail, audio-visual presentations and other new technology has both changed the function of many managers and created ergonomic and other hazards associated with the machines which assist these functions. The term *techno-stress* has been coined to describe the impact of the introduction of new information technologies. In 1991 for the first time in history, US companies spent more on computing and communications hardware than on industrial, mining, farm and construction machines.

Computers affect how professional work and work processes are organized today. Such effects can include eye strain, headaches, and other VDU effects. The World Health Organization (WHO) in 1989 reported that psychological and sociological factors are at least as important as physical ergonomics in working with computers. Unintended consequences of computer use include the isolation of the computer operator, and the increase in working with computers in remote locations using high-speed modems. (See also the article "Telework" in this chapter.)

Occupational Stress

A well-known hazard is that of occupational stress, now linked to physiological outcomes, especially cardiovascular diseases. Stress is discussed extensively in several chapters in this *Encyclopaedia*.

A Swedish study of professional telecommunication engineers suggests that most studies of stress, which have usually been based on low- and medium-skill jobs, are not applicable to skilled professionals. In this study, three stress-reduction interventions were applied to the professional workforce with the following beneficial results: a feeling of being in control of one's own work (thought to protect against high mental strain work); a lessening of mental strain; a lasting effect on social interactions and support; an improvement in elevated prolactin levels; a lessening of circulating thrombocytes (which may be a factor in stroke); and an improvement in cardiovascular risk indicators (Arnetz 1996).

As the human and financial costs of occupational stress have become known, many organizations have introduced initiatives that reduce stress and improve employee health in the workplace. Such interventions can focus on the individual (relaxation techniques and employee assistance programmes); on the individual-organizational interface (person-environment fit, participation and autonomy); or on the organization (organizational structures, training, selection and placement).

Violence

Managerial and professional workers are at risk for violence and assault because of their visibility and the possibility of adverse reactions to their decisions. Most commonly, violence and assault occur where money changes hands in retail settings or where troubled clients are seen. Workplaces at greatest risk for homicide (in descending order) are taxicab establishments, liquor stores, gas stations, detective services, justice and public order establishments, grocery stores, jewellery stores, hotels/motels, and eat-

ing/drinking places. Homicide in the workplace was the leading cause of occupational death for women, and the third leading cause of death for all workers in the United States from the mid-1980s to the mid-1990s (NIOSH 1993; Stout, Jenkins and Pizatella 1989).

Travel Hazards

Approximately 30 million people travelled from industrialized countries to developing countries in 1991, many of these business travellers. One-half of the travellers were US and Canadian residents, most commonly travelling to Mexico. European travellers were 40% of the total, with the majority visiting Africa and Asia. Health risks to international travellers occur when travelling to developing countries with high endemic rates of disease for which the traveller may have low levels of protective antibodies. An example is the hepatitis A virus (HAV), which is transmitted to 3 in 1,000 for the average traveller to developing countries and which increases to 20 in 1,000 people for those who travel to rural areas and were not careful with food and hygiene. Hepatitis A is a food- and water-borne disease. A vaccine is available that was introduced in Switzerland in 1992 and is recommended by the Advisory Committee on Immunization Practices for individuals travelling to areas with a high incidence of HAV (Perry 1996). Background and references for such hazards are provided elsewhere in this *Encyclopaedia*.

Other travel hazards include motor vehicle accidents (the highest rated cause of workplace fatality in the United States), jet lag due to diurnal disturbances, extended family absences, gastrointestinal disturbances, public transport accidents, crime, terrorism or violence. Traveller advisories for specific hazards are available from disease control agencies and embassies.

Health and Safety Interventions

Measure for the improvement of professional and managerial workers' working conditions include the following:

- All managerial, supervisory and professional workers should be included in health and safety training on the worksite.
- Worksite smoking cessation programmes are appropriate as they are convenient, allow practice of cessation behaviours during working hours (when they are often most needed to cope with stressful events) and provide incentive to quit smoking.
- Stress- and time-management programmes lead to improved worker satisfaction and productivity.
- Diversity in the workplace will be commonplace in the coming century. Diversity training improves cross-cultural understanding.
- Female professional and managerial staff need workplace support for their demanding roles at home and in the workplace: family leave, support groups and increased opportunities for advancement and control over their work.
- Employee assistance programmes that are non-judgemental and confidential should be provided to all workers.
- Computer work hazards require organizational, environmental, equipment and training emphasis, as well as engineering improvements in workstation, monitor and remote worksite designs.
- Travellers need time to reorient to other time zones and countries, updated health information to protect them, time off to provide for family needs and security protections.
- All workers need engineering, work practice and protective equipment controls to protect against violent acts and assaults by others. Training in personal and office protection should deal with prevention, personal protection, and post-assault help and counselling.

OFFICES: A HAZARD SUMMARY

Wendy Hord

Office workers may perform a wide variety of tasks, including: answering the telephone; interacting with the public; handling money; receiving and delivering mail; opening mail; typing and transcribing; operating office machinery (e.g., computers, adding machines, duplicating machines and so on); filing; lifting supplies, parcels and so on; and professional work such as writing, editing, accounting, research, interviewing and the like. Table 99.2 lists standard clerical jobs.

Office workers are often thought to have pleasant, safe environments to work in. Even though office work is not as hazardous as many other workplaces, there are a variety of safety and health problems that may be present in an office. Some of these can pose significant risks to office workers.

Some Hazards and Health Problems

Slips, trips and falls are a common cause of office injuries. Poor weather conditions such as rain, snow and ice create slip hazards outside of buildings, and inside when wet floors are not cleaned up promptly. Electrical and telephone cords placed in aisles and walkways are a common cause of trips. Carpeted offices can create trip hazards when old, frayed and buckling carpet is not repaired and shoe heels catch on it. Electrical floor outlet boxes can cause trips when they are located in aisles and walkways.

Table 99.2 • Standard clerical jobs.

Clerks

Secretaries and keyboard-operating clerks
  Stenographers and typists
  Word-processor and related operators
  Data entry operators
  Calculating-machine operators
  Secretaries

Numerical clerks
  Accounting and bookkeeping clerks
  Statistical and finance clerks

Material-recording and transport clerks
  Stock clerks
  Production clerks
  Transport clerks

Library, mail and related clerks
  Library and filing clerks
  Mail carriers and sorting clerks
  Coding, proof-reading and related clerks
  Scribes and related clerks
  Other office clerks

Cashiers, tellers and related clerks
  Cashiers and ticket clerks
  Tellers and other counter clerks
  Bookmakers and croupiers
  Pawnbrokers and money-lenders
  Debt-collectors and related workers

Client information clerks
  Travel agency and related clerks
  Receptionists and information clerks
  Telephone and switchboard operators

Source: ILO 1990a.

Cuts and bruises are seen in office settings from a variety of causes. Paper cuts are common from file folders, envelopes and paper edges. Workers can be injured from walking into tables, doors or drawers that have been left open and are unseen. Office supplies and materials that are improperly stored can cause injury if they fall onto a worker or are placed where a worker would inadvertently walk into them. Cuts can also be caused by office equipment such as paper cutters and sharp edges of drawers, cabinets and tables.

Electrical hazards occur when electrical cords are placed across aisles and walkways, subjecting the cords to damage. Improper use of extension cords is often seen in offices, for example, when these cords are used in place of fixed (permanently installed) outlets, have too many items plugged into them (so that there could be an electrical overload) or are the wrong size (thin extension cords used to energize heavy-duty cords). Adapter or "cheater" plugs are used in many offices. Most often they are used to connect equipment that must be grounded (three-pronged plug) into two-pronged outlets without connecting the plug to ground. This creates an unsafe electrical connection. Ground pins are sometimes broken off a plug to allow for the same two-prong connection.

Stress is a significant psychosocial health problem for many offices. Stress is caused by many factors, including noise from overcrowding and equipment, poor relationships with supervisors and/or co-workers, increase in workload and lack of control of work.

Musculoskeletal problems and soft tissue injuries such as tendinitis result from office furniture and equipment which is not fitted to a worker's individual physical needs. Tendinitis can occur from repeated movement of certain body parts, such as finger problems from constant writing, or filing and retrieving files from cabinets that are too full. Many office workers suffer from a variety of RSIs such as carpal tunnel syndrome, thoracic outlet syndrome and ulner nerve damage because of the ill-fitting equipment and the lack of rest breaks from continuous keying (on a computer) or other repetitive activities. Poorly designed furniture and equipment also contribute to poor posture and nerve compression of lower extremities, since many office workers sit for long periods of time; all of these factors contribute to low-back and lower-extremity problems, as does constant standing.

Continual use of computers and poor overall lighting create *eye strain* for office workers. Because of this, many workers experience a worsening of vision, headaches, burning eyes and eye fatigue. Adjustments in lighting and computer screen contrast, as well as frequent breaks in eye focus, are necessary to help eliminate eye problems. Lighting must be appropriate for the task.

Fire and emergency procedures are essential in an office. Many offices lack adequate procedures for workers to exit a building in case of fire or other emergency. These procedures, or emergency plans, should be in writing and should be practised (through fire drills) so that office occupants are familiar with where to go and what to do. This insures that all workers will promptly and safely evacuate in the event of a real fire or other emergency. Fire safety is often compromised in offices by blocking of exits, lack of exit signage, storage of incompatible chemicals or combustible materials, inoperative alarm or firefighting systems or total lack of adequate means of notification of workers in emergencies.

Violence

Violence in the workplace is now being recognized as a significant workplace hazard. As discussed in the chapter *Violence*, in the United States, for example, homicide is the leading cause of death for women workers and the third-leading cause of death for all workers. Non-fatal assaults occur much more frequently than most people realize. Office workers who interact with the

Table 99.3 • Indoor air pollutants that may be found in office buildings.

Pollutant	Sources	Health effects
Ammonia	Blueprint machines, cleaning solutions	Respiratory system, eye and skin irritation
Asbestos	Insulation products, spackling compounds, fire retardants, ceiling and floor tiles	Pulmonary (lung) fibrosis, cancer
Carbon dioxide	Humans' exhaled air, combustion	Headache, nausea, dizziness
Carbon monoxide	Automobile exhaust, tobacco smoke, combustion	Headache, weakness, dizziness, nausea; long-term exposure related to heart disease
Formaldehyde	Urea-formaldehyde foam insulation and urea-formaldehyde resin used to bind laminated wood products such as particleboard and plywood; tobacco smoke	Respiratory system, eye and skin irritation, nausea, headache, fatigue, possibility of cancer
Freons	Leaking air conditioning systems	Respiratory system irritation; heart arrhythmia at high concentrations
Methyl alcohol	Spirit duplicating machines	Respiratory system and skin irritation
Micro-organisms (viruses, bacteria, fungi)	Humidifying and air conditioning systems, evaporative condensers, cooling towers, mildewed papers, old books, damp newsprint	Respiratory infections, allergic responses
Motor vehicle exhaust (carbon monoxide, nitrogen oxides, lead particulates, sulphur oxides)	Parking garages, outside traffic	Respiratory system and eye irritation, headache (see carbon monoxide), genetic damage
Nitrogen oxides	Gas heaters and stoves, combustion, motor vehicle exhaust, tobacco smoke	Respiratory system and eye irritation
Ozone	Photocopying and other electrical machines	Respiratory system and eye irritation, headache, genetic damage
Paint vapours and dusts (organics, lead, mercury)	Freshly painted surfaces, old, cracking paint	Respiratory system and eye irritation; neurological, kidney and bone-marrow damage at high levels of exposure
PCBs (polychlorinated biphenyls), dioxin, dibenzofuran	Electrical transformers, old fluorescent light ballasts	Sperm and foetal defects, skin rashes, liver and kidney damage, cancer
Pesticides	Spraying of plants and premises	Depending on chemical components: liver damage, cancer, neurological damage, skin, respiratory system and eye irritation
Radon and decay products	Building construction materials such as concrete and stone; basements	Genetic damage, cancer, foetal and sperm damage, etc., due to ionizing radiation
Solvents (methylene chloride, 1,1,1-trichloroethane, perchloroethylene, hexane, heptane, ethyl alcohol, glycol ethers, xylene, etc.)	Typewriter cleaners and correction fluids, spray adhesives, rubber cement, stamp pad inks, felt-tip markers, printing press inks and cleaners	Depending upon solvent: skin, eye and respiratory system irritation; headaches, dizziness, nausea; liver and kidney damage
Sterilant gases (such as ethylene oxide)	Systems to sterilize humidifying and air-conditioning systems	Depending on chemical components: respiratory system and eye irritation, genetic damage, cancer
Tobacco smoke (passive exposure to particulates, carbon monoxide, formaldehyde, coal tars and nicotine)	Cigarettes, pipes, cigars	Respiratory system and eye irritation; may lead to diseases associated with smokers
Volatile organic compounds (VOCs)	Photocopiers and other office machines, carpets, new plastics	Respiratory system and eye irritation, allergic reactions

Source: Stellman and Henifin 1983.

public—for example, cashiers—can be at greater risk of violence. Violence can also be internal (worker against worker). The vast majority of office workplace violence, however, comes from people coming to the office from the outside. Government office workers are much more at risk for workplace violence incidents because these workers administer laws and regulations to which many citizens have hostile reactions, be they verbal or physical. In the United States, 18% of the workforce are government workers, but they constitute 30% of the victims of workplace violence.

Offices can be made safer by restricting access to work areas, changing or creating policies and procedures which help eliminate sources of hostility and provide for emergency procedures and installing security equipment which is appropriate for the particular office being improved. Measures for improving safety are illustrated in the article describing German requirements for bank teller safety.

Indoor Air Quality

Poor indoor air quality (IAQ) is probably the most frequent safety and health complaint from office workers. The effect of poor IAQ on productivity, absenteeism and morale is substantial. The US Environmental Protection Agency (EPA) has listed poor IAQ in their top 5 public health problems of the 1990s. Many reasons exist for poor air quality. Among them are closed or sealed buildings with inadequate amounts of outside air, overcrowding of offices, inadequate maintenance of ventilation systems, presence of chemicals such as pesticides and cleaning compounds, water damage and mould growth, installation of cubicles and walls which block off air flow to work areas, too much or too little humidity and dirty work environments (or poor housekeeping).

Table 99.3 lists common indoor air pollutants found in many offices. Office machines are also a source of many indoor air pollutants. Unfortunately, most offices have not designed their ventilation systems to take into account emissions from office equipment.

The prevalence of poor IAQ has contributed to a rise in occupational asthma and other respiratory disorders, chemical sensitivity and allergies. Dry or irritated skin and eyes are also common health complaints that can be linked to poor IAQ. Action must be taken to investigate and correct problems that are causing poor IAQ according to air quality standards and recommendations.

Dermatitis (both allergic and irritant) can be caused by many of the air pollutants listed in table 99.3—for example, solvents, pesticide residues, inks, coated papers, typewriter ribbons, cleaners and so forth can cause skin problems. The best solutions for office workers are identification of the cause and substitution.

BANK TELLER SAFETY: THE SITUATION IN GERMANY

Manfred Fischer

Working in the Bank: Now Safer for the Personnel

What long-term measures can be taken to reduce the attraction of robbing a bank? The new provisions in Germany's Accident Prevention Regulation (APR) for "Teller's window" (VBG 120) significantly minimizes the risk to employees of being injured or killed in bank robberies.

A precise knowledge of the conduct of bank robbers is crucial. To this end, the Administration Trade Organization has been studying bank robberies since 1966. These studies have shown that, for example, bank robbers prefer small bank branches with few employees. Approximately one-third of bank robberies occur shortly after opening or just before closing. The goal is to leave the robbed bank as quickly as possible (after 2 or 3 minutes) and with the largest possible haul. Many bank robbers work under the wide-spread misconception that DM 100,000 and more can be taken from a teller's window. The results of these and other studies are contained in the sections "Building and equipping" and "Operations" in the "Teller's window" APR. Measures that drastically reduce the bank robbers' expectations are proposed here to protect the employee. The success of these measures depends upon the employees strictly adhering to them in daily practice.

What basic requirements are set in the "Teller's window" APR? In paragraph 7 of the "Teller's window" APR, the central requirement is laid out: "Protecting the insured requires securing the banknotes so as to considerably reduce the incentive for robbery".

What does that mean in daily practice? Easily accessible money should be kept and worked with in publicly accessible areas only within rooms separated from the public by bullet-proof or break-proof sections.

The maximum amount of accessible money allowed is given in paragraph 32: a combined maximum of DM 50,000 is allowed if there are bullet-proof tellers' windows, other break-proof safeguards and at least 6 employees present. DM 10,000 may not be exceeded when using break-proof safeguards (but not bullet-proof tellers' windows) in connection with containers equipped with time-staggered releases. There must be at least 2 employees present at all times, who must be in eye-contact.

To keep the incentive for bank robbery as low as possible, amounts of accessible money should be kept well below the maximums set in the "Teller's window" APR. In addition, paragraph 25 calls for company instructions to set the maximum allowable accessible amounts for each branch. Larger amounts necessary for business and other needs should be secured in time-lock containers to make access by bank robbers more difficult.

Tellers' windows that are not equipped with bullet-proof or break-proof safety guards and have no central money supply facility or employee-operated automatic teller machine should not have any accessible banknotes on hand.

Securing Windows and Doors

Personnel entrance and exit doors to teller areas containing cash must be secured against viewing or entering from outside, so that bank robbers cannot easily intercept employees entering and leaving bank rooms. The employee must be able to ensure, with built-in peepholes, that no danger exists.

To prevent unnoticed entrance by bank robbers into bank rooms, door closers must ensure that doors are always kept closed.

Since a considerable incentive for theft arises from viewing banknotes, windows behind which banknotes are handled must be secured against viewing or penetrating. Statistics show that holding strictly to this requirement results in very few bank robberies through windows or personnel entrances.

In contrast to personnel entrance and exit doors, doors for public traffic must have a clear view. Bank robbers can thereby be recognized early and an alarm sounded to bring assistance. Therefore it is important that the view not be obstructed by placards or the like.

Optimal Room Surveillance

In order to be able to identify the bank robber as quickly as possible, and to have effective evidence for court, optimal room surveillance equipment is prescribed in the "Teller's window" APR. This is also important for determining whether the robber extorted money or threatened employees, since particularly brutal actions increase the penalty. Good pictures reduce the incentive to rob a bank.

The instruction "Installation directions for optimal room surveillance equipment (ORSE) SP 9.7/5" of July 1993 permitted only individual cameras as standard ORSE. Photographs are superior to video shots for identification because of greater detail recognition, resulting in better evidence. The disadvantage lies in the fact that photos are available only after the camera is triggered. Because of technical advances, the Administration technical committee now also permits the use of video cameras as possible ORSE. The corresponding instruction is now being prepared; it provides that the limited resolution of video pictures should be compensated for by using 2 views. For this, at least 2 cameras must be installed for recognizing the robber and for videotaping essential events.

Appropriate installation of the video technology can continuously record, and a "wanted" photo can thus be available without special triggering. The further advantages of the system include colour shots, quicker availability of "wanted" photos, transmission of the pictures to the police even during the robbery and the ability to constantly check the functioning of the camera.

Teller's Window Security

The "Teller's window" APR authorizes:

- bullet-proof and break-proof glass enclosures and tellers' booths
- power-driven separations
- break-proof separations in connection with bullet-proof screens
- central money supply equipment
- employee-operated teller machines.

Furthermore, customer-operated teller machines support the requirements of paragraph 7, since their use can reduce the amount of money in the booth or separated room.

In order to comply with the "Teller's window" APR, the number of employees needed at the counter and the amounts to be taken in and paid out (quantity and number) must be known before a tellers' counter is built or remodeled. Optimal security can be achieved only when counter security corresponds to the actual flow of business.

Constant Presence with Eye contact

Certain teller security measures require a minimum of 2 to 6 employees having eye contact with each other. This requirement flows from the recognition that bank robbers prefer smaller branches with higher yields, where the tellers, when threatened with a gun, cannot withdraw behind bullet-proof shielding.

Break-proof teller shielding can be used only when 6 employees with eye contact are always present in the counter area. This does not mean a 6-person location, where not everyone is always at their workplace due to vacation, sickness, customer visits and so on. Experience shows that this condition can be fulfilled only when 8 to 10 employees work at the location. Alternatively, a floater service can possibly be used to ensure the necessary minimum number of employees.

To guarantee the constant presence of 2 employees with eye contact, the location must have 3 to 4 positions.

It is important that the facility not be opened before the required minimum number of employees are present. When consultations are taking place in adjoining rooms, the minimum number of employees at the windows must still be maintained.

Security through Separation

Small branches

"Small branches" are those where the presence of at least 2 employees with eye contact in the counter area is not ensured. For these branches, bullet-proof shielding in connection with break-proof separations offers good protection, since the employee does not have to leave the secured area in the event of a robbery. Consultations are carried on in an area protected by break-proof shielding. Good communication is possible here. The bullet-proof shield, behind which the accessible cash must be kept, should be placed so that employees cannot be threatened with a weapon from the customer area. Money transactions take place by way of a prescribed hatch or sliding drawer. Since the employee must go into the bullet-proof-secured area in the event of an attack, the necessary personal security is provided. This area must not be left under any circumstances, including while handing money over to the robber.

Bullet-proof full separation presents an alternative for 1- to 3-person teller operations. It offers mechanical protection against the typical bank robbery, since all employees are separated from the robber by bullet-proof shielding. The disadvantage here is that communication with customers is reduced in the interest of security. So full bullet-proof separation is appropriate only for small branches.

Larger branches

The teller's booth is a form of security in which only the teller's work station is separated from the customer area. This possibility makes sense only for teller jobs in which the teller is fully occupied by his or her work in the booth and does not have to leave it.

Before installing a booth, it is necessary to determine whether the teller is fully occupied handling money. In smaller branches with only 2 to 4 employees, this is often not the case. If the teller has other tasks outside the booth, the security requirements of the APR are not met, since the teller is supposed to always be separated from the customers for protection against bodily attack. In practice what repeatedly happens is that while the teller is performing tasks outside the booth, the door is held open with a wedge or the key is left in the lock. Thus the security of the teller's booth is compromised, which is of great interest to potential robbers.

The bullet-proof teller's booth does hinder communication between the teller and customers. But since longer discussions take place in unsecured workplaces anyway, this does not present a big problem. More serious problems include ensuring draft-free ventilation and air-conditioning in small teller's booths.

For power-driven separations, a movable steel wall, built into the counter, is raised in emergencies by way of several arranged triggers in second intervals. This creates a bullet-proof separation, with the employees behind it in a secure area. To prevent a robber from entering unnoticed, it must be activated whenever there are no employees in the vault area, or when work is being done that requires personnel to turn away from the counters. In order to avoid constant activation of the steel wall, this type of security should be used only in 2- to 4-person teller areas.

Furthermore, the tellers' workstations can be isolated with bullet-proof separations. For this, full separations for all employees as well as tellers' booths can be installed. This form of security, however, requires the constant presence of at least 6 employees with constant eye contact in the main hall.

Bullet-proof full separation and tellers' booths can also be used when a minimum of 2 employees are present with eye contact and the accessible cash does not exceed DM 10,000. A time-release money container is required in this case so that the teller does not constantly have to leave the secured area to restock. Bank robbers avoid teller positions where they can expect only a small amount of cash or have to wait a long time for it. In this case, notice of the time-release container at the entrance and in the tellers' area is important for the employees' protection. This makes immediately clear to the potential robber that the employee has no control over the container and that only a small haul can be expected.

Security without Accessible Banknotes in the Main Hall

Security is possible even without building a separation between the employees and the customer area. But for this to reduce the incentive, no accessible quantities of money can be in the tellers' area. Money taken in must be immediately secured. The money is kept in a cash box in an area not open to the public, so it cannot be threatened by the robber. The employees receive the necessary amounts of money through a tube delivery system in the main hall. Money taken in is sent to the cash box by this means. No minimum number of employees in the main hall is prescribed in this case. This type of security, however, results in longer waiting times for customers. The advantage is that bank robbers have virtually no chance of getting anything in a robbery.

Employee-operated automatic teller machines (ATMs) are a second way to make payments with cash that is not accessible in the main hall. These, referred to by the bank as AKT-designated machines, contain 4 to 6 magazines for holding banknotes in a time-released secured container. For payments, the required amount is called up using a keyboard, with which an alarm can also be sounded in emergencies. The money is delivered to the employee after a time delay. The length of the delay depends upon the amount of money and is set in paragraph 32 of the "Teller's window" APR. These are set so that good service is possible, but the robber is scared off by the longer waiting times for larger amounts. Cash receipts should be secured by use of time- or double-closing containers.

At least 2 employees with eye contact must be constantly present when using an employee-operated ATM. For this reason, this form of security is appropriate only for locations in which 3 to 4 employees work. Discussions can take place in a conference room only when 2 or more employees are present in the customer area during the discussion.

In the case of a technical problem in an employee-operated ATM, appropriate instructions and measures should be prepared. These should include an emergency cash box and corresponding organizational procedures to ensure that work proceeds in accordance with the "Teller's window" APR.

Company Directives and Instructions

The employer must prepare company directives for every teller's window and regularly check on compliance. These directives should outline the possible events during a robbery and describe what to do during and after the robbery. Furthermore, daily instructions should be given, and use of the installed security equipment should be mandated. This is especially true when larger amounts of accessible banknotes are present. Instructions should also prescribe the manner of safekeeping for other valuable objects. Employees at the windows should be instructed in these company policies at least twice a year.

The purpose of these instructions is clear—to ensure that the employees follow the requirements of the "Teller's window" APR for their own protection, and to significantly reduce the incentive for robbing a teller's window.

● TELEWORK

Jamie Tessler

Telework—or working out of one's home—is a growing trend in businesses internationally. This article discusses the occupational health and safety hazards of telework (from the Greek *tele*, meaning "far off"). The employer's responsibility to provide safe and healthy working conditions to such employees will vary depending on the contract or understanding that exists between each teleworker and employer and on the applicable labour laws.

While telework is most widespread in the United States, where it involves over 8 million workers and accounts for 6.5% of the workforce, other countries also have significant numbers of teleworkers. There are more than 560,000 in the United Kingdom, 150,000 in Germany and 100,000 in Spain. There are over 32,000 in Ireland, which amount to 3.8% of the workforce (ILO 1997).

The growing trend toward telework arrangements can be explained by the following factors:

- business efforts to reduce the time, expense and environmental impact of commuting
- legislative efforts to reduce traffic-induced air pollution trends
- changes in technology, computerization and electronic communication that enable businesses to employ workers in disparate geographic locations

- costs of maintaining large office spaces needed to accommodate large numbers of employees
- accommodation of workers who prefer telework due to physical disability, parenting needs or other family responsibilities or other reasons
- a strategy to reduce absenteeism
- recognition that workers have varying internal cycles of productivity and creativity.

Increased productivity is another factor, as a number of studies have demonstrated that telework can result in large productivity gains (ILO 1990b).

Telework may be contracted in several ways:

- The employee works full time (or part time) at home for their employer and is entitled to all of the same benefits provided by that employer to all onsite workers.
- The employee works full time for the employer but only works out of the home during a specified number of days per week or month.
- The worker is defined as an independent contractor and does not receive benefits or equipment provided by the employer.

Health and Safety Hazards of Telework

The health and safety hazards of telework can include all of the same hazards found in conventional office environments, with several additional concerns.

Indoor air quality

Most homes are not equipped with mechanical ventilation systems. Instead, air exchanges in the home rely on natural ventilation. The effectiveness of this can depend on such factors as the type of insulation of the building and so on. Provision of a fresh supply of outside air cannot be guaranteed. If the natural ventilation is inadequate to remove sources of indoor air pollutants in the home work environment, then additional ventilation may be necessary.

Indoor air pollutants in the home environment may include the following:

- natural gas or carbon monoxide exposure from inefficient heating systems or leaky stoves
- vapours and gases from photocopiers, printers or other office machines
- ongoing passive exposure to chemicals, gases or dusts resulting from renovation or construction in the worker's home
- exposure to the effluents of other activities if housed in a multi-use building (such as an apartment building with a nail salon, dry cleaner or fast food restaurant on the ground floor).
- exposure to radon hazards if office is located in the basement in parts of the world where radon arises from construction materials or the earth.

Fire hazards

Home electrical wiring is rarely designed to accommodate the needs of the electrical equipment typically used in telework, such as printers, copiers and other office machines. Installing such equipment without assessing the wiring limits of the dwelling could create a fire hazard. Local building codes may prohibit the adjustments necessary to accommodate increased equipment needs.

Teleworkers who rent their apartments may live in multi-unit dwellings with inadequate fire evacuation plans, blocked means of egress to fire exits or locked exit doors.

Ergonomics hazards

Home work environments often rely on the employee's personal furnishings such as chairs, tables, shelves and other items to perform required tasks. Computer workstations in the home environment may not allow for the adjustments necessary for computer-intensive work. A shortage of adequate surface area, shelf space or storage areas may result in excessive bending, awkward postures, excessive reaching and other risk factors for cumulative trauma disorders (CTDs). Working in cold or unevenly heated environments can also contribute to musculoskeletal injuries.

Lighting

Inadequate lighting may result in awkward body postures, eye strain and visual disturbances. Task lighting may be necessary for work surfaces or document holders. Wall and furniture surfaces should be neutral with a non-glare finish. While this glare-reducing strategy is increasingly utilized in office environments, it is not yet a standard of home decoration and design.

Occupational stress

Full-time employment in the home environment deprives the worker of the interpersonal and professional benefits of continuous interaction with co-workers, colleagues and mentors. The isolation created by telework can prevent the worker from engaging in professional development activities, taking advantage of promotional opportunities and contributing ideas to the organization. Gregarious workers in particular may depend on human contact and suffer personally and professionally without it. The lack of administrative support services for employees who require clerical assistance presents an additional burden to teleworkers. The employer should make an effort to incorporate the teleworker into staff meetings and other group activities, either in person or electronically (tele-conferencing) as per physical and geographical limitations.

Employees with children, disabled family members or ageing parents may perceive distinct advantages of working at home. But attending to the needs of dependent family members can affect the concentration needed to focus on job responsibilities. The ensuing stress can negatively impact on the worker who is unable to perform to capacity in the home and fails to meet employer expectations. Telework should not be considered as a substitute for child or elder care. Since workers vary tremendously in their capacity to balance work and other responsibilities in the home environment, the need for support services must be evaluated on a case-by-case basis to prevent excessive occupational stress and subsequent loss in productivity. No worker should be required to adopt a telework arrangement against his or her will.

Injury and Illness Compensation

Occupational illnesses often occur over long periods of time from cumulative exposures. Prevention of these illnesses depends on rapid identification of risk factors, fixing the problem using a variety of methods and medical management of the affected worker when the first signs or symptoms of illness appear.

To date, employer responsibility for accidents and injuries in the home environment have been debated on a case-by-case basis. Most national occupational health and safety standards do not include formal policies addressing the safety of teleworkers. The serious impact of this trend must be carefully evaluated and addressed via international standard-setting.

When telework arrangements shift the employee's status to that of an independent contractor, the burden of many responsibilities shift to the employee as well. Once the work is performed in the home by an independent contractor, the employer no longer feels obligated to provide a healthy and safe workplace, access to preventive and curative medical care for the worker and his or her family, social security, disability insurance and compensation for injured workers who need to recuperate. This trend eliminates worker benefits and protections that were won after decades of struggle and negotiation.

Protection for the Teleworker

The contract between the teleworker and the employer must address the overall work environment, safety and health standards, training and equipment. Employers should inspect the home workspace (at agreed-upon times) to ensure worker safety and to identify and correct risk factors that could contribute to illness or injury. The inspection should evaluate indoor air, ergonomics, trip hazards, lighting, chemical exposure and other concerns. Clear policy must be established regarding the provision of office supplies required for job tasks. Liability issues must be clearly defined regarding employer (and worker) assets that are lost or damaged due to fire, natural disaster or theft. Employees must be exempt from financial liability unless found to be negligent.

In addition, telework arrangements should be evaluated on a regular basis in order to identify workers who discover that working at home does not *work* for them.

Summary

The advantages of telework are extensive, and beneficial telework arrangements should be encouraged for job tasks and mature workers who will have much to gain by working at home. Telework has enabled disabled workers to achieve greater independence and seek professional opportunities not previously offered or available. In return, employers are able to retain valuable workers. However, the telework arrangement must ensure continuation of employee benefits and occupational health and safety protections.

THE RETAIL INDUSTRY

Adrienne Markowitz

The retail trade is the selling of goods to consumers. Enterprises sell everything from automobiles to clothing, from food to television sets. In many countries what once was an industry comprised mainly of small shops and stores, now largely consists of multinational conglomerates which own huge megastores competing for the global market. Competition and technological changes have changed job descriptions, the hazards associated with those jobs and the nature of the workforce itself.

In the developed nations, small retailers struggle to compete with large corporate retailers. In the United States, Canada and throughout the European Community and the Pacific Rim, the retail trade has moved from the city centre to suburban shopping malls. Instead of the neighbourhood "mom and pop" stores, multinational chain stores sell the same products and the same brand names, effectively limiting consumer choice of product and forcing competition out of the market by their buying power, advertising capabilities and lower prices. Many times a large store will take a loss on certain products in order to bring customers into a store; this technique frequently generates other sales.

In developing countries with predominantly agrarian economies, bartering systems and open marketplaces are still common. However, in many developing countries, the large multinational retailers are beginning to enter the retail market.

Each type of establishment has its own hazards. Retail work in developing countries and countries in transition is often very different from retail work in developed countries; conglomerates with large chain stores are not yet dominant and retail work is mainly conducted in an open-air market, in all types of weather.

Outdoor markets

The informal sector accounts for between 20 and 70% of the urban workforce in developing countries (with the average being 40%); and the traders and hawkers of outdoor markets comprise a significant portion of this sector. Such work is by its very nature precarious. It involves long hours and low pay. Average earnings may not total 40% of levels found in the formal sector. Not only do many workers in outdoor markets lack permanent locations to conduct their business, they also may be compelled to do without supporting infrastructural facilities. They do not enjoy the same legal protection or social insurance as workers in the formal sector and are subject to harassment. Occupationally related morbidity and mortality rates generally go unrecorded (Bequele 1985).

Workers in outdoor markets in both developing and developed countries, such as those shown in figures 99.1 and 99.2, are exposed to numerous health and safety hazards. They are exposed to exhaust from motor vehicles, which contains such things as carbon monoxide and polycyclic aromatic hydrocarbons. Workers are also exposed to the weather. In tropical and desert locations they are subject to heat stress and dehydration. In cooler climates they are exposed to freezing temperatures, which can cause problems such as numbness, shivering and frostbite. Workers in outdoor markets may not have access to adequate hygiene facilities.

The informal sector generally and outdoor markets specifically involve child labour. Roughly 250 million children are engaged in full- and part-time work around the world (ILO 1996); street traders are the most visible child workers. Children who work, including street traders, typically are denied education and often are forced to perform tasks, such as lifting heavy loads, which can result in permanent disabilities.

John G. Rodwan, Jr.

Figure 99.1 • Outdoor food market in Malatia, Solomon Islands, 1995.

C. Geefhuyson

Figure 99.2 • Heavy baskets of sea urchins being distributed by a small operator-owner, Japan, 1989.

L. Manderson

There is a trend among multinational conglomerates to try and change employment conditions: trade unionism is discouraged, staff is reduced to a bare minimum, wages go down, stores predominantly hire part-time workers, the average age of the workforce is lowered and benefit packages diminish.

Throughout the world store opening hours have changed so that some establishments even remain open 24 hours a day, 7 days per week. In the past, a worker who worked late at night or on a holiday received extra compensation; now, premium pay for working those hours has been taken away as such long hours become the norm. In the US, for example, traditional holidays are now negotiable when the store stays open on a 24-hour, 7-day basis.

The changes in the nature of how business is conducted has forced several fundamental changes in the workforce. Since many jobs have been marginalized to part-time work, the jobs themselves require little skill and workers receive no training. Workers who once saw a career in retail work, now find themselves changing jobs frequently or even leaving the field of retail work, which has become short term and part time.

The size of the workforce in the retail industry is difficult to estimate. The informal sector plays a significant role in developing countries (see accompanying box). Many times, health and safety problems go unnoticed, are not recorded by government and are considered to be part of the job.

In many of the countries that do keep statistics, retail, wholesale and restaurant and hotel workers are grouped into one category. Statistics from around the world show that the percentage of people who work in the wholesale, retail, restaurant and hotel trades ranges from over 20% in some countries in Asia to less

Table 99.4 • Labour statistics in the retail industry (selected countries).

Country	Men in the labour force (%)	Men in wholesale and retail trade; restaurants and hotels (%)	Women in the labour force (%)	Women in wholesale and retail trade; restaurants and hotels (%)	Total population in wholesale and retail trade; restaurants and hotels (%)	Total number of people injured	Injured people in the retail industry (%)
Burkina Faso	51.3	1.0	48.7	1.5	2.6	1,858	8.7[1]
Costa Rica	69.9	11.0	30.1	7.4	18.4	156,782	7.0[2]
Egypt	75.9	7.3	24.1	1.2	8.4	60,859	2.5[2]
Germany	52.3	4.5	47.7	7.0	11.5	29,847	20.1[3]
Greece	63.0	10.9	37.0	7.0	17.0	23,959	10.5[4]
Italy	63.1	11.7	36.9	6.9	8.6	767,070	8.1[5]
Japan	59.5	11.0	40.5	10.9	21.9	2,245	9.7
Mexico	69.1	10.8	30.9	9.6	20.5	456,843	16.9[6]
Netherlands	58.9	9.1	41.1	8.0	17.1	64,657	16.5
Norway	54.5	7.9	45.5	8.9	16.7	26,473	5.0
Singapore	59.8	13.2	40.2	9.0	22.0	4,019	0.2[7]
Sweden	52.0	6.8	48.0	6.5	13.3	43,459	6.6
Thailand	55.5	5.8	49.5	6.8	12.6	103,296	3.1[8]
United Kingdom	56.2	8.3	43.8	9.5	17.8	157,947	11.0[9]
United States	54	11.1	46.0	10.0	21	295,340	23.6[10]

[1] Including commuting accidents; including occupational diseases.
[2] Including commuting accidents; establishments employing 100 or more workers.
[3] The series related to the territory of the Federal Republic of Germany before 1990; including commuting accidents.
[4] Including occupational diseases; including non-fatal cases without lost workdays.
[5] Including commuting accidents; persons losing more than three workdays per period of disability.
[6] Including non-fatal cases without lost workdays.
[7] Including commuting accidents; including occupational diseases; including non-fatal cases without lost workdays.
[8] Including commuting accidents.
[9] Employees only; excluding traffic accidents; year beginning April, 1993.
[10] Including occupational diseases.

Sources: Country reports: Costa Rica 1994; Greece 1992, 1994; Mexico 1992, 1996; Singapore 1994, 1995; Thailand 1994, 1995; Euro-FIET Commerce Trade Section 1996; ILO 1994, 1995; Price Waterhouse 1991.

than 3% in Burkina Faso (see table 99.4). Although men outnumber women in the labour force, the percentage of women in the retail industry is higher in at least half of the countries for which statistics are available.

Operations, Hazards and Prevention

Cashiers

Many cashiers work at mechanized registers that require them to punch a keypad thousands of times per day to ring up the price of the article. The key punching is usually done with the right hand while products are moved from in front of the cashier to the rear of the cashier for packaging with the left hand. These work activities frequently involve poorly designed workstations, causing cashiers to lift heavy products, reach extensively for products and frequently twist the body in order to move products from one area to another. This job function places different burdens on each side of the body, causing lower-back pain, upper-extremity illnesses and repetitive-motion illnesses including tendinitis, carpal tunnel syndrome, tenosynovitis, thoracic outlet syndrome and hip, leg and foot problems.

Well-designed workstations, with automatic scanners, flexible work height conveyors, lowered bagging stations, extra personnel to bag the products and flexible seats (so that cashiers can sit to relieve lower-back and leg pressures) help eliminate upper-extremity pressures, strains and twisting motions.

Lasers

Bar-code readers and hand-held scanners in supermarkets are generally Class 2 lasers, which produce infrared radiation in the wavelength range of 760 to 1,400 nm; they are considered non-hazardous unless there is prolonged viewing of the laser beam. A laser produces a high-intensity light which can damage the retina of the eye. The eyes are vulnerable to heat, have no heat sensors and do not dissipate heat efficiently. Recommended safe practices should include, at a minimum, training workers about the hazards of looking into the beam of light and the damage to the eye that can result. Baseline eye examinations should be included in a worker protection programme to ensure that no damage has occurred.

Clerks

Retail clerks move large quantities of product from trucks to the loading dock and then to the shelves in the sales area of the store. Products come packaged in cartons of various weights. Manually unloading trucks and moving the product cartons to the front of the store may cause musculoskeletal problems. Pricing the items and placing them on the shelves puts tremendous pressure on the back, legs and neck. Using a pricing gun can cause carpal tunnel syndrome and other RSIs by putting excessive and repeated strain on the wrist, fingers and palm of the hand. Opening cartons with a knife or blade can lead to cuts on the hands, arms and other parts of the body. Cutting through cardboard with a dull knife requires extra pressure, which puts extra strain on the palms of the hands.

Mechanical lifting aids, such as fork-lift trucks, manual high-low trucks, dollies and carts help move items from one part of the store to another. Tables, scissor jacks and movable carts can help bring the items to a good height and help clerks place product on the shelves without back strain from lifting and twisting. Automated pricing guns or packaged goods already labelled will prevent wrist and upper extremity strains from repeated motions. Sharp knives will prevent forceful motions when opening cartons.

Meat cutters and delicatessen workers

Meat cutters and delicatessen workers work with saws, grinders, slicers and knives (see figure 99.3). When machine blades are not guarded, get jammed or become loose, fingers can be severed, cut, crushed or bruised. Machines must be securely anchored to the floor to prevent tipping and moving. Blades must be kept free of debris. If a machine is jammed, wooden devices should be used to unjam the machine with the power off. No machines should be unjammed with the power still on. Knives should be kept sharp to avoid problems in the wrists, hands and arms. The handles of knives, cleavers and clubs should be kept clean and unslippery.

When meat is mechanically weighed and packaged on a styrofoam tray in a plastic film sealed with a heating element, vapours and gases from the heated plastic may cause "meat wrapper's asthma" and eye, nose and throat irritation, difficulty in breathing, chest pains, chills and fever. Local exhaust ventilation (LEV) should be placed near the heating element so that these vapours are not breathed in by workers, but are vented outside the workplace.

Meat cutters enter and leave freezers many times during the day. Work clothing should include heavy clothing for freezer work.

Floors and walkways can become slippery from meat, grease and water. Slips, trips and falls are common causes of injury. All waste material must be carefully discarded and kept off walking surfaces. Walking and standing mats must be cleaned daily or whenever they become soiled.

Chemical exposures

Retail workers are increasingly exposed to hazardous chemicals in cleaning products, pesticides, rodenticides, fungicides and preservatives. Hardware store workers, automotive distributive workers and others are potentially exposed to hazardous chemicals because of the stock of paints, solvents, acids, caustics and compressed gases. The hazardous or toxic chemicals vary depending on the nature of the products that are stocked in each establishment. These can include materials not necessarily considered hazardous. Department store workers, for example, can develop sensitivities and allergies to perfumes that are sprayed as demonstrations.

Cleaning products that are used to clean surfaces in supermarkets and other retail establishments may contain chlorine, ammonia, alcohols, caustics and organic solvents. These products may be used by cleaning crews during the night shift, in stores without natural ventilation and when the mechanical ventilation system is not working at full capacity. These chemical products affect the body when used in the workplace in industrial strengths and amounts. Chemical safety information must be readily available in the workplace for workers to read. Chemical containers must be labelled with the name of the chemical and how the product affects the body, as well as which protective equipment must be used to prevent illness. Workers need to be trained about the health hazards associated with the use of chemicals, how the chemicals enter the body and how to avoid exposure.

Figure 99.3 • Small-scale manual cutting of dried meat for local sale, Japan, 1989.

L. Manderson.

Retail workers who set up shop on the street are exposed to exhaust from motor vehicle traffic, as are the back-of-the-store workers who inhale exhaust from idling delivery trucks in the truck bays. The incomplete combustion products in motor vehicle exhaust include, among other things, carbon monoxide and polycyclic aromatic hydrocarbons. Exhaust gases and particulates affect the body is several ways. Carbon monoxide causes dizziness and nausea and acts as an asphyxiant, limiting the blood's ability to use oxygen. Delivery trucks should turn off their engines while unloading. Mechanical general exhaust ventilation may be needed to vent the contaminated air away from workers. Routine scheduled maintenance and cleaning is needed to maintain the ventilation system.

Formaldehyde is frequently used on clothing and other textiles to prevent mildew. It can affect those who breathe it in. In stores with larger stocks of clothing and textiles without adequate natural or mechanical ventilation systems, formaldehyde gas can build up and irritate the eyes, nose and throat. Formaldehyde can cause skin and respiratory irritation and allergies and is considered a probable carcinogen.

Pesticides, rodenticides and fungicides are frequently used to keep vermin out of establishments. They can affect the nervous, respiratory and circulatory systems of human beings as well as insects, rodents and plants. It is important not to spray chemicals indiscriminately when people are present and to keep people away from sprayed areas until it is safe to enter them again. The pesticide applicator must be trained in safe work methods before pesticides are applied.

"Tight" buildings—those without windows that can open and without natural ventilation—are dependent on mechanical ventilation systems. These systems must provide an adequate exchange of air within the space and must include adequate fresh outdoor air. The air must be heated or cooled depending on the ambient temperature outside.

Sanitation

Personal hygiene is important in the retail industry, especially when employees handle food, money and hazardous chemicals. Toilets and washing and drinking facilities must be sanitary and available in areas where employees can use them while on duty. Facilities must have clean running water, soap and towels. Employees must be encouraged to wash their hands thoroughly after using the toilet and before returning to work. Clean, cool drinking water should be available throughout the work area. Good housekeeping is necessary to prevent vermin and accumulation of garbage. Trash should be picked up on a regular basis.

Sanitation facilities are difficult to maintain in open-air markets, but an attempt must be made to provide toilets and washing facilities.

Weather

In open-air markets, retail workers are exposed to the elements and subject to the problems relating to heat and cold. In supermarkets, cashiers often work at the front of the store close to the doors that the public uses to enter and exit, exposing cashiers to hot and cold air drafts. Air shields in front of the doors that go to the outside will help block drafts and keep the air temperature at the cash register consistent with the rest of the store.

Fire prevention

There are many fire hazards in retail stores, including locked or blocked exits, limited entry and exits, combustible and flammable materials and faulty or temporary electrical wiring and heating systems. If workers are required to fight a fire, they must be trained in how to call for help, use fire extinguishers and evacuate the space. Fire extinguishers must be of the appropriate type for the type of fire and must be inspected regularly and maintained. Fire drills are necessary so that workers know how to get out of the facility during an emergency.

Stress

A new trend in retail work, when the establishment is owned by a large conglomerate, is to change full-time work to part-time work. Many large retail stores are now staying open 24 hours per day, and many stay open every day of the year, forcing workers to work "unsocial" hours. Disruption of the internal biological clock which controls natural physical phenomena such as sleep, causes symptoms such as sleepiness, gastro-intestinal disturbances, headaches and depression. Changing shifts, working on holidays and part-time work cause emotional and physical stress on the job and at home. "Normal" family life is severely compromised and meaningful social life is restricted.

Late night hours are more and more prevalent, increasing the feeling of insecurity about personal safety and the fear of robberies and other types of violence on the job. In the United States, for example, homicide is a major cause of death on the job for women, with many of these deaths occurring during robberies. Handling money or working alone or during late night hours should be avoided. A regular review of security measures should be part of a violence prevention and security programme.

Part-time pay, with few or no benefits, increases job stress and forces many workers to find additional jobs in order to support their families and maintain health benefits.

References

American Federation of Labour and Congress of Industrial Organizations (AFL-CIO). 1995. *Current Statistics on White Collar Employees.* Publication #95-3. Washington, DC: AFL-CIO, Department for Professional Employees.

Arnetz, BB. 1996. Techno-stress: A prospective psycho-physiological study of the impact of a controlled stress reduction program in advanced telecommunications system design work. *Journal of Occupational and Environmental Medicine* 38(1):53-65.

Bequele, A. 1985. Workers in the rural and urban informal sectors in developing countries. In *Introduction to Working Conditions and Environment*, edited by J-M Clerc. Geneva: ILO.

Biener, L. 1988. *Gender and Stress.* New York: Free Press.

De Grip, A, J Hoevenberg, and E Willems. 1997. Atypical employment in the European Union. *Int Labour Rev* 136(1):49–71.

Euro-FIET Commerce Trade Section. 1996. Conference on Economic Transformation and Internationalisation in the Services and Finance Sectors of Central and Eastern Europe, April, Prague, Czech Republic.

Frankenhaeuser, M, U Lundberg, and M. Chesney. 1991. *Women, Work, and Health: Stress and Opportunities.* New York and London: Plenum Press.

Hetes, R, M Moore, and C Northheim. 1995. *Office Equipment: Design, Indoor Air Emissions, and Pollution Prevention Opportunities.* Washington, DC: US Environmental Protection Agency.

International Labour Organization (ILO). 1990a. *International Standard Classification of Occupations: ISCO-88.* Geneva: ILO.

—. 1990b. *Telework. Conditions of Work Digest.* Vol. 9(1). Geneva: ILO.

—. 1994. *Yearbook of Labour Statistics.* Geneva: ILO.

—. 1995. *Yearbook of Labour Statistics.* Geneva: ILO.

—. 1996. *Child Labour: Targeting the Intolerable.* Report VI(1), International Labour Conference, 86th Session. Geneva: ILO.

—. 1997. Working trends: Labour trends. *World Work Mag ILO* 19:26-27.

Karasek, RA. 1979. Job demands, job decision latitude, and mental strain: Implications for job design. *Adm Sci Q* 24:285–308.

—. 1990. Lower health risk with increased job control among white collar workers. *J Organ Behav* 11:171–185.

Maddi, SR and Kobasa, SC. 1984. *The Hardy Executive: Health Under Stress.* Homewood, IL: Dow Jones-Irwin.

Marsella, AJ. 1994. Work and well-being in an ethnoculturally pluralistic society: Conceptual and methodological issues. In *Job Stress in a Changing Workforce.* Washington, DC: American Psychological Association.

Murphy, L and J Hurrell, Jr. 1995. Job stress interventions. In *Managing Workplace Safety and Health: The Case of Contract Labor in the U.S. Petrochemical Industry.* Washington, DC: American Psychological Association.

National Institute for Occupational Safety and Health (NIOSH). 1993. *NIOSH Update: NIOSH Urges Immediate Action to Prevent Workplace Homicide.* DHHS (NIOSH) Publication No. 94-101. Cincinatti, OH: NIOSH.

Perry, GF. 1996. Occupational medicine forum. *Journal of Occupational and Environmental Medicine* 38(4):339-341.

Price Waterhouse. 1991. *Doing Business in Sweden.* New York: Price Waterhouse.

Silvestri, G. 1993. The American workforce, 1992-2005: Occupational employment: Wide variations in growth. *Monthly Labor Review* (November).

Stellman, JM and MS Henifin. 1983. *Office Work Can Be Dangerous to Your Health.* New York: Pantheon Books.

Stout, N, EL Jenkins, and TJ Pizatella. 1996. Occupational injury mortality rates in the United States: Changes from 1980 to 1989. *Am J Public Health* 86(1):73-77.

Tagliacozzo, R and S Vaughn. 1982. Stress and smoking in hospital nurses. *Am J Public Health.* 72:441-448.

Other relevant readings

Amott, T. 1993. *Caught in the Crisis: Women and the U.S. Economy Today.* New York: Monthly Review Press.

Bachman, R. 1994. Violence and theft in the workplace. In *US Department of Justice Crime Data Brief.* NCJ-148199. Washington, DC: US Department of Justice.

Bair, FE. 1988. *International Marketing Handbook,* 3rd edition. Detroit, MI: Gale Research.

Blascovich, J and E Katkin. 1995. *Cardiovascular Reactivity to Psychological Stress and Disease.* Washington, DC: American Psychological Association.

Greenbaum, J. 1995. *Windows on the Workplace: Computers, Jobs and the Future of Office Work in the Late Twentieth Century.* New York: Monthly Review Press.

Huws, U (ed.). 1995. *Action Programmes for the Protection of Homeworkers: Ten Case-studies from around the World.* Geneva: ILO.

Huws, U and S Pordo. 1995. *Employment of Homeworkers: Examples of Good Practice.* Working Paper CONDI/T/WP.5/1995. Geneva: ILO.

International Confederation of Free Trade Unions (ICFTU). 1996. *The Global Market—Trade Unionism's Greatest Challenge.* Brussels: ICFTU.

International Federation of Commercial, Clerical, Professional and Technical Employees (FIET). 1993. *World Action Programme.* Geneva: International Federation of Commercial, Clerical, Professional and Technical Employees.

International Labour Organization (ILO). 1992. *Preventing Stress at Work. Conditions of Work Digest.* Vol 11. Geneva: ILO.

Makower, J. 1981. *Office Hazards.* Washington, DC: Tilden Press.

National Institute for Occupational Safety and Health (NIOSH). 1996. *NIOSH Current Intelligence Bulletin 57: Violence in the Workplace, Risk Factors and Prevention Strategies.* DHSS (NIOSH) Publication No. 96-100. Cincinatti, OH: NIOSH.

Rosenstock, L. 1986. *Clinical Occupational Medicine.* Philadelphia, PA: WB Saunders.

PERSONAL AND COMMUNITY SERVICES

100

Chapter Editor
Angela Babin

Contents

● INDOOR CLEANING SERVICES

Karen Messing

General Profile

Cleaning consists of dusting, washing and polishing surfaces; washing walls; mopping, sweeping and polishing floors; as well as disposing of waste and waste water. It is done in offices, public and commercial buildings, homes and factories. It may be done in confined spaces with little ventilation and in spaces not designed with cleaning in mind. Cleaners may be independent or be employed by the enterprise which owns the facilities being cleaned, or they may work for private contractors. Those who clean may be called cleaners, housekeepers, chars, custodians or janitors, depending on the spaces cleaned and the details of the assigned tasks. For example, janitors and custodians may combine cleaning with maintenance and repair work.

Cleaners have usually worked relatively autonomously, compared to other employment categories of similar prestige. Inspection is done by supervisors, although the users of the cleaned spaces also comment on the cleaners' work. Workers tend to order the tasks themselves and develop their own procedures (Messing, Haëntjens and Doniol-Shaw 1993). However, in commercial spaces in North America, cleaners' routes have increasingly been determined using software programmed to take account of furniture, floor surfaces and crowding. The desired frequency of operations, area to be cleaned and time estimated for the type of area are used to calculate the total time required. Inspection may be done using a computer-programmed spot check procedure. Some of these procedures may severely underestimate the task as performed in shared space, especially if the inventory is not brought regularly up to date (Messing, Chatigny and Courville 1996).

In Canada, cleaning is the eighth most common profession of men and the tenth most common profession of women; women make up 46% of the profession (Armstrong and Armstrong 1994). In France in 1991, 229,000 cleaners worked for 9,000 cleaning companies; about a third were immigrants and 64% were women (Bretin 1994). In Denmark 85% of the 130,000 cleaners are women (Nielsen 1995). In some countries, tasks in factories and services have often been divided into "light" and "heavy", assigned formally or informally to female and male workers respectively, who may be paid at different rates (Government of Quebec 1994). Women may dust and polish surfaces, clean bathrooms and empty wastebaskets while men sweep, mop and polish floors

and carry waste to incinerators (Messing, Haëntjens and Doniol-Shaw 1993; Messing, Doniol-Shaw and Haëntjens 1993; Messing, Chatigny and Courville 1996). In other countries, men and women can be assigned to all cleaning tasks (Nielsen 1995; Hagner and Hagberg 1989). Cleaners are often relatively old compared to other workers (Bretin et al. 1992; Messing 1991; Nielsen 1995).

Risk Factors and Prevention Strategies

Cleaning may be done with hand-held tools such as brushes, brooms, rags and mops, or may be aided by machines. A variety of chemicals are used to dissolve dirt and to make surfaces appear clean and shiny. The difficulty of the task varies according to the type of surface (rough, smooth, pitted), the height and geometry of the objects cleaned, the degree of crowding of spaces and the vocations exercised in the spaces cleaned. In some places, the need for cleaning may be reduced or eliminated by design changes in the object cleaned (such as self-flushing toilets).

Musculoskeletal load

Cleaning, particularly cleaning furniture and bathrooms and emptying wastebaskets, involves rapid postural changes and many awkward and constrained postures (see table 100.1). Many objects must be cleaned, at a variety of heights; a typical sequence observed for dusting in a hospital room was: table (81 cm), television (196 cm), table (81 cm), telephone (81 cm), lamp (extends to 188 cm), table foot (11 cm), chair (46 cm), screen (81 cm), armchair (46 cm), window ledge (89 cm), wall sphygmomanometer (154 cm), chair legs (floor to 46 cm), oxygen fixture (137 cm) (Messing, Chatigny and Courville 1995).

Floor cleaning requires repeated movements (fundamental cycle time of 1 to 2 seconds in the Sogaard, Fallentin and Nielsen (1996) study) and a sustained moderate bending of the back. Constant pressure is exerted by the hands to push vacuum cleaners or buffers, tasks requiring forces near 10 kg (Messing, Chatigny and Courville 1996). Sogaard, Fallentin and Nielsen (1996) found mean back bending during floor mopping to be 28° and mean neck bending to be 51°. Hagner and Hagberg (1989) also noted static muscular loads especially at the shoulder joint. Nordin et al. (1986) found extensive forward trunk bending in a simulated janitorial task involving floor mopping. Cleaning floors and objects is usually done with repeated movements. Sogaard (1994) suggests that the sustained repetitive motions with infrequent pauses in activity may exhaust the relatively small numbers of muscle fibres involved and result in muscular disorders.

Table 100.1 • Postures observed during dusting in a hospital.

Activity	Duration	Extension (%)	Neutral (%)	Bending <45° (%)	Bending ≥45° (%)	Not observable on video (%)
Clean nurse station	3 m, 26 s	—	13.6	86.4	—	—
Waste-basket (3)	1 m, 26 s	—	19.8	71.1	9.2	—
Bath (2)	5 m, 17 s	2.8	26.6	63.1	7.5	—
Bathroom corridor (2)	3 m, 53 s	6.6	18.6	71.0	3.8	0.3
Clean rooms	8 m, 45 s	3.7	29.8	60.1	2.9	3.5
Reception area	3 m, 13 s	—	24.7	74.4	—	0.9
Secretaries' office	10 m, 20 s	3.6	32.0	59.7	0.3	4.4
Overall	36 m, 20 s	3.0	26.4	65.8	2.7	2.2

Source: Messing, Chatigny and Courville 1995.

In order to clean, many objects must be moved. During 66 minutes cleaning and polishing floors, 0.7 objects had to be moved per minute, with weights up to 10 kg; during 23 minutes of dusting, 3.7 objects were moved per minute, with weights up to 2 kg (Messing, Chatigny and Courville 1995).

Winkel et al. (1983) and Hagner and Hagberg (1989) note that increasing specialization and standardization have reduced the number of opportunities to vary body movements and postures during cleaning work. It is therefore important to provide adequate break time. Formal or informal division of tasks according to sex may increase the likelihood of musculoskeletal problems by decreasing the variation in movements (Messing, Haëntjens and Doniol-Shaw 1993).

Cardiovascular load

The cardiovascular load can be quite heavy. Johansson and Ljunggren (1989) recorded the heart rate of female cleaners during office or toilet cleaning at 123 beats/minute, 65% of the maximum for their average age of 29.8 years (corresponding to about 35% of their estimated maximal oxygen uptake or $VO_{2\,max}$, close to that of construction workers). Swabbing or mopping resulted in similar heart rates of 122 to 127 beats/minute. Hagner and Hagberg (1989) found a high level of oxygen consumption (up to 40% of the $VO_{2\,max}$) among cleaners doing floor mopping under experimental conditions. Sogaard (1994) found that relative cardiovascular strain of female school cleaners measured in the workplace was 53% of the $VO_{2\,max}$.

To prevent musculoskeletal problems and decrease the cardiovascular load, workload should be appropriate and sufficient rest time should be allowed. Attention should be paid to ease of cleaning when spaces and procedures are being designed and when furnishings are purchased. Vacuuming requires less force if carpets are carefully laid so as not to wrinkle when the vacuum cleaner is passed. The use of adequate tools is important. For example, extendable brushes for dusting can reduce the necessity to reach or climb. Prolonged bending can be minimized if efficient chemicals and tools make it possible to clean quickly, and if cleaning is frequent enough so that dirt does not become hardened. The common practice of reducing the rate of ventilation in buildings during the evening or night hours, when cleaning is done, reduces air quality for cleaning workers who work during these times and should be avoided. To prevent overwork in the case where cleaning is planned using purchased software, careful observation and verification should be done in order to make sure that times allotted are realistic and take into account multiple use of spaces cleaned. Inventories of rooms and objects cleaned should be updated frequently.

Procedures and apparatus for emptying wastebaskets into bins, and bins into incinerators, have been developed so that manual lifting can be avoided.

Chemicals

Chemicals can be classed as soaps, detergents, disinfectants, porcelain cleaners, scouring powders, wax removers and strippers, solvents, pesticides and drain cleaners. They may contain other ingredients such as fragrances and colouring agents. There may be surface skin contact or they may be inhaled or absorbed through the skin into the system. Damage to the skin, eyes, throat or lungs can result. The risk of exposure depends on the concentration of the chemical and how it is used. Sprays volatilize chemicals and increase exposure. Some chemicals are irritants at low concentration and corrosive at high concentration (acids, oxidizing agents or bases). Others are effective solvents or detergents which may damage the skin barrier and make it more vulnerable to other chemical agents. Still others contain metals (nickel, cobalt, chrome) or other substances which can act as allergens.

Cleaning agents are often sold at high concentrations and diluted on site for use. The common practice of using chemicals at a higher concentration than recommended, in the hope of cleaning more quickly or more efficiently, is a source of overexposure and should be remedied by proper education and by adjusting the workload. Mixing different chemicals can cause accidental intoxication or burns. Work with strong chemicals in poorly ventilated spaces can be a hazard for cleaners and should be avoided.

The Danish Product Register Data Base PROBAS contains information on 2,567 washing and cleaning agents. Of these, 70 are considered to be potentially harmful agents causing chronic or acute health damage, such as corrosives, carcinogens, reproductive toxicants, allergens and neurotoxic agents (Borglum and Hansen 1994). These agents are presented in table 100.2. A study of the PROBAS register found 33 contact allergens in cleaning agents (Flyvholm 1993).

Cleaners who work in factories or hospitals may be exposed to chemicals (or biohazards) associated with the ongoing activities in the spaces they clean. If cleaners are not integrated into the training programmes and social network of the regular workforce, they may be less aware of these hazards than other workers. For example, one study showed that cleaners were the group most often exposed to harmful chemicals of all categories of hospital workers (Weaver et al. 1993).

There is some controversy about the use of gloves for cleaning work. Gloves play an important role in protecting the skin from hazardous agents if they fit correctly and are made of impermeable and resistant materials. But wearing gloves constantly can keep perspiration from evaporating. The resulting damp area is a favourable growth medium for infectious agents. Wearing gloves was associated with skin problems in a large sample of Danish cleaners (Nielsen 1996). It is therefore best to wear gloves the minimum time compatible with protection. The necessity for wearing gloves can often be obviated by using tools with long handles, or by other changes in methods. Wearing cotton gloves under rubber or plastic gloves may reduce humidity and protect against allergies to some glove materials (Foussereau et al. 1982). Some hand creams may contain irritants and should be avoided (Hansen 1983).

Several other practices diminish exposure to chemicals. When cleaning solutions are stored or prepared, there should be good ventilation, and procedures should permit preparation without any danger of touching or breathing the chemicals. The temptation to work with undiluted chemicals will diminish if workers have adequate time and implements. Also, cleaners may use undiluted chemicals or chemicals that have allergenic fragrances in order to signal to others that they have done their job. This can be done by other means, such as clear inspection procedures and communication links with other workers and with clients of cleaning services.

Useful information on prevention of exposure to chemicals can be found in a handbook published by the City of New York (Michaels, undated).

Other health risks

Cleaners often work evening or night shifts, so as not to interfere with the other activities being carried out in the same spaces. They may therefore suffer the usual effects of shift work on biorhythms. In addition, they may risk violence if they work alone in isolated areas.

Cleaners, particularly those who work outside regular building hours and/or who are not part of the regular personnel, may be ignored and excluded from the social network in their workplaces (Messing in press). They may not be given access to the appropriate facilities for breaks and meals. Aside from the psychological effects of exclusion, cleaners may be deprived of information on

Table 100.2 • Dangerous chemicals used in cleaning.[†]

Chemical	Health damage codes	Other hazards
Solvents		
Butylglycol	N*	
Isopropyl benzene	N	
Naphtha, white spirit, Stoddard solvent	N,R	
Toluene	N,R	Flammable
Ethanol	R	Flammable
2-Ethoxyethanol	N,R	
2-Methoxyethanol	R	
1-Methyl-2-pyrrolido	R	
Base oil, crude oil	N	
Tetrachloroethylene	N,R	
1,1,1-Trichloroethane	N	
Xylene	N,R*	Flammable
Butyldiglycol	I	
Acids and bases		
Acetic acid	C	
Ammonium hydroxide	I	Reacts with chlorine bleaches to liberate toxic gas
Potassium hydroxide	C	
Sodium carbonate	I	
Sodium hydroxide	C	
Phosphoric acid	C	
Sulphuric acid	C	
Residual monomers and impurities		
Formaldehyde	A,K*	
Phenol	N*	
Benzene	K,R,N	
Acrylonitrile	A,K	
Butylacrylate	A	
Methylmethacrylate	A,R	
Styrene	R	Flammable
1-Propanol	N	Flammable
Ethyl acrylate	A,K*	
1,2-Ethylene diamine	A	
Ethylene oxide	A,K,R	Flammable
Propylene oxide	K	Flammable
2-Methylaniline	K	
2-Propyn-1-ol	N	
Chelators		
Sodium EDTA (ethylene diamine tetraacetic acid)	R	
Sodium NTA (nitrilotriacetic acid)	K	

Chemical	Health damage codes	Other hazards
Anti-rusts		
2-Aminoethanol	N	
Triethanolamine	A	
Hexamethylene tetramine	A	
2-Butyn-1,4-diol	C,T	
Disodium metasilicate	C,I	
2-(3H)-Benzothiazolethione	A	
Disinfectants		
Borax	R	
Disodium tetraborate	R	
Morpholine	N	
Benzalkonium chloride	C	
Sodium dichloroisocyanurate	I	Reacts with acid to liberate toxic gas
Sodium hypochlorite	C	Reacts with acid or ammonia to release toxic gases
Preserving agents		
1,2-Bensisothiazol-3(2H)-one	A	
5-Chlor-2-methyl-3-isothiazolone	A	
2-Methyl-3-isothiazolone	A	
2-Chloracetamide	A	
p-Chlor-m-cresol	A	
Hexahydro-1,3,5-tris-(2-hydroxyethyl)1,3,5-triazine	A	
1,5-Pentadiol	A	
2-Bromo-2-nitro-1,3-propanediol	T	
Fillers		
Quartz	K	
Silicon dioxide	K	
Sodium hydrogen sulphate	C	
Others		
Subtilisin (Enzyme)	A	
Sodium saccharine	K	
Ammonium peroxodisulphate (bleaching agent)	A	

A = allergen; C = corrosive; I = irritant; K = carcinogen; N = neurotoxic agent; R = reproductive toxic agent; T = toxic if swallowed; * = danger dependent on concentration.

Determination of toxicity was done by the Danish Institute of Occupational Health.

[†] Note that not all cleaning agents have been tested for all toxic properties, so that this list is not necessarily complete or comprehensive.

Source: Summarized from Borglum and Hansen 1994.

hazards routinely given to other workers, despite legal requirements in many jurisdictions to provide this information. Also, despite the importance of surface textures and design for their work, they and their supervisors may not be consulted when relevant purchasing and planning decisions are made. This is especially true if cleaning is contracted out. It is therefore important that a special effort be made to include cleaners in occupational health and safety promotion activities in the workplace. Information on characteristics of chemicals, on work procedures and on safety should be discussed with cleaners and clearly posted in the workplace.

Health Effects and Disease Patterns

Cleaners as a profession have poorer health than others (Nielsen 1995; ASSTSAS 1993; Sogaard 1994). Comparing cleaners with other workers, an analysis of the Quebec Health Survey found, after controlling for age, that women cleaners had the highest prevalence of chronic back problems and cardiopathies of all categories of women workers and that male cleaners had the highest prevalence of musculoskeletal problems and cardiopathies (Gervais 1993). Pregnant cleaners have an increased likelihood of miscarriage (McDonald et al. 1986), giving birth prematurely (McDonald et al. 1988) or bearing children with low birth weight (McDonald et al. 1987).

Some large population-based epidemiological studies have found high cancer rates among cleaners. Rates of some brain tumours among US White men have been found to be especially high for cleaning service workers (Demers, Vaughan and Schommer 1991). Among women, invasive cervical cancer is almost five times more common among cleaners than other women (Savitz, Andrews and Brinton 1995). These results are attributed to chemical exposures, particularly solvents.

Musculoskeletal problems are often encountered. In Denmark, Nielsen (1995) found that those who left cleaning had a reduced frequency of musculoskeletal symptoms compared to those who stayed in the profession. Cleaning was one of the five trades reporting the most shoulder/neck pain, tendovaginitis and low back pain (Sogaard, Fallentin and Nielsen 1996). A population-based epidemiological study found female cleaners to be particularly likely to have osteoarthritis of the knee, compared to other Swedish workers (Vingard et al. 1991). Cleaners in Quebec hospitals suffer almost twice as many occupational accidents and illnesses as the average Quebec health care worker: 23.8 compared to 13.9 per 100 full-time equivalent workers per year (ASSTSAS 1993). Most lesions involved the trunk or upper limbs (ASSTSAS 1993). Comparing male with female cleaners, a survey of cleaners in the Paris region in France found that men had more back pain and women had more joint pain (Opatowski et al. 1995). These differences are probably attributable to specificities in the tasks assigned to women and men cleaners (Messing, Haëntjens and Doniol-Shaw 1993; Messing, Doniol-Shaw and Haëntjens 1993; Messing, Chatigny and Courville 1996).

Cleaners have a high level of skin problems, including dermatitis and eczema (Gawkrodger, Lloyd and Hunter 1986; Singgih et al. 1986). Point prevalences of skin diseases of 15 to 18% and a duration of employment prevalence of 39% have been found among large samples of hospital cleaners (Hansen 1983; Delaporte et al. 1990). Cleaners who spend more time with wet hands have more skin problems (Nielsen 1996). Cleaners may also be injured or infected by broken glass, needles or other sharp objects while handling waste (ASSTSAS 1993).

Recently, occupational health specialists have noted symptoms of stress related to work among hospital cleaners, for which they suggest re-examination of the work process (Toivanen, Helin and Hänninen 1993). Low prestige of the profession may be a cause of distress for cleaners (Messing, in press).

Accidents, infection and environmental contamination may be prevented by clear and well-publicized guidelines for disposal of dangerous waste in factories, hospitals, offices and public buildings. Since constraints placed on other workers may prevent them from paying full attention to prevention of hazards for cleaners, consultations between cleaners and other workers should be arranged, in order to decide on the appropriate size and placement of wastebaskets, waste separation and labelling. Cleaners should be included whenever waste disposal practices are being planned or reviewed so that realistic methods can be proposed.

BARBERING AND COSMETOLOGY

Laura Stock and James Cone

General Profile

It has been estimated that over a million people work in approximately 150,000 salons and barber shops in the United States. These men and women, barbers and cosmetologists (also referred to as "technicians"), perform a wide range of services, including shaving; cutting and styling hair; giving manicures and pedicures; applying artificial nails; and performing a variety of chemical hair processes including bleaching, colouring, hair relaxing and permanent waving. In addition, some technicians provide facial treatments and removal of body hair.

Technicians may be exposed to a variety of potential health and safety hazards on the job, including:

Chemicals. According to an analysis conducted by the US National Institute for Occupational Safety and Health (NIOSH), 30% of the nearly 3,000 chemicals used in cosmetology are classified by the US government as toxic substances. Ventilation in many shops is often inadequate to eliminate chemical exposure.

Diseases. Because of their close contact with clients, technicians may be exposed to a variety of infectious diseases, ranging from colds and flu to impetigo, chicken pox and hepatitis.

Ergonomic hazards. Barbers and cosmetologists also suffer from a range of musculoskeletal disorders associated with repetitive motion, prolonged standing, cramped work spaces and poorly designed tools and equipment.

Scheduling. Working hours may be irregular and extended. Many technicians work in "split shifts", splitting their work day to cover 12 to 14 hours of client services.

Other problems. These include poor housekeeping and electrical and fire hazards.

As a result of exposure to these and other hazards, an increasing number of people are being forced to leave their chosen profession. A recent study by Nellie Brown, director of the Chemical Hazards Information Program at Cornell University, found that 20% of US hair stylists leave their jobs because of work-related illness (*New York Times Magazine*, 7 March 1993).

Despite increasing evidence of risk, there are few regulations protecting barbers and cosmetologists. In the United States, cosmetic products are regulated by the Food and Drug Administration (FDA), which is oriented towards consumer protection and has a limited ability to address worker health and safety issues. Like regulatory agencies in many countries, the FDA does not require product manufacturers to conduct safety tests before public marketing, to list ingredients on the labels of products sold for professional use only or to give the FDA information on consumer complaints. Nor does the FDA routinely test products on its own initiative; any testing done by the FDA focuses on risks to consumers, not workers, although workers may be at greater risk due to their daily and prolonged use of cosmetic chemicals.

Attempts to regulate this industry are further complicated by the differing local, national and international definitions of the tasks barbers and cosmetologists perform. In the United States, licensing requirements vary from state to state. Many countries have no licensing requirements at all.

Major Processes and Hazards

Chemical hazards

Barbers and cosmetologists are exposed to a wide variety of chemicals during the course of a working day. Technicians are at risk for absorbing chemicals through the skin or eyes, inhaling dangerous vapours or particulates and ingesting toxins that have contaminated food, drink or cigarettes. Some guidelines for reducing hazardous exposure are given in figure 100.1.

Chemicals can affect the body in different ways depending on the concentration of the chemical in a product; how toxic the chemical is; the route by which it enters the body (inhalation, skin contact, ingestion); and the length of time of the exposure. Individual characteristics, such as general health status, pregnancy and smoking, can also affect a person's risk.

There are thousands of different chemicals associated with cosmetology processes. In order to determine the specific chemicals contained in a product and their effects, it is important that technicians have access to, and understand, product labels and material safety data sheets (MSDSs).

Common chemical processes

Colouring hair. Hair colouring solutions are applied manually to the hair with an applicator bottle or brush. It also is becoming very common for clients to request an eyebrow or eyelash tints.

Chemicals used in hair colouring include synthetic organic colorants, complex metallic colorants and vegetable dyes. Synthetic hair colorants often include permanent oxidative dyes which use hydrogen peroxide to oxidize aromatic diamines. These chemicals are eye, nose and throat irritants. Synthetic organic hair dyes containing an amine group are also among the most frequent causes of allergic sensitization. Metallic dyes may include lead-containing compounds.

Coal tar-based hair dyes may contain mutagens. Hair dyes which have been found to be mutagenic in *in vitro* testing pose uncertain human health risks. However, the production of non-mutagenic hair dyes appears to be possible and should be encouraged. For example, henna, a vegetable dye, is one of the oldest hair dyes and is not known to be either a mutagen or a carcinogen.

Bleaching hair. Bleaching solutions are applied manually with an applicator bottle or brush. These solutions may contain hydrogen peroxide, sodium peroxide, ammonium hydroxide, ammonium persulphate or potassium persulphate. These chemicals can cause skin, eye, nose, throat or lung irritation. Persulphate bleach powders have also been associated with asthma among cosmetologists (Blainey et al. 1986).

Permanent waving. Permanent waves usually involve several steps: washing the hair; rolling the hair in curlers; applying a thioglycolate or similar solution; and rinsing and neutralizing with an oxidizing agent. Water sprays may also be used.

Permanent-wave solutions may contain alcohol, bromates, sodium hydroxide, boric acid (perborate or borate), ammonium thioglycolate or glycerol monothioglycolate. Some of these chemicals may cause central nervous system effects (headache, dizziness, nausea, drowsiness); eye, nose and throat irritation; lung problems (breathing difficulty or coughing); skin irritation; burns; or allergic reactions (stuffy or runny nose, sneezing, asthma or allergic dermatitis).

Figure 100.1 • Reducing exposure to chemical hazards.

AVOID HAZARDOUS CHEMICALS.
- Obtain labels and material safety data sheets (MSDSs) for all salon products.
- Use substitute chemicals which are less toxic. Avoid products with highly toxic ingredients such as coal tar dyes, formaldehyde, glycol ethers and methyl methacrylate.
- Use substitute methods that involve few or no chemicals:
  – Heat straightening instead of chemical hair straightening
  – Plastic tips or linen strips instead of artificial nails
- Use wet styling aids or pump sprays instead of aerosol hair sprays.

USE WORK PRACTICES THAT REDUCE EXPOSURE.
- Keep bottles and other containers closed when not in use.
- Isolate hazardous work processes (e.g., mix chemicals in a separately vented room).
- Do not eat, drink or smoke while using chemical products, to avoid contamination.
- Wash hands thoroughly after using chemical products; before touching eyes, face or mouth; and before eating, drinking or smoking.
- Dispose of chemicals properly. Do not discard dangerous chemicals down the drain or in the trash.
- Maintain good housekeeping (e.g., clean up spills immediately).
- Avoid performing the same chemical procedure all day.
- Store chemical products in a cool, dry place with no direct sunlight. Secure containers from breakage.
- Do not store incompatible chemicals (such as acids and bases) together.

ENSURE ADEQUATE VENTILATION.
- Provide good general ventilation for the entire shop. Supply air mechanically through vents and air returns. If mechanical ventilation is not feasible, supply fresh air by opening windows and doors and using fans.
- Never position a fan to blow chemicals toward the face (breathing zone).
- Always blow chemicals away from the face.
- Provide local exhaust ventilation (a hood) for each chemical mixing area, manicurist's table and artificial nail station:
  – Make sure the fan in the unit is powerful enough to be effective.
  – Place the hood as close as possible to the process generating the chemical (e.g., to the customer's hand).
  – Vent the unit to the outside.
  – If it is impossible to vent to a window, exhaust duct or drain, then be sure the system has appropriate filters and change them regularly.

USE APPROPRIATE PERSONAL PROTECTIVE EQUIPMENT.
- Always use gloves when doing permanents, straightening, dyeing and shampooing.
- Select the right kind of glove for the particular chemical.
- Discard gloves when they are damaged or when chemicals have broken through to the skin.
- Wear a long-sleeved shirt, coat or smock to avoid getting chemicals on the skin.
- Use an approved dust mask to protect from dust when filing nails. Since a dust mask protects only against dusts, use a cartridge respirator for chemical vapours or aerosols.
- Wear safety glasses or goggles while mixing, pouring or using chemical products that may damage the eyes.

Manicures, pedicures and artificial nails. Nail care involves soaking the cuticles in softening agents, using nail clippers, using emery boards or nail files to file the nails, using hand lotions and applying and removing polish. Artificial nails (acrylics, gels, fibreglass, porcelains and fabric wraps and tips) may be brushed onto the nail or attached to it with glue. They are allowed to harden and then filed to the desired shape.

The many chemicals found in nail products include acetone, ethyl methacrylate and other acrylates, methyl ethyl ketone, ethyl acetate, lanolin and dimethyl-*p*-toluidine. These can cause skin, eye, nose, throat and lung irritation, as well as central nervous system effects. Some nail products also contain formaldehyde, associated with allergies as well as cancer with long term use. Some products contain glycol ethers, xylene and toluene, all linked to reproductive problems in laboratory animals.

The use of methyl methacrylate (MMA) in artificial nail products was banned in the United States in 1974. Despite the ban, this chemical continues to be used. A 1982 study found that methyl methacrylate was present in 8 of 29 artificial nail products, and a 1986 study found measurable levels of MMA in the air of some nail salons. This chemical, if in contact with the skin, can cause tingling, numbness and whitening of the fingers. It also causes skin allergy in many people. An allergy to MMA can result in cross-sensitivity to other more commonly used methacrylates. In some products MMA has been replaced by other acrylates that may also be sensitizers. Figure 100.2 shows a downdraft table designed to minimize a manicurist's exposure to the chemicals.

Washing and styling hair. Hair washing involves shampooing and rinsing with water. During this service, conditioners and other hair treatment products may also be applied. Hair drying is done in many ways: drying manually with towels, using a hand-held dryer or having the client sit under a fixed dryer. Styling generally involves the use of gels, creams or aerosol sprays. Washing the hair is often the first step for other services such as setting the hair, hair colouring and permanent waving. In large salons, one person may be assigned the job of washing clients' hair, and do nothing other than that.

Shampoos and conditioners may contain alcohol, petroleum distillates and formaldehyde. All have been linked to dermatitis and allergies, including asthma. Long-term use of formaldehyde has also been linked to cancer.

Aerosol hair sprays may contain polyvinylpyrrolidone, which has been associated with lung and other respiratory diseases, including thesaurosis. They also contain a variety of solvents.

Straightening hair. Hair-straightening or hair-relaxing solutions are applied to the hair with a brush; then the hair is stretched to relax the natural curl. Hair straightener may contain sodium hydroxide, hydrogen peroxide, bromates, ammonium, thioglycolate and glycerol monothioglycolate. These chemicals may cause eye, nose and throat irritation, central nervous system effects and dermatitis.

Other chemical processes. A variety of cosmetics, including face creams and powders, mascara, eye liners, lipsticks and other products, may also be applied by cosmetologists. These can contain a wide variety of solvents, dyes, pigments, preservatives, oils, waxes and other chemicals that can cause skin allergies and/or irritation.

Cosmetologists may also remove body hair. Hair removal treatments can involve the application of hot wax and use of chemical depilatory products. These products often contain alkaline ingredients that can cause dermatitis.

Ergonomic hazards
Barbers and cosmetologists are at risk for musculoskeletal disorders due to the physical demands of their work and to poorly designed equipment, tools and work spaces. Such disorders can include:

- *Wrist and hand problems,* such as tendinitis and carpal tunnel syndrome. Risk factors include bending and twisting of the wrist while cutting and styling hair, holding hair dryers and using a round brush or curling iron. These disorders are also linked to forceful gripping or pinching caused by cutting with dull and/or poorly fitting shears.
- *Shoulder problems,* including tendinitis and bursitis. These are associated with constant reaching for supplies, or holding arms above shoulder height while cutting or styling hair. See figure 100.3.
- *Neck and back problems,* ranging from common aches and pains to serious conditions such as pinched nerves and ruptured discs. These are associated with frequent bending or twisting during activities such as shampooing, cutting hair below ear level, and performing manicures and pedicures.
- *Foot and leg problems,* including swelling, calluses and varicose veins. These may occur as a result of long periods of standing on hard floors in shoes with poor arch support.

Preventing musculoskeletal disorders
To prevent musculoskeletal disorders, it is important to apply ergonomic principles to the design of tasks, tools and workstations. Ergonomics is the science of adapting the workplace to the needs of the human body. It suggests ways to minimize awkward postures and repetitive motions, as well as the use of excessive force. It maximizes safety, health and comfort.

Ergonomic solutions may include:

- *Adjustable furniture.* For example, client chairs are available that can be raised, lowered and swiveled. Manicurist chairs are available with back support, armrests and seat pans that can be tilted to accommodate forward bending.
- *Shears* that are sharp, well-lubricated and designed to fit the individual's hand.

Figure 100.2 • A modified commercial downdraft manicure table for application of artificial fingernails.

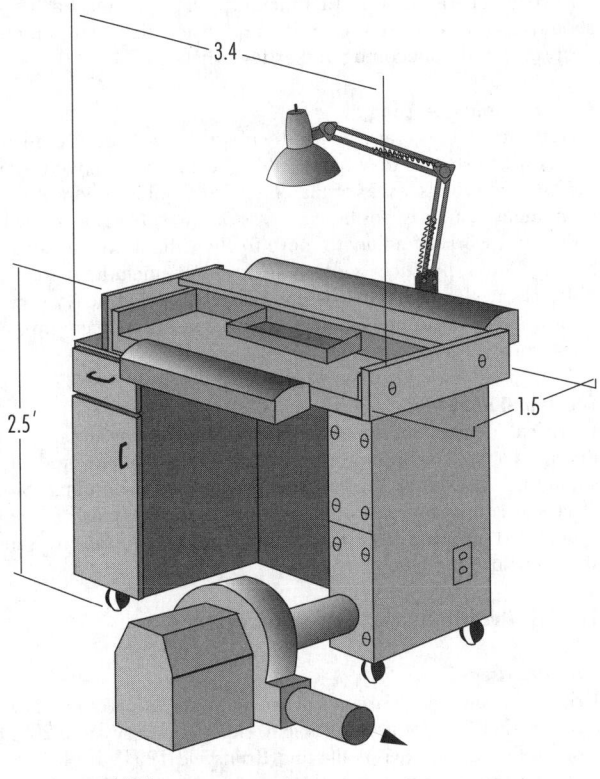

3.4

2.5'

1.5

Source: Spencer et al 1996.

100. PERSONAL AND COMMUNITY SERVICES

Figure 100.3 • Working with arms above shoulder level in a hairdressing salon in Zimbabwe.

- *Curling irons and hair dryers* with flexible handles. These can be used without excessive bending or twisting of the wrist.
- *Free-standing sinks* that allow technicians to wash hair without twisting and bending their backs.
- *Rolling seats or stools* that allow technicians to perform many procedures while seated, or to alternate between sitting and standing.
- *Proper workstation* designs such as storing commonly used supplies within easy reach; providing cushioned floor mats; and ensuring that cabinets are at the correct height to minimize reaching or bending.
- *Client scheduling* that varies the tasks and processes that a technician performs throughout the day.
- *Training* for technicians in good body mechanics and work practices such as proper lifting methods; bending at the hips instead of the waist; and using hair-cutting techniques that minimize reaching and bending of the wrist.

Infectious diseases

Work performed by barbers and cosmetologists involves close contact with clients. Understanding how infectious diseases are transmitted will help technicians prevent infection. Infectious diseases may be spread in the salon in the following ways:

- Through the air (e.g., upper respiratory illnesses such as colds and flu)
- Through contaminated water or food (e.g., hepatitis A, salmonella and giardia)
- Through insect or animal bites (e.g., lice)
- Through direct skin contact with infected persons (e.g., scabies, lice, ringworm, impetigo, herpes simplex, colds and chickenpox)
- Rarely, through exposure to the blood of an infected person (e.g., hepatitis B and HIV/AIDS)

While there is no recorded case of a barber or cosmetologist becoming infected with HIV/AIDS on the job, and work-related hepatitis B infection is extremely rare in these occupations, exposure to these bloodborne pathogens could possibly occur in rare instances of blood contact. Possible sources of exposure could include puncturing the skin with tools that carry infected blood (razors, tweezers, tattoo needles or clippers), or infected blood entering the body through an open wound, sore or skin rash.

This is one reason that shaving clients with razors has become uncommon in many countries. In addition to the risk to technicians, there is the possibility of skin and other infections being transferred from one client to another through unsterilized equipment.

Exposure to harmful organisms can be prevented by taking simple precautions:

- Hands should be washed frequently with soap and water.
- Latex gloves should be worn to protect technician and client if either has sores, lesions or skin rashes.
- Sharp instruments should be handled carefully and disposed of in approved puncture-proof containers.
- All tools, equipment and surfaces should be disinfected properly.
- Towels should be sanitized.
- Workers should be vaccinated against hepatitis B.

Other hazards

Fire hazards
Some products used in the salon may contain flammable or combustible chemicals. Sources of ignition can include flame from a cigarette, match or burner; a spark from a light switch, electric plug or frayed cord; or a hot object such as a curling iron, stove, light bulb or hotplate. To prevent accidents, it should be made sure that chemicals are used and stored properly. Flammables and combustibles should be kept away from flames, sparks or hot objects, and electrical equipment should be checked for broken or frayed cords that might spark or get hot. Each shop should also have a fire-prevention and evacuation plan, and appropriate and functioning fire extinguishers.

General housekeeping
Salons are often cramped and crowded work environments. Overstocked shelves may be unstable. Technicians may be at risk for slips and falls as a result of spilled liquids, poorly stored equipment or poorly positioned cords or wires. Narrow, crowded aisles limit workers' ability to move freely without obstruction. All shops should practice good housekeeping, including: keeping aisles clear, cleaning up spills immediately, storing heavy objects on low shelves and making sure people can move freely through their workspace.

Electrical hazards
Electrical devices in the salon can include hair clippers, hair dryers, facial machines and electrolysis equipment and they should be checked for frayed wires and proper grounding. Since electrical equipment and outlets are often within splash range of water, red ground fault circuit interrupters to prevent shock should be used.

Health Problems and Disease Patterns

Skin diseases
Irritant and allergic dermatitis of the hands alone, or of hands and face together, is a common problem, experienced by 10 to 20% of cosmetologists (van der Walle and Brunsveld 1994). It often produces a characteristic rash in the spaces between the fingers. Signs of dermatitis generally include redness, drying and cracking on

the skin of the hands. Eczema of the tips of the fingers may also occur, with ridging of the nail folds. Younger workers appear to be at highest risk, possibly because those with lower seniority tend to be assigned most often to shampooing and permanent-waving jobs. Most frequent causes of allergic skin rash in cosmetologists include glycerol thioglycolate, ammonium thioglycolate, nickel sulphate, ammonium persulphate preservatives and hair dyes (*p*-phenylenediamine or resorcinol) (Villaplana, Romaguera and Grimalt 1991).

In most cases, once an allergic dermatitis develops it does not improve, even with the wearing of gloves. Rubber latex glove use may itself be a significant risk factor for allergic responses, and vinyl gloves may need to be substituted if latex allergy develops. If one worker in a salon develops latex allergy, the entire salon may need to become latex-free to protect that worker from repeated allergic responses.

Other skin diseases of hairdressers include granuloma from hair implantation, and hot water burns. Also, varicose veins may result from the prolonged standing common to this occupation. Sharp tools such as scissors, shaving equipment and electric hair-cutting tools can cause skin lacerations. Such cuts may predispose the cosmetologist to dermatitis due to chemical exposures.

Lung problems

Allergic rhinitis ("hay fever") and asthma have been associated with exposure to permanent-wave solution (Schwartz, Arnold and Strohl 1990), and in particular to ammonium persulphate (Gamboa et al. 1989). Hair bleach as well as henna (Starr, Yunginger and Brahser 1982) have been associated with occupational asthma in cosmetologists.

Reproductive health

A recent study found a moderately increased risk of spontaneous abortion among cosmetologists who worked full time and performed a large number of chemical services. The use of formaldehyde and exposure to manicuring and nail-sculpting chemicals were specifically associated with an increased risk of spontaneous abortion (John, Savitz and Shy 1994).

Cancer

Cosmetologists have been found to have a possible increased risk of developing certain types of cancer, including non-Hodgkin's lymphoma (Zahm et al. 1992; Pearce 1992), bladder/urothelial cancer (Steineck et al. 1990) and breast cancer (Koenig 1994).

• LAUNDRIES, GARMENT AND DRY CLEANING

Gary S. Earnest, Lynda Ewers and Avima M. Ruder

General Profile

Commercial laundries began as domestic enterprises, but have developed into businesses with many unique health and safety concerns. Laundries specializing in services for hospitals must deal with possible biological hazards, and those laundering work clothes for manufacturing or service workers may risk exposure to specific chemical hazards.

Dry cleaning reputedly originated in France in 1825 when a worker in a dye and cleaning factory spilled lamp oil on a soiled tablecloth (IARC 1995a). After the tablecloth dried, the spots had disappeared. Lamp oil is a hydrocarbon. Similar hydrocarbon solvents—turpentine, kerosene, benzene and gasoline—were used in the fledgling dry-cleaning industry. All these solvents had one

major disadvantage: they were flammable, often resulting in fires and explosions (Wentz 1995). In 1928, W.J. Stoddard introduced a nearly odourless, petroleum-based solvent with a higher flash-point, which reduced the risk of fire. Stoddard solvent gained widespread acceptance in the industry and is still used today.

At the turn of the century, advances in the synthesis of chlorinated hydrocarbons permitted development of nonflammable solvents for dry cleaning. Initially, carbon tetrachloride was preferred, but because of its toxicity and aggressiveness to metals, textiles and dyes, it was gradually replaced in the 1940s and 1950s by trichloroethylene and tetrachloroethylene (also commonly known as perchloroethylene, or PERC) (Wentz 1995). PERC (C_2Cl_4) is a colourless, clear, heavy liquid with an ethereal odour. Today, approximately 90% of US dry cleaners use PERC (EPA 1991a).

Although cleaning practices vary from country to country and from shop to shop, laundries and dry-cleaning shops are usually small businesses; about 70% of US dry-cleaning shops have fewer than four employees, who usually perform the cleaning at the same location as the shop. The employees of such a small business, many of whom typically labour more than eight hours per day, may be members of one family, sometimes including children. In many countries, the dry-cleaning family lives in the same building as the shop. An increasing trend among larger corporations is to operate multiple "drop" shops where customers leave soiled garments. The garments are transported to a central facility for cleaning, and later returned to the drop shops for customer pick-up. This arrangement confines hazardous waste to one site and reduces the solvent exposure of drop shop workers.

The Laundry and Dry-Cleaning Process

The dry-cleaning or laundry process usually begins when a customer brings soiled garments to a shop. Modern clothing is made from many different fibres and fabrics. Garments are inspected and sorted according to weight, colour, finish and fabric type prior to machine loading. Visible stains are treated at a spotting station with various chemicals, before or after cleaning, depending on the type of stain.

Cleaning is a three-step process: washing, extracting and drying (figure 100.4). Wet-process washing (laundering) uses detergent, water and possibly steam. In dry cleaning, detergent and water are added to the solvent to aid in soil removal. Clothes are manually loaded into the machine, and the cleaning solution is automatically injected. Machine contents are agitated for a period, then spun at high speed to extract the water or solvent and tumbled dry. Once garments have been removed from the dryer, they are pressed to remove wrinkles and restore their shape.

Many countries have recently imposed stringent regulations for the control of PERC exposures and emissions because of associated health effects and environmental problems. In response to these regulations, dry-cleaning processes are changing. Improved solvent purification and vapour-recovery systems are available, alternative solvents are being developed, and wet methods using water immersion are being refined to clean garments traditionally cleaned in solvent. These processes are described below.

Transfer versus dry-to-dry equipment

Two basic types of machines used in dry cleaning are transfer and dry-to-dry. Transfer machines, older and less expensive, require manual transfer of solvent-laden clothing from the washer to the dryer. The transfer activity causes excessive worker exposure to PERC. Because of high solvent usage rates, emissions and exposures during transfer, PERC transfer machines are no longer manufactured in the United States; however, older used or reconditioned ones can still be purchased.

Figure 100.4 • The dry cleaning process flow diagram.

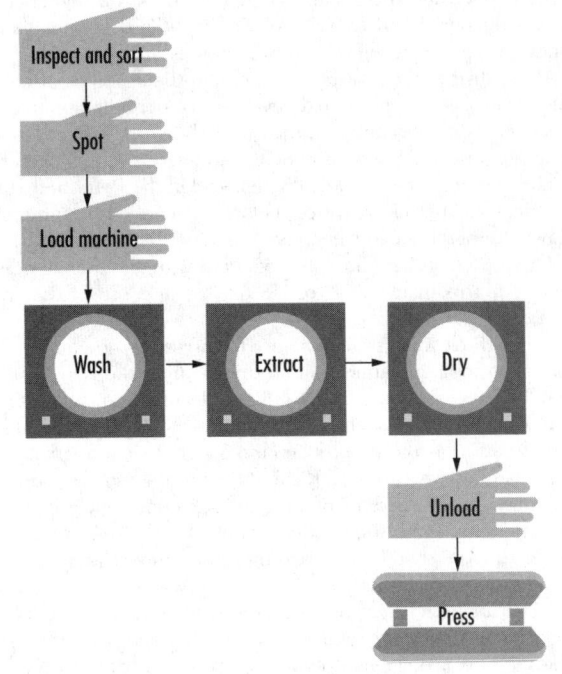

In 1994, at least 70% of PERC machines in the United States, for example, were dry-to-dry machines, using a one-step process that eliminates clothing transfer. Many shops are replacing or have replaced transfer machines with dry-to-dry machines because of the trend towards stricter environmental regulations; however, some shops still use transfer equipment for increased productivity and to avoid the capital expenditure required for new machines. In the United States, petroleum machines are primarily transfer units.

Dry-to-dry machines may be vented or ventless. Vented dry-to-dry machines vent residual solvent vapours directly to the atmosphere or through some form of vapour-recovery system during the aeration process. Ventless dry-to-dry machines are essentially closed systems, open to the atmosphere only when the machine door is opened. They recirculate the heated drying air through a vapour-recovery system and back to the drying drum. There is no aeration step.

Solvent purification: Filtration and distillation

Dry cleaners use filtration and/or distillation to recover and purify solvents. Filtration removes insoluble soils, non-volatile residues and loose dyes from the solvent. It is also sometimes used, primarily in the United States, to remove soluble soils. Filtration is a continuous process. The solvent passes through an adsorbent powder, cartridge or spin-disc filter, all requiring some level of periodic maintenance. Each filtration system produces contaminated cartridges or powders.

Distillation, used by 90% of US cleaners, removes soluble oils, fatty acids and greases not removed by filtration (International Fabricare Institute 1990). Distillation occurs when PERC is heated to its boiling point so that it vaporizes and later condenses back to liquid form. During this process, non-volatile impurities, which cannot be boiled off, remain in the still and are discarded as hazardous waste. Both filtration and distillation produce some solid wastes containing PERC; however, dry-cleaning machine manufacturers are striving to develop new filtration and distilla-

tion technologies that reduce the amount of hazardous waste produced. This ultimately results in important savings to the owner by reducing the cost of hazardous-waste disposal.

Recovery of PERC vapours

Two primary technologies are used to recover PERC vapours: the *carbon adsorber* and the *refrigerated condenser*. These two technologies, traditionally separate, are used together in more modern machines. Carbon adsorption is used in about 35% of the controlled machines in the United States, for example. Carbon adsorbers achieve a 95 to 99% vapour reduction by removing PERC from the air. Solvent-laden vapours pass over activated carbon having a high adsorption capacity. The carbon is later desorbed and the PERC recovered, or the carbon is discarded as hazardous waste when it becomes saturated with PERC. Carbon desorption typically occurs with steam or hot air. Desorption can be done automatically after each load, or it can be done at the end of the day. If not performed regularly, the carbon bed will become saturated and be ineffective for PERC recovery. The adsorption system can handle high volumes of air, having relatively low solvent concentrations while maintaining a high PERC removal efficiency, but frequent desorbing is needed and steam regeneration produces contaminated waste water.

Refrigerated condensers cool solvent-laden air below the dew point of the vapour to recover PERC, and operate on the principle that the ability of air to hold a solvent in the vapour state varies with temperature. Refrigerated condensers are used in approximately 65% of controlled machines. The process can achieve 95% vapour control in dry-to-dry machines and 85% control in transfer machines. Condensers require little maintenance and minimize the potential for waste water because steam regeneration is not required. They do require higher solvent concentrations than a carbon adsorber. Water vapour may pose a problem because it can condense and freeze, impeding gas flow and heat transfer (EPA 1991b).

Solvent alternatives to PERC

Alternative dry-cleaning solvents have been substituted for PERC. Flammable, petroleum-based solvents generally have higher exposure limits than PERC. These petroleum-based solvents are less aggressive at removing soils than PERC. Because their vapour pressures are lower than PERC, exposures from inhalation will generally be lower. However, adverse health effects are possible, including asphyxiation, central nervous system depression and skin and mucous membrane irritation. Contamination of aliphatic hydrocarbons with benzene will significantly increase the hazard.

Two different approaches have been taken in Germany to reduce the fire hazard posed by petroleum-based solvents: developing safer solvents and redesigning machines.

Recently developed petroleum-based solvents, widely used in Germany, are either straight-chain, branched or cyclic paraffins with a chain length of between 10 and 12 carbons. These petroleum-based solvents have an atmospheric lifetime of only a few days, are halogen-free, do not lead to ozone depletion and play only a minor role in the greenhouse effect. Some of the German requirements for petroleum-based, dry-cleaning solvents are outlined below (Hohenstein Institute 1995):

- Boiling range between 180° and 210 °C
- Aromatic, benzene, halogen and polycyclic aromatic content less than 0.01 wt%
- Flashpoint higher than 55 °C
- Thermally stable at operating conditions.

Dry-cleaning machines manufactured for petroleum-based solvents in Germany today are much safer than those of the past. Because petroleum-based solvents are combustible, additional safety measures are required on machines using them. Technical advances improve machine safety and greatly reduce the risk of fire/explosion. The following measures can be taken in combination or separately:

- Using an inert gas, such as nitrogen or argon, to displace oxygen in the drum and ensure that oxygen concentration is sufficiently low (approximately 4%) to prevent combustion
- Operating under a vacuum to remove oxygen and lower its concentration to below 4%
- Ensuring that the lower explosive limit (LEL) is not exceeded, or if the LEL is not known, ensuring that operating temperature remains 15 °C below the flashpoint
- Ensuring that vapour concentration remains below 50% of the LEL, by controlling operating temperatures or by providing sufficiently high airflow.

Wet cleaning

Wet cleaning is a developing technology, distinct from traditional laundering in that it is a more gentle process and can be used on many fabrics that were formerly dry cleaned. Four factors play an essential role in soil removal: temperature, time, mechanical action and chemical agents. Only the proper blend of these factors achieves the best cleaning results (Vasquez 1995). There are minor variations of machine wet cleaning, but all techniques use:

- Specially formulated wet-cleaning soaps and spotting agents
- Increased extraction of water prior to drying (extraction speeds as high as approximately 1,000 revolutions per minute)
- Close monitoring of heat and moisture content during the drying process
- Machines having less mechanical action during washing, accomplished by speed reduction and time limits.

Garments are washed with various levels of limited mechanical action, based on garment type and amount of soilage. The greatest risk occurs during drying. Many fibres can be fully dried with little or no difficulty. However, delicate garments or garments susceptible to shrinkage must be dried for only a few minutes before being hung to air dry. Because of these problems, most wet-cleaned garments require more finishing work than solvent-cleaned garments. Long drying times and more finishing work substantially increase processing time (Earnest and Spencer 1996).

Today, wet cleaning use is limited because the technology does not yet completely eliminate the need for solvents. It has been estimated that wet cleaning can safely clean approximately 30 to 70% of garments traditionally cleaned in solvent (Rice and Weinberg 1994). There are still problems with fibre damage, bleeding of dyes and, most importantly, cleaning ability. Inappropriate use of wet cleaning can expose shop owners to liability for damaged clothing. For this reason wet-cleaning advocates are working to persuade garment manufacturers to use fabrics that can be more easily wet cleaned.

Hazards in Laundries and Dry Cleaning Facilities

PERC hazards

In the workplace PERC can enter the human body through both respiratory and dermal exposure (ATSDR 1995). Symptoms associated with respiratory exposure include depression of the central nervous system; damage to the liver and kidneys (RSC 1986); impaired memory; confusion; dizziness; headache; drowsiness; and eye, nose and throat irritation. Repeated dermal exposure may result in dry, scaly and fissured dermatitis (NIOSH 1977).

US National Cancer Institute and National Toxicology Program studies have established a link between PERC exposure and cancer in animals. Human studies show an elevated risk of uri-

nary tract (Duh and Asal 1984; Blair et al. 1990b; Katz and Jowett 1981), oesophageal (Duh and Asal 1984; Ruder, Ward and Brown 1994) and pancreatic cancer (Lin and Kessler 1981) among dry-cleaning workers. The International Agency for Research on Cancer (IARC) recently classified PERC in group 2A (probably carcinogenic to humans) and dry cleaning in group 2B (possibly carcinogenic to humans) (IARC 1995b). The Environmental Protection Agency (EPA) regulates PERC as a hazardous air pollutant.

US Occupational Safety and Health Administration (OSHA) data include numerous personal samples in dry-cleaning shops over the permissible exposure limit (PEL) of 100 ppm, 8-hour time-weighted average (TWA) (OSHA 1993). The machine operator is typically exposed to the greatest concentrations of PERC. US National Institute for Occupational Safety and Health (NIOSH) studies have shown that in many dry-cleaning shops having traditional machines, extremely high operator exposures occur during loading and unloading. Because loading/unloading occurs frequently throughout the day, in many instances exposure during this activity can account for 50 to 75% of the operator's TWA exposure (Earnest 1996). Occupational exposures can be reduced by using modern dry-cleaning machines, solvent substitution, isolation of the process and effective local and general ventilation near the dry-cleaning machines.

Exposure to chemicals other than PERC

A wide variety of chemicals is present in laundries and dry-cleaning establishments. There is potential exposure through skin or eye contact or inhalation of vapours. Skin damage may occur from chronic or acute exposure. Chemicals that readily vaporize and have a high toxicity may pose a risk from inhalation, although this is generally considered to be of less concern than injury to the eyes or skin. The chemicals commonly used in the United States to treat stains through spotting are trichloroethylene; ketones, especially methyl isobutyl ketone (MIBK); petroleum naphtha; and hydrofluoric acid. Oxidizers, such as chlorine bleaches, may pose a hazard if used in the presence of many common compounds, such as turpentine, ammonia or fuel gases. Detergents containing enzymes may cause immune reactions in many workers. The combined exposures of the dry-cleaning solvent, PERC and various other chemicals is also a concern.

Ergonomic risk factors

Ergonomic hazards in the cleaning industry primarily occur among pressers. Pressing is a dynamic and repetitive task requiring reaching, precision gripping and awkward postures. Ergonomic risk factors are also present during material handling when heavy lifting may occur, especially in commercial laundries.

Fire hazards

The dry-cleaning industry has traditionally had a problem with fires. Part of the reason for this problem has been the widespread use of flammable and combustible liquids as a cleaning medium. The flammability of petroleum-based solvents continues to present an acute health and safety hazard. Approximately 10% of dry-cleaning shops in the United States use traditional, petroleum-based solvents, such as Stoddard solvent or mineral spirits. Even dry-cleaning shops that use non-flammable PERC face important fire hazards. If heated sufficiently, PERC will decompose into hydrogen chloride and phosgene gases. The production of hydrogen cyanide or carbon monoxide is another cause for concern during a fire. Hydrogen cyanide is produced when materials that contain nitrogen, such as many natural and synthetic fibres burn. Carbon monoxide is formed during incomplete combustion. All dry-cleaning shops have a large number of potential fuels and ignition sources.

Dry-cleaning machine designers must avoid conditions that can lead to a fire to occur and must ensure that their machines operate safely. Likewise, shop owners must take appropriate steps to prevent hazardous conditions from developing. Some common causes of fires in all businesses are electrical malfunctions, friction, open flames, sparks, static electricity, hot surfaces and smoking (NIOSH 1975).

Thermal burns

Cleaning facilities have several possible sources of severe burns. In the pressing station, burns may result from contact with the head of a press, lines transporting steam, or the steam itself. Insulation of pipes and surfaces, and use of various guarding techniques, can help prevent burns.

Although modern boilers are of safer design than earlier models, they are still used to produce large quantities of steam and must be operated safely. Many of the needed precautions can be found in the US National Fire Protection Association's Code 32, Standard for Dry Cleaning Plants, and its *Fire Protection Handbook* (NFPA 1991). Recommendations in these documents include building code requirements, proper storage and isolation of flammables, fire extinguishers and sprinkler systems. Recommendations concerning the build-up of gases around the boiler address ways to eliminate gas leakage and ensure proper ventilation.

Mechanical hazards

Mechanical hazards are always a concern when powered equipment is used. Presses pose a significant mechanical hazard. Presses designed to be activated by only one hand leave a potential for the worker's free hand to be caught between the presses. Belts, drive chains, shafts and couplings should be guarded to prevent accidental contact. All moving components of machines should be guarded to prevent body parts from becoming caught in a pinch, nip or shear point. The most common methods of guarding a hazard are enclosing the operation, interlocking devices, moving barriers, removal devices, remote controls, two-hand tripping devices and electronic safety devices.

Electrical hazards

Numerous measures can be taken to limit electrical hazards. Especially important is proper insulation and grounding. Identification and guarding of live parts also helps to prevent injury from electrical current. Electrical hazards can be compounded by the presence of moisture. Ground-fault circuit interrupters are designed to shut off power if high current passes through an unintended path. When selecting electrical equipment, the recommendations of established codes and standards, such as the US National Fire Protection Association 70, the National Electrical Code and the American National Standards Institute's C2, should be followed. Guidelines for appropriate use of electrical equipment are given elsewhere in this *Encyclopaedia*.

Heat stress

Heat stress can afflict workers who must labour for extended periods of time in the hot environments that exist in many cleaning facilities. Heat stress may be compounded in the summer months, particularly if the shop is not air conditioned (air conditioning is not common in this industry). Both physical and environmental factors will modify the effects of heat. Acclimatization, body surface area to weight ratio, age and diseases, water and salt balance and physical fitness all play a role in the likelihood an individual will be affected by heat stress.

Slips, trips and falls

The hazard of slips, trips and falls are especially pertinent to cleaning facilities, which are often crowded with people and equipment. Without clearly established aisles and with a large number of containers holding solvents or water, spills can easily occur, resulting in a slippery floor. To control this hazard, regular housekeeping must be emphasized, facility layout must be carefully planned, and floor surfaces should be of non-slip materials. The workplace should be maintained in a clean, orderly, sanitary condition, and any spills should be cleaned up promptly.

Biological hazards

Laundering hospital linens puts sorters at risk from overlooked sharp objects in sheets or uniform pockets. Both dry cleaners and launderers may encounter freshly soiled garments that have been contaminated with human body fluids. Garments that have come from dental and medical offices or labs, blood banks, drug treatment centers, clinics, mortuaries, ambulances and other health-care facilities can be reasonably suspected to contain potentially infectious materials. In many countries, shops that handle garments from these sources must comply with the occupational standards governing exposures, such as the OSHA regulations governing bloodborne pathogens.

Environmental and Public Health Concerns

Environmental and public health concerns have resulted in dramatic changes in environmental regulations affecting the dry-cleaning industry in recent years. Adjacent apartments and businesses can be exposed to PERC vapours by diffusion through walls or ceilings; indoor airflow through holes in ceilings, pipe chases or vents; and through PERC emissions vented outside of the shop that are re-entrained through opened windows or ventilation units. Groundwater or soil contamination can occur through frequent or large solvent spills that might occur during transfer of solvent from a delivery truck to the dry-cleaning machine. Soil contamination might also occur through improper disposal of separator water into the sanitary sewer. Finally, consumers may be exposed from PERC residuals in poorly dried garments. This is of particular concern if the cleaning machine is not functioning properly or the dry cycle is shortened to improve productivity.

Acknowledgement: This article is largely based on materials assembled and published by the US National Institute for Occupational Safety and Health (NIOSH).

FUNERAL SERVICES

Mary O. Brophy and Jonathan T. Haney

General Profile

Assuming a world population of 5 billion, between one-quarter and one-half of a million people die each day. Many of the dead are infants or children, but eventually everyone who is born will also die. Despite the diversity in culture and religious beliefs surrounding death, the bodily remains of each person must be disposed of. In general, the two main methods of disposing of human remains consist of burial and cremation. Both of these disposal methods often have been applied to the untreated human remains. Many cultures, however, have developed funeral rites that prescribe some treatment of the dead body. Simpler rites may include the washing of the external surface with herbs and spices to slow or mask the onset of decay and the smell associated with dead tissue. More sophisticated rites include intrusive procedures such as embalming and removal of internal organs. Embalming usually involves replacement of blood with an embalming or preserving fluid. The Egyptians were among the first culture to develop and practice embalming of the dead. Embalming has been extensively practiced in the twentieth century throughout Western Europe and North America. Embalming may be followed either by burial or cremation. Outside of Western Europe and North America, burial or cremation is usually not preceded by embalming.

Funeral Processes

The preparation and burial of a deceased person can involve many processes, including:

- washing the surface of the body with various preparations
- dressing the body in burial clothes
- autopsies, in certain circumstances, which involve intrusive procedure, such as dissection and analysis of blood and body tissues
- embalming and removal of internal organs
- application of cosmetics to cover up visible damage if the body is to be viewed
- transporting the body to place of burial or cremation
- lifting of body and casket, and lowering it into the grave
- digging and filling of the grave
- possible exhumation of the body and subsequent autopsy.

Three types of hazard are always associated with the handling of deceased humans: microbial, psychological and ergonomic. A fourth type of hazard—chemical exposure—is introduced when embalming is performed. In the United States many states have enacted laws that require a body to be embalmed if the deceased person will be viewed in a open casket.

Microbial Hazards

Death is often caused by disease. After death the germs that caused the disease may continue to live in the deceased person and can infect the people handling the dead body. Contagious diseases such as the plague and smallpox have been spread by improper handling of victims who died from the diseases. The route of exposure must be considered when evaluating the microbial hazard associated with the handling of dead bodies. Many diseases are spread by touching a source of contamination and then introducing that disease-causing organism, or pathogen, to one's mucous membranes by rubbing the eyes or nose, or by ingesting the pathogen. Some diseases can be contracted simply by inhaling the pathogen. Inhalation can be a special hazard during exhumation, when the remains are dry, or during procedures that aerosolize parts of the human body, such as sawing through the bone of a deceased person. The contagion of diseases is further exacerbated when procedures with sharp instruments are used in funeral rites. Such practices introduce the possibility of parenteral exposure.

Microbial hazards can be classified in many different ways, including the type of disease-causing organism, the type of disease, the severity of the disease and the route of infection. Perhaps the most useful way of discussing microbial hazards encountered by funeral workers is by route of infection. The routes of infection are ingestion, inhalation, touch or surface contact and parenteral, or puncture of a body surface.

Ingestion as a route of exposure can be controlled by proper personal hygiene—that is, always washing hands before eating or smoking, and by keeping food, drink or any object that will be put in the mouth (such as cigarettes) out of areas of possible contamination. This is important for controlling chemical exposure as well. In addition to careful personal hygiene, wearing imperme-

able gloves when handling the dead can reduce the probability of infection.

Inhalation exposure occurs only when disease-causing organisms become airborne. For funeral workers the two primary ways that pathogens can become airborne are during an exhumation or during autopsy procedures in which a saw is used to cut through bone. A third possibility of aerosolizing a pathogen—tuberculosis, for example—is when air is forced out of the lungs of a corpse during handling. Although the epidemics of the past have included plague, cholera, typhoid, tuberculosis, anthrax and smallpox, only the organisms causing anthrax and smallpox appear capable of surviving any length of time after burial (Healing, Hoffman and Young 1995). These pathogens would be found in any of the soft tissues, not the bones, and particularly in soft tissues that have become mummified and/or dried out and friable. The anthrax bacterium can form spores that remain viable for long periods, especially under dry conditions. Intact smallpox viruses taken from the tissues of bodies buried in the 1850s were identified under the electron microscope. None of the viruses grew in tissue culture and they were deemed to be non-infective (Baxter, Brazier and Young 1988). Smallpox virus has remained infective, however, after 13 years in dry storage under laboratory conditions (Wolff and Croon 1968). An article appearing in the *Journal of Public Health* (UK) during the 1850s reports concern about smallpox infectivity from remains buried two hundred years earlier in Montreal, when smallpox was widespread in the New World (Sly 1994).

Perhaps a more probable source of inhalation exposure during exhumation are fungal spores. Whenever old material of any sort is disturbed, protection against the inhalation of fungal spores should be provided. Disposable high efficiency particulate (HEPA) respirators, developed primarily for protection against tuberculosis and lead dust, are quite effective against fungal spores as well. In addition to microbial concerns, the possibility of exposure to wood dust and/or lead needs to be evaluated before any exhumation proceeds.

The primary route of infection for tuberculosis is inhalation. The incidence of tuberculosis has increased during the last quarter of the twentieth century, primarily due to decreased public health vigilance and the emergence of bacterial strains that are resistant to several groups of antibiotics. A recent study conducted at Johns Hopkins School of Public Health (Baltimore, Maryland, US) indicates that 18.8% of embalmers demonstrated positive results to tuberculin skin tests. Only 6.8% of people employed in the funeral business who are not embalmers demonstrated positive results to the same test. The lower rate of reactivity is similar to the general public (Gershon and Karkashion 1996).

Hepatitis B virus (HBV) and the human immunodeficiency virus (HIV) are infective if they come in contact with mucous membranes or are introduced into the bloodstream through a cut or puncture. A study of funeral service practitioners in Maryland indicated that 10% had a mucous membrane exposure within the past 6 months and 15% reported a needle stick within the past 6 months (Gershon et al. 1995). Other US studies reported that between 39 and 53% of morticians had a needle stick within the past 12 months (Nwanyanwu, Tubasuri and Harris 1989). In the United States, the reported prevalence of HBV is between 7.5 and 12.0% in unvaccinated funeral directors, and 2.6% or less in vaccinated funeral workers. The reported vaccination rate varies between 19 and 60% of morticians in the United States. Although there is a vaccine for HBV, there is currently no vaccine for HIV.

HIV and HBV are infective only when the virus comes into contact with the mucous membranes or is introduced into the bloodstream of another human. The virus is not absorbed through intact skin. Mucous membranes include the mouth, nose and eyes. These viruses can be introduced into the bloodstream through a cut or abrasion in the skin, or by puncturing or cutting the skin with an instrument that is contaminated with the virus. Hands that are cracked due to dryness or a hangnail may provide routes of entry for these viruses. Therefore, to prevent transmission of these diseases it is important to provide a barrier impermeable to body fluids, to avoid splashing contaminated fluids on the eyes, nose or mouth, and to prevent puncturing or cutting the skin with an instrument contaminated with HIV or HBV. Use of latex gloves and a face shield can often provide this protection. Latex gloves, however, have a limited shelf life depending on the amount of sunlight and heat to which they have been exposed. In general, the latex should be stress tested if the gloves have been stored for more than a year. Stress testing involves filling the glove with water and observing if any leaks develop during a minimum of two minutes. Some countries in the West, such as the United States and Great Britain, have adopted the idea of universal precautions, which means that every corpse is treated as if it were infected with HIV and HBV.

Psychological Hazards

In many cultures the family of the deceased prepares the body of their dead relative for burial or cremation. In other cultures a specialized group of individuals prepares the bodies of the dead for burial or cremation. There is a psychological effect on the living when they are involved in handling dead bodies. The psychological effect is real regardless of the procedures used in the funeral rites. Recently there has been an interest in identifying and evaluating the effects of performing funeral rites on those who actually perform them.

Although the psychological hazards of being a professional funeral worker have not been extensively studied, the psychological effects of dealing with the human remains of traumatic death have been recently analyzed. The main psychological effects appear to be anxiety, depression and somatization (the tendency to report physical ailments), as well as irritability, appetite and sleep disturbances, and increased alcohol use (Ursano et al. 1995). Post-traumatic stress disorder (PTSD) occurred in a significant number of individuals who handled the victims of traumatic deaths. Immediately after a disaster in which human remains were handled by rescue workers, between 20 and 40% of the rescue workers were considered to be in a high risk category, as demonstrated by psychological testing, but only about 10% of the rescue workers were diagnosed with PTSD. The psychological effects were still present in rescue workers one year after the disaster, but the incidence was greatly reduced. Adverse psychological effects, however, have been detected in individuals several years after the traumatic event.

Many of these studies were performed on military personnel. They indicate that generalized stress rates are higher in inexperienced individuals who were not volunteers, and that there was an increased incidence of stress indicators up to one year after a traumatic incident. Empathy or self-identification of the mortuary worker with the deceased appeared to be associated with an increased level of psychological stress (McCarroll et al. 1993; McCarroll et al. 1995).

One study evaluated the causes of death in 4,046 embalmers and funeral directors in the United States between 1975 and 1985, and reported a proportionate mortality ratio (PMR) of 130 for suicide. The PMR is a ratio of the actual number of suicides in the embalmers and funeral directors divided by the number of suicides that would be expected in a group of individuals comparable in age, race and sex who are not embalmers or funeral directors. This ratio is then multiplied by 100. The purpose of this study was to assess the risk of cancer in morticians, and the suicide statistic was not elaborated any further.

Ergonomics

A deceased human adult is heavy and usually must be carried to a designated place of burial or cremation. Even when mechanical means of transportation are used, the dead body must be transferred from the place of death to the vehicle and from the vehicle to the burial or cremation site. Out of respect for the dead person, this transfer is usually performed by other humans.

Morticians are required to move corpses many times during the course of body preparation and funerals. Although there were no studies found that addressed this issue, low-back pain and injury is associated with prolonged repetitive lifting of heavy objects. There are lifting devices available which can assist with these types of lifts.

Chemical Hazards

Embalming procedures introduce a number of potent chemicals into the workspace of funeral workers. Perhaps the most widely used and toxic of these is formaldehyde. Formaldehyde is irritating to the mucous membranes, the eyes, the nasal lining and the respiratory system, and has been associated with mutagenic cell changes and the development of cancer, as well as occupational asthma. During the past several decades the occupational exposure level associated with no adverse effects has been consistently lowered. Current 8-hour time-weighted average permissible exposure limits range from 0.5 ppm in Germany, Japan, Norway, Sweden and Switzerland to 5 ppm in Egypt and Taiwan (IARC 1995c). Formaldehyde levels between 0.15 and 4.3 ppm, with instantaneous levels as high as 6.6 ppm, have been reported for individual embalmings. An embalming typically takes between 1 and 2 hours. Additional formaldehyde exposure is associated with the application of embalming creams and drying and hardening powders, and during spills.

Rats that have been chronically exposed to 6 to 15 ppm of formaldehyde (Albert et al. 1982; Kerns et al. 1982; Tobe et al. 1985), or repeatedly exposed to 20 ppm for 15-minute periods (Feron et al. 1988), have developed nasal carcinomas (Hayes et al. 1990). The IARC reports limited epidemiological evidence for an association between formaldehyde exposure in industry and the development of human nasal and pharyngeal cancers (Olsen and Asnaes 1986; Hayes et al. 1986; Roush et al. 1987; Vaughan et al. 1986; Blair et al. 1986; Stayner et al. 1988). Several studies of morticians, however, have reported an increased incidence of leukaemias and brain tumours (Levine, Andjelkovich and Shaw 1984; Walrath and Fraumeni 1983). In addition to the carcinogenic effects, formaldehyde is irritating to the mucous membranes and has been considered a strong sensitizer in the development of adult-onset asthma. The mechanism or mechanisms by which formaldehyde precipitates asthma are even less well characterized than its role in the development of cancer.

Other potentially toxic chemicals used in embalming fluids include phenol, methanol, isopropyl alcohol and glutaraldehyde (Hayes et al. 1990). Glutaraldehyde appears to be even more irritating than formaldehyde to the mucous membranes, and affects the central nervous system at levels well above 500 ppm. Methanol also affects the central nervous system and, in particular, the vision system. Phenol appears to affect the nervous system as well as the lungs, heart, liver and kidneys, and is absorbed quite rapidly through the skin. Our understanding of the toxicology of, and our ability to perform risk assessment for, exposure to multiple chemicals simultaneously are not sufficiently sophisticated to analyse the physiological effects of the mixtures to which embalmers and funeral directors are exposed. Blair et al. (1990a) thought that the increased incidence of leukaemias and brain tumours reported in professional, but not industrial, workers was a result of exposure to chemicals other than formaldehyde.

Recent advances in the design of dissecting tables indicate that local downdrafting of vapours significantly reduces the exposure of individuals working in the vicinity (Coleman 1995). Wearing gloves while performing procedures that require skin contact with embalming fluids and creams also reduces the hazard. There has been some concern, however, that some of the latex gloves on the market may be permeable to formaldehyde. Therefore, protective gloves should be selected carefully. In addition to the immediate concerns about the hazards of formaldehyde exposure, evidence has been accumulating that leachate from cemeteries may lead to formaldehyde contamination of groundwater.

Exhumation of bodies may also involve chemical exposures. Although used sporadically for centuries, lead was commonly used to line coffins beginning in the eighteenth and continuing into the nineteenth century. Inhalation of wood dust is associated with respiratory problems, and fungus-contaminated wood dust is a double-edged sword. Arsenic and mercury compounds were also used as preservatives in the past and could present a hazard during exhumation.

● DOMESTIC WORKERS

Angela Babin

General Profile

Domestic work is characterized by labour for another family within their home. The term *domestic workers* should not be confused with *homemakers* and *housewives*, who work in their own home, or *housekeepers*, who work in institutions such as a hospital or school. The position of employment within a home is a unique and often isolated work environment. The position of domestic worker is almost always considered menial or inferior to the family for which they are employed. Indeed in the past, domestic work was sometimes done by slaves or indentured or bonded servants. Some of the job titles today for domestic workers include: servant, maid, housekeeper, au pair and nanny. While domestic workers can be either female or male, female workers are both much more commonly employed and most often paid less than males. Domestic workers are customarily immigrants or members of ethnic, national or religious minorities of the country of employment.

One should distinguish between domestic workers who are employed as live-in servants from those who live in their own home and commute to their place of work. Live-in domestic workers are isolated from their own family, as well as often from their own country of nationality. Because of the worker's disenfranchisement, work contracts and health and other benefits are negligible. Sometimes, room and board are considered part or even complete payment for services rendered. This situation is particularly critical for the overseas domestic worker. Sometimes, infractions concerning agreed-upon salary, sick leave, working hours, vacation pay and regulation of working hours and duties cannot even be addressed because the worker is not fluent in the language, and lacks an advocate, union, work contract or money with which to exit a dangerous situation (Anderson 1993; ILO 1989). Domestic workers usually have no workers' compensation, nowhere to report a violation, and are often unable to quit their employment.

Places where major employers of domestic workers are found include Britain, the Persian Gulf and Arab States, Greece, Hong Kong, Italy, Nigeria, Singapore and the United States. These domestic workers are from various countries, including Bangladesh, Brazil, Colombia, Ethiopia, Eritrea, India, Indonesia, Morocco, Nepal, Nigeria, the Philippines, Sierra Leone and Sri Lanka (Anderson 1993). In the United States, many domestic workers are immigrants from Central and Latin America and the Caribbean islands. Domestic workers are sometimes illegal immigrants, or have special limited visas. They are often not eligible for the basic social services available to others.

General Tasks

Tasks for domestic workers can include:

- *Kitchen work:* shopping for food, cooking and preparation of meals, waiting on the family and serving meals, cleaning up after mealtime and taking care of tableware
- *Housecleaning and housekeeping:* care of furniture and bric-a-brac, washing dishes, polishing silver and cleaning the house including bathrooms, floors, walls, windows and sometimes annexes, such as guest houses, garages and sheds
- *Clothing care:* washing, drying, ironing of clothing, sometimes mending of clothing or delivery/pick-up of clothing that is dry cleaned
- *Child and elder care:* babysitting or childcare, changing diapers and other clothes, washing children, supervision of meals and activities and delivery to and from school. Domestic workers will sometimes be given tasks that revolve around elder care such as supervision, bathing, companionship tasks, delivery to and from doctor visits and light medical chores.

Hazards and Precautions

In general, the intensity of hazards associated with live-in domestic workers is much greater than domestic workers who commute to work daily.

Physical hazards

Some physical hazards include: long working hours, insufficient rest time and sometimes insufficient food, exposures to hot and cold water, exposure to hot kitchen environments, musculoskeletal problems, especially back and spinal pain, from lifting children and furniture, and kneeling to clean floors. "Housemaid's knee" has been likened to "carpet layer's knee", the injury sustained by carpet layers. While mechanization of certain floor-polishing and waxing processes has resulted in less work from the knees, many domestics still must work from their knees, and almost always without padding or protection (Tanaka et al. 1982; Turnbull et al. 1992).

Precautions include limitations of working hours, adequate rest and food breaks, gloves for dishwashing and other water immersion, training in proper lifting techniques, mechanized carpet cleaners and floor polishers to minimize the time spent on the knees and provision of knee pads for occasional tasks.

Chemical hazards

Domestic workers can be exposed to a wide variety of acids, alkalis, solvents and other chemicals in household cleaning products which can cause dermatitis. (See also "Indoor cleaning services" in this chapter.). Dermatitis can often be exacerbated by the immersion of hands in hot or cold water (Scolari and Gardenghi 1966). Domestic workers may not know enough about the materials they use or how to use these products safely. There is inadequate training in chemical handling or hazard communication for materials that they use. For example, a severe poisoning case in a servant who was using cadmium carbonate silver-cleaning powder has been reported. The worker used the product for one-and-a-half days, and suffered abdominal cramps, tightness of the throat, vomiting and low pulse. Recovery took 24 days (Sovet 1958).

Many products used or handled by domestic workers are known allergens. These include natural rubber protective gloves, house plants, waxes and polishes, detergents, hand creams, antiseptics and impurities in detergents and whiteners. Irritant dermatitis may be a precursor to allergic contact dermatitis in housekeepers, and often starts with the development of erythema patches on the backs of hands (Foussereau et al. 1982). Inhalation of solvents, household pesticides, dusts, moulds and so on can cause respiratory problems.

Precautions include using the least toxic household cleaning products possible, training in materials handling and safety of the various detergents and cleaning fluids, as well as the use of protective hand creams and gloves. Unscented products may be better for those individuals prone to allergy (Foussereau et al. 1982).

Biological hazards

Domestic workers with responsibility for the care of young children in particular are at greater risk of becoming infected with a variety of illnesses, especially from changing diapers, and from contaminated food and water. Precautions include washing hands carefully after changing and handling soiled diapers, proper disposal of soiled items and proper food-handling procedures.

Psychological and stress hazards

Some psychological and stress hazards include isolation from one's family and community; lack of paid vacation and sick or maternity leave; inadequate protection of wages; rape, physical and mental abuse; over-extended working hours; and general lack of benefits or contracts. Live-in domestic workers face greater danger from hazards including violence, harassment, physical and mental abuse and rape (Anderson 1993).

During a six-month period in 1990, there were eight deaths—six suicides and two murders—of Filipino domestic helpers recounted in a report filed by the Philippine Embassy in Singapore. Suicide is under-reported and not well documented; however, there were as many as 40 suicides reported to the Philippine Embassy in one time period (Gulati 1993).

To a lesser extent, these same hazards are relevant to non-residential domestic workers. In an Ohio (United States) study that looked at workers' compensation claims filed for sexual assault from 1983 to 1985, 14% of the rapes occurred in motel maids and housekeepers (Seligman et al. 1987).

Prevention of abuses of domestic workers can be aided by establishment of laws that protect these comparatively defenceless workers. In the United States, the hiring of illegal immigrants as domestic workers was a common practice until the passage of the Immigration Reform and Control Act of 1986. This act increased the penalties that could be imposed on the employers of these workers. However, in developed countries the demand for domestic help is steadily increasing. In the United States, domestic workers must be paid at least the minimum wage and, if they earn $1,000 or more annually from any single employer, they are entitled to unemployment compensation and social security (Anderson 1993).

Other countries have taken steps to protect these vulnerable domestic workers. Canada started its Live-in Care-giver Program in 1981, which was amended in 1992. This programme involves recognition of immigrant domestic workers.

Acknowledgement of the immigrant domestic worker is the first step in being able to address heath and safety preventive issues for them. As initial recognition of these workers and their difficulties is achieved, dangerous working conditions can be addressed and improved with government regulations, unionization, private support groups and women's health initiatives.

Health Effects and Disease Patterns

One study of mortality data of 1,382 female domestic workers in British Columbia (Canada) showed higher mortality than expected from cirrhosis of the liver, accidental death due to exposure, homicides and accidents of all types combined. Also, deaths due to pneumonia and rectal and eye cancer were higher than anticipated. The authors suggest that a major factor in the elevated deaths due to liver cirrhosis is because many domestic workers in British Columbia are from the Philippines, where hepatitis B is endemic (McDougal et al. 1992). Other studies point to alcoholism as a factor. In a review of a California (United States) mortality study, it was noted that the following occupations were associated with increased cirrhosis mortality rates in women: private housecleaner and servant; waitress; and nursing aide, orderly and attendant. The authors conclude that the study supports an association between occupation and cirrhosis mortality and, furthermore, that the greatest cirrhosis mortality is associated with low-status employment and jobs where alcohol is easily available (Harford and Brooks 1992).

In their 1989 study of occupational skin disease, the British Association of Dermatologists found that of 2,861 reported cases (of which 96% were contact dermatitis), the occupation of "cleaners and domestics" was the second-highest category of work listed for women (8.4%) (Cherry, Beck and Owen-Smith 1994). Similarly, in positive responses to dermatological patch tests performed on 6,818 patients, the most common professions of women studied were housekeeper, office worker, cleaner, needleworker and cosmetologist. Housework accounted for 943 of the positive responses to the patch tests (Dooms-Goossens 1986).

Other research has pointed to respiratory allergy and disease. Organic chemical-induced occupational allergic lung diseases were reviewed, and the category of domestic workers was noted as one occupation particularly affected by respiratory allergens (Pepys 1986). A Swedish study on mortality due to asthma looked at women who reported employment in the 1960 National Census. Smoking-adjusted standardized mortality ratios were calculated for each occupation. Increased mortality due to asthma was seen in caretakers, maids, waitresses and housekeepers (Horte and Toren 1993).

There is a lack of statistics and health information concerning domestic workers, especially for overseas immigrant workers, perhaps because of these workers' temporary or even illegal status in their countries of employment. Governmental acknowledgement will only help enable more research and protection of these workers' health.

Environmental issues

Many of the processes described in the articles in this chapter can generate hazardous waste such as solvents, acids, alkalis, formaldehyde and so forth.

In dry cleaning, there has been concern about perchloroethylene vapours polluting the air of apartments above the dry-cleaning shops. The installation of machinery for purification and recovery of solvent vapours, the centralization of dry cleaning (using local shops just as drop-off and pickup places) and the development of wet cleaning methods that minimize solvent use are all methods that can minimize these problems.

Funeral parlours using embalming generate both chemical hazardous waste (e.g., formaldehyde) and biological hazardous waste (blood and blood-containing materials). Most countries where embalming is practised require these to be disposed of as hazardous waste. In crematoria, airborne mercury contamination can result from mercury amalgam fillings in teeth.

Most cosmetology shops that generate chemical waste pour it down the drain or place containers with residues in the trash. This is also true of cleaning personnel, both in homes and in institutions, who can generate waste in the form of solvents, acids and other cleaning products containing hazardous chemicals. The existence of many generators individually producing small amounts of waste creates a control problem; focused and standard control technologies are not easily implemented in these cases. For example, even in large institutions like hospitals, the cleaning chemicals are used in small amounts throughout the building, with cleaning chemicals often stored at many locations.

There are several solutions to this problem. One is the ongoing development of less hazardous substitutes, especially the replacement of solvents with water-based products. Another solution is the adoption of procedures to ensure that only the amounts of products needed for the near future are purchased, to avoid the accumulation of old products that must be disposed of. Using all the product in a container before discarding it in the trash can reduce the pollution from that source. In recent years, some countries, like the United States and Canada, have established local household hazardous waste programmes where waste such as solvents and cleaning products can be taken to central collection points that will accept the hazardous waste free of charge and dispose of it according to proper procedures.

Michael McCann

References

Agency for Toxic Substances and Disease Registry (ATSDR). 1995. *Toxicological Profile for Tetrachloroethylene (Update-draft for Public Comment)*. Atlanta, GA: US ATSDR.

Albert, RE, AR Sellakumar, S Laskin, K Kuschner, N Nelson, and CA Snyder. 1982. Gaseous formaldehyde and hydrogen chloride induction of nasal cancer in the rat. *JNCI* 68: 597-603.

Anderson, B. 1993. *Britain's Secret Slaves: An Investigation into the Plight of Overseas Domestic Workers*. Human Right Series No. 5, Anti-slavery International and Kalayaan: Justice for Overseas Domestic Workers.

Armstrong, P and H Armstrong. 1994. *The Double Ghetto*, 3rd edition. Toronto: McClelland and Stewart.

Association pour la santé et la sécurité au travail, secteur affaires sociales (ASSTSAS). 1993. *Entretien sanitaire*. Montreal: ASSTSAS.

Baxter, PJ, AM Brazier, and SEJ Young. 1988. Is smallpox a hazard in church crypts? *Br J Ind Med* 45: 359-360.

Blainey, AD, S Ollier, D Cundell, RE Smith, and RJ Davies. 1986. Occupational asthma in hairdressing salons. *Thorax* 41:42-50.

Blair, A, R Saracci, PA Stewart, RB Hayes, and C Shy. 1990a. Epidemiologic evidence on the relationship between formaldehyde exposure and cancer. *Scand J Work, Environ and Health* 16:381-391.

Blair, A, P Stewart, PE Tolbert, D Grauman, FX Moran, J Faught, and J Rayner. 1990b. Cancer and other causes of death among laundry and dry cleaning workers. *Br J Ind Med* 47:162-168.

Blair, A, PA Stewart, M O'Berg, W Gaffey, J Walrath, J Ward, R Bales, S Kaplan, and D Cubit. 1986. Mortality among industrial workers exposed to formaldehyde. *JNCI* 76: 1071-1084.

Borglum, B and AM Hansen. 1994. *A Survey of Washing and Cleaning Agents* (in Danish, abstract in English). AMI Report 44. Copenhagen, Denmark: Danish Institute of Occupational Health.

Bretin, H. 1994. *Santé des ouvriers du nettoyage à Montréal et à Paris: La face cachée du travail dans la ville*. Kremlin-Bicêtre, France: INSERM Unité 292.

Bretin, H, N Frigul, I Metenier, L Aussel, and A Thébaud-Mony. 1992. *Des femmes chomeuses en mauvaise santé*. Kremlin-Bicêtre, France: INSERM Unité 292.

Cherry, NM, MH Beck, and V Owen-Smith. 1994. *Surveillance of Occupational Skin Disease in the United Kingdom: The OCC-Derm Project*. US NIOSH Publication No. 94-112. Proceedings of the 9th International Symposium on Epidemiology in Occupational Health, 23-25 September 1992, Cincinnati, OH: US NIOSH.

Coleman, R. 1995. Reducing the levels of formaldehyde exposure in gross anatomy laboratories. *Anat Rec* 243: 531-533.

Delaporte, M-F, M Estryn-Behar, G Brucker, E Peigne, and A Pelletier. 1990. Pathologie dermatologique et exercice professionnel en milieu hospitalier. *Arch mal prof* 51(2):83-88.

Demers, PA, TL Vaughan, and RR Schommer. 1991. Occupation, socioeconomic status and brain tumor mortality: A death certificate-based case-control study. *JOM* 33(9):1001-1006.

Dooms-Goossens, A. 1986. A computerized retrieval system of contact allergenic substances. *Seminars in Dermatology* 5(3):249-254.

Duh, RW and NR Asal. 1984. Mortality among laundry and dry cleaning workers in Oklahoma. *Am J Public Health* 74:1278-1280.

Earnest, GS. 1996. Evaluation and control of perchloroethylene exposures during dry cleaning. *Appl Occup Environ Hyg* 11(2):125-132.

Earnest, GS and AB Spencer. 1996. *Lessons from Europe: Reducing Occupational Exposure and Environmental Emissions to Perchloroethylene in Commercial Dry Cleaning* (ECTB No. 201-07). Cincinnati, OH: US NIOSH.

Environmental Protection Agency (EPA). 1991a. *Dry-cleaning Facilities—Background Information for Proposed Standards* (EPA Publication No. 50/3-91-020a). Research Triangle Park, NC: Office of Air Quality Planning and Standards, Environmental Protection Agency.

—. 1991b. National emission standards for hazardous air pollutants for source categories: Perchloroethylene emissions from dry cleaning facilities, proposed rule and notice of public hearing. *Federal Reg* 56(236):64382-64402.

Feron, VJ, JP Bruyntjes, RA Woutersen, HR Immel, and LM Appelman. 1988. Nasal tumors in rats after short-term exposure to a cytotoxic concentration of formaldehyde. *Canc Lett* 39: 101-111.

Flyvholm, M-A. 1993. Contact allergens in registered cleaning agents for industrial and household use. *Br J Ind Med* 50:1043-1050.

Foussereau, J, C Benezra, HI Maibach, and N Hjorth. 1982. House personnel. In *Occupational Contact Dermatitis, Clinical and Chemical Aspects*. Philadelphia: W. B. Saunders Company.

Gamboa, PM, CG de la Cuesta, BE Garcia, JG Castillo, and A Oehling. 1989. Late asthmatic reaction in a hairdresser, due to inhalation of ammonium persulfate salts. *Allergologia et immunopathologia* 17:109-111.

Gawkrodger, DJ, MH Lloyd, and JAA Hunter. 1986. Occupational skin disease in hospital cleaning and kitchen workers. *Contact Dermatitis* 15:132-135.

Gershon, RRM and C Karkashion. 1996. The risk of TB in funeral service workers: Preliminary results. Presented at the American Public Health Association meetings, November, New York City.

Gershon, RRM, D Vlahox, H Farzadegan, and A Miriam. 1995. Occupational risk of human immunodeficiency virus, hepatitis B virus, and hepatitis C virus infections among funeral service practitioners in Maryland. 1995. *Infec Contr Hosp Epid* 16: 194-197.

Gervais, M. 1993. *Bilan de santé des travailleurs québécois*. Montréal: Institut de recherche en santé et en sécurité du travail du Quebec.

Government of Quebec. 1994. *Décret sur le personnel d'entretien d'édifices publics de la région de Montréal*. Québec: Éditeur officiel.

Gulati, L. 1993. *Women Migrant Workers in Asia: A Review*. New Delhi. ILO Asian Regional Team for Employment Protection.

Hagner, I-M and M Hagberg. 1989. Evaluation of two floor-mopping work methods by measurement of load. *Ergonomics* 32 (4): 401-408.

Hansen, KS. 1983. Occupational dermatoses in hospital cleaning women. *Contact Dermatitis* 9:343-351.

Harford, TC and SD Brooks. 1992. Cirrhosis mortality and occupation. *J Stud Alcohol* 53(5):463-468.

Hayes, RB, A Blair, PA Stewart, RF Herrick, and H Mahar. 1990. Mortality of U.S. embalmers and funeral directors. *Am J Ind Med* 18: 641-652.

Hayes, RB, JW Raatgever, A de Bruyn, and M Gerin. 1986. Cancer of the nasal cavity and paranasal sinuses and formaldehyde exposure. *Int J Canc* 37: 487-492.

Healing, TD, PN Hoffman, and SEJ Young. 1995. The infection hazards of human cadavers. *Communicable Dis Rev* 5: R61-R68.

Hohenstein Institute. 1995. *Requirements for the Use of Hydrocarbon Solvents in the Dry Cleaning Industry*. Boennigheim, Germany: Hohenstein Institute.

Horte, LG and K Toren. 1993. Smoking adjusted mortality due to asthma in a population of Swedish working women. *Br J Ind Med* 50(6):575-576.

International Agency for Research on Cancer (IARC). 1995a. Dry cleaning, some chlorinated solvents and other industrial chemicals (Dry cleaning). In *IARC Monographs on the Evaluation of Carcinogenic Risk to Humans*. Vol. 63. Lyon: IARC.

—. 1995b. Dry cleaning, some chlorinated solvents and other industrial chemicals (Tetrachloroethylene). In *IARC Monographs on the Evaluation of Carcinogenic Risks to Humans*. Lyon: IARC.

—. 1995c. Wood dust and formaldehyde. In *IARC Monographs on the Evaluation of Carcinogenic Risks to Humans*. Lyon: IARC.

International Fabricare Institute. 1990. *Focus on Dry Cleaning: Distillation*. Silver Spring, MD: International Fabricare Institute.

International Labour Organization (ILO). 1989. *Conditions of Work Digest: Home Work*. Vol. 8, No. 2. Geneva: ILO.

Johannsson, S-E and G Ljunggren. 1989. Perceived exertion during a self-imposed pace of work for a group of cleaners. *Applied Ergonomics* 20 (4):307-312.

John, EM, DA Savitz, and CM Shy. 1994. Spontaneous abortion among cosmetologists. *Epidemiology* 5:147-155.

Katz, RM and D Jowett. 1981. Female laundry and dry cleaning workers in Wisconsin: A mortality analysis. *Am J Public Health* 71:305-307.

Kerns, WD, KL Pavkov, DJ Donofrio, EJ Gralla, and JA Swenberg. 1982. Carcinogenicity of formaldehyde in rats and mice after long-term inhalation exposure. *Canc Res* 43: 4382-4392.

Koenig, KL. 1994. Hair dye use and breast cancer: A case-control study among screening participants. *Am J Epi* 133:985-995.

Levine, RJ, DA Andjelkovich, and LK Shaw. 1984. The mortality of Ontario undertakers and a review of formaldehyde-related mortality studies. *J Occ Med* 26: 740-746.

Lin, RS and II Kessler. 1981. A multifactorial model for pancreatic cancer in man: Epidemiologic evidence. *JAMA* 245:147-152.

McCarroll, JE, RJ Ursano, CS Fullerton, and A Lundy. 1993. Traumatic stress of a wartime mortuary, anticipation of exposure to mass death. *J Nerv Ment Dis* 181: 545-551.

—. 1995. Anticipatory stress of handling human remains from the Persian Gulf War. *J Nerv Ment Dis* 183: 698-703.

McDonald, AD, B Armstrong, N Cherry, C Delorme, AD Nolin, JC McDonald, and D Robert. 1986. Spontaneous abortion and occupation. *J Occ Med* 28:1232-1238.

McDonald, AD, JC McDonald, B Armstrong, N Cherry, C Delorme, AD Nolin, and D Robert. 1987. Occupation and pregnancy outcome. *Br J Ind Med* 44:521-526.

McDonald, AD, JC McDonald, B Armstrong, N Cherry, AD Nolin, and D Robert. 1988. Prematurity and work in pregnancy. *Br J Ind Med* 45:56-62.

McDougal, L, PR Band, JJ Spinelli, WJ Threlfall, and RP Gallagher. 1992. Mortality patterns in female domestic workers. *Am J Ind Med* 21(4):595-599.

Messing, K. 1991. *Occupational Health Concerns of Canadian Women/La santé et la sécurité des travailleuses canadiennes*. Ottawa: Human Resources Canada.

—. In press. Hospital trash: Cleaners speak of their role in disease prevention. *Med Anthropol Quar*.

Messing, K, C Chatigny, and J Courville. 1995. Travail prescrit, travail réel, travail perçu: l'entretien sanitaire «lourd» et «léger» en milieu hospitalier. *Annals of the Société d'ergonomie de langue française*: 578-585.

—. 1996. L'invisibilité du travail et la division léger/lourd dans l'entretien sanitaire: Impact sur la santé et la sécurité du travail. *Objectif Prévention*. 19(2):13-16.

Messing, K, G Doniol-Shaw, and C Haëntjens. 1993. Sugar and spice: Health effects of the sexual division of labour among train cleaners. *Int J Health Services* 23 (1):133-146.

Messing, K, C Haëntjens, and G Doniol-Shaw. 1993. L'invisible nécessaire: l'activité de nettoyage des toilettes sur les trains de voyageurs en gare. *Le travail humain* 55:353-370.

Michaels, David. Undated. *Right-to-know Handbook for Custodial Assistants*. New York: City of New York Mayor's Office of Operations, Citywide Office of Occupational Safety and Health and District Council 37 Education Fund.

National Fire Protection Association (NFPA). 1991. *Fire Protection Handbook*. Quincy, MA: NFPA.

National Institute for Occupational Safety and Health (NIOSH). 1975. *Health and Safety Guide for Laundries and Dry Cleaners*. NIOSH Publication No. 273-831. Cincinnati, OH: US NIOSH.

—. 1977. *Occupational Diseases: A Guide to Their Recognition*. NIOSH Publication No. 77-181. Cincinnati, OH: US NIOSH.

Nielsen, J. 1995. *Occupational Health of Cleaners* (in Danish, summary in English). Ph.D. thesis. Copenhagen, Denmark: Arbejdsmiljjoinstituttet.

—. 1996. The occurrence and course of skin symptoms on the hands among female cleaners. *Contact Dermatitis* 34: 284-291.

Nordin, M, G Hultman, R Philipsson, S Ortelius, and GBJ Andersson. 1986. Dynamic measurements of trunk movements during work tasks. In *The Ergonomics of Working Postures*, edited by N Corlett, J Wilson and I Manenica. Philadelphia: Taylor & Francis.

Nwanyanwu, OC, TH Tubasuri, and G Harris. 1989. Exposure to and precautions for blood and body fluids among workers in the funeral home franchises of Fort Worth, Texas. *Am J Infect Control* 17: 208-212.

Occupational Safety and Health Administration (OSHA). 1993. Occupational Safety and Health Administration, database, regulations, documents and technical information. OSHA-CD-ROM (OSHA A93-2). Unpublished database.

Olsen, JH and S Asnaes. 1986. Formaldehyde and the risk of squamous cell carcinoma of the sinonasal cavities. *Br J Ind Med* 43: 769-774.

Opatowski, S, P Varaillac, C Richoux, N Sandret, L Peres, D Riffiod, and Y Iwatsubo. 1995. Enquête sur les ouvriers nettoyeurs d'Ile-de-France. *Archives des maladies professionnelles* 56 (3):219-220.

Pearce, N. 1992. Increasing incidence of Non-Hodgkin's lymphoma: Occupational and environmental factors. *Canc Res* 52 (Supplement): 5496s-5500s.

Pepys, J. 1986. Occupational allergic lung disease caused by organic agents. *J Allergy Clin Immunol* 78(5) Part 2: 1,058-1,062.

Rice, B and J Weinberg. 1994. *Dressed to Kill: The Dangers of Dry Cleaning and the Case for Chlorine-free Alternatives*. A Greenpeace/Pollution Probe Report. Toronto. Pollution Probe, Sunset Chemicals Project for the Great Lakes.

Roush, GC, J Walrath, LT Stayner, SA Kaplan, JT Flannery, and A Blair. 1987. Nasopharyngeal cancer, sinonasal cancer and occupations related to formaldehyde: A case-control study. *JNCI* 79: 1221-1225.

Royal Society of Chemistry (RSC). 1986. *Organochlorine Solvents: Health Risks to Workers* (EUR10531EN). Luxembourg: Royal Society of Chemistry, Commission of the European Communities.

Ruder, AM, EM Ward, and DP Brown. 1994. Cancer mortality in female and male dry cleaning workers. *J Occup Med* 36:867-874.

Savitz, DA, KW Andrews, and LA Brinton. 1995. Occupation and cervical cancer. *J Occup and Envir Med* 37(3):357-361.

Schwartz, HJ, JL Arnold, and KP Strohl. 1990. Occupational allergic rhinitis in the hair care industry. Reactions to permanent wave solutions. *J Occ Med* 32:473-475.

Scolari, FG and B Gardenghi. 1966. Problems of preselection, prevention, and recovery in occupational dermatology. *Giornale Italiano di Dermatologia* 107 (5):1259-1270.

Seligman, PJ, SC Newman, CL Timbrook, and WE Halperin. 1987. Sexual assault of women at work. *Am J Ind Med* 12 (4):445-450.

Singgih, SIR, H Latinga, JP Nater, TE Woest, and JA Kruyt-Gaspersz. 1986. Occupational hand dermatoses in hospital cleaning personnel. *Contact Dermatitis* 14: 14-19.

Sly. 1994. Epidemic of small-pox in Quebec, supposed to depend upon the opening of an intramural cemetery 214 years old. *Can J Publ Hlth* (May-June): 149.

Sogaard, K. 1994. *Biomechanics and Motor Control during Repetitive Work: A Biomechanical and Electromyographical Study of Floor Cleaning*. Ph.D. thesis. Copenhagen, Denmark: Department of Physiology, National Institute of Occupational Health.

Sogaard, K, N Fallentin, and J Nielsen. 1996. Workload during floor cleaning. The effect of cleaning methods and work technique. *Eur J App Physiol*.

Sovet, U. 1958. Poisoning caused by powder used in the cleaning of silver. *Presse Medicale* 10 (9):69-70.

Spencer, AB, CF Estil, JB McCammon, RL Mickelsen, and OE Johnston. 1996. Control of ethyl methacrylate exposures during the application of artificial fingernails. *Amer Ind Hyg Assoc J* 58: 214-218.

Starr, JC, J Yunginger, and GW Brahser. 1982. Immediate type I asthmatic response to henna following occupational exposure in hairdressers. *Annals of Allergy* 48:98-99.

Stayner, LT, L Elliott, L Blade, R Keenlyside, and W Halperin. 1988. A retrospective cohort mortality study of workers exposed to formaldehyde in the garment industry. *Am J Ind Med* 13: 667-681.

Steineck, G, N Plato, SE Norell, and C Hogstedt. 1990. Urothelial cancer and some industry-related chemicals: An evaluation of the epidemiologic literature. *Am J Ind Med* 17:371-391.

Tanaka, S, AB Smith, W Halperin, and R Jensen. 1982. Carpet-layer's knee. *New England J Med* 307(20):1276-1277.

Tobe, M, T Kaneko, Y Uchida, E Kamata, Y Ogawa, Y Ikeda, and M Saito. 1985. *Studies on Inhalation Toxicity of Formaldehyde*. Report of the National Sanitary and Medical Laboratory Service. Tokyo: Toxicity Department of the Organism Safety Research Centre.

Toivanen, H, P Helin, and O Hänninen. 1993. Impact of regular relaxation training and psychosocial working factors on neck-shoulder tension and absenteeism in hospital cleaners. *J Occup Med* 35(11): 1123-1130.

Turnbull, N, J Dornan, B Fletcher, and S Wilson. 1992. Prevalence of spinal pain among the staff of a district health authority. *Occup Med* 42(3):143-148.

Ursano, RJ, CS Fullerton, TC Kao, and VR Bhartiya. 1995. Longitudinal assessment of posttraumatic stress disorder and depression after exposure to traumatic death. *J Nerv and Ment Dis* 183: 36-42.

van der Walle, HB and VM Brunsveld. 1994. Dermatitis in hairdressers. *Contact Dermatitis* 30:217-221.

Vasquez, C. 1995. *Wet Cleaning Equipment.* Chicago: Center for Neighborhood Technology.

Vaughan, TL, C Strader, S Davis, and JR Daling. 1986. Formaldehyde and cancers of the pharynx, sinus and nasal cavity. Occupational exposures. *Int J Canc* 38: 677-683.

Villaplana J, C Romaguera, and F Grimalt. 1991. Contact dermatitis from resorcinol in a hair dye. *Contact Dermatitis* 24:151-152.

Vingard, E, L Alfredsson, I Goldie, and C Hogstedt. 1991. Occupation and osteoarthrosis of the hip and knee: A register-based cohort study. *Int J Epidemiol* 20 (4):1025-1031.

Walrath, J and JF Fraumeni. 1983. Mortality patterns among embalmers. *Int J Canc* 31:407-411.

Weaver, V, MA McDiarmid, JA Guidera, FE Humphrey, and JA Schaefer. 1993. Occupational chemical exposures in an academic medical center. *J Occup Med* 35(7):701-706.

Wentz, M. 1995. The evolution of environmentally responsible fabricare technologies. *American Drycleaner* 62(7):52-62.

Winkel, J, B Ekblom, M Hagberg, and B Jonsson. 1983. The working environment of cleaners. Evaluation of physical strain in mopping and swabbing as a basis for job redesign. In *Ergonomics of Workstation Design*, edited by TO Kialseth. Toronto: Butterworth.

Wolff, HL and JJAB Croon. 1968. The survival of small pox virus (Variola Mivor) in natural circumstances. *Bull World Health Organ* 38: 492-493.

Zahm, SH, DD Weisenburger, PA Babbitt, RC Saal, JB Vaught, and A Blair. 1992. Use of hair coloring products and the risk of lymphoma, multiple myeloma, and chronic lymphocytic leukemia. *Am J Public Health* 82:990-997.

100. PERSONAL AND COMMUNITY SERVICES

Chapter Editor
David LeGrande

Contents

OCCUPATIONAL HEALTH AND SAFETY HAZARDS IN PUBLIC AND GOVERNMENTAL SERVICES

David LeGrande

Public and government services encompass a wide variety of industrial and occupational categories. For example, included are workers employed within telecommunications and postal services, inspection and field services, as well as sewage treatment, recycling, landfill and hazardous waste operations. Depending on the individual country, industrial categories such as telecommunications and postal services may be located within either the public or private sector.

Occupational and environmental safety and health hazards in public and government services include exposure to chemicals, ergonomics, blood-borne pathogens, tuberculosis, machinery hazards, violence, motor vehicles and flammable materials. In the future, as public and government services continue to grow and become more complex, it is anticipated that occupational safety and health hazards will increase and become more widespread. In turn, led by tripartite (labour, management and government) initiatives, improvements in occupational safety and health hazard recognition and control will provide improved resolution of identified hazards.

Health Problems and Disease Patterns

Patterns or identifiable trends of occupational health problems have been associated with the type of work (i.e., use of visual display units (VDUs) or chemicals), as well as where the work is performed (i.e., indoors or outdoors).

Indoor work

The primary hazards associated with indoor work are poor or inadequate physical and work organization ergonomics, inadequate indoor air quality or heating, ventilation and air conditioning systems, chemicals, asbestos, workplace violence and electromagnetic fields (low-level radiation).

Health symptoms and disorders or illnesses have been associated with exposure to these hazards. Since the mid-1980s, a large number of ergonomic-related upper extremity physical illnesses have been reported. Disorders include carpal tunnel syndrome, ulnar deviation, thoracic outlet syndrome and tendinitis. Many of these are related to the introduction of new technology, particularly VDUs, as well as the use of hand tools and equipment. Causes of identified illnesses include physical and work organization factors.

Since the engineering and construction of "tight-buildings" in the 1970s, a pattern of increasing incidence of upper respiratory and dermatological health symptoms and illnesses has been observed. Such health problems are associated with improper maintenance of the heating, ventilation and air conditioning systems; chemical contaminants and microbiological agents; and the inadequate provision of fresh air and air flow.

Exposure to chemicals in indoor work environments has been linked to upper respiratory and dermatological health symptoms and illnesses. A variety of different chemical contaminants are emitted from copying machines, furniture, carpets, cleaning materials (solvents) and the heating, ventilation and air conditioning system. One particular syndrome, multiple chemical sensitivity, has been associated with chemical exposures in indoor work environments.

Asbestos exposure may occur when building renovation and service work are performed and asbestos products or materials are deteriorated or damaged, thus causing asbestos fibres to become airborne.

Since the 1980s, workplace violence and associated safety and health problems have become increasingly widespread. Work environments where increasing rates of workplace violence have been documented are characterized as follows: handling money, working with the public, working alone, coming into contact with patients or clients who may be violent and dealing with customer or client complaints. Health concerns include physical harm and death. For example, homicide was the second leading cause of death in the US workplace in 1992, accounting for 17% of all workplace deaths. In addition, from 1980 to 1989 homicide was the leading cause of death in the workplace for women, as discussed in more detail in the chapter *Violence* in this *Encyclopaedia*.

Work with and exposure to electronic equipment and related electromagnetic fields or non-ionizing radiation has become commonplace, as is exposure to high frequency non-ionizing radiation emitting products such as laser and microwave transmission equipment, radio-frequency heat sealers and electric tools and generation equipment. The relationship between such exposures and consequent health effects such as cancer, visual and skin disorders is not yet clear and much research is still needed. Several chapters in this *Encyclopaedia* are devoted to these areas.

Outdoor Work

Outdoor work environment occupational hazards include exposure to chemicals, lead, hazardous and solid waste, environmental conditions, inadequate ergonomics, motor vehicles, electrical and mechanical equipment and electromagnetic field emissions.

Exposure to chemicals occurs in several identified occupational categories including waste disposal operations, water and sanitation services, sewage treatment, domestic waste collection, postal collection and technician jobs in telecommunications. Such exposure has been related to upper respiratory, dermatological, cardiovascular and central nervous system illnesses. Exposure to lead occurs among telecommunications workers while performing splicing operations with and removing lead telecommunications cables. Such exposure has been liked to a variety of health symptoms and illnesses, including anaemia, peripheral and central nervous system disorders, sterility, kidney damage and birth defects.

Hazardous work environments are common to waste disposal operations, water and sanitation services, sewage treatment and domestic waste collection. Occupational safety and health hazards include microbiological and medical waste, chemicals, inadequate ergonomics, motor vehicles, confined spaces and electrical and mechanical equipment. Identified health symptoms and illnesses include upper respiratory, dermatological, upper and lower extremity musculoskeletal, cardiovascular, central nervous system and visual problems. Additional concerns include lacerations, heat exhaustion and stroke.

Inadequately designed workplace tools and equipment are common to all outside public and government service occupations. Hazards comprise poorly designed hand and power tools, machinery and motor vehicles. Associated health problems include upper and lower extremity musculoskeletal symptoms and illnesses. Safety-related concerns include visual problems, strains, sprains and fractured and broken bones.

Hazards associated with motor vehicles include poorly designed equipment (e.g., hoppers, compaction boxes and aerial equipment), as well as improperly operating machinery and equipment. Associated health problems comprise musculoskeletal injuries and death. Motor vehicle accidents account for the greatest number of injuries and fatalities outdoors.

Case report: Violence and urban park rangers in Ireland

Rangers in parks in large Irish cities are employed to "keep the peace", to "liaise with the public" (i.e., discourage vandalism and respond to any complaints that might be made) and to perform "light cleaning duties" (i.e., cleaning up rubbish and garbage such as broken bottles, needles and syringes discarded by drug abusers and used condoms). Their hours are unsociable: they report around mid-day and remain on duty until dusk when they are supposed to lock the park gates. This means long hours in the summertime that are somewhat compensated for by the shorter days in winter.

The majority of the parks have only one ranger who works alone, although there may be other local authority employees doing landscaping, gardening and other jobs in the park. Usually the only building in the park is the depot where gardening equipment is kept and where the staff may go for shelter in very severe weather. To avoid spoiling the ambiance, the depots are usually located in sequestered areas out of the public view where they are subject to misuse by vandals and marauding gangs of youths.

The park rangers are frequently exposed to violence. An employment policy that favoured the hiring of individuals with mild disabilities as rangers was recently supplanted when it was realized that public knowledge of such problems made these rangers ready targets for violent assault. Public authorities were not covered by the Irish health and safety legislation which, until recently, was applicable only to factories, building sites, docks and other process industries. As a result, there were no formalized arrangements for dealing with violence against park workers who, unlike their counterparts in some other countries, were not provided with firearms or other weapons. Nor was there any access to post-violence counselling.

The tendency to assign rangers who lived in the immediate neighbourhood to a particular park meant that they were more likely to be able to identify the trouble-makers likely to have been the perpetrators of violent acts. However, this also increased the danger of reprisals to the ranger for having "fingered" the culprits,

making him or her less inclined to make formal complaints against their assailants.

Lack of an adequate police presence in the parks and the very early release from prison of convicted perpetrators were often crushing blows to the morale of the victims of the violence.

The trade unions representing the rangers and other public authority personnel have been active in promoting efforts to deal with violence. They now include training in recognizing and preventing violence in the courses they sponsor for safety representatives.

Even though the Irish health and safety legislation now covers public authority workers, the creation of a national committee to deal with both the control of violence and the provision of aftercare for its victims would be beneficial. While guidelines on preventing violence are now available to assist those engaged in assessing the risks of violence in workplaces, their use should be made mandatory for all occupations where violence is a risk. Furthermore, increased resources for and enhanced coordination with the city's police force are desirable for dealing with the problem of violence and assault in the public parks.

Training in how to deal with individuals and groups likely to be violent should be make available to all workers who face this risk in their jobs. Such training might include how to approach and deal with individuals presenting indications of violent assault as well as self-defence manoeuvres.

Improved communications for reporting problem situations and requesting help would also be helpful. Installing telephones in all park depots would be a useful first step while "walkie-talkie" radios and cellular telephones would be useful when away from the depot. Video camera systems for surveillance of sensitive areas, such as the park depots and sports facilities, might help to deter violence.

Daniel Murphy

Hazards associated with electrical and mechanical equipment include poorly designed equipment, electrical shock and electrocution, as well as chemical exposures. Health problems include strains, sprains, broken bones, central nervous and cardiovascular system disorders, as well as upper respiratory and dermatological disorders and death.

Work with or in close proximity to electrical transmission equipment and the associated electromagnetic fields of non-ionizing radiation emissions has been linked with the occurrence of certain central nervous system symptoms and disorders as well as cancer. However, scientific and epidemiological research has, as of yet, not clearly defined the degree of harm posed by electromagnetic fields.

Outdoor public and government services activities present several environmental and public health problems. For example, chemicals, microbiological agents, sewage and domestic waste may be used and disposed of improperly, thus finding their way into the water table as well as streams, lakes and oceans, causing environmental contamination. In turn, such waste may lead to the contamination of public water supplies as well as the creation of toxic dumps or sites. Such contamination has been related to the deterioration and destruction of the environment as well as public health. Associated human health effects include dermatological, central nervous and cardiovascular system health symptoms and disorders, as well as certain types of cancer.

INSPECTION SERVICES

Jonathan Rosen

National, state or provincial, municipal and other local government units employ inspectors in a variety of agencies to verify compliance with laws, ordinances and regulations intended to promote and protect the health and safety of both workers and the public. This is government's traditional role of enacting laws to address socially unacceptable risks and then to assigning agencies to establish programmes to achieve conformance with the regulatory standards. The inspector or investigator is the key person on the front-line in enforcing regulatory standards.

An example of such a legislative mandate is the role of inspection of workplaces for health and safety practices. Worksite inspectors visit workplaces to verify compliance with regulations governing the workplace, potential occupational and environmental hazards, the tools, machines and equipment being used, and the way the work is done, including the use of personal protective equipment (PPE). The inspectors have the authority to initiate penalties (citations, monetary fines and, in egregious cases, criminal prosecution) when deficiencies are encountered. Under laws enacted in some localities, regional authorities share responsibilities for carrying out inspections with federal powers.

Other areas in which governmental agencies have inspection responsibilities include environmental protection, regulation of food and drugs, nuclear energy, interstate commerce and civil aviation, public health and consumer protection. Engineering and building inspections are generally organized at the local level.

Throughout the world the basic functions and protections addressed by inspection services are similar although the particular legislation and governmental structures vary. These are discussed elsewhere in this *Encyclopaedia*.

To protect workers and property, to avoid statutory penalties and the adverse publicity that accompanies them and to minimize legal liability and the costs of workers' compensation benefits, private sector enterprises often conduct in-house inspections and audits to ensure that they are complying with the regulations. These self-audits may be conducted by appropriately qualified staff persons or outside consultants may be retained. A notable recent trend in the US and some other developed countries has been the proliferation of private consulting organizations and academic departments which offer occupational health and safety services to employers.

Hazards

In general, inspectors are faced by the very same hazards they are charged to identify and correct. For example, workplace health and safety inspectors may visit worksites that have toxic environments, harmful noise levels, infectious agents, radiation, fire or explosion hazards and unsafe buildings and equipment. Unlike workers in a fixed environment, the inspectors must anticipate the kinds of hazards they will encounter on a given day and make sure that they have the tools and PPE they might need. In each instance, they must prepare themselves for a worst-case scenario. For example, when entering a mine, inspectors must be prepared for an oxygen-deficient atmosphere, fires and explosions and cave-ins. Inspectors checking isolation units in health care facilities must protect themselves against contagious organisms.

Occupational stress is a prime hazard for inspectors. It stems from a number of factors:

- Work stress is increasing as fiscal retrenchments cause reductions in agency budgets, which often results in understaffing. This brings pressure to manage an increasing work load that inevitably affects the ability to maintain the quality and integrity of inspections.
- There is also the stress of having to enforce the minutiae of guidelines and regulations which the inspector may acknowledge to be unwarranted in particular situations. And, when circumstances do not allow them to be overlooked, the inspector may bear the brunt of abuse for enforcing unpopular rules and regulations.
- Employers, and sometimes the workers as well, may resent the "intrusion" of the inspector into the workplace and his or her need to maintain a high level of suspicion with respect to subterfuges and cover-ups. This often makes the job unpleasant and stressful for the inspector. This antagonism may escalate into threats and actual violence.
- The inspector may suffer from feelings of responsibility when neglected or unrecognized hazards in the workplace result in a worker's loss of life or limb or, even worse, in disaster involving many individuals.
- Like many employees who work in the field on their own, inspectors may suffer from such bureaucratic ills as distant and/or inadequate supervision, lack of support, endless paperwork and separation from home, family and friends.
- The necessity of entering unsafe neighbourhoods may expose them to crime and violence.

- Finally, particularly when they are required to wear uniforms, they may be seen as enemies by those who bear a grudge against the particular agency or the government as a whole. This can culminate in abuse or even violent assaults. The 1996 bombing of the federal office building in Oklahoma City, Oklahoma, in the US is an indication of such hostility to government.

Agencies employing inspectors must have clearly written health and safety policies describing appropriate measures to protect the health and well-being of inspectors, particularly those working in the field. In the US, for example, OSHA includes such information in its compliance directives. In some instances, this agency requires inspectors to document their use of the appropriate protective equipment while performing an inspection. The integrity of the inspection may be compromised if the inspector himself or herself violates health and safety rules and procedures.

Education and training are the key to preparing inspectors to properly protect themselves. When new standards are promulgated and new initiatives or programmes undertaken, the inspectors should be trained in preventing illness and injury to themselves as well as being drilled in the new requirements and enforcement procedures. Unfortunately, such training is rarely offered.

As part of programmes for learning to cope with work stress, also rarely offered, inspectors should be trained in communication skills and contending with angry and abusive people.

Table 101.1 lists some of the categories of government inspectors and hazards to which they may be exposed. More detailed

Table 101.1 • Hazards of inspection services.

Occupations	Tasks	Associated hazards
Occupational safety and health compliance officers	Investigate and cite safety and health hazards	A wide variety of safety and health hazards
Agricultural inspectors	Investigate agricultural and farmworker health and safety	Agricultural equipment, chemicals, pesticides, biological agents and outdoor environment
Environmental inspectors	Investigate industrial and agricultural sites for contaminated air, water and soil	Chemical, physical, biological and safety hazards
Health inspectors	Investigate nursing homes and hospitals for compliance with hospital safety and health standards	Infectious, chemical, radioactive and safety hazards
Food inspectors	Investigate and cite food product safety and establishments	Insects, vermin and associated microbiological agents; chemical agents; violence and dogs
Engineering and building inspectors	Investigate for compliance with building construction and fire operation and maintenance codes	Unsafe structures, building and construction equipment and materials
Customs inspectors	Investigate for contraband and hazardous materials entering territorial boundaries	Explosives, drugs, biological and chemical hazards

information about the recognition and control of such hazards is to be found elsewhere in this *Encyclopaedia*.

A recent phenomenon in many countries that is disturbing to many is the trend toward deregulation and decreased emphasis on inspection as an enforcement mechanism. This has led to the under-financing, degrading and downsizing of agencies and erosion of their inspection services. There is a growing concern not only for the health and safety of the cadres of inspectors but also for the health and well-being of the workers and the public they are charged to protect.

• POSTAL SERVICES

Roxanne Cabral

Although the social obligation of most postal administrations—domestic mail collection, sorting, delivery and international mail processing while preserving the security of mail—has remained unchanged over the last century, the methods by which this obligation is carried out have been transformed due to the rapid advances of technology and increases in mail volumes. Australia, France, Germany, Sweden, the United Kingdom and other industrialized countries each process billions of mail pieces each year. In 1994 the US Postal Service delivered almost two hundred billion pieces of mail, an increase in mail volume of 67% since 1980. Competition by private carriers entering the market, particularly for parcel delivery and express delivery service, as well as from other technological advancements, such as facsimile (fax) machines, computer modems, electronic mail, electronic transfer of funds and satellite systems, have also changed personal and business communications. Since private carriers carry out many of the same operations as postal services, their workers face many of the same hazards.

Most postal administrations are government-owned and operated, although this is changing. For example, Argentina, Australia, Canada, Germany, the Netherlands, Sweden, the United Kingdom and the United States have, to varying degrees, privatized their postal operations. The franchising or contracting of work and services is becoming increasingly common among the postal administrations in the industrialized world.

Postal administrations, especially in industrialized nations, are often one of the largest employers in the country; they employ up to several hundred thousand people in some countries. Although advances in technology have not dramatically changed how postal administrations are structured, they have altered the methods by which mail is sorted and delivered. As postal services have long been highly labour intensive (with wages and benefits accounting for up to 80% of total operating costs in some countries), efforts to reduce these costs as well as to improve productivity and increase operating efficiency have promoted technological advancement through capital investments. For many industrialized nations the objective is to fully automate the processing of mail up to the point of delivery.

Operations

Postal operations are divided into three main phases: collection, sorting and delivery. Administrative and maintenance services are also integral aspects of postal operations. The technological changes in operating methods, especially for the sorting phase, have led to a declining demand for workers. As a result, workers are more isolated because less staffing is required to operate the newer postal equipment. Enhanced technology has also led to a reduction of requisite skills in the workforce as computers have replaced such tasks as memorizing postal codes and performing diagnostic tests on mechanical equipment.

Shift work is still a common practice in postal operations as most mail is collected at the end of the day and then transported and sorted at night. Many postal administrations provide home and business mail delivery six days a week. The frequency of service requires most postal operations to run twenty-four hours a day, seven days a week. Consequently, the psychological and physical stress from shift work and night work still remain problems for many postal workers, particularly during the busy night shift in large processing centres.

Most postal administrations in the industrialized world are organized with large processing centres supporting small retail and delivery offices. Often several stories high and occupying several thousands of square metres, processing centres are equipped with large pieces of machinery, material handling equipment, motor vehicles and repair and paint shops similar to work environments in other industrial workplaces. Smaller retail offices, however, are generally cleaner and less noisy and more akin to office environments.

Hazards and Their Prevention

While technology has eliminated many dangerous and monotonous tasks performed by postal workers, different hazards have emerged that, if not properly addressed, may jeopardize the health and safety of postal workers.

Retail services

For employees who work at retail postal counters, job tasks depend on the size of the post office and the type of services offered by the postal administration. General duties of the retail employee include selling stamps and money orders, weighing and pricing letters and parcels and providing postal information to customers. Since retail personnel are directly involved in the exchange of money with the public, the risk of violent robbery is increased for these workers. For retail personnel who work alone, in proximity to high crime areas or late at night or early in the mornings, workplace violence can be a major occupational hazard if appropriate protective measures are not taken. The potential for such workplace violence also contributes to undue mental stress. Also, the day-to-day pressure from dealing with the public and the responsibility for relatively large amounts of money are contributing stress factors.

Environmental conditions and the physical layout of the retail employee's workstation may also contribute to health and safety hazards. Indoor air quality problems, such as dust, the lack of fresh air and temperature variations may cause discomfort for the retail clerk. Poorly designed work stations that require the operator to work in awkward postures due to the placement of retail equipment (e.g., cash register, scale, mail and parcel containers), prolonged standing postures or sitting in uncomfortable and unadjustable chairs, and lifting heavy parcels can lead to musculoskeletal disorders.

Preventive measures that address these hazards include improving security by installing bright external and internal lighting, doors, windows and partitions of bullet proof glass and silent alarms, ensuring that clerks do not work alone, providing emergency and defensive response training and ensuring that the public has limited and controlled access to the facility. Ergonomic and indoor air quality assessments may also contribute to the improvement of the working conditions for retail personnel.

Sorting

The transition from manual operations to mechanized and automated systems has greatly affected the handling and sorting phase of postal operations. For example, whereas postal workers were once required to memorize various codes that corresponded to address delivery routes, that task is now computerized. Since the early 1980s, technology has improved so that many machines can now "read" an address and apply a code. In the industrialized countries, the task of sorting mail has shifted from humans to machines.

Material handling

Although technology has reduced the amount of manual letter and small parcel sorting, it has had less of an impact on the movement of containers, bundles and sacks of mail inside a postal facility. Mail that is transported by trucks, planes, rail or ship into large processing and sorting centres may be internally transferred to different sorting areas by complex conveyor or belt systems. Fork-lift trucks, mechanical dumpers and smaller conveyors assist postal employees in unloading and loading trucks and placing the mail onto the complex conveyor systems. Some material handling tasks, however, especially those performed in smaller postal facilities, must still be performed manually. Culling operations that separate mail to be processed by machine from mail that which must be sorted by hand is one task that has not been fully automated. Depending on the postal administration's regulations or national health and safety regulations, limits on load weights may be imposed to prevent employees from having to lift and carry containers of mail and parcels that are too heavy (see figure 101.1).

Material handling tasks also expose postal workers to electrical hazards and machine parts that may injure the body. Although paper dust is a nuisance to almost all postal workers, employees who primarily perform material handling tasks commonly inhale dust when they first open mailbags, containers and sacks. Material handling workers are also the first employees to come into contact with any biological or chemical materials that may have spilled during transport.

Figure 101.1 • Manual lifting of heavy parcels is a serious ergonomic hazard. Weight and size limits on parcels are necessary.

Efforts to reduce fatigue and back injuries include automating some of the manual lifting and carrying tasks. Transporting pallets of mail by forklifts, using rolling containers to transport mail inside a facility and installing automatic container unloaders are methods of automating material handling tasks. Some industrialized nations are utilizing robotics to assist in material handling tasks such as loading containers onto conveyors. Regulating the amount of weight workers lift and carry and training workers in proper lifting techniques may also help to reduce the incidence of back injury and pain.

To control exposure to chemicals and biological matter, some postal administrations place prohibitions on the type and amount of hazardous materials that can be sent by mail and also require these materials to be identifiable to postal workers. Since some mail will undoubtedly be sent without proper warnings affixed, workers should be trained in responding to releases of potentially hazardous materials.

Manual/mechanized

As sorting technology improves, manual letter sorting is rapidly being phased out. Some manual letter sorting, however, is still necessary in many postal administrations, particularly in the developing countries. Manual letter sorting involves workers placing individual letters into slots or "pigeon holes" in a case. The worker then bundles the mail from each slot and places the bundles into containers or mail bags for dispatch. Manual sorting is a repetitive activity that the worker performs while either standing or sitting on a stool.

Manual parcel sorting is also still performed by postal workers. Since parcels are generally larger in size and much heavier than letters, workers must often put the parcels into separate hampers or containers that are arranged around them. Workers who perform manual parcel sorting often are at risk for cumulative trauma disorders affecting the shoulders, arms and back.

Automation has addressed many of the ergonomic hazards associated with manual letter and parcel sorting. Where automation technology is not available, workers should have the opportunity to rotate to different tasks to relieve fatigue from one particular body area. Appropriate rest breaks should also be provided to workers performing repetitive tasks.

In modern, mechanized sorting systems, workers sit at a keyboard while letters are mechanically passed in front of them (figure 101.2). Coding desks are arranged either side-by-side or behind one another in a line. Operators must often memorize hundreds of codes that correspond to different zones and enter a code for each letter on a keyboard. Unless adjusted properly, the keyboards may require the operator to use more force to depress the keys than modern computer keyboards. Approximately fifty to sixty letters each minute are processed by the operator. Based upon the code entered by the operator, the letters are segregated into different bins and then removed, bundled and dispatched by the postal workers.

Ergonomic hazards that lead to musculoskeletal disorders, particularly tendinitis and carpal tunnel syndrome, are the biggest problem for mechanized sorting operators. Many of these machines were designed several decades ago when ergonomic principles were not applied with the same degree of diligence as they are today. Automated sorting equipment and VDUs are quickly replacing these mechanized sorting systems. In many postal administrations where mechanized sorting is still the primary system, workers may rotate to other positions and/or take breaks at regular intervals. Providing comfortable chairs and adjusting the keyboard force are other modifications that can improve the job. Although a nuisance and discomfort to the operator, noise and dust from the mail are generally not major hazards.

Figure 101.2 • Coding desk operators sorting letters with the aid of computerized machines.

Automation

The most advanced type of sorting reduces the need for workers to be directly involved in the coding and segregation of individual mail pieces. Generally only 2 or 3 workers are required to operate an automatic sorter. At one end of the machine, a worker loads mail onto a mechanical belt that feeds each letter in front of an optical character reader (OCR). The letter is read or scanned by the OCR and a bar code is printed on it. The letters are then automatically segregated into dozens of bins located at the other end of the machine. Workers then remove the bundles of segregated mail from the bins and transport them to the next stage of the sorting process. Larger automated sorters can process between 30,000 and 40,000 pieces of mail per hour.

Although such automation no longer requires a keyboard to encode mail, workers are still exposed to monotonous, repetitive tasks that put them at risk for musculoskeletal disorders. Removing the bundles of segregated mail from the different bins and placing them into containers or other material handling equipment puts physical stress on the operator's shoulders, back and arms. Operators also complain of wrist and hand problems from constantly grasping handfuls of mail. Dust exposure is sometimes more problematic for automated sorter workers than other postal employees because of the larger volume of mail processed.

Many postal administrations have only recently acquired automated sorting equipment. As complaints of musculoskeletal discomfort mount, equipment designers and engineers will be forced to incorporate ergonomic principles more thoroughly in their attempts to balance productivity needs with the well-being of employees. For example, in the United States, government safety and health officials have concluded that some of the automated mail-sorting equipment poses serious ergonomic deficiencies. While attempts can be made to modify either the equipment or work methods to reduce the risks of musculoskeletal discomfort, such modifications are not as effective as the proper design of equipment (and work methods) in the first place.

Another problem is the risk of injury during the clearing of jams or during maintenance and repair operations. Proper training and lockout/tagout procedures are needed for these operations.

Visual display units

Visual display unit-based sorting terminals are beginning to replace mechanized sorters. Instead of the actual mail pieces being presented to the operator, enlarged images of the addresses appear on the screen. Much of the mail that is processed by VDU sorting has been previously rejected or culled as not machineable by the automatic sorters.

The advantage of VDU sorting is that it does not need to be located in close proximity to the mail. Computer modems can send the images to the VDUs that are located in another facility or even a different city. For the VDU operator, this means that the work environment is generally more comfortable, with no background noise from sorting machines or dust from mail. However, sorting with the VDU is a very visually demanding job and often involves only one task, keying from images of letters. As with most sorting tasks, the job is monotonous but at the same time requires intense concentration from the operator in order to maintain the required productivity levels.

Musculoskeletal discomfort and eye strain are the most common complaints of VDU operators. Steps to reduce physical, visual and mental fatigue include providing adjustable equipment, such as keyboards and chairs, maintaining adequate lighting to reduce glare and scheduling regular breaks. In addition, since VDU operators often work in an office-type environment, consideration should be given to indoor air quality complaints.

Delivery

Postal operations rely upon many methods of transportation to distribute mail including air, rail, water and highway. For short distances and local delivery, mail is transported by motor vehicles. Mail travelling generally less than several hundred kilometres from large processing centres to smaller post offices is usually carried by trains or large trucks, while air and sea travel is reserved for the longer distances between large processing centres.

As the use of motor vehicles for delivery services has increased dramatically during the past two decades, accidents and injuries involving postal trucks, jeeps and automobiles have become for some postal administrations the biggest and most serious occupational safety and health problem. Vehicular accidents constitute the main cause of workplace fatalities. Additionally, while the increased use of motor vehicles for delivery and the installation of more street mail storage boxes have helped to reduce the amount of time letter carriers spend walking, musculoskeletal discomfort and back injuries still are problematic due to the heavy bags of mail that they must carry on their routes. Also, robberies and other violent attacks against letter carriers are on the rise. Injuries caused by slips, trips and falls, particularly during adverse weather conditions, and dog attacks are other serious hazards experienced by letter carriers. Unfortunately, other than increased awareness not much can be done to eliminate these particular hazards.

Steps designed to reduce the likelihood of vehicular accidents include installing anti-lock brakes and extra mirrors to improve visibility, increasing seat belt usage, improving driver training, conducting more frequent vehicle maintenance inspections and improving roadways and vehicle design. To address the ergonomic hazards associated with lifting and carrying mail, some postal administrations provide carts with wheels or specialized mail bags where the weight is more evenly distributed across the worker's shoulders instead of concentrated on one side. To reduce the risk of workplace violence, letter carriers may carry two-way communication devices and their vehicles may be equipped with a tracking system. In addition, to address environmental concerns and concerns of exposure to diesel exhaust, some postal vehicles are powered by natural gas or electricity.

Repair and Maintenance

Workers that are responsible for the day-to-day upkeep, cleaning and repair of postal facilities and equipment, including motor vehicles, face similar hazards as maintenance employees in other industrial operations. Exposure to welding operations, electrical hazards, falls from scaffolding, chemicals found in cleaning fluids and machine lubricants, asbestos from brake linings and dust are examples of hazards associated with maintenance tasks.

● TELECOMMUNICATIONS

David LeGrande

Telecommunications is the act of communicating with others through the use of electronic equipment like telephones, computer modems, satellites and fibre optic cables. Telecommunications systems comprise telecommunications cables from the user to the local switching office (local loops), the switching facilities which provide the communications connection to the user, the trunks or channels that transmit calls between the switching offices and, of course, the user.

During the early to mid-twentieth century, telephone exchanges, electromechanical switching systems, cables, repeaters, carrier systems and microwave equipment were introduced. After this occurrence, telecommunications systems spread to the industrialized areas of the world.

From the 1950s to 1984, technological advances continued to appear. For example, satellite systems, improved cable systems, the use of digital technology, fibre optics, computerization and video telephony were introduced throughout the communications industry. These changes allowed for the expansion of telecommunications systems throughout more areas of the world.

In 1984 a court ruling in the United States led to the breakup of the telecommunications monopoly held by American Telegraph and Telephone (AT&T). This breakup coincided with many rapid, major changes in the technology of the telecommunications industry itself.

Until the 1980s telecommunications services were considered to be public services operating within a legislative framework that provided monopoly status in virtually all countries. Along with the development of economic activity, the advent of new technologies has led to the privatization of the telecommunications industry. This trend culminated in the divestiture of AT&T and the deregulation of the US telecommunications system. Similar privatization activities are underway in a number of other countries.

Since 1984, technological advances have produced and expanded telecommunications systems that can provide universal service to all people throughout the world. This occurs as telecommunications technology is now converging with other information technologies. Related fields such as electronics and data processing are involved.

The impact of the introduction of new technology on employment has been mixed. Without question, it has reduced levels of employment and produced the de-skilling of jobs, radically altering the tasks of telecommunications workers as well as the qualifications and experience required of them. However, it is anticipated by some that employment growth will occur in the future as a result of the new business activity stimulated by the deregulated telecommunications industry that will produce many highly skilled jobs.

Occupations within the telecommunications industry can be categorized as either skilled craft or clerical work. Craft jobs include cable splicers, installers, outside plant technicians, central office technicians and frame technicians. These jobs are highly skilled, particularly as a result of the new technological equipment. For example, employees must be very proficient in the electrical, electronics and/or mechanical fields as they relate to the installation, service and maintenance of telecommunications equipment. Training is acquired through classroom and on-the-job training.

Clerical occupations include directory assistance operators, customer service representatives, account representatives and sales clerks. In general these tasks involve the operation of communications equipment such as VDUs private branch exchange (PBX) and facsimile machines which are used to establish local and/or long distance connections, perform business office work inside or outside the workplace and handle sales contacts with customers.

Hazards and Controls

The occupational safety and health hazards within the telecommunications industry can be categorized by the type of tasks or services performed.

Building and construction operations

In general, the same risks occur as in construction and building operations. However, several noteworthy activities which are specific to telecommunications include working at heights on poles or pylons, installing telecommunications wiring systems and excavating for cable laying. The usual means of protection, such as climbing gaffs, safety harnesses, lines and raise platforms and proper shoring for excavations, are applicable in telecommunications. Often, this work is performed during emergency repairs made necessary by storms, landslides or floods.

Electricity

The safe use of electricity and electrical equipment is extremely important when performing telecommunications work. The normal preventive measures against electrocution, electric shock, short circuits and fires or explosions are fully applicable to telecommunications. Also, a serious source of danger may arise when telecommunications and electricity cables are within close proximity to one another.

Cable laying and maintenance

A significant safety and health concern is cable laying and maintenance. Work on underground cables, pipelines and jointing chambers involves handling heavy cable drums and pulling cables into pipelines with power-driven winches and cable equipment as well as cable splicing or jointing and insulation or waterproofing. During cable splicing and insulation jobs, workers suffer exposure to health hazards such as lead, solvents and isocyanates. Preventive measures include use of the least toxic chemicals, adequate ventilation and PPE. Often, maintenance and repair work is performed in confined spaces like manholes and vaults. Such work necessitates special ventilation equipment, harness and lifting equipment and the provision of a worker stationed above ground who is able to perform emergency cardiopulmonary resuscitation (CPR) and rescue activities.

Another health and safety concern is working with fibre optic telecommunications cables. Fibre optic cables are being installed as an alternative to lead and polyurethane-encased cables because they carry many more communications transmission and they are much smaller in size. Health and safety concerns involve potential burns to the eyes or skin from exposure to the laser beam when cables become disconnected or broken. When this occurs, protective engineering controls and equipment should be provided.

Also, cable installation and maintenance work performed in buildings involves potential exposure to asbestos products. Exposure occurs as a result of the deterioration or break-up of asbestos products like pipes, patching and taping compounds, floor and ceiling tiles and reinforcing fillers in paints and sealants. During the late 1970s, asbestos products were banned or their use was discouraged in many countries. Adherence to a worldwide prohibition will eliminate exposure and resultant health disorders for future generations of workers, but there are still large amounts of asbestos to contend with in older buildings.

Telegraph services

Telegraph workers use VDUs and, in some cases, telegraph equipment to perform their work. A frequent hazard associated with this type of work is upper extremity (particularly hand and wrist) musculoskeletal cumulative trauma. These health problems may be minimized and prevented with attention to ergonomic work stations, work environment and work organization factors.

Telecommunications service

Automatic switching and connecting circuits are the mechanical operations components of modern telecommunications systems. Connections are generally made by microwave and radio frequency waves in addition to cables and wires. Potential hazards are associated with microwave and radio frequency exposures. According to available scientific data, there is no indication that exposure to most types of radiation-emitting telecommunications equipment is directly linked to human health disorders. However, craft employees may be exposed to high levels of radio frequency radiation while working in close proximity to electrical power lines. Data have been collected that suggest a relationship between these emissions and cancer. Further scientific investigations are being conducted to more clearly determine the seriousness of this hazard as well as appropriate prevention equipment and methods. In addition, health concerns have been associated with emissions from cellular telephone equipment. Further research is being conducted to draw conclusions regarding potential health hazards.

The vast majority of telecommunications services are performed with the use of VDUs. Work with VDUs is associated with the occurrence of upper extremity (particularly hand and wrist) musculoskeletal cumulative trauma disorders. Many telecommunications unions, such as the Communications Workers of America (US), Seko (Sweden) and the Communication Workers Union (United Kingdom), have identified catastrophic rates of VDU workplace musculoskeletal cumulative trauma disorders among the workers they represent. Proper design of the VDU workplace with attention to work station, work environment and work organization variables will minimize and prevent these health problems.

Additional health concerns include stress, noise and electrical shock.

Hazards in Sewage (Waste) Treatment Plants

Mary O. Brophy

Without treatment of waste the current concentration of people and industry in many parts of the world would very quickly make portions of the environment incompatible with life. Although reduction of the amount of waste is important, the proper treatment of waste is essential. Two basic types of waste enter a treatment plant, human/animal waste and industrial waste. Humans excrete about 250 grams of solid waste per capita per day, including 2000 million coliform and 450 million streptococci bacteria per person per day (Mara 1974). Industrial solid waste production rates range from 0.12 tons per employee per year at professional and scientific institutions to 162.0 tons per employee per year at sawmills and planing mills (Salvato 1992). Although some waste treatment plants are exclusively dedicated to handling one or the other type of material, most plants handle both animal and industrial waste.

Hazards and Their Prevention

The goal of waste water treatment plants is to remove as much of the solid, liquid and gaseous contaminants as possible within technically feasible and financially achievable constraints. There are a variety of different processes that are used to remove contaminants from waste water including sedimentation, coagulation, flocculation, aeration, disinfection, filtration and sludge treatment. (See also the article "Sewage treatment" in this chapter.) The specific hazard associated with each process varies depending on the design of the treatment plant and the chemicals used in the different processes, but the types of hazard can be classified as physical, microbial and chemical. The key to preventing and/or minimizing the adverse effects associated with working in sewage treatment plants is to anticipate, recognize, evaluate and control the hazards.

Physical hazards

Physical hazards include confined spaces, inadvertent energizing of machines or machine parts and trips and falls. The result of an encounter with a physical hazards can often be immediate, irreversible and serious, even fatal. Physical hazards vary with the design of the plant. Most sewage treatment plants, however, have confined spaces which include underground or below grade vaults with limited access, manholes (figure 101.3) and the sedimentation tanks when they have been emptied of liquid content during, for example, repairs (figure 101.4). Mixing equipment, sludge rakes, pumps and mechanical devices used for a variety of operations in sewage treatment plants can maim, and even kill, if they are inadvertently activated when a worker is servicing them. Wet surfaces, often encountered in sewage treatment plants, contribute to slipping and falling hazards.

Confined-space entry is one of the most common and one of the most serious hazards faced by sewage treatment workers. A universal definition of a confined space is elusive. In general, however, a confined space is an area with limited means of entry and egress that was not designed for continuous human habitation and that does not have adequate ventilation. Hazards occur when the confined space is associated with a deficiency of oxygen, the presence of a toxic chemical or an engulfing material, such as water. Decreased oxygen levels can be the result of a variety of conditions including the replacement of oxygen with another gas, such as methane or hydrogen sulphide, the consumption of oxy-

101. PUBLIC AND GOVERNMENT SERVICES

Figure 101.3 • Manhole with cover removed.

Mary O. Brophy

gen by the decay of organic material contained in the waste water or the scavenging of oxygen molecules in the rusting process of some structure within the confined space. Because low levels of oxygen in confined spaces cannot be detected by unaided human observation it is extremely important to use an instrument that can determine the level of oxygen before entering any confined space.

The earth's atmosphere consists of 21% oxygen at sea level. When the percentage of oxygen in breathing air falls below about 16.5% a person's breathing becomes more rapid and more shallow, the heart rate increases and the person begins to lose coordination. Below about 11% the person experiences nausea, vomiting, inability to move and unconsciousness. Emotional instability and impaired judgement may occur at oxygen levels somewhere between these two points. When individuals enter an atmosphere with oxygen levels below 16.5% they may immediately become too disoriented to get themselves out and eventually

Figure 101.4 • Empty tank in a sewage treatment plant.

Mary O. Brophy

succumb to unconsciousness. If the oxygen depletion is great enough individuals can become unconscious after one breath. Without rescue they can die within minutes. Even if rescued and resuscitated, permanent damage can occur (Wilkenfeld et al. 1992).

Lack of oxygen is not the only hazard in a confined space. Toxic gases can be present in a confined space at a concentration level high enough to do serious harm, even kill, despite adequate oxygen levels. The effects of toxic chemicals encountered in confined spaces are discussed further below. One of the most effective ways to control the hazards associated with low oxygen levels (below 19.5%) and atmospheres contaminated with toxic chemicals is to thoroughly and adequately ventilate the confined space with mechanical ventilation prior to allowing anyone to enter it. This is usually done with a flexible duct through which outside air is blown into the confined space (see figure 101.5). Care must be taken to ensure that fumes from a generator or the fan motor are not also blown into the confined space (Brophy 1991).

Sewage treatment plants often have large pieces of machinery to move sludge or raw sewage from one place in the plant to another. When repairs are made on this type of equipment the entire machine should be de-energized. Furthermore, the switch to re-energize the equipment should be under the control of the person performing the repairs. This prevents another worker in the plant from inadvertently energizing the equipment. Development and implementation of procedures to achieve these goals is called a lockout/tagout programme. Mutilation of body parts, such as fingers, arms and legs, dismemberment and even death can result from ineffective or inadequate lockout/tagout programmes.

Sewage treatment plants often contain large tanks and storage containers. People sometimes need to work on top of the containers, or walk by pits that have been emptied of water and may contain an 8 to 10 foot (2.5 to 3 m) drop (see figure 101.4). Sufficient protection against falls as well as adequate safety training should be provided for the workers.

Microbial hazards

Microbial hazards are primarily associated with the treatment of human and animal waste. Although bacteria are often added to alter the solids contained in waste water, the hazard to sewage treatment workers comes primarily from exposure to micro-organisms contained in human and other animal waste. When aeration is used during the sewage treatment process these micro-organisms can become airborne. The long term effect on the immune system of individuals exposed to these micro-organisms for extended periods of time has not been conclusively evaluated. In addition, workers who remove solid refuse from the influent stream before any treatment is begun are often exposed to micro-organisms contained in material splashing onto their skin and making contact with the mucous membranes. The results of encountering micro-organisms found in sewage treatment plants for extended periods of time are often more subtle than resulting from acute intense exposures. Nevertheless, these effects can also be irreversible and serious.

The three main categories of microbes relevant to this discussion are fungi, bacteria and viruses. All three of these can cause acute illness as well as chronic disease. Acute symptoms including respiratory distress, abdominal pains and diarrhoea have been reported in waste treatment workers (Crook, Bardos and Lacey 1988; Lundholm and Rylander 1980). Chronic diseases, such as asthma and allergic alveolitis, have been traditionally associated with exposure to high levels of airborne microbes and, recently, with microbial exposure during the treatment of domestic waste (Rosas et al. 1996; Johanning, Olmstead and Yang 1995). Reports

Figure 101.5 • Air moving unit for entering a confined space.

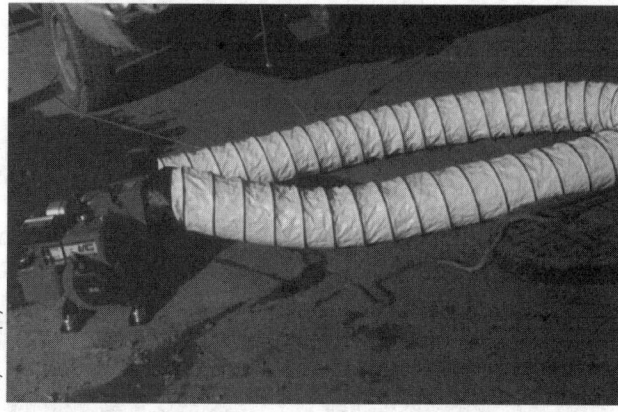

Mary O. Brophy

of significantly elevated concentrations of fungi and bacteria in waste treatment, sludge dewatering and composting facilities are beginning to be published (Rosas et al. 1996; Bisesi and Kudlinski 1996; Johanning Olmstead and Yang 1995). Another source of airborne microbes is the aeration tanks which are used in many sewage treatment plants.

In addition to inhalation, microbes can be transmitted through ingestion and through contact with skin that is not intact. Personal hygiene, including washing hands before eating, smoking and going to the bathroom, is important. Food, drink, eating utensils, cigarettes and anything that would be put into the mouth should be kept away from areas of possible microbial contamination.

Chemical hazards

Chemical encounters at waste treatment plants can be both immediate and fatal, as well as protracted. A variety of chemicals are used in the process of coagulation, flocculation, disinfection and sludge treatment. The chemical of choice is determined by the contaminant or contaminants in the raw sewage; some industrial waste requires somewhat exotic chemical treatment. In general, however, the primary hazards from chemicals used in the coagulation and flocculation processes are skin irritation and eye injury due to direct contact. This is especially true of solutions which have a pH (acidity) less than 3 or greater than 9. The disinfection of effluent is often achieved by using either liquid or gaseous chlorine. Use of liquid chlorine can cause eye injury if splashed into the eyes. Ozone and ultraviolet light are also used to achieve disinfection of the effluent.

One way to monitor the effectiveness of sewage treatment is to measure the amount of organic material which remains in the effluent after treatment is complete. This can be done by determining the amount of oxygen that would be required to biodegrade the organic material contained in 1 litre of liquid over a period of 5 days. This is referred to as the 5-day biological oxygen demand (BOD_5).

Chemical hazards in sewage treatment plants arise from the decomposition of organic material which results in the production of hydrogen sulphide and methane, from toxic waste dumped down the sewer lines and from the contaminants produced by operations performed by the workers themselves.

Hydrogen sulphide is almost always found in waste treatment plants. Hydrogen sulphide, also known as sewer gas, has a distinctive, unpleasant smell, often identified as rotten eggs. The human nose, however, quickly becomes accustomed to the smell. People who are exposed to hydrogen sulphide often lose their ability to detect its odour (i.e., olfactory fatigue). Furthermore, even if the olfactory system is able to detect hydrogen sulphide, it is not able to accurately judge its concentration in the atmosphere. Hydrogen sulphide biochemically interferes with the electron transport mechanism and blocks the utilization of oxygen at the molecular level. The result is asphyxiation and ultimately death due to the lack of oxygen in the brainstem cells that control the breathing rate. High levels of hydrogen sulphide (greater than 100 ppm) can, and often do, occur in the confined spaces found in sewage treatment plants. Exposure to very high levels of hydrogen sulphide can result in almost instantaneous suppression of the respiratory centre in the brainstem. The US National Institute for Occupational Safety and Health (NIOSH) has identified 100 ppm of hydrogen sulphide as immediately dangerous to life and health (IDLH). Lower levels of hydrogen sulphide (less than 10 ppm) are almost always present in some areas of sewage treatment plants. At these lower levels hydrogen sulphide can be irritating to the respiratory system, be associated with headaches and result in conjunctivitis (Smith 1986). Hydrogen sulphide is produced whenever organic matter decays and, industrially, during the production of paper (Kraft process), the tanning of leather (hair removal with sodium sulphide), and the production of heavy water for nuclear reactors.

Methane is another gas produced by the decomposition of organic matter. In addition to displacing oxygen, methane is explosive. Levels can be reached which result in an explosion when a spark or source of ignition is introduced.

Plants that handle industrial waste should have a thorough knowledge of the chemicals used in each of the industrial plants that utilize their services and a working relationship with the management of those plants so that they are promptly informed of any changes in processes and waste contents. Dumping of solvents, fuels and any other substance into sewer systems presents a hazard to treatment workers not only because of the toxicity of the material dumped but also because the dumping is unanticipated.

Whenever any industrial operation, such as welding or spray painting, is performed in a confined space special care must be taken to provide sufficient ventilation to prevent an explosion hazard as well as to remove toxic material produced by the operation. When an operation performed in a confined space produces a toxic atmosphere it is often necessary to equip the worker with a respirator because ventilation of the confined space may not ensure that the concentration of the toxic chemical can be maintained below the permissible exposure limit. Selection and fitting of a proper respirator falls within the purview of industrial hygiene practice.

Another serious chemical hazard in sewage treatment plants is the use of gaseous chlorine to decontaminate the effluent from the plant. The gaseous chlorine comes in a variety of containers weighing from 70 kg to roughly 1 tonne. Some of the very large sewage treatment plants use chlorine delivered in railroad cars. Gaseous chlorine is extremely irritating to the alveolar portion of the lungs, even in levels as low as a few ppm. Inhalation of higher concentrations of chlorine can cause inflammation of the alveoli of the lung and produce the adult respiratory distress syndrome, which has a 50% death rate. When a sewage treatment plant utilizes large amounts of chlorine (1 tonne and greater) the hazard exists not only for the plant workers but for the surrounding community as well. Unfortunately, the plants that use the largest amounts of chlorine are often located in large metropolitan centres with high density of people. Other methods of decontamination of sewage treatment plant effluent are available, including ozone treatment, the use of liquid hypochlorite solution and ultraviolet irradiation.

DOMESTIC WASTE COLLECTION*

Madeleine Bourdouxhe

Overview

Besides the few workers employed by municipalities in the Province of Quebec, Canada, that have their own waste collection boards, thousands of waste collectors and drivers are employed in hundreds of companies in the private sector.

Many private enterprises rely, either wholly or partially, upon jobbers who rent or own trucks and are responsible for the collectors who work for them. Competition in the sector is high, as municipal contracts are awarded to the lowest bidder, and there is a regular annual turnover of enterprises. The high competition also results in low and stable domestic waste-collection rates, and waste collection accounts for the lowest proportion of municipal taxes. However, as the existing landfills fill up, landfill costs rise, obliging municipalities to consider integrated waste-management systems. All municipal workers are unionized. Unionization of private-sector workers began in the 1980s, and 20 to 30% of them are now unionized.

Work Processes

Waste collection is a dangerous trade. If we recognize that garbage trucks are similar to hydraulic presses, it follows that waste collection is like working on a mobile industrial press under conditions much more demanding than those encountered in most factories. In waste collection, the machine travels through traffic in all seasons and workers must feed it by running behind it and tossing irregular objects of variable volume and weight, containing invisible and hazardous objects, into it. On average, collectors handle 2.4 tonnes of waste per hour. The efficiency of waste collection operations is entirely dependent on determinants of work rate and rhythm. The need to avoid rush-hour traffic and bridge line-ups creates time pressures at collection points and during transport. Speed is again of importance during unloading at landfills and incinerators.

Several aspects of waste collection influence workload and hazards. First, remuneration is on a flat-rate basis, that is, the territory specified by contract must be completely cleared of domestic waste on collection day. Since the volume of waste depends on residents' activities and varies from day to day and from season to season, the workload varies enormously. Secondly, workers are in direct contact with the objects and waste collected. This is quite different from the situation in the commercial and industrial waste-collection sectors, where waste-filled containers are collected by either front-loading trucks equipped with automated fork-lifts or by roll-off trucks. This means that workers in those sectors do not handle the waste containers and are not in direct contact with the waste. Working conditions for these collectors therefore more closely resemble those of domestic waste drivers, rather than domestic waste collectors.

Residential collection (also known as domestic collection) is, on the other hand, primarily manual, and workers continue to handle a wide variety of objects and containers of variable size, nature and weight. A few suburban and rural municipalities have implemented semi-automated collection, involving the use of mobile domestic waste bins and side-loading collectors (figure 101.6). However, most domestic waste continues to be collected manually, especially in cities. The principal characteristic of this job is thus significant physical exertion.

In many locations domestic waste collection is performed by municipal employees. In others, by private companies. This article provides an overview of processes and hazards that are based on observations and experiences in the Province of Quebec, Canada. Editor.

Figure 101.6 • Automatic, side-loading refuse collector.

Pak Mor Manufacturing Company

Hazards

A study involving field observations and measurements, interviews with management and workers, statistical analysis of 755 occupational accidents and analysis of video sequences revealed a number of potential hazards (Bourdouxhe, Cloutier and Guertin 1992).

Workload

On average, waste collectors handle 16,000 kg spread out over 500 collection points every day, equivalent to a collection density of 550 kg/km. Collection takes almost 6 hours, equivalent to 2.4 tonnes/hour, and involves walking 11 km during a total work day of 9 hours. Collection speed averages 4.6 km/h, over a territory of almost 30 km of sidewalks, streets and lanes. Rest periods are limited to a few minutes precariously balanced on the rear platform, or, in the case of driver-collectors of side-loading trucks, at the wheel. This demanding workload is exacerbated by such factors as the frequency of truck dismounts and mounts, the distance covered, travel modes, the static effort required to maintain one's balance on the rear platform (a minimum of 13 kg of force), the frequency of handling operations per unit time, the variety of postures required (bending movements), the frequency of tosses and twisting movements of the trunk and the high collection rate per unit time in some sectors. The fact that the Association française de normalisation (AFNOR) adapted weight standard for manual handling was exceeded in 23% of observed trips is eloquent testimony of the impact of these factors. When workers' capacities (established to be 3.0 tonnes/hour for rear-loading trucks, and 1.9 tonnes/hour for side-loading ones) are taken into account, the frequency with which the AFNOR standard is exceeded rises to 37%.

Diversity and nature of objects handled

Manipulation of objects and containers of variable weight and volume interrupts the smooth flow of operations and breaks work rhythms. Objects in this category, often hidden by residents, include heavy, large or bulky objects, sharp or pointed objects and hazardous materials. The most frequently encountered hazards are listed in table 101.2.

Workers are greatly helped by having residents sort waste into colour-coded bags and mobile domestic bins which facilitate the collection and allow better control of work rhythm and effort.

Table 101.2 • Hazardous objects found in domestic waste collections.

Glass, window panes, fluorescent tubing

Battery acid, cans of solvent or paint, aerosol containers, gas cylinders, motor oil

Construction waste, dust, plaster, sawdust, hearth cinders

Pieces of wood with nails in them

Syringes, medical waste

Garden waste, grass, rocks, earth

Furniture, electrical appliances, other large domestic trash

Pre-compacted waste (in apartment buildings)

Excessive numbers of small containers from small businesses and restaurants

Large amounts of vegetable and animal waste in rural sectors

Extra-large bags

Prohibited containers (e.g., no handles, excessive weight, 55-gallon oil drums, thin-necked drums, garbage cans without covers)

Small, apparently light bags that are in fact heavy

Excessive numbers of small bags

Paper bags and boxes that rip

All waste that is hidden because of its excessive weight or toxicity, or that surprises unprepared workers

Commercial containers that must be emptied with an improvised system, which is often inappropriate and dangerous

Climatic conditions and the nature of objects transported
Wet paper bags and poor-quality plastic bags that rip and scatter their contents over the sidewalk, frozen garbage cans and domestic bins stuck in snow banks can cause mishaps and dangerous recovery manoeuvres.

Work schedule
The need to rush, traffic problems, parked cars and crowded streets all can contribute to dangerous situations.

In an attempt to reduce their workload and maintain a high but constant work rhythm in the face of these constraints, workers often attempt to save time or effort by adopting work strategies that may be hazardous. The most commonly observed strategies included kicking bags or cardboard boxes towards the truck, zigzagging across the road to collect from both sides of the street, grabbing bags while the truck is in motion, carrying bags under the arm or against the body, using the thigh to help load bags and garbage cans, hand-picking of waste scattered on the ground and manual compaction (pushing garbage overflowing the hopper with the hands when the compacting system is incapable of processing the load rapidly enough). For example, in suburban collection with a rear-loading truck, almost 1,500 situations were observed per hour that could result in accidents or increase workload. These included:

- 53 mounts and dismounts from the truck's rear platform
- 38 short runs
- 482 bending movements
- 203 tosses
- 159 twisting movements
- 277 potentially hazardous actions (including 255 work strategies aimed at reducing workload by saving time or effort)

- 285 instances of increased workload, including 11 mishap-recovery activities
- 274 dangerous or heavy objects or containers.

Collection with side-loading trucks (see figure 101.6) or small mobile domestic bins reduces the manipulation of heavy or dangerous objects and the frequency of situations that could result in accidents or an increase in workload .

Use of public thoroughfares
The street is the collectors' workplace. This exposes them to such hazards as vehicular traffic, blocked access to residents' waste receptacles, accumulation of water, snow, ice and neighbourhood dogs.

Vehicles
Rear-loading trucks (figure 101.7) often have excessively high or shallow steps and rear platforms that are difficult to mount and render descents perilously similar to jumps. Hand-rails that are too high or too close to the truck body only worsen the situation. These conditions increase the frequency of falls and of collisions with structures adjacent to the rear platform. In addition, the upper edge of the hopper is very high, and shorter workers must expend additional energy lifting objects into it from the ground. In some cases, workers use their legs or thighs for support or additional power when loading the hopper.

The characteristics of side-loading trucks and the operations related to their loading result in specific repetitive movements likely to cause muscle and joint problems in the shoulder and upper back. Driver-collectors of side-loading trucks have an additional constraint, as they must cope with both the physical strain of collection and the mental strain of driving.

Personal protective equipment
While the theoretical value of PPE is beyond question, it may nevertheless prove inadequate in practice. In concrete terms, the equipment may be inappropriate for the conditions under which collection is carried out. Boots, in particular, are incompatible with the narrow utilizable height of rear platforms and the high work rhythm necessitated by the manner in which collection is organized. Strong, puncture-resistant yet flexible gloves are valuable in protecting against hand injuries.

Figure 101.7 • Back-loading enclosed compactor truck.

National Safety Council (US)

The packer-blade comes down within centimetres of the edge of the platform. The blade has the capacity to cut protruding objects.

101. PUBLIC AND GOVERNMENT SERVICES

Table 101.3 • Most common accidents in domestic waste collection, Quebec, Canada.

Injury	Cause	Per cent of accidents studied
Back or shoulder pain	Tossing or twisting movements during collection of bags	19
Back injuries	Excessive efforts while lifting objects	18
Ankle sprains	Falls or slips while dismounting from the truck or moving in its vicinity	18
Crushed hands, fingers, arms or knees	Struck by containers or heavy objects, being caught between the vehicle and containers, or collisions with part of the vehicle or parked cars	18
Hand and thigh lacerations of variable depth	Glass, nails, or syringes, occurring during hopper loading	15
Scrapes and bruises	Contact or collisions	5
Eye or respiratory-tract irritation	Dust or splashes of liquids occurring during work near the hopper during compaction	5
Other		2

Work organization

Some aspects of work organization increase workload and, by extension, hazards. In common with most flat-rate situations, the main advantage to workers of this system is the ability to manage their work time and save time by adopting a rapid work rhythm as they see fit. This explains why attempts, based on safety considerations, to slow down the pace of work have been unsuccessful. Some work schedules exceed workers' capacities.

The role of the myriad variations of residents' behaviour in the creation of additional hazards merits a study in itself. Prohibited or dangerous wastes skilfully hidden in regular waste, non-standard containers, excessively large or heavy objects, disagreements over collection times and non-conformity with bylaws all increase the number of hazards—and the potential for conflicts between residents and collectors. Collectors are often reduced to the role of "garbage police", educators and buffers between municipalities, enterprises and residents.

Collection of materials for recycling is not without its own problems despite a low waste density and collection rates far below those of traditional collection (with the exception of the collection of leaves for composting). The hourly frequency of situations that could result in accidents is often high. The fact that this is a new type of work for which few workers have been trained should be borne in mind.

In several cases, workers are obliged to perform such dangerous activities as mounting the truck's compaction box to get into the compartments and move piles of paper and cardboard with their feet. Several work strategies aimed at speeding up work rhythm have also been observed, e.g., hand re-sorting of the material to be recycled and removing objects from the recycling box and carrying them to the truck, rather than carrying the box to the truck. The frequency of mishaps and disruptions of normal work activity in this type of collection is particularly high. These mishaps result from workers doing ad hoc activities that are themselves dangerous.

Occupational Accidents and Prevention

Domestic waste collection is a dangerous trade. Statistics support this impression. The average annual accident rate in this industry, for all types of enterprise, truck and trade, is almost 80 accidents for every 2,000 hours of collection. This is equivalent to 8 workers of every 10 suffering an injury at least once a year. Four accidents occur for every 1,000 10-tonne truckloads. On average, each accident results in 10 lost workdays and accident compensation of $820 (Canadian). Indices of injury frequency and severity vary among enterprises, with higher rates observed in municipal enterprises (74 accidents/100 workers versus 57/100 workers in private enterprises) (Bourdouxhe, Cloutier and Guertin 1992). The most common accidents are listed in table 101.3.

Collectors typically suffer hand and thigh lacerations, drivers typically suffer sprained ankles resulting from falls during cabin dismounts and driver-collectors of side-loading trucks typically suffer shoulder and upper back pain resulting from tossing movements. The nature of the accidents also depends on the type of truck, although this can also be seen as a reflection of the specific trades associated with rear- and side-loading trucks. These differences are related to equipment design, the type of movements required and the nature and density of waste collected in the sectors in which these two types of truck are used.

Prevention

The following are ten categories in which improvements could make domestic waste collection safer:

1. management of health and safety (for instance, the development of accident-prevention programmes based on workers' knowledge of occupational hazards which are better adapted to actual tasks)
2. training and hiring
3. work organization, organization of collection and workload
4. vehicles
5. training and work conditions of auxiliary, occasional and temporary workers
6. collection contracts
7. public management
8. collaboration between employer associations (municipal and private), workers and municipal or regional decision-making bodies
9. stability of the workforce
10. research on personal protective equipment, ergonomic design of trucks, subcontracting jobbers and safety.

Conclusion

Domestic waste collection is an important but hazardous activity. Protection of workers is made more difficult where this service is contracted out to private sector enterprises which, as in the province of Quebec, may subcontract the work to many smaller jobbers. A large number of ergonomic and accident hazards, compounded by work quotas, adverse weather and local street and traffic problems must be confronted and controlled if workers' health and safety are to be maintained.

STREET CLEANING

J.C. Gunther, Jr. *

Prevention of dirt-borne disease, prevention of damage to vehicles by harmful objects and the joy of viewing a neat, attractive city

*Adapted from 3rd edition, *Encyclopaedia of Occupational Health and Safety*.

are all benefits derived from clean streets. Herded animals or animal-drawn vehicles, which in earlier times caused unsanitary conditions, have generally ceased to be a problem; however, the expansion in world population with the resultant upsurge in waste generated, the increase in the number and size of factories, the growth in the number of vehicles and newspapers and the introduction of disposable containers and products have all contributed to the amount of street refuse and added to the street-cleaning problem.

Organization and Processes

Municipal authorities recognizing the threat to health posed by dirty streets have sought to minimise the danger by organizing street cleaning sections in the public works departments. In these sections, a superintendent responsible for scheduling frequency of cleaning various districts will have forepeople responsible for specific cleaning operations.

Normally, business districts will be swept daily while arterial roads and residential areas will be swept weekly. Frequency will depend upon rain or snowfall, topography and the education of the populace toward prevention of litter.

The superintendent will also decide the most effective means of achieving clean streets. These could be hand sweeping by one worker or a group, hose flushing or machine sweeping or flushing. Generally a combination of methods, depending on the availability of equipment, type of dirt encountered and other factors will be used. In areas of heavy snowfall, special snow-clearing equipment may be used on occasion.

Hand sweeping is generally done in the daytime and confined to cleaning of gutters or spot cleaning of pavements or adjacent areas. The equipment used consists of brooms, scrapers and shovels. One sweeper generally patrols a specified route and cleans about 9 km of curb per shift under favourable conditions; however, this may be reduced in congested business districts.

Dirt collected by one-person sweeping is placed in a cart which he or she pushes ahead and dumps in boxes placed at intervals along his or her route; these boxes are emptied periodically into refuse trucks. In group sweeping, dirt is swept into piles along the gutters and loaded directly into trucks. Normally a group of 8 sweepers will have 2 workers assigned as loaders. Group sweeping is particularly effective for massive clean-up jobs such as after storms, parades or other special events.

Advantages of hand sweeping are: it is easily adjusted to meet changing cleaning loads; it can be used in areas inaccessible to machines; it can be conducted in heavy traffic with minimum interference with vehicle movement; it can be done in freezing weather and it can be used on pavements where surface conditions do not permit machine cleaning. Disadvantages are: the work is dangerous in traffic; it raises dust; dirt piled in gutters may be dispersed by wind or traffic if not collected promptly; and hand sweeping may be costly in labour-expensive areas.

Hose flushing is not considered an economical operation today; however, it is effective where there is a large amount of dirt or mud adhering to the pavement surfaces, where there are large numbers of parked vehicles or in market areas. It is generally done at night by a two-person crew, one of whom handles the hose nozzle and directs the stream and the other connects hose to the hydrant. Equipment consists of hoses, hose nozzles and hydrant wrenches.

Machine sweepers consist of motorized chassis mounted with brushes, conveyors, sprinklers and storage bins. They are generally used in late evening or early morning hours in business districts and during the day in residential areas. Cleaning action is confined to the gutters and adjacent areas where most dirt accumulates.

The machine is operated by one worker and can be expected to clean approximately 36 km of curb during an 8 hour shift. Factors affecting output are: number of times and distance which must be travelled to dump dirt or pick up sprinkling water; traffic density; and amount of dirt collected.

The advantages of machine sweepers are: they clean well, rapidly and raise no dust when sprinklers are used; they pick up the dirt as they clean; they can be used at night; and they are relatively economical. The disadvantages are: they cannot clean under parked cars or in off-pavement areas; they are not effective on rough, wet or muddy streets; the sprinkler cannot be used in freezing weather and dry sweeping raises dust; and they require skilled operators and maintenance personnel.

Flushing machines are essentially water tanks mounted on a motorized chassis which is fitted with a pump and nozzle to provide pressure and direct the stream of water against the pavement surface. The machine can be expected to clean about 36 km of 7 m wide pavement during an 8 hour shift.

The advantages of flushing machines are: they can be used effectively on wet or muddy pavements; they clean rapidly, well and under parked cars without raising dust; and they can operate at night or in light traffic. The disadvantages are: they require additional cleaning to be effective where street, litter or sewer conditions are not favourable; they annoy pedestrians or vehicle operators who are splashed; they cannot be used in freezing weather; and they require skilled operators and maintenance personnel.

Hazards and Their Prevention

Street cleaning is a hazardous occupation due to the fact that it is conducted in traffic and is concerned with dirt and refuse, with the possibility of infection, cuts from broken glass, tins and so on. In crowded areas, hand sweepers may be exposed to a considerable amount of carbon monoxide and to a high level of noise.

Traffic hazards are protected against by training sweepers in ways of avoiding danger, such as arranging work against the traffic flow and providing them with highly visible clothing as well as attaching red flags or other warning devices to their carts. Machine sweepers and flushers are made visible by fitting them with flashing lights, waving flags and painting them distinctively.

Street cleaners, and in particular hand sweepers, are exposed to all the vagaries of weather and occasionally may have to work in very severe conditions. Illness, infection and handling accidents can in part be prevented by the use of PPE and in part by training. Mechanical equipment such as that used for snow cleaning should be operated only by trained workers.

There should be a conveniently accessible central point providing good washing facilities (including showers where practicable), a cloakroom with arrangements for changing and drying clothes, a messroom and a first-aid room. Periodical medical examination is desirable.

Environmental Concerns of Snow Disposal

Snow removal and disposal introduces a set of environmental concerns related to the potential deposition of debris, salts, oil, metals and particulates in local waterbodies. A particular danger exists from the concentration of particulates, such as lead, that originate in atmospheric emissions from industrialized areas and automobiles. The danger of melt-water runoff to aquatic organisms and the risk of soil and groundwater contamination has been countered by the adoption of safe handling practices that protect sensitive areas from exposure. Snow disposal guidelines have been adopted in several Canadian provinces (e.g., Quebec, Ontario, Manitoba).

SEWAGE TREATMENT

M. Agamennone*

Waste water is treated in order to remove pollutants and to comply with the limits set by law. For this purpose an attempt is made to render the pollutants in the water insoluble in the form of solids (e.g., sludge), liquids (e.g., oil) or gases (e.g., nitrogen) by applying appropriate treatments. Well known techniques are then used to separate the treated waste water to be returned to the natural waterways from the pollutants rendered insoluble. The gases are dispersed into the atmosphere, while the liquid and solid residues (sludge, oil, grease) are usually digested before being submitted to further treatment. There may be single or multi-stage treatments according to the characteristics of the waste water and to the degree of purification required. Waste water treatment may be subdivided into physical (primary), biological (secondary) and tertiary processes.

Physical Processes

The various physical treatment processes are designed to remove insoluble pollutants.

Screening

The sewage is made to pass through screens which retain coarse solids that may block or damage the treatment works equipment (e.g., valves and pumps). The screenings are processed according to local situations.

Sand removal

The sand contained in the waste water has to be removed as it tends to settle in the pipework on account of its high density and cause abrasion to the equipment (e.g., centrifugal separators and turbines). Sand is generally removed by passing the waste water through a channel of constant cross-section at a velocity of 15 to 30 cm/s. The sand collects on the channel bottom and may be used, after washing to remove putrescible matter, as an inert material, such as for road building.

Oil removal

Oils and non-emulsifiable fats have to be removed because they would adhere to the equipment of the treatment works (e.g., basins and clarifiers) and interfere with the subsequent biological treatment. Oil and fat particles are made to collect on the surface by passing the waste water at an appropriate velocity through tanks of rectangular cross-section; they are skimmed off mechanically and may be used as a fuel. Multi-plate separators of compact design and high efficiency are frequently used for oil removal: the sewage is made to pass from above through stacks of flat inclined plates; the oil adheres to the bottom surfaces of the plates and moves to the top where it is collected. With both these processes, the de-oiled water is discharged at the bottom.

Sedimentation, flotation and coagulation

These processes enable the solids to be removed from the waste water, heavy ones (greater than 0.4 μm in diameter) by sedimentation and light ones (less than 0.4 μm) by flotation. This treatment, too, relies on the differences in density of the solids and of the flowing waste water which is passed through sedimentation tanks and flotation tanks made of concrete or steel. The particles to be separated collect in the bottom or at the surface, settling or rising at velocities which are proportional to the square of the particle radius and to the difference between the particle density

*Adapted from 3rd edition, *Encyclopaedia of Occupational Health and Safety*.

and the apparent waste water density. Colloidal particles (e.g., proteins, latexes and oily emulsions) with sizes from 0.4 to 0.001 μm are not separated, as these colloids become hydrated and usually negatively charged by adsorption of ions. Consequently the particles repel each other so that they cannot coagulate and separate. However, if these particles are "destabilized", they coagulate to form flocks greater than 4 μm, which can be separated as sludge in conventional sedimentation or flotation tanks. Destabilization is obtained by coagulation, that is, by adding 30 to 60 mg/l of an inorganic coagulant (aluminium sulphate, iron (II) sulphate or iron (III) chloride). The coagulant hydrolyses under given pH (acidity) conditions and forms positive polyvalent metal ions, which neutralize the negative charge of the colloid. Flocculation (the agglomeration of coagulated particles in flocks) is facilitated by adding 1 to 3 mg/l of organic polyelectrolytes (flocculation agents), resulting in flocks of 0.3 to 1 μm diameter which are easier to separate. Sedimentation tanks of the horizontal-flow type may be used; they have rectangular cross-section and flat or sloping bottoms. The waste water enters along one of the head sides, and the clarified water leaves over the edge at the opposite side. Also vertical flow sedimentation tanks can be used which are cylindrical in shape and have a bottom like an inverted right circular cone; the waste water enters in the middle, and the clarified water leaves the tank over the top indented edge to be collected into an external circumferential channel. With the two types of tank, the sludge settles on the bottom and is conveyed (if necessary by means of a raking gear) into a collector. The solids concentration in the sludge is 2 to 10%, whereas that of the clarified water is 20 to 80 mg/l.

The flotation tanks are usually cylindrical in shape and have fine bubble air diffusers installed in their bottoms, the sewage entering the tanks in the centre. The particles adhere to the bubbles, float to the surface and are skimmed off, while the clarified water is discharged below. In the case of the more efficient "dissolved-air floating tanks", the waste water is saturated with air under a pressure of 2 to 5 bars and then allowed to expand in the centre of the floating tank, where the minute bubbles resulting from the decompression make the particles float to the surface.

Compared to sedimentation, flotation yields a thicker sludge at a higher particle separation velocity, and the equipment required is therefore smaller. On the other hand, the operating cost and the concentration of solids in the clarified water are higher.

Several tanks arranged in series are required for coagulating and flocculating a colloidal system. An inorganic coagulant and, if necessary, an acid or an alkali to correct the pH value are added to the waste water in the first tank, which is equipped with an agitator. The suspension is then passed into a second tank equipped with a high-speed agitator; here, the polyelectrolyte is added and dissolved within a few minutes. The flock growth takes place in a third tank with a slow-running agitator and is carried out for 10 to 15 minutes.

Biological Processes

Biological treatment processes remove organic biodegradable pollutants by use of micro-organisms. These organisms digest the pollutant by an aerobic or anaerobic process (with or without supply of atmospheric oxygen) and convert it into water, gases (carbon dioxide and methane) and a solid insoluble microbic mass which can be separated from the treated water. Especially in the case of industrial effluents proper conditions for the development of micro-organisms must be assured: presence of nitrogen and phosphorus compounds, traces of microelements, absence of toxic substances (heavy metals, etc.), optimum temperature and pH value. Biological treatment includes aerobic and anaerobic processes.

Aerobic processes

The aerobic processes are more or less complex according to the space available, the degree of purification required and the composition of the waste water.

Stabilization ponds

These are generally rectangular and 3 to 4 m deep. The sewage enters at one end, is left for 10 to 60 days and leaves the pond partly at the opposite end, partly by evaporation and partly by infiltration into the ground. The purification efficiency ranges from 10 to 90% according to the type of effluent and to the residual 5-day biological oxygen demand (BOD_5) content (<40 mg/l). Oxygen is supplied from the atmosphere by diffusion through the surface of the water and from photosynthetic algae. The solids in suspension in the waste water and those produced by microbial activity settle on the bottom, where they are stabilized by aerobic and/or anaerobic processes according to the depth of the ponds which affects the diffusion both of oxygen and sunlight. The oxygen diffusion is frequently accelerated by surface aerators, which enable the volume of the ponds to be reduced.

This type of treatment is very economical if space is available, but requires clay-like soil to prevent the pollution of underground water by toxic effluents.

Activated sludge

This is used for an accelerated treatment carried out in concrete or steel tanks of 3 to 5 m depth where the waste water comes into contact with a suspension of micro-organisms (2 to 10 g/l) which is oxygenated by means of surface aerators or by blowing in air. After 3 to 24 hours, the mixture of treated water and micro-organisms is passed into a sedimentation tank where the sludge made up by micro-organisms is separated from the water. The micro-organisms are partly returned to the aerated tank and partly evacuated.

There are various types of activated-sludge processes (e.g., contact-stabilization systems and use of pure oxygen) which yield purification efficiencies of greater than 95% even for industrial effluents but they require accurate controls and high energy consumption for oxygen supply.

Percolating filters

With this technique the micro-organisms are not kept in suspension in the waste water, but adhere to the surface of a filling material over which the sewage is sprayed. Air circulates through the material and supplies the required oxygen without any energy consumption. According to the type of waste water and to increase efficiency, part of the treated water is recirculated to the top of the filter bed.

Where land is available, low-cost filling materials of appropriate size (e.g., crushed stone, clinker and limestone) are used, and on account of the weight of the bed the percolating filter is generally constructed as a 1 m high concrete tank usually sunk in the ground. If there is not enough land, more costly lightweight packing materials such as high-rate plastic honeycomb media, with up to 250 square metres of surface area/cubic metre of media, are stacked in percolating towers up to 10 m high.

The waste water is distributed over the filter bed by a mobile or fixed sparging mechanism and collected in the floor to be eventually recirculated to the top and to be passed into a sedimentation tank where the sludge formed can settle. Openings at the bottom of the percolating filter allow for air circulation through the filter bed. Pollutants removal efficiencies of 30 to 90% are achieved. In many cases several filters are arranged in series. This technique, which requires little energy and is easy to operate, has found widespread use and is recommended for cases where land is available, for instance, in developing countries.

Biodiscs

A set of flat plastic discs mounted parallel on a horizontal rotating shaft are partially immersed in the waste water contained in a tank. Due to the rotation the biological felt that covers the discs is brought into contact with the effluents and atmospheric oxygen. The biological sludge coming off the biodiscs remains in suspension in the waste water, and the system acts as activated sludge and sedimentation tank at the same time. Biodiscs are suitable for small to medium-sized industrial factories and communities, take up little space, are easy to operate, require little energy and yield efficiencies of up to 90%.

Anaerobic processes

Anaerobic processes are carried out by two groups of micro-organisms—*hydrolytic bacteria*, which decompose complex substances (polysaccharides, proteins, lipids, etc.) to acetic acid, hydrogen, carbon dioxide and water; and *methanogenic bacteria*, which convert these substances to a biomass (that can be removed from the treated sewage by sedimentation) and to biogas containing 65 to 70% methane, the remainder being carbon dioxide, and having a high heat value.

These two groups of micro-organisms, which are very sensitive to toxic contaminants, act simultaneously in the absence of air at an almost neutral pH value, some requiring a temperature of 20 to 38 °C (mesophilic bacteria) and other, more delicate ones, 60 to 65 °C (thermophilic bacteria). The process is carried out in stirred, closed concrete or steel *digesters*, where the required temperature is held by thermostats. Typical is the *contact process*, where the digester is followed by a sedimentation tank to separate the sludge, which is partially recirculated to the digester, from the treated water.

Anaerobic processes need neither oxygen nor power for oxygen supply and yield biogas, which can be used as a fuel (low operating costs). On the other hand, they are less efficient than aerobic processes (residual BOD_5: 100 to 1,500 mg/l), are slower and more difficult to control, but enable faecal and pathogenic micro-organisms to be destroyed. They are used for treating strong wastes, such as sedimentation sludge from sewage, sludge in excess from activated sludge or percolating-filter treatments and industrial effluents with a BOD_5 up to 30,000 mg/l (e.g., from distilleries, breweries, sugar refineries, abattoirs and paper mills).

Tertiary Processes

The more complex and more expensive tertiary processes make use of chemical reactions or specific chemicophysical or physical techniques to remove water-soluble non-biodegradable pollutants, both organic (e.g., dyes and phenols) and inorganic (e.g., copper, mercury, nickel, phosphates, fluorides, nitrates and cyanides), especially from industrial waste water, because they cannot be removed by other treatments. Tertiary treatment also enables a high degree of water purification to be obtained, and the water thus treated may be used as drinking water or for manufacturing processes (steam generation, cooling systems, process water for particular purposes). The most important tertiary processes are as follows.

Precipitation

Precipitation is carried out in reactors made of an appropriate material and equipped with agitators where chemical reagents are added at a controlled temperature and pH value to convert the pollutant to an insoluble product. The precipitate obtained in the form of sludge is separated by conventional techniques from the treated water. In waste water from the fertilizer industry, for instance, phosphates and fluorides are rendered insoluble by reaction with lime at ambient temperature and at an alkaline pH; chromium (tanning industry), nickel and copper (electroplating shops) are precipitated as hydroxides at an alkaline pH after having been reduced with m-disulphite at a pH of 3 or lower.

Chemical oxidation

The organic pollutant is oxidized with reagents in reactors similar to those used for precipitation. The reaction is generally continued until water and carbon dioxide are obtained as final products. Cyanides, for instance, are destroyed at ambient temperature by adding sodium hypochlorite and calcium hypochlorite at alkaline pH, whereas azo- and anthraquinone-dyes are decomposed by hydrogen peroxide and ferrous sulphate at pH 4.5. Coloured effluents from the chemical industry containing 5 to 10% non-biodegradable organic substance are oxidized at 200 to 300 °C at high pressure in reactors made of special materials by blowing air and oxygen into the liquid (wet oxidation); catalysts are sometimes used. Pathogens left in urban sewage after treatment are oxidized by chlorination or ozonisation to render the water drinkable.

Absorption

Some pollutants (e.g., phenols in waste water from coking plants, dyes in water for industrial or drinking purposes and surfactants) are effectively removed by absorption on activated carbon powder or granules which are highly porous and have a large specific surface area (of 1000 m^2/g or more). The activated carbon powder is added in metered quantities to the waste water in stirred tanks, and 30 to 60 minutes later the spent powder is removed as a sludge. Granulated activated carbon is used in towers arranged in series through which the polluted water is passed. The spent carbon is regenerated in these towers, that is, the absorbed pollutant is removed either by chemical treatment (e.g., phenols are washed out with soda) or by thermal oxidation (e.g., dyes).

Ion exchange

Certain natural substances (e.g., zeolites) or artificial compounds (e.g., Permutit and resins) exchange, in a stoichiometric and reversible manner, the ions bound to them with those contained, even strongly diluted, in the waste water. Copper, chromium, nickel, nitrates and ammonia, for instance, are removed from waste water by percolation through columns packed with resins. When the resins are spent, they are reactivated by washing with regenerating solutions. Metals are thus recovered in a concentrated solution. This treatment, though costly, is efficient and advisable in cases where a high degree of purity is required (e.g., for waste water contaminated by toxic metals).

Reverse osmosis

In special cases it is possible to extract water of high purity, suitable for drinking, from diluted waste water by passing it through semi-permeable membranes. On the waste water side of the membrane the pollutants (chlorides, sulphates, phosphates, dyes, certain metals) are left as concentrated solutions which have to be disposed of or treated for recovery. The diluted waste water is subjected to pressures up to 50 bars in special plant containing synthetic membranes made of cellulose acetate or other polymers. The operating cost of this process is low, and separation efficiencies of greater than 95% may be obtained.

Sludge Treatment

Rendering pollutants insoluble during waste water treatment results in the production of considerable amounts of sludge (20 to 30% of the removed chemical oxygen demand (COD) which is strongly diluted (90 to 99% water)). The disposal of this sludge in a manner acceptable to the environment presupposes treatments with a cost of up to 50% of those required for waste water purification. The types of treatment depend on the destination of

the sludge, depending in turn on its characteristics and on local situations. Sludge may be destined for:

- fertilization or dumping at sea if it is substantially free from toxic substances and contains nitrogen and phosphorus compounds (sludge from biological treatment), using fixed outfalls, lorries or barges
- sanitary landfill into pits dug in the ground, alternating layers of sludge and soil. Impermeabilisation of peats is required if the sludge contains toxic substances that may be washed out by atmospheric precipitations. The pits should be remote from water-bearing strata. Non-stabilized organic sludge is usually mixed with 10 to 15% lime to retard putrefaction.
- incineration in rotary or fluidized-bed furnaces if the sludge is rich in organic substances and free from volatile metals; if necessary, fuel is added, and the smoke emitted is purified.

The sludge is dewatered before its disposal to reduce both its volume and the cost of its treatment, and it is frequently stabilized to prevent its putrefaction and to render harmless any toxic substances it may contain.

Dewatering

Dewatering includes previous thickening in thickeners, similar to sedimentation tanks, where the sludge is left for 12 to 24 hours and loses part of the water which collects on the surface, while the thickened sludge is discharged below. The thickened sludge is dewatered, for example, by centrifugal separation or by filtration (under vacuum or pressure) with conventional equipment, or by exposure to the air in layers of 30 cm thick in sludge-drying beds consisting of rectangular concrete lagoons, approximately 50 cm deep, with a sloped bottom covered with a layer of sand to facilitate water drainage. Sludge containing colloidal substances should be previously destabilized by coagulation and flocculation, according to already described techniques.

Stabilization

Stabilization includes digestion and detoxification. Digestion is a long-term treatment of the sludge during which it loses 30 to 50% of its organic matter, accompanied by an increase in its mineral salt content. This sludge is no longer putrescible, any pathogens are destroyed and the filtrability is improved. Digestion may be of the aerobic type when the sludge is aerated during 8 to 15 days at ambient temperature in concrete tanks, the process being similar to activated-sludge treatment. It may be of the anaerobic type if the sludge is digested in plants similar to those used for the anaerobic waste treatment, at 35 to 40 °C during 30 to 40 days, with the production of biogas. Digestion can be of the thermal type when the sludge is treated with hot air at 200 to 250 °C and at a pressure of more than 100 bars during 15 to 30 minutes (wet combustion), or when it is treated, in the absence of air, at 180 °C and at autogenous pressure, for 30 to 45 minutes.

Detoxification renders harmless sludge containing metals (e.g., chromium, nickel and lead), which are solidified by treatment with sodium silicate and autothermically converted into the corresponding insoluble silicates.

MUNICIPAL RECYCLING INDUSTRY

David E. Malter

Overview

Recycling means different things to different people. To consumers, recycling may mean putting out bottles and cans for curbside collection. To a product maker—a manufacturer of raw materials or fabricator of goods—it means including recycled materials in the process. To recycling service providers, recycling can mean providing cost-efficient collection, sorting and shipping services. For scavengers, it means culling recyclable materials from garbage and waste cans and selling them to recycling depots. To public policy makers in all levels of government, it means establishing regulations governing collection and utilization as well as reducing the volume of waste to be disposed of and deriving revenue from the sale of the recycled materials. For recycling to work effectively and safely, these diverse groups must be educated to work together and share responsibility for its success.

The recycling industry had been growing steadily since its inception a century ago. Until the 1970s, it remained basically unchanged as a voluntary private sector effort conducted largely by scrap dealers. With the advent of incineration in the 1970s, it became desirable to separate out certain materials before putting waste into the furnaces. This concept was introduced to address the emission problems created by metals, batteries, plastics and other materials discarded in urban wastes which were causing many old incinerators to be shut down as environmental polluters. The increasing concern about the environment provided the primary impetus for the organized separation of plastics, aluminium, tin, paper and cardboard from the residential waste stream. Initially, the recycling industry was not economically viable as a self-sustaining business, but by the mid 1980s, the need for the materials and the increase in their prices led to the development of many new material recycling facilities (MRFs) to handle commingled recyclable materials across the US and Europe.

Work Force

The broad range of skills and expertise makes the range of employment for a MRF very wide. Whether it is a full-service MRF or a single sorting-line operation, the following groups of workers are generally employed:

- *Operators of heavy equipment* (front end loaders, grapples, bull-dozers, etc.) work on the tipping floor, coordinating the movement of waste from the staging area of the tipping floor to the area where the materials are sorted.
- *Material sorters*, the majority of the workforce, segregate and sort recyclable materials by product and/or colour. This may be done entirely by hand or with the assistance of equipment. The sorted materials are then baled or crated.
- *Forklift operators* are responsible for moving finished bales from the throat of the baler to the storage area and from there to the trucks or other means of transportation.
- *Maintenance workers* are becoming increasingly important as the technology advances and the machines and equipment become more complicated.

Processes and Facilities

The recycling industry has been growing very rapidly and has evolved many different processes and procedures as the technology of sorting recyclable materials has advanced. The most common types of installation include full-service MRFs, non-waste stream MRFs and simple sorting and processing systems.

Full-service MRFs

The full-service MRF receives recyclable materials mixed in the residential waste streams. Typically, the resident places the recyclables in coloured plastic bags which are then placed in the residential waste container. This allows the community to combine recyclable materials with other residential wastes, eliminating the need for separate collection vehicles and containers. A typical sequence of operations includes the following procedures:

- The waste and recyclables bags are dropped from the collection vehicle onto the tipping/collection floor.
- The mixture of waste and recyclables is moved either by a grapple or a front-end loader to an in-floor conveyer.
- The conveyer moves the material into the sorting area where a rotating trommel (a cylindrical sieve) opens the bags and allows the very small particles of dirt, sand and gravel to pass through the openings to a collection container for discarding.
- The remaining materials are semi-automatically sorted by screens or disks according to weight and bulkiness. Glass is sorted by its heavier weight, plastics by their lighter weight and paper fibre materials by their bulk.
- Employees hand sort materials, typically from an elevated position above bunkers into which the materials can be stored. Materials are sorted according to the grade of paper, the colour of glass, the physical properties of plastic and so on.
- Refuse and other wastes are collected and removed by tractor-trailer loads.
- The separated materials are moved from the bunkers by forklift or by a "walking floor" (i.e., a conveyer) to a baler or a shredding and baling operation.
- The formed bale is discharged from the baler and moved to the storage area by a forklift.
- Collected bales are shipped either by rail or a tractor-trailer. Instead of baling, some MRFs loose load the materials into a rail car or a tractor trailer.

Non-waste stream MRF

In this system, only the recyclables are delivered to the MRF; the residential wastes go elsewhere. It involves an advanced, semi-automated sorting and processing process system in which all of the steps are the same as those described above. Because of the smaller volume, fewer employees are involved.

Simple sorting/processing system

This is a labour-intensive system in which the sorting is performed manually. Typically, a conveyer belt is used to move material from one work station to another with each sorter removing one type of material as the belt passes his station. A typical sequence for such a simple, inexpensive processing system would include these processes:

- Mixed recyclables are received on a tipping floor and are moved by a front-end loader to the main sorting conveyor belt.
- Glass bottles are separated manually by colour (flint, amber, green and so forth).
- Plastic containers are sorted by grade and accumulated for baling.
- Aluminium cans are removed manually and fed to either a compactor or baler.
- The remaining materials are discharged into a residue pile or container for disposal.

Equipment and machinery

The machinery and equipment used in a MRF is determined by the type of process and the volumes of materials handled. In a typical semi-automated MRF, it would include:

- bag openers
- magnetic separators
- screens (disks, shakers or trommel)
- material classification equipment (mechanical or pneumatic)
- glass crushers
- balers and compactors
- eddy current separators (for non-ferrous metal separation)
- conveyer belts
- rolling stock

Health and safety hazards

MRF workers face a large variety of environmental and work hazards, many of which are unpredictable since the content of the waste changes continually. Prominent among them are:

- infectious disease from biological and medical wastes
- acute and chronic toxicity from household chemicals, solvents and other chemicals being discarded. This risk is not very great (except when industrial wastes find their way into the residential stream) since household chemicals are usually not very toxic and only relatively small amounts are present.
- solvents and fuel and exhaust fumes (especially vehicle operators and maintenance workers)
- exposures to heat, cold and bad weather since many MRFs are exposed to the elements
- noise at harmful levels when heavy machines operate in confined spaces
- physical hazards such as slips and falls, puncture wounds, lacerations and abrasions, muscular strains, sprains and repetitive motion injuries. Sorters usually stand continuously, while vehicle operators must sometimes contend with poorly designed seats and operating controls.
- airborne dust and particles.

Table 101.4 lists the most common types of injury in the recycling industry.

Prevention

MRF workers have the potential to be exposed to whatever wastes are delivered to it, as well as the ever-changing environment in which they work. The management of the facility must constantly be aware of the content of the material being delivered, the training and supervision of the workers and their compliance with safety rules and regulations, the proper use of PPE and the maintenance of machinery and equipment. The following safety considerations deserve constant close attention:

- lockout/tagout precautions
- general housekeeping
- egress maintenance
- emergency preparedness and, when needed, access to first-aid and medical assistance
- hearing conservation programmes
- protection against blood-borne pathogens
- preventive maintenance of machines and equipment
- traffic patterns and danger to pedestrians from the rolling stock
- confined spaces
- fire prevention and training and equipment for fire-fighting
- household hazardous waste management
- availability and use of high-quality, properly-sized PPE.

Table 101.4 • Most frequent injuries in the recycling industry.

Injury type	Cause of injury	Body part affected
Cuts, abrasions and lacerations	Contact with sharp materials	Hands and forearms
Strain	Lifting	Lower back
Particles in eye	Airborne dust and flying objects	Eye
Repetitive motion	Manual sorting	Upper extremities

Conclusion

Municipal recycling is a relatively new industry that is changing rapidly as it grows and its technology advances. The health and safety of its workforce depend on proper design of processes and equipment and the proper training and supervision of its workers.

WASTE DISPOSAL OPERATIONS

James W. Platner

Workers involved in municipal waste disposal and handling face occupational health and safety hazards which are as diverse as the materials they are handling. Workers' primary complaints relate to odour and upper respiratory tract irritation usually related to dust. However, actual occupational health and safety concerns vary with the work process and the waste stream characteristics (mixed municipal solid waste (MSW), sanitary and biological waste, recycled wastes, agricultural and food wastes, ash, construction debris and industrial wastes). Biological agents such as bacteria, endotoxins and fungi may present hazards, particularly for immune system-compromised and hypersensitive workers. In addition to safety concerns, health impacts have involved predominantly respiratory health problems among workers, including symptoms of organic dust toxic syndrome (ODTS), irritation of the skin, eyes and upper airways and cases of more severe pulmonary diseases such as asthma, alveolitis and bronchitis.

The World Bank (Beede and Bloom 1995) estimates that 1.3 billion tonnes of MSW were generated in 1990 which represents an average of two-thirds of a kilogram per person per day. In the US alone, an estimated 343,000 workers were involved in MSW collection, transport and disposal according to 1991 US Census Bureau statistics. In industrialized countries waste streams are increasingly distinct and work processes are increasingly complex. Efforts to segregate and better define the compositions of waste streams are often critical for identifying occupational hazards and appropriate controls and for controlling environmental impacts. Most waste disposal workers continue to face unpredictable exposures and risks from mixed wastes in dispersed open dumps, often with open burning.

The economics of waste disposal, reuse and recycling, as well as public health concerns, are driving rapid changes in waste handling globally to maximize recovery of resources and reduce dispersion of refuse into the environment. Depending on local economic factors this results in the adoption of either increasingly labour-intensive or capital-intensive work processes. Labour-intensive practices draw an increasing number of workers into hazardous work environments and commonly involve informal sector scavengers who sort mixed refuse by hand and sell recyclable and reusable materials. Increased capitalization has not automatically led to improvements in working conditions as increased work within confined spaces (e.g., in drum composting operations or incinerators), and increased mechanical processing of wastes can result in increased exposure to both airborne contaminants and mechanical hazards, unless proper controls are implemented.

Waste Disposal Processes

A variety of waste disposal processes are used, and as waste collection, transportation and disposal costs increase to meet increasingly stringent environmental and community standards, an increasing diversity of processes can be cost-justified. These processes break down into four basic approaches which may be used in combination or in parallel for various waste streams. The four basic processes are dispersal (land or water dumping, evaporation), storage/isolation (sanitary and hazardous waste landfills), oxidation (incineration, composting) and reduction (hydrogenation, anaerobic digestion). These processes share some general occupational hazards associated with waste handling, but also involve work-process-specific occupational hazards.

General Occupational Hazards in Waste Handling

Regardless of the specific disposal process being utilized, simply processing MSW and other wastes involves common defined hazards (Colombi 1991; Desbaumes 1968; Malmros and Jonsson 1994; Malmros, Sigsgaard and Bach 1992; Maxey 1978; Mozzon, Brown and Smith 1987; Rahkonen, Ettala and Loikkanen 1987; Robazzi et al. 1994).

Unidentified, highly hazardous materials are often intermixed with normal waste. Pesticides, flammable solvents, paints, industrial chemicals, and biohazardous waste, may all be intermixed with household waste. This hazard can be handled primarily through segregation of the waste stream and in particular separation of industrial and household waste.

Odours and exposure to mixed volatile organic compounds (VOCs) can induce nausea but are typically well below American Conference of Governmental Industrial Hygenists (ACGIH) threshold limit values (TLVs), even within enclosed spaces (ACGIH 1989; Wilkins 1994). Control typically involves isolation of the process, as in sealed anaerobic digesters or drum composters, minimizing worker contact through daily soil cover or transfer station cleanup and controlling biological degradation processes, particularly minimizing anaerobic degradation by controlling moisture content and aeration.

Insect- and rodent-borne pathogens can be controlled through daily cover of waste with soil. Botros et al. (1989) reported that 19% of garbage workers in Cairo had antibodies to *Rickettsia Typhi* (from fleas) which causes human rickettsial disease.

Injection or blood contact with infectious waste, such as needles and blood soiled waste, is best controlled at the generator by segregation and sterilization of such waste prior to disposal and disposal in puncture resistant containers. Tetanus is also a real concern should skin damage occur. Up-to-date immunization is required.

Ingestion of *Giardia* sp. and other gastrointestinal pathogens can be controlled by minimizing handling, reducing hand-to-mouth contact (including tobacco use), supplying safe drinking water, providing toilet and clean up facilities for workers and maintaining appropriate temperature in composting operations in order to destroy pathogens prior to dry handling and bagging. Precautions are particularly appropriate for *Giardia* found in sewage sludge and disposable baby diapers in MSW, as well as for tape and round worms from poultry and slaughterhouse wastes.

Inhalation of airborne bacteria and fungi is of particular concern when mechanical processing increases (Lundholm and Rylander 1980) with compactors (Emery et al. 1992), macerators or shredders, aeration, bagging operations and when moisture content is allowed to drop. This results in increased respiratory disorders (Nersting et al. 1990), bronchial obstruction (Spinaci et al. 1981) and chronic bronchitis (Ducel et al. 1976). Although there are no formal guidelines, the Dutch Occupational Health Association (1989) recommended that total bacteria and fungal counts should be kept below 10,000 colony forming units per cubic metre (cfu/m^3) and below 500 cfu/m^3 for any single pathogenic organism (outdoor air levels are about 500 cfu/m^3 for total bacteria, indoor air is typically less). These levels may be regularly exceeded in composting operations.

Biotoxins are formed by fungi and bacteria including endotoxins formed by gram-negative bacteria. Inhaling or ingesting an endotoxin, even after killing the bacteria which produced it, can cause fever and flu-like symptoms without infection. The Dutch Working Group on Research Methods in Biological Indoor Air Pollution recommends that airborne gram-negative bacteria be kept below 1000 cfu/m^3 to avoid endotoxin effects. Bacteria and fungi can produce a variety of other potent toxins which may also present occupational hazards.

Heat exhaustion and heat stroke can be serious concerns particularly where safe drinking water is limited and where PPE is utilized in sites known to contain hazardous wastes. Simple PVC-Tyvek® suits show a heat stress equivalent of adding 6 to 11 °C (11 to 20 °F) to the ambient wet bulb globe temperature (WBGT) index (Paull and Rosenthal 1987). When the WBGT exceeds 27.7 °C (82 °F) conditions are considered hazardous.

Skin damage or disease are common complaints in waste handling operations (Gellin and Zavon 1970). Direct skin damage from caustic ash and other irritating waste contaminants, combined with high exposures to pathogenic organisms, frequent skin lacerations and punctures and, typically, poor availability of washing facilities result in a high incidence of skin problems.

Wastes contain a variety of materials that can cause lacerations or punctures. These are of particular concern in labour intensive operations such as waste sorting for recycling or manual turning of MSW compost and where mechanical processes such as compacting, crushing or shredding can create projectiles. The most critical control measures are safety glasses and puncture and slash resistant footwear and gloves.

Vehicular-use hazards include both operator hazards such as rollover and engulfment hazards and collision hazards with workers on the ground. Any vehicle that works on unsound or irregular surfaces should be equipped with rollover cages that will support the vehicle and allow the operator to survive. Pedestrian and vehicular traffic should be separated to the extent possible into distinct traffic areas, particularly where visibility is limited such as during open burning, at night and in composting yards where dense ground fogs may develop in cold weather.

Reports of increased atopic bronchopulmonary reactions such as asthma (Sigsgaard, Bach and Malmros 1990) and skin reactions can occur in waste workers, particularly where organic dust exposure levels are high.

Process-specific Hazards

Dispersion

Dispersion includes dumping waste into bodies of water, evaporation into the air or dumping with no effort at containment. Ocean dumping of MSW and hazardous wastes is rapidly declining. However, an estimated 30 to 50% of MSW is not collected in the cities of developing countries (Cointreau-Levine 1994) and is commonly burned or dumped in canals and streets, where it presents a significant public health threat.

Evaporation, sometimes with active heating at low temperatures, is used as a cost-saving alternative to incinerators or kilns, especially for volatile liquid organic contaminants such as solvents or fuel which are mixed with non-combustible wastes such as soil. Workers may face confined-space entry hazards and explosive atmospheres, especially in maintenance operations. Such operations should incorporate appropriate air emissions controls.

Storage/isolation

Isolation involves a combination of remote locations and physical containment in increasingly secure landfills. Typical sanitary landfills involve excavation with earth moving equipment, dumping of waste, compaction and daily cover with soil or compost to reduce pest infestations, odours and dispersion. Clay or impervious plastic caps and/or liners may be installed to limit water infiltration and leachate into groundwater. Test wells may be used to evaluate off-site leachate migration and to allow monitoring of leachate within the landfill. Workers include heavy equipment operators, truck drivers, spotters who may be responsible for rejecting hazardous waste and directing vehicle traffic flows and informal sector scavengers who may sort the waste and remove recyclables.

In areas dependent on coal or wood for fuel, ash can constitute a significant portion of the waste. Quenching prior to dumping, or segregation into ash monofills, may be necessary to avoid fires. Ash can cause skin irritation and caustic burns. Fly ash presents a variety of health hazards including respiratory and mucosal irritation as well as acute respiratory distress (Shrivastava et al. 1994). Low density fly ash can also constitute an engulfment hazard and can be unstable under heavy equipment and in excavations.

In many nations waste disposal continues to consist of simple dumping with open burning, which may be combined with informal scavenging of reusable or recyclable components with value. These informal sector workers face serious safety and health hazards. It is estimated that in Manila, Philippines, 7,000 scavengers work at the MSW dump, 8,000 in Jakarta and 10,000 in Mexico City (Cointreau-Levine 1994). Because of the difficulties in controlling work practices in informal work, an important step in controlling these hazards is to move separation of recyclables and reusables into the formal waste collection process. This may be performed by the waste generators, including consumers or household workers, by collection/sorting workers (e.g., in Mexico City collection workers officially spend 10% of their time sorting waste for sale of recyclables, and in Bangkok 40% (Beede and Bloom 1995)) or in pre-disposal waste separation operations (e.g., magnetic separation of metallic waste).

Open burning exposes workers to a potentially toxic mix of degradation products as discussed below. Because open burning can be used by informal scavengers to assist in separating metal and glass from combustible waste, it may be necessary to recover materials with salvage value prior to dumping in order to eliminate such open burning.

As hazardous wastes are successfully segregated from the waste stream, risks of MSW workers are reduced while quantities handled by hazardous waste site workers increase. Highly secure hazardous waste treatment and disposal sites depend on detailed manifesting of waste composition, high levels of worker PPE, and extensive worker training to control hazards. Secure landfills have unique hazards including slip and fall hazards where excavations are lined with plastic or polymer gels to reduce migration of leachate, potentially serious dermatological problems, heat stress related to work for extended periods in impermeable suits and supplied air quality control. Heavy equipment operators, labourers and technicians depend largely on PPE to minimize their exposures.

Oxidation (incineration and composting)

Open burning, incineration and waste-derived fuel are the most obvious examples of oxidation. Where the moisture content is low enough and the combustible content is high enough, increasing effort is made to utilize the fuel value in MSW either through the generation of waste-derived fuel as compressed briquettes or by incorporating electrical cogeneration or steam plants into municipal waste incinerators. Such operations can involve high levels of dry dusts due to efforts to produce a fuel with consistent heat value. Residual ash must still be disposed of, usually in landfills.

MSW incinerators involve a variety of safety hazards (Knop 1975). Swedish MSW incinerator workers showed increased ischemic heart disease (Gustavsson 1989), while a study of US incinerator workers in Philadelphia, Pennsylvania, failed to show a correlation between health outcomes and exposure groups (Bresnitz et al. 1992). Somewhat elevated blood lead levels have been identified in incinerator workers, primarily related to exposures to electrostatic precipitator ash (Malkin et al. 1992).

Ash exposures (e.g., crystalline silica, radioisotopes, heavy metals) can be significant not only in incinerator operations, but also at landfills and lightweight concrete plants where ash is used as aggregate. Although crystalline silica and heavy metal content vary with the fuel, this may present serious silicosis risk. Schilling (1988) observed lung function and respiratory symptom effects in ash exposed workers, but no changes observable by x ray.

Thermal degradation on pyrolysis products resulting from incomplete oxidation of many waste products can pose significant health risks. These products can include hydrogen chloride, phosgene, dioxins and dibenzofurans from chlorinated wastes, such as polyvinyl chloride (PVC) plastics and solvents. Non-halogenated wastes also can produce hazardous degradation products, including polyaromatic hydrocarbons, acrolein, cyanide from wools and silk, isocyanates from polyurethane and organotin compounds from a variety of plastics. These complex mixtures of degradation products can vary tremendously with waste composition, feed rates, temperature and available oxygen during combustion. While these degradation products are a significant concern in open burning, exposures in MSW incinerator workers appear to be relatively low (Angerer et al. 1992).

In MSW and hazardous waste incinerators and rotary kilns, control of combustion parameters and the residence time for waste vapours and solids at high temperatures is critical in destruction of wastes while minimizing the generation of more hazardous degradation products. Workers are involved in incinerator operation, loading and waste transfer into the incinerator, waste delivery and unloading from trucks, equipment maintenance, housekeeping and ash and slag removal. While incinerator design can limit necessary manual labour and worker exposures, with less capital-intensive designs there may be significant worker exposures and a need for regular confined space entry (e.g., chipping for removal of slag from glass waste from incinerator grates).

Composting

In aerobic biological processes the temperature and speed of oxidation are lower than incineration, but it is nevertheless oxidation. Composting of agricultural and yard wastes, sewage sludge, MSW and food wastes is increasingly common in city-scale operations. Rapidly developing technologies for biological remediation of hazardous and industrial wastes often involve a sequence of aerobic and anaerobic digestion processes.

Composting usually occurs either in wind rows (long piles) or in large vessels which provide aeration and mixing. The objective of composting operations is to create a mix of waste with optimum ratios of carbon and nitrogen (30:1) and then maintain moisture at 40 to 60% by weight, greater than 5% oxygen and temperature levels 32 to 60 °C so that aerobic bacteria and other organisms can grow (Cobb and Rosenfield 1991). Following separation of recyclables and hazardous wastes (which typically involves hand sorting), MSW is shredded to create more surface area for biological action. Shredding can produce high noise and dust levels and significant mechanical guarding concerns. Some operations use ganged hammer-mills to allow reduced front-end sorting.

In-vessel or drum composting operations are capital intensive but allow more effective odour and process control. Confined space entry is a significant hazard for maintenance workers as high levels of CO_2 may be released causing oxygen deficiency. Lockout of equipment prior to maintenance is also critical as mechanisms include internal screw-drives and conveyors.

In less capital intensive wind row composting operations, waste is shredded and placed in long piles which are mechanically aerated through perforated pipes or simply by turning, either with front-end loaders or manually. Wind rows may be covered or roofed to facilitate maintenance of constant moisture content. Where specialized wind row turning equipment is used, chain mixing-flails rotate at high speed through the compost and should be well guarded from human contact. As these flails rotate through the wind row, they eject objects which can become dangerous projectiles. Operators must assure safe clearance distances around and behind the equipment.

Regular temperature measurements with probes allow monitoring the progress of composting and assure high enough temperatures to kill pathogens while allowing adequate survival of beneficial organisms. At moisture contents of 20 to 45% when the temperature exceeds 93 °C there can also be a spontaneous combustion fire hazard (much like a silo fire). This is most likely to occur when piles exceed 4 m in height. Fires can be avoided by keeping pile heights below 3 m, and turning when the temperature exceeds 60 °C. Facilities should provide water hydrants and adequate access between wind rows for control of fires.

Hazards in composting operations include vehicle and mechanical hazards resulting from tractors and trucks involved in turning wind-rows of waste to maintain aeration and moisture content. In cooler climates the elevated temperatures of compost can produce dense ground fogs in a work area occupied by heavy equipment operators and pedestrian workers. Compost workers report more nausea, headache and diarrhoea than their counterparts in a drinking water plant (Lundholm and Rylander 1980). Odour problems can occur as a result of poor control of the moisture and air required for the composting to progress. If anaerobic conditions are allowed to occur, hydrogen sulphide, amines and other odorous materials are generated. In addition to typical disposal worker concerns, composting involving actively growing organisms can raise MSW temperatures high enough to kill pathogens, but can also produce exposures to moulds and fungi and their spores and toxins, especially in compost bagging operations and where compost is allowed to dry. Several studies have evaluated airborne fungi, bacteria, endotoxins and other contaminants (Belin 1985; Clark, Rylander and Larsson 1983; Heida, Bartman and van der Zee 1975; Lacey et al. 1990; Millner et al. 1994; van der Werf 1996; Weber et al. 1993) in composting operations. There is some indication of increased respiratory disorders and hypersensitivity reactions in compost workers (Brown et al. 1995; Sigsgaard et al. 1994). Certainly bacterial and fungal respiratory infections (Kramer, Kurup and Fink 1989) are a concern for immune-suppressed workers such as those with AIDS and those receiving cancer chemotherapy.

Reduction (hydrogenation and anaerobic digestion)
Anaerobic digestion for sewage and agricultural waste involves closed tanks, often with rotating brush contacts if nutrients are dilute, which can pose serious confined space entry concerns for maintenance workers. Anaerobic digesters are also commonly used in many countries as methane generators which may be fuelled with agricultural, sanitary or food wastes. Methane collection from MSW landfills and burning or compression for use is now required in many countries when methane generation exceeds specified thresholds, but most landfills have inadequate moisture for anaerobic digestion to proceed efficiently. Hydrogen sulphide generation is also a common result of anaerobic digestion and can cause eye irritation and olfactory fatigue at low levels.

More recently, high temperature reduction/hydrogenation has become a treatment option for organic chemical wastes. This can involve smaller, and therefore potentially mobile, installations with less energy input than a high temperature incinerator because metallic catalysts allow hydrogenation to proceed at lower temperatures. Organic wastes can be converted into methane and used as fuel to continue the process. Critical worker safety concerns include explosive atmospheres and confined space entry for cleaning, sludge removal and maintenance, hazards of transporting and loading the liquid feed wastes and spill response.

Summary
As wastes are viewed as resources for recycling and reuse, waste processing increases, resulting in rapid change in the waste disposal industry globally. Occupational health and safety risks of waste disposal operations often go beyond obvious safety hazards to a variety of chronic and acute health concerns. These hazards are often faced with minimal PPE and inadequate sanitary and wash-up facilities. Industrial waste reduction and pollution prevention efforts are increasingly shifting recycling and reuse processes away from contracted or external waste disposal operations and into production work areas.

Top priorities in controlling occupational safety and health hazards in this rapidly changing industry sector should include:

- integrating informal sector work into the formal work process
- providing adequate toilet and wash-up facilities and safe drinking water
- eliminating open burning and waste dispersion into the environment
- segregating waste streams to facilitate characterization of wastes and identification of appropriate control measures and work practices
- minimizing mixed vehicular and pedestrian traffic in work areas
- following appropriate excavation practices for soil and waste characteristics
- anticipating and controlling hazards prior to entry into confined spaces
- minimizing respirable dust exposures in high dust operations
- using safety glasses and slash and puncture resistant shoes and gloves
- integrating occupational safety and health concerns when introducing process change plans, particularly during transitions from open dumping and landfills to more complex and potentially more hazardous enclosed operations such as composting, mechanical or manual separation for recycling, waste to energy operations or incinerators.

In this period of rapid change in the industry, significant improvements in worker health and safety can be made at low cost.

THE GENERATION AND TRANSPORT OF HAZARDOUS WASTES: SOCIAL AND ETHICAL ISSUES

Colin L. Soskolne*

Hazardous wastes include, among other things, radioactive materials and chemicals. The movement of these substances from their source to other locations has been termed "toxic trade". It was in the late 1980s that concern was raised about toxic trade, in particular with Africa (Vir 1989). This set the stage for the recently recognized issue of environmental justice, in some situations also known as environmental racism (Coughlin 1996).

Vir (1989) pointed out that as environmental safety laws became increasingly stringent in Europe and in the United States, and as the cost of disposal increased, "dumpers" or "waste mer-

*Adapted from Soskolne 1997, with permission.

chants" began to turn their attention to poorer nations as potential and willing recipients of their waste products, providing a much needed source of revenue to these poorer countries. Some of these countries had been willing to take such waste at a fraction of the cost that developed nations would otherwise have had to pay for their disposal. To "nations that are drowning economically, this is an attractive deal" (Vir 1989).

Asante-Duah, Saccomanno and Shortreed (1992) show the exponential growth in the United States in the production of hazardous wastes since 1970, with the costs associated with treatment and disposal similarly increasing. They argue in favour of a controlled hazardous waste trade, one that is "regulated *and* informed". They note that "countries generating small quantities of hazardous wastes should view the waste trade as an important economic option, as long as the waste recipients do not compromise their environmental sustainability". Hazardous wastes will continue to be generated and there are countries for which an increase in some of these substances would not increase the risk to health of either present or future generations. It might therefore be economically efficient for such countries to accept waste.

There are others who argue that waste should be disposed of only at the source and not be transported at all (Puckett and Fogel 1994; Cray 1991; Southam News 1994). The latter argue from the position that science is incapable of providing any guarantees about the absence of risk.

One ethical principle that emerges from the foregoing argument is that of respect for autonomy (i.e., respect for persons), which also includes questions of national autonomy. The crucial question is one of the ability of a recipient country to adequately assess the level of risk associated with a shipment of hazardous waste. Assessment presupposes full disclosure of the contents of a shipment from the originating country and a level of local expertise to assess any potential impacts on the recipient country.

Because communities in developing countries are less likely to be informed about the potential risks associated with waste shipments, the NIMBY phenomenon (i.e., not in my backyard) so evident in the more affluent regions of the world is less likely to manifest in poorer regions. Furthermore, workers in developing regions of the world tend not to have the infrastructure related to worker protection, including information concerning the labelling of products with which they come into contact. Hence, workers in poorer nations involved in the management, storage and disposal of hazardous waste would lack the training to know how to protect themselves. Regardless of these ethical considerations, in the final analysis the economic benefits to be derived from accepting such waste shipments would need to be weighed against any potential harms that could arise in the short, medium and longer terms.

A second ethical principle emerging from the preceding argument is that of distributive justice, which involves question regarding who takes risks and who derives benefits. When there is an imbalance between those who take risks and those who derive benefits, the principle of distributive justice is not being honoured. It has often been financially poor labourers who have been exposed to hazards without any ability to enjoy the fruits of their efforts. This has occurred in the context of production of relatively expensive merchandise in the developing world for the benefit of first world markets. Another example related to the testing of new vaccines or drugs on people in developing countries who could never afford access to them in their own countries.

Towards Controlling the Transport of Hazardous Wastes

Because of the recognized need to better control the dumping of hazardous wastes, the Basel Convention was entered into by ministers of 33 countries in March 1989 (Asante-Duah, Saccomanno

and Shortreed 1992). The Basel Convention addressed the transboundary movements of hazardous wastes and required the notification and consent of recipient countries before any waste shipments could take place.

Subsequently, the United Nations Environment Programme (UNEP) launched its Cleaner Production Programme, in close cooperation with governments and industry, to advocate low- and non-waste technologies (Rummel-Bulska 1993). In March 1994, a full ban was introduced on all transboundary movements of hazardous wastes from the 24 rich industrialized countries of the Organization for Economic Cooperation and Development (OECD) to other states that are not members of the OECD. The ban was immediate for wastes bound for final disposal and enters into force at the beginning of 1998 for all hazardous wastes that are said to be destined for recycling or recovery operations (Puckett and Fogel 1994). The countries most opposed to the introduction of a total ban were Australia, Canada, Japan and the United States. Despite this opposition from a handful of powerful industrial governments through the penultimate vote, the ban was finally agreed to by consensus (Puckett and Fogel 1994).

Greenpeace has stressed the primary prevention approach to solving the mounting waste crisis by addressing the root cause of the problem, namely minimizing waste generation through clean production technologies (Greenpeace 1994a). In making this point, Greenpeace identified major countries exporting hazardous wastes (Australia, Canada, Germany, the United Kingdom and the United States) and some countries importing them (Bangladesh, China (including Taiwan), India, Indonesia, Malaysia, Pakistan, the Philippines, the Republic of Korea, Sri Lanka and Thailand). In 1993, Canada, for example, had exported some 3.2 million kilograms of ash containing lead and zinc to India, the Republic of Korea and Taiwan, China, and 5.8 million kilograms of plastic waste to Hong Kong (Southam News 1994). Greenpeace (1993, 1994b) also addresses the extent of the problem in terms of specific substances and approaches to disposal.

Risk Assessment

Epidemiology is at the centre of human health risk assessment, which is invoked when concern is raised by a community about the consequences, if any, of exposure to hazardous and potentially toxic substances. The scientific method that epidemiology brings to the study of the environmental determinants of ill health can be fundamental to protecting unempowered communities, both from environmental hazards and from environmental degradation. Risk assessment conducted in advance of a shipment likely would fall into the legal trade arena; when conducted after a shipment has arrived, risk assessment would be undertaken to determine whether or not any health concerns were justified from what likely would have been an illegal shipment.

Among the concerns to the risk assessor would be hazard assessment, i.e., questions about what hazards, if any, exist and in what quantities and in what form they might be present. In addition, depending on the type of hazard, the risk assessor must make an exposure assessment to establish what possibilities there are for people to be exposed to the hazardous substance(s) through inhalation, skin absorption or ingestion (by contamination of the food chain or directly on foodstuffs).

In terms of trade, autonomy would require the informed consent of the parties in a voluntary and non-coercive milieu. However, it is hardly possible that non-coerciveness could ever pertain in such a circumstance by virtue of the financial need of an importing developing world country. The analogue here is the now accepted ethical guideline which does not permit the coercion of participants in research through payment for anything but direct costs (e.g., lost wages) for the time taken to participate in a study (CIOMS 1993). Other ethical issues involved here would include, on the one hand, truth in the presence of unknowns or in the presence of scientific uncertainty and, on the other hand, the principle of *caveat emptor* (buyer beware). The ethical principle of non-maleficence requires the doing of more good than harm. Here the short-term economic benefits of any trade agreement to accept toxic wastes must be weighed against the longer term damage to the environment, the public health and possibly also to future generations.

Finally, the principle of distributive justice requires recognition by the parties involved in a trade deal as to who would be deriving the benefits and who would be taking the risks in any trade deal. In the past, general practices for dumping waste and for locating hazardous waste sites in unempowered communities in the United States have led to the recognition of the concern now known as environmental justice or environmental racism (Coughlin 1996). In addition, questions of environmental sustainability and integrity have become central concerns in the public forum.

Acknowledgements: Dr. Margaret-Ann Armour, Department of Chemistry, University of Alberta, provided valuable references on the topic of toxic trade as well as materials from the November 1993 Pacific Basin "Conference on Hazardous Waste" at the University of Hawaii.

The Greenpeace office in Toronto, Ontario, Canada, was most helpful in providing copies of the Greenpeace references cited in this article.

References

American Conference of Governmental Industrial Hygienists (ACGIH). 1989. *Guidelines for the Assessment of Bioaerosols in the Indoor Environment.* Cincinnati, OH: ACGIH.

Angerer, J, B Heinzow, DO Reimann, W Knorz, and G Lehnert. 1992. Internal exposure to organic substances in a municipal waste incinerator. *Int Arch Occup Environ Health*; 64(4):265-273.

Asante-Duah, DK, FK Saccomanno, and JH Shortreed. 1992. The hazardous waste trade: Can it be controlled? *Environ Sci Technol* 26:1684-1693.

Beede, DE and DE Bloom. 1995. The economics of municipal solid waste. *World Bank Research Observer.* 10(2):113-115.

Belin, L. 1985. Health problems caused by actinomycetes and moulds in the industrial environment. *Allergy Suppl.* 40:24-29.

Bisesi, M and D Kudlinski. 1996. Measurement of airborne gram-negative bacteria in selected areas of a sludge dewatering building. Presented at the American Industrial Hygiene Conference and Exposition, 20-24 May, Washington, DC.

Botros, BA, AK Soliman, M Darwish, S el Said, JC Morrill, and TG Ksiazek. 1989. Seroprevalence of murine typhus and fievre boutonneuse in certain human populations in Egypt. *J Trop Med Hyg.* 92(6):373-378.

Bourdouxhe, M, E Cloutier, and S Guertin. 1992. *Étude des risques d'accidents dans la collecte des ordures ménagères.* Montreal: Institut de recherche en santé de la sécurité du travail.

Bresnitz, EA, J Roseman, D Becker, and E Gracely. 1992. Morbidity among municipal waste incinerator workers. *Am J Ind Med* 22 (3):363-378.

Brophy, M. 1991. Confined space entry programs. *Water Pollution Control Federation Safety and Health Bulletin* (Spring):4.

Brown, JE, D Masood, JI Couser, and R Patterson. 1995. Hypersensitivity pneumonitis from residential composting: residential composter's lung. *Ann Allergy, Asthma & Immunol* 74:45-47.

Clark, CS, R Rylander, and L Larsson. 1983. Levels of gram-negative bacteria, *aspergillus fumigatus*, dust and endotoxin at compost plants. *Appl Environ Microbiol* 45:1501-1505.

Cobb, K and J Rosenfield. 1991. *Municipal Compost Management Home Study Program.* Ithaca, NY: Cornell Waste Management Institute.

Cointreau-Levine, SJ. 1994. *Private Sector Participation in MSW Services in Developing Countries. The Formal Sector,* Vol. 1. Washington, DC: World Bank.

Colombi, A. 1991. Health risks for waste disposal industry workers (in Italian). *Med Lav* 82(4):299-313.

Coughlin, SS. 1996. Environmental justice: The role of epidemiology in protecting unempowered communities from environmental hazards. *Sci Total Environ* 184:67-76.

Council for International Organizations of Medical Sciences (CIOMS). 1993. *International Ethical Guidelines for Biomedical Research Involving Human Subjects.* Geneva: CIOMS.

Cray, C. 1991. *Waste Management Inc.: An Encyclopedia of Environmental Crimes and Other Misdeeds,* 3rd (revised) edition. Chicago, IL: Greenpeace USA.

Crook, B, P Bardos, and J Lacey. 1988. Domestic waste composting plants as source of airborne microorganisms. In *Aerosols: Their Generation, Behavior and Application,* edited by WD Griffiths. London: Aerosol Society.

Desbaumes, P. 1968. Study of risks inherent in industries treating refuse and sewage (in French). *Rev Med Suisse Romande* 88(2):131-136.

Ducel, G, JJ Pitteloud, C Rufener-Press, M Bahy, and P Rey. 1976. The importance of bacterial exposure in sanitation employees when collecting refuse (in French). *Soz Praventivmed* 21(4):136-138.

Dutch Occupational Health Association. 1989. *Protocol Onderzoeksmethoden Micro-biologische Binnenluchtverontreinigingen* [Research Methods in Biological Indoor Air Pollution]. Working Group Report. The Hague, The Netherlands: Dutch Occupational Health Association.

Emery, R, D Sprau, YJ Lao, and W Pryor. 1992. Release of bacterial aerosols during infectious waste compaction: An initial hazard evaluation for health-care workers. *Am Ind Hyg Assoc J* 53(5):339-345.

Gellin, GA and MR Zavon. 1970. Occupational dermatoses of solid waste workers. *Arch Environ Health* 20(4):510-515.

Greenpeace. 1993. *We've Been Had! Montreal's Plastics Dumped Overseas.* Greenpeace International Toxic Trade Report. Washington, DC: Greenpeace Public Information.

—. 1994a. *The Waste Invasion of Asia: A Greenpeace Inventory.* Greenpeace Toxic Trade Report. Washington, DC: Greenpeace Public Information.

—. 1994b. *Incineration.* Greenpeace Inventory of Toxic Technologies. Washington, DC: Greenpeace Public Information.

Gustavsson, P. 1989. Mortality among workers at a municipal waste incinerator. *Am J Ind Med* 15(3):245-253.

Heida, H, F Bartman, and SC van der Zee. 1975. Occupational exposure and indoor air quality monitoring in a composting facility. *Am Ind Hyg Assoc J* 56(1): 39-43.

Johanning, E, E Olmsted, and C Yang. 1995. Medical issues related to municipal waste composting. Presented at the American Industrial Hygiene Conference and Exposition, 22-26 May, Kansas City, KS.

Knop W. 1975. Work safety in incinerator plants (in German) *Zentralbl Arbeitsmed* 25(1):15-19.

Kramer, MN, VP Kurup, and JN Fink. 1989. Allergic bronchopulmonary aspergillosis from a contaminated dump site. *Am Rev Respir Dis* 140:1086-1088.

Lacey, J, PAM Williamson, P King, and RP Barbos. 1990. *Airborne Microorganisms Associated with Domestic Waste Composting.* Stevenage, UK: Warren Spring Laboratory.

Lundholm, M and R Rylander. 1980. Occupational symptoms among compost workers. *J Occup Med* 22(4):256-257.

Malkin, R, P Brandt-Rauf, J Graziano, and M Parides. 1992. Blood lead levels in incinerator workers. *Environ Res* 59(1):265-270.

Malmros, P and P Jonsson. 1994. Wastes management: Planning for recycling workers' safety. *Waste Management & Resource Recovery* 1:107-112.

Malmros, P, T Sigsgaard and B Bach. 1992. Occupational health problems due to garbage sorting. *Waste Management & Research* 10:227-234.

Mara, DD. 1974. *Bacteriology for Sanitary Engineers.* London: Churchill Livingstone.

Maxey, MN. 1978. Hazards of solid waste management: bioethical problems, principles, and priorities. *Environ Health Perspect* 27:223-230.

Millner, PD, SA Olenchock, E Epstein, R Rylander, J Haines, and J Walker. 1994. Bioaerosols associated with composting facilities. *Compost Science and Utilization* 2:3-55.

Mozzon, D, DA Brown, and JW Smith. 1987. Occupational exposure to airborne dust, respirable quartz and metals arising from refuse handling, burning and landfilling. *Am Ind Hyg Assoc J* 48(2):111-116.

Nersting, L, P Malmros, T Sigsgaard, and C Petersen. 1990. Biological health risk associated with resource recovery, sorting of recycle waste and composting. *Grana* 30:454-457.

Paull, JM and FS Rosenthal. 1987. Heat strain and heat stress for workers wearing protective suits at a hazardous waste site. *Am Ind Hyg Assoc J* 48(5):458-463.

Puckett, J and C Fogel 1994. *A Victory for Environment and Justice: The Basel Ban and How It Happened.* Washington, DC: Greenpeace Public Information.

Rahkonen, P, M Ettala, and I Loikkanen. 1987. Working conditions and hygiene at sanitary landfills in Finland. *Ann Occup Hyg* 31(4A):505-513.

Robazzi, ML, E Gir, TM Moriya, and J Pessuto. 1994. The trash collection service: Occupational risks versus damages to health (in Portuguese). *Rev Esc Enferm USP* 28(2):177-190.

Rosas, I, C Calderon, E Salinas, and J Lacey. 1996. Airborne microorganisms in a domestic waste transfer station. In *Aerobiology,* edited by M Muilenberg and H Burge. New York: Lewis Publishers.

101. PUBLIC AND GOVERNMENT SERVICES

Rummel-Bulska, I. 1993. The Basel Convention: A global approach for the management of hazardous wastes. Paper presented at the Pacific Basin Conference on Hazardous Waste, University of Hawaii, November.

Salvato, JA. 1992. *Environmental Engineering and Sanitation*. New York: John Wiley and Sons.

Schilling, CJ, IP Tams, RS Schilling, A Nevitt, CE Rossiter, and B Wilkinson. 1988. A survey into the respiratory effects of prolonged exposure to pulverised fuel ash. *Br J Ind Med* 45(12):810-817.

Shrivastava, DK, SS Kapre, K Cho, and YJ Cho. 1994. Acute lung disease after exposure to fly ash. *Chest* 106(1):309-311.

Sigsgaard, T, A Abel, L Donbk, and P Malmros. 1994. Lung function changes among recycling workers exposed to organic dust. *Am J Ind Med* 25:69-72.

Sigsgaard, T, B Bach, and P Malmros. 1990. Respiratory impairment among workers in a garbage-handling plant. *Am J Ind Med* 17(1):92-93.

Smith, RP. 1986. Toxic responses of the blood. In *Casarett and Doull's Toxicology*, edited by CD Klaassen, MO Amdur, and J Doull. New York: Macmillan Publishing Company.

Soskolne, C. 1997. International transport of hazardous waste: Legal and illegal trade in the context of professional ethics. *Global Bioethics* (September/October).

Spinaci, S, W Arossa, G Forconi, A Arizio, and E Concina. 1981. Prevalence of functional bronchial obstruction and identification of groups at risk in a population of industrial workers (in Italian). *Med Lav* 72(3):214-221.

Southam News. 1994. Export ban on toxic waste proposed. *Edmonton Journal* (9 March):A12.

van der Werf, P. 1996. Bioaerosols at a Canadian composting facility. *Biocycle* (September): 78-83.

Vir, AK. 1989. Toxic trade with Africa. *Environ Sci Technol* 23:23-25.

Weber, S, G Kullman, E Petsonk, WG Jones, S Olenchock, and W Sorensen. 1993. Organic dust exposures from compost handling: Case presentation and respiratory exposure assessment. *Am J Ind Med* 24:365-374.

Wilkenfeld, C, M Cohen, SL Lansman, M Courtney, MR Dische, D Pertsemlidis, and LR Krakoff. 1992. Heart transplantation for end-stage cardiomyopathy caused by an occult pheochromocytoma. *J Heart Lung Transplant* 11:363-366.

TRANSPORT INDUSTRY AND WAREHOUSING

102

Chapter Editor
LaMont Byrd

Contents

● GENERAL PROFILE

LaMont Byrd

The transport sector encompasses industries that are involved in the transportation of goods and passengers throughout the world. This sector is structurally complex and vitally important to economies locally, nationally and globally.

Economic Importance

The transport sector is vitally important to the economic viability of nations. Transportation plays a key role in economically important factors such as employment, utilization of raw and manufactured goods, investment of private and public capital and generation of tax revenues.

In most industrialized countries, transport accounts for 2 to 12% of the paid employment (ILO 1992). In the United States alone, the Department of Transportation reported that in 1993, there were approximately 7.8 million employees in trucking-related firms (DOT 1995). The transport sector's share in the gross domestic product (GDP) and total employment tends to decrease as the country's income increases.

The transport sector is also a major consumer of raw materials and finished goods in most industrialized countries. For example, in the United States, the transport sector utilizes approximately 71% of all rubber produced, 66% of all petroleum refined, 24% of all zinc, 23% of all cement, 23% of all steel, 11% of all copper and 16% of all aluminium (Sampson, Farris and Shrock 1990).

Capital investment utilizing public and private funds to purchase trucks, ships, airplanes, terminals and other equipment and facilities easily exceeds hundreds of billions of dollars in industrialized countries.

The transport sector also plays a major role in generating revenues in the form of taxes. In industrialized countries, transport of passengers and freight is often heavily taxed (Sampson, Farris and Shrock 1990; Gentry, Semeijn and Vellenga 1995). Typically these taxes take the form of fuel taxes on gasoline and diesel fuels, and excise taxes on freight bills and passenger tickets, and easily exceed hundreds of billions of dollars annually.

Evolution of the Sector

In the early stages of the transport sector, geography greatly influenced what was the dominant mode of transportation. As advances were made in construction technology, it became possible to overcome many of the geographical barriers that limited the development of the transport sector. As a result, the modes of transport that have dominated the sector evolved in accordance with the technology available.

Initially, water travel over the oceans was the primary mode of transport of freight and passengers. As large rivers were navigated and canals were built, the volume of inland transport over the waterways increased significantly. In the late nineteenth century, transport over railways began to emerge as the dominant mode of transport. Rail transport, because of its ability to overcome natural barriers such as mountains and valleys through the use of tunnels and bridges, offered flexibility that waterways could not

Figure 102.1 • World road network distribution 1988–89, in kilometres.

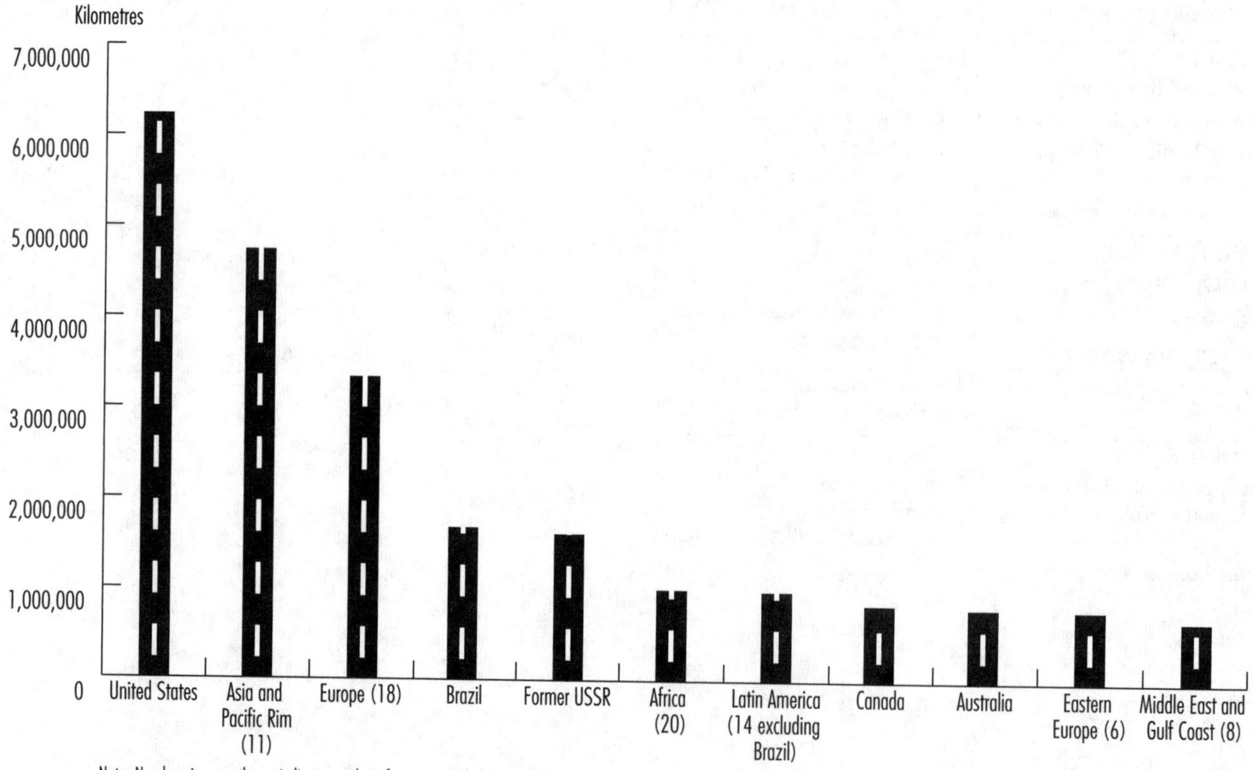

Note: Numbers in parentheses indicate number of countries included in survey.

Source: ILO 1992.

Figure 102.2 • World railroad network distribution, 1988–89, in kilometres.

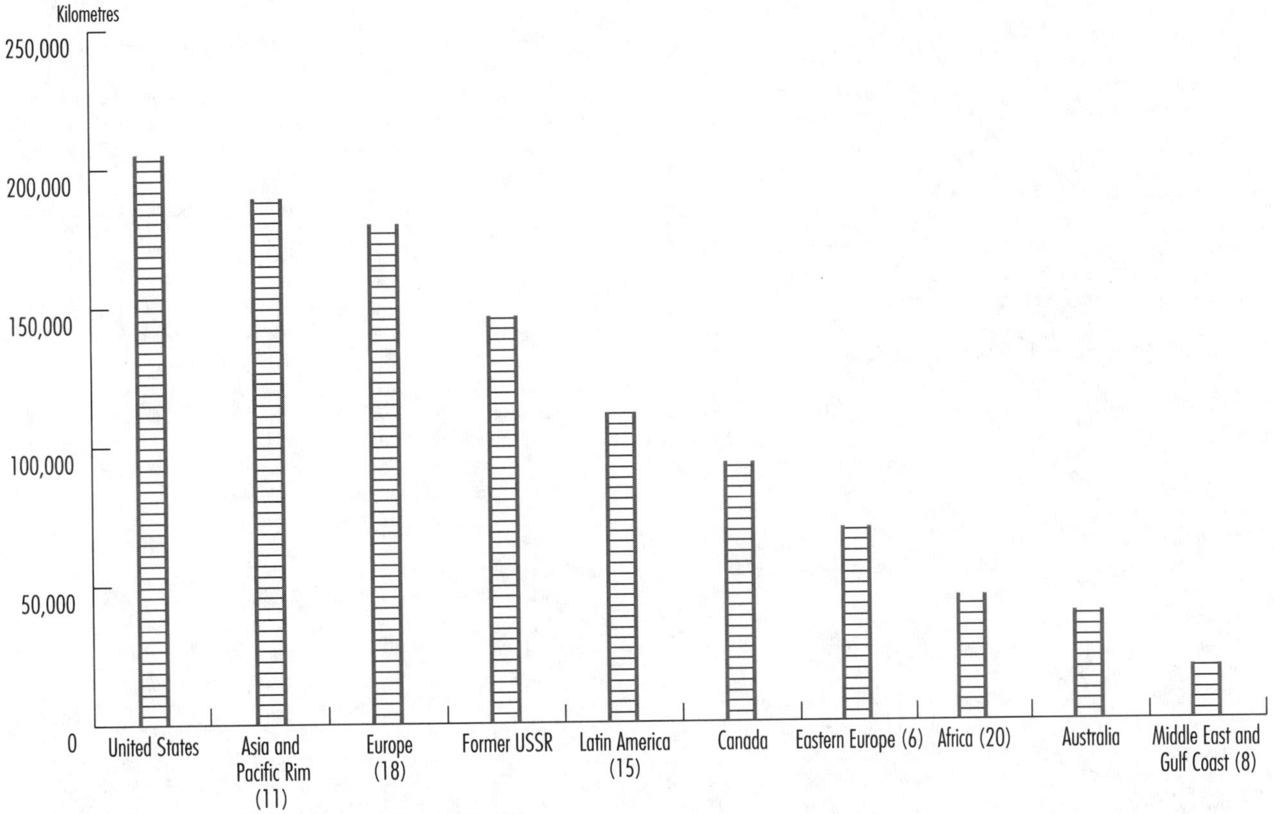

Note: Numbers in parentheses indicate number of countries included in survey.

Source: ILO 1992.

provide. Furthermore, unlike transport over waterways, transport over the rails was virtually unaffected by winter conditions.

Many national governments recognized the strategic and economic advantages of rail transport. Consequently, rail companies were awarded governmental financial assistance to facilitate the expansion of rail networks.

In the early twentieth century, the development of the combustion engine combined with the increased use of motor vehicles enabled road transport to become an increasingly popular mode of transport. As the highway and throughway systems were developed, road transport enabled door-to-door deliveries of goods. This flexibility far surpassed that of railways and waterways. Eventually, as advances were made in road construction and improvements were made to the internal combustion engine, in many parts of the world road transport became faster than rail transport. Consequently, road transport has become the most used mode of transport of goods and passengers.

The transport sector continued to evolve with the advent of airplanes. The use of airplanes as a means to transport freight and passengers began during the Second World War. Initially, airplanes were primarily used to transport mail and soldiers. However, as aircraft construction was perfected and an increasing number of persons learned to operate airplanes, air transport grew in popularity. Today, air transport is a very fast, reliable mode of transport. However, in terms of total tonnage, air transport handles only a very small percentage of freight.

Structure of the Sector

Information on the structure of rail systems in industrialized countries is generally reliable and comparable (ILO 1992). Similar information on road systems is somewhat less reliable. Information on the structure of waterways is reliable, having not changed substantially in the past few decades. However, similar information regarding developing countries is scarce and unreliable.

European countries developed economic and political blocs that have had a significant impact on the transport sector. In Europe, road transport dominates the movement of freight and passengers. Trucking, with a heavy emphasis on less-than-trailer-load freight, is conducted by small national and regional carriers. This industry is heavily regulated and highly fractured. Since the early 1970s, the total volume of freight transported by road has increased by 240%. Conversely, rail transport has declined by approximately 8% (Violland 1996). However, several European countries are working diligently to increase the efficiency of rail transport and are promoting intermodal transport.

In the United States, the primary mode of transport is over the roadways. The Department of Transportation, Office of Motor Carriers, reported in 1993 that there were over 335,000 firms operating medium and heavy trucks (DOT 1995). This included large companies that transport their own products, smaller private firms, and for-hire truckload and less-than-truckload common and contract carriers. The majority of these fleets (58%) operate six or fewer trucks. These companies operate a total of 1.7 million

Challenges to workers' health and safety in the transportation and warehousing industry

The transportation and warehousing industry is fraught with challenges to worker health and safety. Those involved in loading and unloading of cargo and in storing, stacking and retrieving materials are prone to musculoskeletal injuries, slips and falls due to uncertain, irregular or slippery work surfaces and being struck by falling objects. See figure 102.3. Those operating and maintaining vehicles and other machinery are not only vulnerable to such injuries but also to the toxic effects of fuels, lubricants and exhaust fumes. If ergonomic principles are not heeded in the design of seats, pedals and instrument panels, drivers of trains, planes and motor vehicles (those used in warehousing as well on roads) will not only be subject to musculoskeletal disorders and undue fatigue, but will also be prone to operating mishaps that can lead to accidents.

All workers—and the general public as well—may be exposed to toxic substances in the event of leaks, spills and fires. Since much of the work is done out-of-doors, transportation and warehousing workers are also subject to extremes of weather such as heat, cold, rain, snow and ice, which can not only make the work more arduous but also more dangerous. Aviation crews must adjust to changes in barometric pressure. Noise is a perennial problem for those operating or working near noisy vehicles and machinery.

Stress

Perhaps the most pervasive hazard in this industry is work stress. It has many sources:

Adjusting to work hours. Many workers in this industry are burdened by the necessity of adjusting to changing shifts, while flight crews who travel long east-west or west-east distances must adjust to changes in circadian body rhythms; both of these factors may cause drowsiness and fatigue. The danger of functional impairment due to fatigue has led to laws and regulations stipulating the number of hours or shifts that may be worked without a rest period. These are generally applicable to aviation flight crews, railroad train crews and, in most countries, drivers of road buses and trucks. Many of the last group are independent contractors or work for small enterprises and are frequently forced by economic pressures to flout these regulations. There are always emergencies dictated by problems with traffic, weather or accidents which require exceeding the work hours limits. Led by the airlines, large transportation companies are now using computers to track employees' work schedules to verify their compliance with the regulations and to minimize the amount of down time for both workers and equipment.

Timetables. Most passenger and a good part of freight transport is guided by timetables stipulating departure and arrival times. The necessity of keeping to schedules which often allow too little leeway is often a very potent stressor for the drivers and their crews.

Dealing with the public. Meeting the sometimes unreasonable and often forcefully expressed demands of the public can be a significant source of stress for those dealing with passengers at terminals and ticket offices and en route. Drivers of road transport must contend with other vehicles, traffic regulations and diligent highway traffic officers.

Accidents. Accidents, whether due to equipment failure, human error or environmental conditions, place the transportation industry at or near the top of listings of occupational fatalities in most countries. Even when a particular worker's injuries may not be serious, post-traumatic stress disorder (PTSD) can lead to profound and prolonged disability, and in some instances it can prompt changing to another job.

Isolation. Many employees in the transportation industry work alone with little or no human contact (e.g., truck drivers, workers in control rooms and in railroad switch and signal towers). If problems arise, there may be difficulty and delays in getting help. And, if they are not kept busy, boredom may lead to a drop in attentiveness that can presage accidents. Working alone, especially for those driving taxis, limousines and delivery trucks, is an important risk factor for felonious assaults and other forms of violence.

Being away from home. Transportation workers are frequently required to be away from home for periods of days or weeks (in the maritime industry, for months). In addition to the stress of living out of a suitcase, strange food and strange sleeping accommodations, there is the reciprocal stress of separation from family and friends.

Health problems

Most industrialized countries require transportation workers, especially drivers and operating crew members, to take periodic medical examinations to verify that their physical and mental capacities meet the requirements established by regulations. Visual and hearing acuity, colour vision, muscular strength and flexibility and freedom from causes of syncope are some of the factors tested for. Accommodations, however, make it possible for many individuals with chronic disorders or disabilities to work without danger to themselves or others. (In the United States, for example, employers are mandated by the federal Americans With Disabilities Act to provide such accommodations.)

Drugs and alcohol

Prescription and over-the-counter medications taken for a variety of disorders (e.g., hypertension, anxiety and other hyperkinetic conditions, allergies, diabetes, epilepsy, headaches and the common cold) may cause drowsiness and affect alertness, reaction time and coordination, especially when alcoholic beverages are also consumed. Abuse of alcohol and/or illegal drugs is found frequently enough among transportation workers to have led to voluntary or legislatively mandated drug testing programmes.

Summary

The health and safety of workers in the transportation and warehousing industry are critical considerations, not only for the workers themselves but also for the public being transported or involved as bystanders. Safeguarding health and safety, therefore, is the joint responsibility of the employers, the employees and their unions and governments on all levels.

Leon J. Warshaw

combination units, 4.4 million single-unit medium and heavy trucks and 3.8 million trailers. The road system in the United States increased by roughly 2% from 1980 to 1989 (ILO 1992).

The rail systems in the United States have declined, due primarily to the loss of Class 1 status of some rail lines, and due to the abandonment of less profitable lines. Canada has increased its rail system by some 40%, due mainly to a change in the classifica-

tion system. The road system in Canada has decreased by 9% (ILO 1992).

In the industrialized nations of the Pacific Rim, there is great variability of the rail and road systems, due mainly to the different levels of industrialization of the respective countries. For example, rail and road networks in the Republic of Korea are similar to those in Europe, whereas in Malaysia, the rail and road networks

Figure 102.3 • Lifting parcels above shoulder height is an ergonomic hazard.

Teamsters Union

are significantly smaller, but experiencing tremendous growth rates (over 53% for roads since 1980) (ILO 1992).

In Japan, the transport sector is heavily dominated by road transport, which accounts for 90.5% of the total Japanese freight transport tonnage. Approximately 8.2% of the tonnage is transported by water and 1.2% by rail (Magnier 1996).

Developing countries in Asia, Africa and Latin America typically suffer from inadequate transport systems. There is significant work underway to improve the systems, but a lack of hard currency, skilled workers and equipment inhibits the growth. Transport systems have grown significantly in Venezuela, Mexico and Brazil.

The Middle East in general has experienced growth in the transport sector, with countries such as Kuwait and Iran leading the way. It should be noted that due to the large size of the countries, sparse populations and arid climatic conditions, unique problems are encountered that limit the development of transport systems in this region.

An overview of railroad and road systems for selected countries and world regions is shown in figures 102.1 and 102.2.

Workforce Characteristics

The transportation sector contributes significantly to employment in most countries in both the private and public sectors. However, as per capita income increases, the impact of the sector on total employment decreases. The overall number of workers in the transport industries has declined steadily since the 1980s. This loss of workforce in the sector is due to several factors, especially technological advances that have automated many of the jobs related to the construction, maintenance and operation of transport systems. In addition, many countries have passed legislation which deregulated many transport-related industries; this has ultimately resulted in the loss of jobs.

Workers who are currently employed in transport-related industries must be highly skilled and competent. Due to the rapid advances in technology experienced in the transport sector, these workers and prospective workers must receive continual training and retraining.

AIR TRANSPORT

• AIRPORT AND FLIGHT CONTROL OPERATIONS

Christine Proctor, Edward A. Olmsted and E. Evrard*

Commercial air transport involves the interaction of several groups including governments, airport operators, aircraft operators and aircraft manufacturers. Governments are generally involved in overall air transport regulation, oversight of aircraft operators (including maintenance and operations), manufacturing certification and oversight, air traffic control, airport facilities and security. Airport operators can either be local governments or commercial entities. They are usually responsible for the general operation of the airport. Types of aircraft operators include general airlines and commercial transport (either privately or publicly owned), cargo carriers, corporations and individual aircraft owners. Aircraft operators in general are responsible for operation and maintenance of the aircraft, training of personnel and operation of ticketing and boarding operations. Responsibility for security can vary; in some countries the aircraft operators

* Some text was adapted from the 3rd edition Encyclopaedia article "Aviation– ground personnel" authored by E. Evrard.

are responsible, and in others the government or airport operators are responsible. Manufacturers are responsible for design, manufacturing and testing, and for aircraft support and improvement. There are also international agreements con- cerning international flights.

This article deals with the personnel involved with all aspects of flight control (i.e., those who control commercial aircraft from takeoff to landing and who maintain the radar towers and other facilities used for flight control) and with those airport personnel who perform maintenance on and load aircraft, handle baggage and air freight and provide passenger services. Such personnel are divided into the following categories:

- air traffic controllers
- airways facilities and radar towers maintenance personnel
- ground crews
- baggage handlers
- passenger service agents.

Flight Control Operations

Government aviation authorities such as the Federal Aviation Administration (FAA) in the United States maintain flight control over commercial aircraft from takeoff to landing. Their primary mission involves the handling of airplanes using radar and other surveillance equipment to keep aircraft separated and on course.

Figure 102.4 • Air traffic controller at a manual local control centre radar screen.

Flight control personnel work at airports, terminal radar approach control facilities (Tracons) and regional long-distance centres, and consist of air traffic controllers and airways facilities maintenance personnel. Airways facilities maintenance personnel maintain the airport control towers, air traffic Tracons and regional centres, radio beacons, radar towers and radar equipment, and consist of electronics technicians, engineers, electricians and facilities maintenance workers. The guidance of planes using instruments is accomplished following instrument flight rules (IFR). Planes are tracked using the General National Air Space System (GNAS) by air traffic controllers working at airport control towers, Tracons and regional centres. Air traffic controllers keep planes separated and on course. As a plane moves from one jurisdiction to another, responsibility for the plane is handed from one type of controller to another.

Regional centres, terminal radar approach control and airport control towers

Regional centres direct planes after they have reached high altitudes. A centre is the largest of the aviation authority's facilities. Regional centre controllers hand off and receive planes to and from Tracons or other regional control centres and use radio and radar to maintain communication with aircraft. A plane flying across a country will always be under surveillance by a regional centre and passed along from one regional centre to the next. The regional centres all overlap each other in the surveillance range and receive radar information from long-range radar facilities. Radar information is sent to these facilities via microwave links and telephone lines, thus providing a redundancy of information so that if one form of communication is lost, the other is available. Oceanic air traffic, which cannot be seen by radar, is handled by the regional centres via radio. Technicians and engineers maintain the electronic surveillance equipment and the uninterrupted power systems, which includes emergency generators and large banks of back-up batteries.

Air traffic controllers at Tracons handle planes flying at low altitudes and within 80 km of airports, using radio and radar to maintain communication with aircraft. Tracons receive radar tracking information from the airport surveillance radar (ASR). The radar tracking system identifies the plane moving in space but also queries the plane beacon and identifies the plane and its flight information. Personnel and work tasks at Tracons are similar to those at the regional centres.

Regional and approach control systems exist in two variants: non-automated or manual systems and automated systems.

With *manual air traffic control systems*, radio communications between controller and pilot are supplemented by information from primary or secondary radar equipment. The trace of the aeroplane can be followed as a mobile echo on display screens formed by cathode-ray tubes (see figure 102.4). Manual systems have been replaced by automated systems in most countries.

With *automated air traffic control systems*, information on the aeroplane is still based on the flight plan and primary and secondary radar, but computers make it possible to present in alphanumeric form on the display screen all data concerning each aeroplane and to follow its route. Computers are also used to anticipate conflict between two or more aircraft on identical or converging routes on the basis of the flight plans and standard separations. Automation relieves the controller of many of the activities he or she carries out in a manual system, leaving more time for taking decisions.

Conditions of work are different in manual and automated control centre systems. In the manual system the screen is horizontal or sloping, and the operator leans forward in an uncomfortable position with his or her face between 30 and 50 cm from it. The perception of mobile echoes in the form of spots depends on their brightness and their contrast with the illuminance of the screen. As some mobile echoes have a very low luminous intensity, the working environment must be very weakly illuminated to ensure the greatest possible visual sensitivity to contrast.

In the automated system the electronic data display screens are vertical or almost vertical, and the operator can work in a normal sitting position with a greater reading distance. The operator has horizontally arranged keyboards within reach to regulate the presentation of the characters and symbols conveying the various types of information and can alter the shape and brightness of the characters. The lighting of the room can approach the intensity of daylight, for contrast remains highly satisfactory at 160 lux. These features of the automated system place the operator in a much better position to increase efficiency and reduce visual and mental fatigue.

Work is carried out in a huge, artificially lighted room without windows, which is filled with display screens. This closed environment, often far from the airports, allows little social contact during the work, which calls for great concentration and powers of decision. The comparative isolation is mental as well as physical, and there is hardly any opportunity of diversion. All this has been held to produce stress.

Each airport has a control tower. Controllers at airport control towers direct planes in and out of the airport, using radar, radio and binoculars to maintain communication with aircraft both while taxiing and while taking off and landing. Airport tower controllers hand off to or receive planes from controllers at Tracons. Most of the radar and other surveillance systems are located at the airports. These systems are maintained by technicians and engineers.

The walls of the tower room are transparent, for there must be perfect visibility. The working environment is thus completely different from that of regional or approach control. The air traffic controllers have a direct view of aircraft movements and other activities. They meet some of the pilots and take part in the life of the airport. The atmosphere is no longer that of a closed environment, and it offers a greater variety of interest.

Airways facilities maintenance personnel

Airways facilities and radar towers maintenance personnel consist of radar technicians, navigational and communication technicians and environmental technicians.

Radar technicians maintain and operate the radar systems, including airport and long-range radar systems. The work involves electronic equipment maintenance, calibration and troubleshooting.

Navigational and communication technicians maintain and operate the radio communications equipment and other related navigational equipment used in controlling air traffic. The work involves electronic equipment maintenance, calibration and troubleshooting.

Environmental technicians maintain and operate the aviation authority buildings (regional centres, Tracons and airport facilities, including the control towers) and equipment. The work requires running heating, ventilation and air-conditioning equipment and maintaining emergency generators, airport lighting systems, large banks of batteries in uninterrupted power supply (UPS) equipment and related electrical power equipment.

The occupational hazards for all three jobs include: noise exposure; working on or near live electrical parts including exposure to high voltage, x-ray exposure from klystron and magnitron tubes, fall hazards while working on elevated radar towers or using climbing poles and ladders to access towers and radio antenna and possibly PCBs exposure when handling older capacitors and working on utility transformers. Workers may also be exposed to microwave and radio-frequency exposure. According to a study of a group of radar workers in Australia (Joyner and Bangay 1986), personnel are not generally exposed to levels of microwave radiation exceeding 10 W/m^2 unless they are working on open waveguides (microwave cables) and components utilizing waveguide slots, or working within transmitter cabinets when high-voltage arcing is occurring. The environmental technicians also work with chemicals related to building maintenance, including boiler and other related water treatment chemicals, asbestos, paints, diesel fuel and battery acid. Many of the electrical and utility cables at airports are underground. Inspection and repair work on these systems often involves confined space entry and exposure to confined space hazards—noxious or asphyxiating atmospheres, falls, electrocution and engulfment.

Airways facilities maintenance workers and other ground crews in the airport operating area are frequently exposed to jet exhaust. Several airport studies where sampling of jet engine exhaust has been conducted demonstrated similar results (Eisenhardt and Olmsted 1996; Miyamoto 1986; Decker 1994): the presence of aldehydes including butyraldehyde, acetaldehyde, acrolein, methacrolein, isobutyraldehyde, propionaldehyde, croton-aldehyde and formaldehyde. Formaldehyde was present at significantly higher concentrations then the other aldehydes, followed by acetaldehyde. The authors of these studies have concluded that the formaldehyde in the exhaust was probably the main causative factor in the eye and respiratory irritation reported by exposed persons. Depending on the study, nitrogen oxides either were not detected or were present in concentrations below 1 part per million (ppm) in the exhaust stream. They concluded that neither nitrogen oxides nor other oxides play a major role in the irritation. Jet exhaust was also found to contain 70 different hydrocarbon species with up to 13 consisting mostly of olefins (alkenes). Heavy-metal exposure from jet exhaust has been shown not to pose a health hazard for areas surrounding airports.

Radar towers should be equipped with standard railings around the stairs and platforms to prevent falls and with interlocks to prevent access to the radar dish while it is operating. Workers accessing towers and radio antennas should use approved devices for ladder climbing and personal fall protection.

Personnel work on both de-energized and energized electrical systems and equipment. Protection from electrical hazards should involve training in safe work practices, lockout/tagout procedures and the use of personal protective equipment (PPE).

The radar microwave is generated by high-voltage equipment using a klystron tube. The klystron tube generates x rays and can be a source of exposure when the panel is opened, allowing personnel to come in close proximity to it to work on it. The panel should always remain in place except when servicing the klystron tube, and work time should be kept to a minimum.

Personnel should wear the appropriate hearing protection (e.g., ear plugs and/or ear muffs) when working around noise sources such as jet planes and emergency generators.

Other controls involve training in materials handling, vehicle safety, emergency response equipment and evacuation procedures and confined space entry procedures equipment (including direct-reading air monitors, blowers and mechanical retrieval systems).

Air traffic controllers and flight services personnel

Air traffic controllers work in regional control centres, Tracons and airport control towers. This work generally involves working at a console tracking planes on radar scopes and communicating with pilots by radio. Flight services personnel provide weather information for pilots.

The hazards to air traffic controllers include possible visual problems, noise, stress and ergonomic problems. At one time there was concern about x-ray emissions from the radar screens. This, however, has not turned out to be a problem at the operating voltages used.

Standards of fitness for air traffic controllers have been recommended by the International Civil Aviation Organization (ICAO), and detailed standards are set out in national military and civil regulations, those relating to sight and hearing being particularly precise.

Visual problems

The broad, transparent surfaces of air traffic control towers at airports sometimes result in dazzling by the sun, and reflection from surrounding sand or concrete can increase the luminosity. This strain on the eyes may produce headaches, though often of a temporary nature. It may be prevented by surrounding the control tower with grass and avoiding concrete, asphalt or gravel and by giving a green tint to the transparent walls of the room. If the colour is not too strong, visual acuity and colour perception remain adequate while the excess radiation that causes dazzle is absorbed.

Until about 1960 there was a good deal of disagreement among authors on the frequency of eyestrain among controllers from viewing radar screens, but it does seem to have been high. Since then, attention given to visual refractive errors in the selection of radar controllers, their correction among serving controllers and the constant improvement of working conditions at the screen have helped to lower it considerably. Sometimes, however, eyestrain appears among controllers with excellent sight. This may be attributed to too low a level of lighting in the room, irregular illumination of the screen, the brightness of the echoes themselves and, in particular, flickering of the image. Progress in viewing conditions and insistence on higher technical specifications for new equipment are leading to a marked reduction in this source of eyestrain, or even its elimination. Strain in accommodation has also been considered until recently to be a possible cause of eyestrain among operators who have worked very close to the screen for an hour without interruption. Visual problems are becoming much less frequent and are likely to disappear or to occur only very occasionally in the automated radar system, for example, when there is a fault in a scope or where the rhythm of the images is badly adjusted.

A rational arrangement of the premises is mainly one that facilitates the adaptation of the scope readers to the intensity of the ambient lighting. In a non-automated radar station, adaptation to the semi-darkness of the scope room is achieved by spending 15 to 20 minutes in another dimly lighted room. The general lighting of the scope room, the luminous intensity of the scopes and the brightness of the spots must all be studied with care. In the automated system the signs and symbols are read under an ambient lighting of from 160 to 200 lux, and the disadvantages of the dark environment of the non-automated system are avoided. With regard to noise, despite modern sound-insulating techniques, the problem remains acute in control towers installed near the runways.

Readers of radar screens and electronic display screens are sensitive to changes in the ambient lighting. In the non-automated system the controllers must wear glasses absorbing 80% of the light for between 20 and 30 minutes before entering their workplace. In the automated system special glasses for adaptation are no longer essential, but persons particularly sensitive to the contrast between the lighting of the symbols on the display screen and that of the working environment find that glasses of medium absorptive power add to the comfort of their eyes. There is also a reduction in eyestrain. Runway controllers are well advised to wear glasses absorbing 80% of the light when they are exposed to strong sunlight.

Stress

The most serious occupational hazard for air traffic controllers is stress. The chief duty of the controller is to make decisions on the movements of aircraft in the sector he or she is responsible for: flight levels, routes, changes of course when there is conflict with the course of another aircraft or when congestion in one sector leads to delays, air traffic and so on. In non-automated systems the controller must also prepare, classify and organize the information his or her decision is based on. The data available are comparatively crude and must first be digested. In highly automated systems the instruments can help the controller in taking decisions, and he or she may then only have to analyse data produced by teamwork and presented in rational form by these instruments. Although the work may be greatly facilitated, the responsibility for approving the decision proposed to the controller remains the controller's, and his or her activities still give rise to stress. The responsibilities of the job, pressure of work at certain hours of dense or complex traffic, increasingly crowded air space, sustained concentration, rotating shift work and awareness of the catastrophe that may result from an error all create a situation of continuous tension, which may lead to stress reactions. The fatigue of the controller may assume the three classic forms of acute fatigue, chronic fatigue or overstrain and nervous exhaustion. (See also the box on case studies of air traffic controllers in the United States and Italy.)

Air traffic control calls for an uninterrupted service 24 hours a day, all year long. The conditions of work of controllers thus include shift work, an irregular rhythm of work and rest and periods of work when most other people are enjoying holidays. Periods of concentration and of relaxation during working hours and days of rest during a week of work are indispensable to the avoidance of operational fatigue. Unfortunately, this principle cannot be embodied in general rules, for the arrangement of work in shifts is influenced by variables that may be legal (maximum number of consecutive hours of work authorized) or purely professional (workload depending on the hour of the day or the night), and by many other factors based on social or family considerations. With regard to the most suitable length for periods of sustained concentration during work, experiments show that there should be short breaks of at least a few minutes after periods of uninterrupted work of from half an hour to an hour-and-a-half, but that there is no need to be bound by rigid patterns to achieve the desired aim: the maintenance of the level of concentration and the prevention of operational fatigue. What is essential is to be able to interrupt the periods of work at the screen with periods of rest without interrupting the continuity of the shift work. Further study is necessary to establish the most suitable length of the periods of sustained concentration and of relaxation during work and the best rhythm for weekly and annual rest periods and holidays, with a view to drawing up more unified standards.

Other hazards

There are also ergonomic issues while working at the consoles similar to those of computer operators, and there may be indoor air quality problems. Air traffic controllers also experience tone incidents. Tone incidents are loud tones coming into the headsets. The tones are of short duration (a few seconds) and have sound levels up to 115 dBA.

In flight services work, there are hazards associated with lasers, which are used in ceilorometer equipment used to measure cloud ceiling height, as well as ergonomic and indoor air quality issues.

Other flight control services personnel

Other flight control services personnel include flight standards, security, airport facilities renovation and construction, administrative support and medical personnel.

Flight standards personnel are aviation inspectors who conduct airline maintenance and flight inspections. Flight standards personnel verify the airworthiness of the commercial airlines. They often inspect airplane maintenance hangers and other airport facilities, and they ride in the cockpits of commercial flights. They also investigate plane crashes, incidents or other aviation-related mishaps.

The hazards of the job include noise exposure from aircraft, jet fuel and jet exhaust while working in hangers and other airport areas, and potential exposure to hazardous materials and bloodborne pathogens while investigating aircraft crashes. Flight standards personnel face many of the same hazards as airport ground crews, and thus many of the same precautions apply.

Security personnel include sky marshals. Sky marshals provide internal security on airplanes and external security at airport ramps. They are essentially police and investigate criminal activities related to aircraft and airports.

Airport facilities renovation and construction personnel approve all plans for airport modifications or new construction. The personnel are usually engineers, and their work largely involves office work.

Administrative workers include personnel in accounting, management systems and logistics. Medical personnel in the flight surgeon's office provide occupational medical services to aviation authority workers.

Air traffic controllers, flight services personnel and personnel who work in office environments should have ergonomic training on proper sitting postures and on emergency response equipment and evacuation procedures.

Airport Operations

Airport ground crews conduct maintenance on and load aircraft. Baggage handlers handle passenger baggage and air freight, whereas passenger service agents register passengers and check passenger baggage.

All loading operations (passengers, baggage, freight, fuel, supplies and so on) are controlled and integrated by a supervisor who

Case Studies of Air Traffic Controllers in the United States and Italy

United States

High levels of stress among air traffic controllers (ATCs) were first widely reported in the United States in the 1970 Corson Report (US Senate 1970), which focused on working conditions such as overtime, few regular work breaks, increasing air traffic, few vacations, poor physical work environment and "mutual resentment and antagonism" between management and labour. Such conditions contributed to ATC job actions in 1968–69. In addition, early medical research, including a major 1975–78 Boston University study (Rose, Jenkins and Hurst 1978), suggested that ATCs may face a higher risk of stress-related illness, including hypertension.

Following the 1981 US ATC strike, in which job stress was a major issue, the Department of Transportation again appointed a task force to examine stress and morale. The resulting 1982 Jones Report indicated that FAA employees in a wide variety of job titles reported negative results for job design, work organization, communication systems, supervisory leadership, social support and satisfaction. The typical form of ATC stress was an acute episodic incident (such as a near mid-air collision) along with interpersonal tensions stemming from management style. The task force reported that 6% of the ATC sample was "burned out" (having a large and debilitating loss of self-confidence in ability to do the job). This group represented 21% of those 41 years of age and older and 69% of those with 19 or more years of service.

A 1984 review by the Jones task force of its recommendations concluded that "conditions are as bad as in 1981, or perhaps a bit worse". Major concerns were increasing traffic volume, inadequate staffing, low morale and an increasing burnout rate. Such conditions led to the re-unionization of US ATCs in 1987 with the election of the National Air Traffic Controllers Organization (NATCA) as their bargaining representative.

In a 1994 survey, New York City area ATCs reported continuing staffing shortages and concerns about job stress, shift work and indoor air quality. Recommendations for improving morale and health included transfer opportunities, early retirement, more flexible schedules, exercise facilities at work and increased staffing. In 1994, a greater proportion of Level 3 and 5 ATCs reported high burnout than ATCs in 1981 and 1984 national surveys (except for ATCs working in centres in 1984). Level 5 facilities have the highest level of air traffic, and Level 1, the lowest (Landsbergis et al. 1994). Feelings of burnout were related to having experienced a "near miss" in the past 3 years, age, years working as an ATC,

working in high-traffic Level 5 facilities, poor work organization and poor supervisor and co-worker support.

Research also continues on appropriate shift schedules for ATCs, including the possibility of a 10-hour, 4-day shift schedule. The long-term health effects of the combination of rotating shifts and compressed work weeks are not known.

A collectively bargained programme to reduce ATC job stress in Italy

The company in charge of all civil air traffic in Italy (AAAV) employs 1,536 ATCs. AAAV and union representatives drew up several agreements between 1982 and 1991 to improve working conditions. These include:

1. *Modernizing radio systems and automating aeronautical information, flight data processing and air traffic management.* This provided for more reliable information and more time for making decisions, eliminating many risky traffic peaks and providing for a more balanced workload.
2. *Reducing work hours.* The operative work week is now 28 to 30 hours.
3. *Changing shift schedules:*
   - rapid shift speed: one day on each shift
   - one night shift followed by 2 days rest
   - adjust of shift length to workload: 5 to 6 hours for morning; 7 hours for afternoon; 11 to 12 hours for night
   - short naps on the night shift
   - keeping shift rotation as regular as possible to allow better organization of personal, family and social life
   - a long break (45 to 60 minutes) for a meal during work shifts.
4. *Reduce environmental stressors.* Attempts have been made to reduce noise and provide more light.
5. *Improving the ergonomics of new consoles, screens and chairs.*
6. *Improving physical fitness.* Gyms are provided in the largest facilities.

Research during this period suggests that the programme was beneficial. The night shift was not very stressful; ATCs' performance did not worsen significantly at the end of three shifts; only 28 ATCs were dismissed for health reasons in 7 years; and a large decline in "near misses" occurred despite major increases in air traffic.

Paul A. Landsbergis

---

prepares the loading plan. This plan is given to the pilot prior to take-off. When all operations have been completed and any checks or inspections considered necessary by the pilot have been made, the airport controller gives authorization for take-off.

Ground crews

Aircraft maintenance and servicing

Every aircraft is serviced every time it lands. Ground crews performing routine turnaround maintenance; conduct visual inspections, including checking the oils; perform equipment checks, minor repairs and internal and external cleaning; and refuel and restock the aircraft. As soon as the aircraft lands and arrives in the unloading bays, a team of mechanics begins a series of maintenance checks and operations which vary with the type of aircraft. These mechanics refuel the aircraft, check a number of safety systems which must be inspected after each landing, investigate

the logbook for any reports or defects the flight crew may have noticed during the flight and, where necessary, make repairs. (See also the article "Aircraft maintenance operations" in this chapter.) In cold weather, the mechanics may have to perform additional tasks, such as de-icing of wings, landing gear, flaps and so on. In hot climates special attention is paid to the condition of the aircraft's tyres. Once this work has been completed, the mechanics can declare the aircraft flightworthy.

More thorough maintenance inspections and aircraft overhauls are performed at specific intervals of flying hours for each aircraft.

Fuelling aircraft is one of the most potentially hazardous servicing operations. The amount of fuel to be loaded is determined on the basis of such factors as flight duration, take-off weight, flight path, weather and possible diversions.

A cleaning team cleans and services the aircraft cabins, replacing dirty or damaged material (cushions, blankets and so on), empties the toilets and refills the water tanks. This team may also disinfect or disinfest the aircraft under the supervision of public health authorities.

Another team stocks the aircraft with food and drink, emergency equipment and supplies needed for passenger comfort. Meals are prepared under high standards of hygiene to eliminate the risk of food poisoning, particularly among the flight crew. Certain meals are deep frozen to –40 °C, stored at –29 °C and reheated in flight.

Ground service work includes the use of motorized and non-motorized equipment.

Baggage and air cargo loading

Baggage and cargo handlers move passenger baggage and air freight. Freight can range from fresh fruits and vegetables and live animals to radioisotopes and machinery. Because baggage and cargo handling requires physical effort and the use of mechanized equipment, workers may be more at risk for injuries and ergonomic problems.

Ground crews and baggage and freight handlers are exposed to many of the same hazards. These hazards include working outdoors in all types of weather, exposure to potential airborne contaminants from jet fuel and jet engine exhaust and exposure to prop wash and jet blast. Prop wash and jet blast can slam doors shut, knock people or unsecured equipment over, cause turboprop propellers to rotate and blow debris into engines or onto people. Ground crews are also exposed to noise hazards. A study in China showed ground crews were exposed to noise at aircraft engine hatches that exceeds 115 dBA (Wu et al. 1989). Vehicle traffic on the airport ramps and apron is very heavy, and the risk of accidents and collision is high. Fuelling operations are very hazardous, and workers may be exposed to fuel spills, leaks, fires and explosions. Workers on lifting devices, aerial baskets, platforms or access stands are at risk of falling. Job hazards also include rotating shift work carried out under pressure of time.

Strict regulations must be implemented and enforced for vehicle movement and driver training. Driver training should emphasize complying with speed limits, obeying off-limit areas and ensuring that there is adequate room for planes to manoeuvre. There should be good maintenance of ramp surfaces and efficient control of ground traffic. All vehicles authorized to operate on the airfield should be conspicuously marked so they can be readily identified by air traffic controllers. All equipment used by the ground crews should be regularly inspected and maintained. Workers on lifting devices, aerial baskets, platforms or access stands must be protected from falls either through the use of guardrails or personal fall protection equipment. Hearing protection equipment (earplugs and earmuffs) must be used for protection against noise hazards. Other PPE includes suitable work clothing depending on the weather, non-slip reinforced-toe-cap foot protection and appropriate eye, face, glove and body protection when applying de-icing fluids. Rigorous fire prevention and protection measures including bonding and grounding and prevention of electric sparking, smoking, open flames and the presence of other vehicles within 15 m of aircraft, must be implemented for refuelling operations. Fire-fighting equipment should be maintained and located in the area. Training on procedures to follow in the event of a fuel spill or fire should be conducted regularly.

Baggage and freight handlers should store and stack cargo securely and should receive training on proper lifting techniques and back postures. Extreme care should be used when entering and leaving aircraft cargo areas from carts and tractors. Appropriate protective clothing should be worn, depending on the type of cargo or baggage (such as gloves when handling live animal cargo). Baggage and freight conveyors, carousels and dispensers should have emergency shut-offs and built-in guards.

Passenger service agents

Passenger service agents issue tickets, register and check in passengers and passenger baggage. These agents may also guide passengers when boarding. Passenger service agents who sell airline tickets and check in passengers may spend all day on their feet using a video display unit (VDU). Precautions against these ergonomic hazards include resilient floor mats and seats for relief from standing, work breaks and ergonomic and anti-glare measures for the VDUs. In addition, dealing with passengers can be a source of stress, particularly when there are delays in flights or problems with making flight connections and so on. Breakdowns in the computerized airline reservations systems can also be a major source of stress.

Baggage check-in and weigh-in facilities should minimize the need for employees and passengers to lift and handle bags, and baggage conveyors, carousels and dispensers should have emergency shut-offs and built-in guards. Agents should also receive training on proper lifting techniques and back postures.

Baggage inspection systems use fluoroscopic equipment to examine baggage and other carry-on items. Shielding protects workers and the public from x-ray emissions, and if the shielding is not properly positioned, interlocks prevent the system from operating. According to an early study by the US National Institute for Occupational Safety and Health (NIOSH) and the Air Transport Association at five US airports, maximum documented whole-body x-ray exposures were considerably lower than maximum levels set by the US Food and Drug Administration (FDA) and the Occupational Safety and Health Administration (OSHA) (NIOSH 1976). Workers should wear whole-body monitoring devices to measure radiation exposures. NIOSH recommended periodic maintenance programmes to check effectiveness of shielding.

Passenger service agents and other airport personnel must be thoroughly familiar with the airport emergency evacuation plan and procedures.

AIRCRAFT MAINTENANCE OPERATIONS

Buck Cameron

Aircraft maintenance operations are broadly distributed within and across nations and are performed by both military and civilian mechanics. Mechanics work at airports, maintenance bases, private fields, military installations and aboard aircraft carriers. Mechanics are employed by passenger and freight carriers, by maintenance contractors, by operators of private fields, by agricultural operations and by public and private fleet owners. Small airports may provide employment for a few mechanics, while major hub airports and maintenance bases may employ thousands. Maintenance work is divided between that which is necessary to maintain ongoing daily operations (line maintenance) and those procedures that periodically check, maintain and refurbish the aircraft (base maintenance). Line maintenance comprises en route (between landing and takeoff) and overnight maintenance. En route maintenance consists of operational checks and flight-essential repairs to address discrepancies noted during flight. These repairs are typically minor, such as replacing warning lights, tyres and avionic components, but may be as extensive as replacing an engine. Overnight maintenance is more extensive and includes making any repairs deferred during the day's flights.

The timing, distribution and nature of aircraft maintenance is controlled by each airline company and is documented in its maintenance manual, which in most jurisdictions must be submitted for approval to the appropriate aviation authority. Maintenance is performed during regular checks, designated as A through D checks, specified by the maintenance manual. These scheduled maintenance activities ensure that the entire aircraft has been inspected, maintained and refurbished at appropriate intervals. Lower level maintenance checks may be incorporated into line maintenance work, but more extensive work is performed at a maintenance base. Aircraft damage and component failures are repaired as required.

Line Maintenance Operations and Hazards

En route maintenance is typically performed under a great time constraint at active and crowded flight lines. Mechanics are exposed to prevailing conditions of noise, weather and vehicular and aircraft traffic, each of which may amplify the hazards intrinsic to maintenance work. Climatic conditions may include extremes of cold and heat, high winds, rain, snow and ice. Lightning is a significant hazard in some areas.

Although the current generation of commercial aircraft engines are significantly quieter than previous models, they can still produce sound levels well above those set by regulatory authorities, particularly if the aircraft are required to use engine power in order to exit gate positions. Older jet and turboprop engines can produce sound level exposures in excess of 115 dBA. Aircraft auxiliary-power units (APUs), ground-based power and air-conditioning equipment, tugs, fuel trucks and cargo-handling equipment add to the background noise. Noise levels in the ramp or aircraft parking area are seldom below 80 dBA, thus necessitating the careful selection and routine use of hearing protectors. Protectors must be selected that provide excellent noise attenuation while being reasonably comfortable and permitting essential communication. Dual systems (ear plugs plus ear muffs) provide enhanced protection and allow accom-modation for higher and lower noise levels.

Mobile equipment, in addition to aircraft, may include baggage carts, personnel buses, catering vehicles, ground support equipment and jetways. To maintain departure schedules and customer satisfaction, this equipment must move quickly within often congested ramp areas, even under adverse ambient conditions. Aircraft engines pose the danger of ramp personel being ingested into jet engines or being struck by a propeller or exhaust blasts. Reduced visibility during night and inclement weather increase the risk that mechanics and other ramp personnel might be struck by mobile equipment. Reflective materials on work clothing help to improve visibility, but it is essential that all ramp personnel be well trained in ramp traffic rules, which must be rigorously enforced. Falls, the most frequent cause of serious injuries among mechanics, are discussed elsewhere in this *Encyclopaedia*.

Chemical exposures in the ramp area include de-icing fluids (usually containing ethylene or propylene glycol), oils and lubricants. Kerosene is the standard commercial jet fuel (Jet A). Hydraulic fluids containing tributyl phosphate cause severe but transient eye irritation. Fuel tank entry, while relatively rare on the ramp, must be included in a comprehensive confined-space-entry programme. Exposure to resin systems used for patching composite areas such as cargo hold panelling may also occur.

Overnight maintenance is typically performed under more controlled circumstances, either in line-service hangers or on inactive flight lines. Lighting, work stands and traction are far better than on the flight line but are likely to be inferior to those found in maintenance bases. Several mechanics may be working on an aircraft simultaneously, necessitating careful planning and coordination to control personnel movement, aircraft component activation (drives, flight control surfaces and so on) and chemical usage. Good housekeeping is essential to prevent clutter from air lines,

parts and tools, and to clean spills and drips. These requirements are of even greater importance during base maintenance.

Base Maintenance Operations and Hazards

Maintenance hangars are very large structures capable of accommodating numerous aircraft. The largest hangars can simultaneously accommodate several wide-body aircraft, such as the Boeing 747. Separate work areas, or bays, are assigned to each aircraft undergoing maintenance. Specialized shops for the repair and refitting of components are associated with the hangars. Shop areas typically include sheet metal, interiors, hydraulics, plastics, wheels and brakes, electrical and avionics and emergency equipment. Separate welding areas, paint shops and non-destructive testing areas may be established. Parts-cleaning operations are likely to be found throughout the facility.

Paint hangars with high ventilation rates for workplace air contaminant controls and environmental pollution protection should be available if painting or paint stripping is to be performed. Paint strippers often contain methylene chloride and corrosives, including hydrofluoric acid. Aircraft primers typically contain a chromate component for corrosion protection. Top coats may be epoxy or polyurethane based. Toluene diisocyanate (TDI) is now seldom used in these paints, having been replaced with higher molecular weight isocyanates such as 4,4-diphenylmethane diisocyanate (MDI) or by prepolymers. These still present a risk of asthma if inhaled.

Engine maintenance may be performed within the maintenance base, at a specialized engine overhaul facility or by a sub-contractor. Engine overhaul requires the use of metalworking techniques including grinding, blasting, chemical cleaning, plating and plasma spray. Silica has in most cases been replaced with less hazardous materials in parts cleaners, but the base materials or coatings may create toxic dusts when blasted or ground. Numerous materials of worker health and environmental concern are used in metal cleaning and plating. These include corrosives, organic solvents and heavy metals. Cyanide is generally of the greatest immediate concern, requiring special emphasis in emergency preparedness planning. Plasma spray operations also merit particular attention. Finely divided metals are fed into a plasma stream generated using high-voltage electrical sources and plated onto parts with the concomitant generation of very high noise levels and light energies. Physical hazards include work at height, lifting and work in uncomfortable positions. Precautions include local exhaust ventilation, PPE, fall protection, training in proper lifting and use of mechanized lifting equipment when possible and ergonomic redesign. For example, repetitive motions involved in tasks such as wire tying may be reduced by use of specialized tools.

Military and Agricultural Applications

Military aircraft operations may present unique hazards. JP4, a more volatile jet fuel that Jet A, may be contaminated with *n*-hexane. Aviation gasoline, used in some propeller-driven aircraft, is highly flammable. Military aircraft engines, including those on transport aircraft, may use less noise abatement than those on commercial aircraft and may be augmented by afterburners. Aboard aircraft carriers the many hazards are significantly increased. Engine noise is augmented by steam catapults and afterburners, flight deck space is extremely limited, and the deck itself is in motion. Because of combat demands, asbestos insulation is present in some cockpits and around hot areas.

The need for lowered radar visibility (stealth) has resulted in the increased use of composite materials on fuselage, wings and flight control structures. These areas may be damaged in combat or from exposure to extremes of climate, requiring extensive repair. Repairs performed under field conditions may result in heavy exposures to resins and composite dusts. Beryllium is also common in military applications. Hydrazide may be present as part of auxiliary-power units, and anti-tank armament may include radioactive depleted uranium rounds. Precautions include appropriate PPE, including respiratory protection. Where possible, portable exhaust systems should be used.

Maintenance work on agricultural aircraft (crop dusters) may result in exposures to pesticides either as a single product or, more likely, as a mixture of products contaminating a single or multiple aircraft. Degradation products of some pesticides are more hazardous than the parent product. Dermal routes of exposure may be significant and may be enhanced by perspiration. Agricultural aircraft and external parts should be thoroughly cleaned before repair, and/or PPE, including skin and respiratory protection, should be used.

● AIRCRAFT FLIGHT OPERATIONS

Nancy Garcia and H. Gartmann*

This article deals with the occupational safety and health of the crew members of civil aviation aircraft; see also the articles "Airport and flight control operations", "Aircraft maintenance operations" and "Helicopters" for additional information.

Technical Crew Members

The technical personnel, or flight crew members, are responsible for the operation of the aircraft. Depending on aircraft type, the technical crew includes the pilot-in-command (PIC), the co-pilot (or *first officer*), and the flight engineer or a *second officer* (a pilot).

The PIC (or *captain*) has the responsibility for the safety of the aircraft, the passengers and the other crew members. The captain is the legal representative of the air carrier and is vested by the air carrier and the national aviation authority with the authority to carry out all actions necessary to fulfil this mandate. The PIC directs all duties on the flight deck and is in command of the entire aircraft.

The co-pilot takes his or her orders directly from the PIC and acts as the captain's deputy upon delegation or in the latter's absence. The co-pilot is the primary assistant to the PIC in a flight crew; in newer generation, two-person flight deck operations and in older two-engine aircraft, he or she is the only assistant.

Many older generation aircraft carry a third technical crew member. This person may be a flight engineer or a third pilot (usually called the *second officer*). The flight engineer, when present, is responsible for the mechanical condition of the aircraft and its equipment. New generation aircraft have automated many of the functions of the flight engineer; in these two-person operations, the pilots perform such duties as a flight engineer might otherwise perform that have not been automated by design.

On certain long-distance flights, the crew may be supplemented by a pilot with the qualifications of the PIC, an additional first officer and, when required, an additional flight engineer.

National and international laws stipulate that aircraft technical personnel may operate aircraft only when in possession of a valid licence issued by the national authority. In order to maintain their licences, technical crew members are given ground school training once every year; they are also tested in a flight simulator (a device that simulates real flight and flight emergency conditions) twice a year and in actual operations at least once a year.

Another condition for the receipt and renewal of a valid licence is a medical examination every 6 months for airline transport and

* Adapted from the 3rd edition *Encyclopaedia* article "Aviation – flying personnel" authored by H. Gartmann.

commercial pilots over 40 years old, or every 12 months for commercial pilots under 40 years old and for flight engineers. The minimum requirements for these examinations are specified by the ICAO and by national regulations. A certain number of physicians experienced in aviation medicine may be authorized to provide such examinations by the national authorities concerned. These may include air ministry physicians, airforce flight surgeons, airline medical officers or private practitioners designated by the national authority.

Cabin Crew Members

The cabin crew (or *flight attendants*) are primarily responsible for passenger safety. Flight attendants perform routine safety duties; in addition, they are responsible for monitoring the aircraft cabin for security and safety hazards. In the event of an emergency, the cabin crew members are responsible for the organization of emergency procedures and for the safe evacuation of the passengers. In flight, cabin crew may need to respond to emergencies such as smoke and fire in the cabin, turbulence, medical trauma, aircraft decompressions, and hijackings or other terrorist threats. In addition to their emergency responsibilities, flight attendants also provide passenger service.

The minimum cabin crew ranges from 1 to 14 flight attendants, depending on the type of aircraft, the aircraft's passenger capacity and national regulations. Additional staffing requirements may be determined by labour agreements. The cabin crew may be supplemented by a purser or service manager. The cabin crew is usually under the supervision of a lead or "in-charge" flight attendant, who, in turn, is responsible and reports directly to the PIC.

National regulations do not usually stipulate that the cabin crew should hold licences in the same way as the technical crew; however, cabin crew are required by all national regulations to have received appropriate instruction and training in emergency procedures. Periodic medical examinations are not usually required by law, but some air carriers require medical examinations for the purposes of health maintenance.

Hazards and Their Prevention

All air crew members are exposed to a wide variety of stress factors, both physical and psychological, to the hazards of an aircraft accident or other flight incident and to the possible contraction of a number of diseases.

Physical stress

Lack of oxygen, one of the main concerns of aviation medicine in the early days of flying, had until recently become a minor consideration in modern air transport. In the case of a jet aircraft flying at 12,000 m altitude, the equivalent altitude in the pressurized cabin is only 2,300 m and, consequently, symptoms of oxygen deficiency or hypoxia will not normally be encountered in healthy persons. Oxygen deficiency tolerance varies from individual to individual, but for a healthy, non-trained subject the presumed altitude threshold at which the first symptoms of hypoxia occur is 3,000 m.

With the advent of new generation aircraft, however, concerns about cabin air quality have resurfaced. Aircraft cabin air consists of air drawn from compressors in the engine and often also contains recirculated air from within the cabin. The flow rate of outside air within an aircraft cabin can vary from as little as 0.2 m³ per minute per person to 1.42 m³ per minute per person, depending upon aircraft type and age, and depending on location within the cabin. New aircraft use recirculated cabin air to a much greater degree than do older models. This air quality issue is specific to the cabin environment. The flight deck compartment air flow rates are often as high as 4.25 m³ per minute per crew member. These higher air flow rates are provided on the flight deck to meet the cooling requirements of the avionic and electronic equipment.

Complaints of poor cabin air quality from cabin crew and passengers have increased in recent years, prompting some national authorities to investigate. Minimal ventilation rates for aircraft cabins are not defined in national regulations. Actual cabin airflow is seldom measured once an aircraft is put into service, since there is no requirement to do so. Minimal air flow and the use of recirculated air, combined with other issues of air quality, such as the presence of chemical contaminants, micro-organisms, other allergens, tobacco smoke and ozone, require further evaluation and study.

Maintaining a comfortable air temperature in the cabin does not represent a problem in modern aircraft; however, the humidity of this air cannot be raised to a comfortable level, due to the large temperature difference between the aircraft interior and exterior. Consequently, both crew and passengers are exposed to extremely dry air, especially on long-distance flights. Cabin humidity depends on the cabin ventilation rate, passenger load, temperature and pressure. The relative humidity found on aircraft today varies from about 25% to less than 2%. Some passengers and crew members experience discomfort, such as dryness of the eyes, nose and throat, on flights that exceed 3 or 4 hours. There is no conclusive evidence of extensive or serious adverse health effects of low relative humidity on flight personnel. However, precautions should be taken to avoid dehydration; adequate intake of liquids such as water and juices should be sufficient to prevent discomfort.

Motion sickness (dizziness, malaise and vomiting due to the abnormal movements and altitudes of the aircraft) was a problem for civil aviation crews and passengers for many decades; the problem still exists today in the case of small sports aircraft, military aircraft and aerial acrobatics. In modern jet transport aircraft, it is much less serious and occurs less frequently due to higher aircraft speeds and take-off weights, higher cruising altitudes (which take the aircraft above the turbulence zones) and the use of airborne radar (which enables squalls and storms to be located and circumnavigated). Additionally, the lack of motion sickness also may be attributed to the more spacious, open design of today's aircraft cabin, which provides a greater feeling of security, stability and comfort.

Other physical and chemical hazards

Aircraft noise, while a significant problem for ground personnel, is less serious for the crew members of a modern jet aircraft than was the case with the piston-engined plane. The efficiency of noise control measures such as insulation in modern aircraft have helped to eliminate this hazard in most flight environments. Additionally, improvements in communications equipment have minimized background noise levels from these sources.

Ozone exposure is a known but poorly monitored hazard for air crew and passengers. Ozone is present in the upper atmosphere as a result of the photochemical conversion of oxygen by solar ultraviolet radiation at altitudes used by commercial jet aircraft. The mean ambient ozone concentration increases with increasing latitude and is most prevalent during spring. It can also vary with weather systems, with the result of high ozone plumes descending down to lower altitudes.

Symptoms of ozone exposure include cough, upper airway irritation, tickle in the throat, chest discomfort, substantial pain or soreness, difficulty or pain in taking a deep breath, shortness of breath, wheezing, headache, fatigue, nasal congestion and eye irritation. Most people can detect ozone at 0.02 ppm, and studies have shown that ozone exposure at 0.5 ppm or more causes significant decrements in pulmonary function. The effects of

ozone contamination are felt more readily by persons engaged in moderate to heavy activity than those who are at rest or engaged in light activity. Thus flight attendants (who are physically active in flight) have experienced the effects of ozone earlier and more frequently than technical crew or passengers on the same flight when ozone contamination was present.

In one study conducted in the late 1970s by the aviation authority in the United States (Rogers 1980), several flights (mostly at 9,150 to 12,200 m) were monitored for ozone contamination. Eleven per cent of the flights monitored were found to exceed that authority's permissible ozone concentration limits. Methods of minimizing ozone exposure include choice of routes and altitudes that avoid areas of high ozone concentration and the use of air treatment equipment (usually a catalytic converter). The catalytic converters, however, are subject to contamination and loss of efficiency. Regulations (when they exist) do not require their periodic removal for efficiency testing, nor do they require monitoring of ozone levels in actual flight operations. Crew members, especially cabin crew, have requested that better monitoring and control of ozone contamination be implemented.

Another serious concern for technical and cabin crew members is cosmic radiation, which includes radiation forms that are transmitted through space from the sun and other sources in the universe. Most cosmic radiation that travels through space is absorbed by the earth's atmosphere; however, the higher the altitude, the less the protection. The earth's magnetic field also provides some shielding, which is greatest near the equator and decreases at the higher latitudes. Air crew members are exposed to cosmic radiation levels inflight that are higher than those received on the ground.

The amount of radiation exposure depends on the type and the amount of flying; for example, a crew member who flies many hours at high altitudes and high latitudes (e.g., polar routes) will receive the greatest amount of radiation exposure. The civil aviation authority in the United States (the FAA) has estimated that the long-term average cosmic radiation dose for air crew members ranges from 0.025 to 0.93 millisieverts (mSv) per 100 block hours (Friedberg et al. 1992). Based on FAA estimates, a crew member flying 960 block hours per year (or an average of 80 hours/month) would receive an estimated annual radiation dose of between 0.24 and 8.928 mSv. These levels of exposure are lower than the recommended occupational limit of 20 millisieverts per year (5-year average) established by the International Commission on Radiological Protection (ICRP).

The ICRP, however, recommends that occupational exposure to ionizing radiation should not exceed 2 mSv during pregnancy. In addition, the US National Council on Radiation Protection and Measurements (NCRP) recommends that exposure not exceed 0.5 mSv in any month once a pregnancy is known. If a crew member worked an entire month on flights with the highest exposures, the monthly dose rate could exceed the recommended limit. Such a pattern of flying over 5 or 6 months could result in an exposure which also would exceed the recommended pregnancy limit of 2 mSv.

The health effects of low-level radiation exposure over a period of years include cancer, genetic defects and birth defects to a child exposed in the womb. The FAA estimates that the added risk of fatal cancer resulting from exposure to inflight radiation would range from 1 in 1,500 to 1 in 94, depending on the type of routes and number of hours flown; the level of added risk of a serious genetic defect resulting from one parent's exposure to cosmic radiation ranges from 1 in 220,000 live births to 1 in 4,600 live births; and the risk of mental retardation and childhood cancer in a child exposed in utero to cosmic radiation would range between 1 in 20,000 to 1 in 680, depending upon the type and amount of flying the mother did while pregnant.

The FAA report concludes that "radiation exposure is not likely to be a factor that would limit flying for a non-pregnant crew member" because even the largest amount of radiation received annually by a crew member working as much as 1,000 block hours a year is less than half the ICRP recommended average annual limit. However, for a pregnant crew member, the situation is different. The FAA calculates that a pregnant crew member working 70 block hours per month would exceed the recommended 5-month limit on about one-third of the flights they studied (Friedberg et al. 1992).

It should be stressed that these exposure and risk estimates are not universally accepted. Estimates are dependent upon assumptions about the types and mix of radioactive particles encountered at altitude and the weight or quality factor used to determine dose estimates for some of these forms of radiation. Some scientists believe that the actual radiation hazard to air crew members may be greater than described above. Additional monitoring of the flight environment with reliable instrumentation is needed to more clearly determine the extent of inflight radiation exposure.

Until more is known about exposure levels, air crew members should keep their exposure to all types of radiation as low as possible. With respect to inflight radiation exposure, minimizing the amount of flight time and maximizing the distance from the source of radiation can have a direct effect on the dose received. Reducing monthly and yearly flight time and/or selecting flights which fly at lower altitudes and latitudes will reduce exposure. An air crew member who has the ability to control his or her flight assignments might choose to fly fewer hours per month, to bid for a mix of domestic and international flights or to request leaves periodically. A pregnant air crew member might choose to take a leave for the duration of the pregnancy. Since the first trimester is the most crucial time to guard against radiation exposure, an air crew member planning a pregnancy also may want to consider a leave especially if she is flying long-distance polar routes on a regular basis and has no control over her flight assignments.

Ergonomic problems

The main ergonomic problem for technical crew is the need to work for many hours in a sitting but unsettled position and in a very limited working area. In this position (restrained by lap and shoulder harness), it is necessary to carry out a variety of tasks such as movements of the arms, legs and head in different directions, consulting instruments at a distance of about 1 m above, below, to the front and to the side, scanning the far distance, reading a map or manual at close distance (30 cm), listening through earphones or talking through a microphone. Seating, instrumentation, lighting, cockpit microclimate and radio communications equipment comfort have been and still remain the object of continuous improvement. Today's modern flight deck, often referred to as the "glass cockpit", has created yet another challenge with its use of leading-edge technology and automation; maintaining vigilance and situational awareness under these conditions has created new concerns for both the designers of aircraft and the technical personnel who fly them.

Cabin crew have an entirely different set of ergonomic problems. One main problem is that of standing and moving around during flight. During climb and descent, and in turbulence, the cabin crew is required to walk on an inclined floor; in some aircraft the cabin incline may remain at approximately 3% during cruise as well. Also, many cabin floors are designed in a manner that creates a rebound effect while walking, putting an additional stress on the flight attendants who are constantly moving about during a flight. Another important ergonomic problem for flight attendants has been the use of mobile carts. These carts can weigh up to 100 to 140 kg and must be pushed and pulled up and down the length of the cabin. Additionally, the poor design and maintenance of the braking mechanisms on many of these carts have caused an increase in repetitive-strain injuries (RSIs) among flight attendants. Air carriers and cart manufacturers are now taking a more serious look at this equipment, and new designs have resulted in ergonomic improvements. Additional ergonomic problems result from the need to lift and carry heavy or bulky items in restricted spaces or while maintaining uncomfortable body posture.

Workload

The workload for air crew members depends on the task, the ergonomic layout, the hours of work/duty and many other factors. The additional factors affecting the technical crew include:

- duration of rest time between present and last flight and the duration of sleep time during the rest period
- the pre-flight briefing and problems encountered during the pre-flight briefing
- delays preceding departure
- timing of flights
- meteorological conditions at the point of departure, en route and at the destination
- number of flight segments
- type of equipment being flown
- quality and quantity of radio communications
- visibility during descent, glare and protection from the sun
- turbulence
- technical problems with the aircraft
- experience of other crew members
- air traffic (especially at point of departure and destination)
- presence of air carrier or national authority personnel for purposes of checking crew competency.

Certain of these factors may be equally important for the cabin crew. In addition, the latter are subject to the following specific factors:

- pressure of time due to short duration of flight, high number of passengers and extensive service requirements
- extra services demanded by passengers, the character of certain passengers and, occasionally, verbal or physical abuse by passengers
- passengers requiring special care and attention (e.g., children, the disabled, the elderly, a medical emergency)
- extent of preparatory work
- lack of necessary service items (e.g., insufficient meals, beverages and so on) and equipment.

The measures taken by air carrier managements and government administrations to keep crew workload within reasonable limits include: improvement and extension of air-traffic control; reasonable limits on hours of duty and requirements for minimum rest provisions; execution of preparatory work by dispatchers, maintenance, catering and cleaning personnel; automation of cockpit equipment and tasks; the standardization of service procedures; adequate staffing; and the provision of efficient and easy-to-handle equipment.

Hours of work

One of the most important factors affecting both technical and cabin crew member occupational health and safety (and certainly the most widely discussed and controversial) is the issue of flight fatigue and recovery. This issue covers the broad spectrum of activity encompassing crew scheduling practices—length of duty periods, amount of flight time (daily, monthly and yearly), reserve or standby duty periods and availability of time for rest both while on flight assignment and at domicile. Circadian rhythms, especially sleep intervals and duration, with all their physiological and psychological implications, are especially significant for air crew members. Time shifts due either to night flights or to east/west or west/east travel across a number of time zones create the greatest problems. Newer generation aircraft, which have the capability of remaining aloft for up to 15 to 16 hours at a time, have exacerbated the conflict between airline schedules and human limitations.

National regulations to limit duty and flight periods and to provide minimum rest limitations exist on a nation by nation basis. In some instances, these regulations have not kept pace with technology or science, nor do they necessarily guarantee flight safety. Until recently there has been little attempt to standardize these regulations. Current attempts at harmonization have given rise to concerns among air crew members that those countries with more protective regulations may be required to accept lower and less adequate standards. In addition to national regulations, many air crew members have been able to negotiate more protective hours of service requirements in their labour agreements. While these negotiated agreements are important, most crew members feel that hours of service standards are essential to their health and safety (and to that of the flying public), and thus minimum standards should be adequately regulated by the national authorities.

Psychological stress

In recent years, aircraft crew have been confronted with a serious mental stress factor: the likelihood of hijacking, bombs and armed attacks on aircraft. Although security measures in civil aviation worldwide have been considerably increased and upgraded, the sophistication of terrorists has likewise increased. Air piracy, terrorism and other criminal acts remain a real threat to all air crew members. The commitment and cooperation of all national authorities as well as the force of worldwide public opinion are needed to prevent these acts. Additionally, air crew members must continue to receive special training and information on security measures and must be informed on a timely basis of suspected threats of air piracy and terrorism.

Air crew members understand the importance of starting flight duty in a sufficiently good mental and physical state to ensure that the fatigue and stresses occasioned by the flight itself will not affect safety. Fitness for flight duty may occasionally be impaired by psychological and physical stress, and it is the responsibility of the crew member to recognize whether or not he or she is fit for duty. Sometimes, however, these effects may not be readily apparent to the person under duress. For this reason, most airlines and air crew member associations and labour unions have professional standards committees to assist crew members in this area.

Accidents

Fortunately, catastrophic aircraft accidents are rare events; nonetheless, they do represent a hazard for air crew members. An aircraft accident is practically never a hazard resulting from a single, well-defined cause; in almost every instance, a number of technical and human factors coincide in the causal process.

Defective equipment design or equipment failure, especially as a result of inadequate maintenance, are two mechanical causes of aircraft accidents. One important, although relatively rare, type of human failure is sudden death due, for example, to myocardial infarction; other failures include sudden loss of consciousness (e.g., epileptic fit, cardiac syncope and fainting due to food poisoning or other intoxication). Human failure may also result from the slow deterioration of certain functions such as hearing or vision, although no major aircraft accident has been attributed to such a cause. Preventing accidents from medical causes is one of the most important tasks of aviation medicine. Careful personnel selection, regular medical examinations, surveys of absence due to illness and accidents, continuous medical contact with working conditions and industrial hygiene surveys can considerably decrease the danger of sudden incapacitation or slow deterioration in technical crew. Medical personnel should also routinely monitor flight scheduling practices to prevent fatigue-related incidents and accidents. A well-operated, modern airline of significant size should have its own medical service for these purposes.

Advances in aircraft accident prevention are often made as a result of careful investigation of accidents and incidents. Systematic screening of all, even minor, accidents and incidents by an accident investigation board comprising technical, operational, structural, medical and other experts is essential to determine all causal factors in an accident or incident and to make recommendations for preventing future occurrences.

A number of strict regulations exist in aviation to prevent accidents caused by use of alcohol or other drugs. Crew members should not consume quantities of alcohol in excess of what is compatible with professional requirements, and no alcohol at all should be consumed during and for at least 8 hours prior to flight duty. Illegal drug use is strictly prohibited. Drug use for medicinal purposes is strictly controlled; such drugs are generally not allowed during or immediately preceding flight, although exceptions may be allowed by a recognized flight physician.

The transport of hazardous materials by air is yet another cause of aircraft accident and incidents. A recent survey covering a 2-year period (1992 to 1993) identified over 1,000 aircraft incidents involving hazardous materials on passenger and cargo air carriers in one nation alone. More recently, an accident in the United States which resulted in the deaths of 110 passengers and crew involved the carriage of hazardous cargo. Hazardous materials incidents in air transportation occur for a number of reasons. Shippers and passengers may be unaware of the dangers presented by the materials they bring aboard aircraft in their baggage or offer for transport. Occasionally, unscrupulous persons may choose to illegally ship forbidden hazardous materials. Additional restrictions on the carriage of hazardous materials by air and improved training for air crew members, passengers, shippers and loaders may help to prevent future incidents. Other accident prevention regulations deal with oxygen supply, crew meals and procedures in case of illness.

Diseases

Specific occupational disease of crew members are not known or documented. However, certain diseases may be more prevalent among crew members than among persons in other occupations. Common colds and upper respiratory system infections are frequent; this may be due in part to the low humidity during flight, irregularities of schedules, exposure to att large number of people in a confined space and so on. A common cold, especially with upper respiratory congestion, that is not significant for an office worker may incapacitate a crew member if it prevents the clearing of pressure on the middle ear during ascent and, particularly, during descent. Additionally, illnesses that require some form of drug therapy may also preclude the crew member from engaging in work for a period of time. Frequent travel to tropical areas may also entail increased exposure to infectious diseases, the most important being malaria and infections of the digestive system.

The close confines of an aircraft for extended periods of time also carry an excess risk of airborne infectious diseases like tuberculosis, if a passenger or crew member has such a disease in its contagious stage.

102. TRANSPORT INDUSTRY AND WAREHOUSING

AEROSPACE MEDICINE: EFFECTS OF GRAVITY, ACCELERATION AND MICROGRAVITY IN THE AEROSPACE ENVIRONMENT

Relford Patterson and Russell B. Rayman

Since the first sustained flight of a powered aircraft at Kitty Hawk, North Carolina (United States), in 1903, aviation has become a major international activity. It is estimated that from 1960 to 1989, the annual number of air passengers of regularly scheduled flights increased from 20 million to over 900 million (Poitrast and deTreville 1994). Military aircraft have become indispensable weapons systems for the armed forces of many nations. Advances in aviation technology, in particular the design of life support systems, have contributed to the rapid development of space programmes with human crews. Orbital space flights occur relatively frequently, and astronauts and cosmonauts work in space vehicles and space stations for extended periods of time.

In the aerospace environment, physical stressors that may affect the health of aircrew, passengers and astronauts to some degree include reduced concentrations of oxygen in the air, decreased barometric pressure, thermal stress, acceleration, weightlessness and a variety of other potential hazards (DeHart 1992). This article describes aeromedical implications of exposure to gravity and acceleration during flight in the atmosphere and the effects of microgravity experienced in space.

Gravity and Acceleration

The combination of gravity and acceleration encountered during flight in the atmosphere produces a variety of physiological effects experienced by aircrew and passengers. At the surface of the earth, the forces of gravity affect virtually all forms of human physical activity. The weight of a person corresponds to the force exerted upon the mass of the human body by the earth's gravitational field. The symbol used to express the magnitude of the acceleration of an object in free fall when it is dropped near the earth's surface is referred to as g, which corresponds to an acceleration of approximately 9.8 m/s^2 (Glaister 1988a; Leverett and Whinnery 1985).

Acceleration occurs whenever an object in motion increases its velocity. *Velocity* describes the rate of movement (speed) and direction of motion of an object. *Deceleration* refers to acceleration that involves a reduction in established velocity. Acceleration (as well as deceleration) is a vector quantity (it has magnitude and direction). There are three types of acceleration: linear acceleration, a change of speed without change in direction; radial acceleration, a change in direction without a change of speed; and angular acceleration, a change in speed and direction. During flight, aircraft are capable of manoeuvring in all three directions, and crew and passengers may experience linear, radial and angular accelerations. In aviation, applied accelerations are commonly expressed as multiples of the acceleration due to gravity. By convention, G is the unit expressing the ratio of an applied acceleration to the gravitational constant (Glaister 1988a; Leverett and Whinnery 1985).

Biodynamics

Biodynamics is the science dealing with the force or energy of living matter and is a major area of interest within the field of aerospace medicine. Modern aircraft are highly manoeuvrable and capable of flying at very high speeds, causing accelerative forces upon the occupants. The influence of acceleration upon the human body depends upon the intensity, rate of onset and direction of acceleration. The direction of acceleration is generally described by the use of a three-axis coordinate system (x, y, z) in which the vertical (z) axis is parallel to the long axis of the body, the x axis is oriented from front to back, and the y axis oriented side to side (Glaister 1988a). These accelerations can be categorized into two general types: sustained and transitory.

Sustained acceleration

The occupants of aircraft (and spacecraft operating in the atmosphere under the influence of gravity during launch and re-entry) commonly experience accelerations in response to aerodynamic forces of flight. Prolonged changes in velocity involving accelerations lasting longer than 2 seconds may result from changes in an aircraft's speed or direction of flight. The physiological effects of sustained acceleration result from the sustained distortion of tissues and organs of the body and changes in the flow of blood and distribution of body fluids (Glaister 1988a).

Positive or headward acceleration along the z axis ($+G_z$) represents the major physiological concern. In civil air transportation, G_z accelerations are infrequent, but may occasionally occur to a mild degree during some take-offs and landings, and while flying in conditions of air turbulence. Passengers may experience brief sensations of weightlessness when subject to sudden drops (negative G_z accelerations), if unrestrained in their seats. An unexpected abrupt acceleration may cause unrestrained aircrew or passengers to be thrown against internal surfaces of the aircraft cabin, resulting in injuries.

In contrast to civil transport aviation, the operation of high-performance military aircraft and stunt and aerial spray planes may generate significantly higher linear, radial and angular accelerations. Substantial positive accelerations may be generated as a high-performance aircraft changes its flight path during a turn or a pull-up manoeuvre from a steep dive. The $+G_z$ performance characteristics of current combat aircraft may expose occupants to positive accelerations of 5 to 7 G for 10 to 40 seconds (Glaister 1988a). Aircrew may experience an increase in the weight of tissues and of the extremities at relatively low levels of acceleration of only $+2 G_z$. As an example, a pilot weighing 70 kg who performed an aircraft manoeuvre which generated $+2 G_z$ would experience an increase of body weight from 70 kg to 140 kg.

The cardiovascular system is the most important organ system for determining the overall tolerance and response to $+G_z$ stress (Glaister 1988a). The effects of positive acceleration on vision and mental performance are due to decreases in blood flow and delivery of oxygen to eye and brain. The capability of the heart to pump blood to the eyes and brain is dependent upon its capability to exceed the hydrostatic pressure of blood at any point along the circulatory system and the inertial forces generated by the positive G_z acceleration. The situation may be likened to that of pulling upward a balloon partially full of water and observing the downward distension of the balloon because of the resultant inertial force acting upon the mass of water. Exposure to positive accelerations may cause temporary loss of peripheral vision or complete loss of consciousness. Military pilots of high-performance aircraft may risk development of G-induced black-outs when exposed to rapid onset or extended periods of positive acceleration in the $+G_z$ axis. Benign cardiac arrhythmias frequently occur following exposure to high sustained levels of $+G_z$ acceleration, but usually are of minimal clinical significance unless pre-existing disease is present; $-G_z$ acceleration seldom occurs because of limitations in aircraft design and performance, but may occur during inverted flight, outside loops and spins and other similar manoeuvres. The physiological effects associated with exposure to $-G_z$ acceleration primarily involve increased vascular pressures in the upper body, head and neck (Glaister 1988a).

Accelerations of sustained duration which act at right angles to the long axis of the body are termed *transverse accelerations* and are relatively uncommon in most aviation situations, with the exception of catapult and jet- or rocket-assisted take-offs from aircraft carriers, and during launch of rocket systems such as the space shuttle. The accelerations encountered in such military operations are relatively small, and usually do not affect the body in a major fashion because the inertial forces act at right angles to the long axis of the body. In general, the effects are less pronounced than in G_z accelerations. Lateral acceleration in $\pm G_y$ axis are uncommon, except with experimental aircraft.

Transitory acceleration

The physiological responses of individuals to transitory accelerations of short duration are a major consideration in the science of aircraft accident prevention and crew and passenger protection. Transitory accelerations are of such brief duration (considerably less than 1 second) that the body is unable to attain a steady-state status. The most common cause of injury in aircraft accidents results from the abrupt deceleration that occurs when an aircraft impacts the ground or water (Anton 1988). When an aircraft impacts the ground, a tremendous amount of kinetic energy applies damaging forces to the aircraft and its occupants. The human body responds to these applied forces by a combination of acceleration and strain. Injuries result from deformation of tissues and organs and trauma to anatomic parts caused by collision with structural components of the aircraft cockpit and/or cabin.

Human tolerance to abrupt deceleration is variable. The nature of injuries will depend on the nature of the applied force (whether it primarily involves penetrating or blunt impact). At impact, the forces which are generated are dependent on the longitudinal and horizontal decelerations which are generally applied to an occupant. Abrupt decelerative forces are often categorized into tolerable, injurious and fatal. *Tolerable* forces produce traumatic injuries such as abrasions and bruises; *injurious* forces produce moderate to severe trauma which may not be incapacitating. It is estimated that an acceleration pulse of approximately 25 G maintained for 0.1 second is the limit of tolerability along the $+G_z$ axis, and that about 15 G for 0.1 sec is the limit for the $-G_z$ axis (Anton 1988).

Multiple factors affect human tolerance to short-duration acceleration. These factors include the magnitude and duration of the applied force, the rate of onset of the applied force, its direction and the site of application. It should be noted that people can withstand much greater forces perpendicular to the long axis of the body.

Protective Countermeasures

Physical screening of crew members to identify serious pre-existing diseases which might put them at increased risk in the aerospace environment is a key function of aeromedical programmes. In addition, countermeasures are available to crew of high-performance aircraft to protect against the adverse effects of extreme accelerations during flight. Crew members must be trained to recognize that multiple physiological factors may decrease their tolerance to G stress. These risk factors include fatigue, dehydration, heat stress, hypoglycemia and hypoxia (Glaister 1988b).

Three types of manoeuvres which crew members of high-performance aircraft employ to minimize adverse effects of sustained acceleration during flight are muscle tensing, forced expiration against a closed or partially closed glottis (back of the tongue) and positive-pressure breathing (Glaister 1988b; DeHart

1992). Forced muscle contractions exert increased pressure on blood vessels to decrease venous pooling and increase venous return and cardiac output, resulting in increased blood flow to the heart and upper body. While effective, the procedure requires extreme, active effort and may rapidly result in fatigue. Expiration against a closed glottis, termed the *Valsalva manoeuver* (or *M-1 procedure*) can increase pressure in the upper body and raise the intrathoracic pressure (inside the chest); however, the result is short lived and may be detrimental if prolonged, because it reduces venous blood return and cardiac output. Forcibly exhaling against a partially closed glottis is a more effective anti-G straining manoeuver. Breathing under positive pressure represents another method to increase intrathoracic pressure. Positive pressures are transmitted to the small artery system, resulting in increased blood flow to the eyes and brain. Positive-pressure breathing must be combined with the use of anti-G suits to prevent excessive pooling in the lower body and limbs.

Military aircrew practise a variety of training methods to enhance G tolerance. Crews frequently train in a centrifuge consisting of a gondola attached to a rotating arm which spins and generates $+G_z$ acceleration. Aircrew become familiar with the spectrum of physiological symptoms which may develop and learn the proper procedures to control them. Physical fitness training, particularly whole-body strength training, also has been found to be effective. One of the most common mechanical devices used as protective equipment to reduce the effects of $+G$ exposure consists of pneumatically inflated anti-G suits (Glaister 1988b). The typical trouser-like garment consists of bladders over the abdomen, thighs and calves which automatically inflate by means of an anti-G valve in the aircraft. The anti-G valve inflates in reaction to an applied acceleration upon the aircraft. Upon inflation, the anti-G suit produces a rise in the tissue pressures of the lower extremities. This maintains peripheral vascular resistance, reduces the pooling of blood in the abdomen and lower limbs and minimizes downward displacement of the diaphragm to prevent the increase in the vertical distance between the heart and brain that may be caused by positive acceleration (Glaister 1988b).

Surviving transitory accelerations associated with aircraft crashes is dependent on effective restraint systems and the maintenance of the cockpit/cabin integrity to minimize intrusion of damaged aircraft components into the living space (Anton 1988). The function of lap belts, harnesses and other types of restraint systems are to limit the movement of the aircrew or passengers and to attenuate the effects of sudden deceleration during impact. The effectiveness of the restraint system depends on how well it transmits loads between the body and the seat or vehicle structure. Energy-attenuating seating and rearward facing seats are other features in aircraft design which limit injury. Other accident-protection technology includes the design of airframe components to absorb energy and improvements in seat structures to reduce mechanical failure (DeHart 1992; DeHart and Beers 1985).

Microgravity

Since the 1960s, astronauts and cosmonauts have flown numerous missions into space, including 6 lunar landings by Americans. Mission duration has been from several days to a number of months, with a few Russian cosmonauts logging approximately 1-year flights. Subsequent to these space flights, a large body of literature has been written by physicians and scientists describing in-flight and post-flight physiological aberrations. For the most part, these aberrations have been attributed to exposure to weightlessness or microgravity. Although these changes are transient, with total recovery within several days to several months after returning to Earth, nobody can say with complete certitude whether astronauts would be so fortunate after missions lasting 2 to 3 years, as envisioned for a round trip to Mars. The major physiological aberrations (and countermeasures) can be categorized as cardiovascular, musculoskeletal, neurovestibular, haematological and endocrinological (Nicogossian, Huntoon and Pool 1994).

Cardiovascular hazards

Thus far, there have been no serious cardiac problems in space, such as heart attacks or heart failure, although several astronauts have developed abnormal heart rhythms of a transient nature, particularly during extra-vehicular activity (EVA). In one case, a Russian cosmonaut had to return to Earth earlier than planned, as a precautionary measure.

On the other hand, microgravity seems to induce a lability of blood pressure and pulse. Although this does not cause impaired health or crew performance during flight, approximately half of astronauts immediately post-flight do become extremely dizzy and giddy, with some experiencing fainting (syncope) or near fainting (pre-syncope). The cause of this intolerance to being vertical is thought to be a drop in blood pressure upon re-entering the earth's gravitational field, combined with the dysfunction of the body's compensatory mechanisms. Hence, a low blood pressure and decreasing pulse unopposed by the body's normal response to such physiological aberrations results in these symptoms.

Although these pre-syncopal and syncopal episodes are transient and without sequelae, there remains great concern for several reasons. First, in the event that a returning space vehicle were to have an emergency, such as a fire, upon landing, it would be extremely difficult for astronauts to rapidly escape. Second, astronauts landing on the moon after periods of time in space would be prone to some extent to pre-fainting and fainting, even though the moon's gravitational field is one-sixth that of Earth. And finally, these cardiovascular symptoms might be far worse or even lethal after very long missions.

It is for these reasons that there has been an aggressive search for countermeasures to prevent or at least ameliorate the microgravity effects upon the cardiovascular system. Although there are a number of countermeasures now being studied that show some promise, none so far has been proven truly effective. Research has focused on in-flight exercise utilizing a treadmill, bicycle ergometer and rowing machine. In addition, studies are also being conducted with lower body negative pressure (LBNP). There is some evidence that lowering the pressure around the lower body (using compact special equipment) will enhance the body's ability to compensate (i.e., raise blood pressure and pulse when they fall too low). The LBNP countermeasure might be even more effective if the astronaut drinks moderate amounts of specially constituted salt water simultaneously.

If the cardiovascular problem is to be solved, not only is more work needed on these countermeasures, but also new ones must be found.

Musculoskeletal hazards

All astronauts returning from space have some degree of muscle wasting or atrophy, regardless of mission duration. Muscles at particular risk are those of the arms and legs, resulting in decreased size as well as strength, endurance and work capacity. Although the mechanism for these muscle changes is still ill-defined, a partial explanation is prolonged disuse; work, activity and movement in microgravity are almost effortless, since nothing has any weight. This may be a boon for astronauts working in space, but is clearly a liability when returning to a gravitational field, whether it be that of the moon or Earth. Not only could a

weakened condition impede post-flight activities (including work on the lunar surface), it could also compromise rapid ground emergency escape, if required upon landing. Another factor is the possible requirement during EVA to do space vehicle repairs, which can be very strenuous. Countermeasures under study include in-flight exercises, electrical stimulation and anabolic medication (testosterone or testosterone-like steroids). Unfortunately, these modalities at best only retard muscle dysfunction.

In addition to muscle wasting, there is also a slow but inexorable loss of bone in space (about 300 mg per day, or 0.5% of total bone calcium per month) experienced by all astronauts. This has been documented by post-flight x rays of bones, particularly of those that bear weight (i.e., the axial skeleton). This is due to a slow but unremitting loss of calcium into the urine and faeces. Of great concern is the continuing loss of calcium, regardless of flight duration. Consequently, this calcium loss and bone erosion could be a limiting factor of flight, unless an effective countermeasure can be found. Although the precise mechanism of this very significant physiological aberration is not fully understood, it undoubtedly is due in part to the absence of gravitational forces on bone, as well as disuse, similar to muscle wasting. If bone loss were to continue indefinitely, particularly over long missions, bones would become so brittle that eventually there would be risk of fractures with even low levels of stress. Furthermore, with a constant flow of calcium into the urine via the kidneys, a possibility of renal stone formation exists, with accompanying severe pain, bleeding and infection. Clearly, any of these complications would be a very serious matter were they to occur in space.

Unfortunately, there are no known countermeasures that effectively prevent calcium loss during space flight. A number of modalities are being tested, including exercise (treadmill, bicycle ergometer and rowing machine), the theory being that such voluntary physical stresses would normalize bone metabolism, thereby preventing or at least ameliorating bone loss. Other countermeasures under investigation are calcium supplements, vitamins and various medications (such as diphosphonates—a class of medications that has been shown to prevent bone loss in patients with osteoporosis). If none of these simpler countermeasures prove to be effective, it is possible that the solution lies in artificial gravity that could be produced by continuous or intermittent rotation of the space vehicle. Although such motion could generate gravitational forces similar to that of the earth, it would represent an engineering "nightmare", in addition to major add-on costs.

Neurovestibular hazards

More than half of the astronauts and cosmonauts suffer from space motion sickness (SMS). Although the symptoms vary somewhat from individual to individual, most suffer from stomach awareness, nausea, vomiting, headache and drowsiness. Often there is an exacerbation of symptoms with rapid head movement. If an astronaut develops SMS, it usually occurs within a few minutes to a few hours after launch, with complete remission within 72 hours. Interestingly, the symptoms sometimes recur after returning to the earth.

SMS, particularly vomiting, can not only be disconcerting to the crew members, it also has the potential to cause performance decrement in an astronaut who is ill. Furthermore, the risk of vomiting while in a pressure suit doing EVA cannot be ignored, as the vomitus could cause the life-support system to malfunction. It is for these reasons that no EVA activities are ever scheduled during the first 3 days of a space mission. If an EVA becomes necessary, for example, to do emergency repairs on the space vehicle, the crew would have to take that risk.

Much neurovestibular research has been directed toward finding a way to prevent as well as to treat SMS. Various modalities, including anti-motion-sickness pills and patches, as well as using pre-flight adaptation trainers such as rotating chairs to habituate astronauts, have been attempted with very limited success. However, in recent years it has been discovered that the antihistamine phenergan, given by injection, is an extremely effective treatment. Hence, it is carried onboard all flights and given as required. Its efficacy as a preventive has yet to be demonstrated.

Other neurovestibular symptoms reported by astronauts include dizziness, vertigo, dysequilibrium and illusions of self-motion and motion of the surrounding environment, sometimes making walking difficult for a short time post-flight. The mechanisms for these phenomena are very complex and are not completely understood. They could be problematical, particularly after a lunar landing following several days or weeks in space. As of now, there are no known effective countermeasures.

Neurovestibular phenomena are most likely caused by dysfunction of the inner ear (the semicircular canals and utricle-saccule), because of microgravity. Either erroneous signals are sent to the central nervous system or signals are misinterpreted. In any event, the results are the aforementioned symptoms. Once the mechanism is better understood, effective countermeasures can be identified.

Haematological hazards

Microgravity has an effect upon the body's red and white blood cells. The former serve as a conveyor of oxygen to the tissues, and the latter as an immunological system to protect the body from invading organisms. Hence, any dysfunction could cause deleterious effects. For reasons not understood, astronauts lose approximately 7 to 17% of their red blood cell mass early in flight. This loss appears to plateau within a few months, returning to normal 4 to 8 weeks post-flight.

So far, this phenomenon has not been clinically significant, but, rather, a curious laboratory finding. However, there is clear potential for this loss of red blood cell mass to be a very serious aberration. Of concern is the possibility that with very long missions envisioned for the twenty-first century, red blood cells could be lost at an accelerated rate and in far greater quantities. If this were to occur, anaemia could develop to the point that an astronaut could become seriously ill. It is hoped that this will not be the case, and that the red blood cell loss will remain very small, regardless of mission duration.

In addition, several components of the white blood cell system are affected by microgravity. For example, there is an overall increase in the white blood cells, mainly neutrophils, but a decrease in lymphocytes. There is also evidence that some white blood cells do not function normally.

As of now, in spite of these changes, no illness has been attributed to these white blood cell changes. It is unknown whether or not a long mission will cause further decrease in numbers as well as further dysfunction. Should this occur, the body's immune system would be compromised, making astronauts very susceptible to infectious disease, and possibly incapacitated by even minor illness that would otherwise easily be fended off by a normally functioning immunological system.

As with the red blood cell changes, the white blood cell changes, at least on missions of approximately one year, are not of clinical significance. Because of the potential risk of serious illness in-flight or post-flight, it is critical that research continue on the effects of microgravity on the haematological system.

Endocrinological hazards

During space flight, it has been noted that there are a number of fluid and mineral changes within the body due in part to changes in the endocrine system. In general, there is a loss of total body

fluids, as well as calcium, potassium and calcium. A precise mechanism for these phenomena has eluded definition, although changes in various hormonal levels offer a partial explanation. To further confound matters, laboratory findings are often inconsistent among the astronauts who have been studied, making it impossible to discern a unitary hypothesis as to the cause of these physiological aberrations. In spite of this confusion, these changes have caused no known impairment of health of astronauts and no performance decrement in flight. What the significance of these endocrine changes are for very long flight, as well as the possibility that they may be harbingers of very serious sequelae, is unknown.

Acknowledgements: The authors would like to recognize the work of the Aerospace Medical Association in this area.

HELICOPTERS

David L. Huntzinger

The helicopter is a very special type of aircraft. It is used in every part of the world and serves a variety of purposes and industries. Helicopters vary in size from the smallest single-seat helicopters to giant heavy-lift machines with gross weights in excess of 100,000 kg, which is about the same size as a Boeing 757. The purpose of this article is to discuss some of the safety and health challenges of the machine itself, the different missions it are used for, both civilian and military, and the helicopter's operating environment.

The helicopter itself presents some very unique safety and health challenges. All helicopters use a main rotor system. This is the lifting body for the machine and serves the same purpose as the wings on a conventional airplane. Rotor blades are a significant hazard to people and property because of their size, mass and rotational speed, which also makes them difficult to see from certain angles and in different lighting conditions.

The tail rotor is also a hazard. It is usually much smaller than the main rotor and turns at a very high rate, so it too is very difficult to see. Unlike the main rotor system, which sits atop the helicopter's mast, the tail rotor is often near ground level. People should approach a helicopter from the front, in view of the pilot, to avoid coming into contact with the tail rotor. Extra care should be taken to identify or remove obstacles (such as bushes or fences) in a temporary or unimproved helicopter landing area. Contact with the tail rotor can cause injury or death as well as serious damage to the property or helicopter.

Many people recognize the characteristic slap sound of a helicopter's rotor system. This noise is encountered only when the helicopter is in forward flight, and is not considered a health problem. The compressor section of the engine produces extremely loud noise, often in excess of 140 dBA, and unprotected exposure must be avoided. Hearing protection (ear plugs *and* a noise attenuating headset or helmet) should be worn when working in and around helicopters.

There are several other hazards to consider when working with helicopters. One is flammable or combustible liquids. All helicopters require fuel to run the engine(s). The engine and the main and tail rotor transmissions use oil for lubrication and cooling. Some helicopters have one or more hydraulic systems and use hydraulic fluid.

Helicopters build a static electric charge when the rotor system is turning and/or the helicopter is flying. The static charge will

Figure 102.5 • H-46 helicopter landing in the Arizona, US, desert.

dissipate when the helicopter touches the ground. If an individual is required to grab a line from a hovering helicopter, as during logging, external lifts or rescue efforts, that person should let the load or line touch the ground before grabbing it in order to avoid a shock.

The Helicopter Operating Environment

The helicopter is used all over the world in a variety of ways (see, for example, figures 102.5 and 102.6). In addition, it is often working very near the ground and other obstructions. This requires constant vigilance from the pilots and those who work with or ride on the aircraft. By contrast, the fixed-wing aircraft environment is more predictable, since they fly (especially the commercial airplanes) primarily from airports whose airspace is tightly controlled.

The combat environment presents special dangers. The military helicopter also operates in a low-level environment and is subject to the same hazards. The proliferation of inexpensive, hand-carried, heat-seeking missiles represents another danger to rotorcraft. The military helicopter can use the terrain to hide itself or to mask its telltale signature, but when in the open it is vulnerable to small-arms fire and missiles.

Military forces also use night vision goggles (NVG) to enhance the pilot's view of the area in low-light conditions. While the NVGs do increase the pilot's ability to see, they have severe operating limitations. One major drawback is the lack of peripheral vision, which has contributed to mid-air collisions.

Accident Prevention Measures

Preventive measures can be grouped into several categories. Any one prevention category or item will not, in and of itself, prevent accidents. All of them must be used in concert to maximize their effectiveness.

Operational policies

Operational policies are formulated in advance of any operations. They are usually provided by the company with the operating certificate. They are crafted from governmental regulations, manufacturer's recommended guidelines, industry standards, best practices and common sense. In general, they have proven to be effective in preventing incidents and accidents and include:

- *Establishment of best practices and procedures.* Procedures are essential for accident prevention. When not used, such as in early helicopter ambulance operations, there were extremely high accident rates. In the absence of regulatory guidance, pilots attempted to support humanitarian missions at night and/or in poor weather conditions with minimal training and helicopters that were ill equipped for such flights, leading to accidents.
- *Crew resource management (CRM).* CRM began as "cockpit resource management" but has since progressed to crew resource management. CRM is based on the idea that people in the crew should be free to discuss any situation among themselves to assure the successful completion of the flight. While many helicopters are flown by a single pilot, they are often working with other people who are either in the helicopter or on the ground. These people can provide information about the operation if consulted or allowed to speak. When such interaction occurs, CRM then becomes *company* resource management. Such collaboration is an acquired skill and should be taught to crews, company employees and others that work with and around helicopters.
- *Provision of a threat-free company environment.* Helicopter operations can be seasonal. This means long, tiring days. Crews should be able to end their duty day without fear of recrimination. If there are other, similar, operational deficiencies, crews should be permitted to openly identify, discuss and correct them.
- *Physical hazards awareness.* The helicopter presents an array of hazards. The aircraft's dynamic components, its main and tail rotors, must be avoided. All passengers and crew members should be briefed on their location and on how to avoid coming into contact with them. The component's surfaces should be painted to enhance their visibility. The helicopter should be positioned so that it is difficult for people to get to the tail rotor. Noise protection must be provided, especially to those with continuous exposure.
- *Training for abnormal conditions.* Training is often limited, if available at all, to practising autorotations for engine-out conditions. Simulators can provide exposure to a much wider range of atypical conditions without exposing the crew or machine to the real condition.

Figure 102.6 • 5-76A Cougar helicopter landing in field at accident site.

Helicopter operations

The uses of helicopters are numerous. The diversity of operations can be divided into two categories: civil and military.

Civil

Rescue/air ambulance. The helicopter was originally designed with rescue in mind, and one of its most widespread uses is as an ambulance. These are often found at the scene of an accident or disaster (see figure 102.6). They can land in confined areas with qualified medical teams on board who care for the injured at the scene while en route to a medical facility. Helicopters are also used for non-emergency flights when speed of transport or patient comfort is required.

Offshore oil support. Helicopters are used to help supply offshore oil operations. They transport people and supplies between land and platform and between platforms.

Executive/personal transport. The helicopter is used for point-to-point transportation. This is usually done over short distances where geography or sluggish traffic conditions prevent rapid ground transportation. Corporations build helipads on company property to allow easy access to airports or to facilitate transportation between facilities.

Sightseeing. The use of helicopters in the tourist industry has seen continuous growth. The excellent view from the helicopter combined with its ability to access remote areas make it a popular attraction.

Law enforcement. Many police departments and governmental agencies use helicopters for this type of work. The helicopter's mobility in crowded urban areas and remote rural areas makes it invaluable. The largest rooftop helipad in the world is at the Los Angeles Police Department.

Film operations. Helicopters are a staple in action movies. Other types of movies and film-based entertainment are filmed from helicopters.

News gathering. Television and radio stations employ helicopters for traffic spotting and news gathering. Their ability to land at the place where the news is happening makes them a valuable asset. Many of them are also equipped with microwave transceivers so they can send their stories, live, over fairly long distances, while en route.

Heavy lift. Some helicopters are designed to carry heavy loads at the end of external lines. Aerial logging is one application of this concept. Construction and oil exploration crews make extensive use of the helicopter's capacity for lifting large or bulky objects into place.

Aerial application. Helicopters can be fitted with spray booms and loaded to dispense herbicides, pesticides and fertilizers. Other devices can be added that allow helicopters to fight fires. They can drop either water or chemical retardants.

Military

Rescue/aerial ambulance. The helicopter is used widely in humanitarian efforts. Many nations around the world have coast guards that engage in maritime rescue work. Helicopters are used to transport the sick and wounded from battle areas. Still others are sent to rescue or recover people from behind enemy lines.

Attack. Helicopters can be armed and used as attack platforms over land or sea. Weapon systems include machine guns, rockets and torpedoes. Sophisticated targeting and guidance systems are used to lock on to and destroy targets at longe range.

Transport. Helicopters of all sizes are used to transport people and supplies over land or sea. Many ships are equipped with helipads to facilitate offshore operations.

Crew practices

- *Published procedures.* One study of accidents has shown that, in more than half the cases, the accident would have been prevented had the pilot followed known, published procedures.
- *Crew resource management.* CRM should be used.
- *Anticipating and avoiding known problems.* Most helicopters are not equipped to fly in icing conditions and are prohibited from flying in moderate or severe turbulence, yet numerous accidents result from these circumstances. Pilots should anticipate and avoid these and other equally compromising conditions.
- *Special or non-standard operations.* Pilots must be thoroughly briefed for such circumstances.

Support operations

The following are crucial support operations for the safe use of helicopters:

- following published procedures
- briefing all passengers prior to boarding the helicopter
- keeping facilities free of obstructions
- keeping facilities well lit for night operations.

ROAD TRANSPORT

• TRUCK AND BUS DRIVING

Bruce A. Millies

Transport by road includes the movement of people, livestock and freight of all kinds. Freight and livestock generally move in some form of truck, although buses often carry packages and passenger baggage and may transport fowl and small animals. People generally move by bus on the road, although in many areas trucks of various kinds serve this function.

Truck (lorry) drivers may operate several different types of vehicles, including, for example, semi-trailers, tanker trucks, dump trucks, double and triple trailer combinations, mobile cranes, delivery trucks and panel or pickup vehicles. Legal gross vehicle weights (which vary by jurisdiction) range from 2,000 kg to over 80,000 kg. Truck cargo may include any imaginable item—for example, small and large packages, machinery, rock and sand, steel, lumber, flammable liquids, compressed gases, explosives, radioactive materials, corrosive or reactive chemicals, cryogenic liquids, food products, frozen foods, bulk grain, sheep and cattle.

In addition to driving the vehicle, truck drivers are responsible for inspecting the vehicle prior to use, checking shipping papers, verifying that proper placards and markings are in place and maintaining a log book. Drivers may also be responsible for servicing and repairing the vehicle, loading and unloading cargo (either by hand or using a fork truck, crane or other equipment) and collecting money received for goods delivered. In the event of an accident, the driver is responsible for securing the cargo and summoning assistance. If the incident involves hazardous materials, the driver may attempt, even without proper training or necessary equipment, to control spills, stop leaks or put out a fire.

Bus drivers may carry a few people in a small van or operate medium and large buses carrying 100 or more passengers. They are responsible for boarding and discharging passengers safely, providing information and possibly collecting fares and maintaining order. Bus drivers may also be responsible for servicing and repairing the bus and loading and unloading cargo and baggage.

Motor vehicle accidents are one of the most serious hazards facing both truck and bus drivers. This hazard is aggravated if the vehicle is not properly maintained, especially if the tyres are worn or the brake system is faulty. Driver fatigue caused by a long or irregular schedules, or by other stress, increases the likelihood of accidents. Excessive speed and hauling excessive weight add to the risk, as do heavy traffic and adverse weather conditions which impair traction or visibility. An accident involving hazardous materials may cause additional injury (toxic exposure, burns and so on) to the driver or passengers and may affect a wide area surrounding the accident.

Drivers face a variety of ergonomic hazards. The most obvious are back and other injuries caused by lifting excessive weight or using improper lifting technique. The use of back belts is quite common, although their efficacy has been questioned, and their use may create a false sense of security. The necessity of loading and unloading cargo at locations where fork-lift trucks, cranes or even dollies are not available and the great variety of package weights and configurations add to the risk of lifting injuries.

Driver's seats are often poorly designed and cannot be adjusted to provide proper support and long-term comfort, resulting in back problems or other musculoskeletal damage. Drivers may experience damage to the shoulder caused by vibration as the arm may rest for long periods in a somewhat raised position on the window opening. Whole-body vibration can cause damage to the kidneys and back. Ergonomic injury may also result from repetitive use of poorly placed vehicle controls or fare box keypads.

Drivers are at risk of industrial hearing loss caused by long-term exposure to loud engine noises. Poor maintenance, faulty mufflers and inadequate cab insulation aggravate this hazard. Hearing loss may be more pronounced in the ear adjacent to the driver's window.

Drivers, especially long-haul truck drivers, often work excessive hours without adequate rest. The International Labour Organization (ILO) Hours of Work and Rest Periods (Road Transport) Convention, 1979 (No. 153), requires a break after 4 hours of driving, limits total driving time to 9 hours per day and 48 hours per week and requires at least 10 hours of rest in each 24-hour period. Most nations also have laws which govern driving times and rest periods and require drivers to maintain logbooks indicating hours worked and rest periods taken. However, management expectations and economic necessity, as well as certain terms of remuneration, such as pay per load or the lack of pay for an empty return trip, put strong pressure on the driver to operate for excessive hours and to make bogus log entries. Long hours cause psychological stress, aggravate ergonomic problems, contribute to accidents (including accidents caused by falling asleep at the wheel) and may cause the driver to use artificial, addictive stimulants.

In addition to ergonomic conditions, long work hours, noise and economic anxiety, drivers experience psychological and physiological stress and fatigue caused by adverse traffic conditions, poor road surfaces, bad weather, night driving, the fear of assault and robbery, concern about faulty equipment and continuous intense concentration.

Truck drivers are potentially exposed to any chemical, radioactive or biological hazard associated with their load. Leaking containers, faulty valves on tanks and emissions during loading or unloading may cause worker exposures to toxic chemicals. Improper packaging, inadequate shielding or improper placement of radioactive cargo may allow radiation exposure. Workers transporting livestock may be infected with animal-borne infections such as brucellosis. Bus drivers are exposed to infectious diseases of their passengers. Drivers are also exposed to fuel vapours and engine exhaust, especially if there are fuel-line or exhaust system leaks or if the driver makes repairs or handles freight while the engine is running.

In the event of an accident involving hazardous materials, the driver may experience acute chemical or radiation exposures or may be injured by a fire, explosion or chemical reaction. Drivers generally lack the training or equipment to deal with hazardous materials incidents. Their responsibility should be limited to protecting themselves and summoning emergency responders. The driver faces additional risks in attempting emergency response actions for which he or she is not properly trained and adequately equipped.

The driver may be injured in the course of making mechanical repairs to the vehicle. A driver could be struck by another vehicle while working on a truck or bus alongside the road. Wheels with split rims pose a special injury hazard. Improvised or inadequate jacks may cause a crushing injury.

Truck drivers face the risk of assault and robbery, especially if the vehicle carries a valuable cargo or if the driver is responsible for collecting money for goods delivered. Bus drivers are at risk of fare box robberies and abuse or assault by impatient or inebriated passengers.

Many aspects of a driver's life may contribute to poor health. Because they work long hours and need to eat on the road, drivers often suffer from poor nutrition. Stress and peer pressure may lead to drug and alcohol use. Using the services of prostitutes increases the risk of AIDS and other sexually transmitted diseases. The drivers appear to be one of the main vectors for carrying AIDS in some countries.

The risks described above are all preventable, or at least controllable. As with most safety and health issues, what is needed is a combination of adequate remuneration, worker training, a strong union contract and strict adherence to applicable standards on the part of management. If drivers receive adequate pay for their work, based on proper work schedules, there is less incentive to speed, work excessive hours, drive unsafe vehicles, carry overweight loads, take drugs or make bogus log entries. Management must require drivers to comply with all safety laws, including keeping an honest logbook.

If management invests in well-made vehicles and assures their regular inspection, maintenance and servicing, breakdowns and accidents can be greatly reduced. Ergonomic injury can be reduced if management is willing to pay for the well-designed cabs, fully adjustable driver's seats and good vehicle control arrangements that are now available. Proper maintenance, especially of exhaust systems, will reduce noise exposure.

Toxic exposures can be reduced if management assures compliance with packaging, labelling, loading and placarding standards for hazardous materials. Measures which reduce vehicular accidents also reduce the risk of a hazardous materials incident.

Drivers must be given time to thoroughly inspect the vehicle prior to use and must not face any penalty or disincentive for refusing to operate a vehicle that is not functioning properly. Drivers must also receive adequate driver training, vehicle inspection training, hazard recognition training and first-responder training.

If drivers are responsible for loading and unloading, they must receive training in proper lifting technique and be provided with hand-trucks, fork-lifts, cranes or other equipment necessary to handle goods without excessive strain. If drivers are expected to make repairs to vehicles, they must be provided with the correct tools and proper training. Adequate security measures must be taken to protect drivers who transport valuables or handle passenger fares or money received for goods delivered. Bus drivers should have proper supplies for dealing with body fluids from sick or injured passengers.

Drivers must receive medical services both to assure their fitness for work and to maintain their health. Medical surveillance must be provided for drivers who handle hazardous materials or are involved in an incident with exposure to blood-borne pathogens or hazardous materials . Both management and drivers must comply with standards governing the evaluation of medical fitness.

● ERGONOMICS OF BUS DRIVING

Alfons Grösbrink and Andreas Mahr

Bus driving is characterized by psychological and physical stresses. Most severe are the stresses of traffic in big cities, because of the heavy traffic and frequent stops. In most transit companies, the drivers must, in addition to driving responsibilities, handle tasks such as selling tickets, observing passenger loading and unloading and providing information to passengers.

Psychological stresses result from the responsibility for the safe transport of passengers, scant opportunity to communicate with colleagues and the time pressure of holding to a fixed schedule. Rotating shift work is also psychologically and physically stressful. Ergonomic shortcomings in the driver's workstation increase physical stresses.

Numerous studies of the activity of bus drivers have shown that the individual stresses are not great enough to cause an immediate health hazard. But the sum of the stresses and the resulting strain leads to bus drivers having more frequent health problems than other workers. Especially significant are diseases of the stomach and digestive tract, of the motor system (especially the spine) and of the cardiovascular system. This results in drivers often not reaching retirement age, but rather having to quit driving early for health reasons (Beiler and Tränkle 1993; Giesser-Weigt and Schmidt 1989; Haas, Petry and Schühlein 1989; Meifort, Reiners and Schuh 1983; Reimann 1981).

In order to achieve more effective occupational safety in the field of commercial driving, technical as well as organizational measures are necessary. An important work practice is the arranging of shift schedules so that the stress on the drivers is minimized and their personal desires are also taken into account to the extent possible. Informing the personnel of and motivating them to health-conscious conduct (e.g., proper diet, adequate movement within and outside of the workstation) can play an important role in promoting health. An especially necessary technical measure is

the ergonomically optimal design of the driver's workstation. In the past, the requirements of the driver's workstation were considered only after other requirements, such as design of the passenger area. Ergonomic design of the driver's workstation is a necessary component of driver safety and health protection. In recent years, research projects on, among other things, the ergonomically optimal driver's workstation were conducted in Canada, Sweden, Germany and the Netherlands (Canadian Urban Transit Association 1992; Peters et al. 1992; Wallentowitz et al. 1996; Streekvervoer Nederland 1991). The results of the interdisciplinary project in Germany resulted in a new, standardized driver's workstation (Verband Deutscher Verkehrsunternehmen 1996).

The driver's workstation in buses is normally designed in the form of a half-open cabin. The measurements of the driver's cabin and the adjustments that can be made to the seat and steering wheel must fall within a range that is applicable to all drivers. For central Europe, this means a body-size range of 1.58 to 2.00 m. Special proportions, such as being overweight and having long or short limbs, should also be taken into account in the design.

The adjustability and the ways of adjusting the driver's seat and steering wheel should be coordinated so that all drivers within the design range can find positions for their arms and legs that are comfortable and ergonomically healthy. For this purpose, the optimal seat placement has a back incline about 20°, which is further from the vertical than has previously been the norm in commercial vehicles. Furthermore, the instrument panel should also be adjustable for optimal access to adjustment levers and for good visibility of the instruments. This can be coordinated with the steering wheel adjustment. Using a smaller steering wheel also improves spatial relations. The steering wheel diameter now in general use apparently comes from a time when power steering was not common in buses. See figure 102.7.

Figure 102.7 • Ergonomically optimized and unified driver's workstation for buses in Germany.

Courtesy of Ercobus GmbH, Mannheim, Germany

The instrument panel with controls can be adjusted in coordination with the steering wheel.

---

102. TRANSPORT INDUSTRY AND WAREHOUSING

Table 102.1 • Bus driver seat measurements and seat adjustment ranges.

Component	Measurement/ adjustment range	Standard value (mm)	Adjustment range (mm)	Memorized
Entire seat	Horizontal	—	≥ 200	Yes
	Vertical	—	≥ 100	Yes
Seat surface	Seat surface depth	—	390–450	Yes
	Seat surface width (total)	Min. 495	—	—
	Seat surface width (flat part, in pelvic area)	430	—	—
	Side upholstering in pelvic area (crosswise)	40–70	—	—
	Depth of seat recess	10–20	—	—
	Seat surface slope	—	0–10° (rising toward front)	Yes
Seatback	Seatback height			
	Min. height	495	—	—
	Max. height	640	—	—
	Seatback width (total)*	Min. 475	—	—
	Seatback width (flat part)			
	—lumbar area (lower)	340	—	—
	—shoulder area (upper)	385	—	—
Seatback	Side upholstering* (side depth)			
	—lumbar area (lower)	50	—	—
	—shoulder area (upper)	25	—	—
	Seatback slope (to vertical)	—	0°–25°	Yes
Headrest	Height of headrest upper edge above seat surface	—	Min. 840	—
	Height of headrest itself	Min. 120	—	—
	Width of headrest	Min. 250	—	—
Lumbar pad	Forward arch of lumbar support from lumbar surface	—	10–50	—
	Height of lumbar support lower edge over seat surface	—	180–250	—

— Not applicable

* The width of the lower part of the backrest should correspond approximately to the width of the seat surface and grow narrower as it goes up.

** The side upholstering of the seat surface applies only to the recess area.

The instrument panel with the controls can be adjusted in coordination with the steering wheel.

Since stumbling and falling are the most common causes of workplace accidents among drivers, particular attention should be paid to the design of the entrance to the driver's workstation. Anything that can be stumbled on should be avoided. Steps in the entrance area must be of equal height and have adequate step depth.

The driver's seat should have a total of five adjustments: seat length and height settings, seat back angle, seat bottom angle and seat depth. Adjustable lumbar support is strongly advised. To the extent that it is not already legally required, equipping the driver's seat with a three-point seat-belt and head rest are recommended. Since experience shows that manually adjusting to the ergonomically right position is time-consuming, in the future some way of electronically storing the adjustment functions listed in table 102.1 should be used, allowing for quickly and easily refinding the individual seating adjustment (e.g., by entering it onto an electronic card).

Stress through whole-body vibrations in the driver's workstation is low in modern buses compared to other commercial vehicles, and it falls well below the international standards. Experience shows that driver's seats in buses are often not optimally adjusted to the vehicle's actual vibration. An optimal adaptation is advised to avoid certain frequency ranges causing an increase in whole-body vibration on the driver, which can interfere with productivity.

Noise levels that are a hazard to hearing are not anticipated in the bus driver's workstation. High-frequency noise can be irritating and should be eliminated because it could interfere with the drivers' concentration.

All adjustment and service components in the driver's workstation should be arranged for comfortable access. A large number of adjustment components are often required due to the amount of equipment added to the vehicle. For this reason, switches should be grouped and consolidated according to use. Frequently used service components such as door openers, bus stop brakes and windshield wipers should be placed in the main access area. Less frequently used switches can be located outside the main access area (e.g., on a side console).

Analyses of visual movements have shown that driving the vehicle in traffic and observing the loading and unloading of passengers at the stops is a serious burden on the driver's attention. Thus, the information conveyed by instruments and indicator lights in the vehicle should be limited to those absolutely necessary. Vehicle computerized electronics offer the possibility of eliminating numerous instruments and indicator lights, and instead installing a liquid crystal display (LCD) in a central location to convey information, as shown in the instrument panel in figures 102.8 and 102.9.

With the proper computer software, the display will show only a selection of information that is needed for the particular situation. In the case of malfunction, a description of the problem and brief instructions in clear text, rather than in difficult-to-understand pictograms, can provide the driver with important assistance. A hierarchy of malfunction notifications can also be established (e.g., "advisory" for less significant malfunctions, "alarm" when the vehicle must be stopped immediately).

Heating systems in buses often heat the interior with warm air only. For real comfort, however, a higher proportion of radiant heat is desirable (e.g., by heating the side walls, whose surface temperature often lies significantly below the interior air temperature). This, for example, can be achieved by circulating warm air through perforated wall surfaces, which thereby will also have the right temperature. Large window surfaces are used in the driver's area in buses to improve visibility and also for

Figure 102.8 • View of an instrument panel.

Courtesy of Erobus GmbH, Mannheim, Germany

With the exception of the speedometer and a few legally required indicator lights, the functions of the instrument and indicator displays have been assumed by a central LCD display.

appearance. These can lead to a significant warming of the inside by sun rays. The use of air conditioning is thus advisable.

The air quality of the driver's cabin depends heavily on the quality of the outside air. Depending on the traffic, high concentrations of harmful substances, such as carbon monoxide and diesel motor emissions, can briefly occur. Providing fresh air from less-used areas, such as the roof instead of the vehicle front, lessens the problem significantly. Fine-particle filters should also be used.

In most transit companies, an important part of the driving personnel's activity consists of selling tickets, operating devices to provide information to passengers and communicating with the company. Until now, separate devices, located in the available work space and often hard for the driver to reach, have been used for these activities. An integrated design should be sought from the start that arranges the devices in an ergonomically convenient manner in the driver's area, especially the input keys and display panels.

Finally, the assessment of the driver's area by the drivers, whose personal interests should be taken into account, is of great importance. Supposedly minor details, such as placement of the driver's bag or storage lockers for personal effects, are important for driver satisfaction.

Figure 102.9 • Illustration of an instrument panel with legend.

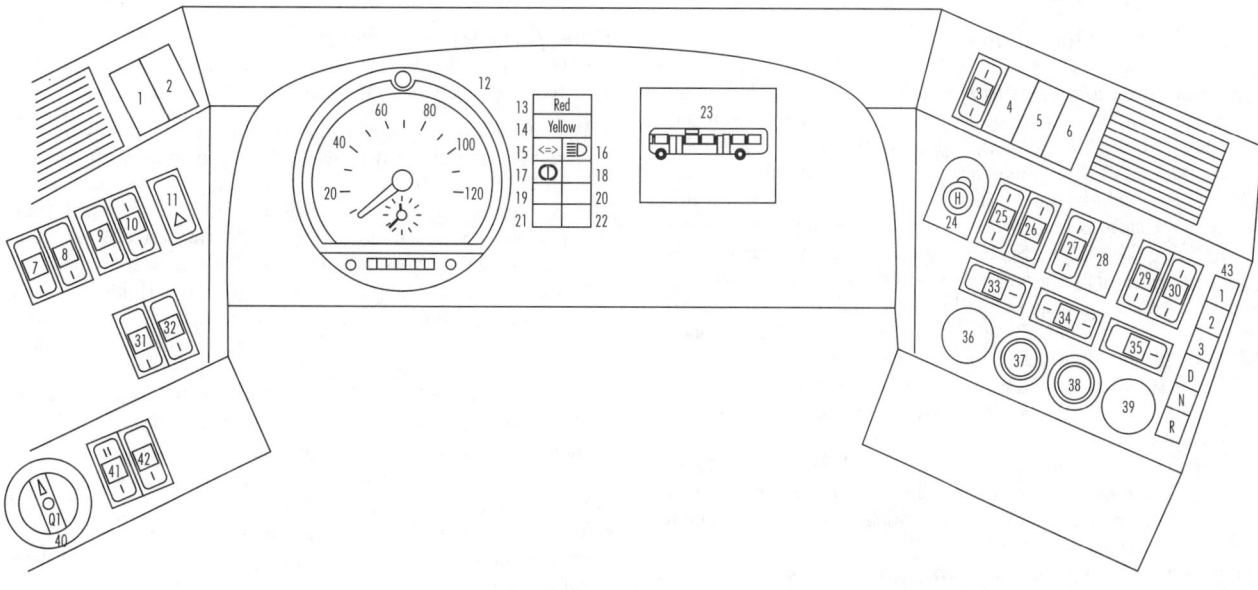

1. Unused
2. Unused
3. Receipt button display
4. Unused
5. Unused
6. Unused
7. Emergency brake on/off
8. Emergency brake direct
9. Step lift
10. Sun screen adjustment*
11. Warning indicator
12. Speedometer
13. Central warning lights (alarm level, red)
14. Central warning lights (warning level, yellow)
15. Travel direction indicator/warning light

16. High beam control
17. Brake malfunction indicator
18. Unused
19. Unused
20. Unused
21. Unused
22. Unused
23. LCD display
24. Bus stop brake
25. Kneeling or kneeling preselection
26. Emergency kneeling raiser
27. Automatic door closer*
28. Unused
29. Loading ramp release*
30. Lift/ramp raise/lower

31. Inside/outside loudspeaker switch
32. Radio
33. Bus stop warning light switch
34. Door leaf lock*
35. Door release*
36. Unused
37. Front door button
38. Rear door button
39. Unused
40. Headlights/fog lights/tail light
41. Passenger area lights
42. Cashbox and driver's area lights
43. Gear selection
 * Optional
** Tachometer optionally integrated into speedometer

MOTOR VEHICLE FUELLING AND SERVICING OPERATIONS

Richard S. Kraus

Petroleum-based fuels and lubricants are sold directly to consumers at full-service and self-service (with or without repair bays) service stations, car washes, automotive service centres, motor vehicle agencies, truck stops, repair garages, automotive parts stores and convenience stores. Service station attendants, mechanics and other employees who fuel, lubricate and service motor vehicles should be aware of the physical and chemical hazards of the petroleum fuels, lubricants, additives and waste products they come into contact with and follow appropriate safe work procedures and personal protection measures. The same physical and chemical hazards and exposures are present at commercial facilities, such as those operated by motor truck fleets, automobile rental agencies and bus companies for fuelling and servicing their own vehicles.

Because they are the facilities where motor fuels are delivered direct to the user's vehicle, service stations, particularly those where drivers fuel their own vehicles, are where employees and the general public are most likely to come into direct contact with hazardous petroleum products. Other than those drivers who change their own oil and lubricate their own vehicles, the likelihood of contact with lubricants or used oil by motorists, except for incidental contact when checking fluid levels, is very small.

Service Station Operations

Fuel island area and dispensing system

Employees should be aware of the potential fire, safety and health hazards of gasoline, kerosene, diesel and other fuels dispensed at service stations. They should also be aware of suitable precautions. These include: safe dispensing of fuels into vehicles and containers, clean-up and disposal of spills, fighting incipient fires and draining fuels safely. Service stations should provide fuel-dispenser pumps which operate only when the fuel-hose nozzles are removed from the dispensers' brackets and the switches are manually or automatically activated. Fuel-dispensing devices should be mounted on islands or protected against collision damage by barriers or curbs. Dispensing equipment, hoses and nozzles should be inspected regularly for leaks, damage and malfunctions. Safety features may be installed on fuel dispensers such as emergency breakaway devices on hoses, which retain liquid on each side of the break point, and impact valves with fusible links at the base of dispensers, which close automatically in event of severe impact or fire.

Government regulations and company policies may require that signs be posted in dispensing areas similar to the following signs, which are required in the United States:

- "No Smoking—Shut off engine"
- "WARNING: It is unlawful and dangerous to dispense gasoline into unapproved containers"
- "Federal Law prohibits the introduction of any gasoline containing lead or phosphorus into any motor vehicle labelled UNLEADED GASOLINE ONLY"
- "UNLEADED GASOLINE", posted at unleaded gasoline dispensers and "CONTAINS LEAD ANTIKNOCK COMPOUNDS", posted at leaded gasoline dispensers.

Fuelling vehicles

Service station employees should know where the fuel dispenser pump emergency shut-off switches are located and how to activate them, and should be aware of potential hazards and procedures for safely dispensing fuel into vehicles, such as the following:

- Vehicle engines should be shut off and smoking prohibited while fuelling to reduce the hazards of accidental vehicle movement, spills and fuel vapour ignition.
- When fuel is dispensed, the nozzle should be inserted into the vehicle's fill pipe and contact between the nozzle and the fill pipe maintained to provide for an electric bond until the delivery has been completed. Nozzles should not be blocked open with fuel caps or other objects. Where allowed, approved latches should be used to hold open automatic nozzles.
- Vehicles such as cement mixers and recreation vehicles with auxiliary internal combustion engines should not be fuelled until both the vehicle's engines and auxiliary engines are shut off. Care should be taken when fuelling recreational or other vehicles equipped with gas-fired stoves, refrigerators and water heaters to ensure that fuel vapours are not ignited by pilot lights. Employees should not fuel trucks while standing on the side rail, truck bed or fuel tank.
- Fuel tanks on motorcycles, motor bicycles, fork-lift trucks and similar vehicles should not be filled while the engine is running or when anyone is seated on the vehicle. The tanks should be filled at a slow rate to prevent fuel spills that could run onto hot engines and start fires.
- After fuelling, hose nozzles should be promptly replaced on the dispensers, pumps turned off and caps replaced on fill pipes or containers.

Filling portable fuel containers

Service stations should establish procedures such as the following for safely dispensing fuel into portable containers:

- Where required by government regulation or company policies, fuel should be dispensed only into approved, properly identified and labelled portable containers, with or without dispensing spouts, nozzles or hoses and equipped with vents and screw tops or self-closing gravity, spring action or combination fusible link covers designed to provide pressure relief.
- Containers should be placed on the ground and filled slowly to avoid splash filling and overfills and to provide for grounding (earthing). Containers should not be filled while in a vehicle or in the bed of a truck, particularly one with a plastic liner, as proper grounding cannot be achieved. Bonding wires and clamps should be provided and used, or contact should be maintained between dispenser nozzles and containers to provide a bond while filling, and between container spouts or funnels and tanks during refuelling from containers.
- When pouring fuel from containers which do not have built-in spouts, funnels should be used to minimize spillage and avoid splash filling.
- Portable containers which contain fuel or vapours should be properly stored in approved storage cabinets or rooms away from sources of heat and ignition.

Storage tanks, fill pipes, fill caps and vents

Service station underground and aboveground storage-tank gauge and fill-caps should be kept closed except when filling and gauging to minimize release of fuel vapours. When tank-gauge openings are located inside buildings, spring-loaded check valves or similar devices should be provided to protect each of the openings against fluid overflow and possible vapour release. Storage-tank vents should be located in accordance with government regulations and company policy. Where venting to open air is permitted, vent-pipe openings from both underground and aboveground storage tanks should be located at a high level so that flammable vapours are directed away from potential sources of ignition and will not enter windows or air intakes or doors or become trapped under eaves or overhangs.

Improper mixing of different products during deliveries may be caused by lack of identification or improper colour coding or markings on storage tanks. Storage-tank covers, fill pipes, caps and fill-box rims or pads should be properly identified as to products and grades so as to reduce the potential of a delivery into the wrong tank. Identification symbols and colour coding should conform to government regulations, company policies or industry standards, such as the American Petroleum Institute's (API) Recommended Practice 1637, *Using the API Color Symbol System to Mark Equipment and Vehicles for Product Identification at Service Stations and Distribution Terminals*. A chart indicating the symbols or colour codes in use should be available at the service station during deliveries.

Delivery of fuel to service stations

Service stations should establish and implement procedures such as the following, for the safe delivery of fuel into aboveground and underground service station storage tanks:

Prior to delivery

- Vehicles and other objects should be moved from the area where the delivery tank truck and delivery hoses will be located.
- Delivery tank trucks should be positioned away from traffic areas, and vehicles should be restricted from driving near the unloading area or over hoses by the use of traffic cones or barriers.
- Receiving storage tanks should be gauged prior to delivery to determine if there is sufficient capacity, and checked to see if any water is in the tank.
- Drivers should assure that fuel is delivered into the correct tanks, that gauge caps are replaced before starting delivery and that all tank openings not being used for delivery are covered.
- Where required by company policies or government regulation, the tank truck vapour recovery system should be connected to the receiving storage tank prior to starting delivery.

During delivery

- Drivers should monitor the area near the receiving tank's vents for potential ignition sources and check that the vents operate properly during delivery.
- Drivers should remain where they can observe the delivery and be able to stop delivery or take other appropriate action in event of an emergency, such as ejection of liquid from vents or if an overfill device or tank vent alarm activates.

After delivery

- Storage tanks may be gauged after delivery to verify that specific tanks have received the correct products and the proper amount of products as indicated on the delivery ticket or record. Samples may be taken from the tanks after delivery for quality-control purposes.
- After delivery, spill containment devices should be drained if necessary and the correct fill and gauge caps and storage tank covers replaced on the proper tanks.

Other Service Station Functions

Storage of flammable and combustible liquids

Government regulations and company policies may control the storage, handling and dispensing of flammable and combustible liquids and automotive chemicals such as paints, starter fluids, antifreeze, battery acids, window washer fluids, solvents and lubricants in service stations. Service stations should store aerosols and flammable liquids in closed containers in approved, well-ventilated areas, away from sources of heat or ignition, in appropriate flammable liquid rooms, lockers or cabinets, or in separate, outside buildings.

Electrical safety and lighting

Service station employees should be familiar with electrical safety fundamentals applicable to service stations, such as the following:

- Lighting and electrical installations, equipment and fixtures of the proper electrical classification should be provided and maintained in accordance with codes and regulations and should not be replaced by equipment of lesser classification.
- Electric tools, water coolers, ice machines, refrigerators and similar electrical equipment should be properly grounded (earthed). Portable lights should be protected against breakage to minimize the chance that a spark might ignite flammable vapours in case bulbs break.

Adequate illumination should be provided at appropriate locations in service stations to reduce the potential for accidents and injuries. Government regulations, company policies or voluntary standards may be used to determine appropriate illumination levels. See table 102.2.

Lockout/tagout

Service stations should establish and implement lockout/tagout procedures to prevent the release of potentially hazardous energy while performing maintenance, repair and service work on electrical, mechanical, hydraulic and pneumatic powered tools, equipment, machinery and systems such as lifts, hoists and jacks, lubrication equipment, fuel-dispenser pumps and compressors. Safe work procedures to prevent the accidental start-up of vehicle engines during servicing or repair should include disconnecting the battery or removing the key from the ignition.

Service station fluids

Fluid and coolant levels

Before working under a hood (bonnet), employees should assure that it will stay open by testing the tension or using a rod or brace. Employees should exercise caution when checking vehicle engine fluids to avoid burns from exhaust manifolds and to prevent contact between dipsticks and electrical terminals or wires; care is also necessary when checking transmission fluid levels (since the engine must be running). Employees should follow safe work procedures when opening radiators, such as allowing pressurized radiators to cool and covering radiator caps with a heavy cloth when opening, using PPE and standing with face turned away from radiators so as to not inhale any escaping steam or vapours.

Table 102.2 • Illumination levels for service station areas.

Service station area	Suggested foot candles
Active traffic areas	20
Storage areas and stockrooms	10–20
Washrooms and waiting areas	30
Dispenser islands, work benches and cashier areas	50
Service, repair, lubrication and washing areas	100
Offices	100–150

Source: ANSI 1967.

Antifreeze and window washer fluids

Employees servicing vehicles should be aware of the hazards of both glycol and alcohol antifreezes and window washer fluid concentrates and how to safely handle them. This includes precautions such as storing alcohol-based products in tightly closed drums or packaged containers, in separate rooms or lockers, away from all heating equipment, and providing containment to prevent contamination of drains and ground in the event of a spill or leak of glycol-type antifreeze. Antifreeze or washer fluid should be dispensed from upright drums by using tightly connected hand pumps equipped with drip returns, rather than by using faucets or valves on horizontal drums, which may leak or be knocked open or broken off, causing spills. Air pressure should not be used to pump antifreeze or washer fluid concentrates from drums. Empty portable antifreeze and washer fluid concentrate containers should be completely drained prior to disposal, and applicable regulations governing the disposal of glycol antifreeze solutions should be followed.

Lubrication

Service stations should ensure that employees are aware of the characteristics and uses of the different fuels, oils, lubricants, greases, automotive fluids and chemicals available in the facility and their correct selection and application. The proper tools should be used to remove crankcase, transmission and differential drains, test plugs and oil filters so as to not damage vehicles or equipment. Pipe wrenches, extenders and chisels should be used only by employees who know how to safely remove frozen or rusted plugs. Because of the potential hazards involved, high-pressure lubricating equipment should not be started until the nozzles are set firmly against grease fittings. If testing is to be done prior to use, the nozzle should be aimed into an empty drum or similar receptacle, and not into a hand-held rag or cloth.

Lift operations

Employees working in and around vehicle service areas should be aware of unsafe conditions and follow safe work practices such as not standing in front of vehicles while they are being driven into service bays, over lubrication pits or onto lifts, or when vehicles are being lifted.

- Vehicles should be properly aligned on two-rail, free-wheel or frame-contact lifts, since an off-centre position may cause a vehicle to fall.
- Lifts should not be raised until occupants have left the vehicles and a check of overhead clearance has been made.
- Once the vehicle is in position, the emergency stop device should be set so the lift will not fall in the event of a pressure drop. If a lift is in a position where the emergency stop device cannot be engaged, blocks or safety stands should be placed under the lift or vehicle.
- A hydraulic lift may be equipped with a low-oil control valve, which prevents operation if the oil in the supply tank falls below a minimum level, since the lift can drop accidentally under those conditions.

When wheel-bearing lubrication, brake repair, tyre changing or other services are performed on free-wheel or frame-contact lifts, vehicles should be raised slightly above the floor to allow employees to work from a squatting position, to reduce the possibility of back strain. After vehicles are raised, the wheels should be blocked to prevent rolling, and safety stands should be placed underneath for support in case of jack or lift failure. When removing wheels from vehicles on drive-on lifts, the vehicles should be blocked securely to prevent rolling. If jacks or stands are used to lift and support vehicles, they should be of the proper capacity, placed at appropriate lift points on the vehicles and checked for stability.

Servicing tyres

Employees should be aware of how to safely check pressures and inflate tyres; tyres should be inspected for excessive wear, maximum tyre pressures should not be exceeded, and the worker should stand or kneel to the side and turn the face when inflating tyres. Employees should be aware of hazards and follow safe work practices when servicing wheels with multi-piece and single-piece rims and lock-ring-rim wheels on trucks and trailers. When repairing tyres with flammable or toxic patching compounds or liquids, precautions such as controlling ignition sources, using PPE and providing adequate ventilation, should be observed.

Parts cleaning

Service station employees should be aware of the fire and health hazards of using gasoline or low-flashpoint solvents to clean parts and should follow safe practices such as using approved solvents with a flashpoint above 60 °C. Parts washers should have a protective cover that is kept closed when the washer is not in use; when the washer is open, there should be a hold-open device such as fusible links, which allows the cover to close automatically in case of fire. Employees should take precautions so that gasoline or other flammable liquids do not contaminate the cleaning solvent and lower its flashpoint to create a fire hazard. Contaminated cleaning solvent should be removed and placed in approved containers for proper disposal or recycling. Employees who clean parts and equipment using cleaning solvents should avoid skin and eye contact and use appropriate PPE. Solvents should not be used for hand-washing and other personal hygiene.

Compressed air

Safe work practices should be established by service stations for the operation of air compressors and the use of compressed air. The air hoses should be used only for inflating tyres and for lubrication, maintenance and auxiliary services. Employees should be aware of the hazards of pressurizing fuel tanks, air horns, water tanks and other non-air pressure containers. Compressed air should not be used for cleaning or to blow residue from vehicle brake systems, since many brake linings, especially on older model vehicles, contain asbestos. Safer methods such as cleaning with vacuums or liquid solutions should be used.

Storage battery service and handling

Service stations should establish procedures to ensure that storage, handling and disposal of batteries and battery electrolyte fluids follow government regulations and company policies. Employees should be aware of the hazards of electrical short circuits when charging, removing, installing or handling batteries; disconnect the ground (negative) cable first before removing batteries; and reconnect the ground (negative) cable last when installing batteries. When removing and replacing batteries, a carrier may be used to facilitate lifting and to avoid touching the battery.

Employees should be aware of safe practices such as the following for handling battery solution:

- Containers of electrolyte solution should be stored at temperature ranges between 16 and 32 °C in safe areas where they cannot overturn. Any electrolyte solution spilled on the batteries or in the filling area should be flushed with water. Baking soda (sodium bicarbonate) may be used on spills, since it is an effective neutralizer for battery electrolyte solution.
- New batteries should be placed on the floor or work table when being filled with electrolyte solution, and the caps should be replaced prior to installation. New batteries should not be filled when they are inside vehicles.
- Face shields and chemical goggles, aprons and gloves may be used to minimize exposure to battery solution. Battery solution

should be handled and dispensed where a supply of potable water or eye wash fluid is available, in case the battery solution spills or contacts an employee's skin or eyes. Do not use neutralizing solutions on skin or eyes.

- When servicing batteries, corrosive particles which accumulate around the terminals should be brushed away, washed with clean water, neutralized with baking soda or other similar agents and prevented from contacting eyes or clothing.

Employees should check fluid levels in batteries prior to charging and periodically check them during charging to determine whether batteries are overheating. Chargers should be turned off before disconnecting cables from batteries, to avoid creating sparks which may ignite hydrogen gas generated during the charge. When "quick charging" batteries are installed in vehicles, the vehicles should be moved away from the fuel-dispensing islands, and the battery ground (negative) cables should be disconnected before connecting the charger units. If the batteries are located within passenger compartments or under vehicle floorboards, they should be removed before charging.

Employees should be familiar with the hazards and safe procedures to "jump start" vehicles that have dead batteries, in order to avoid electrical system damage or injury from exploding batteries if the jumper cables are hooked up incorrectly. Employees should never jump start or charge frozen batteries.

Driving vehicles and towing

Employees should be trained, qualified and have proper motor vehicle operator's licences to drive customer or company vehicles, service trucks or towing equipment either on or off the premises. All vehicles should be operated in compliance with government regulations and company policies. Operators should check the vehicle's brakes immediately, and vehicles with faulty brakes should not be driven. Employees operating tow trucks should be familiar with safe operating procedures, such as operating the hoist, checking the transmission and frame of the vehicle to be towed and not exceeding the tow truck's maximum lifting capacity.

Confined spaces in service stations

Service station employees should be aware of the hazards associated with entry into confined spaces such as aboveground and underground tanks, sumps, pump pits, waste containment tanks, septic tanks and environmental collection wells. Unauthorized entry should not be allowed, and confined-space entry permit procedures should be established that apply to both employee and contractor entrants.

Emergency procedures

Service stations should develop emergency procedures, and employees should know how to sound the alarms, how to notify authorities of emergencies when and how to evacuate and what appropriate response actions should be taken (such as shutting off emergency switches in the event of spills or fires in the dispensing pump areas). Service stations may establish security programmes to familiarize employees with robbery and violence prevention, depending on the service station's location, hours of operation and potential threats.

Service Station Health and Safety

Fire protection

Gasoline vapours are heavier than air and may travel long distances to reach sources of ignition when released during fuel filling, spills, overflows or repairs. Proper ventilation should be provided in enclosed areas to allow for dissipation of gasoline vapours. Fires may occur from spills and overflows when fuelling or servicing vehicles or delivering product into service station tanks, particularly if smoking is not restricted or if vehicle engines remain running during fuelling. To avoid fires, vehicles should be pushed away from spill areas or the spilled gasoline should be cleaned from under or around vehicles before starting their engines. Vehicles should not be permitted to enter or drive through spills.

Employees should be aware of other causes of fires in service stations, such as improper handling, transfer and storage of flammable and combustible liquids, accidental releases during fuel system repairs, electrostatic discharge when changing filters on gasoline dispensers and the use of improper or unprotected work lights. Draining gasoline from vehicle fuel tanks could be very hazardous due to the potential for release of fuel and vapours, especially in enclosed service areas when sources of ignition may be present.

Hot-work permits should be issued when work other than vehicle repair and servicing is performed which introduces sources of ignition in areas where flammable vapours may be present. Employees should be aware that carburettor priming should not be attempted while vehicle engines are running or being turned over with their starters, since flashbacks could ignite the fuel vapours. Employees should follow safe procedures, such as using starter fluid and not gasoline for priming carburettors and using clamps to hold the chokes open while attempting to start the engine.

Although government regulations or company policies may require the installation of fixed fire-protection systems, fire extinguishers are usually the primary means of fire protection in service stations. Service stations should provide fire extinguishers of the proper classification for the expected hazards. Fire extinguishers and fixed fire protection systems should be regularly inspected, maintained and serviced, and employees should know when, where and how to use the fire extinguishers and how to activate the fixed systems.

Service stations should install fuel-dispenser emergency shutdown controls at clearly identified and accessible locations and ensure that employees know the purpose, location and operation of these controls. To prevent spontaneous combustion, oily rags should be kept in covered metal containers until they are recycled or discarded.

Safety

Employee injuries at service stations may result from improper use of tools, equipment and ladders; not wearing PPE; falling or tripping; working in awkward positions; and lifting or carrying cases of materials incorrectly. Injuries and accidents may also occur from not following safe practices when working on hot radiators, transmissions, engines and exhaust systems, servicing tyres and batteries, and working with lifts, jacks, electrical equipment and machinery; from robbery and assault; and from improper use of or exposure to automotive cleaners, solvents and chemicals.

Service stations should develop and implement programmes to prevent accidents and incidents which can be attributed to problems associated with service station physical conditions, such as poor maintenance, storage and housekeeping practices. Other factors contributing toward accidents in service stations include employees' lack of attention, training or skills, which may result in the improper use of equipment, tools, automotive parts, supplies and maintenance materials. Figure 102.10 provides a safety checklist.

Robberies are a major safety hazard in service stations. Appropriate precautions and training are discussed in the accompanying box and elsewhere in this *Encyclopaedia*.

Figure 102.10 • Service station safety and health checklist.

This checklist may be used as a guide to the items which may be included in an assessment of service station fire protection, safety and health activities.

SAFETY AND HEALTH
- ❑ Record keeping and reporting
- ❑ Medical and first aid

EMPLOYEE TRAINING, EDUCATION AND QUALIFICATION
- ❑ Hazard awareness, prevention and protection
- ❑ Mechanical skills
- ❑ Emergency response
- ❑ Safe lifting practices
- ❑ Personal protective equipment
- ❑ Employee shoes, jewellery and clothing

FIRE PROTECTION AND PREVENTION
- ❑ Hot work
- ❑ Fire extinguishers
- ❑ Fixed protection systems
- ❑ Emergency shut-down switches
- ❑ Storage, handling and dispensing of flammable and combustible liquids in containers

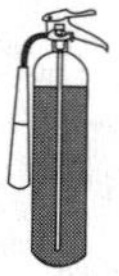

EMERGENCY PREPAREDNESS
- ❑ Emergency/incident response plan and procedures
- ❑ Emergency telephone numbers
- ❑ Emergency alarms, evacuation routes and exits

SAFETY, HEALTH, FIRE PREVENTION AND REGULATORY NOTICES, SIGNS AND LABELS
- ❑ Service station hazard communications
- ❑ Signs and notices

FUEL DISPENSER ISLAND
- ❑ Fuel island protection
- ❑ Fuel dispensing system
- ❑ Fuel spills and drainage
- ❑ Fueling vehicles
- ❑ Fueling motorcycles and small vehicles
- ❑ Filling portable fuel containers
- ❑ Cleaning windshields
- ❑ Checking lubricants, coolants and fluids levels

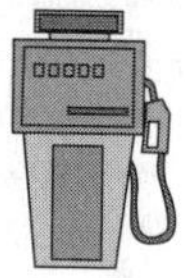

FUEL SAFETY
- ❑ Flammable liquid vapour hazards
- ❑ Priming carburettors

DELIVERY OPERATIONS
- ❑ Receiving and storing fuel
- ❑ Underground and aboveground storage tanks
- ❑ Storage-tank fill pipes and fill caps
- ❑ Storage-tank vents
- ❑ Inventory control

GENERAL SERVICE-BAY OPERATIONS
- ❑ Lift operations
- ❑ Oils, greases and fluids
- ❑ Lubrication service
- ❑ Filter replacement and disposal
- ❑ Draining oil and transmission fluid

REPAIRS AND MAINTENANCE OF VEHICLES AND EQUIPMENT
- ❑ Lockout/tagout
- ❑ Hand and power tools
- ❑ Fan belts, drive belts, etc.
- ❑ Exhaust system repairs and replacement
- ❑ Spark plugs, carburetor and fuel injection service and repair
- ❑ Compressed gas for welding, cutting and brazing
- ❑ Electric arc welding
- ❑ Bench or pedestal grinders
- ❑ Parts washers and fluids
- ❑ Spray-paint finishing operations
- ❑ Auto-body plastic resin fillers

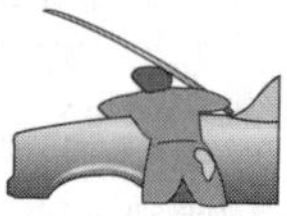

RADIATOR SERVICING
- ❑ Checking radiator coolant levels 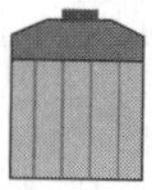
- ❑ Antifreeze storage, handling and disposal
- ❑ Radiator repair and replacement

AIR COMPRESSOR
- ❑ Air compressor operation, inspection and maintenance
- ❑ Air compressor hoses and nozzles

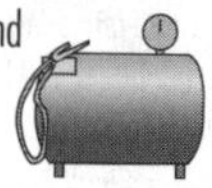

BRAKE SERVICE
- ❑ Asbestos awareness
- ❑ Improper use of air for cleaning

BATTERY SERVICE
- ❑ Battery storage and handling
- ❑ Battery charging
- ❑ Battery jumper cables and jump starting
- ❑ Battery fluids
- ❑ Battery removal and installation

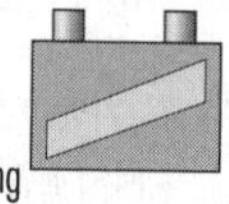

MISCELLANEOUS WORKPLACE SAFETY AND HEALTH
- ❑ Car wash operations
- ❑ Driving customers' vehicles
- ❑ Tow truck operations

TYRE SERVICING
- ❑ Checking and inflating tyres
- ❑ Removing wheels
- ❑ Repairing and mounting tyres
- ❑ Tyre rack and storage
- ❑ Truck tyres
- ❑ Tyre balancing and alignment

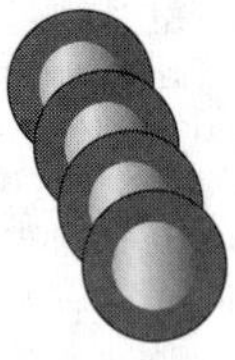

PHYSICAL CONDITIONS
- ❑ Housekeeping, maintenance and physical conditions
- ❑ Lighting
- ❑ Handling and storing merchandise
- ❑ Snow, ice and rainwater removal
- ❑ Heating, ventilation and air conditioning equipment
- ❑ Ventilation of vapours and exhaust gases
- ❑ Ladders
- ❑ Confined spaces in service stations
- ❑ Electrical safety
- ❑ Safe food handling and storage (where applicable)
- ❑ Washrooms and sanitation

ENVIRONMENTAL
- ❑ Spills, clean-up and disposal
- ❑ Handling used oil, fluids, filters and batteries
- ❑ Hazardous waste storage, handling and recycling or disposal

Health

Employees should be aware of health hazards associated with working in service stations, such as the following:

Carbon monoxide. Internal combustion engine exhaust gases contain carbon monoxide, a highly toxic, odourless and colourless gas. Employees should be aware of the dangers of exposure to carbon monoxide, particularly when vehicles are inside service bays, garages or car washes with their engines running. Vehicle exhaust gases should be piped outside through flexible hoses, and ventilation should be provided to assure an adequate supply of fresh air. Fuel oil appliances and heaters should be checked to assure that carbon monoxide is not vented to inside areas.

Toxicity of petroleum fuels. Employees who come in contact with gasoline, diesel fuel, heating oil or kerosene should be aware of the potential hazards of exposure and know how to handle these fuels safely. Inhaling sufficient concentrations of petroleum fuel vapours for extended periods of time may result in mild intoxication, anaesthesia or more serious conditions. Short exposure to high concentrations will cause dizziness, headaches and nausea, and irritate the eyes, nose and throat. Gasoline, solvents or fuel oils should never be siphoned from containers or tanks by mouth, since the toxicity of low viscosity liquid hydrocarbons aspired directly into the lungs is 200 times greater than if they are ingested. Aspiration into the lungs may cause pneumonia with extensive pulmonary oedema and haemorrhage, leading to serious

Violence in gasoline stations

Gasoline station workers rank fourth among US occupations with the highest rates of occupational homicides, with almost all occurring during attempted armed robberies or other crimes (NIOSH 1993b). The recent trend to replace repair shops with convenience stores has made them even more of a target. Study of the circumstances involved has led to the delineation of the following risk factors for such criminal violence:

- exchange of money with the public
- working alone or in small numbers
- working late night or early morning hours
- working in high-crime areas
- guarding valuable property or possessions
- working in community settings.

An additional risk factor is being in locations that are readily accessible and particularly suited to quick getaways.

To defend themselves against attempted robberies, some gasoline station workers have provided themselves with baseball bats or other cudgels and even acquired firearms. Most police authorities oppose such measures, arguing that they are likely to provoke violent reactions on the part of the criminals. The following preventive measures are suggested as more effective deterrents of robbery attempts:

- bright lighting of the gasoline pump and parking areas and of the interiors of stores and cashier's areas
- large, unobstructed, bullet-resistant windows to enhance the visibility of the interior of the store and enclosures of bullet-resistant glass for the cashier

- separate outside entrances to any public rest rooms so that persons using them do not have to enter the store. (A separate, indoor, employee-only rest room would provide privacy for employees and obviate the need for them to go outside to use the public restroom.)
- provision of drop-boxes and time-release safes to hold all but a very limited amount of cash, as well as highly visible signs indicating their use
- establishing a policy of not making change for cash purchases during night and early morning hours
- hiring an additional worker or a security guard so that the worker is never alone (operators of gasoline stations and convenience stores object to the additional cost)
- installing an electrical or electronic alarm system (triggered by easily accessed "panic" buttons) that will provide audible and visual distress signals to attract police or other assistance—this can be combined with an alarm wired directly to a local police station
- installing high-fidelity television monitors to assist in identifying and, ultimately, apprehending the perpetrator(s).

Consultation with local police authorities and crime-prevention experts will assist in the selection of the most appropriate and cost-effective deterrents. It must be remembered that the equipment should be properly installed and periodically tested and maintained, and that the workers must be trained in its use.

Leon J. Warshaw

---

injury or death. Vomiting should not be induced. Immediate medical assistance should be sought.

Benzene. Service station employees should be aware of the potential hazards of benzene, which is found in gasoline, and avoid inhaling gasoline vapours. Although gasoline contains benzene, low-level exposure to gasoline vapours is unlikely to cause cancer. Numerous scientific studies have shown that service station employees are not exposed to excessive levels of benzene during the course of their normal work activities; however, there is always the possibility that overexposure could occur.

Dermatitis hazards. Employees who handle and come into contact with petroleum products as part of their jobs should be aware of the hazards of dermatitis and other skin disorders and the personal hygiene and personal protective measures needed to control exposure. If eye contact with gasoline, lubricants or antifreeze occurs, the eyes should be flushed with clean, lukewarm potable water, and medical assistance should be provided.

Lubricants, used motor oil and automotive chemicals. Employees who change oil and other motor vehicle fluids, including antifreeze, should be aware of the hazards and know how to minimize exposure to products such as gasoline in used motor oil, glycol in antifreeze and other contaminants in transmission fluids and gear lubricants by the use of PPE and good hygiene practices. If high-pressure lubricating guns are discharged against an employee's body, the affected area should be examined immediately to see if petroleum products have penetrated the skin. These injuries cause little pain or bleeding, but involve almost instant separation of the skin tissues and possible deeper damage, which should receive immediate medical attention. The attending physician should be informed of the cause and the product involved in the injury.

Welding. Welding, besides being a fire hazard, can involve exposure to lead pigments from welding on car exteriors, as well as metal fumes and welding gases. Local exhaust ventilation or respiratory protection is needed.

Spray painting and auto body fillers. Spray painting can involve exposure to solvent vapours and pigment particulates (e.g., lead chromate). Auto body fillers often are epoxy or polyester resins and can involve skin and respiratory hazards. Drive-in spray booths for spray painting, local exhaust ventilation and skin and eye protection are recommended while using auto body fillers.

Storage batteries. Batteries contain corrosive electrolyte solutions of sulphuric acid that can cause burns and other injuries to the eyes or skin. Exposure to battery solution should be minimized by the use of PPE, including rubber gloves and eye protection. Employees should immediately flush electrolyte solution from the eyes or skin with clean potable water or eye wash fluid for at least 15 minutes and seek immediate medical attention. Employees should thoroughly wash their hands after servicing batteries and keep their hands away from the face and eyes. Employees should be aware that overcharging batteries can create explosive and toxic quantities of hydrogen gas. Because of the potential harmful effects of exposure to lead, used storage batteries should be properly disposed of or recycled in accordance with government regulations or company policies.

Asbestos. Employees who check and service brakes should be aware of the hazards of asbestos, know how to recognize whether brake shoes contain asbestos and take appropriate protective measures to reduce exposure and contain waste for proper disposal (see figure 102.11).

Personal protective equipment (PPE)

Injuries to employees may occur from contact with automotive fuels, solvents and chemicals or from chemical burns caused by exposure to battery acids or caustic solutions. Service station employees should be familiar with the need to use and wear PPE such as the following:

Figure 102.11 • Portable enclosure for preventing exposure to asbestos dust from brake drums. It is equipped with an enclosed compressed-air gun with a cotton sleeve and is connected to a HEPA vacuum cleaner.

Courtesy of Nilfisk of America, Inc.

- Work shoes with oil- and slip-resistant soles should be worn for general work in service stations, and approved protective-toe safety shoes with oil/slip-resistant soles should be worn where there is a danger of foot injuries due to rolling or falling objects or equipment.
- Safety goggles and respiratory protection should be used for protection against exposures to chemicals, dust or steam, such as when painting or working around batteries and radiators. Industrial safety glasses or face shields with goggles should be worn when the potential exists for exposure to impact materials, such as working with grinders or wire buffers, repairing or mounting tyres, or replacing exhaust systems. Welding glasses should be worn when cutting or welding to prevent flash burns and injuries from particles.
- Impervious gloves, aprons, footwear, face shields and chemical goggles should be worn when handling automotive chemicals and solvents, battery acid and caustic solutions and when cleaning up chemical or fuel spills. Leather work gloves should be worn when handling sharp objects such as broken glass, motor vehicle parts or tyre rims and while emptying trash cans.
- Head protection may be needed when working beneath vehicles in pits or changing overhead signage or lights and in other areas where a potential exists for injury to the head.

- Employees working on vehicles should not wear rings, wristwatches, bracelets or long chains, since the jewellery may contact the vehicle's moving parts or electrical system and cause injury.

To prevent fires, dermatitis or chemical burns to the skin, clothing that is soaked with gasoline, antifreeze or oil should be immediately removed in an area or room with good ventilation and where no sources of ignition, such as electric heaters, engines, cigarettes, lighters or electric hand dryers, are present. The affected areas of the skin should then be thoroughly washed with soap and warm water to remove all traces of contamination. Clothing should be air dried outside or in well-ventilated areas away from sources of ignition before laundering to minimize contamination of wastewater systems.

Service Station Environmental Issues

Storage tank inventory control

Service stations should maintain and reconcile accurate inventory records on all gasoline and fuel oil storage tanks on a regular basis to control losses. Manual stick gauging may be used to provide a check of the integrity of underground storage tanks and connecting pipes. Where automatic gauging or leak detection equipment is installed, its accuracy should be verified regularly by manual stick gauging. Any storage tank or system suspected of leaking should be investigated, and if leakage is detected, the tank should be made safe or emptied and repaired, removed or replaced. Service station employees should be aware that leaking gasoline can travel long distances underground, contaminate water supplies, enter sewer and drainage systems and cause fires and explosions.

Handling and disposal of waste materials

Waste lubricants and automotive chemicals, used motor oil and solvents, spilled gasoline and fuel oil and glycol-type antifreeze solutions should be drained into approved, properly labelled tanks or containers and stored until disposed of or recycled in accordance with government regulations and company policies.

Because engines with worn cylinders or other defects may allow small amounts of gasoline to enter their crankcases, precautions are needed to prevent vapours which could be released from tanks and containers with crankcase drainings from reaching sources of ignition.

Used oil filters and transmission fluid filters should be drained of oil prior to disposal. Used fuel filters which have been removed from vehicles or fuel dispenser pumps should be drained into approved containers and stored in well-ventilated locations away from sources of ignition until dry before disposal.

Used battery-electrolyte containers should be thoroughly rinsed with water before discarding or recycling. Used batteries contain lead and should be properly disposed of or recycled.

Cleaning large spills may require special training and PPE. Recovered spilled fuel may be returned to the terminal or bulk plant or otherwise disposed of according to government regulations or company policy. Lubricants, used oil, grease, antifreeze, spilled fuel and other materials should not be swept, washed or flushed into floor drains, sinks, toilets, sewers, sumps or other drains or the street. Accumulated grease and oil should be removed from floor drains and sumps to prevent these materials from flowing into sewers. Asbestos dust and used asbestos brake linings should be handled and disposed of according to government regulations and company policies. Employees should be aware of the environmental impact and potential health, safety and fire hazards of these wastes.

● RAIL OPERATIONS

Neil McManus

Railroads provide a major mode of transportation around the world. Today, even with competition from road and airborne transport, rail remains an important means of land-based movement of bulk quantities of goods and materials. Railroad operations are carried out in an enormously wide variety of terrains and climates, from Arctic permafrost to equatorial jungle, from rainforest to desert. The roadbed of partly crushed stone (ballast) and track consisting of steel rails and ties of wood, concrete or steel are common to all railroads. Ties and ballast maintain the position of the rails.

The source of power used in railroad operations worldwide (steam, diesel-electric and current electricity) spans the history of development of this mode of transportation.

Administration and Train Operations

Administration and train operations create the public profile of the railroad industry. They ensure that goods move from origin to destination. Administration includes office personnel involved in business and technical functions and management. Train operations include dispatchers, rail traffic control, signal maintainers, train crews and yard workers.

Dispatchers ensure that a crew is available at the appropriate point and time. Railroads operate 24 hours per day, 7 days per week throughout the year. Rail traffic control personnel coordinate train movements. Rail traffic control is responsible for assigning track to trains in the appropriate sequence and time. This function is complicated by single sets of track that must be shared by trains moving in both directions. Since only one train can occupy a particular section of track at any time, rail traffic control must assign occupancy of the main line and sidings, in a manner that assures safety and minimizes delay.

Signals provide visual cues to train operators, as well as to drivers of road vehicles at level train crossings. For train operators, signals must provide unambiguous messages about the status of the track ahead. Signals today are used as an adjunct to rail traffic control, the latter being conducted by radio on channels received by all operating units. Signal maintainers must ensure operation of these units at all times, which can sometimes involve working alone in remote areas in all weather at any time, day or night.

Yard workers' duties include ensuring that the rolling stock is prepared to receive cargo, which is an increasingly important function in this era of quality management. Tri-level automobile transporter cars, for example, must be cleaned prior to use and readied to accept vehicles by moving chocks to appropriate positions. The distance between levels in these cars is too short for the average male to stand upright, so that work is done in a hunched over position. Similarly, the handholds on some cars force yard workers to assume an awkward posture during shunting operations.

For long runs, a train crew operates the train between designated transfer points. A replacement crew takes over at the transfer point and continues the journey. The first crew must wait at the transfer point for another train to make the return trip. The combined trips and the wait for the return train can consume many hours.

A train trip on single track can be very fragmented, in part because of problems in scheduling, track work and the breakdown of equipment. Occasionally a crew returns home in the cab of a trailing locomotive, in the caboose (where still in use) or even by taxi or bus.

The train crew's duties may include dropping off some cars or picking up additional ones en route. This could occur at any hour of the day or night under any imaginable weather conditions. The assembly and disassembly of trains are the sole duties of some train crews in yards.

On occasion there is a failure of one of the knuckles that couple cars together or a break in a hose that carries braking system air between cars. This necessitates investigative work by one of the train crew and repair or replacement of the defective part. The spare knuckle (about 30 kg) must be carried along the roadbed to the repair point, and the original removed and replaced. Work between cars must reflect careful planning and preparation to ensure that the train does not move during the procedure.

In mountainous areas, breakdown may occur in a tunnel. The locomotive must maintain power above idle under these conditions in order to keep the braking functional and to prevent train runaway. Running the engine in a tunnel could cause the tunnel to fill with exhaust gases (nitrogen dioxide, nitric oxide, carbon monoxide and sulphur dioxide).

Table 102.3 summarizes potential hazardous conditions associated with administration and train operations.

Maintenance of Rolling Stock and Track Equipment

Rolling stock includes locomotives and railcars. Track equipment is specialized equipment used for track patrol and maintenance, construction and rehabilitation. Depending on the size of the railroad, maintenance can range from onsite (small-scale repairs) to complete stripdown and rebuilding. Rolling stock must not fail in operation, since failure carries serious adverse safety, environmental and business consequences. If a car carries a hazardous commodity, the consequences that can arise from failure to find and repair a mechanical defect can be enormous.

Larger rail operations have running shops and centralized stripdown and rebuild facilities. Rolling stock is inspected and prepared for the trip at running shops. Minor repair is performed on both cars and locomotives.

Railcars are rigid structures that have pivot points near each end. The pivot point accepts a vertical pin located in the *truck* (the wheels and their support structure). The body of the car is lifted from the truck for repairs. Minor repair can involve the body of the car or attachments or brakes or other parts of the truck. Wheels may require machining on a lathe to remove flat spots.

Major repair could include removal and replacement of damaged or corroded metal sheeting or frame and abrasive blasting and repainting. It could also include removal and replacement of wooden flooring. Trucks, including wheel-axle sets and bearings, may require disassembly and rebuilding. Rehabilitation of truck castings involves build-up welding and grinding. Rebuilt wheel-axle sets require machining to true the assembly.

Locomotives are cleaned and inspected prior to each trip. The locomotive may also require mechanical service. Minor repairs include oil changes, work on brakes and servicing of the diesel engine. Removal of a truck for wheel truing or evening may also be needed. Operation of the engine may be required in order to position the locomotive inside the service building or to remove it from the building. Prior to re-entry into service the locomotive could require a load test, during which the engine is operated at full throttle. Mechanics work in close proximity to the engine during this procedure.

Subways

While railroad safety comes under the jurisdiction of national governments, which issue rules and policies for safety governance and enforcement, subways are usually governed by local public authorities, which in essence govern themselves.

Subway fares usually do not cover operating cost and, through subsidies, are kept at certain levels to maintain an affordable public transportation service. Subway and other city mass transit systems make city roads more accessible and reduce the pollution associated with urban automobile traffic.

Budget cuts that have become so common in many countries in recent years also affect mass transit systems. Preventive maintenance personnel and the upgrade of tracks, signals and rolling stock are the first to be affected. The controlling authorities are often unwilling or unable to enforce their own regulatory procedures on a rapid transit system abandoned by government subsidies. Inevitably in such circumstances, a transportation accident with catastrophic loss of life during the budget cuts results in a public outcry demanding improvements in safety.

While it is recognized that great variation exists in the design, construction and age of the physical facilities of the rapid transit properties in Canada, the United States and other countries, certain standard maintenance functions must be carried out to keep operating track, aerial and underground structures, passenger stations and related facilities in the safest possible condition.

Subway Operation and Maintenance

Subways differ from railroads in several basic ways:
- most subways run underground in tunnels
- subways run on electricity rather than diesel or steam (although there are also some electrical trains)
- subways run much more frequently than railroad trains
- graffiti removal is a major problem.

These factors influence the degree of risk for subway train operators and maintenance crews.

Collisions between subway trains on the same track and with maintenance crews on the track are a serious problem. These collisions are controlled by proper scheduling, central communications systems to alert subway train operators of problems and signal light systems indicating when operators can proceed safely. Break-downs in these control procedures resulting in collisions can occur due to radio communication problems, broken or improperly placed signal lights that do not give operators adequate time to stop and fatigue problems from shift work and excessive overtime, resulting in inattention.

Maintenance crews patrol the subway tracks doing repairs to tracks, signal lights and other equipment, picking up rubbish and performing other duties. They face electrical hazards from the third rail carrying the electricity to operate the subways, fire and smoke hazards from burning rubbish and possible electrical fires, inhalation hazards from steel dust and other particulates in the air from the subway wheels and rails and the hazard of being hit by subway cars. Floods in subways can also create electrical shock and fire hazards. Because of the nature of subway tunnels, many of these hazardous situations are confined-space hazards.

Adequate ventilation to remove air contaminants, proper confined-space and other emergency procedures (e.g., evacuation procedures) for fires and floods and adequate communication procedures including radios and signal lights to notify subway train operators of the presence of maintenance crews on the tracks are essential to protect these crews. There should be frequent emergency spaces along subway walls or adequate space between tracks to allow maintenance crew members to avoid passing subway cars.

Graffiti removal from both the inside and outside of subway cars is a hazard in addition to regular painting and cleaning of cars. Graffiti removers often contained strong alkalis and hazardous solvents and can be a hazard both by skin contact and inhalation. Exterior graffiti removal is done by driving the cars through a car wash where the chemicals are sprayed on the exterior of the car. The chemicals are also applied by brushing and spraying inside subway cars. Applying hazardous graffiti removers inside cars could be a confined-space hazard.

Precautions include using the least toxic chemicals possible, proper respirator protection and other personal protective equipment and proper procedures to ensure that car operators know what chemicals are being used.

George J. McDonald

Major servicing could involve complete stripdown of the locomotive. The diesel engine and engine compartment, compressor, generator and traction motors require thorough degreasing and cleaning owing to heavy service and contact of fuel and lubricants with hot surfaces. Individual components may then be stripped and rebuilt.

Traction motor casings may require build-up welding. Armatures and rotors may need machining in order to remove old insulation, then be repaired and impregnated with a solution of varnish.

Track maintenance equipment includes trucks and other equipment that can operate on road and rail, as well as specialized equipment that operates only on rail. The work may include highly specialized units, such as track inspection units or rail-grinding machines, which may be "one of a kind", even in large railroad companies. Track maintenance equipment may be serviced in garage settings or in field locations. The engines in this equipment may produce considerable exhaust emissions due to long periods between service and lack of familiarity of mechanics. This can have major pollution consequences during operation in confined spaces, such as tunnels and sheds and enclosing formations.

Table 102.4 summarizes potential hazardous conditions associated with maintenance of rolling stock and track equipment as well as transportation accidents.

Maintenance of Track and Right of Way

Maintenance of track and right of way primarily involves work in the outdoor environment in conditions associated with the outdoors: sun, rain, snow, wind, cold air, hot air, blowing sand, biting and stinging insects, aggressive animals, snakes and poisonous plants.

Track and right-of-way maintenance can include track patrol, as well as the maintenance, rehabilitation and replacement of buildings and structures, track and bridges, or service functions, such as snowplowing and herbicide application, and may involve local operating units or large, specialized work gangs that deal with replacement of rails, ballast or ties. Equipment is available to almost completely mechanize each of these activities. Small-scale

Table 102.3 • Hazardous conditions associated with administration and train operations.

Conditions	Affected groups	Comments
Exhaust emissions	Train crew, supervisors, technical advisors	Emissions primarily include nitrogen dioxide, nitric oxide, carbon monoxide, sulphur dioxide and particulates containing polycyclic aromatic hydrocarbons (PAHs). Potential for exposure is most likely in unventilated tunnels.
Noise	Train crew, supervisors, technical advisors	In-cab noise could exceed regulated limits.
Whole-body vibration	Train crew	Structure-borne vibration transmitted through the floor and seats in the cab originates from the engine and motion along the track and over gaps between rails.
Electromagnetic fields	Train crew, signal maintainers	AC and DC fields are possible, depending on design of power unit and traction motors.
Radio-frequency fields	Users of two-way radios	Effects on humans are not fully established.
Weather	Train crew, yard workers, signal maintainers	Ultraviolet energy can cause sunburn, skin cancer and cataracts. Cold can cause cold stress and frostbite. Heat can cause heat stress.
Shiftwork	Dispatchers, rail traffic control, train crews, signal maintainers	Train crews can work irregular hours; remuneration is often based on travelling a fixed distance within a time period.
Musculoskeletal injury	Train crew, yard workers	Ankle injury can occur during disembarkment from moving equipment. Shoulder injury can occur during embarkment onto moving equipment. Injury can occur at various sites while carrying knuckles on rough terrain. Work is performed in awkward postures.
Video displays units	Management, administrative and technical staff, dispatchers, rail traffic control	Effective use of computerized workstations depends on application of visual and office ergonomic principles.
Rundown accidents	All workers	Rundown can occur when the individual stands on an active track and fails to hear approach of trains, track equipment and moving cars.

work, however, could involve small, powered equipment units or even be a completely manual activity.

In order to carry out maintenance of operating lines, a block of time must be available during which the work can occur. The block could become available at any time of day or night, depending on train scheduling, especially on a single-track main line. Thus, time pressure is a main consideration during this work, since the line must be returned to service at the end of the assigned block of time. Equipment must proceed to the site, the work must be completed, and the track vacated within the set period.

Ballast replacement and tie and rail replacement are complex tasks. Ballast replacement first involves removal of contaminated or deteriorated material in order to expose the track. A sled, a plow-like unit that is pulled by a locomotive, or an undercutter performs this task. The undercutter uses a continuous toothed chain to pull ballast to the side. Other equipment is used to remove and replace rail spikes or tie clips, tie plates (the metal plate on which the rail sits on the tie) and ties. Continuous rail is akin to a noodle of wet spaghetti that can flex and whip and that is easily moved vertically and laterally. Ballast is used to stabilize the rail. The ballast train delivers new ballast and pushes it into position. Labourers walk along with the train and systematically open chutes located at the bottom of the cars in order to enable ballast to flow.

After the ballast is dropped, a tamper uses hydraulic fingers to pack the ballast around and under the ties and lifts the track. A spud liner drives a metal spike into the roadbed as an anchor and moves the track into the desired position. The ballast regulator grades the ballast to establish the final contours of the roadbed and sweeps clean the surface of the ties and rails. Considerable dust is generated during ballast dumping, regulating and sweeping.

There are a variety of settings in which track work can take place—open areas, semi-enclosed areas such as cuts, and hill and cliff faces and confined spaces, such as tunnels and sheds. These have a profound influence on working conditions. Enclosed spaces, for example, will confine and concentrate exhaust emissions, ballast dust, dust from grinding, fumes from thermite welding, noise and other hazardous agents and conditions. (Thermite welding uses powdered aluminium and iron oxide. Upon ignition the aluminium burns intensely and converts the iron oxide to molten iron. The molten iron flows into the gap between the rails, welding them together end to end.)

Switching structures are associated with track. The switch contains moveable, tapered rails (points) and a wheel guide (frog). Both are manufactured from specially hardened steel containing a high level of manganese and chromium. The frog is an assembled structure containing several pieces of specially bent rail. The self-locking nuts which are used to bolt together these and other track structures may be cadmium-plated. Frogs are built up by welding and are ground during refurbishing, which can occur onsite or in shop facilities.

Bridge repainting is also an important part of right-of-way maintenance. Bridges often are situated in remote locations; this can considerably complicate provision of personal hygiene facilities which are needed to prevent contamination of individuals and the environment.

Table 102.5 summarizes the hazards of track and right-of-way maintenance.

Transportation Accidents

Possibly the greatest single concern in rail operations is the transportation accident. The large quantities of material that could be involved could cause serious problems of exposure of personnel and the environment. No amount of preparation for a worst-case accident is ever enough. Therefore, minimizing risk and the consequences of an accident are imperative. Transportation accidents occur for a variety of reasons: collisions at level crossings, obstruction of the track, failure of equipment and operator error.

The potential for such accidents can be minimized through conscientious and ongoing inspection and maintenance of track and right-of-way and equipment. The impact of a transportation accident involving a train carrying mixed cargo can be minimized through strategic positioning of cars that carry incompatible freight. Such strategic positioning, however, is not possible for a train hauling a single commodity. Commodities of particular concern include: pulverized coal, sulphur, liquefied petroleum (fuel) gases, heavy metal concentrates, solvents and process chemicals.

All of the groups in a rail organization are involved in transportation accidents. Rehabilitation activities can literally involve all groups working simultaneously at the same location on the site. Thus, coordination of these activities is extremely important, so that the actions of one group do not interfere with those of another.

Hazardous commodities generally remain contained during such accidents because of the attention given to crashproofing in the design of shipping containers and bulk rail cars. During an accident, the contents are removed from the damaged car by emergency response crews that represent the shipper. Equipment maintainers repair the damage to the extent possible and put the car back on the track, if possible. However, the track under the derailed car may have been destroyed. If so, repair or replacement of track occurs next, using prefabricated sections and techniques similar to those described above.

In some situations, loss of containment occurs and the contents of the car or shipping container spill onto the ground. If substances are shipped in quantities sufficient to require placarding because of transportation laws, they are readily identifiable on shipping manifests. However, highly hazardous substances that are shipped in smaller quantities than mandated for listing in a

Table 102.4 • Hazardous conditions associated with maintenance and transportation accidents.

Conditions	Affected groups	Comments
Skin contamination with waste oils and lubricants	Diesel mechanics, traction motor mechanics	Decomposition of hydrocarbons in contact with hot surfaces can produce polycyclic aromatic hydrocarbons (PAHs).
Exhaust emissions	All workers in diesel shop, wash facility, refuelling area, load test area	Emissions primarily include nitrogen dioxide, nitric oxide, carbon monoxide, sulphur dioxide and particulates containing (PAHs). Potential for exposure most likely where exhaust emissions are confined by structures.
Welding emissions	Welders, tackers, fitters, operators of overhead cranes	Work primarily involves carbon steel; aluminium and stainless steel are possible. Emissions include shield gases and fluxes, metal fumes, ozone, nitrogen dioxide, visible and ultraviolet energy.
Brazing emissions	Electricians working on traction motors	Emission include cadmium end lead in solder.
Thermal decomposition products from coatings	Welders, tackers, fitters, grinders, operators of overhead cranes	Emissions can include carbon monoxide, inorganic pigments containing lead and other chromates, decomposition products from paint resins. PCBs may have been used prior to 1971. PCBs can form furans and dioxins when heated.
Cargo residues	Welders, fitters, tackers, grinders, mechanics, strippers	Residues reflect service in which car was used; cargoes could include heavy metal concentrates, coal, sulphur, lead ingots, etc.
Abrasive blasting dust	Abrasive blaster, bystanders	Dust can contain cargo residues, blast material, paint dust. Paint applied prior to 1971 may contain PCBs.
Solvent vapours	Painter, bystanders	Solvent vapours can be present in paint storage and mixing areas and paint booth; flammable mixtures may develop inside confined spaces, such as hoppers and tanks, during spraying.
Paint aerosols	Painter, bystanders	Paint aerosols contain sprayed paint plus diluent; solvent in droplets and vapour can form flammable mixtures; resin system can include isocyanates, epoxys, amines, peroxides and other reactive intermediates.
Confined spaces	All shop workers	Interior of some railcars, tanks and hoppers, nose of locomotive, ovens, degreasers, varnish impregnator, pits, sumps and other enclosed and partially enclosed structures
Noise	All shop workers	Noise generated by many sources and tasks can exceed regulated limits.
Hand-arm vibration	Users of powered hand tools and hand-held equipment	Vibration is transmitted through hand grips.
Electromagnetic fields	Users of electrical welding equipment	AC and DC fields are possible, depending on design of the unit.
Weather	Outside workers	Ultraviolet energy can cause sunburn, skin cancer and cataracts. Cold can cause cold stress and frostbite. Heat can cause heat stress.
Shiftwork	All workers	Crews can work irregular hours.
Musculoskeletal injury	All workers	Ankle injury can occur during disembarkment from moving equipment. Shoulder injury can occur during embarkment onto moving equipment or climbing onto cars. Work is performed in awkward posture especially when welding, burning, cutting and operating powered hand tools.
Rundown accidents	All workers	Rundown can occur when the individual stands on active track and fails to hear approach of track equipment and moving cars.

Table 102.5 • Hazardous conditions associated with maintenance on track and right of way.

Condition	Affected group(s)	Comments
Exhaust emissions	All workers	Emissions include nitrogen dioxide, nitric oxide, carbon monoxide, sulphur dioxide and particulates containing polycyclic aromatic hydrocarbons (PAHs). Potential for exposure is most likely in unventilated tunnels and other circumstances where exhaust is confined by structures.
Ballast dust/spilled cargo	Track equipment operators, labourers	Depending on the source, ballast dust can contain silica (quartz), heavy metals or asbestos. Track work around operations that produce and handle bulk commodities can cause exposure to these products: coal, sulphur, heavy metal concentrates, etc.
Welding, cutting and grinding emissions	Field and shop welders	Welding primarily involves hardened steel; emissions can include shield gases and fluxes, metal fumes, ozone, nitrogen dioxide, carbon monoxide, ultraviolet and visible energy. Exposure to manganese and chromium can occur during work involving rail; cadmium may occur in plated nuts and bolts.
Abrasive blasting dust	Abrasive blaster, bystanders	Dust contains blast material and paint dust; paint likely contains lead and other chromates.
Solvent vapours	Painter, bystanders	Solvent vapours can be present in paint storage and mixing areas; flammable mixtures could develop inside enclosed spray structure during spraying.
Paint aerosols	Painter, bystanders	Paint aerosols contain sprayed paint plus diluent; solvent in droplets and vapour can form flammable mixture; resin system can include isocyanates, epoxys, amines, peroxides and other reactive intermediates.
Confined spaces	All workers	Interior of tunnels, culverts, tanks, hoppers, pits, sumps and other enclosed and partially enclosed structures
Noise	All workers	Noise generated by many sources and tasks can exceed regulated limits.
Whole-body vibration	Truck drivers, track equipment operators	Structure-borne vibration transmitted through the floor and seat in the cab originates from the engine and motion along roads and track and over gaps between rails.
Hand-arm vibration	Users of powered hand tools and hand-held equipment	Vibration transmitted through hand grips
Electromagnetic fields	Users of electrical welding equipment	AC and DC fields are possible, depending on design of the unit.
Radio-frequency fields	Users of two-way radios	Effects on humans not fully established
Weather-related	Outside workers	Ultraviolet energy can cause sunburn, skin cancer and cataracts; cold can cause cold stress and frostbite; heat can cause heat stress.
Shiftwork	All workers	Gangs work irregular hours due to problems in scheduling blocks of track time.
Musculoskeletal injury	All workers	Ankle injury during disembark from moving equipment; shoulder injury during embark onto moving equipment; work in awkward posture, especially when welding and operating powered hand tools
Rundown accident	All workers	Rundown can occur when the individual stands on active track and fails to hear approach of track equipment, trains and moving cars.

shipping manifest can escape identification and characterization for a considerable period. Containment at the site and collection of the spilled material are the responsibility of the shipper.

Railway personnel can be exposed to materials that remain in snow, soil or vegetation during rehabilitation efforts. The severity of exposure depends on the properties and quantity of the substance, the geometry of the site and weather conditions. The situation could also pose fire, explosion, reactivity and toxic hazards to humans, animals and the surrounding environment.

At some point following the accident, the site must be cleared so that the track can be put back into service. Transfer of cargo and repair of equipment and track may still be required.

These activities could be dramatically complicated by the loss of containment and the presence of spilled material. Any action taken to address this type of situation requires considerable prior planning that includes input from specialized knowledgeable professionals.

Hazards and Precautions

Tables 102.3, 102.4 and 102.5 summarize the hazardous conditions associated with the various groups of workers involved in railroad operations. Table 102.6 summarizes the types of precautions used to control these hazardous conditions.

Table 102.6 • Railway industry approaches to controlling hazardous conditions.

Hazardous conditions	Comments/control measures
Exhaust emissions	Locomotives have no exhaust stack. Exhaust discharges vertically from the top surface. Cooling fans also located on the top of the locomotive can direct exhaust-contaminated air into the airspace of tunnels and buildings. In-cab exposure during normal transit through a tunnel does not exceed exposure limits. Exposure during stationary operations in tunnels, such as investigation of mechanical problems, rerailing of derailed cars or track repair, can considerably exceed exposure limits. Stationary operation in shops also can create significant overexposure. Track maintenance and construction equipment and heavy vehicles usually have vertical exhaust stacks. Low-level discharge or discharge through horizontal deflectors can cause overexposure. Small vehicles and portable gasoline-powered equipment discharge exhaust downward or have no stack. Proximity to these sources can cause overexposure. Control measures include: · extended exhaust stacks that discharge vertically · elimination of exhaust leaks · roofspace exhaust fans in buildings · local exhaust systems that collect exhaust at source · roof level fans in tunnels to boost natural airflow in the roofspace · catalytic converters in exhaust systems · not operating locomotives in buildings · respiratory protection: full-facepiece respirators equipped with cartridges (meeting European standards) can provide satisfactory protection under these conditions.
Noise	Control measures include: · cabs incorporating noise control technology · noise control technology installed in existing equipment during rebuilding and remanufacturing · personal hearing protection (consult regulations to ensure compliance during train or vehicle operation).
Whole-body vibration	Control measures include: · cabs incorporating vibration-control technology · vibration control technology installed in existing equipment during rebuilding and remanufacturing.
Electromagnetic fields	Hazard not established below present limits.
Radio-frequency fields	Hazard not established below present limits.
Weather	Control measures include: · work clothing that protects against cold · work clothing that shields against solar radiation · eye protection that provides protection against solar radiation · sunscreen lotions (seek medical advisement for prolonged use).
Shiftwork	Arrange work schedules to reflect current knowledge about circadian rhythms.
Musculoskeletal injury	Control measures include: · equipment designed to reflect ergonomic principles · training in muscle conditioning, lifting and back care · work practices chosen to minimize occurrence of musculoskeletal injury.
Video display units	Apply office ergonomic principles to selection and utilization of video display units.
Rundown accidents	Rail equipment is confined to the track. Unpowered rail equipment creates little noise when in motion. Natural features can block noise from powered rail equipment. Equipment noise can mask warning sound from the horn of an approaching train. During operations in rail yards, switching can occur under remote control with the result that all tracks could be live. Control measures include: · track occupancy permits (TOPs) and signals to regulate movement of trains and track equipment. The TOP authorizes unique occupancy of a section of track. · alarms in buildings indicating movement of equipment · practices and procedures for safe conditions of work around track and rail equipment.
Ballast operations/ spilled cargo	Wetting ballast prior to track work eliminates dust from ballast and cargo residues. Personal and respiratory protective equipment should be provided.
Skin contamination by waste oils and lubricants	Equipment should be cleaned prior to dismantling to remove contamination. Protective clothing, gloves and/or barrier creams should be used.

Continues on next page

Table 102.6 • Railway industry approaches to controlling hazardous conditions.
Continued

Hazardous conditions	Comments/control measures
Welding, cutting and brazing emissions, grinding dust	Control measures include: · local exhaust ventilation · personal protective equipment (PPE) · respiratory protection · personal hygiene measures · medical surveillance (depends on composition of base metal and metal in wire or rod).
Thermal decomposition products from coatings	Control measures include: · local exhaust ventilation · respiratory protection · personal hygiene measures · medical surveillance (depends on composition of the coating).
Cargo residues	Control measures include: · wash residues from car prior to servicing (depends on circumstances) · PPE (depends on circumstances) · respiratory protection (depends on circumstances) · personal hygiene measures (depends on circumstances) · medical surveillance (depends on cargo).
Abrasive blasting dust	Control measures include: · enclosed abrasive blasting facility · robotic blasting operation · dust collection system · PPE · respiratory protection · personal hygiene measures · medical surveillance (depends on abrasive, coating and cargo residue).
Solvent vapours, paint aerosols	Control measures include: · robotic painting system for interior of hoppers · low-solvent coating system · premixed coatings · piped coating transfer system · spray booth · PPE · respiratory protection · medical surveillance (depends on circumstances).
Confined spaces	Control measures include: · portable ventilation systems · PPE · respiratory protection.
Hand-arm vibration	Control measures include: · utilize tools meeting current standards for hand-arm vibration · vibration-absorbing gloves.

WATER TRANSPORT

WATER TRANSPORTATION AND THE MARITIME INDUSTRIES

Timothy J. Ungs and Michael Adess

The very definition of the maritime setting is work and life that takes place in or around a watery world (e.g., ships and barges, docks and terminals). Work and life activities must first accommodate the macro-environmental conditions of the oceans, lakes or waterways in which they take place. Vessels serve as both work-place and home, so most habitat and work exposures are coexistent and inseparable.

The maritime industry comprises a number of sub-industries, including freight transportation, passenger and ferry service, commercial fishing, tankships and barge shipping. Individual maritime sub-industries consist of a set of merchant or commercial activities that are characterized by the type of vessel, targeted goods and services, typical practices and area of operations, and community of owners, operators and workers. In turn, these activities and the context in which they take place define the occupational and environmental hazards and exposures experienced by maritime workers.

Table 102.7 • Merchant vessel types

Vessel types	Description	Crew size
Freight ships		
Bulk carrier	Large vessel (200–600 feet (61–183 m)) typified by large open cargo holds and many voids; carry bulk cargoes such as grain and ore; cargo is loaded by chute, conveyor or shovel	25–50
Break bulk	Large vessel (200–600 feet (61–183 m)); cargo carried in bales, pallets, bags or boxes; expansive holds with between decks; may have tunnels	25–60
Container	Large vessel (200–600 (61–183 m)) with open holds; may or may not have booms or cranes to handle cargo; containers are 20–40 feet (6.1–12.2 m) and stackable	25–45
Ore, bulk, oil (OBO)	Large vessel (200–600 feet (61–183 m)); holds are expansive and shaped to hold bulk ore or oil; holds are water tight, may have pumps and piping; many voids	25–55
Vehicle	Large vessel (200–600 feet (61–183 m)) with big sail area; many levels; vehicles can be self loading or boomed aboard	25–40
Roll-on roll-off (RORO)	Large vessel (200–600 feet (61–183 m)) with big sail area; many levels; can carry other cargo in addition to vehicles	25–40
Tank ships		
Oil	Large vessel (200–1000 feet (61–305 m)) typified by stern house piping on deck; may have hose handling booms and large ullages with many tanks; can carry crude or processed oil, solvents and other petroleum products	25–50
Chemical	Large vessel (200–1000 feet (61–305 m)) similar to oil tankship, but may have additional piping and pumps to handle multiple cargoes simultaneously; cargoes can be liquid, gas, powders or compressed solids	25–50
Pressurized	Usually smaller (200–700 feet (61–213.4 m)) than typical tankship, having fewer tanks, and tanks which are pressurized or cooled; can be chemical or petroleum products such as liquid natural gas; tanks are usually covered and insulated; many voids, pipes and pumps	15–30
Tug boats	Small to mid-size vessel (80–200 feet (24.4–61 m)); harbour, push boats, ocean going	3–15
Barge	Mid-size vessel (100–350 feet (30.5–106.7 m)); can be tank, deck, freight or vehicle; usually not manned or self-propelled; many voids	
Drillships and rigs	Large, similar profile to bulk carrier; typified by large derrick; many voids, machinery, hazardous cargo and large crew; some are towed, others self propelled	40–120
Passenger	All sizes (50–700 feet (15.2–213.4 m)); typified by large number of crew and passengers (up to 1000+)	20–200

Organized merchant maritime activities date back to the earliest days of civilized history. The ancient Greek, Egyptian and Japanese societies are examples of great civilizations where the development of power and influence was closely associated with having an extensive maritime presence. The importance of maritime industries to development of national power and prosperity has continued into the modern era.

The dominant maritime industry is water transportation, which remains the primary mode of international trade. The economies of most countries with ocean borders are heavily influenced by the receipt and export of goods and services by water. However, national and regional economies heavily dependent on the transport of goods by water are not limited to those which border oceans. Many countries removed from the sea have extensive networks of inland waterways.

Modern merchant vessels may process materials or produce goods as well as transport them. Globalized economies, restrictive land use, favourable tax laws and technology are among the factors which have spurred the growth of vessels that serve as both factory and means of transportation. Catcher-processor fishing vessels are a good example of this trend. These factory ships are capable of catching, processing, packaging and delivering finished sea food products to regional markets, as discussed in the chapter *Fishing industry*.

Merchant Transport Vessels

Similar to other transport vehicles, the structure, form and function of vessels closely parallel the vessel's purpose and major environmental circumstances. For example, craft that transport liquids short distances on inland waterways will differ substantially in form and crew from those that carry dry bulk on trans-oceanic voyages. Vessels can be free moving, semi-mobile or permanently fixed structures (e.g., offshore oil-drilling rigs) and be self-propelled or towed. At any given time, existing fleets are comprised of a spectrum of vessels with a wide range of original construction dates, materials and degrees of sophistication.

Crew size will depend on the typical duration of trip, vessel purpose and technology, expected environmental conditions and sophistication of shore facilities. Larger crew size entails more extensive needs and elaborate planning for berthing, dining, sanitation, health care and personnel support. The international trend is toward vessels of increasing size and complexity, smaller crews and expanding reliance on automation, mechanization and containerization. Table 102.7 provides a categorization and descriptive summary of merchant vessel types.

Morbidity and Mortality in the Maritime Industries

Health care providers and epidemiologists are often challenged to distinguish adverse health states due to work-related exposures from those due to exposures outside the workplace. This difficulty is compounded in the maritime industries because vessels serve as both workplace and home, and both exist in the greater environment of the maritime milieu itself. The physical boundaries found on most vessels result in close confinement and sharing of workspaces, engine-room, storage areas, passageways and other compartments with living spaces. Vessels often have a single water, ventilation or sanitation system that serves both work and living quarters.

The social structure aboard vessels is typically stratified into vessel officers or operators (ship's master, first mate and so on) and remaining crew. Ship officers or operators are generally relatively more educated, affluent and occupationally stable. It is not uncommon to find vessels with crew members of an entirely different national or ethnic background from that of the officers or operators. Historically, maritime communities are more transient, heterogeneous and somewhat more independent than non-mari-

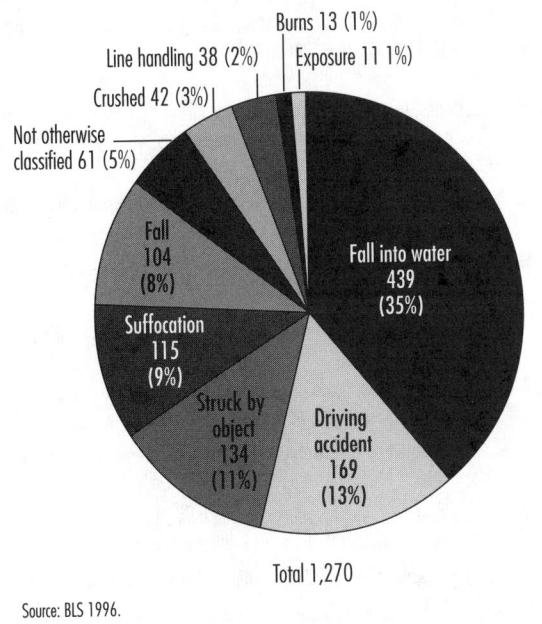

Figure 102.12 • Causes of leading fatal unintentional injuries attributed to personal reasons (US maritime industries 1983–1993).

Source: BLS 1996.

time communities. Work schedules aboard ship are often more fragmented and intermingled with non-work time than are land-based employment situations.

These are some reasons why it is difficult to describe or quantify health problems in the maritime industries, or to correctly associate problems with exposures. Data on maritime worker morbidity and mortality suffer from being incomplete and not representative of entire crews or sub-industries. Another shortfall of many data sets or information systems that report on the maritime industries is the inability to distinguish among health problems due to work, vessel or macro-environmental exposures. As with other occupations, difficulties in capturing morbidity and mortality information is most obvious with chronic disease conditions (e.g., cardiovascular disease), particularly those with a long latency (e.g., cancer).

Review of 11 years (1983 to 1993) of US maritime data demonstrated that half of all fatalities due to maritime injuries, but only 12% of non-fatal injuries, are attributed to the vessel (i.e., collision or capsizing). The remaining fatalities and non-fatal injuries are attributed to personnel (e.g., mishaps to an individual while aboard ship). Reported causes of such mortality and morbidity are described in figures 102.12 and 102.13 respectively. Comparable information on non-injury-related mortality and morbidity is not available.

Combined vessel and personal US maritime casualty data reveal that the highest proportion (42%) of all maritime fatalities (N = 2,559), occurred among commercial fishing vessels. The next highest were among towboats/barges (11%), freight ships (10%) and passenger vessels (10%).

Analysis of reported work-related injuries for the maritime industries shows similarities to patterns reported for the manufacturing and construction industries. Commonalities are that most injuries are due to falls, being struck, cuts and bruises or muscular strains and overuse. Caution is needed when interpreting these data, however, as there is reporting bias: acute injuries are likely to be over-represented and chronic/latent injuries, which are less obviously connected to work, under-reported.

Occupational and Environmental Hazards

Most health hazards found in the maritime setting have land-based analogs in the manufacturing, construction and agricultural industries. The difference is that the maritime environment constricts and compresses available space, forcing close proximity of potential hazards and the intermingling of living quarters and workspaces with fuel tanks, engine and propulsion areas, cargo and storage spaces.

Table 102.8 summaries health hazards common across different vessel types. Health hazards of particular concern with specific vessel types are highlighted in table 102.9. The following paragraphs of this section expand discussion of selected environmental, physical and chemical, and sanitation health hazards.

Environmental hazards

Arguably the most characteristic exposure defining the maritime industries is the pervasive presence of the water itself. The most variable and challenging of water environments is the open ocean. Oceans present constantly undulating surfaces, extremes of weather and hostile travel conditions, which combine to cause constant motion, turbulence and shifting surfaces and can result in vestibular disturbances (motion sickness), object instability (e.g., swinging latches and sliding gear) and the propensity to fall.

Humans have limited capability to survive unaided in open water; drowning and hypothermia are immediate threats upon immersion. Vessels serve as platforms that permit the human presence at sea. Ships and other water craft generally operate at some distance from other resources. For these reasons, vessels must dedicate a large proportion of total space to life support, fuel, structural integrity and propulsion, often at the expense of habitability, personnel safety and human factor considerations.

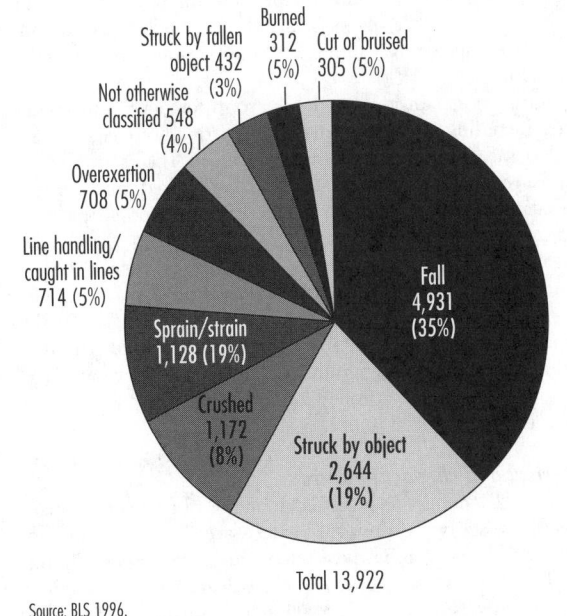

Figure 102.13 • Causes of leading non-fatal unintentional injuries attributed to personal reasons (US maritime industries 1983–1993).

Source: BLS 1996.

Table 102.8 • Health hazards common across vessel types.

Hazards	Description	Examples
Mechanical	Unguarded or exposed moving objects or their parts, which strike, pinch, crush or entangle. Objects can be mechanized (e.g., fork-lift) or simple (hinged door).	Winches, pumps, fans, drive shafts, compressors, propellers, hatches, doors, booms, cranes, mooring lines, moving cargo
Electrical	Static (e.g., batteries) or active (e.g., generators) sources of electricity, their distribution system (e.g., wiring) and powered devices (e.g., motors), all of which can cause direct electrical-induced physical injury	Batteries, vessel generators, dockside electrical sources, unprotected or ungrounded electric motors (pumps, fans, etc.), exposed wiring, navigation and communication electronics
Thermal	Heat- or cold-induced injury	Steam pipes, cold storage spaces, power plant exhaust, cold- or warm-weather exposure above deck
Noise	Adverse auditory and other physiological problems due to excessive and prolonged sound energy	Vessel propulsion system, pumps, ventilation fans, winches, steam-powered devices, conveyor belts
Fall	Slips, trips and falls resulting in kinetic-energy-induced injuries	Steep ladders, deep vessel holds, missing railings, narrow gangways, elevated platforms
Chemical	Acute and chronic disease or injury resulting from exposure to organic or inorganic chemicals and heavy metals	Cleaning solvents, cargo, detergents, welding, rusting/corrosion processes, refrigerants, pesticides, fumigants
Sanitation	Disease related to unsafe water, poor food practices or improper waste disposal	Contaminated potable water, food spoilage, deteriorated vessel waste system
Biologic	Disease or illness causes by exposure to living organisms or their products	Grain dust, raw wood products, cotton bales, bulk fruit or meat, seafood products, communicable disease agents
Radiation	Injury due to non-ionizing radiation	Intense sunlight, arc welding, radar, microwave communications
Violence	Interpersonal violence	Assault, homicide, violent conflict among crew
Confined space	Toxic or anoxic injury resulting from entering an enclosed space with limited entry	Cargo holds, ballast tanks, crawl spaces, fuel tanks, boilers, storage rooms, refrigerated holds
Physical work	Health problems due to overuse, disuse or unsuitable work practices	Shovelling ice in fish tanks, moving awkward cargo in restricted spaces, handling heavy mooring lines, prolonged stationary watch standing

Modern supertankers, which provide more generous human space and liveability, are an exception.

Excessive noise exposure is a prevalent problem because sound energy is readily transmitted through a vessel's metallic structure to nearly all spaces, and limited noise attenuation materials are used. Excessive noise can be nearly continuous, with no available quiet areas. Sources of noise include the engine, propulsion system, machinery, fans, pumps and the pounding of waves on the vessel hull.

Mariners are an identified risk group for developing skin cancers, including malignant melanoma, squamous cell carcinoma and basal cell carcinoma. The increased risk is due to excess exposure to direct and water-surface-reflected ultraviolet solar radiation. Body areas of particular risk are exposed parts of the face, neck, ears and forearms.

Limited insulation, inadequate ventilation, internal sources of heat or cold (e.g., engine rooms or refrigerated spaces) and metallic surfaces all account for potential thermal stress. Thermal stress compounds physiological stress from other sources, resulting in reduced physical and cognitive performance. Thermal stress that is not adequately controlled or protected against can result in heat- or cold-induced injury.

Physical and chemical hazards

Table 102.7 highlights hazards unique or of particular concern to specific vessel types. Physical hazards are the most common and pervasive hazard aboard vessels of any type. Space limitations result in narrow passageways, limited clearance, steep ladders and low overheads. Confined vessel spaces means that machinery, piping, vents, conduits, tanks and so forth are squeezed in, with limited physical separation. Vessels commonly have openings that allow direct vertical access to all levels. Inner spaces below the surface deck are characterized by a combination of large holds, compact spaces and hidden compartments. Such physical structure places crew members at risk for slips, trips and falls, cuts and bruises, and being struck by moving or falling objects.

Constricted conditions result in being in close proximity to machinery, electrical lines, high-pressure tanks and hoses, and dangerously hot or cold surfaces. If unguarded or energized, contact can result in burns, abrasions, lacerations, eye damage, crushing or more serious injury.

Since vessels are basically a composite of spaces housed within a water-tight envelope, ventilation can be marginal or deficient in some spaces, creating a hazardous confined space situation. If oxygen levels are depleted or air is displaced, or if toxic gases enter these confined spaces, entry can be life threatening.

Refrigerants, fuels, solvents, cleaning agents, paints, inert gases and other chemical substances are likely to be found on any vessel. Normal ship activities, such as welding, painting and trash burning can have toxic effects. Transport vessels (e.g., freight ships, container ships and tank ships) can carry a host of biological or chemical products, many of which are toxic if inhaled, ingested or touched with the bare skin. Others can become toxic if allowed to degrade, become contaminated or mix with other agents. Toxicity can be acute, as evidenced by dermal rashes and ocular burns, or chronic, as evidenced by neurobehavioural disorders and fertility problems or even carcinogenic. Some exposures can be immediately life-threatening. Examples of toxic chemicals carried by vessels are benzene-containing petrochemicals, acrylonitrile, butadiene, liquefied natural gas, carbon tetrachloride, chloroform, ethylene dibromide, ethylene oxide, formaldehyde solutions, nitropropane, *o*-toluidine and vinyl chloride.

Asbestos remains a hazard on some vessels, principally those constructed prior to the early 1970s. The thermal insulation, fire protection, durability and low cost of asbestos made this a preferred material in ship building. The primary hazard of asbestos occurs when the material becomes airborne when it is disturbed during renovations, construction or repair activities.

Sanitation and communicable disease hazards

One of the realities aboard ship is that the crew is often in close contact. In the work, recreation and living environments, crowding is often a fact of life that heightens the requirement for maintaining an effective sanitation programme. Critical areas include: berthing spaces, including toilet and shower facilities; food service and storage areas; laundry; recreation areas; and, if present, the barbershop. Pest and vermin control is also of critical importance; many of these animals can transmit disease. There are many opportunities for insects and rodents to infest a vessel, and once entrenched they are very difficult to control or eradicate, especially while underway. All vessels must have a safe and effective pest control programme. This requires training of individuals for this task, including annual refresher training.

Table 102.9 • Notable physical and chemical hazards for specific vessel types.

Vessel Types	Hazards
Tank vessels	Benzene and various hydrocarbon vapours, hydrogen sulphide off-gassing from crude oil, inert gases used in tanks to create oxygen-deficient atmosphere for explosion control, fire and explosion due to combustion of hydrocarbon products
Bulk cargo vessels	Pocketing of fumigants used on agricultural products, personnel entrapment/suffocation in loose or shifting cargo, confined space risks in conveyor or man tunnels deep in vessel, oxygen deficiency due to oxidation or fermentation of cargo
Chemical carriers	Venting of toxic gases or dusts, pressurized air or gas release, leakage of hazardous substances from cargo holds or transfer pipes, fire and explosion due to combustion of chemical cargoes
Container ships	Exposure to spills or leakage due to failed or improperly stored hazardous substances; release of agricultural inerting gases; venting from chemical or gas containers; exposure to mislabeled substances that are hazardous; explosions, fire or toxic exposures due to mixing of separate substances to form a dangerous agent (e.g., acid and sodium cyanide)
Break bulk vessels	Unsafe conditions due to shifting of cargo or improper storage; fire, explosion or toxic exposures due to mixing of incompatible cargoes; oxygen deficiency due to oxidation or fermentation of cargoes; release of refrigerant gases
Passenger ships	Contaminated potable water, unsafe food preparation and storage practices, mass evacuation concerns, acute health problems of individual passengers
Fishing vessels	Thermal hazards from refrigerated holds, oxygen deficiency due to decomposition of seafood products or use of antioxidant preservatives, release of refrigerant gases, entanglement in netting or lines, contact with dangerous or toxic fish or sea animals

Table 102.10 • Vessel hazard control and risk-reduction activities.

Topics	Activities
Programme development and evaluation	Identify hazards, shipboard and dockside. Assess nature, extent and magnitude of potential exposures. Identify crew members at risk. Determine suitable methods for hazard elimination or control and protection of personnel. Develop health surveillance and reporting system. Evaluate and follow at-risk members' health status. Measure programme effectiveness. Adapt and modify programme.
Hazard identification	Inventory shipboard chemical, physical, biological, and environmental hazards, in both work and living spaces (e.g., broken railings, use and storage of cleaning agents, presence of asbestos). Investigate hazards of cargo and those dockside.
Assessment of exposure	Understand work practices and job tasks (prescribed as well as those actually done). Qualify and quantify exposure levels (e.g., number of hours in hazardous cargo hold areas, ambient H2S levels due to off-gassing, type of organisms in potable water, sound levels in ship's spaces).
Personnel at risk	Review work logs, employment records and monitoring data of entire ship's complement, both seasonal and permanent.
Hazard control and personnel protection	Know established and recommended exposure standards (e.g., NIOSH, ILO, EU). Eliminate hazards where possible (replace live watches in hazardous holds with remote electronic monitoring). Control hazards that cannot be eliminated (e.g., enclose and isolate winches rather than leave exposed, and post warning signs). Provide necessary personal protective equipment (wear toxic gas and O2 detectors when entering confined spaces).
Health surveillance	Develop health information gathering and reporting system for all injuries and illnesses (e.g., maintain a ship's daily binnacle).
Monitor crew health	Establish occupational medical monitoring, determine performance standards, and establish fitness-for-work criteria (e.g., pre-placement and periodic pulmonary testing of crew handling grain).
Hazard control and risk reduction effectiveness	Devise and set priorities for goals (e.g., reduce shipboard falls). Set and measure outcomes toward goals (reduce annual number of days crew members not able to work due to falls aboard ship). Determine effectiveness of efforts in achieving goals.
Programme evolution	Modify prevention and control activities based on changing circumstances and prioritization.

Berthing areas must be kept free of debris, soiled laundry and perishable food. Bedding should be changed at least weekly (more often if soiled), and adequate laundry facilities for the size of the crew should be available. Food service areas must be rigorously maintained in a sanitary manner. The food service staff must receive training in proper techniques of food preparation, storage and galley sanitation, and adequate storage facilities must be provided aboard ship. The staff must adhere to recommended standards to ensure that food is prepared in a wholesome manner and is free of chemical and biological contamination. The occurrence of a food-borne disease outbreak aboard a vessel can be serious. A debilitated crew cannot carry out its duties. There may be insufficient medication to treat the crew, especially underway, and there may not be competent medical staff to care for the ill. In addition, if the ship is forced to change its destination, there may be significant economic loss to the shipping company.

The integrity and maintenance of a vessel's potable water system is also of vital importance. Historically, water-borne outbreaks aboard ship have been the most common cause of acute disability and death among crews. Therefore, the potable water supply must come from an approved source (wherever possible) and be free from chemical and biological contamination. Where this is not possible, the vessel must have the means to effectively decontaminate the water and render it potable. A potable water system must be protected against contamination by every known source, including cross-contaminations with any non-potable liquids. The system also must be protected from chemical contamination. It must be cleaned and disinfected periodically. Filling the system with clean water containing at least 100 parts per million (ppm) of chlorine for several hours and then flushing the entire system with water containing 100 ppm chlorine is effective disinfection. The system should then be flushed with fresh potable water. A potable water supply must have at least 2 ppm residual of chlorine at all times, as documented by periodic testing.

Communicable disease transmission aboard ship is a serious potential problem. Lost work time, the cost of medical treatment and the possibility of having to evacuate crew members make this an important consideration. Besides the more common disease agents (e.g., those that cause gastroenteritis, such as *Salmonella*, and those that cause upper respiratory disease, such as the influenza virus), there has been a re-emergence of disease agents that were thought to be under control or eliminated from the general population. Tuberculosis, highly pathogenic strains of *Escherichia coli* and *Streptococcus*, and syphilis and gonorrhoea have reappeared in increasing incidence and/or virulence. In addition, previously unknown or uncommon disease agents such as the HIV virus and the Ebola virus, which are not only highly resistant to treatment, but highly lethal, have appeared. It is therefore important that assessment be made of appropriate crew immunization for such diseases as polio, diphtheria, tetanus, measles, and hepatitis A and B. Additional immunizations may be required for specific potential or unique exposures, since crew members may have occasion to visit a wide variety of ports around the world and at the same time come in contact with a number of disease agents.

It is vital that crew members receive periodic training in the avoidance of contact with disease agents. The topic should include blood-borne pathogens, sexually transmitted diseases (STDs), food- and water-borne diseases, personal hygiene, symptoms of the more common communicable diseases and appropriate action by the individual on discovering these symptoms. Communicable disease outbreaks aboard ship can have a devastating effect on the vessel's operation; they can result in a high level of illness among the crew, with the possibility of serious debilitating disease and in some cases death. In some instances, vessel diversion has been required with resultant heavy economic losses. It is in the best interest of the vessel owner to have an effective and efficient communicable disease programme.

Hazard Control and Risk Reduction

Conceptually, the principles of hazard control and risk reduction are similar to other occupational settings, and include:

- hazard identification and characterization
- inventory and analysis of exposures and at-risk populations
- hazard elimination or control
- personnel monitoring and surveillance
- disease/injury prevention and intervention
- programme evaluation and adjustment (see table 102.9).

To be effective, however, the means and methods to implement these principles must be tailored to the specific maritime arena of interest. Occupational activities are complex and take place in integrated systems (e.g., vessel operations, employee/employer associations, commerce and trade determinants). The key to prevention is to understand these systems and the context in which they take place, which requires close cooperation and interaction between all organizational levels of the maritime community, from general deck hand through vessel operators and company upper management. There are many government and regulatory interests that impact the maritime industries. Partnerships between government, regulators, management and workers are essential for meaningful programmes for improving the health and safety status of the maritime industries.

The ILO has established a number of Conventions and Recommendations relating to shipboard work, such as the Prevention of Accidents (Seafarers) Convention, 1970 (No. 134), and Recommendation, 1970 (No. 142), the Merchant Shipping (Minimum Standards) Convention, 1976 (No. 147), the Merchant Shipping (Improvement of Standards) Recommendation, 1976 (No. 155), and the Health Protection and Medical Care (Seafarers) Convention, 1987 (No. 164). The ILO has also published a Code of Practice regarding the prevention of accidents at sea (ILO 1996).

Approximately 80% of vessel casualties are attributed to human factors. Similarly, the majority of reported injury-related morbidity and mortality have human factor causes. Reduction in maritime injury and death requires successful application of principles of human factors to work and life activities aboard vessels. Successful application of human factors principles means that vessel operations, vessel engineering and design, work activities, systems and management policies are developed that integrate human anthropometrics, performance, cognition and behaviours. For example, cargo loading/unloading presents potential hazards. Human factor considerations would highlight the need for clear communication and visibility, ergonomic matching of worker to task, safe separation of workers from moving machinery and cargo and a trained workforce, well acquainted with work processes.

Prevention of chronic diseases and adverse health states with long latency periods is more problematic than injury prevention and control. Acute injury events generally have readily recognized cause-effect relationships. Also, the association of injury cause and effect with work practices and conditions is usually less complicated than for chronic diseases. Hazards, exposures and health data specific to the maritime industries are limited. In general, health surveillance systems, reporting and analyses for the maritime industries are less developed than those for many of their land-based counterparts. The limited availability of chronic or latent disease health data specific to maritime industries hinders development and application of targeted prevention and control programmes.

STORAGE AND TRANSPORTATION OF CRUDE OIL, NATURAL GAS, LIQUID PETROLEUM PRODUCTS AND OTHER CHEMICALS

Richard S. Kraus

Pipelines, marine vessels, tank trucks, rail tank cars and so forth are used to transport crude oils, compressed and liquefied hydrocarbon gases, liquid petroleum products and other chemicals from their point of origin to pipeline terminals, refineries, distributors and consumers.

Crude oils and liquid petroleum products are transported, handled and stored in their natural liquid state. Hydrocarbon gases are transported, handled and stored in both the gaseous and liquid states and must be completely confined in pipelines, tanks, cylinders or other containers prior to use. The most important characteristic of liquefied hydrocarbon gases (LHGs) is that they are stored, handled and shipped as liquids, taking up a relatively small amount of space and then expanding into a gas when used. For example, liquefied natural gas (LNG) is stored at −162 °C, and when it is released the difference in storage and atmospheric temperatures causes the liquid to expand and gasify. One gallon (3.8 l) of LNG converts to approximately 2.5 m^3 of natural gas at normal temperature and pressure. Because liquefied gas is much more "concentrated" than compressed gas, more useable gas can be transported and provided in the same size container.

Pipelines

It is generally the case that all crude oils, natural gas, liquefied natural gas, liquefied petroleum gas (LPG) and petroleum products flow through pipelines at some time in their migration from the well to a refinery or gas plant, then to a terminal and eventually to the consumer. Aboveground, underwater and underground pipelines, varying in size from several centimetres to a metre or more in diameter, move vast amounts of crude oil, natural gas, LHGs and liquid petroleum products. Pipelines run throughout the world, from the frozen tundra of Alaska and Siberia to the hot deserts of the Middle East, across rivers, lakes, seas, swamps and forests, over and through mountains and under cities and towns. Although the initial construction of pipelines is difficult and expensive, once they are built, properly maintained and operated, they provide one of the safest and most economical means of transporting these products.

The first successful crude-oil pipeline, a 5-cm-diameter wrought iron pipe 9 km long with a capacity of about 800 barrels a day, was opened in Pennsylvania (US) in 1865. Today, crude oil, compressed natural gas and liquid petroleum products are moved long distances through pipelines at speeds from 5.5 to 9 km per hour by large pumps or compressors located along the route of the pipeline at intervals ranging from 90 km to over 270 km. The distance between pumping or compressor stations is determined by the pump capacity, viscosity of the product, size of the pipeline and the type of terrain crossed. Regardless of these factors, pipeline pumping pressures and flow rates are controlled throughout the system to maintain a constant movement of product within the pipeline.

Types of pipelines

The four basic types of pipelines in the oil and gas industry are flow lines, gathering lines, crude trunk pipelines and petroleum product trunk pipelines.

- *Flow lines.* Flow lines move crude oil or natural gas from producing wells to producing field storage tanks and reservoirs. Flow lines may vary in size from 5 cm in diameter in older, lower-pressure fields with only a few wells, to much larger lines in multi-well, high-pressure fields. Offshore platforms use flow lines to move crude and gas from wells to the platform storage and loading facility. A *lease line* is a type of flow line which carries all of the oil produced on a single lease to a storage tank.
- *Gathering and feeder lines.* Gathering lines collect oil and gas from several locations for delivery to central accumulating points, such as from field crude oil tanks and gas plants to marine docks. Feeder lines collect oil and gas from several locations for delivery direct into trunk lines, such as moving crude oil from offshore platforms to onshore crude trunk pipelines. Gathering lines and feeder lines are typically larger in diameter than flow lines.
- *Crude trunk pipelines.* Natural gas and crude oil are moved long distances from producing areas or marine docks to refineries and from refineries to storage and distribution facilities by 1- to 3-m- or larger-diameter trunk pipelines.
- *Petroleum product trunk pipelines.* These pipelines move liquid petroleum products such as gasoline and fuel oil from refineries to terminals, and from marine and pipeline terminals to distribution terminals. Product pipelines may also distribute products from terminals to bulk plants and consumer storage facilities, and occasionally from refineries direct to consumers. Product pipelines are used to move LPG from refineries to distributor storage facilities or large industrial users.

Regulations and standards

Pipelines are constructed and operated to meet safety and environmental standards established by regulatory agencies and industry associations. Within the United States, the Department of Transportation (DOT) regulates the operation of pipelines, the Environmental Protection Agency (EPA) regulates spills and releases, the Occupational Safety and Health Administration (OSHA) promulgates standards covering worker health and safety, and the Interstate Commerce Commission (ICC) regulates common carrier pipelines. A number of industry organizations, such as the American Petroleum Institute and the American Gas Association, also publish recommended practices covering pipeline operations.

Pipeline construction

Pipeline routes are planned using topographic maps developed from aerial photogrammetric surveys, followed by actual ground surveying. After planning the route, obtaining right-of-way and permission to proceed, base camps are established and a means of access for construction equipment is required. Pipelines can be constructed working from one end to another or simultaneously in sections which are then connected.

The first step in laying pipeline is to construct a 15- to 30-m-wide service road along the planned route to provide a stable base for the pipe-laying and pipe-joining equipment and for underground pipeline excavation and backfill equipment. The pipe sections are laid on the ground alongside the service road. The ends of the pipe are cleaned, the pipe is bent horizontally or vertically, as necessary, and the sections are held in position by chocks above the ground and joined by multi-pass electrical arc-welding. The welds are checked visually and then with gamma radiation to assure that no defects are present. Each connected section is then coated with liquid soap and air-pressure tested to detect leaks.

102. TRANSPORT INDUSTRY AND WAREHOUSING

Figure 102.14 • A terminal operator transfers product from the Pasagoula Refinery into holding tanks in the Deraville Terminal near Atlanta, Georgia, US.

American Petroleum Institute

The pipeline is cleaned, primed and coated with a hot, tar-like material to prevent corrosion and wrapped in an outer layer of heavy paper, mineral wool or plastic. If the pipe is to be buried, the bottom of the trench is prepared with a sand or gravel bed. The pipe may be weighed down by short, concrete sleeves to prevent its lifting out of the trench from groundwater pressure. After the underground pipeline is placed in the trench, the trench is backfilled and the surface of the ground returned to normal appearance. After coating and wrapping, aboveground piping is lifted up onto prepared stanchions or casements, which may have various design features such as anti-earthquake shock absorption. Pipelines may be insulated or have heat trace capabilities to keep products at desired temperatures throughout transport. All pipeline sections are hydrostatically tested prior to entering gas or liquid hydrocarbon service.

Pipeline operations

Pipelines may be either privately owned and operated, carrying only the owner's products, or they may be common carriers, required to carry any company's products provided that the pipeline's product requirements and tariffs are met. The three major pipeline operations are pipeline control, pumping or compressor stations and delivery terminals. Storage, cleaning, communication and shipment are also important functions.

- *Pipeline control.* Regardless of the product being transported, the size and length of the pipeline or the terrain, pipeline pumping stations, pressures and flow rates are completely controlled in order to ensure appropriate flow rates and continuous operations. Typically an operator and computer control the pumps, valves, regulators and compressors throughout the pipeline system from a central location.
- *Oil pumping and gas compressor stations.* Crude oil and petroleum products pumping stations and gas compressor stations are located at wellheads and along the pipeline route as needed to maintain pressure and volume. Pumps are driven by electric motors or diesel engines, and turbines may be powered by fuel oil, gas or steam. Many of these stations are automatically controlled and not staffed at most times.

Pumps, with and without vapour return lines or pressure equalizing lines, are commonly used in smaller pipelines for transport of LNG, LPG and compressed natural gas (CNG). Pressure drop detectors are installed to signal any leaks in pipelines, and excess flow valves or other flow limiting devices are used to minimize the rate of flow in case of a pipeline leak. Storage vessels and reservoirs may be isolated from main pipelines by manually operated or remote control valves or fusible link valves.

- *Pipeline product storage.* Crude and petroleum product pipeline terminals have breakout storage tanks to which shipments may be diverted, where they are held until required by a refinery, terminal or user (see figure 102.14). Other tanks at pipeline pumping stations contain fuel for operating diesel-driven pump motors or for running electrical generators. Because gas fields produce continuously and gas pipelines operate continuously, during times of reduced demand, such as summertime, liquefied natural and petroleum gases are stored underground in natural caverns or salt domes until needed.
- *Pipeline cleaning.* Pipelines are cleaned on a scheduled basis or as necessary in order to continue flow by reducing friction and maintaining as large a diameter interior as possible. A special cleaning device, called a *pig* or *go-devil*, is placed into the pipeline and pushed along by the flow of oil from one pumping station to the next. As the pig passes through the pipeline it scrapes off any dirt, wax or other deposits which have built up inside the pipeline walls. When it reaches a pumping station, the pig is removed, cleaned and reinserted into the pipeline to travel to the next station.
- *Communications.* It is important that there be communication and agreement concerning schedules, pumping rates and pressures and emergency procedures between pipeline stations and operators and those shipping and receiving crude oil, gas and petroleum products. Some pipeline companies have private telephone systems which transmit the signal along the pipeline, while others use radios or public telephones. Many pipelines use ultra-high-frequency microwave transmitter systems for computer communications between control centres and pumping stations.
- *Petroleum product shipment.* Petroleum products may be shipped a number of different ways on pipelines. A company operating a refinery may blend a specific grade of its own gasoline with appropriate additives (additize) and ship a batch through a pipeline directly to its own terminal for distribution to its customers. Another method is for a refinery to produce a batch of gasoline, called a frangible or specification product, which is blended to meet a common carrier pipeline company's product specifications. The gasoline is placed into the pipeline for delivery to any company's terminals which are connected to the pipeline system. In a third method, products are shipped by companies to each other's terminals and exchanged in order to avoid extra transportation and handling. Frangible and exchange products are usually blended and additized at the terminal which receives the product from the pipeline, to meet the specific requirements of each company operating from the terminal. Finally, some products are delivered by pipeline from terminals and refineries direct to large commercial consumers—jet fuel to airports, gas to gas distribution companies and fuel oil to electric generating plants.
- *Product receipt and delivery.* Pipeline operators and terminal operators should jointly establish programmes to provide for the safe receipt and transfer of products and to coordinate actions in case an emergency occurs on the pipeline or at the terminal during shipment which requires shutdown or diversion of

product. Instructions for receiving pipeline deliveries should include verification of the availability of the storage tanks to hold the shipment, opening and aligning tank and terminal valves in anticipation of delivery, checking to assure that the proper tank is receiving product immediately after the start of delivery, conducting required sampling and testing of batches at the start of delivery, performing batch changes and tank switches as required, monitoring receipts to assure that overfills do not occur and maintaining communications between the pipeline and the terminal. The use of written communications between terminal workers, especially when shift changes occur during product transfer, should be considered.

Batch shipments and interface

Although pipelines originally were used to move only crude oil, they evolved into carrying all types and different grades of liquid petroleum products. Because petroleum products are transported in pipelines by batches, in succession, there is commingling or mixing of the products at the interfaces. The product intermix is controlled by one of three methods: downgrading (derating), using liquid and solid spacers for separation or reprocessing the intermix. Radioactive tracers, colour dyes and spacers may be placed into the pipeline to identify where the interfaces occur. Radioactive sensors, visual observation or gravity tests are conducted at the receiving facility to identify different pipeline batches.

Petroleum products are normally transported through pipelines in batch sequences with compatible crude oils or products adjoining one another. One method of maintaining product quality and integrity, downgrading or derating, is accomplished by lowering the interface between the two batches to the level of the least affected product. For example, a batch of high-octane premium gasoline is typically shipped immediately before or after a batch of lower-octane regular gasoline. The small quantity of the two products which has intermixed will be downgraded to the lower octane rating regular gasoline. When shipping gasoline before or after diesel fuel, a small amount of diesel interface is allowed to blend into the gasoline, rather than blending gasoline into the diesel fuel, which could lower its flashpoint. Batch interfaces are typically detected by visual observation, gravitometers or sampling.

Liquid and solid spacers or cleaning pigs may be used to physically separate and identify different batches of products. The solid spacers are detected by a radioactive signal and diverted from the pipeline into a special receiver at the terminal when the batch changes from one product to another. Liquid separators may be water or another product that does not commingle with either of the batches it is separating and is later removed and reprocessed. Kerosene, which is downgraded (derated) to another product in storage or is recycled, can also be used to separate batches.

A third method of controlling the interface, often used at the refinery ends of pipelines, is to return the interface to be reprocessed. Products and interfaces which have been contaminated with water may also be returned for reprocessing.

Environmental protection

Because of the large volumes of products which are transported by pipelines on a continuous basis, there is opportunity for environmental damage from releases. Depending on company and regulatory safety requirements and the pipeline's construction, location, weather, accessibility and operation, a considerable amount of product may be released should a break in the line or leak occur. Pipeline operators should have emergency response and spill contingency plans prepared and have containment and clean-up materials, personnel and equipment available or on call. Simple field solutions such as building earth dykes and drainage ditches can be quickly implemented by trained operators to contain and divert spilled product.

Maintaining pipelines and worker health and safety

The first pipelines were made of cast iron. Modern trunk pipelines are constructed of welded, high-strength steel, which can withstand high pressures. Pipe walls are periodically tested for thickness to determine whether internal corrosion or deposits have occurred. Welds are checked visually and with gamma radiation to assure that no defects are present. Plastic pipe may be used for low-pressure, small-diameter flow lines and gathering lines in gas and crude-oil-producing fields, since plastic is light in weight and easy to handle, assemble and move.

When a pipeline is separated by cutting, spreading flanges, removing a valve or opening the line, an electrostatic arc may be created by impressed cathodic protection voltage, corrosion, sacrificial anodes, nearby high-voltage power lines or stray ground currents. This should be minimized by grounding (earthing) the pipe, de-energizing the cathodic rectifiers closest to both sides of the separation and connecting a bonding cable to each side of the piping prior to starting work. As additional pipeline sections, valves and so on are added to an existing line, or during construction, they should first be bonded to the pipelines in place.

Work on pipelines should cease during electrical storms. Equipment used to lift and place pipe should not be operated within 3 m of high-voltage electric lines. Any vehicles or equipment working in the vicinity of high-voltage lines should have trailing grounding straps attached to the frames. Temporary metal buildings should also be grounded.

Pipelines are specially coated and wrapped to prevent corrosion. Cathodic electrical protection may also be required. After the pipeline sections are coated and insulated, they are joined by special clamps connected to metallic anodes. The pipeline is subjected to a grounded source of direct current of sufficient capacity so that the pipeline acts as a cathode and does not corrode.

All pipeline sections are hydrostatically tested prior to entering gas or liquid hydrocarbon service and, depending on regulatory and company requirements, at regular intervals during the life of the pipeline. Air must be eliminated from pipelines prior to hydrostatic testing, and hydrostatic pressure built up and reduced at safe rates. Pipelines are regularly patrolled, usually by aerial surveillance, to visually detect leaks, or monitored from the control centre to detect a drop in flow rate or pressure, which would signify that a break in the pipeline has occurred.

Pipeline systems are provided with warning and signalling systems to alert operators so they may take corrective action in an emergency. Pipelines may have automatic shutdown systems which activate emergency pressure valves upon sensing increased or reduced pipeline pressure. Manually or automatically operated isolation valves are typically located at strategic intervals along pipelines, such as at pumping stations and at both sides of river crossings.

An important consideration when operating pipelines is to provide a means of warning contractors and others who may be working or conducting excavations along the pipeline route, so that the pipeline is not inadvertently ruptured, breached or punctured, resulting in a vapour or gas explosion and fire. This is usually done by regulations which require construction permits or by pipeline companies and associations providing a central number which contractors can call prior to excavation.

Because crude oil and flammable petroleum products are transported in pipelines, the possibility exists for fire or explosion in case of a line break or release of vapour or liquid. Pressure should be reduced to a safe level before working on high-pressure pipelines. Combustible gas testing should be conducted and a permit issued prior to repair or maintenance involving hot work or hot

Figure 102.15 • *SS Paul L. Fahrney oil tanker.*

American Petroleum Institute

tapping on pipelines. The pipeline should be cleared of flammable liquids and vapours or gas prior to starting work. If a pipeline cannot be cleared and an approved plug is used, safe work procedures should be established and followed by qualified workers. The line should be vented a safe distance from the hot work area to relieve any build-up of pressure behind the plug.

Proper safety procedures should be established and followed by qualified workers when hot tapping pipelines. If welding or hot tapping is conducted in an area where a spill or leak has occurred, the outside of the pipe should be cleaned of liquid, and contaminated soil should be removed or covered to prevent ignition.

It is very important to notify operators at the nearest pumping stations on each side of the operating pipeline where maintenance or repair is to be performed, in case shutdown is required. When crude oil or gas is being pumped into pipelines by producers, the pipeline operators must provide specific instructions to the producers as to actions to take during repair, maintenance or in an emergency. For example, prior to tie-in of production tanks and lines to pipelines, all gate valves and bleeders for the tanks and lines involved in the tie-in should be closed and locked or sealed until the operation is completed.

Normal safety precautions concerning pipe and materials handling, toxic and hazardous exposures, welding and excavation apply during pipeline construction. Workers clearing right-of-way should protect themselves from climatic conditions; poisonous plants, insects and snakes; falling trees and rocks; and so on. Excavations and trenches should be sloped or shored to prevent collapse during underground pipeline construction or repair (see the article "Trenching" in the chapter *Construction*). Workers should follow safe work practices when opening and de-energizing electrical transformers and switches.

Pipeline operating and maintenance personnel often work alone and are responsible for long stretches of pipeline. Atmospheric testing and the use of personal and respiratory protective equipment is needed to determine oxygen and flammable vapour levels and protect against toxic exposures to hydrogen sulphide and benzene when gauging tanks, opening lines, cleaning spills, sampling and testing, shipping, receiving and performing other pipeline activities. Workers should wear dosimeters or film badges and avoid exposure when working with density gauges, source holders or other radioactive materials. The use of personal and respiratory protective equipment should be considered for exposure to burns from the hot protective tar used in pipe-coating

operations and from toxic vapours which contain polynuclear aromatic hydrocarbons.

Marine Tankers and Barges

The majority of the world's crude oil is transported by tankers from producing areas such as the Middle East and Africa to refineries in consumer areas such as Europe, Japan and the United States. Oil products were originally transported in large barrels on cargo ships. The first tanker ship, which was built in 1886, carried about 2,300 SDWT (2,240 pounds per ton) of oil. Today's supertankers can be over 300 m long and carry almost 200 times as much oil (see figure 102.15). Gathering and feeder pipelines often end at marine terminals or offshore platform loading facilities, where the crude oil is loaded into tankers or barges for transport to crude trunk pipelines or refineries. Petroleum products also are transported from refineries to distribution terminals by tanker and barge. After delivering their cargoes, the vessels return in ballast to loading facilities to repeat the sequence.

Liquefied natural gas is shipped as a cryogenic gas in specialized marine vessels with heavily insulated compartments or reservoirs (see figure 102.16). At the delivery port, the LNG is off-loaded to storage facilities or regasification plants. Liquefied petroleum gas may be shipped both as a liquid in uninsulated marine vessels and barges and as a cryogenic in insulated marine vessels. Additionally, LPG in containers (bottled gas) may be shipped as cargo on marine vessels and barges.

LPG and LNG marine vessels

The three types of marine vessels used for transport of LPG and LNG are:

- vessels with reservoirs pressurized up to 2 mPa (LPG only)
- vessels with heat-insulated reservoirs and a reduced pressure of 0.3 to 0.6 mPa (LPG only)
- cryogenic vessels with heat-insulated reservoirs pressurized close to atmospheric pressure (LPG and LNG).

Shipment of LHGs on marine vessels requires constant safety awareness. Transfer hoses must be suitable for the correct temperatures and pressures of the LHGs being handled. To prevent a flammable mixture of gas vapour and air, inert gas (nitrogen) blanketing is provided around reservoirs, and the area is continually monitored to detect leaks. Before loading, storage reservoirs should be inspected to ensure that they are free of contaminants. If reservoirs contain inert gas or air, they should be purged with LHG vapour prior to loading the LHG. Reservoirs should be constantly inspected to ensure integrity, and safety valves should be installed to relieve the LHG vapour generated at maximum heat load. Marine vessels are provided with fire suppression systems and have comprehensive emergency response procedures in place.

Crude oil and petroleum products marine vessels

Oil tankers and barges are vessels designed with the engines and quarters at the rear of the vessel and the remainder of the vessel divided into special compartments (tanks) to carry crude oil and liquid petroleum products in bulk. Cargo pumps are located in pump rooms, and forced ventilation and inerting systems are provided to reduce the risk of fires and explosions in pump rooms and cargo compartments. Modern oil tankers and barges are built with double hulls and other protective and safety features required by the United States Oil Pollution Act of 1990 and the International Maritime Organization (IMO) tanker safety standards. Some new ship designs extend double hulls up the sides of the tankers to provide additional protection. Generally, large tankers carry crude oil and small tankers and barges carry petroleum products.

- *Supertankers*. Ultra-large and very large crude carriers (ULCCs and VLCCs) are restricted by their size and draft to specific routes of travel. ULCCs are vessels whose capacity is over 300,000 SDWTs, and VLCCs have capacities ranging from 160,000 to 300,000 SDWTs. Most large crude carriers are not owned by oil companies, but are chartered from transportation companies which specialize in operating these super-sized vessels.
- *Oil tankers*. Oil tankers are smaller than VLCCs, and, in addition to ocean travel, they can navigate restricted passages such as the Suez and Panama Canals, shallow coastal waters and estuaries. Large oil tankers, which range from 25,000 to 160,000 SDWTs, usually carry crude oil or heavy residual products. Smaller oil tankers, under 25,000 SDWT, usually carry gasoline, fuel oils and lubricants.
- *Barges*. Barges operate mainly in coastal and inland waterways and rivers, alone or in groups of two or more, and are either self-propelled or moved by tugboat. They may carry crude oil to refineries, but more often are used as an inexpensive means of transporting petroleum products from refineries to distribution terminals. Barges are also used to off-load cargo from tankers offshore whose draft or size does not allow them to come to the dock.

Barge and ship loading and unloading

Vessel-to-shore procedures, safety checklists and guidelines should be established and agreed upon by terminal and marine vessel operators. The *International Safety Guide for Oil Tankers and Terminals* (International Chamber of Shipping 1978) contains information and samples of checklists, guidelines, permits and other procedures covering safe operations when loading or unloading vessels, which may be used by vessel and terminal operators.

Although marine vessels sit in water and are thereby intrinsically grounded, there is a need to provide protection from static electricity which can build up during loading or unloading. This is accomplished by bonding or connecting metal objects on the dock or loading/unloading apparatus to the metal of the vessel. Bonding is also accomplished by use of conductive loading hose or piping. An electrostatic spark of ignitable intensity may also be generated when lowering equipment, thermometers or gauging devices into compartments immediately after loading; enough time must be allowed for the static charge to dissipate.

Ship-to-shore electric currents, which are different from static electricity, may be generated by cathodic protection of the vessel's hull or dock, or by galvanic potential differences between the vessel and the shore. These currents also build up in metal loading/unloading apparatus. Insulating flanges may be installed within the length of the loading arm and at the point where flexible hoses connect to the shore pipeline system. When the connections are broken, there is no opportunity for a spark to jump from one metal surface to another.

All vessels and terminals need mutually agreed upon emergency response procedures in case of a fire or release of product, vapour or toxic gas. These must cover emergency operations, stopping product flow and emergency removal of a vessel from the dock. The plans should consider communications, fire-fighting, vapour cloud mitigation, mutual aid, rescue, clean-up and remediation measures. Fire protection portable equipment and fixed systems should be in accord with government and company requirements and appropriate to the size, function, exposure potential and value of the dock and wharf facilities. The *International Safety Guide for Oil Tankers and Terminals* (International Chamber of Shipping 1978) contains a sample fire notice which may be used as a guide by terminals for dock fire prevention.

Marine vessel health and safety

In addition to the usual maritime working hazards, transporting crude oil and flammable liquids by marine vessel creates a number of special health, safety and fire prevention situations. These include surging and expansion of liquid cargo, flammable vapour hazards during transport and when loading and unloading, possibility of pyrophoric ignition, toxic exposures to materials such as hydrogen sulphide and benzene and safety considerations when venting, flushing and cleaning compart-ments. The economics of operating modern tankers requires them to be at sea for extended periods of time with only short intervals in port to load or unload cargo. This, together with the fact that tankers are highly automated, creates unique mental and physical demands on the few crew members used to operate the vessels.

Fire and explosion protection

Emergency plans and procedures should be developed and implemented that are appropriate for the type of cargo on board and other potential hazards. Fire-fighting equipment must be supplied. Response team members who have shipboard fire-fighting, rescue and spill clean-up responsibilities should be trained, drilled and equipped to handle potential emergencies. Water, foam, dry chemicals, halon, carbon dioxide and steam are used as cooling, inhibiting and smothering fire-fighting agents aboard marine vessels, although halon is being phased out due to environmental concerns. The requirements for vessel fire-fighting equipment and systems are established by the country under whose flag the vessel sails and by company policy, but usually follow the recommendations of the 1974 International Convention for the Safety of Life at Sea (SOLAS).

Strict control of flames or naked lights, lighted smoking materials and other sources of ignition, such as welding or grinding sparks, electrical equipment and unprotected light bulbs, is required on vessels at all times to reduce the risk of fire and explosion. Prior to conducting hot work on board marine vessels, the area should be examined and tested to assure that conditions are safe, and permits should be issued for each specific task allowed.

One method of preventing explosions and fires in the vapour space of cargo compartments is to maintain the level of oxygen below 11% by making the atmosphere inert with a noncombustible gas. Sources for inert gas are exhaust gases from the vessel's boilers or an independent gas generator or a gas turbine fitted with an afterburner. The 1974 SOLAS Convention implies that vessels carrying cargo with flashpoints below 60 °C should have

Figure 102.16 • LNG *Leo* tanker loading at Arun, Sumatra, Indonesia.

American Petroleum Institute

102.TRANSPORT INDUSTRY AND WAREHOUSING

compartments fitted with inert systems. Vessels using inert gas systems should maintain cargo compartments in non-flammable conditions at all times. Inert gas compartments should be constantly monitored to assure safe conditions and should not be allowed to become flammable, because of the danger of ignition from pyrophoric deposits.

Confined spaces

Confined spaces on marine vessels, such as cargo compartments, paint lockers, pump rooms, fuel tanks and spaces between double hulls, must be treated the same as any confined space for entry, hot work and cold work. Tests for oxygen content, flammable vapours and toxic substances, in that order, must be conducted prior to entering confined spaces. A permit system should be established and followed for all confined space entry, safe (cold) work and hot work, which indicates safe exposure levels and required personal and respiratory protective equipment. In waters of the United States, these tests may be conducted by qualified individuals called "marine chemists".

Compartments on marine vessels such as cargo tanks and pump rooms are confined spaces; when cleaning those which have been made inert or have flammable vapour, toxic or unknown atmospheres, they should be tested, and special safety and respiratory protection procedures should be followed. After crude oil has been unloaded, a small amount of residue, called clingage, remains on the interior surfaces of the compartments, which may then be washed and filled with water for ballast. One method of reducing the amount of residue is to install fixed equipment which removes up to 80% of the clingage by washing down the sides of inerted compartments with crude oil during unloading.

Pumps, valves and equipment

A work permit should be issued and safe work procedures followed, such as bonding, draining and vapour freeing, flammable vapour and toxic exposure testing, and providing stand-by fire protection equipment when operations, maintenance or repair requires opening cargo pumps, lines, valves or equipment on board marine vessels.

Toxic exposures

There is an opportunity for vented gases such as flue gas or hydrogen sulphide to reach the decks of vessels, even from specially designed vent systems. Testing should be continuously conducted to determine inert gas levels on all vessels and hydrogen sulphide levels on vessels which contain or previously carried sour crude oil or residual fuel. Tests should be conducted for benzene exposure on vessels carrying crude oil and gasoline. Inert gas scrubber effluent water and condensate water is acidic and corrosive; PPE should be used when contact is possible.

Environmental protection

Marine vessels and terminals should establish procedures and provide equipment to protect the environment from spills on water and land, and from releases of vapour to the air. The use of large vapour recovery systems at marine terminals is growing. Care must be taken to comply with air pollution requirements when vessels vent compartments and enclosed spaces. Emergency response procedures should be established, and equipment and trained personnel should be available to respond to spills and releases of crude oil and flammable and combustible liquids. A responsible person should be designated to ensure that notifications are made to both the company and the appropriate authorities should a reportable spill or release occur.

In the past, the oil-contaminated ballast water and tank washings were flushed out of the compartments at sea. In 1973, the International Convention for Prevention of Pollution from Ships

established requirements that before the water is discharged at sea, the oily residue must be separated and retained on board for eventual onshore processing. Modern tankers have segregated ballast systems, with different lines, pumps and tanks than those used for cargo (in accordance with international recommen-dations), so that there is no possibility of contamination. Older vessels still carry ballast in cargo tanks, so special procedures, such as pumping oily water into designated onshore tanks and processing facilities, must be followed when discharging ballast in order to prevent pollution.

Motor Vehicle and Railroad Transport of Petroleum Products

Crude oil and petroleum products were initially transported by horse-drawn tank wagons, then by railroad tank cars and finally by motor vehicles. Following receipt at terminals from marine vessels or pipelines, bulk liquid petroleum products are delivered by non-pressure tank trucks or rail tank cars directly to service stations and consumers or to smaller terminals, called bulk plants, for redistribution. LPG, gasoline anti-knock compounds, hydrofluoric acid and many other products, chemicals and additives used in the oil and gas industry are transported in pressure tank cars and tank trucks. Crude oil may also be transported by tank truck from small producing wells to gathering tanks, and by tank truck and railroad tank car from storage tanks to refineries or main pipelines. Packaged petroleum products in bulk bins or drums and pallets and cases of smaller containers are carried by package truck or railroad box car.

Government regulations

Transportation of petroleum products by motor vehicle or railroad tank car is regulated by government agencies throughout most of the world. Agencies such as the US DOT and the Canadian Transport Commission (CTC) have established regulations governing the design, construction, safety devices, testing, preventive maintenance, inspection and operation of tank trucks and tank cars. Regulations governing railroad tank car and tank truck operations typically include tank pressure and pressure relief device testing and certification before being placed into initial service and at regular intervals thereafter. The Association of American Railroads and the National Fire Protection Association (NFPA) are typical of organizations which publish specifications and requirements for the safe operation of tank cars and tank trucks. Most governments have regulations or adhere to United Nations Conventions which require the identification of and information concerning hazardous materials and petroleum products which are shipped in bulk or in containers. Railroad tank cars, tank trucks and package trucks are placarded to identify any hazardous products being transported and to provide emergency response information.

Railroad tank cars

Railroad tank cars are constructed of carbon steel or aluminium and may be pressurized or unpressurized. Modern tank cars can hold up to 171,000 l of compressed gas at pressures up to 600 psi (1.6 to 1.8 mPa). Non-pressure tank cars have evolved from small wooden tank cars of the late 1800s to jumbo tank cars which transport as much as 1.31 million litres of product at pressures up to 100 psi (0.6 mPa). Non-pressure tank cars may be individual units with one or multiple compartments or a string of interconnected tank cars, called a tank train. Tank cars are loaded individually, and entire tank trains can be loaded and unloaded from a single point. Both pressure and non-pressure tank cars may be heated, cooled, insulated and thermally protected against fire, depending on their service and the products transported.

All railroad tank cars have top- or bottom-liquid or vapour valves for loading and unloading and hatch entries for cleaning. They are also equipped with devices intended to prevent the increase of internal pressure when exposed to abnormal con-ditions. These devices include safety relief valves held in place by a spring which can open to relieve pressure and then close; safety vents with rupture discs that burst open to relieve pressure but cannot reclose; or a combination of the two devices. A vacuum relief valve is provided for non-pressure tank cars to prevent vacuum formation when unloading from the bottom. Both pressure and non-pressure tank cars have protective housings on top surrounding the loading connections, sample lines, thermometer wells and gauging devices. Platforms for loaders may or may not be provided on top of cars. Older non-pressure tank cars may have one or more expansion domes. Fittings are provided on the bottom of tank cars for unloading or cleaning. Head shields are provided on the ends of tank cars to prevent puncture of the shell by the coupler of another car during derailments.

LNG is shipped as a cryogenic gas in insulated tank truck and rail pressure tank cars. Pressure tank trucks and rail tank cars for LNG transport have a stainless steel inner reservoir suspended in an outer reservoir of carbon steel. The annular space is a vacuum filled with insulation to maintain low temperatures during ship-ment. To prevent gas from igniting back to the tanks, they are equipped with two independent, remotely controlled fail-safe emergency shut-off valves on the filling and discharge lines and have gauges on both the inside and outside reservoirs.

LPG is transported on land in specially designed rail tank cars (up to 130 m^3 capacity) or tank trucks (up to 40 m^3 capacity). Tank trucks and rail tank cars for LPG transport are typically uninsulated steel cylinders with spherical bottoms, equipped with gauges, thermometers, two safety relief valves, a gas level meter and maximum fill indicator and baffles.

Rail tank cars transporting LNG or LPG should not be over-loaded, since they may sit on a siding for some period of time and be exposed to high ambient temperatures, which could cause overpressure and venting. Bond wires and grounding cables are provided at rail and tank truck loading racks to help neutralize and dissipate static electricity. They should be connected before operations commence and not disconnected until operations are complete and all valves are closed. Truck and rail loading facili-ties are typically protected by fire water spray or mist systems and fire extinguishers.

Tank trucks

Petroleum products and crude oil tank trucks are typically con-structed of carbon steel, aluminium or a plasticized fibreglass material, and vary in size from 1,900-l tank wagons to jumbo 53,200-l tankers. The capacity of tank trucks is governed by regulatory agencies, and usually is dependent upon highway and bridge capacity limitations and the allowable weight per axle or total amount of product allowed.

There are pressurized and non-pressurized tank trucks, which may be non-insulated or insulated depending on their service and the products transported. Pressurized tank trucks are usually single compartment, and non-pressurized tank trucks may have single or multiple compartments. Regardless of the number of compartments on a tank truck, each compartment must be treated individually, with its own loading, unloading and safety-relief devices. Compartments may be separated by single or dou-ble walls. Regulations may require that incompatible products and flammable and combustible liquids carried in different com-partments on the same vehicle be separated by double walls. When pressure testing compartments, the space between the walls should also be tested for liquid or vapour.

Tank trucks have either hatches which open for top loading, valves for closed top- or bottom-loading and unloading, or both. All compartments have hatch entries for cleaning and are equipped with safety relief devices to mitigate internal pressure when exposed to abnormal conditions. These devices include safety relief valves held in place by a spring which can open to relieve pressure and then close, hatches on non-pressure tanks which pop open if the relief valves fail and rupture discs on pressurized tank trucks. A vacuum relief valve is provided for each non-pressurized tank truck compartment to prevent vacuum when unloading from the bottom. Non-pressurized tank trucks have railings on top to protect the hatches, relief valves and vapour recovery system in case of a rollover. Tank trucks are usually equipped with breakaway, self-closing devices installed on compartment bottom loading and unloading pipes and fittings to prevent spills in case of damage in a rollover or collision.

Rail tank car and tank truck loading and unloading

While railroad tank cars are almost always loaded and unloaded by workers assigned to these specific duties, tank trucks may be loaded and unloaded by either loaders or drivers. Tank cars and tank trucks are loaded at facilities called loading racks, and may be top loaded through open hatches or closed connections, bottom loaded through closed connections, or a combination of both.

Loading

Workers who load and unload crude oil, LPG, petroleum prod-ucts, and acids and additives used in the oil and gas industry, should have a basic understanding of the characteristics of the products handled, their hazards and exposures and the operating procedures and work practices needed to perform the job safely. Many government agencies and companies require the use and completion of inspection forms upon receipt and shipment and prior to loading and unloading railroad tank cars and tank trucks. Tank trucks and railroad tank cars may be loaded through open hatches on the top or through fittings and valves at the top or bottom of each tank or compartment. Closed connections are required when pressure loading and where vapour recovery sys-tems are provided. If loading systems do not activate for any reason (such as improper operation of the vapour recovery system or a fault in the grounding or bonding system), by-pass should not be attempted without approval. All hatches should be closed and securely latched during transit.

Workers should follow safe work practices to avoid slips and falls when top loading. If loading controls use pre-set meters, loaders must be careful to load the correct products into the assigned tanks and compartments. All compartment hatches should be shut when bottom loading, and when top loading, only the compartment being loaded should be open. When top load-ing, splash loading should be avoided by placing the loading tube or hose close to the bottom of the compartment and starting to load slowly until the opening is submerged. During manual top loading operations, loaders should remain in attendance, not tie down the loading shut-off (deadman) control and not overfill the compartment. Loaders should avoid exposures to product and vapour by standing upwind and averting the head when top loading through open hatches and by wearing protective equip-ment when handling additives, obtaining samples and draining hoses. Loaders should be aware of and follow prescribed response actions in case of a hose or line rupture, spill, release, fire or other emergency.

Unloading and delivery

When unloading tank cars and tank trucks, it is important first to assure that each product is unloaded into the proper designated

102. TRANSPORT INDUSTRY AND WAREHOUSING

storage tank and that the tank has sufficient capacity to hold all of the product being delivered. Although valves, fill pipes, lines and fill covers should be colour coded or otherwise marked to identify the product contained, the driver should still be responsible for product quality during delivery. Any misdelivery of product, mixing or contamination should be immediately reported to the recipient and to the company to prevent serious consequences. When drivers or operators are required to additize products or obtain samples from storage tanks following delivery to assure product quality or for any other reason, all safety and health provisions specific to the exposure should be followed. Persons engaged in delivery and unloading operations should remain in the vicinity at all times and know what to do in an emergency, including notification, stopping product flow, cleaning spills and when to leave the area.

Pressurized tanks may be unloaded by compressor or pump, and unpressurized tanks by gravity, vehicle pump or recipient pump. Tank trucks and tank cars which carry lubrication or industrial oils, additives and acids are sometimes unloaded by pressurizing the tank with an inert gas such as nitrogen. Tank cars or tank trucks may need to be heated using steam or electric coils in order to unload heavy crude oils, viscous products and waxes. All of these activities have inherent dangers and exposures. Where required by regulation, unloading should not commence until the vapour recovery hoses have been connected between the delivery tank and the storage tank. When delivering petroleum products to residences, farms and commercial accounts, drivers should gauge any tank which is not equipped with a vent alarm in order to prevent an overfill.

Loading-rack fire protection

Fires and explosions at top and bottom tank car and tank truck loading racks may occur from causes such as electrostatic build-up and incendiary spark discharge in a flammable atmosphere, unauthorized hot work, flashback from a vapour recovery unit, smoking or other unsafe practices.

Sources of ignition, such as smoking, running internal combustion engines and hot work activity, should be controlled at the loading rack at all times, and particularly during loading or other operations when a spill or release may occur. Loading racks may be equipped with portable fire extinguishers and manually or automatically operated foam, water or dry chemical fire extinguishing systems. If vapour recovery systems are in use, flame arrestors should be provided to prevent flashback from the recovery unit to the loading rack.

Drainage should be provided at loading racks to divert product spills away from the loader, tank truck or tank car and the loading rack pad. Drains should be provided with fire traps to prevent migration of flames and vapours through sewer systems. Other loading-rack safety considerations include emergency shut-down controls placed at loading spots and other strategic locations in the terminal and automatic pressure-sensing valves which stop product flow to the rack in case of a leak in the product lines. Some companies have installed automatic brake lock systems on their tank truck fill connections, which lock the brakes and will not allow the truck to be moved from the rack until the fill lines have been disconnected.

Electrostatic ignition hazards

Some products such as intermediate distillates and low-vapour-pressure fuels and solvents tend to accumulate electrostatic charges. When loading tank cars and tank trucks, there is always an opportunity for electrostatic charges to be generated by friction as product goes through lines and filters and by splash loading. This can be mitigated by designing loading racks to allow for relaxation time in piping downstream from pumps and filters.

Compartments should be checked to assure that they do not contain any unbonded or floating objects which could act as static accumulators. Bottom loaded compartments may be provided with internal cables to help dissipate electrostatic charges. Sample containers, thermometers or other items should not be lowered into compartments until a waiting period of at least 1 minute has elapsed, to allow any electrostatic charge which has accumulated in the product to dissipate.

Bonding and grounding are important considerations in dissipating electrostatic charges which build up during loading operations. By keeping the fill pipe in contact with the metal side of the hatch when top loading, and through the use of metal loading arms or conductive hose when loading through closed connections, the tank truck or tank car is bonded to the loading rack, maintaining the same electrical charge between the objects so that a spark is not created when the loading tube or hose is removed. The tank car or tank truck may also be bonded to the loading rack by use of a bonding cable, which carries any accumulated charge from a terminal on the tank to the rack, where it is then grounded by a grounding cable and rod. Similar bonding precautions are needed when unloading from tank cars and tank trucks. Some loading racks are provided with electronic connectors and sensors which will not allow loading pumps to activate until a positive bond is achieved.

During cleaning, maintenance or repair, pressurized LPG tank cars or tank trucks are usually opened to the atmosphere, allowing air to enter the tank. In order to prevent combustion from electrostatic charges when loading these cars for the first time after such activities, it is necessary to reduce the oxygen level below 9.5% by blanketing the tank with inert gas, such as nitrogen. Precautions are needed to prevent liquid nitrogen from entering the tank if the nitrogen is provided from portable containers.

Switch loading

Switch loading occurs when intermediate- or low-vapour-pressure products such as diesel fuel or fuel oil are loaded into a tank car or tank truck compartment which previously contained a flammable product such as gasoline. The electrostatic charge generated during loading can discharge in an atmosphere which is within the flammable range, with a resultant explosion and fire. This hazard can be controlled when top loading by lowering the fill tube to the bottom of the compartment and loading slowly until the end of the tube is submerged to avoid splash loading or agitation. Metal to metal contact should be maintained during loading in order to provide a positive bond between the loading tube and the tank hatchway. When bottom loading, initial slow fill or splash deflectors are used to reduce static build-up. Prior to switch loading, tanks which cannot be drained dry may be flushed out with a small amount of the product to be loaded, to remove any flammable residue in sumps, lines, valves and onboard pumps.

Shipping products by rail box cars and package vans

Petroleum products are shipped by motor truck package vans and railroad box cars in metal, fibre and plastic containers of various sizes, from 55-gallon (209-l) drums to 5-gallon (19-l) pails and from 2-1/2-gallon (9.5-l) to 1-quart (.95-l) containers, in corrugated boxes, usually on pallets. Many industrial and commercial petroleum products are shipped in large metal, plastic or combination intermediate bulk containers ranging in size from 380 to over 2,660 l capacity. LPG is shipped in large and small pressure containers. In addition, samples of crude oil, finished products and used products are shipped by mail or express freight carrier to laboratories for assay and analysis. All of these products, containers and packages have to be handled in accordance with government regulations for hazardous chemicals, flammable and combustible liquids and toxic materials. This requires the use of hazardous materials manifests, shipping documents, permits, receipts and other regulatory requirements, such as marking the outsides of packages, containers, motor trucks and box cars with proper identification and a hazard warning label. Proper utilization of tank trucks and tank cars is important to the petroleum industry. Because storage capacity is finite, delivery schedules need to be met, from the delivery of crude oil to keep refineries running to the delivery of gasoline to service stations, and from the delivery of lubricants to commercial and industrial accounts to the delivery of heating oil to homes.

LPG is supplied to consumers by bulk tank trucks which pump directly into smaller onsite storage tanks, both above ground and below ground (e.g., service stations, farms, commercial and industrial consumers). LPG is also delivered to consumers by truck or van in containers (gas cylinders or bottles). LNG is delivered in special cryogenic containers which have an inner fuel tank surrounded by insulation and an outer shell. Similar containers are provided for vehicles and appliances which use LNG as a fuel. Compressed natural gas is normally delivered in conventional compressed gas cylinders, such as those used on industrial lift trucks.

In addition to the normal safety and health precautions required in rail car and package trucking operations, such as moving and handling heavy objects and operating industrial trucks, workers should be familiar with the hazards of the products they are handling and delivering, and know what to do in case of a spill, release or other emergency. For example, intermediate bulk containers and drums should not be dropped out of box cars or from the tailgates of trucks onto the ground. Both companies and government agencies have established special regulations and requirements for drivers and operators who are involved in the transport and delivery of flammable and hazardous petroleum products.

Tank truck and package van drivers often work alone and may have to travel great distances for a number of days to deliver their loads. They work both day and night and in all sorts of weather conditions. Manoeuvring super-sized tank trucks into service stations and customer locations without hitting parked vehicles or fixed objects requires patience, skill and experience. Drivers should have the physical and mental characteristics required for this work.

Driving tank trucks is different from driving package vans in that the liquid product tends to shift forward as the truck stops, backwards as the truck accelerates and from side to side as the truck turns. Tank truck compartments should be fitted with baffles which restrict the movement of product during transport. Considerable skill is required by drivers to overcome the inertia created by this phenomenon, called "mass in motion". Occasionally, tank truck drivers are required to pump out storage tanks. This activity requires special equipment, including suction hose and transfer pumps, and safety precautions, such as bonding and grounding to dissipate electrostatic build-up and to prevent any release of vapours or liquids.

Motor vehicle and rail car emergency response

Drivers and operators should be familiar with notification requirements and emergency response actions in case of a fire or a release of product, gas or vapour. Product identification and hazard warning placards in compliance with industry, association or national marking standards are posted on trucks and rail cars to allow emergency responders to determine the precautions needed in case of a spill or release of vapour, gas or product. Motor vehicle drivers and train operators may also be required to carry material safety data sheets (MSDSs) or other documentation describing the hazards and precautions for handling the products being transported. Some companies or government agencies require that vehicles transporting flammable liquids or hazardous materials carry first aid kits, fire extinguishers, spill clean-up materials and portable hazard warning devices or signals to alert motorists if the vehicle is stopped alongside a highway.

Special equipment and techniques are required if a tank car or tank truck needs to be emptied of product as the result of an accident or rollover. Removal of product through fixed piping and valves or by using special knock-out plates on tank truck hatches is preferred; however, under certain conditions holes may be drilled in tanks using prescribed safe work procedures. Regardless of the method of removal, tanks should be grounded and a bond connection provided between the tank being emptied and the receiving tank.

Cleaning tank cars and tank trucks

Entering a tank car or tank truck compartment for inspection, cleaning, maintenance or repair is a hazardous activity requiring that all ventilation, testing, gas freeing and other confined-space entry and permit system requirements be followed in order to assure a safe operation. Cleaning tank cars and tank trucks is not any different from cleaning petroleum-product storage tanks, and all the same safety and health exposure precautions and procedures apply. Tank cars and tank trucks may contain residue of flammable, hazardous or toxic materials in sumps and unloading piping, or have been unloaded using an inert gas, such as nitrogen, so that what may appear to be a clean, safe space is not. Tanks which have contained crude oil, residues, asphalt or high-melting-point products may need to be steam or chemically cleaned prior to ventilation and entry, or may have a pyrophoric hazard. Ventilating tanks to free them from vapours and toxic or inert gases may be accomplished by opening the lowest and furthest valve or connection on each tank or compartment and placing an air eductor at the furthest top opening. Monitoring should be performed prior to entry without respiratory protection to assure that all of the corners and low spots in the tank, such as sumps, have been thoroughly vented, and ventilation should continue while working in the tank.

Aboveground Tank Storage of Liquid Petroleum Products

Crude oil, gas, LNG and LPG, processing additives, chemicals and petroleum products are stored in aboveground and underground atmospheric (non-pressure) and pressure storage tanks. Storage tanks are located at the ends of feeder lines and gathering lines, along truck pipelines, at marine loading and unloading facilities and in refineries, terminals and bulk plants. This section covers aboveground atmospheric storage tanks in refinery, terminal and bulk plant tank farms. (Information concerning aboveground pressure tanks is covered below, and information concerning underground tanks and small aboveground tanks is in the article "Motor vehicle fuelling and servicing operations".)

Terminals and bulk plants

Terminals are storage facilities which generally receive crude oil and petroleum products by trunk pipeline or marine vessel. Terminals store and redistribute crude oil and petroleum products to refineries, other terminals, bulk plants, service stations and consumers by pipelines, marine vessels, railroad tank cars and tank trucks. Terminals may be owned and operated by oil companies, pipeline companies, independent terminal operators, large industrial or commercial consumers or petroleum product distributors.

Bulk plants are usually smaller than terminals and typically receive petroleum products by rail tank car or tank truck, normally from terminals but occasionally direct from refineries. Bulk plants store and redistribute products to service stations and consumers by tank truck or tank wagon (small tank trucks of approxi-

102. TRANSPORT INDUSTRY AND WAREHOUSING

mately 9,500 to 1,900 l capacity). Bulk plants may be operated by oil companies, distributors or independent owners.

Tank farms

Tank farms are groupings of storage tanks at producing fields, refineries, marine, pipeline and distribution terminals and bulk plants which store crude oil and petroleum products. Within tank farms, individual tanks or groups of two or more tanks are usually surrounded by enclosures called berms, dykes or fire walls. These tank farm enclosures may vary in construction and height, from 45-cm earth berms around piping and pumps inside dykes to concrete walls that are taller than the tanks they surround. Dykes may be built of earth, clay or other materials; they are covered with gravel, limestone or sea shells to control erosion; they vary in height and are wide enough for vehicles to drive along the top. The primary functions of these enclosures are to contain, direct and divert rain water, physically separate tanks to prevent the spread of fire in one area to another, and to contain a spill, release, leak or overflow from a tank, pump or pipe within the area.

Dyke enclosures may be required by regulation or company policy to be sized and maintained to hold a specific amount of product. For example, a dyke enclosure may need to contain at least 110% of the capacity of the largest tank therein, allowing for the volume displaced by the other tanks and the amount of product remaining in the largest tank after hydrostatic equilibrium is reached. Dyke enclosures may also be required to be constructed with impervious clay or plastic liners to prevent spilled or released product from contaminating soil or groundwater.

Storage tanks

There are a number of different types of vertical and horizontal aboveground atmospheric and pressure storage tanks in tank farms, which contain crude oil, petroleum feedstocks, intermediate stocks or finished petroleum products. Their size, shape, design, configuration, and operation depend on the amount and type of products stored and company or regulatory requirements. Aboveground vertical tanks may be provided with double bottoms to prevent leakage onto the ground and cathodic protection to minimize corrosion. Horizontal tanks may be constructed with double walls or placed in vaults to contain any leakage.

Atmospheric cone roof tanks

Cone roof tanks are aboveground, horizontal or vertical, covered, cylindrical atmospheric vessels. Cone roof tanks have external stairways or ladders and platforms, and weak roof to shell seams, vents, scuppers or overflow outlets; they may have appurtenances such as gauging tubes, foam piping and chambers, overflow sensing and signalling systems, automatic gauging systems and so on.

When volatile crude oil and flammable liquid petroleum products are stored in cone roof tanks there is an opportunity for the vapour space to be within the flammable range. Although the space between the top of the product and the tank roof is normally vapour rich, an atmosphere in the flammable range can occur when product is first put into an empty tank or as air enters the tank through vents or pressure/vacuum valves when product is withdrawn and as the tank breathes during temperature changes. Cone roof tanks may be connected to vapour recovery systems.

Conservation tanks are a type of cone roof tank with an upper and lower section separated by a flexible membrane designed to contain any vapour produced when the product warms up and expands due to exposure to sunlight in the daytime and to return the vapour to the tank when it condenses as the tank cools down at night. Conservation tanks are typically used to store aviation gasoline and similar products.

Atmospheric floating roof tanks

Floating roof tanks are aboveground, vertical, open top or covered cylindrical atmospheric vessels that are equipped with floating roofs. The primary purpose of the floating roof is to minimize the vapour space between the top of the product and the bottom of the floating roof so that it is always vapour rich, thus precluding the chance of a vapour-air mixture in the flammable range. All floating roof tanks have external stairways or ladders and platforms, adjustable stairways or ladders for access to the floating roof from the platform, and may have appurtenances such as shunts which electrically bond the roof to the shell, gauging tubes, foam piping and chambers, overflow sensing and signalling systems, automatic gauging systems and so on. Seals or boots are provided around the perimeter of floating roofs to prevent product or vapour from escaping and collecting on the roof or in the space above the roof.

Floating roofs are provided with legs which may be set in high or low positions depending on the type of operation. Legs are normally maintained in the low position so that the greatest possible amount of product can be withdrawn from the tank without creating a vapour space between the top of the product and the bottom of the floating roof. As tanks are brought out of service prior to entry for inspection, maintenance, repair or cleaning, there is a need to adjust the roof legs into the high position to allow room to work under the roof once the tank is empty. When the tank is returned to service, the legs are readjusted into the low position after it is filled with product.

Aboveground floating roof storage tanks are further classified as external floating roof tanks, internal floating roof tanks or covered external floating roof tanks.

External (open top) floating roof tanks are those with floating covers installed on open-top storage tanks. External floating roofs are usually constructed of steel and provided with pontoons or other means of flotation. They are equipped with roof drains to remove water, boots or seals to prevent vapour releases and adjustable stairways to reach the roof from the top of the tank regardless of its position. They may also have secondary seals to minimize release of vapour to the atmosphere, weather shields to protect the seals and foam dams to contain foam in the seal area in case of a fire or seal leak. Entry onto external floating roofs for gauging, maintenance or other activities may be considered confined-space entry, depending on the level of the roof below the top of the tank, the products contained in the tank and government regulations and company policy.

Internal floating roof tanks usually are cone roof tanks which have been converted by installing buoyant decks, rafts or internal floating covers inside the tank. Internal floating roofs are typically constructed of various types of sheet metal, aluminium, plastic or metal-covered plastic expanded foam, and their construction may be of the pontoon or pan type, solid buoyant material, or a combination of these. Internal floating roofs are provided with perimeter seals to prevent vapour from escaping into the portion of the tank between the top of the floating roof and the exterior roof. Pressure/vacuum valves or vents are usually provided at the top of the tank to control any hydrocarbon vapours which may accumulate in the space above the internal floater. Internal floating roof tanks have ladders installed for access from the cone roof to the floating roof. Entry onto internal floating roofs for any purpose should be considered confined-space entry.

Covered (external) floating roof tanks are basically external floating roof tanks that have been retrofitted with a geodesic dome, snow cap or similar semi-fixed cover or roof so that the floating roof is no longer open to the atmosphere. Newly constructed covered external floating roof tanks may incorporate typical floating roofs designed for internal floating roof tanks. Entry onto covered external floating roofs for gauging, maintenance or other activities may be considered confined-space entry, depending on the construction of the dome or cover, the level of the roof below the top of the tank, the products contained in the tank and government regulations and company policy.

Pipeline and marine receipts

An important safety, product quality and environmental concern in tank storage facilities is to prevent intermixing of products and overfilling tanks by developing and implementing safe operating procedures and work practices. Safe operation of storage tanks depends on receiving product into tanks within their defined capacity by designating receiving tanks prior to delivery, gauging tanks to determine the available capacity and ensuring that valves are properly aligned and that only the receiving tank inlet is opened, so the correct amount of product is delivered into the assigned tank. Drains in dyke areas surrounding tanks receiving product should normally be kept closed during receipt in case an overfill or spill occurs. Overfill protection and prevention can be accomplished by a variety of safe operating practices, including manual controls and automatic detection, signalling and shut-down systems and a means of communication, all of which should be mutually understood and acceptable to product transfer personnel at the pipeline, marine vessel and terminal or refinery.

Government regulations or company policy may require that automatic product level detection devices and signal and shut-down systems be installed on tanks receiving flammable liquids and other products from trunk pipelines or marine vessels. Where such systems are installed, electronic system integrity tests should be conducted on a regular basis or prior to product transfer, and if the system fails, transfers should follow manual receipt procedures. Receipts should be monitored manually or automatically, onsite or from a remote control location, to ensure that operations are proceeding as planned. Upon completion of transfer, all valves should be returned to normal operating position or set for the next receipt. Pumps, valves, pipe connections, bleeder and sample lines, manifold areas, drains and sumps should be inspected and maintained to assure good condition and to prevent spills and leakage.

Tank gauging and sampling

Tank storage facilities should establish procedures and safe work practices for gauging and sampling crude oil and petroleum products which take into consideration the potential hazards involved with each product stored and each type of tank in the facility. Although tank gauging is often done using automatic mechanical or electronic devices, manual gauging should be performed at scheduled intervals to assure the accuracy of the automatic systems.

Manual gauging and sampling operations usually require the operator to climb to the top of the tank. When gauging floating roof tanks, the operator then has to descend onto the floating roof unless the tank is fitted with gauging and sampling tubes that are accessible from the platform. With cone roof tanks, the gauger must open a roof hatch in order to lower the gauge into the tank. Gaugers should be aware of the confined-space entry requirements and potential hazards when entering onto covered floating roofs or down upon open-top floating roofs which are below established height levels. This may require the use of monitoring devices, such as oxygen, combustible gas and hydrogen sulphide detectors and personal and respiratory protective equipment.

Product temperatures and samples may be taken at the same time as manual gauging is conducted. Temperatures may also be recorded automatically and samples obtained from built-in sample connections. Manual gauging and sampling should be restricted while tanks are receiving product. Following the completion of receipt, a relaxation period of from 30 minutes to 4 hours, depending on the product and company policy, should be required to allow any electrostatic build-up to dissipate before conducting manual sampling or gauging. Some companies require that communications or visual contact be established and maintained between gaugers and other facility personnel when descending upon floating roofs. Entry onto tank roofs or platforms for gauging, sampling or other activities should be restricted during thunderstorms.

Tank venting and cleaning

Storage tanks are taken out of service for inspection, testing, maintenance, repair, retrofitting and tank cleaning as needed or at regular intervals dependent on government regulations, company policy and operating service requirements. Although tank venting, cleaning and entry is a potentially hazardous operation, this work can be accomplished without incident, provided that proper procedures are established and safe work practices followed. Without such precautions, injury or damage can occur from explosions, fires, lack of oxygen, toxic exposures and physical hazards.

Preliminary preparations

A number of preliminary preparations are required after it has been decided that a tank needs to be taken out of service for inspection, maintenance or cleaning. These include: scheduling storage and supply alternatives; reviewing the tank history to determine whether it has ever contained leaded product or has previously been cleaned and certified lead free; determining the amount and type of products contained and how much residue will remain in the tank; inspecting the outside of the tank, the surrounding area and the equipment to be used for product removal, vapour freeing and cleaning; assuring that personnel are trained, qualified and familiar with facility permit and safety procedures; assigning job responsibilities in accordance with the facility's confined-space entry and hot- and safe-work permit requirements; and holding a meeting between terminal and tank cleaning personnel or contractors before tank cleaning or construction starts.

Control of ignition sources

After the removal of all available product from the tank through fixed piping, and before any water draws or sample lines are opened, all sources of ignition should be removed from the surrounding area until the tank is declared vapour free. Vacuum trucks, compressors, pumps and other equipment which is electrically or motor driven should be located upwind, either on top of or outside the dyke area, or, if inside the dyke area, at least 20 m from the tank or any other sources of flammable vapours. Tank preparation, venting and cleaning activities should cease during electrical storms.

Removing residue

The next step is to remove as much remaining product or residue in the tank as possible through pipeline and waterdraw connections. A safe-work permit may be issued for this work. Water or distillate fuel may be injected into the tank through fixed connections to help float product out of the tank. Residue removed from tanks that have contained sour crude should be kept wet until disposal to avoid spontaneous combustion.

Isolating the tank

After all available product has been removed through fixed piping, all piping connected to the tank, including product lines, vapour recovery lines, foam piping, sample lines and so on, should be disconnected by closing the valves nearest the tank and inserting blinds in the lines on the tank side of the valve to prevent any vapours from entering the tank from the lines. The portion of piping between the blinds and the tank should be drained and flushed. Valves outside the dyke area should be closed and locked or tagged. Tank pumps, internal mixers, cathodic protection systems, electronic gauging and level detection systems and so on should be disconnected, de-energized and locked or tagged out.

Vapour freeing

The tank is now ready to be made vapour free. Intermittent or continuous vapour testing should be conducted and work in the area restricted during tank ventilation. Natural ventilation, through opening the tank to the atmosphere, is not usually preferred, since it is neither as fast nor as safe as forced ventilation. There are a number of methods of mechanically venting a tank, depending on its size, construction, condition and internal configuration. In one method, cone roof tanks may be vapour freed by placing an eductor (a portable ventilator) at a hatch on the top of the tank, starting it slowly while a hatch at the bottom of the tank is opened and then setting it on high speed to draw air and vapours through the tank.

A safe- or hot-work permit should be issued covering ventilation activities. All blowers and eductors should be securely bonded to the tank shell to prevent electrostatic ignition. For safety purposes, blowers and eductors should preferably be operated by compressed air; however, explosion-proof electric- or steam-driven motors have been used. Internal floating roof tanks may need to have the portions above and below the floating roof vented separately. If vapours are discharged from a bottom hatch, a vertical tube at least 4 m above ground level and no lower than the surrounding dyke wall is needed in order to prevent vapours from collecting at low levels or reaching a source of ignition before dissipating. If necessary, vapours may be directed to the facility vapour recovery system.

As ventilation progresses, the remaining residue can be washed down and removed through the open bottom hatch by water and suction hoses, both of which should be bonded to the tank shell to prevent electrostatic ignition. Tanks which have contained sour crude oil or high-sulphur residual products may generate spontaneous heat and ignite as they dry out during ventilation. This should be avoided by wetting the inside of the tank with water to blanket the deposits from air and prevent a rise in temperature. Any iron sulphide residue should be removed from the open hatch to prevent ignition of vapours during ventilation. Workers engaged in washdown, removal and wetting activities should wear appropriate personal and respiratory protection.

Initial entry, inspection and certification

An indication of the progress being made in vapour freeing the tank can be obtained by monitoring vapours at the point of eduction during ventilation. Once it appears that the flammable vapour level is below that established by regulatory agencies or company policy, entry can be made into the tank for inspection and testing purposes. The entrant should wear appropriate personal and air-supplied respiratory protection; after testing the atmosphere at the hatch and obtaining an entry permit, the worker may enter the tank to continue testing and inspection. Checks for obstructions, falling roofs, weak supports, holes in the floor and other physical hazards should be conducted during the inspection.

Cleaning, maintenance and repair

As ventilation continues and the vapour levels in the tank drop lower, permits may be issued allowing entry by workers with appropriate personal and respiratory equipment, if needed, to start cleaning the tank. Monitoring for oxygen, flammable vapours and toxic atmospheres should continue, and if the levels inside the tank exceed those established for entry, the permit should automatically expire and the entrants should immediately leave the tank until the safe level is again achieved and the permit is reissued. Ventilation should continue during cleaning operations as long as any residue or sludge remains in the tank. Only low-voltage lighting or approved flashlights should be used during inspection and clean-up.

After tanks have been cleaned and dried, a final inspection and testing should be conducted before maintenance, repair or retrofitting work is started. Careful inspection of sumps, wells, floor plates, floating roof pontoons, supports and columns is needed to assure that no leaks have developed which allowed product to enter these spaces or seep beneath the floor. Spaces between foam seals and weather shields or secondary containment should also be inspected and tested for vapours. If the tank has previously contained leaded gasoline, or if no tank history is available, a lead-in-air test should be conducted and the tank certified lead free before workers are allowed inside without air-supplied respiratory equipment.

A hot-work permit should be issued covering welding, cutting and other hot work, and a safe-work permit issued to cover other repair and maintenance activities. Welding or hot work can create toxic or noxious fumes inside the tank, requiring monitoring, respiratory protection and continued ventilation. When tanks are to be retrofitted with double bottoms or internal floating roofs, a large hole is often cut into the side of the tank to provide unrestricted access and avoid the need for confined-space entry permits.

Blast cleaning and painting the outside of tanks usually follows tank cleaning and is completed before the tank is returned to service. These activities, together with cleaning and painting tank farm piping, may be performed while tanks and pipes are in service, by implementing and following prescribed safety procedures, such as conducting monitoring for hydrocarbon vapours and stopping blast cleaning while nearby tanks are receiving flammable liquid products. Blast cleaning with sand has the potential for hazardous exposure to silica; therefore, many government agencies and companies require the use of special non-toxic blast cleaning materials or grit, which may be collected, cleaned and recycled. Special vacuum collection blast cleaning devices may be used in order to avoid contamination when cleaning leaded paint from tanks and piping. Following blast cleaning, spots in the tank walls or piping suspected of having leaks and seeps should be tested and repaired before being painted.

Returning the tank to service

In preparation for return to service upon completion of tank cleaning, inspection, maintenance or repair, the hatches are closed, all blinds are removed and the piping is reconnected to the tank. Valves are unlocked, opened and aligned, and mechanical and electrical devices are reactivated. Many government agencies and companies require tanks to be hydrostatically tested to assure that there are no leaks before they are returned to service. Since a considerable amount of water is required to obtain the necessary pressure head for an accurate test, a water bottom topped with diesel fuel is often used. Upon completion of the testing, the tank is emptied and made ready to receive product. After receipt is completed and a relaxation time has elapsed, the legs on floating roof tanks are reset into the low position.

Fire protection and prevention

Whenever hydrocarbons are present in closed containers such as storage tanks in refineries, terminals and bulk plants, the potential exists for release of liquids and vapours. These vapours could mix with air in the flammable range and, if subjected to a source of ignition, cause an explosion or fire. Regardless of the capability of fire protection systems and personnel in the facility, the key to fire protection is fire prevention. Spills and releases should be stopped from entering sewers and drainage systems. Small spills should be covered with wet blankets, and larger spills with foam, to prevent vapours from escaping and mixing with air. Sources of ignition in areas when hydrocarbon vapours may be present should be eliminated or controlled. Portable fire extinguishers should be carried on service vehicles and located at accessible and strategic positions throughout the facility.

The establishment and implementation of safe work procedures and practices such as hot- and safe- (cold-) work permit systems, electrical classification programmes, lockout/tagout programmes, and employee and contractor training and education is critical to preventing fires. Facilities should develop preplanned emergency procedures, and employees should be knowledgeable in their responsibilities for reporting and responding to fires and evacuation. Telephone numbers of responsible persons and agencies to be notified in case of an emergency should be posted at the facility and a means of communication provided. Local fire departments, emergency response, public safety and mutual aid organizations should also be aware of the procedures and familiar with the facility and its hazards.

Hydrocarbon fires are controlled by one or a combination of methods, as follows:

- *Removing fuel.* One of the best and easiest methods of controlling and extinguishing a hydrocarbon fire is to shut off the source of fuel by closing a valve, diverting product flow or, if a small amount of product is involved, controlling exposures while allowing the product to burn away. Foam may also be used to cover hydrocarbon spills to prevent vapours from being emitted and mixing with the air.
- *Removing oxygen.* Another method is to shut off the supply of air or oxygen by smothering fires with foam or water fog, or by using carbon dioxide or nitrogen to displace air in enclosed spaces.
- *Cooling.* Water fog, mist or spray and carbon dioxide may be used to extinguish certain petroleum product fires by cooling the temperature of the fire below the product's ignition temperature and by stopping vapours from forming and mixing with air.
- *Interrupting combustion.* Chemicals such as dry powders and halon extinguish fires by interrupting the chemical reaction of the fire.

Storage tank fire protection

Storage tank fire protection and prevention is a specialized science which depends on the interrelationship of tank type, condition and size; product and amount stored in the tank; tank spacing, dyking and drainage; facility fire protection and response capabilities; outside assistance; and company philosophy, industry standards and government regulations. Storage tank fires may be easy or very difficult to control and extinguish, depending primarily on whether the fire is detected and attacked during its initial inception. Storage tank operators should refer to the numerous recommended practices and standards developed by organizations such as the American Petroleum Institute (API) and the US National Fire Protection Association (NFPA), which cover storage tank fire prevention and protection in great detail.

If open-top floating roof storage tanks are out of round or if the seals are worn or not tight against the tank shells, vapours can escape and mix with air, forming flammable mixtures. In such situations, when lightning strikes, fires may occur at the point where the roof seals meet the shell of the tank. If detected early, small seal fires can often be extinguished by a hand-carried dry powder extinguisher or with foam applied from a foam hose or foam system.

If a seal fire cannot be controlled with hand extinguishers or hose streams, or if a large fire is in progress, foam may be applied onto the roof through fixed or semi-fixed systems or by large foam monitors. Precautions are necessary when applying foam onto the roofs of floating roof tanks; if too much weight is placed on the roof, it may tilt or sink, allowing a large surface area of product to be exposed and become involved in the fire. Foam dams are used on floating roof tanks to trap foam in the area between the seals and the tank shell. As the foam settles, water drains out under the foam dams and should be removed through the tank roof drain system to avoid overweighing and sinking the roof.

Depending on government regulations and company policy, storage tanks may be provided with fixed or semi-fixed foam systems which include: piping to the tanks, foam risers and foam chambers on the tanks; subsurface injection piping and nozzles inside the bottom of tanks; and distribution piping and foam dams on the tops of tanks. With fixed systems, foam-water solutions are generated in centrally located foam houses and pumped to the tank through a piping system. Semi-fixed foam systems typically use portable foam tanks, foam generators and pumps which are brought to the tank involved, connected to a water supply and connected to the tank's foam piping. Water-foam solutions may also be centrally generated and distributed within the facility through a system of piping and hydrants, and hoses would be used to connect the nearest hydrant to the tank's semi-fixed foam system.

Where tanks are not provided with fixed or semi-fixed foam systems, foam may be applied onto the tops of tanks, using foam monitors, fire hoses and nozzles. Regardless of the method of application, in order to control a fully involved tank fire, a specific amount of foam must be applied using special techniques at a specific concentration and rate of flow for a minimum amount of time depending primarily on the size of the tank, the product involved and the surface area of the fire. If there is not enough foam concentrate available to meet the required application criteria, the possibility of control or extinguishment is minimal.

Only trained and knowledgeable fire-fighters should be allowed to use water to fight liquid petroleum tank fires. Instantaneous eruptions, or boil-overs, can occur when water turns into steam upon direct application onto tank fires involving crude or heavy petroleum products. As water is heavier than most hydrocarbon fuels, it will sink to the bottom of a tank and, if enough is applied, fill the tank and push the burning product up and over the top of the tank.

Water is typically used to control or extinguish spill fires around the outside of tanks so that valves can be operated to control product flow, to cool the sides of involved tanks to prevent boiling liquid–expanding vapour explosions (BLEVEs—see the section "Fire hazards of LHGs" below) and to reduce the effect of heat and flame impingement on adjacent tanks and equipment. Because of the need for specialized training, materials and equipment, rather than allow employees to attempt to extinguish tank fires, many terminals and bulk plants have established a policy to remove as much product as possible from the involved tank, protect adjacent structures from heat and flame and allow the remaining product in the tank to burn under controlled conditions until the fire burns out.

Terminal and bulk plant health and safety

Storage tank foundations, supports and piping should be regularly inspected for corrosion, erosion, settling or other visible damage to prevent loss or degradation of product. Tank pressure/vacuum valves, seals and shields, vents, foam chambers, roof drains, water draw-off valves and overfill detection devices should be inspected, tested and maintained on a regular schedule, including removal of ice in the winter. Where flame arrestors are installed on tank vents or in vapour recovery lines, they have to be inspected and cleaned regularly and kept free of frost in the winter to ensure proper operation. Valves on tank outlets which close automatically in case of fire or drop in pressure should be checked for operability.

Dyke surfaces should drain or slope away from tanks, pumps and piping to remove any spilled or released product to a safe area. Dyke walls should be maintained in good condition, with drain valves kept closed except when draining water and dyke areas excavated as needed to maintain design capacity. Stairways, ramps, ladders, platforms and railings to loading racks, dykes and tanks should be maintained in a safe condition, free of ice, snow and oil. Leaking tanks and piping should be repaired as soon as possible. The use of victaulic or similar couplings on piping within dyked areas which could be exposed to heat should be discouraged to prevent lines from opening during fires.

Safety procedures and safe work practices should be established and implemented, and training or education provided, so that terminal and bulk plant operators, maintenance personnel, tank truck drivers and contractor personnel can work safely. These should include, as a minimum, information concerning the basics of hydrocarbon fire ignition, control and extinguishment; hazards and protection from exposures to toxic substances such as hydrogen sulphide and polynuclear aromatics in crude oil and residual fuels, benzene in gasoline and additives such as tetraethyl lead and methyl-*tert*-butyl ether (MTBE); emergency response actions; and normal physical and climatic hazards associated with this activity.

Asbestos or other insulation may be present in the facility as protection for tanks and piping. Appropriate safe-work and personal protective measures should be established and followed for handling, removing and disposing of such materials.

Environmental protection

Terminal operators and employees should be aware of and comply with government regulations and company policies covering environmental protection of ground and surface water, soil and air from pollution by petroleum liquids and vapours, and for handling and removing hazardous waste.

- *Water contamination.* Many terminals have oil/water separators to handle contaminated water from tank containment areas, run-off from loading racks and parking areas and water drained from tanks and open-top tank roofs. Terminals may be required to meet established water quality standards and obtain permits before discharging water.
- *Air pollution.* Air pollution prevention includes minimizing releases of vapours from valves and vents. Vapour recovery units collect vapours from loading racks and marine docks, even when tanks are vented prior to entry. These vapours are either processed and returned to storage as liquids or burned.
- *Spills on land and water.* Government agencies and companies may require that oil storage facilities have spill prevention control and counter-measure plans, and that personnel be trained and aware of the potential hazards, notifications to be made and the actions to take in case of a spill or release. In addition to handling spills within the terminal facility, personnel are often trained and equipped to respond to offsite emergencies, such as a tank truck rollover.
- *Sewage and hazardous waste.* Terminals may be required to meet regulatory requirements and obtain permits for discharge of sewage and oily waste to public or privately owned treatment

works. Various government requirements and company procedures may apply to the onsite storage and handling of hazardous waste such as asbestos insulation, tank cleaning residue and contaminated product. Workers should be trained in this activity and be made aware of the potential hazards from exposures which could occur.

LHG Storage and Handling

Bulk storage tanks

LHGs are stored in large bulk storage tanks at the point of process (gas and oil fields, gas plants and refineries) and at the point of distribution to the consumer (terminals and bulk plants). The two most commonly used methods of bulk storage of LHGs are:

- *Under high pressure at ambient temperature.* LHG is stored in steel pressure tanks (at 1.6 to 1.8 mPa) or in underground impermeable rock or salt formations.
- *Under pressure close to atmospheric at low temperature.* LHG is stored in thin-walled, heat-insulated steel storage tanks; in reinforced concrete tanks above and below ground; and in underground cryogenic storage tanks. Pressure is maintained close to atmospheric (0.005 to 0.007 mPa) at a temperature of −160 °C for LNG stored in cryogenic underground storage tanks.

LPG bulk storage vessels are either cylindrically (bullet) shaped horizontal tanks (40 to 200 m^3) or spheres (up to 8,000 m^3). Refrigerated storage is typical for storage in excess of 2,400 m^3. Both horizontal tanks, which are fabricated in shops and transported to the storage site, and spheres, which are built onsite, are designed and constructed in accordance with rigid specifications, codes and standards.

The design pressure of storage tanks should not be less than the vapour pressure of the LHG to be stored at the maximum service temperature. Tanks for propane-butane mixtures should be designed for 100% propane pressure. Consideration should be given to additional pressure requirements resulting from the hydrostatic head of the product at maximum fill and the partial pressure of non-condensible gases in the vapour space. Ideally, liquefied hydrocarbon gas storage vessels should be designed for full vacuum. If not, vacuum relief valves must be provided. Design features should also include pressure relief devices, liquid level gauges, pressure and temperature gauges, internal shut-off valves, back flow preventers and excess flow check valves. Emergency fail-safe shut-down valves and high level signals may also be provided.

Horizontal tanks are either installed aboveground, placed on mounds or buried underground, typically downwind from any existing or potential sources of ignition. If the end of a horizontal tank ruptures from over-pressurization, the shell will be propelled in the direction of the other end. Therefore, it is prudent to place an aboveground tank so that its length is parallel to any important structure (and so that neither end points toward any important structure or equipment). Other factors include tank spacing, location, and fire prevention and protection. Codes and regulations specify minimum horizontal distances between pressurized liquefied hydrocarbon gas storage vessels and adjoining properties, tanks and important structures as well as potential sources of ignition, including processes, flares, heaters, power transmission lines and transformers, loading and unloading facilities, internal combustion engines and gas turbines.

Drainage and spill containment are important considerations in designing and maintaining liquid hydrocarbon gas tank storage areas in order to direct spills to a location where they will minimize risk to the facility and surrounding areas. Dyking and impounding may be used where spills present a potential hazard to other facilities or to the public. Storage tanks are not usually dyked, but the ground is graded so that vapours and liquids do not collect underneath or around the storage tanks, in order to keep burning spills from impinging upon storage tanks.

Cylinders

LHGs for use by consumers, either LNG or LPG, are stored in cylinders at temperatures above their boiling points at normal temperature and pressure. All LNG and LPG cylinders are provided with protective collars, safety valves and valve caps. The basic types of consumer cylinders in use are:

- vapour withdrawal (1/2 to 50 kg) cylinders used by consumers, with larger ones usually refillable on an exchange basis with the supplier
- liquid withdrawal cylinders for dispensing into small consumer-owned refillable cylinders
- motor vehicle fuel cylinders, including vehicle cylinders (40 kg) permanently installed as fuel tanks on motor vehicles and filled and used in the horizontal position, and industrial truck cylinders designed to be stored, filled and handled in the upright position, but used in the horizontal position.

Properties of hydrocarbon gases

According to the NFPA, flammable (combustible) gases are those which burn in the normal concentrations of oxygen in air. The burning of flammable gases is similar to flammable hydrocarbon liquid vapours, as a specific ignition temperature is needed to initiate the burning reaction, and each will burn only within a certain defined range of gas-air mixtures. Flammable liquids have a flashpoint, which is the temperature (always below the boiling point) at which they emit sufficient vapours for combustion. There is no apparent flashpoint for flammable gases, since they are normally at temperatures above their boiling points, even when liquefied, and are therefore always at temperatures well in excess of their flashpoints.

The NFPA (1976) defines compressed and liquefied gases as follows:

- "Compressed gases are those which at all normal atmospheric temperatures inside their containers, exist solely in the gaseous state under pressure."
- "Liquefied gases are those which at normal atmospheric temperatures inside their containers, exist partly in the liquid state and partly in the gaseous state, and are under pressure as long as any liquid remains in the container."

The major factor which determines the pressure inside the vessel is the temperature of the liquid stored. When exposed to the atmosphere, the liquefied gas very rapidly vaporizes, travelling along the ground or water surface unless dispersed into the air by wind or mechanical air movement. At normal atmospheric temperatures, about one-third of the liquid in the container will vaporize.

Flammable gases are further classified as fuel gas and industrial gas. Fuel gases, including natural gas (methane) and LPGs (propane and butane), are burned with air to produce heat in ovens, furnaces, water heaters and boilers. Flammable industrial gases,

such as acetylene, are used in processing, welding, cutting and heat-treating operations. The differences in combustion properties of LNG and LPGs are shown in table 102.11.

Safety hazards of LPG and LNG

The safety hazards applicable to all LHGs are associated with flammability, chemical reactivity, temperature and pressure. The most serious hazard with LHGs is the unplanned release from containers (canisters or tanks) and contact with an ignition source. Release can occur by failure of the container or valves for a variety of reasons, such as overfilling a container or from over-pressure venting when the gas expands due to heating.

The liquid phase of LPG has a high coefficient of expansion, with liquid propane expanding 16 times and liquid butane 11 times as much as water with the same rise in temperature. This property must be considered when filling containers, as free space must be left for the vapour phase. The correct quantity to be filled is determined by a number of variables, including the nature of the liquefied gas, temperature at time of filling and expected ambient temperatures, size, type (insulated or uninsulated) and location of container (above or below ground). Codes and regulations establish allowable quantities, known as "filling densities", which are specific for individual gases or families of similar gases. Filling densities may be expressed by weight, which are absolute values, or by liquid volume, which must always be temperature corrected.

The maximum amount that LPG pressure containers should be filled with liquid is 85% at 40 °C (less at higher temperatures). Because LNG is stored under low temperatures, LNG containers may be liquid filled from 90% to 95%. All containers are provided with overpressure relief devices which normally discharge at pressures relating to liquid temperatures above normal atmospheric temperatures. As these valves cannot reduce the internal pressure to atmospheric, the liquid will always be at a temperature above its normal boiling point. Pure compressed and liquefied hydrocarbon gases are non-corrosive to steel and most copper alloys. However, corrosion can be a serious problem when sulphur compounds and impurities are present in the gas.

LPGs are 1-1/2 to 2 times heavier than air and, when released in air, tend to quickly disperse along the ground or water surface and collect in low areas. However, as soon as the vapour is diluted by air and forms a flammable mixture, its density is essentially the same as air, and it disperses differently. Wind will significantly reduce the dispersion distance for any size of leak. LNG vapours react differently from LPG. Because natural gas has a low vapour density (0.6), it will mix and disperse rapidly in open air, reducing the chance of forming a flammable mixture with air. Natural gas will collect in enclosed spaces and form vapour clouds which could be ignited. Figure 102.17 indicates how a liquefied natural gas vapour cloud spreads downwind in different spill situations.

Although LHG is colourless, when released in air its vapours will be noticeable due to the condensation and freezing of water vapour contained in the atmosphere which is contacted by the

Table 102.11 • Typical approximate combustion properties of liquified hydrocarbon gases.

Type gas	Flammable range (% gas in air)	Vapour pressure (psig at 21 °C)	Normal init. boiling point (°C)	Weight (pounds/gal)	BTU per ft³	Specific gravity (Air = 1)
LNG	4.5–14	1.47	−162	3.5–4	1,050	9.2–10
LPG (propane)	2.1–9.6	132	−46	4.24	2,500	1.52
LPG (butane)	1.9–8.5	17	−9	4.81	3,200	2.0

Figure 102.17 • Extension of LNG vapour cloud down-wind from different spills (wind speed 8.05 km/h).

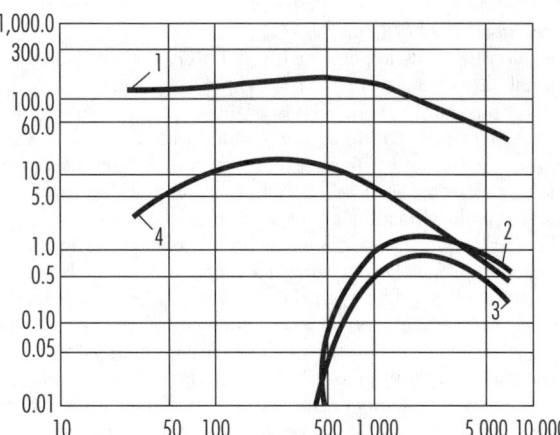

1 Ground spill within 175m square x 5 m high dike
2. Ground spill within 72m diameter x 35 m high dike
3. 62 m diameter above ground tank (100,000 m³), with LNG vapour discharge 35 m above grade
4. 50 m diameter below ground tank (100,000 m³), with LNG vapour discharge 6 m above grade

vapour. This may not occur if the vapour is near ambient temperature and its pressure is relatively low. Instruments are available which can detect the presence of leaking LHG and signal an alarm at levels as low as 15 to 20% of the lower flammable limit (LFL). These devices may also stop all operations and activate suppression systems, should the concentrations of gas reach 40 to 50% of the LFL. Some industrial operations provide forced ventilation to keep leaking fuel-air concentrations below the lower flammable limit. Heater and furnace burners may also have devices which automatically stop the flow of gas if the flame is extinguished.

LHG leakage from tanks and containers may be minimized by the use of limiting and flow control devices. When decompressed and released, LHG will flow out of containers with a low negative pressure and low temperature. The auto refrigeration temperature of the product at the lower pressure must be considered when selecting materials of construction for containers and valves, to prevent metal embrittlement followed by rupture or failure due to exposure to low temperatures.

LHG can contain water in both its liquid and gaseous phases. Water vapour can saturate gas in a specific amount at a given temperature and pressure. If the temperature or pressure changes, or the water vapour content exceeds the evaporation limits, the water condenses. This can create ice plugs in valves and regulators and form hydrocarbon hydrate crystals in pipe-

lines, devices and other apparatus. These hydrates can be decomposed by heating the gas, lowering the gas pressure or introducing materials, such as methanol, which reduce the water vapour pressure.

There are differences in the characteristics of compressed and liquefied gases which must be considered from safety, health and fire aspects. As an example, the differences in the characteristics of compressed natural gas and LNG are illustrated in table 102.12.

Health hazards of LHGs

The primary occupational injury concern in handling LHGs is the potential hazard of frostbite to the skin and eyes from contact with liquid during handling and storage activities including sampling, measuring, filling, receiving and delivery. As with other fuel gases, when improperly burned, compressed and liquefied hydrocarbon gases will emit undesirable levels of carbon monoxide.

Under atmospheric pressures and low concentrations, compressed and liquefied hydrocarbon gases are normally non-toxic, but they are asphyxiants—they will displace oxygen (air) if released in enclosed or confined spaces. Compressed and liquefied hydrocarbon gases may be toxic if they contain sulphur compounds, especially hydrogen sulphide. Because LHGs are colourless and odourless, safeguards include adding odourants, such as mercaptans, to consumer fuel gases to aid in leak detection. Safe work practices should be implemented to protect workers from exposure to mercaptans and other additives during storage and injection. Exposure to LPG vapours in concentrations at or above the LFL may cause a general central nervous system depression similar to anaesthesia gases or intoxicants.

Fire hazards of LHGs

Failure of liquefied gas (LNG and LPG) containers constitutes a more severe hazard than failure of compressed gas containers, as they release greater quantities of gas. When heated, liquefied gases react differently from compressed gases, because they are two-phase (liquid-vapour) products. As the temperature rises, the vapour pressure of the liquid is increased, resulting in increased pressure inside the container. The vapour phase first expands, followed by expansion of the liquid, which then compresses the vapour. The design pressure for LHG vessels is therefore assumed to be near that of the gas pressure at maximum possible ambient temperature.

When a liquefied gas container is exposed to fire, a serious condition can occur if the metal in the vapour space is allowed to heat. Unlike the liquid phase, the vapour phase absorbs little heat. This allows the metal to heat rapidly until a critical point is reached at which an instantaneous, catastrophic explosive failure of the container occurs. This phenomenon is known as a BLEVE. The magnitude of a BLEVE depends on the amount of liquid vaporizing when the container fails, the size of the pieces of exploded container, the distance they travel and the areas they impact. Uninsulated LPG containers may be protected against a

Table 102.12 • Comparison of characteristics of compressed and liquified gas.

Type gas	Flammable range (% gas in air)	Heat release rate (BTU/gal)	Storage condition	Fire risks	Health risks
Compressed natural gas	5.0–15	19,760	Gas at 2,400 to 4,000 psi	Flammable gas	Asphyxiant; overpressure
LNG	4.5–14	82,450	Liquid at 40–140 psi	Flammable gas 625:1 expansion ratio; BLEVE	Asphyxiant; cryogenic liquid

BLEVE by applying cooling water to those areas of the container which are in the vapour phase (not in contact with LPG).

Other more common fire hazards associated with compressed and liquefied hydrocarbon gases include electrostatic discharge, combustion explosions, large open-air explosions and small leaks from pump seals, containers, valves, pipes, hoses and connections.

- Electrostatic charges may be generated when LHG is shipped in pipelines, when loaded and unloaded, in blending and filtering and during tank cleaning.
- Combustion explosions result when escaping gas or vapour is contained in a confined space or structure and combines with air to create a flammable mixture. When this flammable mixture contacts a source of ignition, it burns instantaneously and rapidly, producing extreme heat. The very hot air expands quickly, causing a considerable rise in pressure. If the space or structure is not strong enough to contain this pressure, a combustion explosion occurs.
- Flammable gas fires result when there is no confinement of the escaping gas or vapours, or ignition occurs when only a small amount of gas has been released.
- Large open-air explosions occur when a massive failure of a container releases a large vapour cloud of gas which is ignited before it disperses.

Controlling sources of ignition in hazardous areas is essential for the safe handling of compressed and liquefied hydrocarbon gases. This may be accomplished by establishing a permit system to authorize and control hot work, smoking, operation of motor vehicles or other internal combustion engines, and the use of open flames in areas where compressed and liquefied hydrocarbon gas is transported, stored and handled. Other safeguards include the use of properly classified electrical equipment and bonding and grounding systems to neutralize and dissipate static electricity.

The best means of reducing the fire hazard of leaking compressed or liquefied hydrocarbon gas is to stop the release, or shut off the flow of product, if possible. Although most LHGs will vaporize upon contact with air, lower vapour pressure LPGs, such as butane, and even some higher vapour pressure LPGs, such as propane, will pool if ambient temperatures are low. Water should not be applied to these pools, as it will create turbulence and increase the rate of vaporization. Vaporization from pool spills can be controlled by the careful application of foam. Water, if correctly applied against a leaking valve or small rupture, can freeze upon contact with the cold LHG and block the leak. LHG fires require controlling heat impingement upon storage tanks and containers by the application of cooling water. While compressed and liquefied hydrocarbon gas fires can be extinguished by the use of water spray and dry powder extinguishers, it is often more prudent to allow controlled burning so that a combustible explosive vapour cloud does not form and re-ignite should the gas continue to escape after the fire is extinguished.

• WAREHOUSING

John Lund

Warehousing has long been a global industry; warehouses are integrally linked to commerce and transportation of goods—by rail, sea, air and road. Warehouses may be classified by the type of products stored: food products stored in dry, chilled or frozen sections; clothing or textiles; construction equipment or materials; machinery or machine parts. In the United States in 1995, for exemple, 1,877,000 workers were employed in trucking and ware-

housing (BLS 1996); this statistic cannot presently be disaggregated into workers by warehouse type or category. Warehouses might sell directly to external (retail) or internal (wholesale) customers, and the quantities retrieved for customers may be either full-pallet or less-than-full-pallet (one or more cases selected from a single pallet). Mechanical means (fork-lifts, conveyors or automatic storage and retrieval systems (AS/RS)) may be used to transport full-pallet or less-than-full-pallet loads; or workers, working without pallet movers and conveyors, may manually handle stored materials. Regardless of the nature of the business, the products stored or the mode of transportation servicing the warehouse, the basic layout is quite uniform, although the operational scale, terminology and technology will likely differ. (For additional information on AS/RS in warehousing, see Martin 1987.)

Products are delivered by shippers or suppliers to a receiving dock, where they are then entered into either a manual or computerized inventory system, assigned a storage rack or "slot" location (an address) and then transported to that location, usually by mechanical means (conveyors, AS/RS, fork-lift trucks or tractors). Once a customer order is received, the desired containers or cases must be retrieved from their slot location. Where full pallets are retrieved, mechanical means (a fork-lift or tractor operator) are used (see figure 102.18). When less than a full pallet load (one or more cases from a rack or slot) is to be retrieved, manual material handling is required, using a worker called a *selector*, who will choose the desired number of cases and place them either onto a mechanical pallet mover, a push cart or a conveyor. The individual customer order is assembled onto a pallet or similar container for shipment to the customer; a label, tag or other mark containing invoice/billing and/or routing instructions is then applied. This task may be performed by the order selector or fork-lift operator, or, where conveyors are used to deliver single cases for final assembly, by an assembler. When the order is ready for shipment, it is loaded by mechanical means onto the truck, trailer, railroad car or ship. (See figure 102.19.)

Approximately 60% of the work activity in the warehouse is directly related to travel; the remainder relates to manual material

---

Figure 102.18 • A fork-lift truck in a warehouse in the United Kingdom being loaded with apples.

Figure 102.19 • A dockworker in the United Kingdom using lifting machines to move quarters of beef.

handling. Aside from the important work of clerks, dispatchers, cleaners, supervisors and managers, the main work of the warehouse relating to the transporting and handling of goods is performed primarily by two classes of workers: fork-lift operators and selectors.

Intense worldwide competition and the rapid entrance of new firms have created the drive for increased labour and space efficiency, spawning a new discipline called *warehouse management systems* (WMSs) (Register 1994). These systems are becoming increasingly less expensive and more powerful; they rely on computer networks, bar coding, computer software and radio-frequency communications systems to vastly increase management and control of warehouse inventory and operations, allowing warehouses to improve customer order response times and responsiveness while dramatically increasing inventory accuracy and reducing costs (Firth 1995).

WMSs essentially computerize inventory and order dispatch systems. When incoming product from a supplier or shipper arrives at the receiving dock, bar code scanners record the product code and name, instantly updating the inventory database while assigning the incoming product an address in the warehouse. A fork-lift operator is then alerted to pick up and deliver the stock via a radio-frequency communications system mounted on the vehicle.

Orders from customers are received by another computer program which looks up the product address and availability of each item ordered in the inventory database and then sorts the customer order by the most efficient travel path to minimize travel. Labels with the product name, code and location are printed out for use by the order selectors who must then fill this order. While these features clearly help improve customer service and improve efficiency, they are important preconditions for *engineered work standards* (EWSs), which may pose additional health and safety hazards for both fork-lift operators and order selectors.

Information about each order—the number of cases, travel distances and so on—which is generated by the order dispatch programme can be further combined with standard or allowed times for each activity to calculate an overall standard time for

selecting a particular customer order; it would be extremely time-consuming and difficult to retrieve this information without the use of the computer hardware and databases. Computer monitoring can then be used to record the elapsed time on each order, compare the actual with the allowed time and then compute an efficiency index, which any supervisor or manager can look up by pressing a few computer keys.

Warehouse EWSs have spread from the United States to Australia, Canada, the United Kingdom, Germany, Austria, Finland, Sweden, Italy, South Africa, the Netherlands and Belgium. While WMS systems themselves do not necessarily add safety and health hazards, there is considerable evidence to suggest that the resulting increased workload, lack of control over work pace and the impact of increased frequency of lifting contribute significantly to increased injury risk. In addition, the time pressure imposed by work standards may force workers to take risky short cuts and not utilize proper safe work methods. These risks and hazards are described below.

Hazards

In the most basic warehouse, regardless of the level of technology and computerization, there are a myriad of basic health and safety hazards; modern WMSs can be linked with a different order of health and safety hazards.

Basic health hazards begin with potentially toxic materials which may be stored in warehouses; examples include petroleum products, solvents and dyestuffs. These require proper labelling, employee education and training and an effective hazard communication programme (including MSDSs) for all affected workers, who often know little about the health effects of what they are handling, much less proper handling, spill and clean-up procedures. (See, for example, the ILO Chemicals Convention, 1990 (No. 170), and Recommendation, 1990 (No. 177).) Noise may be present from gasoline or LP-powered fork-lifts, conveyors, ventilation systems and pneumatically-actuated equipment. Additionally, workers who operate such equipment may be subject to whole-body vibration. (See, for example, the ILO Working Environment (Air Pollution, Noise and Vibration) Convention, 1977 (No. 148), and Recommendation, 1977 (No. 156).)

Figure 102.20 • An overhead guard fitted to a fork-lift truck.

Veiligheidsinstituut, Amsterdam

US NIOSH studies of injuries among grocery order selectors

The National Institute for Occupational Safety and Health (NIOSH) studied lifting and other related injuries at two grocery warehouses (referred to hereafter as "Warehouse A" and "Warehouse B") (NIOSH 1993a; NIOSH 1995). Both warehouses have engineered standards against which order selector performance is measured; those who fall below their standard are subject to disciplinary action. The data in table 102.13 are expressed in percentages of order selectors only, reporting either all injuries or back injuries alone each year.

At the risk of generalizing these data beyond their context, by any reckoning, the magnitude of *recordable* injury and illness percentages in these warehouses are quite significant and considerably higher than the aggregate data for the industry as a whole for all job classifications. While the total injuries at Warehouse A show a slight decline, they actually increase at Warehouse B. But the back injuries, with the exception of 1992 at Warehouse B, are both quite stable and significant. In general terms, these data suggest that order selectors have virtually a 3 in 10 chance of experiencing a back injury involving medical treatment and/or lost time in any given year.

The US National Association of Grocery Warehouses of America (NAGWA), an industry group, reported that back strains and sprains accounted for 30% of all injuries involving grocery warehouses and that one-third of all warehouse workers (not just order selectors) will experience one recordable injury per year; these data are consistent with the NIOSH studies. Moreover, they estimated the cost of paying for these injuries (workers' compensation primarily) at $0.61 per hour for the 1990–1992 period (almost US$1,270 per year per worker). They also determined that manual lifting was the primary cause of back injuries in 54% of all cases studied.

In addition to a review of injury and illness statistics, NIOSH utilized a questionnaire instrument which was administered to all grocery order selectors. At Warehouse A, of the 38 full-time selectors, 50% reported at least one injury in the last 12 months, and 18% of full-time selectors reported at least one back injury in the previous 12 months. For Warehouse B, 63% of the 19 full-time selectors reported at least one recordable injury in the last 12 months, and 47% reported having at least one back injury in the same period. Seventy per cent of full-time workers at Warehouse A reported significant back pain in the previous year, as did 47% of

the full-time selectors at Warehouse B. These self-reported data closely correspond with the injury and illness survey data.

In addition to reviewing injury data regarding back injuries, NIOSH applied its revised lifting equation to a sample of lifting tasks of order selectors and found that all the sampled lifting tasks exceeded the recommended weight limit by significant margins, which indicates the tasks studied were highly stressful from an ergonomic point of view. In addition, compressive forces were estimated on the L5/S1 vertebral disc; all exceeded the recommended biomechanical limits of 3.4 kN (kilonewtons), which has been identified as an upper limit for protecting most workers from the risk of low-back injury.

Finally, NIOSH, using both energy expenditure and oxygen consumption methodologies, estimated energy demand on grocery order selectors in both warehouses. Average energy demands of the order selector exceeded the established criterion of 5 kcal/minute (4 METS) for an 8-hour day, which is recognized as moderate to heavy work for a majority of healthy workers. At Warehouse A, the working metabolic rate ranged from 5.4 to 8.0 kcal/minute, and the working heart rate ranged from 104 to 131 beats per minute; at Warehouse B, it was 2.6 to 6.3 kcal/minute, and 138 to 146 beats per minute, respectively. Order selectors' energy demands from continuous lifting at a rate of 4.1 to 4.9 lifts per minute would probably result in fatigued muscles, especially when working shifts of 10 or more hours. This clearly illustrates the physiological cost of work in the two warehouses studied to date. In summing up its findings, NIOSH reached the following conclusion concerning the risks faced by grocery warehouse order selectors:

> In summary, all order assemblers (order selectors) have an elevated risk for musculoskeletal disorders, including low back pain, because of the combination of adverse job factors all contributing to fatigue, a high metabolic load and the workers' inability to regulate their work rate because of the work requirements. According to recognized criteria defining worker capability and accompanying risk of low back injury, the job of order assembler at this work site will place even a highly selected work force at substantial risk of developing low back injuries. Moreover, in general, we believe that the existing performance standards encourage and contribute to these excessive levels of exertion (NIOSH 1995).

Table 102.13 • Back and all reported workplace injuries and illnesses involving order selectors at two grocery warehouses studied by NIOSH, 1987-1992.

Year	Warehouse A: all injuries (%)	Warehouse B: all injuries (%)	Warehouse A: back injuries only (%)	Warehouse B: back injuries only (%)
1987	79	N/A	28	N/A
1988	88	N/A	31	N/A
1989	87	62	39	21
1990	81	62	31	31
1991	52	83	28	29
1992	N/A	86	N/A	17

Sources: NIOSH 1993a, 1995.

Both fork-lift operators and selectors may be exposed to diesel and gasoline exhaust from trucks at the loading and receiving docks, as well as from fork-lifts. Lighting may not be adequate for fork-lift and other vehicle traffic or for ensuring proper identification of products desired by customers. Workers assigned to work in cold and frozen storage areas may experience cold stress from exposure to cold temperatures and air recirculation systems; temperatures in many freezer storage areas can approach –20°C, even without wind chill factors being considered. Moreover, since few warehouses are air conditioned during warm months, warehouse workers, particularly those performing manual material handling, may be exposed to heat stress problems.

Safety hazards and risks are also many and varied. Besides the more obvious hazards evident when pedestrians and any motor-driven vehicle are put into the same work area, many of the injuries occurring among warehouse workers include slips, trips and falls from floors not kept free of ice, water or spilled product or that are poorly maintained; a number of injuries involve fork-lift operators who slip or fall while mounting or dismounting their fork-lift trucks. Workers are often exposed to falling product from overhead racks. Workers may be caught in or between fork-lift masts, forks and cargo, resulting in serious physical injury. Wooden pallets handled by workers often result in exposure to slivers and related puncture wounds. Using knives to cut apart boxes and cases often results in cuts and lacerations. Workers who move boxes or containers on or off conveyors may be exposed to in-running nip points. Selectors, assemblers and other workers engaged in manual material handling are exposed to varying degrees of risk of developing low-back pain and other related injuries. Weight-lifting regulations and recommended methods for materials handling are discussed elsewhere in the *Encyclopaedia*.

Recordable injuries and lost workday cases in the US warehouse industry, for example, are considerably higher than those for all industry.

Data regarding injuries (and particular back injuries) among grocery order selectors, the group at greatest risk from lifting-related injuries, are not available on a national or international scale. The US NIOSH, however, has studied lifting and other related injuries at two grocery warehouses in the United States (see sidebar) and found that "all order selectors have an elevated risk for musculoskeletal disorders, including low-back pain, because of the combination of adverse job factors, all contributing to fatigue, a high metabolic load and the workers' inability to regulate their work rate because of the work requirements" (NIOSH 1995).

A comprehensive application of ergonomics to the warehouse should not be confined to lifting and to order selectors. A wide focus is required, involving detailed job analysis, careful measurement and assessment (part of the job analysis begins with the job safety analyses below). A more comprehensive look at the design of racks and shelves is required, as is establishment of a closer working relationship with suppliers to design or retrofit fork-lift controls to reduce ergonomic risk factors (extensive reaches, foot flexion and extension, winging, awkward neck and body positions) and to design containers that are less heavy and bulky, with handles or grips to reduce lifting risk.

Corrective Actions

Basic health hazards

Employers, workers and trade unions should cooperate to develop and implement an effective hazard communication programme which emphasizes the three following fundamentals:

Table 102.14 • Job safety analysis: Fork-lift operator.

Job elements or tasks	Hazards present	Recommended protective actions
Mounting/dismounting fork-lift	Slipping/tripping on floor (grease, water, cardboard) during mounting/dismounting; back or shoulder strain from repeated incorrect entry/exit and bumping head on protective structure	Proper maintenance and clean-up of floors, particularly in high-traffic areas; exercising caution when mounting/dismounting; using three-point method to get in and out of fork-lift cab, being careful not to bump your head on overhead protective structure: grasping the support beams for the overhead protective structure with both hands, placing the left foot into the foot-hold (if one is provided) and then pushing off with the right foot and levering oneself into the cab.
Driving with and without loads	Pedestrian traffic and other vehicles might cross path suddenly; inadequate lighting; noise and vibration hazards; turning and twisting neck into awkward postures; steering may require wrist deviation, winging and/or excessive force; brake and accelerator pedals often require awkward foot and leg posture together with static loading	Slowing down in high traffic areas; waiting and sounding horn at all crossings with other aisles; exercising caution around other pedestrians; observing speed limits; ensuring proper lighting is provided and maintained through periodic inspections of illumination; installing and maintaining material that dampens noise and vibration on all vehicles and equipment; regular noise testing; operators should twist their upper torso at their waist, not at their neck, particularly when looking behind mirrors installed on the fork-lift and throughout the work facility will also help reduce this risk factor; purchasing, retrofitting and maintaining power steering and steering wheels which can tilt and raise to fit operators and avoiding winging; providing frequent rest breaks for recovery from static loading fatigue; considering redesign of foot pedals to reduce angle of foot (extension) and by hinging accelerator pedals to the floor
Raising or lowering forks with or without loads	Leaning and twisting of neck in order to see load clearly; reaching for hand controls which may involve excess reach or winging	Twisting or leaning from the waist, not from the neck; selecting fork-lifts which provide adequate visibility about the mast and which have hand controls within easy reach (located at side of operator, not on control console by steering wheel), but which are not so close or high as to involve winging; possibly retrofitting fork-lifts, with manufacturer's permission.
Filling gas tanks or changing batteries	Changing LPG or gasoline tanks or batteries may require excessive and awkward lifting	Using at least two employees to lift, or using a mechanical hoist; considering redesign of fork-lift to facilitate a more accessible location for fuel tank

Table 102.15 • Job safety analysis: Order selector.

Job elements or tasks	Hazards present	Recommended protective actions
Mounting/dismounting pallet jack	Slipping/tripping on floor (grease, water, cardboard) during mounting/dismounting	Proper maintenance and clean-up of floors, particularly in high-traffic areas; exercising caution when mounting/dismounting
Travel up and down aisles	Pedestrian traffic and other vehicles might cross path suddenly; lighting; noise	Slowing down in high-traffic areas; waiting and sounding horn at all crossings with other aisles; exercising caution around other pedestrians; observing speed limits; ensuring that proper lighting is provided and maintained; installing and maintaining material that dampens noise and vibration on all vehicles and equipment; regular noise testing
Select case from rack, walk to pallet, place case on pallet	Lifting injuries, shoulder, back and neck strain; bumping head on racks; heat stress; cold stress in freezer or cold rooms	Working in conjunction with vendors to reduce container weight to lowest possible levels and to install handles or better grips on bulky or heavy products; storing heavy products at knuckle height or higher; not storing products to require significant lifting over the shoulder, or provide steps, stairs or platforms; providing "turntable" pallets which can be rotated when selecting products, to avoid stretching; modifying carts or pallet jacks to raise higher, to minimize bending and stooping when placing product on the cart or pallet jack; restricting the "cube" of the pallet so that over-the-shoulder lifting is minimized; providing regular heat and cold stress monitoring; providing adequate fluids, conditioning programmes, clothing and frequent rest breaks
Separate pallets to wrap, mark or drop off at loading docks	Slipping/tripping on floor (grease, water, cardboard) during mounting/dismounting	Proper maintenance and clean-up of floors, particularly in high traffic areas; exercising caution when mounting/dismounting

1. adequate labelling of all toxic substances
2. availability of detailed MSDSs that provide more detailed information about health effects, fire, reactivity, PPE, first aid, spill clean-up and other emergency procedures
3. regular and relevant worker training in proper handling of these substances.

Lack of an effective hazard communication programme is one of the most frequent standards violations cited in this industry by the US Occupational Safety and Health Administration (OSHA).

Noise and vibration from mechanical equipment, conveyors and other sources require frequent noise and vibration testing and worker training, as well as engineering controls where needed. These controls are most effective when applied at the source of the noise in the form of noise insulation, mufflers and other controls (since most fork-lift operators are seated on top of the engine, vibration and noise dampening at this point are generally most effective). Lighting should be checked frequently and maintained at levels sufficient to reduce vehicle-pedestrian accidents and ensure that product identification and other information can be easily read. Heat (or cold) stress prevention programmes should be implemented for workplaces in warm and humid climates and for selectors or fork-lift operators assigned to cold storage or freezer rooms, to ensure that workers receive adequate breaks, fluids, training and information and that other preventive measures are implemented. Finally, where diesel or petroleum-based fuels are used, exhaust systems should be periodically tested for emissions of carbon monoxide and nitrogen oxides to ensure that they are within safe levels. Proper maintenance of vehicles and restricting their use to adequately ventilated areas will also help reduce the risk of over-exposure to these emissions.

Safety hazards for fork-lift and vehicle operators
Vehicle-pedestrian accidents are a constant risk in any warehouse. Pedestrian lanes should be clearly marked and respected. All vehicle operators should receive training in the safe operation of the vehicle, including traffic rules and speed limits; refresher training should also be considered. Mirrors should be installed at busy intersections or at blind corners to enable vehicle operators to check for traffic or pedestrians before proceeding, and operators should sound their horn before proceeding; back-up beepers or signals may also be considered. Dockplates from loading and receiving docks to the truck, railroad car or barge need to be sufficient to support the load and adequately secured.

Table 102.14 gives a job safety analysis for fork-lift operators, with recommendations.

Implementing ergonomic solutions will require closer coordination with fork-lift and vehicle manufacturers; relying solely upon operator training and traffic rules will not eliminate hazards by itself. In addition, safety and health regulatory agencies have prepared mandatory standards for the design and use of fork-lifts—for example, requiring overhead guards to offer protection against falling objects (see figure 102.20).

Safety hazards for order selectors
Table 102.15 is a job safety analysis listing most of the corrective actions necessary to reduce the safety and lifting hazards for order selectors. However, just as improved fork-lift design to reduce ergonomic risk factors requires closer coordination with vehicle manufacturers, reducing safety and lifting hazards for order selectors requires similar coordination with designers of racking systems, consultants who design and install warehouse control systems and engineered standards systems and the vendors who store their products in the warehouse. The latter can be enlisted to design products that are less bulky, weigh less and have better handles or grips. Rack manufacturers can be very helpful in designing and retrofitting rack systems which allow the selector to stand upright during selection.

Consultants who design and install warehouse control systems and engineered standards need to be more aware of the health and safety risks concerning the effect of work intensification on manual material-handling injuries. NIOSH (1993a, 1995)has recommended that more objective forms of determining fatigue allowance, such as oxygen consumption or heart rate, be used. They have also recommended that the height of the pallet being constructed (the "cube") be limited to no more than 150 cm, and that there be an "order break" after one pallet has been assembled by the order selector, thus increasing the frequency of recovery periods between orders. In addition to more frequent breaks, NIOSH has recommended restricting overtime for workers based on engineered standards, considering worker rotation and installing "light duty" programmes for order selectors who return from injury or leave.

References

American National Standards Institute (ANSI). 1967. *Illumination.* ANSI A11.1-1967. New York: ANSI.

Anton, DJ. 1988. Crash dynamics and restraint systems. In *Aviation Medicine*, 2nd edition, edited by J Ernsting and PF King. London: Butterworth.

Beiler, H and U Tränkle. 1993. Fahrerarbeit als Lebensarbeitsperpektive. In *Europäische Forschungsansätze zur Gestaltung der Fahrtätigkeit im ÖPNV* (S. 94-98) Bundesanstat für Arbeitsschutz. Bremerhaven: Wirtschaftsverlag NW.

Bureau of Labor Statistics (BLS). 1996. *Safety and Health Statistics.* Washington, DC: BLS.

Canadian Urban Transit Association. 1992. *Ergonomic Study of the Driver's Workstation in Urban Buses.* Toronto: Canadian Urban Transit Association.

Decker, JA. 1994. *Health Hazard Evaluation: Southwest Airlines, Houston Hobby Airport, Houston, Texas.* HETA-93-0816-2371. Cincinnati, OH: NIOSH.

DeHart RL. 1992. Aerospace medicine. In *Public Health and Preventive Medicine*, 13th edition, edited by ML Last and RB Wallace. Norwalk, CT: Appleton and Lange.

DeHart, RL and KN Beers. 1985. Aircraft accidents, survival, and rescue. In *Fundamentals of Aerospace Medicine*, edited by RL DeHart. Philadelphia, PA: Lea and Febiger.

Eisenhardt, D and E Olmsted. 1996. *Investigation of Jet Exhaust Infiltration into a Building Located on John F. Kennedy (JFK) Airport Taxiway.* New York: US Department of Health and Human Services, Public Health Service, Division of Federal Occupational Health, New York Field Office.

Firth, R. 1995. Steps to successfully installing a warehouse management system. *Industrial Engineering* 27(2):34–36.

Friedberg, W, L Snyder, DN Faulkner, EB Darden, Jr., and K O'Brien. 1992. *Radiation Exposure of Air Carrier Crewmembers II.* DOT/FAA/AM-92-2.19. Oklahoma City, OK: Civil Aeromedical Institute; Washington, DC: Federal Aviation Administration.

Gentry, JJ, J Semeijn, and DB Vellenga. 1995. The future of road haulage in the new European Union—1995 and beyond. *Logistics and Transportation Review* 31(2):149.

Giesser-Weigt, M and G Schmidt. 1989. *Verbesserung des Arbeitssituation von Fahrern im öffentlichen Personennahverkehr.* Bremerhaven: Wirtschaftsverlag NW.

Glaister, DH. 1988a. The effects of long duration acceleration. In *Aviation Medicine*, 2nd edition, edited by J Ernsting and PF King. London: Butterworth.

—. 1988b. Protection against long duration acceleration. In *Aviation Medicine*, 2nd edition, edited by J Ernsting and PF King. London: Butterworth.

Haas, J, H Petry and W Schühlein. 1989. *Untersuchung zur Verringerung berufsbedingter Gesundheitsrisien im Fahrdienst des öffentlichen Personennahverkehr.* Bremerhaven; Wirtschaftsverlag NW.

International Chamber of Shipping. 1978. *International Safety Guide for Oil Tankers and Terminals.* London: Witherby.

International Labour Organization (ILO). 1992. *Recent Developments in Inland Transportation.* Report I, Sectoral Activities Programme, Twelfth Session. Geneva: ILO.

—. 1996. *Accident Prevention on Board Ship at Sea and in Port.* An ILO Code of Practice. 2nd edition. Geneva: ILO.

Joyner, KH and MJ Bangay. 1986. Exposure survey of civilian airport radar workers in Australia. *Journal of Microwave Power and Electromagnetic Energy* 21(4):209–219.

Landsbergis, PA, D Stein, D Iacopelli and J Fruscella. 1994. Work environment survey of air traffic controllers and development of an occupational safety and health training program. Presented at the American Public Health Association, 1 November, Washington, DC.

Leverett, SD and JE Whinnery. 1985. Biodynamics: Sustained acceleration. In *Fundamentals of Aerospace Medicine*, edited by RL DeHart. Philadelphia, PA: Lea and Febiger.

Magnier, M. 1996. Experts: Japan has the structure but not the will for intermodalism. *Journal of Commerce and Commercial* 407:15.

Martin, RL. 1987. AS/RS: From the warehouse to the factory floor. *Manufacturing Engineering* 99:49–56.

Meifort, J, H Reiners, and J Schuh. 1983. *Arbeitsbedingungen von Linienbus- und Strassenbahnfahrem des Dortmunder Staatwerke Aktiengesellschaft.* Bremen- haven: Wirtschaftsverlag.

Miyamoto, Y. 1986. Eye and respiratory irritants in jet engine exhaust. *Aviation, Space and Environmental Medicine* 57(11):1104–1108.

National Fire Protection Association (NFPA). 1976. *Fire Protection Handbook*, 14th edition. Quincy, MA: NFPA.

National Institute for Occupational Safety and Health (NIOSH). 1976. *Documented Personnel Exposures from Airport Baggage Inspection Systems.* DHHS (NIOSH) Publication 77-105. Cincinnati, OH: NIOSH.

—. 1993a. *Health Hazard Evaluation: Big Bear Grocery Warehouse.* HETA 91-405-2340. Cincinnati, OH: NIOSH.

—. 1993b. *Alert: Preventing Homicide in the Workplace.* DHHS (NIOSH) Publication 93-108. Cincinatti, OH: NIOSH.

—. 1995. *Health Hazard Evaluation: Kroger Grocery Warehouse.* HETA 93-0920-2548. Cincinnati, OH: NIOSH.

National Safety Council. 1988. *Aviation Ground Operation Safety Handbook*, 4th edition. Chicago, IL: National Safety Council.

Nicogossian, AE, CL Huntoon and SL Pool (eds.). 1994. *Space Physiology and Medicine*, 3rd edition. Philadelphia, PA: Lea and Febiger.

Peters, Gustavsson, Morén, Nilsson and Wenäll. 1992. *Forarplats I Buss, Etapp 3; Kravspecifikation.* Linköping, Sweden: Väg och Trafikinstitutet.

Poitrast, BJ and deTreville. 1994. Occupational medical considerations in the aviation industry. In *Occupational Medicine*, 3rd edition, edited by C Zenz, OB Dickerson, and EP Hovarth. St. Louis, MO: Mosby.

Register, O. 1994. Make Auto-ID work in your world. *Transportation and Distribution* 35(10):102–112.

Reimann, J. 1981. *Beanspruchung von Linienbusfahrern. Untersuchungen zur Beanspruchung von Linienbusfahrern im innerstädtischen Verkehr.* Bremerhaven: Wirtschafts-verlag NW.

Rogers, JW. 1980. *Results of FAA Cabin Ozone Monitoring Program in Commercial Aircraft in 1978 and 1979.* FAA-EE-80-10. Washington, DC: Federal Aviation Administration, Office of Environment and Energy.

Rose, RM, CD Jenkins, and MW Hurst. 1978. *Air Traffic Controller Health Change Study.* Boston, MA: Boston University School of Medicine.

Sampson, RJ, MT Farris, and DL Shrock. 1990. *Domestic Transportation: Practice, Theory, and Policy*, 6th edition. Boston, MA: Houghton Mifflin Company.

Streekvervoer Nederland. 1991. *Chaufferscabine* [Driver's cabin]. Amsterdam, Netherlands: Streekvervoer Nederland.

US Senate. 1970. *Air Traffic Controllers (Corson Report).* Senate Report 91-1012. 91st Congress, 2nd Session, 9 July. Washington, DC: GPO.

US Department of Transportation (DOT). 1995. Senate Report 103–310, June 1995. Washington, DC: GPO.

Verband Deutscher Verkehrsunternehmen. 1996. *Fahrerarbeitsplatz im Linienbus* [Driver's workstation in buses]. *VDV Schrift 234 (Entwurf).* Cologne, Germany: Verband Deutscher Verkehrsunternehmen.

Violland, M. 1996. Whither railways? *OECD Observer* No. 198, 33.

Wallentowitz H, M Marx, F Luczak, J Scherff. 1996. *Forschungsprojekt. Fahrerarbeitsplatz im Linienbus— Abschlußbericht* [Research project. Driver's workstation in buses—Final report]. Aachen, Germany: RWTH.

Wu, YX, XL Liu, BG Wang, and XY Wang. 1989. Aircraft noise-induced temporary threshold shift. *Aviation Space and Medicine* 60(3):268–270.

Other relevant readings

American Petroleum Institute (API). 1971. *Chemistry and Petroleum for Classroom Use in Chemistry Courses.* Washington, DC: API.

—. 1973. *Industrial Hygiene Monitoring Manual for Petroleum Refineries and Selected Petrochemical Operations.* Washington, DC: API.

—. 1980. *Facts about Oil.* Washington, DC: API.

—. 1984. *Safe Operation of Inland Bulk Plants.* Washington, DC: API.

—. 1984. *Service Station Safety.* Washington, DC: API.

—. 1988. *Design and Construction of LP Gas Installations.* Washington, DC: API.

—. 1995. *Overfill Protection for Storage Tanks in Petroleum Facilities.* Recommended Practice 2350. Washington, DC: API.

—. 1995. *Using the API Color Symbol System to Mark Equipment and Vehicles for Product Identification at Service Stations and Distribution Terminals.* Recommended Practice 1637. Washington, DC: API.

Armistead, G, Jr. 1950. *Safety in Petroleum Refining and Related Industries.* New York: John G. Simmons & Co.

Aschof, J. 1981. Circadian rhythms: Interference with and dependence on work-rest schedules. In *Biological*

Rhythms, Sleep and Shift Work, edited by L Johnson. New York: SP Medical and Scientific Books.

Association of American Railroads. 1982. *Manual of Standards and Recommended Practices, Specifications for Tank Cars*. Washington, DC: Association of American Railroads.

Benenson, AS (ed.). 1995. *Control of Communicable Diseases Manual*, 16th edition. Washington, DC: American Public Health Association.

Bowers, DG. 1983. What would make 11,500 people quit their jobs. *Organizational Dynamics* 5–19.

Chevron Corporation. 1983. *It's Chevron Safety Time*. San Francisco, CA: Chevron Corporation.

Costa, G. 1992. A seven-point programme to reduce stress in air traffic controllers in Italy. In *Preventing Stress at Work. Conditions of Work Digest*. Vol. 11. Geneva: ILO.

Davis, RG. 1987. Providing effective warehouse lighting. *Plant Engineering* 41:88–90.

Exxon Company. 1987. *Encyclopedia for the User of Petroleum Products*. Houston, TX: Exxon Company.

Gentry, JJ, J Semeijn, and DB Vellenga. 1995. The future of road haulage in the new European Union—1995 and beyond. *Logistics and Transportation Review* 31(2):149.

Graeber, RC. 1988. Aircrew fatigue and circadian rhythmicity. In *Human Factors in Aviation*, edited by Weiner and Nagel. San Diego, CA: Academic Press.

Gulf Publishing Company. 1964. *Petroleum Marketing and Transportation*. Houston, TX: Gulf Publishing Company.

Hakkola, M. 1994. Neuropsychological symptoms among tanker drivers with exposure to solvents. *Occupational Medicine* 44(5):243–246.

Hertz, RP. 1988. Tractor-trailer driver fatality and the role of nonconsecutive rest in a sleeper berth. *Accident Analysis and Prevention* 20(6):431–439.

International Labour Organization (ILO). 1977. *Occupational Health and Safety in Civil Aviation*. Tripartite technical meeting for civil aviation. Geneva: ILO.

—. 1993. *Workers' Privacy, Part II: Monitoring and Surveillance in the Workplace. Conditions of Work Digest*. Vol. 12. Geneva: ILO.

—. 1996. *International Labour Conventions and Recommendations 1919-1995*. 3 Vols. Geneva: ILO.

Landsbergis, PA. 1986. Is air traffic control a stressful occupation? *Labor Studies Journal* 11:117–134.

Lund, J. 1991. Computerised work performance monitoring and production standards: A review of labour law issues. *Labor Law Journal* 42(4):195–202.

Marine Safety Agency. 1995. *Merchant Shipping Notice No. M.1607: The Merchant Shipping and Fishing Vessel (Medical Stores) Regulations 1995*. SI 1995 No 1802. Southampton, UK: Department of Transport.

Mobil Oil Corporation. 1972. *Light Products Refining, Fuels Manufacture*. Mobil Technical Bulletin. Fairfax, VA: Mobil Oil Corporation.

—. 1974. *The Language of Oil*. Fairfax, VA: Mobil Oil Corporation.

—. 1990. *Handling, Storing and Dispensing Industrial Lubricants*. Mobil Technical Bulletin. Fairfax, VA: Mobil Oil Corporation.

—. 1992. *LPG Manual*. Fairfax, VA: Mobil Oil Corporation.

National Fire Protection Association (NFPA). 1992. *National Fuel Gas Code*. NFPA 54. Quincy, MA: NFPA.

—. 1992. *Liquified Petroleum Gases Handbook*. Quincy, MA: NFPA.

—. 1993. *Automotive and Marine Service Station Code*. NFPA 30A. Quincy, MA: NFPA.

—. 1993. *Flammable and Combustible Liquids Code*. NFPA 30. Quincy, MA: NFPA.

—. 1994. *Liquified Natural Gas (LNG)*. NFPA 59A. Quincy, MA: NFPA.

—. 1995. *Storage and Handling of Liquified Petroleum Gases*. NFPA 58. Quincy, MA: NFPA.

National Institute for Occupational Safety and Health (NIOSH). 1975. *Health and Safety Guide for Service Stations*. Cincinnati, OH: NIOSH.

—. 1994. *Applications Manual for the Revised NIOSH Lifting Equation*. NIOSH Publication 94-110. Cincinnati, OH: NIOSH.

—. 1994. *Workplace Use of Back Belts: Review and Recommendations*. Cincinnati, OH: NIOSH.

National L-P Gas Association. 1968. *LP Gas Safety Handbook*. Chicago, IL: National L-P Gas Association.

National Research Council. 1986. *The Airliner Cabin Environment: Air Quality and Safety*. Washington, DC: Committee on Airliner Cabin Air Quality, Board on Environmental Studies and Toxicology, Commission on Life Sciences, National Research Council, National Academy Press.

National Safety Council. 1978. *Service Sense: A Guide to Safety around the Automotive Shop*. Itasca, IL: National Safety Council.

—. 1988. Motorized equipment. *Accident Prevention Manual for Industrial Operations: Administration and Programs*, 9th edition. Itasca, IL: National Safety Council.

—. 1995. *Petroleum Section Safety and Health Fact Sheets: Service Station Safety Series, 1988–1995*. Itasca, IL: National Safety Council.

Ribak, J, RB Rayman and P Froom (eds.). 1995. *Occupational Health in Aviation: Maintenance and Support Personnel*. San Diego, CA: Academic Press.

Rosa, RR. 1993. Performance and alertness on 8 h and 12 h rotating shifts at a natural gas utility. *Ergonomics* 36:1177–1193.

Rosa, RR, MH Bonnet, RR Bootzin, CI Eastman, T Monk, PE Penn, DI Tepas, and JK Walsh. 1990. Intervention factors for promoting adjustment to nightwork and shiftwork. *Occ Med: State Art Rev* 5(2):391–414.

Schroeder, DJ, RR Rosa, and LA Witt. *Effects of 8- vs. 1-hour Work Schedules on the Performance/alterness of Air Traffic Control Specialists*. Oklahoma City, OK: Civil Aeromedical Institute.

Shostak, AB and D Skocik. 1986. *The Air Controllers Controversy*. New York: Human Sciences Press.

Transport and General Workers Union. 1993. *Good Bus Cab Design*. Code of Practice. London: Transport and General Workers Union.

US Coast Guard. 1992. *Recommended Program for Protection of Merchant Mariners from Occupational Health Problems*. Navigation and Vessel Inspection Circular No. 3-92. COMDTPUB P6700.4. Washington, DC: US Coast Guard.

—. 1994. *International Safety Management Code for the Safe Operations of Ships and for Pollution Prevention*. Navigation and Vessel Inspection Circular No. 2-94. Washington, DC: US Coast Guard.

—. 1996. *Marine Safety Manual*. COMDTINST M16465.6. Washington, DC: Department of Transportation, US Coast Guard.

US Department of Transportation (DOT). 1994. *Hazardous Materials Air Incidents by Date (January 1, 1992 to December 31, 1993)*. Washington, DC: DOT, Hazardous Materials Safety, Hazardous Materials Information System.

—. 1996. *Hazardous Materials Regulations*. 49 CFR 171-177. Washington, DC: DOT.

US Public Health Service. 1996. *Ship's Medicine Chest and Medical Aid at Sea*. Washington, DC: Deptartment of Health and Human Services.

Witt, CE. 1992. Warehouse lighting brightens path to productivity. *Material Handling Engineering* 47:65–6.